■ PEDAGOGICAL COLOR CHART

Mechanics and Thermodynamics

Displacement and
   position vectors

Displacement and position
   component vectors

Linear ($\vec{\mathbf{v}}$) and angular ($\vec{\boldsymbol{\omega}}$)
   velocity vectors

Velocity component vectors

Force vectors ($\vec{\mathbf{F}}$)

Force component vectors

Acceleration vectors ($\vec{\mathbf{a}}$)

Acceleration component vectors

Energy transfer arrows

W_{eng}

Q_c

Q_h

Process arrow

Linear ($\vec{\mathbf{p}}$) and
   angular ($\vec{\mathbf{L}}$)
   momentum vectors

Linear and
   angular momentum
   component vectors

Torque vectors ($\vec{\boldsymbol{\tau}}$)

Torque component
   vectors

Schematic linear or
   rotational motion
   directions

Dimensional rotational
   arrow

Enlargement arrow

Springs

Pulleys

Electricity and Magnetism

Electric fields

Electric field vectors

Electric field component vectors

Magnetic fields

Magnetic field vectors

Magnetic field
   component vectors

Positive charges

Negative charges

Resistors

Batteries and other
   DC power supplies

Switches

Capacitors

Inductors (coils)

Voltmeters

Ammeters

AC Sources

Lightbulbs

Ground symbol

Current

Light and Optics

Light ray

Focal light ray

Central light ray

Converging lens

Diverging lens

Mirror

Curved mirror

Objects

Images

■ CONVERSION FACTORS

Length

1 m = 39.37 in. = 3.281 ft

1 in. = 2.54 cm (exact)

1 km = 0.621 mi

1 mi = 5 280 ft = 1.609 km

1 lightyear (ly) = 9.461×10^{15} m

1 angstrom (Å) = 10^{-10} m

Mass

1 kg = 10^3 g = 6.85×10^{-2} slug

1 slug = 14.59 kg

1 u = 1.66×10^{-27} kg = 931.5 MeV/c^2

Time

1 min = 60 s

1 h = 3 600 s

1 day = 24 h = 1.44×10^3 min = 8.64×10^4 s

1 yr = 365.242 days = 3.156×10^7 s

Volume

1 L = 1 000 cm^3 = 0.035 3 ft^3

1 ft^3 = 2.832×10^{-2} m^3

1 gal = 3.786 L = 231 in.^{3}

Angle

180° = π rad

1 rad = 57.30°

1° = 60 min = 1.745×10^{-2} rad

Speed

1 km/h = 0.278 m/s = 0.621 mi/h

1 m/s = 2.237 mi/h = 3.281 ft/s

1 mi/h = 1.61 km/h = 0.447 m/s = 1.47 ft/s

Force

1 N = 0.224 8 lb = 10^5 dynes

1 lb = 4.448 N

1 dyne = 10^{-5} N = 2.248×10^{-6} lb

Work and energy

1 J = 10^7 erg = 0.738 ft·lb = 0.239 cal

1 cal = 4.186 J

1 ft·lb = 1.356 J

1 Btu = 1.054×10^3 J = 252 cal

1 J = 6.24×10^{18} eV

1 eV = 1.602×10^{-19} J

1 kWh = 3.60×10^6 J

Pressure

1 atm = 1.013×10^5 N/m^2 (or Pa) = 14.70 lb/in.^{2}

1 Pa = 1 N/m^2 = 1.45×10^{-4} lb/in.^{2}

1 lb/in.^{2} = 6.895×10^3 N/m^2

Power

1 hp = 550 ft·lb/s = 0.746 kW

1 W = 1 J/s = 0.738 ft·lb/s

1 Btu/h = 0.293 W

College Physics

AP* Edition

Ninth Edition

College Physics

Raymond A. Serway | *Emeritus, James Madison University*

Chris Vuille | *Embry-Riddle Aeronautical University*

BROOKS/COLE
CENGAGE Learning™

Australia • Brazil • Canada • Mexico • Singapore • Spain • United Kingdom • United States

BROOKS/COLE
CENGAGE Learning™

College Physics, Ninth Edition
Serway/Vuille

Publisher: Charles Hartford

Development Editor: Ed Dodd

VP, Director, Advanced and Elective Products
Program: Alison Zetterquist

Editorial Coordinator, Advanced and Elective
Products Program: Jean Woy

Associate Developmental Editor: Brandi
Kirksey

Editorial Assistant: Brendan Killion

Senior Media Editor: Rebecca Berardy
Schwartz

Marketing Manager: Nicole Mollica

Marketing Coordinator: Kevin Carroll

Content Project Manager: Cathy Brooks

Art Director: Cate Rickard Barr

Print Buyer: Diane Gibbons

Rights Acquisition Specialists: Amanda
Groszko; Katie Huha

Production Service: Lachina Publishing
Services

Text Designer: Brian Salisbury

Cover Designer: Brian Salisbury

Cover Image: Aflo Sports/Masterfile

Compositor: Lachina Publishing Services

For product information and technology assistance, contact us at
Cengage Learning Customer & Sales Support, 1-800-354-9706

For permission to use material from this text or product,
submit all requests online at **cengage.com/permissions.**
Further permissions questions can be emailed to
permissionrequest@cengage.com.

Library of Congress Control Number: 2010930876

ISBN-13: 978-0-8400-6875-0

ISBN-10: 0-8400-6875-1

Brooks/Cole
20 Channel Center Street
Boston, MA 02210
USA

Cengage Learning is a leading provider of customized learning solutions with
office locations around the globe, including Singapore, the United Kingdom,
Australia, Mexico, Brazil, and Japan. Locate your local office at:
international.cengage.com/region

Cengage Learning products are represented in Canada by Nelson Education, Ltd.

For your course and learning solutions, visit **www.cengage.com.**

Purchase any of our products at our preferred online store
www.cengagebrain.com.

*AP and Advanced Placement Program are registered trademarks of the College
Entrance Examination Board, which was not involved in the production of, and does
not endorse, this product.*

Printed in the United States of America
2 3 4 5 6 7 15 14 13 12

We dedicate this book to our wives, children, grandchildren, relatives, and friends who have provided so much love, support, and understanding through the years, and to the students for whom this book was written.

■ Contents Overview

*AP and Advanced Placement Program are registered trademarks of the College Entrance Examination Board, which was not involved in the production of, and does not endorse, this product.

■ Contents

Raymond A. Serway earned his undergraduate degree in physics at Utica College in 1959, his masters degree in physics at the University of Colorado in 1961, and his doctorate in physics at Illinois Institute of Technology in 1967. He is currently Emeritus Professor of Physics at James Madison University. In 1990, he received the Madison Scholar Award at James Madison University, where he taught for 17 years. Dr. Serway began his teaching career at Clarkson University, where he conducted research and taught from 1967 to 1980. He was the recipient of the Distinguished Teaching Award at Clarkson University in 1977 and the Alumni Achievement Award from Utica College in 1985. As Guest Scientist at the IBM Research Laboratory in Zurich, Switzerland, he worked with K. Alex Müller, 1987 Nobel Prize recipient. Dr. Serway also was a visiting scientist at Argonne National Laboratory, where he collaborated with his mentor and friend, the late Sam Marshall. Early in his career, he was employed as a research scientist at Rome Air Development Center from 1961 to 1963 and at IIT Research Institute from 1963 to 1967. Dr. Serway is also the coauthor of *Physics for Scientists and Engineers*, eighth edition, *Principles of Physics: A Calculus-Based Text*, fourth edition, *Essentials of College Physics*, *Modern Physics*, third edition, and the high school textbook *Physics*, published by Holt, Rinehart and Winston. In addition, Dr. Serway has published more than 40 research papers in the field of condensed matter physics and has given more than 60 presentations at professional meetings. Dr. Serway and his wife Elizabeth enjoy traveling, playing golf, fishing, gardening, singing in the church choir, and especially spending quality time with their four children, nine grandchildren, and a recent great grandson.

Chris Vuille is an associate professor of physics at Embry-Riddle Aeronautical University (ERAU), Daytona Beach, Florida, the world's premier institution for aviation higher education. He received his doctorate in physics from the University of Florida in 1989 and moved to Daytona after a year at ERAU's Prescott, Arizona, campus. Although he has taught courses at all levels, including postgraduate, his primary interest has been instruction at the level of introductory physics. He has received several awards for teaching excellence, including the Senior Class Appreciation Award (three times). He conducts research in general relativity and quantum theory, and was a participant in the JOVE program, a special three-year NASA grant program during which he studied neutron stars. His work has appeared in a number of scientific journals, and he has been a featured science writer in Analog Science Fiction/Science Fact magazine. In addition to this textbook, he is coauthor of *Essentials of College Physics*. Dr. Vuille enjoys tennis, swimming, and playing classical piano, and he is a former chess champion of St. Petersburg and Atlanta. In his spare time he writes fiction and goes to the beach. His wife, Dianne Kowing, is an optometrist for a local Veterans' Administration clinic. His daughter, Kira Vuille-Kowing, is a recent meteorology/communications graduate of ERAU and of her father's first-year physics course. He has two sons, Christopher, a cellist and pilot, and James, avid reader of Disney comics.

College Physics is written for a one-year course in introductory physics usually taken by students majoring in biology, the health professions, and other disciplines including environmental, earth, and social sciences, and technical fields such as architecture. The mathematical techniques used in this book include algebra, geometry, and trigonometry, but not calculus. Drawing on positive feedback from users of the eighth edition, analytics gathered from both teachers and students who use Enhanced WebAssign, as well as reviewers' suggestions, we have refined the text to better meet the needs of students and teachers.

This textbook, which covers the standard topics in classical physics and twentieth-century physics, is divided into six parts. Part 1 (Chapters 1–9) deals with Newtonian mechanics and the physics of fluids; Part 2 (Chapters 10–12) is concerned with heat and thermodynamics; Part 3 (Chapters 13 and 14) covers wave motion and sound; Part 4 (Chapters 15–21) develops the concepts of electricity and magnetism; Part 5 (Chapters 22–25) treats the properties of light and the field of geometric and wave optics; and Part 6 (Chapters 26–30) provides an introduction to special relativity, quantum physics, atomic physics, and nuclear physics.

Objectives

The main objectives of this introductory textbook are twofold: to provide the student with a clear and logical presentation of the basic concepts and principles of physics, and to strengthen an understanding of the concepts and principles through a broad range of interesting applications to the real world. To meet those objectives, we have emphasized sound physical arguments and problem-solving methodology. At the same time we have attempted to motivate the student through practical examples that demonstrate the role of physics in other disciplines.

Changes to the Ninth Edition

A large number of changes and improvements have been made in preparing the ninth edition of this text. Some of the new features are based on our experiences and on current trends in science education. Other changes have been incorporated in response to comments and suggestions offered by users of the eighth edition and by reviewers of the manuscript. The features listed here represent the major changes in the ninth edition.

AP* Multiple-Choice and Free-Response Questions

For the ninth edition, we have added AP*-format multiple-choice questions and free-response questions so your students can practice on questions similar to those found on the AP Physics B examination. The questions were contributed by Lance Argano-Rush, *Viewpoint School* (Calabasas, CA); Tyler Berzina, *Millard West High School* (Omaha, NE); Greg Jacobs, *Woodberry Forest School* (Woodberry Forest, VA); Bill Pappas; and Michelle Strand, *West Fargo High School* (West Fargo, ND).

Multiple-Choice Questions can be found at the end of every chapter of the text. These questions are drawn from and address AP Physics B learning objectives covered in each chapter.

Free-Response Questions are organized into two complete, 90-minute exams that can be found in Appendix E at the end of the text. Each exam is designed to mimic the actual free-response test students will encounter when taking the AP Physics B examination.

Analytics from Enhanced WebAssign Used to Revise Questions and Problems

As part of the revision of the questions and problems sets, the authors utilized extensive user analytics gathered by WebAssign, from both teachers who assigned and students who worked on problems from previous editions of *College Physics*. These analytics helped tremendously, indicating where the phrasing in problems could be clearer, and providing guidance on how to revise problems so they were more easily understandable for students and more easily assignable in Enhanced WebAssign. Finally, the analytics were used to ensure that the problems most often assigned were retained for this new edition. In each chapter's problems set, the top quartile of problems that were assigned in WebAssign have blue-shaded problem numbers for easy identification, allowing teachers to quickly and easily find the most popular problems that were assigned in Enhanced WebAssign.

Integration with Enhanced WebAssign

The textbook's tight integration with Enhanced WebAssign content facilitates an online learning environment that helps students improve their problem-solving skills and gives them a variety of tools to meet their individual learning styles. New to this edition, Master It tutorials help students solve problems by having them work through a stepped-out solution. Problems with Master It tutorials are indicated in each chapter's problem set with a **M** icon. In addition, Watch It solution videos explain fundamental problem-solving strategies to help students step through selected problems. The problems most often assigned in Enhanced Web-Assign (shaded in blue) have feedback to address student misconceptions, helping students avoid common pitfalls.

Thorough Revision of Artwork

Every piece of artwork in the ninth edition was revised in a new and modern style that helps express the physics principles at work in a clearer and more precise fashion. Every piece of art was also revised to make certain that the physical situations presented corresponded exactly to the text discussion at hand.

Also added for this edition is a new feature for many pieces of art: "guidance labels" that point out important features of the figure and guide students through figures without having to go back-and-forth from the figure legend to the figure itself. This format also helps those students who are visual learners. An example of this kind of figure appears below.

Active Figure 3.14

The parabolic trajectory of a particle that leaves the origin with a velocity of $\vec{v}_0$. Note that $\vec{v}$ changes with time. However, the x-component of the velocity, v_x, remains constant in time, equal to its initial velocity, v_{0x}. Also, $v_y = 0$ at the peak of the trajectory, but the acceleration is always equal to the free-fall acceleration and acts vertically downward.

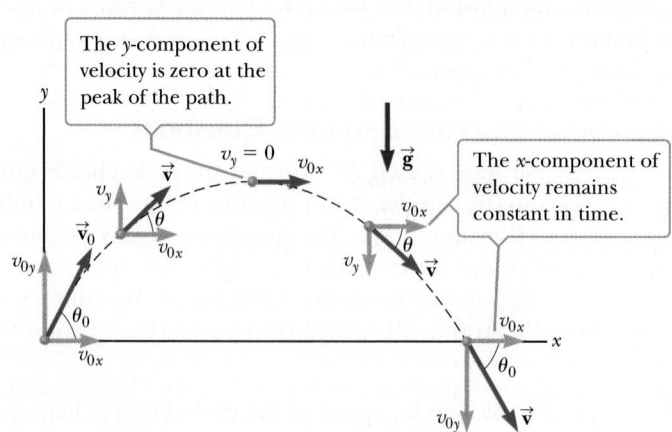

Content Changes

The text has been carefully edited to improve clarity of presentation and precision of language. We hope that the result is a book both accurate and enjoyable to read. Although the overall content and organization of the textbook are similar to the eighth edition, a few changes were implemented.

- **Chapter 1 (Introduction)** The discussion of accuracy of measurements has been improved and Example 1.3, illustrating the use of significant figures, has been greatly expanded.

- **Chapter 2 (Motion in One Dimension)** For this edition the concept of "path length," often called (inaccurately) "total distance," was introduced, as were the conceptual reasons why such a definition (used in mathematics) is important. The general discussion of the concept was also reworked for enhanced clarity. Finally, a new part to Example 2.4 better illustrates the concept of average speed.

- **Chapter 3 (Vectors and Two-Dimensional Motion)** New Figures 3.16 and 3.17 explain and illustrate the independence of horizontal and vertical motion. A new part to Example 3.5 shows how to find the direction of motion given the two components of the velocity vector, while a new part added to Example 3.10 better shows how to handle relative motion in one dimension.

- **Chapter 4 (The Laws of Motion)** New Figures 4.3 and 4.5 illustrate the first and second laws of motion, respectively. Example 4.3 on Newton's law of gravitation now introduces the concept of tidal forces in the example and exercise, all through straightforward calculations. New Example 4.5 illustrates the third law in a simple context. Finally, a new part to Example 4.15 gives an additional example of the system approach.

- **Chapter 5 (Energy)** The definitions of work were refined to include the simplest intuitive definition first, followed by two generalizations. The general discussion of work was enhanced, and an additional part added to the first example on work, Example 5.1.

- **Chapter 6 (Momentum and Collisions)** Example 6.3 on recoil velocity was thoroughly revised and improved, as was Example 6.5 on the ballistic pendulum.

- **Chapter 7 (Rotational Motion and the Law of Gravity)** Example 7.2 on rotational kinematics was extended, allowing the elimination of the now-redundant Example 7.3. Figure 7.10 was reconceptualized and redrawn and now better illustrates the concept of angular velocity. New Figure 7.20 helps the students understand gravitational potential energy.

- **Chapter 8 (Rotational Equilibrium and Rotational Dynamics)** New Figures 8.2 and 8.5 help visually explain the ideas behind torque. Example 8.4 on the center of gravity was extended to better illustrate the concept and technique of applying it.

- **Chapter 9 (Solids and Fluids)** The sections of Chapter 9 were slightly rearranged so the concept of pressure could be introduced before stress and strain. New Example 9.1 helps the student understand the concept of pressure as well as lay the groundwork for grasping the equation of hydrostatic equilibrium.

Example 9.4 on the volume stress-strain problem was significantly upgraded, and now includes the pressure change calculation that causes the change in volume.

- **Chapter 10 (Thermal Physics)** New Example 10.9 focuses on a high-energy electron beam, showing how a large number of particle impacts creates an observed macroscopic force and associated pressure.

- **Chapter 11 (Energy in Thermal Processes)** New Example 11.8 bears on the conductive losses from the human body. This same example also discusses minke whales in the accompanying exercise. A new, more comprehensive example on insulation was created (Example 11.9), which replaces two example problems that are now redundant.

- **Chapter 12 (The Laws of Thermodynamics)** The difference between work done by a gas and work done on a gas was further clarified. New Figure 12.2 compares the concept of work on a gas to the mechanical work done on an object. New Figure 12.5 illustrates the concept of the First Law of Thermodynamics, and is accompanied by further discussion of the first law in a more general context. Finally, Example 12.7 was significantly improved with more parts and a discussion of both monatomic and diatomic gases.

- **Chapter 13 (Vibrations and Waves)** Example 13.1 from the eighth edition was switched with Example 13.2 and greatly enhanced with more parts that better show how to handle single and multiple springs and their spring constants.

- **Chapter 14 (Sound)** A new and exciting physics application concerns a device that uses ultrasound technology in brain surgery. This device allows surgeons to operate without cutting the skin or opening the skull, reducing many such surgeries to an outpatient procedure.

- **Chapter 16 (Electrical Energy and Capacitance)** A new example shows how to handle a capacitor having two dielectric materials layered between the plates. In addition, the summary features new art illustrating the rules for series and parallel combinations of capacitors.

- **Chapter 17 (Current and Resistance)** Further explanation of the relationship between moving charges and energy is introduced, better connecting the early part of Chapter 17 with the concepts of electrical energy described in Chapter 16. New parts to Example 17.1 and its exercise reinforce the conceptual development. In addition, a new part was added to both Example 17.6 and its exercise.

- **Chapter 18 (Direct-Current Circuits)** Example 18.1 on resistors in series has two new parts and a new exercise. Example 18.3 was revised to improve the clarity of the solution. New art in the summary illustrates the two rules for series and parallel combinations of resistors.

- **Chapter 19 (Magnetism)** New Example 19.7 shows how to use Ampère's Law to compute the magnetic field due to a coaxial cable. A new discussion explains the difference between hard and soft magnetic materials and their general applications. Further applications of magnetic fields to directing beams of charged particles have been introduced.

- **Chapter 20 (Induced Voltages and Inductance)** This chapter features a clarified discussion of magnetic flux, explaining the concept of the orientation of a surface and how it relates to the sign of the flux. The discussion of Lenz's Law in Section 20.2 is thoroughly revised, featuring several examples of the law embedded in the text with diagrams. With the enhanced discussion in Section 20.2 it was possible to eliminate the previous edition's Section 20.4, resulting in a smoother, more comprehensive presentation of the concept.

- **Chapter 21 (Alternating-Current Circuits and Electromagnetic Waves)** A new physics application, "Light and Wound Treatment," describes how irradiating wounds with laser light can accelerate healing. Examples 21.8 and 21.9 were revised.

- **Chapter 22 (Reflection and Refraction of Light)** The revising of Example 22.2 on Snell's Law, making it more comprehensive, allowed the elimination of the last edition's Example 22.4.

- **Chapter 23 (Mirrors and Lenses)** A new example combines a thin lens and a spherical mirror.

- **Chapter 24 (Wave Optics)** A new physics application, "Perfect Mirrors," explains how dielectric materials can enhance reflectivity. Fibers constructed with this technology can guide light without any significant loss of intensity.

- **Chapter 26 (Relativity)** Relative velocity in special relativity, reintroduced in this edition, relates the relativistic treatment to the elementary treatment of relative velocity presented in Chapter 3. The connection with elementary physics will facilitate student understanding of this difficult topic. A new example illustrates the concept and its use.

- **Chapter 30 (Nuclear Energy and Elementary Particles)** A new discussion on nuclear power and breeder reactors focuses on efforts to extract the nearly limitless supply of uranium dissolved in the world's oceans. A new section on cosmology includes discussion of dark matter, dark energy, and cosmic inflation, together with new figures.

Textbook Features

Most teachers would agree that the textbook assigned in a course should be the student's primary guide for understanding and learning the subject matter. Further, the textbook should be easily accessible and written in a style that facilitates instruction and learning. With that in mind, we have included many pedagogical features that are intended to enhance the textbook's usefulness to both students and teachers. The following features are included.

Examples For this ninth edition we have reviewed all the worked examples, made improvements, and added or revised many end-of-Example Questions and Exercises. Every effort has been made to ensure the collection of examples, as a whole, is comprehensive in covering all the physical concepts, physics problem types, and required mathematical techniques. The Questions usually require a conceptual response or determination, but they also include estimates requiring knowledge of the relationships between concepts. The answers for the Questions can be found at the back of the book. The examples have been put in a two-column format for a pedagogic purpose: students can study the example, then cover up the right column and attempt to solve the problem using the cues in the left column. Once successful in that exercise, the student can cover up both solution columns and attempt to solve the problem using only the strategy statement, and finally just the problem statement. Here is a sample of an in-text worked example, with an explanation of each of the example's main parts:

The **Goal** describes the physical concepts being explored within the worked example.

The **Problem** statement presents the problem itself.

The **Strategy** section helps students analyze the problem and create a framework for working out the solution.

The **Solution** section uses a two-column format that gives the explanation for each step of the solution in the left-hand column, while giving each accompanying mathematical step in the right-hand column. This layout facilitates matching the idea with its execution and helps students learn how to organize their work. Another benefit: students can easily use this format as a training tool, covering up the solution on the right and solving the problem using the comments on the left as a guide.

■ EXAMPLE 13.7 | Measuring the Value of g

GOAL Determine g from pendulum motion.

PROBLEM Using a small pendulum of length 0.171 m, a geophysicist counts 72.0 complete swings in a time of 60.0 s. What is the value of g in this location?

STRATEGY First calculate the period of the pendulum by dividing the total time by the number of complete swings. Solve Equation 13.15 for g and substitute values.

SOLUTION

Calculate the period by dividing the total elapsed time by the number of complete oscillations:

$$T = \frac{\text{time}}{\text{\# of oscillations}} = \frac{60.0\ \text{s}}{72.0} = 0.833\ \text{s}$$

Solve Equation 13.15 for g and substitute values:

$$T = 2\pi\sqrt{\frac{L}{g}} \quad \rightarrow \quad T^2 = 4\pi^2\frac{L}{g}$$

$$g = \frac{4\pi^2 L}{T^2} = \frac{(39.5)(0.171\ \text{m})}{(0.833\ \text{s})^2} = \boxed{9.73\ \text{m/s}^2}$$

Remarks follow each Solution and highlight some of the underlying concepts and methodology used in arriving at a correct solution. In addition, the remarks are often used to put the problem into a larger, real-world context.

REMARKS Measuring such a vibration is a good way of determining the local value of the acceleration of gravity.

QUESTION 13.7 True or False: A simple pendulum of length 0.50 m has a larger frequency of vibration than a simple pendulum of length 1.0 m.

EXERCISE 13.7 What would be the period of the 0.171-m pendulum on the Moon, where the acceleration of gravity is 1.62 m/s²?

ANSWER 2.04 s

Question Each worked example features a conceptual question that promotes student understanding of the underlying concepts contained in the example.

Exercise/Answer Every Question is followed immediately by an exercise with an answer. These exercises allow students to reinforce their understanding by working a similar or related problem, with the answers giving them instant feedback. At the option of the teacher, the exercises can also be assigned as homework. Students who work through these exercises on a regular basis will find the end-of-chapter problems less intimidating.

ENHANCED
WebAssign

Many Worked Examples are also available to be assigned as Active Examples in the Enhanced WebAssign homework management system (visit **www.cengage.com/physics/serway** for more details and ask your sales representative about available discounts).

Multiple-Choice Questions These questions serve several purposes: Some require calculations designed to facilitate students' familiarity with the equations, the variables used, the concepts the variables represent, and the relationships between the concepts. The rest are conceptual and are designed to encourage physical thinking. Finally, many students are required to take multiple-choice tests, so some practice with that form of question is desirable. The teacher may select multiple-choice questions to assign as homework or use them in the classroom, possibly with "peer instruction" methods or in conjunction with "clicker" systems. (Multiple-choice questions are written with the personal response system user in mind, and most of the questions could easily be used in these systems.) Almost 400 multiple-choice questions are included in this text. Answers to odd-numbered multiple-choice questions are included in the Answers section at the end of the book. Answers to all multiple-choice questions are in the *Instructor's Solutions Manual* and on the teacher's *Power Lecture DVD-ROM*.

Conceptual Questions At the end of each chapter are approximately a dozen conceptual questions. The Applying Physics examples presented in the text serve as models for students when conceptual questions are assigned and show how the concepts can be applied to understanding the physical world. The conceptual questions provide the student with a means of self-testing the concepts presented in the chapter. Some conceptual questions are appropriate for initiating classroom discussions. Answers to odd-numbered conceptual questions are included in the Answers section at the end of the book. Answers to all conceptual questions are in the *Instructor's Solutions Manual*.

Problems All questions and problems for this revision were carefully reviewed to improve their variety, interest, and pedagogical value while maintaining their clarity and quality. An extensive set of problems is included at the end of each chapter (in all, more than 2 000 problems are provided in the ninth edition), and approximately 25% of the questions and problems in this edition are new. Answers to odd-numbered problems are given at the end of the book. For the convenience of both the student and teacher, about two-thirds of the problems are keyed to specific sections of the chapter. The remaining problems, labeled "Additional Problems," are not keyed to specific sections. The three levels of problems are graded according to their difficulty. Straightforward problems are numbered in **black**, intermediate level problems are numbered in blue, and the most challenging problems are numbered in red. The BIO icon identifies problems dealing with applications to the life sciences and medicine. Solutions to approximately 12 problems in each chapter are in the *Student Solutions Manual and Study Guide*.

There are three types of problems we think teachers and students will find interesting as they use the text:

- S **Symbolic problems** require the student to obtain an answer in terms of symbols. In general, some guidance is built into the problem statement. The goal is to better train the student to deal with mathematics at a level appropriate to this course. Most students at this level are uncomfortable with symbolic equations, which is unfortunate because symbolic equations are the most efficient vehicle for presenting relationships between physics concepts. Once students understand the physical concepts, their ability to solve problems is greatly enhanced. As soon as the numbers are substituted into an equation, however, all the concepts and their relationships to one another are lost, melded together in the student's calculator. Symbolic problems train the student to postpone substitution of values, facilitating their ability to think conceptually using the equations. An example of a symbolic problem is provided on the next page:

14. **S** An object of mass m is dropped from the roof of a building of height h. While the object is falling, a wind blowing parallel to the face of the building exerts a constant horizontal force F on the object. (a) How long does it take the object to strike the ground? Express the time t in terms of g and h. (b) Find an expression in terms of m and F for the acceleration a_x of the object in the horizontal direction (taken as the positive x-direction). (c) How far is the object displaced horizontally before hitting the ground? Answer in terms of m, g, F, and h. (d) Find the magnitude of the object's acceleration while it is falling, using the variables F, m, and g.

■ **QC Quantitative/conceptual problems** encourage the student to think conceptually about a given physics problem rather than rely solely on computational skills. Research in physics education suggests that standard physics problems requiring calculations may not be entirely adequate in training students to think conceptually. Students learn to substitute numbers for symbols in the equations without fully understanding what they are doing or what the symbols mean. Quantitative/conceptual problems combat this tendency by asking for answers that require something other than a number or a calculation. An example of a quantitative/conceptual problem is provided here:

5. **QC** Starting from rest, a 5.00-kg block slides 2.50 m down a rough 30.0° incline. The coefficient of kinetic friction between the block and the incline is $\mu_k = 0.436$. Determine (a) the work done by the force of gravity, (b) the work done by the friction force between block and incline, and (c) the work done by the normal force. (d) Qualitatively, how would the answers change if a shorter ramp at a steeper angle were used to span the same vertical height?

■ **GP Guided problems** help students break problems into steps. A physics problem typically asks for one physical quantity in a given context. Often, however, several concepts must be used and a number of calculations are required to get that final answer. Many students are not accustomed to this level of complexity and often don't know where to start. A guided problem breaks a problem into smaller steps, enabling students to grasp all the concepts and strategies required to arrive at a correct solution. Unlike standard physics problems, guidance is often built into the problem statement. For example, the problem might say "Find the speed using conservation of energy" rather than only asking for the speed. In any given chapter there are usually two or three problem types that are particularly suited to this problem form. The problem must have a certain level of complexity, with a similar problem-solving strategy involved each time it appears. Guided problems are reminiscent of how a student might interact with a teacher. These problems help train students to break down complex problems into a series of simpler problems, an essential problem-solving skill. An example of a guided problem is provided here:

32. **GP** Two blocks of masses m_1 and m_2 ($m_1 > m_2$) are placed on a frictionless table in contact with each other. A horizontal force of magnitude F is applied to the block of mass m_1 in Figure P4.32. (a) If P is the magnitude of the contact force between the blocks, draw the free-body diagrams for each block. (b) What is the net force on the system consisting of both blocks? (c) What is the net force acting on m_1? (d) What is the net force acting on m_2? (e) Write the x-component of Newton's second law for each block. (f) Solve the resulting system of two equations and two unknowns, expressing the acceleration a and contact force P in terms of the masses and force. (g) How would the answers change if the force had been applied to m_2 instead? (*Hint:* use symmetry; don't calculate!) Is the contact force larger, smaller, or the same in this case? Why?

Figure P4.32

Quick Quizzes All the Quick Quizzes (see example below) are cast in an objective format, including multiple-choice, true–false, matching, and ranking questions. Quick Quizzes provide students with opportunities to test their understanding of the physical concepts presented. The questions require students to make decisions on the basis of sound reasoning, and some have been written to help students overcome common misconceptions. Answers to all Quick Quiz questions are found at the end of the textbook, and answers with detailed explanations are provided in the *Instructor's Solutions Manual*. Many teachers choose to use Quick Quiz questions in a "peer instruction" teaching style.

■ *Quick Quiz*

4.4 A small sports car collides head-on with a massive truck. The greater impact force (in magnitude) acts on (a) the car, (b) the truck, (c) neither, the force is the same on both. Which vehicle undergoes the greater magnitude acceleration? (d) the car, (e) the truck, (f) the accelerations are the same.

Problem-Solving Strategies A general problem-solving strategy to be followed by the student is outlined at the end of Chapter 1. This strategy provides students with a structured process for solving problems. In most chapters more specific strategies and suggestions (see example below) are included for solving the types of problems featured in both the worked examples and the end-of-chapter problems. This feature helps students identify the essential steps in solving problems and increases their skills as problem solvers.

■ **PROBLEM-SOLVING STRATEGY**

Newton's Second Law
Problems involving Newton's second law can be very complex. The following protocol breaks the solution process down into smaller, intermediate goals:

1. **Read** the problem carefully at least once.
2. **Draw** a picture of the system, identify the object of primary interest, and indicate forces with arrows.
3. **Label** each force in the picture in a way that will bring to mind what physical quantity the label stands for (e.g., *T* for tension).
4. **Draw** a free-body diagram of the object of interest, based on the labeled picture. If additional objects are involved, draw separate free-body diagrams for them. Choose convenient coordinates for each object.
5. **Apply Newton's second law.** The *x*- and *y*-components of Newton's second law should be taken from the vector equation and written individually. This usually results in two equations and two unknowns.
6. **Solve** for the desired unknown quantity, and substitute the numbers.

Biomedical Applications For biology and pre-med students, **BIO** icons point the way to various practical and interesting applications of physical principles to biology and medicine. Whenever possible, more problems that are relevant to these disciplines were included.

Applying Physics The Applying Physics features provide students with an additional means of reviewing concepts presented in that section. Some Applying Physics examples demonstrate the connection between the concepts presented in that chapter and other scientific disciplines. These examples also serve as models for students when assigned the task of responding to the Conceptual Questions presented at the end of each chapter. For examples of Applying Physics boxes, see Applying Physics 9.5 (Home Plumbing) on page 307 and Applying Physics 13.1 (Bungee Jumping) on page 447.

Tips Placed in the margins of the text, Tips address common student misconceptions and situations in which students often follow unproductive paths (see example at the right). More than 95 Tips are provided in this edition to help students avoid common mistakes and misunderstandings.

Tip 4.3 Newton's Second Law Is a *Vector* Equation

In applying Newton's second law, add all of the forces on the object as vectors and then find the resultant vector acceleration by dividing by *m*. Don't find the individual magnitudes of the forces and add them like scalars.

Newton's third law ▶

BIO APPLICATION
Diet Versus Exercise in Weight-loss
Programs

Marginal Notes Comments and notes appearing in the margin (see example at the right) can be used to locate important statements, equations, and concepts in the text.

Applications Although physics is relevant to so much in our modern lives, it may not be obvious to students in an introductory course. Application margin notes (see example to the right) make the relevance of physics to everyday life more obvious by pointing out specific applications in the text. Some of these applications pertain to the life sciences and are marked with a **BIO** icon. A list of the Applications appears after this Preface.

Style To facilitate rapid comprehension, we have attempted to write the book in a style that is clear, logical, relaxed, and engaging. The somewhat informal and relaxed writing style is designed to connect better with students and enhance their reading enjoyment. New terms are carefully defined, and we have tried to avoid the use of jargon.

Introductions All chapters begin with a brief preview that includes a discussion of the chapter's objectives and content.

Units The international system of units (SI) is used throughout the text. The U.S. customary system of units is used only to a limited extent in the chapters on mechanics and thermodynamics.

Pedagogical Use of Color Readers should consult the pedagogical color chart (inside the front cover) for a listing of the color-coded symbols used in the text diagrams. This system is followed consistently throughout the text.

Important Statements and Equations Most important statements and definitions are set in **boldface** type or are highlighted with a background screen for added emphasis and ease of review. Similarly, important equations are highlighted with a tan background screen to facilitate location.

Illustrations and Tables The readability and effectiveness of the text material, worked examples, and end-of-chapter conceptual questions and problems are enhanced by the large number of figures, diagrams, photographs, and tables. Full color adds clarity to the artwork and makes illustrations as realistic as possible. Three-dimensional effects are rendered with the use of shaded and lightened areas where appropriate. Vectors are color coded, and curves in graphs are drawn in color. Color photographs have been carefully selected, and their accompanying captions have been written to serve as an added instructional tool. A complete description of the pedagogical use of color appears on the inside front cover.

Summary The end-of-chapter Summary is organized by individual section heading for ease of reference. For the ninth edition, most chapter summaries now also feature key figures from the chapter.

Significant Figures Significant figures in both worked examples and end-of-chapter problems have been handled with care. Most numerical examples and problems are worked out to either two or three significant figures, depending on the accuracy of the data provided. Intermediate results presented in the examples are rounded to the proper number of significant figures, and only those digits are carried forward.

Appendices and Endpapers Several appendices are provided at the end of the textbook. Most of the appendix material (Appendix A) represents a review of mathematical concepts and techniques used in the text, including scientific notation, algebra, geometry, and trigonometry. Reference to these appendices is made as needed throughout the text. Most of the mathematical review sections include worked examples and exercises with answers. In addition to the mathematical review, some appendices contain useful tables that supplement textual information. For easy reference, the front endpapers contain a chart explaining the use of color throughout the book and a list of frequently used conversion factors.

Active Figures Many diagrams from the text have been animated to become Active Figures (identified in the figure legend), part of the Enhanced WebAssign online homework system. By viewing animations of phenomena and processes that cannot be fully represented on a static page, students greatly increase their conceptual understanding. In addition to viewing animations of the figures, students can see the outcome of changing variables to see the effects, conduct suggested explorations of the principles involved in the figure, and take and receive feedback on quizzes related to the figure.

Teaching Options

This book contains more than enough material for a one-year course in introductory physics, which serves two purposes. First, it gives the teacher more flexibility in choosing topics for a specific course. Second, the book becomes more useful as a resource for students. On average, it should be possible to cover about one chapter each week for a class that meets three hours per week. Those sections, examples, and end-of-chapter problems dealing with applications of physics to life sciences are identified with the **BIO** icon. We offer the following suggestions for shorter courses for those teachers who choose to move at a slower pace through the year.

> *Option A:* If you choose to place more emphasis on contemporary topics in physics, you could omit all or parts of Chapter 8 (Rotational Equilibrium and Rotational Dynamics), Chapter 21 (Alternating-Current Circuits and Electromagnetic Waves), and Chapter 25 (Optical Instruments).

> *Option B:* If you choose to place more emphasis on classical physics, you could omit all or parts of Part 6 of the textbook, which deals with special relativity and other topics in twentieth-century physics.

The *Instructor's Solutions Manual* offers additional suggestions for specific sections and topics that may be omitted without loss of continuity if time presses.

Course Solutions That Fit Your Teaching Goals and Your Students' Learning Needs

Recent advances in educational technology have made homework management systems and audience response systems powerful and affordable tools to enhance the way you teach your course. Whether you offer a more traditional text-based course, are interested in using or are currently using an online homework management system such as Enhanced WebAssign, or are ready to turn your lecture into an interactive learning environment with JoinIn on TurningPoint, you can be confident that the text's proven content provides the foundation for each and every component of our technology and ancillary package.

Homework Management Systems

Enhanced WebAssign Online homework has never been easier! Whether you're an experienced veteran or a beginner, WebAssign is the market leader in online homework solutions and the perfect solution to fit your homework management needs. Designed by physicists for physicists, this system is a reliable and user-friendly teaching companion. Enhanced WebAssign is available for *College Physics*, giving you the freedom to assign

- Every end-of-chapter problem and question

- Selected problems enhanced with targeted feedback. An example of targeted feedback appears below:

A ball is thrown directly downward with an initial speed of 7.65 m/s from a height of 29.0 m. After what time interval does it strike the ground?

| 3.66 | s

You know the initial velocity, the distance and the acceleration. Which equation in Table 2.2 will allow you to find the time? You may need to use the quadratic equation.

Need Help? | Read It | Watch It |

> Selected problems include feedback to address common mistakes that students make. This feedback was developed by teachers with years of classroom experience.

- Master It tutorials, to help students work through the problem one step at a time. An example of a Master It tutorial appears below:

Master It

One gallon of paint (volume = 3.78×10^{-3} m^3) covers an area of 35.0 m^2. What is the thickness of the fresh paint on the wall?

Part 1 of 3 - Conceptualize

We assume the paint keeps the same volume in the can and on the wall.

Part 2 of 3 - Categorize

We model the film on the wall as a rectangular solid, with its volume given by its "footprint" area, which is the area of the wall, multiplied by its thickness t perpendicular to this area and assumed to be uniform.

Part 3 of 3 - Analyze

Solving for t in $V = At$ gives the following.

$$t = \frac{V}{A} = \frac{3.78 \quad \checkmark \; 3.78 \; \times 10^{-3} \text{m}^3}{35.0 \quad \checkmark \; 35 \text{ m}^2} = 1.08 \quad \checkmark \; 1.08 \times 10^{-4} \text{ m}$$

> **Master It** tutorials help students work through each step of the problem.

- Watch It solution videos that explain fundamental problem-solving strategies, to help students step through the problem. In addition, teachers can choose to include video hints of problem-solving strategies. A screen shot from a Watch It solution video appears below:

Watch It solution videos help students visualize the steps needed to solve a problem.

- Most worked examples, enhanced with hints and feedback, to help strengthen students' problem-solving skills
- Every Quick Quiz, giving your students ample opportunity to test their conceptual understanding

Also available in Enhanced WebAssign are

- animated Active Figures, enhanced with hints and feedback, to help students develop their visualization skills
- a math review to help students brush up on key quantitative concepts in algebra and trigonometry
- an interactive eBook

Please visit **www.webassign.net/brookscole** to view a live demonstration of Enhanced WebAssign and ask your sales representative about available discounts.

CengageBrain.com

On **CengageBrain.com** students will be able to save up to 60% on their course materials through our full spectrum of options. Students will have the option to rent their textbooks, purchase print textbooks, e-textbooks, or individual e-chapters and audio books all for substantial savings over average retail prices. **CengageBrain.com** also includes access to Cengage Learning's broad range of homework and study tools and features a selection of free content.

Personal Response Systems

JoinIn on TurningPoint   Pose book-specific questions and display students' answers seamlessly within the Microsoft PowerPoint® slides of your own lecture in conjunction with the "clicker" hardware of your choice. JoinIn on TurningPoint works with most infrared or radio frequency keypad systems, including Responsecard,

EduCue, H-ITT, and even laptops. Contact your local sales representative to learn more about purchasing our personal response software and hardware.

Audience Response System Solutions

Regardless of the response system you are using, we provide the tested content to support it. Our ready-to-go content includes

- all the questions from the Quick Quizzes
- all end-of-chapter objective questions to provide helpful conceptual checkpoints to drop into your lecture
- animated Active Figures enhanced with multiple-choice questions to help test students' observational skills

Our exclusive audience response system content is perfect for amateur, intermediate, or advanced users of this new learning technology. Our platform-neutral content is perfect for use with the "clicker" program of your choice. Interested in adopting audience response system technology? Consider our Microsoft PowerPoint®-compatible JoinIn on TurningPoint® software and our infrared or radio frequency hardware solutions.

Visit **www.cengage.com/physics/serway** to download samples of our personal response system content.

Lecture Presentation Resources

The following resources provide support for your presentations in lecture.

***PowerLecture*™** DVD-ROM is an easy-to-use multimedia tool allowing teachers to assemble art, animations, and digital video to create fluid lectures quickly. The two-volume DVD-ROM (Volume 1: Chapters 1–14; Volume 2: Chapters 15–30) includes prepared PowerPoint® lectures and files for all of the line art from the text as well as editable solutions available through Solution Builder. The DVD-ROM also includes the ExamView® Computerized Test Bank, giving you the ability to build tests featuring an unlimited number of new questions or any of the existing questions from the preloaded Test Bank. Finally, the DVD-ROM includes audience response system content specific to the textbook. Contact your local sales representative to find out about our audience response software and hardware.

Assessment and Course Preparation Resources

A number of resources listed below will assist with your assessment and preparation processes.

Instructor's Solutions Manual by Charles Teague. This two-volume manual contains complete worked solutions to all end-of-chapter multiple-choice, conceptual questions, and problems in the text, and full answers with explanations to the Quick Quizzes. Volume 1 contains Chapters 1 through 14, and Volume 2 contains Chapters 15 through 30. Electronic files of the *Instructor's Solutions Manual* are available on the PowerLecture DVD-ROM as well.

Teachers Guide to AP* Physics B for Serway/Vuille's College Physics, Ninth Edition with contributions from Lance Argano-Rush, *Viewpoint School* (Calabasas, CA); Tyler Berzina, *Millard West High School* (Omaha, NE); Greg Jacobs, *Woodberry Forest School* (Woodberry Forest, VA); Bill Pappas; and Michelle Strand, *West Fargo High School* (West Fargo, ND). The Teachers Guide is the complete resource for high school teachers. It contains sample lesson plans, additional teaching resources and activities, a correlation of the current AP standards to the chapters in the ninth edition, and much more. Contact your sales representative for more information.

Test Bank by Ed Oberhofer (University of North Carolina at Charlotte and Lake-Sumter Community College). The test bank is available on the two-volume PowerLecture DVD-ROM via the ExamView® test software. This two-volume test bank contains approximately 1 750 multiple-choice questions. Teachers may print and duplicate pages for distribution to students. Volume 1 contains Chapters 1 through 14, and Volume 2 contains Chapters 15 through 30. WebCT and Blackboard versions of the test bank are available on the teacher's companion site at **www.cengage/physics/serway**.

Teacher's Companion Website Consult the teacher's site by pointing your browser to **www.cengage.com/physics/serway** for a problem correlation guide, PowerPoint lectures, and JoinIn audience response content. Teachers adopting the ninth edition of *College Physics* may download these materials after securing the appropriate password from their local sales representative.

Supporting Materials for the Teacher

Supporting teacher materials are available to qualified adopters. Please consult your local sales representative for details. Visit **www.holtmcdougal.com** to

- request a desk copy
- locate your local representative
- download electronic files of select support materials

Student Resources

Visit the *College Physics* website at **www.cengage.com/physics/serway** to see samples of select student supplements. Go to **CengageBrain.com** to purchase and access this product at Cengage Learning's preferred online store.

Fast Track to a 5 The *Fast Track to a 5* is a test preparation manual designed to help students prepare for the AP Exam for Physics B. It includes an introduction about the course and exam, a diagnostic test so that students can assess their level of preparedness, a review of the course with practice questions, and two complete practice tests. The *Fast Track to a 5* was written by Edward Pascuzzi, G. Patrick Zober, *Yough Senior High School* (Herminie, PA), and Patricia Zober, *Ringgold High School* (Monongahela, PA). Ask your sales representative about price and ordering.

Student Solutions Manual and Study Guide by John R. Gordon, Charles Teague, and Raymond A. Serway. Now offered in two volumes, the *Student Solutions Manual and Study Guide* features detailed solutions to approximately 12 problems per chapter. Boxed numbers identify those problems in the textbook for which complete solutions are found in the manual. The manual also features a skills section, important notes from key sections of the text, and a list of important equations and concepts. Volume 1 contains Chapters 1 through 14, and Volume 2 contains Chapters 15 through 30. Ask your sales representative about available discounts.

Premium eBook This rich, interactive eBook includes links to animated Active Figures and allows students to highlight the text, add their own notes, and bookmark pages. Students can access the eBook through Enhanced WebAssign. Ask your sales representative about available discounts.

Physics CourseMate includes

- an interactive eBook
- interactive teaching and learning tools including:
  - quizzes
  - flashcards
  - solution videos
  - animations with interactive exercises
  - and more
- Engagement Tracker, a first-of-its-kind tool that monitors student engagement in the course

Cengage Learning's Physics CourseMate brings course concepts to life with interactive learning, study, and exam preparation tools that support the printed textbook. Watch student comprehension soar as your class works with the printed textbook and the textbook-specific website. Physics CourseMate goes beyond the book to deliver what you need! Learn more at **www.cengage.com/coursemate.** Ask your sales representative about available discounts.

Physics Laboratory Manual, third edition by David Loyd (Angelo State University) supplements the learning of basic physical principles while introducing laboratory procedures and equipment. Each chapter includes a prelaboratory assignment, objectives, an equipment list, the theory behind the experiment, experimental procedures, graphing exercises, and questions. A laboratory report form is included with each experiment so that the student can record data, calculations, and experimental results. Students are encouraged to apply statistical analysis to their data. A complete *Instructor's Manual* is also available to facilitate use of this lab manual. Ask your sales representative about available discounts.

Acknowledgments

In preparing the ninth edition of this textbook, we have been guided by the expertise of many people who have reviewed manuscript or provided pre-revision suggestions. We wish to acknowledge the following reviewers and express our sincere appreciation for their helpful suggestions, criticism, and encouragement.

Ninth edition reviewers:

Thomas K. Bolland, *The Ohio State University*
Kevin R. Carter, *School of Science and Engineering Magnet*
David Cinabro, *Wayne State University*
Mark Giroux, *East Tennessee State University*
Torgny Gustafsson, *Rutgers University*
Martha Lietz, *Niles West High School*

Rafael Lopez-Mobilia, *University of Texas at San Antonio*
Sylvio May, *North Dakota State University*
Alexey A. Petrov, *Wayne State University*
Scott Pratt, *Michigan State University*
Scott Saltman, *Phillips Exeter Academy*
Bartlett M. Sheinberg, *Houston Community College*
Gay Stewart, *University of Arkansas*
Michael Willis, *Glen Burnie High School*

College Physics, ninth edition, was carefully checked for accuracy by Phil Adams, *Louisiana State University;* Dolores Gende, *Parish Episcopal School* (Dallas, TX); Grant W. Hart, *Brigham Young University;* John Hughes, *Embry-Riddle Aeronautical University;* Ed Oberhofer, *Lake-Sumter Community College;* M. Anthony Reynolds, *Embry-Riddle Aeronautical University;* and Eugene Surdutovich, *Oakland University.* Although responsibility for any remaining errors rests with us, we thank them for their dedication and vigilance.

Gerd Kortemeyer and Randall Jones contributed several end-of-chapter problems, especially those of interest to the life sciences. Edward F. Redish of the University of Maryland graciously allowed us to list some of his problems from the Activity Based Physics Project.

Special thanks and recognition go to the professional staff at Brooks/Cole Cengage Learning—in particular, Mary Finch, Charlie Hartford, Ed Dodd, Brandi Kirksey (who managed the ancillary program and so much more), Cathy Brooks, Joshua Duncan, Laura Bowen, Brendan Killion, Rebecca Berardy Schwartz, Sam Subity, Nicole Molica, and Michelle Julet—for their fine work during the development, production, and promotion of this textbook. We recognize the skilled production service and excellent artwork provided by the staff at Lachina Publishing Services, and the dedicated photo research efforts of Jaime Jankowski and Sara Golden at PreMediaGlobal.

Finally, we are deeply indebted to our wives and children for their love, support, and long-term sacrifices.

Raymond A. Serway
St. Petersburg, Florida

Chris Vuille
Daytona Beach, Florida

The percentages of the exam that are devoted to each major category
and the corresponding *College Physics* page numbers are:

Topics

Page number

I. Newtonian Mechanics (35%)

A. Kinematics (Including Vectors, Vector Algebra, Components of Vectors, Coordinate Systems, Displacement, Velocity, and Acceleration) (7%)

1. Motion in one dimension — 25–55
2. Motion in two dimensions, including projectile motion — 56–85

B. Newton's Laws of Motion (9%)

1. Static equilibrium (first law) — 86–89, 98–100, 112–116
2. Dynamics of a single particle (second law) — 89–95, 98–99, 101–123
3. Systems of two or more bodies (third law) — 95–98, 113–115, 117–118

C. Work, Energy, Power (5%)

1. Work and work-energy theorem — 124–132, 154–159
2. Conservative forces and potential energy — 132–145, 154–160, 441–444, 463, 464–467
3. Conservation of energy — 135–138, 145–147, 155–166
4. Power — 147–152, 155–157, 162–166

D. Systems of Particles, Linear Momentum (4%)

1. Center of mass — 151, 241–244
2. Impulse and momentum — 167–172, 187–192
3. Conservation of linear momentum, collisions — 172–190, 192–197

E. Circular Motion and Rotation (4%)

1. Uniform circular motion — 207–214, 224–230
2. Torque and rotational statics — 235–241, 244–247, 261–268, 272–276

F. Oscillations and Gravitation (6%)

1. Simple harmonic motion — 437–441, 443–448, 463–465, 467–472
2. Mass on a spring — 446–448, 463–468, 470–472
3. Pendulum and other oscillations — 451–455, 464–466, 468–472
4. Newton's law of gravity — 214–221
5. Orbits of planets and satellites
   a. Circular — 221–227, 230–234

II. Fluid Mechanics and Thermal Physics (15%)

A. Fluid Mechanics (6%)

1. Hydrostatic pressure — 279–282, 288–293, 319–322, 323–324, 328–330
2. Buoyancy — 293–299, 319–322, 324–327, 328–330
3. Fluid flow continuity — 299–302, 319–322, 326–330
4. Bernoulli's equation — 302–308, 319–322, 326–330

B. Temperature and Heat (2%)

1. Mechanical equivalent of heat — 362–363, 386
2. Heat transfer and thermal expansion — 337–341, 354, 355–358, 359–361, 375–385, 386–387, 392

C. Kinetic Theory and Thermodynamics (7%)

1. Ideal gases
   a. Kinetic model — 348–361
   b. Ideal gas law — 343–348, 354–361
2. Laws of thermodynamics
   a. First law (including processes on *PV* diagrams) — 395–415, 427–433, 435–436
   b. Second law (including heat engines) — 415–418, 427–430

■ Engaging Applications

Although physics is relevant to so much in our lives, it may not be obvious to students in an introductory course. In this ninth edition of *College Physics*, we continue a design feature begun in the seventh edition. This feature makes the relevance of physics to everyday life more obvious by pointing out specific applications in the form of a marginal note. Some of these applications pertain to the life sciences and are marked with the **BIO** icon. The list below is not intended to be a complete listing of all the applications of the principles of physics found in this textbook. Many other applications are to be found within the text and especially in the worked examples, conceptual questions, and end-of-chapter problems.

As a student, it's important that you understand how to use this book most effectively and how best to go about learning physics. Scanning through the preface will acquaint you with the various features available, both in the book and online. Awareness of your educational resources and how to use them is essential. Although physics is challenging, it can be mastered with the correct approach.

How to Study

Students often ask how best to study physics and prepare for examinations. There is no simple answer to this question, but we'd like to offer some suggestions based on our own experiences in learning and teaching over the years.

First and foremost, maintain a positive attitude toward the subject matter. Like learning a language, physics takes time. Those who keep applying themselves on a *daily basis* can expect to reach understanding and succeed in the course. Keep in mind that physics is the most fundamental of all natural sciences. Other science courses that follow will use the same physical principles, so it is important that you understand and are able to apply the various concepts and theories discussed in the text. They're relevant!

Concepts and Principles

Students often try to do their homework without first studying the basic concepts. It is essential that you understand the basic concepts and principles *before* attempting to solve assigned problems. You can best accomplish this goal by carefully reading the textbook *before* you attend your lecture on the covered material. When reading the text, you should jot down those points that are not clear to you. Also be sure to make a diligent attempt at answering the questions in the Quick Quizzes as you come to them in your reading. We have worked hard to prepare questions that help you judge for yourself how well you understand the material. Pay careful attention to the many Tips throughout the text. They will help you avoid misconceptions, mistakes, and misunderstandings as well as maximize the efficiency of your time by minimizing adventures along fruitless paths. During class, take careful notes and ask questions about those ideas that are unclear to you. Keep in mind that few people are able to absorb the full meaning of scientific material after only one reading. Your lectures and laboratory work supplement your textbook and should clarify some of the more difficult material. You should minimize rote memorization of material. Successful memorization of passages from the text, equations, and derivations does not necessarily indicate that you understand the fundamental principles.

Your understanding will be enhanced through a combination of efficient study habits, discussions with other students and with teachers, and your ability to solve the problems presented in the textbook. Ask questions whenever you think clarification of a concept is necessary.

Study Schedule

It is important for you to set up a regular study schedule, preferably a daily one. Make sure you read the syllabus for the course and adhere to the schedule set by your teacher. As a general rule, you should devote about two hours of study time for every one hour you are in class. If you are having trouble with the course, seek the advice of the teacher or other students who have taken the course. You may find it necessary to seek further instruction from experienced students. Very often, teachers offer review sessions in addition to regular class periods. It is important that you avoid the practice of delaying study until a day or two before an exam.

One hour of study a day for 14 days is far more effective than 14 hours the day before the exam. "Cramming" usually produces disastrous results, especially in science. Rather than undertake an all-night study session immediately before an exam, briefly review the basic concepts and equations and get a good night's rest.

Visit the *College Physics* website at **www.cengage.com/physics/serway** to see samples of select student supplements. Go to **CengageBrain.com** to purchase and access this product at Cengage Learning's preferred online store.

Use the Features

You should make full use of the various features of the text discussed in the preface. For example, marginal notes are useful for locating and describing important equations and concepts, and **boldfaced** type indicates important statements and definitions. Many useful tables are contained in the appendices, but most tables are incorporated in the text where they are most often referenced. Appendix A is a convenient review of mathematical techniques.

Answers to all Quick Quizzes and Example Questions, as well as odd-numbered multiple-choice questions, conceptual questions, and problems, are given at the end of the textbook. Problem-Solving Strategies included in selected Chapters throughout the text give you additional information about how you should solve problems. The contents provides an overview of the entire text, and the index enables you to locate specific material quickly. Footnotes sometimes are used to supplement the text or to cite other references on the subject discussed.

After reading a Chapter, you should be able to define any new quantities introduced in that Chapter and to discuss the principles and assumptions used to arrive at certain key relations. The Chapter summaries and the review sections of the *Student Solutions Manual and Study Guide* should help you in this regard. In some cases, it may be necessary for you to refer to the index of the text to locate certain topics. You should be able to correctly associate with each physical quantity the symbol used to represent that quantity and the unit in which the quantity is specified. Further, you should be able to express each important relation in a concise and accurate prose statement.

Problem Solving

R. P. Feynman, Nobel laureate in physics, once said, "You do not know anything until you have practiced." In keeping with this statement, we strongly advise that you develop the skills necessary to solve a wide range of problems. Your ability to solve problems will be one of the main tests of your knowledge of physics, so you should try to solve as many problems as possible. It is essential that you understand basic concepts and principles before attempting to solve problems. It is good practice to try to find alternate solutions to the same problem. For example, you can solve problems in mechanics using Newton's laws, but very often an alternate method that draws on energy considerations is more direct. You should not deceive yourself into thinking you understand a problem merely because you have seen it solved in class. You must be able to solve the problem and similar problems on your own. We have cast the examples in this book in a special, two-column format to help you in this regard. After studying an example, see if you can cover up the right-hand side and do it yourself, using only the written descriptions on the left as hints. Once you succeed at that, try solving the example using only the strategy statement as a guide. Finally, try to solve the problem completely on your own. At this point you are ready to answer the associated question and solve the exercise. Once you have accomplished all these steps, you will have a good mastery of the problem, its concepts, and mathematical technique. After studying all the Example Problems in this way, you are ready to tackle the problems at the end of the Chapter. Of those, the guided problems provide another aid to learning how to solve some of the more complex problems.

The approach to solving problems should be carefully planned. A systematic plan is especially important when a problem involves several concepts. First, read the problem several times until you are confident you understand what is being asked. Look for any key words that will help you interpret the problem and perhaps allow you to make certain assumptions. Your ability to interpret a question properly is an integral part of problem solving. Second, you should acquire the habit of writing down the information given in a problem and those quantities that need to be found; for example, you might construct a table listing both the quantities given and the quantities to be found. This procedure is sometimes used in the worked examples of the textbook. After you have decided on the method you think is appropriate for a given problem, proceed with your solution. Finally, check your results to see if they are reasonable and consistent with your initial understanding of the problem. General problem-solving strategies of this type are included in the text and are highlighted with a surrounding box. If you follow the steps of this procedure, you will find it easier to come up with a solution and will also gain more from your efforts.

Often, students fail to recognize the limitations of certain equations or physical laws in a particular situation. It is very important that you understand and remember the assumptions underlying a particular theory or formalism. For example, certain equations in kinematics apply only to a particle moving with constant acceleration. These equations are not valid for describing motion whose acceleration is not constant, such as the motion of an object connected to a spring or the motion of an object through a fluid.

Experiments

Because physics is a science based on experimental observations, we recommend that you supplement the text by performing various types of "hands-on" experiments, either at home or in the laboratory. For example, the common Slinky™ toy is excellent for studying traveling waves, a ball swinging on the end of a long string can be used to investigate pendulum motion, various masses attached to the end of a vertical spring or rubber band can be used to determine their elastic nature, an old pair of Polaroid sunglasses and some discarded lenses and a magnifying glass are the components of various experiments in optics, and the approximate measure of the free-fall acceleration can be determined simply by measuring with a stopwatch the time it takes for a ball to drop from a known height. The list of such experiments is endless. When physical models are not available, be imaginative and try to develop models of your own.

New Media

If available, we strongly encourage you to use the **Enhanced WebAssign** product that is available with this textbook. It is far easier to understand physics if you see it in action, and the materials available in Enhanced WebAssign will enable you to become a part of that action. Enhanced WebAssign is described in the Preface, and it is our sincere hope that you will find physics an exciting and enjoyable experience and that you will benefit from this experience, regardless of your chosen profession.

An Invitation to Physics

It is our hope that you too will find physics an exciting and enjoyable experience and that you will profit from this experience, regardless of your chosen profession. Welcome to the exciting world of physics!

> *To see the World in a Grain of Sand*
> *And a Heaven in a Wild Flower,*
> *Hold infinity in the palm of your hand*
> *And Eternity in an hour.*

William Blake, "Auguries of Innocence"

Advanced Placement can be exhilarating. Whether you are taking an AP course at your school or you are working on AP independently, the stage is set for a great intellectual experience.

Sometime after New Year's Day, however, when the examination begins to loom on a very real horizon, Advanced Placement can seem downright intimidating. In fact, offered the opportunity to take the examination for a lark, even adults long out of high school refuse. If you dread taking the test, you are in good company.

The best way to deal with an AP examination is to master it, not let it master you. If you can think of these examinations as a way to show off how much physics you know, you have a leg up. Attitude *does* help. If you are not one of those students, there is still a lot you can do to sideline your anxiety. Focused review and practice time will help you master the examination so that you can walk in with confidence and score a 5.

By February, long before the exam, you need to make sure that you are registered to take the test. Many schools take care of the paperwork and handle the fees for their AP students, but check with your teacher or the AP coordinator to make sure that you are on the list (especially if you have a documented disability and need test accommodations). If you are studying AP independently, call AP Services at the College Board for the name of the local AP coordinator, who will help you through the registration process.

The evening before the exam is not a great time for partying, nor is it a great time for cramming. If you like, look over class notes or drift through your textbook, concentrating on the broad outlines, not the small details, of the course.

The evening before the exam *is* a great time to get your things together for the next day. Sharpen a fistful of no. 2 pencils with good erasers; bring a scientific calculator with fresh batteries. You may bring a programmable calculator; the memory will not be erased or cleared by the test administrator. It must not have a typewriter-style keyboard. Get a watch and turn off the alarm if it has one; get a piece of fruit or a power bar and a bottle of water for the break. Make sure that you have your social security number and whatever photo identification and admission ticket are required. Then relax. Get a good night's sleep.

On the day of the examination, it is wise not to skip breakfast; studies show that students who eat a hot breakfast before testing get higher grades than students who do not. Be careful not to drink a lot of liquids, necessitating a trip to the bathroom during the test. Breakfast will give you the energy you need to power you through the test, and more. You will spend some time waiting while everyone is seated in the correct room for the correct test, and that's before the test has even begun. With a short break between Section I and Section II, the AP Physics B exam lasts for more than three hours, so be prepared for a long morning. You do not want to be distracted by a growling stomach or hunger pangs.

Be sure to wear comfortable clothes, taking along a sweater in case the heating or air conditioning is erratic. Be sure, too, to wear clothes you like—everyone performs better when they think they look better—and by all means wear your lucky socks.

You have been on the fast track. Now go get a 5!

*AP and Advanced Placement Program are registered trademarks of the College Entrance Examination Board, which was not involved in the production of, and does not endorse, this product.

xxxix

The AP Physics examination consists of two sections: Section I has 70 multiple-choice questions, and Section II has 6 or 7 free-response problems. You will have 90 minutes for the multiple-choice portion. You will not be allowed to use a calculator for the multiple-choice questions. The questions are collected, and you will be given a short break. Then you then have 90 minutes for the free-response problem section.

AP Physics B Exam—Distribution of Questions and Problems			
	Weighting	Possible Topics	Time Allowed
Section I	50%	Multiple-choice questions	90 minutes
Section II	50%	Free-response problems	90 minutes

Strategies for the Multiple-Choice Section

Here are some rules of thumb to help you work your way through the multiple-choice questions.

- **There is no longer a penalty for wrong answers,** so it is to your advantage to answer every question, even if you have to guess. Some students scan the test quickly and answer all the questions to which they know the answers. Then they go back to look at the more difficult questions. If you do this, be sure to skip lines on the answer sheet.
- **Read the question carefully** Pressured for time, many students make the mistake of reading the questions too quickly or merely skimming them. By reading a question carefully, you may already have some idea about the correct answer. You can then look for it in the responses.
- **Eliminate answers you know are incorrect** You can write on the multiple-choice questions in the test book. As you read through the responses, draw a line through any answer you know is wrong.
- **Read all the possible answers and then choose the one you believe is correct** AP examinations are written to test your precise knowledge of a subject. Some of the responses may be partially correct, but there is only one response that is completely true.
- **Mark and skip tough questions** If you are hung up on a question, mark it in the margin of the question book. You can come back to it later if you have time. Make sure to skip that question on your answer sheet, too.
- **Calculational questions** In either calculational or approximation type multiple-choice questions, you may be asked to find the solution to a problem that requires minimal mathematics. These computations are done without the use of a calculator. These types of questions usually end with the word *nearly*.
- **The acceleration due to gravity** In the multiple-choice part of the test, it is advisable to use 10 m/s^2 as the acceleration to approximate an answer.

Types of Multiple-Choice Questions

There are various types of multiple-choice questions. Here are some suggestions for approaching each type.

Classic/Best Response Questions

These questions are the most common type of multiple-choice question. They simply require you to read the question and select the most correct answer. For example:

1. Sources of electromagnetic radiation whose waves have the same phase relationship at all times are described as _____.
   (A) continuous
   (B) coherent
   (C) dispersed
   (D) interfered
   (E) monochromatic

Answer: (B). By definition, coherent sources of electromagnetic radiation are those whose emitted waves have the same phase relationship at all times. Other sources are described as incoherent.

List and Group Questions

In this type of question, there is a list of possible answers, and you must select the answer that contains the correct group of responses. For example:

1. Which of the following quantities are vectors?
   I. instantaneous velocity
   II. distance traveled
   III. average acceleration
      (A) II only
      (B) I and II
      (C) II and III
      (D) I and III
      (E) I, II, and III

Answer: (D). A vector quantity expresses both magnitude and direction. Both instantaneous velocity and average acceleration are vectors. Distance traveled is a scalar because direction is not specified. Cross out all items that contain response II. You have narrowed down the possible responses to (D).

Noncalculational Computations

These questions require computations without the use of a calculator. Simple mathematics and the choice of the correct physics equation will be involved. For example:

1. The work done by friction on a 15 kg body pulling it horizontally in a straight line for 15 m when the coefficient of friction between the contact surfaces is given by $\mu_k = 0.4$ is most nearly what value?
   (A) 60 J
   (B) 90 J
   (C) −60 J
   (D) −590 J
   (E) −890 J

Answer: (E). The work done by friction is negative because friction is a degrading forces, thus eliminating responses (A) and (B) because they are both positive. The force of friction is given by $f = -\mu_k N = -\mu_k mg = -(0.4)(15\text{ kg})(10\text{ m/s}^2) = -60\text{ N}$. The work done by friction is $W = fx = (-60\text{ N})(15\text{ m}) = -900\text{ J}$. This answer is most nearly choice (E).

Strategies for the Free-Response Problem Section

Section II of the AP Physics B exam comes with a table of equations and constants. This table includes numerical values of some physical constants and conversion factors and states some conventions used in the exams.

- Check the radian/degree mode on your calculator. Set it in the degree mode.
- Scan all the questions in the section you are working in and mark those that you know you can answer correctly. Do these problems first.
- You will be provided with an answer booklet as well as an insert that contains the same questions as the answer booklet, but without the spaces. You can remove the insert for reference. All your work and answers for each problem must be shown in the answer booklet. No credit will be given for work shown on the insert, but you may write on it.
- Show all your work. Partial credit will be awarded for problems if the correct work is shown but the answer is not present or is incorrect. In problems involving calculations, box or circle your final answer.
- Points are awarded in the scoring of a problem. The awarding of the points is done by the problem rubric. Points are never taken away.
- Cross out incorrect answers and work with an "X" rather than spending time erasing.
- Be clear and organized in your work. If a grader cannot clearly understand your work, you may not receive full credit. Neatness goes a long way.
- Free-response problems will have sets of parts: (a), (b), (c), and so on. Attempt to solve each part. Even if your answer to part (a) is incorrect, you still may be awarded points for the remaining parts of the question if the work is correct to that point.
- Some free-response problems may not have numbers associated with them.
- Units are important in your answers. Place units in each and every step and in the final answer.
- You do not need to work the problems in order.
- You should be able to recognize that equations of the form $y = mx + b$ are linear with a slope m and a vertical intercept b. An equation of the form $x = at^2 + bt + c$ is parabolic. An equation of the form $PV = k$ is hyperbolic. You should be able to distinguish between these curves.
- In graphing P versus V, P is plotted along the vertical axis and V along the horizontal axis. When graphing $s = f(t)$, s is plotted along the vertical axis and t along the horizontal axis.
- An answer by itself is not enough. The reader (grader) must see how the solution evolves. A good rule of thumb to follow is to write or derive a working equation, substituting using units, and the final answer with correct units. Circle or box the answer.

Sample Problems and Scoring

Sample Problem 1

(15 points) A wood block of mass M is held at rest at the top of an inclined plane of length x and height h that makes an angle θ with the horizontal. The block is released from rest and undergoes uniform acceleration down the plane. The coefficient of friction between the contact surfaces is μ.

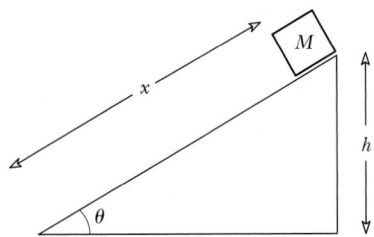

(a) The block slides a short distance down the plane; show and label all the forces acting on the block.

(b) In terms of the coefficient of friction μ, the mass M of the block, the acceleration due to gravity g, and the angle θ of inclination of the inclined plane, what is the frictional force f acting on the block?

(c) Using energy considerations and in terms of the length of the plane x, μ, g, and θ, what is the velocity of the block at the instant it reaches the bottom of the plane?

(d) In terms of g, μ, and θ, what is the acceleration of the block down the plane?

(e) In terms of M, x, μ, g, and θ, what impulse is generated on the block?

Sample Problem 1 Rubric

15 points total

(a) 3 points

1 point is awarded for each correctly drawn and labeled vector.	*(force diagram showing N, f, and Mg vectors on block)*

(b) 2 points

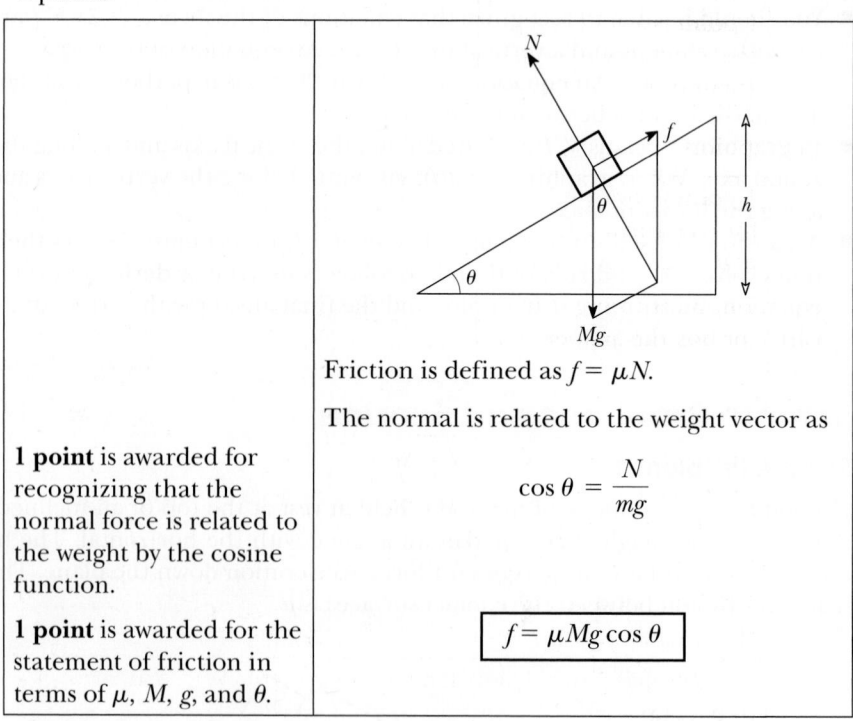

Friction is defined as $f = \mu N$.

The normal is related to the weight vector as

$$\cos \theta = \frac{N}{mg}$$

$$\boxed{f = \mu Mg \cos \theta}$$

1 point is awarded for recognizing that the normal force is related to the weight by the cosine function.

1 point is awarded for the statement of friction in terms of μ, M, g, and θ.

(c) 4 points

1 point is awarded for writing an expression of the Law of Mechanical Energy, including the work done by a nonconservative force.	$-W_f = \Delta K + \Delta U$ $-fx = K - K_0 + U - U_0$
1 point is awarded for showing that the work done by the nonconservative force is negative $(-)$.	The initial kinetic energy is zero and the final potential energy is zero, giving $-fx = K - 0 + 0 - U_0$ $K = U_0 - fx$ Substituting yields $\frac{1}{2}Mv^2 = Mgh - (\mu Mg \cos \theta)x$ Next, h must be eliminated:
1 point is awarded for expressing h in terms of x and θ.	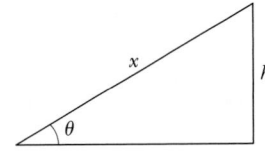 $h = x \sin \theta$ Substituting and dividing out mass M gives $\frac{1}{2}v^2 = gx \sin \theta - \mu gx \cos \theta$ $v^2 = 2gx \,(\sin \theta = \mu \cos \theta)$
1 point is awarded for the expression of v in terms of x, g, μ, and q.	$\boxed{v = \sqrt{2gx \,(\sin \theta - \mu \cos \theta)}}$

(d) 2 points

1 point is awarded for recognizing the equation to be used.	$v^2 = v_0^{\,2} + 2ax$
1 point is awarded for the correct expression.	$2gx \,(\sin \theta - \mu \cos \theta) = 0 + 2ax$ $\boxed{a = (\sin \theta - \mu \cos \theta)g}$

(e) 3 points

2 points are awarded for a statement of the impulse–momentum theorem.	$J = \Delta p$ $J = M(v - v_0)$ $J = Mv$
1 point is awarded for the correct expression.	$\boxed{J = M\sqrt{2gx \,(\sin \theta - \mu \cos \theta)}}$
1 additional point is awarded if no extraneous forces are drawn in part (a).	

Sample Problem 2

(15 points) A 3.00 g bullet leaves the muzzle of a horizontally mounted rifle with a speed v_0 of 300.0 m/s. The bullet strikes and passes completely through a 0.400 kg wooden block suspended from a long cord. The impulse gives the block a speed V of 1.50 m/s as it exits the block. Ignore air resistance.

  (a) Determine the speed of the bullet as it exits the block.
  (b) Find the elevation of the center of mass of the block just after the bullet exits.
  (c) What is the work done on the block by the bullet?
  (d) Calculate the quantity of thermal energy produced as the bullet passes through the block.

300 m/s $v = ?$

Sample Problem 2 Rubric

15 points total
  (a) 3 points

	The total initial momentum equals the total final momentum.
1 point is awarded for the Law of Conservation of Linear Momentum.	$\Sigma p_0 = \Sigma p$ $Mv_0 = MV + mv$ $v = \dfrac{mv_0 - MV}{m}$
1 point is awarded for the correct substitution with the correct units.	$v = \dfrac{(0.003\ \text{kg})(300.0\ \text{m/s}) - (0.40\ \text{kg})(1.50\ \text{m/s})}{0.003\ \text{kg}}$
1 point is awarded for the correct answer with the correct proper units.	The velocity v of the bullet as it exits the block is $\boxed{v = 100\ \text{m/s}}$

(b) 5 points

2 points are awarded for recognizing that energy is conserved.	The kinetic energy of the block just after the bullet leaves equals the gravitational energy the block gains. $\frac{1}{2}MV^2 = Mgh$ 300 m/s $v = ?$ The mass M on both side divides out, giving $$V^2 = 2gh$$
1 point is awarded for the correct substitution with the correct units.	$$h = \sqrt{\frac{V^2}{2g}} = \sqrt{\frac{(1.50 \text{ m/s})^2}{2(9.8 \text{ m/s})}}$$
2 points are awarded for the correct answer with the correct proper units.	The block is elevated by $$\boxed{h = 0.34 \text{ m}}$$

(c) 4 points

2 points are awarded for recognizing that the work done is the gain in potential energy.	Work done equals the change in gravitational energy.
1 point is awarded for the correct working equation.	$W = \Delta U = Mgh$ $W = (0.40 \text{ kg})(9.8 \text{ m/s}^2)(0.34 \text{ m})$
1 point is awarded for the correct answer with the correct proper units.	$$\boxed{W = 1.3 \text{ J}}$$

(d) 3 points

1 point is awarded for expressing the thermal energy in terms of the kinetic energies and the gain in gravitational potential energy.	Total energy before = total energy after $$K_0 = K + U + Q$$ $$Q = K_0 - K - U$$ $$Q = \frac{1}{2}mv_0^2 - \frac{1}{2}mv^2 - Mgh$$
1 point is awarded for the correct substitution with the correct units.	$$Q = \frac{1}{2}(0.003 \text{ kg})(300.0 \text{ m/s})^2 - \frac{1}{2}(0.003 \text{ kg})(100 \text{ m/s})^2$$ $$-(0.40 \text{ kg})(9.8 \text{ m/s})^2(0.34 \text{ m})$$
1 point is awarded for the correct answer with the correct proper units.	The thermal energy developed in the block is $$\boxed{Q = 120 \text{ J}}$$

Image copyright Stephen Inglis. Used under license from Shutterstock.com

Stonehenge, in southern England, was built thousands of years ago to help keep track of the seasons. At dawn on the summer solstice the sun can be seen through these giant stone slabs.

Introduction

The goal of physics is to provide an understanding of the physical world by developing theories based on experiments. A physical theory, usually expressed mathematically, describes how a given physical system works. The theory makes certain predictions about the physical system which can then be checked by observations and experiments. If the predictions turn out to correspond closely to what is actually observed, then the theory stands, although it remains provisional. No theory to date has given a complete description of all physical phenomena, even within a given subdiscipline of physics. Every theory is a work in progress.

The basic laws of physics involve such physical quantities as force, velocity, volume, and acceleration, all of which can be described in terms of more fundamental quantities. In mechanics, it is conventional to use the quantities of **length** (L), **mass** (M), and **time** (T); all other physical quantities can be constructed from these three.

1.1 Standards of Length, Mass, and Time

To communicate the result of a measurement of a certain physical quantity, a *unit* for the quantity must be defined. If our fundamental unit of length is defined to be 1.0 meter, for example, and someone familiar with our system of measurement reports that a wall is 2.0 meters high, we know that the height of the wall is twice the fundamental unit of length. Likewise, if our fundamental unit of mass is defined as 1.0 kilogram and we are told that a person has a mass of 75 kilograms, then that person has a mass 75 times as great as the fundamental unit of mass.

In 1960 an international committee agreed on a standard system of units for the fundamental quantities of science, called **SI** (Système International). Its units of length, mass, and time are the meter, kilogram, and second, respectively.

Length

In 1799 the legal standard of length in France became the meter, defined as one ten-millionth of the distance from the equator to the North Pole. Until 1960, the official length of the meter was the distance between two lines on a specific bar of platinum-iridium alloy stored under controlled conditions. This standard was abandoned for several reasons, the principal one being that measurements of the separation between the lines are not precise enough. In 1960 the meter was defined as 1 650 763.73 wavelengths of orange-red light emitted from a krypton-86 lamp. In October 1983 this definition was abandoned also, and **the meter was redefined as the distance traveled by light in vacuum during a time interval of 1/299 792 458 second**. This latest definition establishes the speed of light at 299 792 458 meters per second.

◀ Definition of the meter

Mass

The SI unit of mass, the kilogram, is defined as the mass of a specific platinum–iridium alloy cylinder kept at the International Bureau of Weights and Measures at Sèvres, France (similar to that shown in Fig. 1.1a). As we'll see in Chapter 4, mass is a quantity used to measure the resistance to a change in the motion of an object. It's more difficult to cause a change in the motion of an object with a large mass than an object with a small mass.

◀ Definition of the kilogram

> ### Tip 1.1 No Commas in Numbers with Many Digits
>
> In science, numbers with more than three digits are written in groups of three digits separated by spaces rather than commas; so that 10 000 is the same as the common American notation 10,000. Similarly, $\pi = 3.14159265$ is written as 3.141 592 65.

Time

Before 1960, the time standard was defined in terms of the average length of a solar day in the year 1900. (A solar day is the time between successive appearances of the Sun at the highest point it reaches in the sky each day.) The basic unit of time, the second, was defined to be $(1/60)(1/60)(1/24) = 1/86\ 400$ of the average solar day. In 1967 the second was redefined to take advantage of the high precision attainable with an atomic clock, which uses the characteristic frequency of the light emitted from the cesium-133 atom as its "reference clock." **The second is now defined as 9 192 631 700 times the period of oscillation of radiation from the cesium atom.** The newest type of cesium atomic clock is shown in Figure 1.1b.

◀ Definition of the second

Figure 1.1 (a) The National Standard Kilogram No. 20, an accurate copy of the International Standard Kilogram kept at Sèvres, France, is housed under a double bell jar in a vault at the National Institute of Standards and Technology. (b) A cesium fountain atomic clock. The clock will neither gain nor lose a second in 20 million years.

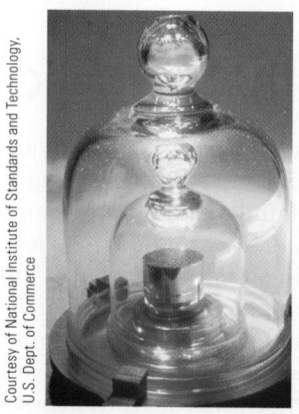

Courtesy of National Institute of Standards and Technology. U.S. Dept. of Commerce

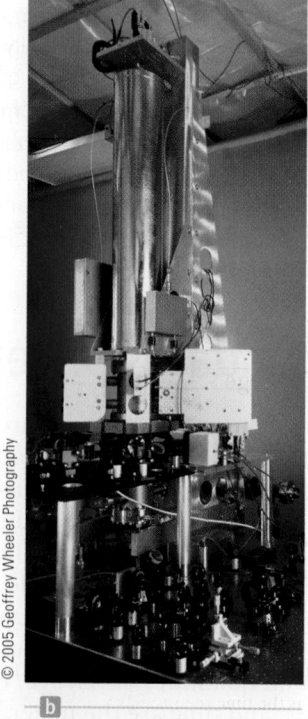

© 2005 Geoffrey Wheeler Photography

Table 1.1 Approximate Values of Some Measured Lengths

	Length (m)
Distance from Earth to most remote known quasar	1×10^{26}
Distance from Earth to most remote known normal galaxies	4×10^{25}
Distance from Earth to nearest large galaxy (M31, the Andromeda galaxy)	2×10^{22}
Distance from Earth to nearest star (Proxima Centauri)	4×10^{16}
One light year	9×10^{15}
Mean orbit radius of Earth about Sun	2×10^{11}
Mean distance from Earth to Moon	4×10^{8}
Mean radius of Earth	6×10^{6}
Typical altitude of satellite orbiting Earth	2×10^{5}
Length of football field	9×10^{1}
Length of housefly	5×10^{-3}
Size of smallest dust particles	1×10^{-4}
Size of cells in most living organisms	1×10^{-5}
Diameter of hydrogen atom	1×10^{-10}
Diameter of atomic nucleus	1×10^{-14}
Diameter of proton	1×10^{-15}

Table 1.2 Approximate Values of Some Masses

	Mass (kg)
Observable Universe	1×10^{52}
Milky Way galaxy	7×10^{41}
Sun	2×10^{30}
Earth	6×10^{24}
Moon	7×10^{22}
Shark	1×10^{2}
Human	7×10^{1}
Frog	1×10^{-1}
Mosquito	1×10^{-5}
Bacterium	1×10^{-15}
Hydrogen atom	2×10^{-27}
Electron	9×10^{-31}

Approximate Values for Length, Mass, and Time Intervals

Approximate values of some lengths, masses, and time intervals are presented in Tables 1.1, 1.2, and 1.3, respectively. Note the wide ranges of values. Study these tables to get a feel for a kilogram of mass (this book has a mass of about 2 kilograms), a time interval of 10^{10} seconds (one century is about 3×10^{9} seconds), or two meters of length (the approximate height of a forward on a basketball team). Appendix A reviews the notation for powers of 10, such as the expression of the number 50 000 in the form 5×10^{4}.

Systems of units commonly used in physics are the Système International, in which the units of length, mass, and time are the meter (m), kilogram (kg), and second (s); the cgs, or Gaussian, system, in which the units of length, mass, and time are the centimeter (cm), gram (g), and second; and the U.S. customary system, in which the units of length, mass, and time are the foot (ft), slug, and second. SI units are almost universally accepted in science and industry, and will be used throughout the book. Limited use will be made of Gaussian and U.S. customary units.

Some of the most frequently used "metric" (SI and cgs) prefixes representing powers of 10 and their abbreviations are listed in Table 1.4. For example, 10^{-3} m is

Table 1.3 Approximate Values of Some Time Intervals

	Time Interval (s)
Age of Universe	5×10^{17}
Age of Earth	1×10^{17}
Average age of college student	6×10^{8}
One year	3×10^{7}
One day	9×10^{4}
Time between normal heartbeats	8×10^{-1}
Period[a] of audible sound waves	1×10^{-3}
Period[a] of typical radio waves	1×10^{-6}
Period[a] of vibration of atom in solid	1×10^{-13}
Period[a] of visible light waves	2×10^{-15}
Duration of nuclear collision	1×10^{-22}
Time required for light to travel across a proton	3×10^{-24}

[a]A *period* is defined as the time required for one complete vibration.

Table 1.4 Some Prefixes for Powers of Ten Used with "Metric" (SI and cgs) Units

Power	Prefix	Abbreviation
10^{-18}	atto-	a
10^{-15}	femto-	f
10^{-12}	pico-	p
10^{-9}	nano-	n
10^{-6}	micro-	μ
10^{-3}	milli-	m
10^{-2}	centi-	c
10^{-1}	deci-	d
10^{1}	deka-	da
10^{3}	kilo-	k
10^{6}	mega-	M
10^{9}	giga-	G
10^{12}	tera-	T
10^{15}	peta-	P
10^{18}	exa-	E

equivalent to 1 millimeter (mm), and 10^3 m is 1 kilometer (km). Likewise, 1 kg is equal to 10^3 g, and 1 megavolt (MV) is 10^6 volts (V). It's a good idea to memorize the more common prefixes early on: femto- to centi-, and kilo- to giga- are used routinely by most physicists.

1.2 The Building Blocks of Matter

A 1-kg ($\approx$ 2-lb) cube of solid gold has a length of about 3.73 cm ($\approx$ 1.5 in.) on a side. If the cube is cut in half, the two resulting pieces retain their chemical identity. But what happens if the pieces of the cube are cut again and again, indefinitely? The Greek philosophers Leucippus and Democritus couldn't accept the idea that such cutting could go on forever. They speculated that the process ultimately would end when it produced a particle that could no longer be cut. In Greek, *atomos* means "not sliceable." From this term comes our English word *atom*, once believed to be the smallest particle of matter but since found to be a composite of more elementary particles.

The atom can be naively visualized as a miniature solar system, with a dense, positively charged nucleus occupying the position of the Sun and negatively charged electrons orbiting like planets. This model of the atom, first developed by the great Danish physicist Niels Bohr nearly a century ago, led to the understanding of certain properties of the simpler atoms such as hydrogen but failed to explain many fine details of atomic structure.

Notice the size of a hydrogen atom, listed in Table 1.1, and the size of a proton—the nucleus of a hydrogen atom—one hundred thousand times smaller. If the proton were the size of a Ping Pong ball, the electron would be a tiny speck about the size of a bacterium, orbiting the proton a kilometer away! Other atoms are similarly constructed. So there is a surprising amount of empty space in ordinary matter.

After the discovery of the nucleus in the early 1900s, questions arose concerning its structure. Although the structure of the nucleus remains an area of active research even today, by the early 1930s scientists determined that two basic entities—protons and neutrons—occupy the nucleus. The *proton* is nature's most common carrier of positive charge, equal in magnitude but opposite in sign to the charge on the electron. The number of protons in a nucleus determines what the element is. For instance, a nucleus containing only one proton is the nucleus of an atom of hydrogen, regardless of how many neutrons may be present. Extra neutrons correspond to different isotopes of hydrogen—deuterium and tritium—which react chemically in exactly the same way as hydrogen, but are more massive. An atom having two protons in its nucleus, similarly, is always helium, although again, differing numbers of neutrons are possible.

The existence of *neutrons* was verified conclusively in 1932. A neutron has no charge and has a mass about equal to that of a proton. Except for hydrogen, all atomic nuclei contain neutrons, which, together with the protons, interact through the strong nuclear force. That force opposes the strongly repulsive electrical force of the protons, which otherwise would cause the nucleus to disintegrate.

The division doesn't stop here; strong evidence over many years indicates that protons, neutrons, and a zoo of other exotic particles are composed of six particles called **quarks** (rhymes with "sharks" though some rhyme it with "forks"). These particles have been given the names *up, down, strange, charm, bottom,* and *top*. The up, charm, and top quarks each carry a charge equal to $+\frac{2}{3}$ that of the proton, whereas the down, strange, and bottom quarks each carry a charge equal to $-\frac{1}{3}$ the proton charge. The proton consists of two up quarks and one down quark (see Fig. 1.2), giving the correct charge for the proton, +1. The neutron is composed of two down quarks and one up quark and has a net charge of zero.

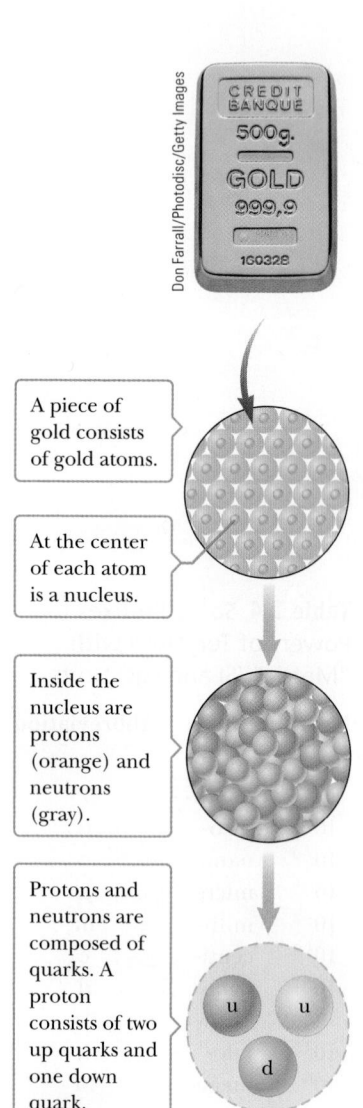

Don Farrall/Photodisc/Getty Images

A piece of gold consists of gold atoms.

At the center of each atom is a nucleus.

Inside the nucleus are protons (orange) and neutrons (gray).

Protons and neutrons are composed of quarks. A proton consists of two up quarks and one down quark.

Figure 1.2 Levels of organization in matter.

The up and down quarks are sufficient to describe all normal matter, so the existence of the other four quarks, indirectly observed in high-energy experiments, is something of a mystery. Despite strong indirect evidence, no isolated quark has ever been observed. Consequently, the possible existence of yet more fundamental particles remains purely speculative.

1.3 Dimensional Analysis

In physics the word *dimension* denotes the physical nature of a quantity. The distance between two points, for example, can be measured in feet, meters, or furlongs, which are different ways of expressing the dimension of *length*.

The symbols used in this section to specify the dimensions of length, mass, and time are L, M, and T, respectively. Brackets [ ] will often be used to denote the dimensions of a physical quantity. In this notation, for example, the dimensions of velocity v are written $[v] = L/T$, and the dimensions of area A are $[A] = L^2$. The dimensions of area, volume, velocity, and acceleration are listed in Table 1.5, along with their units in the three common systems. The dimensions of other quantities, such as force and energy, will be described later as they are introduced.

In physics it's often necessary to deal with mathematical expressions that relate different physical quantities. One way to analyze such expressions, called **dimensional analysis,** makes use of the fact that **dimensions can be treated as algebraic quantities.** Adding masses to lengths, for example, makes no sense, so it follows that quantities can be added or subtracted only if they have the same dimensions. If the terms on the opposite sides of an equation have the same dimensions, then that equation may be correct, although correctness can't be guaranteed on the basis of dimensions alone. Nonetheless, dimensional analysis has value as a partial check of an equation and can also be used to develop insight into the relationships between physical quantities.

The procedure can be illustrated by using it to develop some relationships between acceleration, velocity, time, and distance. Distance x has the dimension of length: $[x] = L$. Time t has dimension $[t] = T$. Velocity v has the dimensions length over time: $[v] = L/T$, and acceleration the dimensions length divided by time squared: $[a] = L/T^2$. Notice that velocity and acceleration have similar dimensions, except for an extra dimension of time in the denominator of acceleration. It follows that

$$[v] = \frac{L}{T} = \frac{L}{T^2}\,T = [a][t]$$

From this it might be guessed that velocity equals acceleration multiplied by time, $v = at$, and that is true for the special case of motion with constant acceleration starting at rest. Noticing that velocity has dimensions of length divided by time and distance has dimensions of length, it's reasonable to guess that

$$[x] = L = L\frac{T}{T} = \frac{L}{T}\,T = [v][t] = [a][t]^2$$

Table 1.5 Dimensions and Some Units of Area, Volume, Velocity, and Acceleration

System	Area (L^2)	Volume (L^3)	Velocity (L/T)	Acceleration (L/T^2)
SI	m^2	m^3	m/s	m/s^2
cgs	cm^2	cm^3	cm/s	cm/s^2
U.S. customary	ft^2	ft^3	ft/s	ft/s^2

Here it appears that $x = at^2$ might correctly relate the distance traveled to acceleration and time; however, that equation is not even correct in the case of constant acceleration starting from rest. The correct expression in that case is $x = \frac{1}{2}at^2$. These examples serve to show the limitations inherent in using dimensional analysis to discover relationships between physical quantities. Nonetheless, such simple procedures can still be of value in developing a preliminary mathematical model for a given physical system. Further, because it's easy to make errors when solving problems, dimensional analysis can be used to check the consistency of the results. When the dimensions in an equation are not consistent, that indicates an error has been made in a prior step.

■ EXAMPLE 1.1 | Analysis of an Equation

GOAL Check an equation using dimensional analysis.

PROBLEM Show that the expression $v = v_0 + at$ is dimensionally correct, where v and v_0 represent velocities, a is acceleration, and t is a time interval.

STRATEGY Analyze each term, finding its dimensions, and then check to see if all the terms agree with each other.

SOLUTION

Find dimensions for v and v_0.

$$[v] = [v_0] = \frac{L}{T}$$

Find the dimensions of at.

$$[at] = [a][t] = \frac{L}{T^2}(T) = \frac{L}{T}$$

REMARKS All the terms agree, so the equation is dimensionally correct.

QUESTION 1.1 True or False. An equation that is dimensionally correct is always physically correct, up to a constant of proportionality.

EXERCISE 1.1 Determine whether the equation $x = vt^2$ is dimensionally correct. If not, provide a correct expression, up to an overall constant of proportionality.

ANSWER Incorrect. The expression $x = vt$ is dimensionally correct.

■ EXAMPLE 1.2 | Find an Equation

GOAL Derive an equation by using dimensional analysis.

PROBLEM Find a relationship between a constant acceleration a, speed v, and distance r from the origin for a particle traveling in a circle.

STRATEGY Start with the term having the most dimensionality, a. Find its dimensions, and then rewrite those dimensions in terms of the dimensions of v and r. The dimensions of time will have to be eliminated with v, because that's the only quantity (other than a, itself) in which the dimension of time appears.

SOLUTION

Write down the dimensions of a:

$$[a] = \frac{L}{T^2}$$

Solve the dimensions of speed for T:

$$[v] = \frac{L}{T} \quad \rightarrow \quad T = \frac{L}{[v]}$$

Substitute the expression for T into the equation for $[a]$:

$$[a] = \frac{L}{T^2} = \frac{L}{(L/[v])^2} = \frac{[v]^2}{L}$$

Substitute L = $[r]$, and guess at the equation:

$$[a] = \frac{[v]^2}{[r]} \quad \rightarrow \quad a = \frac{v^2}{r}$$

REMARKS This is the correct equation for the magnitude of the centripetal acceleration—acceleration toward the center of motion—to be discussed in Chapter 7. In this case it isn't necessary to introduce a numerical factor. Such a factor is often displayed explicitly as a constant k in front of the right-hand side; for example, $a = kv^2/r$. As it turns out, $k = 1$ gives the correct expression. A good technique sometimes introduced in calculus-based textbooks involves using unknown powers of the dimensions. This problem would then be set up as $[a] = [v]^b[r]^c$. Writing out the dimensions and equating powers of each dimension on both sides of the equation would result in $b = 2$ and $c = -1$.

QUESTION 1.2 True or False: Replacing v by r/t in the final answer also gives a dimensionally correct equation.

EXERCISE 1.2 In physics, energy E carries dimensions of mass times length squared divided by time squared. Use dimensional analysis to derive a relationship for energy in terms of mass m and speed v, up to a constant of proportionality. Set the speed equal to c, the speed of light, and the constant of proportionality equal to 1 to get the most famous equation in physics. (Note, however, that the first relationship is associated with energy of motion, and the second with energy of mass. See Chapter 26.)

ANSWER $E = kmv^2 \rightarrow E = mc^2$ when $k = 1$ and $v = c$.

1.4 Uncertainty in Measurement and Significant Figures

Physics is a science in which mathematical laws are tested by experiment. No physical quantity can be determined with complete accuracy because our senses are physically limited, even when extended with microscopes, cyclotrons, and other instruments. Consequently, it's important to develop methods of determining the accuracy of measurements.

All measurements have uncertainties associated with them, whether or not they are explicitly stated. The accuracy of a measurement depends on the sensitivity of the apparatus, the skill of the person carrying out the measurement, and the number of times the measurement is repeated. Once the measurements, along with their uncertainties, are known, it's often the case that calculations must be carried out using those measurements. Suppose two such measurements are multiplied. When a calculator is used to obtain this product, there may be eight digits in the calculator window, but often only two or three of those numbers have any significance. The rest have no value because they imply greater accuracy than was actually achieved in the original measurements. In experimental work, determining how many numbers to retain requires the application of statistics and the mathematical propagation of uncertainties. In a textbook it isn't practical to apply those sophisticated tools in the numerous calculations, so instead a simple method, called *significant figures,* is used to indicate the approximate number of digits that should be retained at the end of a calculation. Although that method is not mathematically rigorous, it's easy to apply and works fairly well.

Suppose that in a laboratory experiment we measure the area of a rectangular plate with a meter stick. Let's assume that the accuracy to which we can measure a particular dimension of the plate is ±0.1 cm. If the length of the plate is measured to be 16.3 cm, we can claim only that it lies somewhere between 16.2 cm and 16.4 cm. In this case, we say that the measured value has three significant figures. Likewise, if the plate's width is measured to be 4.5 cm, the actual value lies between 4.4 cm and 4.6 cm. This measured value has only two significant figures. We could write the measured values as 16.3 ± 0.1 cm and 4.5 ± 0.1 cm. In general, **a significant figure is a reliably known digit** (other than a zero used to locate a decimal point). Note that in each case, the final number has some uncertainty associated with it, and is therefore not 100% reliable. Despite the uncertainty, that number is retained and considered significant because it does convey some information.

Suppose we would like to find the area of the plate by multiplying the two measured values together. The final value can range between $(16.3 - 0.1 \text{ cm})(4.5 - 0.1 \text{ cm}) = (16.2 \text{ cm})(4.4 \text{ cm}) = 71.28 \text{ cm}^2$ and $(16.3 + 0.1 \text{ cm})(4.5 + 0.1 \text{ cm}) = (16.4 \text{ cm})(4.6 \text{ cm}) = 75.44 \text{ cm}^2$. Claiming to know anything about the hundredths place, or even the tenths place, doesn't make any sense, because it's clear we can't even be certain of the units place, whether it's the 1 in 71, the 5 in 75, or somewhere in between. The tenths and the hundredths places are clearly not significant. We have *some* information about the units place, so that number is significant. Multiplying the numbers at the middle of the uncertainty ranges gives $(16.3 \text{ cm})(4.5 \text{ cm}) = 73.35 \text{ cm}^2$, which is also in the middle of the area's uncertainty range. Because the hundredths and tenths are not significant, we drop them and take the answer to be 73 cm^2, with an uncertainty of $\pm 2 \text{ cm}^2$. Note that the answer has two significant figures, the same number of figures as the least accurately known quantity being multiplied, the 4.5-cm width.

Calculations as carried out in the preceding paragraph can indicate the proper number of significant figures, but those calculations are time-consuming. Instead, two rules of thumb can be applied. The first, concerning multiplication and division, is as follows: **In multiplying (dividing) two or more quantities, the number of significant figures in the final product (quotient) is the same as the number of significant figures in the *least accurate* of the factors being combined, where *least accurate* means *having the lowest number of significant figures*.**

To get the final number of significant figures, it's usually necessary to do some rounding. If the last digit dropped is less than 5, simply drop the digit. If the last digit dropped is greater than or equal to 5, raise the last retained digit by one.[1]

Zeros may or may not be significant figures. Zeros used to position the decimal point in such numbers as 0.03 and 0.007 5 are not considered significant figures. Hence, 0.03 has one significant figure, and 0.007 5 has two.

When zeros are placed after other digits in a whole number, there is a possibility of misinterpretation. For example, suppose the mass of an object is given as 1 500 g. This value is ambiguous, because we don't know whether the last two zeros are being used to locate the decimal point or whether they represent significant figures in the measurement.

Using scientific notation to indicate the number of significant figures removes this ambiguity. In this case, we express the mass as 1.5×10^3 g if there are two significant figures in the measured value, 1.50×10^3 g if there are three significant figures, and 1.500×10^3 g if there are four. Likewise, 0.000 15 is expressed in scientific notation as 1.5×10^{-4} if it has two significant figures or as 1.50×10^{-4} if it has three significant figures. The three zeros between the decimal point and the digit 1 in the number 0.000 15 are not counted as significant figures because they only locate the decimal point. In this book, **most of the numerical examples and end-of-chapter problems will yield answers having two or three significant figures.**

For addition and subtraction, it's best to focus on the number of decimal places in the quantities involved rather than on the number of significant figures. **When numbers are added (subtracted), the number of decimal places in the result should equal the smallest number of decimal places of any term in the sum (difference).** For example, if we wish to compute 123 (zero decimal places) + 5.35 (two decimal places), the answer is 128 (zero decimal places) and not 128.35. If we compute the sum 1.000 1 (four decimal places) + 0.000 3 (four decimal places) = 1.000 4, the result has the correct number of decimal places, namely four. Observe that the rules for multiplying significant figures don't work here because the answer has five significant figures even though one of the terms in the sum, 0.000 3, has only one significant figure. Likewise, if we perform the subtraction

---

[1]Some prefer to round to the nearest even digit when the last dropped digit is 5, which has the advantage of rounding 5 up half the time and down half the time. For example, 1.55 would round to 1.6, but 1.45 would round to 1.4. Because the final significant figure is only one representative of a range of values given by the uncertainty, this very slight refinement will not be used in this text.

$1.002 - 0.998 = 0.004$, the result has three decimal places because each term in the subtraction has three decimal places.

To show why this rule should hold, we return to the first example in which we added 123 and 5.35, and rewrite these numbers as 123.*xxx* and 5.35*x*. Digits written with an *x* are completely unknown and can be any digit from 0 to 9. Now we line up 123.*xxx* and 5.35*x* relative to the decimal point and perform the addition, using the rule that an unknown digit added to a known or unknown digit yields an unknown:

$$
\begin{array}{r}
123.xxx \\
+ \quad 5.35x \\
\hline
128.xxx
\end{array}
$$

The answer of 128.*xxx* means that we are justified only in keeping the number 128 because everything after the decimal point in the sum is actually unknown. The example shows that the controlling uncertainty is introduced into an addition or subtraction by the term with the smallest number of decimal places.

■ EXAMPLE 1.3 | Carpet Calculations

GOAL Apply the rules for significant figures.

PROBLEM Several carpet installers make measurements for carpet installation in the different rooms of a restaurant, reporting their measurements with inconsistent accuracy, as compiled in Table 1.6. Compute the areas for **(a)** the banquet hall, **(b)** the meeting room, and **(c)** the dining room, taking into account significant figures. **(d)** What total area of carpet is required for these rooms?

Table 1.6 Dimensions of Rooms in Example 1.3

	Length (m)	Width (m)
Banquet hall	14.71	7.46
Meeting room	4.822	5.1
Dining room	13.8	9

STRATEGY For the multiplication problems in parts (a)–(c), count the significant figures in each number. The smaller result is the number of significant figures in the answer. Part (d) requires a sum, where the area with the least accurately known decimal place determines the overall number of significant figures in the answer.

SOLUTION

(a) Compute the area of the banquet hall.

Count significant figures:

14.71 m $\rightarrow$ 4 significant figures

7.46 m $\rightarrow$ 3 significant figures

To find the area, multiply the numbers keeping only three digits:

14.71 m $\times$ 7.46 m $= 109.74$ m^2 $\rightarrow$ $\boxed{1.10 \times 10^2 \text{ m}^2}$

(b) Compute the area of the meeting room.

Count significant figures:

4.822 m $\rightarrow$ 4 significant figures

5.1 m $\rightarrow$ 2 significant figures

To find the area, multiply the numbers keeping only two digits:

4.822 m $\times$ 5.1 m $= 24.59$ m^2 $\rightarrow$ $\boxed{25 \text{ m}^2}$

(c) Compute the area of the dining room.

Count significant figures:

13.8 m $\rightarrow$ 3 significant figures

9 m $\rightarrow$ 1 significant figure

To find the area, multiply the numbers keeping only one digit:

13.8 m $\times$ 9 m $= 124.2$ m^2 $\rightarrow$ $\boxed{100 \text{ m}^2}$

(Continued)

(d) Calculate the total area of carpet required, with the proper number of significant figures.

Sum all three answers without regard to significant figures:

$$1.10 \times 10^2 \text{ m}^2 + 25 \text{ m}^2 + 100 \text{ m}^2 = 235 \text{ m}^2$$

The least accurate number is 100 m², with one significant figure in the hundred's decimal place:

$$235 \text{ m}^2 \;\rightarrow\; \boxed{2 \times 10^2 \text{ m}^2}$$

REMARKS Notice that the final answer in part (d) has only one significant figure, in the hundredth's place, resulting in an answer that had to be rounded down by a sizable fraction of its total value. That's the consequence of having insufficient information. The value of 9 m, without any further information, represents a true value that could be anywhere in the interval [8.5 m, 9.5 m), all of which round to 9 when only one digit is retained.

QUESTION 1.3 How would the final answer change if the width of the dining room were given as 9.0 m?

EXERCISE 1.3 A ranch has two fenced rectangular areas. Area A has a length of 750 m and width 125 m, and area B has length 400 m and width 150 m. Find (a) area A, (b) area B, and (c) the total area, with attention to the rules of significant figures. Assume trailing zeros are not significant.

ANSWERS (a) $9.4 \times 10^4 \text{ m}^2$ (b) $6 \times 10^4 \text{ m}^2$ (c) $1.5 \times 10^5 \text{ m}^2$

In performing any calculation, especially one involving a number of steps, there will always be slight discrepancies introduced by both the rounding process and the algebraic order in which steps are carried out. For example, consider $2.35 \times 5.89/1.57$. This computation can be performed in three different orders. First, we have $2.35 \times 5.89 = 13.842$, which rounds to 13.8, followed by $13.8/1.57 = 8.7898$, rounding to 8.79. Second, $5.89/1.57 = 3.7516$, which rounds to 3.75, resulting in $2.35 \times 3.75 = 8.8125$, rounding to 8.81. Finally, $2.35/1.57 = 1.4968$ rounds to 1.50, and $1.50 \times 5.89 = 8.835$ rounds to 8.84. So three different algebraic orders, following the rules of rounding, lead to answers of 8.79, 8.81, and 8.84, respectively. Such minor discrepancies are to be expected, because the last significant digit is only one representative from a range of possible values, depending on experimental uncertainty. To avoid such discrepancies, some carry one or more extra digits during the calculation, although it isn't conceptually consistent to do so because those extra digits are not significant. As a practical matter, in the worked examples in this text, intermediate reported results will be rounded to the proper number of significant figures, and only those digits will be carried forward. In the problem sets, however, given data will usually be assumed accurate to two or three digits, even when there are trailing zeros. In solving the problems, the student should be aware that slight differences in rounding practices can result in answers varying from the text in the last significant digit, which is normal and not cause for concern. The method of significant figures has its limitations in determining accuracy, but it's easy to apply. In experimental work, however, statistics and the mathematical propagation of uncertainty must be used to determine the accuracy of an experimental result.

1.5 Conversion of Units

Sometimes it's necessary to convert units from one system to another. Conversion factors between the SI and U.S. customary systems for units of length are as follows:

$$1 \text{ mi} = 1\,609 \text{ m} = 1.609 \text{ km} \qquad 1 \text{ ft} = 0.304\,8 \text{ m} = 30.48 \text{ cm}$$
$$1 \text{ m} = 39.37 \text{ in.} = 3.281 \text{ ft} \qquad 1 \text{ in.} = 0.025\,4 \text{ m} = 2.54 \text{ cm}$$

A more extensive list of conversion factors can be found on the front endsheets of this book. In all the given conversion equations, the "1" on the left is assumed to have the same number of significant figures as the quantity given on the right of the equation.

Units can be treated as algebraic quantities that can "cancel" each other. We can make a fraction with the conversion that will cancel the units we don't want,

The speed limit is given in both kilometers per hour and miles per hour on this road sign. How accurate is the conversion?

and multiply that fraction by the quantity in question. For example, suppose we want to convert 15.0 in. to centimeters. Because 1 in. = 2.54 cm, we find that

$$15.0 \text{ in.} = 15.0 \text{ in.} \times \left(\frac{2.54 \text{ cm}}{1.00 \text{ in.}}\right) = 38.1 \text{ cm}$$

The next two examples show how to deal with problems involving more than one conversion and with powers.

▪ EXAMPLE 1.4 | Pull Over, Buddy!

GOAL Convert units using several conversion factors.

PROBLEM If a car is traveling at a speed of 28.0 m/s, is the driver exceeding the speed limit of 55.0 mi/h?

STRATEGY Meters must be converted to miles and seconds to hours, using the conversion factors listed on the front end-sheets of the book. Here, three factors will be used.

SOLUTION

Convert meters to miles:

$$28.0 \text{ m/s} = \left(28.0 \frac{\text{m}}{\text{s}}\right)\left(\frac{1.00 \text{ mi}}{1\,609 \text{ m}}\right) = 1.74 \times 10^{-2} \text{ mi/s}$$

Convert seconds to hours:

$$1.74 \times 10^{-2} \text{ mi/s} = \left(1.74 \times 10^{-2} \frac{\text{mi}}{\text{s}}\right)\left(60.0 \frac{\text{s}}{\text{min}}\right)\left(60.0 \frac{\text{min}}{\text{h}}\right)$$
$$= \boxed{62.6 \text{ mi/h}}$$

REMARKS The driver should slow down because he's exceeding the speed limit.

QUESTION 1.4 Repeat the conversion, using the relationship 1.00 m/s = 2.24 mi/h. Why is the answer slightly different?

EXERCISE 1.4 Convert 152 mi/h to m/s.

ANSWER 67.9 m/s

▪ EXAMPLE 1.5 | Press the Pedal to the Metal

GOAL Convert a quantity featuring powers of a unit.

PROBLEM The traffic light turns green, and the driver of a high-performance car slams the accelerator to the floor. The accelerometer registers 22.0 m/s^2. Convert this reading to km/min^2.

STRATEGY Here we need one factor to convert meters to kilometers and another two factors to convert seconds squared to minutes squared.

SOLUTION

Multiply by the three factors:

$$\frac{22.0 \text{ m}}{1.00 \text{ s}^2}\left(\frac{1.00 \text{ km}}{1.00 \times 10^3 \text{ m}}\right)\left(\frac{60.0 \text{ s}}{1.00 \text{ min}}\right)^2 = \boxed{79.2 \frac{\text{km}}{\text{min}^2}}$$

REMARKS Notice that in each conversion factor the numerator equals the denominator when units are taken into account. A common error in dealing with squares is to square the units inside the parentheses while forgetting to square the numbers!

QUESTION 1.5 What time conversion factor would be used to further convert the answer to km/h^2?

EXERCISE 1.5 Convert 4.50×10^3 kg/m^3 to g/cm^3.

ANSWER 4.50 g/cm^3

1.6 Estimates and Order-of-Magnitude Calculations

Getting an exact answer to a calculation may often be difficult or impossible, either for mathematical reasons or because limited information is available. In these cases, estimates can yield useful approximate answers that can determine whether a more precise calculation is necessary. Estimates also serve as a partial check if the exact calculations are actually carried out. If a large answer is expected but a small exact answer is obtained, there's an error somewhere.

For many problems, knowing the approximate value of a quantity—within a factor of 10 or so—is sufficient. This approximate value is called an **order-of-magnitude** estimate, and requires finding the power of 10 that is closest to the actual value of the quantity. For example, 75 kg $\sim 10^2$ kg, where the symbol $\sim$ means "is on the order of" or "is approximately." Increasing a quantity by three orders of magnitude means that its value increases by a factor of $10^3 = 1\,000$.

Occasionally the process of making such estimates results in fairly crude answers, but answers ten times or more too large or small are still useful. For example, suppose you're interested in how many people have contracted a certain disease. Any estimates under ten thousand are small compared with Earth's total population, but a million or more would be alarming. So even relatively imprecise information can provide valuable guidance.

In developing these estimates, you can take considerable liberties with the numbers. For example, $\pi \sim 1$, $27 \sim 10$, and $65 \sim 100$. To get a less crude estimate, it's permissible to use slightly more accurate numbers (e.g., $\pi \sim 3$, $27 \sim 30$, $65 \sim 70$). Better accuracy can also be obtained by systematically underestimating as many numbers as you overestimate. Some quantities may be completely unknown, but it's standard to make reasonable guesses, as the examples show.

■ EXAMPLE 1.6 | Brain Cells Estimate

GOAL Develop a simple estimate.

PROBLEM Estimate the number of cells in the human brain.

STRATEGY Estimate the volume of a human brain and divide by the estimated volume of one cell. The brain is located in the upper portion of the head, with a volume that could be approximated by a cube $\ell = 20$ cm on a side.

Brain cells, consisting of about 10% neurons and 90% glia, vary greatly in size, with dimensions ranging from a few microns to a meter or so. As a guess, take $d = 10$ microns as a typical dimension and consider a cell to be a cube with each side having that length.

SOLUTION

Estimate of the volume of a human brain:

$$V_{\text{brain}} = \ell^3 \approx (0.2 \text{ m})^3 = 8 \times 10^{-3} \text{ m}^3 \approx 1 \times 10^{-2} \text{ m}^3$$

Estimate the volume of a cell:

$$V_{\text{cell}} = d^3 \approx (10 \times 10^{-6} \text{ m})^3 = 1 \times 10^{-15} \text{ m}^3$$

Divide the volume of a brain by the volume of a cell:

$$\text{number of cells} = \frac{V_{\text{brain}}}{V_{\text{cell}}} = \frac{0.01 \text{ m}^3}{1 \times 10^{-15} \text{ m}^3} = \boxed{1 \times 10^{13} \text{ cells}}$$

REMARKS Notice how little attention was paid to obtaining precise values. Some general information about a problem is required if the estimate is to be within an order of magnitude of the actual value. Here, knowledge of the approximate dimensions of brain cells and the human brain were essential to developing the estimate.

QUESTION 1.6 Would 10^{12} cells also be a reasonable estimate? What about 10^9 cells? Explain.

EXERCISE 1.6 Estimate the total number of cells in the human body.

ANSWER 10^{14} (Answers may vary.)

■ EXAMPLE 1.7 | Stack One-Dollar Bills to the Moon

GOAL Estimate the number of stacked objects required to reach a given height.

PROBLEM How many one-dollar bills, stacked one on top of the other, would reach the Moon?

STRATEGY The distance to the Moon is about 400 000 km. Guess at the number of dollar bills in a millimeter, and multiply the distance by this number, after converting to consistent units.

SOLUTION

We estimate that ten stacked bills form a layer of 1 mm. Convert mm to km:

$$\frac{10 \text{ bills}}{1 \text{ mm}}\left(\frac{10^3 \text{ mm}}{1 \text{ m}}\right)\left(\frac{10^3 \text{ m}}{1 \text{ km}}\right) = \frac{10^7 \text{ bills}}{1 \text{ km}}$$

Multiply this value by the approximate lunar distance:

$$\text{# of dollar bills} \sim (4 \times 10^5 \text{ km})\left(\frac{10^7 \text{ bills}}{1 \text{ km}}\right) = \boxed{4 \times 10^{12} \text{ bills}}$$

REMARKS That's within an order of magnitude of the U.S. national debt!

QUESTION 1.7 Based on the answer, about how many stacked pennies would reach the Moon?

EXERCISE 1.7 How many pieces of cardboard, typically found at the back of a bound pad of paper, would you have to stack up to match the height of the Washington monument, about 170 m tall?

ANSWER $\sim 10^5$ (Answers may vary.)

■ EXAMPLE 1.8 | Number of Galaxies in the Universe

GOAL Estimate a volume and a number density, and combine.

PROBLEM Given that astronomers can see about 10 billion light years into space and that there are 14 galaxies in our local group, 2 million light years from the next local group, estimate the number of galaxies in the observable universe. (Note: One light year is the distance traveled by light in one year, about 9.5×10^{15} m.) (See Fig. 1.3.)

STRATEGY From the known information, we can estimate the number of galaxies per unit volume. The local group of 14 galaxies is contained in a sphere a million light years in radius, with the Andromeda group in a similar sphere, so there are about 10 galaxies within a volume of radius 1 million light years. Multiply that number density by the volume of the observable universe.

Figure 1.3 In this deep-space photograph, there are few stars—just galaxies without end.

SOLUTION

Compute the approximate volume V_{lg} of the local group of galaxies:

$$V_{lg} = \tfrac{4}{3}\pi r^3 \sim (10^6 \text{ ly})^3 = 10^{18} \text{ ly}^3$$

Estimate the density of galaxies:

$$\text{density of galaxies} = \frac{\text{# of galaxies}}{V_{lg}}$$

$$\sim \frac{10 \text{ galaxies}}{10^{18} \text{ ly}^3} = 10^{-17} \frac{\text{galaxies}}{\text{ly}^3}$$

Compute the approximate volume of the observable universe:

$$V_u = \tfrac{4}{3}\pi r^3 \sim (10^{10} \text{ ly})^3 = 10^{30} \text{ ly}^3$$

Multiply the density of galaxies by V_u:

$$\text{# of galaxies} \sim (\text{density of galaxies})V_u$$

$$= \left(10^{-17} \frac{\text{galaxies}}{\text{ly}^3}\right)(10^{30} \text{ ly}^3)$$

$$= \boxed{10^{13} \text{ galaxies}}$$

(Continued)

REMARKS Notice the approximate nature of the computation, which uses $4\pi/3 \sim 1$ on two occasions and $14 \sim 10$ for the number of galaxies in the local group. This is completely justified: Using the actual numbers would be pointless, because the other assumptions in the problem—the size of the observable universe and the idea that the local galaxy density is representative of the density everywhere—are also very rough approximations. Further, there was nothing in the problem that required using volumes of spheres rather than volumes of cubes. Despite all these arbitrary choices, the answer still gives useful information, because it rules out a lot of reasonable possible answers. Before doing the calculation, a guess of a billion galaxies might have seemed plausible.

QUESTION 1.8 About one in ten galaxies in the local group are not dwarf galaxies. Estimate the number of galaxies in the universe that are not dwarfs.

EXERCISE 1.8 (a) Given that the nearest star is about 4 light years away, develop an estimate of the density of stars per cubic light year in our galaxy. (b) Estimate the number of stars in the Milky Way galaxy, given that it's roughly a disk 100 000 light years across and a thousand light years thick.

ANSWER (a) 0.02 stars/ly^3 (b) 2×10^{11} stars (Estimates will vary. The actual answer is probably about twice that number.)

1.7 Coordinate Systems

Many aspects of physics deal with locations in space, which require the definition of a coordinate system. A point on a line can be located with one coordinate, a point in a plane with two coordinates, and a point in space with three.

A coordinate system used to specify locations in space consists of the following:

- A fixed reference point O, called the *origin*
- A set of specified axes, or directions, with an appropriate scale and labels on the axes
- Instructions on labeling a point in space relative to the origin and axes

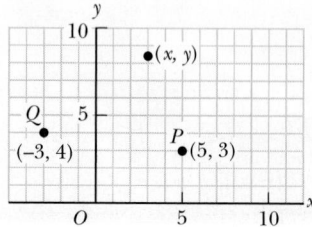

Figure 1.4 Designation of points in a two-dimensional Cartesian coordinate system. Every point is labeled with coordinates (x, y).

One convenient and commonly used coordinate system is the **Cartesian coordinate system,** sometimes called the **rectangular coordinate system.** Such a system in two dimensions is illustrated in Figure 1.4. An arbitrary point in this system is labeled with the coordinates (x, y). For example, the point P in the figure has coordinates $(5, 3)$. If we start at the origin O, we can reach P by moving 5 meters horizontally to the right and then 3 meters vertically upward. In the same way, the point Q has coordinates $(-3, 4)$, which corresponds to going 3 meters horizontally to the left of the origin and 4 meters vertically upward from there.

Positive x is usually selected as right of the origin and positive y upward from the origin, but in two dimensions this choice is largely a matter of taste. (In three dimensions, however, there are "right-handed" and "left-handed" coordinates, which lead to minus sign differences in certain operations. These will be addressed as needed.)

Sometimes it's more convenient to locate a point in space by its **plane polar coordinates** (r, θ), as in Figure 1.5. In this coordinate system, an origin O and a reference line are selected as shown. A point is then specified by the distance r from the origin to the point and by the angle θ between the reference line and a line drawn from the origin to the point. The standard reference line is usually selected to be the positive x-axis of a Cartesian coordinate system. The angle θ is considered positive when measured counterclockwise from the reference line and negative when measured clockwise. For example, if a point is specified by the polar coordinates 3 m and 60°, we locate this point by moving out 3 m from the origin at an angle of 60° above (counterclockwise from) the reference line. A point specified by polar coordinates 3 m and −60° is located 3 m out from the origin and 60° below (clockwise from) the reference line.

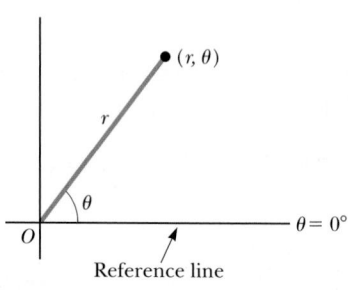

Figure 1.5 The plane polar coordinates of a point are represented by the distance r and the angle θ, where θ is measured counterclockwise from the positive x-axis.

1.8 Trigonometry

Consider the right triangle shown in Active Figure 1.6, where side y is opposite the angle θ, side x is adjacent to the angle θ, and side r is the hypotenuse of the triangle. The basic trigonometric functions defined by such a triangle are the ratios of the lengths of the sides of the triangle. These relationships are called the sine (sin), cosine (cos), and tangent (tan) functions. In terms of θ, the basic trigonometric functions are as follows:[2]

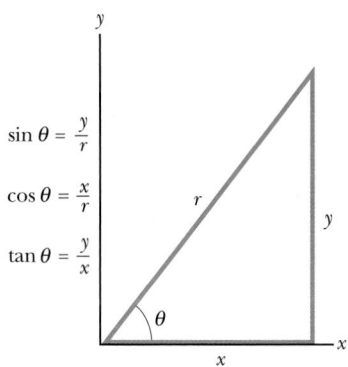

$$\sin \theta = \frac{\text{side opposite } \theta}{\text{hypotenuse}} = \frac{y}{r}$$

$$\cos \theta = \frac{\text{side adjacent to } \theta}{\text{hypotenuse}} = \frac{x}{r} \qquad [1.1]$$

$$\tan \theta = \frac{\text{side opposite } \theta}{\text{side adjacent to } \theta} = \frac{y}{x}$$

Active Figure 1.6
Certain trigonometric functions of a right triangle.

For example, if the angle θ is equal to $30°$, then the ratio of y to r is always 0.50; that is, $\sin 30° = 0.50$. Note that the sine, cosine, and tangent functions are quantities without units because each represents the ratio of two lengths.

Another important relationship, called the **Pythagorean theorem,** exists between the lengths of the sides of a right triangle:

$$r^2 = x^2 + y^2 \qquad [1.2]$$

Finally, it will often be necessary to find the values of inverse relationships. For example, suppose you know that the sine of an angle is 0.866, but you need to know the value of the angle itself. The inverse sine function may be expressed as $\sin^{-1}(0.866)$, which is a shorthand way of asking the question "What angle has a sine of 0.866?" Punching a couple of buttons on your calculator reveals that this angle is $60.0°$. Try it for yourself and show that $\tan^{-1}(0.400) = 21.8°$. Be sure that your calculator is set for degrees and not radians. In addition, the inverse tangent function can return only values between $-90°$ and $+90°$, so when an angle is in the second or third quadrant, it's necessary to add $180°$ to the answer in the calculator window.

The definitions of the trigonometric functions and the inverse trigonometric functions, as well as the Pythagorean theorem, can be applied to *any* right triangle, regardless of whether its sides correspond to x- and y-coordinates.

These results from trigonometry are useful in converting from rectangular coordinates to polar coordinates, or vice versa, as the next example shows.

Tip 1.3 Degrees vs. Radians

When calculating trigonometric functions, make sure your calculator setting—degrees or radians—is consistent with the degree measure you're using in a given problem.

■ EXAMPLE 1.9   Cartesian and Polar Coordinates

GOAL Understand how to convert from plane rectangular coordinates to plane polar coordinates and vice versa.

PROBLEM **(a)** The Cartesian coordinates of a point in the xy-plane are $(x, y) = (-3.50 \text{ m}, -2.50 \text{ m})$, as shown in Active Figure 1.7. Find the polar coordinates of this point. **(b)** Convert $(r, \theta) = (5.00 \text{ m}, 37.0°)$ to rectangular coordinates.

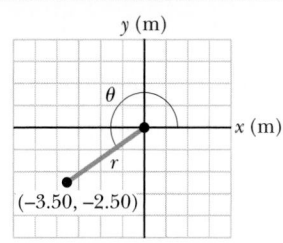

Active Figure 1.7
(Example 1.9) Converting from Cartesian coordinates to polar coordinates.

STRATEGY Apply the trigonometric functions and their inverses, together with the Pythagorean theorem.

(Continued)

---

[2]Many people use the mnemonic *SOHCAHTOA* to remember the basic trigonometric formulas: *S*ine = *O*pposite/*H*ypotenuse, *C*osine = *A*djacent/*H*ypotenuse, and *T*angent = *O*pposite/*A*djacent. (Thanks go to Professor Don Chodrow for pointing this out.)

SOLUTION

(a) Cartesian to Polar conversion

Take the square root of both sides of Equation 1.2 to find the radial coordinate:

$$r = \sqrt{x^2 + y^2} = \sqrt{(-3.50 \text{ m})^2 + (-2.50 \text{ m})^2} = \boxed{4.30 \text{ m}}$$

Use Equation 1.1 for the tangent function to find the angle with the inverse tangent, adding 180° because the angle is actually in third quadrant:

$$\tan \theta = \frac{y}{x} = \frac{-2.50 \text{ m}}{-3.50 \text{ m}} = 0.714$$

$$\theta = \tan^{-1}(0.714) = 35.5° + 180° = \boxed{216°}$$

(b) Polar to Cartesian conversion

Use the trigonometric definitions, Equation 1.1.

$$x = r \cos \theta = (5.00 \text{ m}) \cos 37.0° = \boxed{3.99 \text{ m}}$$

$$y = r \sin \theta = (5.00 \text{ m}) \sin 37.0° = \boxed{3.01 \text{ m}}$$

REMARKS When we take up vectors in two dimensions in Chapter 3, we will routinely use a similar process to find the direction and magnitude of a given vector from its components, or, conversely, to find the components from the vector's magnitude and direction.

QUESTION 1.9 Starting with the answers to part (b), work backwards to recover the given radius and angle. Why are there slight differences from the original quantities?

EXERCISE 1.9 **(a)** Find the polar coordinates corresponding to $(x, y) = (-3.25 \text{ m}, 1.50 \text{ m})$. **(b)** Find the Cartesian coordinates corresponding to $(r, \theta) = (4.00 \text{ m}, 53.0°)$

ANSWERS (a) $(r, \theta) = (3.58 \text{ m}, 155°)$ (b) $(x, y) = (2.41 \text{ m}, 3.19 \text{ m})$

■ EXAMPLE 1.10 | How High Is the Building?

GOAL Apply basic results of trigonometry.

PROBLEM A person measures the height of a building by walking out a distance of 46.0 m from its base and shining a flashlight beam toward the top. When the beam is elevated at an angle of 39.0° with respect to the horizontal, as shown in Figure 1.8, the beam just strikes the top of the building. **(a)** If the flashlight is held at a height of 2.00 m, find the height of the building. **(b)** Calculate the length of the light beam.

STRATEGY Refer to the right triangle shown in the figure. We know the angle, 39.0°, and the length of the side adjacent to it. Because the height of the building is the side opposite the angle, we can use the tangent function. With the adjacent and opposite sides known, we can then find the hypotenuse with the Pythagorean theorem.

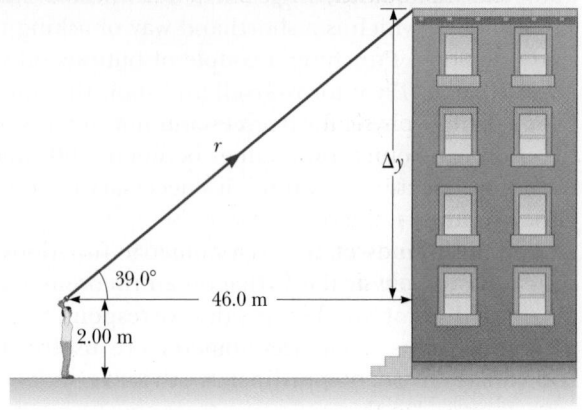

Figure 1.8 (Example 1.10)

SOLUTION

(a) Find the height of the building.

Use the tangent of the given angle:

$$\tan 39.0° = \frac{\Delta y}{46.0 \text{ m}}$$

Solve for the height:

$$\Delta y = (\tan 39.0°)(46.0 \text{ m}) = (0.810)(46.0 \text{ m}) = 37.3 \text{ m}$$

Add 2.00 m to Δy to obtain the height:

$$\text{height} = \boxed{39.3 \text{ m}}$$

(b) Calculate the length of the light beam.

Use the Pythagorean theorem:

$$r = \sqrt{x^2 + y^2} = \sqrt{(37.3 \text{ m})^2 + (46.0 \text{ m})^2} = \boxed{59.2 \text{ m}}$$

REMARKS In a later chapter, right-triangle trigonometry is often used when working with vectors.

QUESTION 1.10 Could the distance traveled by the light beam be found without using the Pythagorean theorem? How?

EXERCISE 1.10 While standing atop a building 50.0 m tall, you spot a friend standing on a street corner. Using a protractor and dangling a plumb bob, you find that the angle between the horizontal and the direction to the spot on the sidewalk where your friend is standing is 25.0°. Your eyes are located 1.75 m above the top of the building. How far away from the foot of the building is your friend?

ANSWER 111 m

1.9 Problem-Solving Strategy

Most courses in general physics require the student to learn the skills used in solving problems, and examinations usually include problems that test such skills. This brief section presents some useful suggestions that will help increase your success in solving problems. An organized approach to problem solving will also enhance your understanding of physical concepts and reduce exam stress. Throughout the book, there will be a number of sections labeled "Problem-Solving Strategy," many of them just a specializing of the list given below (and illustrated in Fig. 1.9).

General Problem-Solving Strategy

Problem
1. **Read** the problem carefully at least twice. Be sure you understand the nature of the problem before proceeding further.
2. **Draw** a diagram while rereading the problem.
3. **Label** all physical quantities in the diagram, using letters that remind you what the quantity is (e.g., *m* for mass). Choose a coordinate system and label it.

Strategy
4. **Identify** physical principles, the knowns and unknowns, and list them. Put circles around the unknowns. There must be as many equations as there are unknowns.
5. **Equations**, the relationships between the labeled physical quantities, should be written down next. Naturally, the selected equations should be consistent with the physical principles identified in the previous step.

Solution
6. **Solve** the set of equations for the unknown quantities in terms of the known. Do this algebraically, without substituting values until the next step, except where terms are zero.
7. **Substitute** the known values, together with their units. Obtain a numerical value with units for each unknown.

Check Answer
8. **Check** your answer. Do the units match? Is the answer reasonable? Does the plus or minus sign make sense? Is your answer consistent with an order of magnitude estimate?

Figure 1.9 A guide to problem solving.

This same procedure, with minor variations, should be followed throughout the course. The first three steps are extremely important, because they get you mentally oriented. Identifying the proper concepts and physical principles assists you in choosing the correct equations. The equations themselves are essential, because when you understand them, you also understand the relationships between the physical quantities. This understanding comes through a lot of daily practice.

Equations are the tools of physics: To solve problems, you have to have them at hand, like a plumber and his wrenches. Know the equations, and understand

Tip 1.4 Get Used to Symbolic Algebra

Whenever possible, solve problems symbolically and then substitute known values. This process helps prevent errors and clarifies the relationships between physical quantities.

what they mean and how to use them. Just as you can't have a conversation without knowing the local language, you can't solve physics problems without knowing and understanding the equations. This understanding grows as you study and apply the concepts and the equations relating them.

Carrying through the algebra for as long as possible, substituting numbers only at the end, is also important, because it helps you think in terms of the physical quantities involved, not merely the numbers that represent them. Many beginning physics students are eager to substitute, but once numbers are substituted it's harder to understand relationships and easier to make mistakes.

The physical layout and organization of your work will make the final product more understandable and easier to follow. Although physics is a challenging discipline, your chances of success are excellent if you maintain a positive attitude and keep trying.

EXAMPLE 1.11 | A Round Trip by Air

GOAL Illustrate the Problem-Solving Strategy.

PROBLEM An airplane travels $x = 4.50 \times 10^2$ km due east and then travels an unknown distance y due north. Finally, it returns to its starting point by traveling a distance of $r = 525$ km. How far did the airplane travel in the northerly direction?

STRATEGY We've finished reading the problem (step 1), and have drawn a diagram (step 2) in Figure 1.10 and labeled it (step 3). From the diagram, we recognize a right triangle and identify (step 4) the principle involved: the Pythagorean theorem. Side y is the unknown quantity, and the other sides are known.

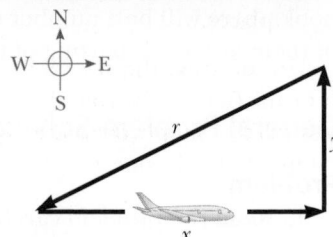

Figure 1.10 (Example 1.11)

SOLUTION

Write the Pythagorean theorem (step 5):

$$r^2 = x^2 + y^2$$

Solve symbolically for y (step 6):

$$y^2 = r^2 - x^2 \quad \rightarrow \quad y = +\sqrt{r^2 - x^2}$$

Substitute the numbers, with units (step 7):

$$y = \sqrt{(525 \text{ km})^2 - (4.50 \times 10^2 \text{ km})^2} = \boxed{2.70 \times 10^2 \text{ km}}$$

REMARKS Note that the negative solution has been disregarded, because it's not physically meaningful. In checking (step 8), note that the units are correct and that an approximate answer can be obtained by using the easier quantities, 500 km and 400 km. Doing so gives an answer of 300 km, which is approximately the same as our calculated answer of 270 km.

QUESTION 1.11 What is the answer if both the distance traveled due east and the direct return distance are both doubled?

EXERCISE 1.11 A plane flies 345 km due south, then turns and flies 615 km at a heading north of east, until it's due east of its starting point. If the plane now turns and heads for home, how far will it have to go?

ANSWER 509 km

SUMMARY

1.1 Standards of Length, Mass, and Time
The physical quantities in the study of mechanics can be expressed in terms of three fundamental quantities: length, mass, and time, which have the SI units meters (m), kilograms (kg), and seconds (s), respectively.

1.2 The Building Blocks of Matter
Matter is made of atoms, which in turn are made up of a relatively small nucleus of protons and neutrons within a

cloud of electrons. Protons and neutrons are composed of still smaller particles, called quarks.

1.3 Dimensional Analysis
Dimensional analysis can be used to check equations and to assist in deriving them. When the dimensions on both sides of the equation agree, the equation is often correct up to a numerical factor. When the dimensions don't agree, the equation must be wrong.

1.4 Uncertainty in Measurement and Significant Figures

No physical quantity can be determined with complete accuracy. The concept of significant figures affords a basic method of handling these uncertainties. A significant figure is a reliably known digit, other than a zero, used to locate the decimal point. The two rules of significant figures are as follows:

1. When multiplying or dividing using two or more quantities, the result should have the same number of significant figures as the quantity having the fewest significant figures.
2. When quantities are added or subtracted, the number of decimal places in the result should be the same as in the quantity with the fewest decimal places.

Use of scientific notation can avoid ambiguity in significant figures. In rounding, if the last digit dropped is less than 5, simply drop the digit; otherwise, raise the last retained digit by one.

1.5 Conversion of Units

Units in physics equations must always be consistent. In solving a physics problem, it's best to start with consistent units, using the table of conversion factors on the front endsheets as necessary.

Converting units is a matter of multiplying the given quantity by a fraction, with one unit in the numerator and its equivalent in the other units in the denominator, arranged so the unwanted units in the given quantity are canceled out in favor of the desired units.

1.6 Estimates and Order-of-Magnitude Calculations

Sometimes it's useful to find an approximate answer to a question, either because the math is difficult or because information is incomplete. A quick estimate can also be used to check a more detailed calculation. In an order-of-magnitude calculation, each value is replaced by the closest power of ten, which sometimes must be guessed or estimated when the value is unknown. The computation is then carried out. For quick estimates involving known values, each value can first be rounded to one significant figure.

1.7 Coordinate Systems

The Cartesian coordinate system consists of two perpendicular axes, usually called the x-axis and y-axis, with each axis labeled with all numbers from negative infinity to positive infinity. Points are located by specifying the x- and y-values. Polar coordinates consist of a radial coordinate r, which is the distance from the origin, and an angular coordinate θ, which is the angular displacement from the positive x-axis.

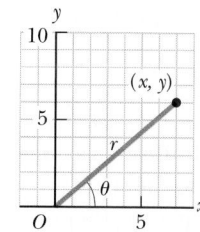

A point in the plane can be described with Cartesian coordinates (x, y) or with the polar coordinates (r, θ).

1.8 Trigonometry

The three most basic trigonometric functions of a right triangle are the sine, cosine, and tangent, defined as follows:

$$\sin \theta = \frac{\text{side opposite } \theta}{\text{hypotenuse}} = \frac{y}{r}$$

$$\cos \theta = \frac{\text{side adjacent to } \theta}{\text{hypotenuse}} = \frac{x}{r} \qquad [1.1]$$

$$\tan \theta = \frac{\text{side opposite } \theta}{\text{side adjacent to } \theta} = \frac{y}{x}$$

The **Pythagorean theorem** is an important relationship between the lengths of the sides of a right triangle:

$$r^2 = x^2 + y^2 \qquad [1.2]$$

where r is the hypotenuse of the triangle and x and y are the other two sides.

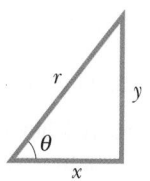

■ MULTIPLE-CHOICE QUESTIONS

WebAssign The multiple-choice questions in this chapter may be assigned online in Enhanced WebAssign.

1. A rectangular airstrip measures 32.30 m by 210 m, with the width measured more accurately than the length. Find the area, taking into account significant figures. (a) $6.783\ 0 \times 10^3$ m^2 (b) 6.783×10^3 m^2 (c) 6.78×10^3 m^2 (d) 6.8×10^3 m^2 (e) 7×10^3 m^2

2. Suppose two quantities, A and B, have different dimensions. Determine which of the following arithmetic operations *could* be physically meaningful. (a) $A + B$ (b) $B - A$ (c) $A - B$ (d) A/B (e) AB

3. Newton's second law of motion (Chapter 4) says that the mass of an object times its acceleration is equal to the net force on the object. Which of the following gives the correct units for force? (a) kg · m/s^2 (b) kg · m^2/s^2 (c) kg/m · s^2 (d) kg · m^2/s (e) none of these

4. Use the rules for significant figures to find the answer to the addition problem $21.4 + 15 + 17.17 + 4.003$. (a) 57.573 (b) 57.57 (c) 57.6 (d) 58 (e) 60

5. The Roman cubitus is an ancient unit of measure equivalent to about 445 mm. Convert the 2.00-m height of a basketball forward to cubiti. (a) 2.52 cubiti (b) 3.12 cubiti (c) 4.49 cubiti (d) 5.33 cubiti (e) none of these

6. A house is advertised as having 1 420 square feet under roof. What is the area of this house in square meters? (a) 115 m² (b) 132 m² (c) 176 m² (d) 222 m² (e) none of these

7. Answer each question yes or no. Must two quantities have the same dimensions (a) if you are adding them? (b) If you are multiplying them? (c) If you are subtracting them? (d) If you are dividing them? (e) If you are equating them?

8. Find the polar coordinates corresponding to a point located at (−5.00, 12.00) in Cartesian coordinates. (a) (13.0, −67.4°) (b) (13.0, 113°) (c) (14.2, −67.4°) (d) (14.2, 113°) (e) (19, −72.5°)

9. Which of the following relationships is dimensionally consistent with an expression yielding a value for accel-
eration? Acceleration has the units of distance divided by time squared. In these equations, x is a distance, t is time, and v is velocity with units of distance divided by time. (a) v/t^2 (b) v/x^2 (c) v^2/t (d) v^2/x (e) none of these

10. The price of gasoline at a particular station is 1.5 euros per liter. An American student can use 33 euros to buy gasoline. Knowing that 4 quarts make a gallon and that one liter is close to one quart, she quickly reasons that she can buy how many gallons of gasoline? (a) less than 1 gallon (b) about 5 gallons (c) about 8 gallons (d) more than 10 gallons

11. At a horizontal distance of 45 m from a tree, the angle of elevation to the top of the tree is 26°. How tall is the tree? (a) 22 m (b) 31 m (c) 45 m (d) 16 m (e) 11 m

12. A calculator displays a result as 1.365 248 0 × 10⁷ kg. The estimated uncertainty in the result is ±2 × 10⁵ kg. How many digits should be included as significant when the result is written down? (a) zero (b) one (c) two (d) three (e) four

CONCEPTUAL QUESTIONS

WebAssign The conceptual questions in this chapter may be assigned online in Enhanced WebAssign.

1. Estimate the order of magnitude of the length, in meters, of each of the following: (a) a mouse, (b) a pool cue, (c) a basketball court, (d) an elephant, (e) a city block.

2. What types of natural phenomena could serve as time standards?

3. Find the order of magnitude of your age in seconds.

4. An object with a mass of 1 kg weighs approximately 2 lb. Use this information to estimate the mass of the following objects: (a) a baseball; (b) your physics textbook; (c) a pickup truck.

5. BIO (a) Estimate the number of times your heart beats in a month. (b) Estimate the number of human heartbeats in an average lifetime.

6. Estimate the number of atoms in 1 cm³ of a solid. (Note that the diameter of an atom is about 10⁻¹⁰ m.)

7. The height of a horse is sometimes given in units of "hands." Why is this a poor standard of length?

8. How many of the lengths or time intervals given in Tables 1.2 and 1.3 could you verify, using only equipment found in a typical dormitory room?

9. (a) If an equation is dimensionally correct, does this mean that the equation must be true? (b) If an equation is not dimensionally correct, does this mean that the equation can't be true? Explain your answers.

10. Why is the metric system of units considered superior to most other systems of units?

11. How can an estimate be of value even when it is off by an order of magnitude? Explain and give an example.

PROBLEMS

WebAssign The problems in this chapter may be assigned online in Enhanced WebAssign. Selected problems also have Watch It video solutions.
1. denotes straightforward problem; 2. denotes intermediate problem;
3. denotes challenging problem
1. denotes full solution available in *Student Solutions Manual/ Study Guide*

1. denotes problems most often assigned in Enhanced WebAssign
BIO denotes biomedical problems
GP denotes guided problems
M denotes Master It tutorial available in Enhanced WebAssign
QC denotes asking for quantitative and conceptual reasoning
S denotes symbolic reasoning problem

1.3 Dimensional Analysis

1. The period of a simple pendulum, defined as the time necessary for one complete oscillation, is measured in time units and is given by

$$T = 2\pi\sqrt{\frac{\ell}{g}}$$

where ℓ is the length of the pendulum and g is the acceleration due to gravity, in units of length divided by time squared. Show that this equation is dimensionally consistent. (You might want to check the formula using your keys at the end of a string and a stopwatch.)

2. (a) Suppose that the displacement of an object is related to time according to the expression $x = Bt^2$. What are the dimensions of B? (b) A displacement is related to time as $x = A \sin (2\pi ft)$, where A and f are constants. Find the dimensions of A. (*Hint:* A trigonometric function appearing in an equation must be dimensionless.)

3. **S** A shape that covers an area A and has a uniform height h has a volume $V = Ah$. (a) Show that $V = Ah$ is dimensionally correct. (b) Show that the volumes of a cylinder and of a rectangular box can be written in the form $V = Ah$, identifying A in each case. (Note that A, sometimes called the "footprint" of the object, can have any shape and that the height can, in general, be replaced by the average thickness of the object.)

4. Each of the following equations was given by a student during an examination: (a) $\frac{1}{2}mv^2 = \frac{1}{2}mv_0{}^2 + \sqrt{mgh}$ (b) $v = v_0 + at^2$ (c) $ma = v^2$. Do a dimensional analysis of each equation and explain why the equation can't be correct.

5. Newton's law of universal gravitation is represented by

$$F = G\frac{Mm}{r^2}$$

where F is the gravitational force, M and m are masses, and r is a length. Force has the SI units $kg \cdot m/s^2$. What are the SI units of the proportionality constant G?

6. **Q|C** Kinetic energy KE (Chapter 5) has dimensions $kg \cdot m^2/s^2$. It can be written in terms of the momentum p (Chapter 6) and mass m as

$$KE = \frac{p^2}{2m}$$

(a) Determine the proper units for momentum using dimensional analysis. (b) Refer to Problem 5. Given the units of force, write a simple equation relating a constant force F exerted on an object, an interval of time t during which the force is applied, and the resulting momentum of the object, p.

1.4 Uncertainty in Measurement and Significant Figures

7. A carpet is to be installed in a room of length 9.72 m and width 5.3 m. Find the area of the room retaining the proper number of significant figures.

8. **Q|C** Use your calculator to determine $(\sqrt{8})^3$ to three significant figures in two ways: (a) Find $\sqrt{8}$ to four significant figures; then cube this number and round to three significant figures. (b) Find $\sqrt{8}$ to three significant figures; then cube this number and round to three significant figures. (c) Which answer is more accurate? Explain.

9. How many significant figures are there in (a) 78.9 ± 0.2, (b) 3.788×10^9, (c) 2.46×10^{-6}, (d) $0.003\,2$

10. The speed of light is now defined to be $2.997\,924\,58 \times 10^8$ m/s. Express the speed of light to (a) three significant figures, (b) five significant figures, and (c) seven significant figures.

11. **Q|C** A block of gold has length 5.62 cm, width 6.35 cm, and height 2.78 cm. (a) Calculate the length times the width and round the answer to the appropriate number of significant figures. (b) Now multiply the rounded result of part (a) by the height and again round, obtaining the volume. (c) Repeat the process, first finding the width times the height, rounding it, and then obtaining the volume by multiplying by the length. (d) Explain why the answers don't agree in the third significant figure.

12. The radius of a circle is measured to be (10.5 ± 0.2) m. Calculate (a) the area and (b) the circumference of the circle, and give the uncertainty in each value.

13. The edges of a shoebox are measured to be 11.4 cm, 17.8 cm, and 29 cm. Determine the volume of the box retaining the proper number of significant figures in your answer.

14. Carry out the following arithmetic operations: (a) the sum of the measured values 756, 37.2, 0.83, and 2.5; (b) the product $0.003\,2 \times 356.3$; (c) the product $5.620 \times \pi$.

1.5 Conversion of Units

15. A fathom is a unit of length, usually reserved for measuring the depth of water. A fathom is approximately 6 ft in length. Take the distance from Earth to the Moon to be 250 000 miles, and use the given approximation to find the distance in fathoms.

16. A small turtle moves at a speed of 186 furlongs per fortnight. Find the speed of the turtle in centimeters per second. Note that 1 furlong = 220 yards and 1 fortnight = 14 days.

17. A firkin is an old British unit of volume equal to 9 gallons. How many cubic meters are there in 6.00 firkins?

18. Find the height or length of these natural wonders in kilometers, meters, and centimeters: (a) The longest cave system in the world is the Mammoth Cave system in Central Kentucky, with a mapped length of 348 miles. (b) In the United States, the waterfall with the greatest single drop is Ribbon Falls in California, which drops 1 612 ft. (c) At 20 320 feet, Mount McKinley in Alaska is America's highest mountain. (d) The

deepest canyon in the United States is King's Canyon in California, with a depth of 8 200 ft.

19. A car is traveling at a speed of 38.0 m/s on an interstate highway where the speed limit is 75.0 mi/h. Is the driver exceeding the speed limit? Justify your answer.

20. A certain car has a fuel efficiency of 25.0 miles per gallon (mi/gal). Express this efficiency in kilometers per liter (km/L).

21. The diameter of a sphere is measured to be 5.36 in. Find (a) the radius of the sphere in centimeters, (b) the surface area of the sphere in square centimeters, and (c) the volume of the sphere in cubic centimeters.

22. **BIO** Suppose your hair grows at the rate of 1/32 inch per day. Find the rate at which it grows in nanometers per second. Because the distance between atoms in a molecule is on the order of 0.1 nm, your answer suggests how rapidly atoms are assembled in this protein synthesis.

23. The speed of light is about 3.00×10^8 m/s. Convert this figure to miles per hour.

24. **M** A house is 50.0 ft long and 26 ft wide and has 8.0-ft-high ceilings. What is the volume of the interior of the house in cubic meters and in cubic centimeters?

25. The amount of water in reservoirs is often measured in acre-ft. One acre-ft is a volume that covers an area of one acre to a depth of one foot. An acre is 43 560 ft^2. Find the volume in SI units of a reservoir containing 25.0 acre-ft of water.

26. The base of a pyramid covers an area of 13.0 acres (1 acre = 43 560 ft^2) and has a height of 481 ft (Fig. P1.26). If the volume of a pyramid is given by the expression $V = bh/3$, where b is the area of the base and h is the height, find the volume of this pyramid in cubic meters.

Figure P1.26

27. A quart container of ice cream is to be made in the form of a cube. What should be the length of a side, in centimeters? (Use the conversion 1 gallon = 3.786 liter.)

1.6 Estimates and Order-of-Magnitude Calculations

Note: In developing answers to the problems in this section, you should state your important assumptions, including the numerical values assigned to parameters used in the solution.

28. Estimate the number of steps you would have to take to walk a distance equal to the circumference of the Earth.

29. **BIO** Estimate the number of breaths taken by a human being during an average lifetime.

30. **BIO** Estimate the number of people in the world who are suffering from the common cold on any given day. (Answers may vary. Remember that a person suffers from a cold for about a week.)

31. **BIO** **Q|C** (a) About how many microorganisms are found in the human intestinal tract? (A typical bacterial length scale is one micron = 10^{-6} m. Estimate the intestinal volume and assume bacteria occupy one hundredth of it.) (b) Discuss your answer to part (a). Are these bacteria beneficial, dangerous, or neutral? What functions could they serve?

32. **BIO** Treat a cell in a human as a sphere of radius 1.0 μm. (a) Determine the volume of a cell. (b) Estimate the volume of your body. (c) Estimate the number of cells in your body.

33. An automobile tire is rated to last for 50 000 miles. Estimate the number of revolutions the tire will make in its lifetime.

34. **BIO** **Q|C** Bacteria and other prokaryotes are found deep underground, in water, and in the air. One micron (10^{-6} m) is a typical length scale associated with these microbes. (a) Estimate the total number of bacteria and other prokaryotes in the biosphere of the Earth. (b) Estimate the total mass of all such microbes. (c) Discuss the relative importance of humans and microbes to the ecology of planet Earth. Can *Homo sapiens* survive without them?

1.7 Coordinate Systems

35. **M** A point is located in a polar coordinate system by the coordinates $r = 2.5$ m and $\theta = 35°$. Find the *x*- and *y*-coordinates of this point, assuming that the two coordinate systems have the same origin.

36. A certain corner of a room is selected as the origin of a rectangular coordinate system. If a fly is crawling on an adjacent wall at a point having coordinates (2.0, 1.0), where the units are meters, what is the distance of the fly from the corner of the room?

37. Express the location of the fly in Problem 36 in polar coordinates.

38. Two points in a rectangular coordinate system have the coordinates (5.0, 3.0) and (−3.0, 4.0), where the units are centimeters. Determine the distance between these points.

39. Two points are given in polar coordinates by $(r, \theta) =$ (2.00 m, 50.0°) and $(r, \theta) = $ (5.00 m, −50.0°), respectively. What is the distance between them?

40. **S** Given points (r_1, θ_1) and (r_2, θ_2) in polar coordinates, obtain a general formula for the distance between them. Simplify it as much as possible using

the identity $\cos^2\theta + \sin^2\theta = 1$. *Hint:* Write the expressions for the two points in Cartesian coordinates and substitute into the usual distance formula.

1.8 Trigonometry

41. M For the triangle shown in Figure P1.41, what are (a) the length of the unknown side, (b) the tangent of θ, and (c) the sine of ϕ?

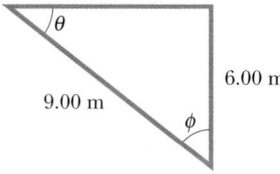

Figure P1.41

42. A ladder 9.00 m long leans against the side of a building. If the ladder is inclined at an angle of 75.0° to the horizontal, what is the horizontal distance from the bottom of the ladder to the building?

43. A high fountain of water is located at the center of a circular pool as shown in Figure P1.43. Not wishing to get his feet wet, a student walks around the pool and measures its circumference to be 15.0 m. Next, the student stands at the edge of the pool and uses a protractor to gauge the angle of elevation at the bottom of the fountain to be 55.0°. How high is the fountain?

Figure P1.43

44. A right triangle has a hypotenuse of length 3.00 m, and one of its angles is 30.0°. What are the lengths of (a) the side opposite the 30.0° angle and (b) the side adjacent to the 30.0° angle?

45. In Figure P1.45, find (a) the side opposite θ, (b) the side adjacent to ϕ, (c) $\cos\theta$, (d) $\sin\phi$, and (e) $\tan\phi$.

46. In a certain right triangle, the two sides that are perpendicular to each other are 5.00 m and 7.00 m long. What is the length of the third side of the triangle?

Figure P1.45

47. In Problem 46, what is the tangent of the angle for which 5.00 m is the opposite side?

48. GP S A woman measures the angle of elevation of a mountaintop as 12.0°. After walking 1.00 km closer to the mountain on level ground, she finds the angle to be 14.0°. (a) Draw a picture of the problem, neglecting the height of the woman's eyes above the ground. *Hint:* Use two triangles. (b) Select variable names for the mountain height (suggestion: y) and the woman's original distance from the mountain (suggestion: x) and label the picture. (c) Using the labeled picture and the tangent function, write two trigonometric equations relating the two selected variables. (d) Find the height

y of the mountain by first solving one equation for x and substituting the result into the other equation.

49. A surveyor measures the distance across a straight river by the following method: Starting directly across from a tree on the opposite bank, he walks $x = 100$ m along the riverbank to establish a baseline. Then he sights across to the tree. The angle from his baseline to the tree is $\theta = 35.0°$ (Fig. P1.49). How wide is the river?

Figure P1.49

50. S Refer to Problem 48. Suppose the mountain height is y, the woman's original distance from the mountain is x, and the angle of elevation she measures from the horizontal to the top of the mountain is θ. If she moves a distance d closer to the mountain and measures an angle of elevation ϕ, find a general equation for the height of the mountain y in terms of d, ϕ, and θ, neglecting the height of her eyes above the ground.

Additional Problems

51. (a) One of the fundamental laws of motion states that the acceleration of an object is directly proportional to the resultant force on it and inversely proportional to its mass. If the proportionality constant is defined to have no dimensions, determine the dimensions of force. (b) The newton is the SI unit of force. According to the results for (a), how can you express a force having units of newtons by using the fundamental units of mass, length, and time?

52. (a) Find a conversion factor to convert from miles per hour to kilometers per hour. (b) For a while, federal law mandated that the maximum highway speed would be 55 mi/h. Use the conversion factor from part (a) to find the speed in kilometers per hour. (c) The maximum highway speed has been raised to 65 mi/h in some places. In kilometers per hour, how much of an increase is this over the 55-mi/h limit?

53. BIO One cubic centimeter (1.0 cm³) of water has a mass of 1.0×10^{-3} kg. (a) Determine the mass of 1.0 m³ of water. Assuming that biological substances are 98% water, estimate the masses of (b) a cell with a diameter of 1.0 μm, (c) a human kidney, and (d) a fly. Take a kidney to be roughly a sphere with a radius of 4.0 cm and a fly to be roughly a cylinder 4.0 mm long and 2.0 mm in diameter.

54. Soft drinks are commonly sold in aluminum containers. (a) To an order of magnitude, how many such containers are thrown away or recycled each year by U.S.

consumers? (b) How many tons of aluminum does this represent? In your solution, state the quantities you measure or estimate and the values you take for them.

55. The displacement of an object moving under uniform acceleration is some function of time and the acceleration. Suppose we write this displacement as $s = ka^m t^n$, where k is a dimensionless constant. Show by dimensional analysis that this expression is satisfied if $m = 1$ and $n = 2$. Can the analysis give the value of k?

56. Assume that it takes 7.00 minutes to fill a 30.0-gal gasoline tank. (a) Calculate the rate at which the tank is filled in gallons per second. (b) Calculate the rate at which the tank is filled in cubic meters per second. (c) Determine the time interval, in hours, required to fill a 1.00-m³ volume at the same rate. (1 U.S. gal = 231 in.³)

57. M One gallon of paint (volume = 3.79×10^{-3} m³) covers an area of 25.0 m². What is the thickness of the fresh paint on the wall?

58. S Sphere 1 has surface area A_1 and volume V_1, and sphere 2 has surface area A_2 and volume V_2. If the radius of sphere 2 is double the radius of sphere 1, what is the ratio of (a) the areas, A_2/A_1 and (b) the volumes, V_2/V_1?

59. M Assume that there are 100 million passenger cars in the United States and that the average fuel consumption is 20 mi/gal of gasoline. If the average distance traveled by each car is 10 000 mi/yr, how much gasoline would be saved per year if average fuel consumption could be increased to 25 mi/gal?

60. At the time of this book's printing, the U.S. national debt was about $10 trillion. (a) If payments were made at the rate of $1 000 per second, how many years would it take to pay off the debt, assuming that no interest were charged? (b) A dollar bill is about 15.5 cm long. If ten trillion dollar bills were laid end to end around the Earth's equator, how many times would they encircle the planet? Take the radius of the Earth at the equator to be 6 378 km. (*Note:* Before doing any of these calculations, try to guess at the answers. You may be very surprised.)

61. (a) How many seconds are there in a year? (b) If one micrometeorite (a sphere with a diameter on the order of 10^{-6} m) struck each square meter of the Moon each second, estimate the number of years it would take to cover the Moon with micrometeorites to a depth of one meter. (*Hint:* Consider a cubic box, 1 m on a side, on the Moon, and find how long it would take to fill the box.)

62. Imagine that you are the equipment manager of a professional baseball team. One of your jobs is to keep baseballs on hand for games. Balls are sometimes lost when players hit them into the stands as either home runs or foul balls. Estimate how many baseballs you have to buy per season in order to make up for such losses. Assume that your team plays an 81-game home schedule in a season.

63. The nearest neutron star (a collapsed star made primarily of neutrons) is about 3.00×10^{18} m away from Earth. Given that the Milky Way galaxy (Fig. P1.63) is roughly a disk of diameter $\sim 10^{21}$ m and thickness $\sim 10^{19}$ m, estimate the number of neutron stars in the Milky Way to the nearest order of magnitude.

Figure P1.63

■ AP* REVIEW QUESTIONS

1. Which of the following units are used as fundamental SI quantities to derive additional quantities?

      I. Newton

      II. kilogram

      III. meter

      IV. Joule

(A) I and III

(B) I, II, and III

(C) II and III

(D) I and IV

(E) All units above are fundamental quantities

Questions 2–3

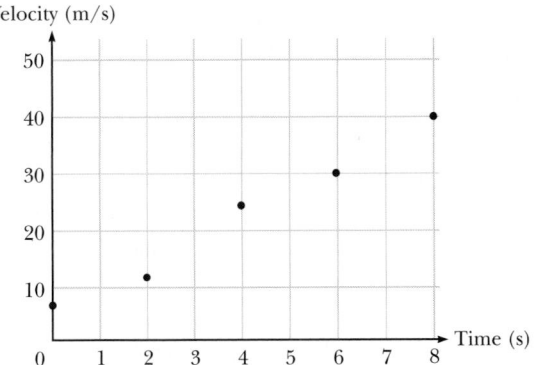

A student collects and plots data for a cart changing speed, as shown on the graph above.

2. The approximate area under the "best fit" straight line is most nearly. . .

(A) 180 m

(B) 220 m

(C) 250 m

(D) 300 m

(E) cannot be determined

3. The slope of the "best fit" straight line is most nearly. . .

(A) 0.25 m/s^2

(B) 0.42 m/s^2

(C) 3.5 m/s^2

(D) 4.3 m/s^2

(E) 5.0 m/s^2

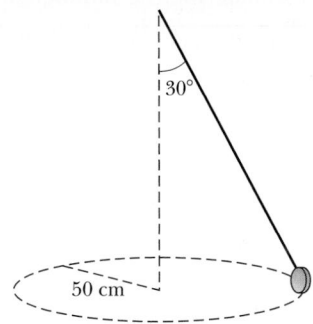

4. A yo-yo follows a circular path with radius 50 cm around a vertical axis. What length is the string attached to the yo-yo if 30 degrees separate the vertical axis from the string? (Note: not drawn to scale.)

(A) 25 cm

(B) 43 cm

(C) 50 cm

(D) 100 cm

(E) 125 cm

5. Which of the following represent the same coordinates?

      I. $(-3 \text{ m}, 4 \text{ m})$

      II. $(5 \text{ m}, 127°)$

      III. $(3 \text{ m}, -4 \text{ m})$

      IV. $(5 \text{ m}, 233°)$

(A) I and II

(B) I, II, and III

(C) II and III

(D) I, II, and IV

(E) All values above represent the same coordinates

6. What order of magnitude estimate would best describe the number of minutes it takes for the Earth to orbit the sun?

(A) $\sim 10^4$

(B) $\sim 10^5$

(C) $\sim 10^6$

(D) $\sim 10^7$

(E) $\sim 10^8$

7. Which of the following would be a reasonable order of magnitude estimate for the number of printed characters (e.g. T, ?, s, μ, 7) in a typical college physics textbook?

(A) $\sim 10^2$

(B) $\sim 10^3$

(C) $\sim 10^6$

(D) $\sim 10^8$

(E) $\sim 10^{10}$

8. The speed limit on many rural interstates in the United States is 65 miles/hour. Which of the following are SI units that would most likely be used to represent this speed in physics?

(A) miles/hour

(B) meters/second

(C) kilometers/hour

(D) centimeters/second

(E) feet/second

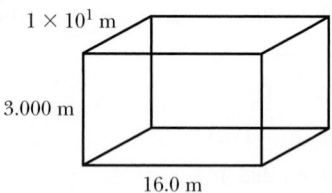

1 × 10¹ m

3.000 m

16.0 m

9. A physicist measures the dimensions of her laboratory to calculate its volume, and records her measurements in her lab notebook, as shown above. What volume can she truthfully claim?

(A) 48.0 m^3

(B) 480 m^3

(C) 480.000 m^3

(D) 500.0 m^3

(E) $5 \times 10^2 \text{ m}^3$

10. Which of the following quantities are dimensionally equivalent?

I. $vaxt^2$

II. xv

III. $2a/v^2$

IV. x^2/t^2

V. $x^3/2t$

(A) I and II

(B) I and V

(C) I, II, and IV

(D) III and V

(E) All quantities above are unique

11. Rank the following prefixes from smallest (left) to largest (right).

(A) femto, giga, mega, kilo, micro, nano

(B) nano, milli, micro, kilo, mega, giga

(C) femto, nano, micro, kilo, mega, giga

(D) nano, micro, milli, kilo, femto, mega

(E) micro, milli, kilo, nano, mega, femto

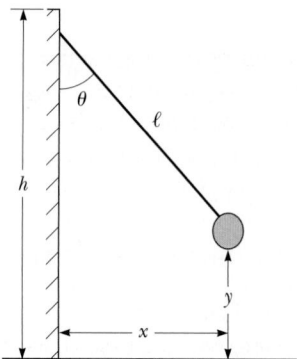

12. What is the height, y, of the charged sphere shown above if it is suspended at an angle θ from a charged vertical wall with height h, the string has length ℓ, and the sphere is located distance x from the wall?

(A) $h - x \sin \theta$

(B) $h - \ell \sin \theta$

(C) $h - x \cos \theta$

(D) $h - \ell \cos \theta$

(E) $h - \ell \tan \theta$

AP Photo/Ben Margot

The current absolute land speed record holder is the British designed ThrustSSC, a twin turbofan-powered car which achieved 763 miles per hour (1,228 km/h) for the mile (1.6 km), breaking the sound barrier. The car was driven by Andy Green (UK) on 10/15/1997 in the Black Rock Desert in Gerlach, Nevada.

Motion in One Dimension

2

Life is motion. Our muscles coordinate motion microscopically to enable us to walk and jog. Our hearts pump tirelessly for decades, moving blood through our bodies. Cell wall mechanisms move select atoms and molecules in and out of cells. From the prehistoric chase of antelopes across the savanna to the pursuit of satellites in space, mastery of motion has been critical to our survival and success as a species.

The study of motion and of physical concepts such as force and mass is called **dynamics.** The part of dynamics that describes motion without regard to its causes is called **kinematics.** In this chapter the focus is on kinematics in one dimension: motion along a straight line. This kind of motion—and, indeed, *any* motion—involves the concepts of displacement, velocity, and acceleration. Here, we use these concepts to study the motion of objects undergoing constant acceleration. In Chapter 3 we will repeat this discussion for objects moving in two dimensions.

The first recorded evidence of the study of mechanics can be traced to the people of ancient Sumeria and Egypt, who were interested primarily in understanding the motions of heavenly bodies. The most systematic and detailed early studies of the heavens were conducted by the Greeks from about 300 B.C. to A.D. 300. Ancient scientists and laypeople regarded the Earth as the center of the Universe. This **geocentric model** was accepted by such notables as Aristotle (384–322 B.C.) and Claudius Ptolemy (about A.D. 140). Largely because of the authority of Aristotle, the geocentric model became the accepted theory of the Universe until the seventeenth century.

About 250 B.C., the Greek philosopher Aristarchus worked out the details of a model of the solar system based on a spherical Earth that rotated on its axis and revolved around the Sun. He proposed that the sky appeared to turn westward because the Earth was turning eastward. This model wasn't given much consideration because it was believed that a turning Earth would generate powerful winds as it moved through the air. We now know that the Earth carries the air and everything else with it as it rotates.

The Polish astronomer Nicolaus Copernicus (1473–1543) is credited with initiating the revolution that finally replaced the geocentric model. In his system, called the **heliocentric model,** Earth and the other planets revolve in circular orbits around the Sun.

This early knowledge formed the foundation for the work of Galileo Galilei (1564–1642), who stands out as the dominant facilitator of the entrance of physics into the modern era. In 1609 he became one of the first to make astronomical observations with a telescope. He observed mountains on the Moon, the larger satellites of Jupiter, spots on the Sun, and the phases of Venus. Galileo's observations convinced him of the correctness of the Copernican theory. His quantitative study of motion formed the foundation of Newton's revolutionary work in the next century.

2.1 Displacement

Motion involves the displacement of an object from one place in space and time to another. Describing motion requires some convenient coordinate system and a specified origin. A **frame of reference** is a choice of coordinate axes that defines the starting point for measuring any quantity, an essential first step in solving virtually any problem in mechanics (Fig. 2.1). In Active Figure 2.2a, for example, a car moves along the x-axis. The coordinates of the car at any time describe its position in space and, more importantly, its *displacement* at some given time of interest.

Definition of displacement ▶

> The **displacement** Δx of an object is defined as its *change in position* and is given by
>
> $$\Delta x \equiv x_f - x_i \qquad [2.1]$$
>
> where x_i is the coordinate of the initial position of the car and x_f is the coordinate of the car's final position. (The indices i and f stand for initial and final, respectively.)
>
> **SI unit: meter (m)**

Tip 2.1 A Displacement Isn't a Distance!

The displacement of an object is *not* the same as the distance it travels. Toss a tennis ball up and catch it. The ball travels a *distance* equal to twice the maximum height reached, but its *displacement* is zero.

We will use the Greek letter delta, Δ, to denote a change in any physical quantity. From the definition of displacement, we see that Δx (read "delta ex") is positive if x_f is greater than x_i and negative if x_f is less than x_i. For example, if the car moves from point Ⓐ to point Ⓑ so that the initial position is $x_i = 30$ m and the final position is $x_f = 52$ m, the displacement is $\Delta x = x_f - x_i = 52$ m − 30 m = +22 m. However, if the car moves from point Ⓒ to point Ⓕ, then the initial position is $x_i = 38$ m and the final position is $x_f = -53$ m, and the displacement is $\Delta x = x_f - x_i = -53$ m − 38 m = −91 m. A positive answer indicates a displacement in

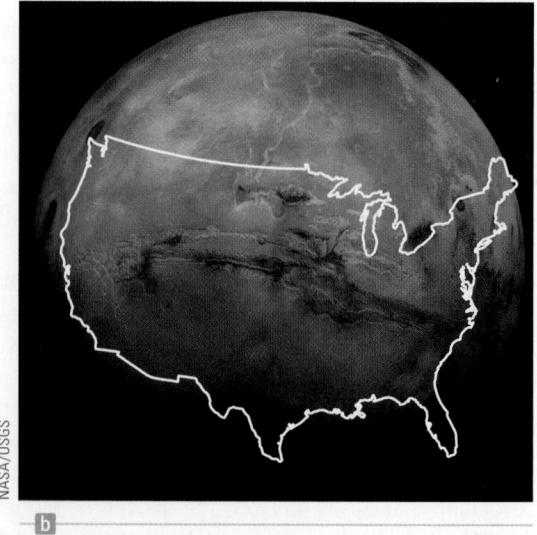

Figure 2.1 (a) How large is the canyon? Without a frame of reference, it's hard to tell. (b) The canyon is Valles Marineris on Mars, and with a frame of reference provided by a superposed outline of the United States, its size is easily grasped.

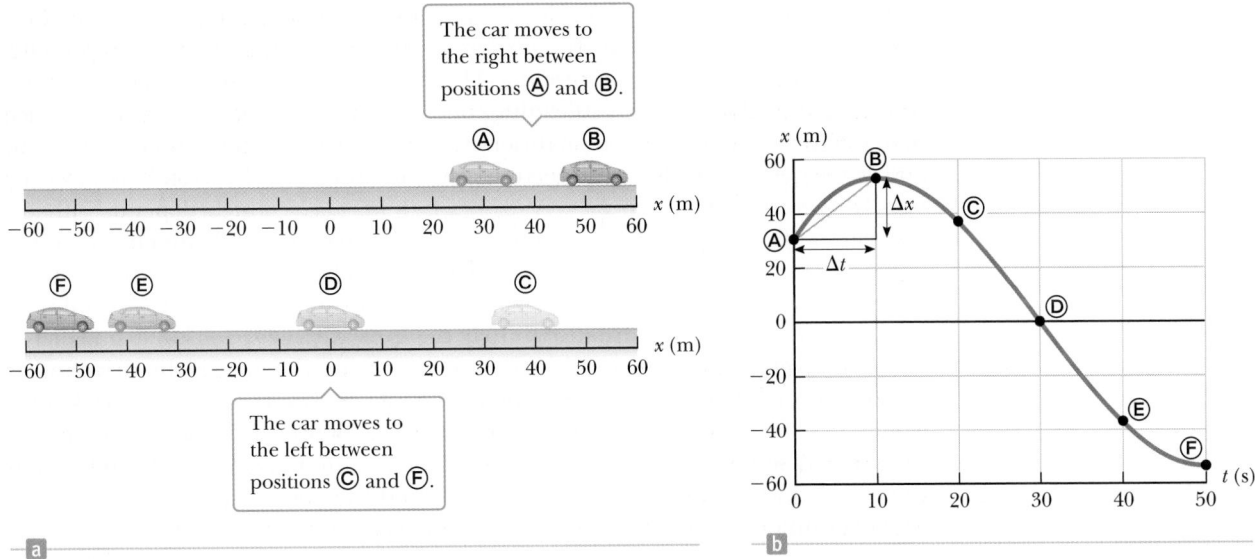

Active Figure 2.2
(a) A car moves back and forth along a straight line taken to be the *x*-axis. Because we are interested only in the car's translational motion, we can model it as a particle. (b) Graph of position vs. time for the motion of the "particle."

the positive *x*-direction, whereas a negative answer indicates a displacement in the negative *x*-direction. Active Figure 2.2b displays the graph of the car's position as a function of time.

Because displacement has both a magnitude (size) and a direction, it's a vector quantity, as are velocity and acceleration. In general, **a vector quantity is characterized by having both a magnitude and a direction.** By contrast, **a scalar quantity has magnitude, but no direction.** Scalar quantities such as mass and temperature are completely specified by a numeric value with appropriate units; no direction is involved.

Vector quantities will be usually denoted in boldface type with an arrow over the top of the letter. For example, $\vec{v}$ represents velocity and $\vec{a}$ denotes an acceleration, both vector quantities. In this chapter, however, it won't be necessary to use that notation because in one-dimensional motion an object can only move in one of two directions, and these directions are easily specified by plus and minus signs.

> **Tip 2.2 Vectors Have Both a Magnitude and a Direction**
>
> Scalars have size. Vectors, too, have size, but they also indicate a direction.

2.2 Velocity

In everyday usage the terms *speed* and *velocity* are interchangeable. In physics, however, there's a clear distinction between them: Speed is a scalar quantity, having only magnitude, whereas velocity is a vector, having both magnitude and direction.

Why must velocity be a vector? If you want to get to a town 70 km away in an hour's time, it's not enough to drive at a speed of 70 km/h; you must travel in the correct direction as well. That's obvious, but it shows that velocity gives considerably more information than speed, as will be made more precise in the formal definitions.

The **average speed** of an object over a given time interval is the length of the path it travels divided by the total elapsed time:

◄ Definition of average speed

$$\text{Average speed} \equiv \frac{\text{path length}}{\text{elapsed time}}$$

SI unit: meter per second (m/s)

In symbols this equation might be written $v = d/t$, where v represents the average speed (not average velocity), d represents the path length, and t represents the elapsed time during the motion. The path length is often called the "total distance," but that can be misleading, because distance has a different, precise mathematical meaning based on differences in the coordinates between the initial and final points. Distance (neglecting any curvature of the surface) is given by the Pythagorean theorem, $\Delta s = \sqrt{(x_f - x_i)^2 + (y_f - y_i)^2}$, which depends only on the endpoints, (x_i, y_i) and (x_f, y_f), and not on what happens in between. The same equation gives the magnitude of a displacement. The straight-line distance from Atlanta, Georgia, to St. Petersburg, Florida, for example, is about 500 miles. If someone drives a car that distance in 10 h, the car's average speed is 500 mi/10 h = 50 mi/h, even if the car's speed varies greatly during the trip. If the driver takes scenic detours off the direct route along the way, however, or doubles back for a while, the path length increases while the distance between the two cities remains the same. A side trip to Jacksonville, Florida, for example, might add 100 miles to the path length, so the car's average speed would then be 600 mi/10 h = 60 mi/h. The magnitude of the average velocity, however, would remain 50 mi/h.

■ EXAMPLE 2.1 | The Tortoise and the Hare

GOAL Apply the concept of average speed.

PROBLEM A turtle and a rabbit engage in a footrace over a distance of 4.00 km. The rabbit runs 0.500 km and then stops for a 90.0-min nap. Upon awakening, he remembers the race and runs twice as fast. Finishing the course in a total time of 1.75 h, the rabbit wins the race. **(a)** Calculate the average speed of the rabbit. **(b)** What was his average speed before he stopped for a nap? Assume no detours or doubling back.

STRATEGY Finding the overall average speed in part (a) is just a matter of dividing the path length by the elapsed time. Part (b) requires two equations and two unknowns, the latter turning out to be the two different average speeds: v_1 before the nap and v_2 after the nap. One equation is given in the statement of the problem ($v_2 = 2v_1$), whereas the other comes from the fact the rabbit ran for only 15 minutes because he napped for 90 minutes.

SOLUTION

(a) Find the rabbit's overall average speed.

Apply the equation for average speed:

$$\text{Average speed} \equiv \frac{\text{path length}}{\text{elapsed time}} = \frac{4.00 \text{ km}}{1.75 \text{ h}}$$

$$= \boxed{2.29 \text{ km/h}}$$

(b) Find the rabbit's average speed before his nap.

Sum the running times, and set the sum equal to 0.25 h:

$$t_1 + t_2 = 0.250 \text{ h}$$

Substitute $t_1 = d_1/v_1$ and $t_2 = d_2/v_2$:

$$(1) \quad \frac{d_1}{v_1} + \frac{d_2}{v_2} = 0.250 \text{ h}$$

Substitute $v_2 = 2v_1$ and the values of d_1 and d_2 into Equation (1):

$$(2) \quad \frac{0.500 \text{ km}}{v_1} + \frac{3.50 \text{ km}}{2v_1} = 0.250 \text{ h}$$

Solve Equation (2) for v_1:

$$v_1 = \boxed{9.00 \text{ km/h}}$$

REMARKS As seen in this example, average speed can be calculated regardless of any variation in speed over the given time interval.

QUESTION 2.1 Does a doubling of an object's average speed always double the magnitude of its displacement in a given amount of time? Explain.

EXERCISE 2.1 Estimate the average speed of the *Apollo* spacecraft in meters per second, given that the craft took five days to reach the Moon from Earth. (The Moon is 3.8×10^8 m from Earth.)

ANSWER ~ 900 m/s

Unlike average speed, **average velocity** is a vector quantity, having both a magnitude and a direction. Consider again the car of Figure 2.2, moving along the road (the x-axis). Let the car's position be x_i at some time t_i and x_f at a later time t_f. In the time interval $\Delta t = t_f - t_i$, the displacement of the car is $\Delta x = x_f - x_i$.

The average velocity $\bar{v}$ during a time interval Δt is the displacement Δx divided by Δt:

$$\bar{v} \equiv \frac{\Delta x}{\Delta t} = \frac{x_f - x_i}{t_f - t_i}$$ [2.2]

◀ Definition of average velocity

SI unit: meter per second (m/s)

Unlike the average speed, which is always positive, the average velocity of an object in one dimension can be either positive or negative, depending on the sign of the displacement. (The time interval Δt is always positive.) In Figure 2.2a, for example, the average velocity of the car is positive in the upper illustration, a positive sign indicating motion to the right along the x-axis. Similarly, a negative average velocity for the car in the lower illustration of the figure indicates that it moves to the left along the x-axis.

As an example, we can use the data in Table 2.1 to find the average velocity in the time interval from point Ⓐ to point Ⓑ (assume two digits are significant):

$$\bar{v} = \frac{\Delta x}{\Delta t} = \frac{52\ \text{m} - 30\ \text{m}}{10\ \text{s} - 0\ \text{s}} = 2.2\ \text{m/s}$$

Aside from meters per second, other common units for average velocity are feet per second (ft/s) in the U.S. customary system and centimeters per second (cm/s) in the cgs system.

To further illustrate the distinction between speed and velocity, suppose we're watching a drag race from a stationary blimp. In one run we see a car follow the straight-line path from Ⓟ to Ⓠ shown in Figure 2.3 during the time interval Δt, and in a second run a car follows the curved path during the same interval. From the definition in Equation 2.2, the two cars had the same average velocity because they had the same displacement $\Delta x = x_f - x_i$ during the same time interval Δt. The car taking the curved route, however, traveled a greater path length and had the higher average speed.

Table 2.1 Position of the Car at Various Times

Position	t (s)	x (m)
Ⓐ	0	30
Ⓑ	10	52
Ⓒ	20	38
Ⓓ	30	0
Ⓔ	40	−37
Ⓕ	50	−53

Figure 2.3 A drag race viewed from a stationary blimp. One car follows the rust-colored straight-line path from Ⓟ to Ⓠ, and a second car follows the blue curved path.

■ *Quick Quiz*

2.1 Figure 2.4 shows the unusual path of a confused football player. After receiving a kickoff at his own goal, he runs downfield to within inches of a touchdown, then reverses direction and races back until he's tackled at the exact location where he first caught the ball. During this run, which took 25 s, what is (a) the path length he travels, (b) his displacement, and (c) his average velocity in the x-direction? (d) What is his average speed?

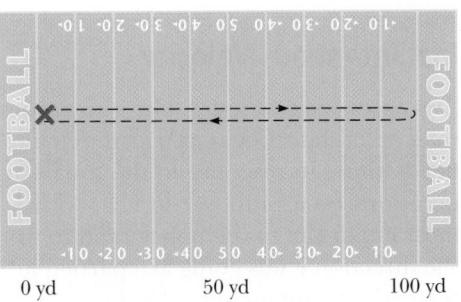

0 yd   50 yd   100 yd

Figure 2.4 (Quick Quiz 2.1) The path followed by a confused football player.

Graphical Interpretation of Velocity

If a car moves along the x-axis from Ⓐ to Ⓑ to Ⓒ, and so forth, we can plot the positions of these points as a function of the time elapsed since the start of the motion. The result is a **position vs. time graph** like those of Figure 2.5 (page 30). In Figure 2.5a, the graph is a straight line because the car is moving at constant

Active Figure 2.5

(a) Position vs. time graph for the motion of a car moving along the *x*-axis at constant velocity. (b) Position vs. time graph for the motion of a car with changing velocity, using the data in Table 2.1.

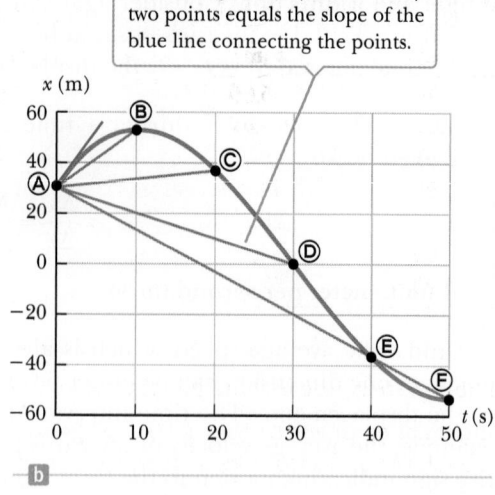

The average velocity between any two points equals the slope of the blue line connecting the points.

---

velocity. The same displacement Δx occurs in each time interval Δt. In this case, the average velocity is always the same and is equal to $\Delta x/\Delta t$. Figure 2.5b is a graph of the data in Table 2.1. Here, the position vs. time graph is not a straight line because the velocity of the car is changing. Between any two points, however, we can draw a straight line just as in Figure 2.5a, and the slope of that line is the average velocity $\Delta x/\Delta t$ in that time interval. In general, **the average velocity of an object during the time interval Δt is equal to the slope of the straight line joining the initial and final points on a graph of the object's position versus time.**

From the data in Table 2.1 and the graph in Figure 2.5b, we see that the car first moves in the positive *x*-direction as it travels from Ⓐ to Ⓑ, reaches a position of 52 m at time $t = 10$ s, then reverses direction and heads backwards. In the first 10 s of its motion, as the car travels from Ⓐ to Ⓑ, its average velocity is 2.2 m/s, as previously calculated. In the first 40 seconds, as the car goes from Ⓐ to Ⓔ, its displacement is $\Delta x = -37$ m $-$ (30 m) $= -67$ m. So the average velocity in this interval, which equals the slope of the blue line in Figure 2.5b from Ⓐ to Ⓔ, is $\bar{v} = \Delta x/\Delta t = (-67$ m$)/(40$ s$) = -1.7$ m/s. In general, there will be a different average velocity between any distinct pair of points.

Instantaneous Velocity

Average velocity doesn't take into account the details of what happens during an interval of time. On a car trip, for example, you may speed up or slow down a number of times in response to the traffic and the condition of the road, and on rare occasions even pull over to chat with a police officer about your speed. What is most important to the police (and to your own safety) is the speed of your car and the direction it was going at a particular instant in time, which together determine the car's **instantaneous velocity.**

So in driving a car between two points, the average velocity must be computed over an interval of time, but the magnitude of instantaneous velocity can be read on the car's speedometer.

Definition of instantaneous ▶
velocity

The instantaneous velocity v is the limit of the average velocity as the time interval Δt becomes infinitesimally small:

$$v \equiv \lim_{\Delta t \to 0} \frac{\Delta x}{\Delta t} \qquad [2.3]$$

SI unit: meter per second (m/s)

Table 2.2 Positions of a Car at Specific Instants of Time

t (s)	x (m)
1.00	5.00
1.01	5.47
1.10	9.67
1.20	14.3
1.50	26.3
2.00	34.7
3.00	52.5

Table 2.3 Calculated Values of the Time Intervals, Displacements, and Average Velocities of the Car of Table 2.2

Time Interval (s)	Δt (s)	Δx (m)	$\bar{v}$ (m/s)
1.00 to 3.00	2.00	47.5	23.8
1.00 to 2.00	1.00	29.7	29.7
1.00 to 1.50	0.50	21.3	42.6
1.00 to 1.20	0.20	9.30	46.5
1.00 to 1.10	0.10	4.67	46.7
1.00 to 1.01	0.01	0.470	47.0

The notation $\lim_{\Delta t \to 0}$ means that the ratio $\Delta x/\Delta t$ is repeatedly evaluated for smaller and smaller time intervals Δt. As Δt gets extremely close to zero, the ratio $\Delta x/\Delta t$ gets closer and closer to a fixed number, which is defined as the instantaneous velocity.

To better understand the formal definition, consider data obtained on our vehicle via radar (Table 2.2). At $t = 1.00$ s, the car is at $x = 5.00$ m, and at $t = 3.00$ s, it's at $x = 52.5$ m. The average velocity computed for this interval $\Delta x/\Delta t = (52.5$ m $- 5.00$ m$)/(3.00$ s $- 1.00$ s$) = 23.8$ m/s. This result could be used as an estimate for the velocity at $t = 1.00$ s, but it wouldn't be very accurate because the speed changes considerably in the 2-second time interval. Using the rest of the data, we can construct Table 2.3. As the time interval gets smaller, the average velocity more closely approaches the instantaneous velocity. Using the final interval of only 0.010 0 s, we find that the average velocity is $\bar{v} = \Delta x/\Delta t = 0.470$ m/0.010 0 s $= 47.0$ m/s. Because 0.010 0 s is a very short time interval, the actual instantaneous velocity is probably very close to this latter average velocity, given the limits on the car's ability to accelerate. Finally using the conversion factor on the front endsheets of the book, we see that this is 105 mi/h, a likely violation of the speed limit.

As can be seen in Figure 2.6, the chords formed by the blue lines gradually approach a tangent line as the time interval becomes smaller. **The slope of the line tangent to the position vs. time curve at "a given time" is defined to be the instantaneous velocity at that time.**

The instantaneous speed of an object, which is a scalar quantity, is defined as the magnitude of the instantaneous velocity. Like average speed, instantaneous speed (which we will usually call, simply, "speed") has no direction associated with it and hence carries no algebraic sign. For example, if one object has an

◄ Definition of instantaneous speed

Figure 2.6 Graph representing the motion of the car from the data in Table 2.2.

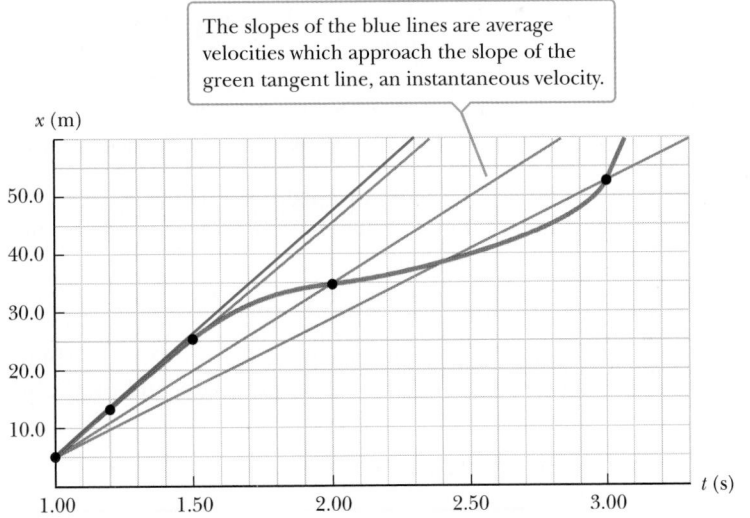

The slopes of the blue lines are average velocities which approach the slope of the green tangent line, an instantaneous velocity.

instantaneous velocity of +15 m/s along a given line and another object has an instantaneous velocity of −15 m/s along the same line, both have an instantaneous speed of 15 m/s.

■ EXAMPLE 2.2 | Slowly Moving Train

GOAL Obtain average and instantaneous velocities from a graph.

PROBLEM A train moves slowly along a straight portion of track according to the graph of position versus time in Figure 2.7a. Find **(a)** the average velocity for the total trip, **(b)** the average velocity during the first 4.00 s of motion, **(c)** the average velocity during the next 4.00 s of motion, **(d)** the instantaneous velocity at $t = 2.00$ s, and **(e)** the instantaneous velocity at $t = 9.00$ s.

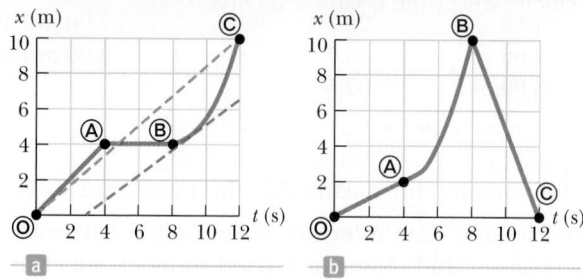

Figure 2.7 (a) (Example 2.2) (b) (Exercise 2.2)

STRATEGY The average velocities can be obtained by substituting the data into the definition. The instantaneous velocity at $t = 2.00$ s is the same as the average velocity at that point because the position vs. time graph is a straight line, indicating constant velocity. Finding the instantaneous velocity when $t = 9.00$ s requires sketching a line tangent to the curve at that point and finding its slope.

SOLUTION

(a) Find the average velocity from ⊚ to ©.

Calculate the slope of the dashed blue line:

$$\bar{v} = \frac{\Delta x}{\Delta t} = \frac{10.0 \text{ m}}{12.0 \text{ s}} = \boxed{+0.833 \text{ m/s}}$$

(b) Find the average velocity during the first 4 seconds of the train's motion.

Again, find the slope:

$$\bar{v} = \frac{\Delta x}{\Delta t} = \frac{4.00 \text{ m}}{4.00 \text{ s}} = \boxed{+1.00 \text{ m/s}}$$

(c) Find the average velocity during the next 4 seconds.

Here, there is no change in position as the train moves from Ⓐ to Ⓑ, so the displacement Δx is zero:

$$\bar{v} = \frac{\Delta x}{\Delta t} = \frac{0 \text{ m}}{4.00 \text{ s}} = \boxed{0 \text{ m/s}}$$

(d) Find the instantaneous velocity at $t = 2.00$ s.

This is the same as the average velocity found in (b), because the graph is a straight line:

$$v = \boxed{1.00 \text{ m/s}}$$

(e) Find the instantaneous velocity at $t = 9.00$ s.

The tangent line appears to intercept the x-axis at (3.0 s, 0 m) and graze the curve at (9.0 s, 4.5 m). The instantaneous velocity at $t = 9.00$ s equals the slope of the tangent line through these points:

$$v = \frac{\Delta x}{\Delta t} = \frac{4.5 \text{ m} - 0 \text{ m}}{9.0 \text{ s} - 3.0 \text{ s}} = \boxed{0.75 \text{ m/s}}$$

REMARKS From the origin to Ⓐ, the train moves at constant speed in the positive x-direction for the first 4.00 s, because the position vs. time curve is rising steadily toward positive values. From Ⓐ to Ⓑ, the train stops at $x = 4.00$ m for 4.00 s. From Ⓑ to ©, the train travels at increasing speed in the positive x-direction.

QUESTION 2.2 Would a vertical line in a graph of position versus time make sense? Explain.

EXERCISE 2.2 Figure 2.7b graphs another run of the train. Find (a) the average velocity from ⊚ to ©; (b) the average and instantaneous velocities from ⊚ to Ⓐ; (c) the approximate instantaneous velocity at $t = 6.0$ s; and (d) the average and instantaneous velocity at $t = 9.0$ s.

ANSWERS (a) 0 m/s (b) both are +0.5 m/s (c) 2 m/s (d) both are −2.5 m/s

2.3 Acceleration

Going from place to place in your car, you rarely travel long distances at constant velocity. The velocity of the car increases when you step harder on the gas pedal and decreases when you apply the brakes. The velocity also changes when you round a curve, altering your direction of motion. The changing of an object's velocity with time is called **acceleration.**

Figure 2.8 A car moving to the right accelerates from a velocity of v_i to a velocity of v_f in the time interval $\Delta t = t_f - t_i$.

Average Acceleration

A car moves along a straight highway as in Figure 2.8. At time t_i it has a velocity of v_i, and at time t_f its velocity is v_f, with $\Delta v = v_f - v_i$ and $\Delta t = t_f - t_i$.

> The average acceleration $\bar{a}$ during the time interval Δt is the change in velocity Δv divided by Δt:
>
> $$\bar{a} \equiv \frac{\Delta v}{\Delta t} = \frac{v_f - v_i}{t_f - t_i} \qquad [2.4]$$
>
> **SI unit: meter per second per second (m/s^2)**

◀ Definition of average acceleration

For example, suppose the car shown in Figure 2.8 accelerates from an initial velocity of $v_i = +10$ m/s to a final velocity of $v_f = +20$ m/s in a time interval of 2 s. (Both velocities are toward the right, selected as the positive direction.) These values can be inserted into Equation 2.4 to find the average acceleration:

$$\bar{a} = \frac{\Delta v}{\Delta t} = \frac{20 \text{ m/s} - 10 \text{ m/s}}{2 \text{ s}} = +5 \text{ m/s}^2$$

Acceleration is a vector quantity having dimensions of length divided by the time squared. Common units of acceleration are meters per second per second ((m/s)/s, which is usually written m/s^2) and feet per second per second (ft/s^2). An average acceleration of $+5$ m/s^2 means that, on average, the car increases its velocity by 5 m/s every second in the positive x-direction.

For the case of motion in a straight line, the direction of the velocity of an object and the direction of its acceleration are related as follows: **When the object's velocity and acceleration are in the same direction, the speed of the object increases with time. When the object's velocity and acceleration are in opposite directions, the speed of the object decreases with time.**

To clarify this point, suppose the velocity of a car changes from -10 m/s to -20 m/s in a time interval of 2 s. The minus signs indicate that the velocities of the car are in the negative x-direction; they do *not* mean that the car is slowing down! The average acceleration of the car in this time interval is

$$\bar{a} = \frac{\Delta v}{\Delta t} = \frac{-20 \text{ m/s} - (-10 \text{ m/s})}{2 \text{ s}} = -5 \text{ m/s}^2$$

The minus sign indicates that the acceleration vector is also in the negative x-direction. Because the velocity and acceleration vectors are in the same direction, the speed of the car must increase as the car moves to the left. Positive and negative accelerations specify directions relative to chosen axes, not "speeding up" or "slowing down." The terms *speeding up* or *slowing down* refer to an increase and a decrease in speed, respectively.

Tip 2.5 Negative Acceleration

Negative acceleration doesn't necessarily mean an object is slowing down. If the acceleration is negative and the velocity is also negative, the object is speeding up!

Tip 2.6 Deceleration

The word *deceleration* means a reduction in speed, a slowing down. Some confuse it with a negative acceleration, which can speed something up. (See Tip 2.5.)

■ Quick Quiz

2.2 True or False? (a) A car must always have an acceleration in the same direction as its velocity. **(b)** It's possible for a slowing car to have a positive acceleration. **(c)** An object with constant nonzero acceleration can never stop and remain at rest.

An object with nonzero acceleration can have a velocity of zero, but only instantaneously. When a ball is tossed straight up, its velocity is zero when it reaches its maximum height. Gravity still accelerates the ball at that point, however; otherwise, it wouldn't fall down.

Instantaneous Acceleration

The value of the average acceleration often differs in different time intervals, so it's useful to define the **instantaneous acceleration,** which is analogous to the instantaneous velocity discussed in Section 2.2.

◀ Definition of instantaneous acceleration

The instantaneous acceleration a is the limit of the average acceleration as the time interval Δt goes to zero:

$$a \equiv \lim_{\Delta t \to 0} \frac{\Delta v}{\Delta t} \qquad [2.5]$$

SI unit: meter per second per second (m/s^2)

Here again, the notation $\lim_{\Delta t \to 0}$ means that the ratio $\Delta v/\Delta t$ is evaluated for smaller and smaller values of Δt. The closer Δt gets to zero, the closer the ratio gets to a fixed number, which is the instantaneous acceleration.

Figure 2.9, a **velocity vs. time graph,** plots the velocity of an object against time. The graph could represent, for example, the motion of a car along a busy street. The average acceleration of the car between times t_i and t_f can be found by determining the slope of the line joining points Ⓟ and Ⓠ. If we imagine that point Ⓠ is brought closer and closer to point Ⓟ, the line comes closer and closer to becoming tangent at Ⓟ. The **instantaneous acceleration of an object at a given time equals the slope of the tangent to the velocity vs. time graph at that time.** From now on, we will use the term *acceleration* to mean "instantaneous acceleration."

In the special case where the velocity vs. time graph of an object's motion is a straight line, the instantaneous acceleration of the object at any point is equal to its average acceleration. That also means that the tangent line to the graph overlaps the graph itself. In that case, the object's acceleration is said to be *uniform*, which means that it has a constant value. Constant acceleration problems are important in kinematics and will be studied extensively in this and the next chapter.

■ Quick Quiz

2.3 Parts (a), (b), and (c) of Figure 2.10 represent three graphs of the velocities of different objects moving in straight-line paths as functions of time. The possible accelerations of each object as functions of time are shown in parts (d), (e), and (f). Match each velocity vs. time graph with the acceleration vs. time graph that best describes the motion.

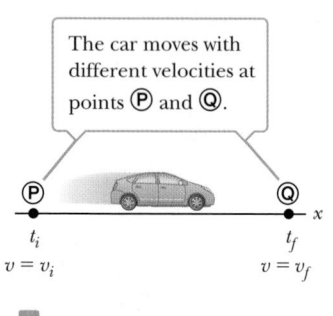

The car moves with different velocities at points Ⓟ and Ⓠ.

a

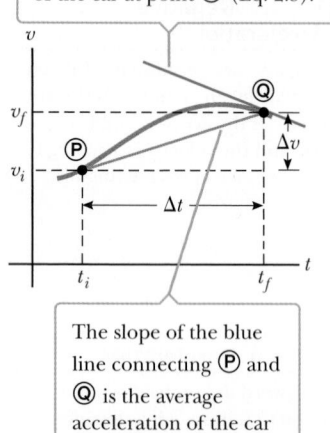

The slope of the green line is the instantaneous acceleration of the car at point Ⓠ (Eq. 2.5).

The slope of the blue line connecting Ⓟ and Ⓠ is the average acceleration of the car during the time interval $\Delta t = t_f - t_i$ (Eq. 2.4).

b

Figure 2.9 (a) A car, modeled as a particle, moving along the x-axis from Ⓟ to Ⓠ, has velocity v_{xi} at $t = t_i$ and velocity v_{xf} at $t = t_f$. (b) Velocity vs. time graph for an object moving in a straight line.

Active Figure 2.10 (Quick Quiz 2.3) Match each velocity vs. time graph to its corresponding acceleration vs. time graph.

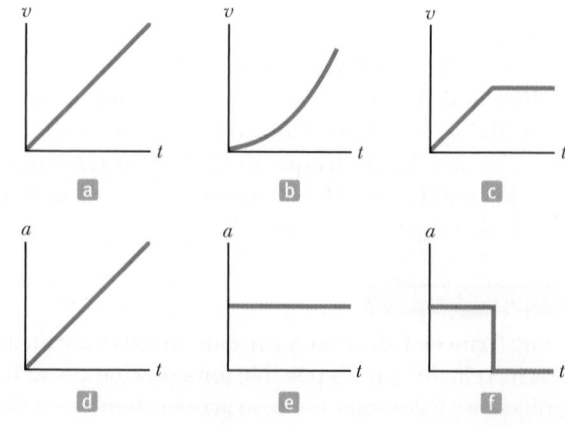

■ **EXAMPLE 2.3** | **Catching a Fly Ball**

GOAL Apply the definition of instantaneous acceleration.

PROBLEM A baseball player moves in a straight-line path in order to catch a fly ball hit to the outfield. His velocity as a function of time is shown in Figure 2.11a. Find his instantaneous acceleration at points Ⓐ, Ⓑ, and Ⓒ.

STRATEGY At each point, the velocity vs. time graph is a straight line segment, so the instantaneous acceleration will be the slope of that segment. Select two points on each segment and use them to calculate the slope.

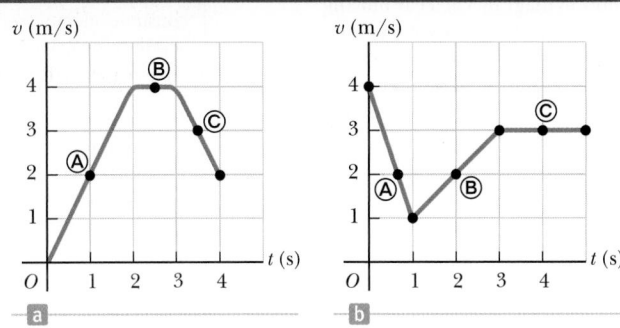

Figure 2.11 (a) (Example 2.3) (b) (Exercise 2.3)

SOLUTION

Acceleration at Ⓐ.

The acceleration at Ⓐ equals the slope of the line connecting the points (0 s, 0 m/s) and (2.0 s, 4.0 m/s):

$$a = \frac{\Delta v}{\Delta t} = \frac{4.0 \text{ m/s} - 0}{2.0 \text{ s} - 0} = \boxed{+2.0 \text{ m/s}^2}$$

Acceleration at Ⓑ.

$\Delta v = 0$, because the segment is horizontal:

$$a = \frac{\Delta v}{\Delta t} = \frac{4.0 \text{ m/s} - 4.0 \text{ m/s}}{3.0 \text{ s} - 2.0 \text{ s}} = \boxed{0 \text{ m/s}^2}$$

Acceleration at Ⓒ.

The acceleration at Ⓒ equals the slope of the line connecting the points (3.0 s, 4.0 m/s) and (4.0 s, 2.0 m/s):

$$a = \frac{\Delta v}{\Delta t} = \frac{2.0 \text{ m/s} - 4.0 \text{ m/s}}{4.0 \text{ s} - 3.0 \text{ s}} = \boxed{-2.0 \text{ m/s}^2}$$

REMARKS Assume the player is initially moving in the positive *x*-direction. For the first 2.0 s, the ballplayer moves in the positive *x*-direction (the velocity is positive) and steadily accelerates (the curve is steadily rising) to a maximum speed of 4.0 m/s. He moves for 1.0 s at a steady speed of 4.0 m/s and then slows down in the last second (the *v* vs. *t* curve is falling), still moving in the positive *x*-direction (*v* is always positive).

QUESTION 2.3 Can the tangent line to a velocity vs. time graph ever be vertical? Explain.

EXERCISE 2.3 Repeat the problem, using Figure 2.11b.

ANSWER The accelerations at Ⓐ, Ⓑ, and Ⓒ are −3.0 m/s², 1.0 m/s², and 0 m/s², respectively.

2.4 Motion Diagrams

Velocity and acceleration are sometimes confused with each other, but they're very different concepts, as can be illustrated with the help of motion diagrams. A **motion diagram** is a representation of a moving object at successive time intervals, with velocity and acceleration vectors sketched at each position, red for velocity vectors and violet for acceleration vectors, as in Active Figure 2.12 (page 36). The time intervals between adjacent positions in the motion diagram are assumed equal.

A motion diagram is analogous to images resulting from a stroboscopic photograph of a moving object. Each image is made as the strobe light flashes. Active Figure 2.12 represents three sets of strobe photographs of cars moving along a straight roadway from left to right. The time intervals between flashes of the stroboscope are equal in each diagram.

In Active Figure 2.12a, the images of the car are equally spaced: The car moves the same distance in each time interval. This means that the car moves with *constant positive velocity* and has *zero acceleration*. The red arrows are all the same length (constant velocity) and there are no violet arrows (zero acceleration).

In Active Figure 2.12b, the images of the car become farther apart as time progresses and the velocity vector increases with time, because the car's displacement

Active Figure 2.12

Motion diagrams of a car moving along a straight roadway in a single direction. The velocity at each instant is indicated by a red arrow, and the constant acceleration is indicated by a purple arrow.

This car moves at constant velocity (zero acceleration).

This car has a constant acceleration in the direction of its velocity.

This car has a constant acceleration in the direction opposite its velocity.

between adjacent positions increases as time progresses. The car is moving with a *positive velocity* and a constant *positive acceleration*. The red arrows are successively longer in each image, and the violet arrows point to the right.

In Active Figure 2.12c, the car slows as it moves to the right because its displacement between adjacent positions decreases with time. In this case, the car moves initially to the right with a constant negative acceleration. The velocity vector decreases in time (the red arrows get shorter) and eventually reaches zero, as would happen when the brakes are applied. Note that the acceleration and velocity vectors are *not* in the same direction. The car is moving with a *positive velocity*, but with a *negative acceleration*.

Try constructing your own diagrams for various problems involving kinematics.

■ *Quick Quiz*

2.4 The three graphs in Figure 2.13 represent the position vs. time for objects moving along the *x*-axis. Which, if any, of these graphs is not physically possible?

2.5 Figure 2.14a is a diagram of a multiflash image of an air puck moving to the right on a horizontal surface. The images sketched are separated by equal time intervals, and the first and last images show the puck at rest. **(a)** In Figure 2.14b, which color graph best shows the puck's position as a function of time? **(b)** In Figure 2.14c, which color graph best shows the puck's velocity as a function of time? **(c)** In Figure 2.14d, which color graph best shows the puck's acceleration as a function of time?

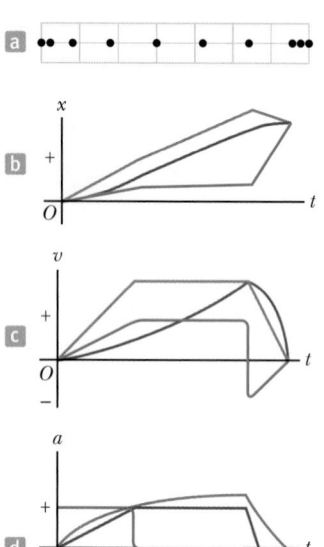

Figure 2.14 (Quick Quiz 2.5) Choose the correct graphs.

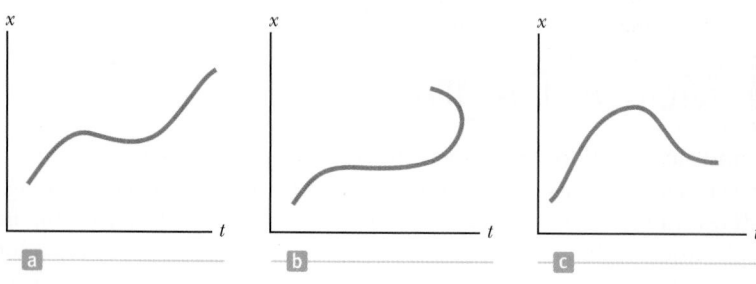

Figure 2.13
(Quick Quiz 2.4) Which position vs. time curve is impossible?

2.5 One-Dimensional Motion with Constant Acceleration

Many applications of mechanics involve objects moving with *constant acceleration*. This type of motion is important because it applies to numerous objects in nature, such as an object in free fall near Earth's surface (assuming air resistance can be neglected). A graph of acceleration versus time for motion with constant acceleration is shown in Active Figure 2.15a. **When an object moves with constant acceleration, the instantaneous acceleration at any point in a time interval is equal to the value of the average acceleration over the entire time interval.** Consequently, the velocity increases or decreases at the same rate throughout the motion, and a plot of v versus t gives a straight line with either positive, zero, or negative slope.

Because the average acceleration equals the instantaneous acceleration when a is constant, we can eliminate the bar used to denote average values from our defining equation for acceleration, writing $\bar{a} = a$, so that Equation 2.4 becomes

$$a = \frac{v_f - v_i}{t_f - t_i}$$

The observer timing the motion is always at liberty to choose the initial time, so for convenience, let $t_i = 0$ and t_f be any arbitrary time t. Also, let $v_i = v_0$ (the initial velocity at $t = 0$) and $v_f = v$ (the velocity at any arbitrary time t). With this notation, we can express the acceleration as

$$a = \frac{v - v_0}{t}$$

or

$$\boxed{v = v_0 + at} \qquad \text{(for constant } a\text{)} \qquad \text{[2.6]}$$

Equation 2.6 states that the acceleration a steadily changes the initial velocity v_0 by an amount at. For example, if a car starts with a velocity of $+2.0$ m/s to the right and accelerates to the right with $a = +6.0$ m/s^2, it will have a velocity of $+14$ m/s after 2.0 s have elapsed:

$$v = v_0 + at = +\,2.0 \text{ m/s} + (6.0 \text{ m/s}^2)(2.0 \text{ s}) = +14 \text{ m/s}$$

The graphical interpretation of v is shown in Active Figure 2.15b. The velocity varies linearly with time according to Equation 2.6, as it should for constant acceleration.

Because the velocity is increasing or decreasing *uniformly* with time, we can express the average velocity in any time interval as the arithmetic average of the initial velocity v_0 and the final velocity v:

$$\bar{v} = \frac{v_0 + v}{2} \qquad \text{(for constant } a\text{)} \qquad \text{[2.7]}$$

Remember that this expression is valid only when the acceleration is constant, in which case the velocity increases uniformly.

We can now use this result along with the defining equation for average velocity, Equation 2.2, to obtain an expression for the displacement of an object as a function of time. Again, we choose $t_i = 0$ and $t_f = t$, and for convenience, we write $\Delta x = x_f - x_i = x - x_0$. This results in

$$\Delta x = \bar{v}t = \left(\frac{v_0 + v}{2}\right)t$$

$$\boxed{\Delta x = \tfrac{1}{2}(v_0 + v)t} \qquad \text{(for constant } a\text{)} \qquad \text{[2.8]}$$

We can obtain another useful expression for displacement by substituting the equation for v (Eq. 2.6) into Equation 2.8:

$$\Delta x = \tfrac{1}{2}(v_0 + v_0 + at)t$$

$$\boxed{\Delta x = v_0 t + \tfrac{1}{2}at^2} \qquad \text{(for constant } a\text{)} \qquad \text{[2.9]}$$

This equation can also be written in terms of the position x, since $\Delta x = x - x_0$. Active Figure 2.15c shows a plot of x versus t for Equation 2.9, which is related to the graph of velocity vs. time: The area under the curve in Active Figure 2.15b is equal to $v_0 t + \tfrac{1}{2}at^2$, which is equal to the displacement Δx. In fact, **the area under the graph of v versus t for any object is equal to the displacement Δx of the object.**

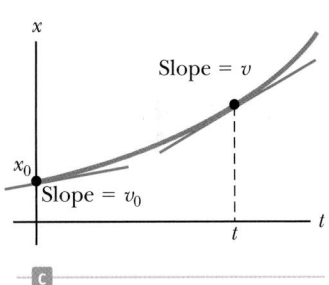

Active Figure 2.15
A particle moving along the x-axis with constant acceleration a.
(a) the acceleration vs. time graph,
(b) the velocity vs. time graph, and
(c) the position vs. time graph.

Table 2.4 Equations for Motion in a Straight Line Under Constant Acceleration

Equation	Information Given by Equation
$v = v_0 + at$	Velocity as a function of time
$\Delta x = v_0 t + \frac{1}{2}at^2$	Displacement as a function of time
$v^2 = v_0{}^2 + 2a\Delta x$	Velocity as a function of displacement

Note: Motion is along the x-axis. At $t = 0$, the velocity of the particle is v_0.

Finally, we can obtain an expression that doesn't contain time by solving Equation 2.6 for t and substituting into Equation 2.8, resulting in

$$\Delta x = \tfrac{1}{2}(v + v_0)\left(\frac{v - v_0}{a}\right) = \frac{v^2 - v_0^2}{2a}$$

$$v^2 = v_0{}^2 + 2a\Delta x \quad \text{(for constant a)} \qquad \text{[2.10]}$$

Equations 2.6 and 2.9 together can solve any problem in one-dimensional motion with constant acceleration, but Equations 2.7, 2.8, and, especially, 2.10 are sometimes convenient. The three most useful equations—Equations 2.6, 2.9, and 2.10—are listed in Table 2.4.

The best way to gain confidence in the use of these equations is to work a number of problems. There is usually more than one way to solve a given problem, depending on which equations are selected and what quantities are given. The difference lies mainly in the algebra.

■ PROBLEM-SOLVING STRATEGY

Motion in One Dimension at Constant Acceleration

The following procedure is recommended for solving problems involving accelerated motion.

1. **Read** the problem.
2. **Draw** a diagram, choosing a coordinate system, labeling initial and final points, and indicating directions of velocities and accelerations with arrows.
3. **Label** all quantities, circling the unknowns. Convert units as needed.
4. **Equations** from Table 2.4 should be selected next. All kinematics problems in this chapter can be solved with the first two equations, and the third is often convenient.
5. **Solve** for the unknowns. Doing so often involves solving two equations for two unknowns.
6. **Check** your answer, using common sense and estimates.

Tip 2.7 Pigs Don't Fly

After solving a problem, you should think about your answer and decide whether it seems reasonable. If it isn't, look for your mistake!

Most of these problems reduce to writing the kinematic equations from Table 2.4 and then substituting the correct values into the constants a, v_0, and x_0 from the given information. Doing this produces two equations—one linear and one quadratic—for two unknown quantities.

■ EXAMPLE 2.4 | The Daytona 500

GOAL Apply the basic kinematic equations.

PROBLEM **(a)** A race car starting from rest accelerates at a constant rate of 5.00 m/s^2. What is the velocity of the car after it has traveled 1.00×10^2 ft? **(b)** How much time has elapsed? **(c)** Calculate the average velocity two different ways.

STRATEGY **(a)** We've read the problem, drawn the diagram in Figure 2.16, and chosen a coordinate system (steps 1 and 2). We'd like to find the velocity v after a certain known displacement Δx. The acceleration a is also known, as is the initial velocity v_0 (step 3, labeling, is complete), so the third equation in Table 2.4 looks most useful for solving part (a). Given the velocity,

Figure 2.16 (Example 2.4)

the first equation in Table 2.4 can then be used to find the time in part (b). Part (c) requires substitution into Equations 2.2 and 2.7, respectively.

SOLUTION

(a) Convert units of Δx to SI, using the information in the inside front cover.

$$1.00 \times 10^2 \text{ ft} = (1.00 \times 10^2 \text{ ft})\left(\frac{1 \text{ m}}{3.28 \text{ ft}}\right) = 30.5 \text{ m}$$

Write the kinematics equation for v^2 (step 4):

$$v^2 = v_0^2 + 2a\,\Delta x$$

Solve for v, taking the positive square root because the car moves to the right (step 5):

$$v = \sqrt{v_0^2 + 2a\,\Delta x}$$

Substitute $v_0 = 0$, $a = 5.00$ m/s^2, and $\Delta x = 30.5$ m:

$$v = \sqrt{v_0^2 + 2a\,\Delta x} = \sqrt{(0)^2 + 2(5.00 \text{ m/s}^2)(30.5 \text{ m})}$$
$$= \boxed{17.5 \text{ m/s}}$$

(b) How much time has elapsed?

Apply the first equation of Table 2.4:

$$v = at + v_0$$

Substitute values and solve for time t:

$$17.5 \text{ m/s} = (5.00 \text{ m/s}^2)t$$
$$t = \frac{17.5 \text{ m/s}}{5.00 \text{ m/s}^2} = \boxed{3.50 \text{ s}}$$

(c) Calculate the average velocity in two different ways.

Apply the definition of average velocity, Equation 2.2:

$$\bar{v} = \frac{x_f - x_i}{t_f - t_i} = \frac{30.5 \text{ m}}{3.50 \text{ s}} = \boxed{8.71 \text{ m/s}}$$

Apply the definition of average velocity in Equation 2.7:

$$\bar{v} = \frac{v_0 + v}{2} = \frac{0 + 17.5 \text{ m/s}}{2} = \boxed{8.75 \text{ m/s}}$$

REMARKS The answers are easy to check. An alternate technique is to use $\Delta x = v_0 t + \frac{1}{2}at^2$ to find t and then use the equation $v = v_0 + at$ to find v. Notice that the two different equations for calculating the average velocity, due to rounding, give slightly different answers.

QUESTION 2.4 What is the final speed if the displacement is increased by a factor of 4?

EXERCISE 2.4 Suppose the driver in this example now slams on the brakes, stopping the car in 4.00 s. Find (a) the acceleration, (b) the distance the car travels while braking, assuming the acceleration is constant, and (c) the average velocity.

ANSWERS (a) -4.38 m/s^2 (b) 35.0 m (c) 8.75 m/s

■ EXAMPLE 2.5 | Car Chase

GOAL Solve a problem involving two objects, one moving at constant acceleration and the other at constant velocity.

PROBLEM A car traveling at a constant speed of 24.0 m/s passes a trooper hidden behind a billboard, as in Figure 2.17. One second after the speeding car passes the billboard, the trooper sets off in chase with a constant acceleration of 3.00 m/s^2. **(a)** How long does it take the trooper to overtake the speeding car? **(b)** How fast is the trooper going at that time?

STRATEGY Solving this problem involves two simultaneous kinematics equations of position, one for the trooper and the other for the car. Choose $t = 0$ to correspond to the time the trooper takes up the chase, when the car is at $x_{car} = 24.0$ m because of its head start

Figure 2.17 (Example 2.5) A speeding car passes a hidden trooper. When does the trooper catch up to the car?

(24.0 m/s × 1.00 s). The trooper catches up with the car when their positions are the same, which suggests setting $x_{trooper} = x_{car}$ and solving for time, which can then be used to find the trooper's speed in part (b).

(Continued)

SOLUTION

(a) How long does it take the trooper to overtake the car?

Write the equation for the car's displacement:

$$\Delta x_{car} = x_{car} - x_0 = v_0 t + \tfrac{1}{2}a_{car}t^2$$

Take $x_0 = 24.0$ m, $v_0 = 24.0$ m/s, and $a_{car} = 0$. Solve for x_{car}:

$$x_{car} = x_0 + vt = 24.0 \text{ m} + (24.0 \text{ m/s})t$$

Write the equation for the trooper's position, taking $x_0 = 0$, $v_0 = 0$, and $a_{trooper} = 3.00$ m/s²:

$$x_{trooper} = \tfrac{1}{2}a_{trooper}t^2 = \tfrac{1}{2}(3.00 \text{ m/s}^2)t^2 = (1.50 \text{ m/s}^2)t^2$$

Set $x_{trooper} = x_{car}$, and solve the quadratic equation. (The quadratic formula appears in Appendix A, Equation A.8.) Only the positive root is meaningful.

$$(1.50 \text{ m/s}^2)t^2 = 24.0 \text{ m} + (24.0 \text{ m/s})t$$
$$(1.50 \text{ m/s}^2)t^2 - (24.0 \text{ m/s})t - 24.0 \text{ m} = 0$$
$$t = \boxed{16.9 \text{ s}}$$

(b) Find the trooper's speed at that time.

Substitute the time into the trooper's velocity equation:

$$v_{trooper} = v_0 + a_{trooper}\, t = 0 + (3.00 \text{ m/s}^2)(16.9 \text{ s})$$
$$= \boxed{50.7 \text{ m/s}}$$

REMARKS The trooper, traveling about twice as fast as the car, must swerve or apply his brakes strongly to avoid a collision! This problem can also be solved graphically by plotting position versus time for each vehicle on the same graph. The intersection of the two graphs corresponds to the time and position at which the trooper overtakes the car.

QUESTION 2.5 The graphical solution corresponds to finding the intersection of what two types of curves in the tx-plane?

EXERCISE 2.5 A motorist with an expired license tag is traveling at 10.0 m/s down a street, and a policeman on a motorcycle, taking another 5.00 s to finish his donut, gives chase at an acceleration of 2.00 m/s². Find (a) the time required to catch the car and (b) the distance the trooper travels while overtaking the motorist.

ANSWERS (a) 13.7 s (b) 188 m

■ EXAMPLE 2.6 | Runway Length

GOAL Apply kinematics to horizontal motion with two phases.

PROBLEM A typical jetliner lands at a speed of 1.60×10^2 mi/h and decelerates at the rate of (10.0 mi/h)/s. If the plane travels at a constant speed of 1.60×10^2 mi/h for 1.00 s after landing before applying the brakes, what is the total displacement of the aircraft between touchdown on the runway and coming to rest?

STRATEGY See Figure 2.18. First, convert all quantities to SI units. The problem must be solved in two parts, or phases, corresponding to the initial coast after touchdown, followed by braking. Using the kinematic equations, find the displacement during each part and add the two displacements.

Figure 2.18 (Example 2.6) Coasting and braking distances for a landing jetliner.

SOLUTION

Convert units of speed and acceleration to SI:

$$v_0 = (1.60 \times 10^2 \text{ mi/h})\left(\frac{0.447 \text{ m/s}}{1.00 \text{ mi/h}}\right) = 71.5 \text{ m/s}$$

$$a = (-10.0 \text{ (mi/h)/s})\left(\frac{0.447 \text{ m/s}}{1.00 \text{ mi/h}}\right) = -4.47 \text{ m/s}^2$$

Taking $a = 0$, $v_0 = 71.5$ m/s, and $t = 1.00$ s, find the displacement while the plane is coasting:

$$\Delta x_{coasting} = v_0 t + \tfrac{1}{2}at^2 = (71.5 \text{ m/s})(1.00 \text{ s}) + 0 = 71.5 \text{ m}$$

Use the time-independent kinematic equation to find the displacement while the plane is braking.

$$v^2 = v_0^2 + 2a\Delta x_{braking}$$

Take $a = -4.47 \text{ m/s}^2$ and $v_0 = 71.5$ m/s. The negative sign on a means that the plane is slowing down.

$$\Delta x_{\text{braking}} = \frac{v^2 - v_0^{\;2}}{2a} = \frac{0 - (71.5 \text{ m/s})^2}{2.00(-4.47 \text{ m/s}^2)} = 572 \text{ m}$$

Sum the two results to find the total displacement:

$$\Delta x_{\text{coasting}} + \Delta x_{\text{braking}} = 71.5 \text{ m} + 572 \text{ m} = \boxed{644 \text{ m}}$$

REMARKS To find the displacement while braking, we could have used the two kinematics equations involving time, namely, $\Delta x = v_0 t + \frac{1}{2}at^2$ and $v = v_0 + at$, but because we weren't interested in time, the time-independent equation was easier to use.

QUESTION 2.6 How would the answer change if the plane coasted for 2.00 s before the pilot applied the brakes?

EXERCISE 2.6 A jet lands at 80.0 m/s, the pilot applying the brakes 2.00 s after landing. Find the acceleration needed to stop the jet within 5.00×10^2 m after touchdown.

ANSWER -9.41 m/s^2

▪ EXAMPLE 2.7 | The Acela: The Porsche of American Trains

GOAL Find accelerations and displacements from a velocity vs. time graph.

PROBLEM The sleek high-speed electric train known as the Acela (pronounced ahh-sell-ah) is currently in service on the Washington-New York-Boston run. The Acela consists of two power cars and six coaches and can carry 304 passengers at speeds up to 170 mi/h. In order to negotiate curves comfortably at high speeds, the train carriages tilt as much as 6° from the vertical, preventing passengers from being pushed to the side. A velocity vs. time graph for the Acela is shown in Figure 2.19a (page 42). **(a)** Describe the motion of the Acela. **(b)** Find the peak acceleration of the Acela in miles per hour per second ((mi/h)/s) as the train speeds up from 45 mi/h to 170 mi/h. **(c)** Find the train's displacement in miles between $t = 0$ and $t = 200$ s. **(d)** Find the average acceleration of the Acela and its displacement in miles in the interval from 200 s to 300 s. (The train has regenerative braking, which means that it feeds energy back into the utility lines each time it stops!) **(e)** Find the total displacement in the interval from 0 to 400 s.

STRATEGY For part (a), remember that the slope of the tangent line at any point of the velocity vs. time graph gives the acceleration at that time. To find the peak acceleration in part (b), study the graph and locate the point at which the slope is steepest. In parts (c) through (e), estimating the area under the curve gives the displacement during a given period, with areas below the time axis, as in part (e), subtracted from the total. The average acceleration in part (d) can be obtained by substituting numbers taken from the graph into the definition of average acceleration, $\bar{a} = \Delta v / \Delta t$.

SOLUTION

(a) Describe the motion.

From about -50 s to 50 s, the Acela cruises at a constant velocity in the $+x$-direction. Then the train accelerates in the $+x$-direction from 50 s to 200 s, reaching a top speed of about 170 mi/h, whereupon it brakes to rest at 350 s and reverses, steadily gaining speed in the $-x$-direction.

(b) Find the peak acceleration.

Calculate the slope of the steepest tangent line, which connects the points (50 s, 50 mi/h) and (100 s, 150 mi/h) (the light blue line in Figure 2.19b):

$$a = \text{slope} = \frac{\Delta v}{\Delta t} = \frac{(1.5 \times 10^2 - 5.0 \times 10^1) \text{ mi/h}}{(1.0 \times 10^2 - 5.0 \times 10^1) \text{s}}$$

$$= \boxed{2.0 \text{ (mi/h)/s}}$$

(c) Find the displacement between 0 s and 200 s.

Using triangles and rectangles, approximate the area in Figure 2.19c (see page 42):

$$\Delta x_{0 \to 200 \text{ s}} = \text{area}_1 + \text{area}_2 + \text{area}_3 + \text{area}_4 + \text{area}_5$$

$$\approx (5.0 \times 10^1 \text{ mi/h})(5.0 \times 10^1 \text{ s})$$

$$+ (5.0 \times 10^1 \text{ mi/h})(5.0 \times 10^1 \text{ s})$$

$$+ (1.6 \times 10^2 \text{ mi/h})(1.0 \times 10^2 \text{ s})$$

$$+ \tfrac{1}{2}(5.0 \times 10^1 \text{ s})(1.0 \times 10^2 \text{ mi/h})$$

$$+ \tfrac{1}{2}(1.0 \times 10^2 \text{ s})(1.7 \times 10^2 \text{ mi/h} - 1.6 \times 10^2 \text{ mi/h})$$

$$= 2.4 \times 10^4 \text{ (mi/h)s}$$

(Continued)

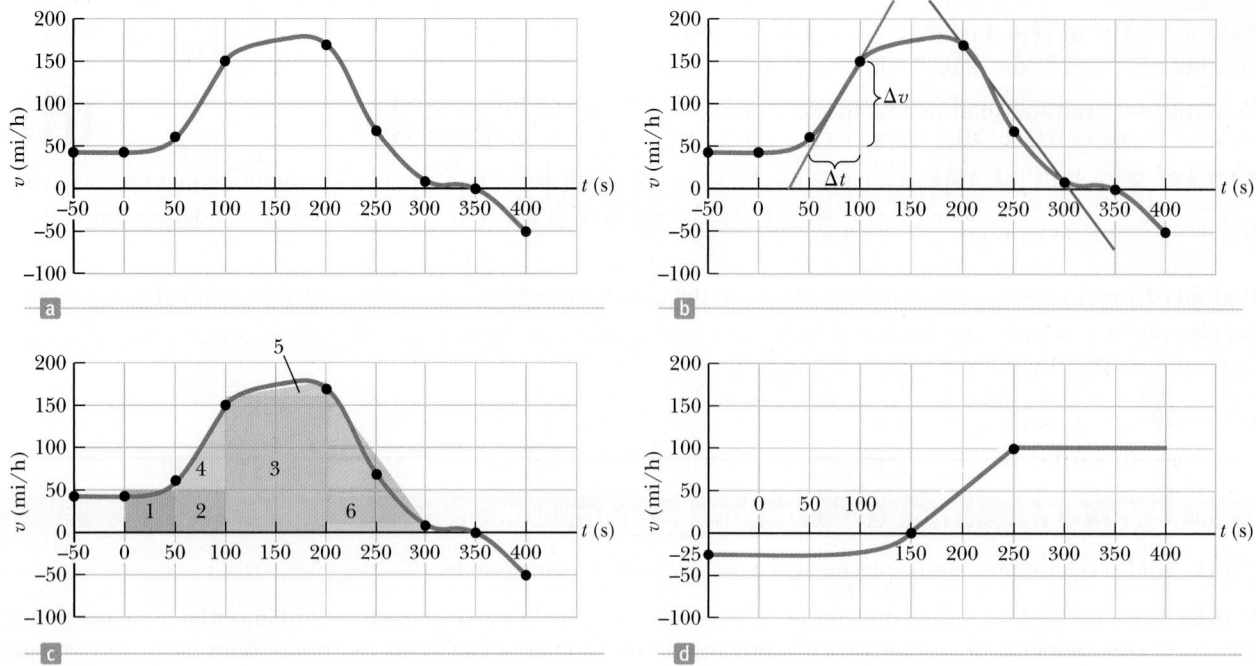

Figure 2.19 (Example 2.7) (a) Velocity vs. time graph for the Acela. (b) The slope of the steepest tangent blue line gives the peak acceleration, and the slope of the green line is the average acceleration between 200 s and 300 s. (c) The area under the velocity vs. time graph in some time interval gives the displacement of the Acela in that time interval. (d) (Exercise 2.7).

Convert units to miles by converting hours to seconds:

$$\Delta x_{0 \to 200 \text{ s}} \approx 2.4 \times 10^4 \frac{\text{mi} \cdot \text{s}}{\text{h}} \left(\frac{1 \text{ h}}{3\ 600 \text{ s}} \right) = \boxed{6.7 \text{ mi}}$$

(d) Find the average acceleration from 200 s to 300 s, and find the displacement.

The slope of the green line is the average acceleration from 200 s to 300 s (Fig. 2.19b):

$$\bar{a} = \text{slope} = \frac{\Delta v}{\Delta t} = \frac{(1.0 \times 10^1 - 1.7 \times 10^2) \text{ mi/h}}{1.0 \times 10^2 \text{ s}}$$
$$= \boxed{-1.6 \text{ (mi/h)/s}}$$

The displacement from 200 s to 300 s is equal to area$_6$, which is the area of a triangle plus the area of a very narrow rectangle beneath the triangle:

$$\Delta x_{200 \to 300 \text{ s}} \approx \tfrac{1}{2}(1.0 \times 10^2 \text{ s})(1.7 \times 10^2 - 1.0 \times 10^1) \text{ mi/h}$$
$$+ (1.0 \times 10^1 \text{ mi/h})(1.0 \times 10^2 \text{ s})$$
$$= 9.0 \times 10^3 (\text{mi/h})(\text{s}) = \boxed{2.5 \text{ mi}}$$

(e) Find the total displacement from 0 s to 400 s.

The total displacement is the sum of all the individual displacements. We still need to calculate the displacements for the time intervals from 300 s to 350 s and fromv 350 s to 400 s. The latter is negative because it's below the time axis.

$$\Delta x_{300 \to 350 \text{ s}} \approx \tfrac{1}{2}(5.0 \times 10^1 \text{ s})(1.0 \times 10^1 \text{ mi/h})$$
$$= 2.5 \times 10^2 (\text{mi/h})(\text{s})$$
$$\Delta x_{350 \to 400 \text{ s}} \approx \tfrac{1}{2}(5.0 \times 10^1 \text{ s})(-5.0 \times 10^1 \text{ mi/h})$$
$$= -1.3 \times 10^3 (\text{mi/h})(\text{s})$$

Find the total displacement by summing the parts:

$$\Delta x_{0 \to 400 \text{ s}} \approx (2.4 \times 10^4 + 9.0 \times 10^3 + 2.5 \times 10^2$$
$$-1.3 \times 10^3)(\text{mi/h})(\text{s}) = \boxed{8.9 \text{ mi}}$$

REMARKS There are a number of ways to find the approximate area under a graph. Choice of technique is a personal preference.

QUESTION 2.7 According to the graph in Figure 2.19a, at what different times is the acceleration zero?

EXERCISE 2.7 Suppose the velocity vs. time graph of another train is given in Figure 2.19d. Find (a) the maximum instantaneous acceleration and (b) the total displacement in the interval from 0 s to 4.00×10^2 s.

ANSWERS (a) 1.0 (mi/h)/s (b) 4.7 mi

2.6 Freely Falling Objects

When air resistance is negligible, all objects dropped under the influence of gravity near Earth's surface fall toward Earth with the same constant acceleration. This idea may seem obvious today, but it wasn't until about 1600 that it was accepted. Prior to that time, the teachings of the great philosopher Aristotle (384–322 B.C.) had held that heavier objects fell faster than lighter ones.

According to legend, Galileo discovered the law of falling objects by observing that two different weights dropped simultaneously from the Leaning Tower of Pisa hit the ground at approximately the same time. Although it's unlikely that this particular experiment was carried out, we know that Galileo performed many systematic experiments with objects moving on inclined planes. In his experiments he rolled balls down a slight incline and measured the distances they covered in successive time intervals. The purpose of the incline was to reduce the acceleration and enable Galileo to make accurate measurements of the intervals. (Some people refer to this experiment as "diluting gravity.") By gradually increasing the slope of the incline he was finally able to draw mathematical conclusions about freely falling objects, because a falling ball is equivalent to a ball going down a vertical incline. Galileo's achievements in the science of mechanics paved the way for Newton in his development of the laws of motion, which we will study in Chapter 4.

Try the following experiment: Drop a hammer and a feather simultaneously from the same height. The hammer hits the floor first because air drag has a greater effect on the much lighter feather. On August 2, 1971, this same experiment was conducted on the Moon by astronaut David Scott, and the hammer and feather fell with exactly the same acceleration, as expected, hitting the lunar surface at the same time. In the idealized case where air resistance is negligible, such motion is called *free fall*.

The expression *freely falling object* doesn't necessarily refer to an object dropped from rest. **A freely falling object is any object moving freely under the influence of gravity alone, regardless of its initial motion.** Objects thrown upward or downward and those released from rest are all considered freely falling.

We denote the magnitude of the **free-fall acceleration** by the symbol g. The value of g decreases with increasing altitude, and varies slightly with latitude as well. At Earth's surface, the value of g is approximately 9.80 m/s^2. Unless stated otherwise, we will use this value for g in doing calculations. For quick estimates, use $g \approx 10$ m/s^2.

If we neglect air resistance and assume that the free-fall acceleration doesn't vary with altitude over short vertical distances, then the motion of a freely falling object is the same as motion in one dimension under constant acceleration. This means that the kinematics equations developed in Section 2.5 can be applied. It's conventional to define "up" as the $+y$-direction and to use y as the position variable. In that case the acceleration is $a = -g = -9.80$ m/s^2. In Chapter 7, we study the variation in g with altitude.

Galileo Galilei
Italian Physicist and Astronomer
(1564–1642)
Galileo formulated the laws that govern the motion of objects in free fall. He also investigated the motion of an object on an inclined plane, established the concept of relative motion, invented the thermometer, and discovered that the motion of a swinging pendulum could be used to measure time intervals. After designing and constructing his own telescope, he discovered four of Jupiter's moons, found that our own Moon's surface is rough, discovered sunspots and the phases of Venus, and showed that the Milky Way consists of an enormous number of stars. Galileo publicly defended Nicolaus Copernicus's assertion that the Sun is at the center of the Universe (the heliocentric system). He published *Dialogue Concerning Two New World Systems* to support the Copernican model, a view the Church declared to be heretical. After being taken to Rome in 1633 on a charge of heresy, he was sentenced to life imprisonment and later was confined to his villa at Arcetri, near Florence, where he died in 1642.

North Wind Archive

■ Quick Quiz

2.6 A tennis player on serve tosses a ball straight up. While the ball is in free fall, does its acceleration (a) increase, (b) decrease, (c) increase and then decrease, (d) decrease and then increase, or (e) remain constant?

2.7 As the tennis ball of Quick Quiz 2.6 travels through the air, does its speed (a) increase, (b) decrease, (c) decrease and then increase, (d) increase and then decrease, or (e) remain the same?

2.8 A skydiver jumps out of a hovering helicopter. A few seconds later, another skydiver jumps out, so they both fall along the same vertical line relative to the helicopter. Both skydivers fall with the same acceleration. Does the vertical distance between them (a) increase, (b) decrease, or (c) stay the same? Does the difference in their velocities (d) increase, (e) decrease, or (f) stay the same? (Assume g is constant.)

■ **EXAMPLE 2.8**   **Not a Bad Throw for a Rookie!**

GOAL Apply the kinematic equations to a freely falling object with a nonzero initial velocity.

PROBLEM A ball is thrown from the top of a building with an initial velocity of 20.0 m/s straight upward, at an initial height of 50.0 m above the ground. The ball just misses the edge of the roof on its way down, as shown in Figure 2.20. Determine **(a)** the time needed for the ball to reach its maximum height, **(b)** the maximum height, **(c)** the time needed for the ball to return to the height from which it was thrown and the velocity of the ball at that instant, **(d)** the time needed for the ball to reach the ground, and **(e)** the velocity and position of the ball at $t = 5.00$ s. Neglect air drag.

STRATEGY The diagram in Figure 2.20 establishes a coordinate system with $y_0 = 0$ at the level at which the ball is released from the thrower's hand, with y positive upward. Write the velocity and position kinematic equations for the ball, and substitute the given information. All the answers come from these two equations by using simple algebra or by just substituting the time. In part (a), for example, the ball comes to rest for an instant at its maximum height, so set $v = 0$ at this point and solve for time. Then substitute the time into the displacement equation, obtaining the maximum height.

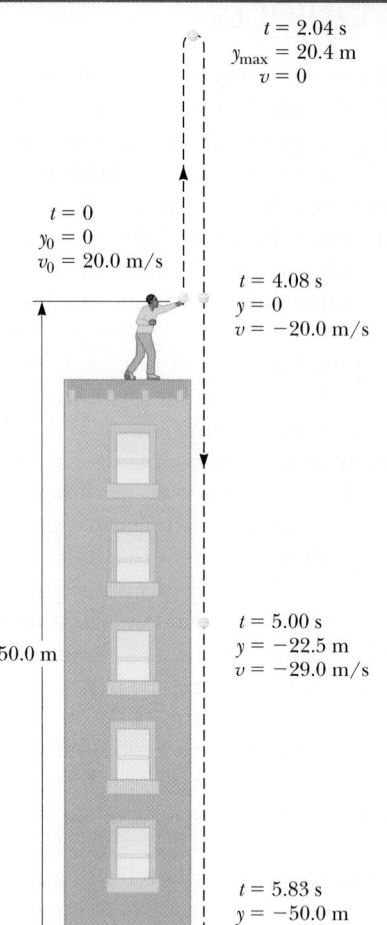

$t = 2.04$ s
$y_{max} = 20.4$ m
$v = 0$

$t = 0$
$y_0 = 0$
$v_0 = 20.0$ m/s

$t = 4.08$ s
$y = 0$
$v = -20.0$ m/s

50.0 m

$t = 5.00$ s
$y = -22.5$ m
$v = -29.0$ m/s

$t = 5.83$ s
$y = -50.0$ m
$v = -37.1$ m/s

Figure 2.20 (Example 2.8) A ball is thrown upward with an initial velocity of $v_0 = +20.0$ m/s. Positions and velocities are given for several times.

SOLUTION

(a) Find the time when the ball reaches its maximum height.

Write the velocity and position kinematic equations:

$$v = at + v_0$$
$$\Delta y = y - y_0 = v_0 t + \tfrac{1}{2}at^2$$

Substitute $a = -9.80$ m/s², $v_0 = 20.0$ m/s, and $y_0 = 0$ into the preceding two equations:

(1) $v = (-9.80 \text{ m/s}^2)t + 20.0 \text{ m/s}$

(2) $y = (20.0 \text{ m/s})t - (4.90 \text{ m/s}^2)t^2$

Substitute $v = 0$, the velocity at maximum height, into Equation (1) and solve for time:

$$0 = (-9.80 \text{ m/s}^2)t + 20.0 \text{ m/s}$$

$$t = \frac{-20.0 \text{ m/s}}{-9.80 \text{ m/s}^2} = \boxed{2.04 \text{ s}}$$

(b) Determine the ball's maximum height.

Substitute the time $t = 2.04$ s into Equation (2):

$$y_{max} = (20.0 \text{ m/s})(2.04 \text{ s}) - (4.90 \text{ m/s}^2)(2.04 \text{ s})^2 = \boxed{20.4 \text{ m}}$$

(c) Find the time the ball takes to return to its initial position, and find the velocity of the ball at that time.

Set $y = 0$ in Equation (2) and solve t:

$$0 = (20.0 \text{ m/s})t - (4.90 \text{ m/s}^2)t^2$$
$$= t(20.0 \text{ m/s} - 4.90 \text{ m/s}^2 t)$$
$$t = \boxed{4.08 \text{ s}}$$

Substitute the time into Equation (1) to get the velocity:

$v = 20.0 \text{ m/s} + (-9.80 \text{ m/s}^2)(4.08 \text{ s}) = \boxed{-20.0 \text{ m/s}}$

(d) Find the time required for the ball to reach the ground.

In Equation (2), set $y = -50.0$ m:

$-50.0 \text{ m} = (20.0 \text{ m/s})t - (4.90 \text{ m/s}^2)t^2$

Apply the quadratic formula and take the positive root:

$t = \boxed{5.83 \text{ s}}$

(e) Find the velocity and position of the ball at $t = 5.00$ s.

Substitute values into Equations (1) and (2):

$v = (-9.80 \text{ m/s}^2)(5.00 \text{ s}) + 20.0 \text{ m/s} = \boxed{-29.0 \text{ m/s}}$

$y = (20.0 \text{ m/s})(5.00 \text{ s}) - (4.90 \text{ m/s}^2)(5.00 \text{ s})^2 = \boxed{-22.5 \text{ m}}$

REMARKS Notice how everything follows from the two kinematic equations. Once they are written down and the constants correctly identified as in Equations (1) and (2), the rest is relatively easy. If the ball were thrown downward, the initial velocity would have been negative.

QUESTION 2.8 How would the answer to part (b), the maximum height, change if the person throwing the ball jumped upward at the instant he released the ball?

EXERCISE 2.8 A projectile is launched straight up at 60.0 m/s from a height of 80.0 m, at the edge of a sheer cliff. The projectile falls, just missing the cliff and hitting the ground below. Find (a) the maximum height of the projectile above the point of firing, (b) the time it takes to hit the ground at the base of the cliff, and (c) its velocity at impact.

ANSWERS (a) 184 m (b) 13.5 s (c) −72.3 m/s

◼ EXAMPLE 2.9 | Maximum Height Derived

GOAL Find the maximum height of a thrown projectile using symbols.

PROBLEM Refer to Example 2.8. Use symbolic manipulation to find **(a)** the time t_{max} it takes the ball to reach its maximum height and **(b)** an expression for the maximum height that doesn't depend on time. Answers should be expressed in terms of the quantities v_0, g, and y_0 only.

STRATEGY When the ball reaches its maximum height, its velocity is zero, so for part (a) solve the kinematics velocity equation for time t and set $v = 0$. For part (b), substitute the expression for time found in part (a) into the displacement equation, solving it for the maximum height.

SOLUTION

(a) Find the time it takes the ball to reach its maximum height.

Write the velocity kinematics equation:

$v = at + v_0$

Move v_0 to the left side of the equation:

$v - v_0 = at$

Divide both sides by a:

$\dfrac{v - v_0}{a} = \dfrac{\acute{a}t}{\acute{a}} = t$

Turn the equation around so that t is on the left and substitute $v = 0$, corresponding to the velocity at maximum height:

(1) $\quad t = \dfrac{-v_0}{a}$

Replace t by t_{max} and substitute $a = -g$:

(2) $\quad t_{max} = \boxed{\dfrac{v_0}{g}}$

(b) Find the maximum height.

Write the equation for the position y at any time:

$y = y_0 + v_0 t + \frac{1}{2}at^2$

(Continued)

Substitute $t = -v_0/a$, which corresponds to the time it takes to reach y_{max}, the maximum height:

$$y_{max} = y_0 + v_0\left(\frac{-v_0}{a}\right) + \frac{1}{2}a\left(\frac{-v_0}{a}\right)^2$$

$$= y_0 - \frac{v_0^2}{a} + \frac{1}{2}\frac{v_0^2}{a}$$

Combine the last two terms and substitute $a = -g$:

(3) $\quad y_{max} = y_0 + \dfrac{v_0^2}{2g}$

REMARKS Notice that $g = +9.8 \text{ m/s}^2$, so the second term is positive overall. Equations (1)–(3) are much more useful than a numerical answer because the effect of changing one value can be seen immediately. For example, doubling the initial velocity v_0 quadruples the displacement above the point of release. Notice also that y_{max} could be obtained more readily from the time-independent equation, $v^2 - v_0^2 = 2a\Delta y$.

QUESTION 2.9 By what factor would the maximum displacement above the rooftop be increased if the building were transported to the Moon, where $a = -\frac{1}{6}g$?

EXERCISE 2.9 (a) Using symbols, find the time t_E it takes for a ball to reach the ground on Earth if released from rest at height y_0. (b) In terms of t_E, how much time t_M would be required if the building were on Mars, where $a = -0.385g$?

ANSWERS (a) $t_E = \sqrt{\dfrac{2y_0}{g}}$ (b) $t_M = 1.61t_E$

▪ EXAMPLE 2.10 | **A Rocket Goes Ballistic**

GOAL Solve a problem involving a powered ascent followed by free-fall motion.

PROBLEM A rocket moves straight upward, starting from rest with an acceleration of $+29.4 \text{ m/s}^2$. It runs out of fuel at the end of 4.00 s and continues to coast upward, reaching a maximum height before falling back to Earth. **(a)** Find the rocket's velocity and position at the end of 4.00 s. **(b)** Find the maximum height the rocket reaches. **(c)** Find the velocity the instant before the rocket crashes on the ground.

STRATEGY Take $y = 0$ at the launch point and y positive upward, as in Figure 2.21. The problem consists of two phases. In phase 1 the rocket has a net *upward* acceleration of 29.4 m/s^2, and we can use the kinematic equations with constant acceleration a to find the height and velocity of the rocket at the end of phase 1, when the fuel is burned up. In phase 2 the rocket is in free fall and has an acceleration of -9.80 m/s^2, with initial velocity and position given by the results of phase 1. Apply the kinematic equations for free fall.

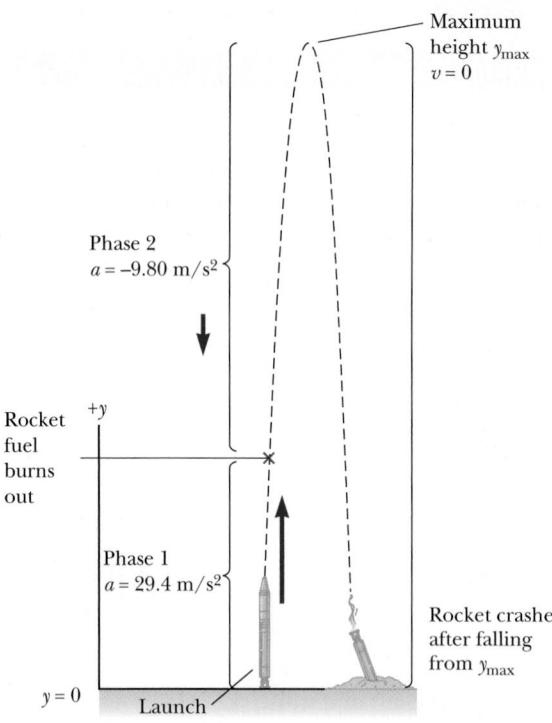

Figure 2.21 (Example 2.10) Two linked phases of motion for a rocket that is launched, uses up its fuel, and crashes.

SOLUTION

(a) Phase 1: Find the rocket's velocity and position after 4.00 s.

Write the velocity and position kinematic equations:

(1) $\quad v = v_0 + at$

(2) $\quad \Delta y = y - y_0 = v_0 t + \frac{1}{2}at^2$

Adapt these equations to phase 1, substituting
$a = 29.4 \text{ m/s}^2$, $v_0 = 0$, and $y_0 = 0$:

(3) $v = (29.4 \text{ m/s}^2)t$
(4) $y = \frac{1}{2}(29.4 \text{ m/s}^2)t^2 = (14.7 \text{ m/s}^2)t^2$

Substitute $t = 4.00$ s into Equations (3) and (4) to find the rocket's velocity v and position y at the time of burnout. These will be called v_b and y_b, respectively.

$v_b = 118 \text{ m/s}$ and $y_b = 235 \text{ m}$

(b) Phase 2: Find the maximum height the rocket attains.

Adapt Equations (1) and (2) to phase 2, substituting
$a = -9.8 \text{ m/s}^2$, $v_0 = v_b = 118 \text{ m/s}$, and $y_0 = y_b = 235 \text{ m}$:

(5) $v = (-9.8 \text{ m/s}^2)t + 118 \text{ m/s}$
(6) $y = 235 \text{ m} + (118 \text{ m/s})t - (4.90 \text{ m/s}^2)t^2$

Substitute $v = 0$ (the rocket's velocity at maximum height) in Equation (5) to get the time it takes the rocket to reach its maximum height:

$0 = (-9.8 \text{ m/s}^2)t + 118 \text{ m/s} \rightarrow t = \frac{118 \text{ m/s}}{9.80 \text{ m/s}^2} = 12.0 \text{ s}$

Substitute $t = 12.0$ s into Equation (6) to find the rocket's maximum height:

$y_{max} = 235 \text{ m} + (118 \text{ m/s})(12.0 \text{ s}) - (4.90 \text{ m/s}^2)(12.0 \text{ s})^2$
$= 945 \text{ m}$

(c) Phase 2: Find the velocity of the rocket just prior to impact.

Find the time to impact by setting $y = 0$ in Equation (6) and using the quadratic formula:

$0 = 235 \text{ m} + (118 \text{ m/s})t - (4.90 \text{ m/s})t^2$
$t = 25.9 \text{ s}$

Substitute this value of t into Equation (5):

$v = (-9.80 \text{ m/s}^2)(25.9 \text{ s}) + 118 \text{ m/s} = -136 \text{ m/s}$

REMARKS You may think that it is more natural to break this problem into three phases, with the second phase ending at the maximum height and the third phase a free fall from maximum height to the ground. Although this approach gives the correct answer, it's an unnecessary complication. Two phases are sufficient, one for each different acceleration.

QUESTION 2.10 If, instead, some fuel remains, at what height should the engines be fired again to brake the rocket's fall and allow a perfectly soft landing? (Assume the same acceleration as during the initial ascent.)

EXERCISE 2.10 An experimental rocket designed to land upright falls freely from a height of 2.00×10^2 m, starting at rest. At a height of 80.0 m, the rocket's engines start and provide constant upward acceleration until the rocket lands. What acceleration is required if the speed on touchdown is to be zero? (Neglect air resistance.)

ANSWER 14.7 m/s^2

■ SUMMARY

2.1 Displacement
The **displacement** of an object moving along the x-axis is defined as the change in position of the object,
$$\Delta x \equiv x_f - x_i \quad [2.1]$$
where x_i is the initial position of the object and x_f is its final position.

A **vector** quantity is characterized by both a magnitude and a direction. A **scalar** quantity has a magnitude only.

2.2 Velocity
The **average speed** of an object is given by
$$\text{Average speed} \equiv \frac{\text{path length}}{\text{elapsed time}}$$
The **average velocity** $\bar{v}$ during a time interval Δt is the displacement Δx divided by Δt.

$$\bar{v} \equiv \frac{\Delta x}{\Delta t} = \frac{x_f - x_i}{t_f - t_i} \quad [2.2]$$

The average velocity is equal to the slope of the straight line joining the initial and final points on a graph of the position of the object versus time.

The slope of the line tangent to the position vs. time curve at some point is equal to the **instantaneous velocity** at that time. The **instantaneous speed** of an object is defined as the magnitude of the instantaneous velocity.

2.3 Acceleration
The **average acceleration** $\bar{a}$ of an object undergoing a change in velocity Δv during a time interval Δt is
$$\bar{a} \equiv \frac{\Delta v}{\Delta t} = \frac{v_f - v_i}{t_f - t_i} \quad [2.4]$$

The **instantaneous acceleration** of an object at a certain time equals the slope of a velocity vs. time graph at that instant.

2.5 One-Dimensional Motion with Constant Acceleration

The most useful equations that describe the motion of an object moving with constant acceleration along the x-axis are as follows:

$$v = v_0 + at \qquad [2.6]$$

$$\Delta x = v_0 t + \tfrac{1}{2}at^2 \qquad [2.9]$$

$$v^2 = v_0^2 + 2a\Delta x \qquad [2.10]$$

All problems can be solved with the first two equations alone, the last being convenient when time doesn't explicitly enter the problem. After the constants are properly identified, most problems reduce to one or two equations in as many unknowns.

2.6 Freely Falling Objects

An object falling in the presence of Earth's gravity exhibits a free-fall acceleration directed toward Earth's center. If air friction is neglected and if the altitude of the falling object is small compared with Earth's radius, then we can assume that the free-fall acceleration $g = 9.8$ m/s^2 is constant over the range of motion. Equations 2.6, 2.9, and 2.10 apply, with $a = -g$.

■ MULTIPLE-CHOICE QUESTIONS

WebAssign The multiple-choice questions in this chapter may be assigned online in Enhanced WebAssign.

1. An arrow is shot straight up in the air at an initial speed of 15.0 m/s. After how much time is the arrow heading downward at a speed of 8.00 m/s? (a) 0.714 s (b) 1.24 s (c) 1.87 s (d) 2.35 s (e) 3.22 s

2. One drop of oil falls straight down onto the road from the engine of a moving car every 5 s. Figure MCQ2.2 shows the pattern of the drops left behind on the pavement. What is the average speed of the car over this section of its motion? (a) 20 m/s (b) 24 m/s (c) 30 m/s (d) 100 m/s (e) 120 m/s.

── 600 m ──

Figure MCQ2.2

3. When applying the equations of kinematics for an object moving in one dimension, which of the following statements *must* be true? (a) The velocity of the object must remain constant. (b) The acceleration of the object must remain constant. (c) The velocity of the object must increase with time. (d) The position of the object must increase with time. (e) The velocity of the object must always be in the same direction as its acceleration.

4. A juggler throws a bowling pin straight up in the air. After the pin leaves his hand and while it is in the air, which statement is true? (a) The velocity of the pin is always in the same direction as its acceleration. (b) The velocity of the pin is never in the same direction as its acceleration. (c) The acceleration of the pin is zero. (d) The velocity of the pin is opposite its acceleration on the way up. (e) The velocity of the pin is in the same direction as its acceleration on the way up.

5. A racing car starts from rest and reaches a final speed v in a time t. If the acceleration of the car is constant during this time, which of the following statements must be true? (a) The car travels a distance vt. (b) The average speed of the car is $v/2$. (c) The acceleration of the car is v/t. (d) The velocity of the car remains constant. (e) None of these

6. When the pilot reverses the propeller in a boat moving north, the boat moves with an acceleration directed south. Assume the acceleration of the boat remains constant in magnitude and direction. What happens to the boat? (a) It eventually stops and remains stopped. (b) It eventually stops and then speeds up in the northward direction. (c) It eventually stops and then speeds up in the southward direction. (d) It never stops but loses speed more and more slowly forever. (e) It never stops but continues to speed up in the northward direction.

7. An object moves along the x-axis, its position measured at each instant of time. The data are organized into an accurate graph of x vs. t. Which of the following quantities *cannot* be obtained from this graph? (a) the velocity at any instant (b) the acceleration at any instant (c) the displacement during some time interval (d) the average velocity during some time interval (e) the speed of the particle at any instant

8. A skateboarder starts from rest and moves down a hill with constant acceleration in a straight line, traveling for 6 s. In a second trial, he starts from rest and moves along the same straight line with the same acceleration for only 2 s. How does his displacement from his starting point in this second trial compare with the first trial? (a) one-third as large (b) three times larger (c) one-ninth as large (d) nine times larger (e) $1/\sqrt{3}$ times as large

9. Races are timed to an accuracy of 1/1 000 of a second. What distance could a person in-line skating at a speed of 8.5 m/s travel in that period of time? (a) 85 mm (b) 85 cm (c) 8.5 m (d) 8.5 mm (e) 8.5 km

10. A student at the top of a building throws a red ball upward with speed v_0 and then throws a blue ball downward with the same initial speed v_0. Immediately before the two balls reach the ground, which of the following statements are true? (Choose all correct statements; neglect air friction.) (a) The speed of the red ball is less than that of the blue ball. (b) The speed of the red ball is greater than that of the blue ball. (c) Their velocities are equal. (d) The speed of each ball is greater than v_0. (e) The acceleration of the blue ball is greater than that of the red ball.

11. A ball is thrown downward from the top of a 40.0 m tower with an initial speed of 12 m/s. Assuming negligible air resistance, what is the speed of the ball just before hitting the ground? (a) 28 m/s (b) 30 m/s (c) 56 m/s (d) 784 m/s (e) More information is needed.

12. A ball is thrown straight up in the air. For which situation are both the instantaneous velocity and the acceleration zero? (a) on the way up (b) at the top of the flight path (c) on the way down (d) halfway up and halfway down (e) none of these

■ CONCEPTUAL QUESTIONS

WebAssign The conceptual questions in this chapter may be assigned online in Enhanced WebAssign.

1. If the velocity of a particle is nonzero, can the particle's acceleration be zero? Explain.

2. If the velocity of a particle is zero, can the particle's acceleration be nonzero? Explain.

3. If a car is traveling eastward, can its acceleration be westward? Explain.

4. (a) Can the equations in Table 2.4 be used in a situation where the acceleration varies with time? (b) Can they be used when the acceleration is zero?

5. Two cars are moving in the same direction in parallel lanes along a highway. At some instant, the velocity of car A exceeds the velocity of car B. Does that mean that the acceleration of A is greater than that of B at that instant? Explain.

6. Figure CQ2.6 shows strobe photographs taken of a disk moving from left to right under different conditions. The time interval between images is constant. Tak-

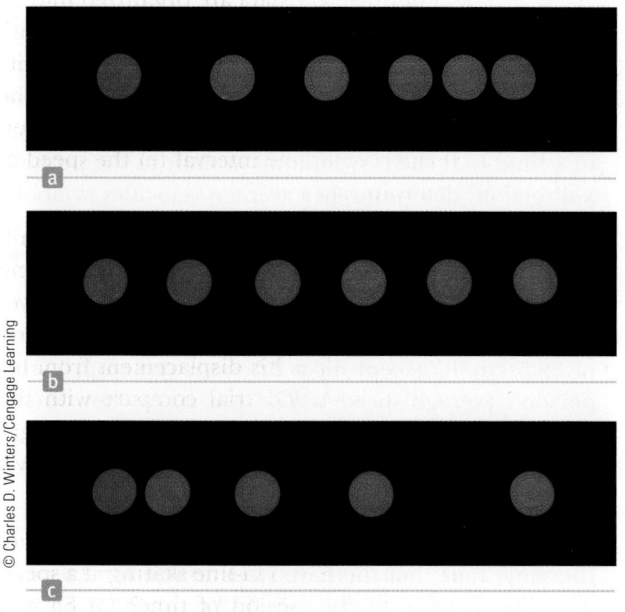

ing the direction to the right to be positive, describe the motion of the disk in each case. For which case is (a) the acceleration positive? (b) the acceleration negative? (c) the velocity constant?

7. (a) Can the instantaneous velocity of an object at an instant of time ever be greater in magnitude than the average velocity over a time interval containing that instant? (b) Can it ever be less?

8. A ball is thrown vertically upward. (a) What are its velocity and acceleration when it reaches its maximum altitude? (b) What is the acceleration of the ball just before it hits the ground?

9. Consider the following combinations of signs and values for the velocity and acceleration of a particle with respect to a one-dimensional x-axis:

	Velocity	Acceleration
a.	Positive	Positive
b.	Positive	Negative
c.	Positive	Zero
d.	Negative	Positive
e.	Negative	Negative
f.	Negative	Zero
g.	Zero	Positive
h.	Zero	Negative

Describe what the particle is doing in each case and give a real-life example for an automobile on an east–west one-dimensional axis, with east considered the positive direction.

10. A ball rolls in a straight line along the horizontal direction. Using motion diagrams (or multiflash photographs), describe the velocity and acceleration of the ball for each of the following situations: (a) The ball moves to the right at a constant speed. (b) The ball moves from right to left and continually slows down. (c) The ball moves from right to left and continually speeds up. (d) The ball moves to the right, first speeding up at a constant rate and then slowing down at a constant rate.

Figure CQ2.6

PROBLEMS

WebAssign The problems in this chapter may be assigned online in Enhanced WebAssign. Selected problems also have Watch It video solutions.

1. denotes straightforward problem; **2.** denotes intermediate problem;

3. denotes challenging problem

1. denotes full solution available in *Student Solutions Manual/ Study Guide*

1. denotes problems most often assigned in Enhanced WebAssign

BIO denotes biomedical problems

GP denotes guided problems

M denotes Master It tutorial available in Enhanced WebAssign

Q|C denotes asking for quantitative and conceptual reasoning

S denotes symbolic reasoning problem

2.1 Displacement

2.2 Velocity

1. **BIO** The speed of a nerve impulse in the human body is about 100 m/s. If you accidentally stub your toe in the dark, estimate the time it takes the nerve impulse to travel to your brain.

2. Light travels at a speed of about 3×10^8 m/s. (a) How many miles does a pulse of light travel in a time interval of 0.1 s, which is about the blink of an eye? (b) Compare this distance to the diameter of Earth.

3. A person travels by car from one city to another with different constant speeds between pairs of cities. She drives for 30.0 min at 80.0 km/h, 12.0 min at 100 km/h, and 45.0 min at 40.0 km/h and spends 15.0 min eating lunch and buying gas. (a) Determine the average speed for the trip. (b) Determine the distance between the initial and final cities along the route.

4. The current indoor world record time in the 200-m race is 19.92 s, held by Frank Fredericks of Namibia (1996), while the indoor record time in the one-mile race is 228.5 s, held by Hicham El Guerrouj of Morroco (1997). Find the mean speed in meters per second corresponding to these record times for (a) the 200-m event and (b) the one-mile event.

5. Two boats start together and race across a 60-km-wide lake and back. Boat A goes across at 60 km/h and returns at 60 km/h. Boat B goes across at 30 km/h, and its crew, realizing how far behind it is getting, returns at 90 km/h. Turnaround times are negligible, and the boat that completes the round trip first wins. (a) Which boat wins and by how much? (Or is it a tie?) (b) What is the average velocity of the winning boat?

6. A graph of position versus time for a certain particle moving along the *x*-axis is shown in Figure P2.6. Find the average velocity in the time intervals from (a) 0 to 2.00 s, (b) 0 to 4.00 s, (c) 2.00 s to 4.00 s, (d) 4.00 s to 7.00 s, and (e) 0 to 8.00 s.

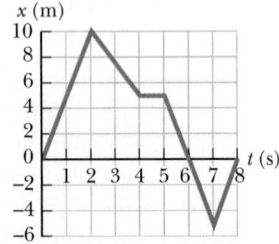

Figure P2.6 Problems 6 and 17

7. A motorist drives north for 35.0 minutes at 85.0 km/h and then stops for 15.0 minutes. He then continues north, traveling 130 km in 2.00 h. (a) What is his total displacement? (b) What is his average velocity?

8. A tennis player moves in a straight-line path as shown in Figure P2.8. Find her average velocity in the time intervals from (a) 0 to 1.0 s, (b) 0 to 4.0 s, (c) 1.0 s to 5.0 s, and (d) 0 to 5.0 s.

Figure P2.8

9. A jet plane has a takeoff speed of $v_{to} = 75$ m/s and can move along the runway at an average acceleration of 1.3 m/s². If the length of the runway is 2.5 km, will the plane be able to use this runway safely? Defend your answer.

10. Two cars travel in the same direction along a straight highway, one at a constant speed of 55 mi/h and the other at 70 mi/h. (a) Assuming they start at the same point, how much sooner does the faster car arrive at a destination 10 mi away? (b) How far must the faster car travel before it has a 15-min lead on the slower car?

11. The cheetah can reach a top speed of 114 km/h (71 mi/h). While chasing its prey in a short sprint, a cheetah starts from rest and runs 45 m in a straight line, reaching a final speed of 72 km/h. (a) Determine the cheetah's average acceleration during the short sprint, and (b) find its displacement at $t = 3.5$ s.

12. **S** An athlete swims the length L of a pool in a time t_1 and makes the return trip to the starting position in a time t_2. If she is swimming initially in the positive *x*-direction, determine her average velocities symbolically in (a) the first half of the swim, (b) the second half of the swim, and (c) the round trip. (d) What is her average speed for the round trip?

13. **M** A person takes a trip, driving with a constant speed of 89.5 km/h, except for a 22.0-min rest stop. If the person's average speed is 77.8 km/h, (a) how much time is spent on the trip and (b) how far does the person travel?

14. A tortoise can run with a speed of 0.10 m/s, and a hare can run 20 times as fast. In a race, they both start at the same time, but the hare stops to rest for 2.0 minutes. The tortoise wins by a shell (20 cm). (a) How long does the race take? (b) What is the length of the race?

15. To qualify for the finals in a racing event, a race car must achieve an average speed of 250 km/h on a track with a total length of 1 600 m. If a particular car covers the first half of the track at an average speed of 230 km/h, what minimum average speed must it have in the second half of the event in order to qualify?

16. **QC** **S** One athlete in a race running on a long, straight track with a constant speed v_1 is a distance d behind a second athlete running with a constant speed v_2. (a) Under what circumstances is the first athlete able to overtake the second athlete? (b) Find the time t it takes the first athlete to overtake the second athlete, in terms of d, v_1, and v_2. (c) At what minimum distance d_2 from the leading athlete must the finish line be located so that the trailing athlete can at least tie for first place? Express d_2 in terms of d, v_1, and v_2 by using the result of part (b).

17. A graph of position versus time for a certain particle moving along the x-axis is shown in Figure P2.6. Find the instantaneous velocity at the instants (a) $t = 1.00$ s, (b) $t = 3.00$ s, (c) $t = 4.50$ s, and (d) $t = 7.50$ s.

18. A race car moves such that its position fits the relationship

$$x = (5.0 \text{ m/s})t + (0.75 \text{ m/s}^3)t^3$$

where x is measured in meters and t in seconds. (a) Plot a graph of the car's position versus time. (b) Determine the instantaneous velocity of the car at $t = 4.0$ s, using time intervals of 0.40 s, 0.20 s, and 0.10 s. (c) Compare the average velocity during the first 4.0 s with the results of part (b).

19. Runner A is initially 4.0 mi west of a flagpole and is running with a constant velocity of 6.0 mi/h due east. Runner B is initially 3.0 mi east of the flagpole and is running with a constant velocity of 5.0 mi/h due west. How far are the runners from the flagpole when they meet?

2.3 Acceleration

20. A particle starts from rest and accelerates as shown in Figure P2.20. Determine (a) the particle's speed at $t = 10.0$ s and at $t = 20.0$ s, and (b) the distance traveled in the first 20.0 s.

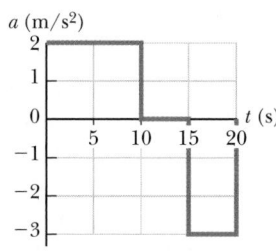

Figure P2.20

21. A 50.0-g Super Ball traveling at 25.0 m/s bounces off a brick wall and rebounds at 22.0 m/s. A high-speed camera records this event. If the ball is in contact with the wall for 3.50 ms, what is the magnitude of the average acceleration of the ball during this time interval?

22. **BIO** The average person passes out at an acceleration of $7g$ (that is, seven times the gravitational acceleration on Earth). Suppose a car is designed to accelerate at this rate. How much time would be required for the

car to accelerate from rest to 60.0 miles per hour? (The car would need rocket boosters!)

23. A certain car is capable of accelerating at a rate of 0.60 m/s². How long does it take for this car to go from a speed of 55 mi/h to a speed of 60 mi/h?

24. The velocity vs. time graph for an object moving along a straight path is shown in Figure P2.24. **(i)** Find the average acceleration of the object during the time intervals (a) 0 to 5.0 s, (b) 5.0 s to 15 s, and (c) 0 to 20 s. **(ii)** Find the instantaneous acceleration at (a) 2.0 s, (b) 10 s, and (c) 18 s.

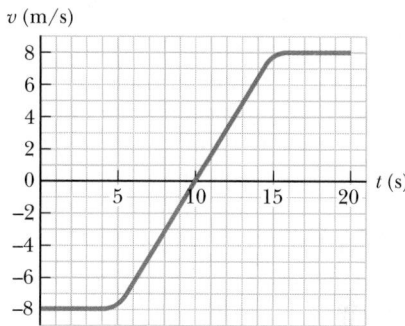

Figure P2.24

25. A steam catapult launches a jet aircraft from the aircraft carrier *John C. Stennis*, giving it a speed of 175 mi/h in 2.50 s. (a) Find the average acceleration of the plane. (b) Assuming the acceleration is constant, find the distance the plane moves.

2.5 One-Dimensional Motion with Constant Acceleration

26. Solve Example 2.5, "Car Chase" by a graphical method. On the same graph, plot position versus time for the car and the trooper. From the intersection of the two curves, read the time at which the trooper overtakes the car.

27. **M** An object moving with uniform acceleration has a velocity of 12.0 cm/s in the positive x-direction when its x-coordinate is 3.00 cm. If its x coordinate 2.00 s later is −5.00 cm, what is its acceleration?

28. In 1865 Jules Verne proposed sending men to the Moon by firing a space capsule from a 220-m-long cannon with final speed of 10.97 km/s. What would have been the unrealistically large acceleration experienced by the space travelers during their launch? (A human can stand an acceleration of $15g$ for a short time.) Compare your answer with the free-fall acceleration, 9.80 m/s².

29. A truck covers 40.0 m in 8.50 s while uniformly slowing down to a final velocity of 2.80 m/s. (a) Find the truck's original speed. (b) Find its acceleration.

30. **GP** A speedboat increases its speed uniformly from $v_i = 20.0$ m/s to $v_f = 30.0$ m/s in a distance of 2.00×10^2 m. (a) Draw a coordinate system for this situation

and label the relevant quantities, including vectors. (b) For the given information, what single equation is most appropriate for finding the acceleration? (c) Solve the equation selected in part (b) symbolically for the boat's acceleration in terms of v_f, v_i, and Δx. (d) Substitute given values, obtaining that acceleration. (e) Find the time it takes the boat to travel the given distance.

31. A Cessna aircraft has a liftoff speed of 120 km/h. (a) What minimum constant acceleration does the aircraft require if it is to be airborne after a takeoff run of 240 m? (b) How long does it take the aircraft to become airborne?

32. An object moves with constant acceleration 4.00 m/s² and over a time interval reaches a final velocity of 12.0 m/s. (a) If its original velocity is 6.00 m/s, what is its displacement during the time interval? (b) What is the distance it travels during this interval? (c) If its original velocity is −6.00 m/s, what is its displacement during this interval? (d) What is the total distance it travels during the interval in part (c)?

33. **Q|C** In a test run, a certain car accelerates uniformly from zero to 24.0 m/s in 2.95 s. (a) What is the magnitude of the car's acceleration? (b) How long does it take the car to change its speed from 10.0 m/s to 20.0 m/s? (c) Will doubling the time always double the change in speed? Why?

34. **Q|C** A jet plane lands with a speed of 100 m/s and can accelerate at a maximum rate of −5.00 m/s² as it comes to rest. (a) From the instant the plane touches the runway, what is the minimum time needed before it can come to rest? (b) Can this plane land on a small tropical island airport where the runway is 0.800 km long?

35. **Q|C** Speedy Sue, driving at 30.0 m/s, enters a one-lane tunnel. She then observes a slow-moving van 155 m ahead traveling at 5.00 m/s. Sue applies her brakes but can accelerate only at −2.00 m/s² because the road is wet. Will there be a collision? State how you decide. If yes, determine how far into the tunnel and at what time the collision occurs. If no, determine the distance of closest approach between Sue's car and the van.

36. A record of travel along a straight path is as follows:

    1. Start from rest with a constant acceleration of 2.77 m/s² for 15.0 s.

    2. Maintain a constant velocity for the next 2.05 min.

    3. Apply a constant negative acceleration of −9.47 m/s² for 4.39 s.

    (a) What was the total displacement for the trip? (b) What were the average speeds for legs 1, 2, and 3 of the trip, as well as for the complete trip?

37. A train is traveling down a straight track at 20 m/s when the engineer applies the brakes, resulting in an acceleration of −1.0 m/s² as long as the train is in motion. How far does the train move during a 40-s time interval starting at the instant the brakes are applied?

38. A car accelerates uniformly from rest to a speed of 40.0 mi/h in 12.0 s. Find (a) the distance the car travels during this time and (b) the constant acceleration of the car.

39. A car starts from rest and travels for 5.0 s with a uniform acceleration of +1.5 m/s². The driver then applies the brakes, causing a uniform acceleration of −2.0 m/s². If the brakes are applied for 3.0 s, (a) how fast is the car going at the end of the braking period, and (b) how far has the car gone?

40. **S** A car starts from rest and travels for t_1 seconds with a uniform acceleration a_1. The driver then applies the brakes, causing a uniform acceleration a_2. If the brakes are applied for t_2 seconds, (a) how fast is the car going just before the beginning of the braking period? (b) How far does the car go before the driver begins to brake? (c) Using the answers to parts (a) and (b) as the initial velocity and position for the motion of the car during braking, what total distance does the car travel? Answers are in terms of the variables a_1, a_2, t_1, and t_2.

41. In the Daytona 500 auto race, a Ford Thunderbird and a Mercedes Benz are moving side by side down a straightaway at 71.5 m/s. The driver of the Thunderbird realizes that she must make a pit stop, and she smoothly slows to a stop over a distance of 250 m. She spends 5.00 s in the pit and then accelerates out, reaching her previous speed of 71.5 m/s after a distance of 350 m. At this point, how far has the Thunderbird fallen behind the Mercedes Benz, which has continued at a constant speed?

42. A certain cable car in San Francisco can stop in 10 s when traveling at maximum speed. On one occasion, the driver sees a dog a distance d in front of the car and slams on the brakes instantly. The car reaches the dog 8.0 s later, and the dog jumps off the track just in time. If the car travels 4.0 m beyond the position of the dog before coming to a stop, how far was the car from the dog? (Hint: You will need three equations.)

43. **M** A hockey player is standing on his skates on a frozen pond when an opposing player, moving with a uniform speed of 12 m/s, skates by with the puck. After 3.0 s, the first player makes up his mind to chase his opponent. If he accelerates uniformly at 4.0 m/s², (a) how long does it take him to catch his opponent, and (b) how far has he traveled in that time? (Assume the player with the puck remains in motion at constant speed.)

44. A train 400 m long is moving on a straight track with a speed of 82.4 km/h. The engineer applies the brakes at a crossing, and later the last car passes the crossing with a speed of 16.4 km/h. Assuming constant acceleration, determine how long the train blocked the crossing. Disregard the width of the crossing.

2.6 Freely Falling Objects

45. A ball is thrown vertically upward with a speed of 25.0 m/s. (a) How high does it rise? (b) How long does

it take to reach its highest point? (c) How long does the ball take to hit the ground after it reaches its highest point? (d) What is its velocity when it returns to the level from which it started?

46. A ball is thrown directly downward with an initial speed of 8.00 m/s, from a height of 30.0 m. After what time interval does it strike the ground?

47. A certain freely falling object, released from rest, requires 1.50 s to travel the last 30.0 m before it hits the ground. (a) Find the velocity of the object when it is 30.0 m above the ground. (b) Find the total distance the object travels during the fall.

48. **Q|C** An attacker at the base of a castle wall 3.65 m high throws a rock straight up with speed 7.40 m/s at a height of 1.55 m above the ground. (a) Will the rock reach the top of the wall? (b) If so, what is the rock's speed at the top? If not, what initial speed must the rock have to reach the top? (c) Find the change in the speed of a rock thrown straight down from the top of the wall at an initial speed of 7.40 m/s and moving between the same two points. (d) Does the change in speed of the downward-moving rock agree with the magnitude of the speed change of the rock moving upward between the same elevations? Explain physically why or why not.

49. **BIO** Traumatic brain injury such as concussion results when the head undergoes a very large acceleration. Generally, an acceleration less than 800 m/s² lasting for any length of time will not cause injury, whereas an acceleration greater than 1 000 m/s² lasting for at least 1 ms will cause injury. Suppose a small child rolls off a bed that is 0.40 m above the floor. If the floor is hardwood, the child's head is brought to rest in approximately 2.0 mm. If the floor is carpeted, this stopping distance is increased to about 1.0 cm. Calculate the magnitude and duration of the deceleration in both cases, to determine the risk of injury. Assume the child remains horizontal during the fall to the floor. Note that a more complicated fall could result in a head velocity greater or less than the speed you calculate.

50. A small mailbag is released from a helicopter that is descending steadily at 1.50 m/s. After 2.00 s, (a) what is the speed of the mailbag, and (b) how far is it below the helicopter? (c) What are your answers to parts (a) and (b) if the helicopter is rising steadily at 1.50 m/s?

51. A tennis player tosses a tennis ball straight up and then catches it after 2.00 s at the same height as the point of release. (a) What is the acceleration of the ball while it is in flight? (b) What is the velocity of the ball when it reaches its maximum height? Find (c) the initial velocity of the ball and (d) the maximum height it reaches.

52. **S** A package is dropped from a helicopter that is descending steadily at a speed v_0. After t seconds have elapsed, (a) what is the speed of the package in terms of v_0, g, and t? (b) What distance d is it from the heli-

copter in terms of g and t? (c) What are the answers to parts (a) and (b) if the helicopter is rising steadily at the same speed?

53. **Q|C** A model rocket is launched straight upward with an initial speed of 50.0 m/s. It accelerates with a constant upward acceleration of 2.00 m/s² until its engines stop at an altitude of 150 m. (a) What can you say about the motion of the rocket after its engines stop? (b) What is the maximum height reached by the rocket? (c) How long after liftoff does the rocket reach its maximum height? (d) How long is the rocket in the air?

54. A baseball is hit so that it travels straight upward after being struck by the bat. A fan observes that it takes 3.00 s for the ball to reach its maximum height. Find (a) the ball's initial velocity and (b) the height it reaches.

Additional Problems

55. A truck tractor pulls two trailers, one behind the other, at a constant speed of 100 km/h. It takes 0.600 s for the big rig to completely pass onto a bridge 400 m long. For what duration of time is all or part of the truck–trailer combination on the bridge?

56. **M** **BIO** Colonel John P. Stapp, USAF, participated in studying whether a jet pilot could survive emergency ejection. On March 19, 1954, he rode a rocket-propelled sled that moved down a track at a speed of 632 mi/h (see Fig. P2.56). He and the sled were safely brought to rest in 1.40 s. Determine in SI units (a) the negative acceleration he experienced and (b) the distance he traveled during this negative acceleration.

Figure P2.56

57. A bullet is fired through a board 10.0 cm thick in such a way that the bullet's line of motion is perpendicular to the face of the board. If the initial speed of the bullet is 400 m/s and it emerges from the other side of the board with a speed of 300 m/s, find (a) the acceleration of the bullet as it passes through the board and (b) the total time the bullet is in contact with the board.

58. A speedboat moving at 30.0 m/s approaches a no-wake buoy marker 100 m ahead. The pilot slows the boat with a constant acceleration of −3.50 m/s² by reducing the throttle. (a) How long does it take the boat to reach

the buoy? (b) What is the velocity of the boat when it reaches the buoy?

59. A student throws a set of keys vertically upward to his fraternity brother, who is in a window 4.00 m above. The brother's outstretched hand catches the keys 1.50 s later. (a) With what initial velocity were the keys thrown? (b)? What was the velocity of the keys just before they were caught?

60. **S** A student throws a set of keys vertically upward to his fraternity brother, who is in a window a distance h above. The brother's outstretched hand catches the keys on their way up a time t later. (a) With what initial velocity were the keys thrown? (b) What was the velocity of the keys just before they were caught? (Answers should be in terms of h, g, and t.)

61. **BIO** It has been claimed that an insect called the froghopper (*Philaenus spumarius*) is the best jumper in the animal kingdom. This insect can accelerate at 4 000 m/s^2 over a distance of 2.0 mm as it straightens its specially designed "jumping legs." (a) Assuming a uniform acceleration, what is the velocity of the insect after it has accelerated through this short distance, and (b) how long did it take to reach that velocity? (c) How high would the insect jump if air resistance could be ignored? Note that the actual height obtained is about 0.7 m, so air resistance is important here.

62. **QC** Draw motion diagrams (see Section 2.5) for (a) an object moving to the right at constant speed, (b) an object moving to the right and speeding up at a constant rate, (c) an object moving to the right and slowing down at a constant rate, (d) an object moving to the left and speeding up at a constant rate, and (e) an object moving to the left and slowing down at a constant rate. (f) How would your drawings change if the changes in speed were not uniform; that is, if the speed were not changing at a constant rate?

63. **M** A ball is thrown upward from the ground with an initial speed of 25 m/s; at the same instant, another ball is dropped from a building 15 m high. After how long will the balls be at the same height?

64. To pass a physical education class at a university, a student must run 1.0 mi in 12 min. After running for 10 min, she still has 500 yd to go. If her maximum acceleration is 0.15 m/s^2, can she make it? If the answer is no, determine what acceleration she would need to be successful.

65. In Chapter 5 we will define the center of mass of an object. The center of mass moves with constant acceleration when constant forces act on the object. A gymnast jumps straight up, with her center of mass moving at 2.80 m/s as she leaves the ground. How high above this point is her center of mass (a) 0.100 s, (b) 0.200 s, (c) 0.300 s, and (d) 0.500 s thereafter?

66. **S** Two students are on a balcony a distance h above the street. One student throws a ball vertically down-

ward at a speed v_0; at the same time, the other student throws a ball vertically upward at the same speed. Answer the following symbolically in terms of v_0, g, h, and t. (a) Write the kinematic equation for the y-coordinate of each ball. (b) Set the equations found in part (a) equal to height 0 and solve each for t symbolically using the quadratic formula. What is the difference in the two balls' time in the air? (c) Use the time-independent kinematics equation to find the velocity of each ball as it strikes the ground. (d) How far apart are the balls at a time t after they are released and before they strike the ground?

67. You drop a ball from a window on an upper floor of a building and it is caught by a friend on the ground when the ball is moving with speed v_f. You now repeat the drop, but you have a friend on the street below throw another ball upward at speed v_f exactly at the same time that you drop your ball from the window. The two balls are initially separated by 28.7 m. (a) At what time do they pass each other? (b) At what location do they pass each other relative the window?

68. The driver of a truck slams on the brakes when he sees a tree blocking the road. The truck slows down uniformly with an acceleration of -5.60 m/s^2 for 4.20 s, making skid marks 62.4 m long that end at the tree. With what speed does the truck then strike the tree?

69. **QC** Emily challenges her husband, David, to catch a $1 bill as follows. She holds the bill vertically as in Figure P2.69, with the center of the bill between David's index finger and thumb. David must catch the bill after Emily releases it without moving his hand downward. If his reaction time is 0.2 s, will he succeed? Explain your reasoning. (This challenge is a good trick you might want to try with your friends.)

Figure P2.69

70. A mountain climber stands at the top of a 50.0-m cliff that overhangs a calm pool of water. She throws two stones vertically downward 1.00 s apart and observes that they cause a single splash. The first stone had an initial velocity of -2.00 m/s. (a) How long after release of the first stone did the two stones hit the water? (b) What initial velocity must the second stone have had, given that they hit the water simultaneously? (c) What was the velocity of each stone at the instant it hit the water?

71. An ice sled powered by a rocket engine starts from rest on a large frozen lake and accelerates at $+40$ ft/s^2. After some time t_1, the rocket engine is shut down and the sled moves with constant velocity v for a time t_2. If

the total distance traveled by the sled is 17 500 ft and the total time is 90 s, find (a) the times t_1 and t_2 and (b) the velocity v. At the 17 500-ft mark, the sled begins to accelerate at -20 ft/s^2. (c) What is the final position of the sled when it comes to rest? (d) How long does it take to come to rest?

72. In Bosnia, the ultimate test of a young man's courage used to be to jump off a 400-year-old bridge (destroyed in 1993; rebuilt in 2004) into the River Neretva, 23 m below the bridge. (a) How long did the jump last? (b) How fast was the jumper traveling upon impact with the river? (c) If the speed of sound in air is 340 m/s, how long after the jumper took off did a spectator on the bridge hear the splash?

73. A person sees a lightning bolt pass close to an airplane that is flying in the distance. The person hears thunder 5.0 s after seeing the bolt and sees the airplane overhead 10 s after hearing the thunder. The speed of sound in air is 1 100 ft/s. (a) Find the distance of the airplane from the person at the instant of the bolt. (Neglect the time it takes the light to travel from the bolt to the eye.) (b) Assuming the plane travels with a constant speed toward the person, find the velocity of the airplane. (c) Look up the speed of light in air and defend the approximation used in part (a).

74. **QC** A glider on an air track carries a flag of length ℓ through a stationary photogate, which measures the time interval Δt_d during which the flag blocks a beam of infrared light passing across the photogate. The ratio $v_d = \ell/\Delta t_d$ is the average velocity of the glider over this part of its motion. Suppose the glider moves with constant acceleration. (a) Is v_d necessarily equal to the instantaneous velocity of the glider when it is halfway through the photogate in space? Explain. (b) Is v_d equal to the instantaneous velocity of the glider when it is halfway through the photogate in time? Explain.

75. A stuntman sitting on a tree limb wishes to drop vertically onto a horse galloping under the tree. The constant speed of the horse is 10.0 m/s, and the man is initially 3.00 m above the level of the saddle. (a) What must be the horizontal distance between the saddle and the limb when the man makes his move? (b) How long is he in the air?

■ AP* REVIEW QUESTIONS

Motion sensor

1. A cart with negligible friction is given an initial velocity up the ramp. The cart rises a distance, turns around, and travels back towards a motion sensor. Which set of signs would describe the cart's displacement, velocity, and acceleration the moment the cart is at the highest point on the ramp if the direction away from the sensor is determined to be positive?

	Displacement	Velocity	Acceleration
(A)	+	0	−
(B)	+	0	0
(C)	−	−	−
(D)	+	+	0
(E)	0	+	+

2. Which of the following acceleration versus time graphs represent a train that speeds up, cruises at a constant velocity, slows down, and stops?

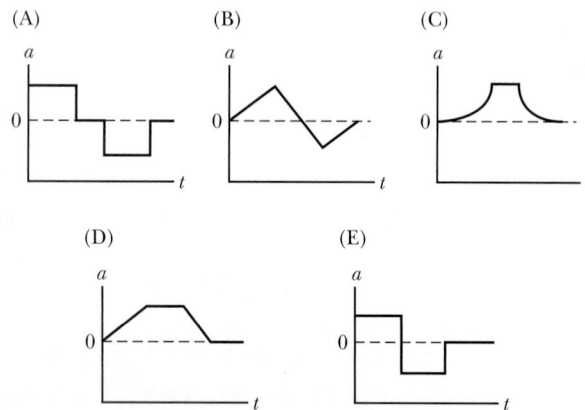

3. A hot air balloon ascends from the ground at a rate of 6.0 m/s and its passenger releases a small sand bag after 5.0 s. Neglecting air resistance, how long after the balloon is launched will it take for the sandbag to reach the ground?

(A) 2.5 s

(B) 3.0 s

(C) 7.5 s

(D) 8.0 s

(E) 11 s

4. How far does an object near Earth's surface fall if it starts from rest and freefalls for 1 second?

(A) 0 m

(B) 4.9 m

(C) 9.8 m

(D) 19.6 m

(E) Not enough information to solve

5. A cannon attached to the top of an armored vehicle points in the reverse direction of its forward motion. The vehicle undergoes an acceleration, a, for time t from rest. After time t, the cannon is fired with a speed v_p relative to the vehicle. What is the velocity of the projectile relative to the ground the moment it emerges from the cannon?

(A) $v_p - at$

(B) $\dfrac{at^2}{2} + v_p$

(C) $at - v_p$

(D) $\dfrac{at^2}{2} - v_p$

(E) $at + v_p$

6. A softball is thrown straight up. Identify the magnitude of the following quantities the moment the softball is at the top of its path.

	Displacement	Velocity	Acceleration
(A)	max	max	max
(B)	min	min	max
(C)	max	min	min
(D)	max	constant	constant
(E)	max	min	constant

7. What altitude from the launching point does a model rocket achieve if its rocket fires for 5 seconds, accelerating the rocket at a constant 50 m/s²?

(A) 10 m

(B) 125 m

(C) 250 m

(D) 625 m

(E) 875 m

8. Which of the following set of graphs represents the same motion?

I. Displacement vs. Time   II. Velocity vs. Time   III. Acceleration vs. Time

(A) I and II

(B) II and III

(C) I and III

(D) All represent a unique motion

(E) All represent the same motion

9. A mass in motion experiences an acceleration $-a$ for time t. Assuming left as the negative direction, which of the following vectors could NEVER represent the velocity after time t?

    I. ⟶

    II. ⟵

    III. zero magnitude

(A) I only

(B) II only

(C) III only

(D) I and III

(E) All are possible

Questions 10–12

Consider the following velocity versus time graph for a moving car for questions 10–12:

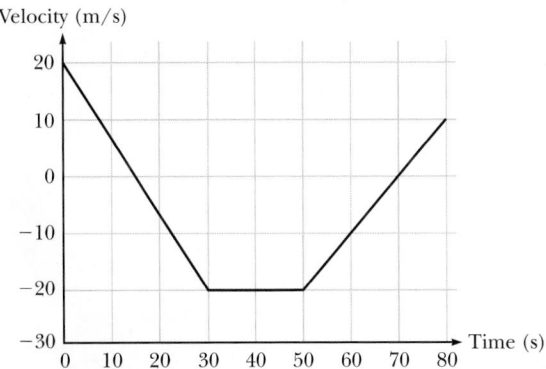

10. What is the car's instantaneous acceleration at 15 seconds?

(A) 0.5 m/s^2

(B) 0.75 m/s^2

(C) 1.0 m/s^2

(D) -1.0 m/s^2

(E) -0.75 m/s^2

11. What would the car's position be at 80 seconds if it started at a position $x_0 = -10$ m at $t = 0$ seconds?

(A) -560 m

(B) -550 m

(C) 960 m

(D) 950 m

(E) 940 m

12. Which of the following best describes the motion of the car for the graphed trip?

(A) The car travels in reverse getting faster and faster, cruises at a constant speed in reverse, and then gets faster and faster in the forward direction.

(B) The car travels in reverse getting slower and slower, stops, and then speeds up in the forward direction.

(C) The car slows in the forward direction, stops, gets faster in the reverse direction, cruises at a constant speed, gets slower in reverse, stops, and then gets faster in the forward direction.

(D) The car slows in the forward direction, stops, gets slower in the reverse direction, cruises at a constant speed, gets faster in reverse, and then gets faster in the forward direction.

(E) A graph of acceleration would have to be provided to fully verbally describe the car's motion.

Dave "Human Cannonball" Smith hurtles through the air along a parabolic path, depending on the correct initial velocity and cannon angle to send him safely over the U.S.-Mexico border fence and into a net.

3 Vectors and Two-Dimensional Motion

In our discussion of one-dimensional motion in Chapter 2, we used the concept of vectors only to a limited extent. In our further study of motion, manipulating vector quantities will become increasingly important, so much of this chapter is devoted to vector techniques. We'll then apply these mathematical tools to two-dimensional motion, especially that of projectiles, and to the understanding of relative motion.

3.1 Vectors and Their Properties

Each of the physical quantities we will encounter in this book can be categorized as either a *vector quantity* or a *scalar quantity*. As noted in Chapter 2, a vector has both direction and magnitude (size). A scalar can be completely specified by its magnitude with appropriate units; it has no direction. An example of each kind of quantity is shown in Figure 3.1.

As described in Chapter 2, displacement, velocity, and acceleration are vector quantities. Temperature is an example of a scalar quantity. If the temperature of an object is $-5°C$, that information completely specifies the temperature of the object; no direction is required. Masses, time intervals, and volumes are scalars as well. Scalar quantities can be manipulated with the rules of ordinary arithmetic. Vectors can also be added and subtracted from each other, and multiplied, but there are a number of important differences, as will be seen in the following sections.

When a vector quantity is handwritten, it is often represented with an arrow over the letter ($\vec{\mathbf{A}}$). As mentioned in Section 2.1, a vector quantity in this book will

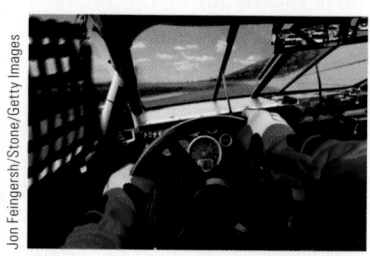

Figure 3.1 A vector such as velocity has a magnitude, shown on the race car's speedometer, and a direction, straight out through the race car's front windshield. The mass of the car is a scalar quantity, as is the volume of gasoline in its fuel tank.

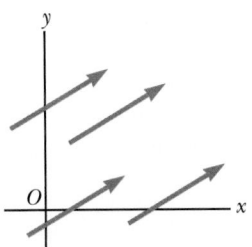

Figure 3.2 These four vectors are equal because they have equal lengths and point in the same direction.

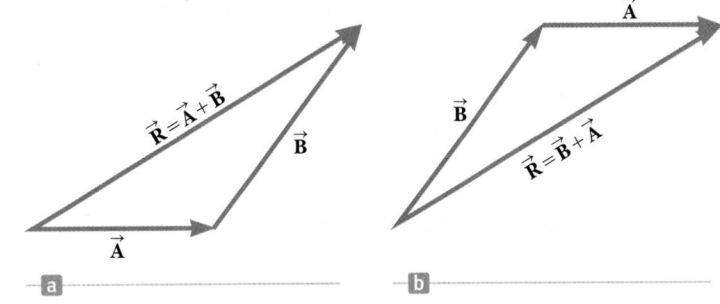

Active Figure 3.3
(a) When vector $\vec{B}$ is added to vector $\vec{A}$, the vector sum $\vec{R}$ is the vector that runs from the tail of $\vec{A}$ to the tip of $\vec{B}$. (b) Here the resultant runs from the tail of $\vec{B}$ to the tip of $\vec{A}$. These constructions prove that $\vec{A} + \vec{B} = \vec{B} + \vec{A}$.

be represented by boldface type with an arrow on top (for example, $\vec{A}$). The magnitude of the vector $\vec{A}$ will be represented by italic type, as A. Italic type will also be used to represent scalars.

Equality of Two Vectors Two vectors $\vec{A}$ and $\vec{B}$ are equal if they have the same magnitude and the same direction. This property allows us to translate a vector parallel to itself in a diagram without affecting the vector. In fact, for most purposes, any vector can be moved parallel to itself without being affected. (See Fig. 3.2.)

Adding Vectors When two or more vectors are added, they must all have the same units. For example, it doesn't make sense to add a velocity vector, carrying units of meters per second, to a displacement vector, carrying units of meters. Scalars obey the same rule: It would be similarly meaningless to add temperatures to volumes or masses to time intervals.

Vectors can be added geometrically or algebraically. (The latter is discussed at the end of the next section.) To add vector $\vec{B}$ to vector $\vec{A}$ geometrically, first draw $\vec{A}$ on a piece of graph paper to some scale, such as 1 cm = 1 m, so that its direction is specified relative to a coordinate system. Then draw vector $\vec{B}$ to the same scale with the tail of $\vec{B}$ starting at the tip of $\vec{A}$, as in Active Figure 3.3a. Vector $\vec{B}$ must be drawn along the direction that makes the proper angle relative vector $\vec{A}$. The **resultant vector** $\vec{R} = \vec{A} + \vec{B}$ is the vector drawn from the tail of $\vec{A}$ to the tip of $\vec{B}$. This procedure is known as the **triangle method of addition.**

When two vectors are added, their sum is independent of the order of the addition: $\vec{A} + \vec{B} = \vec{B} + \vec{A}$. This relationship can be seen from the geometric construction in Active Figure 3.3b, and is called the **commutative law of addition.**

This same general approach can also be used to add more than two vectors, as is done in Figure 3.4 for four vectors. The resultant vector sum $\vec{R} = \vec{A} + \vec{B} + \vec{C} + \vec{D}$ is the vector drawn from the tail of the first vector to the tip of the last. Again, the order in which the vectors are added is unimportant.

Negative of a Vector The negative of the vector $\vec{A}$ is defined as the vector that gives zero when added to $\vec{A}$. This means that $\vec{A}$ and $-\vec{A}$ have the same magnitude but opposite directions.

Subtracting Vectors Vector subtraction makes use of the definition of the negative of a vector. We define the operation $\vec{A} - \vec{B}$ as the vector $-\vec{B}$ added to the vector $\vec{A}$:

$$\vec{A} - \vec{B} = \vec{A} + (-\vec{B}) \qquad [3.1]$$

Vector subtraction is really a special case of vector addition. The geometric construction for subtracting two vectors is shown in Figure 3.5.

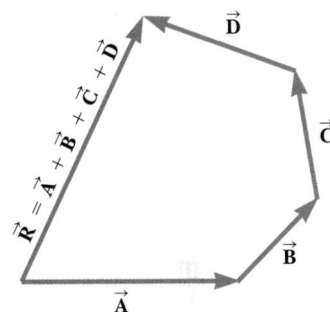

Figure 3.4 A geometric construction for summing four vectors. The resultant vector $\vec{R}$ is the vector that completes the polygon.

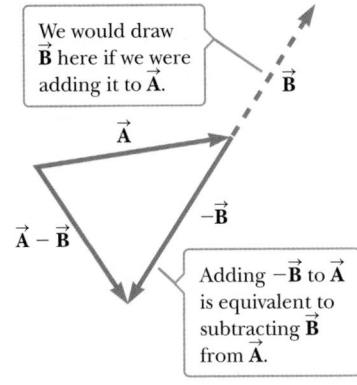

We would draw $\vec{B}$ here if we were adding it to $\vec{A}$.

Adding $-\vec{B}$ to $\vec{A}$ is equivalent to subtracting $\vec{B}$ from $\vec{A}$.

Figure 3.5 This construction shows how to subtract vector $\vec{B}$ from vector $\vec{A}$. The vector $-\vec{B}$ has the same magnitude as the vector $\vec{B}$, but points in the opposite direction.

Multiplying or Dividing a Vector by a Scalar Multiplying or dividing a vector by a scalar gives a vector. For example, if vector $\vec{\mathbf{A}}$ is multiplied by the scalar number 3, the result, written $3\vec{\mathbf{A}}$, is a vector with a magnitude three times that of $\vec{\mathbf{A}}$ and pointing in the same direction. If we multiply vector $\vec{\mathbf{A}}$ by the scalar -3, the result is $-3\vec{\mathbf{A}}$, a vector with a magnitude three times that of $\vec{\mathbf{A}}$ and pointing in the opposite direction (because of the negative sign).

■ *Quick Quiz*

3.1 The magnitudes of two vectors $\vec{\mathbf{A}}$ and $\vec{\mathbf{B}}$ are 12 units and 8 units, respectively. What are the largest and smallest possible values for the magnitude of the resultant vector $\vec{\mathbf{R}} = \vec{\mathbf{A}} + \vec{\mathbf{B}}$? (a) 14.4 and 4 (b) 12 and 8 (c) 20 and 4 (d) none of these.

■ **EXAMPLE 3.1** | **Taking a Trip**

GOAL Find the sum of two vectors by using a graph.

PROBLEM A car travels 20.0 km due north and then 35.0 km in a direction 60.0° west of north, as in Figure 3.6. Using a graph, find the magnitude and direction of a single vector that gives the net effect of the car's trip. This vector is called the car's *resultant displacement*.

STRATEGY Draw a graph and represent the displacement vectors as arrows. Graphically locate the vector resulting from the sum of the two displacement vectors. Measure its length and angle with respect to the vertical.

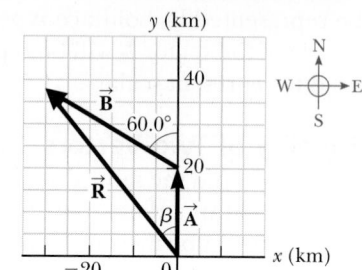

Figure 3.6 (Example 3.1) A graphical method for finding the resultant displacement vector $\vec{\mathbf{R}} = \vec{\mathbf{A}} + \vec{\mathbf{B}}$.

SOLUTION

Let $\vec{\mathbf{A}}$ represent the first displacement vector, 20.0 km north, and $\vec{\mathbf{B}}$ the second displacement vector, extending west of north. Carefully graph the two vectors, drawing a resultant vector $\vec{\mathbf{R}}$ with its base touching the base of $\vec{\mathbf{A}}$ and extending to the tip of $\vec{\mathbf{B}}$. Measure the length of this vector, which turns out to be about 48 km. The angle β, measured with a protractor, is about 39° west of north.

REMARKS Notice that ordinary arithmetic doesn't work here: the correct answer of 48 km is not equal to 20.0 km + 35.0 km = 55.0 km!

QUESTION 3.1 Suppose two vectors are added. Under what conditions would the sum of the magnitudes of the vectors equal the magnitude of the resultant vector?

EXERCISE 3.1 Graphically determine the magnitude and direction of the displacement if a man walks 30.0 km 45° north of east and then walks due east 20.0 km.

ANSWER 46 km, 27° north of east

3.2 Components of a Vector

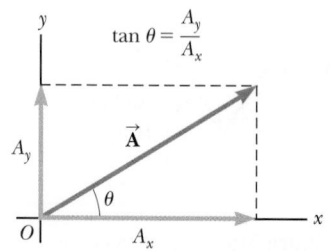

Figure 3.7 Any vector $\vec{\mathbf{A}}$ lying in the *xy*-plane can be represented by its rectangular components A_x and A_y.

One method of adding vectors makes use of the projections of a vector along the axes of a rectangular coordinate system. These projections are called **components.** Any vector can be completely described by its components.

Consider a vector $\vec{\mathbf{A}}$ in a rectangular coordinate system, as shown in Figure 3.7. $\vec{\mathbf{A}}$ can be expressed as the sum of two vectors: $\vec{\mathbf{A}}_x$, parallel to the *x*-axis, and $\vec{\mathbf{A}}_y$, parallel to the *y*-axis. Mathematically,

$$\vec{\mathbf{A}} = \vec{\mathbf{A}}_x + \vec{\mathbf{A}}_y$$

where $\vec{\mathbf{A}}_x$ and $\vec{\mathbf{A}}_y$ are the component vectors of $\vec{\mathbf{A}}$. The projection of $\vec{\mathbf{A}}$ along the *x*-axis, A_x, is called the *x*-component of $\vec{\mathbf{A}}$, and the projection of $\vec{\mathbf{A}}$ along the *y*-axis,

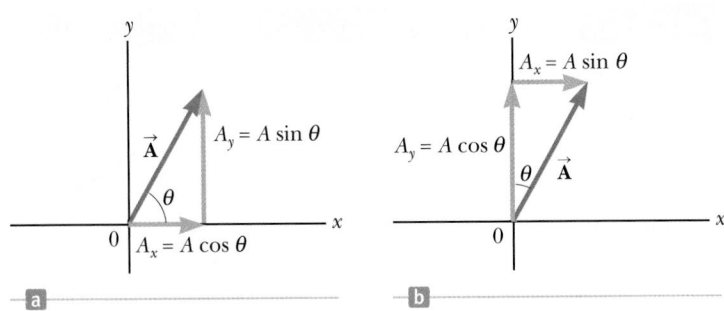

a

b

Figure 3.8 The angle θ need not always be defined from the positive x-axis.

A_y, is called the y-component of $\vec{\mathbf{A}}$. These components can be either positive or negative numbers with units. From the definitions of sine and cosine, we see that $\cos \theta = A_x/A$ and $\sin \theta = A_y/A$, so the components of $\vec{\mathbf{A}}$ are

$$A_x = A \cos \theta \qquad [3.2a]$$

$$A_y = A \sin \theta \qquad [3.2b]$$

These components form two sides of a right triangle having a hypotenuse with magnitude A. It follows that $\vec{\mathbf{A}}$'s magnitude and direction are related to its components through the Pythagorean theorem and the definition of the tangent:

$$A = \sqrt{A_x^2 + A_y^2} \qquad [3.3]$$

$$\tan \theta = \frac{A_y}{A_x} \qquad [3.4]$$

To solve for the angle θ, which is measured counterclockwise from the positive x-axis by convention, the inverse tangent can be taken of both sides of Equation (3.4):

$$\theta = \tan^{-1}\left(\frac{A_y}{A_x}\right)$$

This formula gives the right answer for θ only half the time! The inverse tangent function returns values only from $-90°$ to $+90°$, so the answer in your calculator window will only be correct if the vector happens to lie in the first or fourth quadrant. If it lies in the second or third quadrant, adding $180°$ to the number in the calculator window will always give the right answer. The angle in Equations 3.2 and 3.4 must be measured from the positive x-axis. Other choices of reference line are possible, but certain adjustments must then be made. (See Tip 3.2 and Fig. 3.8.)

If a coordinate system other than the one shown in Figure 3.7 is chosen, the components of the vector must be modified accordingly. In many applications it's more convenient to express the components of a vector in a coordinate system having axes that are not horizontal and vertical, but are still perpendicular to each other. Suppose a vector $\vec{\mathbf{B}}$ makes an angle θ' with the x'-axis defined in Figure 3.9. The rectangular components of $\vec{\mathbf{B}}$ along the axes of the figure are given by $B_{x'} = B \cos \theta'$ and $B_{y'} = B \sin \theta'$, as in Equations 3.2. The magnitude and direction of $\vec{\mathbf{B}}$ are then obtained from expressions equivalent to Equations 3.3 and 3.4.

Tip 3.2 x- and y-components

Equation 3.2 for the x- and y-components of a vector associates cosine with the x-component and sine with the y-component, as in Figure 3.8a. This association is due *solely* to the fact that we chose to measure the angle θ with respect to the positive x-axis. If the angle were measured with respect to the y-axis, as in Figure 3.8b, the components would be given by $A_x = A \sin \theta$ and $A_y = A \cos \theta$.

Tip 3.3 Inverse Tangents on Calculators: Right Half the Time

The inverse tangent function on calculators returns an angle between $-90°$ and $+90°$. If the vector lies in the second or third quadrant, the angle, as measured from the positive x-axis, will be the angle returned by your calculator plus $180°$.

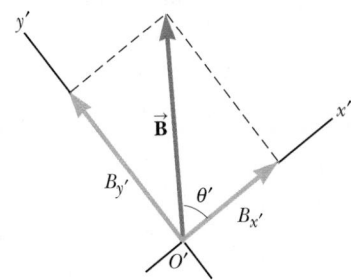

Figure 3.9 The components of vector $\vec{\mathbf{B}}$ in a tilted coordinate system.

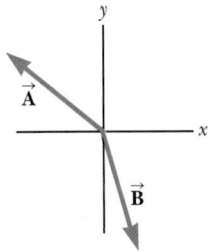

Figure 3.10 (Quick Quizzes 3.2 and 3.3)

■ Quick Quiz

3.2 Figure 3.10 shows two vectors lying in the xy-plane. Determine the signs of the x- and y-components of $\vec{\mathbf{A}}$, $\vec{\mathbf{B}}$, and $\vec{\mathbf{A}} + \vec{\mathbf{B}}$.

3.3 Which vector has an angle with respect to the positive x-axis that is in the range of the inverse tangent function?

■ EXAMPLE 3.2   Help Is on the Way!

GOAL Find vector components, given a magnitude and direction, and vice versa.

PROBLEM **(a)** Find the horizontal and vertical components of the $d = 1.00 \times 10^2$ m displacement of a superhero who flies from the top of a tall building along the path shown in Figure 3.11a. **(b)** Suppose instead the superhero leaps in the other direction along a displacement vector $\vec{B}$ to the top of a flagpole where the displacement components are given by $B_x = -25.0$ m and $B_y = 10.0$ m. Find the magnitude and direction of the displacement vector.

STRATEGY **(a)** The triangle formed by the displacement and its components is shown in Figure 3.11b. Simple trigonometry gives the components relative to the standard xy-coordinate system: $A_x = A \cos \theta$ and $A_y = A \sin \theta$ (Eqs. 3.2). Note that $\theta = -30.0°$, negative because it's measured clockwise from the positive x-axis. **(b)** Apply Equations 3.3 and 3.4 to find the magnitude and direction of the vector.

Figure 3.11 (Example 3.2)

SOLUTION

(a) Find the vector components of $\vec{A}$ from its magnitude and direction.

Use Equations 3.2 to find the components of the displacement vector $\vec{A}$:

$$A_x = A \cos \theta = (1.00 \times 10^2 \text{ m}) \cos(-30.0°) = \boxed{+86.6 \text{ m}}$$

$$A_y = A \sin \theta = (1.00 \times 10^2 \text{ m}) \sin(-30.0°) = \boxed{-50.0 \text{ m}}$$

(b) Find the magnitude and direction of the displacement vector $\vec{B}$ from its components.

Compute the magnitude of $\vec{B}$ from the Pythagorean theorem:

$$B = \sqrt{B_x^2 + B_y^2} = \sqrt{(-25.0 \text{ m})^2 + (10.0 \text{ m})^2} = \boxed{26.9 \text{ m}}$$

Calculate the direction of $\vec{B}$ using the inverse tangent, remembering to add 180° to the answer in your calculator window, because the vector lies in the second quadrant:

$$\theta = \tan^{-1}\left(\frac{B_y}{B_x}\right) = \tan^{-1}\left(\frac{10.0}{-25.0}\right) = -21.8°$$

$$\theta = \boxed{158°}$$

REMARKS In part (a), note that $\cos(-\theta) = \cos \theta$; however, $\sin(-\theta) = -\sin \theta$. The negative sign of A_y reflects the fact that displacement in the y-direction is *downward*.

QUESTION 3.2 What other functions, if any, can be used to find the angle in part (b)?

EXERCISE 3.2 **(a)** Suppose the superhero had flown 150 m at a 120° angle with respect to the positive x-axis. Find the components of the displacement vector. **(b)** Suppose instead the superhero had leaped with a displacement having an x-component of 32.5 m and a y-component of 24.3 m. Find the magnitude and direction of the displacement vector.

ANSWERS (a) $A_x = -75$ m, $A_y = 130$ m (b) 40.6 m, 36.8°

Adding Vectors Algebraically

The graphical method of adding vectors is valuable in understanding how vectors can be manipulated, but most of the time vectors are added algebraically in terms of their components. Suppose $\vec{R} = \vec{A} + \vec{B}$. Then the components of the resultant vector $\vec{R}$ are given by

$$R_x = A_x + B_x \qquad\qquad\qquad \text{[3.5a]}$$

$$R_y = A_y + B_y \qquad\qquad\qquad \text{[3.5b]}$$

So x-components are added only to x-components, and y-components only to y-components. The magnitude and direction of $\vec{R}$ can subsequently be found with Equations 3.3 and 3.4.

Subtracting two vectors works the same way because it's a matter of adding the negative of one vector to another vector. You should make a rough sketch when adding or subtracting vectors, in order to get an approximate geometric solution as a check.

■ EXAMPLE 3.3 | Take a Hike

GOAL Add vectors algebraically and find the resultant vector.

PROBLEM A hiker begins a trip by first walking 25.0 km 45.0° south of east from her base camp. On the second day she walks 40.0 km in a direction 60.0° north of east, at which point she discovers a forest ranger's tower. **(a)** Determine the components of the hiker's displacements in the first and second days. **(b)** Determine the components of the hiker's total displacement for the trip. **(c)** Find the magnitude and direction of the displacement from base camp.

STRATEGY This problem is just an application of vector addition using components, Equations 3.5. We denote the displacement vectors on the first and second days by $\vec{A}$ and $\vec{B}$, respectively.

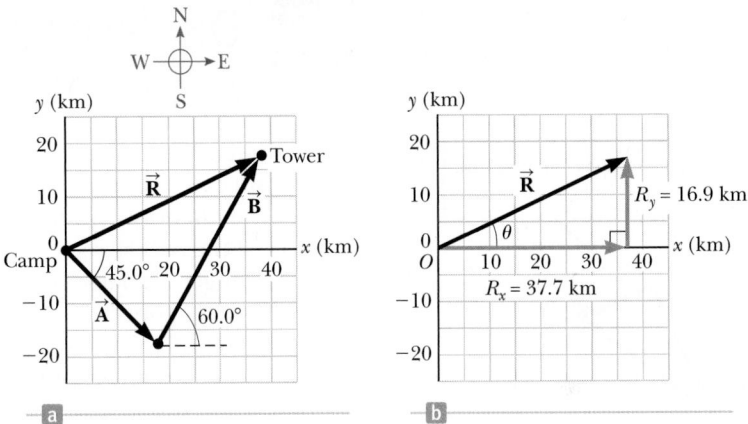

Figure 3.12 (Example 3.3) (a) Hiker's path and the resultant vector. (b) Components of the hiker's total displacement from camp.

Using the camp as the origin of the coordinates, we get the vectors shown in Figure 3.12a. After finding x- and y-components for each vector, we add them "componentwise." Finally, we determine the magnitude and direction of the resultant vector $\vec{R}$, using the Pythagorean theorem and the inverse tangent function.

....

SOLUTION

(a) Find the components of $\vec{A}$.

Use Equations 3.2 to find the components of $\vec{A}$:

$A_x = A \cos(-45.0°) = (25.0 \text{ km})(0.707) = \boxed{17.7 \text{ km}}$

$A_y = A \sin(-45.0°) = -(25.0 \text{ km})(0.707) = \boxed{-17.7 \text{ km}}$

Find the components of $\vec{B}$:

$B_x = B \cos 60.0° = (40.0 \text{ km})(0.500) = \boxed{20.0 \text{ km}}$

$B_y = B \sin 60.0° = (40.0 \text{ km})(0.866) = \boxed{34.6 \text{ km}}$

(b) Find the components of the resultant vector, $\vec{R} = \vec{A} + \vec{B}$.

To find R_x, add the x-components of $\vec{A}$ and $\vec{B}$:

$R_x = A_x + B_x = 17.7 \text{ km} + 20.0 \text{ km} = \boxed{37.7 \text{ km}}$

To find R_y, add the y-components of $\vec{A}$ and $\vec{B}$:

$R_y = A_y + B_y = -17.7 \text{ km} + 34.6 \text{ km} = \boxed{16.9 \text{ km}}$

(c) Find the magnitude and direction of $\vec{R}$.

Use the Pythagorean theorem to get the magnitude:

$R = \sqrt{R_x^2 + R_y^2} = \sqrt{(37.7 \text{ km})^2 + (16.9 \text{ km})^2} = \boxed{41.3 \text{ km}}$

Calculate the direction of $\vec{R}$ using the inverse tangent function:

$\theta = \tan^{-1}\left(\dfrac{16.9 \text{ km}}{37.7 \text{ km}}\right) = \boxed{24.1°}$

....

REMARKS Figure 3.12b shows a sketch of the components of $\vec{R}$ and their directions in space. The magnitude and direction of the resultant can also be determined from such a sketch.

(Continued)

QUESTION 3.3 A second hiker follows the same path the first day, but then walks 15.0 km east on the second day before turning and reaching the ranger's tower. Is the second hiker's resultant displacement vector the same as the first hiker's, or different?

EXERCISE 3.3 A cruise ship leaving port travels 50.0 km 45.0° north of west and then 70.0 km at a heading 30.0° north of east. Find (a) the ship's displacement vector and (b) the displacement vector's magnitude and direction.

ANSWER (a) $R_x = 25.3$ km, $R_y = 70.4$ km (b) 74.8 km, 70.2° north of east

3.3 Displacement, Velocity, and Acceleration in Two Dimensions

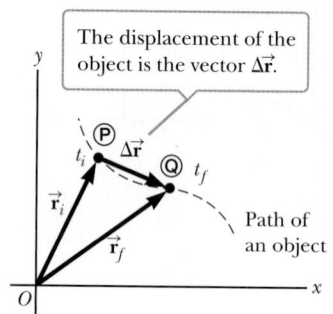

Figure 3.13 An object moving along some curved path between points ⓟ and ⓠ. The displacement vector $\Delta\vec{r}$ is the difference in the position vectors: $\Delta\vec{r} = \vec{r}_f - \vec{r}_i$.

In one-dimensional motion, as discussed in Chapter 2, the direction of a vector quantity such as a velocity or acceleration can be taken into account by specifying whether the quantity is positive or negative. The velocity of a rocket, for example, is positive if the rocket is going up and negative if it's going down. This simple solution is no longer available in two or three dimensions. Instead, we must make full use of the vector concept.

Consider an object moving through space as shown in Figure 3.13. When the object is at some point ⓟ at time t_i, its position is described by the position vector $\vec{r}_i$, drawn from the origin to ⓟ. When the object has moved to some other point ⓠ at time t_f, its position vector is $\vec{r}_f$. From the vector diagram in Figure 3.13, the final position vector is the sum of the initial position vector and the displacement $\Delta\vec{r}$: $\vec{r}_f = \vec{r}_i + \Delta\vec{r}$. From this relationship, we obtain the following one:

An object's **displacement** is defined as the change in its position vector, or

$$\Delta\vec{r} \equiv \vec{r}_f - \vec{r}_i \qquad [3.6]$$

SI unit: meter (m)

We now present several generalizations of the definitions of velocity and acceleration given in Chapter 2.

◄ Average velocity

An object's **average velocity** during a time interval Δt is its displacement divided by Δt:

$$\vec{v}_{av} \equiv \frac{\Delta\vec{r}}{\Delta t} \qquad [3.7]$$

SI unit: meter per second (m/s)

Because the displacement is a vector quantity and the time interval is a scalar quantity, we conclude that the average velocity is a *vector* quantity directed along $\Delta\vec{r}$.

◄ Instantaneous velocity

An object's **instantaneous velocity** $\vec{v}$ is the limit of its average velocity as Δt goes to zero:

$$\vec{v} \equiv \lim_{\Delta t \to 0} \frac{\Delta\vec{r}}{\Delta t} \qquad [3.8]$$

SI unit: meter per second (m/s)

The direction of the instantaneous velocity vector is along a line that is tangent to the object's path and in the direction of its motion.

An object's **average acceleration** during a time interval Δt is the change in its velocity $\Delta \vec{\mathbf{v}}$ divided by Δt, or

$$\vec{\mathbf{a}}_{av} \equiv \frac{\Delta \vec{\mathbf{v}}}{\Delta t} \qquad \qquad [3.9]$$

SI unit: meter per second squared (m/s²)

◄ Average acceleration

An object's **instantaneous acceleration** vector $\vec{\mathbf{a}}$ is the limit of its average acceleration vector as Δt goes to zero:

$$\vec{\mathbf{a}} \equiv \lim_{\Delta t \to 0} \frac{\Delta \vec{\mathbf{v}}}{\Delta t} \qquad \qquad [3.10]$$

SI unit: meter per second squared (m/s²)

◄ Instantaneous acceleration

It's important to recognize that an object can accelerate in several ways. First, the magnitude of the velocity vector (the speed) may change with time. Second, the direction of the velocity vector may change with time, even though the speed is constant, as can happen along a curved path. Third, both the magnitude and the direction of the velocity vector may change at the same time.

■ Quick Quiz

3.4 Which of the following objects can't be accelerating? (a) An object moving with a constant speed; (b) an object moving with a constant velocity; (c) an object moving along a curve.

3.5 Consider the following controls in an automobile: gas pedal, brake, steering wheel. The controls in this list that cause an acceleration of the car are (a) all three controls, (b) the gas pedal and the brake, (c) only the brake, or (d) only the gas pedal.

3.4 Motion in Two Dimensions

In Chapter 2 we studied objects moving along straight-line paths, such as the *x*-axis. In this chapter, we look at objects that move in both the *x*- and *y*-directions simultaneously under constant acceleration. An important special case of this two-dimensional motion is called **projectile motion.**

◄ Projectile motion

Anyone who has tossed any kind of object into the air has observed projectile motion. If the effects of air resistance and the rotation of Earth are neglected, the path of a projectile in Earth's gravity field is curved in the shape of a parabola, as shown in Active Figure 3.14.

The positive *x*-direction is horizontal and to the right, and the *y*-direction is vertical and positive upward. The most important experimental fact about projectile

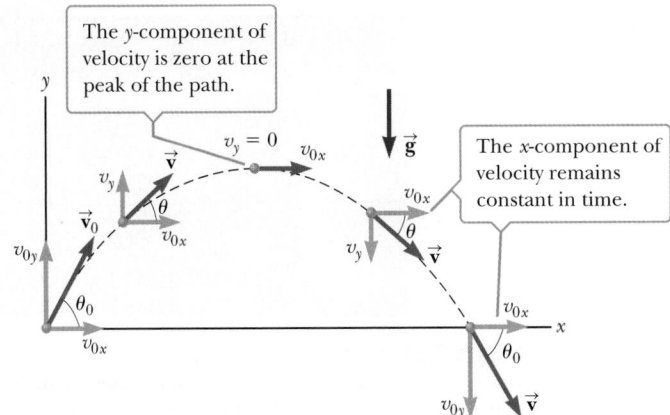

Active Figure 3.14
The parabolic trajectory of a particle that leaves the origin with a velocity of $\vec{\mathbf{v}}_0$. Note that $\vec{\mathbf{v}}$ changes with time. However, the *x*-component of the velocity, v_x, remains constant in time, equal to its initial velocity, v_{0x}. Also, $v_y = 0$ at the peak of the trajectory, but the acceleration is always equal to the free-fall acceleration and acts vertically downward.

Active Figure 3.15

A projectile launched from the origin with an initial speed of 50 m/s at various angles of projection.

motion in two dimensions is that **the horizontal and vertical motions are completely independent of each other.** This means that motion in one direction has no effect on motion in the other direction. If a baseball is tossed in a parabolic path, as in Active Figure 3.14, the motion in the y-direction will look just like a ball tossed straight up under the influence of gravity. Active Figure 3.15 shows the effect of various initial angles; note that complementary angles give the same horizontal range.

Figure 3.16 is an experiment illustrating the independence of horizontal and vertical motion. The gun is aimed directly at the target ball and fired at the instant the target is released. In the absence of gravity, the projectile would hit the target because the target wouldn't move. However, the projectile still hits the target in the presence of gravity. That means the projectile is falling through the same vertical displacement as the target despite its horizontal motion. The experiment also works when set up as in Figure 3.17, when the initial velocity has a vertical component.

In general, the equations of constant acceleration developed in Chapter 2 follow separately for both the x-direction and the y-direction. An important difference is that the initial velocity now has two components, not just one as in that chapter. We assume that at $t = 0$ the projectile leaves the origin with an initial velocity $\vec{v}_0$. If the velocity vector makes an angle θ_0 with the horizontal, where θ_0 is called the *projection angle*, then from the definitions of the cosine and sine functions and Active Figure 3.14 we have

$$v_{0x} = v_0 \cos \theta_0 \qquad \text{and} \qquad v_{0y} = v_0 \sin \theta_0$$

where v_{0x} is the initial velocity (at $t = 0$) in the x-direction and v_{0y} is the initial velocity in the y-direction.

Tip 3.4 Acceleration at the Highest Point

The acceleration in the y-direction is *not* zero at the top of a projectile's trajectory. Only the y-component of the velocity is zero there. If the acceleration were zero, too, the projectile would never come down!

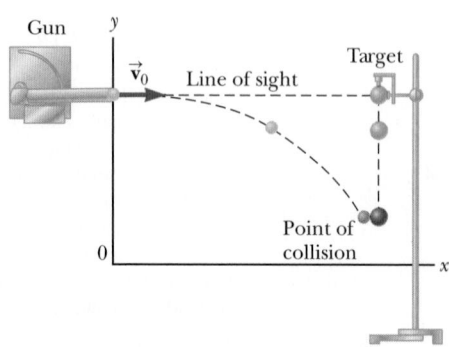

Figure 3.16 A ball is fired at a target at the same instant the target is released. Both fall vertically at the same rate and collide.

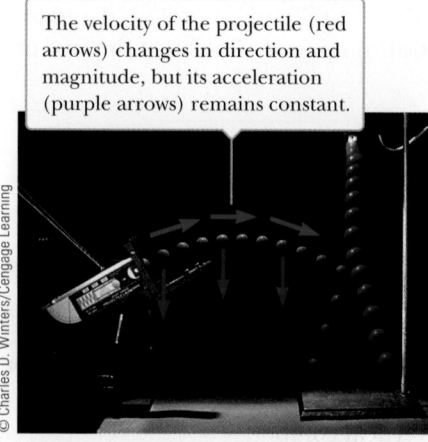

The velocity of the projectile (red arrows) changes in direction and magnitude, but its acceleration (purple arrows) remains constant.

© Charles D. Winters/Cengage Learning

Figure 3.17 Multiflash photograph of the projectile–target demonstration. If the gun is aimed directly at the target and is fired at the same instant the target begins to fall, the projectile will hit the target.

Now, Equations 2.6, 2.9, and 2.10 developed in Chapter 2 for motion with constant acceleration in one dimension carry over to the two-dimensional case; there is one set of three equations for each direction, with the initial velocities modified as just discussed. In the x-direction, with a_x constant, we have

$$v_x = v_{0x} + a_x t \qquad \text{[3.11a]}$$

$$\Delta x = v_{0x} t + \tfrac{1}{2} a_x t^2 \qquad \text{[3.11b]}$$

$$v_x^2 = v_{0x}^2 + 2a_x \Delta x \qquad \text{[3.11c]}$$

where $v_{0x} = v_0 \cos \theta_0$. In the y-direction, we have

$$v_y = v_{0y} + a_y t \qquad \text{[3.12a]}$$

$$\Delta y = v_{0y} t + \tfrac{1}{2} a_y t^2 \qquad \text{[3.12b]}$$

$$v_y^2 = v_{0y}^2 + 2a_y \Delta y \qquad \text{[3.12c]}$$

where $v_{0y} = v_0 \sin \theta_0$ and a_y is constant. The object's speed v can be calculated from the components of the velocity using the Pythagorean theorem:

$$v = \sqrt{v_x^2 + v_y^2}$$

The angle that the velocity vector makes with the x-axis is given by

$$\theta = \tan^{-1}\left(\frac{v_y}{v_x}\right)$$

This formula for θ, as previously stated, must be used with care, because the inverse tangent function returns values only between $-90°$ and $+90°$. Adding $180°$ is necessary for vectors lying in the second or third quadrant.

The kinematic equations are easily adapted and simplified for projectiles close to the surface of the Earth. In that case, assuming air friction is negligible, the acceleration in the x-direction is 0 (because air resistance is neglected). **This means that $a_x = 0$, and the projectile's velocity component along the x-direction remains constant.** If the initial value of the velocity component in the x-direction is $v_{0x} = v_0 \cos \theta_0$, then this is also the value of v- at any later time, so

$$v_x = v_{0x} = v_0 \cos \theta_0 = \text{constant} \qquad \text{[3.13a]}$$

whereas the horizontal displacement is simply

$$\Delta x = v_{0x} t = (v_0 \cos \theta_0) t \qquad \text{[3.13b]}$$

For the motion in the y-direction, we make the substitution $a_y = -g$ and $v_{0y} = v_0 \sin \theta_0$ in Equations 3.12, giving

$$v_y = v_0 \sin \theta_0 - gt \qquad \text{[3.14a]}$$

$$\Delta y = (v_0 \sin \theta_0)t - \tfrac{1}{2}gt^2 \qquad \text{[3.14b]}$$

$$v_y^2 = (v_0 \sin \theta_0)^2 - 2g \Delta y \qquad \text{[3.14c]}$$

The important facts of projectile motion can be summarized as follows:

1. Provided air resistance is negligible, the horizontal component of the velocity v_x remains constant because there is no horizontal component of acceleration.
2. The vertical component of the acceleration is equal to the free-fall acceleration $-g$.
3. The vertical component of the velocity v_y and the displacement in the y-direction are identical to those of a freely falling body.
4. Projectile motion can be described as a superposition of two independent motions in the x- and y-directions.

GOAL Approximate answers in projectile motion using a motion diagram.

PROBLEM A ball is thrown so that its initial vertical and horizontal components of velocity are 40 m/s and 20 m/s, respectively. Use a motion diagram to estimate the ball's total time of flight and the distance it traverses before hitting the ground.

STRATEGY Use the diagram, estimating the acceleration of gravity as −10 m/s². By symmetry, the ball goes up and comes back down to the ground at the same y-velocity as when it left, except with opposite sign. With this fact and the fact that the acceleration of gravity decreases the velocity in the y-direction by 10 m/s every second, we can find the total time of flight and then the horizontal range.

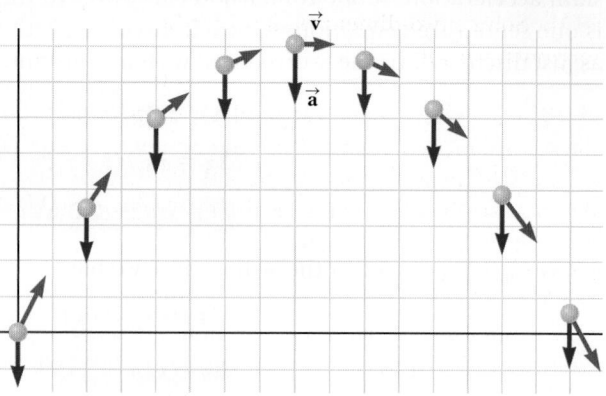

Figure 3.18 (Example 3.4) Motion diagram for a projectile.

SOLUTION

In the motion diagram shown in Figure 3.18, the acceleration vectors are all the same, pointing downward with magnitude of nearly 10 m/s². By symmetry, we know that the ball will hit the ground at the same speed in the y-direction as when it was thrown, so the velocity in the y-direction goes from 40 m/s to −40 m/s in steps of −10 m/s every second; hence, approximately 8 seconds elapse during the motion.

The velocity vector constantly changes direction, but the horizontal velocity never changes because the acceleration in the horizontal direction is zero. Therefore, the displacement of the ball in the x-direction is given by Equation 3.13b, $\Delta x \approx v_{0x}t = (20 \text{ m/s})(8 \text{ s}) = 160$ m.

REMARKS This example emphasizes the independence of the x- and y-components in projectile motion problems.

QUESTION 3.4 Is the magnitude of the velocity vector at impact greater than, less than, or equal to the magnitude of the initial velocity vector? Why?

EXERCISE 3.4 Estimate the maximum height in this same problem.

ANSWER 80 m

■ *Quick Quiz*

3.6 Suppose you are carrying a ball and running at constant speed, and wish to throw the ball and catch it as it comes back down. Should you (a) throw the ball at an angle of about 45° above the horizontal and maintain the same speed, (b) throw the ball straight up in the air and slow down to catch it, or (c) throw the ball straight up in the air and maintain the same speed?

3.7 As a projectile moves in its parabolic path, the velocity and acceleration vectors are perpendicular to each other (a) everywhere along the projectile's path, (b) at the peak of its path, (c) nowhere along its path, or (d) not enough information is given.

■ **PROBLEM-SOLVING STRATEGY**

Projectile Motion

1. **Select** a coordinate system and sketch the path of the projectile, including initial and final positions, velocities, and accelerations.
2. **Resolve** the initial velocity vector into x- and y-components.
3. **Treat** the horizontal motion and the vertical motion independently.
4. **Follow** the techniques for solving problems with constant velocity to analyze the horizontal motion of the projectile.
5. **Follow** the techniques for solving problems with constant acceleration to analyze the vertical motion of the projectile.

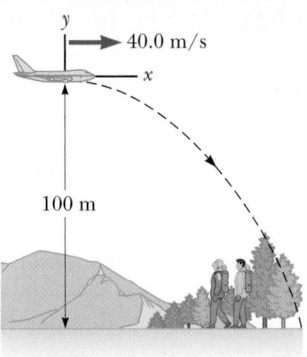

Figure 3.19 (Example 3.5)
From the point of view of an observer on the ground, a package released from the rescue plane travels along the path shown.

■ **EXAMPLE 3.5** | **Stranded Explorers**

GOAL Solve a two-dimensional projectile motion problem in which an object has an initial horizontal velocity.

PROBLEM An Alaskan rescue plane drops a package of emergency rations to stranded hikers, as shown in Figure 3.19. The plane is traveling horizontally at 40.0 m/s at a height of 1.00×10^2 m above the ground. **(a)** Where does the package strike the ground relative to the point at which it was released? **(b)** What are the horizontal and vertical components of the velocity of the package just before it hits the ground? **(c)** Find the angle of the impact.

STRATEGY Here, we're just taking Equations 3.13 and 3.14, filling in known quantities, and solving for the remaining unknown quantities. Sketch the problem using a coordinate system as in Figure 3.19. In part (a), set the y-component of the displacement equations equal to -1.00×10^2 m—the ground level where the package lands—and solve for the time it takes the package to reach the ground. Substitute this time into the displacement equation for the x-component to find the range. In part (b), substitute the time found in part (a) into the velocity components. Notice that the initial velocity has only an x-component, which simplifies the math. Solving part (c) requires the inverse tangent function.

SOLUTION

(a) Find the range of the package.

Use Equation 3.14b to find the y-displacement:

$$\Delta y = y - y_0 = v_{0y}t - \tfrac{1}{2}gt^2$$

Substitute $y_0 = 0$ and $v_{0y} = 0$, and set $y = -1.00 \times 10^2$ m, the final vertical position of the package relative to the airplane. Solve for time:

$$y = -(4.90 \text{ m/s}^2)t^2 = -1.00 \times 10^2 \text{ m}$$
$$t = 4.52 \text{ s}$$

Use Equation 3.13b to find the x-displacement:

$$\Delta x = x - x_0 = v_{0x}t$$

Substitute $x_0 = 0$, $v_{0x} = 40.0$ m/s, and the time:

$$x = (40.0 \text{ m/s})(4.52 \text{ s}) = \boxed{181 \text{ m}}$$

(b) Find the components of the package's velocity at impact:

Find the x-component of the velocity at the time of impact:

$$v_x = v_0 \cos \theta = (40.0 \text{ m/s}) \cos 0° = \boxed{40.0 \text{ m/s}}$$

Find the y-component of the velocity at the time of impact:

$$v_y = v_0 \sin \theta - gt = 0 - (9.80 \text{ m/s}^2)(4.52 \text{ s}) = \boxed{-44.3 \text{ m/s}}$$

(c) Find the angle of the impact.

Write Equation 3.4 and substitute values:

$$\tan \theta = \frac{v_y}{v_x} = \frac{-44.3 \text{ m/s}}{40.0 \text{ m/s}} = -1.11$$

Apply the inverse tangent functions to both sides:

$$\theta = \tan^{-1}(-1.11) = \boxed{-48.0°}$$

REMARKS Notice how motion in the x-direction and motion in the y-direction are handled separately.

QUESTION 3.5 Neglecting air friction effects, what path does the package travel as observed by the pilot? Explain.

EXERCISE 3.5 A bartender slides a beer mug at 1.50 m/s toward a customer at the end of a frictionless bar that is 1.20 m tall. The customer makes a grab for the mug and misses, and the mug sails off the end of the bar. **(a)** How far away from the end of the bar does the mug hit the floor? **(b)** What are the speed and direction of the mug at impact?

ANSWERS (a) 0.742 m (b) 5.08 m/s, $\theta = -72.8°$

■ **EXAMPLE 3.6** | **The Long Jump**

GOAL Solve a two-dimensional projectile motion problem involving an object starting and ending at the same height.

PROBLEM A long jumper (Fig. 3.20) leaves the ground at an angle of 20.0° to the horizontal and at a speed of 11.0 m/s. **(a)** How long does it take for him to reach maximum height? **(b)** What is the maximum height? **(c)** How far does he jump? (Assume his motion is equivalent to that of a particle, disregarding the motion of his arms and legs.) **(d)** Use Equation 3.14c to find the maximum height he reaches.

technotr/iStockphoto.com

Figure 3.20 (Example 3.6) This multiple-exposure shot of a long jumper shows that in reality, the jumper's motion is not the equivalent of the motion of a particle. The center of mass of the jumper follows a parabola, but to extend the length of the jump before impact, the jumper pulls his feet up so he strikes the ground later than he otherwise would have.

STRATEGY Again, we take the projectile equations, fill in the known quantities, and solve for the unknowns. At the maximum height, the velocity in the y-direction is zero, so setting Equation 3.14a equal to zero and solving gives the time it takes him to reach his maximum height. By symmetry, given that his trajectory starts and ends at the same height, doubling this time gives the total time of the jump.

SOLUTION

(a) Find the time t_{max} taken to reach maximum height.

Set $v_y = 0$ in Equation 3.14a and solve for t_{max}:

$$v_y = v_0 \sin \theta_0 - g t_{max} = 0$$

$$(1) \quad t_{max} = \frac{v_0 \sin \theta_0}{g}$$

$$= \frac{(11.0 \text{ m/s})(\sin 20.0°)}{9.80 \text{ m/s}^2} = \boxed{0.384 \text{ s}}$$

(b) Find the maximum height he reaches.

Substitute the time t_{max} into the equation for the y-displacement, equation 3.14b:

$$y_{max} = (v_0 \sin \theta_0) t_{max} - \tfrac{1}{2} g (t_{max})^2$$

$$y_{max} = (11.0 \text{ m/s})(\sin 20.0°)(0.384 \text{ s})$$
$$- \tfrac{1}{2}(9.80 \text{ m/s}^2)(0.384 \text{ s})^2$$

$$y_{max} = \boxed{0.722 \text{ m}}$$

(c) Find the horizontal distance he jumps.

First find the time for the jump, which is twice t_{max}:

$$t = 2t_{max} = 2(0.384 \text{ s}) = 0.768 \text{ s}$$

Substitute this result into the equation for the x-displacement:

$$(2) \quad \Delta x = (v_0 \cos \theta_0)t$$
$$= (11.0 \text{ m/s})(\cos 20.0°)(0.768 \text{ s}) = \boxed{7.94 \text{ m}}$$

(d) Use an alternate method to find the maximum height.

Use Equation 3.14c, solving for Δy:

$$v_y^2 - v_{0y}^2 = -2g \, \Delta y$$

$$\Delta y = \frac{v_y^2 - v_{0y}^2}{-2g}$$

Substitute $v_y = 0$ at maximum height, and the fact that $v_{0y} = (11.0 \text{ m/s}) \sin 20.0°$:

$$\Delta y = \frac{0 - [(11.0 \text{ m/s}) \sin 20.0°]^2}{-2(9.80 \text{ m/s}^2)} = \boxed{0.722 \text{ m}}$$

REMARKS Although modeling the long jumper's motion as that of a projectile is an oversimplification, the values obtained are reasonable.

QUESTION 3.6 True or False: Because the *x*-component of the displacement doesn't depend explicitly on *g*, the horizontal distance traveled doesn't depend on the acceleration of gravity.

EXERCISE 3.6 A grasshopper jumps a horizontal distance of 1.00 m from rest, with an initial velocity at a 45.0° angle with respect to the horizontal. Find (a) the initial speed of the grasshopper and (b) the maximum height reached.

ANSWERS (a) 3.13 m/s (b) 0.250 m

EXAMPLE 3.7 │ The Range Equation

GOAL Find an equation for the maximum horizontal displacement of a projectile fired from ground level.

PROBLEM An athlete participates in a long-jump competition, leaping into the air with a velocity v_0 at an angle θ_0 with the horizontal. Obtain an expression for the length of the jump in terms of v_0, θ_0, and *g*.

STRATEGY Use the results of Example 3.6, eliminating the time *t* from Equations (1) and (2).

SOLUTION

Use Equation (1) of Example 3.6 to find the time of flight, *t*:

$$t = 2t_{max} = \frac{2v_0 \sin \theta_0}{g}$$

Substitute that expression for *t* into Equation (2) of Example 3.6:

$$\Delta x = (v_0 \cos \theta_0)t = (v_0 \cos \theta_0)\left(\frac{2v_0 \sin \theta_0}{g}\right)$$

Simplify:

$$\Delta x = \frac{2v_0^2 \cos \theta_0 \sin \theta_0}{g}$$

Substitute the identity $2 \cos \theta_0 \sin \theta_0 = \sin 2\theta_0$ to reduce the foregoing expression to a single trigonometric function:

$$(1) \quad \Delta x = \frac{v_0^2 \sin 2\theta_0}{g}$$

REMARKS The use of a trigonometric identity in the final step isn't necessary, but it makes Question 3.7 easier to answer.

QUESTION 3.7 What angle θ_0 produces the longest jump?

EXERCISE 3.7 Obtain an expression for the athlete's maximum displacement in the vertical direction, Δy_{max} in terms of v_0, θ_0, and *g*.

ANSWER $\Delta y_{max} = \dfrac{v_0^2 \sin^2 \theta_0}{2g}$

EXAMPLE 3.8 │ That's Quite an Arm

GOAL Solve a two-dimensional kinematics problem with a nonhorizontal initial velocity, starting and ending at different heights.

PROBLEM A ball is thrown upward from the top of a building at an angle of 30.0° to the horizontal and with an initial speed of 20.0 m/s, as in Figure 3.21. The point of release is 45.0 m above the ground. **(a)** How long does it take for the ball to hit the ground? **(b)** Find the ball's speed at impact. **(c)** Find the horizontal range of the stone. Neglect air resistance.

STRATEGY Choose coordinates as in the figure, with the origin at the point of release. **(a)** Fill in the constants of Equation 3.14b for the *y*-displacement and set the displacement equal to −45.0 m, the *y*-displacement when the ball hits the ground. Using the quadratic formula, solve for the time. To solve part **(b)**, substitute the time from part (a) into the components of the velocity, and substitute the same time into the equation for the *x*-displacement to solve part **(c)**.

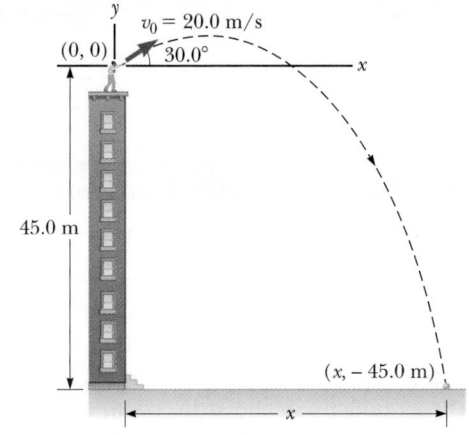

Figure 3.21 (Example 3.8)

(Continued)

SOLUTION

(a) Find the ball's time of flight.

Find the initial x- and y-components of the velocity:

$$v_{0x} = v_0 \cos \theta_0 = (20.0 \text{ m/s})(\cos 30.0°) = +17.3 \text{ m/s}$$
$$v_{0y} = v_0 \sin \theta_0 = (20.0 \text{ m/s})(\sin 30.0°) = +10.0 \text{ m/s}$$

Find the y-displacement, taking $y_0 = 0$, $y = -45.0$ m, and $v_{0y} = 10.0$ m/s:

$$\Delta y = y - y_0 = v_{0y}t - \tfrac{1}{2}gt^2$$
$$-45.0 \text{ m} = (10.0 \text{ m/s})t - (4.90 \text{ m/s}^2)t^2$$

Reorganize the equation into standard form and use the quadratic formula (see Appendix A) to find the positive root:

$$t = \boxed{4.22 \text{ s}}$$

(b) Find the ball's speed at impact.

Substitute the value of t found in part (a) into Equation 3.14a to find the y-component of the velocity at impact:

$$v_y = v_{0y} - gt = 10.0 \text{ m/s} - (9.80 \text{ m/s}^2)(4.22 \text{ s})$$
$$= -31.4 \text{ m/s}$$

Use this value of v_y, the Pythagorean theorem, and the fact that $v_x = v_{0x} = 17.3$ m/s to find the speed of the ball at impact:

$$v = \sqrt{v_x^2 + v_y^2} = \sqrt{(17.3 \text{ m/s})^2 + (-31.4 \text{ m/s})^2}$$
$$= \boxed{35.9 \text{ m/s}}$$

(c) Find the horizontal range of the ball.

Substitute the time of flight into the range equation:

$$\Delta x = x - x_0 = (v_0 \cos \theta)t = (20.0 \text{ m/s})(\cos 30.0°)(4.22 \text{ s})$$
$$= \boxed{73.1 \text{ m}}$$

REMARKS The angle at which the ball is thrown affects the velocity vector throughout its subsequent motion, but doesn't affect the speed at a given height. This is a consequence of the conservation of energy, described in Chapter 5.

QUESTION 3.8 True or False: All other things being equal, if the ball is thrown at half the given speed it will travel half as far.

EXERCISE 3.8 Suppose the ball is thrown from the same height as in the example at an angle of 30.0° degrees below the horizontal. If it strikes the ground 57.0 m away, find (a) the time of flight, (b) the initial speed, and (c) the speed and the angle of the velocity vector with respect to the horizontal at impact. (*Hint:* For part (a), use the equation for the x-displacement to eliminate v_0t from the equation for the y-displacement.)

ANSWERS (a) 1.57 s (b) 41.9 m/s (c) 51.3 m/s, $-45.0°$

Two-Dimensional Constant Acceleration

So far we have studied only problems in which an object with an initial velocity follows a trajectory determined by the acceleration of gravity alone. In the more general case, other agents, such as air drag, surface friction, or engines, can cause accelerations. These accelerations, taken together, form a vector quantity with components a_x and a_y. When both components are constant, we can use Equations 3.11 and 3.12 to study the motion, as in the next example.

▪ EXAMPLE 3.9 │ The Rocket

GOAL Solve a problem involving accelerations in two directions.

PROBLEM A jet plane traveling horizontally at 1.00×10^2 m/s drops a rocket from a considerable height. (See Fig. 3.22.) The rocket immediately fires its engines, accelerating at 20.0 m/s² in the x-direction while falling under the influence of gravity in the y-direction. When the rocket has fallen 1.00 km, find **(a)** its velocity in the y-direction, **(b)** its velocity in the x-direction, and **(c)** the magnitude and direction of its velocity. Neglect air drag and aerodynamic lift.

STRATEGY Because the rocket maintains a horizontal orientation (say, through gyroscopes), the x- and y-components of acceleration are independent of each other. Use the

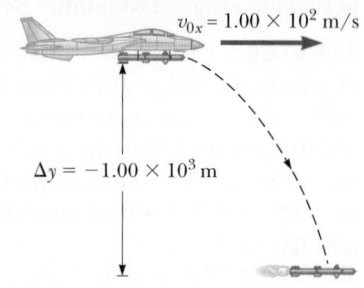

Figure 3.22 (Example 3.9)

time-independent equation for the velocity in the y-direction to find the y-component of the velocity after the rocket falls 1.00 km. Then calculate the time of the fall and use that time to find the velocity in the x-direction.

SOLUTION

(a) Find the velocity in the y-direction.

Use Equation 3.14c:

$$v_y^2 = v_{0y}^2 - 2g\,\Delta y$$

Substitute $v_{0y} = 0$, $g = -9.80 \text{ m/s}^2$, and $\Delta y = -1.00 \times 10^3$ m, and solve for v_y:

$$v_y^2 - 0 = 2(-9.8 \text{ m/s}^2)(-1.00 \times 10^3 \text{ m})$$
$$v_y = \boxed{-1.40 \times 10^2 \text{ m/s}}$$

(b) Find the velocity in the x-direction.

Find the time it takes the rocket to drop 1.00×10^3 m, using the y-component of the velocity:

$$v_y = v_{0y} + a_y t$$
$$-1.40 \times 10^2 \text{ m/s} = 0 - (9.80 \text{ m/s}^2)t \quad \rightarrow \quad t = 14.3 \text{ s}$$

Substitute t, v_{0x}, and a_x into Equation 3.11a to find the velocity in the x-direction:

$$v_x = v_{0x} + a_x t = 1.00 \times 10^2 \text{ m/s} + (20.0 \text{ m/s}^2)(14.3 \text{ s})$$
$$= \boxed{386 \text{ m/s}}$$

(c) Find the magnitude and direction of the velocity.

Find the magnitude using the Pythagorean theorem and the results of parts (a) and (b):

$$v = \sqrt{v_x^2 + v_y^2} = \sqrt{(-1.40 \times 10^2 \text{ m/s})^2 + (386 \text{ m/s})^2}$$
$$= \boxed{411 \text{ m/s}}$$

Use the inverse tangent function to find the angle:

$$\theta = \tan^{-1}\left(\frac{v_y}{v_x}\right) = \tan^{-1}\left(\frac{-1.40 \times 10^2 \text{ m/s}}{386 \text{ m/s}}\right) = \boxed{-19.9°}$$

REMARKS Notice the symmetry: The kinematic equations for the x- and y-directions are handled in exactly the same way. Having a nonzero acceleration in the x-direction doesn't greatly increase the difficulty of the problem.

QUESTION 3.9 True or False: Neglecting air friction and lift effects, a projectile with a horizontal acceleration always stays in the air longer than a projectile that is freely falling.

EXERCISE 3.9 Suppose a rocket-propelled motorcycle is fired from rest horizontally across a canyon 1.00 km wide. (a) What minimum constant acceleration in the x-direction must be provided by the engines so the cycle crosses safely if the opposite side is 0.750 km lower than the starting point? (b) At what speed does the motorcycle land if it maintains this constant horizontal component of acceleration? Neglect air drag, but remember that gravity is still acting in the negative y-direction.

ANSWERS (a) 13.1 m/s² (b) 202 m/s

In a stunt similar to that described in Exercise 3.9, motorcycle daredevil Evel Knievel tried to vault across Hells Canyon, part of the Snake River system in Idaho, on his rocket-powered Harley-Davidson X-2 "Skycycle." He lost consciousness at takeoff and released a lever, prematurely deploying his parachute and falling short of the other side. He landed safely in the canyon.

3.5 Relative Velocity

Relative velocity is all about relating the measurements of two different observers, one moving with respect to the other. The measured velocity of an object depends on the velocity of the observer with respect to the object. On highways, for example, cars moving in the same direction are often moving at high speed relative to Earth, but relative to each other they hardly move at all. To an observer at rest at the side of the road, a car might be traveling at 60 mi/h, but to an observer in a

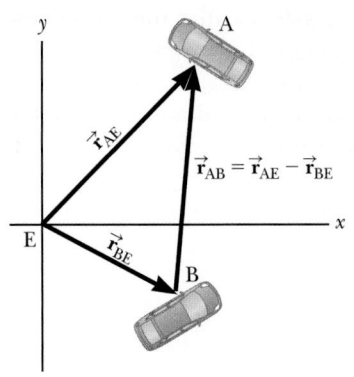

Figure 3.23 The position of Car A relative to Car B can be found by vector subtraction. The rate of change of the resultant vector with respect to time is the relative velocity equation.

truck traveling in the same direction at 50 mi/h, the car would appear to be traveling only 10 mi/h.

So measurements of velocity depend on the **reference frame** of the observer. Reference frames are just coordinate systems. Most of the time, we use a **stationary frame of reference** relative to Earth, but occasionally we use a **moving frame of reference** associated with a bus, car, or plane moving with constant velocity relative to Earth.

In two dimensions relative velocity calculations can be confusing, so a systematic approach is important and useful. Let E be an observer, assumed stationary with respect to Earth. Let two cars be labeled A and B, and introduce the following notation (see Fig. 3.23):

$\vec{r}_{AE}$ = the position of Car A as measured by E (in a coordinate system fixed with respect to Earth).

$\vec{r}_{BE}$ = the position of Car B as measured by E.

$\vec{r}_{AB}$ = the position of Car A as measured by an observer in Car B.

According to the preceding notation, the first letter tells us what the vector is pointing at and the second letter tells us where the position vector starts. The position vectors of Car A and Car B relative to E, $\vec{r}_{AE}$ and $\vec{r}_{BE}$, are given in the figure. How do we find $\vec{r}_{AB}$, the position of Car A as measured by an observer in Car B? We simply draw an arrow pointing from Car B to Car A, which can be obtained by subtracting $\vec{r}_{BE}$ from $\vec{r}_{AE}$:

$$\vec{r}_{AB} = \vec{r}_{AE} - \vec{r}_{BE} \qquad [3.15]$$

Now, the rate of change of these quantities with time gives us the relationship between the associated velocities:

$$\vec{v}_{AB} = \vec{v}_{AE} - \vec{v}_{BE} \qquad [3.16]$$

The coordinate system of observer E need not be fixed to Earth, although it often is. Take careful note of the pattern of subscripts; rather than memorize Equation 3.16, it's better to study the short derivation based on Figure 3.23. Note also that the equation doesn't work for observers traveling a sizable fraction of the speed of light, when Einstein's theory of special relativity comes into play.

■ PROBLEM-SOLVING STRATEGY

Relative Velocity

1. **Label** each object involved (usually three) with a letter that reminds you of what it is (for example, E for Earth).
2. **Look** through the problem for phrases such as "The velocity of A relative to B" and write the velocities as $\vec{v}_{AB}$. When a velocity is mentioned but it isn't explicitly stated as relative to something, it's almost always relative to Earth.
3. **Take** the three velocities you've found and assemble them into an equation just like Equation 3.16, with subscripts in an analogous order.
4. **There will be** two unknown components. Solve for them with the x- and y-components of the equation developed in step 3.

■ EXAMPLE 3.10 | Pitching Practice on the Train

GOAL Solve a one-dimensional relative velocity problem.

PROBLEM A train is traveling with a speed of 15 m/s relative to Earth. A passenger standing at the rear of the train pitches a baseball with a speed of 15 m/s relative to the train off the back end, in the direction opposite the motion of the train. **(a)** What is the velocity of the baseball relative to Earth? **(b)** What is the velocity of the baseball relative to the Earth if thrown in the opposite direction at the same speed?

STRATEGY Solving these problems involves putting the proper subscripts on the velocities and arranging them as in Equation 3.16. In the first sentence of the problem statement, we are informed that the train travels at "15 m/s relative to Earth." This quantity is $\vec{\mathbf{v}}_{TE}$, with T for train and E for Earth. The passenger throws the baseball at "15 m/s relative to the train," so this quantity is $\vec{\mathbf{v}}_{BT}$, where B stands for baseball. The second sentence asks for the velocity of the baseball relative to Earth, $\vec{\mathbf{v}}_{BE}$. The rest of the problem can be solved by identifying the correct components of the known quantities and solving for the unknowns, using an analog of Equation 3.16. Part(b) just requires a change of sign.

SOLUTION

(a) What is the velocity of the baseball relative to the Earth?

Write the x-components of the known quantities:

$$(\vec{\mathbf{v}}_{TE})_x = +15 \text{ m/s}$$
$$(\vec{\mathbf{v}}_{BT})_x = -15 \text{ m/s}$$

Follow Equation 3.16:

(1) $(\vec{\mathbf{v}}_{BT})_x = (\vec{\mathbf{v}}_{BE})_x - (\vec{\mathbf{v}}_{TE})_x$

Insert the given values and solve:

$$-15 \text{ m/s} = (\vec{\mathbf{v}}_{BE})_x - 15 \text{ m/s}$$
$$(\vec{\mathbf{v}}_{BE})_x = \boxed{0}$$

(b) What is the velocity of the baseball relative the to Earth if thrown in the opposite direction at the same speed?

Substitute $(\vec{\mathbf{v}}_{BT})_x = +15 \text{ m/s}$ into Equation (1):

$$+15 \text{ m/s} = (\vec{\mathbf{v}}_{BT})_x - 15 \text{ m/s}$$

Solve for $(\vec{\mathbf{v}}_{BT})_x$:

$$(\vec{\mathbf{v}}_{BT})_x = \boxed{+3.0 \times 10^1 \text{ m/s}}$$

QUESTION 3.10 Describe the motion of the ball in part (a) as related by an observer on the ground.

EXERCISE 3.10 A train is traveling at 27 m/s relative to Earth in the positive x-direction. A passenger standing on the ground throws a ball at 15 m/s relative to Earth in the same direction as the train's motion. **(a)** Find the speed of the ball relative to an observer on the train. **(b)** Repeat the exercise if the ball is thrown in the opposite direction.

ANSWERS (a) −12 m/s (b) −42 m/s

■ **EXAMPLE 3.11** | **Crossing a River**

GOAL Solve a simple two-dimensional relative motion problem.

PROBLEM The boat in Figure 3.24 is heading due north as it crosses a wide river with a velocity of 10.0 km/h relative to the water. The river has a uniform velocity of 5.00 km/h due east. Determine the magnitude and direction of the boat's velocity with respect to an observer on the riverbank.

STRATEGY Again, we look for key phrases. "The boat . . . (has) a velocity of 10.0 km/h relative to the water" gives $\vec{\mathbf{v}}_{BR}$. "The river has a uniform velocity of 5.00 km/h due east" gives $\vec{\mathbf{v}}_{RE}$, because this implies velocity with respect to Earth. The observer on the riverbank is in a reference frame at rest with respect to Earth. Because we're looking for the velocity of the boat with respect to that observer, this last velocity is designated $\vec{\mathbf{v}}_{BE}$. Take east to be the $+x$-direction, north the $+y$-direction.

Figure 3.24 (Example 3.10)

SOLUTION

Arrange the three quantities into the proper relative velocity equation:

$$\vec{\mathbf{v}}_{BR} = \vec{\mathbf{v}}_{BE} - \vec{\mathbf{v}}_{RE}$$

(Continued)

Write the velocity vectors in terms of their components. For convenience, these are organized in the following table:

Vector	x-Component (km/h)	y-Component (km/h)
$\vec{\mathbf{v}}_{BR}$	0	10.0
$\vec{\mathbf{v}}_{BE}$	v_x	v_y
$\vec{\mathbf{v}}_{RE}$	5.00	0

Find the x-component of velocity:

$0 = v_x - 5.00 \text{ km/h} \rightarrow v_x = 5.00 \text{ km/h}$

Find the y-component of velocity:

$10.0 \text{ km/h} = v_y - 0 \rightarrow v_y = 10.0 \text{ km/h}$

Find the magnitude of $\vec{\mathbf{v}}_{BE}$:

$$v_{BE} = \sqrt{v_x^2 + v_y^2}$$
$$= \sqrt{(5.00 \text{ km/h})^2 + (10.0 \text{ km/h})^2} = \boxed{11.2 \text{ km/h}}$$

Find the direction of $\vec{\mathbf{v}}_{BE}$:

$$\theta = \tan^{-1}\left(\frac{v_x}{v_y}\right) = \tan^{-1}\left(\frac{5.00 \text{ m/s}}{10.0 \text{ m/s}}\right) = \boxed{26.6°}$$

REMARKS The boat travels at a speed of 11.2 km/h in the direction 26.6° east of north with respect to Earth.

QUESTION 3.11 If the speed of the boat relative to the water is increased, what happens to the angle?

EXERCISE 3.11 Suppose the river is flowing east at 3.00 m/s and the boat is traveling south at 4.00 m/s with respect to the river. Find the speed and direction of the boat relative to Earth.

ANSWER 5.00 m/s, 53.1° south of east

■ **EXAMPLE 3.12** | **Bucking the Current**

GOAL Solve a complex two-dimensional relative motion problem.

PROBLEM If the skipper of the boat of Example 3.11 moves with the same speed of 10.0 km/h relative to the water but now wants to travel due north, as in Figure 3.25a, in what direction should he head? What is the speed of the boat, according to an observer on the shore? The river is flowing east at 5.00 km/h.

Figure 3.25
(a) (Example 3.12)
(b) (Exercise 3.12)

STRATEGY Proceed as in the previous example. In this situation, we must find the heading of the boat and its velocity with respect to the water, using the fact that the boat travels due north.

SOLUTION

Arrange the three quantities, as before:

$\vec{\mathbf{v}}_{BR} = \vec{\mathbf{v}}_{BE} - \vec{\mathbf{v}}_{RE}$

Organize a table of velocity components:

Vector	x-Component (km/h)	y-Component (km/h)
$\vec{\mathbf{v}}_{BR}$	$-(10.0 \text{ km/h}) \sin\theta$	$(10.0 \text{ km/h}) \cos\theta$
$\vec{\mathbf{v}}_{BE}$	0	v
$\vec{\mathbf{v}}_{RE}$	5.00 km/h	0

The x-component of the relative velocity equation can be used to find θ:

$-(10.0 \text{ m/s}) \sin\theta = 0 - 5.00 \text{ km/h}$

$$\sin\theta = \frac{5.00 \text{ km/h}}{10.0 \text{ km/h}} = \frac{1.00}{2.00}$$

Apply the inverse sine function and find θ, which is the boat's heading, east of north:

$$\theta = \sin^{-1}\left(\frac{1.00}{2.00}\right) = \boxed{30.0°}$$

The *y*-component of the relative velocity equation can be used to find *v*:

$$(10.0 \text{ km/h}) \cos \theta = v \quad \rightarrow \quad v = \boxed{8.66 \text{ km/h}}$$

REMARKS From Figure 3.25, we see that this problem can be solved with the Pythagorean theorem, because the problem involves a right triangle: the boat's *x*-component of velocity exactly cancels the river's velocity. When this is not the case, a more general technique is necessary, as shown in the following exercise. Notice that in the *x*-component of the relative velocity equation a minus sign had to be included in the term $-(10.0 \text{ km/h})\sin \theta$ because the *x*-component of the boat's velocity with respect to the river is negative.

QUESTION 3.12 The speeds in this example are the same as in Example 3.11. Why isn't the angle the same as before?

EXERCISE 3.12 Suppose the river is moving east at 5.00 km/h and the boat is traveling 45.0° south of east with respect to Earth. Find (a) the speed of the boat with respect to Earth and (b) the speed of the boat with respect to the river if the boat's heading in the water is 60.0° south of east. (See Fig. 3.25b.) You will have to solve two equations with two unknowns. (As an alternative, the law of sines can be used.)

ANSWERS (a) 16.7 km/h (b) 13.7 km/h

■ SUMMARY

3.1 Vectors and Their Properties

Two vectors $\vec{A}$ and $\vec{B}$ can be added geometrically with the **triangle method.** The two vectors are drawn to scale on graph paper, with the tail of the second vector located at the tip of the first. The **resultant** vector is the vector drawn from the tail of the first vector to the tip of the second.

The negative of a vector $\vec{A}$ is a vector with the same magnitude as $\vec{A}$, but pointing in the opposite direction. A vector can be multiplied by a scalar, changing its magnitude, and its direction if the scalar is negative.

3.2 Components of a Vector

A vector $\vec{A}$ can be split into two components, one pointing in the *x*-direction and the other in the *y*-direction. These components form two sides of a right triangle having a hypotenuse with magnitude A and are given by

$$A_x = A \cos \theta \qquad [3.2a]$$
$$A_y = A \sin \theta \qquad [3.2b]$$

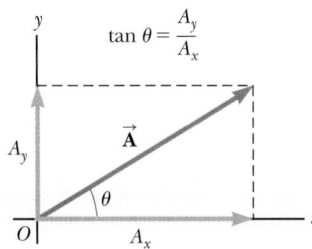

A vector can be written in terms of components in the *x*- and *y*-directions.

The magnitude and direction of $\vec{A}$ are related to its components through the Pythagorean theorem and the definition of the tangent:

$$A = \sqrt{A_x^2 + A_y^2} \qquad [3.3]$$
$$\tan \theta = \frac{A_y}{A_x} \qquad [3.4]$$

In Equation (3.4), $\theta = \tan^{-1}(A_y/A_x)$ gives the correct vector angle only for vectors with $-90° < \theta < 90°$. If the vector has a negative *x*-component, 180° must be added to the answer in the calculator window.

If $\vec{R} = \vec{A} + \vec{B}$, then the components of the resultant vector $\vec{R}$ are

$$R_x = A_x + B_x \qquad [3.5a]$$
$$R_y = A_y + B_y \qquad [3.5b]$$

3.3 Displacement, Velocity, and Acceleration in Two Dimensions

The displacement of an object in two dimensions is defined as the change in the object's position vector:

$$\Delta \vec{r} \equiv \vec{r}_f - \vec{r}_i \qquad [3.6]$$

The average velocity of an object during the time interval Δt is

$$\vec{v}_{av} \equiv \frac{\Delta \vec{r}}{\Delta t} \qquad [3.7]$$

Taking the limit of this expression as Δt gets arbitrarily small gives the instantaneous velocity $\vec{v}$:

$$\vec{v} \equiv \lim_{\Delta t \to 0} \frac{\Delta \vec{r}}{\Delta t} \qquad [3.8]$$

The direction of the instantaneous velocity vector is along a line that is tangent to the path of the object and in the direction of its motion.

The average acceleration of an object with a velocity changing by $\Delta \vec{v}$ in the time interval Δt is

$$\vec{a}_{av} \equiv \frac{\Delta \vec{v}}{\Delta t} \qquad [3.9]$$

Taking the limit of this expression as Δt gets arbitrarily small gives the instantaneous acceleration vector $\vec{a}$:

$$\vec{a} \equiv \lim_{\Delta t \to 0} \frac{\Delta \vec{v}}{\Delta t} \qquad [3.10]$$

3.4 Motion in Two Dimensions

The general kinematic equations in two dimensions for objects with constant acceleration are, for the x-direction,

$$v_x = v_{0x} + a_x t \qquad [3.11a]$$

$$\Delta x = v_{0x}t + \tfrac{1}{2}a_x t^2 \qquad [3.11b]$$

$$v_x^2 = v_{0x}^2 + 2a_x \Delta x \qquad [3.11c]$$

where $v_{0x} = v_0 \cos \theta_0$, and, for the y-direction,

$$v_y = v_{0y} + a_y t \qquad [3.12a]$$

$$\Delta y = v_{0y}t + \tfrac{1}{2}a_y t^2 \qquad [3.12b]$$

$$v_y^2 = v_{0y}^2 + 2a_y \Delta y \qquad [3.12c]$$

where $v_{0y} = v_0 \sin \theta_0$. The speed v of the object at any instant can be calculated from the components of velocity at that instant using the Pythagorean theorem:

$$v = \sqrt{v_x^2 + v_y^2}$$

The angle that the velocity vector makes with the x-axis is given by

$$\theta = \tan^{-1}\left(\frac{v_y}{v_x}\right)$$

The horizontal and vertical motions of a projectile are completely independent of each other.

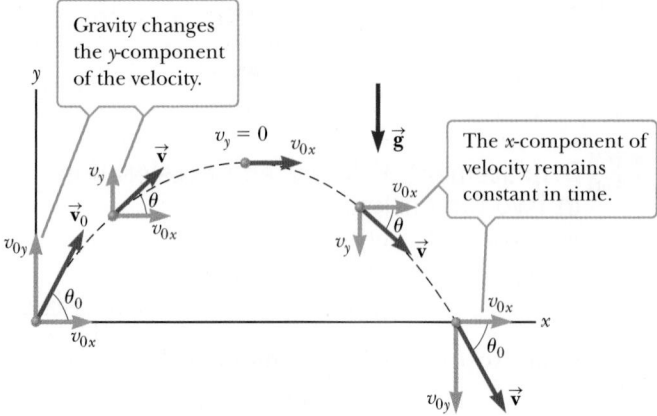

Gravity acts on the y-component of the velocity and has no effect on the x-component, illustrating the independence of horizontal and vertical projectile motion.

The kinematic equations are easily adapted and simplified for projectiles close to the surface of the Earth. The equations for the motion in the horizontal or x-direction are

$$v_x = v_{0x} = v_0 \cos \theta_0 = \text{constant} \qquad [3.13a]$$

$$\Delta x = v_{0x}t = (v_0 \cos \theta_0)t \qquad [3.13b]$$

while the equations for the motion in the vertical or y-direction are

$$v_y = v_0 \sin \theta_0 - gt \qquad [3.14a]$$

$$\Delta y = (v_0 \sin \theta_0)t - \tfrac{1}{2}gt^2 \qquad [3.14b]$$

$$v_y^2 = (v_0 \sin \theta_0)^2 - 2g \Delta y \qquad [3.14c]$$

Problems are solved by algebraically manipulating one or more of these equations, which often reduces the system to two equations and two unknowns.

3.5 Relative Velocity

Let E be an observer, and B a second observer traveling with velocity $\vec{v}_{BE}$ as measured by E. If E measures the velocity of an object A as $\vec{v}_{AE}$, then B will measure A's velocity as

$$\vec{v}_{AB} = \vec{v}_{AE} - \vec{v}_{BE} \qquad [3.16]$$

Equation 3.16 can be derived from Figure 3.21 by dividing the relative position equation by the Δt and taking the limit as Δt goes to zero.

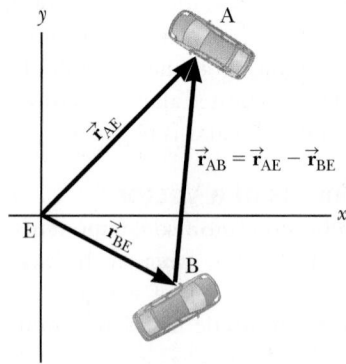

The time rate of change of the difference of the two position vectors $\vec{r}_{AE}$ and $\vec{r}_{BE}$ gives the relative velocity equation, Equation 3.16.

Solving relative velocity problems involves identifying the velocities properly and labeling them correctly, substituting into Equation 3.16, and then solving for unknown quantities.

■ MULTIPLE-CHOICE QUESTIONS

WebAssign The multiple-choice questions in this chapter may be assigned online in Enhanced WebAssign.

1. A cruise ship sails due north at 4.50 m/s while a coast guard patrol boat heads 45.0° north of west at 5.20 m/s. What is the velocity of the cruise ship relative to the patrol boat? (a) $v_x = 3.68$ m/s; $v_y = 0.823$ m/s (b) $v_x = -3.68$ m/s; $v_y = 8.18$ m/s (c) $v_x = 3.68$ m/s; $v_y = 8.18$ m/s (d) $v_x = -3.68$ m/s; $v_y = -0.823$ m/s (e) $v_x = 3.68$ m/s; $v_y = 1.82$ m/s

2. A skier leaves the end of a horizontal ski jump at 22.0 m/s and falls 3.20 m before landing. Neglecting friction, how far horizontally does the skier travel in the air before landing? (a) 9.8 m (b) 12.2 m (c) 14.3 m (d) 17.8 m (e) 21.6 m

3. A catapult launches a large stone at a speed of 45.0 m/s at an angle of 55.0° with the horizontal. What maxi-

mum height does the stone reach? (Neglect air friction.) (a) 45.7 m (b) 32.7 m (c) 69.3 m (d) 83.2 m (e) 102 m

4. A vector lying in the *xy*-plane has components of opposite sign. The vector must lie in which quadrant? (a) the first quadrant (b) the second quadrant (c) the third quadrant (d) the fourth quadrant (e) either the second or the fourth quadrant

5. A NASA astronaut hits a golf ball on the Moon. Which of the following quantities, if any, remain constant as the ball travels through the lunar vacuum? (a) speed (b) acceleration (c) velocity (d) horizontal component of velocity (e) vertical component of velocity

6. A car moving around a circular track with constant speed (a) has zero acceleration, (b) has an acceleration component in the direction of its velocity, (c) has an acceleration directed away from the center of its path, (d) has an acceleration directed toward the center of its path, or (e) has an acceleration with a direction that cannot be determined from the information given.

7. An athlete runs three-fourths of the way around a circular track. Which of the following statements is true? (a) His average speed is greater than the magnitude of his average velocity. (b) The magnitude of his average velocity is greater than his average speed. (c) His average speed is equal to the magnitude of his average velocity. (d) His average speed is the same as the magnitude of his average velocity if his instantaneous speed is constant. (e) None of statements (a) through (d) is true.

8. A projectile is launched from Earth's surface at a certain initial velocity at an angle above the horizontal, reaching maximum height after time t_{max}. Another projectile is launched with the same initial velocity and angle from the surface of the Moon, where the acceleration of gravity is one-sixth that of Earth. Neglecting air resistance (on Earth) and variations in the acceleration of gravity with height, how long does it take the projectile on the Moon to reach its maximum height? (a) t_{max} (b) $t_{max}/6$ (c) $\sqrt{6}t_{max}$ (d) $36t_{max}$ (e) $6t_{max}$

9. A sailor drops a wrench from the top of a sailboat's vertical mast while the boat is moving rapidly and steadily straight forward. Where will the wrench hit the deck? (a) ahead of the base of the mast (b) at the base of the mast (c) behind the base of the mast (d) on the windward side of the base of the mast (e) None of choices (a) through (d) is correct.

10. A baseball is thrown from the outfield toward the catcher. When the ball reaches its highest point, which statement is true? (a) Its velocity and its acceleration are both zero. (b) Its velocity is not zero, but its acceleration is zero. (c) Its velocity is perpendicular to its acceleration. (d) Its acceleration depends on the angle at which the ball was thrown. (e) None of statements (a) through (d) is true.

11. A student throws a heavy red ball horizontally from a balcony of a tall building with an initial speed v_0. At the same time, a second student drops a lighter blue ball from the same balcony. Neglecting air resistance, which statement is true? (a) The blue ball reaches the ground first. (b) The balls reach the ground at the same instant. (c) The red ball reaches the ground first. (d) Both balls hit the ground with the same speed. (e) None of statements (a) through (d) is true.

12. As an apple tree is transported by a truck moving to the right with a constant velocity, one of its apples shakes loose and falls toward the bed of the truck. Of the curves shown in Figure MCQ3.12, (i) which best describes the path followed by the apple as seen by a stationary observer on the ground, who observes the truck moving from his left to his right? (ii) Which best describes the path as seen by an observer sitting in the truck?

Figure MCQ3.12

13. Which of the following quantities are vectors? (a) the velocity of a sports car (b) temperature (c) the volume of water in a can (d) the displacement of a tennis player from the backline of the court to the net (e) the height of a building

■ CONCEPTUAL QUESTIONS

WebAssign The conceptual questions in this chapter may be assigned online in Enhanced WebAssign.

1. If $\vec{B}$ is added to $\vec{A}$, under what conditions does the resultant vector have a magnitude equal to $A + B$? Under what conditions is the resultant vector equal to zero?

2. Under what circumstances would a vector have components that are equal in magnitude?

3. As a projectile moves in its path, is there any point along the path where the velocity and acceleration vectors are (a) perpendicular to each other? (b) Parallel to each other?

4. Construct motion diagrams showing the velocity and acceleration of a projectile at several points along its

path, assuming (a) the projectile is launched horizontally and (b) the projectile is launched at an angle θ with the horizontal.

5. Explain whether the following particles do or do not have an acceleration: (a) a particle moving in a straight line with constant speed and (b) a particle moving around a curve with constant speed.

6. A ball is projected horizontally from the top of a building. One second later, another ball is projected horizontally from the same point with the same velocity. (a) At what point in the motion will the balls be closest to each other? (b) Will the first ball always be traveling faster than the second? (c) What will be the time difference between them when the balls hit the ground? (d) Can the horizontal projection velocity of the second ball be changed so that the balls arrive at the ground at the same time?

7. A spacecraft drifts through space at a constant velocity. Suddenly, a gas leak in the side of the spacecraft causes it to constantly accelerate in a direction perpendicular to the initial velocity. The orientation of the spacecraft does not change, so the acceleration remains perpendicular to the original direction of the velocity. What is the shape of the path followed by the spacecraft?

8. Determine which of the following moving objects obey the equations of projectile motion developed in this chapter. (a) A ball is thrown in an arbitrary direction. (b) A jet airplane crosses the sky with its engines thrusting the plane forward. (c) A rocket leaves the launch pad. (d) A rocket moves through the sky after its engines have failed. (e) A stone is thrown under water.

9. Two projectiles are thrown with the same initial speed, one at an angle θ with respect to the level ground and the other at angle $90° - \theta$. Both projectiles strike the ground at the same distance from the projection point. Are both projectiles in the air for the same length of time?

10. A ball is thrown upward in the air by a passenger on a train that is moving with constant velocity. (a) Describe the path of the ball as seen by the passenger. Describe the path as seen by a stationary observer outside the train. (b) How would these observations change if the train were accelerating along the track?

11. A projectile is launched at some angle to the horizontal with some initial speed v_i, and air resistance is negligible. (a) Is the projectile a freely falling body? (b) What is its acceleration in the vertical direction? (c) What is its acceleration in the horizontal direction?

■ PROBLEMS

WebAssign The problems in this chapter may be assigned online in Enhanced WebAssign. Selected problems also have Watch It video solutions.
1. denotes straightforward problem; 2. denotes intermediate problem;
3. denotes challenging problem
1. denotes full solution available in *Student Solutions Manual/ Study Guide*

1. denotes problems most often assigned in Enhanced WebAssign
BIO denotes biomedical problems
GP denotes guided problems
M denotes Master It tutorial available in Enhanced WebAssign
QC denotes asking for quantitative and conceptual reasoning
S denotes symbolic reasoning problem

3.1 Vectors and Their Properties

1. Vector $\vec{A}$ has a magnitude of 29 units and points in the positive y-direction. When vector $\vec{B}$ is added to $\vec{A}$, the resultant vector $\vec{A} + \vec{B}$ points in the negative y-direction with a magnitude of 14 units. Find the magnitude and direction of $\vec{B}$.

2. Vector $\vec{A}$ has a magnitude of 8.00 units and makes an angle of 45.0° with the positive x-axis. Vector $\vec{B}$ also has a magnitude of 8.00 units and is directed along the negative x-axis. Using graphical methods, find (a) the vector sum $\vec{A} + \vec{B}$ and (b) the vector difference $\vec{A} - \vec{B}$.

3. Vector $\vec{A}$ is 3.00 units in length and points along the positive x-axis. Vector $\vec{B}$ is 4.00 units in length and points along the negative y-axis. Use graphical methods to find the magnitude and direction of the vectors (a) $\vec{A} + \vec{B}$ and (b) $\vec{A} - \vec{B}$.

4. QC Three displacements are $\vec{A}$ = 200 m due south, $\vec{B}$ = 250 m due west, and $\vec{C}$ = 150 m at 30.0° east of north. (a) Construct a separate diagram for each of the following possible ways of adding these vectors: $\vec{R}_1 = \vec{A} + \vec{B} + \vec{C}$; $\vec{R}_2 = \vec{B} + \vec{C} + \vec{A}$; $\vec{R}_3 = \vec{C} + \vec{B} + \vec{A}$. (b) Explain what you can conclude from comparing the diagrams.

5. A roller coaster moves 200 ft horizontally and then rises 135 ft at an angle of 30.0° above the horizontal. Next, it travels 135 ft at an angle of 40.0° below the horizontal. Use graphical techniques to find the roller coaster's displacement from its starting point to the end of this movement.

6. QC An airplane flies 200 km due west from city A to city B and then 300 km in the direction of 30.0° north of west from city B to city C. (a) In straight-line dis-

tance, how far is city C from city A? (b) Relative to city A, in what direction is city C? (c) Why is the answer only approximately correct?

7. A plane flies from base camp to lake A, a distance of 280 km at a direction of 20.0° north of east. After dropping off supplies, the plane flies to lake B, which is 190 km and 30.0° west of north from lake A. Graphically determine the distance and direction from lake B to the base camp.

8. A force $\vec{F}_1$ of magnitude 6.00 units acts on an object at the origin in a direction $\theta = 30.0°$ above the positive x-axis (Fig. P3.8). A second force $\vec{F}_2$ of magnitude 5.00 units acts on the object in the direction of the positive y-axis. Find graphically the magnitude and direction of the resultant force $\vec{F}_1 + \vec{F}_2$.

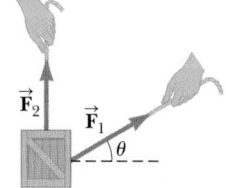

Figure P3.8

9. A man in a maze makes three consecutive displacements. His first displacement is 8.00 m westward, and the second is 13.0 m northward. At the end of his third displacement he is back to where he started. Use the graphical method to find the magnitude and direction of his third displacement.

3.2 Components of a Vector

10. A person walks 25.0° north of east for 3.10 km. How far due north and how far due east would she have to walk to arrive at the same location?

11. The magnitude of vector $\vec{A}$ is 35.0 units and points in the direction 325° counterclockwise from the positive x-axis. Calculate the x- and y-components of this vector.

12. A figure skater glides along a circular path of radius 5.00 m. If she coasts around one half of the circle, find (a) the magnitude of the displacement vector and (b) what distance she skated. (c) What is the magnitude of the displacement if she skates all the way around the circle?

13. A girl delivering newspapers covers her route by traveling 3.00 blocks west, 4.00 blocks north, and then 6.00 blocks east. (a) What is her resultant displacement? (b) What is the total distance she travels?

14. **Q|C** A hiker starts at his camp and moves the following distances while exploring his surroundings: 75.0 m north, 2.50×10^2 m east, 125 m at an angle 30.0° north of east, and 1.50×10^2 m south. (a) Find his resultant displacement from camp. (Take east as the positive x-direction and north as the positive y-direction.) (b) Would changes in the order in which the hiker makes the given displacements alter his final position? Explain.

15. A vector has an x-component of -25.0 units and a y-component of 40.0 units. Find the magnitude and direction of the vector.

16. A quarterback takes the ball from the line of scrimmage, runs backwards for 10.0 yards, then runs sideways parallel to the line of scrimmage for 15.0 yards. At this point, he throws a 50.0-yard forward pass straight downfield, perpendicular to the line of scrimmage. What is the magnitude of the football's resultant displacement?

17. **M** The eye of a hurricane passes over Grand Bahama Island in a direction 60.0° north of west with a speed of 41.0 km/h. Three hours later the course of the hurricane suddenly shifts due north, and its speed slows to 25.0 km/h. How far from Grand Bahama is the hurricane 4.50 h after it passes over the island?

18. A map suggests that Atlanta is 730 miles in a direction 5.00° north of east from Dallas. The same map shows that Chicago is 560 miles in a direction 21.0° west of north from Atlanta. Figure P3.18 shows the location of these three cities. Modeling the Earth as flat, use this information to find the displacement from Dallas to Chicago.

Figure P3.18

19. A commuter airplane starts from an airport and takes the route shown in Figure P3.19. The plane first flies to city A, located 175 km away in a direction 30.0° north of east. Next, it flies for 150 km 20.0° west of north, to city B. Finally, the plane flies 190 km due west, to city C. Find the location of city C relative to the location of the starting point.

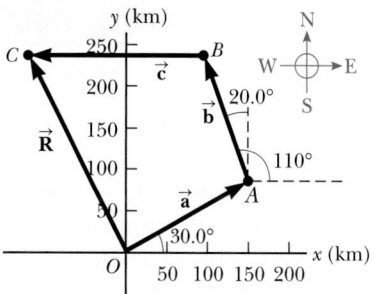

Figure P3.19

20. The helicopter view in Figure P3.20 shows two people pulling on a stubborn mule. Find (a) the single force that is equivalent to the two forces shown and (b) the force a third person would have to exert on the mule to make the net force equal to zero. The forces are measured in units of newtons (N).

Figure P3.20

21. A novice golfer on the green takes three strokes to sink the ball. The successive displacements of the ball are 4.00 m to the north, 2.00 m northeast, and 1.00 m at 30.0° west of south (Fig. P3.21). Starting at the same initial point, an expert golfer could make the hole in what single displacement?

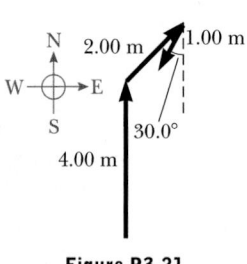

Figure P3.21

3.3 Displacement, Velocity, and Acceleration in Two Dimensions

3.4 Motion in Two Dimensions

22. One of the fastest recorded pitches in major-league baseball, thrown by Tim Lincecum in 2009, was clocked at 101.0 mi/h (Fig. P3.22). If a pitch were thrown horizontally with this velocity, how far would the ball fall vertically by the time it reached home plate, 60.5 ft away?

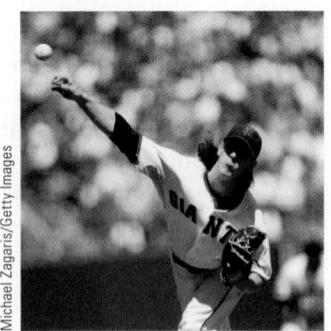

Figure P3.22 Tim Lincecum throws a baseball.

23. **GP** A student stands at the edge of a cliff and throws a stone horizontally over the edge with a speed of 18.0 m/s. The cliff is 50.0 m above a flat, horizontal beach as shown in Figure P3.23. (a) What are the coordinates of the initial position of the stone? (b) What are the components of the initial velocity? (c) Write the equations for the x- and y-components of the velocity of the stone with time. (d) Write the equations for the position of the stone with time, using the coordinates in Figure P3.23. (e) How long after being released does the stone strike the beach below the cliff? (f) With what speed and angle of impact does the stone land?

Figure P3.23

24. **QC** **S** A rock is thrown upward from the level ground in such a way that the maximum height of its flight is equal to its horizontal range R. (a) At what angle θ is the rock thrown? (b) In terms of the original range R, what is the range R_{max} the rock can attain if it is launched at the same speed but at the optimal angle for maximum range? (c) Would your answer to part (a) be different if the rock is thrown with the same speed on a different planet? Explain.

25. The best leaper in the animal kingdom is the puma, which can jump to a height of 3.7 m when leaving the ground at an angle of 45°. With what speed must the animal leave the ground to reach that height?

26. **QC** The record distance in the sport of throwing cowpats is 81.1 m. This record toss was set by Steve Urner of the United States in 1981. Assuming the initial launch angle was 45° and neglecting air resistance, determine (a) the initial speed of the projectile and (b) the total time the projectile was in flight. (c) Qualitatively, how would the answers change if the launch angle were greater than 45°? Explain.

27. **M** A place-kicker must kick a football from a point 36.0 m (about 40 yards) from the goal. Half the crowd hopes the ball will clear the crossbar, which is 3.05 m high. When kicked, the ball leaves the ground with a speed of 20.0 m/s at an angle of 53.0° to the horizontal. (a) By how much does the ball clear or fall short of clearing the crossbar? (b) Does the ball approach the crossbar while still rising or while falling?

28. **GP** From the window of a building, a ball is tossed from a height y_0 above the ground with an initial velocity of 8.00 m/s and angle of 20.0° below the horizontal. It strikes the ground 3.00 s later. (a) If the base of the building is taken to be the origin of the coordinates, with upward the positive y-direction, what are the initial coordinates of the ball? (b) With the positive x-direction chosen to be out the window, find the x- and y-components of the initial velocity. (c) Find the equations for the x- and y-components of the position as functions of time. (d) How far horizontally from the

base of the building does the ball strike the ground? (e) Find the height from which the ball was thrown. (f) How long does it take the ball to reach a point 10.0 m below the level of launching?

29. A brick is thrown upward from the top of a building at an angle of 25° to the horizontal and with an initial speed of 15 m/s. If the brick is in flight for 3.0 s, how tall is the building?

30. An artillery shell is fired with an initial velocity of 300 m/s at 55.0° above the horizontal. To clear an avalanche, it explodes on a mountainside 42.0 s after firing. What are the x- and y-coordinates of the shell where it explodes, relative to its firing point?

31. A car is parked on a cliff overlooking the ocean on an incline that makes an angle of 24.0° below the horizontal. The negligent driver leaves the car in neutral, and the emergency brakes are defective. The car rolls from rest down the incline with a constant acceleration of 4.00 m/s² for a distance of 50.0 m to the edge of the cliff, which is 30.0 m above the ocean. Find (a) the car's position relative to the base of the cliff when the car lands in the ocean and (b) the length of time the car is in the air.

32. A fireman $d = 50.0$ m away from a burning building directs a stream of water from a ground-level fire hose at an angle of $\theta_i = 30.0°$ above the horizontal as shown in Figure P3.32. If the speed of the stream as it leaves the hose is $v_i = 40.0$ m/s, at what height will the stream of water strike the building?

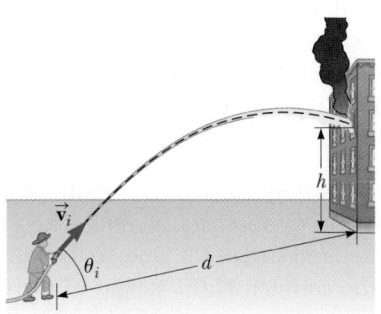

Figure P3.32

33. A projectile is launched with an initial speed of 60.0 m/s at an angle of 30.0° above the horizontal. The projectile lands on a hillside 4.00 s later. Neglect air friction. (a) What is the projectile's velocity at the highest point of its trajectory? (b) What is the straight-line distance from where the projectile was launched to where it hits its target?

34. A playground is on the flat roof of a city school, 6.00 m above the street below (Fig. P3.34). The vertical wall of the building is $h = 7.00$ m high, to form a 1-m-high railing around the playground. A ball has fallen to the street below, and a passerby returns it by launching it at an angle of $\theta = 53.0°$ above the horizontal at a point $d = 24.0$ m from the base of the building wall. The ball takes 2.20 s to reach a point vertically above the wall. (a) Find the speed at which the ball was launched. (b) Find the vertical distance by which the ball clears the wall. (c) Find the horizontal distance from the wall to the point on the roof where the ball lands.

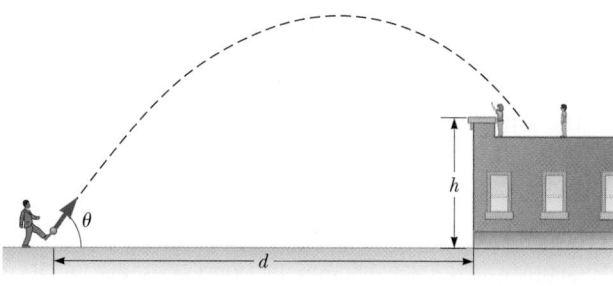

Figure P3.34

3.5 Relative Velocity

35. GP A jet airliner moving initially at 3.00×10^2 mi/h due east enters a region where the wind is blowing 1.00×10^2 mi/h in a direction 30.0° north of east. (a) Find the components of the velocity of the jet airliner relative to the air, $\vec{v}_{JA}$. (b) Find the components of the velocity of the air relative to Earth, $\vec{v}_{AE}$. (c) Write an equation analogous to Equation 3.16 for the velocities $\vec{v}_{JA}$, $\vec{v}_{AE}$, and $\vec{v}_{JE}$. (d) What are the speed and direction of the aircraft relative to the ground?

36. M A car travels due east with a speed of 50.0 km/h. Raindrops are falling at a constant speed vertically with respect to the Earth. The traces of the rain on the side windows of the car make an angle of 60.0° with the vertical. Find the velocity of the rain with respect to (a) the car and (b) the Earth.

37. QC A bolt drops from the ceiling of a moving train car that is accelerating northward at a rate of 2.50 m/s². (a) What is the acceleration of the bolt relative to the train car? (b) What is the acceleration of the bolt relative to the Earth? (c) Describe the trajectory of the bolt as seen by an observer fixed on the Earth.

38. A Coast Guard cutter detects an unidentified ship at a distance of 20.0 km in the direction 15.0° east of north. The ship is traveling at 26.0 km/h on a course at 40.0° east of north. The Coast Guard wishes to send a speedboat to intercept and investigate the vessel. (a) If the speedboat travels at 50.0 km/h, in what direction should it head? Express the direction as a compass bearing with respect to due north. (b) Find the time required for the cutter to intercept the ship.

39. An airplane maintains a speed of 630 km/h relative to the air it is flying through, as it makes a trip to a city 750 km away to the north. (a) What time interval is required for the trip if the plane flies through a headwind blowing at 35.0 km/h toward the south? (b) What time interval is required if there is a tailwind with the same speed? (c) What time interval is required if there is a crosswind blowing at 35.0 km/h to the east relative to the ground?

40. **BIO** Suppose a chinook salmon needs to jump a waterfall that is 1.50 m high. If the fish starts from a distance 1.00 m from the base of the ledge over which the waterfall flows, (a) find the x- and y-components of the initial velocity the salmon would need to just reach the ledge at the top of its trajectory. (b) Can the fish make this jump? (Note that a chinook salmon can jump out of the water with an initial speed of 6.26 m/s.)

41. **Q|C** A river has a steady speed of 0.500 m/s. A student swims upstream a distance of 1.00 km and swims back to the starting point. (a) If the student can swim at a speed of 1.20 m/s in still water, how long does the trip take? (b) How much time is required in still water for the same length swim? (c) Intuitively, why does the swim take longer when there is a current?

42. **Q|C** **S** *This is a symbolic version of Problem 41.* A river has a steady speed of v_s. A student swims upstream a distance d and back to the starting point. (a) If the student can swim at a speed of v in still water, how much time t_{up} does it take the student to swim upstream a distance d? Express the answer in terms of d, v, and v_s. (b) Using the same variables, how much time t_{down} does it take to swim back downstream to the starting point? (c) Sum the answers found in parts (a) and (b) and show that the time t_a required for the whole trip can be written as

$$t_a = \frac{2d/v}{1 - v_s^2/v^2}$$

(d) How much time t_b does the trip take in still water? (e) Which is larger, t_a or t_b? Is it always larger?

43. A bomber is flying horizontally over level terrain at a speed of 275 m/s relative to the ground and at an altitude of 3.00 km. (a) The bombardier releases one bomb. How far does the bomb travel horizontally between its release and its impact on the ground? Ignore the effects of air resistance. (b) Firing from the people on the ground suddenly incapacitates the bombardier before he can call, "Bombs away!" Consequently, the pilot maintains the plane's original course, altitude, and speed through a storm of flak. Where is the plane relative to the bomb's point of impact when the bomb hits the ground? (c) The plane has a telescopic bombsight set so that the bomb hits the target seen in the sight at the moment of release. At what angle from the vertical was the bombsight set?

Additional Problems

44. **S** A moving walkway at an airport has a speed v_1 and a length L. A woman stands on the walkway as it moves from one end to the other, while a man in a hurry to reach his flight walks on the walkway with a speed of v_2 relative to the moving walkway. (a) How long does it take the woman to travel the distance L? (b) How long does it take the man to travel this distance?

45. How long does it take an automobile traveling in the left lane of a highway at 60.0 km/h to overtake (become even with) another car that is traveling in the right lane at 40.0 km/h when the cars' front bumpers are initially 100 m apart?

46. You can use any coordinate system you like to solve a projectile motion problem. To demonstrate the truth of this statement, consider a ball thrown off the top of a building with a velocity $\vec{v}$ at an angle θ with respect to the horizontal. Let the building be 50.0 m tall, the initial horizontal velocity be 9.00 m/s, and the initial vertical velocity be 12.0 m/s. Choose your coordinates such that the positive y-axis is upward, the x-axis is to the right, and the origin is at the point where the ball is released. (a) With these choices, find the ball's maximum height above the ground and the time it takes to reach the maximum height. (b) Repeat your calculations choosing the origin at the base of the building.

47. **Q|C** A Nordic jumper goes off a ski jump at an angle of 10.0° below the horizontal, traveling 108 m horizontally and 55.0 m vertically before landing. (a) Ignoring friction and aerodynamic effects, calculate the speed needed by the skier on leaving the ramp. (b) Olympic Nordic jumpers can make such jumps with a jump speed of 23.0 m/s, which is considerably less than the answer found in part (a). Explain how that is possible.

48. **S** In a local diner, a customer slides an empty coffee cup down the counter for a refill. The cup slides off the counter and strikes the floor at distance d from the base of the counter. If the height of the counter is h, (a) find an expression for the time t it takes the cup to fall to the floor in terms of the variables h and g. (b) With what speed does the mug leave the counter? Answer in terms of the variables d, g, and h. (c) In the same terms, what is the speed of the cup immediately before it hits the floor? (d) In terms of h and d, what is the direction of the cup's velocity immediately before it hits the floor?

49. **M** Towns A and B in Figure P3.49 are 80.0 km apart. A couple arranges to drive from town A and meet a couple driving from town B at the lake, L. The two couples leave simultaneously and drive for 2.50 h in the directions shown. Car 1 has a speed of 90.0 km/h. If the cars arrive simultaneously at the lake, what is the speed of car 2?

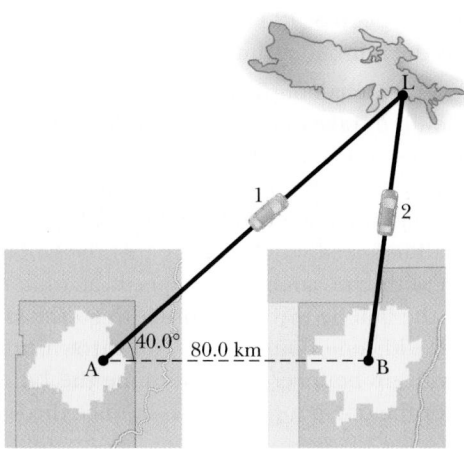

Figure P3.49

50. **BIO** A chinook salmon has a maximum underwater speed of 3.58 m/s, but it can jump out of water with a speed of 6.26 m/s. To move upstream past a waterfall, the salmon does not need to jump to the top of the fall, but only to a point in the fall where the water speed is less than 3.58 m/s; it can then swim up the fall for the remaining distance. Because the salmon must make forward progress in the water, let's assume it can swim to the top if the water speed is 3.00 m/s. If water has a speed of 1.50 m/s as it passes over a ledge, (a) how far below the ledge will the water be moving with a speed of 3.00 m/s? (Note that water undergoes projectile motion once it leaves the ledge.) (b) If the salmon is able to jump vertically upward from the base of the fall, what is the maximum height of waterfall that the salmon can clear?

51. A rocket is launched at an angle of 53.0° above the horizontal with an initial speed of 100 m/s. The rocket moves for 3.00 s along its initial line of motion with an acceleration of 30.0 m/s². At this time, its engines fail and the rocket proceeds to move as a projectile. Find (a) the maximum altitude reached by the rocket, (b) its total time of flight, and (c) its horizontal range.

52. Two canoeists in identical canoes exert the same effort paddling and hence maintain the same speed relative to the water. One paddles directly upstream (and moves upstream), whereas the other paddles directly downstream. With downstream as the positive direction, an observer on shore determines the velocities of the two canoes to be −1.2 m/s and +2.9 m/s, respectively. (a) What is the speed of the water relative to the shore? (b) What is the speed of each canoe relative to the water?

53. (a) If a person can jump a maximum horizontal distance (by using a 45° projection angle) of 3.0 m on Earth, what would be his maximum range on the Moon, where the free-fall acceleration is g/6 and g = 9.80 m/s²? (b) Repeat for Mars, where the acceleration due to gravity is 0.38g.

54. **QC** A farm truck moves due east with a constant velocity of 9.50 m/s on a limitless, horizontal stretch of road. A boy riding on the back of the truck

Figure P3.54

throws a can of soda upward (Fig. P3.54) and catches the projectile at the same location on the truck bed, but 16.0 m farther down the road. (a) In the frame of reference of the truck, at what angle to the vertical does the boy throw the can? (b) What is the initial speed of the can relative to the truck? (c) What is the shape of the can's trajectory as seen by the boy? An observer on the ground watches the boy throw the can and catch it. In this observer's frame of reference, (d) describe the shape of the can's path and (e) determine the initial velocity of the can.

55. **M** A home run is hit in such a way that the baseball just clears a wall 21 m high, located 130 m from home plate. The ball is hit at an angle of 35° to the horizontal, and air resistance is negligible. Find (a) the initial speed of the ball, (b) the time it takes the ball to reach the wall, and (c) the velocity components and the speed of the ball when it reaches the wall. (Assume the ball is hit at a height of 1.0 m above the ground.)

56. A ball is thrown straight upward and returns to the thrower's hand after 3.00 s in the air. A second ball thrown at an angle of 30.0° with the horizontal reaches the same maximum height as the first ball. (a) At what speed was the first ball thrown? (b) At what speed was the second ball thrown?

57. A quarterback throws a football toward a receiver with an initial speed of 20 m/s at an angle of 30° above the horizontal. At that instant the receiver is 20 m from the quarterback. In (a) what direction and (b) with what constant speed should the receiver run in order to catch the football at the level at which it was thrown?

58. A 2.00-m-tall basketball player is standing on the floor 10.0 m from the basket, as in Figure P3.58. If he shoots the ball at a 40.0° angle with the horizontal, at what initial speed must he throw the basketball so that it goes through the hoop without striking the backboard? The height of the basket is 3.05 m.

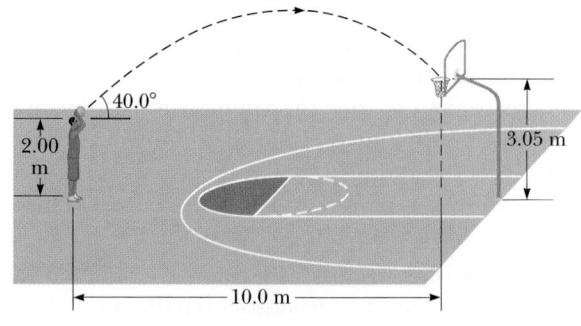

Figure P3.58

59. QC S In a very popular lecture demonstration, a projectile is fired at a falling target as in Figure P3.59. The projectile leaves the gun at the same instant the target is dropped from rest. Assuming the gun is initially aimed at the target, show that the projectile will hit the target. (One restriction of this experiment is that the projectile must reach the target before the target strikes the floor.)

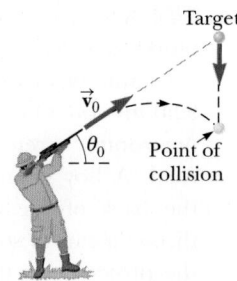

Figure P3.59

60. BIO Figure P3.60 illustrates the difference in proportions between the male (m) and female (f) anatomies. The displacements $\vec{d}_{1m}$ and $\vec{d}_{1f}$ from the bottom of the feet to the navel have magnitudes of 104 cm and 84.0 cm, respectively. The displacements $\vec{d}_{2m}$ and $\vec{d}_{2f}$ have magnitudes of 50.0 cm and 43.0 cm, respectively. (a) Find the vector sum of the displacements $\vec{d}_{d1}$ and $\vec{d}_{d2}$ in each case. (b) The male figure is 180 cm tall, the female 168 cm. Normalize the displacements of each figure to a common height of 200 cm and re-form the vector sums as in part (a). Then find the vector difference between the two sums.

Figure P3.60

61. QC By throwing a ball at an angle of 45°, a girl can throw the ball a maximum horizontal distance R on a level field. How far can she throw the same ball vertically upward? Assume her muscles give the ball the same speed in each case. (Is this assumption valid?)

62. S The equation of a parabola is $y = ax^2 + bx + c$, where a, b, and c are constants. The x- and y-coordinates of a projectile launched from the origin as a function of time are given by $x = v_{0x}t$ and $y = v_{0y}t - \frac{1}{2}gt^2$, where v_{0x} and v_{0y} are the components of the initial velocity. (a) Eliminate t from these two equations and show that the path of a projectile is a parabola and has the form $y = ax + bx^2$. (b) What are the values of a, b, and c for the projectile?

63. A hunter wishes to cross a river that is 1.5 km wide and flows with a speed of 5.0 km/h parallel to its banks. The hunter uses a small powerboat that moves at a maximum speed of 12 km/h with respect to the water. What is the minimum time necessary for crossing?

64. S When baseball outfielders throw the ball, they usually allow it to take one bounce, on the theory that the ball arrives at its target sooner that way. Suppose that, after the bounce, the ball rebounds at the same angle θ that it had when it was released (as in Fig. P3.64), but loses half its speed. (a) Assuming that the ball is always thrown with the same initial speed, at what angle θ should the ball be thrown in order to go the same distance D with one bounce as a ball thrown upward at 45.0° with no bounce? (b) Determine the ratio of the times for the one-bounce and no-bounce throws.

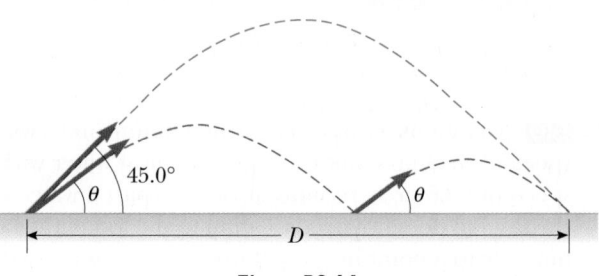

Figure P3.64

65. A daredevil is shot out of a cannon at 45.0° to the horizontal with an initial speed of 25.0 m/s. A net is positioned a horizontal distance of 50.0 m from the cannon. At what height above the cannon should the net be placed in order to catch the daredevil?

66. BIO Chinook salmon are able to move upstream faster by jumping out of the water periodically; this behavior is called *porpoising*. Suppose a salmon swimming in still water jumps out of the water with a speed of 6.26 m/s at an angle of 45°, sails through the air a distance L before returning to the water, and then swims a distance L underwater at a speed of 3.58 m/s before beginning another porpoising maneuver. Determine the average speed of the fish.

67. QC A student decides to measure the muzzle velocity of a pellet shot from his gun. He points the gun horizontally. He places a target on a vertical wall a distance x away from the gun. The pellet hits the target a vertical distance y below the gun. (a) Show that the position of the pellet when traveling through the air is given by $y = Ax^2$, where A is a constant. (b) Express the constant A in terms of the initial (muzzle) velocity and the free-fall acceleration. (c) If $x = 3.00$ m and $y = 0.210$ m, what is the initial speed of the pellet?

68. A sailboat is heading directly north at a speed of 20 knots (1 knot = 0.514 m/s). The wind is blowing toward the east with a speed of 17 knots. (a) Determine the magnitude and direction of the wind velocity as measured on the boat. (b) What is the component of the wind velocity in the direction parallel to the motion of the boat? (See Problem 58 in Chapter 4 for an explanation of how a sailboat can move "into the wind.")

69. A golf ball with an initial speed of 50.0 m/s lands exactly 240 m downrange on a level course. (a) Neglecting air friction, what *two* projection angles would achieve this result? (b) What is the maximum height reached by the ball, using the two angles determined in part (a)?

70. QC A landscape architect is planning an artificial waterfall in a city park. Water flowing at 0.750 m/s leaves the end of a horizontal channel at the top of a vertical wall $h = 2.35$ m high and falls into a pool (Fig. P3.70). (a) How far from the wall will the water land? Will the space behind the waterfall be wide enough for a pedestrian walkway? (b) To sell her plan to the city council, the architect wants to build a model to standard scale, one-twelfth actual size. How fast should the water flow in the channel in the model?

Figure P3.70

71. One strategy in a snowball fight is to throw a snowball at a high angle over level ground. Then, while your opponent is watching that snowball, you throw a second one at a low angle timed to arrive before or at the same time as the first one. Assume both snowballs are thrown with a speed of 25.0 m/s. The first is thrown at an angle of 70.0° with respect to the horizontal. (a) At what angle should the second snowball be thrown to arrive at the same point as the first? (b) How many seconds later should the second snowball be thrown after the first in order for both to arrive at the same time?

72. A dart gun is fired while being held horizontally at a height of 1.00 m above ground level and while it is at rest relative to the ground. The dart from the gun travels a horizontal distance of 5.00 m. A college student holds the same gun in a horizontal position while sliding down a 45.0° incline at a constant speed of 2.00 m/s. How far will the dart travel if the student fires the gun when it is 1.00 m above the ground?

73. The determined Wile E. Coyote is out once more to try to capture the elusive roadrunner. The coyote wears a new pair of power roller skates, which provide a constant horizontal acceleration of 15 m/s², as shown in Figure P3.73. The coyote starts off at rest 70 m from the edge of a cliff at the instant the roadrunner zips by in the direction of the

Figure P3.73

cliff. (a) If the roadrunner moves with constant speed, find the minimum speed the roadrunner must have to reach the cliff before the coyote. (b) If the cliff is 100 m above the base of a canyon, find where the coyote lands in the canyon. (Assume his skates are still in operation when he is in "flight" and that his horizontal component of acceleration remains constant at 15 m/s².)

74. A truck loaded with cannonball watermelons stops suddenly to avoid running over the edge of a washed-out bridge (Fig. P3.74). The quick stop causes a number of melons to fly off the truck. One melon rolls over the edge with an initial speed $v_i = 10.0$ m/s in the horizontal direction. A cross section of the bank has the shape of the bottom half of a parabola with its vertex at the edge of the road, and with the equation $y^2 = (16.0 \text{ m}) x$, where x and y are measured in meters. What are the x- and y-coordinates of the melon when it splatters on the bank?

Figure P3.74 The blue dashed curve shows the parabolic shape of the bank.

■ AP* REVIEW QUESTIONS

1. Which set of measurements is represented by scalar quantities only?

(A)	temperature	mass	weight
	time	velocity	
(B)	weight	acceleration	force
	time	distance	
(C)	force	speed	acceleration
	displacement	time	
(D)	mass	acceleration	time
	velocity	distance	
(E)	time	mass	distance
	speed	temperature	

2. Two vectors, **A** and **B**, are located at angles θ and Φ respectively from a common reference line and are added together. Which of the following expressions represents the magnitude of the resultant?

(A) $\sqrt{(\mathbf{A}\cos\theta + \mathbf{B}\cos\Phi)^2 + (\mathbf{A}\sin\theta + \mathbf{B}\sin\Phi)^2}$

(B) $\sqrt{(\mathbf{A}\cos\theta + \mathbf{B}\cos\Phi)^2 - (\mathbf{A}\sin\theta + \mathbf{B}\sin\Phi)^2}$

(C) $\mathbf{A}\cos\theta + \mathbf{B}\cos\Phi + \mathbf{A}\sin\theta + \mathbf{B}\sin\Phi$

(D) $\mathbf{A}\tan\theta + \mathbf{B}\tan\Phi$

(E) $\mathbf{A} + \mathbf{B}$

3. A lost cat meanders through a city section that has a grid street layout of evenly-spaced blocks. The cat first travels 10 blocks east, 4 blocks south, and then 7 blocks west. What is the cat's displacement from her starting point?

(A) 2.5 blocks southeast

(B) 5 blocks southeast

(C) 7 blocks southeast

(D) 11 blocks northwest

(E) 21 blocks east, south, and west

4. Which of the following descriptions could apply to an accelerating car?

    I. A car rounding a curve

    II. A car speeding up to get on a freeway

    III. A car slowing down to get off a freeway

    IV. A car maintaining a constant speed

(A) II

(B) II and III

(C) I, II, and III

(D) I and IV

(E) All choices could represent an accelerating car

5. Which of the following best represents the total acceleration vector at the top of a projectile's motion for a ball kicked from left to right if air resistance is NOT ignored?

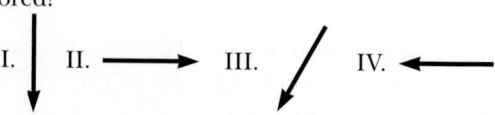

    V. zero acceleration

(A) I

(B) II

(C) III

(D) IV

(E) V

6. Two projectiles, P_1 and P_2, are fired at different angles from a common starting line and ultimately end the same distance away on level ground. If P_1 is launched at 25° from horizontal, what can be concluded about P_2's angle of launch from horizontal, time in the air, and speed at which it lands compared to P_1?

	Launch angle	Time in air	Landing speed
(A)	30°	greater than P_1	greater than P_1
(B)	45°	less than P_1	same as P_1
(C)	45°	same as P_1	zero
(D)	65°	greater than P_1	same as P_1
(E)	65°	less than P_1	greater than P_1

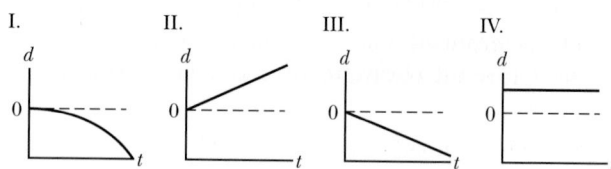

7. A rock is thrown horizontally off a cliff with a positive velocity as shown above. Assume air resistance is negligible. Which graph(s) above represent(s) the horizontal and vertical displacements versus time for the rock?

(A) Horizontal: I, Vertical: II

(B) Horizontal: I, Vertical: III

(C) Horizontal: II, Vertical: I

(D) Horizontal: III, Vertical: III

(E) Horizontal: III, Vertical: IV

8. A rock is thrown horizontally off a cliff with a positive velocity as shown above. Assume air resistance is negligible. Which graph(s) above represent(s) the horizontal and vertical velocities versus time for the rock?

(A) Horizontal: IV, Vertical: I

(B) Horizontal: III, Vertical: IV

(C) Horizontal: II, Vertical: II

(D) Horizontal: IV, Vertical: II

(E) One of the two velocity components is not represented by the graphs

9. A duck can swim at a speed of 2 m/s. Which of the following is true if a duck swims at its maximum speed perpendicular to the bank of a river 100 m wide flowing at 5 m/s?

(A) The duck will arrive at the opposite bank in 50 s.

(B) The duck will have traveled a distance 100 m to get across the river.

(C) The duck will have traveled a distance greater than 100 m to get across the river.

(D) (A) and (B)

(E) (A) and (C)

10. A football is kicked at an angle of 30° from horizontal with an initial velocity v_0 into a head-on breeze. Which of the following statements is true if air resistance is NOT ignored and it lands on ground level to where it was kicked?

(A) The football lands at an angle smaller than 30° from horizontal.

(B) The football lands at an angle larger than 30° from horizontal.

(C) The football lands at an angle of 30° from horizontal.

(D) The initial velocity will equal to the final velocity.

(E) The initial speed will be equal to the final speed.

11. A physics student wishes to measure the speed of a ball launched from a spring-loaded desktop cannon. The student launches the cannon horizontally and notices it strikes a wall located 5 m away 40 cm below the launch height. With what speed is the ball launched?

(A) 32 m/s

(B) 25 m/s

(C) 8.0 m/s

(D) 1.0 m/s

(E) None of the above

12. A tennis player wishes to clear a net of height h by height y at a horizontal distance x from the net. If the ball is hit at velocity v from ground level at an angle θ from horizontal and air resistance is negligible, which of the following expressions best describes y?

(A) $\left\{ \left[x^2 + \left(\dfrac{x}{v \cos \theta} - \dfrac{g \left(\dfrac{x}{v \sin \theta} \right)^2}{2} \right)^2 \right] \right\}^{0.5} - h$

(B) $-\dfrac{g \left(\dfrac{x}{v \cos \theta} \right)^2}{2} - h$

(C) $\dfrac{x \cos \theta}{\sin \theta} - \dfrac{g \left(\dfrac{x}{v \sin \theta} \right)^2}{2} - h$

(D) $\left(x \tan \theta - \dfrac{g \left(\dfrac{x}{v \cos \theta} \right)^2}{2} \right) - h$

(E) None of the expressions above correctly describe y.

By intuitively applying Newton's laws of motion, these two big horn sheep compete for dominance. They each exert forces against the Earth through muscular exertions of their legs, aided by the friction forces that keep them from slipping. The reaction forces of the Earth act back on the sheep and cause them to surge forward and butt heads. The goal is to force the opposing sheep out of equilibrium.

Image copyright Suzann Julien. Used under license from Shutterstock.com

4 The Laws of Motion

Classical mechanics describes the relationship between the motion of objects found in our everyday world and the forces acting on them. As long as the system under study doesn't involve objects comparable in size to an atom or traveling close to the speed of light, classical mechanics provides an excellent description of nature.

This chapter introduces Newton's three laws of motion and his law of gravity. The three laws are simple and sensible. The first law states that a force must be applied to an object in order to change its velocity. Changing an object's velocity means accelerating it, which implies a relationship between force and acceleration. This relationship, the second law, states that the net force on an object equals the object's mass times its acceleration. Finally, the third law says that whenever we push on something, it pushes back with equal force in the opposite direction. Those are the three laws in a nutshell.

Newton's three laws, together with his invention of calculus, opened avenues of inquiry and discovery that are used routinely today in virtually all areas of mathematics, science, engineering, and technology. Newton's theory of universal gravitation had a similar impact, starting a revolution in celestial mechanics and astronomy that continues to this day. With the advent of this theory, the orbits of all the planets could be calculated to high precision and the tides understood. The theory even led to the prediction of "dark stars," now called black holes, more than two centuries before any evidence for their existence was observed.[1] Newton's three laws of motion, together with his law of gravitation, are considered among the greatest achievements of the human mind.

---

[1]In 1783, John Michell combined Newton's theory of light and theory of gravitation, predicting the existence of "dark stars" from which light itself couldn't escape.

4.1 Forces

A **force** is commonly imagined as a push or a pull on some object, perhaps rapidly, as when we hit a tennis ball with a racket. (See Fig. 4.1.) We can hit the ball at different speeds and direct it into different parts of the opponent's court. That means we can control the magnitude of the applied force and also its direction, so force is a vector quantity, just like velocity and acceleration.

If you pull on a spring (Fig. 4.2a), the spring stretches. If you pull hard enough on a wagon (Fig. 4.2b), the wagon moves. When you kick a football (Fig. 4.2c), it deforms briefly and is set in motion. These are all examples of **contact forces,** so named because they result from physical contact between two objects.

Another class of forces doesn't involve any direct physical contact. Early scientists, including Newton, were uneasy with the concept of forces that act between two disconnected objects. Nonetheless, Newton used this "action-at-a-distance" concept in his law of gravity, whereby a mass at one location, such as the Sun, affects the motion of a distant object such as Earth despite no evident physical connection between the two objects. To overcome the conceptual difficulty associated with action at a distance, Michael Faraday (1791–1867) introduced the concept of a *field*. The corresponding forces are called **field forces.** According to this approach, an object of mass *M,* such as the Sun, creates an invisible influence that stretches throughout space. A second object of mass *m,* such as Earth, interacts with the *field* of the Sun, not directly with the Sun itself. So the force of gravitational attraction between two objects, illustrated in Figure 4.2d, is an example of a field force. The force of gravity keeps objects bound to Earth and also gives rise to what we call the *weight* of those objects.

Another common example of a field force is the electric force that one electric charge exerts on another (Fig. 4.2e). A third example is the force exerted by a bar magnet on a piece of iron (Fig. 4.2f).

The known fundamental forces in nature are all field forces. These are, in order of decreasing strength, (1) the strong nuclear force between subatomic particles, (2) the electromagnetic forces between electric charges, (3) the weak nuclear force, which arises in certain radioactive decay processes, and (4) the gravitational force between objects. The strong force keeps the nucleus of an atom from flying apart due to the repulsive electric force of the protons. The weak force is involved in most radioactive processes and plays an important role in the nuclear reactions that generate the Sun's energy output. The strong and weak forces operate only on the nuclear scale, with a very short range on the order of 10^{-15} m. Outside this range they have no influence. Classical physics, however, deals only with gravitational and electromagnetic forces, which have infinite range.

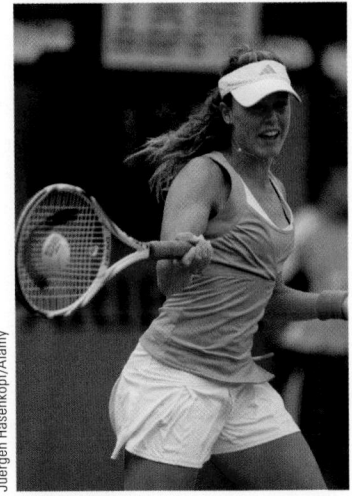

Figure 4.1 A tennis player applies a contact force to the ball with her racket, accelerating and directing the ball toward the open court.

Juergen Hasenkopf/Alamy

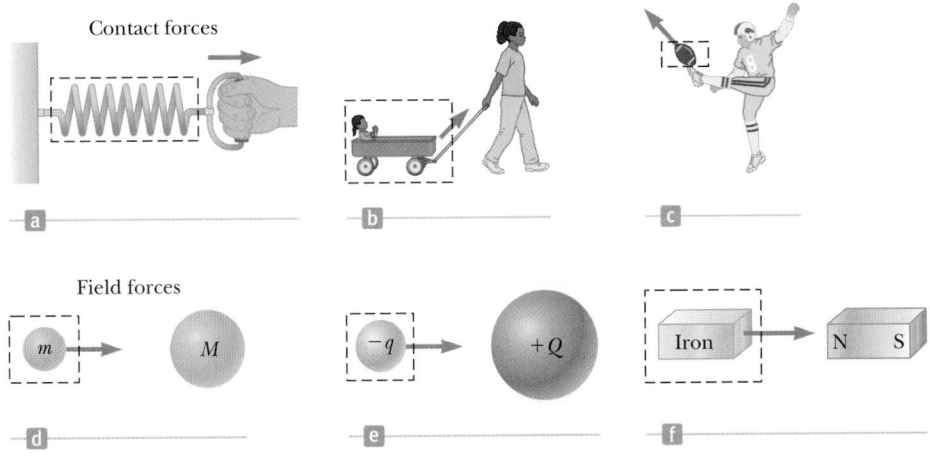

Figure 4.2 Examples of forces applied to various objects. In each case, a force acts on the object surrounded by the dashed lines. Something in the environment external to the boxed area exerts the force.

Forces exerted on an object can change the object's shape. For example, striking a tennis ball with a racket, as in Figure 4.1, deforms the ball to some extent. Even objects we usually consider rigid and inflexible are deformed under the action of external forces. Often the deformations are permanent, as in the case of a collision between automobiles.

4.2 Newton's First Law

Consider a book lying on a table. Obviously, the book remains at rest if left alone. Now imagine pushing the book with a horizontal force great enough to overcome the force of friction between the book and the table, setting the book in motion. Because the magnitude of the applied force exceeds the magnitude of the friction force, the book accelerates. When the applied force is withdrawn (Fig. 4.3a), friction soon slows the book to a stop.

Now imagine pushing the book across a smooth, waxed floor. The book again comes to rest once the force is no longer applied, but not as quickly as before. Finally, if the book is moving on a horizontal frictionless surface (Fig. 4.3b), it continues to move in a straight line with constant velocity until it hits a wall or some other obstruction.

Before about 1600, scientists felt that the natural state of matter was the state of rest. Galileo, however, devised thought experiments—such as an object moving on a frictionless surface, as just described—and concluded that **it's not the nature of an object to stop, once set in motion, but rather to continue in its original state of motion.** This approach was later formalized as **Newton's first law of motion:**

Newton's first law ▶ | An object moves with a velocity that is constant in magnitude and direction unless a non-zero net force acts on it.

The net force on an object is defined as the vector sum of all external forces exerted on the object. External forces come from the object's environment. If an object's velocity isn't changing in either magnitude or direction, then its acceleration and the net force acting on it must both be zero.

Internal forces originate within the object itself and can't change the object's velocity (although they can change the object's rate of rotation, as described in

Figure 4.3 The first law of motion. (a) A book moves at an initial velocity of $\vec{v}$ on a surface with friction. Because there is a friction force acting horizontally, the book slows to rest. (b) A book moves at velocity $\vec{v}$ on a frictionless surface. In the absence of a net force, the book keeps moving at velocity v.

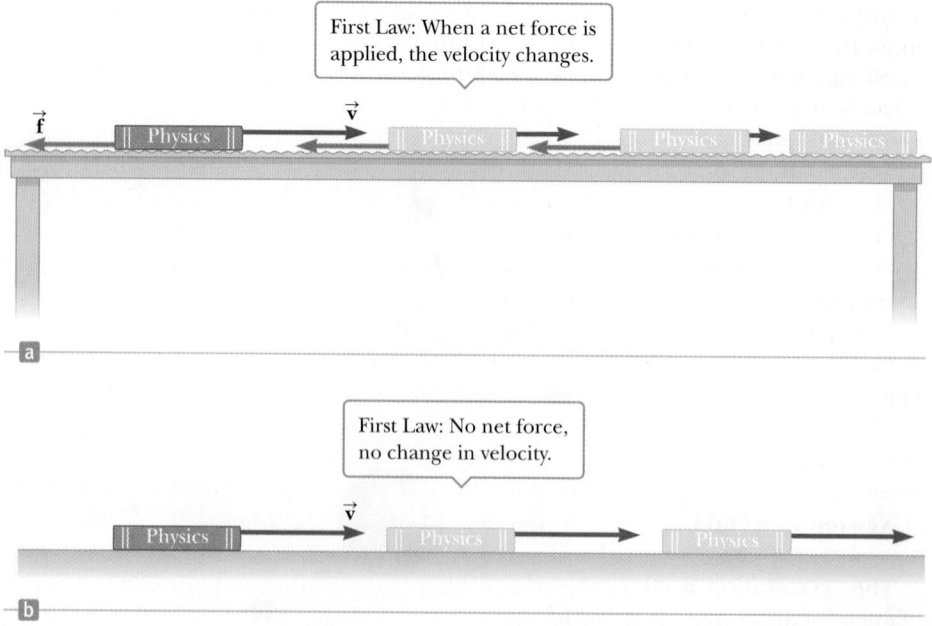

First Law: When a net force is applied, the velocity changes.

First Law: No net force, no change in velocity.

Chapter 8). As a result, internal forces aren't included in Newton's second law. It's not really possible to "pull yourself up by your own bootstraps."

A consequence of the first law is the feasibility of space travel. After just a few moments of powerful thrust, the spacecraft coasts for months or years, its velocity only slowly changing with time under the relatively faint influence of the distant Sun and planets.

Mass and Inertia

Imagine hitting a golf ball off a tee with a driver. If you're a good golfer, the ball will sail over two hundred yards down the fairway. Now imagine teeing up a bowling ball and striking it with the same club (an experiment we don't recommend). Your club would probably break, you might sprain your wrist, and the bowling ball, at best, would fall off the tee, take half a roll, and come to rest.

From this thought experiment, we conclude that although both balls resist changes in their state of motion, the bowling ball offers much more effective resistance. The tendency of an object to continue in its original state of motion is called **inertia.**

Although inertia is the tendency of an object to continue its motion in the absence of a force, **mass** is a measure of the object's resistance to changes in its motion due to a force. The greater the mass of a body, the less it accelerates under the action of a given applied force. The SI unit of mass is the kilogram. Mass is a scalar quantity that obeys the rules of ordinary arithmetic.

Inertia can be used to explain the operation of one type of seat belt mechanism. In the event of an accident, the purpose of the seat belt is to hold the passenger firmly in place relative to the car, to prevent serious injury. Figure 4.4 illustrates how one type of shoulder harness operates. Under normal conditions, the ratchet turns freely to allow the harness to wind on or unwind from the pulley as the passenger moves. In an accident, the car undergoes a large acceleration and rapidly comes to rest. Because of its inertia, the large block under the seat continues to slide forward along the tracks. The pin connection between the block and the rod causes the rod to pivot about its center and engage the ratchet wheel. At this point, the ratchet wheel locks in place and the harness no longer unwinds.

4.3 Newton's Second Law

Newton's first law explains what happens to an object that has no net force acting on it: The object either remains at rest or continues moving in a straight line with constant speed. Newton's second law answers the question of what happens to an object that *does* have a net force acting on it.

Imagine pushing a block of ice across a frictionless horizontal surface. When you exert some horizontal force on the block, it moves with an acceleration of, say, 2 m/s². If you apply a force twice as large, the acceleration doubles to 4 m/s². Pushing three times as hard triples the acceleration, and so on. From such observations, we conclude that **the acceleration of an object is directly proportional to the net force acting on it.**

Mass also affects acceleration. Suppose you stack identical blocks of ice on top of each other while pushing the stack with constant force. If the force applied to one block produces an acceleration of 2 m/s², then the acceleration drops to half that value, 1 m/s², when two blocks are pushed, to one-third the initial value when three blocks are pushed, and so on. We conclude that **the acceleration of an object is inversely proportional to its mass.** These observations are summarized in **Newton's second law:**

The acceleration $\vec{a}$ of an object is directly proportional to the net force acting on it and inversely proportional to its mass.

Unless acted on by an external force, an object at rest will remain at rest and an object in motion will continue in motion with constant velocity. In this case, the wall of the building did not exert a large enough external force on the moving train to stop it.

APPLICATION
Seat Belts

Figure 4.4 A mechanical arrangement for an automobile seat belt.

Tip 4.1 Force Causes Changes in Motion

Motion can occur even in the absence of forces. Force causes *changes* in motion.

◄ Newton's second law

Isaac Newton
English Physicist and Mathematician (1642–1727)
Newton was one of the most brilliant scientists in history. Before he was 30, he formulated the basic concepts and laws of mechanics, discovered the law of universal gravitation, and invented the mathematical methods of the calculus. As a consequence of his theories, Newton was able to explain the motions of the planets, the ebb and flow of the tides, and many special features of the motions of the Moon and Earth. He also interpreted many fundamental observations concerning the nature of light. His contributions to physical theories dominated scientific thought for two centuries and remain important today.

Figure 4.5 The second law of motion. For the block of mass m, the net force $\sum \vec{\mathbf{F}}$ acting on the block equals the mass m times the acceleration vector $\vec{\mathbf{a}}$.

The constant of proportionality is equal to one, so in mathematical terms the preceding statement can be written

$$\vec{\mathbf{a}} = \frac{\sum \vec{\mathbf{F}}}{m}$$

where $\vec{\mathbf{a}}$ is the acceleration of the object, m is its mass, and $\sum \vec{\mathbf{F}}$ is the vector sum of all forces acting on it. Multiplying through by m, we have

$$\sum \vec{\mathbf{F}} = m\vec{\mathbf{a}} \qquad [4.1]$$

Physicists commonly refer to this equation as '$F = ma$.' Figure 4.5 illustrates the relationship between the mass, acceleration, and the net force. The second law is a vector equation, equivalent to the following three component equations:

$$\sum F_x = ma_x \qquad \sum F_y = ma_y \qquad \sum F_z = ma_z \qquad [4.2]$$

When there is no net force on an object, its acceleration is zero, which means the velocity is constant.

Units of Force and Mass

The SI unit of force is the **newton.** When 1 newton of force acts on an object that has a mass of 1 kg, it produces an acceleration of 1 m/s² in the object. From this definition and Newton's second law, we see that the newton can be expressed in terms of the fundamental units of mass, length, and time as

$$1 \text{ N} \equiv 1 \text{ kg} \cdot \text{m/s}^2 \qquad [4.3]$$

In the U.S. customary system, the unit of force is the **pound.** The conversion from newtons to pounds is given by

$$1 \text{ N} = 0.225 \text{ lb} \qquad [4.4]$$

The units of mass, acceleration, and force in the SI and U.S. customary systems are summarized in Table 4.1.

Tip 4.2 $m\vec{\mathbf{a}}$ Is Not a Force

Equation 4.1 does *not* say that the product $m\vec{\mathbf{a}}$ is a force. All forces exerted on an object are summed as vectors to generate the net force on the left side of the equation. This net force is then equated to the product of the mass and resulting acceleration of the object. Do *not* include an "$m\vec{\mathbf{a}}$ force" in your analysis.

■ *Quick Quiz*

4.1 Which of the following statements are true? (a) An object can move even when no force acts on it. (b) If an object isn't moving, no external forces act on it. (c) If a single force acts on an object, the object accelerates. (d) If an object accelerates, a force is acting on it. (e) If an object isn't accelerating, no external force is acting on it. (f) If the net force acting on an object is in the positive x-direction, the object moves only in the positive x-direction.

Table 4.1 Units of Mass, Acceleration, and Force

System	Mass	Acceleration	Force
SI	kg	m/s²	N = kg·m/s²
U.S. customary	slug	ft/s²	lb = slug·ft/s²

■ **EXAMPLE 4.1** | Airboat

GOAL Apply Newton's second law in one dimension, together with the equations of kinematics.

PROBLEM An airboat with mass 3.50×10^2 kg, including the passenger, has an engine that produces a net horizontal force of 7.70×10^2 N, after accounting for forces of resistance (see Fig. 4.6). **(a)** Find the acceleration of the airboat.

(b) Starting from rest, how long does it take the airboat to reach a speed of 12.0 m/s? **(c)** After reaching that speed, the pilot turns off the engine and drifts to a stop over a distance of 50.0 m. Find the resistance force, assuming it's constant.

STRATEGY In part (a), apply Newton's second law to find the acceleration, and in part (b) use that acceleration in the one-dimensional kinematics equation for the velocity. When the engine is turned off in part (c), only the resistance forces act on the boat in the x-direction, so the net acceleration can be found from $v^2 - v_0^2 = 2a\,\Delta x$. Then Newton's second law gives the resistance force.

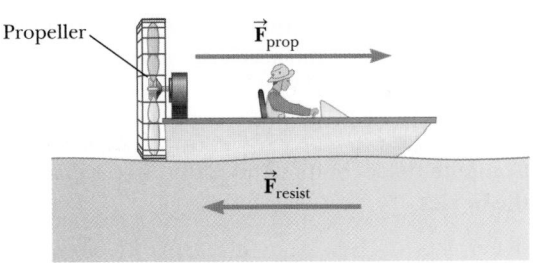

Figure 4.6 (Example 4.1)

SOLUTION

(a) Find the acceleration of the airboat.

Apply Newton's second law and solve for the acceleration:

$$ma = F_{net} \quad \rightarrow \quad a = \frac{F_{net}}{m} = \frac{7.70 \times 10^2 \text{ N}}{3.50 \times 10^2 \text{ kg}}$$
$$= \boxed{2.20 \text{ m/s}^2}$$

(b) Find the time necessary to reach a speed of 12.0 m/s.

Apply the kinematics velocity equation:

$$v = at + v_0 = (2.20 \text{ m/s}^2)t = 12.0 \text{ m/s} \quad \rightarrow \quad t = \boxed{5.45 \text{ s}}$$

(c) Find the resistance force after the engine is turned off.

Using kinematics, find the net acceleration due to resistance forces:

$$v^2 - v_0^2 = 2a\,\Delta x$$
$$0 - (12.0 \text{ m/s})^2 = 2a(50.0 \text{ m}) \quad \rightarrow \quad a = -1.44 \text{ m/s}^2$$

Substitute the acceleration into Newton's second law, finding the resistance force:

$$F_{resist} = ma = (3.50 \times 10^2 \text{ kg})(-1.44 \text{ m/s}^2) = \boxed{-504 \text{ N}}$$

REMARKS The propeller exerts a force on the air, pushing it backwards behind the boat. At the same time, the air exerts a force on the propellers and consequently on the airboat. Forces always come in pairs of this kind, which are formalized in the next section as Newton's third law of motion. The negative answer for the acceleration in part (c) means that the airboat is slowing down.

QUESTION 4.1 What other forces act on the airboat? Describe them.

EXERCISE 4.1 Suppose the pilot, starting again from rest, opens the throttle partway. At a constant acceleration, the airboat then covers a distance of 60.0 m in 10.0 s. Find the net force acting on the boat.

ANSWER 4.20×10^2 N

Tip 4.3 Newton's Second Law Is a *Vector* Equation

In applying Newton's second law, add all of the forces on the object as vectors and then find the resultant vector acceleration by dividing by m. Don't find the individual magnitudes of the forces and add them like scalars.

■ **EXAMPLE 4.2**   **Horses Pulling a Barge**

GOAL Apply Newton's second law in a two-dimensional problem.

PROBLEM Two horses are pulling a barge with mass 2.00×10^3 kg along a canal, as shown in Figure 4.7. The cable connected to the first horse makes an angle of $\theta_1 = 30.0°$ with respect to the direction of the canal, while the cable connected to the second horse makes an angle of $\theta_2 = -45.0°$. Find the initial acceleration of the barge, starting at rest, if each horse exerts a force of magnitude 6.00×10^2 N on the barge. Ignore forces of resistance on the barge.

STRATEGY Using trigonometry, find the vector force exerted by each horse on the barge. Add the x-components

Figure 4.7 (Example 4.2)

(Continued)

together to get the *x*-component of the resultant force, and then do the same with the *y*-components. Divide by the mass of the barge to get the accelerations in the *x*- and *y*-directions.

. . . .

SOLUTION

Compute the *x*-components of the forces exerted by the horses.

$$F_{1x} = F_1 \cos \theta_1 = (6.00 \times 10^2 \text{ N}) \cos (30.0°) = 5.20 \times 10^2 \text{ N}$$

$$F_{2x} = F_2 \cos \theta_2 = (6.00 \times 10^2 \text{ N}) \cos (-45.0°) = 4.24 \times 10^2 \text{ N}$$

Find the total force in the *x*-direction by adding the *x*-components:

$$F_x = F_{1x} + F_{2x} = 5.20 \times 10^2 \text{ N} + 4.24 \times 10^2 \text{ N}$$

$$= 9.44 \times 10^2 \text{ N}$$

Compute the *y*-components of the forces exerted by the horses:

$$F_{1y} = F_1 \sin \theta_1 = (6.00 \times 10^2 \text{ N}) \sin 30.0° = 3.00 \times 10^2 \text{ N}$$

$$F_{2y} = F_2 \sin \theta_2 = (6.00 \times 10^2 \text{ N}) \sin (-45.0°)$$

$$= -4.24 \times 10^2 \text{ N}$$

Find the total force in the *y*-direction by adding the *y*-components:

$$F_y = F_{1y} + F_{2y} = 3.00 \times 10^2 \text{ N} - 4.24 \times 10^2 \text{ N}$$

$$= -1.24 \times 10^2 \text{ N}$$

Obtain the components of the acceleration by dividing each of the force components by the mass:

$$a_x = \frac{F_x}{m} = \frac{9.44 \times 10^2 \text{ N}}{2.00 \times 10^3 \text{ kg}} = 0.472 \text{ m/s}^2$$

$$a_y = \frac{F_y}{m} = \frac{-1.24 \times 10^2 \text{ N}}{2.00 \times 10^3 \text{ kg}} = -0.062 \, 0 \text{ m/s}^2$$

Calculate the magnitude of the acceleration:

$$a = \sqrt{a_x^2 + a_y^2} = \sqrt{(0.472 \text{ m/s}^2)^2 + (-0.062 \, 0 \text{ m/s}^2)^2}$$

$$= \boxed{0.476 \text{ m/s}^2}$$

Calculate the direction of the acceleration using the tangent function:

$$\tan \theta = \frac{a_y}{a_x} = \frac{-0.062 \, 0 \text{ m/s}^2}{0.472 \text{ m/s}^2} = -0.131$$

$$\theta = \tan^{-1}(-0.131) = \boxed{-7.46°}$$

. . . .

REMARKS Notice that the angle is in fourth quadrant, in the range of the inverse tangent function, so it is not necessary to add 180° to the answer. The horses exert a force on the barge through the tension in the cables, while the barge exerts an equal and opposite force on the horses, again through the cables. If that were not true, the horses would easily move forward, as if unburdened. This example is another illustration of forces acting in pairs.

QUESTION 4.2 True or False: In general, the magnitude of the acceleration of an object is determined by the magnitudes of the forces acting on it.

EXERCISE 4.2 Repeat Example 4.2, but assume the first horse pulls at a 40.0° angle, the second horse at 20.0°.

ANSWER 0.520 m/s², 10.0°

The Gravitational Force

The **gravitational force** is the mutual force of attraction between any two objects in the Universe. Although the gravitational force can be very strong between very large objects, it's the weakest of the fundamental forces. A good demonstration of how weak it is can be carried out with a small balloon. Rubbing the balloon in your hair gives the balloon a tiny electric charge. Through electric forces, the balloon then adheres to a wall, resisting the gravitational pull of the entire Earth!

In addition to contributing to the understanding of motion, Newton studied gravity extensively. **Newton's law of universal gravitation states that every particle in the Universe attracts every other particle with a force that is directly proportional to the product of the masses of the particles and inversely proportional to the square of the distance between them.** If the particles have masses m_1 and m_2

◀ Law of universal gravitation

and are separated by a distance r, as in Figure 4.8, the magnitude of the gravitational force F_g is

$$F_g = G\frac{m_1 m_2}{r^2}$$ [4.5]

where $G = 6.67 \times 10^{-11}$ N · m²/kg² is the **universal gravitation constant.** We examine the gravitational force in more detail in Chapter 7.

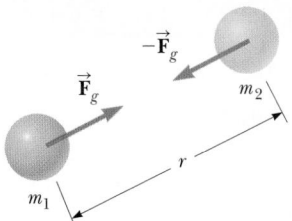

Figure 4.8 The gravitational force between two particles is attractive.

Weight

The magnitude of the gravitational force acting on an object of mass m is called the **weight** w of the object, given by

$$w = mg$$ [4.6]

where g is the acceleration of gravity.
SI unit: newton (N)

From Equation 4.5, an alternate definition of the weight of an object with mass m can be written as

$$w = G\frac{M_E m}{r^2}$$ [4.7]

where M_E is the mass of Earth and r is the distance from the object to Earth's center. If the object is at rest on Earth's surface, then r is equal to Earth's radius R_E. Because r^2 is in the denominator of Equation 4.7, the weight decreases with increasing r. So the weight of an object on a mountaintop is less than the weight of the same object at sea level.

Comparing Equations 4.6 and 4.7, it follows that

$$g = G\frac{M_E}{r^2}$$ [4.8]

Unlike mass, weight is not an inherent property of an object because it can take different values, depending on the value of g in a given location. If an object has a mass of 70.0 kg, for example, then its weight at a location where $g = 9.80$ m/s² is $mg = 686$ N. In a high-altitude balloon, where g might be 9.76 m/s², the object's weight would be 683 N. The value of g also varies slightly due to the density of matter in a given locality. **In this text, unless stated otherwise, the value of g will be understood to be 9.80 m/s², its value near the surface of the Earth.**

Equation 4.8 is a general result that can be used to calculate the acceleration of an object falling near the surface of any massive object if the more massive object's radius and mass are known. Using the values in Table 7.3 (p. 223), you should be able to show that $g_{\text{Sun}} = 274$ m/s² and $g_{\text{Moon}} = 1.62$ m/s². An important fact is that for spherical bodies, distances are calculated from the centers of the objects, a consequence of Gauss's law (explained in Chapter 15), which holds for both gravitational and electric forces.

NASA/Eugene Cernan

The life-support unit strapped to the back of astronaut Harrison Schmitt weighed 300 lb on Earth and had a mass of 136 kg. During his training, a 50-lb mock-up with a mass of 23 kg was used. Although the mock-up had the same weight as the actual unit would have on the Moon, the smaller mass meant it also had a lower inertia. The weight of the unit is caused by the acceleration of the local gravity field, but the astronaut must also accelerate anything he's carrying in order to move it around. Consequently, the actual unit used on the Moon, with the same weight but greater inertia, was harder for the astronaut to handle than the mock-up unit on Earth.

■ Quick Quiz

4.2 Which has greater value, a newton of gold won on Earth or a newton of gold won on the Moon? (a) The newton of gold on the Earth. (b) The newton of gold on the Moon. (c) The value is the same, regardless.

4.3 Respond to each statement, true or false: (a) No force of gravity acts on an astronaut in an orbiting space station. (b) At three Earth radii from the center of Earth, the acceleration of gravity is 1/9 its surface value. (c) If two identical planets, each with surface gravity g and volume V, coalesce into one planet with volume $2V$, the surface gravity of the new planet is $2g$. (d) One kilogram of gold would have greater value on Earth than on the Moon.

EXAMPLE 4.3   Forces of Distant Worlds

GOAL Calculate the magnitude of a gravitational force using Newton's law of gravitation.

PROBLEM (a) Find the gravitational force exerted by the Sun on a 70.0-kg man located at the Earth's equator at noon, when the man is closest to the Sun. (b) Calculate the gravitational force of the Sun on the man at midnight, when he is farthest from the Sun. (c) Calculate the difference in the acceleration due to the Sun between noon and midnight. (For values, see Table 7.3 on page 223.)

STRATEGY To obtain the distance of the Sun from the man at noon, subtract the Earth's radius from the solar distance. At midnight, add the Earth's radius. Retain enough digits so that rounding doesn't remove the small difference between the two answers. For part (c), subtract the answer for (b) from (a) and divide by the man's mass.

. . . .

SOLUTION

(a) Find the gravitational force exerted by the Sun on the man at the Earth's equator at noon.

Write the law of gravitation, Equation 4.5, in terms of the distance from the Sun to the Earth, r_S, and Earth's radius, R_E:

$$(1) \quad F_{\text{Sun}}^{\text{noon}} = \frac{mM_SG}{r^2} = \frac{mM_SG}{(r_S - R_E)^2}$$

Substitute values into (1) and retain two extra digits:

$$F_{\text{Sun}}^{\text{noon}} = \frac{(70.0 \text{ kg})(1.991 \times 10^{30} \text{ kg})(6.67 \times 10^{-11} \text{ kg}^{-1}\text{m}^3/\text{s}^2)}{(1.496 \times 10^{11} \text{ m} - 6.38 \times 10^6 \text{ m})^2}$$

$$= \boxed{0.415 \ 19 \text{ N}}$$

(b) Calculate the gravitational force of the Sun on the man at midnight.

Write the law of gravitation, adding Earth's radius this time:

$$(2) \quad F_{\text{Sun}}^{\text{mid}} = \frac{mM_SG}{r^2} = \frac{mM_SG}{(r_S + R_E)^2}$$

Substitute values into (2):

$$F_{\text{Sun}}^{\text{mid}} = \frac{(70.0 \text{ kg})(1.991 \times 10^{30} \text{ kg})(6.67 \times 10^{-11} \text{ kg}^{-1}\text{m}^3/\text{s}^2)}{(1.496 \times 10^{11} \text{ m} + 6.38 \times 10^6 \text{ m})^2}$$

$$= \boxed{0.415 \ 12 \text{ N}}$$

(c) Calculate the difference in the man's solar acceleration between noon and midnight.

Write an expression for the difference in acceleration and substitute values:

$$a = \frac{F_{\text{Sun}}^{\text{noon}} - F_{\text{Sun}}^{\text{mid}}}{m} = \frac{0.415 \ 19 \text{ N} - 0.415 \ 12 \text{ N}}{70.0 \text{ kg}}$$

$$\cong \boxed{1 \times 10^{-6} \text{ m/s}^2}$$

. . . .

REMARKS The gravitational attraction between the Sun and objects on Earth is easily measurable and has been exploited in experiments to determine whether gravitational attraction depends on the composition of the object. The gravitational force on Earth due to the Moon is much weaker than the gravitational force on Earth due to the Sun. Paradoxically, the Moon's effect on the tides is over twice that of the Sun because the tides depend on *differences* in the gravitational force across the Earth, and those differences are greater for the Moon's gravitational force because the Moon is much closer to Earth than the Sun.

QUESTION 4.3 Mars is about one and a half times as far from the Sun as Earth. Without doing an explicit calculation, estimate to one significant digit the gravitational force of the Sun on a 70.0 kg man standing on Mars.

EXERCISE 4.3 During a new Moon, the Moon is directly overhead in the middle of the day. (a) Find the gravitational force exerted by the Moon on a 70.0-kg man at the Earth's equator at noon. (b) Calculate the gravitational force of the Moon on the man at midnight. (c) Calculate the difference in the man's acceleration due to the Moon between noon and midnight. *Note:* The distance from the Earth to the Moon is 3.84×10^8 m. The mass of the Moon is 7.36×10^{22} kg.

ANSWERS (a) 2.41×10^{-3} N (b) 2.25×10^{-3} N (c) 2.3×10^{-6} m/s^2

■ **EXAMPLE 4.4** | **Weight on Planet X**

GOAL Understand the effect of a planet's mass and radius on the weight of an object on the planet's surface.

PROBLEM An astronaut on a space mission lands on a planet with three times the mass and twice the radius of Earth. What is her weight w_X on this planet as a multiple of her Earth weight w_E?

STRATEGY Write M_X and r_X, the mass and radius of the planet, in terms of M_E and R_E, the mass and radius of Earth, respectively, and substitute into the law of gravitation.

SOLUTION

From the statement of the problem, we have the following relationships:

$$M_X = 3M_E \quad r_X = 2R_E$$

Substitute the preceding expressions into Equation 4.5 and simplify, algebraically associating the terms giving the weight on Earth:

$$w_X = G\frac{M_X m}{r_X^2} = G\frac{3M_E m}{(2R_E)^2} = \frac{3}{4}G\frac{M_E m}{R_E^2} = \boxed{\frac{3}{4}w_E}$$

REMARKS This problem shows the interplay between a planet's mass and radius in determining the weight of objects on its surface. Because of Earth's much smaller radius, the weight of an object on Jupiter is only 2.64 times its weight on Earth, despite the fact that Jupiter has over 300 times as much mass.

QUESTION 4.4 A volume of rock has a mass roughly three times a similar volume of ice. Suppose one world is made of ice whereas another world with the same radius is made of rock. If g is the acceleration of gravity on the surface of the ice world, what is the approximate acceleration of gravity on the rock world?

EXERCISE 4.4 An astronaut lands on Ganymede, a giant moon of Jupiter that is larger than the planet Mercury. Ganymede has one-fortieth the mass of Earth and two-fifths the radius. Find the weight of the astronaut standing on Ganymede in terms of his Earth weight w_E.

ANSWER $w_G = (5/32)w_E$

4.4 Newton's Third Law

In Section 4.1 we found that a force is exerted on an object when it comes into contact with some other object. Consider the task of driving a nail into a block of wood, for example, as illustrated in Figure 4.9a (page 96). To accelerate the nail and drive it into the block, the hammer must exert a net force on the nail. Newton recognized, however, that a single isolated force couldn't exist. Instead, **forces in nature always exist in pairs.** According to Newton, as the nail is driven into the block by the force exerted by the hammer, the hammer is slowed down and stopped by the force exerted by the nail.

Newton described such paired forces with his **third law:**

If object 1 and object 2 interact, the force $\vec{F}_{12}$ exerted by object 1 on object 2 is equal in magnitude but opposite in direction to the force $\vec{F}_{21}$ exerted by object 2 on object 1.

◀ Newton's third law

This law, which is illustrated in Figure 4.9b, states that **a single isolated force can't exist.** The force $\vec{F}_{12}$ exerted by object 1 on object 2 is sometimes called the *action force,* and the force $\vec{F}_{21}$ exerted by object 2 on object 1 is called the *reaction force.* In reality, either force can be labeled the action or reaction force. **The action force is equal in magnitude to the reaction force and opposite in direction. In all cases, the action and reaction forces act on different objects.** For example, the force acting on a freely falling projectile is the force of gravity exerted by Earth on the projectile, $\vec{F}_g$, and the magnitude of this force is its weight mg. The reaction to force $\vec{F}_g$ is the gravitational force exerted by the projectile on Earth, $\vec{F}_g' = -\vec{F}_g$. The reaction force $\vec{F}_g'$ must accelerate the Earth towards the projectile, just

Tip 4.4 Action–Reaction Pairs

In applying Newton's third law, remember that an action and its reaction force always act on *different* objects. Two external forces acting on the same object, even if they are equal in magnitude and opposite in direction, *can't* be an action–reaction pair.

Figure 4.9 Newton's third law.
(a) The force exerted by the hammer on the nail is equal in magnitude and opposite in direction to the force exerted by the nail on the hammer. (b) The force $\vec{\mathbf{F}}_{12}$ exerted by object 1 on object 2 is equal in magnitude and opposite in direction to the force $\vec{\mathbf{F}}_{21}$ exerted by object 2 on object 1.

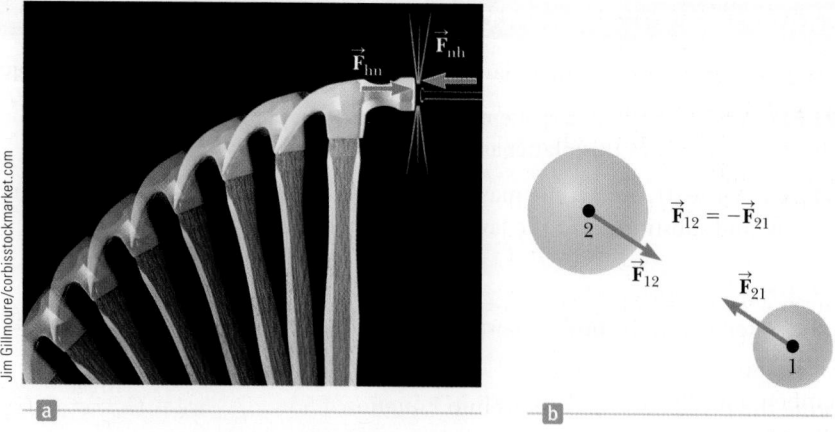

as the action force $\vec{\mathbf{F}}_g$ accelerates the projectile towards Earth. Because Earth has such a large mass, however, its acceleration due to this reaction force is negligibly small.

Newton's third law constantly affects our activities in everyday life. Without it, no locomotion of any kind would be possible, whether on foot, on a bicycle, or in a motorized vehicle. When walking, for example, we exert a frictional force against the ground. The reaction force of the ground against our foot propels us forward. In the same way, the tires on a bicycle exert a frictional force against the ground, and the reaction of the ground pushes the bicycle forward. As we'll see shortly, friction plays a large role in such reaction forces.

APPLICATION

Helicopter Flight

For another example of Newton's third law, consider the helicopter. Most helicopters have a large set of blades rotating in a horizontal plane above the body of the vehicle and another, smaller set rotating in a vertical plane at the back. Other helicopters have two large sets of blades above the body rotating in opposite directions. Why do helicopters always have two sets of blades? In the first type of helicopter, the engine applies a force to the blades, causing them to change their rotational motion. According to Newton's third law, however, the blades must exert a force on the engine of equal magnitude and in the opposite direction. This force would cause the body of the helicopter to rotate in the direction opposite the blades. A rotating helicopter would be impossible to control, so a second set of blades is used. The small blades in the back provide a force opposite to that tending to rotate the body of the helicopter, keeping the body oriented in a stable position. In helicopters with two sets of large counterrotating blades, engines apply forces in opposite directions, so there is no net force rotating the helicopter.

Tip 4.5 Equal and Opposite but Not a Reaction Force

A common error in Figure 4.10b is to consider the normal force on the object to be the reaction force to the gravity force, because in this case these two forces are equal in magnitude and opposite in direction. That is impossible, however, because they act on the same object!

As mentioned earlier, Earth exerts a gravitational force $\vec{\mathbf{F}}_g$ on any object. If the object is a monitor at rest on a table, as in Figure 4.10a, the reaction force to $\vec{\mathbf{F}}_g$ is the gravitational force the monitor exerts on the Earth, $\vec{\mathbf{F}}_g{}'$. The monitor doesn't accelerate downward because it's held up by the table. The table therefore exerts

Figure 4.10 When a monitor is sitting on a table, the forces acting on the monitor are the normal force $\vec{\mathbf{n}}$ exerted by the table and the force of gravity, $\vec{\mathbf{F}}_g$, as illustrated in (b). The reaction to $\vec{\mathbf{n}}$ is the force exerted by the monitor on the table, $\vec{\mathbf{n}}'$. The reaction to $\vec{\mathbf{F}}_g$ is the force exerted by the monitor on Earth, $\vec{\mathbf{F}}_g{}'$.

an upward force $\vec{\mathbf{n}}$, called the **normal force,** on the monitor. (*Normal,* a technical term from mathematics, means "perpendicular" in this context.) The normal force is an elastic force arising from the cohesion of matter and is electromagnetic in origin. It balances the gravitational force acting on the monitor, preventing the monitor from falling through the table, and can have any value needed, up to the point of breaking the table. The reaction to $\vec{\mathbf{n}}$ is the force exerted by the monitor on the table, $\vec{\mathbf{n}}'$. Therefore,

$$\vec{\mathbf{F}}_g = -\vec{\mathbf{F}}_g' \qquad \text{and} \qquad \vec{\mathbf{n}} = -\vec{\mathbf{n}}'$$

The forces $\vec{\mathbf{n}}$ and $\vec{\mathbf{n}}'$ both have the same magnitude as $\vec{\mathbf{F}}_g$. Note that the forces acting on the monitor are $\vec{\mathbf{F}}_g$ and $\vec{\mathbf{n}}$, as shown in Figure 4.10b. The two reaction forces, $\vec{\mathbf{F}}_g'$ and $\vec{\mathbf{n}}'$, are exerted by the monitor on objects other than the monitor. Remember that the two forces in an action–reaction pair always act on two different objects.

Because the monitor is not accelerating in any direction ($\vec{\mathbf{a}} = 0$), it follows from Newton's second law that $m\vec{\mathbf{a}} = 0 = \vec{\mathbf{F}}_g + \vec{\mathbf{n}}$. However, $F_g = -mg$, so $n = mg$, a useful result.

■ Quick Quiz

4.4 A small sports car collides head-on with a massive truck. The greater impact force (in magnitude) acts on (a) the car, (b) the truck, (c) neither, the force is the same on both. Which vehicle undergoes the greater magnitude acceleration? (d) the car, (e) the truck, (f) the accelerations are the same.

APPLICATION

Colliding Vehicles

■ **EXAMPLE 4.5**   Action–Reaction and the Ice Skaters

GOAL Illustrate Newton's third law of motion.

PROBLEM A man of mass $M = 75.0$ kg and woman of mass $m = 55.0$ kg stand facing each other on an ice rink, both wearing ice skates. The woman pushes the man with a horizontal force of $F = 85.0$ N in the positive x-direction. Assume the ice is frictionless. **(a)** What is the man's acceleration? **(b)** What is the reaction force acting on the woman? **(c)** Calculate the woman's acceleration.

STRATEGY Parts (a) and (c) are simple applications of the second law. An application of the third law solves part (b).

SOLUTION

(a) What is the man's acceleration?

Write the second law for the man:

$$Ma_M = F$$

Solve for the man's acceleration and substitute values:

$$a_M = \frac{F}{M} = \frac{85.0\ \text{N}}{75.0\ \text{kg}} = \boxed{1.13\ \text{m/s}^2}$$

(b) What is the reaction force acting on the woman?

Apply Newton's third law of motion, finding that the reaction force R acting on the woman has the same magnitude and opposite direction:

$$R = -F = \boxed{-85.0\ \text{N}}$$

(c) Calculate the woman's acceleration.

Write Newton's second law for the woman:

$$ma_W = R = -F$$

Solve for the woman's acceleration and substitute values:

$$a_W = \frac{-F}{m} = \frac{-85.0\ \text{N}}{55.0\ \text{kg}} = \boxed{-1.55\ \text{m/s}^2}$$

REMARKS Notice that the forces are equal and opposite each other, but the accelerations are not because the two masses differ from each other.

QUESTION 4.5 Name two other forces acting on the man and the two reaction forces that are paired with them.

(*Continued*)

EXERCISE 4.5 A space-walking astronaut of total mass 148 kg exerts a force of 265 N on a free-floating satellite of mass 635 kg, pushing it in the positive x-direction. (a) What is the reaction force exerted by the satellite on the astronaut? Calculate the accelerations of (b) the astronaut, and (c) the satellite.

ANSWERS (a) −265 N (b) −1.79 m/s² (c) 0.417 m/s²

Figure 4.11 Newton's second law applied to a rope gives $T - T' = ma$. However, if $m = 0$, then $T = T'$. Thus, the tension in a massless rope is the same at all points in the rope.

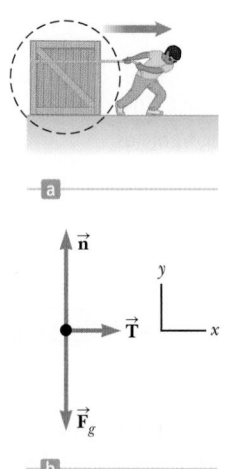

Figure 4.12 (a) A crate being pulled to the right on a frictionless surface. (b) The free-body diagram that represents the forces exerted on the crate.

Tip 4.6 Free-Body Diagrams

The *most important step* in solving a problem by means of Newton's second law is to draw the correct free-body diagram. Include only those forces that act directly on the object of interest.

Tip 4.7 A Particle in Equilibrium

A zero net force on a particle does *not* mean that the particle isn't moving. It means that the particle isn't *accelerating*. If the particle has a nonzero initial velocity and is acted upon by a zero net force, it continues to move with the same velocity.

4.5 Applications of Newton's Laws

This section applies Newton's laws to objects moving under the influence of constant external forces. We assume that objects behave as particles, so we need not consider the possibility of rotational motion. We also neglect any friction effects and the masses of any ropes or strings involved. With these approximations, the magnitude of the force exerted along a rope, called the **tension,** is the same at all points in the rope. This is illustrated by the rope in Figure 4.11, showing the forces $\vec{\mathbf{T}}$ and $\vec{\mathbf{T}}'$ acting on it. If the rope has mass m, then Newton's second law applied to the rope gives $T - T' = ma$. If the mass m is taken to be negligible, however, as in the upcoming examples, then $T = T'$.

When we apply Newton's law to an object, we are interested only in those forces which act *on the object*. For example, in Figure 4.10b, the only external forces acting on the monitor are $\vec{\mathbf{n}}$ and $\vec{\mathbf{F}}_g$. The reactions to these forces, $\vec{\mathbf{n}}'$ and $\vec{\mathbf{F}}_g'$, act on the table and on Earth, respectively, and don't appear in Newton's second law applied to the monitor.

Consider a crate being pulled to the right on a frictionless, horizontal surface, as in Figure 4.12a. Suppose you wish to find the acceleration of the crate and the force the surface exerts on it. The horizontal force exerted on the crate acts through the rope. The force that the rope exerts on the crate is denoted by $\vec{\mathbf{T}}$ (because it's a tension force). The magnitude of $\vec{\mathbf{T}}$ is equal to the tension in the rope. What we mean by the words "tension in the rope" is just the force read by a spring scale when the rope in question has been cut and the scale inserted between the cut ends. A dashed circle is drawn around the crate in Figure 4.12a to emphasize the importance of isolating the crate from its surroundings.

Because we are interested only in the motion of the crate, we must be able to identify all forces acting on it. These forces are illustrated in Figure 4.12b. In addition to displaying the force $\vec{\mathbf{T}}$, the force diagram for the crate includes the force of gravity $\vec{\mathbf{F}}_g$ exerted by Earth and the normal force $\vec{\mathbf{n}}$ exerted by the floor. Such a force diagram is called a **free-body diagram** because the environment is replaced by a series of forces on an otherwise free body. The construction of a correct free-body diagram is an essential step in applying Newton's laws. An incorrect diagram will most likely lead to incorrect answers!

The *reactions* to the forces we have listed—namely, the force exerted by the rope on the hand doing the pulling, the force exerted by the crate on Earth, and the force exerted by the crate on the floor—aren't included in the free-body diagram because they act on other objects and not on the crate. Consequently, they don't directly influence the crate's motion. Only forces acting directly on the crate are included.

Now let's apply Newton's second law to the crate. First we choose an appropriate coordinate system. In this case it's convenient to use the one shown in Figure 4.12b, with the x-axis horizontal and the y-axis vertical. We can apply Newton's second law in the x-direction, y-direction, or both, depending on what we're asked to find in a problem. Newton's second law applied to the crate in the x- and y-directions yields the following two equations:

$$ma_x = T \qquad ma_y = n - mg = 0$$

From these equations, we find that the acceleration in the x-direction is constant, given by $a_x = T/m$, and that the normal force is given by $n = mg$. Because the acceleration is constant, the equations of kinematics can be applied to obtain further information about the velocity and displacement of the object.

■ PROBLEM-SOLVING STRATEGY

Newton's Second Law

Problems involving Newton's second law can be very complex. The following protocol breaks the solution process down into smaller, intermediate goals:

1. **Read** the problem carefully at least once.
2. **Draw** a picture of the system, identify the object of primary interest, and indicate forces with arrows.
3. **Label** each force in the picture in a way that will bring to mind what physical quantity the label stands for (e.g., T for tension).
4. **Draw** a free-body diagram of the object of interest, based on the labeled picture. If additional objects are involved, draw separate free-body diagrams for them. Choose convenient coordinates for each object.
5. **Apply Newton's second law.** The x- and y-components of Newton's second law should be taken from the vector equation and written individually. This usually results in two equations and two unknowns.
6. **Solve** for the desired unknown quantity, and substitute the numbers.

In the special case of equilibrium, the foregoing process is simplified because the acceleration is zero.

Objects in Equilibrium

Objects that are either at rest or moving with constant velocity are said to be in equilibrium. Because $\vec{\mathbf{a}} = 0$, Newton's second law applied to an object in equilibrium gives

$$\sum \vec{\mathbf{F}} = 0 \qquad \textbf{[4.9]}$$

This statement signifies that the *vector* sum of all the forces (the net force) acting on an object in equilibrium is zero. Equation 4.9 is equivalent to the set of component equations given by

$$\sum F_x = 0 \quad \text{and} \quad \sum F_y = 0 \qquad \textbf{[4.10]}$$

We won't consider three-dimensional problems in this book, but the extension of Equation 4.10 to a three-dimensional problem can be made by adding a third equation: $\sum F_z = 0$.

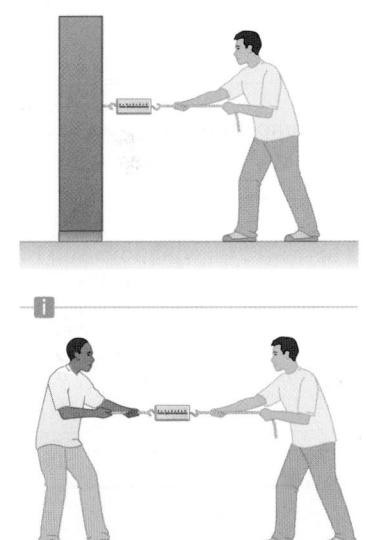

Figure 4.13 (Quick Quiz 4.5) (i) A person pulls with a force of magnitude F on a spring scale attached to a wall. (ii) Two people pull with forces of magnitude F in opposite directions on a spring scale attached between two ropes.

■ Quick Quiz

4.5 Consider the two situations shown in Figure 4.13, in which there is no acceleration. In both cases the men pull with a force of magnitude F. Is the reading on the scale in part (i) of the figure (a) greater than, (b) less than, or (c) equal to the reading in part (ii)?

■ EXAMPLE 4.6 | A Traffic Light at Rest

GOAL Use the second law in an equilibrium problem requiring two free-body diagrams.

PROBLEM A traffic light weighing 1.00×10^2 N hangs from a vertical cable tied to two other cables that are fastened to a support, as in Figure 4.14a. The upper cables make angles of 37.0° and 53.0° with the horizontal. Find the tension in each of the three cables.

STRATEGY There are three unknowns, so we need to generate three equations relating them, which can then be solved. One equation can be obtained by applying Newton's second law to the traffic light, which has forces in the y-direction only. Two more equations can be obtained by applying the second law to the knot joining the cables—one equation from the x-component and one equation from the y-component.

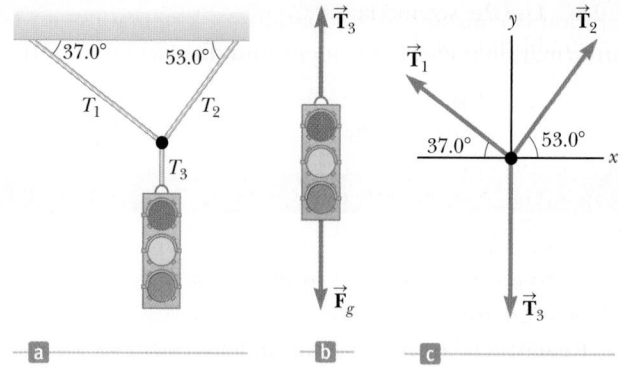

Figure 4.14 (Example 4.6) (a) A traffic light suspended by cables. (b) The forces acting on the traffic light. (c) A free-body diagram for the knot joining the cables.

SOLUTION

Find T_3 from Figure 4.14b, using the condition of equilibrium:

$$\Sigma F_y = 0 \quad \rightarrow \quad T_3 - F_g = 0$$
$$T_3 = F_g = 1.00 \times 10^2 \text{ N}$$

Using Figure 4.14c, resolve all three tension forces into components and construct a table for convenience:

Force	x-Component	y-Component
$\vec{T}_1$	$-T_1 \cos 37.0°$	$T_1 \sin 37.0°$
$\vec{T}_2$	$T_2 \cos 53.0°$	$T_2 \sin 53.0°$
$\vec{T}_3$	0	-1.00×10^2 N

Apply the conditions for equilibrium to the knot, using the components in the table:

(1) $\Sigma F_x = -T_1 \cos 37.0° + T_2 \cos 53.0° = 0$

(2) $\Sigma F_y = T_1 \sin 37.0° + T_2 \sin 53.0° - 1.00 \times 10^2 \text{ N} = 0$

There are two equations and two remaining unknowns. Solve Equation (1) for T_2:

$$T_2 = T_1 \left(\frac{\cos 37.0°}{\cos 53.0°} \right) = T_1 \left(\frac{0.799}{0.602} \right) = 1.33 T_1$$

Substitute the result for T_2 into Equation (2):

$$T_1 \sin 37.0° + (1.33T_1)(\sin 53.0°) - 1.00 \times 10^2 \text{ N} = 0$$
$$T_1 = \boxed{60.1 \text{ N}}$$
$$T_2 = 1.33T_1 = 1.33(60.1 \text{ N}) = \boxed{79.9 \text{ N}}$$

REMARKS It's very easy to make sign errors in this kind of problem. One way to avoid them is to always measure the angle of a vector from the positive x-direction. The trigonometric functions of the angle will then automatically give the correct signs for the components. For example, $\vec{T}_1$ makes an angle of $180° - 37° = 143°$ with respect to the positive x-axis, and its x-component, $T_1 \cos 143°$, is negative, as it should be.

QUESTION 4.6 How would the answers change if a second traffic light were attached beneath the first?

EXERCISE 4.6 Suppose the traffic light is hung so that the tensions T_1 and T_2 are both equal to 80.0 N. Find the new angles they make with respect to the x-axis. (By symmetry, these angles will be the same.)

ANSWER Both angles are 38.7°.

■ EXAMPLE 4.7 | **Sled on a Frictionless Hill**

GOAL Use the second law and the normal force in an equilibrium problem.

PROBLEM A sled is tied to a tree on a frictionless, snow-covered hill, as shown in Figure 4.15a. If the sled weighs 77.0 N, find the magnitude of the tension force $\vec{T}$ exerted by the rope on the sled and that of the normal force $\vec{n}$ exerted by the hill on the sled.

STRATEGY When an object is on a slope, it's convenient to use tilted coordinates, as in Figure 4.15b, so that the normal force $\vec{n}$ is in the y-direction and the tension force $\vec{T}$ is in the x-direction. In the absence of friction, the hill exerts no force on the sled in the x-direction. Because the sled is at rest, the conditions for equilibrium, $\Sigma F_x = 0$ and $\Sigma F_y = 0$, apply, giving two equations for the two unknowns—the tension and the normal force.

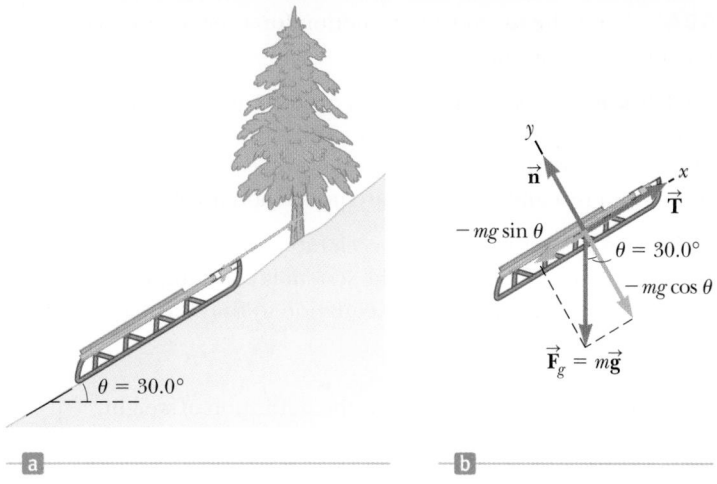

Figure 4.15 (Example 4.7) (a) A sled tied to a tree on a frictionless hill. (b) A diagram of forces acting on the sled.

SOLUTION

Apply Newton's second law to the sled, with $\vec{a} = 0$:

$$\sum \vec{F} = \vec{T} + \vec{n} + \vec{F}_g = 0$$

Extract the x-component from this equation to find T. The x-component of the normal force is zero, and the sled's weight is given by $mg = 77.0$ N.

$$\sum F_x = T + 0 - mg\sin\theta = T - (77.0\text{ N})(\sin 30.0°) = 0$$
$$T = \boxed{38.5\text{ N}}$$

Write the y-component of Newton's second law. The y-component of the tension is zero, so this equation will give the normal force.

$$\sum F_y = 0 + n - mg\cos\theta = n - (77.0\text{ N})(\cos 30.0°) = 0$$
$$n = \boxed{66.7\text{ N}}$$

REMARKS Unlike its value on a horizontal surface, n is less than the weight of the sled when the sled is on the slope. This is because only part of the force of gravity (the x-component) is acting to pull the sled down the slope. The y-component of the force of gravity balances the normal force.

QUESTION 4.7 Consider the same scenario on a hill with a steeper slope. Would the magnitude of the tension in the rope get larger, smaller, or remain the same as before? How would the normal force be affected?

EXERCISE 4.7 Suppose a child of weight w climbs onto the sled. If the tension force is measured to be 60.0 N, find the weight of the child and the magnitude of the normal force acting on the sled.

ANSWERS $w = 43.0$ N, $n = 104$ N

■ Quick Quiz

4.6 For the woman being pulled forward on the toboggan in Figure 4.16, is the magnitude of the normal force exerted by the ground on the toboggan (a) equal to the total weight of the woman plus the toboggan, (b) greater than the total weight, (c) less than the total weight, or (d) possibly greater than or less than the total weight, depending on the size of the weight relative to the tension in the rope?

Accelerating Objects and Newton's Second Law

When a net force acts on an object, the object accelerates, and we use Newton's second law to analyze the motion.

Figure 4.16 (Quick Quiz 4.6)

■ EXAMPLE 4.8 | Moving a Crate

GOAL Apply the second law of motion for a system not in equilibrium, together with a kinematics equation.

PROBLEM The combined weight of the crate and dolly in Figure 4.17 is 3.00×10^2 N. If the man pulls on the rope with a constant force of 20.0 N, what is the acceleration of the system (crate plus dolly), and how far will it move in 2.00 s? Assume the system starts from rest and that there are no friction forces opposing the motion.

STRATEGY We can find the acceleration of the system from Newton's second law. Because the force exerted on the system is constant, its acceleration is constant. Therefore, we can apply a kinematics equation to find the distance traveled in 2.00 s.

Figure 4.17 (Example 4.8)

SOLUTION

Find the mass of the system from the definition of weight, $w = mg$:

$$m = \frac{w}{g} = \frac{3.00 \times 10^2 \text{ N}}{9.80 \text{ m/s}^2} = 30.6 \text{ kg}$$

Find the acceleration of the system from the second law:

$$a_x = \frac{F_x}{m} = \frac{20.0 \text{ N}}{30.6 \text{ kg}} = \boxed{0.654 \text{ m/s}^2}$$

Use kinematics to find the distance moved in 2.00 s, with $v_0 = 0$:

$$\Delta x = \tfrac{1}{2} a_x t^2 = \tfrac{1}{2} (0.654 \text{ m/s}^2)(2.00 \text{ s})^2 = \boxed{1.31 \text{ m}}$$

REMARKS Note that the constant applied force of 20.0 N is assumed to act on the system at all times during its motion. If the force were removed at some instant, the system would continue to move with constant velocity and hence zero acceleration. The rollers have an effect that was neglected, here.

QUESTION 4.8 What effect does doubling the weight have on the acceleration and the displacement?

EXERCISE 4.8 A man pulls a 50.0-kg box horizontally from rest while exerting a constant horizontal force, displacing the box 3.00 m in 2.00 s. Find the force the man exerts on the box. (Ignore friction.)

ANSWER 75.0 N

■ EXAMPLE 4.9 | The Runaway Car

GOAL Apply the second law and kinematic equations to a problem involving an object moving on an incline.

PROBLEM (a) A car of mass m is on an icy driveway inclined at an angle $\theta = 20.0°$, as in Figure 4.18a. Determine the acceleration of the car, assuming the incline is frictionless. (b) If the length of the driveway is 25.0 m and the car starts from rest at the top, how long does it take to travel to the bottom? (c) What is the car's speed at the bottom?

STRATEGY Choose tilted coordinates as in Figure 4.18b so that the normal force $\vec{\mathbf{n}}$ is in the positive y-direction, perpendicular to the driveway, and the positive x-axis is down the slope. The force of gravity $\vec{\mathbf{F}}_g$ then has an x-component, $mg \sin \theta$, and a y-component, $-mg \cos \theta$. The components of Newton's second law form a system of two equations and two unknowns for the acceleration down the slope, a_x, and the normal force. Parts (b) and (c) can be solved with the kinematics equations.

Figure 4.18 (Example 4.9)

SOLUTION

(a) Find the acceleration of the car.

Apply Newton's second law to the car:

$$m\vec{a} = \sum \vec{F} = \vec{F}_g + \vec{n}$$

Extract the *x*- and *y*-components from the second law:

(1) $ma_x = \sum F_x = mg\sin\theta$

(2) $0 = \sum F_y = -mg\cos\theta + n$

Divide Equation (1) by *m* and substitute the given values:

$a_x = g\sin\theta = (9.80 \text{ m/s}^2)\sin 20.0° = \boxed{3.35 \text{ m/s}^2}$

(b) Find the time taken for the car to reach the bottom.

Use Equation 3.11b for displacement, with $v_{0x} = 0$:

$\Delta x = \frac{1}{2}a_x t^2 \rightarrow \frac{1}{2}(3.35 \text{ m/s}^2)t^2 = 25.0 \text{ m}$

$t = \boxed{3.86 \text{ s}}$

(c) Find the speed of the car at the bottom of the driveway.

Use Equation 3.11a for velocity, again with $v_{0x} = 0$:

$v_x = a_x t = (3.35 \text{ m/s}^2)(3.86 \text{ s}) = \boxed{12.9 \text{ m/s}}$

REMARKS Notice that the final answer for the acceleration depends only on *g* and the angle θ, not the mass. Equation (2), which gives the normal force, isn't useful here, but is essential when friction plays a role.

QUESTION 4.9 If the car is parked on a more gentle slope, how will the time required for it to slide to the bottom of the hill be affected? Explain.

EXERCISE 4.9 **(a)** Suppose a hockey puck slides down a frictionless ramp with an acceleration of 5.00 m/s². What angle does the ramp make with respect to the horizontal? **(b)** If the ramp has a length of 6.00 m, how long does it take the puck to reach the bottom? **(c)** Now suppose the mass of the puck is doubled. What's the puck's new acceleration down the ramp?

ANSWER **(a)** 30.7° **(b)** 1.55 s **(c)** unchanged, 5.00 m/s²

■ EXAMPLE 4.10 | Weighing a Fish in an Elevator

GOAL Explore the effect of acceleration on the apparent weight of an object.

PROBLEM A woman weighs a fish with a spring scale attached to the ceiling of an elevator, as shown in Figures 4.19a and 4.19b. While the elevator is at rest, she measures a weight of 40.0 N. **(a)** What weight does the scale read if the elevator accelerates upward at 2.00 m/s²? **(b)** What does the scale read if the elevator accelerates downward at 2.00 m/s², as in Figure 4.19b? **(c)** If the elevator cable breaks, what does the scale read?

STRATEGY Write down Newton's second law for the fish, including the force $\vec{T}$ exerted by the spring scale and the force of gravity, $m\vec{g}$. The scale doesn't measure the true weight, it measures the force T that it exerts on the fish, so in each case solve for this force, which is the apparent weight as measured by the scale.

SOLUTION

(a) Find the scale reading as the elevator accelerates upward, as in Figure 4.19a.

When the elevator accelerates upward, the spring scale reads a value greater than the weight of the fish.

When the elevator accelerates downward, the spring scale reads a value less than the weight of the fish.

Figure 4.19 (Example 4.10)

(Continued)

Apply Newton's second law to the fish, taking upward as the positive direction:

$$ma = \sum F = T - mg$$

Solve for T:

$$T = ma + mg = m(a + g)$$

Find the mass of the fish from its weight of 40.0 N:

$$m = \frac{w}{g} = \frac{40.0 \text{ N}}{9.80 \text{ m/s}^2} = 4.08 \text{ kg}$$

Compute the value of T, substituting $a = +2.00 \text{ m/s}^2$:

$$T = m(a + g) = (4.08 \text{ kg})(2.00 \text{ m/s}^2 + 9.80 \text{ m/s}^2)$$
$$= \boxed{48.1 \text{ N}}$$

(b) Find the scale reading as the elevator accelerates downward, as in Figure 4.19b.

The analysis is the same, the only change being the acceleration, which is now negative: $a = -2.00 \text{ m/s}^2$.

$$T = m(a + g) = (4.08 \text{ kg})(-2.00 \text{ m/s}^2 + 9.80 \text{ m/s}^2)$$
$$= \boxed{31.8 \text{ N}}$$

(c) Find the scale reading after the elevator cable breaks.

Now $a = -9.80 \text{ m/s}^2$, the acceleration due to gravity:

$$T = m(a + g) = (4.08 \text{ kg})(-9.80 \text{ m/s}^2 + 9.80 \text{ m/s}^2)$$
$$= \boxed{0 \text{ N}}$$

REMARKS Notice how important it is to have correct signs in this problem! Accelerations can increase or decrease the apparent weight of an object. Astronauts experience very large changes in apparent weight, from several times normal weight during ascent to weightlessness in free fall.

QUESTION 4.10 Starting from rest, an elevator accelerates upward, reaching and maintaining a constant velocity thereafter until it reaches the desired floor, when it begins to slow down. Describe the scale reading during this time.

EXERCISE 4.10 Find the initial acceleration of a rocket if the astronauts on board experience eight times their normal weight during an initial vertical ascent. (*Hint:* In this exercise, the scale force is replaced by the normal force.)

ANSWER 68.6 m/s^2

■ EXAMPLE 4.11 | Atwood's Machine

GOAL Use the second law to solve a simple two-body problem symbolically.

PROBLEM Two objects of mass m_1 and m_2, with $m_2 > m_1$, are connected by a light, inextensible cord and hung over a frictionless pulley, as in Active Figure 4.20a. Both cord and pulley have negligible mass. Find the magnitude of the acceleration of the system and the tension in the cord.

STRATEGY The heavier mass, m_2, accelerates downward, in the negative y-direction. Because the cord can't be stretched, the accelerations of the two masses are equal in magnitude, but *opposite* in direction, so that a_1 is positive and a_2 is negative, and $a_2 = -a_1$. Each mass is acted on by a force of tension $\vec{T}$ in the upward direction and a force of gravity in the downward direction. Active Figure 4.20b shows free-body diagrams for the two masses. Newton's second law for each mass, together with the equation relating the accelerations, constitutes a set of three equations for the three unknowns—a_1, a_2, and T.

Active Figure 4.20
(Example 4.11) Atwood's machine. (a) Two hanging objects connected by a light string that passes over a frictionless pulley. (b) Free-body diagrams for the objects.

SOLUTION

Apply the second law to each of the two objects individually:

(1) $m_1 a_1 = T - m_1 g$ **(2)** $m_2 a_2 = T - m_2 g$

Substitute $a_2 = -a_1$ into Equation (2) and multiply both sides by -1:

$$\textbf{(3)} \quad m_2 a_1 = -T + m_2 g$$

Add Equations (1) and (3), and solve for a_1:

$$(m_1 + m_2)a_1 = m_2 g - m_1 g$$

$$a_1 = \left(\frac{m_2 - m_1}{m_1 + m_2}\right)g$$

Substitute this result into Equation (1) to find T:

$$T = \left(\frac{2m_1 m_2}{m_1 + m_2}\right)g$$

REMARKS The acceleration of the second object is the same as that of the first, but negative. When m_2 gets very large compared with m_1, the acceleration of the system approaches g, as expected, because m_2 is falling nearly freely under the influence of gravity. Indeed, m_2 is only slightly restrained by the much lighter m_1.

QUESTION 4.11 How could this simple machine be used to raise objects too heavy for a person to lift?

EXERCISE 4.11 Suppose in the same Atwood setup another string is attached to the bottom of m_1 and a constant force f is applied, retarding the upward motion of m_1. If $m_1 = 5.00$ kg and $m_2 = 10.00$ kg, what value of f will reduce the acceleration of the system by 50%?

ANSWER 24.5 N

4.6 Forces of Friction

An object moving on a surface or through a viscous medium such as air or water encounters resistance as it interacts with its surroundings. This resistance is called **friction.** Forces of friction are essential in our everyday lives. Friction makes it possible to grip and hold things, drive a car, walk, and run. Even standing in one spot would be impossible without friction, as the slightest shift would instantly cause you to slip and fall.

Imagine that you've filled a plastic trash can with yard clippings and want to drag the can across the surface of your concrete patio. If you apply an external horizontal force $\vec{\mathbf{F}}$ to the can, acting to the right as shown in Active Figure 4.21a (page 106), the can remains stationary if $\vec{\mathbf{F}}$ is small. The force that counteracts $\vec{\mathbf{F}}$ and keeps the can from moving acts to the left, opposite the direction of $\vec{\mathbf{F}}$, and is called the **force of static friction, $\vec{\mathbf{f}}_s$.** As long as the can isn't moving, $\vec{\mathbf{f}}_s = -\vec{\mathbf{F}}$. If $\vec{\mathbf{F}}$ is increased, $\vec{\mathbf{f}}_s$ also increases. Likewise, if $\vec{\mathbf{F}}$ decreases, $\vec{\mathbf{f}}_s$ decreases. Experiments show that the friction force arises from the nature of the two surfaces: Because of their roughness, contact is made at only a few points.

If we increase the magnitude of $\vec{\mathbf{F}}$, as in Active Figure 4.21b, the trash can eventually slips. When the can is on the verge of slipping, f_s is a maximum, as shown in Figure 4.21c. When F exceeds $f_{s,max}$, the can accelerates to the right. When the can is in motion, the friction force is less than $f_{s,max}$ (Fig. 4.21c). We call the friction force for an object in motion the **force of kinetic friction, $\vec{\mathbf{f}}_k$.** The net force $F - f_k$ in the x-direction produces an acceleration to the right, according to Newton's second law. If $F = f_k$, the acceleration is zero, and the can moves to the right with constant speed. If the applied force is removed, the friction force acting to the left provides an acceleration of the can in the $-x$-direction and eventually brings it to rest, again consistent with Newton's second law.

Experimentally, to a good approximation, both $f_{s,max}$ and f_k for an object on a surface are proportional to the normal force exerted by the surface on the object. The experimental observations can be summarized as follows:

Active Figure 4.21

(a) and (b) When pulling on a trash can, the direction of the force of friction ($\vec{\mathbf{f}}_s$ in part (a) and $\vec{\mathbf{f}}_k$ in part (b)) between the can and a rough surface is opposite the direction of the applied force $\vec{\mathbf{F}}$. (c) A graph of the magnitude of the friction force versus applied force. Note that $f_{s,\text{max}} > f_k$.

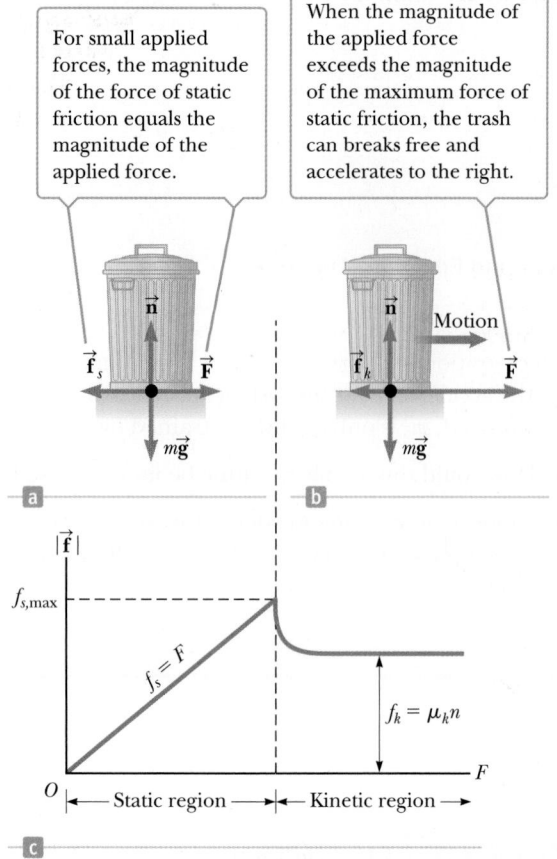

For small applied forces, the magnitude of the force of static friction equals the magnitude of the applied force.

When the magnitude of the applied force exceeds the magnitude of the maximum force of static friction, the trash can breaks free and accelerates to the right.

- The magnitude of the force of static friction between any two surfaces in contact can have the values

$$f_s \le \mu_s n \qquad [4.11]$$

where the dimensionless constant μ_s is called the **coefficient of static friction** and n is the magnitude of the normal force exerted by one surface on the other. Equation 4.11 also holds for $f_s = f_{s,\text{max}} \equiv \mu_s n$ when an object is on the averge of slipping. This situation is called *impending motion*. The strict inequality holds when the component of the applied force parallel to the surfaces is less than $\mu_s n$.

- The magnitude of the force of kinetic friction acting between two surfaces is

$$f_k = \mu_k n \qquad [4.12]$$

where μ_k is the **coefficient of kinetic friction.**

- The values of μ_k and μ_s depend on the nature of the surfaces, but μ_k is generally less than μ_s. Table 4.2 lists some reported values.

- The direction of the friction force exerted by a surface on an object is opposite the actual motion (kinetic friction) or the impending motion (static friction) of the object relative to the surface.

- The coefficients of friction are nearly independent of the area of contact between the surfaces.

Although the coefficient of kinetic friction varies with the speed of the object, we will neglect any such variations. The approximate nature of Equations 4.11 and 4.12 is easily demonstrated by trying to get an object to slide down an incline at constant acceleration. Especially at low speeds, the motion is likely to be characterized by alternate stick and slip episodes.

Tip 4.8 Use the Equals Sign in Limited Situations

In Equation 4.11, the equals sign is used *only* when the surfaces are just about to break free and begin sliding. Don't fall into the common trap of using $f_s = \mu_s n$ in *any* static situation.

Table 4.2 Coefficients of Friction[a]

	μ_s	μ_k
Steel on steel	0.74	0.57
Aluminum on steel	0.61	0.47
Copper on steel	0.53	0.36
Rubber on concrete	1.0	0.8
Wood on wood	0.25–0.5	0.2
Glass on glass	0.94	0.4
Waxed wood on wet snow	0.14	0.1
Waxed wood on dry snow	—	0.04
Metal on metal (lubricated)	0.15	0.06
Ice on ice	0.1	0.03
Teflon on Teflon	0.04	0.04
Synovial joints in humans	0.01	0.003

[a]All values are approximate.

■ Quick Quiz

4.7 If you press a book flat against a vertical wall with your hand, in what direction is the friction force exerted by the wall on the book? (a) downward (b) upward (c) out from the wall (d) into the wall

4.8 A crate is sitting in the center of a flatbed truck. As the truck accelerates to the east, the crate moves with it, not sliding on the bed of the truck. In what direction is the friction force exerted by the bed of the truck on the crate? (a) To the west. (b) To the east. (c) There is no friction force, because the crate isn't sliding.

4.9 Suppose your friend is sitting on a sled and asks you to move her across a flat, horizontal field. You have a choice of (a) pushing her from behind by applying a force downward on her shoulders at 30° below the horizontal (Fig. 4.22a) or (b) attaching a rope to the front of the sled and pulling with a force at 30° above the horizontal (Fig 4.22b). Which option would be easier and why?

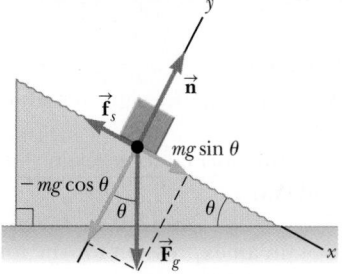

Figure 4.22 (Quick Quiz 4.9)

■ EXAMPLE 4.12 │ A Block on a Ramp

GOAL Apply the concept of static friction to an object resting on an incline.

PROBLEM Suppose a block with a mass of 2.50 kg is resting on a ramp. If the coefficient of static friction between the block and ramp is 0.350, what maximum angle can the ramp make with the horizontal before the block starts to slip down?

STRATEGY This is an application of Newton's second law involving an object in equilibrium. Choose tilted coordinates, as in Active Figure 4.23. Use the fact that the block is just about to slip when the force of static friction takes its maximum value, $f_s = \mu_s n$.

Active Figure 4.23 (Example 4.12)

SOLUTION

Write Newton's laws for a static system in component form. The gravity force has two components, just as in Examples 4.7 and 4.9.

(1) $\sum F_x = mg\sin\theta - \mu_s n = 0$

(2) $\sum F_y = n - mg\cos\theta = 0$

Rearrange Equation (2) to get an expression for the normal force n:

$n = mg\cos\theta$

(Continued)

Substitute the expression for n into Equation (1) and solve for $\tan \theta$:

$$\sum F_x = mg \sin \theta - \mu_s mg \cos \theta = 0 \quad \rightarrow \quad \tan \theta = \mu_s$$

Apply the inverse tangent function to get the answer:

$$\tan \theta = 0.350 \quad \rightarrow \quad \theta = \tan^{-1}(0.350) = \boxed{19.3°}$$

. . . .

REMARKS It's interesting that the final result depends only on the coefficient of static friction. Notice also how similar Equations (1) and (2) are to the equations developed in Examples 4.7 and 4.9. Recognizing such patterns is key to solving problems successfully.

QUESTION 4.12 How would a larger static friction coefficient affect the maximum angle?

EXERCISE 4.12 The ramp in Example 4.12 is roughed up and the experiment repeated. **(a)** What is the new coefficient of static friction if the maximum angle turns out to be 30.0°? **(b)** Find the maximum static friction force that acts on the block.

ANSWER **(a)** 0.577 **(b)** 12.3 N

▪ EXAMPLE 4.13 | The Sliding Hockey Puck

GOAL Apply the concept of kinetic friction.

PROBLEM The hockey puck in Figure 4.24, struck by a hockey stick, is given an initial speed of 20.0 m/s on a frozen pond. The puck remains on the ice and slides 1.20×10^2 m, slowing down steadily until it comes to rest. Determine the coefficient of kinetic friction between the puck and the ice.

STRATEGY The puck slows "steadily," which means that the acceleration is constant. Consequently, we can use the kinematic equation $v^2 = v_0^2 + 2a\Delta x$ to find a, the acceleration in the x-direction. The x- and y-components of Newton's second law then give two equations and two unknowns for the coefficient of kinetic friction, μ_k, and the normal force n.

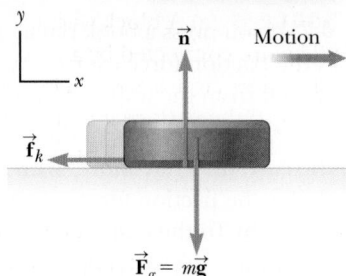

Figure 4.24 (Example 4.13) *After the puck is given an initial velocity to the right, the external forces acting on it are the force of gravity $\vec{\mathbf{F}}_g$, the normal force $\vec{\mathbf{n}}$, and the force of kinetic friction, $\vec{\mathbf{f}}_k$.*

. . . .

SOLUTION

Solve the time-independent kinematic equation for the acceleration a:

$$v^2 = v_0^2 + 2a\Delta x$$
$$a = \frac{v^2 - v_0^2}{2\Delta x}$$

Substitute $v = 0$, $v_0 = 20.0$ m/s, and $\Delta x = 1.20 \times 10^2$ m. Note the negative sign in the answer: $\vec{\mathbf{a}}$ is opposite $\vec{\mathbf{v}}$:

$$a = \frac{0 - (20.0 \text{ m/s})^2}{2(1.20 \times 10^2 \text{ m})} = -1.67 \text{ m/s}^2$$

Find the normal force from the y-component of the second law:

$$\sum F_y = n - F_g = n - mg = 0$$
$$n = mg$$

Obtain an expression for the force of kinetic friction, and substitute it into the x-component of the second law:

$$f_k = \mu_k n = \mu_k mg$$
$$ma = \sum F_x = -f_k = -\mu_k mg$$

Solve for μ_k and substitute values:

$$\mu_k = -\frac{a}{g} = \frac{1.67 \text{ m/s}^2}{9.80 \text{ m/s}^2} = \boxed{0.170}$$

. . . .

REMARKS Notice how the problem breaks down into three parts: kinematics, Newton's second law in the y-direction, and then Newton's law in the x-direction.

QUESTION 4.13 How would the answer be affected if the puck were struck by an astronaut on a patch of ice on Mars, where the acceleration of gravity is $0.35g$, with all other given quantities remaining the same?

EXERCISE 4.13 An experimental rocket plane lands on skids on a dry lake bed. If it's traveling at 80.0 m/s when it touches down, how far does it slide before coming to rest? Assume the coefficient of kinetic friction between the skids and the lake bed is 0.600.

ANSWER 544 m

The System Approach

Two-body problems can often be treated as single objects and solved with a system approach. When the objects are rigidly connected—say, by a string of negligible mass that doesn't stretch—this approach can greatly simplify the analysis. When the two bodies are considered together, one or more of the forces end up becoming forces that are internal to the system, rather than external forces affecting each of the individual bodies. Both approaches will be used in Example 4.14.

■ EXAMPLE 4.14 | Connected Objects

GOAL Use both the general method and the system approach to solve a connected two-body problem involving gravity and friction.

PROBLEM (a) A block with mass $m_1 = 4.00$ kg and a ball with mass $m_2 = 7.00$ kg are connected by a light string that passes over a frictionless pulley, as shown in Figure 4.25a. The coefficient of kinetic friction between the block and the surface is 0.300. Find the acceleration of the two objects and the tension in the string. (b) Check the answer for the acceleration by using the system approach.

STRATEGY Connected objects are handled by applying Newton's second law separately to each object. The force diagrams for the block and the ball are shown in Figure 4.25b, with the $+x$-direction to the right and the $+y$-direction upwards. The magnitude of the acceleration for both objects has the same value, $|a_1| = |a_2| = a$. The block with mass m_1 moves in the positive x-direction, and the ball with mass m_2 moves in the negative y-direction, so $a_1 = -a_2$. Using Newton's second law, we can develop two equations involving the unknowns T and a that can be solved simultaneously. In part (b), treat the two masses as a single object, with the gravity force on the ball increasing the combined object's speed and the friction force on the block retarding it. The tension forces then become internal and don't appear in the second law.

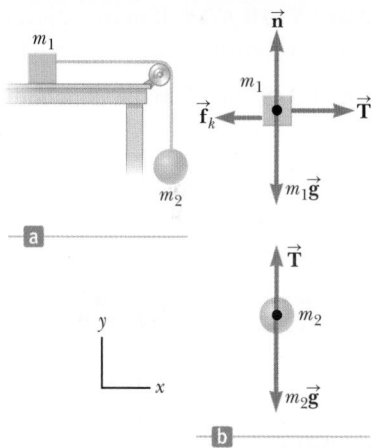

Figure 4.25 (Example 4.14) (a) Two objects connected by a light string that passes over a frictionless pulley. (b) Force diagrams for the objects.

· ·

SOLUTION

(a) Find the acceleration of the objects and the tension in the string.

Write the components of Newton's second law for the block of mass m_1:

$$\sum F_x = T - f_k = m_1 a_1 \quad \sum F_y = n - m_1 g = 0$$

The equation for the y-component gives $n = m_1 g$. Substitute this value for n and $f_k = \mu_k n$ into the equation for the x-component:

$$(1) \quad T - \mu_k m_1 g = m_1 a_1$$

Apply Newton's second law to the ball, recalling that $a_2 = -a_1$:

$$\sum F_y = T - m_2 g = m_2 a_2 = -m_2 a_1$$

$$(2) \quad T - m_2 g = -m_2 a_1$$

Subtract Equation (2) from Equation (1), eliminating T and leaving an equation that can be solved for a_1:

$$m_2 g - \mu_k m_1 g = (m_1 + m_2) a_1$$

$$a_1 = \frac{m_2 g - \mu_k m_1 g}{m_1 + m_2}$$

(Continued)

Substitute the given values to obtain the acceleration:

$$a_1 = \frac{(7.00 \text{ kg})(9.80 \text{ m/s}^2) - (0.300)(4.00 \text{ kg})(9.80 \text{ m/s}^2)}{(4.00 \text{ kg} + 7.00 \text{ kg})}$$

$$= \boxed{5.17 \text{ m/s}^2}$$

Substitute the value for a_1 into Equation (1) to find the tension T:

$$T = \boxed{32.4 \text{ N}}$$

(b) Find the acceleration using the system approach, where the system consists of the two blocks.

Apply Newton's second law to the system and solve for a:

$$(m_1 + m_2)a = m_2 g - \mu_k n = m_2 g - \mu_k m_1 g$$

$$a = \frac{m_2 g - \mu_k m_1 g}{m_1 + m_2}$$

. . . .

REMARKS Although the system approach appears quick and easy, it can be applied only in special cases and can't give any information about the internal forces, such as the tension. To find the tension, you must consider the free-body diagram of one of the blocks separately as was done in part (a) of Example 4.14.

QUESTION 4.14 If mass m_2 is increased, does the acceleration of the system increase, decrease, or remain the same? Does the tension increase, decrease, or remain the same?

EXERCISE 4.14 What if an additional mass is attached to the ball in Example 4.14? How large must this mass be to increase the downward acceleration by 50%? Why isn't it possible to add enough mass to double the acceleration?

ANSWER 14.0 kg. Doubling the acceleration to 10.3 m/s² isn't possible simply by suspending more mass because all objects, regardless of their mass, fall freely at 9.8 m/s² near Earth's surface.

■ **EXAMPLE 4.15** | **Two Blocks and a Cord**

GOAL Apply Newton's second law and static friction to a two-body system.

PROBLEM A block of mass $m = 5.00$ kg rides on top of a second block of mass $M = 10.0$ kg. A person attaches a string to the bottom block and pulls the system horizontally across a frictionless surface, as in Figure 4.26a. Friction between the two blocks keeps the 5.00-kg block from slipping off. If the coefficient of static friction is 0.350, **(a)** what maximum force can be exerted by the string on the 10.0-kg block without causing the 5.00-kg block to slip? **(b)** Use the system approach to calculate the acceleration.

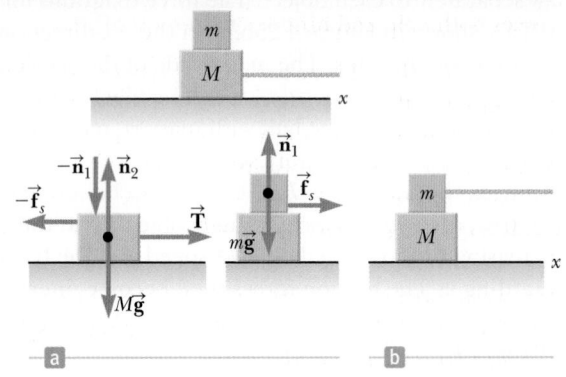

Figure 4.26 (a) (Example 4.15) (b) (Exercise 4.15)

STRATEGY Draw a free-body diagram for each block. The static friction force causes the top block to move horizontally, and the maximum such force corresponds to $f_s = \mu_s n$. That same static friction retards the motion of the bottom block. As long as the top block isn't slipping, the acceleration of both blocks is the same. Write Newton's second law for each block, and eliminate the acceleration a by substitution, solving for the tension T. Once the tension is known, use the system approach to calculate the acceleration.

. . . .

SOLUTION

(a) Find the maximum force that can be exerted by the string.

Write the two components of Newton's second law for the top block:

x-component: $ma = \mu_s n_1$
y-component: $0 = n_1 - mg$

Solve the y-component for n_1, substitute the result into the x-component, and then solve for a:

$$n_1 = mg \quad \rightarrow \quad ma = \mu_s mg \quad \rightarrow \quad a = \mu_s g$$

Write the x-component of Newton's second law for the bottom block:

(1) $Ma = -\mu_s mg + T$

Substitute the expression for $a = \mu_s g$ into Equation (1) and solve for the tension T:	$M\mu_s g = T - \mu_s mg \rightarrow T = (m + M)\mu_s g$

Now evaluate to get the answer:	$T = (5.00 \text{ kg} + 10.0 \text{ kg})(0.350)(9.80 \text{ m/s}^2) = \boxed{51.5 \text{ N}}$

(b) Use the system approach to calculate the acceleration.

Write the second law for the x-component of the force on the system:	$(m + M)a = T$

Solve for the acceleration and substitute values:	$a = \dfrac{T}{m + M} = \dfrac{51.5 \text{ N}}{5.00 \text{ kg} + 10.0 \text{ kg}} = \boxed{3.43 \text{ m/s}^2}$

REMARKS Notice that the y-component for the 10.0-kg block wasn't needed because there was no friction between that block and the underlying surface. It's also interesting to note that the top block was accelerated by the force of static friction. The system acceleration could also have been calculated with $a = \mu_s g$. Does the result agree with the answer found by the system approach?

QUESTION 4.15 What would happen if the tension force exceeded 51.5 N?

EXERCISE 4.15 Suppose instead the string is attached to the top block in Example 4.15 (see Fig. 4.26b). Find the maximum force that can be exerted by the string on the block without causing the top block to slip.

ANSWER 25.7 N

■ APPLYING PHYSICS 4.1 | Cars and Friction

Forces of friction are important in the analysis of the motion of cars and other wheeled vehicles. How do such forces both help and hinder the motion of a car?

EXPLANATION There are several types of friction forces to consider, the main ones being the force of friction between the tires and the road surface and the retarding force produced by air resistance.

Assuming the car is a four-wheel-drive vehicle of mass m, as each wheel turns to propel the car forward, the tire exerts a rearward force on the road. The reaction to this rearward force is a forward force $\vec{f}$ exerted by the road on the tire (Fig. 4.27). If we assume the same forward force $\vec{f}$ is exerted on each tire, the net forward force on the car is $4\vec{f}$, and the car's acceleration is therefore $\vec{a} = 4\vec{f}/m$.

The friction between the moving car's wheels and the road is normally static friction, unless the car is skidding.

When the car is in motion, we must also consider the force of air resistance, $\vec{R}$, which acts in the direction opposite the velocity of the car. The net force exerted on the

Figure 4.27 (Applying Physics 4.1) The horizontal forces acting on the car are the *forward* forces $\vec{f}$ exerted by the road on each tire and the force of air resistance $\vec{R}$, which acts *opposite* the car's velocity. (The car's tires exert a rearward force on the road, not shown in the diagram.)

car is therefore $4\vec{f} - \vec{R}$, so the car's acceleration is $\vec{a} = (4\vec{f} - \vec{R})/m$. At normal driving speeds, the magnitude of $\vec{R}$ is proportional to the first power of the speed, $R = bv$, where b is a constant, so the force of air resistance increases with increasing speed. When R is equal to $4f$, the acceleration is zero and the car moves at a constant speed. To minimize this resistive force, racing cars often have very low profiles and streamlined contours. ■

■ APPLYING PHYSICS 4.2 | Air Drag

Air resistance isn't always undesirable. What are some applications that depend on it?

EXPLANATION Consider a skydiver plunging through the air, as in Figure 4.28 (page 112). Despite falling from a height of several thousand meters, she never exceeds a speed

of around 120 miles per hour. This is because, aside from the downward force of gravity $m\vec{g}$, there is also an upward force of air resistance, $\vec{R}$. Before she reaches a final constant speed, the magnitude of $\vec{R}$ is less than her weight. As her downward speed increases, the force of air resistance increases. The vector sum of the force of gravity and the force of air resistance gives a total force that decreases with time, so her acceleration decreases. Once the two forces balance each other, the net force is zero, so the acceleration is zero, and she reaches a **terminal speed**.

Terminal speed is generally still high enough to be fatal on impact, although there have been amazing stories of survival. In one case, a man fell flat on his back in a freshly plowed field and survived. (He did, however, break virtually every bone in his body.) In another case, a flight attendant survived a fall from thirty thousand feet into a snowbank. In neither case would the person have had any chance of surviving without the effects of air drag.

Parachutes and paragliders create a much larger drag force due to their large area and can reduce the terminal speed to a few meters per second. Some sports enthusiasts have even developed special suits with wings, allowing a long glide to the ground. In each case, a larger cross-sectional area intercepts more air, creating greater air drag, so the terminal speed is lower.

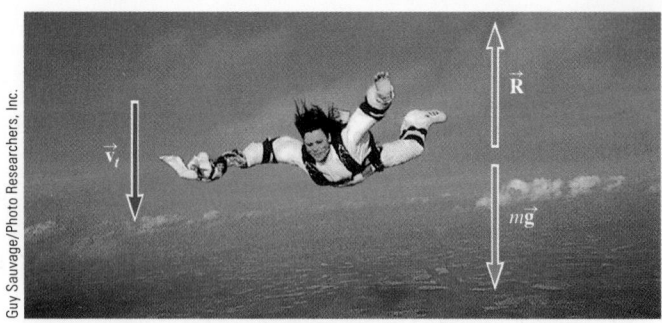

Figure 4.28 (Applying Physics 4.2)

Air drag is also important in space travel. Without it, returning to Earth would require a considerable amount of fuel. Air drag helps slow capsules and spaceships, and aerocapture techniques have been proposed for trips to other planets. These techniques significantly reduce fuel requirements by using air drag to reduce the speed of the spacecraft. ∎

■ SUMMARY

4.1 Forces

There are four known fundamental forces of nature: (1) the strong nuclear force between subatomic particles; (2) the electromagnetic forces between electric charges; (3) the weak nuclear forces, which arise in certain radioactive decay processes; and (4) the gravitational force between objects. These are collectively called field forces. Classical physics deals only with the gravitational and electromagnetic forces.

Forces such as friction or the force of a bat hitting a ball are called contact forces. On a more fundamental level, contact forces have an electromagnetic nature.

4.2 Newton's First Law

Newton's first law states that an object moves at constant velocity unless acted on by a force.

The tendency for an object to maintain its original state of motion is called **inertia. Mass** is the physical quantity that measures the resistance of an object to changes in its velocity.

Newton's Second Law

Newton's second law states that the acceleration of an object is directly proportional to the net force acting on it and inversely proportional to its mass. The net force acting on an object equals the product of its mass and acceleration:

A net force $\sum \vec{F}$ acting on a mass m creates an acceleration proportional to the force and inversely proportional to the mass.

$$\sum \vec{F} = m\vec{a} \qquad [4.1]$$

Newton's universal law of gravitation is

$$F_g = G\frac{m_1 m_2}{r^2} \qquad [4.5]$$

The **weight** w of an object is the magnitude of the force of gravity exerted on that object and is given by

$$w = mg \qquad [4.6]$$

where $g = F_g/m$ is the acceleration of gravity.

Solving problems with Newton's second law involves finding all the forces acting on a system and writing Equation 4.1 for the x-component and y-component separately. These two equations are then solved algebraically for the unknown quantities.

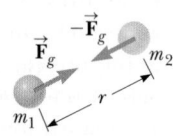

The gravity force between any two objects is proportional to their masses and inversely proportional to the square of the distance between them.

Newton's Third Law

Newton's third law states that if two objects interact, the force $\vec{F}_{12}$ exerted by object 1 on object 2 is equal in magnitude and opposite in direction to the force $\vec{F}_{21}$ exerted by object 2 on object 1:

$$\vec{F}_{12} = -\vec{F}_{21}$$

An isolated force can never occur in nature.

Newton's third law in action: the hammer drives the nail forward into the wall, and the nail slows the head of the hammer down to rest with an equal and opposite force.

4.5 Applications of Newton's Laws

An **object in equilibrium** has no net external force acting on it, and the second law, in component form, implies that $\Sigma F_x = 0$ and $\Sigma F_y = 0$ for such an object. These two equations are useful for solving problems in statics, in which the object is at rest or moving at constant velocity.

An object under acceleration requires the same two equations, but with the acceleration terms included: $\Sigma F_x = ma_x$ and $\Sigma F_y = ma_y$. When the acceleration is constant, the equations of kinematics can supplement Newton's second law.

4.6 Forces of Friction

The magnitude of the maximum force of static friction, $f_{s,max}$, between an object and a surface is proportional to the magnitude of the normal force acting on the object. This maximum force occurs when the object is on the verge of slipping. In general,

$$f_s \leq \mu_s n \qquad [4.11]$$

where μ_s is the **coefficient of static friction.** When an object slides over a surface, the direction of the force of kinetic friction, $\vec{f}_k$, on the object is opposite the direction of the motion of the object relative to the surface and proportional to the magnitude of the normal force. The magnitude of $\vec{f}_k$ is

$$f_k = \mu_k n \qquad [4.12]$$

where μ_k is the **coefficient of kinetic friction.** In general, $\mu_k < \mu_s$.

Solving problems that involve friction is a matter of using these two friction forces in Newton's second law. The static friction force must be handled carefully because it refers to a maximum force, which is not always called upon in a given problem.

■ MULTIPLE-CHOICE QUESTIONS

WebAssign The multiple-choice questions in this chapter may be assigned online in Enhanced WebAssign.

1. A horizontal force of 95.0 N is applied to a 60.0-kg crate on a rough, level surface. If the crate accelerates at 1.20 m/s², what is the magnitude of the force of kinetic friction acting on the crate? (a) 23.0 N (b) 45.0 N (c) 16.0 N (d) 33.0 N (e) 8.80 N

2. As a block slides down a frictionless incline, which of the following statements is true? (a) Both its speed and acceleration increase. (b) Its speed and acceleration remain constant. (c) Its speed increases and its acceleration remains constant. (d) Both its speed and acceleration decrease. (e) Its speed increases and its acceleration decreases.

3. If Earth's mass and radius both suddenly doubled, what would be the new value of the acceleration of gravity near Earth's surface? (a) 9.80 m/s² (b) 4.90 m/s² (c) 2.45 m/s² (d) 19.6 m/s² (e) 12.6 m/s²

4. If a constant non-zero net external force acts on an object during a given period, which of the following statements must be true during that time? (a) The object moves. (b) The magnitude of the object's velocity increases. (c) The acceleration of the object is increasing. (d) The object accelerates. (e) The object's speed remains constant.

5. Two monkeys of equal mass are holding onto a single vine of negligible mass that hangs vertically from a tree, with one monkey a few meters higher than the other. What is the ratio of the tension in the vine above the upper monkey to the tension in the vine between the two monkeys? (a) $\frac{1}{2}$ (b) 1 (c) 1.5 (d) 2 (e) More information is required.

6. A crate remains stationary after it has been placed on a ramp inclined at an angle with the horizontal. Which of the following statements must be true about the magnitude of the frictional force that acts on the crate? (a) It is larger than the weight of the crate. (b) It is at least equal to the weight of the crate. (c) It is equal to $\mu_s n$. (d) It is greater than the component of the gravitational force acting down the ramp. (e) It is equal to the component of the gravitational force acting down the ramp.

7. In the photo on page 89, a locomotive has broken through the wall of a train station. During the collision, what can be said about the force exerted by the locomotive on the wall? (a) The force exerted by the locomotive on the wall was larger than the force the wall could exert on the locomotive. (b) The force exerted by the locomotive on the wall was the same in magnitude as the force exerted by the wall on the locomotive. (c) The force exerted by the locomotive on the wall was less than the force exerted by the wall on the locomotive. (d) The wall cannot be said to "exert" a force; after all, it broke.

8. If an object of mass m moves with constant velocity v, the net force on the object is (a) mg (b) mv (c) mv/t (d) 0 (e) None of these answers is correct.

9. Four forces act on an object, given by $\vec{A}$ = 40 N east, $\vec{B}$ = 50 N north, $\vec{C}$ = 70 N west, and $\vec{D}$ = 90 N south. What is the magnitude of the net force on the object? (a) 50 N (b) 70 N (c) 131 N (d) 170 N (e) 250 N

10. If an object is in equilibrium, which of the following statements is *not* true? (a) The speed of the object remains constant. (b) The acceleration of the object is zero. (c) The net force acting on the object is zero. (d) The object must be at rest. (e) The velocity is constant.

11. A manager of a restaurant pushes horizontally with a force of magnitude 150 N on a box of melons. The box moves across the floor with a constant acceleration in the same direction as the applied force. Which statement is most accurate concerning the magnitude of the force of kinetic friction acting on the box? (a) It is greater than 150 N. (b) It is less than 150 N. (c) It is equal to 150 N. (d) The kinetic friction force is steadily decreasing. (e) The kinetic friction force must be zero.

12. A truck loaded with sand accelerates along a highway. The driving force on the truck remains constant. What happens to the acceleration of the truck as its trailer leaks sand at a constant rate through a hole in its bottom? (a) It decreases at a steady rate. (b) It increases at a steady rate. (c) It increases and then decreases. (d) It decreases and then increases. (e) It remains constant.

13. A large crate of mass m is placed on the back of a truck but not tied down. As the truck accelerates forward with an acceleration a, the crate remains at rest relative to the truck. What force causes the crate to accelerate forward? (a) the normal force (b) the force of gravity (c) the force of friction between the crate and the floor of the truck (d) the "ma" force (e) none of these

14. Two objects are connected by a string that passes over a frictionless pulley as in Active Figure 4.20, where $m_1 < m_2$ and a_1 and a_2 are the respective magnitudes of the accelerations. Which mathematical statement is true concerning the magnitude of the acceleration a_2 of mass m_2? (a) $a_2 < g$ (b) $a_2 > g$ (c) $a_2 = g$ (d) $a_2 < a_1$ (e) $a_2 > a_1$

15. Which of the following statements are true? (a) An astronaut's weight is the same on the Moon as on Earth. (b) An astronaut's mass is the same on the International Space Station as it is on Earth. (c) Earth's gravity has no effect on astronauts inside the International Space Station. (d) An astronaut's mass is greater on Earth than on the Moon. (e) None of these statements are true.

16. An object of mass m undergoes an acceleration $\vec{a}$ down a rough incline. Which of the following forces should *not* appear in the free-body diagram for the object? Choose all correct answers. (a) the force of gravity (b) $m\vec{a}$ (c) the normal force of the incline on the object (d) the force of friction down the incline (e) the force of friction up the incline (f) the force of the object on the incline

CONCEPTUAL QUESTIONS

WebAssign The conceptual questions in this chapter may be assigned online in Enhanced WebAssign.

1. A passenger sitting in the rear of a bus claims that she was injured as the driver slammed on the brakes, causing a suitcase to come flying toward her from the front of the bus. If you were the judge in this case, what disposition would you make? Explain.

2. A space explorer is moving through space far from any planet or star. He notices a large rock, taken as a specimen from an alien planet, floating around the cabin of the ship. Should he push it gently, or should he kick it toward the storage compartment? Explain.

3. (a) If gold were sold by weight, would you rather buy it in Denver or in Death Valley? (b) If it were sold by mass, in which of the two locations would you prefer to buy it? Why?

4. If you push on a heavy box that is at rest, you must exert some force to start its motion. Once the box is sliding, why does a smaller force maintain its motion?

5. A ball is held in a person's hand. (a) Identify all the external forces acting on the ball and the reaction to each. (b) If the ball is dropped, what force is exerted on it while it is falling? Identify the reaction force in this case. (Neglect air resistance.)

6. A weight lifter stands on a bathroom scale. (a) As she pumps a barbell up and down, what happens to the reading on the scale? (b) Suppose she is strong enough to actually *throw* the barbell upward. How does the reading on the scale vary now?

7. (a) What force causes an automobile to move? (b) A propeller-driven airplane? (c) A rowboat?

8. If only one force acts on an object, can it be in equilibrium? Explain.

9. In the motion picture *It Happened One Night* (Columbia Pictures, 1934), Clark Gable is standing inside a stationary bus in front of Claudette Colbert, who is seated. The bus suddenly starts moving forward and Clark falls into Claudette's lap. Why did this happen?

10. Analyze the motion of a rock dropped in water in terms of its speed and acceleration as it falls. Assume a resistive force is acting on the rock that increases as the velocity of the rock increases.

11. Identify the action–reaction pairs in the following situations: (a) a man takes a step, (b) a snowball hits a girl in the back, (c) a baseball player catches a ball, (d) a gust of wind strikes a window.

12. Draw a free-body diagram for each of the following objects: (a) a projectile in motion in the presence of air resistance, (b) a rocket leaving the launch pad with its engines operating, (c) an athlete running along a horizontal track.

13. In a tug-of-war between two athletes, each pulls on the rope with a force of 200 N. What is the tension in the rope? If the rope doesn't move, what horizontal force does each athlete exert against the ground?

14. Suppose you are driving a car at a high speed. Why should you avoid slamming on your brakes when you want to stop in the shortest possible distance? (Newer cars have antilock brakes that avoid this problem.)

■ PROBLEMS

WebAssign The problems in this chapter may be assigned online in Enhanced WebAssign. Selected problems also have Watch It video solutions.

1. denotes straightforward problem; 2. denotes intermediate problem;
3. denotes challenging problem
1. denotes full solution available in *Student Solutions Manual/ Study Guide*

1. denotes problems most often assigned in Enhanced WebAssign
BIO denotes biomedical problems
GP denotes guided problems
M denotes Master It tutorial available in Enhanced WebAssign
QC denotes asking for quantitative and conceptual reasoning
S denotes symbolic reasoning problem

4.1 Forces

4.2 Newton's First Law

4.3 Newton's Second Law

4.4 Newton's Third Law

1. The heaviest invertebrate is the giant squid, which is estimated to have a weight of about 2 tons spread out over its length of 70 feet. What is its weight in newtons?

2. A football punter accelerates a football from rest to a speed of 10 m/s during the time in which his toe is in contact with the ball (about 0.20 s). If the football has a mass of 0.50 kg, what average force does the punter exert on the ball?

3. A 6.0-kg object undergoes an acceleration of 2.0 m/s². (a) What is the magnitude of the resultant force acting on it? (b) If this same force is applied to a 4.0-kg object, what acceleration is produced?

4. QC One or more external forces are exerted on each object enclosed in a dashed box shown in Figure 4.2. Identify the reaction to each of these forces.

5. A bag of sugar weighs 5.00 lb on Earth. What would it weigh in newtons on the Moon, where the free-fall acceleration is one-sixth that on Earth? Repeat for Jupiter, where g is 2.64 times that on Earth. Find the mass of the bag of sugar in kilograms at each of the three locations.

6. A freight train has a mass of 1.5×10^7 kg. If the locomotive can exert a constant pull of 7.5×10^5 N, how long does it take to increase the speed of the train from rest to 80 km/h?

7. A 75-kg man standing on a scale in an elevator notes that as the elevator rises, the scale reads 825 N. What is the acceleration of the elevator?

8. QC Consider a solid metal sphere (S) a few centimeters in diameter and a feather (F). For each quantity in the list that follows, indicate whether the quantity is the same, greater, or lesser in the case of S or in that of F. Explain in each case why you gave the answer you did. Here is the list: (a) the gravitational force, (b) the time it will take to fall a given distance in air, (c) the time it will take to fall a given distance in vacuum, (d) the total force on the object when falling in vacuum.

9. BIO As a fish jumps vertically out of the water, assume that only two significant forces act on it: an upward force F exerted by the tail fin and the downward force due to gravity. A record Chinook salmon has a length of 1.50 m and a mass of 61.0 kg. If this fish is moving upward at 3.00 m/s as its head first breaks the surface and has an upward speed of 6.00 m/s after two-thirds of its length has left the surface, assume constant acceleration and determine (a) the salmon's acceleration and (b) the magnitude of the force F during this interval.

10. A 5.0-g bullet leaves the muzzle of a rifle with a speed of 320 m/s. What force (assumed constant) is exerted on the bullet while it is traveling down the 0.82-m-long barrel of the rifle?

11. A boat moves through the water with two forces acting on it. One is a 2 000-N forward push by the water on the propeller, and the other is a 1 800-N resistive force due to the water around the bow. (a) What is the acceleration of the 1 000-kg boat? (b) If it starts from rest, how far will the boat move in 10.0 s? (c) What will its velocity be at the end of that time?

12. Two forces are applied to a car in an effort to move it, as shown in Figure P4.12. (a) What is the resultant of these

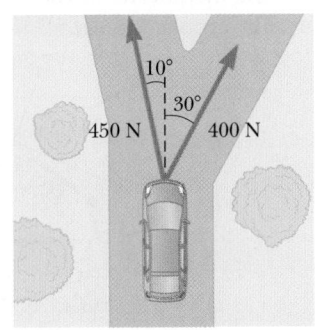

Figure P4.12

two forces? (b) If the car has a mass of 3 000 kg, what acceleration does it have? Ignore friction.

13. A 970-kg car starts from rest on a horizontal roadway and accelerates eastward for 5.00 s when it reaches a speed of 25.0 m/s. What is the average force exerted on the car during this time?

14. **S** An object of mass m is dropped from the roof of a building of height h. While the object is falling, a wind blowing parallel to the face of the building exerts a constant horizontal force F on the object. (a) How long does it take the object to strike the ground? Express the time t in terms of g and h. (b) Find an expression in terms of m and F for the acceleration a_x of the object in the horizontal direction (taken as the positive x-direction). (c) How far is the object displaced horizontally before hitting the ground? Answer in terms of m, g, F, and h. (d) Find the magnitude of the object's acceleration while it is falling, using the variables F, m, and g.

15. After falling from rest from a height of 30 m, a 0.50-kg ball rebounds upward, reaching a height of 20 m. If the contact between ball and ground lasted 2.0 ms, what average force was exerted on the ball?

16. **M** The force exerted by the wind on the sails of a sailboat is 390 N north. The water exerts a force of 180 N east. If the boat (including its crew) has a mass of 270 kg, what are the magnitude and direction of its acceleration?

4.5 Applications of Newton's Laws

17. **QC** (a) Find the tension in each cable supporting the 600-N cat burglar in Figure P4.17. (b) Suppose the horizontal cable were reattached higher up on the wall. Would the tension in the other cable increase, decrease, or stay the same? Why?

Figure P4.17

18. **BIO** A certain orthodontist uses a wire brace to align a patient's crooked tooth as in Figure P4.18. The tension in the wire is adjusted to have a magnitude of 18.0 N. Find the magnitude of the net force exerted by the wire on the crooked tooth.

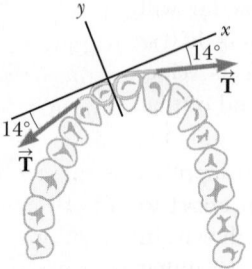

Figure P4.18

19. A 150-N bird feeder is supported by three cables as shown in Figure P4.19. Find the tension in each cable.

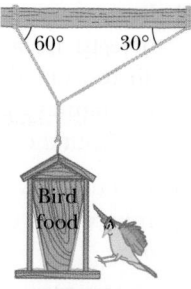

Figure P4.19

20. **BIO** The leg and cast in Figure P4.20 weigh 220 N (w_1). Determine the weight w_2 and the angle α needed so that no force is exerted on the hip joint by the leg plus the cast.

Figure P4.20

21. Two blocks each of mass $m = 3.50$ kg are fastened to the top of an elevator as in Figure P4.21. (a) If the elevator has an upward acceleration $a = 1.60$ m/s², find the tensions T_1 and T_2 in the upper and lower strings. (b) If the strings can withstand a maximum tension of 85.0 N, what maximum acceleration can the elevator have before the upper string breaks?

Figure P4.21
(Problems 21 and 22)

22. **S** Two blocks each of mass m are fastened to the top of an elevator as in Figure P4.21. The elevator has an upward acceleration a. The strings have negligible mass. (a) Find the tensions T_1 and T_2 in the upper and lower strings in terms of m, a, and g. (b) Compare the two tensions and determine which string would break first if a is made sufficiently large. (c) What are the tensions if the cable supporting the elevator breaks?

23. The distance between two telephone poles is 50.0 m. When a 1.00-kg bird lands on the telephone wire midway between the poles, the wire sags 0.200 m. Draw a free-body diagram of the bird. How much tension does the bird produce in the wire? Ignore the weight of the wire.

24. The systems shown in Figure P4.24 are in equilibrium. If the spring scales are calibrated in newtons, what do they read? Ignore the masses of the pulleys and strings and assume the pulleys and the incline in Figure P4.24d are frictionless.

Figure P4.24

25. A 5.0-kg bucket of water is raised from a well by a rope. If the upward acceleration of the bucket is 3.0 m/s², find the force exerted by the rope on the bucket.

26. A crate of mass $m = 32$ kg rides on the bed of a truck attached by a cord to the back of the cab as in Figure P4.26. The cord can withstand a maximum tension of 68 N before breaking.

Figure P4.26

Neglecting friction between the crate and truck bed, find the maximum acceleration the truck can have before the cord breaks.

27. **S** Two blocks of masses m and $2m$ are held in equilibrium on a frictionless incline as in Figure P4.27. In terms of m and θ, find (a) the magnitude of the tension T_1 in the upper cord and (b) the magnitude of the tension T_2 in the lower cord connecting the two blocks.

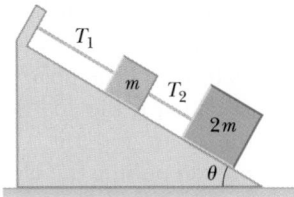

Figure P4.27

28. Two packing crates of masses 10.0 kg and 5.00 kg are connected by a light string that passes over a frictionless pulley as in Figure P4.28. The 5.00-kg crate lies on a smooth incline of angle 40.0°. Find

Figure P4.28

(a) the acceleration of the 5.00-kg crate and (b) the tension in the string.

29. **M** Assume the three blocks portrayed in Figure P4.29 move on a frictionless surface and a 42-N force acts as shown on the 3.0-kg block. Determine (a) the acceleration given this system, (b) the tension in the cord connecting the 3.0-kg and the 1.0-kg blocks, and (c) the force exerted by the 1.0-kg block on the 2.0-kg block.

Figure P4.29

30. A block of mass $m = 5.8$ kg is pulled up a $\theta = 25°$ incline as in Figure P4.30 with a force of magnitude $F = 32$ N. (a) Find the acceleration of the block if the incline is frictionless. (b) Find the acceleration of the block if the coefficient of kinetic friction between the block and incline is 0.10.

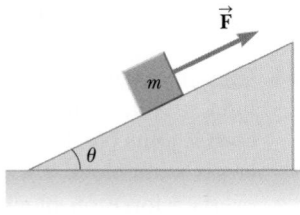

Figure P4.30

31. **BIO** A setup similar to the one shown in Figure P4.31 is often used in hospitals to support and apply a traction force to an injured leg. (a) Determine the force of tension in the rope supporting the leg. (b) What is the traction force exerted on the leg? Assume the traction force is horizontal.

Figure P4.31

32. **GP** Two blocks of masses m_1 and m_2 ($m_1 > m_2$) are placed on a frictionless table in contact with each other. A horizontal force of magnitude F is applied to the block of mass m_1 in Figure P4.32. (a) If P is the magnitude of the contact force between the blocks, draw the free-body diagrams for each block. (b) What is the net force on the system consisting of both blocks? (c) What is the net force acting on m_1? (d) What is the net force acting on m_2? (e) Write the x-component of Newton's second law for each block. (f) Solve the resulting system of two equations and two unknowns, expressing the acceleration a and contact force P in terms of the masses and force.

Figure P4.32

(g) How would the answers change if the force had been applied to m_2 instead? (*Hint:* use symmetry; don't calculate!) Is the contact force larger, smaller, or the same in this case? Why?

33. A 276-kg glider is being pulled by a 1 950-kg airplane along a horizontal runway with an acceleration of $\vec{a} = 2.20 \text{ m/s}^2$ to the right as in Figure P4.33. Find (a) the thrust provided by the airplane's propellers and (b) the magnitude of the tension in the cable connecting the airplane and glider.

Figure P4.33

34. **Q|C** In Figure P4.34, the light, taut, unstretchable cord B joins block 1 and the larger-mass block 2. Cord A exerts a force on block 1 to make it accelerate forward. (a) How does the magnitude of the force exerted by cord A on block 1 compare with the magnitude of the force exerted by cord B on block 2? (b) How does the acceleration of block 1 compare with the acceleration of block 2? (c) Does cord B exert a force on block 1? Explain your answer.

Figure P4.34

35. **Q|C** (a) An elevator of mass m moving upward has two forces acting on it: the upward force of tension in the cable and the downward force due to gravity. When the elevator is accelerating upward, which is greater, T or w? (b) When the elevator is moving at a constant velocity upward, which is greater, T or w? (c) When the elevator is moving upward, but the acceleration is downward, which is greater, T or w? (d) Let the elevator have a mass of 1 500 kg and an upward acceleration of 2.5 m/s². Find T. Is your answer consistent with the answer to part (a)? (e) The elevator of part (d) now moves with a constant upward velocity of 10 m/s. Find T. Is your answer consistent with your answer to part (b)? (f) Having initially moved upward with a constant velocity, the elevator begins to accelerate downward at 1.50 m/s². Find T. Is your answer consistent with your answer to part (c)?

36. An object with mass $m_1 = 5.00$ kg rests on a frictionless horizontal table and is connected to a cable that passes over a pulley and is then fastened to a hanging object with mass $m_2 = 10.0$ kg, as shown in Figure P4.36. Find (a) the acceleration of each object and (b) the tension in the cable.

Figure P4.36
(Problems 36, 40, and 45)

37. A 1 000-kg car is pulling a 300-kg trailer. Together, the car and trailer have an acceleration of 2.15 m/s² in the positive x-direction. Neglecting frictional forces on the trailer, determine (a) the net force on the car, (b) the net force on the trailer, (c) the magnitude and direction of the force exerted by the trailer on the car, and (d) the resultant force exerted by the car on the road.

38. Two objects with masses of 3.00 kg and 5.00 kg are connected by a light string that passes over a frictionless pulley, as in Figure P4.38. Determine (a) the tension in the string, (b) the acceleration of each object, and (c) the distance each object will move in the first second of motion if both objects start from rest.

Figure P4.38

4.6 Forces of Friction

39. A dockworker loading crates on a ship finds that a 20-kg crate, initially at rest on a horizontal surface, requires a 75-N horizontal force to set it in motion. However, after the crate is in motion, a horizontal force of 60 N is required to keep it moving with a constant speed. Find the coefficients of static and kinetic friction between crate and floor.

40. In Figure P4.36, $m_1 = 10$ kg and $m_2 = 4.0$ kg. The coefficient of static friction between m_1 and the horizontal surface is 0.50, and the coefficient of kinetic friction is 0.30. (a) If the system is released from rest, what will its acceleration be? (b) If the system is set in motion with m_2 moving downward, what will be the acceleration of the system?

41. A 1 000-N crate is being pushed across a level floor at a constant speed by a force $\vec{F}$ of 300 N at an angle of 20.0° below the horizontal, as shown in Figure P4.41a. (a) What is the coefficient of kinetic friction between the crate and the floor? (b) If the 300-N force is instead pulling the block at an angle of 20.0° above the horizontal, as shown in Figure P4.41b, what will be the acceleration of the crate? Assume that the coefficient of friction is the same as that found in part (a).

Figure P4.41

42. **Q|C S** A block of mass $3m$ is placed on a frictionless horizontal surface, and a second block of mass

m is placed on top of the first block. The surfaces of the blocks are rough. A constant force of magnitude *F* is applied to the first block as in Figure P4.42. (a) Construct free-body diagrams for each block. (b) Identify the horizontal force that causes the block of mass *m* to accelerate. (c) Assume that the upper block does not slip on the lower block, and find the acceleration of each block in terms of *m* and *F*.

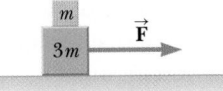

Figure P4.42

43. Consider a large truck carrying a heavy load, such as steel beams. A significant hazard for the driver is that the load may slide forward, crushing the cab, if the truck stops suddenly in an accident or even in braking. Assume, for example, a 10 000-kg load sits on the flatbed of a 20 000-kg truck moving at 12.0 m/s. Assume the load is not tied down to the truck and has a coefficient of static friction of 0.500 with the truck bed. (a) Calculate the minimum stopping distance for which the load will not slide forward relative to the truck. (b) Is any piece of data unnecessary for the solution?

44. A crate of mass 45.0 kg is being transported on the flatbed of a pickup truck. The coefficient of static friction between the crate and the truck's flatbed is 0.350, and the coefficient of kinetic friction is 0.320. (a) The truck accelerates forward on level ground. What is the maximum acceleration the truck can have so that the crate does not slide relative to the truck's flatbed? (b) The truck barely exceeds this acceleration and then moves with constant acceleration, with the crate sliding along its bed. What is the acceleration of the crate relative to the ground?

45. **M** Objects with masses $m_1 = 10.0$ kg and $m_2 = 5.00$ kg are connected by a light string that passes over a frictionless pulley as in Figure P4.36. If, when the system starts from rest, m_2 falls 1.00 m in 1.20 s, determine the coefficient of kinetic friction between m_1 and the table.

46. **S** A hockey puck struck by a hockey stick is given an initial speed v_0 in the positive *x*-direction. The coefficient of kinetic friction between the ice and the puck is μ_k. (a) Obtain an expression for the acceleration of the puck. (b) Use the result of part (a) to obtain an expression for the distance *d* the puck slides. The answer should be in terms of the variables v_0, μ_k, and *g* only.

47. The coefficient of static friction between the 3.00-kg crate and the 35.0° incline of Figure P4.47 is 0.300. What minimum force $\vec{F}$ must be applied to the crate perpendicular to the incline to prevent the crate from sliding down the incline?

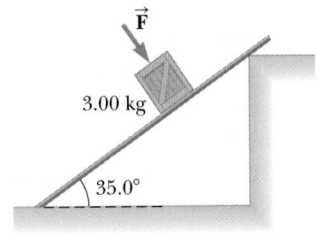

Figure P4.47

48. A student decides to move a box of books into her dormitory room by pulling on a rope attached to the box. She pulls with a force of 80.0 N at an angle of 25.0° above the horizontal. The box has a mass of 25.0 kg, and the coefficient of kinetic friction between box and floor is 0.300. (a) Find the acceleration of the box. (b) The student now starts moving the box up a 10.0° incline, keeping her 80.0 N force directed at 25.0° above the line of the incline. If the coefficient of friction is unchanged, what is the new acceleration of the box?

49. **Q|C** An object falling under the pull of gravity is acted upon by a frictional force of air resistance. The magnitude of this force is approximately proportional to the speed of the object, which can be written as $f = bv$. Assume $b = 15$ kg/s and $m = 50$ kg. (a) What is the terminal speed the object reaches while falling? (b) Does your answer to part (a) depend on the initial speed of the object? Explain.

50. A car is traveling at 50.0 km/h on a flat highway. (a) If the coefficient of friction between road and tires on a rainy day is 0.100, what is the minimum distance in which the car will stop? (b) What is the stopping distance when the surface is dry and the coefficient of friction is 0.600?

51. A 3.00-kg block starts from rest at the top of a 30.0° incline and slides 2.00 m down the incline in 1.50 s. Find (a) the acceleration of the block, (b) the coefficient of kinetic friction between the block and the incline, (c) the frictional force acting on the block, and (d) the speed of the block after it has slid 2.00 m.

52. A 15.0-lb block rests on a horizontal floor. (a) What force does the floor exert on the block? (b) A rope is tied to the block and is run vertically over a pulley. The other end is attached to a free-hanging 10.0-lb object. What now is the force exerted by the floor on the 15.0-lb block? (c) If the 10.0-lb object in part (b) is replaced with a 20.0-lb object, what is the force exerted by the floor on the 15.0-lb block?

53. To meet a U.S. Postal Service requirement, employees' footwear must have a coefficient of static friction of 0.500 or more on a specified tile surface. A typical athletic shoe has a coefficient of 0.800. In an emergency, what is the minimum time interval in which a person starting from rest can move 3.00 m on the tile surface if she is wearing (a) footwear meeting the Postal Service minimum and (b) a typical athletic shoe?

54. Objects of masses $m_1 = 4.00$ kg and $m_2 = 9.00$ kg are connected by a light string that passes over a frictionless pulley as in Figure P4.54. The object m_1 is held at rest on the floor, and m_2 rests on a fixed incline of $\theta = 40.0°$. The objects

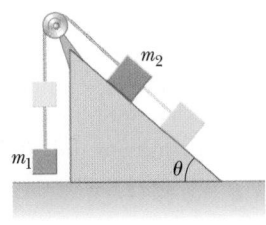

Figure P4.54

are released from rest, and m_2 slides 1.00 m down the incline in 4.00 s. Determine (a) the acceleration of each object, (b) the tension in the string, and (c) the coefficient of kinetic friction between m_2 and the incline.

55. **BIO** The person in Figure P4.55 weighs 170 lb. Each crutch makes an angle of 22.0° with the vertical (as seen from the front). Half of the person's weight is supported by the crutches, the other half by the vertical forces exerted by the ground on his feet. Assuming he is at rest and the force exerted by the ground on the crutches acts along the crutches, determine (a) the smallest possible coefficient of friction between crutches and ground and (b) the magnitude of the compression force supported by each crutch.

Figure P4.55

Additional Problems

56. As a protest against the umpire's calls, a baseball pitcher throws a ball straight up into the air at a speed of 20.0 m/s. In the process, he moves his hand through a distance of 1.50 m. If the ball has a mass of 0.150 kg, find the force he exerts on the ball to give it this upward speed.

57. **QC** Three objects are connected on a table as shown in Figure P4.57. The coefficient of kinetic friction between the block of mass m_2 and the table is 0.350. The objects have masses of $m_1 = 4.00$ kg, $m_2 = 1.00$ kg, and $m_3 = 2.00$ kg as shown, and the pulleys are frictionless. (a) Draw a diagram of the forces on each object. (b) Determine the acceleration of each object, including its direction. (c) Determine the tensions in the two cords. (d) If the tabletop were smooth, would the tensions increase, decrease, or remain the same? Explain.

Figure P4.57

58. The force exerted by the wind on a sailboat is approximately perpendicular to the sail and proportional to the component of the wind velocity perpendicular to the sail. For the 800-kg sailboat shown in Figure P4.58, the force exerted by the wind on the sailboat is

$$F_{sail} = \left(550 \, \frac{N}{m/s}\right) v_{wind\perp}$$

Water exerts a force along the keel (bottom) of the boat that prevents it from moving sideways, as shown in the figure. Once the boat starts moving forward, water also exerts a drag force backwards on the boat, opposing the forward motion. If a 17-knot wind (1 knot = 0.514 m/s) is blowing to the east, what is the initial acceleration of the sailboat?

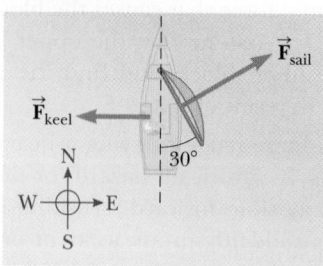

Figure P4.58

59. (a) What is the resultant force exerted by the two cables supporting the traffic light in Figure P4.59? (b) What is the weight of the light?

60. (a) What is the minimum force of friction required to hold the system of Figure P4.60 in equilibrium? (b) What coefficient of static friction between the 100-N block and the table ensures equilibrium? (c) If the coefficient of kinetic friction between the 100-N block and the table is 0.250, what hanging weight should replace the 50.0-N weight to allow the system to move at a constant speed once it is set in motion?

Figure P4.59

Figure P4.60

61. A boy coasts down a hill on a sled, reaching a level surface at the bottom with a speed of 7.0 m/s. If the coefficient of friction between the sled's runners and the snow is 0.050 and the boy and sled together weigh 600 N, how far does the sled travel on the level surface before coming to rest?

62. A woman at an airport is towing her 20.0-kg suitcase at constant speed by pulling on a strap at an angle θ above the horizontal (Fig. 4.62). She pulls on the strap with a 35.0-N force, and the friction force on the suitcase is 20.0 N. (a) Draw a free-body diagram of the suitcase. (b) What angle does the strap make with the horizontal? (c) What is the magnitude of the normal force that the ground exerts on the suitcase?

Figure P4.62

63. [QC] A box rests on the back of a truck. The coefficient of static friction between the box and the bed of the truck is 0.300. (a) When the truck accelerates forward, what force accelerates the box? (b) Find the maximum acceleration the truck can have before the box slides.

64. Three objects are connected by light strings as shown in Figure P4.64. The string connecting the 4.00-kg object and the 5.00-kg object passes over a light frictionless pulley. Determine (a) the acceleration of each object and (b) the tension in the two strings.

Figure P4.64

65. [M] A frictionless plane is 10.0 m long and inclined at 35.0°. A sled starts at the bottom with an initial speed of 5.00 m/s up the incline. When the sled reaches the point at which it momentarily stops, a second sled is released from the top of the incline with an initial speed v_i. Both sleds reach the bottom of the incline at the same moment. (a) Determine the distance that the first sled traveled up the incline. (b) Determine the initial speed of the second sled.

66. A high diver of mass 70.0 kg steps off a board 10.0 m above the water and falls vertical to the water, starting from rest. If her downward motion is stopped 2.00 s after her feet first touch the water, what average upward force did the water exert on her?

67. A 2.00-kg aluminum block and a 6.00-kg copper block are connected by a light string over a frictionless pulley. The two blocks are allowed to move on a fixed steel block wedge (of angle $\theta = 30.0°$) as shown in Figure P4.67. Making use of Table 4.2, determine (a) the acceleration of the two blocks and (b) the tension in the string.

Figure P4.67

68. [S] An object of mass m_1 hangs from a string that passes over a very light fixed pulley P_1 as shown in Figure P4.68. The string connects to a second very light pulley P_2. A second string passes around this pulley with one end attached to a wall and the other to an object of mass m_2 on a frictionless, horizontal table.

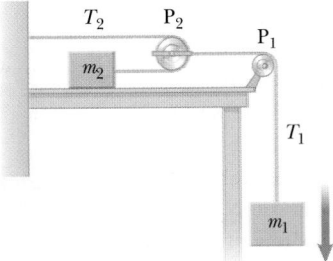

Figure P4.68

(a) If a_1 and a_2 are the accelerations of m_1 and m_2, respectively, what is the relation between these accelerations? Find expressions for (b) the tensions in the strings and (c) the accelerations a_1 and a_2 in terms of the masses m_1 and m_2, and g.

69. Two boxes of fruit on a frictionless horizontal surface are connected by a light string as in Figure P4.69, where $m_1 = 10$ kg and $m_2 = 20$ kg. A force of 50 N is applied to the 20-kg box. (a) Determine the acceleration of each box and the tension in the string. (b) Repeat the problem for the case where the coefficient of kinetic friction between each box and the surface is 0.10.

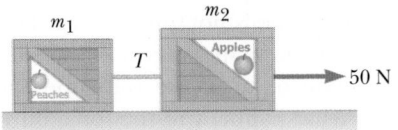

Figure P4.69

70. [QC] *Measuring coefficients of friction* A coin is placed near one edge of a book lying on a table, and that edge of the book is lifted until the coin just slips down the incline as shown in Figure P4.70. The angle of the incline, θ_c, called the critical angle, is measured. (a) Draw a free-body diagram for the coin when it is on the verge of slipping and identify all forces acting on it. Your free-body diagram should include a force of static friction acting up the incline. (b) Is the magnitude of the friction force equal to $\mu_s n$ for angles less than θ_c? Explain. What can you definitely say about the magnitude of the friction force for any angle $\theta \leq \theta_c$? (c) Show that the coefficient of static friction is given by $\mu_s = \tan \theta_c$. (d) Once the coin starts to slide down the incline, the angle can be adjusted to a new value $\theta_c' \leq \theta_c$ such that the coins moves down the incline with constant speed. How does observation enable you to obtain the coefficient of kinetic friction?

Figure P4.70

71. [QC] A fisherman poles a boat as he searches for his next catch. He pushes parallel to the length of the light pole, exerting a force of 240 N on the bottom of a shallow lake. The pole lies in the vertical plane containing the boat's keel. At one moment, the pole makes an angle of 35.0° with the vertical and the water exerts a horizontal drag force of 47.5 N on the boat, opposite to its forward velocity of magnitude 0.857 m/s. The mass of the boat including its cargo and the worker is 370 kg. (a) The water exerts a buoyant force vertically upward on the boat. Find the magnitude of this force. (b) Assume the forces are constant over a short interval of time. Find the velocity of the boat 0.450 s after the moment described. (c) If the angle of the pole with respect to the vertical increased but the exerted force against the bottom remained the same, what would happen to buoyant force and the acceleration of the boat?

72. **Q|C** A rope with mass m_r is attached to a block with mass m_b as in Figure P4.72. Both the rope and the block rest on a horizontal, frictionless surface. The rope

Figure P4.72

does not stretch. The free end of the rope is pulled to the right with a horizontal force *F*. (a) Draw free-body diagrams for the rope and the block, noting that the tension in the rope is not uniform. (b) Find the acceleration of the system in terms of m_b, m_r, and *F*. (c) Find the magnitude of the force the rope exerts on the block. (d) What happens to the force on the block as the rope's mass approaches zero? What can you state about the tension in a *light* cord joining a pair of moving objects?

73. A van accelerates down a hill (Fig. P4.73), going from rest to 30.0 m/s in 6.00 s. During the acceleration, a toy ($m = 0.100$ kg) hangs by a string from the van's ceiling. The acceleration is such that the string remains perpendicular to the ceiling. Determine (a) the angle θ and (b) the tension in the string.

Figure P4.73

74. An inquisitive physics student, wishing to combine pleasure with scientific inquiry, rides on a roller coaster sitting on a bathroom scale. (Do not try this yourself on a roller coaster that forbids loose, heavy packages.) The bottom of the seat in the roller-coaster car is in a plane parallel to the track. The seat has a perpendicular back and a seat belt that fits around the student's chest in a plane parallel to the bottom of the seat. The student lifts his feet from the floor so that the scale reads his weight, 200 lb, when the car is horizontal. At one point during the ride, the car zooms with negligible friction down a straight slope inclined at 30.0° below the horizontal. What does the scale read at that point?

75. The parachute on a race car of weight 8 820 N opens at the end of a quarter-mile run when the car is traveling at 35 m/s. What total retarding force must be supplied by the parachute to stop the car in a distance of 1 000 m?

76. **M** On an airplane's takeoff, the combined action of the air around the engines and wings of an airplane exerts an 8 000-N force on the plane, directed upward at an angle of 65.0° above the horizontal. The plane rises with constant velocity in the vertical direction while continuing to accelerate in the horizontal direction. (a) What is the weight of the plane? (b) What is its horizontal acceleration?

77. The board sandwiched between two other boards in Figure P4.77 weighs 95.5 N. If the coefficient of friction between the boards is 0.663, what must be the magnitude of the compression forces (assumed to be horizontal) acting on both sides of the center board to keep it from slipping?

Figure P4.77

78. A sled weighing 60.0 N is pulled horizontally across snow so that the coefficient of kinetic friction between sled and snow is 0.100. A penguin weighing 70.0 N rides on the sled, as in Figure P4.78. If the coefficient of static friction between penguin and sled is

Figure P4.78

0.700, find the maximum horizontal force that can be exerted on the sled before the penguin begins to slide off.

79. A 72-kg man stands on a spring scale in an elevator. Starting from rest, the elevator ascends, attaining its maximum speed of 1.2 m/s in 0.80 s. The elevator travels with this constant speed for 5.0 s, undergoes a uniform *negative* acceleration for 1.5 s, and then comes to rest. What does the spring scale register (a) before the elevator starts to move? (b) During the first 0.80s of the elevator's ascent? (c) While the elevator is traveling at constant speed? (d) During the elevator's negative acceleration?

80. A magician pulls a tablecloth from under a 200-g mug located 30.0 cm from the edge of the cloth. The cloth exerts a friction force of 0.100 N on the mug and is pulled with a constant acceleration of 3.00 m/s². How far does the mug move relative to the horizontal tabletop before the cloth is completely out from under it? Note that the cloth must move more than 30 cm relative to the tabletop during the process.

81. An inventive child wants to reach an apple in a tree without climbing the tree. Sitting in a chair connected to a rope that passes over a frictionless pulley (Fig. P4.81), the child pulls on the loose end of the rope with such a force that the spring scale reads 250 N. The child's true weight is 320 N, and the chair weighs 160 N. The child's feet are not touching the ground.

Figure P4.81

(a) Show that the acceleration of the system is *upward,* and find its magnitude. (b) Find the force the child exerts on the chair.

82. A fire helicopter carries a 620-kg bucket of water at the end of a 20.0-m-long cable. Flying back from a fire at a constant speed of 40.0 m/s, the cable makes an angle of 40.0° with respect to the vertical. Determine the force exerted by air resistance on the bucket.

83. **S** A crate of weight F_g is pushed by a force $\vec{P}$ on a horizontal floor as shown in Figure P4.83. The coefficient of static friction is μ_s, and $\vec{P}$ is directed at angle θ below the horizontal. (a) Show that the minimum value of P that will move the crate is given by

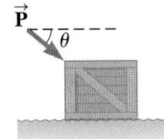

Figure P4.83

$$P = \frac{\mu_s F_g \sec \theta}{1 - \mu_s \tan \theta}$$

(b) Find the condition on θ in terms of μ_s for which motion of the crate is impossible for any value of P.

84. **Q|C** In Figure P4.84, the pulleys and the cord are light, all surfaces are frictionless, and the cord does not stretch. (a) How does the acceleration of block 1 compare with

Figure P4.84

the acceleration of block 2? Explain your reasoning. (b) The mass of block 2 is $m_2 = 1.30$ kg. Derive an expression for the acceleration of the block having mass m_2 as a function of the mass of block 1, m_1. (c) What does the result of part (b) predict if m_1 is very much less than 1.30 kg? (d) What does the result of part (b) predict if m_1 approaches infinity? (e) In this last case, what is the tension in the cord? (f) Could you anticipate the answers to parts (c), (d), and (e) without first doing part (b)? Explain.

85. **S** What horizontal force must be applied to a large block of mass M shown in Figure P4.85 so that the blocks remain stationary relative to M? Assume all surfaces and the pulley are frictionless. Notice that the force exerted by the string accelerates m_2.

Figure P4.85

■ AP* REVIEW QUESTIONS

1. A marble rolls down an incline with friction (as shown above) in such a way that it maintains a constant speed, v. Which of the following free-body diagrams describe the forces on the marble?

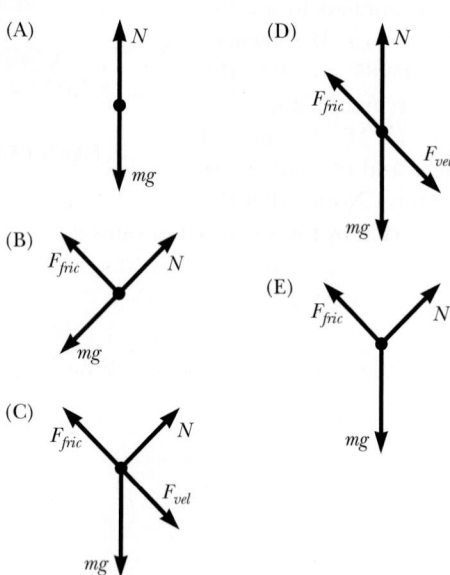

2. A skateboarder rolls down a rough hill with an increasing speed. Which of the following free-body diagrams describe the skateboarder?

3. What is the magnitude of the friction force acting on a 100 N wagon, if the wagon accelerates at 0.5 m/s² by pulling on its handle with 80 N of force at an angle of 60° from horizontal, as shown above?

(A) 5 N   (D) 40 N

(B) 20 N   (E) 50 N

(C) 35 N

4. A train engine can exert a maximum pulling force of $\mathbf{F}_{max}$. By what factor would the resulting maximum acceleration differ if the mass of an entire single-engine train were tripled while the number of pulling engines, each pulling $\mathbf{F}_{max}$, doubled? Assume friction is negligible.

(A) 1

(B) $\dfrac{2}{3}$

(C) $\dfrac{1}{3}$

(D) $\dfrac{3}{2}$

(E) 2

5. Two forces act on a mass, one parallel to the x-axis, and the other parallel to the y-axis. If the force in the y-axis is doubled relative to the magnitude of the x-axis force, by what factor would the mass have to change in order to maintain the same acceleration?

(A) 1

(B) $\dfrac{1}{2}$

(C) $\dfrac{3}{2}$

(D) 2

(E) Impossible to maintain the same acceleration

6. The gravitational attraction between two rocks of equal mass in deep space is 16 N. If both rocks double in mass and the distance separating the two rocks doubles, what is the resulting gravitational force between them?

(A) 8 N

(B) 12 N

(C) 16 N

(D) 32 N

(E) 64 N

7. A large, dense, round asteroid has an acceleration due to gravity of 0.20 m/s² at its surface. What would the acceleration due to gravity be on the surface of another, less dense asteroid of the same mass but with a diameter 3 times larger?

(A) 0.018 m/s²

(B) 0.06 m/s²

(C) 0.18 m/s²

(D) 0.20 m/s²

(E) 0.60 m/s²

8. Which of the following statements is/are true about the collision about to happen between the two billiard balls, as shown in the diagram above? Do not assume the masses are identical.

  I. The force is greater on the white cue ball than the black 8 ball.

  II. The force is less on the white cue ball than the black 8 ball.

  III. The force is the same on the white cue ball as the black 8 ball.

(A) I

(B) II

(C) III

(D) I, II, or III could be correct depending on the particular mass differences of either ball

(E) II is correct only if the mass of the black 8 ball is greater than the white cue ball

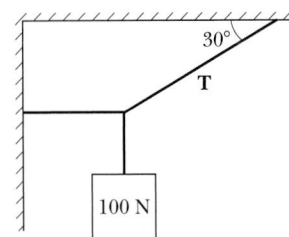

9. A 100 N weight hangs in a stationary position as shown above. What is the tension, **T**, of the supporting cable?

(A) 50 N

(B) 100 N

(C) 150 N

(D) 200 N

(E) 250 N

10. An elevator manufacturer determines the maximum force acting on ascending passengers should not exceed 110% of a standing passenger's weight on their feet. What would be the minimum time possible, according to this manufacturer, to raise an elevator 10 floors from rest if each floor is 5 m apart?

(A) 3 s

(B) 6 s

(C) 10 s

(D) 19 s

(E) 24 s

11. A truck carrying a cargo box on the rough surface of its bed accelerates forward. Which of the following statements is/are true?

  I. The net force accelerating the box is dependent on the weight of the box.

  II. The larger the weight of the box, the larger the resulting net force, thus a larger possible acceleration.

  III. The weight of the box does not affect the maximum acceleration possible before the box slips.

(A) I

(B) II

(C) III

(D) I and II

(E) I and III

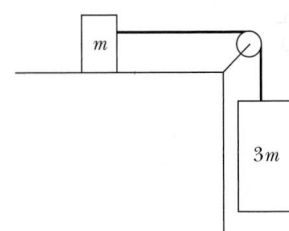

12. Masses m and $3m$ are connected with a light cable over a pulley with negligible friction and mass, as shown above. The coefficient of friction between mass m and the flat surface is μ. What is the acceleration of the two masses when they are allowed to move?

(A) $g = \dfrac{3 - \mu}{4}$

(B) $g = \dfrac{3 - \mu}{2}$

(C) $3g$

(D) g

(E) $\dfrac{3mg(1 - \mu)}{2}$

By timing his jumps, a student does work on the pogo-stick-student system, increasing his height with each jump. The work is transformed into gravitational potential energy at maximum height, converted to kinetic energy while falling, and stored as spring potential energy after contact with the ground.

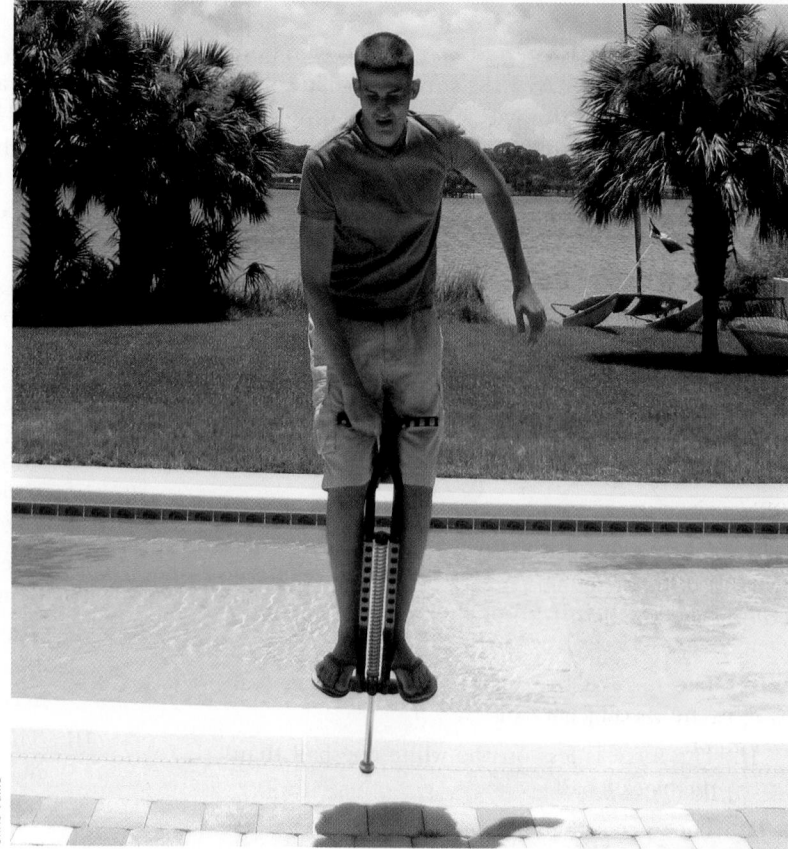

Chris Vuille

5 Energy

Energy is one of the most important concepts in the world of science. In everyday use energy is associated with the fuel needed for transportation and heating, with electricity for lights and appliances, and with the foods we consume. These associations, however, don't tell us what energy *is,* only what it *does,* and that producing it requires fuel. Our goal in this chapter, therefore, is to develop a better understanding of energy and how to quantify it.

Energy is present in the Universe in a variety of forms, including mechanical, chemical, electromagnetic, and nuclear energy. Even the inert mass of everyday matter contains a very large amount of energy. Although energy can be transformed from one kind to another, all observations and experiments to date suggest that the total amount of energy in the Universe never changes. That's also true for an isolated system, which is a collection of objects that can exchange energy with each other, but not with the rest of the Universe. If one form of energy in an isolated system decreases, then another form of energy in the system must increase. For example, if the system consists of a motor connected to a battery, the battery converts chemical energy to electrical energy and the motor converts electrical energy to mechanical energy. Understanding how energy changes from one form to another is essential in all the sciences.

In this chapter the focus is mainly on *mechanical energy,* which is the sum of *kinetic energy,* the energy associated with motion, and *potential energy*—the energy associated with relative position. Using an energy approach to solve certain problems is often much easier than using forces and Newton's three laws. These two very different approaches are linked through the concept of *work.*

5.1 Work

Work has a different meaning in physics than it does in everyday usage. In the physics definition, a physics textbook author does very little work typing away at a computer. A mason, by contrast, may do a lot of work laying concrete blocks. In physics, work is done only if an object is moved through some displacement while a force is applied to it. If either the force or displacement is doubled, the work is doubled. Double them both, and the work is quadrupled. Doing work involves applying a force to an object while moving it a given distance.

The definition for work W might be taken as

$$W = Fd \qquad [5.1]$$

◀ Intuitive definition of work

where F is the magnitude of the force acting on the object and d is the magnitude of the object's displacement. That definition, however, gives only the magnitude of work done on an object when the force is constant and parallel to the displacement, which must be along a line. A more sophisticated definition is required.

Figure 5.1 shows a block undergoing a displacement $\Delta \vec{x}$ along a straight line while acted on by a constant force $\vec{F}$ in the same direction. We have the following definition:

> The work W done on an object by a constant force $\vec{F}$ during a linear displacement along the x-axis is
>
> $$W = F_x \Delta x \qquad [5.2]$$
>
> where F_x is the x-component of the force $\vec{F}$ and $\Delta x = x_f - x_i$ is the object's displacement.
>
> **SI unit: joule (J) = newton · meter (N · m) = kg · m²/s²**

◀ Work by a constant force during a linear displacement

Note that in one dimension, $\Delta x = x_f - x_i$ is a vector quantity, just as it was defined in Chapter 2, not a magnitude as might be inferred from definitions of a vector and its magnitude in Chapter 3. Therefore Δx can be either positive or negative. Work as defined in Equation 5.2 is rigorous for displacements of any object along the x-axis while a constant force acts on it and, therefore, is suitable for many one-dimensional problems. Work is a positive number if F_x and Δx are both positive or both negative, in which case, as discussed in the next section, the work increases the mechanical energy of the object. If F_x is positive and Δx is negative, or vice versa, then the work is negative, and the object loses mechanical energy. The definition in Equation 5.2 works even when the constant force $\vec{F}$ is not parallel to the x-axis. Work is done only by the part of the force acting parallel to the object's direction of motion.

Figure 5.1 A constant force $\vec{F}$ in the same direction as the displacement, $\Delta \vec{x}$, does work $F \Delta x$.

It's easy to see the difference between the physics definition and the everyday definition of work. The author exerts very little force on the keys of a keyboard, creating only small displacements, so relatively little physics work is done. The mason must exert much larger forces on the concrete blocks and move them significant distances, and so performs a much greater amount of work. Even very tiring tasks, however, may not constitute work according to the physics definition. A truck driver, for example, may drive for several hours, but if he doesn't exert a force, then $F_x = 0$ in Equation 5.2 and he doesn't do any work. Similarly, a student pressing against a wall for hours in an isometric exercise also does no work, because the displacement in Equation 5.2, Δx, is zero.[1] Atlas, of Greek mythology, bore the world on his shoulders, but that, too, wouldn't qualify as work in the physics definition.

Work is a scalar quantity—a number rather than a vector—and consequently is easier to handle. No direction is associated with it. Further, work doesn't depend explicitly on time, which can be an advantage in problems involving only velocities and positions. Because the units of work are those of force and

Tip 5.1 Work Is a Scalar Quantity

Work is a simple number—a scalar, not a vector—so there is no direction associated with it. Energy and energy transfer are also scalars.

---

[1]Actually, you do expend energy while doing isometric exercises because your muscles are continuously contracting and relaxing in the process. This internal muscular movement qualifies as work according to the physics definition.

Figure 5.2 A constant force $\vec{F}$ exerted at an angle θ with respect to the displacement, $\Delta\vec{x}$, does work $(F\cos\theta)\Delta x$.

Work by a constant force ▶ at an angle to the displacement

Figure 5.3 No work is done on a bucket when it is moved horizontally because the applied force $\vec{F}$ is perpendicular to the displacement.

Tip 5.2 Work Is Done *by Something, on Something Else*

Work doesn't happen by itself. Work is done *by* something in the environment, *on* the object of interest.

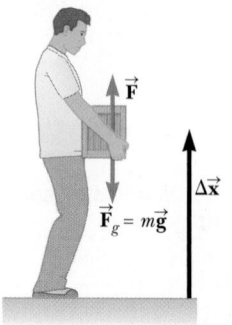

Figure 5.4 The student does positive work when he lifts the box from the floor, because the applied force $\vec{F}$ is in the same direction as the displacement. When he lowers the box to the floor, he does negative work.

distance, the SI unit is the **newton-meter** (N · m). Another name for the newton-meter is the **joule (J)** (rhymes with "pool"). The U.S. customary unit of work is the **foot-pound,** because distances are measured in feet and forces in pounds in that system.

A useful alternate definition relates the work done on an object to the angle the displacement makes with respect to the force. This definition exploits the triangle shown in Figure 5.2. The components of the vector $\vec{F}$ can be written as $F_x = F\cos\theta$ and $F_y = F\sin\theta$. However, only the x-component, which is parallel to the direction of motion, makes a nonzero contribution to the work done on the object.

The work W done on an object by a constant force $\vec{F}$ during a linear displacement $\Delta\vec{x}$ is

$$W = (F\cos\theta)d \qquad [5.3]$$

where d is the magnitude of the displacement and θ is the angle between the vectors $\vec{F}$ and the displacement vector, $\Delta\vec{x}$.

SI unit: joule (J)

The definition in Equation 5.3 can also be used more generally when the displacement is not specifically along the x-axis or any other axis.

In Figure 5.3 a man carries a bucket of water horizontally at constant velocity. The upward force exerted by the man's hand on the bucket is perpendicular to the direction of motion, so it does no work on the bucket. This can also be seen from Equation 5.3 because the angle between the force exerted by the hand and the direction of motion is 90°, giving $\cos 90° = 0$ and $W = 0$. Similarly, the force of gravity does no work on the bucket.

Work always requires a system of more than just one object. A nail, for example, can't do work on itself, but a hammer can do work on the nail by driving it into a board. In general, an object may be moving under the influence of several external forces. In that case, the net work done on the object as it undergoes some displacement is just the sum of the amount of work done by each force.

Work can be either positive or negative. In the definition of work in Equation 5.3, F and d are magnitudes, which are never negative. Work is therefore positive or negative depending on whether $\cos\theta$ is positive or negative. This, in turn, depends on the direction of $\vec{F}$ relative the direction of $\Delta\vec{x}$. When these vectors are pointing in the same direction, the angle between them is 0°, so $\cos 0° = +1$ and the work is positive. For example, when a student lifts a box as in Figure 5.4, the work he does on the box is positive because the force he exerts on the box is upward, in the same direction as the displacement. In lowering the box slowly back down, however, the student still exerts an upward force on the box, but the motion of the box is downwards. Because the vectors $\vec{F}$ and $\Delta\vec{x}$ are now in opposite directions, the angle between them is 180°, and $\cos 180° = -1$ and the work done by the student is negative. In general, when the part of $\vec{F}$ parallel to $\Delta\vec{x}$ points in the same direction as $\Delta\vec{x}$, the work is positive; otherwise, it's negative.

Because Equations 5.1–5.3 assume a force constant in both direction and magnitude, they are only special cases of a more general definition of work—that done by a varying force—treated briefly in Section 5.7.

■ *Quick Quiz*

5.1 In Figure 5.5 (a)–(d), a block moves to the right in the positive x-direction through the displacement $\Delta\vec{x}$ while under the influence of a force with the same magnitude $\vec{F}$. Which of the following is the correct order of the amount of work done by the force $\vec{F}$, from most positive to most negative? (a) d, c, a, b (b) c, a, b, d (c) c, a, d, b

Figure 5.5 (Quick Quiz 5.1) A force $\vec{\mathbf{F}}$ is exerted on an object that undergoes a displacement $\Delta\vec{\mathbf{x}}$ to the right. Both the magnitude of the force and the displacement are the same in all four cases.

■ **EXAMPLE 5.1**   **Sledding Through the Yukon**

GOAL Apply the basic definitions of work done by a constant force.

PROBLEM An Eskimo returning from a successful fishing trip pulls a sled loaded with salmon. The total mass of the sled and salmon is 50.0 kg, and the Eskimo exerts a force of magnitude 1.20×10^2 N on the sled by pulling on the rope. **(a)** How much work does he do on the sled if the rope is horizontal to the ground ($\theta = 0°$ in Fig. 5.6) and he pulls the sled 5.00 m? **(b)** How much work does he do on the sled if $\theta = 30.0°$ and he pulls the sled the same distance? (Treat the sled as a point particle, so details such as the point of attachment of the rope make no difference.) **(c)** At a coordinate position of 12.4 m, the Eskimo lets up on the applied force. A friction force of 45.0 N between the ice and the sled brings the sled to rest at a coordinate position of 18.2 m. How much work does friction do on the sled?

Figure 5.6 (Examples 5.1 and 5.2) An Eskimo pulling a sled with a rope at an angle θ to the horizontal.

STRATEGY Substitute the given values of F and Δx into the basic equations for work, Equations 5.2 and 5.3.

SOLUTION

(a) Find the work done when the force is horizontal.

Use Equation 5.2, substituting the given values:

$$W = F_x \Delta x = (1.20 \times 10^2 \text{ N})(5.00 \text{ m}) = \boxed{6.00 \times 10^2 \text{ J}}$$

(b) Find the work done when the force is exerted at a 30° angle.

Use Equation 5.3, again substituting the given values:

$$W = (F \cos \theta)\, d = (1.20 \times 10^2 \text{ N})(\cos 30°)(5.00 \text{ m})$$
$$= \boxed{5.20 \times 10^2 \text{ J}}$$

(c) How much work does a friction force of 45.0 N do on the sled as it travels from a coordinate position of 12.4 m to 18.2 m?

Use Equation 5.2, with F_x replaced by f_k:

$$W_{\text{fric}} = F_x \Delta x = f_k(x_f - x_i)$$

Substitute $f_k = -45.0$ N and the initial and final coordinate positions into x_i and x_f:

$$W_{\text{fric}} = (-45.0 \text{ N})(18.2 \text{ m} - 12.4 \text{ m}) = \boxed{-261 \text{ J}}$$

REMARKS The normal force $\vec{\mathbf{n}}$, the gravitational force $m\vec{\mathbf{g}}$, and the upward component of the applied force do *no* work on the sled because they're perpendicular to the displacement. The mass of the sled didn't come into play here, but it is important when the effects of friction must be calculated, and in the next section, where we introduce the work–energy theorem.

QUESTION 5.1 How does the answer for the work done by the applied force change if the load is doubled? Explain.

EXERCISE 5.1 Suppose the Eskimo is pushing the same 50.0-kg sled across level terrain with a force of 50.0 N. **(a)** If he does 4.00×10^2 J of work on the sled while exerting the force horizontally, through what distance must he have pushed it? **(b)** If he exerts the same force at an angle of 45.0° with respect to the horizontal and moves the sled through the same distance, how much work does he do on the sled?

ANSWERS (a) 8.00 m (b) 283 J

a

b

The edge of a razor blade looks smooth to the eye, but under a microscope proves to have numerous irregularities.

Work and Dissipative Forces

Frictional work is extremely important in everyday life because doing almost any other kind of work is impossible without it. The Eskimo in the last example, for instance, depends on surface friction to pull his sled. Otherwise, the rope would slip in his hands and exert no force on the sled, while his feet slid out from underneath him and he fell flat on his face. Cars wouldn't work without friction, nor could conveyor belts, nor even our muscle tissue.

The work done by pushing or pulling an object is the application of a single force. Friction, on the other hand, is a complex process caused by numerous microscopic interactions over the entire area of the surfaces in contact. Consider a metal block sliding over a metal surface. Microscopic "teeth" in the block encounter equally microscopic irregularities in the underlying surface. Pressing against each other, the teeth deform, get hot, and weld to the opposite surface. Work must be done breaking these temporary bonds, and that comes at the expense of the energy of motion of the block, to be discussed in the next section. The energy lost by the block goes into heating both the block and its environment, with some energy converted to sound.

The friction force of two objects in contact and in relative motion to each other always dissipates energy in these relatively complex ways. For our purposes, the phrase "work done by friction" will denote the effect of these processes on mechanical energy alone.

■ **EXAMPLE 5.2** | **More Sledding**

GOAL Calculate the work done by friction when an object is acted on by an applied force.

PROBLEM Suppose that in Example 5.1 the coefficient of kinetic friction between the loaded 50.0-kg sled and snow is 0.200. **(a)** The Eskimo again pulls the sled 5.00 m, exerting a force of 1.20×10^2 N at an angle of 0°. Find the work done on the sled by friction, and the net work. **(b)** Repeat the calculation if the applied force is exerted at an angle of 30.0° with the horizontal.

STRATEGY See Figure 5.6. The frictional work depends on the magnitude of the kinetic friction coefficient, the normal force, and the displacement. Use the *y*-component of Newton's second law to find the normal force $\vec{\mathbf{n}}$, calculate the work done by friction using the definitions, and sum with the result of Example 5.1(a) to obtain the net work on the sled. Part (b) is solved similarly, but the normal force is smaller because it has the help of the applied force $\vec{\mathbf{F}}_{app}$ in supporting the load.

. . . .

SOLUTION

(a) Find the work done by friction on the sled and the net work, if the applied force is horizontal.

First, find the normal force from the *y*-component of Newton's second law, which involves only the normal force and the force of gravity:

$$\sum F_y = n - mg = 0 \quad \rightarrow \quad n = mg$$

Use the normal force to compute the work done by friction:

$$W_{fric} = -f_k \Delta x = -\mu_k n \Delta x = -\mu_k mg \Delta x$$
$$= -(0.200)(50.0 \text{ kg})(9.80 \text{ m/s}^2)(5.00 \text{ m})$$
$$= \boxed{-4.90 \times 10^2 \text{ J}}$$

Sum the frictional work with the work done by the applied force from Example 5.1 to get the net work (the normal and gravity forces are perpendicular to the displacement, so they don't contribute):

$$W_{net} = W_{app} + W_{fric} + W_n + W_g$$
$$= 6.00 \times 10^2 \text{ J} + (-4.90 \times 10^2 \text{ J}) + 0 + 0$$
$$= \boxed{1.10 \times 10^2 \text{ J}}$$

(b) Recalculate the frictional work and net work if the applied force is exerted at a 30.0° angle.

Find the normal force from the y-component of Newton's second law:

$$\sum F_y = n - mg + F_{app} \sin \theta = 0$$
$$n = mg - F_{app} \sin \theta$$

Use the normal force to calculate the work done by friction:

$$W_{fric} = -f_k \Delta x = -\mu_k n \Delta x = -\mu_k (mg - F_{app} \sin \theta) \, \Delta x$$
$$= -(0.200)(50.0 \text{ kg} \cdot 9.80 \text{ m/s}^2$$
$$-1.20 \times 10^2 \text{ N} \sin 30.0°)(5.00 \text{ m})$$
$$W_{fric} = \boxed{-4.30 \times 10^2 \text{ J}}$$

Sum this answer with the result of Example 5.1(b) to get the net work (again, the normal and gravity forces don't contribute):

$$W_{net} = W_{app} + W_{fric} + W_n + W_g$$
$$= 5.20 \times 10^2 \text{ J} - 4.30 \times 10^2 \text{ J} + 0 + 0 = \boxed{9.0 \times 10^1 \text{ J}}$$

REMARKS The most important thing to notice here is that exerting the applied force at different angles can dramatically affect the work done on the sled. Pulling at the optimal angle (11.3° in this case) will result in the most net work for the same applied force.

QUESTION 5.2 How does the net work change in each case if the displacement is doubled?

EXERCISE 5.2 (a) The Eskimo pushes the same 50.0-kg sled over level ground with a force of 1.75×10^2 N exerted horizontally, moving it a distance of 6.00 m over new terrain. If the net work done on the sled is 1.50×10^2 J, find the coefficient of kinetic friction. (b) Repeat the exercise with the same data, finding the coefficient of kinetic friction, but assume the applied force is upwards at a 45.0° angle with the horizontal.

ANSWER (a) 0.306   (b) 0.270

5.2 Kinetic Energy and the Work–Energy Theorem

Solving problems using Newton's second law can be difficult if the forces involved are complicated. An alternative is to relate the speed of an object to the net work done on it by external forces. If the net work can be calculated for a given displacement, the change in the object's speed is easy to evaluate.

Figure 5.7 shows an object of mass m moving to the right under the action of a constant net force $\vec{\mathbf{F}}_{net}$, also directed to the right. Because the force is constant, we know from Newton's second law that the object moves with constant acceleration $\vec{\mathbf{a}}$. If the object is displaced by Δx, the work done by $\vec{\mathbf{F}}_{net}$ on the object is

$$W_{net} = F_{net} \, \Delta x = (ma) \, \Delta x \qquad \text{[5.4]}$$

In Chapter 2, we found that the following relationship holds when an object undergoes constant acceleration:

$$v^2 = v_0^2 + 2a\Delta x \qquad \text{or} \qquad a \, \Delta x = \frac{v^2 - v_0^2}{2}$$

We can substitute this expression into Equation 5.4 to get

$$W_{net} = m \left(\frac{v^2 - v_0^2}{2} \right)$$

or

$$W_{net} = \tfrac{1}{2}mv^2 - \tfrac{1}{2}mv_0^2 \qquad \text{[5.5]}$$

So the net work done on an object equals a change in a quantity of the form $\frac{1}{2}mv^2$. Because this term carries units of energy and involves the object's speed, it can be interpreted as energy associated with the object's motion, leading to the following definition:

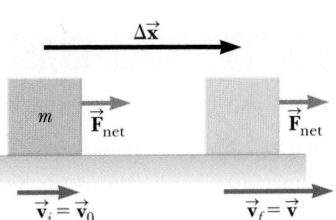

Figure 5.7 An object undergoes a displacement and a change in velocity under the action of a constant net force $\vec{\mathbf{F}}_{net}$.

Kinetic energy ▶

The **kinetic energy KE** of an object of mass m moving with a speed v is

$$KE \equiv \tfrac{1}{2}mv^2 \qquad [5.6]$$

SI unit: joule (J) = kg · m²/s²

Like work, kinetic energy is a scalar quantity. Using this definition in Equation 5.5, we arrive at an important result known as the **work–energy theorem:**

Work–energy theorem ▶

The net work done on an object is equal to the change in the object's kinetic energy:

$$W_{net} = KE_f - KE_i = \Delta KE \qquad [5.7]$$

where the change in the kinetic energy is due entirely to the object's change in speed.

The proviso on the speed is necessary because work that deforms or causes the object to warm up invalidates Equation 5.7, although under most circumstances it remains approximately correct. From that equation, a positive net work W_{net} means that the final kinetic energy KE_f is greater than the initial kinetic energy KE_i. This, in turn, means that the object's final speed is greater than its initial speed. So positive net work increases an object's speed, and negative net work decreases its speed.

We can also turn Equation 5.7 around and think of kinetic energy as the work a moving object can do in coming to rest. For example, suppose a hammer is on the verge of striking a nail, as in Figure 5.8. The moving hammer has kinetic energy and can therefore do work on the nail. The work done on the nail is $F\Delta x$, where F is the average net force exerted on the nail and Δx is the distance the nail is driven into the wall. That work, plus small amounts of energy carried away by heat and sound, is equal to the change in kinetic energy of the hammer, ΔKE.

For convenience, the work–energy theorem was derived under the assumption that the net force acting on the object was constant. A more general derivation, using calculus, would show that Equation 5.7 is valid under all circumstances, including the application of a variable force.

Figure 5.8 The moving hammer has kinetic energy and can do work on the nail, driving it into the wall.

■ APPLYING PHYSICS 5.1   Leaving Skid Marks

Suppose a car traveling at a speed v skids a distance d after its brakes lock. Estimate how far it would skid if it were traveling at speed $2v$ when its brakes locked.

EXPLANATION Assume for simplicity that the force of kinetic friction between the car and the road surface is constant and the same at both speeds. From the work–energy theorem, the net force exerted on the car times the displacement of the car, $F_{net}\Delta x$, is equal in magnitude to its initial kinetic energy, $\tfrac{1}{2}mv^2$. When the speed is doubled, the kinetic energy of the car is quadrupled. So for a given applied friction force, the distance traveled must increase fourfold when the initial speed is doubled, and the estimated distance the car skids is $4d$. ■

■ EXAMPLE 5.3   Collision Analysis

GOAL Apply the work–energy theorem with a known force.

PROBLEM The driver of a 1.00×10^3 kg car traveling on the interstate at 35.0 m/s (nearly 80.0 mph) slams on his brakes to avoid hitting a second vehicle in front of him, which had come to rest because of congestion ahead (Fig. 5.9). After the brakes are applied, a constant kinetic friction force of magnitude 8.00×10^3 N acts on the car. Ignore air resistance. **(a)** At what minimum distance should the brakes be applied to avoid a collision with the other vehicle? **(b)** If the distance between the vehicles is initially only 30.0 m, at what speed would the collision occur?

Figure 5.9 (Example 5.3) A braking vehicle just prior to an accident.

STRATEGY Compute the net work, which involves just the kinetic friction, because the normal and gravity forces are perpendicular to the motion. Then set the net work equal to the change in kinetic energy. To get the minimum distance in part (a), we take the final speed v_f to be zero just as the braking vehicle reaches the rear of the vehicle at rest. Solve for the unknown, Δx. For part (b) proceed similarly, except that the unknown is the final velocity v_f.

SOLUTION

(a) Find the minimum necessary stopping distance.

Apply the work–energy theorem to the car:

$$W_{net} = \tfrac{1}{2}mv_f{}^2 - \tfrac{1}{2}mv_i{}^2$$

Substitute an expression for the frictional work and set $v_f = 0$:

$$-f_k\Delta x = 0 - \tfrac{1}{2}mv_i{}^2$$

Substitute $v_i = 35.0$ m/s, $f_k = 8.00 \times 10^3$ N, and $m = 1.00 \times 10^3$ kg. Solve for Δx:

$$-(8.00 \times 10^3 \text{ N})\,\Delta x = -\tfrac{1}{2}(1.00 \times 10^3 \text{ kg})(35.0 \text{ m/s})^2$$

$$\Delta x = \boxed{76.6 \text{ m}}$$

(b) At the given distance of 30.0 m, the car is too close to the other vehicle. Find the speed at impact.

Write down the work–energy theorem:

$$W_{net} = W_{fric} = -f_k\Delta x = \tfrac{1}{2}mv_f{}^2 - \tfrac{1}{2}mv_i{}^2$$

Multiply by $2/m$ and rearrange terms, solving for the final velocity v_f:

$$v_f{}^2 = v_i{}^2 - \frac{2}{m}f_k\Delta x$$

$$v_f{}^2 = (35.0 \text{ m/s})^2 - \left(\frac{2}{1.00 \times 10^3 \text{ kg}}\right)(8.00 \times 10^3 \text{ N})(30.0 \text{ m})$$

$$= 745 \text{ m}^2/\text{s}^2$$

$$v_f = \boxed{27.3 \text{ m/s}}$$

REMARKS This calculation illustrates how important it is to remain alert on the highway, allowing for an adequate stopping distance at all times. It takes about a second to react to the brake lights of the car in front of you. On a high-speed highway, your car may travel more than 30 meters before you can engage the brakes. Bumper-to-bumper traffic at high speed, as often exists on the highways near big cities, is extremely unsafe.

QUESTION 5.3 Qualitatively, how would the answer for the final velocity change in part (b) if it's raining during the incident? Explain.

EXERCISE 5.3 A police investigator measures straight skid marks 27.0 m long in an accident investigation. Assuming a friction force and car mass the same as in the previous problem, what was the minimum speed of the car when the brakes locked?

ANSWER 20.8 m/s

Conservative and Nonconservative Forces

It turns out there are two general kinds of forces. The first is called a **conservative force.** Gravity is probably the best example of a conservative force. To understand the origin of the name, think of a diver climbing to the top of a 10-meter platform. The diver has to do work against gravity in making the climb. Once at the top, however, he can recover the work as kinetic energy by taking a dive. His speed just before hitting the water will give him a kinetic energy equal to the work he did against gravity in climbing to the top of the platform, minus the effect of some nonconservative forces, such as air drag and internal muscular friction.

A **nonconservative force** is generally dissipative, which means that it tends to randomly disperse the energy of bodies on which it acts. This dispersal of energy often takes the form of heat or sound. Kinetic friction and air drag are good examples. Propulsive forces, like the force exerted by a jet engine on a plane or by a propeller on a submarine, are also nonconservative.

Figure 5.10 Because the gravity field is conservative, the diver regains as kinetic energy the work she did against gravity in climbing the ladder. Taking the frictionless slide gives the same result.

The work done in moving the book is greater along the rust-colored path than along the blue path.

Figure 5.11 Because friction is a nonconservative force, a book pushed along the three segments Ⓐ–Ⓑ, Ⓑ–Ⓒ, and Ⓒ–Ⓓ requires three times the work as pushing the book directly from Ⓐ to Ⓓ.

Conservative force ▶

Work done against a nonconservative force can't be easily recovered. Dragging objects over a rough surface requires work. When the Eskimo in Example 5.2 dragged the sled across terrain having a nonzero coefficient of friction, the net work was smaller than in the frictionless case. The missing energy went into warming the sled and its environment. As will be seen in the study of thermodynamics, such losses can't be avoided, nor all the energy recovered, so these forces are called nonconservative.

Another way to characterize conservative and nonconservative forces is to measure the work done by a force on an object traveling between two points along different paths. The work done by gravity on someone going down a frictionless slide, as in Figure 5.10, is the same as that done on someone diving into the water from the same height. This equality doesn't hold for nonconservative forces. For example, sliding a book directly from point Ⓐ to point Ⓓ in Figure 5.11 requires a certain amount of work against friction, but sliding the book along the three other legs of the square, from Ⓐ to Ⓑ, Ⓑ to Ⓒ, and finally Ⓒ to Ⓓ, requires three times as much work. This observation motivates the following definition of a conservative force:

A force is conservative if the work it does moving an object between two points is the same no matter what path is taken.

Nonconservative forces, as we've seen, don't have this property. The work–energy theorem, Equation 5.7, can be rewritten in terms of the work done by conservative forces W_c and the work done by nonconservative forces W_{nc} because the net work is just the sum of these two:

$$W_{nc} + W_c = \Delta KE \qquad \text{[5.8]}$$

It turns out that conservative forces have another useful property: The work they do can be recast as something called **potential energy,** a quantity that depends only on the beginning and end points of a curve, not the path taken.

5.3 Gravitational Potential Energy

An object with kinetic energy (energy of motion) can do work on another object, just like a moving hammer can drive a nail into a wall. A brick on a high shelf can also do work: it can fall off the shelf, accelerate downwards, and hit a nail squarely, driving it into the floorboards. The brick is said to have **potential energy** associated with it, because from its location on the shelf it can potentially do work.

Potential energy is a property of a **system,** rather than of a single object, because it's due to the relative positions of interacting objects in the system, such as the position of the diver in Figure 5.10 relative to the Earth. In this chapter we define a system as a collection of objects interacting via forces or other processes that are internal to the system. It turns out that potential energy is another way of looking at the work done by conservative forces.

Gravitational Work and Potential Energy

Using the work–energy theorem in problems involving gravitation requires computing the work done by gravity. For most trajectories—say, for a ball traversing a parabolic arc—finding the gravitational work done on the ball requires sophisticated techniques from calculus. Fortunately, for conservative fields there's a simple alternative: potential energy.

Gravity is a conservative force, and for every conservative force a special expression called a potential energy function can be found. Evaluating that function at any two points in an object's path of motion and finding the difference will give the negative of the work done by that force between those two points. It's also advantageous that potential energy, like work and kinetic energy, is a scalar quantity.

Our first step is to find the work done by gravity on an object when it moves from one position to another. The negative of that work is the change in the gravitational potential energy of the system, and from that expression, we'll be able to identify the potential energy function.

In Active Figure 5.12, a book of mass m falls from a height y_i to a height y_f, where the positive y-coordinate represents position above the ground. We neglect the force of air friction, so the only force acting on the book is gravitation. How much work is done? The magnitude of the force is mg and that of the displacement is $\Delta y = y_i - y_f$ (a positive number), while both $\vec{F}$ and $\Delta\vec{y}$ are pointing downwards, so the angle between them is zero. We apply the definition of work in Equation 5.3, with $d = y_i - y_f$:

$$W_g = Fd\cos\theta = mg(y_i - y_f)\cos 0° = -mg(y_f - y_i) \qquad \text{[5.9]}$$

Factoring out the minus sign was deliberate, to clarify the coming connection to potential energy. Equation 5.9 for gravitational work holds for any object, regardless of its trajectory in space, because the gravitational force is conservative. Now, W_g will appear as the work done by gravity in the work–energy theorem. For the rest of this section, assume for simplicity that we are dealing only with systems involving gravity and nonconservative forces. Then Equation 5.8 can be written as

$$W_{\text{net}} = W_{nc} + W_g = \Delta KE$$

where W_{nc} is the work done by the nonconservative forces. Substituting the expression for W_g from Equation 5.9, we obtain

$$W_{nc} - mg(y_f - y_i) = \Delta KE \qquad \text{[5.10a]}$$

Next, we add $mg(y_f - y_i)$ to both sides:

$$W_{nc} = \Delta KE + mg(y_f - y_i) \qquad \text{[5.10b]}$$

Now, by definition, we'll make the connection between gravitational work and gravitational potential energy.

The gravitational potential energy of a system consisting of Earth and an object of mass m near Earth's surface is given by

$$PE \equiv mgy \qquad \text{[5.11]}$$

where g is the acceleration of gravity and y is the vertical position of the mass relative the surface of Earth (or some other reference point).

SI unit: joule (J)

◄ Gravitational potential energy

In this definition, $y = 0$ is usually taken to correspond to Earth's surface, but that is not strictly necessary, as discussed in the next subsection. It turns out that only *differences* in potential energy really matter.

So the gravitational potential energy associated with an object located near the surface of Earth is the object's weight mg times its vertical position y above Earth.

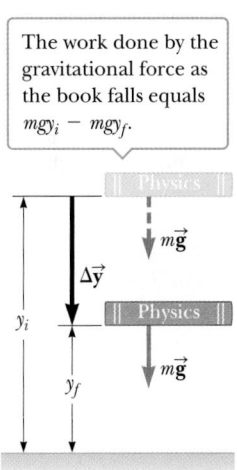

The work done by the gravitational force as the book falls equals $mgy_i - mgy_f$.

Active Figure 5.12 A book of mass m falls from a height y_i to a height y_f.

From this *definition*, we have the relationship between gravitational work and gravitational potential energy:

$$W_g = -(PE_f - PE_i) = -(mgy_f - mgy_i) \qquad [5.12]$$

The work done by gravity is one and the same as the negative of the change in gravitational potential energy.

Finally, using the relationship in Equation 5.12 in Equation 5.10b, we obtain an extension of the work–energy theorem:

$$W_{nc} = (KE_f - KE_i) + (PE_f - PE_i) \qquad [5.13]$$

This equation says that the work done by nonconservative forces, W_{nc}, is equal to the change in the kinetic energy plus the change in the gravitational potential energy.

Equation 5.13 will turn out to be true in general, even when other conservative forces besides gravity are present. The work done by these additional conservative forces will again be recast as changes in potential energy and will appear on the right-hand side along with the expression for gravitational potential energy.

Reference Levels for Gravitational Potential Energy

In solving problems involving gravitational potential energy, it's important to choose a location at which to set that energy equal to zero. Given the form of Equation 5.11, this is the same as choosing the place where $y = 0$. The choice is completely arbitrary because the important quantity is the *difference* in potential energy, and this difference will be the same regardless of the choice of zero level. However, once this position is chosen, it must remain fixed for a given problem.

While it's always possible to choose the surface of Earth as the reference position for zero potential energy, the statement of a problem will usually suggest a convenient position to use. As an example, consider a book at several possible locations, as in Figure 5.13. When the book is at Ⓐ, a natural zero level for potential energy is the surface of the desk. When the book is at Ⓑ, the floor might be a more convenient reference level. Finally, a location such as Ⓒ, where the book is held out a window, would suggest choosing the surface of Earth as the zero level of potential energy. The choice, however, makes no difference: Any of the three reference levels could be used as the zero level, regardless of whether the book is at Ⓐ, Ⓑ, or Ⓒ. Example 5.4 illustrates this important point.

Figure 5.13 Any reference level—the desktop, the floor of the room, or the ground outside the building—can be used to represent zero gravitational potential energy in the book–Earth system.

■ EXAMPLE 5.4 | Wax Your Skis

GOAL Calculate the change in gravitational potential energy for different choices of reference level.

PROBLEM A 60.0-kg skier is at the top of a slope, as shown in Figure 5.14. At the initial point Ⓐ, she is 10.0 m vertically above point Ⓑ. **(a)** Setting the zero level for gravitational potential energy at Ⓑ, find the gravitational potential energy of this system when the skier is at Ⓐ and then at Ⓑ. Finally, find the change in potential energy of the skier–Earth system as the skier goes from point Ⓐ to point Ⓑ. **(b)** Repeat this problem with the zero level at point Ⓐ. **(c)** Repeat again, with the zero level 2.00 m higher than point Ⓑ.

STRATEGY Follow the definition and be careful with signs. Ⓐ is the initial point, with gravitational potential energy PE_i, and Ⓑ is the final point, with gravitational potential energy PE_f. The location chosen for $y = 0$ is also the zero point for the potential energy, because $PE = mgy$.

10.0 m

Figure 5.14 (Example 5.4)

SOLUTION

(a) Let $y = 0$ at Ⓑ. Calculate the potential energy at Ⓐ and at Ⓑ, and calculate the change in potential energy.

Find PE_i, the potential energy at Ⓐ, from Equation 5.11:

$$PE_i = mgy_i = (60.0 \text{ kg})(9.80 \text{ m/s}^2)(10.0 \text{ m}) = 5.88 \times 10^3 \text{ J}$$

$PE_f = 0$ at Ⓑ by choice. Find the difference in potential energy between Ⓐ and Ⓑ:

$$PE_f - PE_i = 0 - 5.88 \times 10^3 \text{ J} = \boxed{-5.88 \times 10^3 \text{ J}}$$

(b) Repeat the problem if $y = 0$ at Ⓐ, the new reference point, so that PE = 0 at Ⓐ.

Find PE_f, noting that point Ⓑ is now at $y = -10.0$ m:

$$PE_f = mgy_f = (60.0 \text{ kg})(9.80 \text{ m/s}^2)(-10.0 \text{ m})$$
$$= -5.88 \times 10^3 \text{ J}$$
$$PE_f - PE_i = -5.88 \times 10^3 \text{ J} - 0 = \boxed{-5.88 \times 10^3 \text{ J}}$$

(c) Repeat the problem, if $y = 0$ two meters above Ⓑ.

Find PE_i, the potential energy at Ⓐ:

$$PE_i = mgy_i = (60.0 \text{ kg})(9.80 \text{ m/s}^2)(8.00 \text{ m}) = 4.70 \times 10^3 \text{ J}$$

Find PE_f, the potential energy at Ⓑ:

$$PE_f = mgy_f = (60.0 \text{ kg})(9.8 \text{ m/s}^2)(-2.00 \text{ m})$$
$$= -1.18 \times 10^3 \text{ J}$$

Compute the change in potential energy:

$$PE_f - PE_i = -1.18 \times 10^3 \text{ J} - 4.70 \times 10^3 \text{ J}$$
$$= \boxed{-5.88 \times 10^3 \text{ J}}$$

REMARKS These calculations show that the change in the gravitational potential energy when the skier goes from the top of the slope to the bottom is -5.88×10^3 J, *regardless of the zero level selected.*

QUESTION 5.4 If the angle of the slope is increased, does the change of gravitational potential energy between two heights (a) increase, (b) decrease, (c) remain the same?

EXERCISE 5.4 If the zero level for gravitational potential energy is selected to be midway down the slope, 5.00 m above point Ⓑ, find the initial potential energy, the final potential energy, and the change in potential energy as the skier goes from point Ⓐ to Ⓑ in Figure 5.14.

ANSWER 2.94 kJ, −2.94 kJ, −5.88 kJ

Gravity and the Conservation of Mechanical Energy

Conservation principles play a very important role in physics. **When a physical quantity is conserved the numeric value of the quantity remains the same throughout the physical process.** Although the form of the quantity may change in some way, **its final value is the same as its initial value.**

The kinetic energy *KE* of an object falling only under the influence of gravity is constantly changing, as is the gravitational potential energy *PE*. Obviously, then, these quantities aren't conserved. Because all nonconservative forces are assumed absent, however, we can set $W_{nc} = 0$ in Equation 5.13. Rearranging the equation, we arrive at the following very interesting result:

$$KE_i + PE_i = KE_f + PE_f \qquad [5.14]$$

According to this equation, **the sum of the kinetic energy and the gravitational potential energy remains constant at all times and hence is a conserved quantity.** We denote the total mechanical energy by $E = KE + PE$, and say that **the total mechanical energy is conserved.**

To show how this concept works, think of tossing a rock off a cliff, ignoring the drag forces. As the rock falls, its speed increases, so its kinetic energy increases. As the rock approaches the ground, the potential energy of the rock–Earth system decreases. Whatever potential energy is lost as the rock moves downward appears as kinetic energy, and Equation 5.14 says that in the absence of nonconservative

Tip 5.4 Conservation Principles

There are many conservation laws like the conservation of mechanical energy in isolated systems, as in Equation 5.14. For example, momentum, angular momentum, and electric charge are all conserved quantities, as will be seen later. Conserved quantities may change form during physical interactions, but their sum total for a system never changes.

forces like air drag, the trading of energy is exactly even. This is true for all conservative forces, not just gravity.

Conservation of ▶
mechanical energy

> In any isolated system of objects interacting only through conservative forces, the total mechanical energy $E = KE + PE$, of the system, remains the same at all times.

If the force of gravity is the *only* force doing work within a system, then the principle of conservation of mechanical energy takes the form

$$\tfrac{1}{2}mv_i^2 + mgy_i = \tfrac{1}{2}mv_f^2 + mgy_f \qquad [5.15]$$

This form of the equation is particularly useful for solving problems explicitly involving only one mass and gravity. In that special case, which occurs commonly, notice that the mass cancels out of the equation. However, that is possible only because any change in kinetic energy of the Earth in response to the gravity field of the object of mass m has been (rightfully) neglected. In general, there must be kinetic energy terms for each object in the system, and gravitational potential energy terms for every pair of objects. Further terms have to be added when other conservative forces are present, as we'll soon see.

■ Quick Quiz

5.2 Three identical balls are thrown from the top of a building, all with the same initial speed. The first ball is thrown horizontally, the second at some angle above the horizontal, and the third at some angle below the horizontal, as in Active Figure 5.15. Neglecting air resistance, rank the speeds of the balls as they reach the ground, from fastest to slowest. (a) 1, 2, 3 (b) 2, 1, 3 (c) 3, 1, 2 (d) All three balls strike the ground at the same speed.

5.3 Bob, of mass m, drops from a tree limb at the same time that Esther, also of mass m, begins her descent down a frictionless slide. If they both start at the same height above the ground, which of the following is true about their kinetic energies as they reach the ground?

(a) Bob's kinetic energy is greater than Esther's.

(b) Esther's kinetic energy is greater than Bob's.

(c) They have the same kinetic energy.

(d) The answer depends on the shape of the slide.

Active Figure 5.15
(Quick Quiz 5.2) A student throws three identical balls from the top of a building, each at the same initial speed but at a different initial angle.

■ PROBLEM-SOLVING STRATEGY

Applying Conservation of Mechanical Energy
Take the following steps when applying conservation of mechanical energy to problems involving gravity:

1. **Define the system,** including all interacting bodies. Verify the absence of nonconservative forces.
2. **Choose a location for $y = 0$,** the zero point for gravitational potential energy.
3. **Select the body of interest and identify two points**—one point where you have given information and the other point where you want to find out something about the body of interest.
4. **Write down the conservation of energy equation,** Equation 5.15, for the system. **Identify the unknown quantity** of interest.
5. **Solve for the unknown quantity,** which is usually either a speed or a position, and substitute known values.

As previously stated, it's usually best to do the algebra with symbols rather than substituting known numbers first, because it's easier to check the symbols for possible errors. The exception is when a quantity is clearly zero, in which case immediate substitution greatly simplifies the ensuing algebra.

■ EXAMPLE 5.5 | Platform Diver

GOAL Use conservation of energy to calculate the speed of a body falling straight down in the presence of gravity.

PROBLEM A diver of mass m drops from a board 10.0 m above the water's surface, as in Figure 5.16. Neglect air resistance. **(a)** Use conservation of mechanical energy to find his speed 5.00 m above the water's surface. **(b)** Find his speed as he hits the water.

STRATEGY Refer to the problem-solving strategy. Step 1: The system consists of the diver and Earth. As the diver falls, only the force of gravity acts on him (neglecting air drag), so the mechanical energy of the system is conserved, and we can use conservation of energy for both parts (a) and (b). Step 2: Choose $y = 0$ for the water's surface. Step 3: In part (a), $y = 10.0$ m and $y = 5.00$ m are the points of interest, while in part (b), $y = 10.0$ m and $y = 0$ m are of interest.

Figure 5.16 (Example 5.5) The zero of gravitational potential energy is taken to be at the water's surface.

SOLUTION

(a) Find the diver's speed halfway down, at $y = 5.00$ m.

Step 4: We write the energy conservation equation and supply the proper terms:

$$KE_i + PE_i = KE_f + PE_f$$
$$\tfrac{1}{2}mv_i^2 + mgy_i = \tfrac{1}{2}mv_f^2 + mgy_f$$

Step 5: Substitute $v_i = 0$, cancel the mass m, and solve for v_f:

$$0 + gy_i = \tfrac{1}{2}v_f^2 + gy_f$$
$$v_f = \sqrt{2g(y_i - y_f)} = \sqrt{2(9.80 \text{ m/s}^2)(10.0 \text{ m} - 5.00 \text{ m})}$$
$$v_f = \boxed{9.90 \text{ m/s}}$$

(b) Find the diver's speed at the water's surface, $y = 0$.

Use the same procedure as in part (a), taking $y_f = 0$:

$$0 + mgy_i = \tfrac{1}{2}mv_f^2 + 0$$
$$v_f = \sqrt{2gy_i} = \sqrt{2(9.80 \text{ m/s}^2)(10.0 \text{ m})} = \boxed{14.0 \text{ m/s}}$$

REMARKS Notice that the speed halfway down is not half the final speed. Another interesting point is that the final answer doesn't depend on the mass. That is really a consequence of neglecting the change in kinetic energy of Earth, which is valid when the mass of the object, the diver in this case, is much smaller than the mass of Earth. In reality, Earth also falls towards the diver, reducing the final speed, but the reduction is so minuscule it could never be measured.

QUESTION 5.5 Qualitatively, how will the answers change if the diver takes a running dive off the end of the board?

EXERCISE 5.5 Suppose the diver vaults off the springboard, leaving it with an initial speed of 3.50 m/s upward. Use energy conservation to find his speed when he strikes the water.

ANSWER 14.4 m/s

■ EXAMPLE 5.6 | The Jumping Bug

GOAL Use conservation of mechanical energy and concepts from ballistics in two dimensions to calculate a speed.

PROBLEM A powerful grasshopper launches itself at an angle of 45° above the horizontal and rises to a maximum height of 1.00 m during the leap. (See Fig. 5.17.) With what speed v_i did it leave the ground? Neglect air resistance.

STRATEGY This problem can be solved with conservation of energy and the relation between the initial velocity and its x-component. Aside from the origin, the other point of interest is the maximum height $y = 1.00$ m, where the grasshopper has a velocity v_x in the x-direction only. Energy conservation then gives one equation with two unknowns: the initial speed v_i and speed at maximum height, v_x. Because there are no forces in the x-direction, however, v_x is the same as the x-component of the initial velocity.

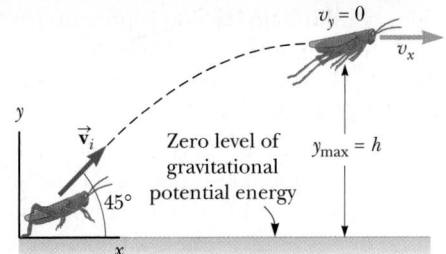

Figure 5.17 (Example 5.6)

(Continued)

SOLUTION

Use energy conservation:

$$\tfrac{1}{2}mv_i^2 + mgy_i = \tfrac{1}{2}mv_f^2 + mgy_f$$

Substitute $y_i = 0$, $v_f = v_x$, and $y_f = h$:

$$\tfrac{1}{2}mv_i^2 = \tfrac{1}{2}mv_x^2 + mgh$$

Multiply each side by $2/m$, obtaining one equation and two unknowns:

$$(1) \quad v_i^2 = v_x^2 + 2gh$$

Eliminate v_x by substituting $v_x = v_i \cos 45°$ into Equation (1), solving for v_i, and substituting known values:

$$v_i^2 = (v_i \cos 45°)^2 + 2gh = \tfrac{1}{2}v_i^2 + 2gh$$

$$v_i = 2\sqrt{gh} = 2\sqrt{(9.80 \text{ m/s}^2)(1.00 \text{ m})} = \boxed{6.26 \text{ m/s}}$$

REMARKS The final answer is a surprisingly high value and illustrates how strong insects are relative to their size.

QUESTION 5.6 All other given quantities remaining the same, how would the answer change if the initial angle were smaller? Why?

EXERCISE 5.6 A catapult launches a rock at a 30.0° angle with respect to the horizontal. Find the maximum height attained if the speed of the rock at its highest point is 30.0 m/s.

ANSWER 15.3 m

> **Tip 5.5 Don't Use Work Done by the Force of Gravity *and* Gravitational Potential Energy!**
>
> Gravitational potential energy is just another way of including the work done by the force of gravity in the work–energy theorem. Don't use both of them in the equation at the same time or you'll count it twice!

Gravity and Nonconservative Forces

When nonconservative forces are involved along with gravitation, the full work–energy theorem must be used, often with techniques from Chapter 4. Solving problems requires the basic procedure of the problem-solving strategy for conservation-of-energy problems in the previous section. The only difference lies in substituting Equation 5.13, the work–energy equation with potential energy, for Equation 5.15.

■ EXAMPLE 5.7   Der Stuka!

GOAL Use the work–energy theorem with gravitational potential energy to calculate the work done by a nonconservative force.

PROBLEM Waterslides are nearly frictionless, hence can provide bored students with high-speed thrills (Fig. 5.18). One such slide, Der Stuka, named for the terrifying German dive bombers of World War II, is 72.0 feet high (21.9 m), found at Six Flags in Dallas, Texas, and at Wet'n Wild in Orlando, Florida. **(a)** Determine the speed of a 60.0-kg woman at the bottom of such a slide, assuming no friction is present. **(b)** If the woman is clocked at 18.0 m/s at the bottom of the slide, find the work done on the woman by friction.

STRATEGY The system consists of the woman, Earth, and the slide. The normal force, always perpendicular to the displacement, does no work. Let $y = 0$ m represent the bottom of the slide. The two points of interest are $y = 0$ m and $y = 21.9$ m. Without friction, $W_{nc} = 0$, and we can apply conservation of mechanical energy, Equation 5.15. For part (b), use Equation 5.13, substitute two velocities and heights, and solve for W_{nc}.

Wet'n Wild Orlando

Figure 5.18 (Example 5.7) If the slide is frictionless, the woman's speed at the bottom depends only on the height of the slide, not on the path it takes.

SOLUTION

(a) Find the woman's speed at the bottom of the slide, assuming no friction.

Write down Equation 5.15, for conservation of energy:

$$\tfrac{1}{2}mv_i^2 + mgy_i = \tfrac{1}{2}mv_f^2 + mgy_f$$

Insert the values $v_i = 0$ and $v_f = 0$:

$$0 + mgy_i = \tfrac{1}{2}mv_f^2 + 0$$

Solve for v_f and substitute values for g and y_i:

$$v_f = \sqrt{2gy_i} = \sqrt{2(9.80\ \text{m/s}^2)(21.9\ \text{m})} = \boxed{20.7\ \text{m/s}}$$

(b) Find the work done on the woman by friction if $v_f = 18.0\ \text{m/s} < 20.7\ \text{m/s}$.

Write Equation 5.13, substituting expressions for the kinetic and potential energies:

$$W_{nc} = (KE_f - KE_i) + (PE_f - PE_i)$$
$$= (\tfrac{1}{2}mv_f^2 - \tfrac{1}{2}mv_i^2) + (mgy_f - mgy_i)$$

Substitute $m = 60.0$ kg, $v_f = 18.0$ m/s, and $v_i = 0$, and solve for W_{nc}:

$$W_{nc} = [\tfrac{1}{2}\cdot 60.0\ \text{kg}\cdot(18.0\ \text{m/s})^2 - 0]$$
$$+ [0 - 60.0\ \text{kg}\cdot(9.80\ \text{m/s}^2)\cdot 21.9\ \text{m}]$$
$$W_{nc} = \boxed{-3.16\times 10^3\ \text{J}}$$

REMARKS The speed found in part (a) is the same as if the woman fell vertically through a distance of 21.9 m, consistent with our intuition in Quick Quiz 5.3. The result of part (b) is negative because the system loses mechanical energy. Friction transforms part of the mechanical energy into thermal energy and mechanical waves, absorbed partly by the system and partly by the environment.

QUESTION 5.7 If the slide were not frictionless, would the shape of the slide affect the final answer? Explain.

EXERCISE 5.7 Suppose a slide similar to Der Stuka is 35.0 meters high, but is a straight slope, inclined at 45.0° with respect to the horizontal. (a) Find the speed of a 60.0-kg woman at the bottom of the slide, assuming no friction. (b) If the woman has a speed of 20.0 m/s at the bottom, find the change in mechanical energy due to friction and (c) the magnitude of the force of friction, assumed constant.

ANSWERS (a) 26.2 m/s (b) -8.58×10^3 J (c) 173 N

EXAMPLE 5.8   Hit the Ski Slopes

GOAL Combine conservation of mechanical energy with the work–energy theorem involving friction on a horizontal surface.

PROBLEM A skier starts from rest at the top of a frictionless incline of height 20.0 m, as in Figure 5.19. At the bottom of the incline, the skier encounters a horizontal surface where the coefficient of kinetic friction between skis and snow is 0.210. **(a)** Find the skier's speed at the bottom. **(b)** How far does the skier travel on the horizontal surface before coming to rest? Neglect air resistance.

Figure 5.19 (Example 5.8) The skier slides down the slope and onto a level surface, stopping after traveling a distance d from the bottom of the hill.

STRATEGY Going down the frictionless incline is physically no different than going down the slide of the previous example and is handled the same way, using conservation of mechanical energy to find the speed $v_{\circledB}$ at the bottom. On the flat, rough surface, use the work–energy theorem, Equation 5.13, with $W_{nc} = W_{\text{fric}} = -f_k d$, where f_k is the magnitude of the force of friction and d is the distance traveled on the horizontal surface before coming to rest.

SOLUTION

(a) Find the skier's speed at the bottom.

Follow the procedure used in part (a) of the previous example as the skier moves from the top, point Ⓐ, to the bottom, point Ⓑ:

$$v_{\circledB} = \sqrt{2gh} = \sqrt{2(9.80\ \text{m/s}^2)(20.0\ \text{m})} = \boxed{19.8\ \text{m/s}}$$

(Continued)

(b) Find the distance traveled on the horizontal, rough surface.

Apply the work–energy theorem as the skier moves from Ⓑ to Ⓒ:

$$W_{net} = -f_k d = \Delta KE = \tfrac{1}{2}mv_{Ⓒ}^2 - \tfrac{1}{2}mv_{Ⓑ}^2$$

Substitute $v_{Ⓒ} = 0$ and $f_k = \mu_k n = \mu_k mg$:

$$-\mu_k mgd = -\tfrac{1}{2}mv_{Ⓑ}^2$$

Solve for d:

$$d = \frac{v_{Ⓑ}^2}{2\mu_k g} = \frac{(19.8 \text{ m/s})^2}{2(0.210)(9.80 \text{ m/s}^2)} = \boxed{95.2 \text{ m}}$$

REMARKS Substituting the symbolic expression $v_{Ⓑ} = \sqrt{2gh}$ into the equation for the distance d shows that d is linearly proportional to h: Doubling the height doubles the distance traveled.

QUESTION 5.8 Give two reasons why skiers typically assume a crouching position when going down a slope.

EXERCISE 5.8 Find the horizontal distance the skier travels before coming to rest if the incline also has a coefficient of kinetic friction equal to 0.210. Assume that $\theta = 20.0°$.

ANSWER 40.3 m

5.4 Spring Potential Energy

Springs are important elements in modern technology. They are found in machines of all kinds, in watches, toys, cars, and trains. Springs will be introduced here, then studied in more detail in Chapter 13.

Work done by an applied force in stretching or compressing a spring can be recovered by removing the applied force, so like gravity, the spring force is conservative, as long as losses through internal friction of the spring can be neglected. This means a potential energy function can be found and used in the work–energy theorem.

Active Figure 5.20a shows a spring in its equilibrium position, where the spring is neither compressed nor stretched. Pushing a block against the spring as in Active Figure 5.20b compresses it a distance x. Although x appears to be merely a coordinate, for springs it also represents a displacement from the equilibrium position, which for our purposes will always be taken to be at $x = 0$. Experimentally, it turns out that doubling a given displacement requires double the force, while tripling it takes triple the force. This means the force exerted by the spring, F_s, must be proportional to the displacement x, or

$$F_s = -kx \qquad [5.16]$$

where k is a constant of proportionality, the *spring constant*, carrying units of newtons per meter. Equation 5.16 is called **Hooke's law**, after Sir Robert Hooke, who discovered the relationship. The force F_s is often called a *restoring force* because the spring always exerts a force in a direction opposite the displacement of its end, tending to restore whatever is attached to the spring to its original position. For positive values of x, the force is negative, pointing back towards equilibrium at $x = 0$, and for negative x, the force is positive, again pointing towards $x = 0$. For a flexible spring, k is a small number (about 100 N/m), whereas for a stiff spring k is large (about 10 000 N/m). The value of the spring constant k is determined by how the spring was formed, its material composition, and the thickness of the wire. The minus sign ensures that the spring force is always directed back towards the equilibrium point.

As in the case of gravitation, a potential energy, called the **elastic potential energy,** can be associated with the spring force. Elastic potential energy is another way of looking at the work done by a spring during motion because it is equal to the negative of the work done by the spring. It can also be considered stored energy arising from the work done to compress or stretch the spring.

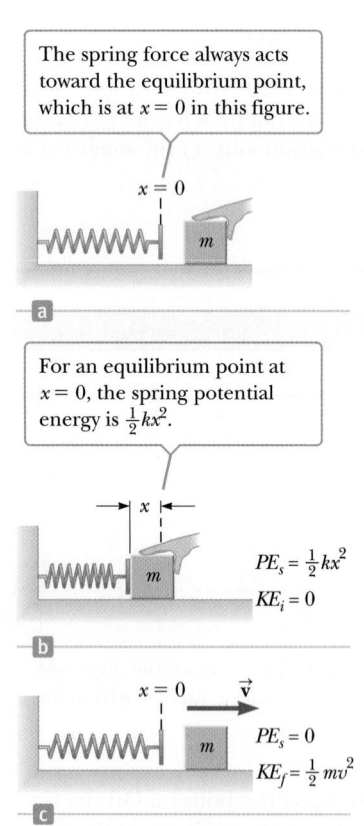

The spring force always acts toward the equilibrium point, which is at $x = 0$ in this figure.

$x = 0$

a

For an equilibrium point at $x = 0$, the spring potential energy is $\frac{1}{2}kx^2$.

$PE_s = \frac{1}{2}kx^2$
$KE_i = 0$

b

$x = 0$ $\vec{v}$

$PE_s = 0$
$KE_f = \frac{1}{2}mv^2$

c

Active Figure 5.20
(a) A spring at equilibrium, neither compressed nor stretched. (b) A block of mass m on a frictionless surface is pushed against the spring. (c) When the block is released, the energy stored in the spring is transferred to the block in the form of kinetic energy.

Consider a horizontal spring and mass at the equilibrium position. We determine the work done by the spring when compressed by an applied force from equilibrium to a displacement x, as in Active Figure 5.20b. The spring force points in the direction opposite the motion, so we expect the work to be negative. When we studied the constant force of gravity near Earth's surface, we found the work done on an object by multiplying the gravitational force by the vertical displacement of the object. However, this procedure can't be used with a varying force such as the spring force. Instead, we use the average force, $\overline{F}$:

$$\overline{F} = \frac{F_0 + F_1}{2} = \frac{0 - kx}{2} = -\frac{kx}{2}$$

Therefore, the work *done by the spring force* is

$$W_s = \overline{F}x = -\tfrac{1}{2}kx^2$$

In general, when the spring is stretched or compressed from x_i to x_f, the work done by the spring is

$$W_s = -\left(\tfrac{1}{2}kx_f{}^2 - \tfrac{1}{2}kx_i{}^2\right)$$

The work done by a spring can be included in the work–energy theorem. Assume Equation 5.13 now includes the work done by springs on the left-hand side. It then reads

$$W_{nc} - \left(\tfrac{1}{2}kx_f{}^2 - \tfrac{1}{2}kx_i{}^2\right) = \Delta KE + \Delta PE_g$$

where PE_g is the gravitational potential energy. We now define the elastic potential energy associated with the spring force, PE_s, by

$$PE_s \equiv \tfrac{1}{2}kx^2 \qquad\qquad [5.17]$$

Inserting this expression into the previous equation and rearranging gives the new form of the work–energy theorem, including both gravitational and elastic potential energy:

$$W_{nc} = (KE_f - KE_i) + (PE_{gf} - PE_{gi}) + (PE_{sf} - PE_{si}) \qquad [5.18]$$

where W_{nc} is the work done by nonconservative forces, KE is kinetic energy, PE_g is gravitational potential energy, and PE_s is the elastic potential energy. PE, formerly used to denote gravitational potential energy alone, will henceforth denote the total potential energy of a system, including potential energies due to all conservative forces acting on the system.

It's important to remember that the work done by gravity and springs in any given physical system is already included on the right-hand side of Equation 5.18 as potential energy and should not also be included on the left as work.

Active Figure 5.20c shows how the stored elastic potential energy can be recovered. When the block is released, the spring snaps back to its original length, and the stored elastic potential energy is converted to kinetic energy of the block. The elastic potential energy stored in the spring is zero when the spring is in the equilibrium position ($x = 0$). As given by Equation 5.17, potential energy is also stored in the spring when it's stretched. Further, the elastic potential energy is a maximum when the spring has reached its maximum compression or extension. Finally, because PE_s is proportional to x^2, the potential energy is always positive when the spring is not in the equilibrium position.

In the absence of nonconservative forces, $W_{nc} = 0$, so the left-hand side of Equation 5.18 is zero, and an extended form for conservation of mechanical energy results:

$$(KE + PE_g + PE_s)_i = (KE + PE_g + PE_s)_f \qquad [5.19]$$

Problems involving springs, gravity, and other forces are handled in exactly the same way as described in the problem-solving strategy for conservation of mechanical energy, except that the equilibrium point of any spring in the problem must be defined, in addition to the zero point for gravitational potential energy.

■ EXAMPLE 5.9 | A Horizontal Spring

GOAL Use conservation of energy to calculate the speed of a block on a horizontal spring with and without friction.

PROBLEM A block with mass of 5.00 kg is attached to a horizontal spring with spring constant $k = 4.00 \times 10^2$ N/m, as in Figure 5.21. The surface the block rests upon is frictionless. If the block is pulled out to $x_i = 0.050\ 0$ m and released, **(a)** find the speed of the block when it first reaches the equilibrium point, **(b)** find the speed when $x = 0.025\ 0$ m, and **(c)** repeat part (a) if friction acts on the block, with coefficient $\mu_k = 0.150$.

STRATEGY In parts (a) and (b) there are no nonconservative forces, so conservation of energy, Equation 5.19, can be applied. In part (c) the definition of work and the work–energy theorem are needed to deal with the loss of mechanical energy due to friction.

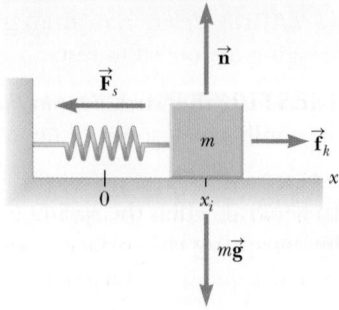

Figure 5.21 (Example 5.9) A mass attached to a spring.

SOLUTION

(a) Find the speed of the block at its equilibrium point.

Start with Equation 5.19:	$(KE + PE_g + PE_s)_i = (KE + PE_g + PE_s)_f$
Substitute expressions for the block's kinetic energy and the potential energy, and set the gravity terms to zero:	**(1)** $\frac{1}{2}mv_i^2 + \frac{1}{2}kx_i^2 = \frac{1}{2}mv_f^2 + \frac{1}{2}kx_f^2$
Substitute $v_i = 0$, $x_f = 0$, and multiply by $2/m$:	$\dfrac{k}{m}x_i^2 = v_f^2$
Solve for v_f and substitute the given values:	$v_f = \sqrt{\dfrac{k}{m}}\,x_i = \sqrt{\dfrac{4.00 \times 10^2\ \text{N/m}}{5.00\ \text{kg}}}\,(0.050\ 0\ \text{m})$
	$= \boxed{0.447\ \text{m/s}}$

(b) Find the speed of the block at the halfway point.

Set $v_i = 0$ in Equation (1) and multiply by $2/m$:	$\dfrac{kx_i^2}{m} = v_f^2 + \dfrac{kx_f^2}{m}$
Solve for v_f and substitute the given values:	$v_f = \sqrt{\dfrac{k}{m}\left(x_i^2 - x_f^2\right)}$
	$= \sqrt{\dfrac{4.00 \times 10^2\ \text{N/m}}{5.00\ \text{kg}}\left[(0.050\ 0\ \text{m})^2 - (0.025\ \text{m})^2\right]}$
	$= \boxed{0.387\ \text{m/s}}$

(c) Repeat part (a), this time with friction.

Apply the work–energy theorem. The work done by the force of gravity and the normal force is zero because these forces are perpendicular to the motion.	$W_{\text{fric}} = \frac{1}{2}mv_f^2 - \frac{1}{2}mv_i^2 + \frac{1}{2}kx_f^2 - \frac{1}{2}kx_i^2$
Substitute $v_i = 0$, $x_f = 0$, and $W_{\text{fric}} = -\mu_k n x_i$:	$-\mu_k n x_i = \frac{1}{2}mv_f^2 - \frac{1}{2}kx_i^2$

Set $n = mg$ and solve for v_f:

$$\tfrac{1}{2}mv_f{}^2 = \tfrac{1}{2}kx_i{}^2 - \mu_k mg x_i$$

$$v_f = \sqrt{\frac{k}{m}x_i{}^2 - 2\mu_k g x_i}$$

$$v_f = \sqrt{\frac{4.00 \times 10^2\,\text{N/m}}{5.00\,\text{kg}}(0.050\,0\,\text{m})^2 - 2(0.150)(9.80\,\text{m/s}^2)(0.050\,0\,\text{m})}$$

$$v_f = \boxed{0.230\,\text{m/s}}$$

REMARKS Friction or drag from immersion in a fluid damps the motion of an object attached to a spring, eventually bringing the object to rest.

QUESTION 5.9 In the case of friction, what percent of the mechanical energy was lost by the time the mass first reached the equilibrium point? (*Hint:* use the answers to parts (a) and (c).)

EXERCISE 5.9 Suppose the spring system in the last example starts at $x = 0$ and the attached object is given a kick to the right, so it has an initial speed of 0.600 m/s. (a) What distance from the origin does the object travel before coming to rest, assuming the surface is frictionless? (b) How does the answer change if the coefficient of kinetic friction is $\mu_k = 0.150$? (Use the quadratic formula.)

ANSWERS (a) 0.067 1 m (b) 0.051 2 m

■ EXAMPLE 5.10 | Circus Acrobat

GOAL Use conservation of mechanical energy to solve a one-dimensional problem involving gravitational potential energy and spring potential energy.

PROBLEM A 50.0-kg circus acrobat drops from a height of 2.00 meters straight down onto a springboard with a force constant of 8.00×10^3 N/m, as in Figure 5.22. By what maximum distance does she compress the spring?

STRATEGY Nonconservative forces are absent, so conservation of mechanical energy can be applied. At the two points of interest, the acrobat's initial position and the point of maximum spring compression, her velocity is zero, so the kinetic energy terms will be zero. Choose $y = 0$ as the point of maximum compression, so the final gravitational potential energy is zero. This choice also means that the initial position of the acrobat is $y_i = h + d$, where h is the acrobat's initial height above the platform and d is the spring's maximum compression.

Figure 5.22 (Example 5.10) An acrobat drops onto a springboard, causing it to compress.

SOLUTION

Use conservation of mechanical energy:

$$(1)\quad (KE + PE_g + PE_s)_i = (KE + PE_g + PE_s)_f$$

The only nonzero terms are the initial gravitational potential energy and the final spring potential energy.

$$0 + mg(h + d) + 0 = 0 + 0 + \tfrac{1}{2}kd^2$$

$$mg(h + d) = \tfrac{1}{2}kd^2$$

Substitute the given quantities and rearrange the equation into standard quadratic form:

$$(50.0\,\text{kg})(9.80\,\text{m/s}^2)(2.00\,\text{m} + d) = \tfrac{1}{2}(8.00 \times 10^3\,\text{N/m})d^2$$

$$d^2 - (0.123\,\text{m})d - 0.245\,\text{m}^2 = 0$$

Solve with the quadratic formula (Equation A.8):

$$d = \boxed{0.560\,\text{m}}$$

REMARKS The other solution, $d = -0.437$ m, can be rejected because d was chosen to be a positive number at the outset. A change in the acrobat's center of mass, say, by crouching as she makes contact with the springboard, also affects the

(*Continued*)

spring's compression, but that effect was neglected. Shock absorbers often involve springs, and this example illustrates how they work. The spring action of a shock absorber turns a dangerous jolt into a smooth deceleration, as excess kinetic energy is converted to spring potential energy.

QUESTION 5.10 Is it possible for the acrobat to rebound to a height greater than her initial height? If so, how?

EXERCISE 5.10 An 8.00-kg block drops straight down from a height of 1.00 m, striking a platform spring having force constant 1.00×10^3 N/m. Find the maximum compression of the spring.

ANSWER $d = 0.482$ m

■ EXAMPLE 5.11 | A Block Projected up a Frictionless Incline

GOAL Use conservation of mechanical energy to solve a problem involving gravitational potential energy, spring potential energy, and a ramp.

PROBLEM A 0.500-kg block rests on a horizontal, frictionless surface as in Figure 5.23. The block is pressed back against a spring having a constant of $k = 625$ N/m, compressing the spring by 10.0 cm to point Ⓐ. Then the block is released. **(a)** Find the maximum distance d the block travels up the frictionless incline if $\theta = 30.0°$. **(b)** How fast is the block going when halfway to its maximum height?

Figure 5.23 (Example 5.11)

STRATEGY In the absence of other forces, conservation of mechanical energy applies to parts (a) and (b). In part (a), the block starts at rest and is also instantaneously at rest at the top of the ramp, so the kinetic energies at Ⓐ and Ⓒ are both zero. Note that the question asks for a distance d along the ramp, not the height h. In part (b), the system has both kinetic and gravitational potential energy at Ⓑ.

· ·

SOLUTION

(a) Find the distance the block travels up the ramp.

Apply conservation of mechanical energy:

$$\tfrac{1}{2}mv_i^2 + mgy_i + \tfrac{1}{2}kx_i^2 = \tfrac{1}{2}mv_f^2 + mgy_f + \tfrac{1}{2}kx_f^2$$

Substitute $v_i = v_f = 0$, $y_i = 0$, $y_f = h = d\sin\theta$, and $x_f = 0$:

$$\tfrac{1}{2}kx_i^2 = mgh = mgd\sin\theta$$

Solve for the distance d and insert the known values:

$$d = \frac{\tfrac{1}{2}kx_i^2}{mg\sin\theta} = \frac{\tfrac{1}{2}(625 \text{ N/m})(-0.100 \text{ m})^2}{(0.500 \text{ kg})(9.80 \text{ m/s}^2)\sin(30.0°)}$$

$$= \boxed{1.28 \text{ m}}$$

(b) Find the velocity at half the height, $h/2$. Note that $h = d\sin\theta = (1.28 \text{ m})\sin 30.0° = 0.640$ m.

Use energy conservation again:

$$\tfrac{1}{2}mv_i^2 + mgy_i + \tfrac{1}{2}kx_i^2 = \tfrac{1}{2}mv_f^2 + mgy_f + \tfrac{1}{2}kx_f^2$$

Take $v_i = 0$, $y_i = 0$, $y_f = \tfrac{1}{2}h$, and $x_f = 0$, yielding

$$\tfrac{1}{2}kx_i^2 = \tfrac{1}{2}mv_f^2 + mg\left(\tfrac{1}{2}h\right)$$

Multiply by $2/m$ and solve for v_f:

$$\frac{k}{m}x_i^2 = v_f^2 + gh$$

$$v_f = \sqrt{\frac{k}{m}x_i^2 - gh}$$

$$= \sqrt{\left(\frac{625 \text{ N/m}}{0.500 \text{ kg}}\right)(-0.100 \text{ m})^2 - (9.80 \text{ m/s}^2)(0.640 \text{ m})}$$

$$v_f = \boxed{2.50 \text{ m/s}}$$

· ·

REMARKS Notice that it wasn't necessary to compute the velocity gained upon leaving the spring: only the mechanical energy at each of the two points of interest was required, where the block was at rest.

QUESTION 5.11 A real spring will continue to vibrate slightly after the mass has left it. How would this affect the answer to part (a), and why?

EXERCISE 5.11 A 1.00-kg block is shot horizontally from a spring, as in the previous example, and travels 0.500 m up along a frictionless ramp before coming to rest and sliding back down. If the ramp makes an angle of 45.0° with respect to the horizontal, and the spring was originally compressed by 0.120 m, find the spring constant.

ANSWER 481 N/m

■ **APPLYING PHYSICS 5.2** | **Accident Reconstruction**

Sometimes people involved in automobile accidents make exaggerated claims of chronic pain due to subtle injuries to the neck or spinal column. The likelihood of injury can be determined by finding the change in velocity of a car during the accident. The larger the change in velocity, the more likely it is that the person suffered spinal injury resulting in chronic pain. How can reliable estimates for this change in velocity be found after the fact?

EXPLANATION The metal and plastic of an automobile acts much like a spring, absorbing the car's kinetic energy by flexing during a collision. When the magnitude of the difference in velocity of the two cars is under 5 miles per hour, there is usually no visible damage, because bumpers are designed to absorb the impact and return to their orig-

inal shape at such low speeds. At greater relative speeds there will be permanent damage to the vehicle. Despite the fact the structure of the car may not return to its original shape, a certain force per meter is still required to deform it, just as it takes a certain force per meter to compress a spring. The greater the original kinetic energy, the more the car is compressed during a collision, and the greater the damage. By using data obtained through crash tests, it's possible to obtain effective spring constants for all the different models of cars and determine reliable estimates of the change in velocity of a given vehicle during an accident. Medical research has established the likelihood of spinal injury for a given change in velocity, and the estimated velocity change can be used to help reduce insurance fraud. ■

5.5 Systems and Energy Conservation

Recall that the work–energy theorem can be written as

$$W_{nc} + W_c = \Delta KE$$

where W_{nc} represents the work done by nonconservative forces and W_c is the work done by conservative forces in a given physical context. As we have seen, any work done by conservative forces, such as gravity and springs, can be accounted for by changes in potential energy. The work–energy theorem can therefore be written in the following way:

$$W_{nc} = \Delta KE + \Delta PE = (KE_f - KE_i) + (PE_f - PE_i) \qquad [5.20]$$

where now, as previously stated, *PE* includes all potential energies. This equation is easily rearranged to

$$W_{nc} = (KE_f + PE_f) - (KE_i + PE_i) \qquad [5.21]$$

Recall, however, that the total mechanical energy is given by $E = KE + PE$. Making this substitution into Equation 5.21, we find that the work done on a system by all nonconservative forces is equal to the change in mechanical energy of that system:

$$W_{nc} = E_f - E_i = \Delta E \qquad [5.22]$$

If the mechanical energy is changing, it has to be going somewhere. The energy either leaves the system and goes into the surrounding environment, or it stays in the system and is converted into a nonmechanical form such as thermal energy.

A simple example is a block sliding along a rough surface. Friction creates thermal energy, absorbed partly by the block and partly by the surrounding environment. When the block warms up, something called *internal energy* increases. The internal energy of a system is related to its temperature, which in turn is a consequence of the activity of its parts, such as the moving atoms of a gas or the vibration of atoms in a solid. (Internal energy will be studied in more detail in Chapter 10–12.)

Energy can be transferred between a nonisolated system and its environment. If positive work is done on the system, energy is transferred from the environment to the system. If negative work is done on the system, energy is transferred from the system to the environment.

So far, we have encountered three methods of storing energy in a system: kinetic energy, potential energy, and internal energy. On the other hand, we've seen only one way of transferring energy into or out of a system: through work. Other methods will be studied in later chapters, but are summarized here:

- **Work,** in the mechanical sense of this chapter, transfers energy to a system by displacing it with an applied force.
- **Heat** is the process of transferring energy through microscopic collisions between atoms or molecules. For example, a metal spoon resting in a cup of coffee becomes hot because some of the kinetic energy of the molecules in the liquid coffee is transferred to the spoon as internal energy.
- **Mechanical waves** transfer energy by creating a disturbance that propagates through air or another medium. For example, energy in the form of sound leaves your stereo system through the loudspeakers and enters your ears to stimulate the hearing process. Other examples of mechanical waves are seismic waves and ocean waves.
- **Electrical transmission** transfers energy through electric currents. This is how energy enters your stereo system or any other electrical device.
- **Electromagnetic radiation** transfers energy in the form of electromagnetic waves such as light, microwaves, and radio waves. Examples of this method of transfer include cooking a potato in a microwave oven and light energy traveling from the Sun to Earth through space.

Conservation of Energy in General

BIO APPLICATION
Flagellar Movement;
Bioluminescence

The most important feature of the energy approach is the idea that energy is conserved; it can't be created or destroyed, only transferred from one form into another. This is the principle of **conservation of energy.**

The principle of conservation of energy is not confined to physics. In biology, energy transformations take place in myriad ways inside all living organisms. One example is the transformation of chemical energy to mechanical energy that causes flagella to move and propel an organism. Some bacteria use chemical energy to produce light. (See Fig. 5.24.) Although the mechanisms that produce these light emissions are not well understood, living creatures often rely on this light for their existence. For example, certain fish have sacs beneath their eyes filled with light-emitting bacteria. The emitted light attracts creatures that become food for the fish.

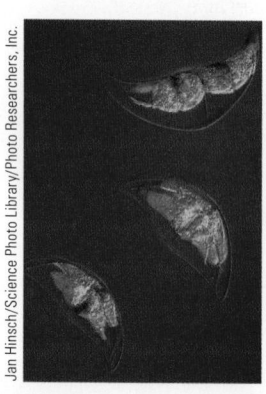

Jan Hinsch/Science Photo Library/Photo Researchers, Inc.

Figure 5.24 This small plant, found in warm southern waters, exhibits bioluminescence, a process in which chemical energy is converted to light. The red areas are chlorophyll, which fluoresce when irradiated with blue light.

■ Quick Quiz

5.4 A book of mass m is projected with a speed v across a horizontal surface. The book slides until it stops due to the friction force between the book and the surface. The surface is now tilted 30°, and the book is projected up the surface with the same initial speed v. When the book has come to rest, how does the decrease in mechanical energy of the book–Earth system compare with that when the book slid over the horizontal surface? (a) It's the same. (b) It's larger on the tilted surface. (c) It's smaller on the tilted surface. (d) More information is needed.

An asteroid about 10 kilometers in diameter has been blamed for the extinction of the dinosaurs 65 million years ago. How can a relatively small object, which could fit inside a college campus, inflict such injury on the vast biosphere of Earth?

EXPLANATION While such an asteroid is comparatively small, it travels at a very high speed relative to Earth, typically on the order of 40 000 m/s. A roughly spherical asteroid 10 kilometers in diameter and made mainly of rock has a mass of approximately 1 000 trillion kilograms—a mountain of matter. The kinetic energy of such an asteroid would be about 10^{24} J, or a trillion trillion joules. By contrast, the atomic bomb that devastated Hiroshima was equivalent to 15 kilotons of TNT, approximately 6×10^{13} J of energy. On striking Earth, the asteroid's enormous kinetic energy changes into other forms, such as thermal energy, sound, and light, with a total energy release greater than ten billion Hiroshima explosions! Aside from the devastation in the immediate blast area and fires across a continent, gargantuan tidal waves would scour low-lying regions around the world and dust would block the Sun for decades.

For this reason, asteroid impacts represent a threat to life on Earth. Asteroids large enough to cause widespread extinction hit Earth only every 60 million years or so.

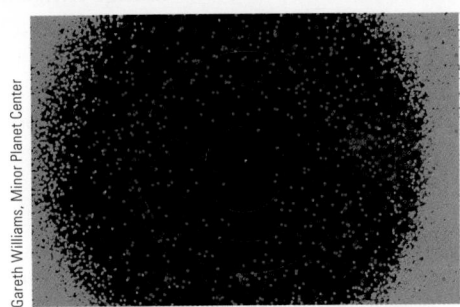

Figure 5.25 Asteroid map of the inner solar system. The violet circles represent the orbits of the inner planets. Green dots stand for asteroids not considered dangerous to Earth; those that are considered threatening are represented by red dots.

Smaller asteroids, of sufficient size to cause serious damage to civilization on a global scale, are thought to strike every five to ten thousand years. There have been several near misses by such asteroids in the last century and even in the last decade. In 1907, a small asteroid or comet fragment struck Tunguska, Siberia, annihilating a region 60 kilometers across. Had it hit northern Europe, millions of people might have perished.

Figure 5.25 is an asteroid map of the inner solar system. More asteroids are being discovered every year. ■

5.6 Power

Power, the rate at which energy is transferred, is important in the design and use of practical devices, such as electrical appliances and engines of all kinds. The concept of power, however, is essential whenever a transfer of any kind of energy takes place. The issue is particularly interesting for living creatures because the maximum work per second, or power output, of an animal varies greatly with output duration. Power is defined as the rate of energy transfer with time:

If an external force does work W on an object in the time interval Δt, then the **average power** delivered to the object is the work done divided by the time interval, or

$$\overline{P} = \frac{W}{\Delta t} \qquad [5.23]$$

◀ Average power

SI unit: watt (W = J/s)

It's sometimes useful to rewrite Equation 5.23 by substituting $W = F \Delta x$ and noticing that $\Delta x / \Delta t$ is the average speed of the object during the time Δt:

$$\overline{P} = \frac{W}{\Delta t} = \frac{F \Delta x}{\Delta t} = F \overline{v} \qquad [5.24]$$

According to Equation 5.24, average power is a constant force times the average speed. The force F is the component of force in the direction of the average velocity. A more general definition, called the **instantaneous power,** can be written down with a little calculus and has the same form as Equation 5.24:

$$P = Fv \qquad [5.25]$$

◀ Instantaneous power

In Equation 5.25 both the force F and the velocity v must be parallel, but can change with time. The SI unit of power is the joule per second (J/s), also called the **watt,** named after James Watt:

$$1 \text{ W} = 1 \text{ J/s} = 1 \text{ kg} \cdot \text{m}^2/\text{s}^3 \qquad [5.26a]$$

The unit of power in the U.S. customary system is the horsepower (hp), where

$$1 \text{ hp} \equiv 550 \, \frac{\text{ft} \cdot \text{lb}}{\text{s}} = 746 \text{ W} \qquad [5.26b]$$

The horsepower was first defined by Watt, who needed a large power unit to rate the power output of his new invention, the steam engine.

The watt is commonly used in electrical applications, but it can be used in other scientific areas as well. For example, European sports car engines are rated in kilowatts.

In electric power generation, it's customary to use the kilowatt-hour as a measure of energy. One kilowatt-hour (kWh) is the energy transferred in 1 h at the constant rate of 1 kW = 1 000 J/s. Therefore,

$$1 \text{ kWh} = (10^3 \text{ W})(3\ 600 \text{ s}) = (10^3 \text{ J/s})(3\ 600 \text{ s}) = 3.60 \times 10^6 \text{ J}$$

It's important to realize that a kilowatt-hour is a unit of energy, *not* power. When you pay your electric bill, you're buying energy, and that's why your bill lists a charge for electricity of about 10 cents/kWh. The amount of electricity used by an appliance can be calculated by multiplying its power rating (usually expressed in watts and valid only for normal household electrical circuits) by the length of time the appliance is operated. For example, an electric bulb rated at 100 W (= 0.100 kW) "consumes" 3.6×10^5 J of energy in 1 h.

> **Tip 5.6 Watts the Difference?**
>
> Don't confuse the nonitalic symbol for watts, W, with the italic symbol W for work. A watt is a unit, the same as joules per second. Work is a concept, carrying units of joules.

■ EXAMPLE 5.12 | Power Delivered by an Elevator Motor

GOAL Apply the force-times-velocity definition of power.

PROBLEM A 1.00×10^3-kg elevator car carries a maximum load of 8.00×10^2 kg. A constant frictional force of 4.00×10^3 N retards its motion upward, as in Figure 5.26. What minimum power, in kilowatts and in horsepower, must the motor deliver to lift the fully loaded elevator car at a constant speed of 3.00 m/s?

STRATEGY To solve this problem, we need to determine the force the elevator car's motor must deliver through the force of tension in the cable, $\vec{\mathbf{T}}$. Substituting this force together with the given speed v into $P = Fv$ gives the desired power. The tension in the cable, T, can be found with Newton's second law.

Figure 5.26 (a) (Example 5.12) The motor exerts an upward force $\vec{\mathbf{T}}$ on the elevator. A frictional force $\vec{\mathbf{f}}$ and the force of gravity $M\vec{\mathbf{g}}$ act downward. (b) The free-body diagram for the elevator car.

· ·

SOLUTION

Apply Newton's second law to the elevator car:

$$\sum \vec{\mathbf{F}} = m\vec{\mathbf{a}}$$

The velocity is constant, so the acceleration is zero. The forces acting on the elevator car are the force of tension in the cable, $\vec{\mathbf{T}}$, the friction $\vec{\mathbf{f}}$, and gravity $M\vec{\mathbf{g}}$, where M is the mass of the elevator car.

$$\vec{\mathbf{T}} + \vec{\mathbf{f}} + M\vec{\mathbf{g}} = 0$$

Write the equation in terms of its components:	$T - f - Mg = 0$
Solve this equation for the tension T and evaluate it:	$T = f + Mg$ $= 4.00 \times 10^3$ N $+ (1.80 \times 10^3$ kg$)(9.80$ m/s$^2)$ $T = 2.16 \times 10^4$ N
Substitute this value of T for F in the power equation:	$P = Fv = (2.16 \times 10^4$ N$)(3.00$ m/s$) = 6.48 \times 10^4$ W $P = 64.8$ kW $= $ 86.9 hp

REMARKS The friction force acts to retard the motion, requiring more power. For a descending elevator car, the friction force can actually reduce the power requirement.

QUESTION 5.12 In general, are the minimum power requirements of an elevator car ascending at constant velocity (a) greater than, (b) less than, or (c) equal to the minimum power requirements of an elevator car descending at constant velocity?

EXERCISE 5.12 Suppose the same elevator car with the same load descends at 3.00 m/s. What minimum power is required? (Here, the motor removes energy from the elevator car by not allowing it to fall freely.)

ANSWER 4.09×10^4 W $= 54.9$ hp

■ **EXAMPLE 5.13** | **Shamu Sprint** BIO

GOAL Calculate the average power needed to increase an object's kinetic energy.

PROBLEM Killer whales are known to reach 32 ft in length and have a mass of over 8 000 kg. They are also very quick, able to accelerate up to 30 mi/h in a matter of seconds. Disregarding the considerable drag force of water, calculate the average power a killer whale named Shamu with mass 8.00×10^3 kg would need to generate to reach a speed of 12.0 m/s in 6.00 s.

STRATEGY Find the change in kinetic energy of Shamu and use the work–energy theorem to obtain the minimum work Shamu has to do to effect this change. (Internal and external friction forces increase the necessary amount of energy.) Divide by the elapsed time to get the average power.

SOLUTION

Calculate the change in Shamu's kinetic energy. By the work–energy theorem, this equals the minimum work Shamu must do:	$\Delta KE = \frac{1}{2}mv_f^2 - \frac{1}{2}mv_i^2$ $= \frac{1}{2} \cdot 8.00 \times 10^3$ kg $\cdot (12.0$ m/s$)^2 - 0$ $= 5.76 \times 10^5$ J
Divide by the elapsed time (Eq. 5.23), noting that $W = \Delta KE$:	$\overline{P} = \dfrac{W}{\Delta t} = \dfrac{5.76 \times 10^5 \text{ J}}{6.00 \text{ s}} = $ 9.60×10^4 W

REMARKS This is enough power to run a moderate-sized office building! The actual requirements are larger because of friction in the water and muscular tissues. Something similar can be done with gravitational potential energy, as the exercise illustrates.

QUESTION 5.13 If Shamu could double his velocity in double the time, by what factor would the average power requirement change?

EXERCISE 5.13 What minimum average power must a 35-kg human boy generate climbing up the stairs to the top of the Washington monument? The trip up the nearly 170-m-tall building takes him 10 minutes. Include only work done against gravity, ignoring biological inefficiency.

ANSWER 97 W

■ EXAMPLE 5.14 | Speedboat Power

GOAL Combine power, the work–energy theorem, and nonconservative forces with one-dimensional kinematics.

PROBLEM (a) What average power would a 1.00×10^3-kg speedboat need to go from rest to 20.0 m/s in 5.00 s, assuming the water exerts a constant drag force of magnitude $f_d = 5.00 \times 10^2$ N and the acceleration is constant. (b) Find an expression for the instantaneous power in terms of the drag force f_d, the mass m, acceleration a, and time t.

STRATEGY The power is provided by the engine, which creates a nonconservative force. Use the work–energy theorem together with the work done by the engine, W_{engine}, and the work done by the drag force, W_{drag}, on the left-hand side. Use one-dimensional kinematics to find the acceleration and then the displacement Δx. Solve the work–energy theorem for W_{engine}, and divide by the elapsed time to get the average power. For part (b), use Newton's second law to obtain an example for F_E, and then substitute into the definition of instantaneous power.

SOLUTION

(a) Write the work–energy theorem:

$$W_{net} = \Delta KE = \tfrac{1}{2}mv_f{}^2 - \tfrac{1}{2}mv_i{}^2$$

Fill in the two work terms and take $v_i = 0$:

$$(1) \quad W_{engine} + W_{drag} = \tfrac{1}{2}mv_f{}^2$$

To get the displacement Δx, first find the acceleration using the velocity equation of kinematics:

$$v_f = at + v_i \quad \rightarrow \quad v_f = at$$
$$20.0 \text{ m/s} = a(5.00 \text{ s}) \quad \rightarrow \quad a = 4.00 \text{ m/s}^2$$

Substitute a into the time-independent kinematics equation and solve for Δx:

$$v_f{}^2 - v_i{}^2 = 2a\,\Delta x$$
$$(20.0 \text{ m/s})^2 - 0^2 = 2(4.00 \text{ m/s}^2)\,\Delta x$$
$$\Delta x = 50.0 \text{ m}$$

Now that we know Δx, we can find the mechanical energy lost due to the drag force:

$$W_{drag} = -f_d\,\Delta x = -(5.00 \times 10^2 \text{ N})(50.0 \text{ m}) = -2.50 \times 10^4 \text{ J}$$

Solve equation (1) for W_{engine}:

$$W_{engine} = \tfrac{1}{2}mv_f{}^2 - W_{drag}$$
$$= \tfrac{1}{2}(1.00 \times 10^3 \text{ kg})(20.0 \text{ m/s})^2 - (-2.50 \times 10^4 \text{ J})$$
$$W_{engine} = 2.25 \times 10^5 \text{ J}$$

Compute the average power:

$$\overline{P} = \frac{W_{engine}}{\Delta t} = \frac{2.25 \times 10^5 \text{ J}}{5.00 \text{ s}} = 4.50 \times 10^4 \text{ W} = \boxed{60.3 \text{ hp}}$$

(b) Find a symbolic expression for the instantaneous power.

Use Newton's second law:

$$ma = F_E - f_d$$

Solve for the force exerted by the engine, F_E:

$$F_E = ma + f_d$$

Substitute the expression for F_E and $v = at$ into Equation 5.25 to obtain the instantaneous power:

$$P = F_E v = (ma + f_d)(at)$$
$$\boxed{P = (ma^2 + af_d)t}$$

REMARKS In fact, drag forces generally get larger with increasing speed.

QUESTION 5.14 How does the instantaneous power at the end of 5.00 s compare to the average power?

EXERCISE 5.14 What average power must be supplied to push a 5.00-kg block from rest to 10.0 m/s in 5.00 s when the coefficient of kinetic friction between the block and surface is 0.250? Assume the acceleration is uniform.

ANSWER 111 W

Energy and Power in a Vertical Jump **BIO**

The stationary jump consists of two parts: extension and free flight.[2] In the extension phase the person jumps up from a crouch, straightening the legs and throw-

---

[2]For more information on this topic, see E. J. Offenbacher, *American Journal of Physics*, **38**, 829 (1969).

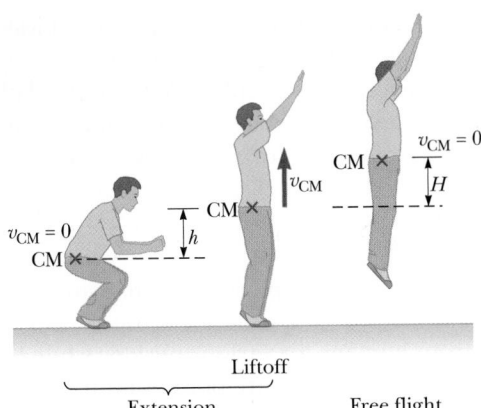

Figure 5.27 Extension and free flight in the vertical jump.

ing up the arms; the free-flight phase occurs when the jumper leaves the ground. Because the body is an extended object and different parts move with different speeds, we describe the motion of the jumper in terms of the position and velocity of the **center of mass (CM),** which is the point in the body at which all the mass may be considered to be concentrated. Figure 5.27 shows the position and velocity of the CM at different stages of the jump.

Using the principle of the conservation of mechanical energy, we can find H, the maximum increase in height of the CM, in terms of the velocity v_{CM} of the CM at liftoff. Taking PE_i, the gravitational potential energy of the jumper–Earth system just as the jumper lifts off from the ground to be zero, and noting that the kinetic energy KE_f of the jumper at the peak is zero, we have

$$PE_i + KE_i = PE_f + KE_f$$

$$\tfrac{1}{2}mv_{CM}^2 = mgH \quad \text{or} \quad H = \frac{v_{CM}^2}{2g}$$

We can estimate v_{CM} by assuming that the acceleration of the CM is constant during the extension phase. If the depth of the crouch is h and the time for extension is Δt, we find that $v_{CM} = 2\bar{v} = 2h/\Delta t$. Measurements on a group of male college students show typical values of $h = 0.40$ m and $\Delta t = 0.25$ s, the latter value being set by the fixed speed with which muscle can contract. Substituting, we obtain

$$v_{CM} = 2(0.40 \text{ m})/(0.25 \text{ s}) = 3.2 \text{ m/s}$$

and

$$H = \frac{v_{CM}^2}{2g} = \frac{(3.2 \text{ m/s})^2}{2(9.80 \text{ m/s}^2)} = 0.52 \text{ m}$$

Measurements on this same group of students found that H was between 0.45 m and 0.61 m in all cases, confirming the basic validity of our simple calculation.

To relate the abstract concepts of energy, power, and efficiency to humans, it's interesting to calculate these values for the vertical jump. The kinetic energy given to the body in a jump is $KE = \tfrac{1}{2}mv_{CM}^2$, and for a person of mass 68 kg, the kinetic energy is

$$KE = \tfrac{1}{2}(68 \text{ kg})(3.2 \text{ m/s})^2 = 3.5 \times 10^2 \text{ J}$$

Although this may seem like a large expenditure of energy, we can make a simple calculation to show that jumping and exercise in general are not good ways to lose weight, in spite of their many health benefits. Because the muscles are at most 25% efficient at producing kinetic energy from chemical energy (muscles always produce a lot of internal energy and kinetic energy as well as work—that's why you perspire when you work out), they use up four times the 350 J (about 1 400 J) of chemical energy in one jump. This chemical energy ultimately comes from the

BIO APPLICATION

Diet Versus Exercise in Weight-loss Programs

Table 5.1 Maximum Power Output from Humans over Various Periods BIO

Power	Time
2 hp, or 1 500 W	6 s
1 hp, or 750 W	60 s
0.35 hp, or 260 W	35 min
0.2 hp, or 150 W	5 h
0.1 hp, or 75 W (safe daily level)	8 h

food we eat, with energy content given in units of food calories and one food calorie equal to 4 200 J. So the total energy supplied by the body as internal energy and kinetic energy in a vertical jump is only about one-third of a food calorie!

Finally, it's interesting to calculate the average mechanical power that can be generated by the body in strenuous activity for brief periods. Here we find that

$$\overline{P} = \frac{KE}{\Delta t} = \frac{3.5 \times 10^2 \text{ J}}{0.25 \text{ s}} = 1.4 \times 10^3 \text{ W}$$

or $(1\,400\text{ W})(1\text{ hp}/746\text{ W}) = 1.9$ hp. So humans can produce about 2 hp of mechanical power for periods on the order of seconds. Table 5.1 shows the maximum power outputs from humans for various periods while bicycling and rowing, activities in which it is possible to measure power output accurately.

5.7 Work Done by a Varying Force

Suppose an object is displaced along the x-axis under the action of a force F_x that acts in the x-direction and varies with position, as shown in Figure 5.28. The object is displaced in the direction of increasing x from $x = x_i$ to $x = x_f$. In such a situation, we can't use Equation 5.2 to calculate the work done by the force because this relationship applies only when $\vec{F}$ is constant in magnitude and direction. However, if we imagine that the object undergoes the *small* displacement Δx shown in Figure 5.28a, then the x-component F_x of the force is nearly constant over this interval and we can approximate the work done by the force for this small displacement as

$$W_1 \cong F_x \Delta x \qquad [5.27]$$

This quantity is just the area of the shaded rectangle in Figure 5.28a. If we imagine that the curve of F_x versus x is divided into a large number of such intervals, then the total work done for the displacement from x_i to x_f is approximately equal to the sum of the areas of a large number of small rectangles:

$$W \cong F_1 \Delta x_1 + F_2 \Delta x_2 + F_3 \Delta x_3 + \cdots \qquad [5.28]$$

Now imagine going through the same process with twice as many intervals, each half the size of the original Δx. The rectangles then have smaller widths and will better approximate the area under the curve. Continuing the process of increas-

Figure 5.28 (a) The work done on a particle by the force component F_x for the small displacement Δx is approximately $F_x \Delta x$, the area of the shaded rectangle. (b) The width Δx of each rectangle is shrunk to zero.

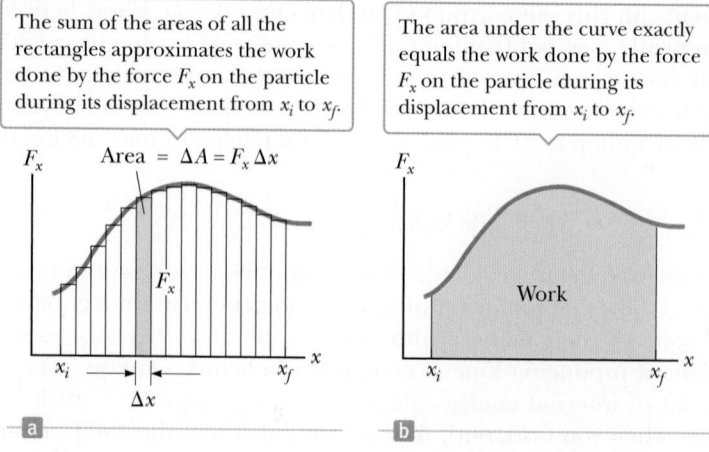

ing the number of intervals while allowing their size to approach zero, the number of terms in the sum increases without limit, but the value of the sum approaches a definite value equal to the area under the curve bounded by F_x and the x-axis in Figure 5.28b. In other words, **the work done by a variable force acting on an object that undergoes a displacement is equal to the area under the graph of F_x versus x.**

A common physical system in which force varies with position consists of a block on a horizontal, frictionless surface connected to a spring, as discussed in Section 5.4. When the spring is stretched or compressed a small distance x from its equilibrium position $x = 0$, it exerts a force on the block given by $F_x = -kx$, where k is the force constant of the spring.

Now let's determine the work done by an external agent on the block as the spring is stretched *very slowly* from $x_i = 0$ to $x_f = x_{max}$, as in Active Figure 5.29a. This work can be easily calculated by noting that at any value of the displacement, Newton's third law tells us that the applied force $\vec{F}_{app}$ is equal in magnitude to the spring force $\vec{F}_s$ and acts in the opposite direction, so that $F_{app} = -(-kx) = kx$. A plot of F_{app} versus x is a straight line, as shown in Active Figure 5.29b. Therefore, the work done by this applied force in stretching the spring from $x = 0$ to $x = x_{max}$ is the area under the straight line in that figure, which in this case is the area of the shaded triangle:

$$W_{F_{app}} = \tfrac{1}{2}kx_{max}^2$$

During this same time the spring has done exactly the same amount of work, but that work is negative, because the spring force points in the direction opposite the motion. The potential energy of the system is exactly equal to the work done by the applied force and is the same sign, which is why potential energy is thought of as stored work.

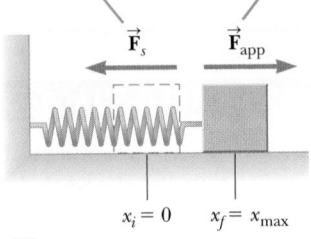

If the process of moving the block is carried out very slowly, the applied force is equal in magnitude and opposite in direction to the spring force at all times.

$x_i = 0$ $x_f = x_{max}$

a

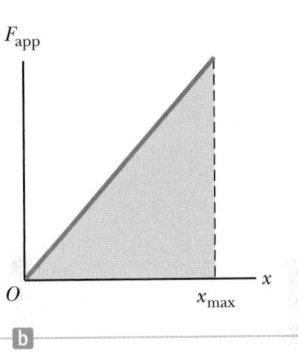

b

Active Figure 5.29
(a) A block being pulled from $x_i = 0$ to $x_f = x_{max}$ on a frictionless surface by a force $\vec{F}_{app}$. (b) A graph of F_{app} versus x.

▪ EXAMPLE 5.15   Work Required to Stretch a Spring

GOAL Apply the graphical method of finding work.

PROBLEM One end of a horizontal spring ($k = 80.0$ N/m) is held fixed while an external force is applied to the free end, stretching it slowly from $x_{\text{Ⓐ}} = 0$ to $x_{\text{Ⓑ}} = 4.00$ cm. **(a)** Find the work done by the applied force on the spring. **(b)** Find the additional work done in stretching the spring from $x_{\text{Ⓑ}} = 4.00$ cm to $x_{\text{Ⓒ}} = 7.00$ cm.

STRATEGY For part (a), simply find the area of the smaller triangle in Figure 5.30, using $A = \tfrac{1}{2}bh$, one-half the base times the height. For part (b), the easiest way to find the additional work done from $x_{\text{Ⓑ}} = 4.00$ cm to $x_{\text{Ⓒ}} = 7.00$ cm is to find the area of the new, larger triangle and subtract the area of the smaller triangle.

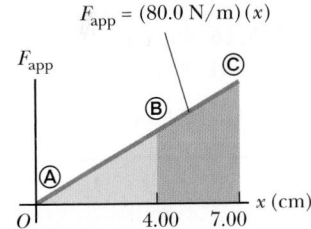

$F_{app} = (80.0 \text{ N/m})(x)$

F_{app}

Ⓒ

Ⓑ

Ⓐ

x (cm)

O 4.00   7.00

Figure 5.30 (Example 5.15) A graph of the external force required to stretch a spring that obeys Hooke's law versus the elongation of the spring.

SOLUTION

(a) Find the work from $x_{\text{Ⓐ}} = 0$ cm to $x_{\text{Ⓑ}} = 4.00$ cm.

Compute the area of the smaller triangle:

$W = \tfrac{1}{2}kx_{\text{Ⓑ}}^2 = \tfrac{1}{2}(80.0 \text{ N/m})(0.040 \text{ m})^2 = \boxed{0.064\,0 \text{ J}}$

(b) Find the work from $x_{\text{Ⓑ}} = 4.00$ cm to $x_{\text{Ⓒ}} = 7.00$ cm.

Compute the area of the large triangle and subtract the area of the smaller triangle:

$W = \tfrac{1}{2}kx_{\text{Ⓒ}}^2 - \tfrac{1}{2}kx_{\text{Ⓑ}}^2$

$W = \tfrac{1}{2}(80.0 \text{ N/m})(0.070\,0 \text{ m})^2 - 0.064\,0 \text{ J}$

$= 0.196 \text{ J} - 0.064\,0 \text{ J}$

$= \boxed{0.132 \text{ J}}$

(Continued)

REMARKS Only simple geometries (rectangles and triangles) can be solved exactly with this method. More complex shapes require calculus or the square-counting technique in the next worked example.

QUESTION 5.15 True or False: When stretching springs, half the displacement requires half as much work.

EXERCISE 5.15 How much work is required to stretch this same spring from $x_i = 5.00$ cm to $x_f = 9.00$ cm?

ANSWER 0.224 J

■ EXAMPLE 5.16 | Estimating Work by Counting Boxes

GOAL Use the graphical method and counting boxes to estimate the work done by a force.

PROBLEM Suppose the force applied to stretch a thick piece of elastic changes with position as indicated in Figure 5.31a. Estimate the work done by the applied force.

STRATEGY To find the work, simply count the number of boxes underneath the curve and multiply that number by the area of each box. The curve will pass through the middle of some boxes, in which case only an estimated fractional part should be counted.

Figure 5.31 (a) (Example 5.16) (b) (Exercise 5.16)

SOLUTION

There are 62 complete or nearly complete boxes under the curve, 6 boxes that are about half under the curve, and a triangular area from $x = 0$ m to $x = 0.10$ m that is equivalent to 1 box, for a total of about 66 boxes. Because the area of each box is 0.10 J, the total work done is approximately 66×0.10 J = 6.6 J.

REMARKS Mathematically, there are a number of other methods for creating such estimates, all involving adding up regions approximating the area. To get a better estimate, make smaller boxes.

QUESTION 5.16 In developing such an estimate, is it necessary for all boxes to have the same length and width?

EXERCISE 5.16 Suppose the applied force necessary to pull the drawstring on a bow is given by Figure 5.31b. Find the approximate work done by counting boxes.

ANSWER About 50 J. (Individual answers may vary.)

■ SUMMARY

5.1 Work
The work done on an object by a constant force is

$$W = (F\cos\theta)d \qquad [5.3]$$

where F is the magnitude of the force, d is the magnitude of the object's displacement, and θ is the angle between the direction of the force $\vec{F}$ and the displacement $\Delta\vec{x}$. Solving simple problems requires substituting values into this equation. More complex problems, such as those involving friction, often require using Newton's second law, $m\vec{a} = \vec{F}_{net}$, to determine forces.

A constant force $\vec{F}$ applied during a displacement $\Delta\vec{x}$ does work $(F\cos\theta)\,\Delta x$.

5.2 Kinetic Energy and the Work–Energy Theorem
The kinetic energy of a body with mass m and speed v is given by

$$KE \equiv \tfrac{1}{2}mv^2 \qquad [5.6]$$

The work–energy theorem states that the net work done on an object of mass m is equal to the change in its kinetic energy, or

$$W_{net} = KE_f - KE_i = \Delta KE \qquad [5.7]$$

Work done by a net force $\vec{F}_{net}$ on an object changes the object's velocity.

Work and energy of any kind carry units of joules. Solving problems involves finding the work done by each force acting on the object and summing them up, which is W_{net}, followed by substituting known quantities into Equation 5.7, solving for the unknown quantity.

Conservative forces are special: Work done against them can be recovered—it's conserved. An example is gravity: The work done in lifting an object through a height is effectively stored in the gravity field and can be recovered in the kinetic energy of the object simply by letting it fall. Nonconservative forces, such as surface friction and drag, dissipate energy in a form that can't be readily recovered. To account for such forces, the work–energy theorem can be rewritten as

$$W_{nc} + W_c = \Delta KE \qquad [5.8]$$

where W_{nc} is the work done by nonconservative forces and W_c is the work done by conservative forces.

5.3 Gravitational Potential Energy

The gravitational force is a conservative field. Gravitational potential energy is another way of accounting for gravitational work W_g:

$$W_g = -(PE_f - PE_i)$$
$$= -(mgy_f - mgy_i) \qquad [5.12]$$

> The work done by the gravitational force as the book falls equals $mgy_i - mgy_f$.

To find the change in gravitational potential energy as an object of mass m moves between two points in a gravitational field, substitute the values of the object's y-coordinates.

The work–energy theorem can be generalized to include gravitational potential energy:

$$W_{nc} = (KE_f - KE_i) + (PE_f - PE_i) \qquad [5.13]$$

Gravitational work and gravitational potential energy should not both appear in the work–energy theorem at the same time, only one or the other, because they're equivalent. Setting the work due to nonconservative forces to zero and substituting the expressions for KE and PE, a form of the conservation of mechanical energy with gravitation can be obtained:

$$\tfrac{1}{2}mv_i^2 + mgy_i = \tfrac{1}{2}mv_f^2 + mgy_f \qquad [5.15]$$

To solve problems with this equation, identify two points in the system—one where information is known and the other where information is desired. Substitute and solve for the unknown quantity.

The work done by other forces, as when frictional forces are present, isn't always zero. In that case, identify two points as before, calculate the work due to all other forces, and solve for the unknown in Equation 5.13.

5.4 Spring Potential Energy

The spring force is conservative, and its potential energy is given by

$$PE_s \equiv \tfrac{1}{2}kx^2 \qquad [5.17]$$

Spring potential energy can be put into the work–energy theorem, which then reads

$$W_{nc} = (KE_f - KE_i) + (PE_{gf} - PE_{gi}) + (PE_{sf} - PE_{si}) \qquad [5.18]$$

When nonconservative forces are absent, $W_{nc} = 0$ and mechanical energy is conserved.

5.5 Systems and Energy Conservation

The principle of the conservation of energy states that energy can't be created or destroyed. It can be transformed, but the total energy content of any isolated system is always constant. The same is true for the universe at large. The work done by all nonconservative forces acting on a system equals the change in the total mechanical energy of the system:

$$W_{nc} = (KE_f + PE_f) - (KE_i + PE_i) = E_f - E_i \qquad [5.21\text{–}5.22]$$

where PE represents all potential energies present.

5.6 Power

Average power is the amount of energy transferred divided by the time taken for the transfer:

$$\overline{P} = \frac{W}{\Delta t} \qquad [5.23]$$

This expression can also be written

$$\overline{P} = F\overline{v} \qquad [5.24]$$

where $\overline{v}$ is the object's average speed. The unit of power is the watt (W = J/s). To solve simple problems, substitute given quantities into one of these equations. More difficult problems usually require finding the work done on the object using the work–energy theorem or the definition of work.

■ MULTIPLE-CHOICE QUESTIONS

WebAssign The multiple-choice questions in this chapter may be assigned online in Enhanced WebAssign.

1. A worker pushes a wheelbarrow 5.0 m along a level surface, exerting a constant horizontal force of 50.0 N. If a frictional force of 43 N acts on the wheelbarrow in a direction opposite to that of the worker, what net work is done on the wheelbarrow? (a) 250 J (b) 215 J (c) 35 J (d) 15 J (e) 45 J

2. What average mechanical power must be delivered by the muscles of a 70.0-kg mountain climber who climbs a summit of height 325 m in 95.0 min? *Note:* Due to inefficiencies in converting chemical energy to mechanical energy, the amount calculated here is only a fraction of the power that must be produced by the

climber's body. See Chapter 12. (a) 39.1 W (b) 54.6 W (c) 25.5 W (d) 67.0 W (e) 88.4 W

3. A 40.0-N crate starting at rest slides down a rough 6.00-m-long ramp, inclined at 30.0° with the horizontal. The magnitude of the force of friction between the crate and the ramp is 6.0 N. What is the speed of the crate at the bottom of the incline? (a) 1.60 m/s (b) 3.32 m/s (c) 4.5 m/s (d) 6.42 m/s (e) 7.75 m/s

4. A skier leaves a ski jump at 15.0 m/s at some angle θ. At what speed is he traveling at his maximum height of 4.50 m above the level of the end of the ski jump? (Neglect air friction.) (a) 11.7 m/s (b) 16.3 m/s (c) 12.2 m/s (d) 8.55 m/s (e) 17.4 m/s

5. The work required to accelerate an object on a frictionless surface from a speed v to a speed $2v$ is (a) equal to the work required to accelerate the object from $v = 0$ to v, (b) twice the work required to accelerate the object from $v = 0$ to v, (c) three times the work required to accelerate the object from $v = 0$ to v, (d) four times the work required to accelerate the object from $2v$ to $3v$, or (e) not known without knowledge of the acceleration.

6. You hold a slingshot at arm's length, pull the light elastic band back to your chin, and release it to launch a pebble horizontally with speed 200 cm/s. With the same procedure, you fire a bean with speed 600 cm/s. What is the ratio of the mass of the bean to the mass of the pebble? (a) 1/9 (b) 1/3 (c) 1 (d) 3 (e) 9

7. Mark and David are loading identical cement blocks onto David's pickup truck. Mark lifts his block straight up from the ground to the truck, whereas David slides his block up a ramp on massless, frictionless rollers. Which statement is true? (a) Mark does more work than David. (b) Mark and David do the same amount of work. (c) David does more work than Mark. (d) None of these statements is necessarily true because the

angle of the incline is unknown. (e) None of these statements is necessarily true because the mass of one block is not given.

8. If the speed of a particle is doubled, what happens to its kinetic energy? (a) It becomes four times larger. (b) It becomes two times larger. (c) It becomes $\sqrt{2}$ times larger. (d) It is unchanged. (e) It becomes half as large.

9. A certain truck has twice the mass of a car. Both are moving at the same speed. If the kinetic energy of the truck is K, what is the kinetic energy of the car? (a) $K/4$ (b) $K/2$ (c) $0.71K$ (d) K (e) $2K$

10. An athlete jumping vertically on a trampoline leaves the surface with a velocity of 8.5 m/s upward. What maximum height does she reach? (a) 13 m (b) 2.3 m (c) 3.7 m (d) 0.27 m (e) The answer can't be determined because the mass of the athlete isn't given.

11. If the net work done on a particle is zero, which of the following statements must be true? (a) The velocity is zero. (b) The velocity is decreased. (c) The velocity is unchanged. (d) The speed is unchanged. (e) More information is needed.

12. A block of mass m is dropped from the fourth floor of an office building, subsequently hitting the sidewalk at speed v. From what floor should the mass be dropped to double that impact speed? (a) the sixth floor (b) the eighth floor (c) the tenth floor (d) the twelfth floor (e) the sixteenth floor

13. A car accelerates uniformly from rest. When does the car require the greatest power? (a) when the car first accelerates from rest (b) just as the car reaches its maximum speed (c) when the car reaches half its maximum speed (d) The question is misleading because the power required is constant. (e) More information is needed.

■ CONCEPTUAL QUESTIONS

WebAssign The conceptual questions in this chapter may be assigned online in Enhanced WebAssign.

1. Consider a tug-of-war as in Figure CQ5.1, in which two teams pulling on a rope are evenly matched so that no

Figure CQ5.1

motion takes place. Is work done on the rope? On the pullers? On the ground? Is work done on anything?

2. **BIO** During a stress test of the cardiovascular system, a patient walks and runs on a treadmill. (a) Is the energy expended by the patient equivalent to the energy of walking and running on the ground? Explain. (b) What effect, if any, does tilting the treadmill upward have? Discuss.

3. (a) If the height of a playground slide is kept constant, will the length of the slide or whether it has bumps make any difference in the final speed of children playing on it? Assume that the slide is slick enough to be considered frictionless. (b) Repeat part (a), assuming that the slide is not frictionless.

4. (a) Can the kinetic energy of a system be negative? (b) Can the gravitational potential energy of a system be negative? Explain.

5. Roads going up mountains are formed into switchbacks, with the road weaving back and forth along the face of the slope such that there is only a gentle rise on any portion of the roadway. Does this configuration require any less work to be done by an automobile climbing the mountain, compared with one traveling on a roadway that is straight up the slope? Why are switchbacks used?

6. A bowling ball is suspended from the ceiling of a lecture hall by a strong cord. The ball is drawn away from its equilibrium position and released from rest at the tip of the demonstrator's nose, as shown in Figure CQ5.6. (a) If the demonstrator remains stationary, explain why the ball does not strike her on its return swing. (b) Would this demonstrator be safe if the ball were given a push from its starting position at her nose?

Figure CQ5.6

7. As a simple pendulum swings back and forth, the forces acting on the suspended object are the force of gravity, the tension in the supporting cord, and air resistance. (a) Which of these forces, if any, does no work on the pendulum? (b) Which of these forces does negative work at all times during the pendulum's motion? (c) Describe the work done by the force of gravity while the pendulum is swinging.

8. Discuss whether any work is being done by each of the following agents and, if so, whether the work is positive or negative: (a) a chicken scratching the ground, (b) a person studying, (c) a crane lifting a bucket of concrete, (d) the force of gravity on the bucket in part (c), (e) the leg muscles of a person in the act of sitting down.

9. When a punter kicks a football, is he doing any work on the ball while the toe of his foot is in contact with it? Is he doing any work on the ball after it loses contact with his toe? Are any forces doing work on the ball while it is in flight?

10. The driver of a car slams on her brakes to avoid colliding with a deer crossing the highway. What happens to the car's kinetic energy as it comes to rest?

11. A weight is connected to a spring that is suspended vertically from the ceiling. If the weight is displaced downward from its equilibrium position and released, it will oscillate up and down. (a) If air resistance is neglected, will the total mechanical energy of the system (weight plus Earth plus spring) be conserved? (b) How many forms of potential energy are there for this situation?

12. In most situations we have encountered in this chapter, frictional forces tend to reduce the kinetic energy of an object. However, frictional forces can sometimes increase an object's kinetic energy. Describe a few situations in which friction causes an increase in kinetic energy.

13. Suppose you are re-shelving books in a library. You lift a book from the floor to the top shelf. The kinetic energy of the book on the floor was zero, and the kinetic energy of the book on the top shelf is zero, so there is no change in kinetic energy. Yet you did some work in lifting the book. Is the work–energy theorem violated?

14. The feet of a standing person of mass m exert a force equal to mg on the floor, and the floor exerts an equal and opposite force upwards on the feet, which we call the normal force. During the extension phase of a vertical jump (see page 151), the feet exert a force on the floor that is greater than mg, so the normal force is greater than mg. As you learned in Chapter 4, we can use this result and Newton's second law to calculate the acceleration of the jumper:

$$a = F_{net}/m = (n - mg)/m.$$

Using energy ideas, we know that work is performed on the jumper to give him or her kinetic energy. But the normal force can't perform any work here because the feet don't undergo any displacement. How is energy transferred to the jumper?

15. An Earth satellite is in a circular orbit at an altitude of 500 km. Explain why the work done by the gravitational force acting on the satellite is zero. Using the work–energy theorem, what can you say about the speed of the satellite?

■ PROBLEMS

5.1 Work

1. A weight lifter lifts a 350-N set of weights from ground level to a position over his head, a vertical distance of 2.00 m. How much work does the weight lifter do, assuming he moves the weights at constant speed?

2. In 1990 Walter Arfeuille of Belgium lifted a 281.5-kg object through a distance of 17.1 cm using only his teeth. (a) How much work did Arfeuille do on the object? (b) What magnitude force did he exert on the object during the lift, assuming the force was constant?

3. The record number of boat lifts, including the boat and its ten crew members, was achieved by Sami Heinonen and Juha Räsänen of Sweden in 2000. They lifted a total mass of 653.2 kg approximately 4 in. off the ground a total of 24 times. Estimate the total mechanical work done by the two men in lifting the boat 24 times, assuming they applied the same force to the boat during each lift. (Neglect any work they may have done allowing the boat to drop back to the ground.)

4. **QC** A shopper in a supermarket pushes a cart with a force of 35 N directed at an angle of 25° below the horizontal. The force is just sufficient to overcome various frictional forces, so the cart moves at constant speed. (a) Find the work done by the shopper as she moves down a 50.0-m length aisle. (b) What is the *net work* done on the cart? Why? (c) The shopper goes down the next aisle, pushing horizontally and maintaining the same speed as before. If the work done by frictional forces doesn't change, would the shopper's applied force be larger, smaller, or the same? What about the work done on the cart by the shopper?

5. **QC** Starting from rest, a 5.00-kg block slides 2.50 m down a rough 30.0° incline. The coefficient of kinetic friction between the block and the incline is $\mu_k = 0.436$. Determine (a) the work done by the force of gravity, (b) the work done by the friction force between block and incline, and (c) the work done by the normal force. (d) Qualitatively, how would the answers change if a shorter ramp at a steeper angle were used to span the same vertical height?

6. A horizontal force of 150 N is used to push a 40.0-kg packing crate a distance of 6.00 m on a rough horizontal surface. If the crate moves at constant speed, find (a) the work done by the 150-N force and (b) the coefficient of kinetic friction between the crate and surface.

7. A sledge loaded with bricks has a total mass of 18.0 kg and is pulled at constant speed by a rope inclined at 20.0° above the horizontal. The sledge moves a distance of 20.0 m on a horizontal surface. The coefficient of kinetic friction between the sledge and surface is 0.500. (a) What is the tension in the rope? (b) How much work is done by the rope on the sledge? (c) What is the mechanical energy lost due to friction?

8. **M** A block of mass $m = 2.50$ kg is pushed a distance $d = 2.20$ m along a frictionless horizontal table by a constant applied force of magnitude $F = 16.0$ N directed at an angle $\theta = 25.0°$ below the horizontal as shown in Figure P5.8. Determine the work done by (a) the applied force, (b) the normal force exerted by the table, (c) the force of gravity, and (d) the net force on the block.

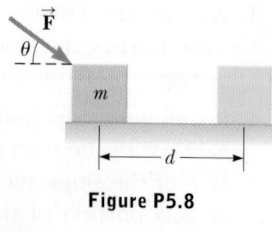

Figure P5.8

5.2 Kinetic Energy and the Work–Energy Theorem

9. A mechanic pushes a 2.50×10^3-kg car from rest to a speed of v, doing 5 000 J of work in the process. During this time, the car moves 25.0 m. Neglecting friction between car and road, find (a) v and (b) the horizontal force exerted on the car.

10. A 7.00-kg bowling ball moves at 3.00 m/s. How fast must a 2.45-g Ping-Pong ball move so that the two balls have the same kinetic energy?

11. A 65.0-kg runner has a speed of 5.20 m/s at one instant during a long-distance event. (a) What is the runner's kinetic energy at this instant? (b) If he doubles his speed to reach the finish line, by what factor does his kinetic energy change?

12. **QC** A worker pushing a 35.0-kg wooden crate at a constant speed for 12.0 m along a wood floor does 350 J of work by applying a constant horizontal force of magnitude F_0 on the crate. (a) Determine the value of F_0. (b) If the worker now applies a force greater than F_0, describe the subsequent motion of the crate. (c) Describe what would happen to the crate if the applied force is less than F_0.

13. A 70-kg base runner begins his slide into second base when he is moving at a speed of 4.0 m/s. The coefficient of friction between his clothes and Earth is 0.70. He slides so that his speed is zero just as he reaches the base. (a) How much mechanical energy is lost due to friction acting on the runner? (b) How far does he slide?

14. A running 62-kg cheetah has a top speed of 32 m/s. (a) What is the cheetah's maximum kinetic energy? (b) Find the cheetah's speed when its kinetic energy is one half of the value found in part (a).

15. A 7.80-g bullet moving at 575 m/s penetrates a tree trunk to a depth of 5.50 cm. (a) Use work and energy considerations to find the average frictional force that stops the bullet. (b) Assuming the frictional force is constant, determine how much time elapses between the moment the bullet enters the tree and the moment it stops moving.

16. A 0.60-kg particle has a speed of 2.0 m/s at point A and a kinetic energy of 7.5 J at point B. What is (a) its kinetic energy at A? (b) Its speed at point B? (c) The total work done on the particle as it moves from A to B?

17. A large cruise ship of mass 6.50×10^7 kg has a speed of 12.0 m/s at some instant. (a) What is the ship's kinetic energy at this time? (b) How much work is required to stop it? (c) What is the magnitude of the constant force required to stop it as it undergoes a displacement of 2.50 km?

18. A man pushing a crate of mass $m = 92.0$ kg at a speed of $v = 0.850$ m/s encounters a rough horizontal surface of length $\ell = 0.65$ m as in Figure P5.18. If the coefficient of kinetic friction between the crate and rough surface is 0.358 and he exerts a constant horizontal force of 275 N on the crate, find (a) the magnitude and direction of the net force on the crate while it is on the rough surface, (b) the net work done on the crate while it is on the rough surface, and (c) the speed of the crate when it reaches the end of the rough surface.

Figure P5.18

5.3 Gravitational Potential Energy

5.4 Spring Potential Energy

19. A 0.20-kg stone is held 1.3 m above the top edge of a water well and then dropped into it. The well has a depth of 5.0 m. Taking $y = 0$ at the top edge of the well, what is the gravitational potential energy of the stone–Earth system (a) before the stone is released and (b) when it reaches the bottom of the well. (c) What is the change in gravitational potential energy of the system from release to reaching the bottom of the well?

20. When a 2.50-kg object is hung vertically on a certain light spring described by Hooke's law, the spring stretches 2.76 cm. (a) What is the force constant of the spring? (b) If the 2.50-kg object is removed, how far will the spring stretch if a 1.25-kg block is hung on it? (c) How much work must an external agent do to stretch the same spring 8.00 cm from its unstretched position?

21. In a control system, an accelerometer consists of a 4.70-g object sliding on a calibrated horizontal rail. A low-mass spring attaches the object to a flange at one end of the rail. Grease on the rail makes static friction negligible, but rapidly damps out vibrations of the sliding object. When subject to a steady acceleration of $0.800g$, the object should be at a location 0.500 cm away from its equilibrium position. Find the force constant of the spring required for the calibration to be correct.

22. **GP** A 60.0-kg athlete leaps straight up into the air from a trampoline with an initial speed of 9.0 m/s. The goal of this problem is to find the maximum height she attains and her speed at half maximum height. (a) What are the interacting objects and how do they interact? (b) Select the height at which the athlete's speed is 9.0 m/s as $y = 0$. What is her kinetic energy at this point? What is the gravitational potential energy associated with the athlete? (c) What is her kinetic energy at maximum height? What is the gravitational potential energy associated with the athlete? (d) Write a general equation for energy conservation in this case and solve for the maximum height. Substitute and obtain a numerical answer. (e) Write the general equation for energy conservation and solve for the velocity at half the maximum height. Substitute and obtain a numerical answer.

23. **M** A 2 100-kg pile driver is used to drive a steel I-beam into the ground. The pile driver falls 5.00 m before coming into contact with the top of the beam, and it drives the beam 12.0 cm farther into the ground as it comes to rest. Using energy considerations, calculate the average force the beam exerts on the pile driver while the pile driver is brought to rest.

24. **S** Two blocks are connected by a light string that passes over two frictionless pulleys as in Figure P5.24. The block of mass m_2 is attached to a spring of force constant k and $m_1 > m_2$. If the system is released from rest, and the spring is initially not stretched or compressed, find an expression for the maximum displacement d of m_2.

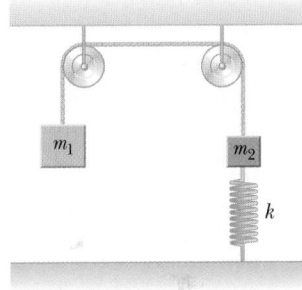

Figure P5.24

25. A daredevil on a motorcycle leaves the end of a ramp with a speed of 35.0 m/s as in Figure P5.25. If his speed is 33.0 m/s when he reaches the peak of the path, what is the maximum height that he reaches? Ignore friction and air resistance.

Figure P5.25

26. Truck suspensions often have "helper springs" that engage at high loads. One such arrangement is a leaf spring with a helper coil spring mounted on the axle, as shown in Figure P5.26 (page 160). When the main leaf spring is compressed by distance y_0, the helper spring engages

and then helps to support any additional load. Suppose the leaf spring constant is 5.25×10^5 N/m, the helper spring constant is 3.60×10^5 N/m, and $y_0 = 0.500$ m. (a) What is the compression of the leaf spring for a load of 5.00×10^5 N? (b) How much work is done in compressing the springs?

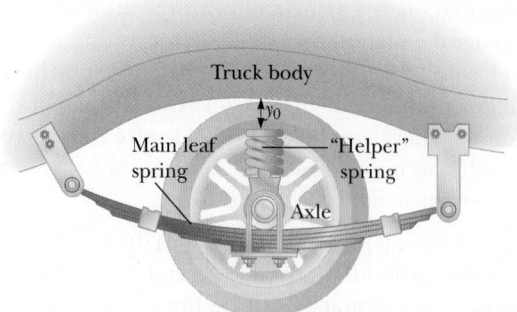

Figure P5.26

27. **BIO** The chin-up is one exercise that can be used to strengthen the biceps muscle. This muscle can exert a force of approximately 800 N as it contracts a distance of 7.5 cm in a 75-kg male.[3] How much work can the biceps muscles (one in each arm) perform in a single contraction? Compare this amount of work with the energy required to lift a 75-kg person 40 cm in performing a chin-up. Do you think the biceps muscle is the only muscle involved in performing a chin-up?

28. **BIO** A flea is able to jump about 0.5 m. It has been said that if a flea were as big as a human, it would be able to jump over a 100-story building! When an animal jumps, it converts work done in contracting muscles into gravitational potential energy (with some steps in between). The maximum force exerted by a muscle is proportional to its cross-sectional area, and the work done by the muscle is this force times the length of contraction. If we magnified a flea by a factor of 1 000, the cross section of its muscle would increase by 1 000² and the length of contraction would increase by 1 000. How high would this "superflea" be able to jump? (Don't forget that the mass of the "superflea" increases as well.)

29. A 50.0-kg projectile is fired at an angle of 30.0° above the horizontal with an initial speed of 1.20×10^2 m/s from the top of a cliff 142 m above level ground, where the ground is taken to be $y = 0$. (a) What is the initial total mechanical energy of the projectile? (b) Suppose the projectile is traveling 85.0 m/s at its maximum height of $y = 427$ m. How much work has been done on the projectile by air friction? (c) What is the speed of the projectile immediately before it hits the ground if air friction does one and a half times as much work

on the projectile when it is going down as it did when it was going up?

30. **S** A projectile of mass m is fired horizontally with an initial speed of v_0 from a height of h above a flat, desert surface. Neglecting air friction, at the instant before the projectile hits the ground, find the following in terms of m, v_0, h, and g: (a) the work done by the force of gravity on the projectile, (b) the change in kinetic energy of the projectile since it was fired, and (c) the final kinetic energy of the projectile. (d) Are any of the answers changed if the initial angle is changed?

31. **GP** A horizontal spring attached to a wall has a force constant of 850 N/m. A block of mass 1.00 kg is attached to the spring and oscillates freely on a horizontal, frictionless surface as in Active Figure 5.20. The initial goal of this problem is to find the velocity at the equilibrium point after the block is released. (a) What objects constitute the system, and through what forces do they interact? (b) What are the two points of interest? (c) Find the energy stored in the spring when the mass is stretched 6.00 cm from equilibrium and again when the mass passes through equilibrium after being released from rest. (d) Write the conservation of energy equation for this situation and solve it for the speed of the mass as it passes equilibrium. Substitute to obtain a numerical value. (e) What is the speed at the halfway point? Why isn't it half the speed at equilibrium?

5.5 Systems and Energy Conservation

32. A 50-kg pole vaulter running at 10 m/s vaults over the bar. Her speed when she is above the bar is 1.0 m/s. Neglect air resistance, as well as any energy absorbed by the pole, and determine her altitude as she crosses the bar.

33. A child and a sled with a combined mass of 50.0 kg slide down a frictionless slope. If the sled starts from rest and has a speed of 3.00 m/s at the bottom, what is the height of the hill?

34. Hooke's law describes a certain light spring of unstretched length 35.0 cm. When one end is attached to the top of a door frame and a 7.50-kg object is hung from the other end, the length of the spring is 41.5 cm. (a) Find its spring constant. (b) The load and the spring are taken down. Two people pull in opposite directions on the ends of the spring, each with a force of 190 N. Find the length of the spring in this situation.

35. **QC** A 0.250-kg block along a horizontal track has a speed of 1.50 m/s immediately before colliding with a light spring of force constant 4.60 N/m located at the end of the track. (a) What is the spring's maximum compression if the track is frictionless? (b) If the track is *not* frictionless, would the spring's maximum compression be greater than, less than, or equal to the value obtained in part (a)?

36. A block of mass $m = 5.00$ kg is released from rest from point Ⓐ and slides on the frictionless track shown in Figure P5.36. Determine (a) the block's speed at points Ⓑ and Ⓒ and (b) the net work done by the gravitational force on the block as it moves from point from Ⓐ to Ⓒ.

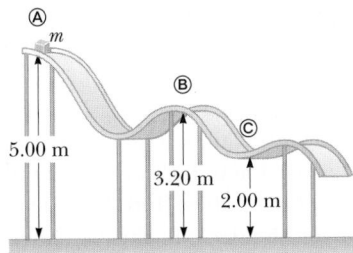

Figure P5.36

37. Tarzan swings on a 30.0-m-long vine initially inclined at an angle of 37.0° with the vertical. What is his speed at the bottom of the swing (a) if he starts from rest? (b) If he pushes off with a speed of 4.00 m/s?

38. **S** Two blocks are connected by a light string that passes over a frictionless pulley as in Figure P5.38. The system is released from rest while m_2 is on the floor and m_1 is a distance h above the floor. (a) Assuming $m_1 > m_2$, find an expression for the speed of m_1 just as it reaches the floor. (b) Taking $m_1 = 6.5$ kg, $m_2 = 4.2$ kg, and $h = 3.2$ m, evaluate your answer to part (a), and (c) find the speed of each block when m_1 has fallen a distance of 1.6 m.

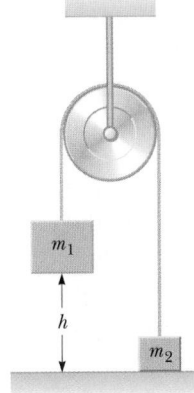

Figure P5.38

39. **M** The launching mechanism of a toy gun consists of a spring of unknown spring constant, as shown in Figure P5.39a. If the spring is compressed a distance of 0.120 m and the gun fired vertically as shown, the gun can launch a 20.0-g projectile from rest to a maximum height of 20.0 m above the starting point of the projectile. Neglecting all resistive forces, (a) describe the mechanical energy transformations that occur from the time the gun is fired until the projectile reaches its maximum height, (b) determine the spring constant, and (c) find the speed of the projectile as it moves through the equilibrium position of the spring (where $x = 0$), as shown in Figure P5.39b.

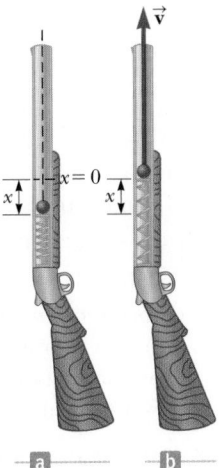

Figure P5.39

40. **GP** (a) A block with a mass m is pulled along a horizontal surface for a distance x by a constant force $\vec{F}$ at an angle θ with respect to the horizontal. The coefficient of kinetic friction between block and table is μ_k. Is the force exerted by friction equal to $\mu_k mg$? If not, what is the force exerted by friction? (b) How much work is done by the friction force and by $\vec{F}$? (Don't forget the signs.) (c) Identify all the forces that do no work on the block. (d) Let $m = 2.00$ kg, $x = 4.00$ m, $\theta = 37.0°$, $F = 15.0$ N, and $\mu_k = 0.400$, and find the answers to parts (a) and (b).

41. **Q|C** (a) A child slides down a water slide at an amusement park from an initial height h. The slide can be considered frictionless because of the water flowing down it. Can the equation for conservation of mechanical energy be used on the child? (b) Is the mass of the child a factor in determining his speed at the bottom of the slide? (c) The child drops straight down rather than following the curved ramp of the slide. In which case will he be traveling faster at ground level? (d) If friction is present, how would the conservation-of-energy equation be modified? (e) Find the maximum speed of the child when the slide is frictionless if the initial height of the slide is 12.0 m.

42. **Q|C** An airplane of mass 1.50×10^4 kg is moving at 60.0 m/s. The pilot then increases the engine's thrust to 7.50×10^4 N. The resistive force exerted by air on the airplane has a magnitude of 4.00×10^4 N. (a) Is the work done by the engine on the airplane equal to the change in the airplane's kinetic energy after it travels through some distance through the air? Is mechanical energy conserved? Explain. (b) Find the speed of the airplane after it has traveled 5.00×10^2 m. Assume the airplane is in level flight throughout the motion.

43. The system shown in Figure P5.43 is used to lift an object of mass $m = 76.0$ kg. A constant downward force of magnitude F is applied to the loose end of the rope such that the hanging object moves upward at constant speed. Neglecting the masses of the rope and pulleys, find (a) the required value of F, (b) the tensions T_1, T_2, and T_3, and (c) the work done by the applied force in raising the object a distance of 1.80 m.

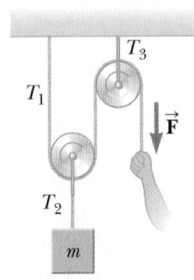

Figure P5.43

44. A 25.0-kg child on a 2.00-m-long swing is released from rest when the ropes of the swing make an angle of 30.0° with the vertical. (a) Neglecting friction, find the child's speed at the lowest position. (b) If the actual speed of the child at the lowest position is 2.00 m/s, what is the mechanical energy lost due to friction?

45. A 2.1×10^3-kg car starts from rest at the top of a 5.0-m-long driveway that is inclined at 20° with the horizontal. If an average friction force of 4.0×10^3 N impedes the motion, find the speed of the car at the bottom of the driveway.

46. **GP** **S** A child of mass m starts from rest and slides without friction from a height h along a curved water-slide (Fig. P5.46). She is launched from a height $h/5$ into the pool. (a) Is mechanical energy conserved? Why? (b) Give the gravitational potential energy associated with the child and her kinetic energy in terms of mgh at the following positions: the top of the water-slide, the launching point, and the point where she lands in the pool. (c) Determine her initial speed v_0 at the launch point in terms of g and h. (d) Determine her maximum airborne height y_{max} in terms of h, g, and the horizontal speed at that height, v_{0x}. (e) Use the x-component of the answer to part (c) to eliminate v_0 from the answer to part (d), giving the height y_{max} in terms of g, h, and the launch angle θ. (f) Would your answers be the same if the waterslide were not friction-less? Explain.

Figure P5.46

47. A skier starts from rest at the top of a hill that is inclined 10.5° with respect to the horizontal. The hillside is 200 m long, and the coefficient of friction between snow and skis is 0.075 0. At the bottom of the hill, the snow is level and the coefficient of friction is unchanged. How far does the skier glide along the horizontal portion of the snow before coming to rest?

48. In a circus performance, a monkey is strapped to a sled and both are given an initial speed of 4.0 m/s up a 20° inclined track. The combined mass of monkey and sled is 20 kg, and the coefficient of kinetic friction between sled and incline is 0.20. How far up the incline do the monkey and sled move?

49. An 80.0-kg skydiver jumps out of a balloon at an altitude of 1 000 m and opens the parachute at an altitude of 200.0 m. (a) Assuming that the total retarding force on the diver is constant at 50.0 N with the parachute closed and constant at 3 600 N with the parachute open, what is the speed of the diver when he lands on the ground? (b) Do you think the skydiver will get hurt? Explain. (c) At what height should the parachute be opened so that the final speed of the skydiver when he hits the ground is 5.00 m/s? (d) How realistic is the assumption that the total retarding force is constant? Explain.

5.6 Power

50. A skier of mass 70 kg is pulled up a slope by a motor-driven cable. (a) How much work is required to pull him 60 m up a 30° slope (assumed frictionless) at a constant speed of 2.0 m/s? (b) What power (expressed in hp) must a motor have to perform this task?

51. A 3.50-kN piano is lifted by three workers at constant speed to an apartment 25.0 m above the street using a pulley system fastened to the roof of the building. Each worker is able to deliver 165 W of power, and the pulley system is 75.0% efficient (so that 25.0% of the mechanical energy is lost due to friction in the pulley). Neglecting the mass of the pulley, find the time required to lift the piano from the street to the apartment.

52. **BIO** While running, a person dissipates about 0.60 J of mechanical energy per step per kilogram of body mass. If a 60-kg person develops a power of 70 W during a race, how fast is the person running? (Assume a running step is 1.5 m long.)

53. The electric motor of a model train accelerates the train from rest to 0.620 m/s in 21.0 ms. The total mass of the train is 875 g. Find the average power delivered to the train during its acceleration.

54. When an automobile moves with constant speed down a highway, most of the power developed by the engine is used to compensate for the mechanical energy loss due to frictional forces exerted on the car by the air and the road. If the power developed by an engine is 175 hp, estimate the total frictional force acting on the car when it is moving at a speed of 29 m/s. One horse-power equals 746 W.

55. An older-model car accelerates from 0 to speed v in 10 s. A newer, more powerful sports car of the same mass accelerates from 0 to $2v$ in the same time period. Assuming the energy coming from the engine appears only as kinetic energy of the cars, compare the power of the two cars.

56. A certain rain cloud at an altitude of 1.75 km contains 3.20×10^7 kg of water vapor. How long would it take for a 2.70-kW pump to raise the same amount of water from Earth's surface to the cloud's position?

57. A 1.50×10^3-kg car starts from rest and accelerates uniformly to 18.0 m/s in 12.0 s. Assume that air resistance remains constant at 400 N during this time. Find (a) the average power developed by the engine and (b) the instantaneous power output of the engine at $t = 12.0$ s, just before the car stops accelerating.

58. A 650-kg elevator starts from rest and moves upward for 3.00 s with constant acceleration until it reaches its cruising speed, 1.75 m/s. (a) What is the average power of the elevator motor during this period? (b) How does this amount of power compare with its power during an upward trip with constant speed?

5.7 Work Done by a Varying Force

59. **M** The force acting on a particle varies as in Figure P5.59. Find the work done by the force as the particle moves (a) from $x = 0$ to $x = 8.00$ m, (b) from $x = 8.00$ m to $x = 10.0$ m, and (c) from $x = 0$ to $x = 10.0$ m.

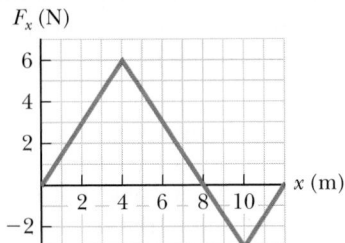

Figure P5.59

60. An object of mass 3.00 kg is subject to a force F_x that varies with position as in Figure P5.60. Find the work done by the force on the object as it moves (a) from $x = 0$ to $x = 5.00$ m, (b) from $x = 5.00$ m to $x = 10.0$ m, and (c) from $x = 10.0$ m to $x = 15.0$ m. (d) If the object has a speed of 0.500 m/s at $x = 0$, find its speed at $x = 5.00$ m and its speed at $x = 15.0$ m.

Figure P5.60

61. The force acting on an object is given by $F_x = (8x - 16)$ N, where x is in meters. (a) Make a plot of this force versus x from $x = 0$ to $x = 3.00$ m. (b) From your graph, find the net work done by the force as the object moves from $x = 0$ to $x = 3.00$ m.

Additional Problems

62. An outfielder throws a 0.150-kg baseball at a speed of 40.0 m/s and an initial angle of 30.0°. What is the kinetic energy of the ball at the highest point of its motion?

63. A person doing a chin-up weighs 700 N, exclusive of the arms. During the first 25.0 cm of the lift, each arm exerts an upward force of 355 N on the torso. If the upward movement starts from rest, what is the person's velocity at that point?

64. **S** A boy starts at rest and slides down a frictionless slide as in Figure P5.64. The bottom of the track is a height h above the ground. The boy then leaves the track horizontally, striking the ground a distance d as shown. Using energy methods, determine the initial height H of the boy in terms of h and d.

Figure P5.64

65. A roller-coaster car of mass 1.50×10^3 kg is initially at the top of a rise at point Ⓐ. It then moves 35.0 m at an angle of 50.0° below the horizontal to a lower point Ⓑ. (a) Find both the potential energy of the system when the car is at points Ⓐ and Ⓑ and the change in potential energy as the car moves from point Ⓐ to point Ⓑ, assuming $y = 0$ at point Ⓑ. (b) Repeat part (a), this time choosing $y = 0$ at point Ⓒ, which is another 15.0 m down the same slope from point Ⓑ.

66. A ball of mass $m = 1.80$ kg is released from rest at a height $h = 65.0$ cm above a light vertical spring of force constant k as in Figure P5.66a. The ball strikes the top of the spring and compresses it a distance $d = 9.00$ cm as in Figure P5.66b. Neglecting any energy losses during the collision, find (a) the speed of the ball just as it touches the spring and (b) the force constant of the spring.

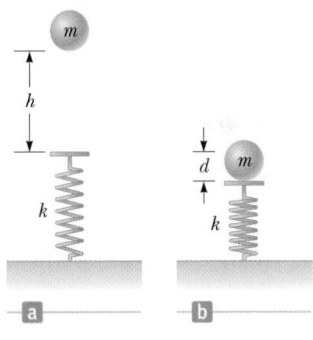

Figure P5.66

67. An archer pulls her bowstring back 0.400 m by exerting a force that increases uniformly from zero to 230 N. (a) What is the equivalent spring constant of the bow? (b) How much work does the archer do in pulling the bow?

68. A block of mass 12.0 kg slides from rest down a frictionless 35.0° incline and is stopped by a strong spring with $k = 3.00 \times 10^4$ N/m. The block slides 3.00 m from the point of release to the point where it comes to rest against the spring. When the block comes to rest, how far has the spring been compressed?

69. **BIO** (a) A 75-kg man steps out a window and falls (from rest) 1.0 m to a sidewalk. What is his speed just before his feet strike the pavement? (b) If the man falls with his knees and ankles locked, the only cushion for his fall is an approximately 0.50-cm give in the pads of his feet. Calculate the average force exerted on him by the ground during this 0.50 cm of travel. This average force is sufficient to cause damage to cartilage in the joints or to break bones.

70. A toy gun uses a spring to project a 5.3-g soft rubber sphere horizontally. The spring constant is 8.0 N/m,

the barrel of the gun is 15 cm long, and a constant frictional force of 0.032 N exists between barrel and projectile. With what speed does the projectile leave the barrel if the spring was compressed 5.0 cm for this launch?

71. Two objects (m_1 = 5.00 kg and m_2 = 3.00 kg) are connected by a light string passing over a light, frictionless pulley as in Figure P5.71. The 5.00-kg object is released from rest at a point h = 4.00 m above the table. (a) Determine the speed of each object when the two pass each other. (b) Determine the speed of each object at the moment the 5.00-kg object hits the table. (c) How much higher does the 3.00-kg object travel after the 5.00-kg object hits the table?

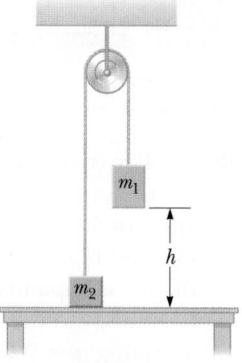

Figure P5.71

72. **BIO** In a needle biopsy, a narrow strip of tissue is extracted from a patient with a hollow needle. Rather than being pushed by hand, to ensure a clean cut the needle can be fired into the patient's body by a spring. Assume the needle has mass 5.60 g, the light spring has force constant 375 N/m, and the spring is originally compressed 8.10 cm to project the needle horizontally without friction. The tip of the needle then moves through 2.40 cm of skin and soft tissue, which exerts a resistive force of 7.60 N on it. Next, the needle cuts 3.50 cm into an organ, which exerts a backward force of 9.20 N on it. Find (a) the maximum speed of the needle and (b) the speed at which a flange on the back end of the needle runs into a stop, set to limit the penetration to 5.90 cm.

73. A 2.00×10^2-g particle is released from rest at point A on the inside of a smooth hemispherical bowl of radius R = 30.0 cm (Fig. P5.73). Calculate (a) its gravitational potential energy at A relative to B, (b) its kinetic energy at B, (c) its speed at B, (d) its potential energy at C relative to B, and (e) its kinetic energy at C.

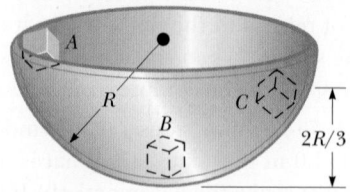

Figure P5.73 Problems 73 and 74.

74. **QC** The particle described in Problem 73 (Fig. P5.73) is released from point A at rest. Its speed at B is 1.50 m/s. (a) What is its kinetic energy at B? (b) How much mechanical energy is lost as a result of friction as the particle goes from A to B? (c) Is it possible to determine μ from these results in a simple manner? Explain.

75. A light spring with spring constant 1.20×10^3 N/m hangs from an elevated support. From its lower end hangs a second light spring, which has spring constant 1.80×10^3 N/m. A 1.50-kg object hangs at rest from the lower end of the second spring. (a) Find the total extension distance of the pair of springs. (b) Find the effective spring constant of the pair of springs as a system. We describe these springs as being *in series*. *Hint:* Consider the forces on each spring separately.

76. **S** *Symbolic Version of Problem 75* A light spring with spring constant k_1 hangs from an elevated support. From its lower end hangs a second light spring, which has spring constant k_2. An object of mass m hangs at rest from the lower end of the second spring. (a) Find the total extension distance x of the pair of springs in terms of the two displacements x_1 and x_2. (b) Find the effective spring constant of the pair of springs as a system. We describe these springs as being *in series*.

77. **BIO** In terms of saving energy, bicycling and walking are far more efficient means of transportation than is travel by automobile. For example, when riding at 10.0 mi/h, a cyclist uses food energy at a rate of about 400 kcal/h above what he would use if he were merely sitting still. (In exercise physiology, power is often measured in kcal/h rather than in watts. Here, 1 kcal = 1 nutritionist's Calorie = 4 186 J.) Walking at 3.00 mi/h requires about 220 kcal/h. It is interesting to compare these values with the energy consumption required for travel by car. Gasoline yields about 1.30×10^8 J/gal. Find the fuel economy in equivalent miles per gallon for a person (a) walking and (b) bicycling.

78. **BIO** Energy is conventionally measured in Calories as well as in joules. One Calorie in nutrition is 1 kilocalorie, which we define in Chapter 11 as 1 kcal = 4 186 J. Metabolizing 1 gram of fat can release 9.00 kcal. A student decides to try to lose weight by exercising. She plans to run up and down the stairs in a football stadium as fast as she can and as many times as necessary. Is this in itself a practical way to lose weight? To evaluate the program, suppose she runs up a flight of 80 steps, each 0.150 m high, in 65.0 s. For simplicity, ignore the energy she uses in coming down (which is small). Assume that a typical efficiency for human muscles is 20.0%. This means that when your body converts 100 J from metabolizing fat, 20 J goes into doing mechanical work (here, climbing stairs). The remainder goes into internal energy. Assume the student's mass is 50.0 kg. (a) How many times must she run the flight of stairs to lose 1 pound of fat? (b) What is her average power output, in watts and in horsepower, as she is running up the stairs?

79. A ski jumper starts from rest 50.0 m above the ground on a frictionless track and flies off the track at an angle of 45.0° above the horizontal and at a height of 10.0 m above the level ground. Neglect air resistance. (a) What is her speed when she leaves the track? (b) What is the

maximum altitude she attains after leaving the track? (c) Where does she land relative to the end of the track?

80. A 5.0-kg block is pushed 3.0 m up a vertical wall with constant speed by a constant force of magnitude F applied at an angle of $\theta = 30°$ with the horizontal, as shown in Figure P5.80. If the coefficient of kinetic friction between block and wall is 0.30, determine the work done by (a) $\vec{F}$, (b) the force of gravity, and (c) the normal force between block and wall. (d) By how much does the gravitational potential energy increase during the block's motion?

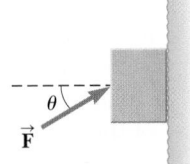

Figure P5.80

81. A child's pogo stick (Fig. P5.81) stores energy in a spring ($k = 2.50 \times 10^4$ N/m). At position Ⓐ ($x_1 = -0.100$ m), the spring compression is a maximum and the child is momentarily at rest. At position Ⓑ ($x = 0$), the spring is relaxed and the child is moving upward. At position Ⓒ, the child is again momentarily at rest at the top of the jump. Assuming that the combined mass of child and pogo stick is 25.0 kg, (a) calculate the total energy of the system if both potential energies are zero at $x = 0$, (b) determine x_2, (c) calculate the speed of the child at $x = 0$, (d) determine the value of x for which the kinetic energy of the system is a maximum, and (e) obtain the child's maximum upward speed.

Figure P5.81

82. **BIO** A hummingbird is able to hover because, as the wings move downward, they exert a downward force on the air. Newton's third law tells us that the air exerts an equal and opposite force (upward) on the wings. The average of this force must be equal to the weight of the bird when it hovers. If the wings move through a distance of 3.5 cm with each stroke, and the wings beat 80 times per second, determine the work performed by the wings on the air in 1 minute if the mass of the hummingbird is 3.0 grams.

83. In the dangerous "sport" of bungee jumping, a daring student jumps from a hot-air balloon with a specially designed elastic cord attached to his waist. The unstretched length of the cord is 25.0 m, the student weighs 700 N, and the balloon is 36.0 m above the surface of a river below. Calculate the required force constant of the cord if the student is to stop safely 4.00 m above the river.

84. **QC** The masses of the javelin, discus, and shot are 0.80 kg, 2.0 kg, and 7.2 kg, respectively, and record throws in the corresponding track events are about 98 m, 74 m, and 23 m, respectively. Neglecting air resistance, (a) calculate the minimum initial kinetic energies that would produce these throws, and (b) estimate the average force exerted on each object during the throw, assuming the force acts over a distance of 2.0 m. (c) Do your results suggest that air resistance is an important factor?

85. A truck travels uphill with constant velocity on a highway with a 7.0° slope. A 50-kg package sits on the floor of the back of the truck and does not slide, due to a static frictional force. During an interval in which the truck travels 340 m, (a) what is the net work done on the package? What is the work done on the package by (b) the force of gravity, (c) the normal force, and (d) the friction force?

86. A daredevil wishes to bungee-jump from a hot-air balloon 65.0 m above a carnival midway. He will use a piece of uniform elastic cord tied to a harness around his body to stop his fall at a point 10.0 m above the ground. Model his body as a particle and the cord as having negligible mass and a tension force described by Hooke's force law. In a preliminary test, hanging at rest from a 5.00-m length of the cord, the jumper finds that his body weight stretches it by 1.50 m. He will drop from rest at the point where the top end of a longer section of the cord is attached to the stationary balloon. (a) What length of cord should he use? (b) What maximum acceleration will he experience?

87. **M** A loaded ore car has a mass of 950 kg and rolls on rails with negligible friction. It starts from rest and is pulled up a mine shaft by a cable connected to a winch. The shaft is inclined at 30.0° above the horizontal. The car accelerates uniformly to a speed of 2.20 m/s in 12.0 s and then continues at constant speed. (a) What power must the winch motor provide when the car is moving at constant speed? (b) What maximum power must the motor provide? (c) What total energy transfers out of the motor by work by the time the car moves off the end of the track, which is of length 1 250 m?

88. **S** An object of mass m is suspended from the top of a cart by a string of length L as in Figure P5.88a. The cart and object are initially moving to the right at a constant speed v_0. The cart comes to rest after colliding and sticking to a bumper, as in Figure P5.88b, and the suspended object swings through an angle θ. (a) Show

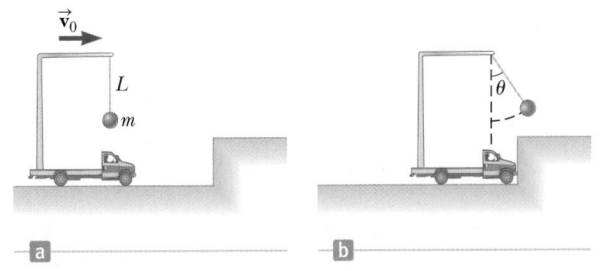

Figure P5.88

that the initial speed is $v_0 = \sqrt{2gL(1 - \cos\theta)}$. (b) If $L = 1.20$ m and $\theta = 35.0°$, find the initial speed of the cart. (*Hint:* The force exerted by the string on the object does no work on the object.)

89. Three objects with masses $m_1 = 5.0$ kg, $m_2 = 10$ kg, and $m_3 = 15$ kg, respectively, are attached by strings over frictionless pulleys as indicated in Figure P5.89. The horizontal surface exerts a force of friction of 30 N on m_2. If the system is released from rest, use energy concepts to find the speed of m_3 after it moves down 4.0 m.

Figure P5.89

90. A light spring with force constant 3.85 N/m is compressed by 8.00 cm as it is held between a 0.250-kg block on the left and a 0.500-kg block on the right, both resting on a horizontal surface. The spring exerts a force on each block, tending to push them apart. The blocks are simultaneously released from rest. Find the acceleration with which each block starts to move, given that the coefficient of kinetic friction between each block and the surface is (a) 0, (b) 0.100, and (c) 0.462.

91. **BIO** In bicycling for aerobic exercise, a woman wants her heart rate to be between 136 and 166 beats per minute. Assume that her heart rate is directly proportional to her mechanical power output. Ignore all forces on the woman-plus-bicycle system, except for static friction forward on the drive wheel of the bicycle and an air resistance force proportional to the square of the bicycler's speed. When her speed is 22.0 km/h, her heart rate is 90.0 beats per minute. In what range should her speed be so that her heart rate will be in the range she wants?

92. Two blocks, *A* and *B* (with mass 50 kg and 100 kg, respectively), are connected by a string, as shown in Figure P5.92. The pulley is frictionless and of negligible mass. The coefficient of kinetic friction between block *A* and the incline is $\mu_k = 0.25$. Determine the change in the kinetic energy of block *A* as it moves from ©️ to Ⓓ, a distance of 20 m up the incline (and block *B* drops downward a distance of 20 m) if the system starts from rest.

Figure P5.92

■ AP* REVIEW QUESTIONS

1. Two identical boxes are pushed by movers over a rough level surface in different paths with a constant velocity, as shown above. Which of the paths identified below represent true statements about the work done by the movers on the boxes?

   I. Path $ABCD$ = Path AD
   II. Path XYZ > Path XZ
   III. Path $ABCD$ = Path XYZ
   IV. Path $ABCD$ > Path XYZ

(A) I
(B) I and III
(C) II and IV
(D) II
(E) None of the statements above are true

2. By what factor would the escape velocity change if a planet's radius is doubled and its mass remains the same?

(A) 1
(B) $\sqrt{2}$
(C) $\dfrac{1}{\sqrt{2}}$
(D) 2
(E) 4

3. A ball attached to a string of length $\ell = 10$ m is released from position A, as shown above. What is the ball's speed when it is at position B, when the string is at an angle of 60° from vertical?

(A) 2 m/s
(B) 5 m/s
(C) 8 m/s
(D) $10\sqrt{2}$ m/s
(E) 10 m/s

4. A 10 kg mass is attached to a large ideal spring with a spring constant of 900 N/m, which is anchored to a ceiling, as shown above. The spring is compressed 2 m

from equilibrium (x_0) and released. What maximum speed does the mass reach?

(A) $6\sqrt{10}$
(B) 15 m/s
(C) 20 m/s
(D) $12\sqrt{5}$
(E) 30 m/s

5. A spring is connected to a string of negligible mass draped over a frictionless, massless pulley. A 6 kg mass is attached to the end of the string, and the spring stretches a distance of 20 cm. The mass is then replaced with a second mass of 10 kg and released from the point at which the spring is in equilibrium. What maximum distance does the second mass reach after released?

(A) 0.33 m
(B) 0.67 m
(C) 1 m
(D) 1.5 m
(E) 3 m

6. By what factor does a 1000 kg automobile's kinetic energy change if its speed is increased from 20 m/s ($\approx$45 mi/hr) to 25 m/s ($\approx$55 mi/hr)?

(A) 0.64
(B) 0.8
(C) 1.25
(D) 1.6
(E) 2

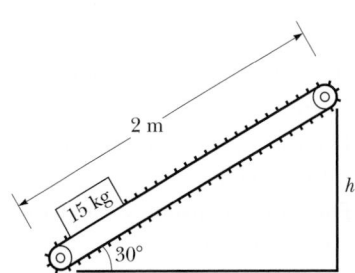

7. The frictionless conveyer belt shown above is used to raise goods at a constant speed. What is the power needed by the motor in order to raise a 15 kg box of bananas height h in 3 s if the belt is at an angle of 30° from horizontal?

(A) 300 W
(B) 150 W
(C) 100 W
(D) 50 W
(E) 33 W

Force vs. Distance
pushing a snow shovel

8. Snow accumulates on a shovel as it is pushed along a snow-covered sidewalk. A graph of the force required to push the shovel versus the distance covered is shown above. About how much work does it take to travel 8 m?

(A) 15 J   (D) 240 J

(B) 100 J   (E) 480 J

(C) 170 J

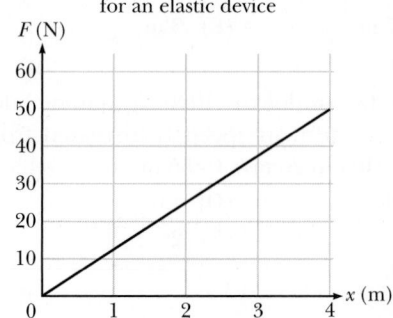

Force vs. Stretch
for an elastic device

9. An elastic device is stretched from a relaxed state to 4 m as shown in the force versus stretch graph above. Which of the following is true about the elastic device's spring constant?

   I. The spring constant remains constant for the entire stretch.

   II. The spring constant varies with the stretch of this elastic device.

   III. The spring constant value at 2 m is less than 15 N/m.

   IV. The spring constant value at 2 m is greater than 15 N/m.

(A) I only   (D) II and III

(B) II only   (E) II and IV

(C) I and III

10. An 18 N force acts horizontally on a 100 N block over a smooth level surface from rest for a distance of 10 m. What is its final velocity?

(A) 180 m/s   (D) 10 m/s

(B) 18 m/s   (E) 6 m/s

(C) 12 m/s

11. A mass, m, is attached to a string with length x and is swung around horizontally in a half circle from point A to point B at a constant speed, as shown above with tension T. How much work is done by the string on the mass?

(A) 0   (D) $\dfrac{Tx}{2}$

(B) Tx (E) $2mgx$

(C) $2Tx$

12. Two students push two identical shopping carts along a rough level surface at constant velocities and argue about who is doing more work. The first student pushes on a cart a distance d with mass m with a horizontal force F. The second pushes the second cart a distance $2d$ with the same force F acting at an angle of 60° below horizontal. Which of the following is true?

(A) Both students do the same amount of work on their respective carts.

(B) The first student is doing twice as much work on the cart as the second.

(C) The second student is doing twice as much work on the cart as the first.

(D) The second student is doing four times as much work on the cart as the first.

(E) The constant velocities of each must be known in order to answer this question.

AP photos/Keystone/Regina Kuehne

The concept of momentum allows the analysis of car collisions even without detailed knowledge of the forces involved. Such analysis can determine the relative velocity of the cars before the collision, and in addition aid engineers in designing safer vehicles.

Momentum and Collisions 6

What happens when two automobiles collide? How does the impact affect the motion of each vehicle, and what basic physical principles determine the likelihood of serious injury? How do rockets work, and what mechanisms can be used to overcome the limitations imposed by exhaust speed? Why do we have to brace ourselves when firing small projectiles at high velocity? Finally, how can we use physics to improve our golf game?

To begin answering such questions, we introduce *momentum*. Intuitively, anyone or anything that has a lot of momentum is going to be hard to stop. In politics, the term is metaphorical. Physically, the more momentum an object has, the more force has to be applied to stop it in a given time. This concept leads to one of the most powerful principles in physics: *conservation of momentum*. Using this law, complex collision problems can be solved without knowing much about the forces involved during contact. We'll also be able to derive information about the average force delivered in an impact. With conservation of momentum, we'll have a better understanding of what choices to make when designing an automobile or a moon rocket, or when addressing a golf ball on a tee.

6.1 Momentum and Impulse

In physics, momentum has a precise definition. A slowly moving brontosaurus has a lot of momentum, but so does a little hot lead shot from the muzzle of a gun. We therefore expect that momentum will depend on an object's mass and velocity.

The linear momentum $\vec{\mathbf{p}}$ of an object of mass m moving with velocity $\vec{\mathbf{v}}$ is the product of its mass and velocity:

$$\vec{\mathbf{p}} \equiv m\vec{\mathbf{v}} \qquad [6.1]$$

SI unit: kilogram-meter per second (kg · m/s)

◀ Linear momentum

Doubling either the mass or the velocity of an object doubles its momentum; doubling both quantities quadruples its momentum. Momentum is a vector quantity with the same direction as the object's velocity. Its components are given in two dimensions by

$$p_x = mv_x \qquad p_y = mv_y$$

where p_x is the momentum of the object in the x-direction and p_y its momentum in the y-direction.

The magnitude of the momentum p of an object of mass m can be related to its kinetic energy KE:

$$KE = \frac{p^2}{2m} \qquad [6.2]$$

This relationship is easy to prove using the definitions of kinetic energy and momentum (see Problem 6) and is valid for objects traveling at speeds much less than the speed of light. Equation 6.2 is useful in grasping the interplay between the two concepts, as illustrated in Quick Quiz 6.1.

■ *Quick Quiz*

6.1 Two masses m_1 and m_2, with $m_1 < m_2$, have equal kinetic energy. How do the magnitudes of their momenta compare? (a) Not enough information is given. (b) $p_1 < p_2$ (c) $p_1 = p_2$ (d) $p_1 > p_2$

Changing the momentum of an object requires the application of a force. This is, in fact, how Newton originally stated his second law of motion. Starting from the more common version of the second law, we have

$$\vec{F}_{net} = m\vec{a} = m\frac{\Delta \vec{v}}{\Delta t} = \frac{\Delta(m\vec{v})}{\Delta t}$$

where the mass m and the forces are assumed constant. The quantity in parentheses is just the momentum, so we have the following result:

The change in an object's momentum $\Delta\vec{p}$ divided by the elapsed time Δt equals the constant net force $\vec{F}_{net}$ acting on the object:

Newton's second law and momentum ▶

$$\frac{\Delta\vec{p}}{\Delta t} = \frac{\text{change in momentum}}{\text{time interval}} = \vec{F}_{net} \qquad [6.3]$$

This equation is also valid when the forces are not constant, provided the limit is taken as Δt becomes infinitesimally small. Equation 6.3 says that if the net force on an object is zero, the object's momentum doesn't change. In other words, the linear momentum of an object is conserved when $\vec{F}_{net} = 0$. Equation 6.3 also tells us that changing an object's momentum requires the continuous application of a force over a period of time Δt, leading to the definition of *impulse*:

If a constant force $\vec{F}$ acts on an object, the **impulse $\vec{I}$** delivered to the object over a time interval Δt is given by

$$\vec{I} \equiv \vec{F}\,\Delta t \qquad [6.4]$$

SI unit: kilogram meter per second (kg · m/s)

Impulse is a vector quantity with the same direction as the constant force acting on the object. When a single constant force $\vec{F}$ acts on an object, Equation 6.3 can be written as

Impulse–momentum ▶ theorem

$$\vec{I} = \vec{F}\Delta t = \Delta\vec{p} = m\vec{v}_f - m\vec{v}_i \qquad [6.5]$$

which is a special case of the **impulse–momentum theorem**. Equation 6.5 shows that **the impulse of the force acting on an object equals the change in momentum**

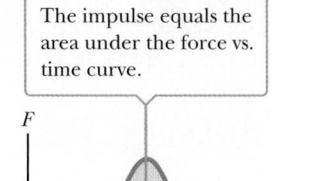

The impulse equals the area under the force vs. time curve.

The impulse of the average force equals the impulse of the actual time-varying force.

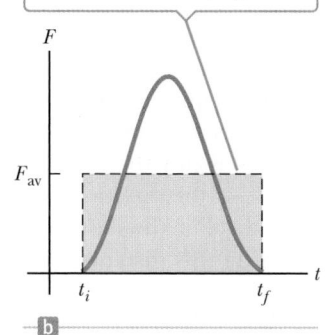

Figure 6.1 (a) A net force acting on a particle may vary in time. (b) The value of the constant force F_{av} (horizontal dashed line) is chosen so that the area of the rectangle $F_{av}\Delta t$ is the same as the area under the curve in (a).

of that object. That equality is true even if the force is not constant, as long as the time interval Δt is taken to be arbitrarily small. (The proof of the general case requires concepts from calculus.)

In real-life situations, the force on an object is only rarely constant. For example, when a bat hits a baseball, the force increases sharply, reaches some maximum value, and then decreases just as rapidly. Figure 6.1(a) shows a typical graph of force versus time for such incidents. The force starts out small as the bat comes in contact with the ball, rises to a maximum value when they are firmly in contact, and then drops off as the ball leaves the bat. In order to analyze this rather complex interaction, it's useful to define an **average force** $\vec{\mathbf{F}}_{av}$, shown as the dashed line in Figure 6.1b. The average force is the constant force delivering the same impulse to the object in the time interval Δt as the actual time-varying force. We can then write the impulse–momentum theorem as

$$\vec{\mathbf{F}}_{av}\,\Delta t = \Delta\vec{\mathbf{p}} \qquad [6.6]$$

The magnitude of the impulse delivered by a force during the time interval Δt is equal to the area under the force vs. time graph as in Figure 6.1a or, equivalently, to $F_{av}\Delta t$ as shown in Figure 6.1b. The brief collision between a bullet and an apple is illustrated in Figure 6.2.

Ted Kinsman/Photo Researchers, Inc.

Figure 6.2 An apple being pierced by a 30-caliber bullet traveling at a supersonic speed of 900 m/s. This collision was photographed with a microflash stroboscope using an exposure time of 0.33 μs. Shortly after the photograph was taken, the apple disintegrated completely. Note that the points of entry and exit of the bullet are visually explosive.

■ APPLYING PHYSICS 6.1   Boxing and Brain Injury BIO

Boxers in the nineteenth century used their bare fists. In modern boxing, fighters wear padded gloves. How do gloves protect the brain of the boxer from injury? Also, why do boxers often "roll with the punch"?

EXPLANATION The brain is immersed in a cushioning fluid inside the skull. If the head is struck suddenly by a bare fist, the skull accelerates rapidly. The brain matches this acceleration only because of the large impulsive force exerted by the skull on the brain. This large and sudden force (large F_{av} and small Δt) can cause severe brain injury.

Padded gloves extend the time Δt over which the force is applied to the head. For a given impulse $F_{av}\Delta t$, a glove results in a longer time interval than a bare fist, decreasing the average force. Because the average force is decreased, the acceleration of the skull is decreased, reducing (but not eliminating) the chance of brain injury. The same argument can be made for "rolling with the punch": If the head is held steady while being struck, the time interval over which the force is applied is relatively short and the average force is large. If the head is allowed to move in the same direction as the punch, the time interval is lengthened and the average force reduced. ■

■ EXAMPLE 6.1   Teeing Off

GOAL Use the impulse–momentum theorem to estimate the average force exerted during an impact.

PROBLEM A golf ball with mass 5.0×10^{-2} kg is struck with a club as in Figure 6.3 (page 170). The force on the ball varies from zero when contact is made up to some maximum value (when the ball is maximally deformed) and then back to zero

(Continued)

when the ball leaves the club, as in the graph of force vs. time in Figure 6.1. Assume that the ball leaves the club face with a velocity of +44 m/s. **(a)** Find the magnitude of the impulse due to the collision. **(b)** Estimate the duration of the collision and the average force acting on the ball.

STRATEGY In part (a), use the fact that the impulse is equal to the change in momentum. The mass and the initial and final speeds are known, so this change can be computed. In part (b), the average force is just the change in momentum computed in part (a) divided by an estimate of the duration of the collision. Guess at the distance the ball travels on the face of the club (about 2 cm, roughly the same as the radius of the ball). Divide this distance by the average velocity (half the final velocity) to get an estimate of the time of contact.

Figure 6.3 (Example 6.1) During impact, the club head momentarily flattens the side of the golf ball.

SOLUTION

(a) Find the impulse delivered to the ball.

The problem is essentially one dimensional. Note that $v_i = 0$, and calculate the change in momentum, which equals the impulse:

$$I = \Delta p = p_f - p_i = (5.0 \times 10^{-2}\,\text{kg})(44\,\text{m/s}) - 0$$
$$= +2.2\,\text{kg} \cdot \text{m/s}$$

(b) Estimate the duration of the collision and the average force acting on the ball.

Estimate the time interval of the collision, Δt, using the approximate displacement (radius of the ball) and its average speed (half the maximum speed):

$$\Delta t = \frac{\Delta x}{v_{av}} = \frac{2.0 \times 10^{-2}\,\text{m}}{22\,\text{m/s}} = 9.1 \times 10^{-4}\,\text{s}$$

Estimate the average force from Equation 6.6:

$$F_{av} = \frac{\Delta p}{\Delta t} = \frac{2.2\,\text{kg} \cdot \text{m/s}}{9.1 \times 10^{-4}\,\text{s}} = +2.4 \times 10^3\,\text{N}$$

REMARKS This estimate shows just how large such contact forces can be. A good golfer achieves maximum momentum transfer by shifting weight from the back foot to the front foot, transmitting the body's momentum through the shaft and head of the club. This timing, involving a short movement of the hips, is more effective than a shot powered exclusively by the arms and shoulders. Following through with the swing ensures that the motion isn't slowed at the critical instant of impact.

QUESTION 6.1 What average club speed would double the average force?

EXERCISE 6.1 A 0.150-kg baseball, thrown with a speed of 40.0 m/s, is hit straight back at the pitcher with a speed of 50.0 m/s. (a) What is the magnitude of the impulse delivered by the bat to the baseball? (b) Find the magnitude of the average force exerted by the bat on the ball if the two are in contact for 2.00×10^{-3} s.

ANSWER (a) 13.5 kg · m/s (b) 6.75 kN

■ EXAMPLE 6.2   How Good Are the Bumpers?

GOAL Find an impulse and estimate a force in a collision of a moving object with a stationary object.

PROBLEM In a crash test, a car of mass 1.50×10^3 kg collides with a wall and rebounds as in Figure 6.4a. The initial and final velocities of the car are $v_i = -15.0$ m/s and $v_f = 2.60$ m/s, respectively. If the collision lasts for 0.150 s, find **(a)** the impulse delivered to the car due to the collision and **(b)** the size and direction of the average force exerted on the car.

STRATEGY This problem is similar to the previous example, except that the initial and final momenta are both nonzero. Find the momenta and substitute into the impulse–momentum theorem, Equation 6.6, solving for F_{av}.

Before
−15.0 m/s

After
+2.60 m/s

Figure 6.4 (Example 6.2) (a) This car's momentum changes as a result of its collision with the wall. (b) In a crash test (an inelastic collision), much of the car's initial kinetic energy is transformed into the energy it took to damage the vehicle.

SOLUTION

(a) Find the impulse delivered to the car.

Calculate the initial and final momenta of the car:

$$p_i = mv_i = (1.50 \times 10^3 \, \text{kg})(-15.0 \, \text{m/s})$$
$$= -2.25 \times 10^4 \, \text{kg} \cdot \text{m/s}$$
$$p_f = mv_f = (1.50 \times 10^3 \, \text{kg})(+2.60 \, \text{m/s})$$
$$= +0.390 \times 10^4 \, \text{kg} \cdot \text{m/s}$$

The impulse is just the difference between the final and initial momenta:

$$I = p_f - p_i$$
$$= +0.390 \times 10^4 \, \text{kg} \cdot \text{m/s} - (-2.25 \times 10^4 \, \text{kg} \cdot \text{m/s})$$
$$I = \boxed{2.64 \times 10^4 \, \text{kg} \cdot \text{m/s}}$$

(b) Find the average force exerted on the car.

Apply Equation 6.6, the impulse–momentum theorem:

$$F_{av} = \frac{\Delta p}{\Delta t} = \frac{2.64 \times 10^4 \, \text{kg} \cdot \text{m/s}}{0.150 \, \text{s}} = \boxed{+1.76 \times 10^5 \, \text{N}}$$

REMARKS When the car doesn't rebound off the wall, the average force exerted on the car is smaller than the value just calculated. With a final momentum of zero, the car undergoes a smaller change in momentum.

QUESTION 6.2 When a person is involved in a car accident, why is the likelihood of injury greater in a head-on collision as opposed to being hit from behind? Answer using the concepts of relative velocity, momentum, and average force.

EXERCISE 6.2 Suppose the car doesn't rebound off the wall, but the time interval of the collision remains at 0.150 s. In this case, the final velocity of the car is zero. Find the average force exerted on the car.

ANSWER $+1.50 \times 10^5$ N

Injury in Automobile Collisions

The main injuries that occur to a person hitting the interior of a car in a crash are brain damage, bone fracture, and trauma to the skin, blood vessels, and internal organs. Here, we compare the rather imprecisely known thresholds for human injury with typical forces and accelerations experienced in a car crash.

BIO APPLICATION
Injury to Passengers in Car Collisions

A force of about 90 kN (20 000 lb) compressing the tibia can cause fracture. Although the breaking force varies with the bone considered, we may take this value as the threshold force for fracture. It's well known that rapid acceleration of the head, even without skull fracture, can be fatal. Estimates show that head accelerations of $150g$ experienced for about 4 ms or $50g$ for 60 ms are fatal 50% of the time. Such injuries from rapid acceleration often result in nerve damage to the spinal cord where the nerves enter the base of the brain. The threshold for damage to skin, blood vessels, and internal organs may be estimated from whole-body impact data, where the force is uniformly distributed over the entire front surface area of 0.7 to 0.9 m². These data show that if the collision lasts for less than about 70 ms, a person will survive if the whole-body impact pressure (force per unit area) is less than 1.9×10^5 N/m² (28 lb/in.²). Death results in 50% of cases in which the whole-body impact pressure reaches 3.4×10^5 N/m² (50 lb/in.²).

Armed with the data above, we can estimate the forces and accelerations in a typical car crash and see how seat belts, air bags, and padded interiors can reduce the chance of death or serious injury in a collision. Consider a typical collision involving a 75-kg passenger not wearing a seat belt, traveling at 27 m/s (60 mi/h) who comes to rest in about 0.010 s after striking an unpadded dashboard. Using $F_{av}\Delta t = mv_f - mv_i$, we find that

$$F_{av} = \frac{mv_f - mv_i}{\Delta t} = \frac{0 - (75 \, \text{kg})(27 \, \text{m/s})}{0.010 \, \text{s}} = -2.0 \times 10^5 \, \text{N}$$

and

$$a = \left|\frac{\Delta v}{\Delta t}\right| = \frac{27 \text{ m/s}}{0.010 \text{ s}} = 2\,700 \text{ m/s}^2 = \frac{2\,700 \text{ m/s}^2}{9.8 \text{ m/s}^2}\,g = 280g$$

If we assume the passenger crashes into the dashboard and windshield so that the head and chest, with a combined surface area of 0.5 m², experience the force, we find a whole-body pressure of

$$\frac{F_{av}}{A} = \frac{2.0 \times 10^5 \text{ N}}{0.5 \text{ m}^2} \cong 4 \times 10^5 \text{ N/m}^2$$

We see that the force, the acceleration, and the whole-body pressure all *exceed* the threshold for fatality or broken bones and that an unprotected collision at 60 mi/h is almost certainly fatal.

What can be done to reduce or eliminate the chance of dying in a car crash? The most important factor is the collision time, or the time it takes the person to come to rest. If this time can be increased by 10 to 100 times the value of 0.01 s for a hard collision, the chances of survival in a car crash are much higher because the increase in Δt makes the contact force 10 to 100 times smaller. Seat belts restrain people so that they come to rest in about the same amount of time it takes to stop the car, typically about 0.15 s. This increases the effective collision time by an order of magnitude. Figure 6.5 shows the measured force on a car versus time for a car crash.

Air bags also increase the collision time, absorb energy from the body as they rapidly deflate, and spread the contact force over an area of the body of about 0.5 m², preventing penetration wounds and fractures. Air bags must deploy very rapidly (in less than 10 ms) in order to stop a human traveling at 27 m/s before he or she comes to rest against the steering column about 0.3 m away. To achieve this rapid deployment, accelerometers send a signal to discharge a bank of capacitors (devices that store electric charge), which then ignites an explosive, thereby filling the air bag with gas very quickly. The electrical charge for ignition is stored in capacitors to ensure that the air bag continues to operate in the event of damage to the battery or the car's electrical system in a severe collision.

The important reduction in potentially fatal forces, accelerations, and pressures to tolerable levels by the simultaneous use of seat belts and air bags is summarized as follows: If a 75-kg person traveling at 27 m/s is stopped by a seat belt in 0.15 s, the person experiences an average force of 9.8 kN, an average acceleration of 18g, and a whole-body pressure of 2.8×10^4 N/m² for a contact area of 0.5 m². These values are about one order of magnitude less than the values estimated earlier for an unprotected person and well below the thresholds for life-threatening injuries.

F (in units of 10⁵ N)

Figure 6.5 Force on a car versus time for a typical collision.

6.2 Conservation of Momentum

When a collision occurs in an isolated system, the total momentum of the system doesn't change with the passage of time. Instead, it remains constant both in magnitude and in direction. The momenta of the individual objects in the system may change, but the vector sum of *all* the momenta will not change. The total momentum is therefore said to be *conserved*. In this section, we will see how the laws of motion lead us to this important conservation law.

A collision may be the result of physical contact between two objects, as illustrated in Active Figure 6.6a. This is a common macroscopic event, as when a pair of billiard balls or a baseball and a bat strike each other. By contrast, because contact on a submicroscopic scale is hard to define accurately, the notion of *collision* must be generalized to that scale. Forces between two objects arise from the electrostatic interaction of the electrons in the surface atoms of the objects. As will be discussed in Chapter 15, electric charges are either positive or negative. Charges with the same sign repel each other, while charges with opposite sign attract each

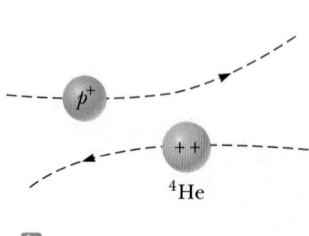

Active Figure 6.6 (a) A collision between two objects resulting from direct contact. (b) A collision between two charged objects (in this case, a proton and a helium nucleus).

other. To understand the distinction between macroscopic and microscopic collisions, consider the collision between two positive charges, as shown in Active Figure 6.6b. Because the two particles in the figure are both positively charged, they repel each other. During such a microscopic collision, particles need not touch in the normal sense in order to interact and transfer momentum.

Active Figure 6.7 shows an isolated system of two particles before and after they collide. By "isolated," we mean that no external forces, such as the gravitational force or friction, act on the system. Before the collision, the velocities of the two particles are $\vec{\mathbf{v}}_{1i}$ and $\vec{\mathbf{v}}_{2i}$; after the collision, the velocities are $\vec{\mathbf{v}}_{1f}$ and $\vec{\mathbf{v}}_{2f}$. The impulse–momentum theorem applied to m_1 becomes

$$\vec{\mathbf{F}}_{21}\,\Delta t = m_1\vec{\mathbf{v}}_{1f} - m_1\vec{\mathbf{v}}_{1i}$$

Likewise, for m_2, we have

$$\vec{\mathbf{F}}_{12}\,\Delta t = m_2\vec{\mathbf{v}}_{2f} - m_2\vec{\mathbf{v}}_{2i}$$

where $\vec{\mathbf{F}}_{21}$ is the average force exerted by m_2 on m_1 during the collision and $\vec{\mathbf{F}}_{12}$ is the average force exerted by m_1 on m_2 during the collision, as in Figure 6.6a.

We use average values for $\vec{\mathbf{F}}_{21}$ and $\vec{\mathbf{F}}_{12}$ even though the actual forces may vary in time in a complicated way, as is the case in Figure 6.8. Newton's third law states that at all times these two forces are equal in magnitude and opposite in direction: $\vec{\mathbf{F}}_{21} = -\vec{\mathbf{F}}_{12}$. In addition, the two forces act over the same time interval. As a result, we have

$$\vec{\mathbf{F}}_{21}\,\Delta t = -\vec{\mathbf{F}}_{12}\,\Delta t$$

or

$$m_1\vec{\mathbf{v}}_{1f} - m_1\vec{\mathbf{v}}_{1i} = -(m_2\vec{\mathbf{v}}_{2f} - m_2\vec{\mathbf{v}}_{2i})$$

after substituting the expressions obtained for $\vec{\mathbf{F}}_{21}$ and $\vec{\mathbf{F}}_{12}$. This equation can be rearranged to give the following important result:

$$m_1\vec{\mathbf{v}}_{1i} + m_2\vec{\mathbf{v}}_{2i} = m_1\vec{\mathbf{v}}_{1f} + m_2\vec{\mathbf{v}}_{2f} \qquad \text{[6.7]}$$

This result is a special case of the law of **conservation of momentum** and is true of isolated systems containing any number of interacting objects.

> When no net external force acts on a system, the total momentum of the system remains constant in time.

◀ Conservation of momentum

Defining the isolated system is an important feature of applying this conservation law. A cheerleader jumping upwards from rest might appear to violate conservation of momentum, because initially her momentum is zero and suddenly she's leaving the ground with velocity $\vec{\mathbf{v}}$. The flaw in this reasoning lies in the fact that the cheerleader isn't an isolated system. In jumping, she exerts a downward force on Earth, changing its momentum. This change in Earth's momentum isn't noticeable,

Before the collision, these particles have equal and opposite velocities.

After the collision both velocities change, but the total momentum of the system remains the same.

Active Figure 6.7
Before and after a head-on collision between two particles. The momentum of each object changes during the collision, but the total momentum of the system is constant. Notice that the magnitude of the change of velocity of the lighter particle is greater than that of the heavier particle, which is true in general.

BIO APPLICATION
Conservation of momentum and squid propulsion

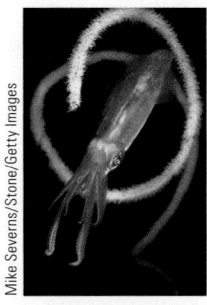
Conservation of momentum is the principle behind a squid's propulsion system. It propels itself by expelling water at a high velocity.

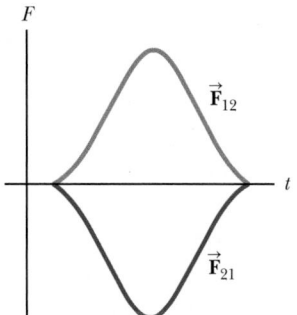
Figure 6.8 Force as a function of time for the two colliding particles in Figures 6.6a and 6.7. Note that $\vec{\mathbf{F}}_{21} = -\vec{\mathbf{F}}_{12}$.

Tip 6.1 Momentum Conservation Applies to a *System*!

The momentum of an isolated system is conserved, but not necessarily the momentum of one particle within that system, because other particles in the system may be interacting with it. Apply conservation of momentum to an isolated system *only*.

however, because of Earth's gargantuan mass compared to the cheerleader's. When we define the system to be *the cheerleader and Earth*, momentum is conserved.

Action and reaction, together with the accompanying exchange of momentum between two objects, is responsible for the phenomenon known as *recoil*. Everyone knows that throwing a baseball while standing straight up, without bracing one's feet against Earth, is a good way to fall over backwards. This reaction, an example of recoil, also happens when you fire a gun or shoot an arrow. Conservation of momentum provides a straightforward way to calculate such effects, as the next example shows.

■ EXAMPLE 6.3 | The Archer

GOAL Calculate recoil velocity using conservation of momentum.

PROBLEM An archer stands at rest on frictionless ice; his total mass including his bow and quiver of arrows is 60.00 kg. (See Fig. 6.9.) **(a)** If the archer fires a 0.030 0-kg arrow horizontally at 50.0 m/s in the positive *x*-direction, what is his subsequent velocity across the ice? **(b)** He then fires a second identical arrow at the same speed relative to the ground but at an angle of 30.0° above the horizontal. Find his new speed. **(c)** Estimate the average normal force acting on the archer as the second arrow is accelerated by the bowstring. Assume a draw length of 0.800 m.

STRATEGY To solve part (a), set up the conservation of momentum equation in the *x*-direction and solve for the final velocity of the archer. The system of the archer (including the bow) and the arrow is not isolated, because the gravitational and normal forces act on it. Those forces, however, are perpendicular to the motion of the system during the release of the arrow and hence do no work on the system, so conservation of momentum can be used. In part (b), conservation of momentum can be applied again, neglecting the tiny effect of gravitation on the arrow during its release. This time there is a non-zero initial velocity. Part (c) requires using the impulse–momentum theorem and estimating the time, which can be carried out with simple ballistics.

Figure 6.9 (Example 6.3) An archer fires an arrow horizontally to the right. Because he is standing on frictionless ice, he will begin to slide to the left across the ice.

- -

SOLUTION

(a) Find the archer's subsequent velocity across the ice.

Write the conservation of momentum equation for the *x*-direction.

$$p_{ix} = p_{fx}$$

Let m_1 and v_{1f} be the archer's mass and velocity after firing the arrow, respectively, and m_2 and v_{2f} the arrow's mass and velocity. Both velocities are in the *x*-direction. Substitute $p_i = 0$ and expressions for the final momenta:

$$0 = m_1 v_{1f} + m_2 v_{2f}$$

Solve for v_{1f} and substitute $m_1 = 59.97$ kg, $m_2 = 0.030\ 0$ kg, and $v_{2f} = 50.0$ m/s:

$$v_{1f} = -\frac{m_2}{m_1} v_{2f} = -\left(\frac{0.030\ 0 \text{ kg}}{59.97 \text{ kg}}\right)(50.0 \text{ m/s})$$

$$v_{1f} = \boxed{-0.025\ 0 \text{ m/s}}$$

(b) Calculate the archer's velocity after he fires a second arrow at an angle of 30.0° above the horizontal.

Write the *x*-component of the momentum equation with m_1 again the archer's mass after firing the first arrow as in part (a) and m_2 the mass of the next arrow:

$$m_1 v_{1i} = (m_1 - m_2)v_{1f} + m_2 v_{2f} \cos\theta$$

Solve for v_{1f}, the archer's final velocity, and substitute:

$$v_{1f} = \frac{m_1}{(m_1 - m_2)} v_{1i} - \frac{m_2}{(m_1 - m_2)} v_{2f} \cos\theta$$

$$= \left(\frac{59.97 \text{ kg}}{59.94 \text{ kg}}\right)(-0.025\ 0 \text{ m/s}) - \left(\frac{0.030\ 0 \text{ kg}}{59.94 \text{ kg}}\right)(50.0 \text{ m/s}) \cos(30.0°)$$

$$v_{1f} = \boxed{-0.046\ 7 \text{ m/s}}$$

(c) Estimate the average normal force acting on the archer as the arrow is accelerated by the bowstring.

Use kinematics in one dimension to estimate the acceleration of the arrow:

$$v^2 - v_0^2 = 2a\Delta x$$

Solve for the acceleration and substitute values setting $v = v_{2f}$, the final velocity of the arrow:

$$a = \frac{v_{2f}^2 - v_0^2}{2\Delta x} = \frac{(50.0 \text{ m/s})^2 - 0}{2(0.800 \text{ m})} = 1.56 \times 10^3 \text{ m/s}^2$$

Find the time the arrow is accelerated using $v = at + v_0$:

$$t = \frac{v_{2f} - v_0}{a} = \frac{50.0 \text{ m/s} - 0}{1.56 \times 10^3 \text{ m/s}^2} = 0.032\,0 \text{ s}$$

Write the y-component of the impulse–momentum theorem:

$$F_{y,av}\,\Delta t = \Delta p_y$$
$$F_{y,av} = \frac{\Delta p_y}{\Delta t} = \frac{m_2 v_{2f} \sin \theta}{\Delta t}$$
$$F_{y,av} = \frac{(0.030\,0 \text{ kg})(50.0 \text{ m/s}) \sin (30.0°)}{0.032\,0 \text{ s}} = 23.4 \text{ N}$$

The average normal force is given by the archer's weight plus the reaction force R of the arrow on the archer:

$$\Sigma F_y = n - mg - R = 0$$
$$n = mg + R = (59.94 \text{ kg})(9.80 \text{ m/s}^2) + (23.4 \text{ N}) = \boxed{6.11 \times 10^2 \text{ N}}$$

REMARKS The negative sign on v_{1f} indicates that the archer is moving opposite the arrow's direction, in accordance with Newton's third law. Because the archer is much more massive than the arrow, his acceleration and velocity are much smaller than the acceleration and velocity of the arrow. A technical point: the second arrow was fired at the same velocity relative to the ground, but because the archer was moving backwards at the time, it was traveling slightly faster than the first arrow relative to the archer. Velocities must always be given relative to a frame of reference.

Notice that conservation of momentum was effective in leading to a solution in parts (a) and (b). The final answer for the normal force is only an average because the force exerted on the arrow is unlikely to be constant. If the ice really were frictionless, the archer would have trouble standing. In general the coefficient of static friction of ice is more than sufficient to prevent sliding in response to such small recoils.

QUESTION 6.3 Would firing a heavier arrow necessarily increase the recoil velocity? Explain, using the result of Quick Quiz 6.1.

EXERCISE 6.3 A 70.0-kg man and a 55.0-kg woman holding a 2.50-kg purse on ice skates stand facing each other. (a) If the woman pushes the man backwards so that his final speed is 1.50 m/s, with what average force did she push him, assuming they were in contact for 0.500 s? (b) What is the woman's recoil speed? (c) If she now throws her 2.50-kg purse at him at a 20.0° angle above the horizontal and at 4.20 m/s relative to the ground, what is her subsequent speed?

ANSWERS (a) 2.10×10^2 N (b) 1.83 m/s (c) 2.09 m/s

■Quick Quiz

6.2 A boy standing at one end of a floating raft that is stationary relative to the shore walks to the opposite end of the raft, away from the shore. As a consequence, the raft (a) remains stationary, (b) moves away from the shore, or (c) moves toward the shore. (*Hint:* Use conservation of momentum.)

6.3 Collisions

We have seen that for any type of collision, the total momentum of the system just before the collision equals the total momentum just after the collision as long as the system may be considered isolated. The total kinetic energy, on the other hand, is generally not conserved in a collision because some of the kinetic energy is converted to internal energy, sound energy, and the work needed to permanently

Tip 6.2 Momentum and Kinetic Energy in Collisions

The momentum of an isolated system is conserved in all collisions. However, the kinetic energy of an isolated system is conserved only when the collision is elastic.

Tip 6.3 Inelastic vs. Perfectly Inelastic Collisions

If the colliding particles stick together, the collision is perfectly inelastic. If they bounce off each other (and kinetic energy is not conserved), the collision is inelastic.

BIO APPLICATION
Glaucoma Testing

Elastic collision ▶
Inelastic collision ▶

Before a perfectly inelastic collision the objects move independently.

m_1 $\vec{\mathbf{v}}_{1i}$ $\vec{\mathbf{v}}_{2i}$ m_2

⟶ $+x$

a

After the collision the objects remain in contact. System momentum *is* conserved, but system energy is *not* conserved.

$m_1 + m_2$ $\vec{\mathbf{v}}_f$

⟶ $+x$

b

Active Figure 6.10
(a) Before and (b) after a perfectly inelastic head-on collision between two objects.

deform the objects involved, such as cars in a car crash. **We define an inelastic collision as a collision in which momentum is conserved, but kinetic energy is not.** The collision of a rubber ball with a hard surface is inelastic, because some of the kinetic energy is lost when the ball is deformed during contact with the surface. **When two objects collide and stick together, the collision is called *perfectly inelastic.*** For example, if two pieces of putty collide, they stick together and move with some common velocity after the collision. If a meteorite collides head on with Earth, it becomes buried in Earth and the collision is considered perfectly inelastic. Only in very special circumstances is all the initial kinetic energy lost in a perfectly inelastic collision.

An elastic collision is defined as one in which both momentum and kinetic energy are conserved. Billiard ball collisions and the collisions of air molecules with the walls of a container at ordinary temperatures are highly elastic. Macroscopic collisions such as those between billiard balls are only approximately elastic, because some loss of kinetic energy takes place—for example, in the clicking sound when two balls strike each other. Perfectly elastic collisions do occur, however, between atomic and subatomic particles. Elastic and perfectly inelastic collisions are *limiting* cases; most actual collisions fall into a range in between them.

As a practical application, an inelastic collision is used to detect glaucoma, a disease in which the pressure inside the eye builds up and leads to blindness by damaging the cells of the retina. In this application, medical professionals use a device called a *tonometer* to measure the pressure inside the eye. This device releases a puff of air against the outer surface of the eye and measures the speed of the air after reflection from the eye. At normal pressure, the eye is slightly spongy, and the pulse is reflected at low speed. As the pressure inside the eye increases, the outer surface becomes more rigid, and the speed of the reflected pulse increases. In this way, the speed of the reflected puff of air can measure the internal pressure of the eye.

We can summarize the types of collisions as follows:

- In an elastic collision, both momentum and kinetic energy are conserved.
- In an inelastic collision, momentum is conserved but kinetic energy is not.
- In a *perfectly* inelastic collision, momentum is conserved, kinetic energy is not, and the two objects stick together after the collision, so their final velocities are the same.

In the remainder of this section, we will treat perfectly inelastic collisions and elastic collisions in one dimension.

■ Quick Quiz

6.3 A car and a large truck traveling at the same speed collide head-on and stick together. Which vehicle undergoes the larger change in the magnitude of its momentum? (a) the car (b) the truck (c) the change in the magnitude of momentum is the same for both (d) impossible to determine without more information.

Perfectly Inelastic Collisions

Consider two objects having masses m_1 and m_2 moving with known initial velocity components v_{1i} and v_{2i} along a straight line, as in Active Figure 6.10. If the two objects collide head-on, stick together, and move with a common velocity component v_f after the collision, then the collision is perfectly inelastic. Because the total momentum of the two-object isolated system before the collision equals the total momentum of the combined-object system after the collision, we can solve for the final velocity using conservation of momentum alone:

$$m_1 v_{1i} + m_2 v_{2i} = (m_1 + m_2) v_f \qquad [6.8]$$

$$v_f = \frac{m_1 v_{1i} + m_2 v_{2i}}{m_1 + m_2} \qquad [6.9]$$

It's important to notice that v_{1i}, v_{2i}, and v_f represent the x-components of the velocity vectors, so care is needed in entering their known values, particularly with regard to signs. For example, in Active Figure 6.10, v_{1i} would have a positive value (m_1 moving to the right), whereas v_{2i} would have a negative value (m_2 moving to the left). Once these values are entered, Equation 6.9 can be used to find the correct final velocity, as shown in Examples 6.4 and 6.5.

■ EXAMPLE 6.4 | A Truck Versus a Compact

GOAL Apply conservation of momentum to a one-dimensional inelastic collision.

PROBLEM A pickup truck with mass 1.80×10^3 kg is traveling eastbound at +15.0 m/s, while a compact car with mass 9.00×10^2 kg is traveling westbound at −15.0 m/s. (See Fig. 6.11.) The vehicles collide head-on, becoming entangled. **(a)** Find the speed of the entangled vehicles after the collision. **(b)** Find the change in the velocity of each vehicle. **(c)** Find the change in the kinetic energy of the system consisting of both vehicles.

STRATEGY The total momentum of the vehicles before the collision, p_i, equals the total momentum of the vehicles after the collision, p_f, if we ignore friction and assume the two vehicles form an isolated system. (This is called the "impulse approximation.") Solve the momentum conservation equation for the final velocity of the entangled vehicles. Once the velocities are in hand, the other parts can be solved by substitution.

Figure 6.11 (Example 6.4)

SOLUTION

(a) Find the final speed after collision.

Let m_1 and v_{1i} represent the mass and initial velocity of the pickup truck, while m_2 and v_{2i} pertain to the compact. Apply conservation of momentum:

$$p_i = p_f$$
$$m_1 v_{1i} + m_2 v_{2i} = (m_1 + m_2)v_f$$

Substitute the values and solve for the final velocity, v_f:

$$(1.80 \times 10^3 \text{ kg})(15.0 \text{ m/s}) + (9.00 \times 10^2 \text{ kg})(-15.0 \text{ m/s})$$
$$= (1.80 \times 10^3 \text{ kg} + 9.00 \times 10^2 \text{ kg})v_f$$
$$v_f = \boxed{+5.00 \text{ m/s}}$$

(b) Find the change in velocity for each vehicle.

Change in velocity of the pickup truck:

$$\Delta v_1 = v_f - v_{1i} = 5.00 \text{ m/s} - 15.0 \text{ m/s} = \boxed{-10.0 \text{ m/s}}$$

Change in velocity of the compact car:

$$\Delta v_2 = v_f - v_{2i} = 5.00 \text{ m/s} - (-15.0 \text{ m/s}) = \boxed{20.0 \text{ m/s}}$$

(c) Find the change in kinetic energy of the system.

Calculate the initial kinetic energy of the system:

$$KE_i = \tfrac{1}{2}m_1 v_{1i}^2 + \tfrac{1}{2}m_2 v_{2i}^2 = \tfrac{1}{2}(1.80 \times 10^3 \text{ kg})(15.0 \text{ m/s})^2$$
$$+ \tfrac{1}{2}(9.00 \times 10^2 \text{ kg})(-15.0 \text{ m/s})^2$$
$$= 3.04 \times 10^5 \text{ J}$$

Calculate the final kinetic energy of the system and the change in kinetic energy, ΔKE.

$$KE_f = \tfrac{1}{2}(m_1 + m_2)v_f^2$$
$$= \tfrac{1}{2}(1.80 \times 10^3 \text{ kg} + 9.00 \times 10^2 \text{ kg})(5.00 \text{ m/s})^2$$
$$= 3.38 \times 10^4 \text{ J}$$
$$\Delta KE = KE_f - KE_i = \boxed{-2.70 \times 10^5 \text{ J}}$$

REMARKS During the collision, the system lost almost 90% of its kinetic energy. The change in velocity of the pickup truck was only 10.0 m/s, compared to twice that for the compact car. This example underscores perhaps the most important safety feature of any car: its mass. Injury is caused by a change in velocity, and the more massive vehicle undergoes a smaller velocity change in a typical accident.

QUESTION 6.4 If the mass of both vehicles were doubled, how would the final velocity be affected? The change in kinetic energy?

(Continued)

EXERCISE 6.4 Suppose the same two vehicles are both traveling eastward, the compact car leading the pickup truck. The driver of the compact car slams on the brakes suddenly, slowing the vehicle to 6.00 m/s. If the pickup truck traveling at 18.0 m/s crashes into the compact car, find (a) the speed of the system right after the collision, assuming the two vehicles become entangled, (b) the change in velocity for both vehicles, and (c) the change in kinetic energy of the system, from the instant before impact (when the compact car is traveling at 6.00 m/s) to the instant right after the collision.

ANSWERS (a) 14.0 m/s   (b) pickup truck: $\Delta v_1 = -4.0$ m/s   compact car: $\Delta v_2 = 8.0$ m/s   (c) -4.32×10^4 J

EXAMPLE 6.5 | The Ballistic Pendulum

GOAL Combine the concepts of conservation of energy and conservation of momentum in inelastic collisions.

PROBLEM The ballistic pendulum (Fig. 6.12a) is a device used to measure the speed of a fast-moving projectile such as a bullet. The bullet is fired into a large block of wood suspended from some light wires. The bullet is stopped by the block, and the entire system swings up to a height h. It is possible to obtain the initial speed of the bullet by measuring h and the two masses. As an example of the technique, assume that the mass of the bullet, m_1, is 5.00 g, the mass of the pendulum, m_2, is 1.000 kg, and h is 5.00 cm. **(a)** Find the velocity of the system after the bullet embeds in the block. **(b)** Calculate the initial speed of the bullet.

STRATEGY Use conservation of energy to find the initial velocity of the block–bullet system, labeling it v_{sys}. Part **(b)** requires the conservation of momentum equation, which can be solved for the initial velocity of the bullet, v_{1i}.

Figure 6.12 (Example 6.5)
(a) Diagram of a ballistic pendulum. Note that $\vec{v}_{sys}$ is the velocity of the system just *after* the perfectly inelastic collision. (b) Multiflash photograph of a laboratory ballistic pendulum.

© Charles D. Winters/Cengage Learning

SOLUTION

(a) Find the velocity of the system after the bullet embeds in the block.

Apply conservation of energy to the block–bullet system after the collision:

$$(KE + PE)_{\text{after collision}} = (KE + PE)_{\text{top}}$$

Substitute expressions for the kinetic and potential energies. Note that both the potential energy at the bottom and the kinetic energy at the top are zero:

$$\tfrac{1}{2}(m_1 + m_2)v_{sys}^2 + 0 = 0 + (m_1 + m_2)gh$$

Solve for the final velocity of the block–bullet system, v_{sys}:

$$v_{sys}{}^2 = 2gh$$
$$v_{sys} = \sqrt{2gh} = \sqrt{2(9.80 \text{ m/s}^2)(5.00 \times 10^{-2} \text{ m})}$$
$$v_{sys} = \boxed{0.990 \text{ m/s}}$$

(b) Calculate the initial speed of the bullet.

Write the conservation of momentum equation and substitute expressions.

$$p_i = p_f$$
$$m_1 v_{1i} + m_2 v_{2i} = (m_1 + m_2)v_{sys}$$

Solve for the initial velocity of the bullet, and substitute values:

$$v_{1i} = \frac{(m_1 + m_2)v_{sys}}{m_1}$$
$$v_{1i} = \frac{(1.005 \text{ kg})(0.990 \text{ m/s})}{5.00 \times 10^{-3} \text{ kg}} = \boxed{199 \text{ m/s}}$$

REMARKS Because the impact is inelastic, it would be incorrect to equate the initial kinetic energy of the incoming bullet to the final gravitational potential energy associated with the bullet–block combination. The energy isn't conserved!

QUESTION 6.5 List three ways mechanical energy can be lost from the system in this experiment.

EXERCISE 6.5 A bullet with mass 5.00 g is fired horizontally into a 2.000-kg block attached to a horizontal spring. The spring has a constant 6.00×10^2 N/m and reaches a maximum compression of 6.00 cm. (a) Find the initial speed of the bullet–block system. (b) Find the speed of the bullet.

ANSWER (a) 1.04 m/s   (b) 417 m/s

■ *Quick Quiz*

6.4 An object of mass m moves to the right with a speed v. It collides head-on with an object of mass $3m$ moving with speed $v/3$ in the opposite direction. If the two objects stick together, what is the speed of the combined object, of mass $4m$, after the collision?

(a) 0   (b) $v/2$ (c) v (d) $2v$

6.5 A skater is using very low-friction rollerblades. A friend throws a Frisbee at her, on the straight line along which she is coasting. Describe each of the following events as an elastic, an inelastic, or a perfectly inelastic collision between the skater and the Frisbee. (a) She catches the Frisbee and holds it. (b) She tries to catch the Frisbee, but it bounces off her hands and falls to the ground in front of her. (c) She catches the Frisbee and immediately throws it back with the same speed (relative to the ground) to her friend.

6.6 In a perfectly inelastic one-dimensional collision between two objects, what condition alone is necessary so that *all* of the original kinetic energy of the system is gone after the collision? (a) The objects must have momenta with the same magnitude but opposite directions. (b) The objects must have the same mass. (c) The objects must have the same velocity. (d) The objects must have the same speed, with velocity vectors in opposite directions.

Elastic Collisions

Now consider two objects that undergo an **elastic head-on collision** (Active Fig. 6.13). In this situation, **both the momentum and the kinetic energy of the system of two objects are conserved.** We can write these conditions as

$$m_1 v_{1i} + m_2 v_{2i} = m_1 v_{1f} + m_2 v_{2f} \qquad \text{[6.10]}$$

and

$$\tfrac{1}{2} m_1 v_{1i}^2 + \tfrac{1}{2} m_2 v_{2i}^2 = \tfrac{1}{2} m_1 v_{1f}^2 + \tfrac{1}{2} m_2 v_{2f}^2 \qquad \text{[6.11]}$$

where v is positive if an object moves to the right and negative if it moves to the left.

In a typical problem involving elastic collisions, there are two unknown quantities, and Equations 6.10 and 6.11 can be solved simultaneously to find them. These two equations are linear and quadratic, respectively. An alternate approach simplifies the quadratic equation to another linear equation, facilitating solution. Canceling the factor $\tfrac{1}{2}$ in Equation 6.11, we rewrite the equation as

$$m_1(v_{1i}^2 - v_{1f}^2) = m_2(v_{2f}^2 - v_{2i}^2)$$

Here we have moved the terms containing m_1 to one side of the equation and those containing m_2 to the other. Next, we factor both sides of the equation:

$$m_1(v_{1i} - v_{1f})(v_{1i} + v_{1f}) = m_2(v_{2f} - v_{2i})(v_{2f} + v_{2i}) \qquad \text{[6.12]}$$

Now we separate the terms containing m_1 and m_2 in the equation for the conservation of momentum (Eq. 6.10) to get

$$m_1(v_{1i} - v_{1f}) = m_2(v_{2f} - v_{2i}) \qquad \text{[6.13]}$$

Before an elastic collision the two objects move independently.

After the collision the object velocities change, but **both** the energy and momentum of the system are conserved.

Active Figure 6.13
(a) Before and (b) after an elastic head-on collision between two hard spheres. Unlike an inelastic collision, both the total momentum and the total energy are conserved.

To obtain our final result, we divide Equation 6.12 by Equation 6.13, producing

$$v_{1i} + v_{1f} = v_{2f} + v_{2i}$$

Gathering initial and final values on opposite sides of the equation gives

$$v_{1i} - v_{2i} = -(v_{1f} - v_{2f}) \qquad [6.14]$$

This equation, in combination with Equation 6.10, will be used to solve problems dealing with perfectly elastic head-on collisions. According to Equation 6.14, the relative velocity of the two objects before the collision, $v_{1i} - v_{2i}$, equals the negative of the relative velocity of the two objects after the collision, $-(v_{1f} - v_{2f})$. To better understand the equation, imagine that you are riding along on one of the objects. As you measure the velocity of the other object from your vantage point, you will be measuring the relative velocity of the two objects. In your view of the collision, the other object comes toward you and bounces off, leaving the collision with the same speed, but in the opposite direction. This is just what Equation 6.14 states.

■ PROBLEM-SOLVING STRATEGY

One-Dimensional Collisions

The following procedure is recommended for solving one-dimensional problems involving collisions between two objects:

1. **Coordinates.** Choose a coordinate axis that lies along the direction of motion.
2. **Diagram.** Sketch the problem, representing the two objects as blocks and labeling velocity vectors and masses.
3. **Conservation of Momentum.** Write a general expression for the *total* momentum of the system of two objects *before* and *after* the collision, and equate the two, as in Equation 6.10. On the next line, fill in the known values.
4. **Conservation of Energy.** If the collision is elastic, write a general expression for the total energy before and after the collision, and equate the two quantities, as in Equation 6.11 or (preferably) Equation 6.14. Fill in the known values. (*Skip* this step if the collision is *not* perfectly elastic.)
5. **Solve** the equations simultaneously. Equations 6.10 and 6.14 form a system of two linear equations and two unknowns. If you have forgotten Equation 6.14, use Equation 6.11 instead.

Steps 1 and 2 of the problem-solving strategy are generally carried out in the process of sketching and labeling a diagram of the problem. This is clearly the case in our next example, which makes use of Figure 6.13 (page 179). Other steps are pointed out as they are applied.

■ EXAMPLE 6.6 | Let's Play Pool

GOAL Solve an elastic collision in one dimension.

PROBLEM Two billiard balls of identical mass move toward each other as in Active Figure 6.13, with the positive *x*-axis to the right (Steps 1 and 2). Assume that the collision between them is perfectly elastic. If the initial velocities of the balls are +30.0 cm/s and −20.0 cm/s, what are the velocities of the balls after the collision? Assume friction and rotation are unimportant.

STRATEGY Solution of this problem is a matter of solving two equations, the conservation of momentum and conservation of energy equations, for two unknowns, the final velocities of the two balls. Instead of using Equation 6.11 for conservation of energy, use Equation 6.14, which is linear, hence easier to handle.

· ·

SOLUTION

Write the conservation of momentum equation. Because $m_1 = m_2$, we can cancel the masses, then substitute $v_{1i} = +30.0$ m/s and $v_{2i} = -20.0$ cm/s (Step 3).

$$m_1 v_{1i} + m_2 v_{2i} = m_1 v_{1f} + m_2 v_{2f}$$
$$30.0 \text{ cm/s} + (-20.0 \text{ cm/s}) = v_{1f} + v_{2f}$$
$$\textbf{(1)} \quad 10.0 \text{ cm/s} = v_{1f} + v_{2f}$$

Next, apply conservation of energy in the form of Equation 6.14 (Step 4):

$$(2) \quad v_{1i} - v_{2i} = -(v_{1f} - v_{2f})$$
$$30.0 \text{ cm/s} - (-20.0 \text{ cm/s}) = v_{2f} - v_{1f}$$
$$(3) \quad 50.0 \text{ cm/s} = v_{2f} - v_{1f}$$

Now solve Equations (1) and (3) simultaneously by adding them together (Step 5):

$$10.0 \text{ cm/s} + 50.0 \text{ cm/s} = (v_{1f} + v_{2f}) + (v_{2f} - v_{1f})$$
$$60.0 \text{ cm/s} = 2v_{2f} \quad \rightarrow \quad v_{2f} = \boxed{30.0 \text{ m/s}}$$

Substitute the answer for v_{2f} into Equation (1):

$$10.0 \text{ cm/s} = v_{1f} + 30.0 \text{ m/s} \quad \rightarrow \quad v_{1f} = \boxed{-20.0 \text{ m/s}}$$

REMARKS Notice the balls exchanged velocities—almost as if they'd passed through each other. This is always the case when two objects of equal mass undergo an elastic head-on collision.

QUESTION 6.6 In this example, is it possible to adjust the initial velocities of the balls so that both are at rest after the collision? Explain.

EXERCISE 6.6 Find the final velocity of the two balls if the ball with initial velocity $v_{2i} = -20.0$ cm/s has a mass equal to one-half that of the ball with initial velocity $v_{1i} = +30.0$ cm/s.

ANSWER $v_{1f} = -3.33$ cm/s; $v_{2f} = +46.7$ cm/s

▪ EXAMPLE 6.7 | Two Blocks and a Spring

GOAL Solve an elastic collision involving spring potential energy.

PROBLEM A block of mass $m_1 = 1.60$ kg, initially moving to the right with a velocity of $+4.00$ m/s on a frictionless horizontal track, collides with a massless spring attached to a second block of mass $m_2 = 2.10$ kg moving to the left with a velocity of -2.50 m/s, as in Figure 6.14a. The spring has a spring constant of 6.00×10^2 N/m. **(a)** Determine the velocity of block 2 at the instant when block 1 is moving to the right with a velocity of $+3.00$ m/s, as in Figure 6.14b. **(b)** Find the maximum compression of the spring.

STRATEGY We identify the system as the two blocks and the spring. Write down the conservation of momentum equations, and solve for the final velocity of block 2, v_{2f}. Then use conservation of energy to find the compression of the spring.

Figure 6.14
(Example 6.7)

SOLUTION

(a) Find the velocity v_{2f} when block 1 has velocity $+3.00$ m/s.

Write the conservation of momentum equation for the system and solve for v_{2f}:

$$(1) \quad m_1 v_{1i} + m_2 v_{2i} = m_1 v_{1f} + m_2 v_{2f}$$
$$v_{2f} = \frac{m_1 v_{1i} + m_2 v_{2i} - m_1 v_{1f}}{m_2}$$
$$= \frac{(1.60 \text{ kg})(4.00 \text{ m/s}) + (2.10 \text{ kg})(-2.50 \text{ m/s}) - (1.60 \text{ kg})(3.00 \text{ m/s})}{2.10 \text{ kg}}$$
$$v_{2f} = \boxed{-1.74 \text{ m/s}}$$

(b) Find the compression of the spring.

Use energy conservation for the system, noticing that potential energy is stored in the spring when it is compressed a distance x:

$$E_i = E_f$$
$$\tfrac{1}{2} m_1 v_{1i}^2 + \tfrac{1}{2} m_2 v_{2i}^2 + 0 = \tfrac{1}{2} m_1 v_{1f}^2 + \tfrac{1}{2} m_2 v_{2f}^2 + \tfrac{1}{2} kx^2$$

(Continued)

Substitute the given values and the result $x =$ $\boxed{0.173\ \text{m}}$
of part (a) into the preceding expression,
solving for x:

. . . .

REMARKS The initial velocity component of block 2 is -2.50 m/s because the block is moving to the left. The negative value for v_{2f} means that block 2 is still moving to the left at the instant under consideration.

QUESTION 6.7 Is it possible for both blocks to come to rest while the spring is being compressed? Explain. *Hint:* Look at the momentum in Equation (1).

EXERCISE 6.7 Find (a) the velocity of block 1 and (b) the compression of the spring at the instant that block 2 is at rest.

ANSWER (a) 0.719 m/s to the right   (b) 0.251 m

6.4 Glancing Collisions

In Section 6.2 we showed that the total linear momentum of a system is conserved when the system is isolated (that is, when no external forces act on the system). For a general collision of two objects in three-dimensional space, the conservation of momentum principle implies that the total momentum of the system in each direction is conserved. However, an important subset of collisions takes place in a plane. The game of billiards is a familiar example involving multiple collisions of objects moving on a two-dimensional surface. We restrict our attention to a single two-dimensional collision between two objects that takes place in a plane, and ignore any possible rotation. For such collisions, we obtain two component equations for the conservation of momentum:

$$m_1 v_{1ix} + m_2 v_{2ix} = m_1 v_{1fx} + m_2 v_{2fx}$$

$$m_1 v_{1iy} + m_2 v_{2iy} = m_1 v_{1fy} + m_2 v_{2fy}$$

We must use three subscripts in this general equation, to represent, respectively, (1) the object in question, and (2) the initial and final values of the components of velocity.

Now, consider a two-dimensional problem in which an object of mass m_1 collides with an object of mass m_2 that is initially at rest, as in Active Figure 6.15. After the collision, object 1 moves at an angle θ with respect to the horizontal, and object 2 moves at an angle ϕ with respect to the horizontal. This is called a *glancing* collision. Applying the law of conservation of momentum in component form, and noting that the initial y-component of momentum is zero, we have

x-component: $m_1 v_{1i} + 0 = m_1 v_{1f}\cos\theta + m_2 v_{2f}\cos\phi$ [6.15]

y-component: $0 + 0 = m_1 v_{1f}\sin\theta + m_2 v_{2f}\sin\phi$ [6.16]

Active Figure 6.15
A glancing collision between two objects.

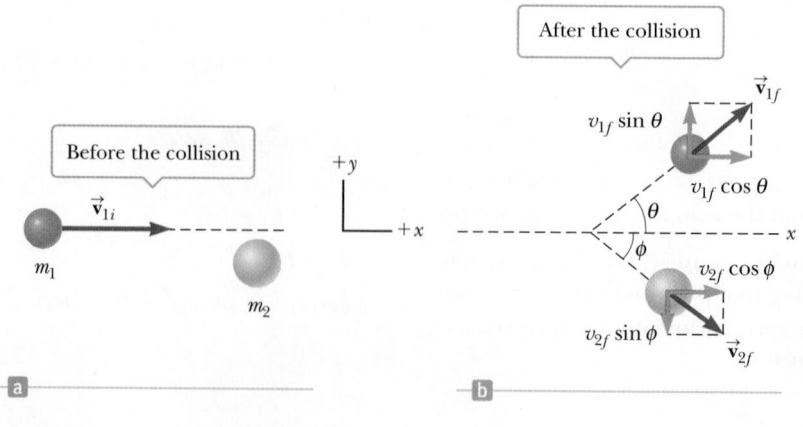

If the collision is elastic, we can write a third equation, for conservation of energy, in the form

$$\tfrac{1}{2}m_1v_{1i}{}^2 = \tfrac{1}{2}m_1v_{1f}{}^2 + \tfrac{1}{2}m_2v_{2f}{}^2 \qquad \text{[6.17]}$$

If we know the initial velocity v_{1i} and the masses, we are left with four unknowns (v_{1f}, v_{2f}, θ, and ϕ). Because we have only three equations, one of the four remaining quantities must be given in order to determine the motion after the collision from conservation principles alone.

If the collision is inelastic, the kinetic energy of the system is *not* conserved, and Equation 6.17 does *not* apply.

■ PROBLEM-SOLVING STRATEGY

Two-Dimensional Collisions

To solve two-dimensional collisions, follow this procedure:

1. **Coordinate Axes.** Use both *x*- and *y*-coordinates. It's convenient to have either the *x*-axis or the *y*-axis coincide with the direction of one of the initial velocities.
2. **Diagram.** Sketch the problem, labeling velocity vectors and masses.
3. **Conservation of Momentum.** Write a separate conservation of momentum equation for each of the *x*- and *y*-directions. In each case, the total initial momentum in a given direction equals the total final momentum in that direction.
4. **Conservation of Energy.** If the collision is elastic, write a general expression for the total energy before and after the collision, and equate the two expressions, as in Equation 6.11. Fill in the known values. (**Skip** this step if the collision is **not perfectly elastic.**) The energy equation can't be simplified as in the one-dimensional case, so a quadratic expression such as Equation 6.11 or 6.17 must be used when the collision is elastic.
5. **Solve** the equations simultaneously. There are two equations for inelastic collisions and three for elastic collisions.

■ EXAMPLE 6.8 | Collision at an Intersection

GOAL Analyze a two-dimensional inelastic collision.

PROBLEM A car with mass 1.50×10^3 kg traveling east at a speed of 25.0 m/s collides at an intersection with a 2.50×10^3-kg van traveling north at a speed of 20.0 m/s, as shown in Figure 6.16. Find the magnitude and direction of the velocity of the wreckage after the collision, assuming that the vehicles undergo a perfectly inelastic collision (that is, they stick together) and assuming that friction between the vehicles and the road can be neglected.

STRATEGY Use conservation of momentum in two dimensions. (Kinetic energy is not conserved.) Choose coordinates as in Figure 6.16. Before the collision, the only object having momentum in the *x*-direction is the car, while the van carries all the momentum in the *y*-direction. After the totally inelastic collision, both vehicles move together at some common speed v_f and angle θ. Solve for these two unknowns, using the two components of the conservation of momentum equation.

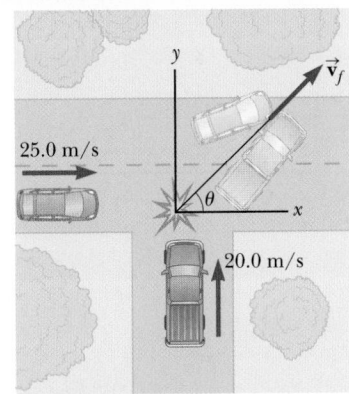

Figure 6.16 (Example 6.8) A top view of a perfectly inelastic collision between a car and a van.

(Continued)

SOLUTION

Find the x-components of the initial and final total momenta:

$$\sum p_{xi} = m_{car}v_{car} = (1.50 \times 10^3 \text{ kg})(25.0 \text{ m/s})$$
$$= 3.75 \times 10^4 \text{ kg} \cdot \text{m/s}$$
$$\sum p_{xf} = (m_{car} + m_{van})v_f \cos\theta = (4.00 \times 10^3 \text{ kg})v_f \cos\theta$$

Set the initial x-momentum equal to the final x-momentum:

(1) $3.75 \times 10^4 \text{ kg} \cdot \text{m/s} = (4.00 \times 10^3 \text{ kg})v_f \cos\theta$

Find the y-components of the initial and final total momenta:

$$\sum p_{iy} = m_{van}v_{van} = (2.50 \times 10^3 \text{ kg})(20.0 \text{ m/s})$$
$$= 5.00 \times 10^4 \text{ kg} \cdot \text{m/s}$$
$$\sum p_{fy} = (m_{car} + m_{van})v_f \sin\theta = (4.00 \times 10^3 \text{ kg})v_f \sin\theta$$

Set the initial y-momentum equal to the final y-momentum:

(2) $5.00 \times 10^4 \text{ kg} \cdot \text{m/s} = (4.00 \times 10^3 \text{ kg})v_f \sin\theta$

Divide Equation (2) by Equation (1) and solve for θ:

$$\tan\theta = \frac{5.00 \times 10^4 \text{ kg} \cdot \text{m/s}}{3.75 \times 10^4 \text{ kg} \cdot \text{m}} = 1.33$$
$$\theta = \boxed{53.1°}$$

Substitute this angle back into Equation (2) to find v_f:

$$v_f = \frac{5.00 \times 10^4 \text{ kg} \cdot \text{m/s}}{(4.00 \times 10^3 \text{ kg}) \sin 53.1°} = \boxed{15.6 \text{ m/s}}$$

REMARKS It's also possible to first find the x- and y-components v_{fx} and v_{fy} of the resultant velocity. The magnitude and direction of the resultant velocity can then be found with the Pythagorean theorem, $v_f = \sqrt{v_{fx}^2 + v_{fy}^2}$, and the inverse tangent function $\theta = \tan^{-1}(v_{fy}/v_{fx})$. Setting up this alternate approach is a simple matter of substituting $v_{fx} = v_f \cos\theta$ and $v_{fy} = v_f \sin\theta$ in Equations (1) and (2).

QUESTION 6.8 If the car and van had identical mass and speed, what would the resultant angle have been?

EXERCISE 6.8 A 3.00-kg object initially moving in the positive x-direction with a velocity of +5.00 m/s collides with and sticks to a 2.00-kg object initially moving in the negative y-direction with a velocity of −3.00 m/s. Find the final components of velocity of the composite object.

ANSWER $v_{fx} = 3.00$ m/s; $v_{fy} = -1.20$ m/s

6.5 Rocket Propulsion

When ordinary vehicles such as cars and locomotives move, the driving force of the motion is friction. In the case of the car, this driving force is exerted by the road on the car, a reaction to the force exerted by the wheels against the road. Similarly, a locomotive "pushes" against the tracks; hence, the driving force is the reaction force exerted by the tracks on the locomotive. However, a rocket moving in space has no road or tracks to push against. How can it move forward?

In fact, reaction forces also propel a rocket. (You should review Newton's third law, discussed in Chapter 4.) To illustrate this point, we model our rocket with a spherical chamber containing a combustible gas, as in Figure 6.17a. When an explosion occurs in the chamber, the hot gas expands and presses against all sides of the chamber, as indicated by the arrows. Because the sum of the forces exerted on the rocket is zero, it doesn't move. Now suppose a hole is drilled in the bottom of the chamber, as in Figure 6.17b. When the explosion occurs, the gas presses against the chamber in all directions, but can't press against anything at the hole, where it simply escapes into space. Adding the forces on the spherical chamber now results in a net force upwards. Just as in the case of cars and locomotives, this is a reaction force. A car's wheels press against the ground, and the reaction force of the ground on the car pushes it forward. The wall of the rocket's combustion chamber exerts a force on the gas expanding against it. The reaction force of the gas on the wall then pushes the rocket upward.

In a now infamous article in *The New York Times,* rocket pioneer Robert Goddard was ridiculed for thinking that rockets would work in space, where, according to the *Times,* there was nothing to push against. The *Times* retracted, rather belatedly, during the first *Apollo* moon landing mission in 1969. The hot gases are not pushing against anything external, but against the rocket itself—and ironically, rockets actually work *better* in a vacuum. In an atmosphere, the gases have to do work against the outside air pressure to escape the combustion chamber, slowing the exhaust velocity and reducing the reaction force.

At the microscopic level, this process is complicated, but it can be simplified by applying conservation of momentum to the rocket and its ejected fuel. In principle, the solution is similar to that in Example 6.3, with the archer representing the rocket and the arrows the exhaust gases.

Suppose that at some time t, the momentum of the rocket plus the fuel is given by $(M + \Delta m)v$, where Δm is an amount of fuel about to be burned (Fig. 6.18a). This fuel is traveling at a speed v relative to, say, Earth, just like the rest of the rocket. During a short time interval Δt, the rocket ejects fuel of mass Δm, and the rocket's speed increases to $v + \Delta v$ (Fig. 6.18b). If the fuel is ejected with exhaust speed v_e *relative to the rocket,* the speed of the fuel relative to the Earth is $v - v_e$. Equating the total initial momentum of the system with the total final momentum, we have

$$(M + \Delta m)v = M(v + \Delta v) + \Delta m(v - v_e)$$

Simplifying this expression gives

$$M\Delta v = v_e \Delta m$$

The increase Δm in the mass of the exhaust corresponds to an equal decrease in the mass of the rocket, so that $\Delta m = -\Delta M$. Using this fact, we have

$$M\Delta v = -v_e \Delta M \qquad \text{[6.18]}$$

This result, together with the methods of calculus, can be used to obtain the following equation:

$$v_f - v_i = v_e \ln\left(\frac{M_i}{M_f}\right) \qquad \text{[6.19]}$$

where M_i is the initial mass of the rocket plus fuel and M_f is the final mass of the rocket plus its remaining fuel. This is the basic expression for rocket propulsion; it tells us that the increase in velocity is proportional to the exhaust speed v_e and to the natural logarithm of M_i/M_f. Because the maximum ratio of M_i to M_f for a single-stage rocket is about 10:1, the increase in speed can reach $v_e \ln 10 = 2.3v_e$ or about twice the exhaust speed! For best results, therefore, the exhaust speed should be as high as possible. Currently, typical rocket exhaust speeds are several kilometers per second.

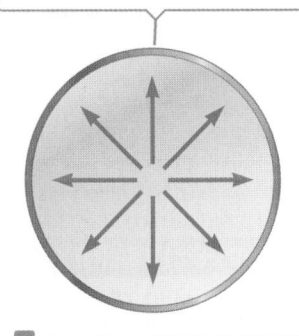

A rocket reaction chamber without a nozzle has reaction forces pushing equally in all directions, so no motion results.

a

An opening at the bottom of the chamber removes the downward reaction force, resulting in a net upward reaction force.

b

Figure 6.17 A rocket reaction chamber containing a combusting gas works because it has a nozzle where gases can escape. The chamber wall acts on the expanding gas; the reaction force of the gas on the chamber wall pushes the rocket forward.

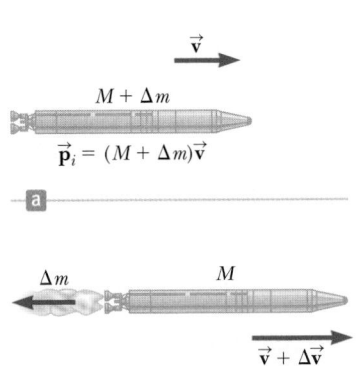

Figure 6.18 Rocket propulsion. (a) The initial mass of the rocket and fuel is $M + \Delta m$ at a time t, and the rocket's speed is v. (b) At a time $t + \Delta t$, the rocket's mass has been reduced to M, and an amount of fuel Δm has been ejected. The rocket's speed increases by an amount Δv.

The **thrust** on the rocket is defined as the force exerted on the rocket by the ejected exhaust gases. We can obtain an expression for the instantaneous thrust by dividing Equation 6.18 by Δt:

Rocket thrust ▶

$$\text{Instantaneous thrust} = Ma = M\frac{\Delta v}{\Delta t} = \left| v_e \frac{\Delta M}{\Delta t} \right| \qquad [6.20]$$

The absolute value signs are used for clarity: In Equation 6.18, $-\Delta M$ is a positive quantity (as is v_e, a speed). Here we see that the thrust increases as the exhaust velocity increases and as the rate of change of mass $\Delta M/\Delta t$ (the burn rate) increases.

■ **APPLYING PHYSICS 6.2** | **Multistage Rockets**

The current maximum exhaust speed of $v_e = 4\,500$ m/s can be realized with rocket engines fueled with liquid hydrogen and liquid oxygen. But this means that the maximum speed attainable for a given rocket with a mass ratio of 10 is $v_e \ln 10 \approx 10\,000$ m/s. To reach the Moon, however, requires a change in velocity of over 11 000 m/s. Further, this change must occur while working against gravity and atmospheric friction. How can that be managed without developing better engines?

EXPLANATION The answer is the multistage rocket. By dropping stages, the spacecraft becomes lighter, so that fuel burned later in the mission doesn't have to accelerate mass that no longer serves any purpose. Strap-on boosters, as used by the space shuttle and a number of other rockets, such as the *Titan 4* or Russian *Proton,* is a similar concept. The boosters are jettisoned after their fuel is exhausted, so the rocket is no longer burdened by their weight. ■

■ **EXAMPLE 6.9** | **Single Stage to Orbit (SSTO)**

GOAL Apply the velocity and thrust equations of a rocket.

PROBLEM A rocket has a total mass of 1.00×10^5 kg and a burnout mass of 1.00×10^4 kg, including engines, shell, and payload. The rocket blasts off from Earth and exhausts all its fuel in 4.00 min, burning the fuel at a steady rate with an exhaust velocity of $v_e = 4.50 \times 10^3$ m/s. **(a)** If air friction and gravity are neglected, what is the speed of the rocket at burnout? **(b)** What thrust does the engine develop at liftoff? **(c)** What is the initial acceleration of the rocket if gravity is not neglected? **(d)** Estimate the speed at burnout if gravity isn't neglected.

STRATEGY Although it sounds sophisticated, this problem is mainly a matter of substituting values into the appropriate equations. Part (a) requires substituting values into Equation 6.19 for the velocity. For part (b), divide the change in the rocket's mass by the total time, getting $\Delta M/\Delta t$, then substitute into Equation 6.20 to find the thrust. (c) Using Newton's second law, the force of gravity, and the result of (b), we can find the initial acceleration. For part (d), the acceleration of gravity is approximately constant over the few kilometers involved, so the velocity found in part (b) will be reduced by roughly $\Delta v_g = -gt$. Add this loss to the result of part (a).

SOLUTION

(a) Calculate the velocity at burnout.

Substitute $v_i = 0$, $v_e = 4.50 \times 10^3$ m/s, $M_i = 1.00 \times 10^5$ kg, and $M_f = 1.00 \times 10^4$ kg into Equation 6.19:

$$v_f = v_i + v_e \ln\left(\frac{M_i}{M_f}\right)$$

$$= 0 + (4.5 \times 10^3 \text{ m/s}) \ln\left(\frac{1.00 \times 10^5 \text{ kg}}{1.00 \times 10^4 \text{ kg}}\right)$$

$$v_f = \boxed{1.04 \times 10^4 \text{ m/s}}$$

(b) Find the thrust at liftoff.

Compute the change in the rocket's mass:

$$\Delta M = M_f - M_i = 1.00 \times 10^4 \text{ kg} - 1.00 \times 10^5 \text{ kg}$$
$$= -9.00 \times 10^4 \text{ kg}$$

Calculate the rate at which rocket mass changes by dividing the change in mass by the time (where the time interval equals 4.00 min $= 2.40 \times 10^2$ s):

$$\frac{\Delta M}{\Delta t} = \frac{-9.00 \times 10^4 \text{ kg}}{2.40 \times 10^2 \text{ s}} = -3.75 \times 10^2 \text{ kg/s}$$

Substitute this rate into Equation 6.20, obtaining the thrust:

$$\text{Thrust} = \left| v_e \frac{\Delta M}{\Delta t} \right| = (4.50 \times 10^3 \text{ m/s})(3.75 \times 10^2 \text{ kg/s})$$

$$= \boxed{1.69 \times 10^6 \text{ N}}$$

(c) Find the initial acceleration.

Write Newton's second law, where T stands for thrust, and solve for the acceleration a:

$$Ma = \sum F = T - Mg$$

$$a = \frac{T}{M} - g = \frac{1.69 \times 10^6 \text{ N}}{1.00 \times 10^5 \text{ kg}} - 9.80 \text{ m/s}^2$$

$$= \boxed{7.10 \text{ m/s}^2}$$

(d) Estimate the speed at burnout when gravity is not neglected.

Find the approximate loss of speed due to gravity:

$$\Delta v_g = -g\Delta t = -(9.80 \text{ m/s}^2)(2.40 \times 10^2 \text{ s})$$

$$= -2.35 \times 10^3 \text{ m/s}$$

Add this loss to the result of part (b):

$$v_f = 1.04 \times 10^4 \text{ m/s} - 2.35 \times 10^3 \text{ m/s}$$

$$= \boxed{8.05 \times 10^3 \text{ m/s}}$$

REMARKS Even taking gravity into account, the speed is sufficient to attain orbit. Some additional boost may be required to overcome air drag.

QUESTION 6.9 What initial normal force would be exerted on an astronaut of mass m in a rocket traveling vertically upward with an acceleration a? Answer symbolically in terms of the positive quantities m, g, and a.

EXERCISE 6.9 A spaceship with a mass of 5.00×10^4 kg is traveling at 6.00×10^3 m/s relative to a space station. What mass will the ship have after it fires its engines in order to reach a relative speed of 8.00×10^3 m/s, traveling the same direction? Assume an exhaust velocity of 4.50×10^3 m/s.

ANSWER 3.21×10^4 kg

■ SUMMARY

6.1 Momentum and Impulse

The **linear momentum** $\vec{p}$ of an object of mass m moving with velocity $\vec{v}$ is defined as

$$\vec{p} \equiv m\vec{v} \qquad [6.1]$$

Momentum carries units of kg · m/s. The **impulse** $\vec{I}$ of a constant force $\vec{F}$ delivered to an object is equal to the product of the force and the time interval during which the force acts:

$$\vec{I} \equiv \vec{F}\Delta t \qquad [6.4]$$

These two concepts are unified in the **impulse–momentum theorem,** which states that the impulse of a constant force delivered to an object is equal to the change in momentum of the object:

$$\vec{I} = \vec{F}\Delta t = \Delta\vec{p} \equiv m\vec{v}_f - m\vec{v}_i \qquad [6.5]$$

Solving problems with this theorem often involves estimating speeds or contact times (or both), leading to an average force.

6.2 Conservation of Momentum

When no net external force acts on an isolated system, the total momentum of the system is constant. This principle is called **conservation of momentum.** In particular, if the isolated system consists of two objects undergoing a collision, the total momentum of the system is the same before and after the collision. Conservation of momentum can be written mathematically for this case as

$$m_1\vec{v}_{1i} + m_2\vec{v}_{2i} = m_1\vec{v}_{1f} + m_2\vec{v}_{2f} \qquad [6.7]$$

In an isolated system of two objects undergoing a collision, the total momentum of the system remains constant.

Collision and recoil problems typically require finding unknown velocities in one or two dimensions. Each vector component gives an equation, and the resulting equations are solved simultaneously.

6.3 Collisions

In an **inelastic collision,** the momentum of the system is conserved, but kinetic energy is not. In a **perfectly inelastic collision,** the colliding objects stick together. In an **elastic collision,** both the momentum and the kinetic energy of the system are conserved.

A one-dimensional **elastic collision** between two objects can be solved by using the conservation of momentum and conservation of energy equations:

$$m_1 v_{1i} + m_2 v_{2i} = m_1 v_{1f} + m_2 v_{2f} \qquad \textbf{[6.10]}$$

$$\tfrac{1}{2} m_1 v_{1i}^2 + \tfrac{1}{2} m_2 v_{2i}^2 = \tfrac{1}{2} m_1 v_{1f}^2 + \tfrac{1}{2} m_2 v_{2f}^2 \qquad \textbf{[6.11]}$$

The following equation, derived from Equations 6.10 and 6.11, is usually more convenient to use than the original conservation of energy equation:

$$v_{1i} - v_{2i} = -(v_{1f} - v_{2f}) \qquad \textbf{[6.14]}$$

These equations can be solved simultaneously for the unknown velocities. Energy is not conserved in **inelastic collisions,** so such problems must be solved with Equation 6.10 alone.

6.4 Glancing Collisions

In glancing collisions, conservation of momentum can be applied along two perpendicular directions: an x-axis and a y-axis. Problems can be solved by using the x- and y-components of Equation 6.7. Elastic two-dimensional collisions will usually require Equation 6.11 as well. (Equa-

tion 6.14 doesn't apply to two dimensions.) Generally, one of the two objects is taken to be traveling along the x-axis, undergoing a deflection at some angle θ after the collision. The final velocities and angles can be found with elementary trigonometry.

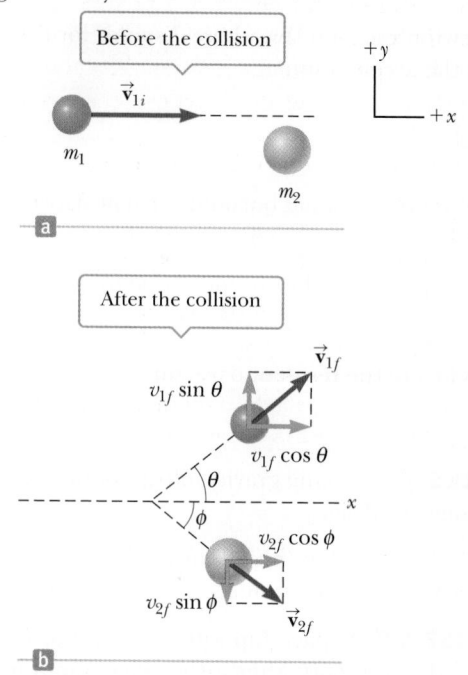

In a two-dimensional collision the system momentum is conserved, whereas the system energy is conserved only if the collision is elastic.

■ MULTIPLE-CHOICE QUESTIONS

WebAssign The multiple-choice questions in this chapter may be assigned online in Enhanced WebAssign.

1. A soccer player runs up behind a 0.450-kg soccer ball traveling at 3.20 m/s and kicks it in the same direction as it is moving, increasing its speed to 12.8 m/s. What magnitude impulse did the soccer player deliver to the ball? (a) 2.45 kg · m/s (b) 4.32 kg · m/s (c) 5.61 kg · m/s (d) 7.08 kg · m/s (e) 9.79 kg · m/s

2. A small china bowl having kinetic energy E is sliding along a frictionless countertop when a server, with perfect timing, places a rice ball into the bowl as it passes him. If the bowl and rice ball have the same mass, what is the kinetic energy of the system thereafter? (a) $2E$ (b) E (c) $E/2$ (d) $E/4$ (e) $E/8$

3. A car of mass m traveling at speed v crashes into the rear of a truck of mass $2m$ that is at rest and in neutral at an intersection. If the collision is perfectly inelastic, what is the speed of the combined car and truck after the collision? (a) v (b) $v/2$ (c) $v/3$ (d) $2v$ (e) None of these

4. A 57.0-g tennis ball is traveling straight at a player at 21.0 m/s. The player volleys the ball straight back at 25.0 m/s. If the ball remains in contact with the

racket for 0.060 s, what average force acts on the ball? (a) 22.6 kg · m/s² (b) 32.5 kg · m/s² (c) 43.7 kg · m/s² (d) 72.1 kg · m/s² (e) 102 kg · m/s²

5. In a game of billiards, a red billiard ball is traveling in the positive x-direction with speed v and the cue ball is traveling in the negative x-direction with speed $3v$ when the two balls collide head on. Which statement is true concerning their velocities subsequent to the collision? Neglect any effects of spin. (a) red ball: $-v$; cue ball: $3v$ (b) red ball: v; cue ball: $2v$ (c) red ball: $-3v$; cue ball: v (d) red ball: v; cue ball: $3v$ (e) The velocities can't be determined without knowing the mass of each ball.

6. A 5-kg cart moving to the right with a velocity of +6 m/s collides with a concrete wall and rebounds with a velocity of −2 m/s. Is the change in momentum of the cart (a) 0, (b) 40 kg · m/s, (c) −40 kg · m/s, (d) −30 kg · m/s, or (e) −10 kg · m/s?

7. A 2-kg object moving to the right with a speed of 4 m/s makes a head-on elastic collision with a 1-kg object that is initially at rest. The velocity of the 1-kg object after

the collision is (a) greater than 4 m/s, (b) less than 4 m/s, (c) equal to 4 m/s, (d) zero, or (e) impossible to say based on the information provided.

8. A 3-kg object moving to the right on a frictionless horizontal surface with a speed of 2 m/s collides head on and sticks to a 2-kg object that is initially moving to the left with a speed of 4 m/s. After the collision, which statement is true? (a) the kinetic energy of the system is 20 J, (b) the momentum of the system is 14 kg · m/s, (c) the kinetic energy of the system is greater than 5 J but less than 20 J, (d) the momentum of the system is −2 kg · m/s, (e) the momentum of the system is less than the momentum of the system before the collision.

9. If two particles have equal kinetic energies, are their momenta equal? (a) yes, always (b) no, never (c) yes, as long as their masses are equal (d) yes, if both their masses and directions of motion are the same (e) no, unless they are moving perpendicular to each other

10. If two particles have equal momenta, are their kinetic energies equal? (a) yes, always (b) no, never (c) no, except when their masses are equal (d) no, except when their speeds are the same (e) yes, as long as they move along parallel lines

11. The kinetic energy of a rocket is increased by a factor of eight after its engines are fired, whereas its total mass is reduced by half through the burning of fuel. By what factor is the magnitude of its momentum changed? *Hint:* Use $KE = p^2/2m$. (a) 2 (b) 8 (c) 4 (d) 16 (e) 1

12. A rocket with total mass 3.00×10^5 kg leaves a launch pad at Cape Kennedy, moving vertically with an acceleration of 36.0 m/s². If the speed of the exhausted gases is 4.50×10^3 m/s, at what rate is the rocket initially burning fuel? (a) 3.05×10^3 kg/s (b) 2.40×10^3 kg/s (c) 7.50×10^2 kg/s (d) 1.50×10^3 kg/s (e) None of these

13. Two particles of different mass start from rest. The same net force acts on both of them as they move over equal distances. How do their final kinetic energies compare? (a) The particle of larger mass has more kinetic energy. (b) The particle of smaller mass has more kinetic energy. (c) The particles have equal kinetic energies. (d) Either particle might have more kinetic energy.

■ CONCEPTUAL QUESTIONS

WebAssign The conceptual questions in this chapter may be assigned online in Enhanced WebAssign.

1. A batter bunts a pitched baseball, blocking the ball without swinging. (a) Can the baseball deliver more kinetic energy to the bat and batter than the ball carries initially? (b) Can the baseball deliver more momentum to the bat and batter than the ball carries initially? Explain each of your answers.

2. If two objects collide and one is initially at rest, (a) is it possible for both to be at rest after the collision? (b) Is it possible for only one to be at rest after the collision? Explain.

3. In perfectly inelastic collisions between two objects, there are events in which all of the original kinetic energy is transformed to forms other than kinetic. Give an example of such an event.

4. Americans will never forget the terrorist attack on September 11, 2001. One commentator remarked that the force of the explosion at the Twin Towers of the World Trade Center was strong enough to blow glass and parts of the steel structure to small fragments. Yet the television coverage showed thousands of sheets of paper floating down, many still intact. Explain how that could be.

5. A ball of clay of mass m is thrown with a speed v against a brick wall. The clay sticks to the wall and stops. Is the principle of conservation of momentum violated in this example?

6. A skater is standing still on a frictionless ice rink. Her friend throws a Frisbee straight at her. In which of the following cases is the largest momentum transferred to the skater? (a) The skater catches the Frisbee and holds onto it. (b) The skater catches the Frisbee momentarily, but then drops it vertically downward. (c) The skater catches the Frisbee, holds it momentarily, and throws it back to her friend.

7. A more ordinary example of conservation of momentum than a rocket ship occurs in a kitchen dishwashing machine. In this device, water at high pressure is forced out of small holes on the spray arms. Use conservation of momentum to explain why the arms rotate, directing water to all the dishes.

8. (a) If two automobiles collide, they usually do not stick together. Does this mean the collision is elastic? (b) Explain why a head-on collision is likely to be more dangerous than other types of collisions.

9. Your physical education teacher throws you a tennis ball at a certain velocity, and you catch it. You are now given the following choice: The teacher can throw you a medicine ball (which is much more massive than the tennis ball) with the same velocity, the same momentum, or the same kinetic energy as the tennis ball. Which option would you choose in order to make the easiest catch, and why?

10. A large bedsheet is held vertically by two students. A third student, who happens to be the star pitcher on the baseball team, throws a raw egg at the sheet. Explain why the egg doesn't break when it hits the sheet, regardless of its initial speed. (If you try this, make sure the pitcher hits the sheet near its center, and don't allow the egg to fall on the floor after being caught.)

11. A sharpshooter fires a rifle while standing with the butt of the gun against his shoulder. If the forward momentum of a bullet is the same as the backward momentum of the gun, why isn't it as dangerous to be hit by the gun as by the bullet?

12. An air bag inflates when a collision occurs, protecting a passenger (the dummy in Figure CQ6.12) from seri-

© David Woods/Terra/Corbis

Figure CQ6.12

ous injury. Why does the air bag soften the blow? Discuss the physics involved in this dramatic photograph.

13. In golf, novice players are often advised to be sure to "follow through" with their swing. (a) Why does this make the ball travel a longer distance? (b) If a shot is taken near the green, very little follow-through is required. Why?

14. An open box slides across a frictionless, icy surface of a frozen lake. What happens to the speed of the box as water from a rain shower falls vertically downward into the box? Explain.

15. Does a larger net force exerted on an object always produce a larger change in the momentum of the object, compared to a smaller net force? Explain.

16. Does a larger net force always produce a larger change in kinetic energy than a smaller net force? Explain.

■ PROBLEMS

ENHANCED
WebAssign The problems in this chapter may be assigned online in Enhanced WebAssign. Selected problems also have Watch It video solutions.

1. denotes straightforward problem; **2.** denotes intermediate problem;

3. denotes challenging problem

1. denotes full solution available in *Student Solutions Manual/ Study Guide*

1. denotes problems most often assigned in Enhanced WebAssign

BIO denotes biomedical problems

GP denotes guided problems

M denotes Master It tutorial available in Enhanced WebAssign

Q|C denotes asking for quantitative and conceptual reasoning

S denotes symbolic reasoning problem

6.1 Momentum and Impulse

1. Calculate the magnitude of the linear momentum for the following cases: (a) a proton with mass equal to 1.67×10^{-27} kg, moving with a speed of 5.00×10^6 m/s; (b) a 15.0-g bullet moving with a speed of 300 m/s; (c) a 75.0-kg sprinter running with a speed of 10.0 m/s; (d) the Earth (mass = 5.98×10^{24} kg) moving with an orbital speed equal to 2.98×10^4 m/s.

2. A high-speed photograph of a club hitting a golf ball is shown in Figure 6.3. The club was in contact with a ball, initially at rest, for about 0.002 0 s. If the ball has a mass of 55 g and leaves the head of the club with a speed of 2.0×10^2 ft/s, find the average force exerted on the ball by the club.

3. A pitcher claims he can throw a 0.145-kg baseball with as much momentum as a 3.00-g bullet moving with a speed of 1.50×10^3 m/s. (a) What must the baseball's speed be if the pitcher's claim is valid? (b) Which has greater kinetic energy, the ball or the bullet?

4. **S** A ball of mass m is thrown straight up into the air with an initial speed v_0. (a) Find an expression for the maximum height reached by the ball in terms of v_0 and g. (b) Using conservation of energy and the result of part (a), find the magnitude of the momentum of the ball at one-half its maximum height in terms of m and v_0.

5. **Q|C** Drops of rain fall perpendicular to the roof of a parked car during a rainstorm. The drops strike the roof with a speed of 12 m/s, and the mass of rain per second striking the roof is 0.035 kg/s. (a) Assuming the drops come to rest after striking the roof, find the average force exerted by the rain on the roof. (b) If hailstones having the same mass as the raindrops fall on the roof at the same rate and with the same speed, how would the average force on the roof compare to that found in part (a)?

6. **S** Show that the kinetic energy of a particle of mass m is related to the magnitude of the momentum p of that particle by $KE = p^2/2m$. *Note:* This expression is invalid for particles traveling at speeds near that of light.

7. An object has a kinetic energy of 275 J and a momentum of magnitude 25.0 kg · m/s. Find the (a) speed and (b) mass of the object.

8. An estimated force vs. time curve for a baseball struck by a bat is shown in Figure P6.8. From this curve, determine (a) the impulse delivered to the ball and (b) the average force exerted on the ball.

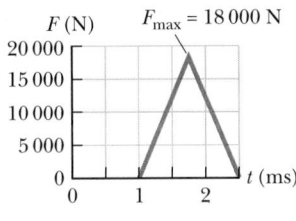

Figure P6.8

9. A 0.280-kg volleyball approaches a player horizontally with a speed of 15.0 m/s. The player strikes the ball with her fist and causes the ball to move in the opposite direction with a speed of 22.0 m/s. (a) What impulse is delivered to the ball by the player? (b) If the player's fist is in contact with the ball for 0.060 0 s, find the magnitude of the average force exerted on the player's fist.

10. **QC** A man claims he can safely hold on to a 12.0-kg child in a head-on collision with a relative speed of 120-mi/h lasting for 0.10 s as long as he has his seat belt on. (a) Find the magnitude of the average force needed to hold onto the child. (b) Based on the result to part (a), is the man's claim valid? (c) What does the answer to this problem say about laws requiring the use of proper safety devices such as seat belts and special toddler seats?

11. A ball of mass 0.150 kg is dropped from rest from a height of 1.25 m. It rebounds from the floor to reach a height of 0.960 m. What impulse was given to the ball by the floor?

12. A tennis player receives a shot with the ball (0.060 0 kg) traveling horizontally at 50.0 m/s and returns the shot with the ball traveling horizontally at 40.0 m/s in the opposite direction. (a) What is the impulse delivered to the ball by the racket? (b) What work does the racket do on the ball?

13. A car is stopped for a traffic signal. When the light turns green, the car accelerates, increasing its speed from 0 to 5.20 m/s in 0.832 s. What are (a) the magnitudes of the linear impulse and (b) the average total force experienced by a 70.0-kg passenger in the car during the time the car accelerates?

14. A 65.0-kg basketball player jumps vertically and leaves the floor with a velocity of 1.80 m/s upward. (a) What impulse does the player experience? (b) What force does the floor exert on the player before the jump? (c) What is the total average force exerted by the floor on the player if the player is in contact with the floor for 0.450 s during the jump?

15. The force shown in the force vs. time diagram in Figure P6.15 acts on a 1.5-kg object. Find (a) the impulse of the force, (b) the final velocity of the object if it is initially at rest, and (c) the final velocity of the object if it is initially moving along the *x*-axis with a velocity of −2.0 m/s.

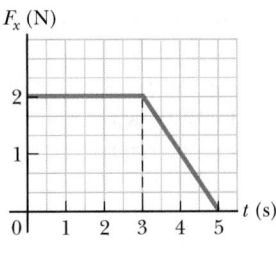

Figure P6.15

16. A force of magnitude F_x acting in the *x*-direction on a 2.00-kg particle varies in time as shown in Figure P6.16. Find (a) the impulse of the force, (b) the final velocity of the particle if it is initially at rest, and (c) the final velocity of the particle if it is initially moving along the *x*-axis with a velocity of −2.00 m/s.

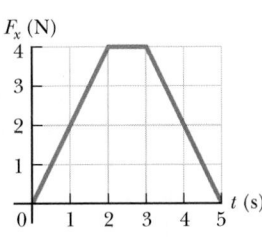

Figure P6.16

17. The forces shown in the force vs. time diagram in Figure P6.17 act on a 1.5-kg particle. Find (a) the impulse for the interval from $t = 0$ to $t = 3.0$ s and (b) the impulse for the interval from $t = 0$ to $t = 5.0$ s. If the forces act on a 1.5-kg particle that is initially at rest, find the particle's speed (c) at $t = 3.0$ s and (d) at $t = 5.0$ s.

Figure P6.17

18. A 3.00-kg steel ball strikes a massive wall at 10.0 m/s at an angle of $\theta = 60.0°$ with the plane of the wall. It bounces off the wall with the same speed and angle (Fig. P6.18). If the ball is in contact with the wall for 0.200 s, what is the average force exerted by the wall on the ball?

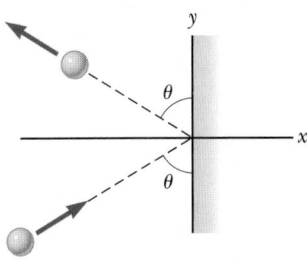

Figure P6.18

19. **M** The front 1.20 m of a 1 400-kg car is designed as a "crumple zone" that collapses to absorb the shock of a collision. If a car traveling 25.0 m/s stops uniformly in 1.20 m, (a) how long does the collision last, (b) what is the magnitude of the average force on the car, and (c) what is the acceleration of the car? Express the acceleration as a multiple of the acceleration of gravity.

20. **QC** A pitcher throws a 0.14-kg baseball toward the batter so that it crosses home plate horizontally and has a speed of 42 m/s just before it makes contact with the bat. The batter then hits the ball straight back at the pitcher with a speed of 48 m/s. Assume the ball travels along the same line leaving the bat as it followed before contacting the bat. (a) What is the magnitude of the impulse delivered by the bat to the baseball? (b) If the ball is in contact with the bat for 0.005 0 s, what is the magnitude of the average force exerted by the bat on the ball? (c) How does your answer to part (b) compare to the weight of the ball?

6.2 Conservation of Momentum

21. High-speed stroboscopic photographs show that the head of a 200-g golf club is traveling at 55 m/s just before it strikes a 46-g golf ball at rest on a tee. After the collision, the club head travels (in the same direction) at 40 m/s. Find the speed of the golf ball just after impact.

22. A rifle with a weight of 30 N fires a 5.0-g bullet with a speed of 300 m/s. (a) Find the recoil speed of the rifle. (b) If a 700-N man holds the rifle firmly against his shoulder, find the recoil speed of the man and rifle.

23. A 45.0-kg girl is standing on a 150-kg plank. The plank, originally at rest, is free to slide on a frozen lake, which is a flat, frictionless surface. The girl begins to walk along the plank at a constant velocity of 1.50 m/s to the right relative to the plank. (a) What is her velocity relative to the surface of the ice? (b) What is the velocity of the plank relative to the surface of the ice?

24. **S** *This is a symbolic version of Problem 23.* A girl of mass m_G is standing on a plank of mass m_p. Both are originally at rest on a frozen lake that constitutes a frictionless, flat surface. The girl begins to walk along the plank at a constant velocity v_{GP} to the right relative to the plank. (The subscript *GP* denotes the girl relative to plank.) (a) What is the velocity v_{PI} of the plank relative to the surface of the ice? (b) What is the girl's velocity v_{GI} relative to the ice surface?

25. **QC** An astronaut in her space suit has a total mass of 87.0 kg, including suit and oxygen tank. Her tether line loses its attachment to her spacecraft while she's on a spacewalk. Initially at rest with respect to her spacecraft, she throws her 12.0-kg oxygen tank away from her spacecraft with a speed of 8.00 m/s to propel herself back toward it (Fig. P6.25). (a) Determine the

Figure P6.25

maximum distance she can be from the craft and still return within 2.00 min (the amount of time the air in her helmet remains breathable). (b) Explain in terms of Newton's laws of motion why this strategy works.

26. A 75-kg fisherman in a 125-kg boat throws a package of mass $m = 15$ kg horizontally toward the right with a speed of $v_i = 4.5$ m/s as in Figure P6.26. Neglecting water resistance, and assuming the boat is at rest before the package is thrown, find the velocity of the boat after the package is thrown.

Figure P6.26

27. A 65.0-kg person throws a 0.045 0-kg snowball forward with a ground speed of 30.0 m/s. A second person, with a mass of 60.0 kg, catches the snowball. Both people are on skates. The first person is initially moving forward with a speed of 2.50 m/s, and the second person is initially at rest. What are the velocities of the two people after the snowball is exchanged? Disregard friction between the skates and the ice.

28. **QC** **S** An amateur skater of mass M (when fully dressed) is trapped in the middle of an ice rink and is unable to return to the side where there is no ice. Every motion she makes causes her to slip on the ice and remain in the same spot. She decides to try to return to safety by removing her gloves of mass m and throwing them in the direction opposite the safe side. (a) She throws the gloves as hard as she can, and they leave her hand with a velocity $\vec{v}_{gloves}$. Explain whether or not she moves. If she does move, calculate her velocity $\vec{v}_{girl}$ relative to the Earth after she throws the gloves. (b) Discuss her motion from the point of view of the forces acting on her.

6.3 Collisions

6.4 Glancing Collisions

29. **GP** A man of mass $m_1 = 70.0$ kg is skating at $v_1 = 8.00$ m/s behind his wife of mass $m_2 = 50.0$ kg, who is skating at $v_2 = 4.00$ m/s. Instead of passing her, he inadvertently collides with her. He grabs her around the waist, and they maintain their balance. (a) Sketch the problem with before-and-after diagrams, representing the skaters as blocks. (b) Is the collision best described as elastic, inelastic, or perfectly inelastic? Why? (c) Write the general equation for conservation of momentum in terms of m_1, v_1, m_2, v_2, and final velocity v_f. (d) Solve the momentum equation for v_f.

(e) Substitute values, obtaining the numerical value for v_f, their speed after the collision.

30. An archer shoots an arrow toward a 300-g target that is sliding in her direction at a speed of 2.50 m/s on a smooth, slippery surface. The 22.5-g arrow is shot with a speed of 35.0 m/s and passes through the target, which is stopped by the impact. What is the speed of the arrow after passing through the target?

31. Gayle runs at a speed of 4.00 m/s and dives on a sled, initially at rest on the top of a frictionless, snow-covered hill. After she has descended a vertical distance of 5.00 m, her brother, who is initially at rest, hops on her back, and they continue down the hill together. What is their speed at the bottom of the hill if the total vertical drop is 15.0 m? Gayle's mass is 50.0 kg, the sled has a mass of 5.00 kg, and her brother has a mass of 30.0 kg.

32. **BIO** A 75.0-kg ice skater moving at 10.0 m/s crashes into a stationary skater of equal mass. After the collision, the two skaters move as a unit at 5.00 m/s. Suppose the average force a skater can experience without breaking a bone is 4 500 N. If the impact time is 0.100 s, does a bone break?

33. A railroad car of mass 2.00×10^4 kg moving at 3.00 m/s collides and couples with two coupled railroad cars, each of the same mass as the single car and moving in the same direction at 1.20 m/s. (a) What is the speed of the three coupled cars after the collision? (b) How much kinetic energy is lost in the collision?

34. **S** *This is a symbolic version of Problem 33.* A railroad car of mass M moving at a speed v_1 collides and couples with two coupled railroad cars, each of the same mass M and moving in the same direction at a speed v_2. (a) What is the speed v_f of the three coupled cars after the collision in terms of v_1 and v_2? (b) How much kinetic energy is lost in the collision? Answer in terms of M, v_1, and v_2.

35. **S** Consider the ballistic pendulum device discussed in Example 6.5 and illustrated in Figure 6.12. (a) Determine the ratio of the momentum immediately after the collision to the momentum immediately before the collision. (b) Show that the ratio of the kinetic energy immediately after the collision to the kinetic energy immediately before the collision is $m_1/(m_1 + m_2)$.

36. **S** A car of mass m moving at a speed v_1 collides and couples with the back of a truck of mass $2m$ moving initially in the same direction as the car at a lower speed v_2. (a) What is the speed v_f of the two vehicles immediately after the collision? (b) What is the change in kinetic energy of the car–truck system in the collision?

37. In a Broadway performance, an 80.0-kg actor swings from a 3.75-m-long cable that is horizontal when he starts. At the bottom of his arc, he picks up his 55.0-kg costar in an inelastic collision. What maximum height do they reach after their upward swing?

38. Two shuffleboard disks of equal mass, one orange and the other green, are involved in a perfectly elastic glancing collision. The green disk is initially at rest and is struck by the orange disk moving initially to the right at 5.00 m/s as in Figure P6.38a. After the collision, the orange disk moves in a direction that makes an angle of 37.0° with the horizontal axis while the green disk makes an angle of 53.0° with this axis as in Figure P6.38b. Determine the speed of each disk after the collision.

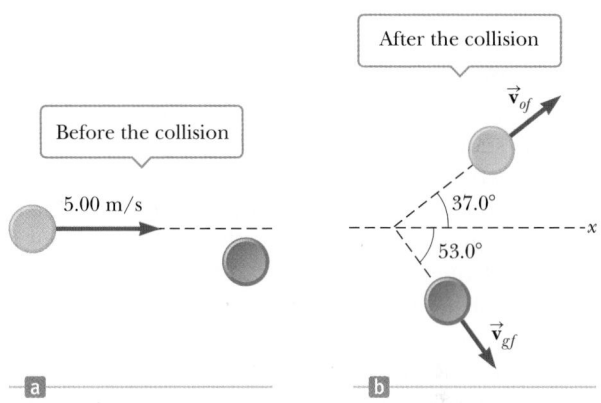

Figure P6.38

39. A 0.030-kg bullet is fired vertically at 200 m/s into a 0.15-kg baseball that is initially at rest. How high does the combined bullet and baseball rise after the collision, assuming the bullet embeds itself in the ball?

40. **M** An bullet of mass $m = 8.00$ g is fired into a block of mass $M = 250$ g that is initially at rest at the edge of a table of height $h = 1.00$ m (Fig. P6.40). The bullet remains in the block, and after the impact the block lands $d = 2.00$ m from the bottom of the table. Determine the initial speed of the bullet.

Figure P6.40

41. A 12.0-g bullet is fired horizontally into a 100-g wooden block that is initially at rest on a frictionless horizontal surface and connected to a spring having spring constant 150 N/m. The bullet becomes embedded in the block. If the bullet–block system compresses the spring by a maximum of 80.0 cm, what was the speed of the bullet at impact with the block?

42. A 1 200-kg car traveling initially with a speed of 25.0 m/s in an easterly direction crashes into the rear end of a 9 000-kg truck moving in the same direction at 20.0 m/s (Fig. P6.42 on page 194). The velocity of the car right after the collision is 18.0 m/s to the east. (a) What is the velocity of the truck right after the collision? (b) How much mechanical energy is lost in the collision? Account for this loss in energy.

Before   After

Figure P6.42

43. **QC** **S** A boy of mass m_b and his girlfriend of mass m_g, both wearing ice skates, face each other at rest while standing on a frictionless ice rink. The boy pushes the girl, sending her away with velocity v_g toward the east. Assume that $m_b > m_g$. (a) Describe the subsequent motion of the boy. (b) Find expressions for the final kinetic energy of the girl and the final kinetic energy of the boy, and show that the girl has greater kinetic energy than the boy. (c) The boy and girl had zero kinetic energy before the boy pushed the girl, but ended up with kinetic energy after the event. How do you account for the appearance of mechanical energy?

44. **GP** **QC** A space probe, initially at rest, undergoes an internal mechanical malfunction and breaks into three pieces. One piece of mass $m_1 = 48.0$ kg travels in the positive x-direction at 12.0 m/s, and a second piece of mass $m_2 = 62.0$ kg travels in the xy-plane at an angle of 105° at 15.0 m/s. The third piece has mass $m_3 = 112$ kg. (a) Sketch a diagram of the situation, labeling the different masses and their velocities. (b) Write the general expression for conservation of momentum in the x- and y-directions in terms of m_1, m_2, m_3, v_1, v_2, and v_3 and the sines and cosines of the angles, taking θ to be the unknown angle. (c) Calculate the final x-components of the momenta of m_1 and m_2. (d) Calculate the final y-components of the momenta of m_1 and m_2. (e) Substitute the known momentum components into the general equations of momentum for the x- and y-directions, along with the known mass m_3. (f) Solve the two momentum equations for $v_3 \cos \theta$ and $v_3 \sin \theta$, respectively, and use the identity $\cos^2 \theta + \sin^2 \theta = 1$ to obtain v_3. (g) Divide the equation for $v_3 \sin \theta$ by that for $v_3 \cos \theta$ to obtain $\tan \theta$, then obtain the angle by taking the inverse tangent of both sides. (h) In general, would three such pieces necessarily have to move in the same plane? Why?

45. A 25.0-g object moving to the right at 20.0 cm/s overtakes and collides elastically with a 10.0-g object moving in the same direction at 15.0 cm/s. Find the velocity of each object after the collision.

46. A billiard ball rolling across a table at 1.50 m/s makes a head-on elastic collision with an identical ball. Find the speed of each ball after the collision (a) when the second ball is initially at rest, (b) when the second ball

is moving toward the first at a speed of 1.00 m/s, and (c) when the second ball is moving away from the first at a speed of 1.00 m/s.

47. **QC** **M** A 90.0-kg fullback running east with a speed of 5.00 m/s is tackled by a 95.0-kg opponent running north with a speed of 3.00 m/s. (a) Why does the tackle constitute a perfectly inelastic collision? (b) Calculate the velocity of the players immediately after the tackle and (c) determine the mechanical energy that is lost as a result of the collision. (d) Where did the lost energy go?

48. Identical twins, each with mass 55.0 kg, are on ice skates and at rest on a frozen lake, which may be taken as frictionless. Twin A is carrying a backpack of mass 12.0 kg. She throws it horizontally at 3.00 m/s to Twin B. Neglecting any gravity effects, what are the subsequent speeds of Twin A and Twin B?

49. A 2 000-kg car moving east at 10.0 m/s collides with a 3 000-kg car moving north. The cars stick together and move as a unit after the collision, at an angle of 40.0° north of east and a speed of 5.22 m/s. Find the speed of the 3 000-kg car before the collision.

50. Two automobiles of equal mass approach an intersection. One vehicle is traveling with velocity 13.0 m/s toward the east, and the other is traveling north with velocity v_{2i}. Neither driver sees the other. The vehicles collide in the intersection and stick together, leaving parallel skid marks at an angle of 55.0° north of east. The speed limit for both roads is 35 mi/h, and the driver of the northward-moving vehicle claims he was within the limit when the collision occurred. Is he telling the truth?

51. A billiard ball moving at 5.00 m/s strikes a stationary ball of the same mass. After the collision, the first ball moves at 4.33 m/s at an angle of 30° with respect to the original line of motion. (a) Find the velocity (magnitude and direction) of the second ball after collision. (b) Was the collision inelastic or elastic?

Additional Problems

52. **BIO** In research in cardiology and exercise physiology, it is often important to know the mass of blood pumped by a person's heart in one stroke. This information can be obtained by means of a *ballistocardiograph*. The instrument works as follows: The subject lies on a horizontal pallet floating on a film of air. Friction on the pallet is negligible. Initially, the momentum of the system is zero. When the heart beats, it expels a mass m of blood into the aorta with speed v, and the body and platform move in the opposite direction with speed V. The speed of the blood can be determined independently (for example, by observing an ultrasound Doppler shift). Assume that the blood's speed is 50.0 cm/s in one typical trial. The mass of the subject plus the pallet is 54.0 kg. The pallet moves at a speed of 6.00×10^{-5} m in 0.160 s after one heartbeat. Calculate

the mass of blood that leaves the heart. Assume that the mass of blood is negligible compared with the total mass of the person. This simplified example illustrates the principle of ballistocardiography, but in practice a more sophisticated model of heart function is used.

53. **Q|C** Most of us know intuitively that in a head-on collision between a large dump truck and a subcompact car, you are better off being in the truck than in the car. Why is this? Many people imagine that the collision force exerted on the car is much greater than that exerted on the truck. To substantiate this view, they point out that the car is crushed, whereas the truck is only dented. This idea of unequal forces, of course, is false; Newton's third law tells us that both objects are acted upon by forces of the same magnitude. The truck suffers less damage because it is made of stronger metal. But what about the two drivers? Do they experience the same forces? To answer this question, suppose that each vehicle is initially moving at 8.00 m/s and that they undergo a perfectly inelastic head-on collision. Each driver has mass 80.0 kg. Including the masses of the drivers, the total masses of the vehicles are 800 kg for the car and 4 000 kg for the truck. If the collision time is 0.120 s, what force does the seat belt exert on each driver?

54. Consider a frictionless track as shown in Figure P6.54. A block of mass $m_1 = 5.00$ kg is released from Ⓐ. It makes a head-on elastic collision at Ⓑ with a block of mass $m_2 = 10.0$ kg that is initially at rest. Calculate the maximum height to which m_1 rises after the collision.

Figure P6.54

55. **M** A 2.0-g particle moving at 8.0 m/s makes a perfectly elastic head-on collision with a resting 1.0-g object. (a) Find the speed of each particle after the collision. (b) Find the speed of each particle after the collision if the stationary particle has a mass of 10 g. (c) Find the final kinetic energy of the incident 2.0-g particle in the situations described in parts (a) and (b). In which case does the incident particle lose more kinetic energy?

56. **S** A bullet of mass m and speed v passes completely through a pendulum bob of mass M as shown in Figure P6.56. The bullet emerges with a speed of $v/2$. The pendulum bob is suspended by a stiff rod of length ℓ and negli-

Figure P6.56

gible mass. What is the minimum value of v such that the bob will barely swing through a complete vertical circle?

57. Two objects of masses $m_1 = 0.56$ kg and $m_2 = 0.88$ kg are placed on a horizontal frictionless surface and a compressed spring of force constant $k = 280$ N/m is placed between them as in Figure P6.57a. Neglect the mass of the spring. The spring is not attached to either object and is compressed a distance of 9.8 cm. If the objects are released from rest, find the final velocity of each object as shown in Figure P6.57b.

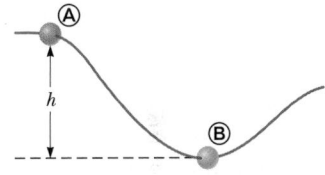

Figure P6.57

58. A 0.400-kg blue bead slides on a frictionless, curved wire, starting from rest at point Ⓐ in Figure P6.58, where $h = 1.50$ m. At point Ⓑ, the bead collides elastically with a 0.600-kg green bead at rest. Find the maximum height the green bead rises as it moves up the wire.

Figure P6.58

59. A 730-N man stands in the middle of a frozen pond of radius 5.0 m. He is unable to get to the other side because of a lack of friction between his shoes and the ice. To overcome this difficulty, he throws his 1.2-kg physics textbook horizontally toward the north shore at a speed of 5.0 m/s. How long does it take him to reach the south shore?

60. An unstable nucleus of mass 1.7×10^{-26} kg, initially at rest at the origin of a coordinate system, disintegrates into three particles. One particle, having a mass of $m_1 = 5.0 \times 10^{-27}$ kg, moves in the positive y-direction with speed $v_1 = 6.0 \times 10^6$ m/s. Another particle, of mass $m_2 = 8.4 \times 10^{-27}$ kg, moves in the positive x-direction with speed $v_2 = 4.0 \times 10^6$ m/s. Find the magnitude and direction of the velocity of the third particle.

61. **S** Two blocks of masses m_1 and m_2 approach each other on a horizontal table with the same constant speed, v_0, as measured by a laboratory observer. The blocks undergo a perfectly elastic collision, and it is observed that m_1 stops but m_2 moves opposite its original motion with some constant speed, v. (a) Determine the ratio of the two masses, m_1/m_2. (b) What is the ratio of their speeds, v/v_0?

62. Two blocks of masses $m_1 = 2.00$ kg and $m_2 = 4.00$ kg are each released from rest at a height of $h = 5.00$ m on a frictionless track, as shown in Figure P6.62 (page 196),

and undergo an elastic head-on collision. (a) Determine the velocity of each block just before the collision. (b) Determine the velocity of each block immediately after the collision. (c) Determine the maximum heights to which m_1 and m_2 rise after the collision.

Figure P6.62

63. A block with mass $m_1 = 0.500$ kg is released from rest on a frictionless track at a distance $h_1 = 2.50$ m above the top of a table. It then collides elastically with an object having mass $m_2 = 1.00$ kg that is initially at rest on the table, as shown in Figure P6.63. (a) Determine the velocities of the two objects just after the collision. (b) How high up the track does the 0.500-kg object travel back after the collision? (c) How far away from the bottom of the table does the 1.00-kg object land, given that the height of the table is $h_2 = 2.00$ m? (d) How far away from the bottom of the table does the 0.500-kg object eventually land?

Figure P6.63

64. **S** Two objects of masses m and $3m$ are moving toward each other along the x-axis with the same initial speed v_0. The object with mass m is traveling to the left, and the object with mass $3m$ is traveling to the right. They undergo an elastic glancing collision such that m is moving downward after the collision at right angles from its initial direction. (a) Find the final speeds of the two objects. (b) What is the angle θ at which the object with mass $3m$ is scattered?

65. A small block of mass $m_1 = 0.500$ kg is released from rest at the top of a curved wedge of mass $m_2 = 3.00$ kg, which sits on a frictionless horizontal surface as in Figure P6.65a. When the block leaves the wedge, its velocity is measured to be 4.00 m/s to the right, as in Figure P6.65b. (a) What is the velocity of the wedge after the

block reaches the horizontal surface? (b) What is the height h of the wedge?

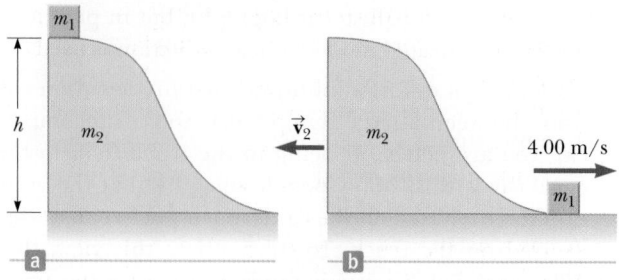

Figure P6.65

66. A cue ball traveling at 4.00 m/s makes a glancing, elastic collision with a target ball of equal mass that is initially at rest. The cue ball is deflected so that it makes an angle of 30.0° with its original direction of travel. Find (a) the angle between the velocity vectors of the two balls after the collision and (b) the speed of each ball after the collision.

67. **Q|C** A cannon is rigidly attached to a carriage, which can move along horizontal rails, but is connected to a post by a large spring, initially unstretched and with force constant $k = 2.00 \times 10^4$ N/m, as in Figure P6.67. The cannon fires a 200-kg projectile at a velocity of 125 m/s directed 45.0° above the horizontal. (a) If the mass of the cannon and its carriage is 5 000 kg, find the recoil speed of the cannon. (b) Determine the maximum extension of the spring. (c) Find the maximum force the spring exerts on the carriage. (d) Consider the system consisting of the cannon, the carriage, and the shell. Is the momentum of this system conserved during the firing? Why or why not?

Figure P6.67

68. The "force platform" is a tool that is used to analyze the performance of athletes by measuring the vertical force as a function of time that the athlete exerts on the ground in performing various activities. A simplified force vs. time graph for an athlete performing a standing high jump is shown in Figure P6.68. The athlete started the jump at $t = 0.0$ s. How high did this athlete jump?

Figure P6.68

69. A neutron in a reactor makes an elastic head-on collision with a carbon atom that is initially at rest. (The mass of the carbon nucleus is about 12 times that of the neutron.) (a) What fraction of the neutron's kinetic energy is transferred to the carbon nucleus? (b) If the neutron's initial kinetic energy is 1.6×10^{-13} J, find its final kinetic energy and the kinetic energy of the carbon nucleus after the collision.

70. QC S Two blocks collide on a frictionless surface. After the collision, the blocks stick together. Block A has a mass M and is initially moving to the right at speed v. Block B has a mass $2M$ and is initially at rest. System C is composed of both blocks. (a) Draw a force diagram for each block at an instant *during* the collision. (b) Rank the magnitudes of the horizontal forces in your diagram. Explain your reasoning. (c) Calculate the change in momentum of block A, block B, and system C. (d) Is kinetic energy conserved in this collision? Explain your answer. (This problem is courtesy of Edward F. Redish. For more such problems, visit http://www.physics.umd.edu/perg.)

71. QC (a) A car traveling due east strikes a car traveling due north at an intersection, and the two move together as a unit. A property owner on the southeast corner of the intersection claims that his fence was torn down in the collision. Should he be awarded damages by the insurance company? Defend your answer. (b) Let the eastward-moving car have a mass of 1 300 kg and a speed of 30.0 km/h and the northward-moving car a mass of 1 100 kg and a speed of 20.0 km/h. Find the velocity after the collision. Are the results consistent with your answer to part (a)?

72. A 60-kg soccer player jumps vertically upwards and heads the 0.45-kg ball as it is descending vertically with a speed of 25 m/s. (a) If the player was moving upward with a speed of 4.0 m/s just before impact, what will be the speed of the ball immediately after the collision if the ball rebounds vertically upwards and the collision is elastic? (b) If the ball is in contact with the player's head for 20 ms, what is the average acceleration of the ball? (Note that the force of gravity may be ignored during the brief collision time.)

73. M A tennis ball of mass 57.0 g is held just above a basketball of mass 590 g. With their centers vertically aligned, both balls are released from rest at the same time, to fall through a distance of 1.20 m, as shown in Figure P6.73. (a) Find the magnitude of the downward velocity with which the basketball reaches the ground. (b) Assume that an elastic collision with the ground instantaneously reverses the velocity of the basketball while the tennis ball is still moving down. Next, the two balls meet in an elastic collision. To what height does the tennis ball rebound?

Figure P6.73

74. A 20.0-kg toboggan with 70.0-kg driver is sliding down a frictionless chute directed 30.0° below the horizontal at 8.00 m/s when a 55.0-kg woman drops from a tree limb straight down behind the driver. If she drops through a vertical displacement of 2.00 m, what is the subsequent velocity of the toboggan immediately after impact?

75. S *Measuring the speed of a bullet.* A bullet of mass m is fired horizontally into a wooden block of mass M lying on a table. The bullet remains in the block after the collision. The coefficient of friction between the block and table is μ, and the block slides a distance d before stopping. Find the initial speed v_0 of the bullet in terms of M, m, μ, g, and d.

76. A flying squid (family Ommastrephidae) is able to "jump" off the surface of the sea by taking water into its body cavity and then ejecting the water vertically downward. A 0.85-kg squid is able to eject 0.30 kg of water with a speed of 20 m/s. (a) What will be the speed of the squid immediately after ejecting the water? (b) How high in the air will the squid rise?

77. A 0.30-kg puck, initially at rest on a frictionless horizontal surface, is struck by a 0.20-kg puck that is initially moving along the x-axis with a velocity of 2.0 m/s. After the collision, the 0.20-kg puck has a speed of 1.0 m/s at an angle of $\theta = 53°$ to the positive x-axis. (a) Determine the velocity of the 0.30-kg puck after the collision. (b) Find the fraction of kinetic energy lost in the collision.

78. QC S A wooden block of mass M rests on a table over a large hole as in Figure P6.78. A bullet of mass m with an initial velocity v_i is fired upward into the bottom of the block and remains in the block after the collision. The block and bullet rise to a maximum height of h. (a) Describe how you would find the initial velocity of the bullet using ideas you have learned in this chapter. (b) Find an expression for the initial velocity of the bullet.

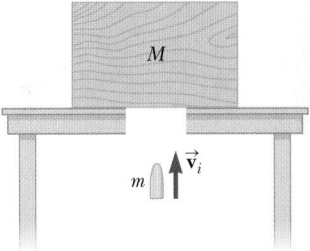

Figure P6.78 Problems 78 and 79.

79. QC A 1.25-kg wooden block rests on a table over a large hole as in Figure P6.78. A 5.00-g bullet with an initial velocity v_i is fired upward into the bottom of the block and remains in the block after the collision. The block and bullet rise to a maximum height of 22.0 cm. (a) Describe how you would find the initial velocity of the bullet using ideas you have learned in this chapter. (b) Calculate the initial velocity of the bullet from the information provided.

■ AP* REVIEW QUESTIONS

1. A lump of clay and a bouncy rubber ball with identical mass are thrown against identical doors with the same speed. The ball bounces off the first door, causing it to move; the clay sticks to the second door, also causing it to move. Which of the following are true statements?

    I. The door struck by the clay will experience a greater change in speed.

    II. The door struck by the bouncy rubber ball will experience a greater change in speed.

    III. The two doors will experience the same change in speed.

    IV. The total kinetic energy of the clay before the collision is the same as the kinetic energy of the clay and door after the collision.

(A) I   (D) I and IV

(B) II   (E) II and IV

(C) III

2. What is the total momentum of the two blocks as a system given the speeds and masses shown above?

(A) $0 \text{ kg} \cdot \text{m/s}$ (D) $30 \text{ kg} \cdot \text{m/s}$

(B) $15 \text{ kg} \cdot \text{m/s}$ (E) $64 \text{ kg} \cdot \text{m/s}$

(C) $-15 \text{ kg} \cdot \text{m/s}$

3. A bullet with mass m passes through a block of mass $4m$ sitting initially at rest on a smooth surface as shown above. The bullet has a velocity v before it enters the block and exits the block with a velocity $v/2$. If the block moves with a velocity $v/8$ after the bullet passes, how much kinetic energy is dissipated in this event?

(A) 0, the kinetic energy is conserved.

(B) mv^2 (D) $\dfrac{mv^2}{4}$

(C) $\dfrac{mv^2}{2}$ (E) $\dfrac{mv^2}{8}$

4. Which of the following is/are true regarding an exploding stick of dynamite bored into solid rock as shown above?

(A) The total momentum is the same before and after the explosion.

(B) The rock wall moves to the right as a result of the dynamite explosion.

(C) The kinetic energy of the rock pieces is equal to the energy of the explosion.

(D) More momentum is created toward the left, away from the solid rock remaining.

(E) Both (A) and (B) are correct statements.

5. How fast was a northbound 1000 kg car traveling if it collided inelastically with a westbound 3000 kg truck and both vehicles traveled at 10 m/s at 30° north of west?

(A) 10 m/s   (D) 30 m/s

(B) 13.3 m/s   (E) 40 m/s

(C) 20 m/s

Questions 6–7

Two masses, M and $3M$, are separated on a frictionless surface as shown below. Mass M has an ideal spring attached only to it. Both masses are set in motion toward each other; mass $3M$ at a velocity $+v$, and mass M at a velocity $-v$. The spring momentarily compresses when the two masses collide and then expands as they separate from this perfectly elastic collision.

Before Collision

6. Which of the following graphs represents the total kinetic energy of the two mass and spring system?

*AP and Advanced Placement Program are registered trademarks of the College Entrance Examination Board, which was not involved in the production of, and does not endorse, this product.

(A) *KE*

(D) *KE*

(B) *KE*

(E) *KE*

(C) *KE*
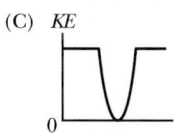

7. Which of the following graphs represents the total momentum of the two mass and spring system during this perfectly elastic collision?

(A) *P*

(D) *P*

(B) *P*

(E) *P*

(C) *P*
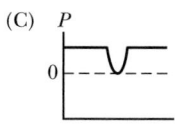

8. Why is it more comfortable to bend your knees when landing from a height onto your feet as compared to landing without bending your knees?

(A) Bending the knees reduces the kinetic energy as compared to a stiff-legged landing.

(B) Bending the knees reduces the momentum as compared to a stiff-legged landing.

(C) Bending the knees decreases the magnitude of impulse from the collision with the floor.

(D) Bending the knees increases the time of the collision, reducing the force.

(E) Answers (A) and (B) are both correct.

9. An object of mass m moves to the right with speed v. It collides head-on in a perfectly inelastic collision with an object of twice the mass but half the speed moving in the opposite direction. What is the speed of the combined mass after the collision?

(A) 0

(D) $2v$

(B) $v/2$

(E) $\frac{2}{3}(v)$

(C) v

10. A baseball pitching machine of mass M (including the mass m of a baseball) rests on wheels on a smooth level surface as shown above. What is the recoil speed of the machine immediately after it fires the baseball at a speed v?

(A) 0

(D) $\dfrac{mv}{M}$

(B) $\dfrac{mv}{(M-v)}$

(E) $\dfrac{2mv}{(M-m)}$

(C) $\dfrac{mv}{(M+v)}$

11. Which of the following is/are always true regarding a force versus time graph that shows a changing force over time acting on an object?

   I. The instantaneous slope of the line indicates the instantaneous impulse delivered.

   II. The area bound between the line and zero indicates the momentum of the object.

   III. The change in momentum is found by the area bound between the line and zero.

   IV. The impulse is always a positive scalar quantity.

(A) I

(D) IV

(B) II

(E) II and III

(C) III

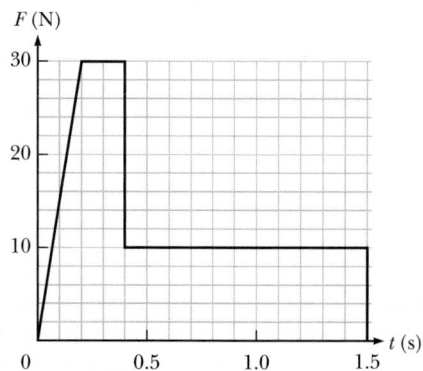

12. A manufacturer of model rocket engines provides a force versus time graph for one of its engines as shown above. Neglecting any change in mass of the engine's fuel and air resistance, what maximum velocity could a 2000 g rocket car reach from rest on a frictionless horizontal track if equipped with this engine?

(A) 2 m/s

(D) 20 m/s

(B) 7.5 m/s

(E) 75 m/s

(C) 10 m/s

The International Space Station falls freely around the Earth at thousands of meters per second, held in orbit by the centripetal force provided by gravity.

NASA

7 Rotational Motion and the Law of Gravity

Rotational motion is an important part of everyday life. The rotation of the Earth creates the cycle of day and night, the rotation of wheels enables easy vehicular motion, and modern technology depends on circular motion in a variety of contexts, from the tiny gears in a Swiss watch to the operation of lathes and other machinery. The concepts of *angular speed, angular acceleration,* and *centripetal acceleration* are central to understanding the motions of a diverse range of phenomena, from a car moving around a circular racetrack to clusters of galaxies orbiting a common center.

Rotational motion, when combined with Newton's law of universal gravitation and his laws of motion, can also explain certain facts about space travel and satellite motion, such as where to place a satellite so it will remain fixed in position over the same spot on the Earth. The generalization of gravitational potential energy and energy conservation offers an easy route to such results as planetary escape speed. Finally, we present Kepler's three laws of planetary motion, which formed the foundation of Newton's approach to gravity.

7.1 Angular Speed and Angular Acceleration

In the study of linear motion, the important concepts are *displacement* Δx, *velocity* v, and *acceleration* a. Each of these concepts has its analog in rotational motion: *angular displacement* $\Delta\theta$, *angular velocity* ω, and *angular acceleration* α.

The *radian*, a unit of angular measure, is essential to the understanding of these concepts. Recall that the distance s around a circle is given by $s = 2\pi r$, where r is the radius of the circle. Dividing both sides by r results in $s/r = 2\pi$. This quantity is dimensionless because both s and r have dimensions of length, but the value 2π corresponds to a displacement around a circle. A half circle would give an answer of π, a quarter circle an answer of $\pi/2$. The numbers 2π, π, and $\pi/2$ correspond to angles of 360°, 180°, and 90°, respectively, so a new unit of angular measure, the **radian,** can be introduced, with 180° = π rad relating degrees to radians.

The angle θ subtended by an arc length s along a circle of radius r, measured in radians counterclockwise from the positive x-axis, is

$$\theta = \frac{s}{r} \qquad [7.1]$$

The angle θ in Equation 7.1 is actually an angular displacement from the positive x-axis, and s the corresponding displacement along the circular arc, again measured from the positive x-axis. Figure 7.1 illustrates the size of 1 radian, which is approximately 57°. Converting from degrees to radians requires multiplying by the ratio $(\pi \text{ rad}/180°)$. For example, 45° $(\pi \text{ rad}/180°) = (\pi/4)$ rad.

Generally, angular quantities in physics must be expressed in radians. Be sure to set your calculator to radian mode; neglecting to do so is a common error.

Armed with the concept of radian measure, we can now discuss angular concepts in physics. Consider Figure 7.2a, a top view of a rotating compact disc. Such a disk is an example of a "rigid body," with each part of the body fixed in position relative to all other parts of the body. When a rigid body rotates through a given angle, all parts of the body rotate through the same angle at the same time. For the compact disc, the axis of rotation is at the center of the disc, O. A point P on the disc is at a distance r from the origin and moves about O in a circle of radius r. We set up a *fixed* reference line, as shown in Figure 7.2a, and assume that at time $t = 0$ the point P is on that reference line. After a time interval Δt has elapsed, P has advanced to a new position (Fig. 7.2b). In this interval, the line OP has moved through the angle θ with respect to the reference line. The angle θ, measured in radians, is called the **angular position** and is analogous to the linear position variable x. Likewise, P has moved an arc length s measured along the circumference of the circle.

In Figure 7.3, as a point on the rotating disc moves from Ⓐ to Ⓑ in a time Δt, it starts at an angle θ_i and ends at an angle θ_f. The difference $\theta_f - \theta_i$ is called the **angular displacement.**

An object's angular displacement, $\Delta\theta$, is the difference in its final and initial angles:

$$\Delta\theta = \theta_f - \theta_i \qquad [7.2]$$

SI unit: radian (rad)

For example, if a point on a disc is at $\theta_i = 4$ rad and rotates to angular position $\theta_f = 7$ rad, the angular displacement is $\Delta\theta = \theta_f - \theta_i = 7$ rad $- 4$ rad $= 3$ rad. Note that we use angular variables to describe the rotating disc because **each point on the disc undergoes the same angular displacement in any given time interval.**

Using the definition in Equation 7.2, Equation 7.1 can be written more generally as $\Delta\theta = \Delta s/r$, where Δs is a displacement along the circular arc subtended by the angular displacement. Having defined angular displacements, it's natural to define an angular speed:

The average angular speed ω_{av} of a rotating rigid object during the time interval Δt is the angular displacement $\Delta\theta$ divided by Δt:

$$\omega_{av} \equiv \frac{\theta_f - \theta_i}{t_f - t_i} = \frac{\Delta\theta}{\Delta t} \qquad [7.3]$$

SI unit: radian per second (rad/s)

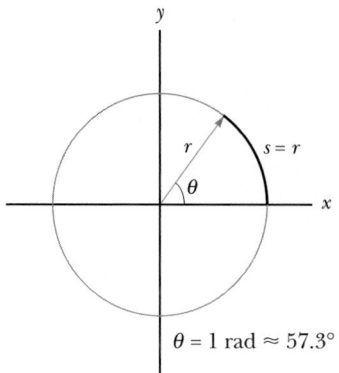

Figure 7.1 For a circle of radius r, one radian is the angle subtended by an arc length equal to r.

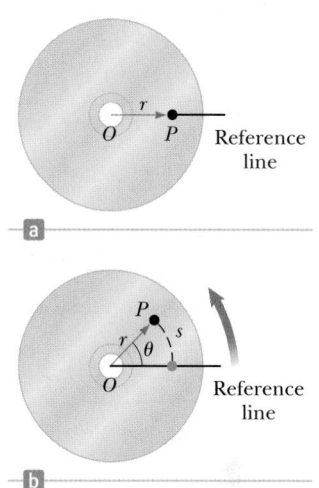

Figure 7.2 (a) The point P on a rotating compact disc at $t = 0$. (b) As the disc rotates, P moves through an arc length s.

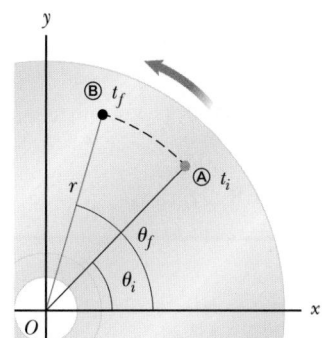

Figure 7.3 As a point on the compact disc moves from Ⓐ to Ⓑ, the disc rotates through the angle $\Delta\theta = \theta_f - \theta_i$.

For very short time intervals, the average angular speed approaches the instantaneous angular speed, just as in the linear case.

The **instantaneous angular speed** ω of a rotating rigid object is the limit of the average speed $\Delta\theta/\Delta t$ as the time interval Δt approaches zero:

$$\omega \equiv \lim_{\Delta t \to 0} \frac{\Delta\theta}{\Delta t} \qquad\qquad \text{[7.4]}$$

SI unit: radian per second (rad/s)

We take ω to be positive when θ is increasing (counterclockwise motion) and negative when θ is decreasing (clockwise motion). When the angular speed is constant, the instantaneous angular speed is equal to the average angular speed.

■ EXAMPLE 7.1 | **Whirlybirds**

GOAL Convert an angular speed in revolutions per minute to radians per second.

PROBLEM The rotor on a helicopter turns at an angular speed of 3.20×10^2 revolutions per minute. (In this book, we sometimes use the abbreviation rpm, but in most cases we use rev/min.) **(a)** Express this angular speed in radians per second. **(b)** If the rotor has a radius of 2.00 m, what arclength does the tip of the blade trace out in 3.00×10^2 s?

STRATEGY During one revolution, the rotor turns through an angle of 2π radians. Use this relationship as a conversion factor.

. . . .

SOLUTION

(a) Express this angular speed in radians per second.

Apply the conversion factors 1 rev = 2π rad and 60.0 s = 1 min:

$$\omega = 3.20 \times 10^2 \, \frac{\text{rev}}{\text{min}}$$

$$= 3.20 \times 10^2 \, \frac{\text{rev}}{\text{min}} \left(\frac{2\pi \text{ rad}}{1 \text{ rev}}\right)\left(\frac{1.00 \text{ min}}{60.0 \text{ s}}\right)$$

$$= \boxed{33.5 \text{ rad/s}}$$

(b) Multiply the angular speed by the time to obtain the angular displacement:

$$\Delta\theta = \omega t = (33.5 \text{ rad/s})(3.00 \times 10^2 \text{ s}) = 1.01 \times 10^4 \text{ rad}$$

Multiply the angular displacement by the radius to get the arc length:

$$\Delta s = r\,\Delta\theta = (2.00 \text{ m})(1.01 \times 10^4 \text{ rad}) = \boxed{2.02 \times 10^4 \text{ m}}$$

. . . .

REMARKS In general, it's best to express angular speeds in radians per second. Consistent use of radian measure minimizes errors.

QUESTION 7.1 Is it possible to express angular speed in degrees per second? If so, what's the conversion factor from radians per second?

EXERCISE 7.1 A waterwheel turns at 1 500 revolutions per hour. Express this rate of rotation in units of radians per second.

ANSWER 2.6 rad/s

■ Quick Quiz

7.1 A rigid body is rotating counterclockwise about a fixed axis. Each of the following pairs of quantities represents an initial angular position and a final angular position of the rigid body. Which of the sets can occur *only* if the rigid body rotates through more than 180°? (a) 3 rad, 6 rad; (b) −1 rad, 1 rad; (c) 1 rad, 5 rad.

Figure 7.4 An accelerating bicycle wheel rotates with (a) angular speed ω_i at time t_i and (b) angular speed ω_f at time t_f.

■ *Quick Quiz*

7.2 Suppose the change in angular position for each of the pairs of values in Quick Quiz 7.1 occurred in 1 s. Which choice represents the lowest average angular speed?

Figure 7.4 shows a bicycle turned upside down so that a repair technician can work on the rear wheel. The bicycle pedals are turned so that at time t_i the wheel has angular speed ω_i (Fig. 7.4a) and at a later time t_f it has angular speed ω_f (Fig. 7.4b). Just as a changing speed leads to the concept of an acceleration, a changing angular speed leads to the concept of an angular acceleration.

An object's average angular acceleration α_{av} during the time interval Δt is the change in its angular speed $\Delta\omega$ divided by Δt:

$$\alpha_{av} \equiv \frac{\omega_f - \omega_i}{t_f - t_i} = \frac{\Delta\omega}{\Delta t} \qquad [7.5]$$

SI unit: radian per second squared (rad/s^2)

◀ Average angular acceleration

As with angular velocity, positive angular accelerations are in the counterclockwise direction, negative angular accelerations in the clockwise direction. If the angular speed goes from 15 rad/s to 9.0 rad/s in 3.0 s, the average angular acceleration during that time interval is

$$\alpha_{av} = \frac{\Delta\omega}{\Delta t} = \frac{9.0 \text{ rad/s} - 15 \text{ rad/s}}{3.0 \text{ s}} = -2.0 \text{ rad/s}^2$$

The negative sign indicates that the angular acceleration is clockwise (although the angular speed, still positive but slowing down, is in the counterclockwise direction). There is also an instantaneous version of angular acceleration:

The instantaneous angular acceleration α is the limit of the average angular acceleration $\Delta\omega/\Delta t$ as the time interval Δt approaches zero:

$$\alpha \equiv \lim_{\Delta t \to 0} \frac{\Delta\omega}{\Delta t} \qquad [7.6]$$

SI unit: radian per second squared (rad/s^2)

◀ Instantaneous angular acceleration

When a rigid object rotates about a fixed axis, as does the bicycle wheel, every portion of the object has the same angular speed and the same angular acceleration. This fact is what makes these variables so useful for describing rotational motion. In contrast, the tangential (linear) speed and acceleration of the object take different values that depend on the distance from a given point to the axis of rotation.

7.2 Rotational Motion Under Constant Angular Acceleration

A number of parallels exist between the equations for rotational motion and those for linear motion. For example, compare the defining equation for the average angular speed,

$$\omega_{av} \equiv \frac{\theta_f - \theta_i}{t_f - t_i} = \frac{\Delta\theta}{\Delta t}$$

with that of the average linear speed,

$$v_{av} \equiv \frac{x_f - x_i}{t_f - t_i} = \frac{\Delta x}{\Delta t}$$

In these equations, ω takes the place of v and θ takes the place of x, so the equations differ only in the names of the variables. In the same way, every linear quantity we have encountered so far has a corresponding "twin" in rotational motion.

The procedure used in Section 2.5 to develop the kinematic equations for linear motion under constant acceleration can be used to derive a similar set of equations for rotational motion under constant angular acceleration. The resulting equations of rotational kinematics, along with the corresponding equations for linear motion, are as follows:

Linear Motion with a Constant (Variables: x and v)	Rotational Motion About a Fixed Axis with α Constant (Variables: θ and ω)	
$v = v_i + at$	$\omega = \omega_i + \alpha t$	[7.7]
$\Delta x = v_i t + \frac{1}{2}at^2$	$\Delta\theta = \omega_i t + \frac{1}{2}\alpha t^2$	[7.8]
$v^2 = v_i^2 + 2a\Delta x$	$\omega^2 = \omega_i^2 + 2\alpha\,\Delta\theta$	[7.9]

Notice that every term in a given linear equation has a corresponding term in the analogous rotational equation.

■ *Quick Quiz*

7.3 Consider again the pairs of angular positions for the rigid object in Quick Quiz 7.1. If the object starts from rest at the initial angular position, moves counterclockwise with constant angular acceleration, and arrives at the final angular position with the same angular speed in all three cases, for which choice is the angular acceleration the highest?

■ **EXAMPLE 7.2** | **A Rotating Wheel**

GOAL Apply the rotational kinematic equations.

PROBLEM A wheel rotates with a constant angular acceleration of 3.50 rad/s². If the angular speed of the wheel is 2.00 rad/s at $t = 0$, **(a)** through what angle does the wheel rotate between $t = 0$ and $t = 2.00$ s? Give your answer in radians and in revolutions. **(b)** What is the angular speed of the wheel at $t = 2.00$ s? **(c)** What angular displacement (in revolutions) results while the angular speed found in part (b) doubles?

STRATEGY The angular acceleration is constant, so this problem just requires substituting given values into Equations 7.7–7.9.

....

SOLUTION
(a) Find the angular displacement after 2.00 s, in both radians and revolutions.

Use Equation 7.8, setting $\omega_i = 2.00$ rad/s, $\alpha = 3.5$ rad/s², and $t = 2.00$ s:

$$\Delta\theta = \omega_i t + \frac{1}{2}\alpha t^2$$
$$= (2.00 \text{ rad/s})(2.00 \text{ s}) + \frac{1}{2}(3.50 \text{ rad/s}^2)(2.00 \text{ s})^2$$
$$= \boxed{11.0 \text{ rad}}$$

Convert radians to revolutions.

$$\Delta\theta = (11.0 \text{ rad})(1.00 \text{ rev}/2\pi \text{ rad}) = \boxed{1.75 \text{ rev}}$$

(b) What is the angular speed of the wheel at $t = 2.00$ s?

Substitute the same values into Equation 7.7:

$$\omega = \omega_i + \alpha t = 2.00 \text{ rad/s} + (3.50 \text{ rad/s}^2)(2.00 \text{ s})$$
$$= \boxed{9.00 \text{ rad/s}}$$

(c) What angular displacement (in revolutions) results during the time in which the angular speed found in part (b) doubles?

Apply the time-independent rotational kinematics equation:

$$\omega_f{}^2 - \omega_i{}^2 = 2\alpha\Delta\theta$$

Substitute values, noting that $\omega_f = 2\omega_i$:

$$(2 \times 9.00 \text{ rad/s})^2 - (9.00 \text{ rad/s})^2 = 2(3.50 \text{ rad/s}^2)\Delta\theta$$

Solve for the angular displacement and convert to revolutions:

$$\Delta\theta = (34.7 \text{ rad})\left(\frac{1 \text{ rev}}{2\pi \text{ rad}}\right) = \boxed{5.52 \text{ rev}}$$

· ·

REMARKS The result of part (b) could also be obtained from Equation 7.9 and the results of part (a).

QUESTION 7.2 Suppose the radius of the wheel is doubled. Are the answers affected? If so, in what way?

EXERCISE 7.2 (a) Find the angle through which the wheel rotates between $t = 2.00$ s and $t = 3.00$ s. (b) Find the angular speed when $t = 3.00$ s. (c) What is the magnitude of the angular speed two revolutions following $t = 3.00$ s?

ANSWERS (a) 10.8 rad   (b) 12.5 rad/s   (c) 15.6 rad/s

7.3 Relations Between Angular and Linear Quantities

Angular variables are closely related to linear variables. Consider the arbitrarily shaped object in Active Figure 7.5 rotating about the z-axis through the point O. Assume the object rotates through the angle $\Delta\theta$, and hence point P moves through the arc length Δs, in the interval Δt. We know from the defining equation for radian measure that

$$\Delta\theta = \frac{\Delta s}{r}$$

Dividing both sides of this equation by Δt, the time interval during which the rotation occurs, yields

$$\frac{\Delta\theta}{\Delta t} = \frac{1}{r}\frac{\Delta s}{\Delta t}$$

When Δt is very small, the angle $\Delta\theta$ through which the object rotates is also small and the ratio $\Delta\theta/\Delta t$ is close to the instantaneous angular speed ω. On the other side of the equation, similarly, the ratio $\Delta s/\Delta t$ approaches the instantaneous linear speed v for small values of Δt. Hence, when Δt gets arbitrarily small, the preceding equation is equivalent to

$$\omega = \frac{v}{r}$$

In Active Figure 7.5, the point P traverses a distance Δs along a circular arc during the time interval Δt at a linear speed of v. The direction of P's velocity vector $\vec{v}$ is *tangent to the circular path*. The magnitude of $\vec{v}$ is the linear speed $v = v_t$, called the **tangential speed** of a particle moving in a circular path, written

$$v_t = r\omega \qquad\qquad\qquad [7.10] \qquad \blacktriangleleft \text{ Tangential speed}$$

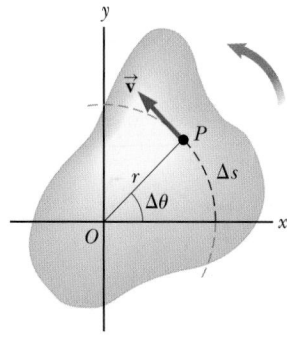

Active Figure 7.5
Rotation of an object about an axis through O (the z-axis) that is perpendicular to the plane of the figure. Note that a point P on the object rotates in a circle of radius r centered at O.

The tangential speed of a point on a rotating object equals the distance of that point from the axis of rotation multiplied by the angular speed. Equation 7.10 shows that the linear speed of a point on a rotating object increases as that point is moved outward from the center of rotation toward the rim, as expected; however, **every point on the rotating object has the same *angular* speed.**

Equation 7.10, derived using the defining equation for radian measure, is valid only when ω is measured in radians per unit time. Other measures of angular speed, such as degrees per second and revolutions per second, shouldn't be used.

To find a second equation relating linear and angular quantities, refer again to Active Figure 7.5 and suppose the rotating object changes its angular speed by $\Delta\omega$ in the time interval Δt. At the end of this interval, the speed of a point on the object, such as P, has changed by the amount Δv_t. From Equation 7.10 we have

$$\Delta v_t = r\,\Delta\omega$$

Dividing by Δt gives

$$\frac{\Delta v_t}{\Delta t} = r\frac{\Delta\omega}{\Delta t}$$

As the time interval Δt is taken to be arbitrarily small, $\Delta\omega/\Delta t$ approaches the instantaneous angular acceleration. On the left-hand side of the equation, note that the ratio $\Delta v_t/\Delta t$ tends to the instantaneous linear acceleration, called the tangential acceleration of that point, given by

Tangential acceleration ▶

$$a_t = r\alpha \qquad\qquad [7.11]$$

The tangential acceleration of a point on a rotating object equals the distance of that point from the axis of rotation multiplied by the angular acceleration. Again, radian measure must be used for the angular acceleration term in this equation.

One last equation that relates linear quantities to angular quantities will be derived in the next section.

■ Quick Quiz

7.4 Andrea and Chuck are riding on a merry-go-round. Andrea rides on a horse at the outer rim of the circular platform, twice as far from the center of the circular platform as Chuck, who rides on an inner horse. When the merry-go-round is rotating at a constant angular speed, Andrea's angular speed is (a) twice Chuck's (b) the same as Chuck's (c) half of Chuck's (d) impossible to determine.

7.5 When the merry-go-round of Quick Quiz 7.4 is rotating at a constant angular speed, Andrea's tangential speed is (a) twice Chuck's (b) the same as Chuck's (c) half of Chuck's (d) impossible to determine.

■ APPLYING PHYSICS 7.1   ESA Launch Site

Why is the launch area for the European Space Agency in South America and not in Europe?

EXPLANATION Satellites are boosted into orbit on top of rockets, which provide the large tangential speed necessary to achieve orbit. Due to its rotation, the surface of Earth is already traveling toward the east at a tangential speed of nearly 1 700 m/s at the equator. This tangential speed is steadily reduced farther north because the distance to the axis of rotation is decreasing. It finally goes to zero at the North Pole. Launching eastward from the equator gives the satellite a starting initial tangential speed of 1 700 m/s, whereas a European launch provides roughly half that speed (depending on the exact latitude). ■

■ **EXAMPLE 7.3** | **Compact Discs**

GOAL Apply the rotational kinematics equations in tandem with tangential acceleration and speed.

PROBLEM A compact disc rotates from rest up to an angular speed of 31.4 rad/s in a time of 0.892 s. **(a)** What is the angular acceleration of the disc, assuming the angular acceleration is uniform? **(b)** Through what angle does the disc turn while coming up to speed? **(c)** If the radius of the disc is 4.45 cm, find the tangential speed of a microbe riding on the rim of the disc when $t = 0.892$ s. **(d)** What is the magnitude of the tangential acceleration of the microbe at the given time?

STRATEGY We can solve parts (a) and (b) by applying the kinematic equations for angular speed and angular displacement (Eqs. 7.7 and 7.8). Multiplying the radius by the angular acceleration yields the tangential acceleration at the rim, whereas multiplying the radius by the angular speed gives the tangential speed at that point.

. . . .

SOLUTION

(a) Find the angular acceleration of the disc.

Apply the angular velocity equation $\omega = \omega_i + \alpha t$, taking $\omega_i = 0$ at $t = 0$:

$$\alpha = \frac{\omega}{t} = \frac{31.4 \text{ rad/s}}{0.892 \text{ s}} = \boxed{35.2 \text{ rad/s}^2}$$

(b) Through what angle does the disc turn?

Use Equation 7.8 for angular displacement, with $t = 0.892$ s and $\omega_i = 0$:

$$\Delta\theta = \omega_i t + \tfrac{1}{2}\alpha t^2 = \tfrac{1}{2}(35.2 \text{ rad/s}^2)(0.892 \text{ s})^2 = \boxed{14.0 \text{ rad}}$$

(c) Find the final tangential speed of a microbe at $r = 4.45$ cm.

Substitute into Equation 7.10:

$$v_t = r\omega = (0.044\ 5 \text{ m})(31.4 \text{ rad/s}) = \boxed{1.40 \text{ m/s}}$$

(d) Find the tangential acceleration of the microbe at $r = 4.45$ cm.

Substitute into Equation 7.11:

$$a_t = r\alpha = (0.044\ 5 \text{ m})(35.2 \text{ rad/s}^2) = \boxed{1.57 \text{ m/s}^2}$$

. . . .

REMARKS Because 2π rad = 1 rev, the angular displacement in part (b) corresponds to 2.23 rev. In general, dividing the number of radians by 6 gives a good approximation to the number of revolutions, because $2\pi \sim 6$.

QUESTION 7.3 If the angular acceleration were doubled for the same duration, by what factor would the angular displacement change? Why is the answer true in this case but not in general?

EXERCISE 7.3 **(a)** What are the angular speed and angular displacement of the disc 0.300 s after it begins to rotate? **(b)** Find the tangential speed at the rim at this time.

ANSWERS **(a)** 10.6 rad/s; 1.58 rad   **(b)** 0.472 m/s

Before MP3s became the medium of choice for recorded music, compact discs and phonographs were popular. There are similarities and differences between the rotational motion of phonograph records and that of compact discs. A phonograph record rotates at a constant angular speed. Popular angular speeds were $33\tfrac{1}{3}$ rev/min for long-playing albums (hence the nickname "LP"), 45 rev/min for "singles," and 78 rev/min used in very early recordings. At the outer edge of the record, the pickup needle (stylus) moves over the vinyl material at a faster tangential speed than when the needle is close to the center of the record. As a result, the sound information is compressed into a smaller length of track near the center of the record than near the outer edge.

CDs, on the other hand, are designed so that the disc moves under the laser pickup at a constant tangential speed. Because the pickup moves radially as it follows the tracks of information, the angular speed of the compact disc must vary according to the radial position of the laser. Because the tangential speed is fixed,

APPLICATION

Phonograph Records and Compact Discs

the information density (per length of track) anywhere on the disc is the same. Example 7.4 demonstrates numerical calculations for both compact discs and phonograph records.

■ EXAMPLE 7.4 | **Track Length of a Compact Disc**

GOAL Relate angular to linear variables.

PROBLEM In a compact disc player, as the read head moves out from the center of the disc, the angular speed of the disc changes so that the linear speed at the position of the head remains at a constant value of about 1.3 m/s. **(a)** Find the angular speed of the compact disc when the read head is at $r = 2.0$ cm and again at $r = 5.6$ cm. **(b)** An old-fashioned record player rotates at a constant angular speed, so the linear speed of the record groove moving under the detector (the stylus) changes. Find the linear speed of a 45.0-rpm record at points 2.0 and 5.6 cm from the center. **(c)** In both the CD and phonograph record, information is recorded in a continuous spiral track. Calculate the total length of the track for a CD designed to play for 1.0 h.

STRATEGY This problem is just a matter of substituting numbers into the appropriate equations. Part (a) requires relating angular and linear speed with Equation 7.10, $v_t = r\omega$, solving for ω and substituting given values. In part (b), convert from rev/min to rad/s and substitute straight into Equation 7.10 to obtain the linear speeds. In part (c), linear speed multiplied by time gives the total distance.

SOLUTION

(a) Find the angular speed of the disc when the read head is at $r = 2.0$ cm and $r = 5.6$ cm.

Solve $v_t = r\omega$ for ω and calculate the angular speed at $r = 2.0$ cm:

$$\omega = \frac{v_t}{r} = \frac{1.3 \text{ m/s}}{2.0 \times 10^{-2} \text{ m}} = \boxed{65 \text{ rad/s}}$$

Likewise, find the angular speed at $r = 5.6$ cm:

$$\omega = \frac{v_t}{r} = \frac{1.3 \text{ m/s}}{5.6 \times 10^{-2} \text{ m}} = \boxed{23 \text{ rad/s}}$$

(b) Find the linear speed in m/s of a 45.0-rpm record at points 2.0 cm and 5.6 cm from the center.

Convert rev/min to rad/s:

$$45.0 \, \frac{\text{rev}}{\text{min}} = 45.0 \, \frac{\text{rev}}{\text{min}} \left(\frac{2\pi \text{ rad}}{\text{rev}} \right) \left(\frac{1.00 \text{ min}}{60.0 \text{ s}} \right) = 4.71 \, \frac{\text{rad}}{\text{s}}$$

Calculate the linear speed at $r = 2.0$ cm:

$$v_t = r\omega = (2.0 \times 10^{-2} \text{ m})(4.71 \text{ rad/s}) = \boxed{0.094 \text{ m/s}}$$

Calculate the linear speed at $r = 5.6$ cm:

$$v_t = r\omega = (5.6 \times 10^{-2} \text{ m})(4.71 \text{ rad/s}) = \boxed{0.26 \text{ m/s}}$$

(c) Calculate the total length of the track for a CD designed to play for 1.0 h.

Multiply the linear speed of the read head by the time in seconds:

$$d = v_t t = (1.3 \text{ m/s})(3\,600 \text{ s}) = \boxed{4\,700 \text{ m}}$$

REMARKS Notice that for the record player in part (b), even though the angular speed is constant at all points along a radial line, the tangential speed steadily increases with increasing r. The calculation for a CD in part (c) is easy only because the linear (tangential) speed is constant. It would be considerably more difficult for a record player, where the tangential speed depends on the distance from the center.

QUESTION 7.4 What is the angular acceleration of a record player while it's playing a song? Can a CD player have the same angular acceleration as a record player? Explain.

EXERCISE 7.4 Compute the linear speed on a record playing at $33\frac{1}{3}$ revolutions per minute (a) at $r = 2.00$ cm and (b) at $r = 5.60$ cm.

ANSWERS (a) 0.069 8 m/s (b) 0.195 m/s

7.4 Centripetal Acceleration

Figure 7.6a shows a car moving in a circular path with *constant linear speed v*. **Even though the car moves at a constant speed, it still has an acceleration.** To understand this, consider the defining equation for average acceleration:

$$\vec{\mathbf{a}}_{av} = \frac{\vec{\mathbf{v}}_f - \vec{\mathbf{v}}_i}{t_f - t_i} \qquad [7.12]$$

The numerator represents the difference between the velocity vectors $\vec{\mathbf{v}}_f$ and $\vec{\mathbf{v}}_i$. These vectors may have the same *magnitude*, corresponding to the same speed, but if they have different *directions*, their difference can't equal zero. The direction of the car's velocity as it moves in the circular path is continually changing, as shown in Figure 7.6b. For circular motion at constant speed, the acceleration vector always points toward the center of the circle. Such an acceleration is called a **centripetal** (center-seeking) **acceleration.** Its magnitude is given by

$$a_c = \frac{v^2}{r} \qquad [7.13]$$

To derive Equation 7.13, consider Figure 7.7a. An object is first at point Ⓐ with velocity $\vec{\mathbf{v}}_i$ at time t_i and then at point Ⓑ with velocity $\vec{\mathbf{v}}_f$ at a later time t_f. We assume $\vec{\mathbf{v}}_i$ and $\vec{\mathbf{v}}_f$ differ only in direction; their magnitudes are the same ($v_i = v_f = v$). To calculate the acceleration, we begin with Equation 7.12,

$$\vec{\mathbf{a}}_{av} = \frac{\vec{\mathbf{v}}_f - \vec{\mathbf{v}}_i}{t_f - t_i} = \frac{\Delta \vec{\mathbf{v}}}{\Delta t} \qquad [7.14]$$

where $\Delta \vec{\mathbf{v}} = \vec{\mathbf{v}}_f - \vec{\mathbf{v}}_i$ is the change in velocity. When Δt is very small, Δs and $\Delta\theta$ are also very small. In Figure 7.7b $\vec{\mathbf{v}}_f$ is almost parallel to $\vec{\mathbf{v}}_i$, and the vector $\Delta \vec{\mathbf{v}}$ is approximately perpendicular to them, pointing toward the center of the circle. In the limiting case when Δt becomes vanishingly small, $\Delta \vec{\mathbf{v}}$ points exactly toward the center of the circle, and the average acceleration $\vec{\mathbf{a}}_{av}$ becomes the instantaneous acceleration $\vec{\mathbf{a}}$. From Equation 7.14, $\vec{\mathbf{a}}$ and $\Delta \vec{\mathbf{v}}$ point in the same direction (in this limit), so the instantaneous acceleration points to the center of the circle.

The triangle in Figure 7.7a, which has sides Δs and r, is similar to the one formed by the vectors in Figure 7.7b, so the ratios of their sides are equal:

$$\frac{\Delta v}{v} = \frac{\Delta s}{r}$$

or

$$\Delta v = \frac{v}{r} \Delta s \qquad [7.15]$$

Substituting the result of Equation 7.15 into $a_{av} = \Delta v / \Delta t$ gives

$$a_{av} = \frac{v}{r} \frac{\Delta s}{\Delta t} \qquad [7.16]$$

But Δs is the distance traveled along the arc of the circle in time Δt, and in the limiting case when Δt becomes very small, $\Delta s / \Delta t$ approaches the instantaneous value of the tangential speed, v. At the same time, the average acceleration a_{av} approaches a_c, the instantaneous centripetal acceleration, so Equation 7.16 reduces to Equation 7.13:

$$a_c = \frac{v^2}{r}$$

Because the tangential speed is related to the angular speed through the relation $v_t = r\omega$ (Eq. 7.10), an alternate form of Equation 7.13 is

$$a_c = \frac{r^2 \omega^2}{r} = r\omega^2 \qquad [7.17]$$

a

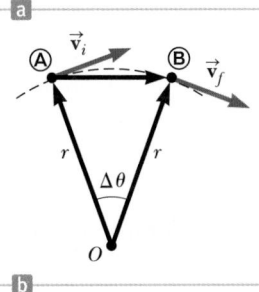

b

Figure 7.6 (a) Circular motion of a car moving with constant speed. (b) As the car moves along the circular path from Ⓐ to Ⓑ, the direction of its velocity vector changes, so the car undergoes a centripetal acceleration.

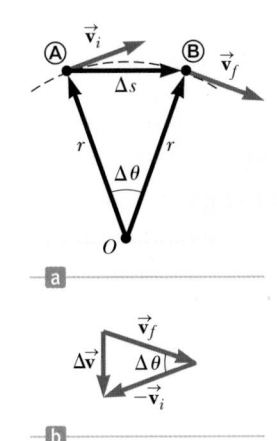

Figure 7.7 (a) As the particle moves from Ⓐ to Ⓑ, the direction of its velocity vector changes from $\vec{\mathbf{v}}_i$ to $\vec{\mathbf{v}}_f$. (b) The construction for determining the direction of the change in velocity $\Delta \vec{\mathbf{v}}$, which is toward the center of the circle.

Dimensionally, $[r] = $ L and $[\omega] = 1/$T, so the units of centripetal acceleration are L/T^2, as they should be. This is a geometric result relating the centripetal acceleration to the angular speed, but physically an acceleration can occur only if some force is present. For example, if a car travels in a circle on flat ground, the force of static friction between the tires and the ground provides the necessary centripetal force.

Note that a_c in Equations 7.13 and 7.17 represents only the *magnitude* of the centripetal acceleration. The acceleration itself is always directed toward the center of rotation.

The foregoing derivations concern circular motion at constant speed. When an object moves in a circle but is speeding up or slowing down, a tangential component of acceleration, $a_t = r\alpha$, is also present. Because the tangential and centripetal components of acceleration are perpendicular to each other, we can find the magnitude of the **total acceleration** with the Pythagorean theorem:

Total acceleration ▶

$$a = \sqrt{a_t^2 + a_c^2}$$ [7.18]

Figure 7.8 (Quick Quiz 7.6)

▪ Quick Quiz

7.6 A racetrack is constructed such that two arcs of radius 80 m at Ⓐ and 40 m at Ⓑ are joined by two stretches of straight track as in Figure 7.8. In a particular trial run, a driver travels at a constant speed of 50 m/s for one complete lap.
  1. The ratio of the tangential acceleration at Ⓐ to that at Ⓑ is
     (a) $\frac{1}{2}$ (b) $\frac{1}{4}$ (c) 2 (d) 4 (e) The tangential acceleration is zero at both points.
  2. The ratio of the centripetal acceleration at Ⓐ to that at Ⓑ is
     (a) $\frac{1}{2}$ (b) $\frac{1}{4}$ (c) 2 (d) 4 (e) The centripetal acceleration is zero at both points.
  3. The angular speed is greatest at
     (a) Ⓐ (b) Ⓑ (c) It is equal at both Ⓐ and Ⓑ.

7.7 An object moves in a circular path with constant speed v. Which of the following statements is true concerning the object? (a) Its velocity is constant, but its acceleration is changing. (b) Its acceleration is constant, but its velocity is changing. (c) Both its velocity and acceleration are changing. (d) Its velocity and acceleration remain constant.

▪ EXAMPLE 7.5 | At the Racetrack

GOAL Apply the concepts of centripetal acceleration and tangential speed.

PROBLEM A race car accelerates uniformly from a speed of 40.0 m/s to a speed of 60.0 m/s in 5.00 s while traveling counterclockwise around a circular track of radius 4.00×10^2 m. When the car reaches a speed of 50.0 m/s, find **(a)** the magnitude of the car's centripetal acceleration, **(b)** the angular speed, **(c)** the magnitude of the tangential acceleration, and **(d)** the magnitude of the total acceleration.

STRATEGY Substitute values into the definitions of centripetal acceleration (Eq. 7.13), tangential speed (Eq. 7.10), and total acceleration (Eq. 7.18). Dividing the change in linear speed by the time yields the tangential acceleration.

· ·

SOLUTION

(a) Find the magnitude of the centripetal acceleration when $v = 50.0$ m/s.

Substitute into Equation 7.13:

$$a_c = \frac{v^2}{r} = \frac{(50.0 \text{ m/s})^2}{4.00 \times 10^2 \text{ m}} = \boxed{6.25 \text{ m/s}^2}$$

(b) Find the angular speed.

Solve Equation 7.10 for ω and substitute:

$$\omega = \frac{v}{r} = \frac{50.0 \text{ m/s}}{4.00 \times 10^2 \text{ m}} = \boxed{0.125 \text{ rad/s}}$$

(c) Find the magnitude of the tangential acceleration.

Divide the change in linear speed by the time:

$$a_t = \frac{v_f - v_i}{\Delta t} = \frac{60.0 \text{ m/s} - 40.0 \text{ m/s}}{5.00 \text{ s}} = \boxed{4.00 \text{ m/s}^2}$$

(d) Find the magnitude of the total acceleration.

Substitute into Equation 7.18:

$$a = \sqrt{a_t^2 + a_c^2} = \sqrt{(4.00 \text{ m/s}^2)^2 + (6.25 \text{ m/s}^2)^2}$$

$$a = \boxed{7.42 \text{ m/s}^2}$$

. . . .

REMARKS We can also find the centripetal acceleration by substituting the derived value of ω into Equation 7.17.

QUESTION 7.5 If the force causing the centripetal acceleration suddenly vanished, would the car (a) slide away along a radius, (b) proceed along a line tangent to the circular motion, or (c) proceed at an angle intermediate between the tangent and radius?

EXERCISE 7.5 Suppose the race car now slows down uniformly from 60.0 m/s to 30.0 m/s in 4.50 s to avoid an accident, while still traversing a circular path 4.00×10^2 m in radius. Find the car's (a) centripetal acceleration, (b) angular speed, (c) tangential acceleration, and (d) total acceleration when the speed is 40.0 m/s.

ANSWERS (a) 4.00 m/s^2 (b) 0.100 rad/s   (c) -6.67 m/s^2 (d) 7.78 m/s^2

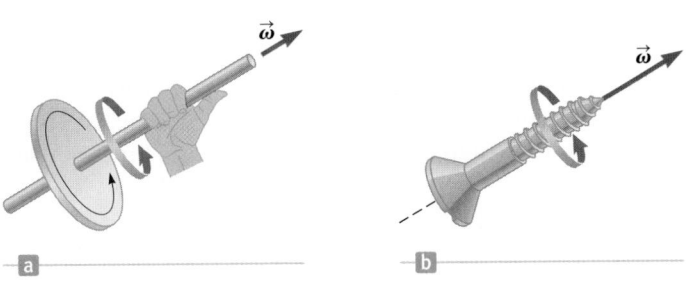

Figure 7.9 (a) The right-hand rule for determining the direction of the angular velocity vector $\vec{\omega}$. (b) The direction of $\vec{\omega}$ is in the direction of advance of a right-handed screw.

Angular Quantities Are Vectors

When we discussed linear motion in Chapter 2, we emphasized that displacement, velocity, and acceleration are all vector quantities. In describing rotational motion, angular displacement, angular velocity, and angular acceleration are also vector quantities.

The direction of the angular velocity vector $\vec{\omega}$ can be found with the **right-hand rule,** as illustrated in Figure 7.9a. Grasp the axis of rotation with your right hand so that your fingers wrap in the direction of rotation. Your extended thumb then points in the direction of $\vec{\omega}$. Figure 7.9b shows that $\vec{\omega}$ is also in the direction of advance of a rotating right-handed screw.

We can apply this rule to a disk rotating about a vertical axis through its center, as in Figure 7.10. When the disk rotates counterclockwise (Fig. 7.10a), the right-hand rule shows that the direction of $\vec{\omega}$ is upward. When the disk rotates clockwise (Fig. 7.10b), the direction of $\vec{\omega}$ is downward.

Finally, the directions of the angular acceleration $\vec{\alpha}$ and the angular velocity $\vec{\omega}$ are the same if the angular speed ω (the magnitude of $\vec{\omega}$) is increasing with time, and are opposite each other if the angular speed is decreasing with time.

Forces Causing Centripetal Acceleration

An object can have a centripetal acceleration *only* if some external force acts on it. For a ball whirling in a circle at the end of a string, that force is the tension in the string. In the case of a car moving on a flat circular track, the force is friction between the car and track. A satellite in circular orbit around Earth has a centripetal acceleration due to the gravitational force between the satellite and Earth.

Some books use the term "centripetal force," which can give the mistaken impression that it is a new force of nature. This is not the case: The adjective

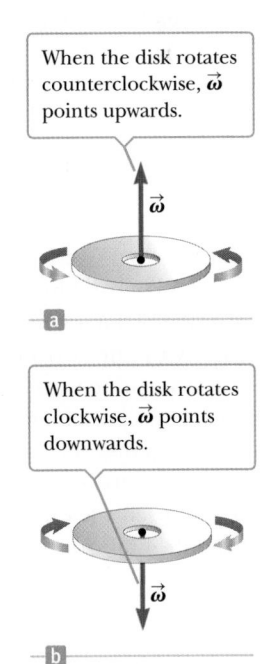

When the disk rotates counterclockwise, $\vec{\omega}$ points upwards.

When the disk rotates clockwise, $\vec{\omega}$ points downwards.

Figure 7.10 The direction of the angular velocity vector $\vec{\omega}$ depends on the direction of rotation.

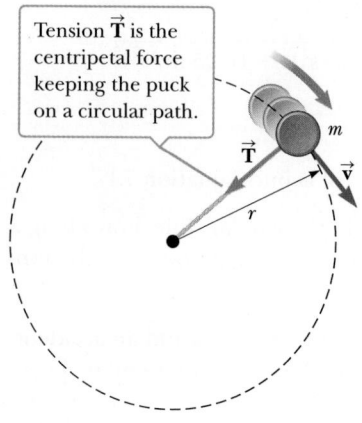

Tension $\vec{\mathbf{T}}$ is the centripetal force keeping the puck on a circular path.

Figure 7.11 A puck attached to a string of length r rotates in a horizontal plane at constant speed.

Tip 7.2 Centripetal Force Is a *Type* of Force, Not a Force in Itself!

"Centripetal force" is a classification that includes forces acting toward a central point, like the horizontal component of the string tension on a tetherball or gravity on a satellite. A centripetal force must be *supplied* by some actual, physical force.

"centripetal" in "centripetal force" simply means that the force in question acts toward a center. The force of tension in the string of a yo-yo whirling in a vertical circle is an example of a centripetal force, as is the force of gravity on a satellite circling the Earth.

Consider a puck of mass m that is tied to a string of length r and is being whirled at constant speed in a horizontal circular path, as illustrated in Figure 7.11. Its weight is supported by a frictionless table. Why does the puck move in a circle? Because of its inertia, the tendency of the puck is to move in a straight line; however, the string prevents motion along a straight line by exerting a radial force on the puck—a tension force—that makes it follow the circular path. The tension $\vec{\mathbf{T}}$ is directed along the string toward *the center of the circle*, as shown in the figure.

In general, converting Newton's second law to polar coordinates yields an equation relating the net centripetal force, F_c, which is the sum of the radial components of all forces acting on a given object, to the centripetal acceleration. The *magnitude* of the net centripetal force equals the mass times the magnitude of the centripetal acceleration:

$$F_c = ma_c = m\,\frac{v^2}{r} \qquad [7.19]$$

A net force causing a centripetal acceleration acts toward the center of the circular path and effects a change in the direction of the velocity vector. If that force should vanish, the object would immediately leave its circular path and move along a straight line tangent to the circle at the point where the force vanished.

■ **APPLYING PHYSICS 7.2** | **Artificial Gravity**

Astronauts spending lengthy periods of time in space experience a number of negative effects due to weightlessness, such as weakening of muscle tissue and loss of calcium in bones. These effects may make it very difficult for them to return to their usual environment on Earth. How could artificial gravity be generated in space to overcome such complications?

SOLUTION A rotating cylindrical space station creates an environment of artificial gravity. The normal force of the rigid walls provides the centripetal force, which keeps the astronauts moving in a circle (Fig. 7.12). To an astronaut, the normal force can't be easily distinguished from a gravitational force as long as the radius of the station is large compared with the astronaut's height. (Otherwise there are unpleasant inner ear effects.) This same principle is used in certain amusement park rides in which passengers are pressed against the inside of a rotating cylinder as it tilts in various directions. The visionary physicist Gerard O'Neill proposed creating a giant space colony a kilometer in radius that rotates slowly, creating Earth-normal artificial gravity for the inhabitants in its interior. These inside-out artificial worlds could enable safe transport on a several-thousand-year journey to another star system. ■

Figure 7.12 Artificial gravity inside a spinning cylinder is provided by the normal force.

■ **PROBLEM-SOLVING STRATEGY**

Forces That Cause Centripetal Acceleration

Use the following steps in dealing with centripetal accelerations and the forces that produce them:

1. **Draw a free-body diagram** of the object under consideration, labeling all forces that act on it.
2. **Choose a coordinate system** that has one axis perpendicular to the circular path followed by the object (the radial direction) and one axis tangent to the circular path (the tangential, or angular, direction). The normal direction, perpendicular to the plane of motion, is also often needed.
3. **Find the net force F_c toward the center** of the circular path, $F_c = \Sigma F_r$, where ΣF_r is the sum of the radial components of the forces. This net radial force causes the centripetal acceleration.
4. **Use Newton's second law for the radial, tangential, and normal directions,** as required, writing $\Sigma F_r = ma_c$, $\Sigma F_t = ma_t$, and $\Sigma F_n = ma_n$. Remember that the magnitude of the centripetal acceleration for uniform circular motion can always be written $a_c = v_t^2/r$.
5. **Solve** for the unknown quantities.

■ **EXAMPLE 7.6** | **Buckle Up for Safety**

GOAL Calculate the frictional force that causes an object to have a centripetal acceleration.

PROBLEM A car travels at a constant speed of 30.0 mi/h (13.4 m/s) on a level circular turn of radius 50.0 m, as shown in the bird's-eye view in Figure 7.13a. What minimum coefficient of static friction, μ_s, between the tires and roadway will allow the car to make the circular turn without sliding?

STRATEGY In the car's free-body diagram (Fig. 7.13b) the normal direction is vertical and the tangential direction is into the page (Step 2). Use Newton's second law. The net force acting on the car in the radial direction is the force of static friction toward the center of the circular path, which causes the car to have a centripetal acceleration. Calculating the maximum static friction force requires the normal force, obtained from the normal component of the second law.

Figure 7.13 (Example 7.6) (a) The centripetal force is provided by the force of static friction, which is directed radially toward the center of the circular path. (b) Gravity, the normal force, and the static friction force act on the car.

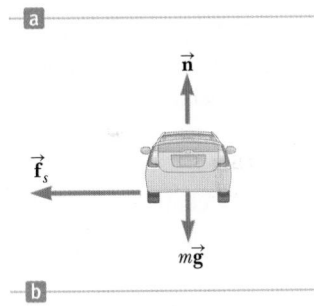

SOLUTION

(Steps 3, 4) Write the components of Newton's second law. The radial component involves only the maximum static friction force, $f_{s,\text{max}}$:

$$m\frac{v^2}{r} = f_{s,\text{max}} = \mu_s n$$

In the vertical component of the second law, the gravity force and the normal force are in equilibrium:

$$n - mg = 0 \quad \rightarrow \quad n = mg$$

(Step 5) Substitute the expression for n into the first equation and solve for μ_s:

$$m\frac{v^2}{r} = \mu_s mg$$

$$\mu_s = \frac{v^2}{rg} = \frac{(13.4 \text{ m/s})^2}{(50.0 \text{ m})(9.80 \text{ m/s}^2)} = \boxed{0.366}$$

REMARKS The value of μ_s for rubber on dry concrete is very close to 1, so the car can negotiate the curve with ease. If the road were wet or icy, however, the value for μ_s could be 0.2 or lower. Under such conditions, the radial force provided by static friction wouldn't be great enough to keep the car on the circular path, and it would slide off on a tangent, leaving the roadway.

(Continued)

QUESTION 7.6 If the static friction coefficient were increased, would the maximum safe speed be reduced, be increased, or remain the same?

EXERCISE 7.6 At what maximum speed can a car negotiate a turn on a wet road with coefficient of static friction 0.230 without sliding out of control? The radius of the turn is 25.0 m.

ANSWER 7.51 m/s

■ EXAMPLE 7.7 | Daytona International Speedway

GOAL Solve a centripetal force problem involving two dimensions.

PROBLEM The Daytona International Speedway in Daytona Beach, Florida, is famous for its races, especially the Daytona 500, held every February. Both of its courses feature four-story, 31.0° banked curves, with maximum radius of 316 m. If a car negotiates the curve too slowly, it tends to slip down the incline of the turn, whereas if it's going too fast, it may begin to slide up the incline. **(a)** Find the necessary centripetal acceleration on this banked curve so the car won't slip down or slide up the incline. (Neglect friction.) **(b)** Calculate the speed of the race car.

Figure 7.14 (Example 7.7) As the car rounds a curve banked at an angle θ, the centripetal force that keeps it on a circular path is supplied by the radial component of the normal force. Friction also contributes, although that is neglected in this example. The car is moving forward, into the page. (a) Force diagram for the car. (b) Components of the forces.

STRATEGY Two forces act on the race car: the force of gravity and the normal force $\vec{n}$. (See Fig. 7.14.) Use Newton's second law in the upward and radial directions to find the centripetal acceleration a_c. Solving $a_c = v^2/r$ for v then gives the race car's speed.

. . . .

SOLUTION

(a) Find the centripetal acceleration.

Write Newton's second law for the car:

$$m\vec{a} = \sum \vec{F} = \vec{n} + m\vec{g}$$

Use the y-component of Newton's second law to solve for the normal force n:

$$n \cos \theta - mg = 0$$
$$n = \frac{mg}{\cos \theta}$$

Obtain an expression for the horizontal component of $\vec{n}$, which is the centripetal force F_c in this example:

$$F_c = n \sin \theta = \frac{mg \sin \theta}{\cos \theta} = mg \tan \theta$$

Substitute this expression for F_c into the radial component of Newton's second law and divide by m to get the centripetal acceleration:

$$ma_c = F_c$$
$$a_c = \frac{F_c}{m} = \frac{mg \tan \theta}{m} = g \tan \theta$$
$$a_c = (9.80 \text{ m/s}^2)(\tan 31.0°) = \boxed{5.89 \text{ m/s}^2}$$

(b) Find the speed of the race car.

Apply Equation 7.13:

$$\frac{v^2}{r} = a_c$$
$$v = \sqrt{ra_c} = \sqrt{(316 \text{ m})(5.89 \text{ m/s}^2)} = \boxed{43.1 \text{ m/s}}$$

REMARKS Both banking and friction assist in keeping the race car on the track.

QUESTION 7.7 What three physical quantities determine the minimum and maximum safe speeds on a banked racetrack?

EXERCISE 7.7 A racetrack is to have a banked curve with radius of 245 m. What should be the angle of the bank if the normal force alone is to allow safe travel around the curve at 58.0 m/s?

ANSWER 54.5°

APPLICATION
Banked Roadways

▪ EXAMPLE 7.8 | Riding the Tracks

GOAL Combine centripetal force with conservation of energy. Derive results symbolically.

PROBLEM Figure 7.15a shows a roller-coaster car moving around a circular loop of radius R. **(a)** What speed must the car have so that it will just make it over the top without any assistance from the track? **(b)** What speed will the car subsequently have at the bottom of the loop? **(c)** What will be the normal force on a passenger at the bottom of the loop if the loop has a radius of 10.0 m?

STRATEGY This problem requires Newton's second law and centripetal acceleration to find an expression for the car's speed at the top of the loop, followed by conservation of energy to find its speed at the bottom. If the car just makes it over the top, the force $\vec{\mathbf{n}}$ must become zero there, so the only force exerted on the car at that point is the force of gravity, $m\vec{\mathbf{g}}$. At the bottom of

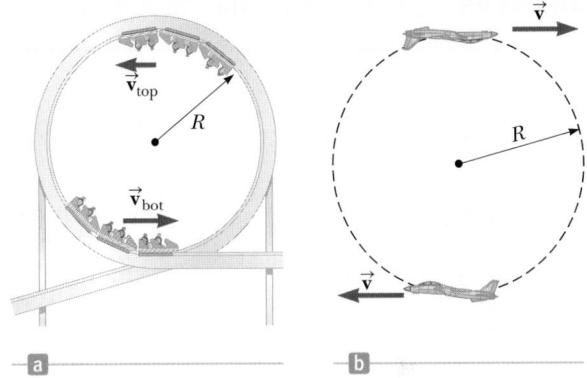

Figure 7.15 (a) (Example 7.8) A roller coaster traveling around a nearly circular track. (b) (Exercise 7.8) A jet executing a vertical loop.

the loop, the normal force acts up toward the center and the gravity force acts down, away from the center. The difference of these two is the centripetal force. The normal force can then be calculated from Newton's second law.

. . . .

SOLUTION

(a) Find the speed at the top of the loop.

Write Newton's second law for the car:

(1) $m\vec{\mathbf{a}}_c = \vec{\mathbf{n}} + m\vec{\mathbf{g}}$

At the top of the loop, set $n = 0$. The force of gravity acts toward the center and provides the centripetal acceleration $a_c = v^2/R$:

$$m\frac{v_{top}^2}{R} = mg$$

Solve the foregoing equation for v_{top}:

$$v_{top} = \boxed{\sqrt{gR}}$$

(b) Find the speed at the bottom of the loop.

Apply conservation of mechanical energy to find the total mechanical energy at the top of the loop:

$$E_{top} = \tfrac{1}{2}mv_{top}^2 + mgh = \tfrac{1}{2}mgR + mg(2R) = 2.5mgR$$

Find the total mechanical energy at the bottom of the loop:

$$E_{bot} = \tfrac{1}{2}mv_{bot}^2$$

Energy is conserved, so these two energies may be equated and solved for v_{bot}:

$$\tfrac{1}{2}mv_{bot}^2 = 2.5mgR$$

$$v_{bot} = \boxed{\sqrt{5gR}}$$

(c) Find the normal force on a passenger at the bottom. (This is the passenger's perceived weight.)

Use Equation (1). The net centripetal force is $n - mg$:

$$m\frac{v_{bot}^2}{R} = n - mg$$

(Continued)

Solve for n:

$$n = mg + m\frac{v_{\text{bot}}^2}{R} = mg + m\frac{5gR}{R} = \boxed{6mg}$$

REMARKS The final answer for n shows that the rider experiences a force six times normal weight at the bottom of the loop! Astronauts experience a similar force during space launches.

QUESTION 7.8 Suppose the car subsequently goes over a rise with the same radius of curvature and at the same speed as part (a). What is the normal force in this case?

EXERCISE 7.8 A jet traveling at a speed of 1.20×10^2 m/s executes a vertical loop with a radius of 5.00×10^2 m. (See Fig. 7.15b.) Find the magnitude of the force of the seat on a 70.0-kg pilot at (a) the top and (b) the bottom of the loop.

ANSWERS (a) 1.33×10^3 N   (b) 2.70×10^3 N

Tip 7.3 Centrifugal Force

A so-called centrifugal force is most often just the *absence* of an adequate *centripetal force*, arising from measuring phenomena from a noninertial (accelerating) frame of reference such as a merry-go-round.

Figure 7.16 A fun-loving student loses his grip and falls along a line tangent to the rim of the merry-go-round.

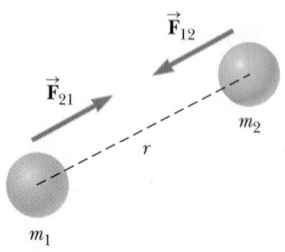

Active Figure 7.17
The gravitational force between two particles is attractive and acts along the line joining the particles. Note that according to Newton's third law, $\vec{\mathbf{F}}_{12} = -\vec{\mathbf{F}}_{21}$.

Fictitious Forces

Anyone who has ridden a merry-go-round as a child (or as a fun-loving grown-up) has experienced what feels like a "center-fleeing" force. Holding onto the railing and moving toward the center feels like a walk up a steep hill.

Actually, this so-called centrifugal force is *fictitious*. In reality, the rider is exerting a centripetal force on his body with his hand and arm muscles. In addition, a smaller centripetal force is exerted by the static friction between his feet and the platform. If the rider's grip slipped, he wouldn't be flung radially away; rather, he would go off on a straight line, tangent to the point in space where he let go of the railing. The rider lands at a point that is farther away from the center, but not by "fleeing the center" along a radial line. Instead, he travels perpendicular to a radial line, traversing an angular displacement while increasing his radial displacement. (See Fig. 7.16.)

7.5 Newtonian Gravitation

Prior to 1686, a great deal of data had been collected on the motions of the Moon and planets, but no one had a clear understanding of the forces affecting them. In that year, Isaac Newton provided the key that unlocked the secrets of the heavens. He knew from the first law that a net force had to be acting on the Moon. If it were not, the Moon would move in a straight-line path rather than in its almost circular orbit around Earth. Newton reasoned that this force arose as a result of an attractive force between the Moon and the Earth, called the force of gravity, and that it was the same kind of force that attracted objects—such as apples—close to the surface of the Earth.

In 1687 Newton published his work on the law of universal gravitation:

If two particles with masses m_1 and m_2 are separated by a distance r, a gravitational force F acts along a line joining them, with magnitude given by

$$F = G\frac{m_1 m_2}{r^2} \qquad [7.20]$$

where $G = 6.673 \times 10^{-11}$ kg$^{-1} \cdot$ m$^3 \cdot$ s^{-2} is a constant of proportionality called the **constant of universal gravitation.** The gravitational force is always attractive.

This force law is an example of an **inverse-square law,** in that it varies as one over the square of the separation of the particles. From Newton's third law, we know that the force exerted by m_1 on m_2, designated $\vec{\mathbf{F}}_{12}$ in Active Figure 7.17, is equal in magnitude but opposite in direction to the force $\vec{\mathbf{F}}_{21}$ exerted by m_2 on m_1, forming an action–reaction pair.

Another important fact is that **the gravitational force exerted by a uniform sphere on a particle outside the sphere is the same as the force exerted if the entire mass of the sphere were concentrated at its center.** This is called Gauss's law, after the German mathematician and astronomer Karl Friedrich Gauss, and is also true of electric fields, which we will encounter in Chapter 15. Gauss's law is a mathematical result, true because the force falls off as an inverse square of the separation between the particles.

Near the surface of the Earth, the expression $F = mg$ is valid. As shown in Table 7.1, however, the free-fall acceleration g varies considerably with altitude above the Earth.

Table 7.1 Free-Fall Acceleration g at Various Altitudes

Altitude (km)[a]	g (m/s²)
1 000	7.33
2 000	5.68
3 000	4.53
4 000	3.70
5 000	3.08
6 000	2.60
7 000	2.23
8 000	1.93
9 000	1.69
10 000	1.49
50 000	0.13

[a]All figures are distances above Earth's surface.

■ *Quick Quiz*

7.8 A ball is falling toward the ground. Which of the following statements are false? (a) The force that the ball exerts on Earth is equal in magnitude to the force that Earth exerts on the ball. (b) The ball undergoes the same acceleration as Earth. (c) The magnitude of the force the Earth exerts on the ball is greater than the magnitude of the force the ball exerts on the Earth.

7.9 A planet has two moons with identical mass. Moon 1 is in a circular orbit of radius r. Moon 2 is in a circular orbit of radius $2r$. The magnitude of the gravitational force exerted by the planet on Moon 2 is (a) four times as large (b) twice as large (c) the same (d) half as large (e) one-fourth as large as the gravitational force exerted by the planet on Moon 1.

Measurement of the Gravitational Constant

The gravitational constant G in Equation 7.20 was first measured in an important experiment by Henry Cavendish in 1798. His apparatus consisted of two small spheres, each of mass m, fixed to the ends of a light horizontal rod suspended by a thin metal wire, as in Figure 7.18. Two large spheres, each of mass M, were placed near the smaller spheres. The attractive force between the smaller and larger spheres caused the rod to rotate in a horizontal plane and the wire to twist. The angle through which the suspended rod rotated was measured with a light beam reflected from a mirror attached to the vertical suspension. (Such a moving spot of light is an effective technique for amplifying the motion.) The experiment was carefully repeated with different masses at various separations. In addition to providing a value for G, the results showed that the force is attractive, proportional to the product mM, and inversely proportional to the square of the distance r. Modern forms of such experiments are carried out regularly today in an effort to determine G with greater precision.

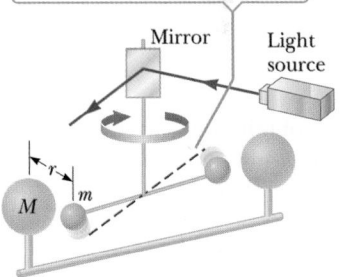

Gravity forces cause the rod to rotate away from its original position (the dashed line).

Mirror   Light source

Figure 7.18 A schematic diagram of the Cavendish apparatus for measuring G. The smaller spheres of mass m are attracted to the large spheres of mass M, and the rod rotates through a small angle. A light beam reflected from a mirror on the rotating apparatus measures the angle of rotation.

■ **EXAMPLE 7.9**   **Billiards, Anyone?**

GOAL Use vectors to find the net gravitational force on an object.

PROBLEM (a) Three 0.300-kg billiard balls are placed on a table at the corners of a right triangle, as shown from overhead in Figure 7.19. Find the net gravitational force on the cue ball (designated as m_1) resulting from the forces exerted by the other two balls. (b) Find the components of the gravitational force of m_2 on m_3.

STRATEGY (a) To find the net gravitational force on the cue ball of mass m_1, we first calculate the force $\vec{F}_{21}$ exerted by m_2 on m_1. This force is the y-component of the net force acting on m_1. Then we find the force $\vec{F}_{31}$ exerted by m_3 on m_1, which is the x-component of the net force acting on m_1. With these two components, we can find the magnitude and direction of the net force on the cue ball. (b) In this case, we must use trigonometry to find the components of the force $\vec{F}_{23}$.

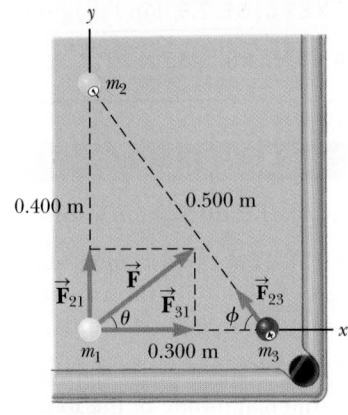

Figure 7.19 (Example 7.9)

(Continued)

SOLUTION

(a) Find the net gravitational force on the cue ball.

Find the magnitude of the force $\vec{\mathbf{F}}_{21}$ exerted by m_2 on m_1 using the law of gravitation, Equation 7.20:

$$F_{21} = G\frac{m_2 m_1}{r_{21}^2} = (6.67 \times 10^{-11}\,\text{N}\cdot\text{m}^2/\text{kg}^2)\frac{(0.300\,\text{kg})(0.300\,\text{kg})}{(0.400\,\text{m})^2}$$

$$F_{21} = 3.75 \times 10^{-11}\,\text{N}$$

Find the magnitude of the force $\vec{\mathbf{F}}_{31}$ exerted by m_3 on m_1, again using Newton's law of gravity:

$$F_{31} = G\frac{m_3 m_1}{r_{31}^2} = (6.67 \times 10^{-11}\,\text{N}\cdot\text{m}^2/\text{kg}^2)\frac{(0.300\,\text{kg})(0.300\,\text{kg})}{(0.300\,\text{m})^2}$$

$$F_{31} = 6.67 \times 10^{-11}\,\text{N}$$

The net force has components $F_x = F_{31}$ and $F_y = F_{21}$. Compute the magnitude of this net force:

$$F = \sqrt{F_x^2 + F_y^2} = \sqrt{(6.67)^2 + (3.75)^2} \times 10^{-11}\,\text{N}$$

$$= \boxed{7.65 \times 10^{-11}\,\text{N}}$$

Use the inverse tangent to obtain the direction of $\vec{\mathbf{F}}$:

$$\theta = \tan^{-1}\left(\frac{F_y}{F_x}\right) = \tan^{-1}\left(\frac{3.75 \times 10^{-11}\,\text{N}}{6.67 \times 10^{-11}\,\text{N}}\right) = \boxed{29.3°}$$

(b) Find the components of the force of m_2 on m_3.

First, compute the magnitude of $\vec{\mathbf{F}}_{23}$:

$$F_{23} = G\frac{m_2 m_1}{r_{23}^2}$$

$$= (6.67 \times 10^{-11}\,\text{kg}^{-1}\text{m}^3\text{s}^{-2})\frac{(0.300\,\text{kg})(0.300\,\text{kg})}{(0.500\,\text{m})^2}$$

$$= 2.40 \times 10^{-11}\,\text{N}$$

To obtain the x- and y-components of F_{23}, we need $\cos\varphi$ and $\sin\varphi$. Use the sides of the large triangle in Figure 7.19:

$$\cos\varphi = \frac{\text{adj}}{\text{hyp}} = \frac{0.300\,\text{m}}{0.500\,\text{m}} = 0.600$$

$$\sin\varphi = \frac{\text{opp}}{\text{hyp}} = \frac{0.400\,\text{m}}{0.500\,\text{m}} = 0.800$$

Compute the components of $\vec{\mathbf{F}}_{23}$. A minus sign must be supplied for the x-component because it's in the negative x-direction.

$$F_{23x} = -F_{23}\cos\varphi = -(2.40 \times 10^{-11}\,\text{N})(0.600)$$

$$= \boxed{-1.44 \times 10^{-11}\,\text{N}}$$

$$F_{23y} = F_{23}\sin\varphi = (2.40 \times 10^{-11}\,\text{N})(0.800) = \boxed{1.92 \times 10^{-11}\,\text{N}}$$

REMARKS Notice how small the gravity forces are between everyday objects. Nonetheless, such forces can be measured directly with torsion balances.

QUESTION 7.9 Is the gravity force a significant factor in a game of billiards? Explain.

EXERCISE 7.9 Find magnitude and direction of the force exerted by m_1 and m_3 on m_2.

ANSWERS $5.85 \times 10^{-11}\,\text{N}$, $-75.8°$

■ EXAMPLE 7.10 | Ceres

GOAL Relate Newton's universal law of gravity to mg and show how g changes with position.

PROBLEM An astronaut standing on the surface of Ceres, the largest asteroid, drops a rock from a height of 10.0 m. It takes 8.06 s to hit the ground. **(a)** Calculate the acceleration of gravity on Ceres. **(b)** Find the mass of Ceres, given that the radius of Ceres is $R_C = 5.10 \times 10^2$ km. **(c)** Calculate the gravitational acceleration 50.0 km from the surface of Ceres.

STRATEGY Part (a) is a review of one-dimensional kinematics. In part (b) the weight of an object, $w = mg$, is the same as the magnitude of the force given by the universal law of gravity. Solve for the unknown mass of Ceres, after which the answer for (c) can be found by substitution into the universal law of gravity, Equation 7.20.

SOLUTION

(a) Calculate the acceleration of gravity, g_C, on Ceres.
Apply the kinematics displacement equation to the falling rock:

(1) $\quad \Delta x = \frac{1}{2}at^2 + v_0 t$

Substitute $\Delta x = -10.0$ m, $v_0 = 0$, $a = -g_C$, and $t = 8.06$ s, and solve for the gravitational acceleration on Ceres, g_C:

$-10.0 \text{ m} = -\frac{1}{2}g_C(8.06 \text{ s})^2 \quad \rightarrow \quad g_C = \boxed{0.308 \text{ m/s}^2}$

(b) Find the mass of Ceres.

Equate the weight of the rock on Ceres to the gravitational force acting on the rock:

$mg_C = G\dfrac{M_C m}{R_C^{\,2}}$

Solve for the mass of Ceres, M_C:

$M_C = \dfrac{g_C R_C^{\,2}}{G} = \boxed{1.20 \times 10^{21} \text{ kg}}$

(c) Calculate the acceleration of gravity at a height of 50.0 km above the surface of Ceres.

Equate the weight at 50.0 km to the gravitational force:

$mg_C' = G\dfrac{mM_C}{r^2}$

Cancel m, then substitute $r = 5.60 \times 10^5$ m and the mass of Ceres:

$g_C' = G\dfrac{M_C}{r^2}$

$= (6.67 \times 10^{-11} \text{ kg}^{-1}\text{m}^3\text{s}^{-2})\dfrac{1.20 \times 10^{21} \text{ kg}}{(5.60 \times 10^5 \text{ m})^2}$

$= \boxed{0.255 \text{ m/s}^2}$

REMARKS This is the standard method of finding the mass of a planetary body: study the motion of a falling (or orbiting) object.

QUESTION 7.10 Give two reasons Equation (1) could not be used for every asteroid as it is used in part (a).

EXERCISE 7.10 An object takes 2.40 s to fall 5.00 m on a certain planet. (a) Find the acceleration due to gravity on the planet. (b) Find the planet's mass if its radius is 5 250 km.

ANSWERS (a) 1.74 m/s² (b) 7.19 × 10²³ kg

Gravitational Potential Energy Revisited

In Chapter 5 we introduced the concept of gravitational potential energy and found that the potential energy associated with an object could be calculated from the equation $PE = mgh$, where h is the height of the object above or below some reference level. This equation, however, is valid *only* when the object is near Earth's surface. For objects high above Earth's surface, such as a satellite, an alternative must be used because g varies with distance from the surface, as shown in Table 7.1.

The gravitational potential energy associated with an object of mass m at a distance r from the center of Earth is

$$PE = -G\dfrac{M_E\, m}{r} \qquad \text{[7.21]}$$

where M_E and R_E are the mass and radius of Earth, respectively, with $r > R_E$.

SI units: Joules (J)

As before, gravitational potential energy is a property of a system, in this case the object of mass m and Earth. Equation 7.21, illustrated in Figure 7.20, is valid for the special case where the zero level for potential energy is at an infinite distance

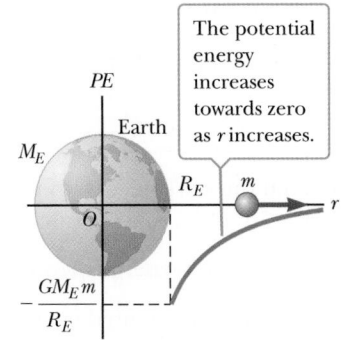

Figure 7.20 As a mass m moves radially away from the Earth, the potential energy of the Earth-mass system, which is $PE = -G(M_E m/R_E)$ at Earth's surface, increases toward a limit of zero as the mass m travels away from Earth, as shown in the graph.

from the center of Earth. Recall that the gravitational potential energy associated with an object is nothing more than the negative of the work done by the force of gravity in moving the object. If an object falls under the force of gravity from a great distance (effectively infinity), the change in gravitational potential energy is negative, which corresponds to a positive amount of gravitational work done on the system. This positive work is equal to the (also positive) change in kinetic energy, as the next example shows.

■ EXAMPLE 7.11 | A Near-Earth Asteroid

GOAL Use gravitational potential energy to calculate the work done by gravity on a falling object.

PROBLEM An asteroid with mass $m = 1.00 \times 10^9$ kg comes from deep space, effectively from infinity, and falls toward Earth. **(a)** Find the change in potential energy when it reaches a point 4.00×10^8 m from the center of the Earth (just beyond the orbital radius of the Moon). In addition, find the work done by the force of gravity. **(b)** Calculate the asteroid's speed at that point, assuming it was initially at rest when it was arbitrarily far away. **(c)** How much work would have to be done on the asteroid by some other agent so the asteroid would be traveling at only half the speed found in (b) at the same point?

STRATEGY Part (a) requires simple substitution into the definition of gravitational potential energy. To find the work done by the force of gravity, recall that the work done on an object by a conservative force is just the negative of the change in potential energy. Part (b) can be solved with conservation of energy, and part (c) is an application of the work–energy theorem.

SOLUTION

(a) Find the change in potential energy and the work done by the force of gravity.

Apply Equation 7.21:

$$\Delta PE = PE_f - PE_i = -\frac{GM_E m}{r_f} - \left(-\frac{GM_E m}{r_i}\right)$$

$$= GM_E m\left(-\frac{1}{r_f} + \frac{1}{r_i}\right)$$

Substitute known quantities. The asteroid's initial position is effectively infinity, so $1/r_i$ is zero:

$$\Delta PE = (6.67 \times 10^{-11} \text{ kg}^{-1} \text{ m}^3/\text{s}^2)(5.98 \times 10^{24} \text{ kg})$$

$$\times (1.00 \times 10^9 \text{ kg})\left(-\frac{1}{4.00 \times 10^8 \text{ m}} + 0\right)$$

$$\Delta PE = \boxed{-9.97 \times 10^{14} \text{ J}}$$

Compute the work done by the force of gravity:

$$W_{\text{grav}} = \boxed{-\Delta PE = 9.97 \times 10^{14} \text{ J}}$$

(b) Find the speed of the asteroid when it reaches $r_f = 4.00 \times 10^8$ m.

Use conservation of energy:

$$\Delta KE + \Delta PE = 0$$

$$\left(\tfrac{1}{2}mv^2 - 0\right) - 9.97 \times 10^{14} \text{ J} = 0$$

$$v = \boxed{1.41 \times 10^3 \text{ m/s}}$$

(c) Find the work needed to reduce the speed to 7.05×10^2 m/s (half the value just found) at this point.

Apply the work–energy theorem:

$$W = \Delta KE + \Delta PE$$

The change in potential energy remains the same as in part (a), but substitute only half the speed in the kinetic-energy term:

$$W = \left(\tfrac{1}{2}mv^2 - 0\right) - 9.97 \times 10^{14} \text{ J}$$

$$W = \tfrac{1}{2}(1.00 \times 10^9 \text{ kg})(7.05 \times 10^2 \text{ m/s})^2 - 9.97 \times 10^{14} \text{ J}$$

$$= \boxed{-7.48 \times 10^{14} \text{ J}}$$

REMARKS The amount of work calculated in part (c) is negative because an external agent must exert a force against the direction of motion of the asteroid. It would take a thruster with a megawatt of output about 24 years to slow down the asteroid to half its original speed. An asteroid endangering Earth need not be slowed that much: A small change in its speed, if applied early enough, will cause it to miss Earth. Timeliness of the applied thrust, however, is important. By the time you can look over your shoulder and see the Earth, it's already far too late, despite how these scenarios play out in Hollywood. Last-minute rescues won't work!

QUESTION 7.11 As the asteroid approaches Earth, does the gravitational potential energy associated with the asteroid–Earth system (a) increase, (b) decrease, (c) remain the same?

EXERCISE 7.11 Suppose the asteroid starts from rest at a great distance (effectively infinity), falling toward Earth. How much work would have to be done on the asteroid to slow it to 425 m/s by the time it reached a distance of 2.00×10^8 m from Earth?

ANSWER -1.90×10^{15} J

■ APPLYING PHYSICS 7.3 | Why Is the Sun Hot?

EXPLANATION The Sun formed when particles in a cloud of gas coalesced, due to gravitational attraction, into a massive astronomical object. Before this occurred, the particles in the cloud were widely scattered, representing a large amount of gravitational potential energy. As the particles fell closer together, their kinetic energy increased, but the gravitational potential energy of the system decreased, as required by the conservation of energy. With further slow collapse, the cloud became more dense

and the average kinetic energy of the particles increased. This kinetic energy is the internal energy of the cloud, which is proportional to the temperature. If enough particles come together, the temperature can rise to a point at which nuclear fusion occurs and the ball of gas becomes a star. Otherwise, the temperature may rise, but not enough to ignite fusion reactions, and the object becomes a brown dwarf (a failed star) or a planet. ■

On inspecting Equation 7.21, some may wonder what happened to mgh, the gravitational potential energy expression introduced in Chapter 5. That expression is still valid when h is small compared with Earth's radius. To see this, we write the change in potential energy as an object is raised from the ground to height h, using the general form for gravitational potential energy (see Fig. 7.21):

$$PE_2 - PE_1 = -G\frac{M_E m}{(R_E + h)} - \left(-G\frac{M_E m}{R_E}\right)$$

$$= -GM_E m\left[\frac{1}{(R_E + h)} - \frac{1}{R_E}\right]$$

After finding a common denominator and applying some algebra, we obtain

$$PE_2 - PE_1 = \frac{GM_E mh}{R_E(R_E + h)}$$

When the height h is very small compared with R_E, h can be dropped from the second factor in the denominator, yielding

$$\frac{1}{R_E(R_E + h)} \cong \frac{1}{R_E^2}$$

Substituting this into the previous expression, we have

$$PE_2 - PE_1 \cong \frac{GM_E}{R_E^2} mh$$

Now recall from Chapter 4 that the free-fall acceleration at the surface of Earth is given by $g = GM_E/R_E^2$, giving

$$PE_2 - PE_1 \cong mgh$$

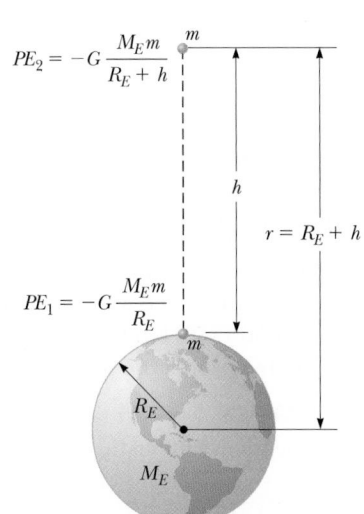

Figure 7.21 Relating the general form of gravitational potential energy to mgh.

Table 7.2 Escape Speeds for the Planets and the Moon

Planet	v_{esc} (km/s)
Mercury	4.3
Venus	10.3
Earth	11.2
Moon	2.3
Mars	5.0
Jupiter	60.0
Saturn	36.0
Uranus	22.0
Neptune	24.0
Pluto[a]	1.1

[a]In August 2006, the International Astronomical Union adopted a definition of a planet that separates Pluto from the other eight planets. Pluto is now defined as a "dwarf planet" (like the asteroid Ceres).

Escape Speed

If an object is projected upward from Earth's surface with a large enough speed, it can soar off into space and never return. This speed is called Earth's **escape speed.** (It is also commonly called the *escape velocity*, but in fact is more properly a speed.)

Earth's escape speed can be found by applying conservation of energy. Suppose an object of mass m is projected vertically upward from Earth's surface with an initial speed v_i. The initial mechanical energy (kinetic plus potential energy) of the object–Earth system is given by

$$KE_i + PE_i = \tfrac{1}{2}mv_i^2 - \frac{GM_E m}{R_E}$$

We neglect air resistance and assume the initial speed is just large enough to allow the object to reach infinity with a speed of zero. This value of v_i is the escape speed v_{esc}. When the object is at an infinite distance from Earth, its kinetic energy is zero because $v_f = 0$, and the gravitational potential energy is also zero because $1/r$ goes to zero as r goes to infinity. Hence the total mechanical energy is zero, and the law of conservation of energy gives

$$\tfrac{1}{2}mv_{esc}^2 - \frac{GM_E m}{R_E} = 0$$

so that

$$v_{esc} = \sqrt{\frac{2GM_E}{R_E}} \qquad \text{[7.22]}$$

The escape speed for Earth is about 11.2 km/s, which corresponds to about 25 000 mi/h. (See Example 7.12.) Note that the expression for v_{esc} doesn't depend on the mass of the object projected from Earth, so a spacecraft has the same escape speed as a molecule. Escape speeds for the planets, the Moon, and the Sun are listed in Table 7.2. Escape speed and temperature determine to a large extent whether a world has an atmosphere and, if so, what the constituents of the atmosphere are. Planets with low escape speeds, such as Mercury, generally don't have atmospheres because the average speed of gas molecules is close to the escape speed. Venus has a very thick atmosphere, but it's almost entirely carbon dioxide, a heavy gas. The atmosphere of Earth has very little hydrogen or helium, but has retained the much heavier nitrogen and oxygen molecules.

■ EXAMPLE 7.12 | From the Earth to the Moon

GOAL Apply conservation of energy with the general form of Newton's universal law of gravity.

PROBLEM In Jules Verne's classic novel *From the Earth to the Moon*, a giant cannon dug into the Earth in Florida fired a spacecraft all the way to the Moon. **(a)** If the spacecraft leaves the cannon at escape speed, at what speed is it moving when 1.50×10^5 km from the center of Earth? Neglect any friction effects. **(b)** Approximately what constant acceleration is needed to propel the spacecraft to escape speed through a cannon bore 1.00 km long?

STRATEGY For part (a), use conservation of energy and solve for the final speed v_f. Part (b) is an application of the time-independent kinematic equation: solve for the acceleration a.

....

SOLUTION

(a) Find the speed at $r = 1.50 \times 10^5$ km.

Apply conservation of energy:

$$\tfrac{1}{2}mv_i^2 - \frac{GM_E m}{R_E} = \tfrac{1}{2}mv_f^2 - \frac{GM_E m}{r_f}$$

Multiply by $2/m$ and rearrange, solving for v_f^2. Then substitute known values and take the square root.

$$v_f^2 = v_i^2 + \frac{2GM_E}{r_f} - \frac{2GM_E}{R_E} = v_i^2 + 2GM_E\left(\frac{1}{r_f} - \frac{1}{R_E}\right)$$

$$v_f^2 = (1.12 \times 10^4 \text{ m/s})^2 + 2(6.67 \times 10^{-11} \text{ kg}^{-1}\text{m}^3\text{s}^{-2})$$

$$\times (5.98 \times 10^{24} \text{ kg})\left(\frac{1}{1.50 \times 10^8 \text{ m}} - \frac{1}{6.38 \times 10^6 \text{ m}}\right)$$

$$v_f = \boxed{2.39 \times 10^3 \text{ m/s}}$$

(b) Find the acceleration through the cannon bore, assuming it's constant.

Use the time-independent kinematics equation:

$$v^2 - v_0{}^2 = 2a\Delta x$$

$$(1.12 \times 10^4 \text{ m/s})^2 - 0 = 2a(1.00 \times 10^3 \text{ m})$$

$$a = \boxed{6.27 \times 10^4 \text{ m/s}^2}$$

REMARKS This result corresponds to an acceleration of over 6 000 times the free-fall acceleration on Earth. Such a huge acceleration is far beyond what the human body can tolerate.

QUESTION 7.12 Suppose the spacecraft managed to go into an elliptical orbit around Earth, with a nearest point (perigee) and farthest point (apogee). At which point is the kinetic energy of the spacecraft higher, and why?

EXERCISE 7.12 Using the data in Table 7.3 (see page 223), find (a) the escape speed from the surface of Mars and (b) the speed of a space vehicle when it is 1.25×10^7 m from the center of Mars if it leaves the surface at the escape speed.

ANSWERS (a) 5.04×10^3 m/s (b) 2.62×10^3 m/s

7.6 Kepler's Laws

The movements of the planets, stars, and other celestial bodies have been observed for thousands of years. In early history scientists regarded Earth as the center of the Universe. This **geocentric model** was developed extensively by the Greek astronomer Claudius Ptolemy in the second century A.D. and was accepted for the next 1 400 years. In 1543 Polish astronomer Nicolaus Copernicus (1473–1543) showed that Earth and the other planets revolve in circular orbits around the Sun (the **heliocentric model**).

Danish astronomer Tycho Brahe (pronounced Brah or BRAH–huh; 1546–1601) made accurate astronomical measurements over a period of 20 years, providing the data for the currently accepted model of the solar system. Brahe's precise observations of the planets and 777 stars were carried out with nothing more elaborate than a large sextant and compass; the telescope had not yet been invented.

German astronomer Johannes Kepler, who was Brahe's assistant, acquired Brahe's astronomical data and spent about 16 years trying to deduce a mathematical model for the motions of the planets. After many laborious calculations, he found that Brahe's precise data on the motion of Mars about the Sun provided the answer. Kepler's analysis first showed that the concept of circular orbits about the Sun had to be abandoned. He eventually discovered that the orbit of Mars could be accurately described by an ellipse with the Sun at one focus. He then generalized this analysis to include the motions of all planets. The complete analysis is summarized in three statements known as **Kepler's laws:**

1. All planets move in elliptical orbits with the Sun at one of the focal points.
2. A line drawn from the Sun to any planet sweeps out equal areas in equal time intervals.
3. The square of the orbital period of any planet is proportional to the cube of the average distance from the planet to the Sun.

◀ Kepler's Laws

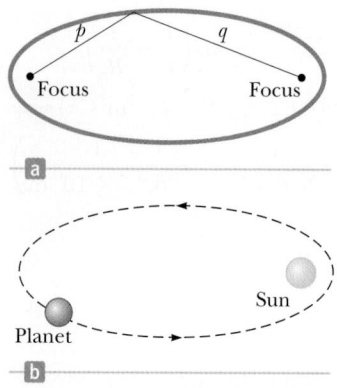

Active Figure 7.22
(a) The sum $p + q$ is the same for every point on the ellipse. (b) In the Solar System, the Sun is at one focus of the elliptical orbit of each planet and the other focus is empty.

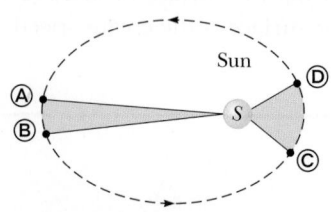

Active Figure 7.23
The two areas swept out by the planet in its elliptical orbit about the Sun are equal if the time interval between points Ⓐ and Ⓑ is equal to the time interval between points Ⓒ and Ⓓ.

Newton later demonstrated that these laws are consequences of the gravitational force that exists between any two objects. Newton's law of universal gravitation, together with his laws of motion, provides the basis for a full mathematical description of the motions of planets and satellites.

Kepler's First Law

The first law arises as a natural consequence of the inverse-square nature of Newton's law of gravitation. Any object bound to another by a force that varies as $1/r^2$ will move in an elliptical orbit. As shown in Active Figure 7.22a, an ellipse is a curve drawn so that the sum of the distances from any point on the curve to two internal points called *focal points* or *foci* (singular, *focus*) is always the same. The semimajor axis a is half the length of the line that goes across the ellipse and contains both foci. For the Sun–planet configuration (Active Fig. 7.22b), the Sun is at one focus and the other focus is empty. Because the orbit is an ellipse, the distance from the Sun to the planet continuously changes.

Kepler's Second Law

Kepler's second law states that a line drawn from the Sun to any planet sweeps out equal areas in equal time intervals. Consider a planet in an elliptical orbit about the Sun, as in Active Figure 7.23. In a given period Δt, the planet moves from point Ⓐ to point Ⓑ. The planet moves more slowly on that side of the orbit because it's farther away from the sun. On the opposite side of its orbit, the planet moves from point Ⓒ to point Ⓓ in the same amount of time, Δt, moving faster because it's closer to the sun. Kepler's second law says that any two wedges formed as in Figure 7.23 will always have the same area. As we will see in Chapter 8, Kepler's second law is related to a physical principle known as conservation of angular momentum.

Kepler's Third Law

The derivation of Kepler's third law is simple enough to carry out for the special case of a circular orbit. Consider a planet of mass M_p moving around the Sun, which has a mass of M_S, in a circular orbit. Because the orbit is circular, the planet moves at a constant speed v. Newton's second law, his law of gravitation, and centripetal acceleration then give the following equation:

$$M_p a_c = \frac{M_p v^2}{r} = \frac{GM_S M_p}{r^2}$$

The speed v of the planet in its orbit is equal to the circumference of the orbit divided by the time required for one revolution, T, called the **period** of the planet, so $v = 2\pi r/T$. Substituting, the preceding expression becomes

$$\frac{GM_S}{r^2} = \frac{(2\pi r/T)^2}{r}$$

Kepler's third law ▶

$$T^2 = \left(\frac{4\pi^2}{GM_S}\right)r^3 = K_S r^3 \qquad \text{[7.23]}$$

where K_S is a constant given by

$$K_S = \frac{4\pi^2}{GM_S} = 2.97 \times 10^{-19} \text{ s}^2/\text{m}^3$$

Equation 7.23 is Kepler's third law for a circular orbit. The orbits of most of the planets are very nearly circular. Comets and asteroids, however, usually have elliptical orbits. For these orbits, the radius r must be replaced with a, the semimajor axis—half the longest distance across the elliptical orbit. (This is also the average distance of the comet or asteroid from the Sun.) A more detailed calculation shows that K_S actually depends on the sum of both the mass of a given planet and

Table 7.3 Useful Planetary Data

Body	Mass (kg)	Mean Radius (m)	Period (s)	Mean Distance from Sun (m)	$\frac{T^2}{r^3}10^{-19}\left(\frac{s^2}{m^3}\right)$
Mercury	3.18×10^{23}	2.43×10^6	7.60×10^6	5.79×10^{10}	2.97
Venus	4.88×10^{24}	6.06×10^6	1.94×10^7	1.08×10^{11}	2.99
Earth	5.98×10^{24}	6.38×10^6	3.156×10^7	1.496×10^{11}	2.97
Mars	6.42×10^{23}	3.37×10^6	5.94×10^7	2.28×10^{11}	2.98
Jupiter	1.90×10^{27}	6.99×10^7	3.74×10^8	7.78×10^{11}	2.97
Saturn	5.68×10^{26}	5.85×10^7	9.35×10^8	1.43×10^{12}	2.99
Uranus	8.68×10^{25}	2.33×10^7	2.64×10^9	2.87×10^{12}	2.95
Neptune	1.03×10^{26}	2.21×10^7	5.22×10^9	4.50×10^{12}	2.99
Pluto[a]	1.27×10^{23}	1.14×10^6	7.82×10^9	5.91×10^{12}	2.96
Moon	7.36×10^{22}	1.74×10^6	—	—	—
Sun	1.991×10^{30}	6.96×10^8	—	—	—

[a]In August 2006, the International Astronomical Union adopted a definition of a planet that separates Pluto from the other eight planets. Pluto is now defined as a "dwarf planet" like the asteroid Ceres.

the Sun's mass. The masses of the planets, however, are negligible compared with the Sun's mass; hence can be neglected, meaning Equation 7.23 is valid for any planet in the Sun's family. If we consider the orbit of a satellite such as the Moon around Earth, then the constant has a different value, with the mass of the Sun replaced by the mass of Earth. In that case, K_E equals $4\pi^2/GM_E$.

The mass of the Sun can be determined from Kepler's third law because the constant K_S in Equation 7.23 includes the mass of the Sun and the other variables and constants can be easily measured. The value of this constant can be found by substituting the values of a planet's period and orbital radius and solving for K_S. The mass of the Sun is then

$$M_S = \frac{4\pi^2}{GK_S}$$

This same process can be used to calculate the mass of Earth (by considering the period and orbital radius of the Moon) and the mass of other planets in the solar system that have satellites.

The last column in Table 7.3 confirms that T^2/r^3 is very nearly constant. When time is measured in Earth years and the semimajor axis in astronomical units (1 AU = the distance from Earth to the Sun), Kepler's law takes the following simple form:

$$T^2 = a^3$$

This equation can be easily checked: Earth has a semimajor axis of one astronomical unit (by definition), and it takes one year to circle the Sun. This equation, of course, is valid only for the sun and its planets, asteroids, and comets.

■ Quick Quiz

7.10 Suppose an asteroid has a semimajor axis of 4 AU. How long does it take the asteroid to go around the Sun? (a) 2 years (b) 4 years (c) 6 years (d) 8 years

■ EXAMPLE 7.13   Geosynchronous Orbit and Telecommunications Satellites

GOAL Apply Kepler's third law to an Earth satellite.

PROBLEM From a telecommunications point of view, it's advantageous for satellites to remain at the same location relative to a location on Earth. This can occur only if the satellite's orbital period is the same as the Earth's period of rotation,

(Continued)

24.0 h. **(a)** At what distance from the center of the Earth can this geosynchronous orbit be found? **(b)** What's the orbital speed of the satellite?

STRATEGY This problem can be solved with the same method that was used to derive a special case of Kepler's third law, with Earth's mass replacing the Sun's mass. There's no need to repeat the analysis; just replace the Sun's mass with Earth's mass in Kepler's third law, substitute the period T (converted to seconds), and solve for r. For part (b), find the circumference of the circular orbit and divide by the elapsed time.

SOLUTION

(a) Find the distance r to geosynchronous orbit.

Apply Kepler's third law:

$$T^2 = \left(\frac{4\pi^2}{GM_E}\right)r^3$$

Substitute the period in seconds, $T = 86\,400$ s, the gravity constant $G = 6.67 \times 10^{-11}$ kg^{-1} m^3/s^2, and the mass of the Earth, $M_E = 5.98 \times 10^{24}$ kg. Solve for r:

$$r = \boxed{4.23 \times 10^7 \text{ m}}$$

(b) Find the orbital speed.

Divide the distance traveled during one orbit by the period:

$$v = \frac{d}{T} = \frac{2\pi r}{T} = \frac{2\pi(4.23 \times 10^7 \text{ m})}{8.64 \times 10^4 \text{ s}} = \boxed{3.08 \times 10^3 \text{ m/s}}$$

REMARKS Both these results are independent of the mass of the satellite. Notice that Earth's mass could be found by substituting the Moon's distance and period into this form of Kepler's third law.

QUESTION 7.13 If the satellite was placed in an orbit three times as far away, about how long would it take to orbit the Earth once? Answer in days, rounding to one digit.

EXERCISE 7.13 Mars rotates on its axis once every 1.02 days (almost the same as Earth does). (a) Find the distance from Mars at which a satellite would remain in one spot over the Martian surface. (b) Find the speed of the satellite.

ANSWERS (a) 2.03×10^7 m   (b) 1.45×10^3 m/s

SUMMARY

7.1 Angular Speed and Angular Acceleration

The **average angular speed** ω_{av} of a rigid object is defined as the ratio of the angular displacement $\Delta\theta$ to the time interval Δt, or

$$\omega_{av} \equiv \frac{\theta_f - \theta_i}{t_f - t_i} = \frac{\Delta\theta}{\Delta t} \qquad [7.3]$$

where ω_{av} is in radians per second (rad/s).

The **average angular acceleration** α_{av} of a rotating object is defined as the ratio of the change in angular speed $\Delta\omega$ to the time interval Δt, or

$$\alpha_{av} \equiv \frac{\omega_f - \omega_i}{t_f - t_i} = \frac{\Delta\omega}{\Delta t} \qquad [7.5]$$

where α_{av} is in radians per second per second (rad/s^2).

7.2 Rotational Motion Under Constant Angular Acceleration

If an object undergoes rotational motion about a fixed axis under a constant angular acceleration α, its motion can be described with the following set of equations:

$$\omega = \omega_i + \alpha t \qquad [7.7]$$
$$\Delta\theta = \omega_i t + \tfrac{1}{2}\alpha t^2 \qquad [7.8]$$
$$\omega^2 = \omega_i^2 + 2\alpha\Delta\theta \qquad [7.9]$$

Problems are solved as in one-dimensional kinematics.

7.3 Relations Between Angular and Linear Quantities

When an object rotates about a fixed axis, the angular speed and angular acceleration are related to the tangential speed and tangential acceleration through the relationships

$$v_t = r\omega \qquad [7.10]$$

and

$$a_t = r\alpha \qquad [7.11]$$

7.4 Centripetal Acceleration

Any object moving in a circular path has an acceleration directed toward the center of the circular path, called a **centripetal acceleration.** Its magnitude is given by

$$a_c = \frac{v^2}{r} = r\omega^2 \qquad [7.13, 7.17]$$

Any object moving in a circular path must have a net force exerted on it that is directed toward the center of the path. Some examples of forces that cause centripetal acceleration are the force of gravity (as in the motion of a satellite) and the force of tension in a string.

7.5 Newtonian Gravitation

Newton's law of universal gravitation states that every particle in the Universe attracts every other particle with a force that is directly proportional to the product of their masses and inversely proportional to the square of the distance r between them:

$$F = G\frac{m_1 m_2}{r^2} \quad \text{[7.20]}$$

where $G = 6.673 \times 10^{-11}$ N · m²/kg² is the **constant of universal gravitation.** A general expression for gravitational potential energy is

$$PE = -G\frac{M_E m}{r} \quad \text{[7.21]}$$

This expression reduces to $PE = mgh$ close to the surface of Earth and holds for other worlds through replacement of the mass M_E. Problems such as finding the escape velocity from Earth can be solved by using Equation 7.21 in the conservation of energy equation.

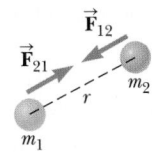

| The gravitational force is attractive and acts along the line joining the particles. |

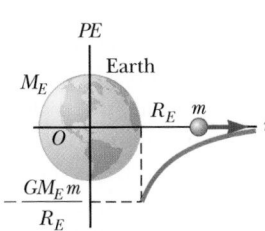

| The gravitational potential energy increases towards zero as r increases. |

7.6 Kepler's Laws

Kepler derived the following three laws of planetary motion:

1. All planets move in elliptical orbits with the Sun at one of the focal points.

| Kepler's first law. |

2. A line drawn from the Sun to any planet sweeps out equal areas in equal time intervals.

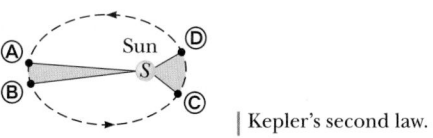

| Kepler's second law. |

3. The square of the orbital period of a planet is proportional to the cube of the average distance from the planet to the Sun:

$$T^2 = \left(\frac{4\pi^2}{GM_S}\right)r^3 \quad \text{| Kepler's third law. |} \quad \text{[7.23]}$$

The third law can be applied to any large body and its system of satellites by replacing the Sun's mass with the body's mass. In particular, it can be used to determine the mass of the central body once the average distance to a satellite and its period are known.

■ **MULTIPLE-CHOICE QUESTIONS**

WebAssign The multiple-choice questions in this chapter may be assigned online in Enhanced WebAssign.

---

1. Find the angular speed of Earth around the Sun in radians per second. (a) 2.22×10^{-6} rad/s (b) 1.16×10^{-7} rad/s (c) 3.17×10^{-8} rad/s (d) 4.52×10^{-7} rad/s (e) 1.99×10^{-7} rad/s

2. A 0.400-kg object attached to the end of a string of length 0.500 m is swung in a circular path and in a vertical plane. If a constant angular speed of 8.00 rad/s is maintained, what is the tension in the string when the object is at the top of the circular path? (a) 8.88 N (b) 10.5 N (c) 12.8 N (d) 19.6 N (e) None of these

3. A cyclist rides a bicycle with a wheel radius of 0.500 m across campus. A piece of plastic on the front rim makes a clicking sound every time it passes through the fork. If the cyclist counts 320 clicks between her apartment and the cafeteria, how far has she traveled? (a) 0.50 km (b) 0.80 km (c) 1.0 km (d) 1.5 km (e) 1.8 km

4. A grindstone increases in angular speed from 4.00 rad/s to 12.00 rad/s in 4.00 s. Through what angle does it turn during that time if the angular acceleration is constant? (a) 8.00 rad (b) 12.0 rad (c) 16.0 rad (d) 32.0 rad (e) 64.0 rad

5. The gravitational force exerted on an astronaut on Earth's surface is 650 N down. When she is in the International Space Station, is the gravitational force on her (a) larger, (b) exactly the same, (c) smaller, (d) nearly but not exactly zero, or (e) exactly zero?

6. Consider an object on a rotating disk a distance r from its center, held in place on the disk by static friction. Which of the following statements is *not* true concerning this object? (a) If the angular speed is constant, the object must have constant tangential speed. (b) If the angular speed is constant, the object is not accelerated. (c) The object has a tangential acceleration only if the disk has an angular acceleration. (d) If the disk has an angular acceleration, the object has both a centripetal and a tangential acceleration. (e) The object always has a centripetal acceleration except when the angular speed is zero.

7. A merry-go-round rotates with constant angular speed. As a rider moves from the rim of the merry-go-round toward the center, what happens to the magnitude of total centripetal force that must be exerted on him? (a) It increases. (b) It is not zero, but remains the same. (c) It decreases. (d) It's always zero. (e) It increases or decreases, depending on the direction of rotation.

8. An object is located on the surface of a spherical planet of mass M and radius R. The escape speed from the planet does *not* depend on which of the following? (a) M (b) the density of the planet (c) R (d) the

acceleration due to gravity on that planet (e) the mass of the object

9. A satellite moves in a circular orbit at a constant speed around Earth. Which of the following statements is true? (a) No force acts on the satellite. (b) The satellite moves at constant speed and hence doesn't accelerate. (c) The satellite has an acceleration directed away from Earth. (d) The satellite has an acceleration directed toward Earth. (e) Work is done on the satellite by the force of gravity.

10. A system consists of four particles. How many terms appear in the expression for the total gravitational potential energy of the system? (a) 4 (b) 6 (c) 10 (d) 12 (e) None of these

11. What is the gravitational acceleration close to the surface of a planet with twice the mass and twice the radius of Earth? Answer as a multiple of g, the gravitational acceleration near Earth's surface. (a) $0.25g$ (b) $0.5g$ (c) g (d) $2g$ (e) $4g$

12. Which of the following statements are true of an object in orbit around Earth? (a) If the orbit is circular, the gravity force is perpendicular to the object's velocity. (b) If the orbit is elliptical, the gravity force is perpendicular to the velocity vector only at the nearest and farthest points. (c) If the orbit is not circular, the speed is greatest when the object is farthest away from Earth. (d) The gravity force on the object always has components both parallel and perpendicular to the object's velocity. (e) All these statements are true.

13. Halley's comet has a period of approximately 76 years and moves in an elliptical orbit in which its distance from the Sun at closest approach is a small fraction of its maximum distance. Estimate the comet's maximum distance from the Sun in astronomical units AU (the distance from Earth to the Sun). (a) 3 AU (b) 6 AU (c) 10 AU (d) 18 AU (e) 36 AU

■ CONCEPTUAL QUESTIONS

WebAssign The conceptual questions in this chapter may be assigned online in Enhanced WebAssign.

1. In a race like the Indianapolis 500, a driver circles the track counterclockwise and feels his head pulled toward one shoulder. To relieve his neck muscles from having to hold his head erect, the driver fastens a strap to one wall of the car and the other to his helmet. The length of the strap is adjusted to keep his head vertical. (a) Which shoulder does his head tend to lean toward? (b) What force or forces produce the centripetal acceleration when there is no strap? (c) What force or forces do so when there is a strap?

2. If someone told you that astronauts are weightless in Earth orbit because they are beyond the force of gravity, would you accept the statement? Explain.

3. If a car's wheels are replaced with wheels of greater diameter, will the reading of the speedometer change? Explain.

4. At night, you are farther away from the Sun than during the day. What's more, the force exerted by the Sun on you is downward into Earth at night and upward into the sky during the day. If you had a sensitive enough bathroom scale, would you appear to weigh more at night than during the day?

5. A pendulum consists of a small object called a bob hanging from a light cord of fixed length, with the top end of the cord fixed, as represented in Figure CQ7.5. The bob moves without friction, swinging equally high on both sides. It moves from its turning point A through point B and reaches its maximum speed at point C.

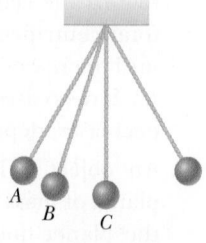

Figure CQ7.5

(a) At what point does the bob have nonzero radial acceleration and zero tangential acceleration? What is the direction of its total acceleration at this point? (b) At what point does the bob have nonzero tangential acceleration and zero radial acceleration? What is the direction of its total acceleration at this point? (c) At what point does the bob have both nonzero tangential and radial acceleration? What is the direction of its total acceleration at this point?

6. Because of Earth's rotation about its axis, you weigh slightly less at the equator than at the poles. Explain.

7. It has been suggested that rotating cylinders about 10 miles long and 5 miles in diameter be placed in space for colonies. The purpose of their rotation is to simulate gravity for the inhabitants. Explain the concept behind this proposal.

8. Describe the path of a moving object in the event that the object's acceleration is constant in magnitude at all times and (a) perpendicular to its velocity; (b) parallel to its velocity.

9. A pail of water can be whirled in a vertical circular path such that no water is spilled. Why does the water remain in the pail, even when the pail is upside down above your head?

10. Use Kepler's second law to convince yourself that Earth must move faster in its orbit during the northern hemisphere winter, when it is closest to the Sun, than during the summer, when it is farthest from the Sun.

11. Is it possible for a car to move in a circular path in such a way that it has a tangential acceleration but no centripetal acceleration?

12. A child is practicing for a BMX race. His speed remains constant as he goes counterclockwise around a level track with two nearly straight sections and two nearly semicircular sections, as shown

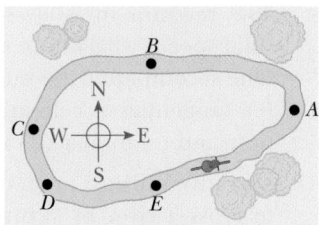

Figure CQ7.12

in the aerial view of Figure CQ7.12. (a) What are the directions of his velocity at points *A*, *B*, and *C*? For each point choose one: north, south, east, west, or nonexistent? (b) What are the directions of his acceleration at points *A*, *B*, and *C*?

13. An object executes circular motion with constant speed whenever a net force of constant magnitude acts perpendicular to the velocity. What happens to the speed if the force is not perpendicular to the velocity?

■ PROBLEMS

7.1 Angular Speed and Angular Acceleration

1. **Q|C** (a) Find the angular speed of Earth's rotation about its axis. (b) How does this rotation affect the shape of Earth?

2. A wheel has a radius of 4.1 m. How far (path length) does a point on the circumference travel if the wheel is rotated through angles of (a) 30°, (b) 30 rad, and (c) 30 rev, respectively?

3. The tires on a new compact car have a diameter of 2.0 ft and are warranted for 60 000 miles. (a) Determine the angle (in radians) through which one of these tires will rotate during the warranty period. (b) How many revolutions of the tire are equivalent to your answer in part (a)?

4. **Q|C** A potter's wheel moves uniformly from rest to an angular speed of 1.00 rev/s in 30.0 s. (a) Find its angular acceleration in radians per second per second. (b) Would doubling the angular acceleration during the given period have doubled final angular speed?

7.2 Rotational Motion Under Constant Angular Acceleration

7.3 Relations Between Angular and Linear Quantities

5. A dentist's drill starts from rest. After 3.20 s of constant angular acceleration, it turns at a rate of 2.51×10^4 rev/min. (a) Find the drill's angular acceleration. (b) Determine the angle (in radians) through which the drill rotates during this period.

6. A centrifuge in a medical laboratory rotates at an angular speed of 3 600 rev/min. When switched off, it rotates through 50.0 revolutions before coming to rest. Find the constant angular acceleration (in rad/s²) of the centrifuge.

7. **Q|C** A machine part rotates at an angular speed of 0.06 rad/s; its speed is then increased to 2.2 rad/s at an angular acceleration of 0.70 rad/s². (a) Find the angle through which the part rotates before reaching this final speed. (b) In general, if both the initial and final angular speed are doubled at the same angular acceleration, by what factor is the angular displacement changed? Why? *Hint:* Look at the form of Equation 7.9.

8. **Q|C** A bicycle is turned upside down while its owner repairs a flat tire. A friend spins the other wheel and observes that drops of water fly off tangentially. She measures the heights reached by drops moving vertically (Fig. P7.8). A drop that breaks loose from the tire on one turn rises

Figure P7.8 Problems 8 and 69.

vertically 54.0 cm above the tangent point. A drop that breaks loose on the next turn rises 51.0 cm above the tangent point. The radius of the wheel is 0.381 m. (a) Why does the first drop rise higher than the second drop? (b) Neglecting air friction and using only the observed heights and the radius of the wheel, find the wheel's angular acceleration (assuming it to be constant).

9. The diameters of the main rotor and tail rotor of a single-engine helicopter are 7.60 m and 1.02 m, respectively. The respective rotational speeds are 450 rev/min and 4 138 rev/min. Calculate the speeds of the tips of both rotors. Compare these speeds with the speed of sound, 343 m/s.

10. The tub of a washer goes into its spin-dry cycle, starting from rest and reaching an angular speed of 5.0 rev/s in

8.0 s. At this point, the person doing the laundry opens the lid, and a safety switch turns off the washer. The tub slows to rest in 12.0 s. Through how many revolutions does the tub turn during the entire 20-s interval? Assume constant angular acceleration while it is starting and stopping.

11. A car initially traveling at 29.0 m/s undergoes a constant negative acceleration of magnitude 1.75 m/s² after its brakes are applied. (a) How many revolutions does each tire make before the car comes to a stop, assuming the car does not skid and the tires have radii of 0.330 m? (b) What is the angular speed of the wheels when the car has traveled half the total distance?

12. A 45.0-cm diameter disk rotates with a constant angular acceleration of 2.50 rad/s². It starts from rest at $t = 0$, and a line drawn from the center of the disk to a point P on the rim of the disk makes an angle of 57.3° with the positive x-axis at this time. At $t = 2.30$ s, find (a) the angular speed of the wheel, (b) the linear velocity and tangential acceleration of P, and (c) the position of P (in degrees, with respect to the positive x-axis).

13. **M** A rotating wheel requires 3.00 s to rotate 37.0 revolutions. Its angular velocity at the end of the 3.00-s interval is 98.0 rad/s. What is the constant angular acceleration (in rad/s²) of the wheel?

14. An electric motor rotating a workshop grinding wheel at a rate of 1.00×10^2 rev/min is switched off. Assume the wheel has a constant negative angular acceleration of magnitude 2.00 rad/s². (a) How long does it take for the grinding wheel to stop? (b) Through how many radians has the wheel turned during the interval found in part (a)?

7.4 Centripetal Acceleration

15. A car initially traveling eastward turns north by traveling in a circular path at uniform speed as shown in Figure P7.15. The length of the arc ABC is 235 m, and the car completes the turn in 36.0 s. (a) Determine the car's speed. (b) What is the magnitude and direction of the acceleration when the car is at point B?

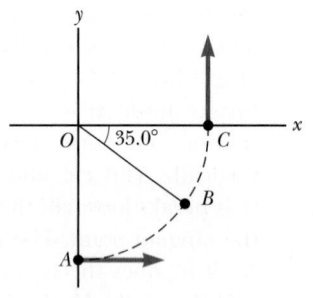

Figure P7.15

16. It has been suggested that rotating cylinders about 10 mi long and 5.0 mi in diameter be placed in space and used as colonies. What angular speed must such a cylinder have so that the centripetal acceleration at its surface equals the free-fall acceleration on Earth?

17. (a) What is the tangential acceleration of a bug on the rim of a 10.0-in.-diameter disk if the disk accelerates uniformly from rest to an angular speed of 78.0 rev/min in 3.00 s? (b) When the disk is at its final speed, what is the tangential velocity of the bug? One second after the bug starts from rest, what are its (c) tangential acceleration, (d) centripetal acceleration, and (e) total acceleration?

18. An adventurous archeologist ($m = 85.0$ kg) tries to cross a river by swinging from a vine. The vine is 10.0 m long, and his speed at the bottom of the swing is 8.00 m/s. The archeologist doesn't know that the vine has a breaking strength of 1 000 N. Does he make it across the river without falling in?

19. **Q|C** One end of a cord is fixed and a small 0.500-kg object is attached to the other end, where it swings in a section of a vertical circle of radius 2.00 m, as shown in Figure P7.19. When $\theta = 20.0°$, the speed of the object is 8.00 m/s. At this instant, find (a) the tension in the string, (b) the tangential and radial components of acceleration, and (c) the total acceleration. (d) Is your answer changed if the object is swinging down toward its lowest point instead of swinging up? (e) Explain your answer to part (d).

Figure P7.19

20. **Q|C** A coin rests 15.0 cm from the center of a turntable. The coefficient of static friction between the coin and turntable surface is 0.350. The turntable starts from rest at $t = 0$ and rotates with a constant angular acceleration of 0.730 rad/s². (a) Once the turntable starts to rotate, what force causes the centripetal acceleration when the coin is stationary relative to the turntable? Under what condition does the coin begin to move relative to the turntable? (b) After what period of time will the coin start to slip on the turntable?

21. A 55.0-kg ice skater is moving at 4.00 m/s when she grabs the loose end of a rope, the opposite end of which is tied to a pole. She then moves in a circle of radius 0.800 m around the pole. (a) Determine the force exerted by the horizontal rope on her arms. (b) Compare this force with her weight.

22. **M** A 40.0-kg child swings in a swing supported by two chains, each 3.00 m long. The tension in each chain at the lowest point is 350 N. Find (a) the child's speed at the lowest point and (b) the force exerted by the seat on the child at the lowest point. (Ignore the mass of the seat.)

23. A certain light truck can go around a flat curve having a radius of 150 m with a maximum speed of 32.0 m/s. With what maximum speed can it go around a curve having a radius of 75.0 m?

24. **BIO** A sample of blood is placed in a centrifuge of radius 15.0 cm. The mass of a red blood cell is 3.0×10^{-16} kg, and the magnitude of the force acting on it as it settles out of the plasma is 4.0×10^{-11} N. At how many revolutions per second should the centrifuge be operated?

25. A 50.0-kg child stands at the rim of a merry-go-round of radius 2.00 m, rotating with an angular speed of 3.00 rad/s. (a) What is the child's centripetal acceleration? (b) What is the minimum force between her feet and the floor of the carousel that is required to keep her in the circular path? (c) What minimum coefficient of static friction is required? Is the answer you found reasonable? In other words, is she likely to stay on the merry-go-round?

26. GP A space habitat for a long space voyage consists of two cabins each connected by a cable to a central hub as shown in Figure P7.26. The cabins are set spinning around the hub axis, which is connected to the rest of the spacecraft to generate artificial gravity. (a) What forces are acting on an astronaut in one of the cabins? (b) Write Newton's second law for an astronaut lying on the "floor" of one of the habitats, relating the astronaut's mass m, his velocity v, his radial distance from the hub r, and the normal force n. (c) What would n have to equal if the 60.0-kg astronaut is to experience half his normal Earth weight? (d) Calculate the necessary tangential speed of the habitat from Newton's second law. (e) Calculate the angular speed from the tangential speed. (f) Calculate the period of rotation from the angular speed. (g) If the astronaut stands up, will his head be moving faster, slower, or at the same speed as his feet? Why? Calculate the tangential speed at the top of his head if he is 1.80 m tall.

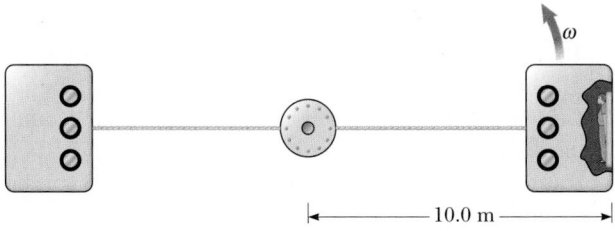

Figure P7.26

27. An air puck of mass $m_1 = 0.25$ kg is tied to a string and allowed to revolve in a circle of radius $R = 1.0$ m on a frictionless horizontal table. The other end of the string passes through a hole in the center of the table, and a mass of $m_2 = 1.0$ kg is tied to it (Fig. P7.27). The suspended mass remains in equilibrium while the puck on the tabletop revolves. (a) What is the tension in the string? (b) What is the horizontal force acting on the puck? (c) What is the speed of the puck?

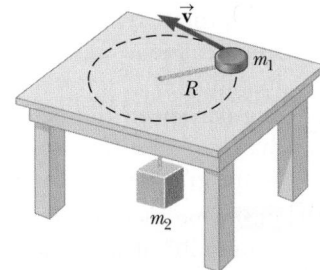

Figure P7.27 Problems 27 and 28.

28. S An air puck of mass m_1 is tied to a string and allowed to revolve in a circle of radius R on a horizontal, frictionless table. The other end of the string passes through a small hole in the center of the table, and an object of mass m_2 is tied to it (Fig. P7.27). The suspended object remains in equilibrium while the puck on the tabletop revolves. (a) Find a symbolic expression for the tension in the string in terms of m_2 and g. (b) Write Newton's second law for the air puck, using the variables m_1, v, R, and T. (c) Eliminate the tension T from the expressions found in parts (a) and (b) and find an expression for the speed of the puck in terms of m_1, m_2, g, and R. (d) Check your answers by substituting the values of Problem 27 and comparing the results with the answers for that problem.

29. Q|C A woman places her briefcase on the backseat of her car. As she drives to work, the car negotiates an unbanked curve in the road that can be regarded as an arc of a circle of radius 62.0 m. While on the curve, the speed of the car is 15.0 m/s at the instant the briefcase starts to slide across the backseat toward the side of the car. (a) What force causes the centripetal acceleration of the briefcase when it is stationary relative to the car? Under what condition does the briefcase begin to move relative to the car? (b) What is the coefficient of static friction between the briefcase and seat surface?

30. Q|C A pail of water is rotated in a vertical circle of radius 1.00 m. (a) What two external forces act on the water in the pail? (b) Which of the two forces is most important in causing the water to move in a circle? (c) What is the pail's minimum speed at the top of the circle if no water is to spill out? (d) If the pail with the speed found in part (c) were to suddenly disappear at the top of the circle, describe the subsequent motion of the water. Would it differ from the motion of a projectile?

31. M A 40.0-kg child takes a ride on a Ferris wheel that rotates four times each minute and has a diameter of 18.0 m. (a) What is the centripetal acceleration of the child? (b) What force (magnitude and direction) does the seat exert on the child at the lowest point of the ride? (c) What force does the seat exert on the child at the highest point of the ride? (d) What force does the seat exert on the child when the child is halfway between the top and bottom?

32. A roller-coaster vehicle has a mass of 500 kg when fully loaded with passengers (Fig. P7.32). (a) If the vehicle

Figure P7.32

has a speed of 20.0 m/s at point Ⓐ, what is the force of the track on the vehicle at this point? (b) What is the maximum speed the vehicle can have at point Ⓑ for gravity to hold it on the track?

7.5 Newtonian Gravitation

33. The average distance separating Earth and the Moon is 384 000 km. Use the data in Table 7.3 to find the net gravitational force exerted by Earth and the Moon on a 3.00×10^4-kg spaceship located halfway between them.

34. A satellite has a mass of 100 kg and is located at 2.00×10^6 m above the surface of Earth. (a) What is the potential energy associated with the satellite at this location? (b) What is the magnitude of the gravitational force on the satellite?

35. A coordinate system (in meters) is constructed on the surface of a pool table, and three objects are placed on the table as follows: a 2.0-kg object at the origin of the coordinate system, a 3.0-kg object at (0, 2.0), and a 4.0-kg object at (4.0, 0). Find the resultant gravitational force exerted by the other two objects on the object at the origin.

36. After the Sun exhausts its nuclear fuel, its ultimate fate may be to collapse to a *white dwarf* state. In this state, it would have approximately the same mass as it has now, but its radius would be equal to the radius of Earth. Calculate (a) the average density of the white dwarf, (b) the surface free-fall acceleration, and (c) the gravitational potential energy associated with a 1.00-kg object at the surface of the white dwarf.

37. Objects with masses of 200 kg and 500 kg are separated by 0.400 m. (a) Find the net gravitational force exerted by these objects on a 50.0-kg object placed midway between them. (b) At what position (other than infinitely remote ones) can the 50.0-kg object be placed so as to experience a net force of zero?

38. Use the data of Table 7.3 to find the point between Earth and the Sun at which an object can be placed so that the net gravitational force exerted by Earth and the Sun on that object is zero.

39. A projectile is fired straight upward from the Earth's surface at the South Pole with an initial speed equal to one third the escape speed. (a) Ignoring air resistance, determine how far from the center of the Earth the projectile travels before stopping momentarily. (b) What is the altitude of the projectile at this instant?

40. Two objects attract each other with a gravitational force of magnitude 1.00×10^{-8} N when separated by 20.0 cm. If the total mass of the objects is 5.00 kg, what is the mass of each?

7.6 Kepler's Laws

41. Ⓜ A satellite is in a circular orbit around the Earth at an altitude of 2.80×10^6 m. Find (a) the period of the orbit, (b) the speed of the satellite, and (c) the accel-

eration of the satellite. *Hint:* Modify Equation 7.23 so it is suitable for objects orbiting the Earth rather than the Sun.

42. An artificial satellite circling the Earth completes each orbit in 110 minutes. (a) Find the altitude of the satellite. (b) What is the value of g at the location of this satellite?

43. A satellite of Mars, called Phoebus, has an orbital radius of 9.4×10^6 m and a period of 2.8×10^4 s. Assuming the orbit is circular, determine the mass of Mars.

44. A 600-kg satellite is in a circular orbit about Earth at a height above Earth equal to Earth's mean radius. Find (a) the satellite's orbital speed, (b) the period of its revolution, and (c) the gravitational force acting on it.

45. Two satellites are in circular orbits around the Earth. Satellite A is at an *altitude* equal to the Earth's radius, while satellite B is at an altitude equal to twice the Earth's radius. What is the ratio of their periods, T_B/T_A?

Additional Problems

46. A synchronous satellite, which always remains above the same point on a planet's equator, is put in circular orbit around Jupiter to study that planet's famous red spot. Jupiter rotates once every 9.84 h. Use the data of Table 7.3 to find the altitude of the satellite.

47. (a) One of the moons of Jupiter, named Io, has an orbital radius of 4.22×10^8 m and a period of 1.77 days. Assuming the orbit is circular, calculate the mass of Jupiter. (b) The largest moon of Jupiter, named Ganymede, has an orbital radius of 1.07×10^9 m and a period of 7.16 days. Calculate the mass of Jupiter from this data. (c) Are your results to parts (a) and (b) consistent? Explain.

48. Neutron stars are extremely dense objects that are formed from the remnants of supernova explosions. Many rotate very rapidly. Suppose the mass of a certain spherical neutron star is twice the mass of the Sun and its radius is 10.0 km. Determine the greatest possible angular speed the neutron star can have so that the matter at its surface on the equator is just held in orbit by the gravitational force.

49. **BIO** One method of pitching a softball is called the "windmill" delivery method, in which the pitcher's arm rotates through approximately 360° in a vertical plane before the 198-gram ball is released at the lowest point of the circular motion. An experienced pitcher can throw a ball with a speed of 98.0 mi/h. Assume the angular acceleration is uniform throughout the pitching motion and take the distance between the softball and the shoulder joint to be 74.2 cm. (a) Determine the angular speed of the arm in rev/s at the instant of release. (b) Find the value of the angular acceleration in rev/s² and the radial and tangential acceleration of the ball just before it is released. (c) Determine the force exerted on the ball by the pitcher's hand (both radial and tangential components) just before it is released.

50. A digital audio compact disc carries data along a continuous spiral track from the inner circumference of the disc to the outside edge. Each bit occupies 0.6 μm of the track. A CD player turns the disc to carry the track counterclockwise above a lens at a constant speed of 1.30 m/s. Find the required angular speed (a) at the beginning of the recording, where the spiral has a radius of 2.30 cm, and (b) at the end of the recording, where the spiral has a radius of 5.80 cm. (c) A full-length recording lasts for 74 min, 33 s. Find the average angular acceleration of the disc. (d) Assuming the acceleration is constant, find the total angular displacement of the disc as it plays. (e) Find the total length of the track.

51. An athlete swings a 5.00-kg ball horizontally on the end of a rope. The ball moves in a circle of radius 0.800 m at an angular speed of 0.500 rev/s. What are (a) the tangential speed of the ball and (b) its centripetal acceleration? (c) If the maximum tension the rope can withstand before breaking is 100 N, what is the maximum tangential speed the ball can have?

52. A car rounds a banked curve where the radius of curvature of the road is R, the banking angle is θ, and the coefficient of static friction is μ. (a) Determine the range of speeds the car can have without slipping up or down the road. (b) What is the range of speeds possible if R = 100 m, θ = 10°, and μ = 0.10 (slippery conditions)?

53. The Solar Maximum Mission Satellite was placed in a circular orbit about 150 mi above Earth. Determine (a) the orbital speed of the satellite and (b) the time required for one complete revolution.

54. A 0.400-kg pendulum bob passes through the lowest part of its path at a speed of 3.00 m/s. (a) What is the tension in the pendulum cable at this point if the pendulum is 80.0 cm long? (b) When the pendulum reaches its highest point, what angle does the cable make with the vertical? (c) What is the tension in the pendulum cable when the pendulum reaches its highest point?

55. **Q|C** A car moves at speed v across a bridge made in the shape of a circular arc of radius r. (a) Find an expression for the normal force acting on the car when it is at the top of the arc. (b) At what minimum speed will the normal force become zero (causing the occupants of the car to seem weightless) if r = 30.0 m?

56. **S** Show that the escape speed from the surface of a planet of uniform density is directly proportional to the radius of the planet.

57. **Q|C** Because of Earth's rotation about its axis, a point on the equator has a centripetal acceleration of 0.034 0 m/s^2, whereas a point at the poles has no

centripetal acceleration. (a) Show that, at the equator, the gravitational force on an object (the object's true weight) must exceed the object's apparent weight. (b) What are the apparent weights of a 75.0-kg person at the equator and at the poles? (Assume Earth is a uniform sphere and take g = 9.800 m/s^2.)

58. A small block of mass m = 0.50 kg is fired with an initial speed of v_0 = 4.0 m/s along a horizontal section of frictionless track, as shown in the top portion of Figure P7.58. The block then moves along the frictionless, semicircular, *vertical* tracks of radius R = 1.5 m. (a) Determine the force exerted by the track on the block at points Ⓐ and Ⓑ. (b) The bottom of the track consists of a section (L = 0.40 m) with friction. Determine the coefficient of kinetic friction between the block and that portion of the bottom track if the block just makes it to point Ⓒ on the first trip. *Hint:* If the block just makes it to point Ⓒ, the force of contact exerted by the track on the block at that point is zero.

Figure P7.58

59. In Robert Heinlein's *The Moon Is a Harsh Mistress*, the colonial inhabitants of the Moon threaten to launch rocks down onto Earth if they are not given independence (or at least representation). Assuming a gun could launch a rock of mass m at twice the lunar escape speed, calculate the speed of the rock as it enters Earth's atmosphere.

60. **Q|C** A roller coaster travels in a circular path. (a) Identify the forces on a passenger at the top of the circular loop that cause centripetal acceleration. Show the direction of all forces in a sketch. (b) Identify the forces on the passenger at the bottom of the loop that produce centripetal acceleration. Show these in a sketch. (c) Based on your answers to parts (a) and (b), at what point, top or bottom, should the seat exert the greatest force on the passenger? (d) Assume the speed of the roller coaster is 4.00 m/s at the top of the loop of radius 8.00 m. Find the force exerted by the seat on a 70.0-kg passenger at the top of the loop. Then, assume the speed remains the same at the bottom of the loop and find the force exerted by the seat on the passenger at this point. Are your answers consistent with your choice of answers for parts (a) and (b)?

61. In a home laundry dryer, a cylindrical tub containing wet clothes is rotated steadily about a horizontal axis,

as shown in Figure P7.61. So that the clothes will dry uniformly, they are made to tumble. The rate of rotation of the smooth-walled tub is chosen so that a small piece of cloth will lose contact with the tub when the cloth is at an angle of $\theta = 68.0°$ above the horizontal. If the radius of the tub is $r = 0.330$ m, what rate of revolution is needed in revolutions per second?

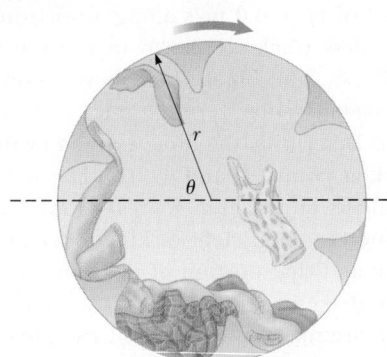

Figure P7.61

62. **M** A model airplane of mass 0.750 kg flies with a speed of 35.0 m/s in a horizontal circle at the end of a 60.0-m control wire as shown in Figure P7.62a. The forces exerted on the airplane are shown in Figure P7.62b; the tension in the control wire, $\theta = 20.0°$ inward from the vertical. Compute the tension in the wire, assuming the wire makes a constant angle of $\theta = 20.0°$ with the horizontal.

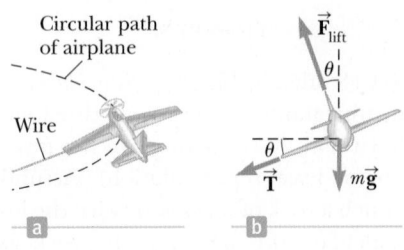

Figure P7.62

63. **S** A skier starts at rest at the top of a large hemispherical hill (Fig. P7.63). Neglecting friction, show that the skier will leave the hill and become airborne at a distance $h = R/3$ below the top of the hill. *Hint:* At this point, the normal force goes to zero.

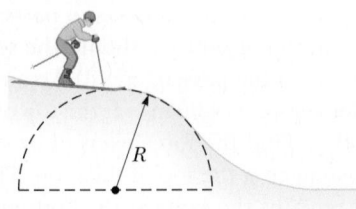

Figure P7.63

64. Casting of molten metal is important in many industrial processes. *Centrifugal casting* is used for manufacturing pipes, bearings, and many other structures. A cylindrical enclosure is rotated rapidly and steadily about a horizontal axis, as in Figure P7.64. Molten metal is poured into the rotating cylinder and then cooled, forming the finished product. Turning the cylinder at a high rotation rate forces the solidifying metal strongly to the outside. Any bubbles are displaced toward the axis so that unwanted voids will not be present in the casting.

Suppose a copper sleeve of inner radius 2.10 cm and outer radius 2.20 cm is to be cast. To eliminate bubbles and give high structural integrity, the centripetal acceleration of each bit of metal should be $100g$. What rate of rotation is required? State the answer in revolutions per minute.

Figure P7.64

65. Suppose a 1 800-kg car passes over a bump in a roadway that follows the arc of a circle of radius 20.4 m, as in Figure P7.65. (a) What force does the road exert on the car as the car passes the highest point of the bump if the car travels at 8.94 m/s? (b) What is the maximum speed the car can have without losing contact with the road as it passes this highest point?

Figure P7.65

66. A stuntman whose mass is 70 kg swings from the end of a 4.0-m-long rope along the arc of a vertical circle. Assuming he starts from rest when the rope is horizontal, find the tensions in the rope that are required to make him follow his circular path (a) at the beginning of his motion, (b) at a height of 1.5 m above the bottom of the circular arc, and (c) at the bottom of the arc.

67. **QC** A minimum-energy orbit to an outer planet consists of putting a spacecraft on an elliptical trajectory with the departure planet corresponding to the perihelion of the ellipse, or closest point to the Sun, and the arrival planet corresponding to the aphelion of the ellipse, or farthest point from the Sun. (a) Use Kepler's third law to calculate how long it would take to go from Earth to Mars on such an orbit. (Answer in years.) (b) Can such an orbit be undertaken at any time? Explain.

68. **QC** The pilot of an airplane executes a constant-speed loop-the-loop maneuver in a vertical circle as in Figure 7.15b. The speed of the airplane is 2.00×10^2 m/s, and the radius of the circle is 3.20×10^3 m. (a) What is the pilot's apparent weight at the lowest

point of the circle if his true weight is 712 N? (b) What is his apparent weight at the highest point of the circle? (c) Describe how the pilot could experience weightlessness if both the radius and the speed can be varied. *Note:* His apparent weight is equal to the magnitude of the force exerted by the seat on his body. Under what conditions does this occur? (d) What speed would have resulted in the pilot experiencing weightlessness at the top of the loop?

69. **S** A piece of mud is initially at point *A* on the rim of a bicycle wheel of radius *R* rotating clockwise about a horizontal axis at a constant angular speed ω (Fig. P7.8). The mud dislodges from point *A* when the wheel diameter through *A* is horizontal. The mud then rises vertically and returns to point *A*. (a) Find a symbolic expression in terms of *R*, ω, and *g* for the total time the mud is in the air and returns to point *A*. (b) If the wheel makes one complete revolution in the time it takes the mud to return to point *A*, find an expression for the angular speed of the bicycle wheel ω in terms of π, *g*, and *R*.

70. **Q|C** A 0.275-kg object is swung in a *vertical* circular path on a string 0.850 m long as in Figure P7.70. (a) What are the forces acting on the ball at any point along this path? (b) Draw free-body diagrams for the ball when it is at the bottom of the circle and when it is at the top. (c) If its speed is 5.20 m/s at the top of the circle, what is the tension in the string there? (d) If the string breaks when its tension exceeds 22.5 N, what is the maximum speed the object can have at the bottom before the string breaks?

Figure P7.70

71. A 4.00-kg object is attached to a vertical rod by two strings as shown in Figure P7.71. The object rotates in a horizontal circle at constant speed 6.00 m/s. Find the tension in (a) the upper string and (b) the lower string.

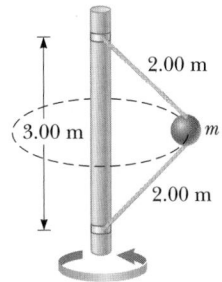

Figure P7.71

72. **BIO** The maximum lift force on a bat is proportional to the square of its flying speed *v*. For the hoary bat (*Lasiurus cinereus*), the magnitude of the lift force is given by

$$F_L \leq (0.018 \text{ N} \cdot \text{s}^2/\text{m}^2)v^2$$

The bat can fly in a horizontal circle by "banking" its wings at an angle θ, as shown in Figure P7.72. In this situation, the magnitude of the vertical component of the lift force must equal the bat's weight. The horizontal component of the force provides the centripetal acceleration. (a) What is the minimum speed that the bat can have if its mass is 0.031 kg? (b) If the maximum speed of the bat is 10 m/s, what is the maximum

banking angle that allows the bat to stay in a horizontal plane? (c) What is the radius of the circle of its flight when the bat flies at its maximum speed? (d) Can the bat turn with a smaller radius by flying more slowly?

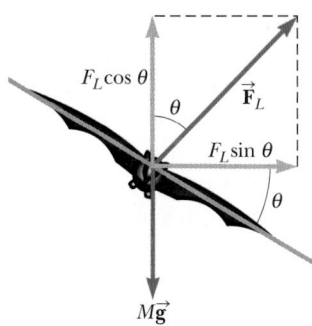

Figure P7.72

73. (a) A luggage carousel at an airport has the form of a section of a large cone, steadily rotating about its vertical axis. Its metallic surface slopes downward toward the outside, making an angle of 20.0° with the horizontal. A 30.0-kg piece of luggage is placed on the carousel, 7.46 m from the axis of rotation. The travel bag goes around once in 38.0 s. Calculate the force of static friction between the bag and the carousel. (b) The drive motor is shifted to turn the carousel at a higher constant rate of rotation, and the piece of luggage is bumped to a position 7.94 m from the axis of rotation. The bag is on the verge of slipping as it goes around once every 34.0 s. Calculate the coefficient of static friction between the bag and the carousel.

74. A 0.50-kg ball that is tied to the end of a 1.5-m light cord is revolved in a horizontal plane, with the cord making a 30° angle with the vertical. (See Fig. P7.74.) (a) Determine the ball's speed. (b) If, instead, the ball is revolved so that its speed is 4.0 m/s, what angle does the cord make with the vertical? (c) If the cord can withstand a maximum tension of 9.8 N, what is the highest speed at which the ball can move?

Figure P7.74

75. In a popular amusement park ride, a rotating cylinder of radius 3.00 m is set in rotation at an angular speed of 5.00 rad/s, as in Figure P7.75. The floor then drops away, leaving the riders suspended against the wall in a vertical position. What minimum coefficient of friction between a rider's clothing and the wall is needed to keep the rider from slipping? *Hint:* Recall that the magnitude of the maximum force

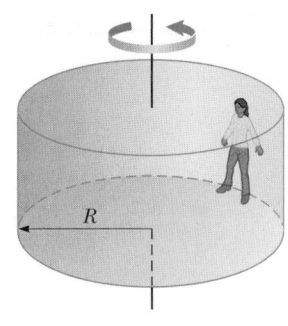

Figure P7.75

of static friction is equal to $\mu_s n$, where n is the normal force—in this case, the force causing the centripetal acceleration.

76. A massless spring of constant $k = 78.4$ N/m is fixed on the left side of a level track. A block of mass $m = 0.50$ kg is pressed against the spring and compresses it a distance d, as in Figure P7.76. The block (initially at rest) is then released and travels toward a circular loop-the-loop of radius $R = 1.5$ m. The entire track and the loop-the-loop are frictionless, except for the section of track between points A and B. Given that the coefficient of kinetic friction between the block and the track along AB is $\mu_k = 0.30$, and that the length of AB is 2.5 m, determine the minimum compression d of the spring that enables the block to just make it through the loop-the-loop at point C. *Hint:* The force exerted by the track on the block will be zero if the block barely makes it through the loop-the-loop.

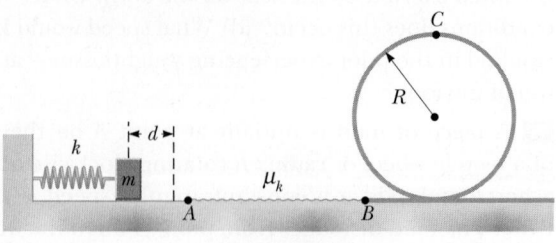

Figure P7.76

■ AP* REVIEW QUESTIONS

1. The acceleration due to gravity at earth's surface is *g*. If *R* is the radius of the Earth, at what height above the surface of the Earth would the acceleration due to gravity be equal to *g*/4?

(A) *R* (D) 4*R*
(B) 2*R* (E) 16*R*
(C) 3*R*

2. Which of the following is a consequence of the universal law of gravitation?

(A) If the distance between two masses is doubled, the gravitational attraction is halved.

(B) If two masses reach a critical distance apart, the gravitational force equals zero.

(C) If one of two masses attracting each other is doubled, the gravitational attraction is four times as great.

(D) The gravitational force between any two masses in the entire universe can never be zero.

(E) A planet's orbiting tangential velocity affects the size of gravitational pull from the Sun.

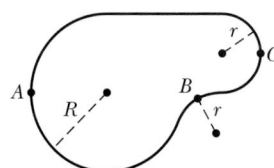

3. A race car driver completes one lap on the track shown above with a constant speed of *v*. Which of the following best describes the acceleration(s) of the car?

(A) The centripetal acceleration at point *A* is equal to the centripetal acceleration at point *B*.

(B) The tangential acceleration remains zero throughout the lap.

(C) The total magnitude of acceleration at *B* is different than that at *C*.

(D) The centripetal acceleration at point *A* is greater than the centripetal acceleration at point *B*.

(E) The tangential acceleration at point *A* is less than the tangential acceleration at point *C*.

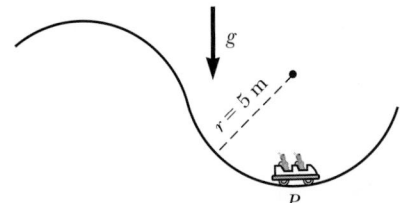

4. A section of track for a roller coaster is shown above. What force does the track exert on the coaster at point *P* if the coaster is traveling at 20 m/s and the mass of the cart plus passengers is 1000 kg and the curve follows a 5 m radius?

(A) 10,000 N (D) 90,000 N
(B) 14,000 N (E) 100,000 N
(C) 80,000 N

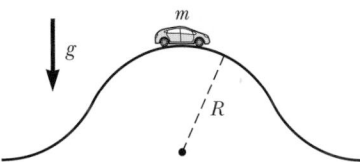

5. A road goes over a rounded hill with a vertical radius *R*, as shown above. What minimum constant speed would an automobile driver with mass *m* have to attain to allow the tires to barely make contact with the road at the top of this hill?

(A) gR (D) $m\sqrt{Rg}$
(B) $R\sqrt{g}$ (E) $\sqrt{2Rg}$
(C) $\sqrt{Rg}$

6. If the speed of an object revolving around another doubles while its radius remains constant, what happens to the magnitude of its centripetal acceleration?

(A) Half (D) Quadruples
(B) Same (E) Only a tangential acceleration
(C) Doubles exists after it has changed speed

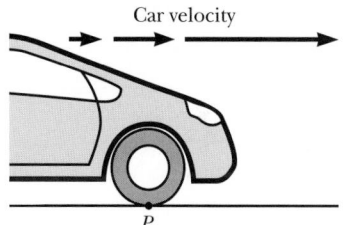

7. Consider the point *P* on a tire that contacts the ground for a forward accelerating car, as shown in the figure above.

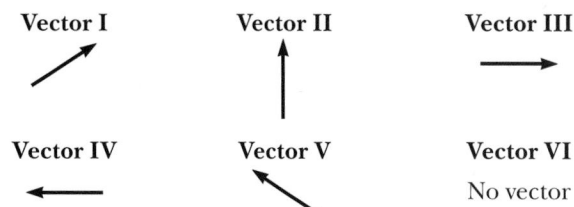

Which of the following set of vectors best describes the velocity and total acceleration for point *P* relative to the ground?

	Velocity	Total acceleration
(A)	III	I
(B)	IV	II
(C)	IV	V
(D)	V	III
(E)	VI	V

8. What would happen to an orbiting satellite around the Earth if suddenly half of its mass were removed?

   (A) The velocity and the orbit distance to the center of the Earth would remain the same.

   (B) The velocity would stay the same and the orbit distance to the center of the Earth would increase.

   (C) The velocity would decrease while its path would remain the same.

   (D) The velocity would stay the same and the orbit distance to the center of the Earth would decrease.

   (E) The velocity would increase while its path would remain the same.

9. A child is riding a horizontal merry-go-round at a position $R/4$, as shown above. What must the tangential speed of the merry-go-round be changed to if the child were to move out to a new position of radius R while maintaining the same centripetal force as before?

   (A) One-fourth the original speed

   (B) One-half the original speed

   (C) The same as the original speed

   (D) Double the original speed

   (E) Quadruple the original speed

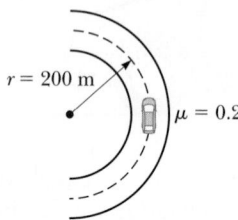

10. A car follows a flat, ice-covered curve with a radius of $r = 200$ m, as shown above. What is the maximum speed at which the car can make this turn if the coefficient of static friction between the icy road and tires is 0.2?

   (A) 5 m/s   (D) 30 m/s

   (B) 10 m/s   (E) 40 m/s

   (C) 20 m/s

Questions 11–12
Problems 11 and 12 relate to a similar setup with different orientations:

11. As shown in the figure at the bottom of the previous column, a cordless force probe is attached to a string that is spinning a rock in a vertical circle with a constant speed. Which of the following graphs would best represent the tension in the string over time if the speed is just great enough to maintain a circular path with the string?

   (A)

   (B)

   (C)

   (D)

   (E)

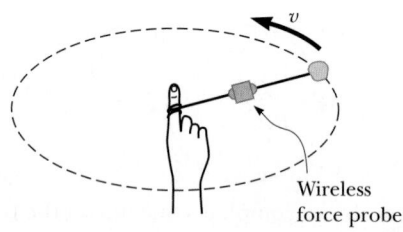

12. The string and force probe are now turned horizontally, as shown above. This time, however, the string is allowed to wrap around the finger of the person whirling the rock, shortening the string with every rotation. If the person whirls it in such a way that the rock maintains at a constant speed, what must the tension versus time graph look like?

   (A)

   (B)

   (C)

   (D)

   (E)

Marnie Burkhart/Fancy/Jupiter Images

Wind exerts forces on the propellers of this wind turbine, producing a torque that causes the turbine to rotate. This process converts the kinetic energy of wind to rotational kinetic energy, which is transformed by electromagnetic induction to electrical energy.

Rotational Equilibrium and Rotational Dynamics

8

In the study of linear motion, objects were treated as point particles without structure. It didn't matter *where* a force was applied, only *whether* it was applied or not.

The reality is that the point of application of a force *does* matter. In football, for example, if the ball carrier is tackled near his midriff, he might carry the tackler several yards before falling. If tackled well below the waistline, however, his center of mass rotates toward the ground, and he can be brought down immediately. Tennis provides another good example. If a tennis ball is struck with a strong horizontal force acting through its center of mass, it may travel a long distance before hitting the ground, far out of bounds. Instead, the same force applied in an upward, glancing stroke will impart topspin to the ball, which can cause it to land in the opponent's court.

The concepts of rotational equilibrium and rotational dynamics are also important in other disciplines. For example, students of architecture benefit from understanding the forces that act on buildings, and biology students should understand the forces at work in muscles and on bones and joints. These forces create torques, which tell us how the forces affect an object's equilibrium and rate of rotation.

We will find that an object remains in a state of uniform rotational motion unless acted on by a net torque. That principle is the equivalent of Newton's first law. Further, the angular acceleration of an object is proportional to the net torque acting on it, which is the analog of Newton's second law. A net torque acting on an object causes a change in its rotational energy.

Finally, torques applied to an object through a given time interval can change the object's angular momentum. In the absence of external torques, angular momentum is conserved, a property that explains some of the mysterious and formidable properties of pulsars, remnants of supernova explosions that rotate at equatorial speeds approaching that of light.

Figure 8.1 A bird's-eye view of a door hinged at O, with a force applied perpendicular to the door.

8.1 Torque

Forces cause accelerations; *torques* cause angular accelerations. There is a definite relationship, however, between the two concepts.

Figure 8.1 depicts an overhead view of a door hinged at point O. From this viewpoint, the door is free to rotate around an axis perpendicular to the page and passing through O. If a force $\vec{\mathbf{F}}$ is applied to the door, there are three factors that determine the effectiveness of the force in opening the door: the *magnitude* of the force, the *position* of application of the force, and the *angle* at which it is applied.

For simplicity, we restrict our discussion to position and force vectors lying in a plane. When the applied force $\vec{\mathbf{F}}$ is perpendicular to the outer edge of the door, as in Figure 8.1, the door rotates counterclockwise with constant angular acceleration. The same perpendicular force applied at a point nearer the hinge results in a smaller angular acceleration. In general, a larger radial distance r between the applied force and the axis of rotation results in a larger angular acceleration. Similarly, a larger applied force will also result in a larger angular acceleration. These considerations motivate the basic definition of **torque** for the special case of forces perpendicular to the position vector:

Basic definition of torque ▶

Let $\vec{\mathbf{F}}$ be a force acting on an object, and let $\vec{\mathbf{r}}$ be a position vector from a chosen point O to the point of application of the force, with $\vec{\mathbf{F}}$ perpendicular to $\vec{\mathbf{r}}$. The magnitude of the torque $\vec{\boldsymbol{\tau}}$ exerted by the force $\vec{\mathbf{F}}$ is given by

$$\tau = rF \qquad [8.1]$$

where r is the length of the position vector and F is the magnitude of the force.

SI unit: Newton-meter (N · m)

The vectors $\vec{\mathbf{r}}$ and $\vec{\mathbf{F}}$ lie in a plane. Active Figure 8.2 illustrates how the point of the force's application affects the magnitude of the torque. As discussed in detail shortly in conjunction with Figure 8.6, the torque $\vec{\boldsymbol{\tau}}$ is then perpendicular to this plane. The point O is usually chosen to coincide with the axis the object is rotating around, such as the hinge of a door or hub of a merry-go-round. (Other choices are possible as well.) In addition, we consider only forces acting in the plane perpendicular to the axis of rotation. This criterion excludes, for example, a force with upward component on a merry-go-round railing, which cannot affect the merry-go-round's rotation.

Under these conditions, an object can rotate around the chosen axis in one of two directions. By convention, counterclockwise is taken to be the positive direction, clockwise the negative direction. When an applied force causes an object to rotate counterclockwise, the torque on the object is positive. When the force causes the object to rotate clockwise, the torque on the object is negative. When two or

Active Figure 8.2 As the force is applied farther out along the wrench, the magnitude of the torque increases.

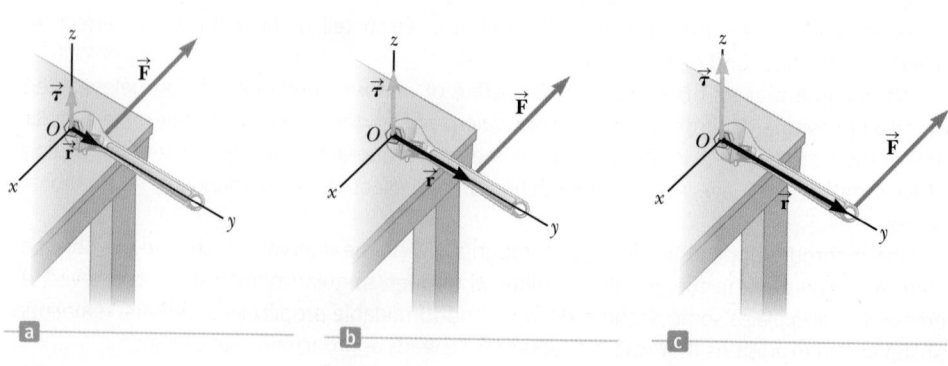

more torques act on an object at rest, the torques are added. If the net torque isn't zero, the object starts rotating at an ever-increasing rate. If the net torque is zero, the object's rate of rotation doesn't change. These considerations lead to the rotational analog of the first law: **the rate of rotation of an object doesn't change, unless the object is acted on by a net torque.**

▪ EXAMPLE 8.1 | Battle of the Revolving Door

GOAL Apply the basic definition of torque.

PROBLEM Two disgruntled businesspeople are trying to use a revolving door, as in Figure 8.3. The woman on the left exerts a force of 625 N perpendicular to the door and 1.20 m from the hub's center, while the man on the right exerts a force of 8.50×10^2 N perpendicular to the door and 0.800 m from the hub's center. Find the net torque on the revolving door.

STRATEGY Calculate the individual torques on the door using the definition of torque, Equation 8.1, and then sum to find the net torque on the door. The woman exerts a negative torque, the man a positive torque. Their positions of application also differ.

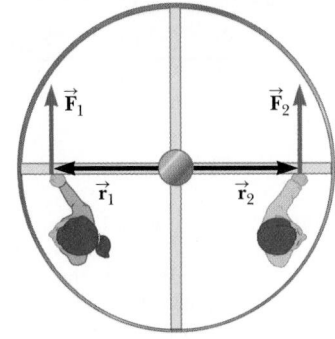

Figure 8.3 (Example 8.1)

SOLUTION

Calculate the torque exerted by the woman. A negative sign must be supplied because $\vec{\mathbf{F}}_1$, if unopposed, would cause a clockwise rotation:

$$\tau_1 = -r_1 F_1 = -(1.20 \text{ m})(625 \text{ N}) = -7.50 \times 10^2 \text{ N} \cdot \text{m}$$

Calculate the torque exerted by the man. The torque is positive because $\vec{\mathbf{F}}_2$, if unopposed, would cause a counterclockwise rotation:

$$\tau_2 = r_2 F_2 = (0.800 \text{ m})(8.50 \times 10^2 \text{ N}) = 6.80 \times 10^2 \text{ N} \cdot \text{m}$$

Sum the torques to find the net torque on the door:

$$\tau_{\text{net}} = \tau_1 + \tau_2 = \boxed{-7.0 \times 10^1 \text{ N} \cdot \text{m}}$$

REMARKS The negative result here means that the net torque will produce a clockwise rotation.

QUESTION 8.1 What happens if the woman suddenly slides closer to the hub by 0.400 m?

EXERCISE 8.1 A businessman enters the same revolving door on the right, pushing with 576 N of force directed perpendicular to the door and 0.700 m from the hub, while a boy exerts a force of 365 N perpendicular to the door, 1.25 m to the left of the hub. Find (a) the torques exerted by each person and (b) the net torque on the door.

ANSWERS (a) $\tau_{\text{boy}} = -456 \text{ N} \cdot \text{m}$, $\tau_{\text{man}} = 403 \text{ N} \cdot \text{m}$ (b) $\tau_{\text{net}} = -53 \text{ N} \cdot \text{m}$

The applied force isn't always perpendicular to the position vector $\vec{\mathbf{r}}$. Suppose the force $\vec{\mathbf{F}}$ exerted on a door is directed away from the axis, as in Figure 8.4a (page 238), say, by someone's grasping the doorknob and pushing to the right. Exerting the force in this direction couldn't possibly open the door. However, if the applied force acts at an angle to the door as in Figure 8.4b, the component of the force *perpendicular* to the door will cause it to rotate. This figure shows that the component of the force perpendicular to the door is $F \sin \theta$, where θ is the angle between the position vector $\vec{\mathbf{r}}$ and the force $\vec{\mathbf{F}}$. When the force is directed away from the axis, $\theta = 0°$, $\sin (0°) = 0$, and $F \sin (0°) = 0$. When the force is directed toward the axis, $\theta = 180°$ and $F \sin (180°) = 0$. The maximum absolute value of $F \sin \theta$ is attained only when $\vec{\mathbf{F}}$ is perpendicular to $\vec{\mathbf{r}}$—that is, when $\theta = 90°$ or $\theta = 270°$. These considerations motivate a more general definition of torque:

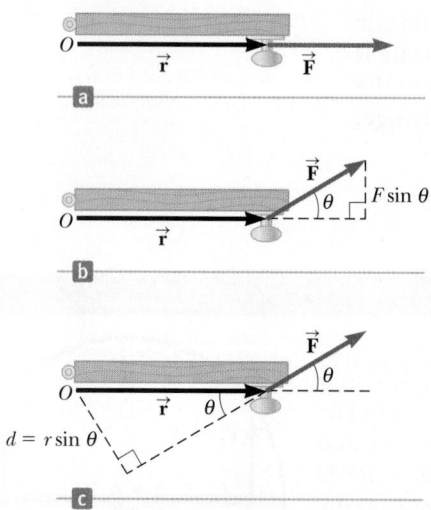

Figure 8.4 (a) A force $\vec{\mathbf{F}}$ acting at an angle $\theta = 0°$ exerts zero torque about the pivot O. (b) The part of the force perpendicular to the door, $F\sin\theta$, exerts torque $rF\sin\theta$ about O. (c) An alternate interpretation of torque in terms of a *lever arm* $d = r\sin\theta$.

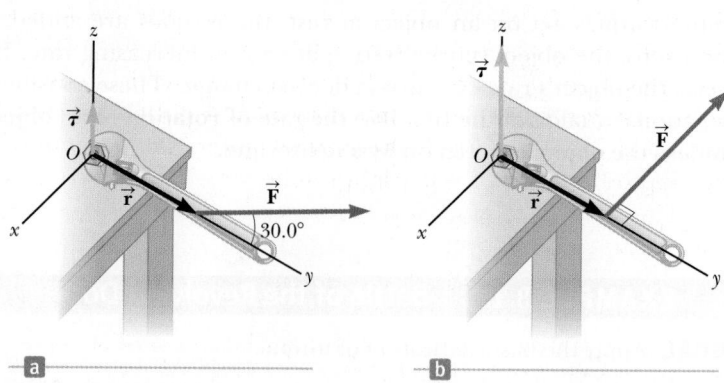

Figure 8.5 As the angle between the position vector and force vector increases in parts (a)–(b), the torque exerted by the wrench increases.

General definition ▶ of torque

Let $\vec{\mathbf{F}}$ be a force acting on an object, and let $\vec{\mathbf{r}}$ be a position vector from a chosen point O to the point of application of the force. The magnitude of the torque $\vec{\tau}$ exerted by the force $\vec{\mathbf{F}}$ is

$$\tau = rF\sin\theta \qquad [8.2]$$

where r is the length of the position vector, F the magnitude of the force, and θ the angle between $\vec{\mathbf{r}}$ and $\vec{\mathbf{F}}$.

SI unit: Newton-meter (N · m)

Again the vectors $\vec{\mathbf{r}}$ and $\vec{\mathbf{F}}$ lie in a plane, and for our purposes the chosen point O will usually correspond to an axis of rotation perpendicular to the plane. Figure 8.5 illustrates how the magnitude of the torque exerted by a wrench increases as the angle between the position vector and the force vector increases at 90°, where the torque is a maximum.

A second way of understanding the $\sin\theta$ factor is to associate it with the magnitude r of the position vector $\vec{\mathbf{r}}$. The quantity $d = r\sin\theta$ is called the **lever arm,** which is the perpendicular distance from the axis of rotation to a line drawn along the direction of the force. This alternate interpretation is illustrated in Figure 8.4c.

It's important to remember that **the value of τ depends on the chosen axis of rotation.** Torques can be computed around any axis, regardless of whether there is some actual, physical rotation axis present. Once the point is chosen, however, it must be used consistently throughout a given problem.

Torque is a vector perpendicular to the plane determined by the position and force vectors, as illustrated in Figure 8.6. The direction can be determined by the *right-hand rule:*

Figure 8.6 The right-hand rule: Point the fingers of your right hand along $\vec{\mathbf{r}}$ and curl them in the direction of $\vec{\mathbf{F}}$. Your thumb then points in the direction of the torque (out of the page, in this case). Note that either θ or θ' can be used in the definition of torque.

1. Point the fingers of your right hand in the direction of $\vec{\mathbf{r}}$.
2. Curl your fingers toward the direction of vector $\vec{\mathbf{F}}$.
3. Your thumb then points approximately in the direction of the torque, in this case out of the page.

Notice the two choices of angle in Figure 8.6. The angle θ is the actual angle between the directions of the two vectors. The angle θ' is literally "between" the two vectors. Which angle is correct? Because $\sin \theta = \sin (180° − \theta) = \sin (180°) \cos \theta − \sin \theta \cos (180°) = 0 − \sin \theta \cdot (−1) = \sin \theta$, either angle is correct. Problems used in this book will be confined to objects rotating around an axis perpendicular to the plane containing $\vec{r}$ and $\vec{F}$, so if these vectors are in the plane of the page, the torque will always point either into or out of the page, parallel to the axis of rotation. If your right thumb is pointed in the direction of a torque, your fingers curl naturally in the direction of rotation that the torque would produce on an object at rest.

■ EXAMPLE 8.2 | The Swinging Door

GOAL Apply the more general definition of torque.

PROBLEM (a) A man applies a force of $F = 3.00 \times 10^2$ N at an angle of 60.0° to the door of Figure 8.7a, 2.00 m from the hinges. Find the torque on the door, choosing the position of the hinges as the axis of rotation. (b) Suppose a wedge is placed 1.50 m from the hinges on the other side of the door. What minimum force must the wedge exert so that the force applied in part (a) won't open the door?

STRATEGY Part (a) can be solved by substitution into the general torque equation. In part (b) the hinges, the wedge, and the applied force all exert torques on the door. The door doesn't open, so the sum of these torques must be zero, a condition that can be used to find the wedge force.

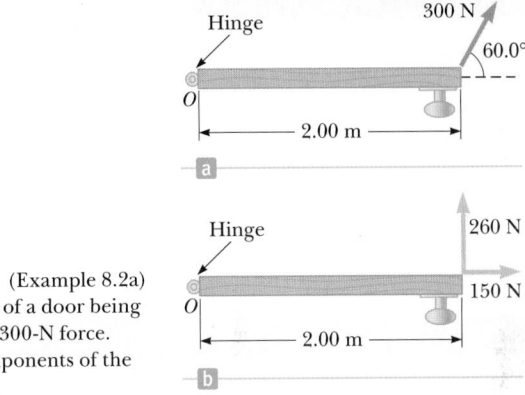

Figure 8.7 (Example 8.2a)
(a) Top view of a door being pushed by a 300-N force.
(b) The components of the 300-N force.

. . . .

SOLUTION

(a) Compute the torque due to the applied force exerted at 60.0°.

Substitute into the general torque equation:

$$\tau_F = rF \sin \theta = (2.00 \text{ m})(3.00 \times 10^2 \text{ N}) \sin 60.0°$$
$$= (2.00 \text{ m})(2.60 \times 10^2 \text{ N}) = \boxed{5.20 \times 10^2 \text{ N} \cdot \text{m}}$$

(b) Calculate the force exerted by the wedge on the other side of the door.

Set the sum of the torques equal to zero:

$$\tau_{\text{hinge}} + \tau_{\text{wedge}} + \tau_F = 0$$

The hinge force provides no torque because it acts at the axis ($r = 0$). The wedge force acts at an angle of −90.0°, opposite the upward 260 N component.

$$0 + F_{\text{wedge}}(1.50 \text{ m}) \sin (−90.0°) + 5.20 \times 10^2 \text{ N} \cdot \text{m} = 0$$
$$F_{\text{wedge}} = \boxed{347 \text{ N}}$$

. . . .

REMARKS Notice that the angle from the position vector to the wedge force is −90°. That's because, starting at the position vector, it's necessary to go 90° clockwise (the negative angular direction) to get to the force vector. Measuring the angle that way automatically supplies the correct sign for the torque term and is consistent with the right-hand rule. Alternately, the magnitude of the torque can be found and the correct sign chosen based on physical intuition. Figure 8.7b illustrates the fact that the component of the force perpendicular to the lever arm causes the torque.

QUESTION 8.2 To make the wedge more effective in keeping the door closed, should it be placed closer to the hinge or to the doorknob?

EXERCISE 8.2 A man ties one end of a strong rope 8.00 m long to the bumper of his truck, 0.500 m from the ground, and the other end to a vertical tree trunk at a height of 3.00 m. He uses the truck to create a tension of 8.00×10^2 N in the rope. Compute the magnitude of the torque on the tree due to the tension in the rope, with the base of the tree acting as the reference point.

ANSWER 2.28×10^3 N · m

8.2 Torque and the Two Conditions for Equilibrium

This large balanced rock at the Garden of the Gods in Colorado Springs, Colorado, is in mechanical equilibrium.

An object in mechanical equilibrium must satisfy the following two conditions:

1. **The net external force must be zero:** $\sum \vec{F} = 0$

2. **The net external torque must be zero:** $\sum \vec{\tau} = 0$

The first condition is a statement of translational equilibrium: The sum of all forces acting on the object must be zero, so the object has no translational acceleration, $\vec{a} = 0$. The second condition is a statement of rotational equilibrium: The sum of all torques on the object must be zero, so the object has no angular acceleration, $\vec{\alpha} = 0$. For an object to be in equilibrium, it must move through space at a constant speed and rotate at a constant angular speed.

Because we can choose any location for calculating torques, it's usually best to select an axis that will make at least one torque equal to zero, just to simplify the net torque equation.

■ EXAMPLE 8.3 | Balancing Act

GOAL Apply the conditions of equilibrium and illustrate the use of different axes for calculating the net torque on an object.

PROBLEM A woman of mass $m = 55.0$ kg sits on the left end of a seesaw—a plank of length $L = 4.00$ m, pivoted in the middle as in Figure 8.8. **(a)** First compute the torques on the seesaw about an axis that passes through the pivot point. Where should a man of mass $M = 75.0$ kg sit if the system (seesaw plus man and woman) is to be balanced? **(b)** Find the normal force exerted by the pivot if the plank has a mass of $m_{pl} = 12.0$ kg. **(c)** Repeat part (a), but this time compute the torques about an axis through the left end of the plank.

STRATEGY In part (a), apply the second condition of equilibrium, $\Sigma\tau = 0$, computing torques around the pivot point. The mass of the plank forming the seesaw is distributed evenly on either side of the pivot point, so the torque exerted by gravity on the plank, $\tau_{gravity}$, can be computed as if all the plank's mass is concentrated at the pivot point. Then $\tau_{gravity}$ is zero, as is the torque exerted by the pivot, because their lever arms are zero. In part (b) the first condition of equilibrium, $\Sigma\vec{F} = 0$, must be applied. Part (c) is a repeat of part (a) showing that choice of a different axis yields the same answer.

Figure 8.8 (Example 8.3) The system consists of two people and a seesaw. Because the sum of the forces and the sum of the torques acting on the system are both zero, the system is said to be in equilibrium.

SOLUTION

(a) Where should the man sit to balance the seesaw?

Apply the second condition of equilibrium to the plank by setting the sum of the torques equal to zero:

$$\tau_{pivot} + \tau_{gravity} + \tau_{man} + \tau_{woman} = 0$$

The first two torques are zero. Let x represent the man's distance from the pivot. The woman is at a distance $L/2$ from the pivot.

$$0 + 0 - Mgx + mg(L/2) = 0$$

Solve this equation for x and evaluate it:

$$x = \frac{m(L/2)}{M} = \frac{(55.0 \text{ kg})(2.00 \text{ m})}{75.0 \text{ kg}} = \boxed{1.47 \text{ m}}$$

(b) Find the normal force n exerted by the pivot on the seesaw.

Apply for first condition of equilibrium to the plank, solving the resulting equation for the unknown normal force, n:

$$-Mg - mg - m_{pl}g + n = 0$$

$$n = (M + m + m_{pl})g$$

$$= (75.0 \text{ kg} + 55.0 \text{ kg} + 12.0 \text{ kg})(9.80 \text{ m/s}^2)$$

$$n = \boxed{1.39 \times 10^3 \text{ N}}$$

(c) Repeat part (a), choosing a new axis through the left end of the plank.

Compute the torques using this axis, and set their sum equal to zero. Now the pivot and gravity forces on the plank result in nonzero torques.

$$\tau_{man} + \tau_{woman} + \tau_{plank} + \tau_{pivot} = 0$$

$$-Mg(L/2 + x) + mg(0) - m_{pl}g(L/2) + n(L/2) = 0$$

Substitute all known quantities:

$$-(75.0 \text{ kg})(9.80 \text{ m/s}^2)(2.00 \text{ m} + x) + 0$$

$$- (12.0 \text{ kg})(9.80 \text{ m/s}^2)(2.00 \text{ m}) + n(2.00 \text{ m}) = 0$$

$$-(1.47 \times 10^3 \text{ N} \cdot \text{m}) - (735 \text{ N})x - (235 \text{ N} \cdot \text{m})$$

$$+ (2.00 \text{ m})n = 0$$

Solve for x, substituting the normal force found in part (b):

$$x = \boxed{1.46 \text{ m}}$$

REMARKS The answers for x in parts (a) and (c) agree except for a small rounding discrepancy. That illustrates how choosing a different axis leads to the same solution.

QUESTION 8.3 What happens if the woman now leans backwards?

EXERCISE 8.3 Suppose a 30.0-kg child sits 1.50 m to the left of center on the same seesaw. A second child sits at the end on the opposite side, and the system is balanced. (a) Find the mass of the second child. (b) Find the normal force acting at the pivot point.

ANSWERS (a) 22.5 kg   (b) 632 N

8.3 The Center of Gravity

In the example of the seesaw in the previous section, we guessed that the torque due to the force of gravity on the plank was the same as if all the plank's weight were concentrated at its center. That's a general procedure: To compute the torque on a rigid body due to the force of gravity, the body's entire weight can be thought of as concentrated at a single point. The problem then reduces to finding the location of that point. If the body is homogeneous (its mass is distributed evenly) and symmetric, it's usually possible to guess the location of that point, as in Example 8.3. Otherwise, it's necessary to calculate the point's location, as explained in this section.

Consider an object of arbitrary shape lying in the xy-plane, as in Figure 8.9. The object is divided into a large number of very small particles of weight m_1g, m_2g, m_3g, ... having coordinates (x_1, y_1), (x_2, y_2), (x_3, y_3), ... If the object is free to rotate around the origin, each particle contributes a torque about the origin that is equal to its weight multiplied by its lever arm. For example, the torque due to the weight m_1g is m_1gx_1, and so forth.

We wish to locate the point of application of the single force of magnitude $w = F_g = Mg$ (the total weight of the object), where the effect on the rotation of the object is the same as that of the individual particles. That point is called the object's **center of gravity.** Equating the torque exerted by w at the center of gravity to the sum of the torques acting on the individual particles gives

$$(m_1g + m_2g + m_3g + \cdots)x_{cg} = m_1gx_1 + m_2gx_2 + m_3gx_3 + \cdots$$

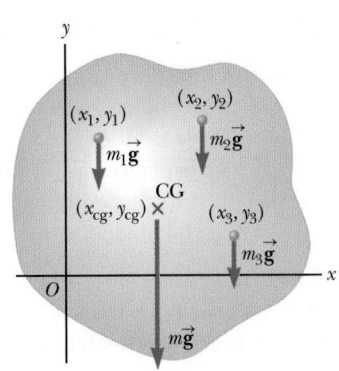

Figure 8.9 The net gravitational torque on an object is zero if computed around the center of gravity. The object will balance if supported at that point (or at any point along a vertical line above or below that point).

We assume that g is the same everywhere in the object (which is true for all objects we will encounter). Then the g factors in the preceding equation cancel, resulting in

$$x_{cg} = \frac{m_1 x_1 + m_2 x_2 + m_3 x_3 + \cdots}{m_1 + m_2 + m_3 + \cdots} = \frac{\sum m_i x_i}{\sum m_i} \qquad \text{[8.3a]}$$

where x_{cg} is the x-coordinate of the center of gravity. Similarly, the y-coordinate and z-coordinate of the center of gravity of the system can be found from

$$y_{cg} = \frac{\sum m_i y_i}{\sum m_i} \qquad \text{[8.3b]}$$

and

$$z_{cg} = \frac{\sum m_i z_i}{\sum m_i} \qquad \text{[8.3c]}$$

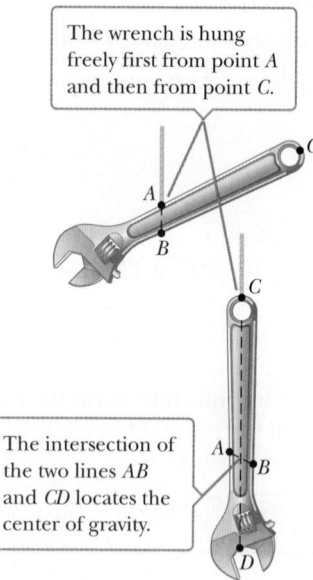

The wrench is hung freely first from point A and then from point C.

The intersection of the two lines AB and CD locates the center of gravity.

Figure 8.10 An experimental technique for determining the center of gravity of a wrench.

These three equations are identical to the equations for a similar concept called **center of mass.** The center of mass and center of gravity of an object are exactly the same when g doesn't vary significantly over the object.

It's often possible to guess the location of the center of gravity. **The center of gravity of a homogeneous, symmetric body must lie on the axis of symmetry.** For example, the center of gravity of a homogeneous rod lies midway between the ends of the rod, and the center of gravity of a homogeneous sphere or a homogeneous cube lies at the geometric center of the object. The center of gravity of an irregularly shaped object, such as a wrench, can be determined experimentally by suspending the wrench from two different arbitrary points (Fig. 8.10). The wrench is first hung from point A, and a vertical line AB (which can be established with a plumb bob) is drawn when the wrench is in equilibrium. The wrench is then hung from point C, and a second vertical line CD is drawn. The center of gravity coincides with the intersection of these two lines. In fact, if the wrench is hung freely from any point, the center of gravity always lies straight below the point of support, so the vertical line through that point must pass through the center of gravity.

Several examples in Section 8.4 involve homogeneous, symmetric objects where the centers of gravity coincide with their geometric centers. A rigid object in a uniform gravitational field can be balanced by a single force equal in magnitude to the weight of the object, as long as the force is directed upward through the object's center of gravity.

▪ EXAMPLE 8.4 ▪ Where Is the Center of Gravity?

GOAL Find the center of gravity of a system of objects.

PROBLEM (a) Three objects are located in a coordinate system as shown in Figure 8.11a. Find the center of gravity. (b) How does the answer change if the object on the left is displaced upward by 1.00 m and the object on the right is displaced downward by 0.500 m (Figure 8.11b)? Treat the objects as point particles.

STRATEGY The y-coordinate and z-coordinate of the center of gravity in part (a) are both zero because all the objects are on the x-axis. We can find the x-coordinate of the center of gravity using Equation 8.3a. Part (b) requires Equation 8.3b.

Figure 8.11 (Example 8.4) Locating the center of gravity of a system of three particles.

....

SOLUTION

(a) Find the center of gravity of the system in Figure 8.11a.

Apply Equation 8.3a to the system of three objects:

$$(1) \quad x_{cg} = \frac{\sum m_i x_i}{\sum m_i} = \frac{m_1 x_1 + m_2 x_2 + m_3 x_3}{m_1 + m_2 + m_3}$$

Compute the numerator of Equation (1):

$$\sum m_i x_i = m_1 x_1 + m_2 x_2 + m_3 x_3$$
$$= (5.00 \text{ kg})(-0.500 \text{ m}) + (2.00 \text{ kg})(0 \text{ m}) + (4.00 \text{ kg})(1.00 \text{ m})$$
$$= 1.50 \text{ kg} \cdot \text{m}$$

Substitute the denominator, $\sum m_i = 11.0$ kg, and the numerator into Equation (1).

$$x_{cg} = \frac{1.50 \text{ kg} \cdot \text{m}}{11.0 \text{ kg}} = \boxed{0.136 \text{ m}}$$

(b) How does the answer change if the positions of the objects are changed as in Figure 8.11b?

Because the x-coordinates have not been changed, the x-coordinate of the center of gravity is also unchanged:

$$x_{cg} = \boxed{0.136 \text{ m}}$$

Write Equation 8.3b:

$$y_{cg} = \frac{\sum m_i y_i}{\sum m_i} = \frac{m_1 y_1 + m_2 y_2 + m_3 y_3}{m_1 + m_2 + m_3}$$

Substitute values:

$$y_{cg} = \frac{(5.00 \text{ kg})(1.00 \text{ m}) + (2.00 \text{ kg})(0 \text{ m}) + (4.00 \text{ kg})(-0.500 \text{ m})}{5.00 \text{ kg} + 2.00 \text{ kg} + 4.00 \text{ kg}}$$

$$y_{cg} = \boxed{0.273 \text{ m}}$$

REMARKS Notice that translating objects in the y-direction doesn't change the x-coordinate of the center of gravity. The three components of the center of gravity are each independent of the other two coordinates.

QUESTION 8.4 If 1.00 kg is added to the masses on the left and right in Figure 8.11a, does the center of mass (a) move to the left, (b) move to the right, or (c) remain in the same position?

EXERCISE 8.4 If a fourth particle of mass 2.00 kg is placed at (0, 0.25 m) in Figure 8.11a, find the x- and y-coordinates of the center of gravity for this system of four particles.

ANSWER $x_{cg} = 0.115$ m; $y_{cg} = 0.038\ 5$ m

■ EXAMPLE 8.5 | **Locating Your Lab Partner's Center of Gravity** BIO

GOAL Use torque to find a center of gravity.

PROBLEM In this example we show how to find the location of a person's center of gravity. Suppose your lab partner has a height L of 173 cm (5 ft, 8 in) and a weight w of 715 N (160 lb). You can determine the position of his center of gravity by having him stretch out on a uniform board supported at one end by a scale, as shown in Figure 8.12. If the board's weight w_b is 49 N and the scale reading F is 3.50×10^2 N, find the distance of your lab partner's center of gravity from the left end of the board.

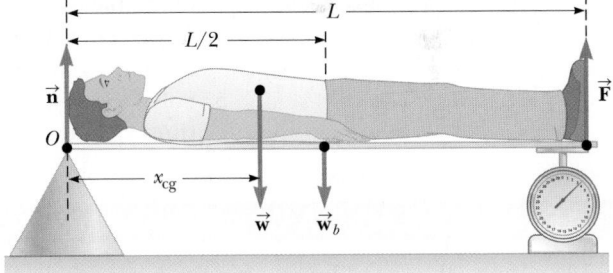

Figure 8.12 (Example 8.5) Determining your lab partner's center of gravity.

STRATEGY To find the position x_{cg} of the center of gravity, compute the torques using an axis through O. There is no torque due to the normal force $\vec{\mathbf{n}}$ because its moment arm is zero about an axis through O. Set the sum of the torques equal to zero and solve for x_{cg}.

SOLUTION

Apply the second condition of equilibrium:

$$\sum \tau_i = \tau_n + \tau_w + \tau_{w_b} + \tau_F = 0$$

Substitute expressions for the torques?

$$0 - wx_{cg} - w_b(L/2) + FL = 0$$

Solve for x_{cg} and substitute known values:

$$x_{cg} = \frac{FL - w_b(L/2)}{w}$$

$$= \frac{(350 \text{ N})(173 \text{ cm}) - (49 \text{ N})(86.5 \text{ cm})}{715 \text{ N}} = \boxed{79 \text{ cm}}$$

(Continued)

REMARKS The given information is sufficient only to determine the x-coordinate of the center of gravity. The other two coordinates can be estimated, based on the body's symmetry.

QUESTION 8.5 What would happen if a support is placed exactly at $x = 79$ cm followed by the removal of the supports at the subject's head and feet?

EXERCISE 8.5 Suppose a 416-kg alligator of length 3.5 m is stretched out on a board of the same length weighing 65 N. If the board is supported on the ends as in Figure 8.12, and the scale reads 1 880 N, find the x-component of the alligator's center of gravity.

ANSWER 1.59 m

Tip 8.2 Rotary Motion Under Zero Torque

If a net torque of zero is exerted on an object, it will continue to rotate at a constant angular speed—which need not be zero. However, zero torque *does* imply that the angular acceleration is zero.

8.4 Examples of Objects in Equilibrium

Recall from Chapter 4 that when an object is treated as a geometric point, equilibrium requires only that the net force on the object is zero. In this chapter we have shown that for extended objects a second condition for equilibrium must also be satisfied: The net torque on the object must be zero. The following general procedure is recommended for solving problems that involve objects in equilibrium.

■ **PROBLEM-SOLVING STRATEGY**

Objects in Equilibrium

1. **Diagram the system.** Include coordinates and choose a convenient rotation axis for computing the net torque on the object.
2. **Draw a force diagram** of the object of interest, showing all external forces acting on it. For systems with more than one object, draw a *separate* diagram for each object. (Most problems will have a single object of interest.)
3. **Apply $\Sigma\tau_i = 0$, the second condition of equilibrium.** This condition yields a single equation for each object of interest. If the axis of rotation has been carefully chosen, the equation often has only one unknotwn and can be solved immediately.
4. **Apply $\Sigma F_x = 0$ and $\Sigma F_y = 0$, the first condition of equilibrium.** This yields two more equations per object of interest.
5. **Solve the system of equations.** For each object, the two conditions of equilibrium yield three equations, usually with three unknowns. Solve by substitution.

■ **EXAMPLE 8.6** | **A Weighted Forearm** BIO

GOAL Apply the equilibrium conditions to the human body.

PROBLEM A 50.0-N (11-lb) bowling ball is held in a person's hand with the forearm horizontal, as in Figure 8.13a. The biceps muscle is attached 0.030 0 m from the joint, and the ball is 0.350 m from the joint. Find the upward force $\vec{F}$ exerted by the biceps on the forearm (the ulna) and the downward force $\vec{R}$ exerted by the humerus on the forearm, acting at the joint. Neglect the weight of the forearm and slight deviation from the vertical of the biceps.

STRATEGY The forces acting on the forearm are equivalent to those acting on a bar of length 0.350 m, as shown in Figure 8.13b. Choose the usual

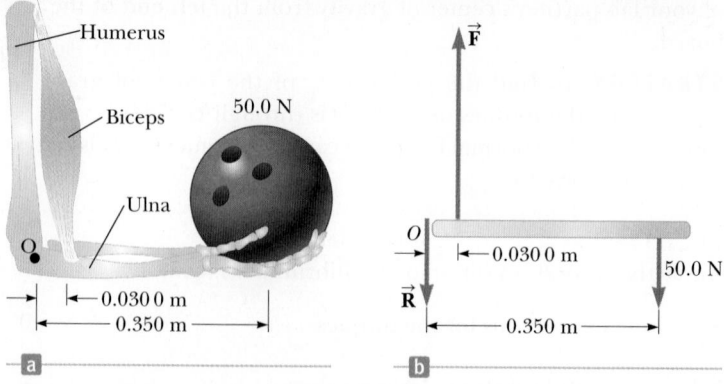

Figure 8.13 (Example 8.6) (a) A weight held with the forearm horizontal. (b) The mechanical model for the system.

x- and y-coordinates as shown and the axis at O on the left end. (This completes Steps 1 and 2.) Use the conditions of equilibrium to generate equations for the unknowns, and solve.

SOLUTION

Apply the second condition for equilibrium (Step 3) and solve for the upward force F:

$$\sum \tau_i = \tau_R + \tau_F + \tau_{BB} = 0$$
$$R(0) + F(0.030\ 0\ \text{m}) - (50.0\ \text{N})(0.350\ \text{m}) = 0$$
$$F = \boxed{583\ \text{N}\ (131\ \text{lb})}$$

Apply the first condition for equilibrium (Step 4) and solve (Step 5) for the downward force R:

$$\sum F_y = F - R - 50.0\ \text{N} = 0$$
$$R = F - 50.0\ \text{N} = 583\ \text{N} - 50\ \text{N} = \boxed{533\ \text{N}\ (120\ \text{lb})}$$

REMARKS The magnitude of the force supplied by the biceps must be about ten times as large as the bowling ball it is supporting!

QUESTION 8.6 Suppose the biceps were surgically reattached three centimeters farther toward the person's hand. If the same bowling ball were again held in the person's hand, how would the force required of the biceps be affected? Explain.

EXERCISE 8.6 Suppose you wanted to limit the force acting on your joint to a maximum value of 8.00×10^2 N. (a) Under these circumstances, what maximum weight would you attempt to lift? (b) What force would your biceps apply while lifting this weight?

ANSWERS (a) 75.0 N   (b) 875 N

■ EXAMPLE 8.7 | Don't Climb the Ladder

GOAL Apply the two conditions of equilibrium.

PROBLEM A uniform ladder 10.0 m long and weighing 50.0 N rests against a smooth vertical wall as in Figure 8.14a. If the ladder is just on the verge of slipping when it makes a 50.0° angle with the ground, find the coefficient of static friction between the ladder and ground.

STRATEGY Figure 8.14b is the force diagram for the ladder. The first condition of equilibrium, $\sum \vec{F}_i = 0$, gives two equations for three unknowns: the magnitudes of the static friction force f and the normal force n, both acting on the base of the ladder, and the magnitude of the force of the wall, P, acting on the top of the ladder. The second condition of equilibrium, $\sum \tau_i = 0$, gives a third equation (for P), so all three quantities can be found. The definition of static friction then allows computation of the coefficient of static friction.

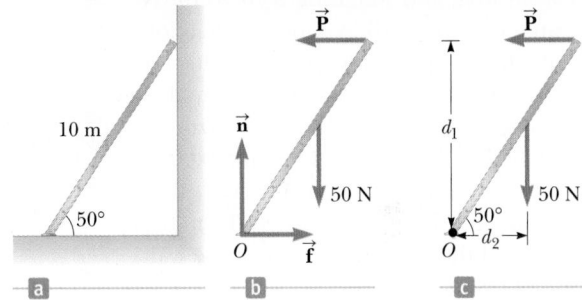

Figure 8.14 (Interactive Example 8.7) (a) A ladder leaning against a frictionless wall. (b) A force diagram of the ladder. (c) Lever arms for the force of gravity and $\vec{P}$.

SOLUTION

Apply the first condition of equilibrium to the ladder:

(1) $\sum F_x = f - P = 0 \quad \rightarrow \quad f = P$

(2) $\sum F_y = n - 50.0\ \text{N} = 0 \quad \rightarrow \quad n = 50.0\ \text{N}$

Apply the second condition of equilibrium, computing torques around the base of the ladder, with τ_{grav} standing for the torque due to the ladder's 50.0-N weight:

$$\sum \tau_i = \tau_f + \tau_n + \tau_{grav} + \tau_P = 0$$

The torques due to friction and the normal force are zero about O because their moment arms are zero. (Moment arms can be found from Fig. 8.14c.)

$$0 + 0 - (50.0\ \text{N})(5.00\ \text{m})\sin 40.0° + P(10.0\ \text{m})\sin 50.0° = 0$$
$$P = 21.0\ \text{N}$$

(Continued)

From Equation (1), we now have $f = P = 21.0$ N. The ladder is on the verge of slipping, so write an expression for the maximum force of static friction and solve for μ_s:

$$21.0 \text{ N} = f = f_{s,\text{max}} = \mu_s n = \mu_s (50.0 \text{ N})$$

$$\mu_s = \frac{21.0 \text{ N}}{50.0 \text{ N}} = \boxed{0.420}$$

REMARKS Note that torques were computed around an axis through the bottom of the ladder so that only $\vec{P}$ and the force of gravity contributed nonzero torques. This choice of axis reduces the complexity of the torque equation, often resulting in an equation with only one unknown.

QUESTION 8.7 If a 50.0 N monkey hangs from the middle rung, would the coefficient of static friction be (a) doubled, (b) halved, or (c) unchanged?

EXERCISE 8.7 If the coefficient of static friction is 0.360, and the same ladder makes a 60.0° angle with respect to the horizontal, how far along the length of the ladder can a 70.0-kg painter climb before the ladder begins to slip?

ANSWER 6.33 m

■ EXAMPLE 8.8 | Walking a Horizontal Beam

GOAL Solve an equilibrium problem with nonperpendicular torques.

PROBLEM A uniform horizontal beam 5.00 m long and weighing 3.00×10^2 N is attached to a wall by a pin connection that allows the beam to rotate. Its far end is supported by a cable that makes an angle of 53.0° with the horizontal (Fig. 8.15a). If a person weighing 6.00×10^2 N stands 1.50 m from the wall, find the magnitude of the tension $\vec{T}$ in the cable and the force $\vec{R}$ exerted by the wall on the beam.

STRATEGY See Figure 8.15a–c (Steps 1 and 2). The second condition of equilibrium, $\Sigma \tau_i = 0$, with torques computed around the pin, can be solved for the tension T in the cable. The first condition of equilibrium, $\Sigma \vec{F}_i = 0$, gives two equations and two unknowns for the two components of the force exerted by the wall, R_x and R_y.

Figure 8.15 (Example 8.8) (a) A uniform beam attached to a wall and supported by a cable. (b) A force diagram for the beam. (c) The component form of the force diagram. (d) (Exercise 8.8)

SOLUTION

From Figure 8.15, the forces causing torques are the wall force $\vec{R}$, the gravity forces on the beam and the man, w_B and w_M, and the tension force $\vec{T}$. Apply the condition of rotational equilibrium (Step 3):

$$\sum \tau_i = \tau_R + \tau_B + \tau_M + \tau_T = 0$$

Compute torques around the pin at O, so $\tau_R = 0$ (zero moment arm). The torque due to the beam's weight acts at the beam's center of gravity.

$$\sum \tau_i = 0 - w_B(L/2) - w_M(1.50 \text{ m}) + TL \sin(53°) = 0$$

Substitute $L = 5.00$ m and the weights, solving for T:

$$-(3.00 \times 10^2\,\text{N})(2.50\,\text{m}) - (6.00 \times 10^2\,\text{N})(1.50\,\text{m})$$
$$+ (T\sin 53.0°)(5.00\,\text{m}) = 0$$
$$T = \boxed{413\,\text{N}}$$

Now apply the first condition of equilibrium to the beam (Step 4):

(1) $\sum F_x = R_x - T\cos 53.0° = 0$
(2) $\sum F_y = R_y - w_B - w_M + T\sin 53.0° = 0$

Substituting the value of T found in the previous step and the weights, obtain the components of $\vec{R}$ (Step 5):

$R_x = \boxed{249\,\text{N}}$ $R_y = \boxed{5.70 \times 10^2\,\text{N}}$

REMARKS Even if we selected some other axis for the torque equation, the solution would be the same. For example, if the axis were to pass through the center of gravity of the beam, the torque equation would involve both T and R_y. Together with Equations (1) and (2), however, the unknowns could still be found—a good exercise. In both Example 8.6 and Example 8.8, notice the steps of the Problem-Solving Strategy could be carried out in the explicit recommended order.

QUESTION 8.8 What happens to the tension in the cable if the man in Figure 8.15a moves farther away from the wall?

EXERCISE 8.8 A person with mass 55.0 kg stands 2.00 m away from the wall on a uniform 6.00-m beam, as shown in Figure 8.15d. The mass of the beam is 40.0 kg. Find the hinge force components and the tension in the wire.

ANSWERS $T = 751$ N, $R_x = -6.50 \times 10^2$ N, $R_y = 556$ N

8.5 Relationship Between Torque and Angular Acceleration

When a rigid object is subject to a net torque, it undergoes an angular acceleration that is directly proportional to the net torque. This result, which is analogous to Newton's second law, is derived as follows.

The system shown in Figure 8.16 consists of an object of mass m connected to a very light rod of length r. The rod is pivoted at the point O, and its movement is confined to rotation on a frictionless *horizontal* table. Assume that a force F_t acts perpendicular to the rod and hence is tangent to the circular path of the object. Because there is no force to oppose this tangential force, the object undergoes a tangential acceleration a_t in accordance with Newton's second law:

$$F_t = ma_t$$

Multiply both sides of this equation by r:

$$F_t r = mra_t$$

Substituting the equation $a_t = r\alpha$ relating tangential and angular acceleration into the above expression gives

$$F_t r = mr^2\alpha \qquad [8.4]$$

The left side of Equation 8.4 is the torque acting on the object about its axis of rotation, so we can rewrite it as

$$\tau = mr^2\alpha \qquad [8.5]$$

Equation 8.5 shows that the torque on the object is proportional to the angular acceleration of the object, where the constant of proportionality mr^2 is called the **moment of inertia** of the object of mass m. (Because the rod is very light, its moment of inertia can be neglected.)

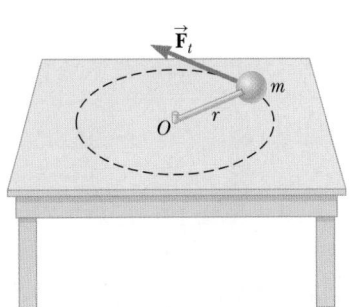

Figure 8.16 An object of mass m attached to a light rod of length r moves in a circular path on a frictionless horizontal surface while a tangential force $\vec{F}_t$ acts on it.

Figure 8.17 (a) A solid disk rotating about its axis. (b) The disk consists of many particles, all with the same angular acceleration.

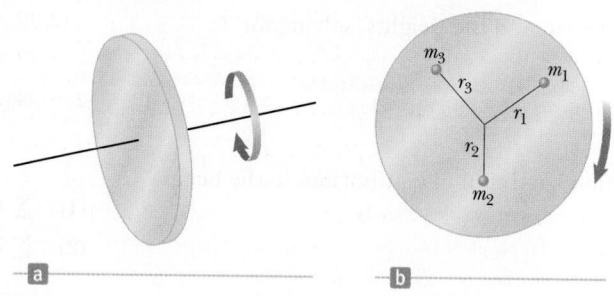

a

b

■ Quick Quiz

8.1 Using a screwdriver, you try to remove a screw from a piece of furniture, but can't get it to turn. To increase the chances of success, you should use a screwdriver that (a) is longer, (b) is shorter, (c) has a narrower handle, or (d) has a wider handle.

Torque on a Rotating Object

Consider a solid disk rotating about its axis as in Figure 8.17a. The disk consists of many particles at various distances from the axis of rotation. (See Fig. 8.17b.) The torque on each one of these particles is given by Equation 8.5. The *net* torque on the disk is given by the sum of the individual torques on all the particles:

$$\sum \tau = (\sum mr^2)\alpha \qquad [8.6]$$

Because the disk is rigid, all of its particles have the *same* angular acceleration, so α is not involved in the sum. If the masses and distances of the particles are labeled with subscripts as in Figure 8.17b, then

$$\sum mr^2 = m_1 r_1^2 + m_2 r_2^2 + m_3 r_3^2 + \cdots$$

This quantity is the moment of inertia, I, of the whole body:

Moment of inertia ▶

$$I \equiv \sum mr^2 \qquad [8.7]$$

The moment of inertia has the SI units kg · m². Using this result in Equation 8.6, we see that the net torque on a rigid body rotating about a fixed axis is given by

Rotational analog of ▶
Newton's second law

$$\sum \tau = I\alpha \qquad [8.8]$$

Equation 8.8 says that **the angular acceleration of an extended rigid object is proportional to the net torque acting on it.** This equation is the rotational analog of Newton's second law of motion, with torque replacing force, moment of inertia replacing mass, and angular acceleration replacing linear acceleration. Although the moment of inertia of an object is related to its mass, there is an important difference between them. The mass m depends only on the quantity of matter in an object, whereas the moment of inertia, I, depends on both the quantity of matter and its distribution (through the r^2 term in $I = \sum mr^2$) in the rigid object.

A

B

Figure 8.18 (Quick Quiz 8.3)

■ Quick Quiz

8.2 A constant net torque is applied to an object. Which one of the following will *not* be constant? (a) angular acceleration, (b) angular velocity, (c) moment of inertia, or (d) center of gravity.

8.3 The two rigid objects shown in Figure 8.18 have the same mass, radius, and angular speed. If the same braking torque is applied to each, which takes longer to stop? (a) A (b) B (c) more information is needed

The gear system on a bicycle provides an easily visible example of the relationship between torque and angular acceleration. Consider first a five-speed gear system in which the drive chain can be adjusted to wrap around any of five gears attached to the back wheel (Fig. 8.19). The gears, with different radii, are concentric with the wheel hub. When the cyclist begins pedaling from rest, the chain is attached to the largest gear. Because it has the largest radius, this gear provides the largest torque to the drive wheel. A large torque is required initially, because the bicycle starts from rest. As the bicycle rolls faster, the tangential speed of the chain increases, eventually becoming too fast for the cyclist to maintain by pushing the pedals. The chain is then moved to a gear with a smaller radius, so the chain has a smaller tangential speed that the cyclist can more easily maintain. This gear doesn't provide as much torque as the first, but the cyclist needs to accelerate only to a somewhat higher speed. This process continues as the bicycle moves faster and faster and the cyclist shifts through all five gears. The fifth gear supplies the lowest torque, but now the main function of that torque is to counter the frictional torque from the rolling tires, which tends to reduce the speed of the bicycle. The small radius of the fifth gear allows the cyclist to keep up with the chain's movement by pushing the pedals.

A 15-speed bicycle has the same gear structure on the drive wheel, but has three gears on the sprocket connected to the pedals. By combining different positions of the chain on the rear gears and the sprocket gears, 15 different torques are available.

Figure 8.19 The drive wheel and gears of a bicycle.

More on the Moment of Inertia

As we have seen, a small object (or a particle) has a moment of inertia equal to mr^2 about some axis. The moment of inertia of a *composite* object about some axis is just the sum of the moments of inertia of the object's components. For example, suppose a majorette twirls a baton as in Figure 8.20. Assume that the baton can be modeled as a very light rod of length 2ℓ with a heavy object at each end. (The rod of a real baton has a significant mass relative to its ends.) Because we are neglecting the mass of the rod, the moment of inertia of the baton about an axis through its center and perpendicular to its length is given by Equation 8.7:

$$I = \Sigma mr^2$$

Because this system consists of two objects with equal masses equidistant from the axis of rotation, $r = \ell$ for each object, and the sum is

$$I = \Sigma mr^2 = m\ell^2 + m\ell^2 = 2m\ell^2$$

If the mass of the rod were not neglected, we would have to include its moment of inertia to find the total moment of inertia of the baton.

We pointed out earlier that I is the rotational counterpart of m. However, there are some important distinctions between the two. For example, mass is an intrinsic property of an object that doesn't change, whereas **the moment of inertia of a system depends on how the mass is distributed and on the location of the axis of rotation.** Example 8.9 illustrates this point.

Figure 8.20 A baton of length 2ℓ and mass $2m$. (The mass of the connecting rod is neglected.) The moment of inertia about the axis through the baton's center and perpendicular to its length is $2m\ell^2$.

■ EXAMPLE 8.9 | The Baton Twirler

GOAL Calculate a moment of inertia.

PROBLEM In an effort to be the star of the halftime show, a majorette twirls an unusual baton made up of four spheres fastened to the ends of very light rods (Fig. 8.21). Each rod is 1.0 m long. **(a)** Find the moment of inertia of the baton about an axis perpendicular to the page and passing through the point where the rods cross. **(b)** The majorette tries spinning her strange baton about the axis OO', as shown in Figure 8.22 on page 250. Calculate the moment of inertia of the baton about this axis.

STRATEGY In Figure 8.21, all four balls contribute to the moment of inertia, whereas in Figure 8.22, with the new axis, only the two balls on the left and right contribute. Technically, the balls on the

Figure 8.21 (Example 8.9a) Four objects connected to light rods rotating in the plane of the page.

(Continued)

top and bottom still make a small contribution because they're not really point particles. However, their moment of inertia can be neglected because the radius of the sphere is much smaller than the radius formed by the rods.

SOLUTION

(a) Calculate the moment of inertia of the baton when oriented as in Figure 8.21.

Apply Equation 8.7, neglecting the mass of the connecting rods:

$$I = \Sigma mr^2 = m_1 r_1^2 + m_2 r_2^2 + m_3 r_3^2 + m_4 r_4^2$$
$$= (0.20 \text{ kg})(0.50 \text{ m})^2 + (0.30 \text{ kg})(0.50 \text{ m})^2$$
$$+ (0.20 \text{ kg})(0.50 \text{ m})^2 + (0.30 \text{ kg})(0.50 \text{ m})^2$$
$$I = \boxed{0.25 \text{ kg} \cdot \text{m}^2}$$

(b) Calculate the moment of inertia of the baton when oriented as in Figure 8.22.

Apply Equation 8.7 again, neglecting the radii of the 0.20-kg spheres.

$$I = \Sigma mr^2 = m_1 r_1^2 + m_2 r_2^2 + m_3 r_3^2 + m_4 r_4^2$$
$$= (0.20 \text{ kg})(0)^2 + (0.30 \text{ kg})(0.50 \text{ m})^2 + (0.20 \text{ kg})(0)^2$$
$$+ (0.30 \text{ kg})(0.50 \text{ m})^2$$
$$I = \boxed{0.15 \text{ kg} \cdot \text{m}^2}$$

Figure 8.22 (Example 8.9b) A double baton rotating about the axis OO'.

REMARKS The moment of inertia is smaller in part (b) because in this configuration the 0.20-kg spheres are essentially located on the axis of rotation.

QUESTION 8.9 If one of the rods is lengthened, which one would cause the larger change in the moment of inertia, the rod connecting bars one and three or the rod connecting balls two and four?

EXERCISE 8.9 Yet another bizarre baton is created by taking four identical balls, each with mass 0.300 kg, and fixing them as before, except that one of the rods has a length of 1.00 m and the other has a length of 1.50 m. Calculate the moment of inertia of this baton (a) when oriented as in Figure 8.19; (b) when oriented as in Figure 8.22, with the shorter rod vertical; and (c) when oriented as in Figure 8.22, but with longer rod vertical.

ANSWERS (a) 0.488 kg · m²   (b) 0.338 kg · m²   (c) 0.150 kg · m²

Calculation of Moments of Inertia for Extended Objects

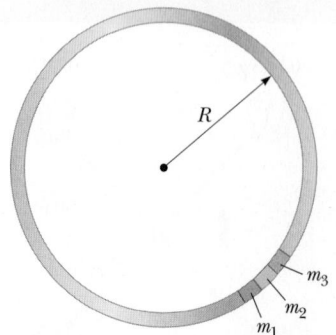

Figure 8.23 A uniform hoop can be divided into a large number of small segments that are equidistant from the center of the hoop.

The method used for calculating moments of inertia in Example 8.9 is simple when only a few small objects rotate about an axis. When the object is an extended one, such as a sphere, a cylinder, or a cone, techniques of calculus are often required, unless some simplifying symmetry is present. One such extended object amenable to a simple solution is a hoop rotating about an axis perpendicular to its plane and passing through its center, as shown in Figure 8.23. (A bicycle tire, for example, would approximately fit into this category.)

To evaluate the moment of inertia of the hoop, we can still use the equation $I = \Sigma mr^2$ and imagine that the mass of the hoop M is divided into n small segments having masses $m_1, m_2, m_3, \cdots, m_n$, as in Figure 8.23, with $M = m_1 + m_2 + m_3 + \cdots + m_n$. This approach is just an extension of the baton problem described in the preceding examples, except that now we have a large number of small masses in rotation instead of only four.

Table 8.1 Moments of Inertia for Various Rigid Objects of Uniform Composition

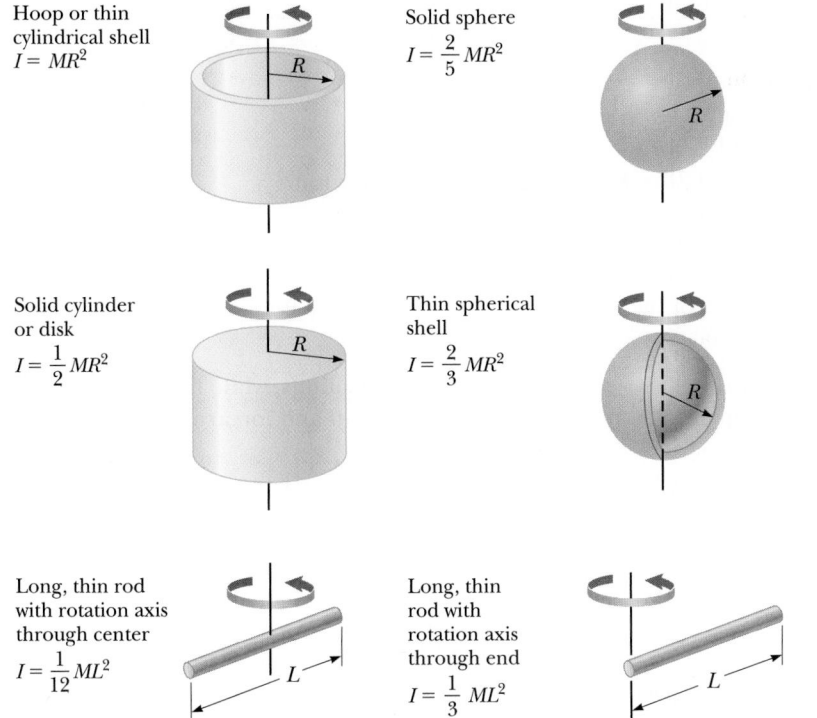

Hoop or thin cylindrical shell
$I = MR^2$

Solid sphere
$I = \frac{2}{5} MR^2$

Solid cylinder or disk
$I = \frac{1}{2} MR^2$

Thin spherical shell
$I = \frac{2}{3} MR^2$

Long, thin rod with rotation axis through center
$I = \frac{1}{12} ML^2$

Long, thin rod with rotation axis through end
$I = \frac{1}{3} ML^2$

We can express the sum for I as

$$I = \Sigma mr^2 = m_1 r_1^{\,2} + m_2 r_2^{\,2} + m_3 r_3^{\,2} + \cdots + m_n r_n^{\,2}$$

All of the segments around the hoop are at the *same distance R* from the axis of rotation, so we can drop the subscripts on the distances and factor out R^2 to obtain

$$I = (m_1 + m_2 + m_3 + \cdots + m_n)R^2 = MR^2 \qquad \text{[8.9]}$$

This expression can be used for the moment of inertia of any ring-shaped object rotating about an axis through its center and perpendicular to its plane. Note that the result is strictly valid only if the thickness of the ring is small relative to its inner radius.

The hoop we selected as an example is unique in that we were able to find an expression for its moment of inertia by using only simple algebra. Unfortunately, for most extended objects the calculation is much more difficult because the mass elements are not all located at the same distance from the axis, so the methods of integral calculus are required. The moments of inertia for some other common shapes are given without proof in Table 8.1. You can use this table as needed to determine the moment of inertia of a body having any one of the listed shapes.

If mass elements in an object are redistributed parallel to the axis of rotation, the moment of inertia of the object doesn't change. Consequently, the expression $I = MR^2$ can be used equally well to find the axial moment of inertia of an embroidery hoop or of a long sewer pipe. Likewise, a door turning on its hinges is described by the same moment-of-inertia expression as that tabulated for a long, thin rod rotating about an axis through its end.

Tip 8.3 No Single Moment of Inertia

Moment of inertia is analogous to mass, but there are major differences. Mass is an inherent property of an object. The moment of inertia of an object depends on the shape of the object, its mass, and the choice of rotation axis.

▪ EXAMPLE 8.10 | Warming Up

GOAL Find a moment of inertia and apply the rotational analog of Newton's second law.

PROBLEM A baseball player loosening up his arm before a game tosses a 0.150-kg baseball, using only the rotation of his forearm to accelerate the ball (Fig. 8.24). The forearm has a mass of 1.50 kg and a length of 0.350 m. The ball starts at rest and is released with a speed of 30.0 m/s in 0.300 s. **(a)** Find the constant angular acceleration of the arm and ball. **(b)** Calculate the moment of inertia of the system consisting of the forearm and ball. **(c)** Find the torque exerted on the system that results in the angular acceleration found in part (a).

Figure 8.24 (Example 8.10) A ball being tossed by a pitcher. The forearm is used to accelerate the ball.

0.350 m

STRATEGY The angular acceleration can be found with rotational kinematic equations, while the moment of inertia of the system can be obtained by summing the separate moments of inertia of the ball and forearm. Multiplying these two results together gives the torque.

SOLUTION

(a) Find the angular acceleration of the ball.

The angular acceleration is constant, so use the angular velocity kinematic equation with $\omega_i = 0$:

$$\omega = \omega_i + \alpha t \quad \rightarrow \quad \alpha = \frac{\omega}{t}$$

The ball accelerates along a circular arc with radius given by the length of the forearm. Solve $v = r\omega$ for ω and substitute:

$$\alpha = \frac{\omega}{t} = \frac{v}{rt} = \frac{30.0 \text{ m/s}}{(0.350 \text{ m})(0.300 \text{ s})} = \boxed{286 \text{ rad/s}^2}$$

(b) Find the moment of inertia of the system (forearm plus ball).

Find the moment of inertia of the ball about an axis that passes through the elbow, perpendicular to the arm:

$$I_{ball} = mr^2 = (0.150 \text{ kg})(0.350 \text{ m})^2 = 1.84 \times 10^{-2} \text{ kg} \cdot \text{m}^2$$

Obtain the moment of inertia of the forearm, modeled as a rod rotating about an axis through one end, by consulting Table 8.1:

$$I_{forearm} = \tfrac{1}{3} ML^2 = \tfrac{1}{3}(1.50 \text{ kg})(0.350 \text{ m})^2$$
$$= 6.13 \times 10^{-2} \text{ kg} \cdot \text{m}^2$$

Sum the individual moments of inertia to obtain the moment of inertia of the system (ball plus forearm):

$$I_{system} = I_{ball} + I_{forearm} = \boxed{7.97 \times 10^{-2} \text{ kg} \cdot \text{m}^2}$$

(c) Find the torque exerted on the system.

Apply Equation 8.8, using the results of parts (a) and (b):

$$\tau = I_{system}\alpha = (7.97 \times 10^{-2} \text{ kg} \cdot \text{m}^2)(286 \text{ rad/s}^2)$$
$$= \boxed{22.8 \text{ N} \cdot \text{m}}$$

REMARKS Notice that having a long forearm can greatly increase the torque and hence the acceleration of the ball. This is one reason it's advantageous for a pitcher to be tall: the pitching arm is proportionately longer. A similar advantage holds in tennis, where taller players can usually deliver faster serves.

QUESTION 8.10 Why do pitchers step forward when delivering the pitch? Why is the timing important?

EXERCISE 8.10 A catapult with a radial arm 4.00 m long accelerates a ball of mass 20.0 kg through a quarter circle. The ball leaves the apparatus at 45.0 m/s. If the mass of the arm is 25.0 kg and the acceleration is constant, find **(a)** the angular acceleration, **(b)** the moment of inertia of the arm and ball, and **(c)** the net torque exerted on the ball and arm.

Hint: Use the time-independent rotational kinematics equation to find the angular acceleration, rather than the angular velocity equation.

ANSWERS (a) 40.3 rad/s² (b) 453 kg · m² (c) 1.83 × 10⁴ N · m

■ EXAMPLE 8.11 | The Falling Bucket

GOAL Combine Newton's second law with its rotational analog.

PROBLEM A solid, uniform, frictionless cylindrical reel of mass $M = 3.00$ kg and radius $R = 0.400$ m is used to draw water from a well (Fig. 8.25a). A bucket of mass $m = 2.00$ kg is attached to a cord that is wrapped around the cylinder. **(a)** Find the tension T in the cord and acceleration a of the bucket. **(b)** If the bucket starts from rest at the top of the well and falls for 3.00 s before hitting the water, how far does it fall?

STRATEGY This problem involves three equations and three unknowns. The three equations are Newton's second law applied to the bucket, $ma = \Sigma F_i$; the rotational version of the second law applied to the cylinder, $I\alpha = \Sigma \tau_i$; and the relationship between linear and angular acceleration, $a = r\alpha$, which connects the dynamics of the bucket and cylinder. The three unknowns are the acceleration a of the bucket, the angular acceleration α of the cylinder, and the tension T in the rope. Assemble the terms of the three equations and solve for the three unknowns by substitution. Part (b) is a review of kinematics.

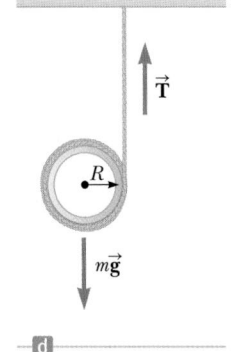

Figure 8.25 (Example 8.11) (a) A water bucket attached to a rope passing over a frictionless reel. (b) A force diagram for the bucket. (c) The tension produces a torque on the cylinder about its axis of rotation. (d) A falling cylinder (Exercise 8.11).

· ·

SOLUTION

(a) Find the tension in the cord and the acceleration of the bucket.

Apply Newton's second law to the bucket in Figure 8.25b. There are two forces: the tension $\vec{T}$ acting upward and gravity $m\vec{g}$ acting downward.

$$(1) \quad ma = -mg + T$$

Apply $\tau = I\alpha$ to the cylinder in Figure 8.25c:

$$\Sigma \tau = I\alpha = \tfrac{1}{2}MR^2\alpha \quad \text{(solid cylinder)}$$

Notice the angular acceleration is clockwise, so the torque is negative. The normal and gravity forces have zero moment arm and don't contribute any torque.

$$(2) \quad -TR = \tfrac{1}{2}MR^2\alpha$$

Solve for T and substitute $\alpha = a/R$ (notice that both α and a are negative):

$$(3) \quad T = -\tfrac{1}{2}MR\alpha = -\tfrac{1}{2}Ma$$

Substitute the expression for T in Equation (3) into Equation (1), and solve for the acceleration:

$$ma = -mg - \tfrac{1}{2}Ma \quad \rightarrow \quad a = -\frac{mg}{m + \tfrac{1}{2}M}$$

Substitute the values for m, M, and g, getting a, then substitute a into Equation (3) to get T:

$$a = \boxed{-5.60 \text{ m/s}^2} \quad T = \boxed{8.40 \text{ N}}$$

(b) Find the distance the bucket falls in 3.00 s.

Apply the displacement kinematic equation for constant acceleration, with $t = 3.00$ s and $v_0 = 0$:

$$\Delta y = v_0 t + \tfrac{1}{2}at^2 = -\tfrac{1}{2}(5.60 \text{ m/s}^2)(3.00 \text{ s})^2 = \boxed{-25.2 \text{ m}}$$

· ·

REMARKS Proper handling of signs is very important in these problems. All such signs should be chosen initially and checked mathematically and physically. In this problem, for example, both the angular acceleration α and the acceleration a are negative, so $\alpha = a/R$ applies. If the rope had been wound the other way on the cylinder, causing counterclockwise rotation, the torque would have been positive, and the relationship would have been $\alpha = -a/R$, with the double negative making the right-hand side positive, just like the left-hand side.

(Continued)

QUESTION 8.11 How would the acceleration and tension change if most of the reel's mass were at its rim?

EXERCISE 8.11 A hollow cylinder of mass 0.100 kg and radius 4.00 cm has a string wrapped several times around it, as in Figure 8.25d. If the string is attached to a rigid support and the cylinder allowed to drop from rest, find (a) the acceleration of the cylinder and (b) the speed of the cylinder when a meter of string has unwound off of it.

ANSWERS (a) -4.90 m/s^2 (b) 3.13 m/s

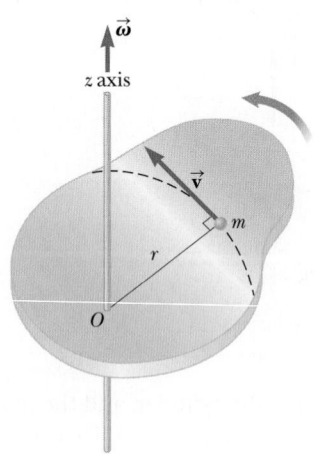

Figure 8.26 A rigid plate rotates about the z-axis with angular speed v. The kinetic energy of a particle of mass m is $\frac{1}{2}mv^2$. The total kinetic energy of the plate is $\frac{1}{2}I\omega^2$.

8.6 Rotational Kinetic Energy

In Chapter 5 we defined the kinetic energy of a particle moving through space with a speed v as the quantity $\frac{1}{2}mv^2$. Analogously, **an object rotating about some axis with an angular speed ω has rotational kinetic energy given by $\frac{1}{2}I\omega^2$.** To prove this, consider an object in the shape of a thin, rigid plate rotating around some axis perpendicular to its plane, as in Figure 8.26. The plate consists of many small particles, each of mass m. All these particles rotate in circular paths around the axis. If r is the distance of one of the particles from the axis of rotation, the speed of that particle is $v = r\omega$. Because the *total* kinetic energy of the plate's rotation is the sum of all the kinetic energies associated with its particles, we have

$$KE_r = \sum \left(\tfrac{1}{2}m\omega^2\right) = \sum \left(\tfrac{1}{2}mr^2\omega^2\right) = \tfrac{1}{2}\left(\sum mr^2\right)\omega^2$$

In the last step, the ω^2 term is factored out because it's the same for every particle. Now, the quantity in parentheses on the right is the moment of inertia of the plate in the limit as the particles become vanishingly small, so

$$KE_r = \tfrac{1}{2}I\omega^2 \qquad\qquad [8.10]$$

where $I = \sum mr^2$ is the moment of inertia of the plate.

A system such as a bowling ball rolling down a ramp is described by three types of energy: **gravitational potential energy PE_g, translational kinetic energy KE_t,** and **rotational kinetic energy KE_r.** All these forms of energy, plus the potential energies of any other conservative forces, must be included in our equation for the conservation of mechanical energy of an isolated system:

◄ Conservation of mechanical energy

$$(KE_t + KE_r + PE)_i = (KE_t + KE_r + PE)_f \qquad\qquad [8.11]$$

where i and f refer to initial and final values, respectively, and PE includes the potential energies of all conservative forces in a given problem. This relation is true *only* if we ignore dissipative forces such as friction. In that case, it's necessary to resort to a generalization of the work–energy theorem:

◄ Work–energy theorem including rotational energy

$$W_{nc} = \Delta KE_t + \Delta KE_r + \Delta PE \qquad\qquad [8.12]$$

■ PROBLEM-SOLVING STRATEGY

Energy Methods and Rotation

1. **Choose two points of interest,** one where all necessary information is known, and the other where information is desired.
2. **Identify** the conservative and nonconservative forces acting on the system being analyzed.
3. **Write the general work–energy theorem,** Equation 8.12, or Equation 8.11 if all forces are conservative.
4. **Substitute general expressions** for the terms in the equation.
5. **Use $v = r\omega$** to eliminate either ω or v from the equation.
6. **Solve** for the unknown.

■ EXAMPLE 8.12 | A Ball Rolling Down an Incline

GOAL Combine gravitational, translational, and rotational energy.

PROBLEM A ball of mass M and radius R starts from rest at a height of 2.00 m and rolls down a 30.0° slope, as in Figure 8.27. What is the linear speed of the ball when it leaves the incline? Assume that the ball rolls without slipping.

STRATEGY The two points of interest are the top and bottom of the incline, with the bottom acting as the zero point of gravitational potential energy. As the ball rolls down the ramp, gravitational potential energy is converted into both translational and rotational kinetic energy without dissipation, so conservation of mechanical energy can be applied with the use of Equation 8.11.

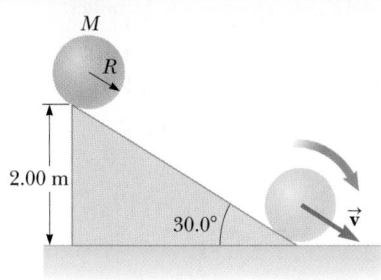

Figure 8.27 (Example 8.12) A ball starts from rest at the top of an incline and rolls to the bottom without slipping.

SOLUTION

Apply conservation of energy with $PE = PE_g$, the potential energy associated with gravity:

$$(KE_t + KE_r + PE_g)_i = (KE_t + KE_r + PE_g)_f$$

Substitute the appropriate general expressions, noting that $(KE_t)_i = (KE_r)_i = 0$ and $(PE_g)_f = 0$ (obtain the moment of inertia of a ball from Table 8.1):

$$0 + 0 + Mgh = \tfrac{1}{2}Mv^2 + \tfrac{1}{2}(\tfrac{2}{5}MR^2)\omega^2 + 0$$

The ball rolls without slipping, so $R\omega = v$, the "no-slip condition," can be applied:

$$Mgh = \tfrac{1}{2}Mv^2 + \tfrac{1}{5}Mv^2 = \tfrac{7}{10}Mv^2$$

Solve for v, noting that M cancels.

$$v = \sqrt{\frac{10gh}{7}} = \sqrt{\frac{10(9.80\ \text{m/s}^2)(2.00\ \text{m})}{7}} = \boxed{5.29\ \text{m/s}}$$

REMARKS Notice the translational speed is less than that of a block sliding down a frictionless slope, $v = \sqrt{2gh}$. That's because some of the original potential energy must go to increasing the rotational kinetic energy.

QUESTION 8.12 Rank from fastest to slowest: (a) a solid ball rolling down a ramp without slipping, (b) a cylinder rolling down the same ramp without slipping, (c) a block sliding down a frictionless ramp with the same height and slope.

EXERCISE 8.12 Repeat this example for a solid cylinder of the same mass and radius as the ball and released from the same height. In a race between the two objects on the incline, which one would win?

ANSWER $v = \sqrt{4gh/3} = 5.11$ m/s; the ball would win.

■ Quick Quiz

8.4 Two spheres, one hollow and one solid, are rotating with the same angular speed around an axis through their centers. Both spheres have the same mass and radius. Which sphere, if either, has the higher rotational kinetic energy? (a) The hollow sphere. (b) The solid sphere. (c) They have the same kinetic energy.

■ EXAMPLE 8.13 | Blocks and Pulley

GOAL Solve a system requiring rotation concepts and the work–energy theorem.

PROBLEM Two blocks with masses $m_1 = 5.00$ kg and $m_2 = 7.00$ kg are attached by a string as in Figure 8.28a (page 256), over a pulley with mass $M = 2.00$ kg. The pulley, which turns on a frictionless axle, is a hollow cylinder with radius 0.050 0 m over which the string moves without slipping. The horizontal surface has coefficient of kinetic friction 0.350. Find the speed of the system when the block of mass m_2 has dropped 2.00 m.

STRATEGY This problem can be solved with the extension of the work–energy theorem, Equation 8.12. If the block of mass m_2 falls from height h to 0, then the block of mass m_1 moves the same distance, $\Delta x = h$. Apply the work-energy theorem, solve for v, and substitute. Kinetic friction is the sole nonconservative force.

(Continued)

Figure 8.28 (a) (Example 8.13) $\vec{T}_1$ and $\vec{T}_2$ exert torques on the pulley. (b) (Exercise 8.13)

a   b

. . . .

SOLUTION

Apply the work–energy theorem, with $PE = PE_g$, the potential energy associated with gravity:

$$W_{nc} = \Delta KE_t + \Delta KE_r + \Delta PE_g$$

Substitute the frictional work for W_{nc}, kinetic energy changes for the two blocks, the rotational kinetic energy change for the pulley, and the potential energy change for the second block:

$$-\mu_k n\,\Delta x = -\mu_k(m_1 g)\,\Delta x = (\tfrac{1}{2}m_1 v^2 - 0) + (\tfrac{1}{2}m_2 v^2 - 0)$$
$$+ (\tfrac{1}{2}I\omega^2 - 0) + (0 - m_2 gh)$$

Substitute $\Delta x = h$, and write I as $(I/r^2)r^2$:

$$-\mu_k(m_1 g)h = \tfrac{1}{2}m_1 v^2 + \tfrac{1}{2}m_2 v^2 + \tfrac{1}{2}\left(\frac{I}{r^2}\right)r^2\omega^2 - m_2 gh$$

For a hoop, $I = Mr^2$ so $(I/r^2) = M$. Substitute this quantity and $v = r\omega$:

$$-\mu_k(m_1 g)h = \tfrac{1}{2}m_1 v^2 + \tfrac{1}{2}m_2 v^2 + \tfrac{1}{2}Mv^2 - m_2 gh$$

Solve for v:

$$m_2 gh - \mu_k(m_1 g)h = \tfrac{1}{2}m_1 v^2 + \tfrac{1}{2}m_2 v^2 + \tfrac{1}{2}Mv^2$$
$$= \tfrac{1}{2}(m_1 + m_2 + M)v^2$$
$$v = \sqrt{\frac{2gh(m_2 - \mu_k m_1)}{m_1 + m_2 + M}}$$

Substitute $m_1 = 5.00$ kg, $m_2 = 7.00$ kg, $M = 2.00$ kg, $g = 9.80$ m/s^2, $h = 2.00$ m, and $\mu_k = 0.350$:

$$v = \boxed{3.83 \text{ m/s}}$$

. . . .

REMARKS In the expression for the speed v, the mass m_1 of the first block and the mass M of the pulley all appear in the denominator, reducing the speed, as they should. In the numerator, m_2 is positive while the friction term is negative. Both assertions are reasonable because the force of gravity on m_2 increases the speed of the system while the force of friction on m_1 slows it down. This problem can also be solved with Newton's second law together with $\tau = I\alpha$, a good exercise.

QUESTION 8.13 How would increasing the radius of the pulley affect the final answer? Assume the angles of the cables are unchanged and the mass is the same as before.

EXERCISE 8.13 Two blocks with masses $m_1 = 2.00$ kg and $m_2 = 9.00$ kg are attached over a pulley with mass $M = 3.00$ kg, hanging straight down as in Atwood's machine (Fig. 8.28b). The pulley is a solid cylinder with radius 0.050 0 m, and there is some friction in the axle. The system is released from rest, and the string moves without slipping over the pulley. If the larger mass is traveling at a speed of 2.50 m/s when it has dropped 1.00 m, how much mechanical energy was lost due to friction in the pulley's axle?

ANSWER 29.5 J

8.7 Angular Momentum

In Figure 8.29, an object of mass m rotates in a circular path of radius r, acted on by a net force, $\vec{F}_{net}$. The resulting net torque on the object increases its angular speed from the value ω_0 to the value ω in a time interval Δt. Therefore, we can write

$$\sum \tau = I\alpha = I\frac{\Delta\omega}{\Delta t} = I\left(\frac{\omega - \omega_0}{\Delta t}\right) = \frac{I\omega - I\omega_0}{\Delta t}$$

If we define the product

$$L \equiv I\omega \qquad \text{[8.13]}$$

as the **angular momentum** of the object, then we can write

$$\sum \tau = \frac{\text{change in angular momentum}}{\text{time interval}} = \frac{\Delta L}{\Delta t} \qquad \text{[8.14]}$$

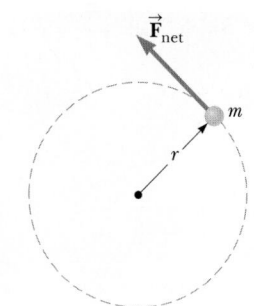

Figure 8.29 An object of mass m rotating in a circular path under the action of a constant torque.

Equation 8.14 is the rotational analog of Newton's second law, which can be written in the form $F = \Delta p/\Delta t$ and states that **the net torque acting on an object is equal to the time rate of change of the object's angular momentum.** Recall that this equation also parallels the impulse–momentum theorem.

When the net external torque ($\Sigma\tau$) acting on a system is zero, Equation 8.14 gives $\Delta L/\Delta t = 0$, which says that the time rate of change of the system's angular momentum is zero. We then have the following important result:

Let L_i and L_f be the angular momenta of a system at two different times, and suppose there is no net external torque, so $\Sigma\tau = 0$. Then

$$L_i = L_f \qquad \text{[8.15]}$$

and angular momentum is said to be *conserved*.

◄ Conservation of angular momentum

Equation 8.15 gives us a third conservation law to add to our list: **conservation of angular momentum.** We can now state that **the mechanical energy, linear momentum, and angular momentum of an isolated system all remain constant.**

If the moment of inertia of an isolated rotating system changes, the system's angular speed will change. Conservation of angular momentum then requires that

$$I_i\omega_i = I_f\omega_f \qquad \text{if} \qquad \sum \tau = 0 \qquad \text{[8.16]}$$

Note that conservation of angular momentum applies to macroscopic objects such as planets and people, as well as to atoms and molecules. There are many examples of conservation of angular momentum; one of the most dramatic is that of a figure skater spinning in the finale of his act. In Figure 8.30a (page 258), the skater has pulled his arms and legs close to his body, reducing their distance from his axis of rotation and hence also reducing his moment of inertia. By conservation of angular momentum, a reduction in his moment of inertia must increase his angular speed. Coming out of the spin in Figure 8.30b, he needs to reduce his angular speed, so he extends his arms and legs again, increasing his moment of inertia and thereby slowing his rotation.

Similarly, when a diver or an acrobat wishes to make several somersaults, she pulls her hands and feet close to the trunk of her body in order to rotate at a greater angular speed. In this case, the external force due to gravity acts through her center of gravity and hence exerts no torque about her axis of rotation, so the angular momentum about her center of gravity is conserved. For example, when a diver wishes to double her angular speed, she must reduce her moment of inertia to half its initial value.

APPLICATION
Figure Skating

APPLICATION
Aerial Somersaults

Tightly curling her body, a diver decreases her moment of inertia, increasing her angular speed.

Figure 8.30 Evgeni Plushenko varies his moment of inertia to change his angular speed.

By pulling in his arms and legs, he reduces his moment of inertia and increases his angular speed (rate of spin).

Upon landing, extending his arms and legs increases his moment of inertia and helps slow his spin.

An interesting astrophysical example of conservation of angular momentum occurs when a massive star, at the end of its lifetime, uses up all its fuel and collapses under the influence of gravitational forces, causing a gigantic outburst of energy called a supernova. The best-studied example of a remnant of a supernova explosion is the Crab Nebula, a chaotic, expanding mass of gas (Fig. 8.31). In a supernova, part of the star's mass is ejected into space, where it eventually condenses into new stars and planets. Most of what is left behind typically collapses into a **neutron star**—an extremely dense sphere of matter with a diameter of about 10 km, greatly reduced from the 10^6-km diameter of the original star and containing a large fraction of the star's original mass. In a neutron star, pressures become so great that atomic electrons combine with protons, becoming neutrons. As the moment of inertia of the system decreases during the collapse, the star's rotational speed increases. More than 700 rapidly rotating neutron stars have been identified since their first discovery in 1967, with periods of rotation ranging from a millisecond to several seconds. The neutron star is an amazing system—an object with a mass greater than the Sun, fitting comfortably within the space of a small county and rotating so fast that the tangential speed of the surface approaches a sizable fraction of the speed of light!

APPLICATION
Rotating Neutron Stars

■ Quick Quiz

8.5 A horizontal disk with moment of inertia I_1 rotates with angular speed ω_1 about a vertical frictionless axle. A second horizontal disk having moment of inertia I_2 drops onto the first, initially not rotating but sharing the same axis as the first disk. Because their surfaces are rough, the two disks eventually reach the same

Figure 8.31 (a) The Crab Nebula in the constellation Taurus. This nebula is the remnant of a supernova seen on Earth in A.D. 1054. It is located some 6 300 light-years away and is approximately 6 light-years in diameter, still expanding outward. A pulsar deep inside the nebula flashes 30 times every second. (b) Pulsar off. (c) Pulsar on.

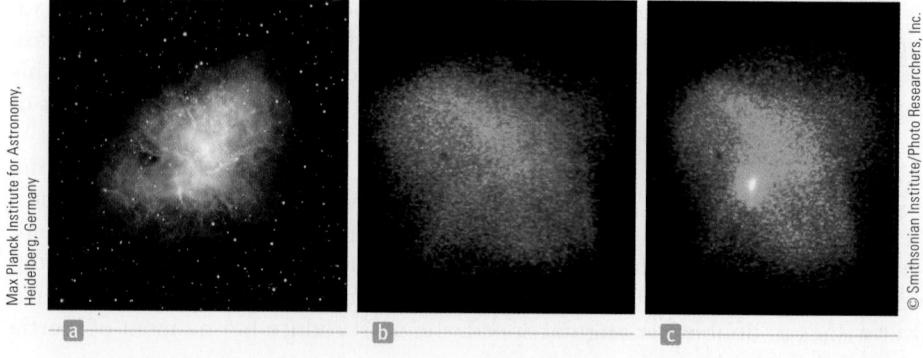

angular speed ω. The ratio ω/ω_1 is equal to (a) I_1/I_2 (b) I_2/I_1 (c) $I_1/(I_1 + I_2)$
(d) $I_2/(I_1 + I_2)$

8.6 If global warming continues, it's likely that some ice from the polar ice caps of
the Earth will melt and the water will be distributed closer to the equator. If this
occurs, would the length of the day (one revolution) (a) increase, (b) decrease, or
(c) remain the same?

■ EXAMPLE 8.14 | The Spinning Stool

GOAL Apply conservation of angular momentum to a simple system.

PROBLEM A student sits on a pivoted stool while holding a pair of weights. (See Fig. 8.32.)
The stool is free to rotate about a vertical axis with negligible friction. The moment of
inertia of student, weights, and stool is 2.25 kg · m². The student is set in rotation with arms
outstretched, making one complete turn every 1.26 s, arms outstretched. **(a)** What is the
initial angular speed of the system? **(b)** As he rotates, he pulls the weights inward so that
the new moment of inertia of the system (student, objects, and stool) becomes 1.80 kg · m².
What is the new angular speed of the system? **(c)** Find the work done by the student on the
system while pulling in the weights. (Ignore energy lost through dissipation in his muscles.)

STRATEGY (a) The angular speed can be obtained from the frequency, which is the
inverse of the period. (b) There are no external torques acting on the system, so the new
angular speed can be found with the principle of conservation of angular momentum.
(c) The work done on the system during this process is the same as the system's change in
rotational kinetic energy.

Figure 8.32 (Example 8.14)
(a) The student is given an initial
angular speed while holding two
weights out. (b) The angular
speed increases as the student
draws the weights inwards.

SOLUTION

(a) Find the initial angular speed of the system.

Invert the period to get the frequency, and multiply by 2π: $\omega_i = 2\pi f = 2\pi/T = $ 4.99 rad/s

(b) After he pulls the weights in, what's the system's new
angular speed?

Equate the initial and final angular momenta of the
system:

(1) $L_i = L_f \rightarrow I_i\omega_i = I_f\omega_f$

Substitute and solve for the final angular speed ω_f:

(2) $(2.25 \text{ kg} \cdot \text{m}^2)(4.99 \text{ rad/s}) = (1.80 \text{ kg} \cdot \text{m}^2)\omega_f$

$\omega_f = $ 6.24 rad/s

(c) Find the work the student does on the system.

Apply the work–energy theorem:

$$W_{\text{student}} = \Delta K_r = \tfrac{1}{2}I_f\omega_f^2 - \tfrac{1}{2}I_i\omega_i^2$$
$$= \tfrac{1}{2}(1.80 \text{ kg} \cdot \text{m}^2)(6.24 \text{ rad/s})^2$$
$$- \tfrac{1}{2}(2.25 \text{ kg} \cdot \text{m}^2)(4.99 \text{ rad/s})^2$$
$$W_{\text{student}} = \boxed{7.03 \text{ J}}$$

REMARKS Although the angular momentum of the system is conserved, mechanical energy is not conserved because the
student does work on the system.

QUESTION 8.14 If the student suddenly releases the weights, will his angular speed increase, decrease, or remain the
same?

EXERCISE 8.14 A star with an initial radius of 1.0×10^8 m and period of 30.0 days collapses suddenly to a radius of
1.0×10^4 m. (a) Find the period of rotation after collapse. (b) Find the work done by gravity during the collapse if the mass
of the star is 2.0×10^{30} kg. (c) What is the speed of an indestructible person standing on the equator of the collapsed star?
(Neglect any relativistic or thermal effects, and assume the star is spherical before and after it collapses.)

ANSWERS (a) 2.6×10^{-2} s   (b) 2.3×10^{42} J   (c) 2.4×10^6 m/s

■EXAMPLE 8.15 | The Merry-Go-Round

GOAL Apply conservation of angular momentum while combining two moments of inertia.

PROBLEM A merry-go-round modeled as a disk of mass $M = 1.00 \times 10^2$ kg and radius $R = 2.00$ m is rotating in a horizontal plane about a frictionless vertical axle (Fig. 8.33 is an overhead view of the system). **(a)** After a student with mass $m = 60.0$ kg jumps on the rim of the merry-go-round, the system's angular speed decreases to 2.00 rad/s. If the student walks slowly from the edge toward the center, find the angular speed of the system when she reaches a point 0.500 m from the center. **(b)** Find the change in the system's rotational kinetic energy caused by her movement to $r = 0.500$ m. **(c)** Find the work done on the student as she walks to $r = 0.500$ m.

STRATEGY This problem can be solved with conservation of angular momentum by equating the system's initial angular momentum when the student stands at the rim to the angular momentum when the student has reached $r = 0.500$ m. The key is to find the different moments of inertia.

Figure 8.33 (Example 8.15) As the student walks toward the center of the merry-go-round, the moment of inertia I of the system becomes smaller. Because angular momentum is conserved and $L = I\omega$, the angular speed must increase.

SOLUTION

(a) Find the angular speed when the student reaches a point 0.500 m from the center.

Calculate the moment of inertia of the disk, I_D:

$$I_D = \tfrac{1}{2}MR^2 = \tfrac{1}{2}(1.00 \times 10^2 \text{ kg})(2.00 \text{ m})^2$$
$$= 2.00 \times 10^2 \text{ kg} \cdot \text{m}^2$$

Calculate the initial moment of inertia of the student. This is the same as the moment of inertia of a mass a distance R from the axis:

$$I_{Si} = mR^2 = (60.0 \text{ kg})(2.00 \text{ m})^2 = 2.40 \times 10^2 \text{ kg} \cdot \text{m}^2$$

Sum the two moments of inertia and multiply by the initial angular speed to find L_i, the initial angular momentum of the system:

$$L_i = (I_D + I_{Si})\omega_i$$
$$= (2.00 \times 10^2 \text{ kg} \cdot \text{m}^2 + 2.40 \times 10^2 \text{ kg} \cdot \text{m}^2)(2.00 \text{ rad/s})$$
$$= 8.80 \times 10^2 \text{ kg} \cdot \text{m}^2/\text{s}$$

Calculate the student's final moment of inertia, I_{Sf}, when she is 0.500 m from the center:

$$I_{Sf} = mr_f^2 = (60.0 \text{ kg})(0.50 \text{ m})^2 = 15.0 \text{ kg} \cdot \text{m}^2$$

The moment of inertia of the platform is unchanged. Add it to the student's final moment of inertia, and multiply by the unknown final angular speed to find L_f:

$$L_f = (I_D + I_{Sf})\omega_f = (2.00 \times 10^2 \text{ kg} \cdot \text{m}^2 + 15.0 \text{ kg} \cdot \text{m}^2)\omega_f$$
$$= (2.15 \times 10^2 \text{ kg} \cdot \text{m}^2)\omega_f$$

Equate the initial and final angular momenta and solve for the final angular speed of the system:

$$L_i = L_f$$
$$(8.80 \times 10^2 \text{ kg} \cdot \text{m}^2/\text{s}) = (2.15 \times 10^2 \text{ kg} \cdot \text{m}^2)\omega_f$$
$$\omega_f = \boxed{4.09 \text{ rad/s}}$$

(b) Find the change in the rotational kinetic energy of the system.

Calculate the initial kinetic energy of the system:

$$KE_i = \tfrac{1}{2}I_i\omega_i^2 = \tfrac{1}{2}(4.40 \times 10^2 \text{ kg} \cdot \text{m}^2)(2.00 \text{ rad/s})^2$$
$$= 8.80 \times 10^2 \text{ J}$$

Calculate the final kinetic energy of the system:

$$KE_f = \tfrac{1}{2}I_f\omega_f^2 = \tfrac{1}{2}(215 \text{ kg} \cdot \text{m}^2)(4.09 \text{ rad/s})^2 = 1.80 \times 10^3 \text{ J}$$

Calculate the change in kinetic energy of the system:

$$KE_f - KE_i = \boxed{920 \text{ J}}$$

(c) Find the work done on the student.

The student undergoes a change in kinetic energy that equals the work done on her. Apply the work–energy theorem:

$$W = \Delta KE_{\text{student}} = \tfrac{1}{2} I_{Sf}\,\omega_f^{\,2} - \tfrac{1}{2} I_{Si}\,\omega_i^{\,2}$$
$$= \tfrac{1}{2}(15.0 \text{ kg} \cdot \text{m}^2)(4.09 \text{ rad/s})^2$$
$$- \tfrac{1}{2}(2.40 \times 10^2 \text{ kg} \cdot \text{m}^2)(2.00 \text{ rad/s})^2$$
$$W = \boxed{-355 \text{ J}}$$

REMARKS The angular momentum is unchanged by internal forces; however, the kinetic energy increases because the student must perform positive work in order to walk toward the center of the platform.

QUESTION 8.15 Is energy conservation violated in this example? Explain why there is a positive net change in mechanical energy. What is the origin of this energy?

EXERCISE 8.15 (a) Find the angular speed of the merry-go-round before the student jumped on, assuming the student didn't transfer any momentum or energy as she jumped on the merry-go-round. (b) By how much did the kinetic energy of the system change when the student jumped on? Notice that energy is lost in this process, as should be expected, since it is essentially a perfectly inelastic collision.

ANSWERS (a) 4.4 rad/s (b) $KE_f - KE_i = -1.06 \times 10^3 \text{ J}$.

■ SUMMARY

8.1 Torque

Let $\vec{F}$ be a force acting on an object, and let $\vec{r}$ be a position vector from a chosen point O to the point of application of the force. Then the magnitude of the torque $\vec{\tau}$ of the force $\vec{F}$ is given by

$$\tau = rF\sin\theta \qquad [8.2]$$

where r is the length of the position vector, F the magnitude of the force, and θ the angle between $\vec{F}$ and $\vec{r}$.

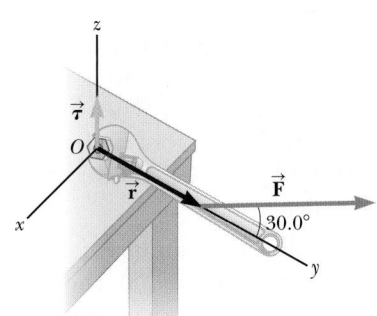

The torque at O depends on the distance to the point of application of the force $\vec{F}$ and the force's magnitude and direction.

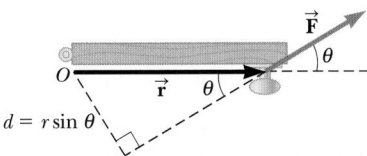

An alternate interpretation of torque involves the concept of a lever arm $d = r\sin\theta$ that is perpendicular to the force.

The quantity $d = r\sin\theta$ is called the *lever arm* of the force.

8.2 Torque and the Two Conditions for Equilibrium

An object in mechanical equilibrium must satisfy the following two conditions:

1. The net external force must be zero: $\sum \vec{F} = 0$.

2. The net external torque must be zero: $\sum \vec{\tau} = 0$.

These two conditions, used in solving problems involving rotation in a plane—result in three equations and three unknowns—two from the first condition (corresponding to the x- and y-components of the force) and one from the second condition, on torques. These equations must be solved simultaneously.

8.5 Relationship Between Torque and Angular Acceleration

The **moment of inertia** of a group of particles is

$$I \equiv \sum mr^2 \qquad [8.7]$$

If a rigid object free to rotate about a fixed axis has a net external torque $\sum\tau$ acting on it, then the object undergoes an angular acceleration a, where

$$\sum \tau = I\alpha \qquad [8.8]$$

This equation is the rotational equivalent of the second law of motion.

Problems are solved by using Equation 8.8 together with Newton's second law and solving the resulting equations simultaneously. The relation $a = r\alpha$ is often key in relating the translational equations to the rotational equations.

8.6 Rotational Kinetic Energy

If a rigid object rotates about a fixed axis with angular speed ω, its **rotational kinetic energy** is

$$KE_r = \tfrac{1}{2}I\omega^2 \qquad [8.10]$$

where I is the moment of inertia of the object around the axis of rotation.

A system involving rotation is described by three types of energy: potential energy PE, translational kinetic energy KE_t, and rotational kinetic energy KE_r. All these forms of energy must be included in the equation for conservation of mechanical energy for an isolated system:

$$(KE_t + KE_r + PE)_i = (KE_t + KE_r + PE)_f \qquad [8.11]$$

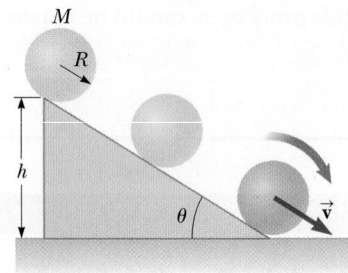

A ball rolling down an incline converts potential energy to translational and rotational kinetic energy.

where i and f refer to initial and final values, respectively. When non-conservative forces are present, it's necessary to use a generalization of the work–energy theorem:

$$W_{nc} = \Delta KE_t + \Delta KE_r + \Delta PE \qquad [8.12]$$

8.7 Angular Momentum

The **angular momentum** of a rotating object is given by

$$L \equiv I\omega \qquad [8.13]$$

Angular momentum is related to torque in the following equation:

$$\sum \tau = \frac{\text{change in angular momentum}}{\text{time interval}} = \frac{\Delta L}{\Delta t} \qquad [8.14]$$

If the net external torque acting on a system is zero, the total angular momentum of the system is constant,

$$L_i = L_f \qquad [8.15]$$

and is said to be conserved. Solving problems usually involves substituting into the expression

$$I_i\omega_i = I_f\omega_f \qquad [8.16]$$

and solving for the unknown.

■ MULTIPLE-CHOICE QUESTIONS

WebAssign The multiple-choice questions in this chapter may be assigned online in Enhanced WebAssign.

---

1. What is the magnitude of the angular acceleration of a 25.0-kg disk of radius 0.800 m when a torque of magnitude 40.0 N · m is applied to it? (a) 2.50 rad/s^2 (b) 5.00 rad/s^2 (c) 7.50 rad/s^2 (d) 10.0 rad/s^2 (e) 12.5 rad/s^2

2. A horizontal plank 4.00 m long and having mass 20.0 kg rests on two pivots, one at the left end and a second 1.00 m from the right end. Find the magnitude of the force exerted on the plank by the second pivot. (a) 32.0 N (b) 45.2 N (c) 112 N (d) 131 N (e) 98.2 N

3. A wrench 0.500 m long is applied to a nut with a force of 80.0 N. Because of the cramped space, the force must be exerted upward at an angle of 60.0° with respect to a line from the bolt through the end of the wrench. How much torque is applied to the nut? (a) 34.6 N · m (b) 4.56 N · m (c) 11.8 N · m (d) 14.2 N · m (e) 20.0 N · m

4. As shown in Figure MCQ8.4, a cord is wrapped onto a cylindrical reel mounted on a fixed, frictionless, horizontal axle. When

Figure MCQ8.4

does the reel have a greater magnitude of angular acceleration? (a) When the cord is pulled down with a constant force of 50 N. (b) When an object of weight 50 N is hung from the cord and released. (c) The angular accelerations in (a) and (b) are equal. (d) It is impossible to determine.

5. Two forces are acting on an object. Which of the following statements is correct? (a) The object is in equilibrium if the forces are equal in magnitude and opposite in direction. (b) The object is in equilibrium if the net torque on the object is zero. (c) The object is in equilibrium if the forces act at the same point on the object. (d) The object is in equilibrium if the net force and the net torque on the object are both zero. (e) The object cannot be in equilibrium because more than one force acts on it.

6. A block slides down a frictionless ramp, while a hollow sphere and a solid ball roll without slipping down a second ramp with the same height and slope. Rank the arrival times at the bottom from shortest to longest. (a) sphere, ball, block (b) ball, block, sphere (c) ball, sphere, block (d) block, sphere, ball (e) block, ball, sphere

7. A constant net nonzero torque is exerted on an object. Which of the following quantities *cannot* be constant for this object? More than one answer may be correct. (a) angular acceleration (b) angular velocity (c) moment of inertia (d) center of mass (e) angular momentum

8. A disk rotates about a fixed axis that is perpendicular to the disk and passes through its center. At any instant, does every point on the disk have the same (a) centripetal acceleration, (b) angular velocity, (c) tangential acceleration, (d) linear velocity, or (e) total acceleration?

9. A solid disk and a hoop are simultaneously released from rest at the top of an incline and roll down without slipping. Which object reaches the bottom first? (a) The one that has the largest mass arrives first. (b) The one that has the largest radius arrives first. (c) The hoop arrives first. (d) The disk arrives first. (e) The hoop and the disk arrive at the same time.

10. A solid cylinder of mass M and radius R rolls down an incline without slipping. Its moment of inertia about an axis through its center of mass is $MR^2/2$. At any instant while in motion, its rotational kinetic energy about its center of mass is what fraction of its total kinetic energy? (a) $\frac{1}{2}$ (b) $\frac{1}{4}$ (c) $\frac{1}{3}$ (d) $\frac{2}{5}$ (e) None of these

11. A mouse is initially at rest on a horizontal turntable mounted on a frictionless, vertical axle. As the mouse begins to walk clockwise around the perimeter, which of the following statements *must* be true of the turntable? (a) It also turns clockwise. (b) It turns counterclockwise with the same angular velocity as the mouse. (c) It remains stationary. (d) It turns counterclock-

wise because angular momentum is conserved. (e) It turns counterclockwise because mechanical energy is conserved.

12. Consider two uniform, solid spheres, a large, massive sphere and a smaller, lighter sphere. They are released from rest simultaneously from the top of a hill and roll down without slipping. Which one reaches the bottom of the hill first? (a) The large sphere reaches the bottom first. (b) The small sphere reaches the bottom first. (c) The sphere with the greatest density reaches the bottom first. (d) The spheres reach the bottom at the same time. (e) The answer depends on the values of the spheres' masses and radii.

13. The cars in a soapbox derby have no engines; they simply coast downhill. Which of the following design criteria is best from a competitive point of view? The car's wheels should (a) have large moments of inertia, (b) be massive, (c) be hoop-like wheels rather than solid disks, (d) be large wheels rather than small wheels, or (e) have small moments of inertia.

14. Two ponies of equal mass are initially at diametrically opposite points on the rim of a large horizontal turntable that is turning freely on a vertical, frictionless axle through its center. The ponies simultaneously start walking toward each other across the turntable. **(i)** As they walk, what happens to the angular speed of the carousel? (a) It increases. (b) It decreases. (c) It stays constant. Consider the ponies–turntable system in this process, and answer yes or no for the following questions. **(ii)** Is the mechanical energy of the system conserved? **(iii)** Is the momentum of the system conserved? **(iv)** Is the angular momentum of the system conserved?

■ CONCEPTUAL QUESTIONS

WebAssign The conceptual questions in this chapter may be assigned online in Enhanced WebAssign.

1. Why can't you put your heels firmly against a wall and then bend over without falling?

2. Explain why changing the axis of rotation of an object changes its moment of inertia.

3. If you see an object rotating, is there necessarily a net torque acting on it?

4. (a) Is it possible to calculate the torque acting on a rigid object without specifying an origin? (b) Is the torque independent of the location of the origin?

5. Why does a long pole help a tightrope walker stay balanced?

6. In the movie *Jurassic Park,* there is a scene in which some members of the visiting group are trapped in the kitchen with dinosaurs outside. The paleontologist is pressing against the center of the door, trying to keep out the dinosaurs on the other side. The botanist throws herself against the door at the edge near the hinge. A pivotal point in the film is that she cannot reach a gun

on the floor because she is trying to hold the door closed. If the paleontologist is pressing at the center of the door, and the botanist is pressing at the edge about 8 cm from the hinge, estimate how far the paleontologist would have to relocate in order to have a greater effect on keeping the door closed than both of them pushing together have in their original positions. (Question 6 is courtesy of Edward F. Redish. For more questions of this type, see www.physics.umd.edu/perg/.)

7. In some motorcycle races, the riders drive over small hills and the motorcycle becomes airborne for a short time. If the motorcycle racer keeps the throttle open while leaving the hill and going into the air, the motorcycle's nose tends to rise upwards. Why does this happen?

8. If you toss a textbook into the air, rotating it each time about one of the three axes perpendicular to it, you will find that it will not rotate smoothly about one of

those axes. (Try placing a strong rubber band around the book before the toss so that it will stay closed.) The book's rotation is stable about those axes having the largest and smallest moments of inertia, but unstable about the axis of intermediate moment. Try this on your own to find the axis that has this intermediate moment of inertia.

9. Stars originate as large bodies of slowly rotating gas. Because of gravity, these clumps of gas slowly decrease in size. What happens to the angular speed of a star as it shrinks? Explain.

10. If a high jumper positions his body correctly when going over the bar, the center of gravity of the athlete may actually pass under the bar. (See Fig. CQ8.10.) Explain how this is possible.

Figure CQ8.10

11. In a tape recorder, the tape is pulled past the read–write heads at a constant speed by the drive mechanism. Consider the reel from which the tape is pulled: As the tape is pulled off, the radius of the roll of remaining tape decreases. (a) How does the torque on the reel change with time? (b) If the tape mechanism is sud-

denly turned on so that the tape is quickly pulled with a large force, is the tape more likely to break when pulled from a nearly full reel or from a nearly empty reel?

12. (a) Give an example in which the net force acting on an object is zero, yet the net torque is nonzero. (b) Give an example in which the net torque acting on an object is zero, yet the net force is nonzero.

13. A ladder rests inclined against a wall. Would you feel safer climbing up the ladder if you were told that the floor was frictionless, but the wall was rough, or that the wall was frictionless, but the floor was rough? Justify your answer.

14. A cat usually lands on its feet regardless of the position from which it is dropped. A slow-motion film of a cat falling shows that the upper half of its body twists in one direction while the lower half twists in the opposite direction. (See Fig. CQ8.14.) Why does this type of rotation occur?

Figure CQ8.14

PROBLEMS

8.1 Torque

1. The fishing pole in Figure P8.1 makes an angle of 20.0° with the horizontal. What is the magnitude of the torque exerted by the fish about an axis perpendicular to the page and passing through the angler's hand if the fish pulls on the fishing line with a force $\vec{F} = 100$ N

at an angle 37.0° below the horizontal? The force is applied at a point 2.00 m from the angler's hands.

2. **M** Find the net torque on the wheel in Figure P8.2 about the axle through O perpendicular to the page, taking $a = 10.0$ cm and $b = 25.0$ cm.

Figure P8.1

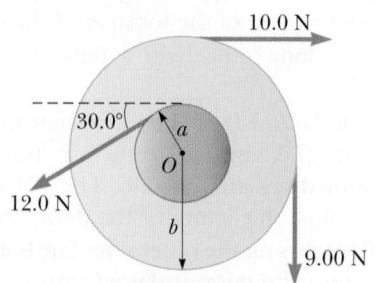

Figure P8.2

3. Calculate the net torque (magnitude and direction) on the beam in Figure P8.3 about (a) an axis through O perpendicular to the page and (b) an axis through C perpendicular to the page.

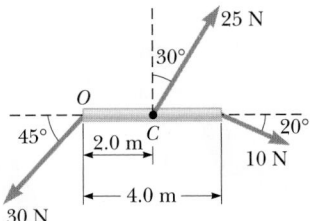

Figure P8.3

4. **BIO** A dental bracket exerts a horizontal force of 80.0 N on a tooth at point B in Figure P8.4. What is the torque on the root of the tooth about point A?

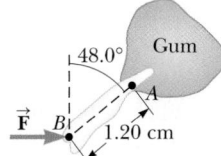

Figure P8.4

5. **QC** A simple pendulum consists of a small object of mass 3.0 kg hanging at the end of a 2.0-m-long light string that is connected to a pivot point. (a) Calculate the magnitude of the torque (due to the force of gravity) about this pivot point when the string makes a 5.0° angle with the vertical. (b) Does the torque increase or decrease as the angle increases? Explain.

6. **S** Write the necessary equations of equilibrium of the object shown in Figure P8.6. Take the origin of the torque equation about an axis perpendicular to the page through the point O.

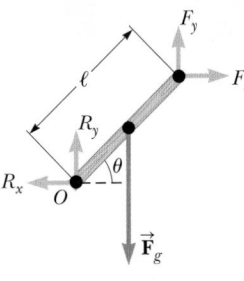

Figure P8.6

8.2 Torque and the Two Conditions for Equilibrium

8.3 The Center of Gravity

8.4 Examples of Objects in Equilibrium

7. **BIO** The arm in Figure P8.7 weighs 41.5 N. The force of gravity acting on the arm acts through point A. Determine the magnitudes of the tension force $\vec{F}_t$ in the deltoid muscle and the force $\vec{F}_s$ exerted by the shoulder on the humerus (upper-arm bone) to hold the arm in the position shown.

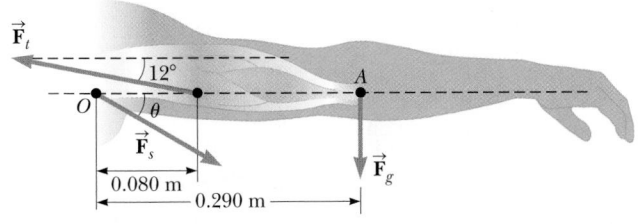

Figure P8.7

8. A uniform 35.0-kg beam of length $\ell = 5.00$ m is supported by a vertical rope located $d = 1.20$ m from its left end as in Figure P8.8. The right end of the beam is supported by a vertical column. Find (a) the tension in the rope and (b) the force that the column exerts on the right end of the beam.

Figure P8.8

9. **BIO** A cook holds a 2.00-kg carton of milk at arm's length (Fig. P8.9). What force $\vec{F}_B$ must be exerted by the biceps muscle? (Ignore the weight of the forearm.)

Figure P8.9

10. A meter stick is found to balance at the 49.7-cm mark when placed on a fulcrum. When a 50.0-gram mass is attached at the 10.0-cm mark, the fulcrum must be moved to the 39.2-cm mark for balance. What is the mass of the meter stick?

11. Find the x- and y-coordinates of the center of gravity of a 4.00-ft by 8.00-ft uniform sheet of plywood with the upper right quadrant removed as shown in Figure P8.11. *Hint:* The mass of any segment of the plywood sheet is proportional to the area of that segment.

Figure P8.11

12. **GP** A beam resting on two pivots has a length of $L = 6.00$ m and mass $M = 90.0$ kg. The pivot under the left end exerts a normal force n_1 on the beam, and the second pivot placed a distance $\ell = 4.00$ m from the left end exerts a normal force n_2. A woman of mass $m = 55.0$ kg steps onto the left end of the beam and begins walking to the right as in Figure P8.12 on page 266. The goal is to find the woman's position when the beam begins to tip. (a) Sketch a free-body diagram, labeling the gravitational and normal forces acting on the beam and placing the woman x meters to the right of the first pivot, which is the origin. (b) Where is the woman when the normal force n_1 is the greatest?

(c) What is n_1 when the beam is about to tip? (d) Use the force equation of equilibrium to find the value of n_2 when the beam is about to tip. (e) Using the result of part (c) and the torque equilibrium equation, with torques computed around the second pivot point, find the woman's position when the beam is about to tip. (f) Check the answer to part (e) by computing torques around the first pivot point. Except for possible slight differences due to rounding, is the answer the same?

Figure P8.12 Problems 12 and 14.

13. Consider the following mass distribution, where x- and y-coordinates are given in meters: 5.0 kg at (0.0, 0.0) m, 3.0 kg at (0.0, 4.0) m, and 4.0 kg at (3.0, 0.0) m. Where should a fourth object of 8.0 kg be placed so that the center of gravity of the four-object arrangement will be at (0.0, 0.0) m?

14. **S** A beam of length L and mass M rests on two pivots. The first pivot is at the left end, taken as the origin, and the second pivot is at a distance ℓ from the left end. A woman of mass m starts at the left end and walks toward the right end as in Figure P8.12. When the beam is on the verge of tipping, find symbolic expressions for (a) the normal force exerted by the second pivot in terms of M, m, and g and (b) the woman's position in terms of M, m, L, and ℓ. (c) Find the minimum value of ℓ that will allow the woman to reach the end of the beam without it tipping.

15. **BIO** Many of the elements in horizontal-bar exercises can be modeled by representing the gymnast by four segments consisting of arms, torso (including the head), thighs, and lower legs, as shown in Figure P8.15a. Inertial parameters for a particular gymnast are as follows:

Segment	Mass (kg)	Length (m)	r_{cg} (m)	I (kg · m²)
Arms	6.87	0.548	0.239	0.205
Torso	33.57	0.601	0.337	1.610
Thighs	14.07	0.374	0.151	0.173
Legs	7.54	—	0.227	0.164

Note that in Figure P8.15a r_{cg} is the distance to the center of gravity measured from the joint closest to the bar and the masses for the arms, thighs, and legs include both appendages. I is the moment of inertia of each segment about its center of gravity. Determine the distance from the bar to the center of gravity of the gymnast for the two positions shown in Figures P8.15b and P8.15c.

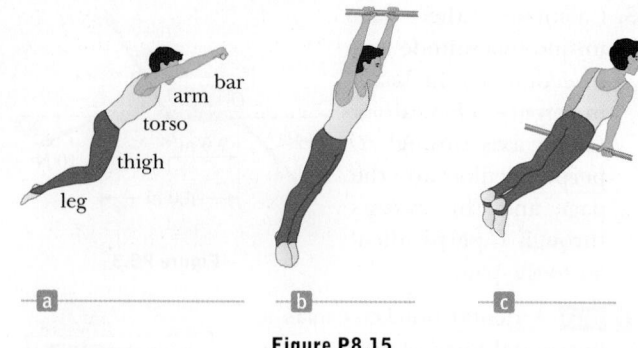

Figure P8.15

16. **BIO** Using the data given in Problem 15 and the coordinate system shown in Figure P8.16b, calculate the position of the center of gravity of the gymnast shown in Figure P8.16a. Pay close attention to the definition of r_{cg} in the table.

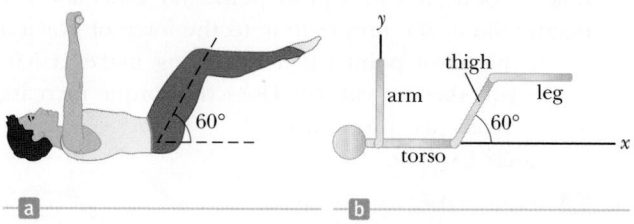

Figure P8.16

17. **BIO** A person bending forward to lift a load "with his back" (Fig. P8.17a) rather than "with his knees" can be injured by large forces exerted on the muscles and vertebrae. The spine pivots mainly at the fifth lumbar vertebra, with the principal supporting force provided by the erector spinalis muscle in the back. To see the magnitude of the forces involved, and to understand why back problems are common among humans, consider the model shown in Figure P8.17b of a person bending forward to lift a 200-N object. The spine and upper body are represented as a uniform horizontal rod of weight 350 N, pivoted at the base of the spine. The erector spinalis muscle, attached at a point two-thirds of the way up the spine, maintains the position of the back. The angle between the spine and this muscle is 12.0°. Find (a) the tension in the back muscle and (b) the compressional force in the spine.

Figure P8.17

18. **BIO** When a person stands on tiptoe (a strenuous position), the position of the foot is as shown in Figure P8.18a. The total gravitational force on the body, $\vec{F}_g$, is supported by the force $\vec{n}$ exerted by the floor on the toes of one foot. A mechanical model of the situation is shown in Figure P8.18b, where $\vec{T}$ is the force exerted by the Achilles tendon on the foot and $\vec{R}$ is the force exerted by the tibia on the foot. Find the values of T, R, and θ when $F_g = n = 700$ N.

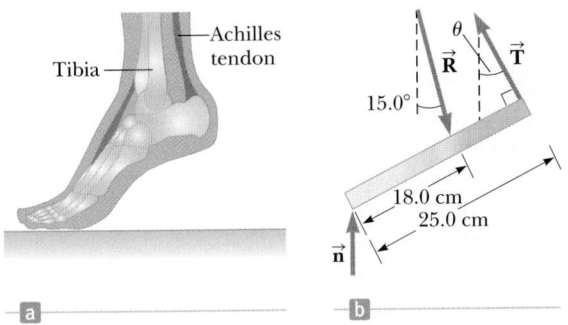

Figure P8.18

19. **M** A 500-N uniform rectangular sign 4.00 m wide and 3.00 m high is suspended from a horizontal, 6.00-m-long, uniform, 100-N rod as indicated in Figure P8.19. The left end of the rod is supported by a hinge, and the right end is supported by a thin cable making a 30.0° angle with the vertical. (a) Find the tension T in the cable.

Figure P8.19

(b) Find the horizontal and vertical components of force exerted on the left end of the rod by the hinge.

20. A window washer is standing on a scaffold supported by a vertical rope at each end. The scaffold weighs 200 N and is 3.00 m long. What is the tension in each rope when the 700-N worker stands 1.00 m from one end?

21. A uniform plank of length 2.00 m and mass 30.0 kg is supported by three ropes, as indicated by the blue vectors in Figure P8.21. Find the tension in each rope when a 700-N person is $d = 0.500$ m from the left end.

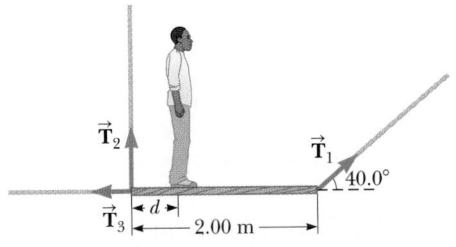

Figure P8.21

22. A hungry bear weighing 700 N walks out on a beam in an attempt to retrieve a basket of goodies hanging at the end of the beam (Fig. P8.22). The beam is uniform, weighs 200 N, and is 6.00 m long, and it is supported by a wire at an angle of $\theta = 60.0°$. The basket weighs 80.0 N. (a) Draw a force diagram for the beam. (b) When the bear is at $x = 1.00$ m, find the tension in the wire supporting the beam and the components of the force exerted by the wall on the left end of the beam. (c) If the wire can withstand a maximum tension of 900 N, what is the maximum distance the bear can walk before the wire breaks?

Figure P8.22

23. **S** Figure P8.23 shows a uniform beam of mass m pivoted at its lower end, with a horizontal spring attached between its top end and a vertical wall. The beam makes an angle θ with the horizontal. Find expressions for (a) the distance d the spring is stretched from equilibrium and (b) the components of the force exerted by the pivot on the beam.

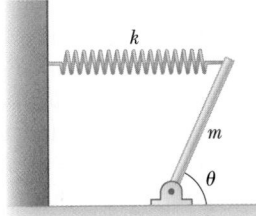

Figure P8.23

24. **GP** A strut of length $L = 3.00$ m and mass $m = 16.0$ kg is held by a cable at an angle of $\theta = 30.0°$ with respect to the horizontal as shown in Figure P8.24. (a) Sketch a force diagram, indicating all the forces and their placement on the strut. (b) Why is the hinge a good place to use for calculating torques? (c) Write the condition for rotational equilibrium symbolically, calculating the torques around the hinge. (d) Use the torque equation to calculate the tension in the cable. (e) Write the x- and y-components of Newton's second law for equilibrium. (f) Use the force equation to find the x- and y-components of the force on the hinge. (g) Assuming the strut position is to remain the same, would it be advantageous to attach the cable higher up on the wall? Explain the benefit in terms of the force on the hinge and cable tension.

Figure P8.24

25. **S** A refrigerator of width w and height h rests on a rough incline as in Figure P8.25 (page 268). Find an expression for the maximum value θ can have before the refrigerator tips over. Note, the contact

point between the refrigerator and incline shifts as θ increases and treat the refrigerator as a uniform box.

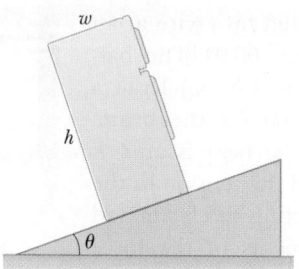

Figure P8.25

26. QC S A uniform beam of length L and mass m shown in Figure P8.26 is inclined at an angle θ to the horizontal. Its upper end is connected to a wall by a rope, and its lower end rests on a rough horizontal surface. The coefficient of static friction between the beam and surface is μ_s. Assume the angle is such that the static friction force is at its maximum value. (a) Draw a force diagram for the beam. (b) Using the condition of rotational equilibrium, find an expression for the tension T in the rope in terms of m, g, and θ. (c) Using Newton's second law for equilibrium, find a second expression for T in terms of μ_s, m, and g. (d) Using the foregoing results, obtain a relationship involving only μ_s and the angle θ. (e) What happens if the angle gets smaller? Is this equation valid for all values of θ? Explain.

Figure P8.26

27. BIO The chewing muscle, the masseter, is one of the strongest in the human body. It is attached to the mandible (lower jawbone) as shown in Figure P8.27a. The jawbone is pivoted about a socket just in front of the auditory canal. The forces acting on the jawbone are equivalent to those acting on the curved bar in Figure P8.27b. $\vec{F}_C$ is the force exerted by the food being chewed against the jawbone, $\vec{T}$ is the force of tension in the masseter, and $\vec{R}$ is the force exerted by the socket on the mandible. Find $\vec{T}$ and $\vec{R}$ for a person who bites down on a piece of steak with a force of 50.0 N.

Figure P8.27

28. A 1200-N uniform boom at $\phi = 65°$ to the horizontal is supported by a cable at an angle $\theta = 25.0°$ to the horizontal as shown in Figure P8.28. The boom is pivoted at the bottom, and an object of weight $w = 2\,000$ N hangs from its top. Find (a) the tension in the support cable and (b) the components of the reaction force exerted by the pivot on the boom.

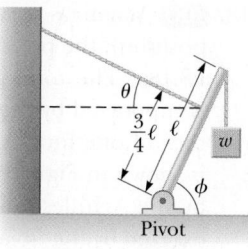

Figure P8.28

29. BIO The large quadriceps muscle in the upper leg terminates at its lower end in a tendon attached to the upper end of the tibia (Fig. P8.29a). The forces on the lower leg when the leg is extended are modeled as in Figure P8.29b, where $\vec{T}$ is the force of tension in the tendon, $\vec{w}$ is the force of gravity acting on the lower leg, and $\vec{F}$ is the force of gravity acting on the foot. Find $\vec{T}$ when the tendon is at an angle of 25.0° with the tibia, assuming that $w = 30.0$ N, $F = 12.5$ N, and the leg is extended at an angle θ of 40.0° with the vertical. Assume that the center of gravity of the lower leg is at its center and that the tendon attaches to the lower leg at a point one-fifth of the way down the leg.

Figure P8.29

30. One end of a uniform 4.0-m-long rod of weight w is supported by a cable at an angle of $\theta = 37°$ with the rod. The other end rests against a wall, where it is held by friction. (See Fig. P8.30.) The coefficient of static friction between the wall and the rod is $\mu_s = 0.50$. Determine the minimum distance x from point A at which an additional weight w (the same as the weight of the rod) can be hung without causing the rod to slip at point A.

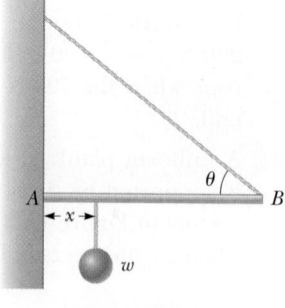

Figure P8.30

8.5 Relationship Between Torque and Angular Acceleration

31. Four objects are held in position at the corners of a rectangle by light rods as shown in Figure P8.31. Find the moment of inertia of the system about (a) the

x-axis, (b) the y-axis, and (c) an axis through O and perpendicular to the page.

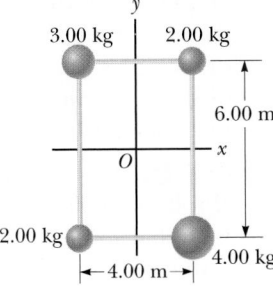

Figure P8.31
Problems 31 and 32.

32. If the system shown in Figure P8.31 is set in rotation about each of the axes mentioned in Problem 31, find the torque that will produce an angular acceleration of 1.50 rad/s² in each case.

33. A large grinding wheel in the shape of a solid cylinder of radius 0.330 m is free to rotate on a frictionless, vertical axle. A constant tangential force of 250 N applied to its edge causes the wheel to have an angular acceleration of 0.940 rad/s². (a) What is the moment of inertia of the wheel? (b) What is the mass of the wheel? (c) If the wheel starts from rest, what is its angular velocity after 5.00 s have elapsed, assuming the force is acting during that time?

34. **GP** An oversized yo-yo is made from two identical solid disks each of mass $M = 2.00$ kg and radius $R = 10.0$ cm. The two disks are joined by a solid cylinder of radius $r = 4.00$ cm and mass $m = 1.00$ kg as in Figure P8.34. Take the center of the cylinder as the axis of the system, with positive torques directed to the left along this axis. All torques and angular variables are to be calculated around this axis. Light string is wrapped around the cylinder, and the system is then allowed to drop from rest. (a) What is the moment of inertia of the system? Give a symbolic answer. (b) What torque does gravity exert on the system with respect to the given axis? (c) Take downward as the negative coordinate direction. As depicted in Figure P8.34, is the torque exerted by the tension positive or negative? Is the angular acceleration positive or negative? What about the translational acceleration? (d) Write an equation for the angular acceleration α in terms of the translational acceleration a and radius r. (Watch the sign!) (e) Write Newton's second law for the system in terms of m, M, a, T, and g. (f) Write Newton's second law for rotation in terms of I, α, T, and r. (g) Eliminate α from the rotational second law with the expression found in

part (d) and find a symbolic expression for the acceleration a in terms of m, M, g, r and R. (h) What is the numeric value for the system's acceleration? (i) What is the tension in the string? (j) How long does it take the system to drop 1.00 m from rest?

35. **QC** A rope of negligible mass is wrapped around a 225-kg solid cylinder of radius 0.400 m. The cylinder is suspended several meters off the ground with its axis oriented horizontally, and turns on that axis without friction. (a) If a 75.0-kg man takes hold of the free end of the rope and falls under the force of gravity, what is his acceleration? (b) What is the angular acceleration of the cylinder? (c) If the mass of the rope were not neglected, what would happen to the angular acceleration of the cylinder as the man falls?

36. A potter's wheel having a radius of 0.50 m and a moment of inertia of 12 kg · m² is rotating freely at 50 rev/min. The potter can stop the wheel in 6.0 s by pressing a wet rag against the rim and exerting a radially inward force of 70 N. Find the effective coefficient of kinetic friction between the wheel and the wet rag.

37. A model airplane with mass 0.750 kg is tethered by a wire so that it flies in a circle 30.0 m in radius. The airplane engine provides a net thrust of 0.800 N perpendicular to the tethering wire. (a) Find the torque the net thrust produces about the center of the circle. (b) Find the angular acceleration of the airplane when it is in level flight. (c) Find the linear acceleration of the airplane tangent to its flight path.

38. A bicycle wheel has a diameter of 64.0 cm and a mass of 1.80 kg. Assume that the wheel is a hoop with all the mass concentrated on the outside radius. The bicycle is placed on a stationary stand, and a resistive force of 120 N is applied tangent to the rim of the tire. (a) What force must be applied by a chain passing over a 9.00-cm-diameter sprocket in order to give the wheel an acceleration of 4.50 rad/s²? (b) What force is required if you shift to a 5.60-cm-diameter sprocket?

39. **M** A 150-kg merry-go-round in the shape of a uniform, solid, horizontal disk of radius 1.50 m is set in motion by wrapping a rope about the rim of the disk and pulling on the rope. What constant force must be exerted on the rope to bring the merry-go-round from rest to an angular speed of 0.500 rev/s in 2.00 s?

40. **QC S** An Atwood's machine consists of blocks of masses $m_1 = 10.0$ kg and $m_2 = 20.0$ kg attached by a cord running over a pulley as in Figure P8.40. The pulley is a solid cylinder with mass $M = 8.00$ kg and radius $r = 0.200$ m. The block of mass m_2 is allowed to drop, and the cord turns the pulley without slipping. (a) Why must the tension T_2 be

Figure P8.34

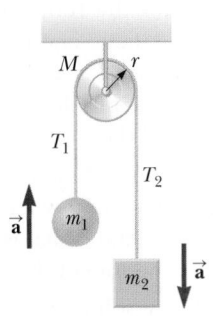

Figure P8.40

greater than the tension T_1? (b) What is the acceleration of the system, assuming the pulley axis is frictionless? (c) Find the tensions T_1 and T_2.

41. An airliner lands with a speed of 50.0 m/s. Each wheel of the plane has a radius of 1.25 m and a moment of inertia of 110 kg · m². At touchdown, the wheels begin to spin under the action of friction. Each wheel supports a weight of 1.40×10^4 N, and the wheels attain their angular speed in 0.480 s while rolling without slipping. What is the coefficient of kinetic friction between the wheels and the runway? Assume that the speed of the plane is constant.

8.6 Rotational Kinetic Energy

42. A car is designed to get its energy from a rotating flywheel with a radius of 2.00 m and a mass of 500 kg. Before a trip, the flywheel is attached to an electric motor, which brings the flywheel's rotational speed up to 5 000 rev/min. (a) Find the kinetic energy stored in the flywheel. (b) If the flywheel is to supply energy to the car as a 10.0-hp motor would, find the length of time the car could run before the flywheel would have to be brought back up to speed.

43. A horizontal 800-N merry-go-round of radius 1.50 m is started from rest by a constant horizontal force of 50.0N applied tangentially to the merry-go-round. Find the kinetic energy of the merry-go-round after 3.00 s. (Assume it is a solid cylinder.)

44. QC Four objects—a hoop, a solid cylinder, a solid sphere, and a thin, spherical shell—each have a mass of 4.80 kg and a radius of 0.230 m. (a) Find the moment of inertia for each object as it rotates about the axes shown in Table 8.1. (b) Suppose each object is rolled down a ramp. Rank the translational speed of each object from highest to lowest. (c) Rank the objects' rotational kinetic energies from highest to lowest as the objects roll down the ramp.

45. A light rod of length $\ell = 1.00$ m rotates about an axis perpendicular to its length and passing through its center as in Figure P8.45. Two particles of masses $m_1 = 4.00$ kg and $m_2 = 3.00$ kg are connected to the ends of the rod. (a) Neglecting the mass of the rod, what is the system's kinetic energy when its angular speed is 2.50 rad/s? (b) Repeat the problem, assuming the mass of the rod is taken to be 2.00 kg.

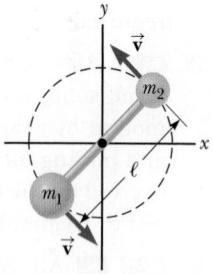

Figure P8.45
Problems 45 and 57.

46. A 240-N sphere 0.20 m in radius rolls without slipping 6.0 m down a ramp that is inclined at 37° with the horizontal. What is the angular speed of the sphere at the bottom of the slope if it starts from rest?

47. A solid, uniform disk of radius 0.250 m and mass 55.0 kg rolls down a ramp of length 4.50 m that makes an angle of 15.0° with the horizontal. The disk starts from rest from the top of the ramp. Find (a) the speed of the disk's center of mass when it reaches the bottom of the ramp and (b) the angular speed of the disk at the bottom of the ramp.

48. QC S A solid uniform sphere of mass m and radius R rolls without slipping down an incline of height h. (a) What forms of mechanical energy are associated with the sphere at any point along the incline when its angular speed is ω? Answer in words and symbolically in terms of the quantities m, g, y, I, ω, and v. (b) What force acting on the sphere causes it to roll rather than slip down the incline? (c) Determine the ratio of the sphere's rotational kinetic energy to its total kinetic energy at any instant.

49. The top in Figure P8.49 has a moment of inertia of 4.00×10^{-4} kg · m² and is initially at rest. It is free to rotate about a stationary axis AA'. A string wrapped around a peg along the axis of the top is pulled in such a manner as to maintain a constant tension of 5.57 N in the string. If the string does not slip while wound around the peg, what is the angular speed of the top after 80.0 cm of string has been pulled off the peg? *Hint:* Consider the work that is done.

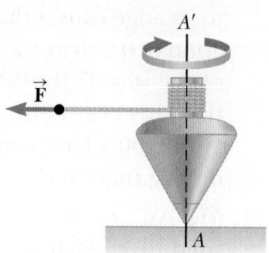

Figure P8.49

50. A constant torque of 25.0 N · m is applied to a grindstone whose moment of inertia is 0.130 kg · m². Using energy principles and neglecting friction, find the angular speed after the grindstone has made 15.0 revolutions. *Hint:* The angular equivalent of $W_{net} = F\Delta x = \frac{1}{2}mv_f^2 - \frac{1}{2}mv_i^2$ is $W_{net} = \tau\Delta\theta = \frac{1}{2}I\omega_f^2 - \frac{1}{2}I\omega_i^2$. You should convince yourself that this last relationship is correct.

51. A 10.0-kg cylinder rolls without slipping on a rough surface. At an instant when its center of gravity has a speed of 10.0 m/s, determine (a) the translational kinetic energy of its center of gravity, (b) the rotational kinetic energy about its center of gravity, and (c) its total kinetic energy.

52. Use conservation of energy to determine the angular speed of the spool shown in Figure P8.52 after the 3.00-kg bucket has fallen 4.00 m, starting from rest. The light string attached to the bucket is wrapped around the spool and does not slip as it unwinds.

53. QC A giant swing at an amusement park consists of a 365-kg uniform arm 10.0 m long, with two seats of negligible mass

Figure P8.52

connected at the lower end of the arm (Fig. P8.53). (a) How far from the upper end is the center of mass of the arm? (b) The gravitational potential energy of the arm is the same as if all its mass were concentrated at the center of mass. If the arm is raised through a 45.0° angle, find the gravitational potential energy, where the zero level is taken to be 10.0 m below the axis. (c) The arm drops from rest from the position described in part (b). Find the gravitational potential energy of the system when it reaches the vertical orientation. (d) Find the speed of the seats at the bottom of the swing.

10.0 m

Figure P8.53

8.7 Angular Momentum

54. Each of the following objects has a radius of 0.180 m and a mass of 2.40 kg, and each rotates about an axis through its center (as in Table 8.1) with an angular speed of 35.0 rad/s. Find the magnitude of the angular momentum of each object. (a) a hoop (b) a solid cylinder (c) a solid sphere (d) a hollow spherical shell

55. (a) Calculate the angular momentum of Earth that arises from its spinning motion on its axis, treating Earth as a uniform solid sphere. (b) Calculate the angular momentum of Earth that arises from its orbital motion about the Sun, treating Earth as a point particle.

56. **QC** A 0.005 00-kg bullet traveling horizontally with a speed of 1.00×10^3 m/s enters an 18.0-kg door, embedding itself 10.0 cm from the side opposite the hinges as in Figure P8.56. The 1.00-m-wide door is free to swing on its hinges. (a) Before it hits the door, does the bullet have angular momentum relative the door's axis of rotation? Explain. (b) Is mechanical energy conserved in this collision? Answer without doing a calculation. (c) At what angular speed does the door swing open immediately after the collision? (The door has the same moment of inertia as a rod with axis at one end.) (d) Calculate the energy of the door–bullet system and determine whether it is less than or equal to the kinetic energy of the bullet before the collision.

Hinge

18.0 kg

0.005 00 kg

Figure P8.56. An overhead view of a bullet striking a door.

57. A light rigid rod of length $\ell = 1.00$ m rotates about an axis perpendicular to its length and through its center, as shown in Figure P8.45. Two particles of masses $m_1 = 4.00$ kg and $m_2 = 3.00$ kg are connected to the ends of the rod. What is the angular momentum of the system if the speed of each particle is 5.00 m/s? (Neglect the rod's mass.)

58. Halley's comet moves about the Sun in an elliptical orbit, with its closest approach to the Sun being 0.59 A.U. and its greatest distance being 35 A.U. (1 A.U. is the Earth–Sun distance). If the comet's speed at closest approach is 54 km/s, what is its speed when it is farthest from the Sun? You may neglect any change in the comet's mass and assume that its angular momentum about the Sun is conserved.

59. **S** A rigid, massless rod has three particles with equal masses attached to it as shown in Figure P8.59. The rod is free to rotate in a vertical plane about a frictionless axle perpendicular to the rod through the point P and is released from rest in the horizontal position at $t = 0$. Assuming m and d are known, find (a) the moment of inertia of the system (rod plus particles) about the pivot, (b) the torque acting on the system at $t = 0$, (c) the angular acceleration of the system at $t = 0$, (d) the linear acceleration of the particle labeled 3 at $t = 0$, (e) the maximum kinetic energy of the system, (f) the maximum angular speed reached by the rod, (g) the maximum angular momentum of the system, and (h) the maximum translational speed reached by the particle labeled 2.

$\frac{2d}{3}$

P

m m m

1   2   3

d d

Figure P8.59

60. **M** A 60.0-kg woman stands at the rim of a horizontal turntable having a moment of inertia of 500 kg · m² and a radius of 2.00 m. The turntable is initially at rest and is free to rotate about a frictionless, vertical axle through its center. The woman then starts walking around the rim clockwise (as viewed from above the system) at a constant speed of 1.50 m/s relative to Earth. (a) In what direction and with what angular speed does the turntable rotate? (b) How much work does the woman do to set herself and the turntable into motion?

61. A solid, horizontal cylinder of mass 10.0 kg and radius 1.00 m rotates with an angular speed of 7.00 rad/s about a fixed vertical axis through its center. A 0.250-kg piece of putty is dropped vertically onto the cylinder at a point 0.900 m from the center of rotation and sticks to the cylinder. Determine the final angular speed of the system.

62. A student sits on a rotating stool holding two 3.0-kg objects. When his arms are extended horizontally, the objects are 1.0 m from the axis of rotation and he rotates with an angular speed of 0.75 rad/s. The moment of inertia of the student plus stool is 3.0 kg · m² and is assumed to be constant. The student then pulls in the objects horizontally to 0.30 m from the rotation axis. (a) Find the new angular speed of the student. (b) Find the kinetic energy of the student before and after the objects are pulled in.

63. The puck in Figure P8.63 has a mass of 0.120 kg. Its original distance from the center of rotation is 40.0 cm, and it moves with a speed of 80.0 cm/s. The string is pulled downward 15.0 cm through the hole in the frictionless table. Determine the work done on the puck. *Hint:* Consider the change in kinetic energy of the puck.

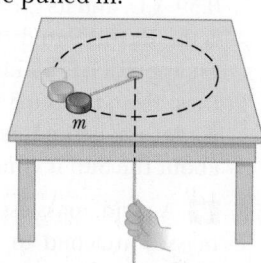

Figure P8.63

64. A space station shaped like a giant wheel has a radius of 100 m and a moment of inertia of 5.00×10^8 kg · m². A crew of 150 lives on the rim, and the station is rotating so that the crew experiences an apparent acceleration of 1g (Fig. P8.64). When 100 people move to the center of the station for a union meeting, the angular speed changes. What apparent acceleration is experienced by the managers remaining at the rim? Assume the average mass of a crew member is 65.0 kg.

Figure P8.64

65. **QC** **S** A cylinder with moment of inertia I_1 rotates with angular velocity ω_0 about a frictionless vertical axle. A second cylinder, with moment of inertia I_2, initially not rotating, drops onto the first cylinder (Fig. P8.65). Because the surfaces are rough, the two cylinders eventually reach the same angular speed ω. (a) Calculate ω. (b) Show that kinetic energy is lost in this situation, and calculate the ratio of the final to the initial kinetic energy.

Figure P8.65

66. **M** A particle of mass 0.400 kg is attached to the 100-cm mark of a meter stick of mass 0.100 kg. The meter stick rotates on a horizontal, frictionless table with an angular speed of 4.00 rad/s. Calculate the angular momentum of the system when the stick is pivoted about an axis (a) perpendicular to the table through the 50.0-cm mark and (b) perpendicular to the table through the 0-cm mark.

Additional Problems

67. **GP** A typical propeller of a turbine used to generate electricity from the wind consists of three blades as in Figure P8.67. Each blade has a length of $L = 35$ m and a mass of $m = 420$ kg. The propeller rotates at the rate of 25 rev/min. (a) Convert the angular speed of the propeller to units of rad/s. Find (b) the moment of inertia of the propeller about the axis of rotation and (c) the total kinetic energy of the propeller.

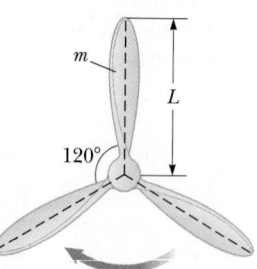

Figure P8.67

68. Figure P8.68 shows a claw-hammer as it is being used to pull a nail out of a horizontal board. If a force of magnitude 150 N is exerted horizontally as shown, find (a) the force exerted by the hammer claws on the nail and (b) the force exerted by the surface at the point of contact with the hammer head. Assume that the force the hammer exerts on the nail is parallel to the nail and perpendicular to the position vector from the point of contact.

Figure P8.68

69. **QC** A 40.0-kg child stands at one end of a 70.0-kg boat that is 4.00 m long (Fig. P8.69). The boat is initially 3.00 m from the pier. The child notices a turtle on a rock beyond the far end of the boat and proceeds to walk to that end to catch the turtle. (a) Neglecting friction between the boat and water, describe the

Figure P8.69

motion of the system (child plus boat). (b) Where will the child be relative to the pier when he reaches the far end of the boat? (c) Will he catch the turtle? (Assume that he can reach out 1.00 m from the end of the boat.)

70. An object of mass $M = 12.0$ kg is attached to a cord that is wrapped around a wheel of radius $r = 10.0$ cm (Fig. P8.70). The acceleration of the object down the frictionless incline is measured to be $a = 2.00$ m/s² and the incline makes an angle $\theta = 37.0°$ with the horizontal. Assuming the axle of the wheel to be frictionless, determine (a) the tension in the rope, (b) the moment of inertia of the wheel, and (c) the angular speed of the wheel 2.00 s after it begins rotating, starting from rest.

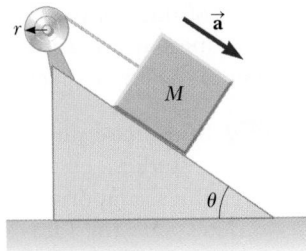

Figure P8.70

71. A uniform ladder of length L and weight w is leaning against a vertical wall. The coefficient of static friction between the ladder and the floor is the same as that between the ladder and the wall. If this coefficient of static friction is $\mu_s = 0.500$, determine the smallest angle the ladder can make with the floor without slipping.

72. Two astronauts (Fig. P8.72), each having a mass of 75.0 kg, are connected by a 10.0-m rope of negligible mass. They are isolated in space, moving in circles around the point halfway between them at a speed of 5.00 m/s. Treating the astronauts as particles, calculate (a) the magnitude of the angular momentum and (b) the rotational energy of the system. By pulling on the rope, the astronauts shorten the distance between them to 5.00 m. (c) What is the new angular momentum of the system? (d) What are their new speeds? (e) What is the new rotational energy of the system? (f) How much work is done by the astronauts in shortening the rope?

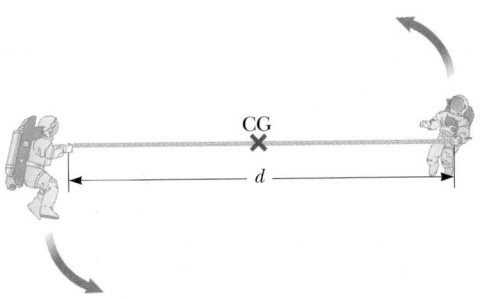

Figure P8.72 Problems 72 and 73.

73. **S** *This is a symbolic version of problem 72.* Two astronauts (Fig. P8.72), each having a mass M, are connected by a rope of length d having negligible mass. They are

isolated in space, moving in circles around the point halfway between them at a speed v. (a) Calculate the magnitude of the angular momentum of the system by treating the astronauts as particles. (b) Calculate the rotational energy of the system. By pulling on the rope, the astronauts shorten the distance between them to $d/2$. (c) What is the new angular momentum of the system? (d) What are their new speeds? (e) What is the new rotational energy of the system? (f) How much work is done by the astronauts in shortening the rope?

74. Two window washers, Bob and Joe, are on a 3.00-m-long, 345-N scaffold supported by two cables attached to its ends. Bob weighs 750 N and stands 1.00 m from the left end, as shown in Figure P8.74. Two meters from the left end is the 500-N washing equipment. Joe is 0.500 m from the right end and weighs 1 000 N. Given that the scaffold is in rotational and translational equilibrium, what are the forces on each cable?

Figure P8.74

75. A 2.35-kg uniform bar of length $\ell = 1.30$ m is held in a horizontal position by three vertical springs as in Figure P8.75. The two lower springs are compressed and exert *upward* forces on the bar of magnitude $F_1 = 6.80$ N and $F_2 = 9.50$ N, respectively. Find (a) the force F_s exerted by the top spring on the bar, and (b) the location x of the upper spring that will keep the bar in equilibrium.

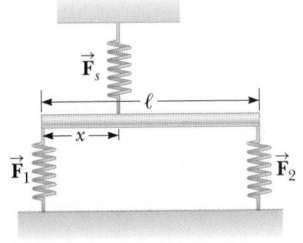

Figure P8.75

76. **QC** **S** A light rod of length $2L$ is free to rotate in a *vertical* plane about a frictionless pivot through its center. A particle of mass m_1 is attached at one end of the rod, and a mass m_2 is at the opposite end, where $m_1 > m_2$. The system is released from rest in the vertical position shown in Figure P8.76a (page 274), and at some later time the system is rotating in the position shown in Figure P8.76b. Take the reference point

of the gravitational potential energy to be at the pivot. (a) Find an expression for the system's total mechanical energy in the vertical position. (b) Find an expression for the total mechanical energy in the rotated position shown in Figure P8.76b. (c) Using the fact that the mechanical energy of the system is conserved, how would you determine the angular speed ω of the system in the rotated position? (d) Find the magnitude of the torque on the system in the vertical position and in the rotated position. Is the torque constant? Explain what these results imply regarding the angular momentum of the system. (e) Find an expression for the magnitude of the angular acceleration of the system in the rotated position. Does your result make sense when the rod is horizontal? When it is vertical? Explain.

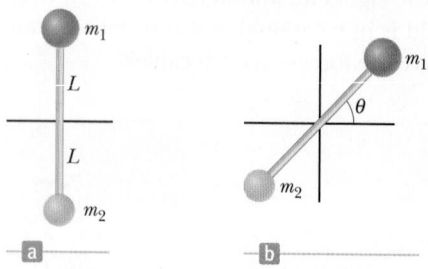

Figure P8.76

77. **QC** A light rope passes over a light, frictionless pulley. One end is fastened to a bunch of bananas of mass M, and a monkey of mass M clings to the other end (Fig. P8.77). The monkey climbs the rope in an attempt to reach the bananas. (a) Treating the system as consisting of the monkey, bananas, rope, and pulley, find the net torque of the system about the pulley axis. (b) Using the result of part (a), determine the total angular momentum about the pulley axis and describe the motion of the system. (c) Will the monkey reach the bananas before they get stuck in the pulley?

Figure P8.77

78. An electric motor turns a flywheel through a drive belt that joins a pulley on the motor and a pulley that is rigidly attached to the flywheel, as shown in Figure P8.78.

Figure P8.78

The flywheel is a uniform disk with a mass of 80.0 kg and a radius of $R = 0.625$ m. It turns on a frictionless axle. Its pulley has much smaller mass and a radius of $r = 0.230$ m. The tension T_u in the upper (taut) segment of the belt is 135 N and the flywheel has a clockwise angular acceleration of 1.67 rad/s^2. Find the tension in the lower (slack) segment of the belt.

79. **BIO** In exercise physiology studies, it is sometimes important to determine the location of a person's center of gravity. This can be done with the arrangement shown in Figure P8.79. A light plank rests on two scales that read $F_{g1} = 380$ N and $F_{g2} = 320$ N. The scales are separated by a distance of 2.00 m. How far from the woman's feet is her center of gravity?

Figure P8.79

80. **S** A uniform thin rod of length L and mass M is free to rotate on a frictionless pin passing through one end (Fig. P8.80). The rod is released from rest in the horizontal position. (a) What is the speed of its center of gravity when the rod reaches its lowest position? (b) What is the tangential speed of the lowest point on the rod when it is in the vertical position?

Figure P8.80

81. **S** A uniform solid cylinder of mass M and radius R rotates on a frictionless horizontal axle (Fig. P8.81). Two objects with equal masses m hang from light cords wrapped around the cylinder. If the system is released from rest, find (a) the tension in each cord and (b) the acceleration of each object after the objects have descended a distance h.

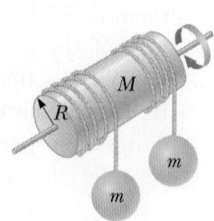

Figure P8.81

82. **QC** **S** A painter climbs a ladder leaning against a smooth wall. At a certain height, the ladder is on the verge of slipping. (a) Explain why the force exerted by the vertical wall on the ladder is horizontal. (b) If the ladder of length L leans at an angle θ with the horizontal, what is the lever arm for this horizontal force with the axis of rotation taken at the base of the ladder? (c) If the ladder is uniform, what is the lever arm for the force of gravity acting on the ladder? (d) Let the mass of the painter be 80 kg, $L = 4.0$ m, the ladder's

mass be 30 kg, $\theta = 53°$, and the coefficient of friction between ground and ladder be 0.45. Find the maximum distance the painter can climb up the ladder.

83. A *war-wolf*, or *trebuchet*, is a device used during the Middle Ages to throw rocks at castles and now sometimes used to fling pumpkins and pianos. A simple trebuchet is shown in Figure P8.83. Model it as a stiff rod of negligible mass 3.00 m long and joining particles of mass $m_1 = 0.120$ kg and $m_2 = 60.0$ kg at its ends. It can turn on a frictionless horizontal axle perpendicular to the rod and 14.0 cm from the particle of larger mass. The rod is released from rest in a horizontal orientation. Find the maximum speed that the object of smaller mass attains.

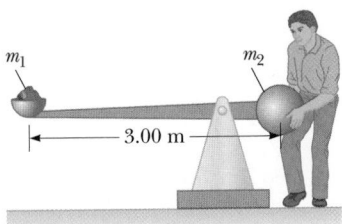

Figure P8.83

84. A string is wrapped around a uniform cylinder of mass M and radius R. The cylinder is released from rest with the string vertical and its top end tied to a fixed bar (Fig. P8.84). Show that (a) the tension in the string is one-third the weight of the cylinder, (b) the magnitude of the acceleration of the center of gravity is $2g/3$, and (c) the speed of the center of gravity is $(4gh/3)^{1/2}$ after the cylinder has descended through distance h. Verify your answer to part (c) with the energy approach.

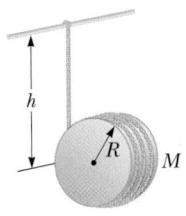

Figure P8.84

85. **BIO** **The Iron Cross** When a gymnast weighing 750 N executes the iron cross as in Figure P8.85a, the primary muscles involved in supporting this position are the latissimus dorsi ("lats") and the pectoralis major ("pecs"). The rings exert an upward force on the arms and support the weight of the gymnast. The force exerted by the shoulder joint on the arm is labeled $\vec{F}_s$ while the two muscles exert a total force $\vec{F}_m$ on the arm. Estimate the magnitude of the force $\vec{F}_m$. Note that one ring supports half the weight of the gymnast, which is 375 N as indicated in Figure P8.85b. Assume that the force $\vec{F}_m$ acts at an angle of 45° below the horizontal at a distance of 4.0 cm from the shoulder joint. In your estimate, take the distance from the shoulder joint to the hand to be $L = 70$ cm and ignore the weight of the arm.

a

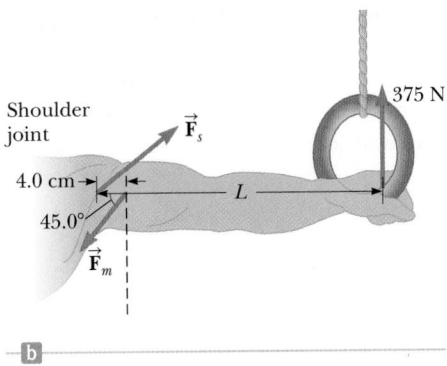

b

Figure P8.85

86. **BIO** In an emergency situation, a person with a broken forearm ties a strap from his hand to clip on his shoulder as in Figure P8.86. His 1.60-kg forearm remains in a horizontal position and the strap makes an angle of $\theta = 50.0°$ with the horizontal. Assume the forearm is uniform, has a length of $\ell = 0.320$ m, assume the biceps muscle is relaxed, and ignore the mass and length of the hand. Find (a) the tension in the strap and (b) the components of the reaction force exerted by the humerus on the forearm.

Figure P8.86

87. An object of mass $m_1 = 4.00$ kg is connected by a light cord to an object of mass $m_2 = 3.00$ kg on a frictionless surface (Fig. P8.87). The pulley rotates about a frictionless axle and has a moment of inertia of 0.500 kg · m² and a radius of 0.300 m. Assuming that the cord does not slip on the pulley, find (a) the acceleration of the two masses and (b) the tensions T_1 and T_2.

Figure P8.87

88. **QC** A 10.0-kg monkey climbs a uniform ladder with weight $w = 1.20 \times 10^2$ N and length $L = 3.00$ m as shown in Figure P8.88 (page 276). The ladder rests against the wall at an angle of $\theta = 60.0°$. The upper and lower ends of the ladder rest on frictionless surfaces, with the lower end fastened to the wall by a horizontal rope that is frayed and that can support a maximum tension of only 80.0 N. (a) Draw a force diagram for

the ladder. (b) Find the normal force exerted by the bottom of the ladder. (c) Find the tension in the rope when the monkey is two-thirds of the way up the ladder. (d) Find the maximum distance d that the monkey can climb up the ladder before the rope breaks. (e) If the horizontal surface were rough and the rope were removed, how would your analysis of the problem be changed and what other information would you need to answer parts (c) and (d)?

Figure P8.88

89. A 3.2-kg sphere is suspended by a cord that passes over a 1.8-kg pulley of radius 3.8 cm. The cord is attached to a spring whose force constant is $k = 86$ N/m as in Figure P8.89. Assume the pulley is a solid disk. (a) If the sphere is released from rest with the spring unstretched, what distance does the sphere fall through before stopping? (b) Find the speed of the sphere after it has fallen 25 cm.

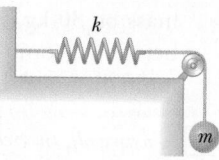

Figure P8.89

■ AP* REVIEW QUESTIONS

1. What conditions must be met in order for an object to be in equilibrium?

    I. The sum of all forces must equal zero

    II. The sum of all torques must equal zero

    III. The acceleration must equal zero

    IV. The velocity must equal zero

(A) I and II only   (D) I, II, and III only

(B) I and III only   (E) I, II, III, and IV

(C) III only

2. What is the magnitude of torque experienced by a hinged door if a 40 N force is directed at an angle of 30° from the plane of the door at a point 50 cm from the hinge, as shown above?

(A) 0 N·m   (D) 720 N·m

(B) 10 N·m   (E) 2000 N·m

(C) 35 N·m

3. A solid ball is allowed to accelerate down a rough incline without slipping, as shown above. Which of the following are true statements?

    I. The ball experiences no net torque in this scenario.

    II. The weight of the ball provides a net torque on the ball.

    III. The force of friction provides a net torque on the ball.

(A) I only   (D) II and III

(B) II only   (E) None of the above statements are true

(C) III only

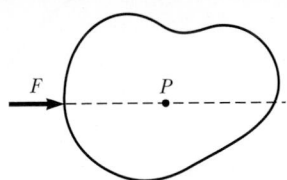

4. A force is acting on a rotating body, as shown above. What is the direction of the resulting torque from this force if the point of rotation is located at point *P*?

(A) Out of the page   (D) To the right

(B) Into the page   (E) No torque is present

(C) To the left

5. A plank with length ℓ and mass m is held in equilibrium by a spring with a spring constant k stretched length x, as shown above. What is the torque due to gravity on this uniform plank?

(A) $mg\ell$ (D) $\ell(mg + kx)$

(B) $mg\ell/2$ (E) $mg\ell + kx$

(C) ℓkx

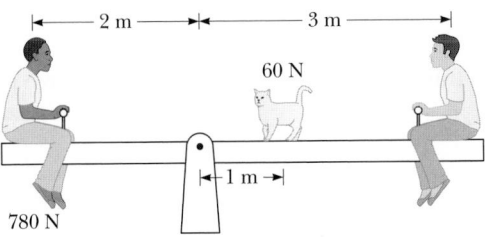

6. Two people and a cat are balanced on a seesaw, as shown above. If the person on the left weighs 780 N and the cat weighs 60 N, how much does the person on the right weigh?

(A) 500 N   (D) 780 N

(B) 560 N   (E) 900 N

(C) 720 N

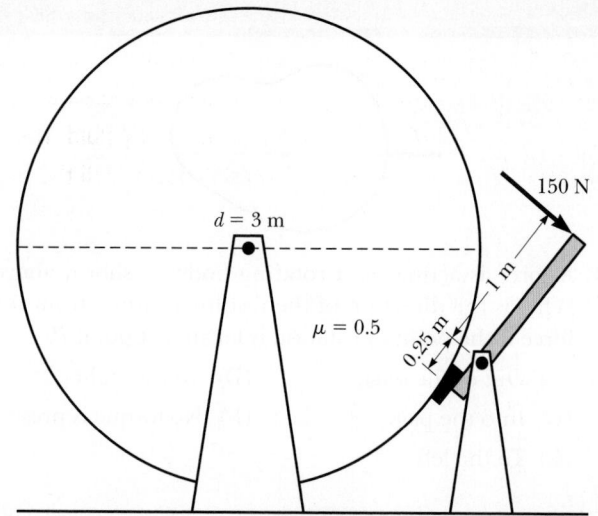

7. A lever is used as a manual brake for a large spinning 3 m diameter flywheel, as shown above. If a 150 N force is applied to the end of the handle and the coefficient of friction between the brake and the flywheel is 0.5, what stopping torque will be provided to the flywheel?

(A) 75 N·m   (D) 600 N·m

(B) 300 N·m   (E) 1800 N·m

(C) 450 N·m

8. A railroad car wheel, shown above, moves forward with a constant speed over a level rail. Using the center of the wheel as the point of rotation, what is the direction of the resulting torque at point P from the normal force between the rail and wheel?

(A) Out of the page   (D) To the right

(B) Into the page   (E) The normal force provides

(C) To the left   no torque to the cart

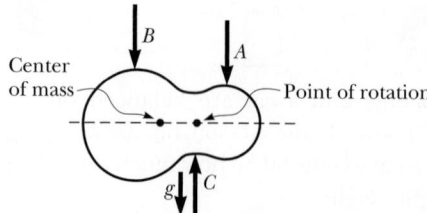

9. An object with mass is allowed to rotate about a point of rotation, as shown above. Which of the potential placement of forces (A, B, or C) will provide a torque in a direction indicated in the answers below that will enable the object to remain in equilibrium?

(A) Force A; Torque out   (D) Force B; Torque into
    of page   page

(B) Force A; Torque into   (E) Force C; Torque out of
    page   page

(C) Force B; Torque out of page

10. What direction of torque must be added at position P in order to maintain equilibrium if the center of mass of this uniform bar is determined to be the point of rotation, as shown above?

(A) Out of the page   (D) To the right

(B) Into the page   (E) No torque is needed

(C) To the left

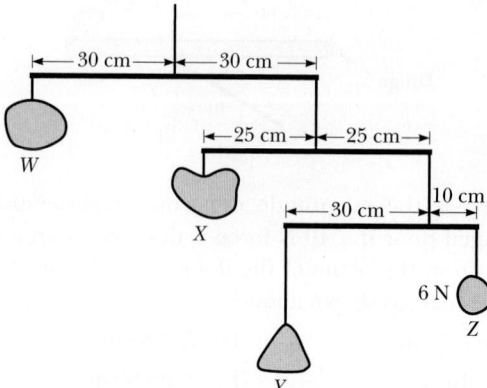

11. A mobile is suspended in equilibrium, as shown above. If object Z weighs 6 N, how much do objects W, X, and Y weigh?

	Object W	Object X	Object Y
(A)	16 N	8 N	2 N
(B)	9 N	7 N	2 N
(C)	24 N	12 N	6 N
(D)	18 N	9 N	3 N
(E)	40 N	20 N	14 N

12. A plank is suspended across a stream and supported by the banks on either side, as shown above. If a wildcat were to walk across this plank, providing the plank could hold the wildcat's weight without breaking, which of the following statement(s) is/are true?

(A) The banks' upward supporting forces vary depending on the location of the wildcat as it crosses the plank.

(B) The net torque on the plank remains zero as the wildcat crosses the plank.

(C) The net force on the plank remains zero as the wildcat crosses the plank.

(D) Both (A) and (C) are correct.

(E) (A), (B), and (C) are all correct.

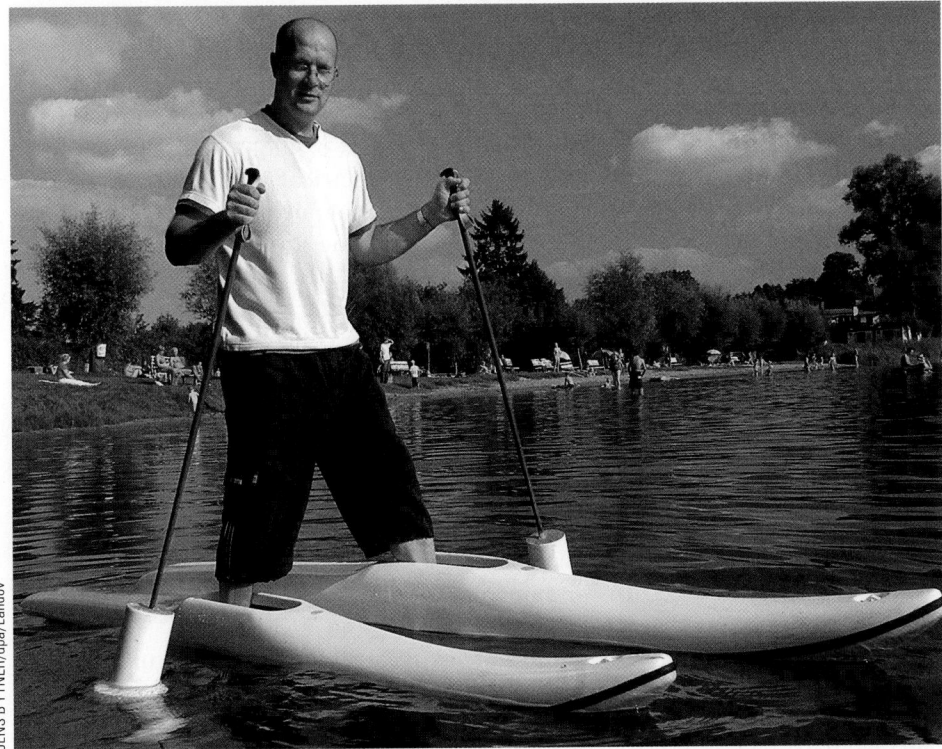

JENS B TTNER/dpa/Landov

Oversized floating shoes allow this man to "walk" on water, using the buoyant force, a consequence of pressure differences in any fluid. The shoes sink down until the weight of displaced water equals the weight of the load.

Solids and Fluids 9

There are four known states of matter: solids, liquids, gases, and plasmas. In the Universe at large, plasmas—systems of charged particles interacting electromagnetically—are the most common. In our environment on Earth, solids, liquids, and gases predominate.

An understanding of the fundamental properties of these different states of matter is important in all the sciences, in engineering, and in medicine. Forces put stresses on solids, and stresses can strain, deform, and break those solids, whether they are steel beams or bones. Fluids under pressure can perform work, or they can carry nutrients and essential solutes, like the blood flowing through our arteries and veins. Flowing gases cause pressure differences that can lift a massive cargo plane or the roof off a house in a hurricane. High-temperature plasmas created in fusion reactors may someday allow humankind to harness the energy source of the Sun.

The study of any one of these states of matter is itself a vast discipline. Here, we'll introduce basic properties of solids and liquids, the latter including some properties of gases. In addition, we'll take a brief look at surface tension, viscosity, osmosis, and diffusion.

9.1 States of Matter

Matter is normally classified as being in one of three states: **solid, liquid,** or **gas.** Often this classification system is extended to include a fourth state of matter, called a **plasma.**

Everyday experience tells us that a solid has a definite volume and shape. A brick, for example, maintains its familiar shape and size day in and day out. A liquid has a definite volume but no definite shape. When you fill the tank on a lawn mower, the gasoline changes its shape from that of the original container to

Crystals of natural quartz (SiO_2), one of the most common minerals on Earth. Quartz crystals are used to make special lenses and prisms and are employed in certain electronic applications.

Figure 9.1 A model of a portion of a solid. The atoms (spheres) are imagined as being attached to each other by springs, which represent the elastic nature of the interatomic forces. A solid consists of trillions of segments like this, with springs connecting all of them.

that of the tank on the mower, but the original volume is unchanged. A gas differs from solids and liquids in that it has neither definite volume nor definite shape. Because gas can flow, however, it shares many properties with liquids.

All matter consists of some distribution of atoms or molecules. The atoms in a solid, held together by forces that are mainly electrical, are located at specific positions with respect to one another and vibrate about those positions. At low temperatures, the vibrating motion is slight and the atoms can be considered essentially fixed. As energy is added to the material, the amplitude of the vibrations increases. A vibrating atom can be viewed as being bound in its equilibrium position by springs attached to neighboring atoms. A collection of such atoms and imaginary springs is shown in Figure 9.1. We can picture applied external forces as compressing these tiny internal springs. When the external forces are removed, the solid tends to return to its original shape and size. Consequently, a solid is said to have *elasticity*.

Solids can be classified as either crystalline or amorphous. In a **crystalline solid** the atoms have an ordered structure. For example, in the sodium chloride crystal (common table salt), sodium and chlorine atoms occupy alternate corners of a cube, as in Figure 9.2a. In an **amorphous solid,** such as glass, the atoms are arranged almost randomly, as in Figure 9.2b.

For any given substance, the liquid state exists at a higher temperature than the solid state. The intermolecular forces in a liquid aren't strong enough to keep the molecules in fixed positions, and they wander through the liquid in random fashion (Fig. 9.2c). Solids and liquids both have the property that when an attempt is made to compress them, strong repulsive atomic forces act internally to resist the compression.

In the gaseous state, molecules are in constant random motion and exert only weak forces on each other. The average distance between the molecules of a gas is quite large compared with the size of the molecules. Occasionally the molecules collide with each other, but most of the time they move as nearly free, noninteracting particles. As a result, unlike solids and liquids, gases can be easily compressed. We'll say more about gases in subsequent chapters.

When a gas is heated to high temperature, many of the electrons surrounding each atom are freed from the nucleus. The resulting system is a collection of free, electrically charged particles—negatively charged electrons and positively charged ions. Such a highly ionized state of matter containing equal amounts of positive and negative charges is called a **plasma.** Unlike a neutral gas, the long-range electric and magnetic forces allow the constituents of a plasma to interact with each other. Plasmas are found inside stars and in accretion disks around black holes, for example, and are far more common than the solid, liquid, and gaseous states because there are far more stars around than any other form of celestial matter.

Normal matter, however, may constitute less than 5% of all matter in the Universe. Observations of the last several years point to the existence of an invisible

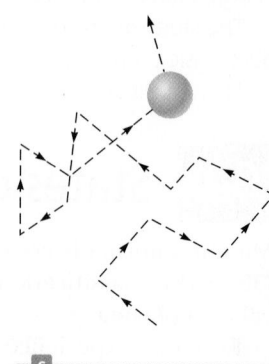

Figure 9.2 (a) The NaCl structure, with the Na^+ (gray) and Cl^- (green) ions at alternate corners of a cube. (b) In an amorphous solid, the atoms are arranged randomly. (c) Erratic motion of a molecule in a liquid.

dark matter, which affects the motion of stars orbiting the centers of galaxies. Dark matter may comprise nearly 25% of the matter in the Universe, several times larger than the amount of normal matter. Finally, the rapid acceleration of the expansion of the Universe may be driven by an even more mysterious form of matter, called **dark energy,** which may account for over 70% of all matter in the Universe.

9.2 Density and Pressure

Equal masses of aluminum and gold have an important physical difference: The aluminum takes up over seven times as much space as the gold. Although the reasons for the difference lie at the atomic and nuclear levels, a simple measure of this difference is the concept of *density*.

> The **density** ρ of an object having uniform composition is its mass M divided by its volume V:
>
> $$\rho \equiv \frac{M}{V} \qquad [9.1]$$
>
> **SI unit: kilogram per meter cubed (kg/m^3)**

◀ Density

For an object with non-uniform composition, Equation 9.1 defines an average density. The most common units used for density are kilograms per cubic meter in the SI system and grams per cubic centimeter in the cgs system. Table 9.1 lists the densities of some substances. The densities of most liquids and solids vary slightly with changes in temperature and pressure; the densities of gases vary greatly with such changes. Under normal conditions, the densities of solids and liquids are about 1 000 times greater than the densities of gases. This difference implies that the average spacing between molecules in a gas under such conditions is about ten times greater than in a solid or liquid.

The **specific gravity** of a substance is the ratio of its density to the density of water at 4°C, which is 1.0×10^3 kg/m^3. (The size of the kilogram was originally defined to make the density of water 1.0×10^3 kg/m^3 at 4°C.) By definition, specific gravity is a dimensionless quantity. For example, if the specific gravity of a substance is 3.0, its density is $3.0(1.0 \times 10^3 \text{ kg/m}^3) = 3.0 \times 10^3$ kg/m^3.

■ Quick Quiz

9.1 Suppose you have one cubic meter of gold, two cubic meters of silver, and six cubic meters of aluminum. Rank them by mass, from smallest to largest. (a) gold, aluminum, silver (b) gold, silver, aluminum (c) aluminum, gold, silver (d) silver, aluminum, gold

Table 9.1 Densities of Some Common Substances

Substance	ρ (kg/m^3)[a]	Substance	ρ (kg/m^3)[a]
Ice	0.917×10^3	Water	1.00×10^3
Aluminum	2.70×10^3	Glycerin	1.26×10^3
Iron	7.86×10^3	Ethyl alcohol	0.806×10^3
Copper	8.92×10^3	Benzene	0.879×10^3
Silver	10.5×10^3	Mercury	13.6×10^3
Lead	11.3×10^3	Air	1.29
Gold	19.3×10^3	Oxygen	1.43
Platinum	21.4×10^3	Hydrogen	8.99×10^{-2}
Uranium	18.7×10^3	Helium	1.79×10^{-1}

[a]All values are at standard atmospheric temperature and pressure (STP), defined as 0°C (273 K) and 1 atm (1.013×10^5 Pa). To convert to grams per cubic centimeter, multiply by 10^{-3}.

Figure 9.3 (a) The force exerted by a fluid on the surfaces of a submerged object. (b) A simple device for measuring pressure in a fluid.

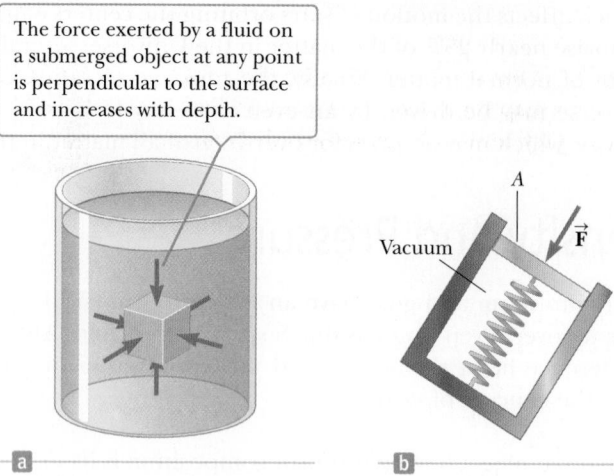

The force exerted by a fluid on a submerged object at any point is perpendicular to the surface and increases with depth.

Vacuum

A

$\vec{F}$

a

b

Tip 9.1 Force and Pressure

Equation 9.2 makes a clear distinction between force and pressure. Another important distinction is that *force is a vector* and *pressure is a scalar*. There is no direction associated with pressure, but the direction of the force associated with the pressure is perpendicular to the surface of interest.

The force exerted by a fluid on an object is always perpendicular to the surfaces of the object, as shown in Figure 9.3a.

The pressure at a specific point in a fluid can be measured with the device pictured in Figure 9.3b: an evacuated cylinder enclosing a light piston connected to a spring that has been previously calibrated with known weights. As the device is submerged in a fluid, the fluid presses down on the top of the piston and compresses the spring until the inward force exerted by the fluid is balanced by the outward force exerted by the spring. Let F be the magnitude of the force on the piston and A the area of the top surface of the piston. Notice that the force that compresses the spring is spread out over the entire area, motivating our formal definition of pressure:

Pressure ▶

If F is the magnitude of a force exerted perpendicular to a given surface of area A, then the average pressure P is the force divided by the area:

$$P \equiv \frac{F}{A} \qquad [9.2]$$

SI unit: pascal (Pa = N/m²)

Pressure can change from point to point, which is why the pressure in Equation 9.2 is called an average. Because pressure is defined as force per unit area, it has units of pascals (newtons per square meter). The English customary unit for pressure is the pound per inch squared. Atmospheric pressure at sea level is 14.7 lb/in.², which in SI units is 1.01×10^5 Pa.

As we see from Equation 9.2, the effect of a given force depends critically on the area to which it's applied. A 700-N man can stand on a vinyl-covered floor in regular street shoes without damaging the surface, but if he wears golf shoes, the metal cleats protruding from the soles can do considerable damage to the floor. With the cleats, the same force is concentrated into a smaller area, greatly elevating the pressure in those areas, resulting in a greater likelihood of exceeding the ultimate strength of the floor material.

Snowshoes use the same principle (Fig. 9.4). The snow exerts an upward normal force on the shoes to support the person's weight. According to Newton's third law, this upward force is accompanied by a downward force exerted by the shoes on the snow. If the person is wearing snowshoes, that force is distributed over the very large area of each snowshoe, so that the pressure at any given point is relatively low and the person doesn't penetrate very deeply into the snow.

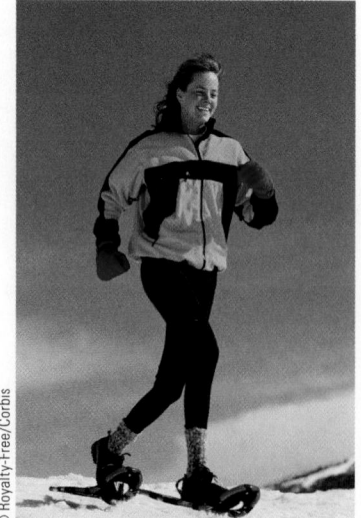

© Royalty-Free/Corbis

Figure 9.4 Snowshoes prevent the person from sinking into the soft snow because the force on the snow is spread over a larger area, reducing the pressure on the snow's surface.

■ APPLYING PHYSICS 9.1 | Bed of Nails Trick

After an exciting but exhausting lecture, a physics professor stretches out for a nap on a bed of nails, as in Figure
9.5, suffering no injury and only moderate discomfort.
How is that possible?

EXPLANATION If you try to support your entire weight
on a single nail, the pressure on your body is your weight
divided by the very small area of the end of the nail. The
resulting pressure is large enough to penetrate the skin.
If you distribute your weight over several hundred nails,
however, as demonstrated by the professor, the pressure is
considerably reduced because the area that supports your
weight is the total area of all nails in contact with your
body. (Why is lying on a bed of nails more comfortable
than sitting on the same bed? Extend the logic to show that
it would be more uncomfortable yet to stand on a bed of
nails without shoes.) ■

Figure 9.5 (Applying Physics 9.1) Does anyone have a pillow?

■ EXAMPLE 9.1 | Pressure and Weight of Water

GOAL Relate density, pressure, and weight.

PROBLEM (a) Calculate the weight of a cylindrical column of water with
height $h = 40.0$ m and radius $r = 1.00$ m. (See Fig. 9.6.) (b) Calculate the
force exerted by air on a disk of radius 1.00 m at the water's surface. (c) What
pressure at a depth of 40.0 m supports the water column?

STRATEGY For part (a), calculate the volume and multiply by the density
to get the mass of water, then multiply the mass by g to get the weight. Part
(b) requires substitution into the definition of pressure. Adding the results
of part (a) and (b) and dividing by the area gives the pressure of water at the
bottom of the column.

The downward
force is caused by
air pressure.

The upward force
is caused by the
pressure of water,
and must equal
the weight plus the
downward force of
air pressure.

Figure 9.6 (Example 9.1)

SOLUTION

(a) Calculate the weight of a cylindrical column of water
with height 40.0 m and radius 1.00 m.

Calculate the volume of the cylinder:

$$V = \pi r^2 h = \pi (1.00 \text{ m})^2 (40.0 \text{ m}) = 126 \text{ m}^3$$

Multiply the volume by the density of water to obtain the
mass of water in the cylinder:

$$m = \rho V = (1.00 \times 10^3 \text{ kg/m}^3)(126 \text{ m}^3) = 1.26 \times 10^5 \text{ kg}$$

Multiply the mass by the acceleration of gravity g to
obtain the weight w:

$$w = mg = (1.26 \times 10^5 \text{ kg})(9.80 \text{ m/s}^2) = \boxed{1.23 \times 10^6 \text{ N}}$$

(b) Calculate the force exerted by air on a disk of radius
1.00 m at the surface of the lake.

Write the equation for pressure:

$$P = \frac{F}{A}$$

Solve the pressure equation for the force and substitute
$A = \pi r^2$:

$$F = PA = P\pi r^2$$

Substitute values:

$$F = (1.01 \times 10^5 \text{ Pa})\pi (1.00 \text{ m})^2 = \boxed{3.17 \times 10^5 \text{ N}}$$

(Continued)

(c) What pressure at a depth of 40.0 m supports the water column?

Write Newton's second law for the water column: $-F_{down} - w + F_{up} = 0$

Solve for the upward force: $F_{up} = F_{down} + w = (3.17 \times 10^5 \text{ N}) + (1.23 \times 10^6 \text{ N}) = 1.55 \times 10^6 \text{ N}$

Divide the force by the area to obtain the required pressure:

$$P = \frac{F_{up}}{A} = \frac{1.55 \times 10^6 \text{ N}}{\pi(1.00 \text{ m})^2} = \boxed{4.93 \times 10^5 \text{ Pa}}$$

REMARKS Notice that the pressure at a given depth is related to the sum of the weight of the water and the force exerted by the air pressure at the water's surface. Water at a depth of 40.0 m must push upward to maintain the column in equilibrium. Notice also the important role of density in determining the pressure at a given depth.

QUESTION 9.1 A giant oil storage facility contains oil to a depth of 40.0 m. How does the pressure at the bottom of the tank compare to the pressure at a depth of 40.0 m in water? Explain.

EXERCISE 9.1 A large rectangular tub is filled to a depth of 2.60 m with olive oil, which has density 915 kg/m³. If the tub has length 5.00 m and width 3.00 m, calculate (a) the weight of the olive oil, (b) the force of air pressure on the surface of the oil, and (c) the pressure exerted upward by the bottom of the tub.

ANSWERS (a) 3.50×10^5 N (b) 1.52×10^6 N (c) 1.25×10^5 Pa

9.3 The Deformation of Solids

Although a solid may be thought of as having a definite shape and volume, it's possible to change its shape and volume by applying external forces. A sufficiently large force will permanently deform or break an object, but otherwise, when the external forces are removed, the object tends to return to its original shape and size. This is called *elastic behavior*.

The elastic properties of solids are discussed in terms of stress and strain. **Stress** is the force per unit area causing a deformation; **strain** is a measure of the amount of the deformation. For sufficiently small stresses, **stress is proportional to strain,** with the constant of proportionality depending on the material being deformed and on the nature of the deformation. We call this proportionality constant the **elastic modulus:**

$$\boxed{\text{stress} = \text{elastic modulus} \times \text{strain}} \qquad [9.3]$$

The elastic modulus is analogous to a spring constant. It can be taken as the stiffness of a material: A material having a large elastic modulus is very stiff and difficult to deform. There are three relationships having the form of Equation 9.3, corresponding to tensile, shear, and bulk deformation, and all of them satisfy an equation similar to Hooke's law for springs:

$$F = -k\,\Delta x \qquad [9.4]$$

where F is the applied force, k is the spring constant, and Δx is essentially the amount by which the spring is stretched or compressed.

Young's Modulus: Elasticity in Length

Consider a long bar of cross-sectional area A and length L_0, clamped at one end (Active Fig. 9.7). When an external force $\vec{F}$ is applied along the bar, perpendicular to the cross section, internal forces in the bar resist the distortion ("stretching") that $\vec{F}$ tends to produce. Nevertheless, the bar attains an equilibrium in which (1) its length is greater than L_0 and (2) the external force is balanced by internal forces. Under these circumstances, the bar is said to be *stressed*. We define the

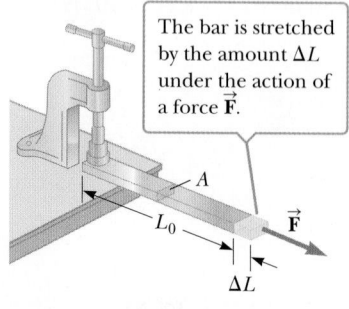

The bar is stretched by the amount ΔL under the action of a force $\vec{F}$.

Active Figure 9.7

A force is applied to a long bar clamped at one end.

tensile stress as the ratio of the magnitude of the external force F to the cross-sectional area A. The word "tensile" has the same root as the word "tension" and is used because the bar is under tension. The SI unit of stress is the newton per square meter (N/m²), called the **pascal** (Pa), the same as the unit of pressure:

$$1 \text{ Pa} \equiv \text{N/m}^2$$

◄ The pascal

The **tensile strain** in this case is defined as the ratio of the change in length ΔL to the original length L_0 and is therefore a dimensionless quantity. Using Equation 9.3, we can write an equation relating tensile stress to tensile strain:

$$\frac{F}{A} = Y\frac{\Delta L}{L_0} \qquad \text{[9.5]}$$

In this equation, Y is the constant of proportionality, called **Young's modulus.** Notice that Equation 9.5 could be solved for F and put in the form $F = k\,\Delta L$, where $k = YA/L_0$, making it look just like Hooke's law, Equation 9.4.

A material having a large Young's modulus is difficult to stretch or compress. This quantity is typically used to characterize a rod or wire stressed under either tension or compression. Because strain is a dimensionless quantity, Y is in pascals. Typical values are given in Table 9.2. Experiments show that (1) the change in length for a fixed external force is proportional to the original length and (2) the force necessary to produce a given strain is proportional to the cross-sectional area. The value of Young's modulus for a given material depends on whether the material is stretched or compressed. A human femur, for example, is stronger under tension than compression.

It's possible to exceed the **elastic limit** of a substance by applying a sufficiently great stress (Fig. 9.8). At the elastic limit, the stress-strain curve departs from a straight line. A material subjected to a stress beyond this limit ordinarily doesn't return to its original length when the external force is removed. As the stress is increased further, it surpasses the **ultimate strength:** the greatest stress the substance can withstand without breaking. The **breaking point** for brittle materials is just beyond the ultimate strength. For ductile metals like copper and gold, after passing the point of ultimate strength, the metal thins and stretches at a lower stress level before breaking.

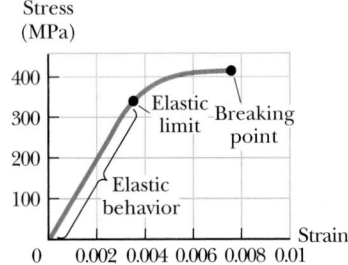

Figure 9.8 Stress-versus-strain curve for an elastic solid.

Shear Modulus: Elasticity of Shape

Another type of deformation occurs when an object is subjected to a force $\vec{\mathbf{F}}$ *parallel* to one of its faces while the opposite face is held fixed by a second force (Active Fig. 9.9a on page 284). If the object is originally a rectangular block, such a parallel

Table 9.2 Typical Values for the Elastic Modulus

Substance	Young's Modulus (Pa)	Shear Modulus (Pa)	Bulk Modulus (Pa)
Aluminum	7.0×10^{10}	2.5×10^{10}	7.0×10^{10}
Bone	1.8×10^{10}	8.0×10^{10}	—
Brass	9.1×10^{10}	3.5×10^{10}	6.1×10^{10}
Copper	11×10^{10}	4.2×10^{10}	14×10^{10}
Steel	20×10^{10}	8.4×10^{10}	16×10^{10}
Tungsten	35×10^{10}	14×10^{10}	20×10^{10}
Glass	$6.5\text{–}7.8 \times 10^{10}$	$2.6\text{–}3.2 \times 10^{10}$	$5.0\text{–}5.5 \times 10^{10}$
Quartz	5.6×10^{10}	2.6×10^{10}	2.7×10^{10}
Rib Cartilage	1.2×10^{7}	—	—
Rubber	0.1×10^{7}	—	—
Tendon	2×10^{7}	—	—
Water	—	—	0.21×10^{10}
Mercury	—	—	2.8×10^{10}

Active Figure 9.9

(a) A shear deformation in which a rectangular block is distorted by forces applied tangent to two of its faces. (b) A book under shear stress.

The shear stress displaces the top face of the block to the right relative the bottom.

Fixed face

The shear stress displaces the front cover of the book to the right relative the back cover.

force results in a shape with the cross section of a parallelogram. This kind of stress is called a **shear stress.** A book pushed sideways, as in Active Figure 9.9b, is being subjected to a shear stress. There is no change in volume with this kind of deformation. It's important to remember that in shear stress, the applied force is *parallel* to the cross-sectional area, whereas in tensile stress the force is *perpendicular* to the cross-sectional area. We define **the shear stress as F/A, the ratio of the magnitude of the parallel force to the area A of the face being sheared. The shear strain is the ratio $\Delta x/h$, where Δx is the horizontal distance the sheared face moves and h is the height of the object.** The shear stress is related to the shear strain according to

$$\frac{F}{A} = S\frac{\Delta x}{h} \qquad [9.6]$$

where S is the **shear modulus** of the material, with units of pascals (force per unit area). Once again, notice the similarity to Hooke's law.

A material having a large shear modulus is difficult to bend. Shear moduli for some representative materials are listed in Table 9.2.

Bulk Modulus: Volume Elasticity

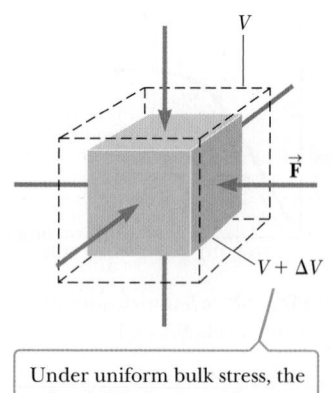

Under uniform bulk stress, the cube shrinks in size without changing shape.

Active Figure 9.10

A solid cube is under uniform pressure and is therefore compressed on all sides by forces normal to its six faces. The arrowheads of force vectors on the sides of the cube that are not visible are hidden by the cube.

Bulk modulus ▶

The bulk modulus characterizes the response of a substance to uniform squeezing. Suppose the external forces acting on an object are all perpendicular to the surface on which the force acts and are distributed uniformly over the surface of the object (Active Fig. 9.10). This occurs when an object is immersed in a fluid. An object subject to this type of deformation undergoes a change in volume but no change in shape. **The volume stress ΔP is defined as the ratio of the change in the magnitude of the applied force ΔF to the surface area A.** From the definition of pressure in Section 9.2, ΔP is also simply a change in pressure. The volume strain is equal to the change in volume ΔV divided by the original volume V. Again using Equation 9.3, we can relate a volume stress to a volume strain by the formula

$$\Delta P = -B\frac{\Delta V}{V} \qquad [9.7]$$

A material having a large bulk modulus doesn't compress easily. Note that a negative sign is included in this defining equation so that B is always positive. An increase in pressure (positive ΔP) causes a decrease in volume (negative ΔV) and vice versa.

Table 9.2 lists bulk modulus values for some materials. If you look up such values in a different source, you may find that the reciprocal of the bulk modulus, called the **compressibility** of the material, is listed. Note from the table that both solids and liquids have bulk moduli. There is neither a Young's modulus nor shear modulus for liquids, however, because liquids simply flow when subjected to a tensile or shearing stress.

■ **EXAMPLE 9.2** | **Built to Last**

GOAL Calculate a compression due to tensile stress, and maximum load.

PROBLEM A vertical steel beam in a building supports a load of 6.0×10^4 N. **(a)** If the length of the beam is 4.0 m and its cross-sectional area is 8.0×10^{-3} m², find the distance the beam is compressed along its length. **(b)** What maximum load in newtons could the steel beam support before failing?

STRATEGY Equation 9.3 pertains to compressive stress and strain and can be solved for ΔL, followed by substitution of known values. For part (b), set the compressive stress equal to the ultimate strength of steel from Table 9.3. Solve for the magnitude of the force, which is the total weight the structure can support.

SOLUTION

(a) Find the amount of compression in the beam.

Solve Equation 9.5 for ΔL and substitute, using the value of Young's modulus from Table 9.2:

$$\frac{F}{A} = Y\frac{\Delta L}{L_0}$$

$$\Delta L = \frac{FL_0}{YA} = \frac{(6.0 \times 10^4 \text{ N})(4.0 \text{ m})}{(2.0 \times 10^{11} \text{ Pa})(8.0 \times 10^{-3} \text{ m}^2)}$$

$$= \boxed{1.5 \times 10^{-4} \text{ m}}$$

(b) Find the maximum load that the beam can support.

Set the compressive stress equal to the ultimate compressive strength from Table 9.3, and solve for F:

$$\frac{F}{A} = \frac{F}{8.0 \times 10^{-3} \text{ m}^2} = 5.0 \times 10^8 \text{ Pa}$$

$$F = \boxed{4.0 \times 10^6 \text{ N}}$$

REMARKS In designing load-bearing structures of any kind, it's always necessary to build in a safety factor. No one would drive a car over a bridge that had been designed to supply the minimum necessary strength to keep it from collapsing.

QUESTION 9.2 Rank by the amount of fractional increase in length under increasing tensile stress, from smallest to largest: rubber, tungsten, steel, aluminum.

EXERCISE 9.2 A cable used to lift heavy materials like steel I-beams must be strong enough to resist breaking even under a load of 1.0×10^6 N. For safety, the cable must support twice that load. **(a)** What cross-sectional area should the cable have if it's to be made of steel? **(b)** By how much will an 8.0-m length of this cable stretch when subject to the 1.0×10^6-N load?

ANSWERS (a) 4.0×10^{-3} m² (b) 1.0×10^{-2} m

Table 9.3 Ultimate Strength of Materials

Material	Tensile Strength (N/m²)	Compressive Strength (N/m²)
Iron	1.7×10^8	5.5×10^8
Steel	5.0×10^8	5.0×10^8
Aluminum	2.0×10^8	2.0×10^8
Bone	1.2×10^8	1.5×10^8
Marble	—	8.0×10^7
Brick	1×10^6	3.5×10^7
Concrete	2×10^6	2×10^7

■ **EXAMPLE 9.3** | **Football Injuries** BIO

GOAL Obtain an estimate of shear stress.

PROBLEM A defensive lineman of mass $M = 125$ kg makes a flying tackle at $v_i = 4.00$ m/s on a stationary quarterback of mass $m = 85.0$ kg, and the lineman's helmet makes solid contact with the quarterback's femur. **(a)** What is the speed v_f of the two athletes immediately after contact? Assume a linear inelastic collision. **(b)** If the collision lasts for 0.100 s, estimate

(Continued)

the average force exerted on the quarterback's femur. **(c)** If the cross-sectional area of the quarterback's femur is equal to 5.00×10^{-4} m², calculate the shear stress exerted on the bone in the collision.

STRATEGY The solution proceeds in three well-defined steps. In part (a), use conservation of linear momentum to calculate the final speed of the system consisting of the quarterback and the lineman. Second, the speed found in part (a) can be used in the impulse-momentum theorem to obtain an estimate of the average force exerted on the femur. Third, dividing the average force by the cross-sectional area of the femur gives the desired estimate of the shear stress.

SOLUTION

(a) What is the speed of the system immediately after contact?

Apply momentum conservation to the system:

$$p_{\text{initial}} = p_{\text{final}}$$

Substitute expressions for the initial and final momenta:

$$Mv_i = (M + m)\, v_f$$

Solve for the final speed v_f:

$$v_f = \frac{Mv_i}{M + m} = \frac{(125\text{ kg})(4.00\text{ m/s})}{125\text{ kg} + 85.0\text{ kg}} = \boxed{2.38\text{ m/s}}$$

(b) Obtain an estimate for the average force delivered to the quarterback's femur.

Apply the impulse-momentum theorem:

$$F_{\text{av}}\,\Delta t = \Delta p = Mv_f - Mv_i$$

Solve for the average force exerted on the quarterback's femur:

$$F_{\text{av}} = \frac{M(v_f - v_i)}{\Delta t}$$

$$= \frac{(125\text{ kg})(4.00\text{ m/s} - 2.38\text{ m/s})}{0.100\text{ s}} = \boxed{2.03 \times 10^3\text{ N}}$$

(c) Obtain the average shear stress exerted on the quarterback's femur.

Divide the average force found in part (b) by the cross-sectional area of the femur:

$$\text{Shear stress} = \frac{F}{A} = \frac{2.03 \times 10^3\text{ N}}{5.00 \times 10^{-4}\text{ m}^2} = \boxed{4.06 \times 10^6\text{ Pa}}$$

REMARKS The ultimate shear strength of a femur is approximately 7×10^7 Pa, so this collision would not be expected to break the quarterback's leg.

QUESTION 9.3 What kind of stress would be sustained by the lineman? What parts of his body would be affected?

EXERCISE 9.3 Calculate the diameter of a horizontal steel bolt if it is expected to support a maximum load hung on it having a mass of 2.00×10^3 kg but for safety reasons must be designed to support three times that load. (Assume the ultimate shear strength of steel is 2.50×10^8 Pa.)

ANSWER 1.73 cm

■ EXAMPLE 9.4 | **Lead Ballast Overboard**

GOAL Apply the concepts of bulk stress and strain.

PROBLEM Ships and sailing vessels often carry lead ballast in various forms, such as bricks, to keep the ship properly oriented and upright in the water. Suppose a ship takes on cargo and the crew jettisons a total of 0.500 m³ of lead ballast into water 2.00 km deep. Calculate **(a)** the change in the pressure at that depth and **(b)** the change in volume of the lead upon reaching the bottom. Take the density of sea water to be 1.025×10^3 kg/m³, and take the bulk modulus of lead to be 4.2×10^{10} Pa.

STRATEGY The pressure difference between the surface and a depth of 2.00 km is due to the weight of the water column. Calculate the weight of water in a column with cross section of 1.00 m². That number in newtons will be the same magnitude as the pressure difference in pascal. Substitute the pressure change into the bulk stress and strain equation to obtain the change in volume of the lead.

SOLUTION

(a) Calculate the pressure difference between the surface and at a depth of 2.00 km.

Use the density, volume, and acceleration of gravity g to compute the weight of water in a column having cross-sectional area of 1.00 m²:

$$w = mg = (\rho V)g$$
$$= (1.025 \times 10^3 \text{ kg/m}^3)(2.00 \times 10^3 \text{ m}^3)(9.80 \text{ m/s}^2)$$
$$= 2.01 \times 10^7 \text{ N}$$

Divide by the area (in this case, 1.00 m²) to obtain the pressure difference due to the column of water:

$$\Delta P = \frac{F}{A} = \frac{2.01 \times 10^7 \text{ N}}{1.00 \text{ m}^2} = \boxed{2.01 \times 10^7 \text{ Pa}}$$

(b) Calculate the change in volume of the lead upon reaching the bottom.

Write the bulk stress and strain equation:

$$\Delta P = -B\frac{\Delta V}{V}$$

Solve for ΔV:

$$\Delta V = -\frac{V\Delta P}{B} = -\frac{(0.500 \text{ m}^3)(2.01 \times 10^7 \text{ Pa})}{4.2 \times 10^{10} \text{ Pa}} = \boxed{-2.4 \times 10^{-4} \text{ m}^3}$$

REMARKS The negative sign indicates a *decrease* in volume. The following exercise shows that even water can be compressed, although not by much.

QUESTION 9.4 Rank the following substances in order of the fractional change in volume in response to increasing pressure, from smallest to largest: copper, steel, water, mercury.

EXERCISE 9.4 (a) By what percentage does a ball of water shrink at that same depth? (b) What is the ratio of the new radius to the initial radius?

ANSWERS (a) 0.96% (b) 0.997

Arches and the Ultimate Strength of Materials

As we have seen, the ultimate strength of a material is the maximum force per unit area the material can withstand before it breaks or fractures. Such values are of great importance, particularly in the construction of buildings, bridges, and roads. Table 9.3 gives the ultimate strength of a variety of materials under both tension and compression. Note that bone and a variety of building materials (concrete, brick, and marble) are stronger under compression than under tension. The greater ability of brick and stone to resist compression is the basis of the semicircular arch, developed and used extensively by the Romans in everything from memorial arches to expansive temples and aqueduct supports.

Before the development of the arch, the principal method of spanning a space was the simple post-and-beam construction (Fig. 9.11a), in which a horizontal

APPLICATION

Arch Structures in Buildings

Figure 9.11 (a) A simple post-and-beam structure. (b) The semicircular arch developed by the Romans. (c) Gothic arch with flying buttresses to provide lateral support.

beam is supported by two columns. This type of construction was used to build the great Greek temples. The columns of these temples were closely spaced because of the limited length of available stones and the low ultimate tensile strength of a sagging stone beam.

The semicircular arch (Fig. 9.11b) developed by the Romans was a great technological achievement in architectural design. It effectively allowed the heavy load of a wide roof span to be channeled into horizontal and vertical forces on narrow supporting columns. The stability of this arch depends on the compression between its wedge-shaped stones. The stones are forced to squeeze against each other by the uniform loading, as shown in the figure. This compression results in horizontal outward forces at the base of the arch where it starts curving away from the vertical. These forces must then be balanced by the stone walls shown on the sides of the arch. It's common to use very heavy walls (buttresses) on either side of the arch to provide horizontal stability. If the foundation of the arch should move, the compressive forces between the wedge-shaped stones may decrease to the extent that the arch collapses. The stone surfaces used in the arches constructed by the Romans were cut to make very tight joints; mortar was usually not used. The resistance to slipping between stones was provided by the compression force and the friction between the stone faces.

Another important architectural innovation was the pointed Gothic arch, shown in Figure 9.11c. This type of structure was first used in Europe beginning in the 12th century, followed by the construction of several magnificent Gothic cathedrals in France in the 13th century. One of the most striking features of these cathedrals is their extreme height. For example, the cathedral at Chartres rises to 118 ft, and the one at Reims has a height of 137 ft. Such magnificent buildings evolved over a very short time, without the benefit of any mathematical theory of structures. However, Gothic arches required flying buttresses to prevent the spreading of the arch supported by the tall, narrow columns.

9.4 Variation of Pressure with Depth

When a fluid is at rest in a container, **all portions of the fluid must be in static equilibrium**—at rest with respect to the observer. Furthermore, **all points at the same depth must be at the same pressure.** If this were not the case, fluid would flow from the higher pressure region to the lower pressure region. For example, consider the small block of fluid shown in Figure 9.12a. If the pressure were greater on the left side of the block than on the right, $\vec{F}_1$ would be greater than $\vec{F}_2$, and the block would accelerate to the right and thus would not be in equilibrium.

Next, let's examine the fluid contained within the volume indicated by the darker region in Figure 9.12b. This region has cross-sectional area A and extends from position y_1 to position y_2 below the surface of the liquid. Three external forces act on this volume of fluid: the force of gravity, Mg; the upward force P_2A exerted by the liquid below it; and a downward force P_1A exerted by the fluid above it. Because the given volume of fluid is in equilibrium, these forces must add to zero, so we get

$$P_2A - P_1A - Mg = 0 \qquad [9.8]$$

From the definition of density, we have

$$M = \rho V = \rho A(y_1 - y_2) \qquad [9.9]$$

Substituting Equation 9.9 into Equation 9.8, canceling the area A, and rearranging terms, we get

$$P_2 = P_1 + \rho g(y_1 - y_2) \qquad [9.10]$$

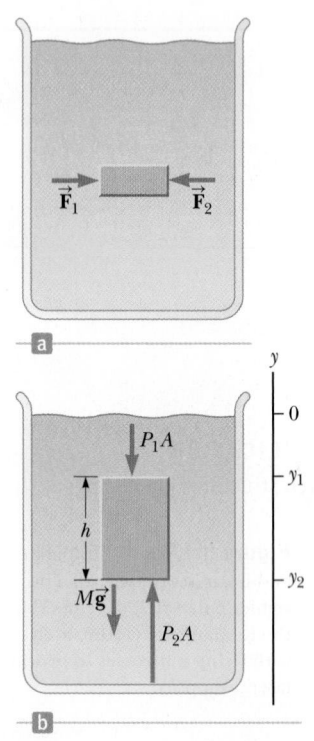

Figure 9.12 (a) In a static fluid, all points at the same depth are at the same pressure, so the force $\vec{F}_1$ must equal the force $\vec{F}_2$. (b) Because the volume of the shaded fluid isn't sinking or rising, the net force on it must equal zero.

Notice that $(y_1 - y_2)$ is positive, because $y_2 < y_1$. The force P_2A is greater than the force P_1A by exactly the weight of water between the two points. This is the same principle experienced by the person at the bottom of a pileup in football or rugby.

Atmospheric pressure is also caused by a piling up of fluid—in this case, the fluid is the gas of the atmosphere. The weight of all the air from sea level to the edge of space results in an atmospheric pressure of $P_0 = 1.013 \times 10^5$ Pa (equivalent to 14.7 lb/in.²) at sea level. This result can be adapted to find the pressure P at any depth $h = (y_1 - y_2) = (0 - y_2)$ below the surface of the water:

$$P = P_0 + \rho g h \qquad [9.11]$$

According to Equation 9.11, **the pressure P at a depth h below the surface of a liquid open to the atmosphere is greater than atmospheric pressure by the amount ρgh.** Moreover, the pressure isn't affected by the shape of the vessel, as shown in Figure 9.13.

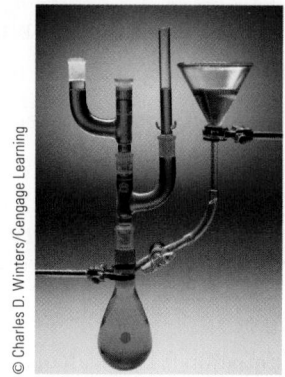

Figure 9.13 This photograph illustrates the fact that the pressure in a liquid is the same at all points lying at the same elevation. Note that the shape of the vessel does not affect the pressure.

■ Quick Quiz

9.2 The pressure at the bottom of a glass filled with water ($\rho = 1\,000$ kg/m³) is P. The water is poured out and the glass is filled with ethyl alcohol ($\rho = 806$ kg/m³). The pressure at the bottom of the glass is now (a) smaller than P (b) equal to P (c) larger than P (d) indeterminate.

■ EXAMPLE 9.5 | Oil and Water

GOAL Calculate pressures created by layers of different fluids.

PROBLEM In a huge oil tanker, salt water has flooded an oil tank to a depth of $h_2 = 5.00$ m. On top of the water is a layer of oil $h_1 = 8.00$ m deep, as in the cross-sectional view of the tank in Figure 9.14. The oil has a density of 0.700 g/cm³. Find the pressure at the bottom of the tank. (Take 1 025 kg/m³ as the density of salt water.)

STRATEGY Equation 9.11 must be used twice. First, use it to calculate the pressure P_1 at the bottom of the oil layer. Then use this pressure in place of P_0 in Equation 9.11 and calculate the pressure P_{bot} at the bottom of the water layer.

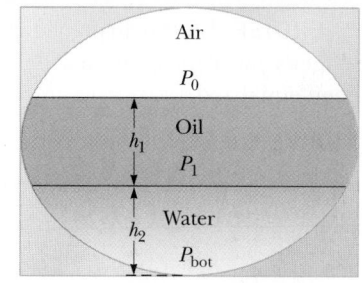

Figure 9.14 (Example 9.5)

SOLUTION

Use Equation 9.11 to calculate the pressure at the bottom of the oil layer:

(1) $\quad P_1 = P_0 + \rho g h_1$
$\quad\quad = 1.01 \times 10^5$ Pa
$\quad\quad\quad + (7.00 \times 10^2\text{ kg/m}^3)(9.80\text{ m/s}^2)(8.00\text{ m})$
$\quad P_1 = 1.56 \times 10^5$ Pa

Now adapt Equation 9.11 to the new starting pressure, and use it to calculate the pressure at the bottom of the water layer:

(2) $\quad P_{bot} = P_1 + \rho g h_2$
$\quad\quad = 1.56 \times 10^5$ Pa
$\quad\quad\quad + (1.025 \times 10^3\text{ kg/m}^3)(9.80\text{ m/s}^2)(5.00\text{ m})$
$\quad P_{bot} = \boxed{2.06 \times 10^5\text{ Pa}}$

REMARKS The weight of the atmosphere results in P_0 at the surface of the oil layer. Then the weight of the oil and the weight of the water combine to create the pressure at the bottom.

QUESTION 9.5 Why does air pressure decrease with increasing altitude?

EXERCISE 9.5 Calculate the pressure on the top lid of a chest buried under 4.00 meters of mud with density equal to 1.75×10^3 kg/m³ at the bottom of a 10.0-m-deep lake.

ANSWER 2.68×10^5 Pa

■ **EXAMPLE 9.6** | **A Pain in the Ear** BIO

GOAL Calculate a pressure difference at a given depth and estimate a force.

PROBLEM Estimate the net force exerted on your eardrum due to the water above when you are swimming at the bottom of a pool that is 5.0 m deep.

STRATEGY Use Equation 9.11 to find the pressure difference across the eardrum at the given depth. The air inside the ear is generally at atmospheric pressure. Estimate the eardrum's surface area, then use the definition of pressure to get the net force exerted on the eardrum.

· ·

SOLUTION

Use Equation 9.11 to calculate the difference between the water pressure at the depth h and the pressure inside the ear:

$$\Delta P = P - P_0 = \rho g h$$
$$= (1.00 \times 10^3 \text{ kg/m}^3)(9.80 \text{ m/s}^2)(5.0 \text{ m})$$
$$= 4.9 \times 10^4 \text{ Pa}$$

Multiply by area A to get the net force on the eardrum associated with this pressure difference, estimating the area of the eardrum as 1 cm².

$$F_{\text{net}} = A\Delta P \approx (1 \times 10^{-4} \text{ m}^2)(4.9 \times 10^4 \text{ Pa}) \approx \boxed{5 \text{ N}}$$

· ·

REMARKS Because a force on the eardrum of this magnitude is uncomfortable, swimmers often "pop their ears" by swallowing or expanding their jaws while underwater, an action that pushes air from the lungs into the middle ear. Using this technique equalizes the pressure on the two sides of the eardrum and relieves the discomfort.

QUESTION 9.6 Why do water containers and gas cans often have a second, smaller cap opposite the spout through which fluid is poured?

EXERCISE 9.6 An airplane takes off at sea level and climbs to a height of 425 m. Estimate the net outward force on a passenger's eardrum assuming the density of air is approximately constant at 1.3 kg/m³ and that the inner ear pressure hasn't been equalized.

ANSWER 0.54 N

Because the pressure in a fluid depends on depth and on the value of P_0, any increase in pressure at the surface must be transmitted to every point in the fluid. This was first recognized by the French scientist Blaise Pascal (1623–1662) and is called **Pascal's principle:**

> A change in pressure applied to an enclosed fluid is transmitted undiminished to every point of the fluid and to the walls of the container.

APPLICATION
Hydraulic Lifts

An important application of Pascal's principle is the hydraulic press (Fig. 9.15a). A downward force $\vec{\mathbf{F}}_1$ is applied to a small piston of area A_1. The pressure

Figure 9.15 (a) In a hydraulic press, an increase of pressure in the smaller area A_1 is transmitted to the larger area A_2. Because force equals pressure times area, the force $\vec{\mathbf{F}}_2$ is larger than $\vec{\mathbf{F}}_1$ by a factor of A_2/A_1. (b) A vehicle under repair is supported by a hydraulic lift in a garage.

A small force $\vec{\mathbf{F}}_1$ on the left produces a much larger force $\vec{\mathbf{F}}_2$ on the right.

Sam Jordash/Digital Vision/Getty Images

a   b

is transmitted through a fluid to a larger piston of area A_2. As the pistons move and the fluids in the left and right cylinders change their relative heights, there are slight differences in the pressures at the input and output pistons. Neglecting these small differences, the fluid pressure on each of the pistons may be taken to be the same; $P_1 = P_2$. From the definition of pressure, it then follows that $F_1/A_1 = F_2/A_2$. Therefore, the magnitude of the force $\vec{F}_2$ is larger than the magnitude of $\vec{F}_1$ by the factor A_2/A_1. That's why a large load, such as a car, can be moved on the large piston by a much smaller force on the smaller piston. Hydraulic brakes, car lifts, hydraulic jacks, forklifts, and other machines make use of this principle.

■ **EXAMPLE 9.7** | **The Car Lift**

GOAL Apply Pascal's principle to a car lift, and show that the input work is the same as the output work.

PROBLEM In a car lift used in a service station, compressed air exerts a force on a small piston of circular cross section having a radius of $r_1 = 5.00$ cm. This pressure is transmitted by an incompressible liquid to a second piston of radius $r_2 = 15.0$ cm. **(a)** What force must the compressed air exert on the small piston in order to lift a car weighing 13 300 N? Neglect the weights of the pistons. **(b)** What air pressure will produce a force of that magnitude? **(c)** Show that the work done by the input and output pistons is the same.

STRATEGY Substitute into Pascal's principle in part (a), while recognizing that the magnitude of the output force, F_2, must be equal to the car's weight in order to support it. Use the definition of pressure in part (b). In part (c), use $W = F\Delta x$ to find the ratio W_1/W_2, showing that it must equal 1. This requires combining Pascal's principle with the fact that the input and output pistons move through the same volume.

SOLUTION

(a) Find the necessary force on the small piston.

Substitute known values into Pascal's principle, using $A = \pi r^2$ for the area of each piston:

$$F_1 = \left(\frac{A_1}{A_2}\right)F_2 = \frac{\pi r_1^{\,2}}{\pi r_2^{\,2}}\,F_2$$

$$= \frac{\pi(5.00 \times 10^{-2}\,\text{m})^2}{\pi(15.0 \times 10^{-2}\,\text{m})^2}\,(1.33 \times 10^4\,\text{N})$$

$$= \boxed{1.48 \times 10^3\,\text{N}}$$

(b) Find the air pressure producing F_1.

Substitute into the definition of pressure:

$$P = \frac{F_1}{A_1} = \frac{1.48 \times 10^3\,\text{N}}{\pi(5.00 \times 10^{-2}\,\text{m})^2} = \boxed{1.88 \times 10^5\,\text{Pa}}$$

(c) Show that the work done by the input and output pistons is the same.

First equate the volumes, and solve for the ratio of A_2 to A_1:

$$V_1 = V_2 \quad \rightarrow \quad A_1\Delta x_1 = A_2\Delta x_2$$

$$\frac{A_2}{A_1} = \frac{\Delta x_1}{\Delta x_2}$$

Now use Pascal's principle to get a relationship for F_1/F_2:

$$\frac{F_1}{A_1} = \frac{F_2}{A_2} \quad \rightarrow \quad \frac{F_1}{F_2} = \frac{A_1}{A_2}$$

Evaluate the work ratio, substituting the preceding two results:

$$\frac{W_1}{W_2} = \frac{F_1\,\Delta x_1}{F_2\,\Delta x_2} = \left(\frac{F_1}{F_2}\right)\left(\frac{\Delta x_1}{\Delta x_2}\right) = \left(\frac{A_1}{A_2}\right)\left(\frac{A_2}{A_1}\right) = 1$$

$$W_1 = W_2$$

REMARKS In this problem, we didn't address the effect of possible differences in the heights of the pistons. If the column of fluid is higher in the small piston, the fluid weight assists in supporting the car, reducing the necessary applied force. If the column of fluid is higher in the large piston, both the car and the extra fluid must be supported, so additional applied force is required.

(Continued)

QUESTION 9.7 True or False: If the radius of the output piston is doubled, the output force increases by a factor of 4.

EXERCISE 9.7 A hydraulic lift has pistons with diameters 8.00 cm and 36.0 cm, respectively. If a force of 825 N is exerted at the input piston, what maximum mass can be lifted by the output piston?

ANSWER 1.70×10^3 kg

■ APPLYING PHYSICS 9.2 | Building the Pyramids

A corollary to the statement that pressure in a fluid increases with depth is that water always seeks its own level. This means that if a vessel is filled with water, then regardless of the vessel's shape the surface of the water is perfectly flat and at the same height at all points. The ancient Egyptians used this fact to make the pyramids level. Devise a scheme showing how this could be done.

EXPLANATION There are many ways it could be done, but Figure 9.16 shows the scheme used by the Egyptians. The builders cut grooves in the base of the pyramid as in (a) and partially filled the grooves with water. The height of the water was marked as in (b), and the rock was chis-

eled down to the mark, as in (c). Finally, the groove was filled with crushed rock and gravel, as in (d). ■

Figure 9.16 (Applying Physics 9.2)

9.5 Pressure Measurements

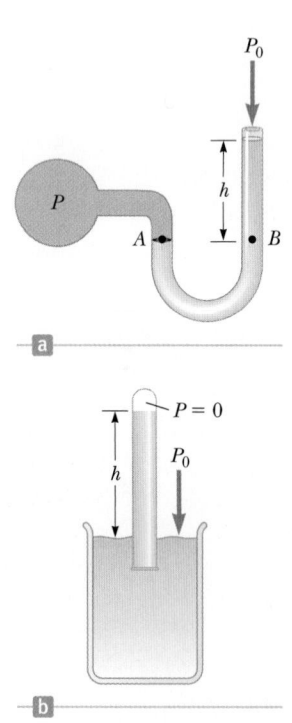

Active Figure 9.17 Two devices for measuring pressure: (a) an open-tube manometer and (b) a mercury barometer.

BIO APPLICATION

Decompression and Injury to the Lungs

A simple device for measuring pressure is the open-tube manometer (Active Fig. 9.17a). One end of a U-shaped tube containing a liquid is open to the atmosphere, and the other end is connected to a system of unknown pressure P. The pressure at point B equals $P_0 + \rho g h$, where ρ is the density of the fluid. The pressure at B, however, equals the pressure at A, which is also the unknown pressure P. We conclude that $P = P_0 + \rho g h$.

The pressure P is called the **absolute pressure,** and $P - P_0$ is called the **gauge pressure.** If P in the system is greater than atmospheric pressure, h is positive. If P is less than atmospheric pressure (a partial vacuum), h is negative, meaning that the right-hand column in Figure 9.16a is lower than the left-hand column.

Another instrument used to measure pressure is the **barometer** (Active Fig. 9.17b), invented by Evangelista Torricelli (1608–1647). A long tube closed at one end is filled with mercury and then inverted into a dish of mercury. The closed end of the tube is nearly a vacuum, so its pressure can be taken to be zero. It follows that $P_0 = \rho g h$, where ρ is the density of the mercury and h is the height of the mercury column. Note that the barometer measures the pressure of the atmosphere, whereas the manometer measures pressure in an enclosed fluid.

One atmosphere of pressure is defined to be the pressure equivalent of a column of mercury that is exactly 0.76 m in height at 0°C with $g = 9.806\ 65$ m/s². At this temperature, mercury has a density of 13.595×10^3 kg/m³; therefore,

$$P_0 = \rho g h = (13.595 \times 10^3 \text{ kg/m}^3)(9.806\ 65 \text{ m/s}^2)(0.760\ 0 \text{ m})$$

$$= 1.013 \times 10^5 \text{ Pa} = 1 \text{ atm}$$

It is interesting to note that the force of the atmosphere on our bodies (assuming a body area of 2 000 in.²) is extremely large, on the order of 30 000 lb! If it were not for the fluids permeating our tissues and body cavities, our bodies would collapse. The fluids provide equal and opposite forces. In the upper atmosphere or in space, sudden decompression can lead to serious injury and death. Air retained in the lungs can damage the tiny alveolar sacs, and intestinal gas can even rupture internal organs.

■ *Quick Quiz*

9.3 Several common barometers are built using a variety of fluids. For which fluid will the column of fluid in the barometer be the highest? (Refer to Table 9.1.) (a) mercury (b) water (c) ethyl alcohol (d) benzene

Blood Pressure Measurements

A specialized manometer (called a sphygmomanometer) is often used to measure blood pressure. In this application, a rubber bulb forces air into a cuff wrapped tightly around the upper arm and simultaneously into a manometer, as in Figure 9.18. The pressure in the cuff is increased until the flow of blood through the brachial artery in the arm is stopped. A valve on the bulb is then opened, and the measurer listens with a stethoscope to the artery at a point just below the cuff. When the pressure in the cuff and brachial artery is just below the maximum value produced by the heart (the systolic pressure), the artery opens momentarily on each beat of the heart. At this point, the velocity of the blood is high and turbulent, and the flow is noisy and can be heard with the stethoscope. The manometer is calibrated to read the pressure in millimeters of mercury, and the value obtained is about 120 mm for a normal heart. Values of 130 mm or above are considered high, and medication to lower the blood pressure is often prescribed for such patients. As the pressure in the cuff is lowered further, intermittent sounds are still heard until the pressure falls just below the minimum heart pressure (the diastolic pressure). At this point, continuous sounds are heard. In the normal heart, this transition occurs at about 80 mm of mercury, and values above 90 require medical intervention. Blood pressure readings are usually expressed as the ratio of the systolic pressure to the diastolic pressure, which is 120/80 for a healthy heart.

■ *Quick Quiz*

9.4 Blood pressure is normally measured with the cuff of the sphygmomanometer around the arm. Suppose the blood pressure is measured with the cuff around the calf of the leg of a standing person. Would the reading of the blood pressure be (a) the same here as it is for the arm, (b) greater than it is for the arm, or (c) less than it is for the arm?

BIO APPLICATION
Measuring Blood Pressure

Figure 9.18 A sphygmomanometer can be used to measure blood pressure.

■ **APPLYING PHYSICS 9.3** | **Ballpoint Pens**

In a ballpoint pen, ink moves down a tube to the tip, where it is spread on a sheet of paper by a rolling stainless steel ball. Near the top of the ink cartridge, there is a small hole open to the atmosphere. If you seal this hole, you will find that the pen no longer functions. Use your knowledge of how a barometer works to explain this behavior.

EXPLANATION If the hole were sealed, or if it were not present, the pressure of the air above the ink would decrease as the ink was used. Consequently, atmospheric pressure exerted against the ink at the bottom of the cartridge would prevent some of the ink from flowing out. The hole allows the pressure above the ink to remain at atmospheric pressure. Why does a ballpoint pen seem to run out of ink when you write on a vertical surface? ■

9.6 Buoyant Forces and Archimedes' Principle

A fundamental principle affecting objects submerged in fluids was discovered by Greek mathematician and natural philosopher Archimedes. **Archimedes' principle** can be stated as follows:

Archimedes' principle ▶

Archimedes
Greek mathematician, physicist, and engineer (287–212 B.C.)
Archimedes was probably the greatest scientist of antiquity. According to legend, King Hieron asked him to determine whether the king's crown was pure gold or a gold alloy. Archimedes allegedly arrived at a solution when bathing, noticing a partial loss of weight on lowering himself into the water. He was so excited that he reportedly ran naked through the streets of Syracuse shouting "Eureka!", which is Greek for "I have found it!"

Any object completely or partially submerged in a fluid is buoyed up by a force with magnitude equal to the weight of the fluid displaced by the object.

Many historians attribute the concept of buoyancy to Archimedes' "bathtub epiphany," when he noticed an apparent change in his weight upon lowering himself into a tub of water. As will be seen in Example 9.8, buoyancy yields a method of determining density.

Everyone has experienced Archimedes' principle. It's relatively easy, for example, to lift someone if you're both standing in a swimming pool, whereas lifting that same individual on dry land may be a difficult task. Water provides partial support to any object placed in it. We often say that an object placed in a fluid is buoyed up by the fluid, so we call this upward force the **buoyant force.**

The buoyant force is *not* a mysterious new force that arises in fluids. In fact, the physical cause of the buoyant force is the pressure difference between the upper and lower sides of the object, which can be shown to be equal to the weight of the displaced fluid. In Figure 9.19a, the fluid inside the indicated sphere, colored darker blue, is pressed on all sides by the surrounding fluid. Arrows indicate the forces arising from the pressure. Because pressure increases with depth, the arrows on the underside are larger than those on top. Adding them all up, the horizontal components cancel, but there is a net force upward. This force, due to differences in pressure, is the buoyant force $\vec{\mathbf{B}}$. The sphere of water neither rises nor falls, so the vector sum of the buoyant force and the force of gravity on the sphere of fluid must be zero, and it follows that $B = Mg$, where M is the mass of the fluid.

Replacing the shaded fluid with a cannon ball of the same volume, as in Figure 9.19b, changes only the mass on which the pressure acts, so the buoyant force is the same: $B = Mg$, where M is the mass of the displaced fluid, *not* the mass of the cannon ball. The force of gravity on the heavier ball is greater than it was on the fluid, so the cannon ball sinks.

Archimedes' principle can also be obtained from Equation 9.8, relating pressure and depth, using Figure 9.12b. Horizontal forces from the pressure cancel, but in the vertical direction P_2A acts upward on the bottom of the block of fluid, and P_1A and the gravity force on the fluid, Mg, act downward, giving

$$B = P_2A - P_1A = Mg \qquad \text{[9.12a]}$$

where the buoyancy force has been identified as a difference in pressure equal in magnitude to the weight of the displaced fluid. This buoyancy force remains the same regardless of the material occupying the volume in question because it's due to the *surrounding* fluid. Using the definition of density, Equation 9.12a becomes

$$B = \rho_{\text{fluid}}V_{\text{fluid}}g \qquad \text{[9.12b]}$$

Tip 9.2 Buoyant Force Is Exerted by the Fluid

The buoyant force on an object is exerted by the fluid and is the same, regardless of the density of the object. Objects more dense than the fluid sink; objects less dense rise.

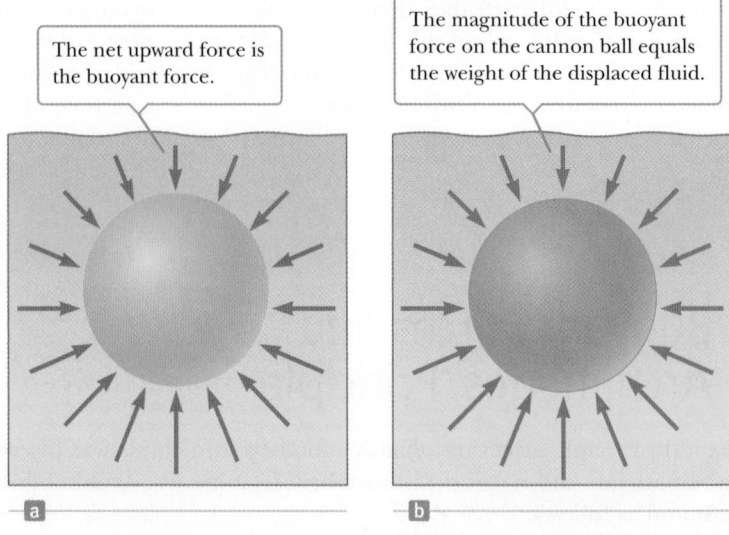

The net upward force is the buoyant force.

The magnitude of the buoyant force on the cannon ball equals the weight of the displaced fluid.

Figure 9.19 (a) The arrows indicate forces on the sphere of fluid due to pressure, larger on the underside because pressure increases with depth. (b) The buoyant force, which is caused by the *surrounding* fluid, is the same on any object of the same volume, including this cannon ball.

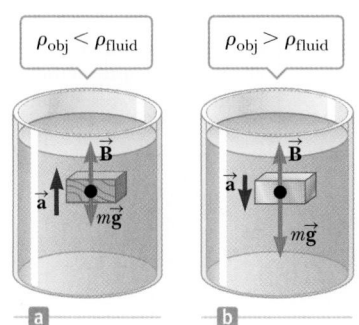

Active Figure 9.20
(a) A totally submerged object that is less dense than the fluid in which it is submerged is acted upon by a net upward force. (b) A totally submerged object that is denser than the fluid sinks.

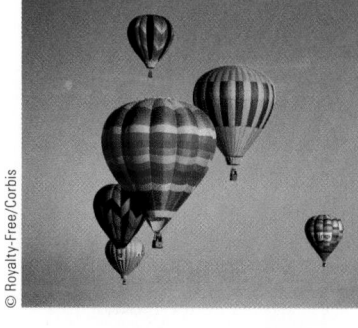

Hot-air balloons. Because hot air is less dense than cold air, there is a net upward force on the balloons.

where ρ_{fluid} is the density of the fluid and V_{fluid} is the volume of the displaced fluid. This result applies equally to all shapes because any irregular shape can be approximated by a large number of infinitesimal cubes.

It's instructive to compare the forces on a totally submerged object with those on a floating object.

Case I: A Totally Submerged Object.
When an object is *totally* submerged in a fluid of density ρ_{fluid}, the upward buoyant force acting on the object has a magnitude of $B = \rho_{fluid}V_{obj}g$, where V_{obj} is the volume of the object. If the object has density ρ_{obj}, the downward gravitational force acting on the object has a magnitude equal to $w = mg = \rho_{obj}V_{obj}g$, and the net force on it is $B - w = (\rho_{fluid} - \rho_{obj})V_{obj}g$. Therefore, if the density of the object is *less* than the density of the fluid, the net force exerted on the object is *positive* (upward) and the object accelerates *upward,* as in Active Figure 9.20a. If the density of the object is *greater* than the density of the fluid, as in Active Figure 9.20b, the net force is *negative* and the object accelerates *downward.*

Case II: A Floating Object.
Now consider a partially submerged object in static equilibrium floating in a fluid, as in Active Figure 9.21. In this case, the upward buoyant force is balanced by the downward force of gravity acting on the object. If V_{fluid} is the volume of the fluid displaced by the object (which corresponds to the volume of the part of the object beneath the fluid level), then the magnitude of the buoyant force is given by $B = \rho_{fluid}V_{fluid}g$. Because the weight of the object is $w = mg = \rho_{obj}V_{obj}g$, and because $w = B$, it follows that $\rho_{fluid}V_{fluid}g = \rho_{obj}V_{obj}g$, or

$$\frac{\rho_{obj}}{\rho_{fluid}} = \frac{V_{fluid}}{V_{obj}} \qquad [9.13]$$

Equation 9.13 neglects the buoyant force of the air, which is slight because the density of air is only 1.29 kg/m^3 at sea level.

Under normal circumstances, the average density of a fish is slightly greater than the density of water, so a fish would sink if it didn't have a mechanism for adjusting its density. By changing the size of an internal swim bladder, fish maintain neutral buoyancy as they swim to various depths.

The human brain is immersed in a fluid (the cerebrospinal fluid) of density 1 007 kg/m^3, which is slightly less than the average density of the brain, 1 040 kg/m^3. Consequently, most of the weight of the brain is supported by the buoyant force of the surrounding fluid. In some clinical procedures, a portion of this fluid must be removed for diagnostic purposes. During such procedures, the nerves and blood vessels in the brain are placed under great strain, which in turn can cause extreme discomfort and pain. Great care must be exercised with such patients until the initial volume of brain fluid has been restored by the body.

When service station attendants check the antifreeze in your car or the condition of your battery, they often use devices that apply Archimedes' principle. Figure 9.22 (page 296) shows a common device that is used to check the antifreeze in a car radiator. The small balls in the enclosed tube vary in density so that all of them float when the tube is filled with pure water, none float in pure antifreeze,

Most of the volume of this iceberg is beneath the water. Can you determine what fraction of the total volume is under water?

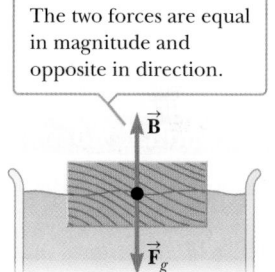

The two forces are equal in magnitude and opposite in direction.

Active Figure 9.21
An object floating on the surface of a fluid is acted upon by two forces: the gravitational force $\vec{F}_g$ and the buoyant force $\vec{B}$.

BIO APPLICATION
Buoyancy Control in Fish

BIO APPLICATION
Cerebrospinal Fluid

APPLICATION
Checking the Battery Charge

Figure 9.23 The orange ball in the plastic tube inside the battery serves as an indicator of whether the battery is (a) charged or (b) discharged.

As the battery loses its charge, the density of the battery fluid decreses, and the ball sinks out of sight.

Battery fluid

Charged battery   Discharged battery

Tubing to draw antifreeze from the radiator

Balls of different densities

Figure 9.22 The number of balls that float in this device is a measure of the density of the antifreeze solution in a vehicle's radiator and, consequently, a measure of the temperature at which freezing will occur.

one floats in a 5% mixture, two in a 10% mixture, and so forth. The number of balls that float is a measure of the percentage of antifreeze in the mixture, which in turn is used to determine the lowest temperature the mixture can withstand without freezing.

Similarly, the degree of charge in some car batteries can be determined with a so-called magic-dot process that is built into the battery (Fig. 9.23). Inside a viewing port in the top of the battery, the appearance of an orange dot indicates that the battery is sufficiently charged; a black dot indicates that the battery has lost its charge. If the battery has sufficient charge, the density of the battery fluid is high enough to cause the orange ball to float. As the battery loses its charge, the density of the battery fluid decreases and the ball sinks beneath the surface of the fluid, leaving the dot to appear black.

■ Quick Quiz

9.5 Atmospheric pressure varies from day to day. The level of a floating ship on a high-pressure day is (a) higher (b) lower, or (c) no different than on a low-pressure day.

9.6 The density of lead is greater than iron, and both metals are denser than water. Is the buoyant force on a solid lead object (a) greater than, (b) equal to, or (c) less than the buoyant force acting on a solid iron object of the same dimensions?

■ EXAMPLE 9.8   A Red-Tag Special on Crowns

GOAL Apply Archimedes' principle to a submerged object.

PROBLEM A bargain hunter purchases a "gold" crown at a flea market. After she gets home, she hangs it from a scale and finds its weight to be 7.84 N (Fig. 9.24a). She then weighs the crown while it is immersed in water, as in Figure 9.24b, and now the scale reads 6.86 N. Is the crown made of pure gold?

STRATEGY The goal is to find the density of the crown and compare it to the density of gold. We already have the weight of the crown in air, so we can get the mass by dividing by the acceleration of gravity. If we can find the volume of the crown, we can obtain the desired density by dividing the mass by this volume.

When the crown is fully immersed, the displaced water is equal to the volume of the crown. This same volume is used in calculating the buoyant force. So our strategy is as follows: (1) Apply Newton's second law to the crown, both in the water and in the air to find the buoyant force. (2) Use the buoyant force to find the crown's volume. (3) Divide the crown's scale weight in air by the acceleration of gravity to get the mass, then by the volume to get the density of the crown.

$\vec{T}_{air}$

$\vec{B}$ $\vec{T}_{water}$

$m\vec{g}$ $m\vec{g}$

a   b

Figure 9.24 (Example 9.8) (a) When the crown is suspended in air, the scale reads $T_{air} = mg$, the crown's true weight. (b) When the crown is immersed in water, the buoyant force $\vec{B}$ reduces the scale reading by the magnitude of the buoyant force, $T_{water} = mg - B$.

SOLUTION

Apply Newton's second law to the crown when it's weighed in air. There are two forces on the crown—gravity $m\vec{g}$ and $\vec{T}_{air}$, the force exerted by the scale on the crown, with magnitude equal to the reading on the scale.

(1) $T_{air} - mg = 0$

When the crown is immersed in water, the scale force is $\vec{T}_{water}$, with magnitude equal to the scale reading, and there is an upward buoyant force $\vec{B}$ and the force of gravity.

(2) $T_{water} - mg + B = 0$

Solve Equation (1) for mg, substitute into Equation (2), and solve for the buoyant force, which equals the difference in scale readings:

$T_{water} - T_{air} + B = 0$

$B = T_{air} - T_{water} = 7.84 \text{ N} - 6.86 \text{ N} = 0.980 \text{ N}$

Find the volume of the displaced water, using the fact that the magnitude of the buoyant force equals the weight of the displaced water:

$B = \rho_{water} g V_{water} = 0.980 \text{ N}$

$V_{water} = \dfrac{0.980 \text{ N}}{g \rho_{water}} = \dfrac{0.980 \text{ N}}{(9.80 \text{ m/s}^2)(1.00 \times 10^3 \text{ kg/m}^3)}$

$= 1.00 \times 10^{-4} \text{ m}^3$

The crown is totally submerged, so $V_{crown} = V_{water}$. From Equation (1), the mass is the crown's weight in air, T_{air}, divided by g:

$m = \dfrac{T_{air}}{g} = \dfrac{7.84 \text{ N}}{9.80 \text{ m/s}^2} = 0.800 \text{ kg}$

Find the density of the crown:

$\rho_{crown} = \dfrac{m}{V_{crown}} = \dfrac{0.800 \text{ kg}}{1.00 \times 10^{-4} \text{ m}^3} = \boxed{8.00 \times 10^3 \text{ kg/m}^3}$

REMARKS Because the density of gold is 19.3×10^3 kg/m^3, the crown is either hollow, made of an alloy, or both. Despite the mathematical complexity, it is certainly conceivable that this was the method that occurred to Archimedes. Conceptually, it's a matter of realizing (or guessing) that equal weights of gold and a silver–gold alloy would have different scale readings when immersed in water because their densities and hence their volumes are different, leading to differing buoyant forces.

QUESTION 9.8 True or False: The magnitude of the buoyant force on a completely submerged object depends on the object's density.

EXERCISE 9.8 The weight of a metal bracelet is measured to be 0.100 00 N in air and 0.092 00 N when immersed in water. Find its density.

ANSWER 1.25×10^4 kg/m^3

■ EXAMPLE 9.9   Floating Down the River

GOAL Apply Archimedes' principle to a partially submerged object.

PROBLEM A raft is constructed of wood having a density of 6.00×10^2 kg/m^3. Its surface area is 5.70 m^2, and its volume is 0.60 m^3. When the raft is placed in fresh water as in Figure 9.25, to what depth h is the bottom of the raft submerged?

STRATEGY There are two forces acting on the raft: the buoyant force of magnitude B, acting upward, and the force of gravity, acting downward. Because the raft is in equilibrium, the sum of these forces is zero. The buoyant force depends on the submerged volume $V_{water} = Ah$. Set up Newton's second law and solve for h, the depth reached by the bottom of the raft.

Figure 9.25 (Example 9.9) A raft partially submerged in water.

SOLUTION

Apply Newton's second law to the raft, which is in equilibrium:

$B - m_{raft} g = 0 \quad \rightarrow \quad B = m_{raft} g$

(Continued)

The volume of the raft submerged in water is given by $V_{water} = Ah$. The magnitude of the buoyant force is equal to the weight of this displaced volume of water:

$$B = m_{water}g = (\rho_{water}V_{water})g = (\rho_{water}Ah)g$$

Now rewrite the gravity force on the raft using the raft's density and volume:

$$m_{raft}g = (\rho_{raft}V_{raft})g$$

Substitute these two expressions into Newton's second law, $B = m_{raft}g$, and solve for h (note that g cancels):

$$(\rho_{water}Ah)g = (\rho_{raft}V_{raft})g$$

$$h = \frac{\rho_{raft}V_{raft}}{\rho_{water}A}$$

$$= \frac{(6.00 \times 10^2 \text{ kg/m}^3)(0.600 \text{ m}^3)}{(1.00 \times 10^3 \text{ kg/m}^3)(5.70 \text{ m}^2)}$$

$$= \boxed{0.063\ 2 \text{ m}}$$

REMARKS How low the raft rides in the water depends on the density of the raft. The same is true of the human body: Fat is less dense than muscle and bone, so those with a higher percentage of body fat float better.

QUESTION 9.9 If the raft is placed in salt water, which has a density greater than fresh water, would the value of h (a) decrease, (b) increase, or (c) not change?

EXERCISE 9.9 Calculate how much of an iceberg is beneath the surface of the ocean, given that the density of ice is 917 kg/m^3 and salt water has density 1 025 kg/m^3.

ANSWER 89.5%

▪ EXAMPLE 9.10 | Floating in Two Fluids

GOAL Apply Archimedes' principle to an object floating in a fluid having two layers with different densities.

PROBLEM A 1.00×10^3-kg cube of aluminum is placed in a tank. Water is then added to the tank until half the cube is immersed. **(a)** What is the normal force on the cube? (See Fig. 9.26a.) **(b)** Mercury is now slowly poured into the tank until the normal force on the cube goes to zero. (See Fig. 9.26b.) How deep is the layer of mercury?

STRATEGY Both parts of this problem involve applications of Newton's second law for a body in equilibrium, together with the concept of a buoyant force. In part (a) the normal, gravitational, and buoyant forces act on the cube. In part (b) there is an additional buoyant force of mercury, while the normal force goes to zero. Using $V_{Hg} = Ah$, solve for the height of mercury, h.

Figure 9.26 (Example 9.10)

SOLUTION

(a) Find the normal force on the cube when half-immersed in water.

Calculate the volume V of the cube and the length d of one side, for future reference (both quantities will be needed for what follows):

$$V_{Al} = \frac{M_{Al}}{\rho_{Al}} = \frac{1.00 \times 10^3 \text{ kg}}{2.70 \times 10^3 \text{ kg/m}^3} = 0.370 \text{ m}^3$$

$$d = V_{Al}^{1/3} = 0.718 \text{ m}$$

Write Newton's second law for the cube, and solve for the normal force. The buoyant force is equal to the weight of the displaced water (half the volume of the cube).

$$n - M_{Al}g + B_{water} = 0$$

$$n = M_{Al}g - B_{water} = M_{Al}g - \rho_{water}(V/2)g$$

$$= (1.00 \times 10^3 \text{ kg})(9.80 \text{ m/s}^2)$$

$$- (1.00 \times 10^3 \text{ kg/m}^3)(0.370 \text{ m}^3/2.00)(9.80 \text{ m/s}^2)$$

$$n = 9.80 \times 10^3 \text{ N} - 1.81 \times 10^3 \text{ N} = \boxed{7.99 \times 10^3 \text{ N}}$$

(b) Calculate the level h of added mercury.

Apply Newton's second law to the cube:

$$n - M_{Al}g + B_{water} + B_{Hg} = 0$$

Set $n = 0$ and solve for the buoyant force of mercury:

$$B_{Hg} = (\rho_{Hg} Ah)g = M_{Al}g - B_{water} = 7.99 \times 10^3 \text{ N}$$

Solve for h, noting that $A = d^2$:

$$h = \frac{M_{Al}g - B_{water}}{\rho_{Hg}Ag} = \frac{7.99 \times 10^3 \text{ N}}{(13.6 \times 10^3 \text{ kg/m}^3)(0.718 \text{ m})^2(9.80 \text{ m/s}^2)}$$

$$h = \boxed{0.116 \text{ m}}$$

REMARKS Notice that the buoyant force of mercury calculated in part (b) is the same as the normal force in part (a). This is naturally the case, because enough mercury was added to exactly cancel out the normal force. We could have used this fact to take a shortcut, simply writing $B_{Hg} = 7.99 \times 10^3 \text{ N}$ immediately, solving for h, and avoiding a second use of Newton's law. Most of the time, however, we wouldn't be so lucky! Try calculating the normal force when the level of mercury is 4.00 cm.

QUESTION 9.10 What would happen to the aluminum cube if more mercury were poured into the tank?

EXERCISE 9.10 A cube of aluminum 1.00 m on a side is immersed one-third in water and two-thirds in glycerin. What is the normal force on the cube?

ANSWER $1.50 \times 10^4 \text{ N}$

9.7 Fluids in Motion

When a fluid is in motion, its flow can be characterized in one of two ways. The flow is said to be **streamline,** or **laminar,** if every particle that passes a particular point moves along exactly the same smooth path followed by previous particles passing that point. This path is called a *streamline* (Fig. 9.27). Different streamlines can't cross each other under this steady-flow condition, and the streamline at any point coincides with the direction of the velocity of the fluid at that point.

In contrast, the flow of a fluid becomes irregular, or **turbulent,** above a certain velocity or under any conditions that can cause abrupt changes in velocity. Irregular motions of the fluid, called *eddy currents*, are characteristic in turbulent flow, as shown in Figure 9.28.

In discussions of fluid flow, the term **viscosity** is used for the degree of internal friction in the fluid. This internal friction is associated with the resistance between two adjacent layers of the fluid moving relative to each other. A fluid such as kerosene has a lower viscosity than does crude oil or molasses.

Many features of fluid motion can be understood by considering the behavior of an **ideal fluid,** which satisfies the following conditions:

1. **The fluid is nonviscous,** which means there is no internal friction force between adjacent layers.
2. **The fluid is incompressible,** which means its density is constant.
3. **The fluid motion is steady,** meaning that the velocity, density, and pressure at each point in the fluid don't change with time.
4. **The fluid moves without turbulence.** This implies that each element of the fluid has zero angular velocity about its center, so there can't be any eddy currents present in the moving fluid. A small wheel placed in the fluid would translate but not rotate.

Equation of Continuity

Figure 9.29a (page 300) represents a fluid flowing through a pipe of nonuniform size. The particles in the fluid move along the streamlines in steady-state flow. In a small time interval Δt, the fluid entering the bottom end of the pipe moves a

Figure 9.27 An illustration of streamline flow around an automobile in a test wind tunnel. The streamlines in the airflow are made visible by smoke particles.

Figure 9.28 Hot gases made visible by smoke particles. The smoke first moves in laminar flow at the bottom and then in turbulent flow above.

Figure 9.29 (a) A fluid moving with streamline flow through a pipe of varying cross-sectional area. The volume of fluid flowing through A_1 in a time interval Δt must equal the volume flowing through A_2 in the same time interval. (b) Water flowing slowly out of a faucet.

The volume flow rate through A_1 must equal the rate through A_2, so $A_1v_1 = A_2v_2$.

The width of the stream narrows as the water falls and speeds up in accord with the continuity equation.

© Cengage Learning/George Semple

distance $\Delta x_1 = v_1 \Delta t$, where v_1 is the speed of the fluid at that location. If A_1 is the cross-sectional area in this region, then the mass contained in the bottom blue region is $\Delta M_1 = \rho_1 A_1 \Delta x_1 = \rho_1 A_1 v_1 \Delta t$, where ρ_1 is the density of the fluid at A_1. Similarly, the fluid that moves out of the upper end of the pipe in the same time interval Δt has a mass of $\Delta M_2 = \rho_2 A_2 v_2 \Delta t$. However, **because mass is conserved and because the flow is steady,** the mass that flows into the bottom of the pipe through A_1 in the time Δt must equal the mass that flows out through A_2 in the same interval. Therefore, $\Delta M_1 = \Delta M_2$, or

$$\rho_1 A_1 v_1 = \rho_2 A_2 v_2 \qquad [9.14]$$

For the case of an incompressible fluid, $\rho_1 = \rho_2$ and Equation 9.14 reduces to

◀ Equation of continuity

$$A_1 v_1 = A_2 v_2 \qquad [9.15]$$

This expression is called the **equation of continuity.** From this result, we see that **the product of the cross-sectional area of the pipe and the fluid speed at that cross section is a constant.** Therefore, the speed is high where the tube is constricted and low where the tube has a larger diameter. The product Av, which has dimensions of volume per unit time, is called the **flow rate. The condition Av = constant is equivalent to the fact that the volume of fluid that enters one end of the tube in a given time interval equals the volume of fluid leaving the tube in the same interval, assuming that the fluid is incompressible and there are no leaks.** Figure 9.29b is an example of an application of the equation of continuity: As the stream of water flows continuously from a faucet, the width of the stream narrows as it falls and speeds up.

There are many instances in everyday experience that involve the equation of continuity. Reducing the cross-sectional area of a garden hose by putting a thumb over the open end makes the water spray out with greater speed; hence the stream goes farther. Similar reasoning explains why smoke from a smoldering piece of wood first rises in a streamline pattern, getting thinner with height, eventually breaking up into a swirling, turbulent pattern. The smoke rises because it's less dense than air and the buoyant force of the air accelerates it upward. As the speed of the smoke stream increases, the cross-sectional area of the stream decreases, in accordance with the equation of continuity. The stream soon reaches a speed so great that streamline flow is not possible. We will study the relationship between speed of fluid flow and turbulence in a later discussion on the Reynolds number.

Tip 9.3 Continuity Equations

The rate of flow of fluid into a system equals the rate of flow out of the system. The incoming fluid occupies a certain volume and can enter the system only if the fluid already inside goes out, thereby making room.

■ **EXAMPLE 9.11** | **Niagara Falls**

GOAL Apply the equation of continuity.

PROBLEM Each second, 5 525 m^3 of water flows over the 670-m-wide cliff of the Horseshoe Falls portion of Niagara Falls. The water is approximately 2 m deep as it reaches the cliff. Estimate its speed at that instant.

STRATEGY This is an estimate, so only one significant figure will be retained in the answer. The volume flow rate is given, and, according to the equation of continuity, is a constant equal to Av. Find the cross-sectional area, substitute, and solve for the speed.

SOLUTION

Calculate the cross-sectional area of the water as it reaches the edge of the cliff:

$$A = (670 \text{ m})(2 \text{ m}) = 1\ 340 \text{ m}^2$$

Multiply this result by the speed and set it equal to the flow rate. Then solve for v:

$$Av = \text{volume flow rate}$$
$$(1\ 340 \text{ m}^2)v = 5\ 525 \text{ m}^3/\text{s} \quad \rightarrow \quad v \approx \boxed{4 \text{ m/s}}$$

QUESTION 9.11 What happens to the speed of blood in an artery when plaque starts to build up on the artery's sides?

EXERCISE 9.11 The Garfield Thomas water tunnel at Pennsylvania State University has a circular cross section that constricts from a diameter of 3.6 m to the test section which has a diameter of 1.2 m. If the speed of flow is 3.0 m/s in the larger-diameter pipe, determine the speed of flow in the test section.

ANSWER 27 m/s

■ **EXAMPLE 9.12** | **Watering a Garden**

GOAL Combine the equation of continuity with concepts of flow rate and kinematics.

PROBLEM A water hose 2.50 cm in diameter is used by a gardener to fill a 30.0-liter bucket. (One liter = 1 000 cm^3.) The gardener notices that it takes 1.00 min to fill the bucket. A nozzle with an opening of cross-sectional area 0.500 cm^2 is then attached to the hose. The nozzle is held so that water is projected horizontally from a point 1.00 m above the ground. Over what horizontal distance can the water be projected?

STRATEGY We can find the volume flow rate through the hose by dividing the volume of the bucket by the time it takes to fill it. After finding the flow rate, apply the equation of continuity to find the speed at which the water shoots horizontally out the nozzle. The rest of the problem is an application of two-dimensional kinematics. The answer obtained is the same as would be found for a ball having the same initial velocity and height.

SOLUTION

Calculate the volume flow rate into the bucket, and convert to m^3/s:

$$\text{volume flow rate} =$$
$$= \frac{30.0 \text{ L}}{1.00 \text{ min}}\left(\frac{1.00 \times 10^3 \text{ cm}^3}{1.00 \text{ L}}\right)\left(\frac{1.00 \text{ m}}{100.0 \text{ cm}}\right)^3\left(\frac{1.00 \text{ min}}{60.0 \text{ s}}\right)$$
$$= 5.00 \times 10^{-4} \text{ m}^3/\text{s}$$

Solve the equation of continuity for v_{0x}, the x-component of the initial velocity of the stream exiting the hose:

$$A_1v_1 = A_2v_2 = A_2v_{0x}$$
$$v_{0x} = \frac{A_1v_1}{A_2} = \frac{5.00 \times 10^{-4} \text{ m}^3/\text{s}}{0.500 \times 10^{-4} \text{ m}^2} = 10.0 \text{ m/s}$$

Calculate the time for the stream to fall 1.00 m, using kinematics. Initially, the stream is horizontal, so v_{0y} is zero:

$$\Delta y = v_{0y}t - \tfrac{1}{2}gt^2$$

Set $v_{0y} = 0$ in the preceding equation and solve for t, noting that $\Delta y = -1.00$ m:

$$t = \sqrt{\frac{-2\Delta y}{g}} = \sqrt{\frac{-2(-1.00 \text{ m})}{9.80 \text{ m/s}^2}} = 0.452 \text{ s}$$

Find the horizontal distance the stream travels:

$$x = v_{0x}t = (10.0 \text{ m/s})(0.452 \text{ s}) = \boxed{4.52 \text{ m}}$$

(Continued)

REMARKS It's interesting that the motion of fluids can be treated with the same kinematics equations as individual objects.

QUESTION 9.12 By what factor would the range be changed if the flow rate were doubled?

EXERCISE 9.12 The nozzle is replaced with a Y-shaped fitting that splits the flow in half. Garden hoses are connected to each end of the Y, with each hose having a 0.400 cm² nozzle. (a) How fast does the water come out of one of the nozzles? (b) How far would one of the nozzles squirt water if both were operated simultaneously and held horizontally 1.00 m off the ground? *Hint:* Find the volume flow rate through each 0.400-cm² nozzle, then follow the same steps as before.

ANSWERS (a) 6.25 m/s (b) 2.83 m

Bernoulli's Equation

The tube of fluid between points Ⓐ and Ⓒ moves forward so it is between points Ⓑ and Ⓓ.

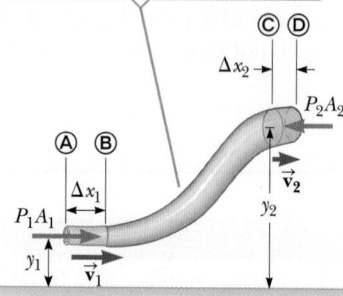

Figure 9.30 By the work-energy theorem, the work done by the opposing pressures P_1 and P_2 equals the difference in mechanical energy between that of the fluid now between points Ⓒ and Ⓓ and the fluid that was formerly between Ⓐ and Ⓑ.

Daniel Bernoulli
Swiss physicist and mathematician (1700–1782)
In his most famous work, *Hydrodynamica*, Bernoulli showed that, as the velocity of fluid flow increases, its pressure decreases. In this same publication, Bernoulli also attempted the first explanation of the behavior of gases with changing pressure and temperature; this was the beginning of the kinetic theory of gases.

As a fluid moves through a pipe of varying cross section and elevation, the pressure changes along the pipe. In 1738 the Swiss physicist Daniel Bernoulli (1700–1782) derived an expression that relates the pressure of a fluid to its speed and elevation. Bernoulli's equation is not a freestanding law of physics; rather, it's **a consequence of energy conservation as applied to an ideal fluid.**

In deriving Bernoulli's equation, we again assume the fluid is incompressible, nonviscous, and flows in a nonturbulent, steady-state manner. Consider the flow through a nonuniform pipe in the time Δt, as in Figure 9.30. The force on the lower end of the fluid is $P_1 A_1$, where P_1 is the pressure at the lower end. The work done on the lower end of the fluid by the fluid behind it is

$$W_1 = F_1 \Delta x_1 = P_1 A_1 \Delta x_1 = P_1 V$$

where V is the volume of the lower blue region in the figure. In a similar manner, the work done on the fluid on the upper portion in the time Δt is

$$W_2 = -P_2 A_2 \Delta x_2 = -P_2 V$$

The volume is the same because, by the equation of continuity, the volume of fluid that passes through A_1 in the time Δt equals the volume that passes through A_2 in the same interval. The work W_2 is negative because the force on the fluid at the top is opposite its displacement. The net work done by these forces in the time Δt is

$$W_{\text{fluid}} = P_1 V - P_2 V$$

Part of this work goes into changing the fluid's kinetic energy, and part goes into changing the gravitational potential energy of the fluid–Earth system. If m is the mass of the fluid passing through the pipe in the time interval Δt, then the change in kinetic energy of the volume of fluid is

$$\Delta KE = \tfrac{1}{2} m v_2^2 - \tfrac{1}{2} m v_1^2$$

The change in the gravitational potential energy is

$$\Delta PE = mg y_2 - mg y_1$$

Because the net work done by the fluid on the segment of fluid shown in Figure 9.30 changes the kinetic energy and the potential energy of the nonisolated system, we have

$$W_{\text{fluid}} = \Delta KE + \Delta PE$$

The three terms in this equation are those we have just evaluated. Substituting expressions for each of the terms gives

$$P_1 V - P_2 V = \tfrac{1}{2} m v_2^2 - \tfrac{1}{2} m v_1^2 + mg y_2 - mg y_1$$

If we divide each term by V and recall that $\rho = m/V$, this expression becomes

$$P_1 - P_2 = \tfrac{1}{2}\rho v_2^2 - \tfrac{1}{2}\rho v_1^2 + \rho g y_2 - \rho g y_1$$

The pressure P_1 is greater than the pressure P_2, because $v_1 < v_2$.

Pressure is lower at the narrow part of the tube, so the fluid level is higher.

© Charles D. Winters/Cengage Learning

a

b

Figure 9.31 (a) This device can be used to measure the speed of fluid flow. (b) A Venturi tube, located at the top of the photograph. The higher level of fluid in the middle column shows that the pressure at the top of the column, which is in the constricted region of the Venturi tube, is lower than the pressure else-where in the column.

Rearrange the terms as follows:

$$P_1 + \tfrac{1}{2}\rho v_1^{\,2} + \rho g y_1 = P_2 + \tfrac{1}{2}\rho v_2^{\,2} + \rho g y_2 \qquad \text{[9.16]}$$

This is **Bernoulli's equation,** often expressed as

$$P + \tfrac{1}{2}\rho v^2 + \rho g y = \text{constant} \qquad \text{[9.17]}$$

Bernoulli's equation states that the sum of the pressure P, the kinetic energy per unit volume, $\tfrac{1}{2}\rho v^2$, and the potential energy per unit volume, $\rho g y$, has the same value at all points along a streamline.

◄ Bernoulli's equation

An important consequence of Bernoulli's equation can be demonstrated by considering Figure 9.31, which shows water flowing through a horizontal con-stricted pipe from a region of large cross-sectional area into a region of smaller cross-sectional area. This device, called a **Venturi tube,** can be used to measure the speed of fluid flow. Because the pipe is horizontal, $y_1 = y_2$, and Equation 9.16 applied to points 1 and 2 gives

$$P_1 + \tfrac{1}{2}\rho v_1^{\,2} = P_2 + \tfrac{1}{2}\rho v_2^{\,2} \qquad \text{[9.18]}$$

Because the water is not backing up in the pipe, its speed v_2 in the constricted region must be greater than its speed v_1 in the region of greater diameter. From Equation 9.18, we see that P_2 must be less than P_1 because $v_2 > v_1$. This result is often expressed by the statement that **swiftly moving fluids exert less pressure than do slowly moving fluids.** This important fact enables us to understand a wide range of everyday phenomena.

Tip 9.4 Bernoulli's Principle for Gases

Equation 9.16 isn't strictly true for gases because they aren't incompressible. The qualitative behavior is the same, however: As the speed of the gas increases, its pressure decreases.

■ Quick Quiz

9.7 You observe two helium balloons floating next to each other at the ends of strings secured to a table. The facing surfaces of the balloons are separated by 1–2 cm. You blow through the opening between the balloons. What happens to the balloons? (a) They move toward each other. (b) They move away from each other. (c) They are unaffected.

■ EXAMPLE 9.13 | Shoot-Out at the Old Water Tank

GOAL Apply Bernoulli's equation to find the speed of a fluid.

PROBLEM A nearsighted sheriff fires at a cattle rustler with his trusty six-shooter. Fortunately for the rustler, the bullet misses him and penetrates the town water tank, causing a leak (Fig. 9.32 on page 304). **(a)** If the top of the tank is open to

(Continued)

the atmosphere, determine the speed at which the water leaves the hole when the water level is 0.500 m above the hole. **(b)** Where does the stream hit the ground if the hole is 3.00 m above the ground?

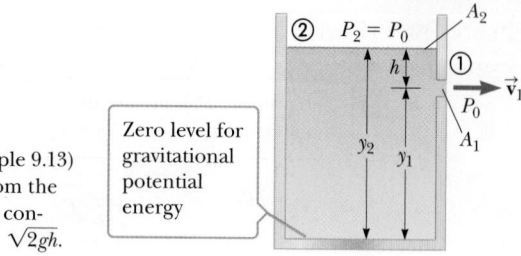

STRATEGY (a) Assume the tank's cross-sectional area is large compared to the hole's $(A_2 \gg A_1)$, so the water level drops very slowly and $v_2 \approx 0$. Apply Bernoulli's equation to points ① and ② in Figure 9.31, noting that P_1 equals atmospheric pressure P_0

Figure 9.32 (Example 9.13) The water speed v_1 from the hole in the side of the container is given by $v_1 = \sqrt{2gh}$.

at the hole and is approximately the same at the top of the water tank. Part (b) can be solved with kinematics, just as if the water were a ball thrown horizontally.

SOLUTION

(a) Find the speed of the water leaving the hole.

Substitute $P_1 = P_2 = P_0$ and $v_2 \approx 0$ into Bernoulli's equation, and solve for v_1:

$$P_0 + \tfrac{1}{2}\rho v_1^2 + \rho g y_1 = P_0 + \rho g y_2$$
$$v_1 = \sqrt{2g(y_2 - y_1)} = \sqrt{2gh}$$
$$v_1 = \sqrt{2(9.80 \text{ m/s}^2)(0.500 \text{ m})} = \boxed{3.13 \text{ m/s}}$$

(b) Find where the stream hits the ground.

Use the displacement equation to find the time of the fall, noting that the stream is initially horizontal, so $v_{0y} = 0$.

$$\Delta y = -\tfrac{1}{2}gt^2 + v_{0y}t$$
$$-3.00 \text{ m} = -(4.90 \text{ m/s}^2)t^2$$
$$t = 0.782 \text{ s}$$

Compute the horizontal distance the stream travels in this time:

$$x = v_{0x}t = (3.13 \text{ m/s})(0.782 \text{ s}) = \boxed{2.45 \text{ m}}$$

REMARKS As the analysis of part (a) shows, the speed of the water emerging from the hole is equal to the speed acquired by an object falling freely through the vertical distance h. This is known as **Torricelli's law.**

QUESTION 9.13 As time passes, what happens to the speed of the water leaving the hole?

EXERCISE 9.13 Suppose, in a similar situation, the water hits the ground 4.20 m from the hole in the tank. If the hole is 2.00 m above the ground, how far above the hole is the water level?

ANSWER 2.21 m above the hole

■ **EXAMPLE 9.14** | **Fluid Flow in a Pipe**

GOAL Solve a problem combining Bernoulli's equation and the equation of continuity.

PROBLEM A large pipe with a cross-sectional area of 1.00 m² descends 5.00 m and narrows to 0.500 m², where it terminates in a valve at point ① (Fig. 9.33). If the pressure at point ② is atmospheric pressure, and the valve is opened wide and water allowed to flow freely, find the speed of the water leaving the pipe.

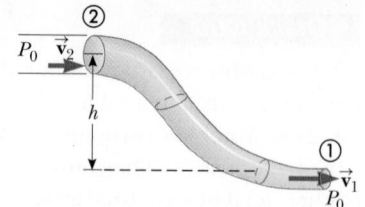

STRATEGY The equation of continuity, together with Bernoulli's equation, constitute two equations in two unknowns: the speeds v_1 and v_2. Eliminate v_2 from Bernoulli's equation with the equation of continuity, and solve for v_1.

Figure 9.33 (Example 9.14)

SOLUTION

Write Bernoulli's equation:

(1) $\quad P_1 + \tfrac{1}{2}\rho v_1^2 + \rho g y_1 = P_2 + \tfrac{1}{2}\rho v_2^2 + \rho g y_2$

Solve the equation of continuity for v_2:

$$A_2 v_2 = A_1 v_1$$

(2) $\quad v_2 = \dfrac{A_1}{A_2} v_1$

In Equation (1), set $P_1 = P_2 = P_0$, and substitute the expression for v_2. Then solve for v_1.

(3) $P_0 + \frac{1}{2}\rho v_1^2 + \rho g y_1 = P_0 + \frac{1}{2}\rho \left(\frac{A_1}{A_2} v_1\right)^2 + \rho g y_2$

$$v_1^2 \left[1 - \left(\frac{A_1}{A_2}\right)^2\right] = 2g(y_2 - y_1) = 2gh$$

$$v_1 = \frac{\sqrt{2gh}}{\sqrt{1 - (A_1/A_2)^2}}$$

Substitute the given values: $v_1 = $ 11.4 m/s

REMARKS Calculating actual flow rates of real fluids through pipes is in fact much more complex than presented here, due to viscosity, the possibility of turbulence, and other factors.

QUESTION 9.14 Find a symbolic expression for the limit of speed v_1 as the lower cross sectional area A_1 opening becomes negligibly small compared to cross section A_2. What is this result called?

EXERCISE 9.14 Water flowing in a horizontal pipe is at a pressure of 1.40×10^5 Pa at a point where its cross-sectional area is 1.00 m². When the pipe narrows to 0.400 m², the pressure drops to 1.16×10^5 Pa. Find the water's speed (a) in the wider pipe and (b) in the narrower pipe.

ANSWERS (a) 3.02 m/s (b) 7.56 m/s

9.8 Other Applications of Fluid Dynamics

In this section we describe some common phenomena that can be explained, at least in part, by Bernoulli's equation.

In general, an object moving through a fluid is acted upon by a net upward force as the result of any effect that causes the fluid to change its direction as it flows past the object. For example, a golf ball struck with a club is given a rapid backspin, as shown in Figure 9.34. The dimples on the ball help entrain the air along the curve of the ball's surface. The figure shows a thin layer of air wrapping partway around the ball and being deflected downward as a result. Because the ball pushes the air down, by Newton's third law the air must push up on the ball and cause it to rise. Without the dimples, the air isn't as well entrained, so the golf ball doesn't travel as far. A tennis ball's fuzz performs a similar function, though the desired result is ball placement rather than greater distance.

Many devices operate in the manner illustrated in Figure 9.35. A stream of air passing over an open tube reduces the pressure above the tube, causing the liquid to rise into the airstream. The liquid is then dispersed into a fine spray of droplets. You might recognize that this so-called atomizer is used in perfume bottles and paint sprayers. The same principle is used in the carburetor of a gasoline engine. In that case, the low-pressure region in the carburetor is produced by air drawn in by the piston through the air filter. The gasoline vaporizes, mixes with the air, and enters the cylinder of the engine for combustion.

In a person with advanced arteriosclerosis, the Bernoulli effect produces a symptom called **vascular flutter.** In this condition, the artery is constricted as a result of accumulated plaque on its inner walls, as shown in Figure 9.36. To maintain a constant flow rate, the blood must travel faster than normal through the constriction. If the speed of the blood is sufficiently high in the constricted region,

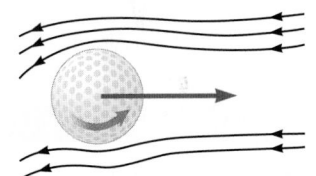

Figure 9.34 A spinning golf ball is acted upon by a lifting force that allows it to travel much further than it would if it were not spinning.

APPLICATION
"Atomizers" in Perfume Bottles and Paint Sprayers

BIO APPLICATION
Vascular Flutter and Aneurysms

Figure 9.35 A stream of air passing over a tube dipped in a liquid causes the liquid to rise in the tube. This effect is used in perfume bottles and paint sprayers.

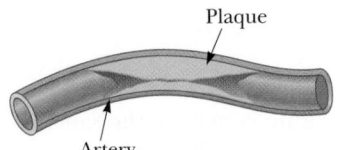

Plaque

Artery

Figure 9.36 Blood must travel faster than normal through a constricted region of an artery.

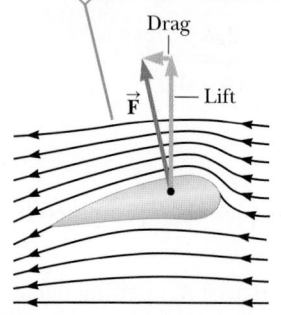

The difference in pressure between the underside and top of the wing creates a dynamic upward lift force.

Figure 9.37 Streamline flow around an airplane wing. The pressure above is less than the pressure below, and there is a dynamic upward lift force.

the blood pressure is low, and the artery may collapse under external pressure, causing a momentary interruption in blood flow. During the collapse there is no Bernoulli effect, so the vessel reopens under arterial pressure. As the blood rushes through the constricted artery, the internal pressure drops and the artery closes again. Such variations in blood flow can be heard with a stethoscope. If the plaque becomes dislodged and ends up in a smaller vessel that delivers blood to the heart, it can cause a heart attack.

An **aneurysm** is a weakened spot on an artery where the artery walls have ballooned outward. Blood flows more slowly though this region, as can be seen from the equation of continuity, resulting in an increase in pressure in the vicinity of the aneurysm relative to the pressure in other parts of the artery. This condition is dangerous because the excess pressure can cause the artery to rupture.

The lift on an aircraft wing can also be explained in part by the Bernoulli effect. Airplane wings are designed so that the air speed above the wing is greater than the speed below. As a result, the air pressure above the wing is less than the pressure below, and there is a net upward force on the wing, called the *lift*. (There is also a horizontal component called the *drag*.) Another factor influencing the lift on a wing, shown in Figure 9.37, is the slight upward tilt of the wing. This causes air molecules striking the bottom to be deflected downward, producing a reaction force upward by Newton's third law. Finally, turbulence also has an effect. If the wing is tilted too much, the flow of air across the upper surface becomes turbulent, and the pressure difference across the wing is not as great as that predicted by the Bernoulli effect. In an extreme case, this turbulence may cause the aircraft to stall.

■ EXAMPLE 9.15 | Lift on an Airfoil

GOAL Use Bernoulli's equation to calculate the lift on an airplane wing.

PROBLEM An airplane has wings, each with area 4.00 m², designed so that air flows over the top of the wing at 245 m/s and underneath the wing at 222 m/s. Find the mass of the airplane such that the lift on the plane will support its weight, assuming the force from the pressure difference across the wings is directed straight upward.

STRATEGY This problem can be solved by substituting values into Bernoulli's equation to find the pressure difference between the air under the wing and the air over the wing, followed by applying Newton's second law to find the mass the airplane can lift.

. . . .

SOLUTION

Apply Bernoulli's equation to the air flowing under the wing (point 1) and over the wing (point 2). Gravitational potential energy terms are small compared with the other terms, and can be neglected.

$$P_1 + \tfrac{1}{2}\rho v_1^2 = P_2 + \tfrac{1}{2}\rho v_2^2$$

Solve this equation for the pressure difference:

$$\Delta P = P_1 - P_2 = \tfrac{1}{2}\rho v_2^2 - \tfrac{1}{2}\rho v_1^2 = \tfrac{1}{2}\rho(v_2^2 - v_1^2)$$

Substitute the given speeds and $\rho = 1.29$ kg/m³, the density of air:

$$\Delta P = \tfrac{1}{2}(1.29 \text{ kg/m}^3)(245^2 \text{ m}^2/\text{s}^2 - 222^2 \text{ m}^2/\text{s}^2)$$

$$\Delta P = 6.93 \times 10^3 \text{ Pa}$$

Apply Newton's second law. To support the plane's weight, the sum of the lift and gravity forces must equal zero. Solve for the mass m of the plane.

$$2A\Delta P - mg = 0 \quad \rightarrow \quad m = \boxed{5.66 \times 10^3 \text{ kg}}$$

. . . .

REMARKS Note the factor of two in the last equation, needed because the airplane has two wings. The density of the atmosphere drops steadily with increasing height, reducing the lift. As a result, all aircraft have a maximum operating altitude.

QUESTION 9.15 Why is the maximum lift affected by increasing altitude?

EXERCISE 9.15 Approximately what size wings would an aircraft need on Mars if its engine generates the same differences in speed as in the example and the total mass of the craft is 400 kg? The density of air on the surface of Mars is approximately one percent Earth's density at sea level, and the acceleration of gravity on the surface of Mars is about 3.8 m/s^2.

ANSWER Rounding to one significant digit, each wing would have to have an area of about 10 m^2. There have been proposals for solar-powered robotic Mars aircraft, which would have to be gossamer-light with large wings.

■ APPLYING PHYSICS 9.4 | Sailing Upwind

How can a sailboat accomplish the seemingly impossible task of sailing into the wind?

EXPLANATION As shown in Figure 9.38, the wind blowing in the direction of the arrow causes the sail to billow out and take on a shape similar to that of an airplane wing. By Bernoulli's equation, just as for an airplane wing, there is a force on the sail in the direction shown. The component of force perpendicular to the boat tends to make the boat move sideways in the water, but the keel prevents this sideways motion. The component of the force in the forward direction drives the boat almost against the wind. The word *almost* is used because a sailboat can move forward only when the wind direction is about 10 to 15° with respect to the forward direction. This means that to sail directly against the wind, a boat must follow a zigzag path, a procedure called *tacking*, so that the wind is always at some angle with respect to the direction of travel. ■

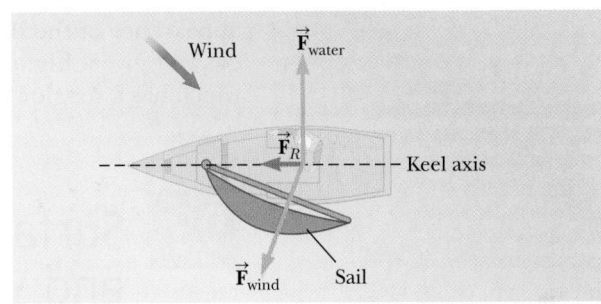

Figure 9.38 (Applying Physics 9.4)

■ APPLYING PHYSICS 9.5 | Home Plumbing

Consider the portion of a home plumbing system shown in Figure 9.39. The water trap in the pipe below the sink captures a plug of water that prevents sewer gas from finding its way from the sewer pipe, up the sink drain, and into the home. Suppose the dishwasher is draining and the water is moving to the left in the sewer pipe. What is the purpose of the vent, which is open to the air above the roof of the house? In which direction is air moving at the opening of the vent, upward or downward?

EXPLANATION Imagine that the vent isn't present so that the drainpipe for the sink is simply connected through the trap to the sewer pipe. As water from the dishwasher moves to the left in the sewer pipe, the pressure in the sewer pipe is reduced below atmospheric pressure, in accordance with Bernoulli's principle. The pressure at the drain in the sink is still at atmospheric pressure. This pressure difference can push the plug of water in the water trap of the sink down the drainpipe and into the sewer pipe, removing it as a barrier to sewer gas. With the addition of the vent to the roof, the reduced pressure of the dishwasher water will result in air entering the vent pipe at the roof. This inflow of air will keep the pressure in the vent pipe and the right-hand side of the sink drainpipe close to atmospheric pressure so that the plug of water in the water trap will remain in place. ■

Figure 9.39 (Applying Physics 9.5)

The exhaust speed of a rocket engine can also be understood qualitatively with Bernoulli's equation, although, in actual practice, a large number of additional variables need to be taken into account. Rockets actually work better in vacuum than in the atmosphere, contrary to an early *New York Times* article criticizing rocket pioneer Robert Goddard, which held that they wouldn't work at all, having

APPLICATION
Rocket Engines

no air to push against. The pressure inside the combustion chamber is P, and the pressure just outside the nozzle is the ambient atmospheric pressure, P_{atm}. Differences in height between the combustion chamber and the end of the nozzle result in negligible contributions of gravitational potential energy. In addition, the gases inside the chamber flow at negligible speed compared to gases going through the nozzle. The exhaust speed can be found from Bernoulli's equation,

$$v_{ex} = \sqrt{\frac{2(P - P_{atm})}{\rho}}$$

This equation shows that the exhaust speed is reduced in the atmosphere, so rockets are actually more effective in the vacuum of space. Also of interest is the appearance of the density ρ in the denominator. A lower density working fluid or gas will give a higher exhaust speed, which partly explains why liquid hydrogen, which has a very low density, is a fuel of choice.

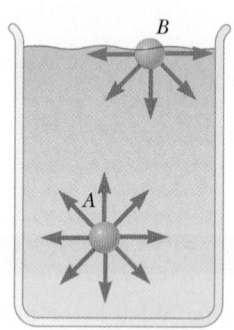

Figure 9.40 The net force on a molecule at A is zero because such a molecule is completely surrounded by other molecules. The net force on a surface molecule at B is downward because it isn't completely surrounded by other molecules.

9.9 Surface Tension, Capillary Action, and Viscous Fluid Flow

If you look closely at a dewdrop sparkling in the morning sunlight, you will find that the drop is spherical. The drop takes this shape because of a property of liquid surfaces called **surface tension.** In order to understand the origin of surface tension, consider a molecule at point A in a container of water, as in Figure 9.40. Although nearby molecules exert forces on this molecule, the net force on it is zero because it's completely surrounded by other molecules and hence is attracted equally in all directions. The molecule at B, however, is not attracted equally in all directions. Because there are no molecules above it to exert upward forces, the molecule at B is pulled toward the interior of the liquid. The contraction at the surface of the liquid ceases when the inward pull exerted on the surface molecules is balanced by the outward repulsive forces that arise from collisions with molecules in the interior of the liquid. **The net effect of this pull on all the surface molecules is to make the surface of the liquid contract and, consequently, to make the surface area of the liquid as small as possible.** Drops of water take on a spherical shape because a sphere has the smallest surface area for a given volume.

If you place a sewing needle very carefully on the surface of a bowl of water, you will find that the needle floats even though the density of steel is about eight times that of water. This phenomenon can also be explained by surface tension. A close examination of the needle shows that it actually rests in a depression in the liquid surface as shown in Figure 9.41. The water surface acts like an elastic membrane under tension. The weight of the needle produces a depression, increasing the surface area of the film. Molecular forces now act at all points along the depression, tending to restore the surface to its original horizontal position. The vertical components of these forces act to balance the force of gravity on the needle. The floating needle can be sunk by adding a little detergent to the water, which reduces the surface tension.

The **surface tension** γ in a film of liquid is defined as the magnitude of the surface tension force F divided by the length L along which the force acts:

The vertical components of the surface tension force balance the gravity force.

$\vec{F}$ $\vec{F}$

$M\vec{g}$

Figure 9.41 End view of a needle resting on the surface of water.

$$\gamma \equiv \frac{F}{L} \qquad\qquad [9.19]$$

The SI unit of surface tension is the newton per meter, and values for a few representative materials are given in Table 9.4.

Surface tension can be thought of as the energy content of the fluid at its surface per unit surface area. To see that this is reasonable, we can manipulate the units of surface tension γ as follows:

$$\frac{N}{m} = \frac{N \cdot m}{m^2} = \frac{J}{m^2}$$

In general, in **any equilibrium configuration of an object, the energy is a minimum.** Consequently, a fluid will take on a shape such that its surface area is as small as possible. For a given volume, a spherical shape has the smallest surface area; therefore, a drop of water takes on a spherical shape.

An apparatus used to measure the surface tension of liquids is shown in Figure 9.42. A circular wire with a circumference L is lifted from a body of liquid. The surface film clings to the inside and outside edges of the wire, holding back the wire and causing the spring to stretch. If the spring is calibrated, the force required to overcome the surface tension of the liquid can be measured. In this case the surface tension is given by

$$\gamma = \frac{F}{2L}$$

We use $2L$ for the length because the surface film exerts forces on both the inside and outside of the ring.

The surface tension of liquids decreases with increasing temperature because the faster moving molecules of a hot liquid aren't bound together as strongly as are those in a cooler liquid. In addition, certain ingredients called surfactants decrease surface tension when added to liquids. For example, soap or detergent decreases the surface tension of water, making it easier for soapy water to penetrate the cracks and crevices of your clothes to clean them better than plain water does. A similar effect occurs in the lungs. The surface tissue of the air sacs in the lungs contains a fluid that has a surface tension of about 0.050 N/m. A liquid with a surface tension this high would make it very difficult for the lungs to expand during inhalation. However, as the area of the lungs increases with inhalation, the body secretes into the tissue a substance that gradually reduces the surface tension of the liquid. At full expansion, the surface tension of the lung fluid can drop to as low as 0.005 N/m.

Table 9.4 Surface Tensions for Various Liquids

Liquid	T (°C)	Surface Tension (N/m)
Ethyl alcohol	20	0.022
Mercury	20	0.465
Soapy water	20	0.025
Water	20	0.073
Water	100	0.059

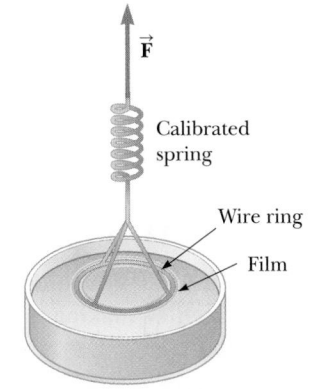

Figure 9.42 An apparatus for measuring the surface tension of liquids. The force on the wire ring is measured just before the ring breaks free of the liquid.

BIO APPLICATION

Air Sac Surface Tension

■ EXAMPLE 9.16 | **Walking on Water** BIO

GOAL Apply the surface tension equation.

PROBLEM Many insects can literally walk on water, using surface tension for their support. To show this is feasible, assume the insect's "foot" is spherical. When the insect steps onto the water with all six legs, a depression is formed in the water around each foot, as shown in Figure 9.43a. The surface tension of the water produces upward forces on the water that tend to restore the water surface to its normally flat shape. If the insect's mass is 2.0×10^{-5} kg and the radius of each foot is 1.5×10^{-4} m, find the angle θ.

STRATEGY Find an expression for the magnitude of the net force F directed tangentially to the depressed part of the water surface, and obtain the part that is acting vertically, in opposition to the downward force of gravity. Assume the radius of depression is the same as the radius of the insect's foot. Because the insect has six legs, one-sixth of the insect's weight must be supported by one of the legs, assuming the weight is distributed evenly. The length L is just the distance around a circle. Using Newton's second law for a body in equilibrium (zero acceleration), solve for θ.

Herman Eisenbeiss/Photo Researchers, Inc.

Figure 9.43 (Example 9.16) (a) One foot of an insect resting on the surface of water. (b) This water strider resting on the surface of a lake remains on the surface, rather than sinking, because an upward surface tension force acts on each leg, balancing the force of gravity on the insect.

(Continued)

SOLUTION

Start with the surface tension equation:

$$F = \gamma L$$

Focus on one circular foot, substituting $L = 2\pi r$. Multiply by $\cos\theta$ to get the vertical component F_v:

$$F_v = \gamma(2\pi r)\cos\theta$$

Write Newton's second law for the insect's one foot, which supports one-sixth of the insect's weight:

$$\sum F = F_v - F_{grav} = 0$$

$$\gamma(2\pi r)\cos\theta - \tfrac{1}{6}mg = 0$$

Solve for $\cos\theta$ and substitute:

$$(1) \quad \cos\theta = \frac{mg}{12\pi r\gamma}$$

$$= \frac{(2.0 \times 10^{-5}\,\text{kg})(9.80\,\text{m/s}^2)}{12\pi(1.5 \times 10^{-4}\,\text{m})(0.073\,\text{N/m})} = 0.47$$

Take the inverse cosine of both sides to find the angle θ:

$$\theta = \cos^{-1}(0.47) = \boxed{62°}$$

REMARKS If the weight of the insect were great enough to make the right side of Equation (1) greater than 1, a solution for θ would be impossible because the cosine of an angle can never be greater than 1. In this circumstance the insect would sink.

QUESTION 9.16 True or False: Warm water gives more support to walking insects than cold water.

EXERCISE 9.16 A typical sewing needle floats on water when its long dimension is parallel to the water's surface. Estimate the needle's maximum possible mass, assuming the needle is two inches long. *Hint:* The cosine of an angle is never larger than 1.

ANSWER 0.8 g

The Surface of Liquid

If you have ever closely examined the surface of water in a glass container, you may have noticed that the surface of the liquid near the walls of the glass curves upward as you move from the center to the edge, as shown in Figure 9.44a. However, if mercury is placed in a glass container, the mercury surface curves downward, as in Figure 9.44b. These surface effects can be explained by considering the forces between molecules. In particular, we must consider the forces that the molecules of the liquid exert on one another and the forces that the molecules of the glass surface exert on those of the liquid. In general terms, forces between like molecules, such as the forces between water molecules, are called **cohesive forces,**

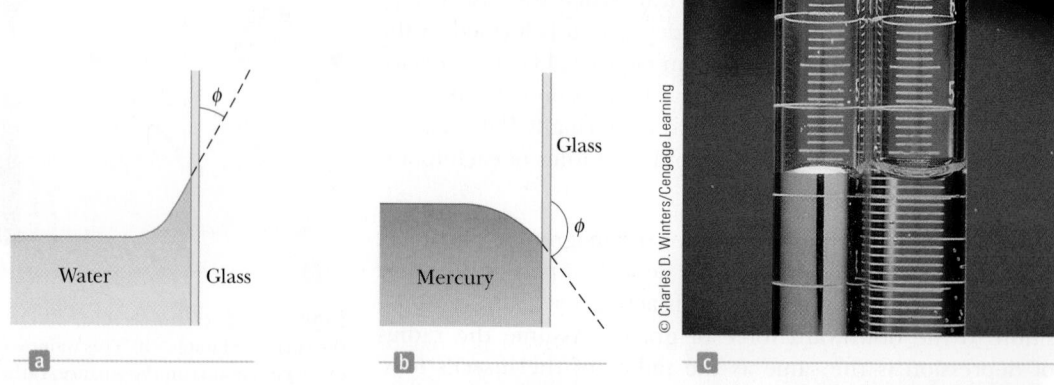

Figure 9.44 A liquid in contact with a solid surface. (a) For water, the adhesive force is greater than the cohesive force. (b) For mercury, the adhesive force is less than the cohesive force. (c) The surface of mercury (*left*) curves downward in a glass container, whereas the surface of water (*right*) curves upward, as you move from the center to the edge.

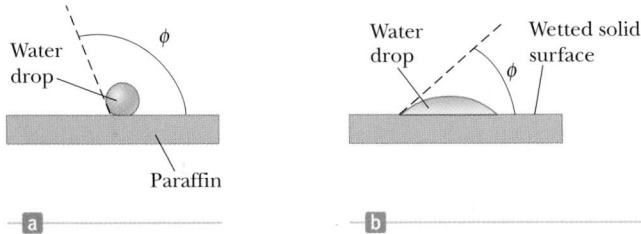

Figure 9.45 (a) The contact angle between water and paraffin is about 107°. In this case, the cohesive force is greater than the adhesive force. (b) When a chemical called a wetting agent is added to the water, it wets the paraffin surface, and $\phi < 90°$. In this case, the adhesive force is greater than the cohesive force.

and forces between unlike molecules, such as those exerted by glass on water, are called **adhesive forces.**

Water tends to cling to the walls of the glass because the adhesive forces between the molecules of water and the glass molecules are *greater* than the cohesive forces between the water molecules. In effect, the water molecules cling to the surface of the glass rather than fall back into the bulk of the liquid. When this condition prevails, the liquid is said to "wet" the glass surface. The surface of the mercury curves downward near the walls of the container because the cohesive forces between the mercury atoms are greater than the adhesive forces between mercury and glass. A mercury atom near the surface is pulled more strongly toward other mercury atoms than toward the glass surface, so mercury doesn't wet the glass surface.

The angle ϕ between the solid surface and a line drawn tangent to the liquid at the surface is called the **contact angle** (Fig. 9.45). The angle ϕ is less than 90° for any substance in which adhesive forces are stronger than cohesive forces and greater than 90° if cohesive forces predominate. For example, if a drop of water is placed on paraffin, the contact angle is approximately 107° (Fig. 9.45a). If certain chemicals, called wetting agents or detergents, are added to the water, the contact angle becomes less than 90°, as shown in Figure 9.45b. The addition of such substances to water ensures that the water makes intimate contact with a surface and penetrates it. For this reason, detergents are added to water to wash clothes or dishes.

On the other hand, it is sometimes necessary to *keep* water from making intimate contact with a surface, as in waterproof clothing, where a situation somewhat the reverse of that shown in Figure 9.45 is called for. The clothing is sprayed with a waterproofing agent, which changes ϕ from less than 90° to greater than 90°. The water beads up on the surface and doesn't easily penetrate the clothing.

Capillary Action

In capillary tubes the diameter of the opening is very small, on the order of a hundredth of a centimeter. In fact, the word *capillary* means "hairlike." If such a tube is inserted into a fluid for which adhesive forces dominate over cohesive forces, the liquid rises into the tube, as shown in Figure 9.46. The rising of the liquid in the tube can be explained in terms of the shape of the liquid's surface and surface tension effects. At the point of contact between liquid and solid, the upward force of surface tension is directed as shown in the figure. From Equation 9.19, the magnitude of this force is

$$F = \gamma L = \gamma(2\pi r)$$

(We use $L = 2\pi r$ here because the liquid is in contact with the surface of the tube at all points around its circumference.) The vertical component of this force due to surface tension is

$$F_v = \gamma(2\pi r)(\cos \phi) \qquad \text{[9.20]}$$

For the liquid in the capillary tube to be in equilibrium, this upward force must be equal to the weight of the cylinder of water of height h inside the capillary tube. The weight of this water is

$$w = Mg = \rho Vg = \rho g \pi r^2 h \qquad \text{[9.21]}$$

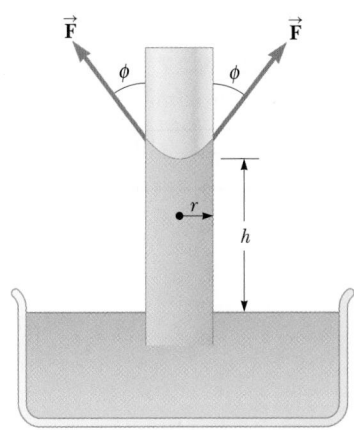

Figure 9.46 A liquid rises in a narrow tube because of capillary action, a result of surface tension and adhesive forces.

viscous fluid have different velocities, as Figure 9.48b indicates. The fluid has the greatest velocity at the center of the pipe, whereas the layer next to the wall doesn't move because of adhesive forces between molecules and the wall surface.

To better understand the concept of viscosity, consider a layer of liquid between two solid surfaces, as in Figure 9.49. The lower surface is fixed in position, and the top surface moves to the right with a velocity $\vec{v}$ under the action of an external force $\vec{F}$. Because of this motion, a portion of the liquid is distorted from its original shape, *ABCD*, at one instant to the shape *AEFD* a moment later. The force required to move the upper plate and distort the liquid is proportional to both the area *A* in contact with the fluid and the speed *v* of the fluid. Further, the force is inversely proportional to the distance *d* between the two plates. We can express these proportionalities as $F \propto Av/d$. The force required to move the upper plate at a fixed speed *v* is therefore

$$F = \eta \frac{Av}{d} \qquad [9.23]$$

where η (the lowercase Greek letter *eta*) is the **coefficient of viscosity** of the fluid.

The SI units of viscosity are $N \cdot s/m^2$. The units of viscosity in many reference sources are often expressed in $dyne \cdot s/cm^2$, called 1 **poise,** in honor of the French scientist J. L. Poiseuille (1799–1869). The relationship between the SI unit of viscosity and the poise is

$$1 \text{ poise} = 10^{-1} \text{ N} \cdot s/m^2 \qquad [9.24]$$

Small viscosities are often expressed in centipoise (cp), where $1 \text{ cp} = 10^{-2}$ poise. The coefficients of viscosity for some common substances are listed in Table 9.5.

Poiseuille's Law

Figure 9.50 shows a section of a tube of length *L* and radius *R* containing a fluid under a pressure P_1 at the left end and a pressure P_2 at the right. Because of this pressure difference, the fluid flows through the tube. The rate of flow (volume per unit time) depends on the pressure difference $(P_1 - P_2)$, the dimensions of the tube, and the viscosity of the fluid. The result, known as **Poiseuille's law,** is

$$\text{Rate of flow} = \frac{\Delta V}{\Delta t} = \frac{\pi R^4 (P_1 - P_2)}{8\eta L} \qquad [9.25] \qquad \blacktriangleleft \text{ Poiseuille's law}$$

where η is the coefficient of viscosity of the fluid. We won't attempt to derive this equation here because the methods of integral calculus are required. However, it is reasonable that the rate of flow should increase if the pressure difference across the tube or the tube radius increases. Likewise, the flow rate should decrease if the viscosity of the fluid or the length of the tube increases. So the presence of *R*

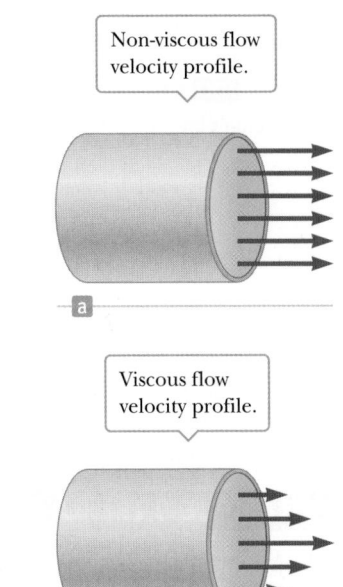

Figure 9.48 (a) The particles in an ideal (nonviscous) fluid all move through the pipe with the same velocity. (b) In a viscous fluid, the velocity of the fluid particles is zero at the surface of the pipe and increases to a maximum value at the center of the pipe.

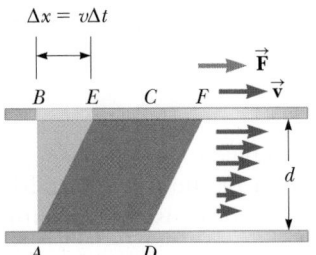

Figure 9.49 A layer of liquid between two solid surfaces in which the lower surface is fixed and the upper surface moves to the right with a velocity $\vec{v}$.

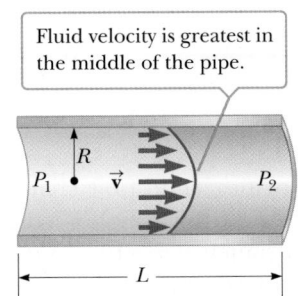

Figure 9.50 Velocity profile of a fluid flowing through a uniform pipe of circular cross section. The rate of flow is given by Poiseuille's law.

Table 9.5 Viscosities of Various Fluids

Fluid	T (°C)	Viscosity η ($N \cdot s/m^2$)
Water	20	1.0×10^{-3}
Water	100	0.3×10^{-3}
Whole blood	37	2.7×10^{-3}
Glycerin	20	$1\,500 \times 10^{-3}$
10-wt motor oil	30	250×10^{-3}

and the pressure difference in the numerator of Equation 9.25 and of L and η in the denominator make sense.

From Poiseuille's law, we see that in order to maintain a constant flow rate, the pressure difference across the tube has to increase if the viscosity of the fluid increases. This fact is important in understanding the flow of blood through the circulatory system. The viscosity of blood increases as the number of red blood cells rises. Blood with a high concentration of red blood cells requires greater pumping pressure from the heart to keep it circulating than does blood of lower red blood cell concentration.

Note that the flow rate varies as the radius of the tube raised to the fourth power. Consequently, if a constriction occurs in a vein or artery, the heart will have to work considerably harder in order to produce a higher pressure drop and hence maintain the required flow rate.

EXAMPLE 9.18 | A Blood Transfusion BIO

GOAL Apply Poiseuille's law.

PROBLEM A patient receives a blood transfusion through a needle of radius 0.20 mm and length 2.0 cm. The density of blood is 1 050 kg/m^3. The bottle supplying the blood is 0.500 m above the patient's arm. What is the rate of flow through the needle?

STRATEGY Find the pressure difference between the level of the blood and the patient's arm. Substitute into Poiseuille's law, using the value for the viscosity of whole blood in Table 9.5.

SOLUTION

Calculate the pressure difference:

$$P_1 - P_2 = \rho g h = (1\,050 \text{ kg/m}^3)(9.80 \text{ m/s}^2)(0.500 \text{ m})$$
$$= 5.15 \times 10^3 \text{ Pa}$$

Substitute into Poiseuille's law:

$$\frac{\Delta V}{\Delta t} = \frac{\pi R^4 (P_1 - P_2)}{8\eta L}$$
$$= \frac{\pi (2.0 \times 10^{-4} \text{ m})^4 (5.15 \times 10^3 \text{ Pa})}{8(2.7 \times 10^{-3} \text{ N} \cdot \text{s/m}^2)(2.0 \times 10^{-2} \text{ m})}$$
$$= \boxed{6.0 \times 10^{-8} \text{ m}^3\text{/s}}$$

REMARKS Compare this to the volume flow rate in the absence of any viscosity. Using Bernoulli's equation, the calculated volume flow rate is approximately five times as great. As expected, viscosity greatly reduces flow rate.

QUESTION 9.18 If the radius of a tube is doubled, by what factor will the flow rate change for a viscous fluid?

EXERCISE 9.18 A pipe carrying water from a tank 20.0 m tall must cross 3.00×10^2 km of wilderness to reach a remote town. Find the radius of pipe so that the volume flow rate is at least 0.050 0 m^3/s. (Use the viscosity of water at 20°C.)

ANSWER 0.118 m

Reynolds Number

At sufficiently high velocities, fluid flow changes from simple streamline flow to turbulent flow, characterized by a highly irregular motion of the fluid. Experimentally, the onset of turbulence in a tube is determined by a dimensionless factor called the **Reynolds number,** *RN*, given by

$$RN = \frac{\rho v d}{\eta} \qquad \text{[9.26]}$$

where ρ is the density of the fluid, v is the average speed of the fluid along the direction of flow, d is the diameter of the tube, and η is the viscosity of the fluid. If

RN is below about 2 000, the flow of fluid through a tube is streamline; turbulence occurs if *RN* is above 3 000. In the region between 2 000 and 3 000, the flow is unstable, meaning that the fluid can move in streamline flow, but any small disturbance will cause its motion to change to turbulent flow.

■ EXAMPLE 9.19 | Turbulent Flow of Blood   BIO

GOAL Use the Reynolds number to determine a speed associated with the onset of turbulence.

PROBLEM Determine the speed at which blood flowing through an artery of diameter 0.20 cm will become turbulent.

STRATEGY The solution requires only the substitution of values into Equation 9.26 giving the Reynolds number and then solving it for the speed *v*.

SOLUTION

Solve Equation 9.26 for *v*, and substitute the viscosity and density of blood from Example 9.18, the diameter *d* of the artery, and a Reynolds number of 3.00×10^3:

$$v = \frac{\eta(RN)}{\rho d} = \frac{(2.7 \times 10^{-3}\,\text{N} \cdot \text{s/m}^2)(3.00 \times 10^3)}{(1.05 \times 10^3\,\text{kg/m}^3)(0.20 \times 10^{-2}\,\text{m})}$$

$$v = \boxed{3.9\ \text{m/s}}$$

REMARKS The exercise shows that rapid ingestion of soda through a straw may create a turbulent state.

QUESTION 9.19 True or False: If the viscosity of a fluid flowing through a tube is increased, the speed associated with the onset of turbulence decreases.

EXERCISE 9.19 Determine the speed *v* at which water at 20°C sucked up a straw would become turbulent. The straw has a diameter of 0.006 0 m.

ANSWER $v = 0.50$ m/s

9.10 Transport Phenomena

When a fluid flows through a tube, the basic mechanism that produces the flow is a difference in pressure across the ends of the tube. This pressure difference is responsible for the transport of a mass of fluid from one location to another. The fluid may also move from place to place because of a second mechanism—one that depends on a difference in *concentration* between two points in the fluid, as opposed to a pressure difference. When the concentration (the number of molecules per unit volume) is higher at one location than at another, molecules will flow from the point where the concentration is high to the point where it is lower. The two fundamental processes involved in fluid transport resulting from concentration differences are called *diffusion* and *osmosis*.

Diffusion

In a diffusion process, molecules move from a region where their concentration is high to a region where their concentration is lower. To understand why diffusion occurs, consider Figure 9.51, which depicts a container in which a high concentration of molecules has been introduced into the left side. The dashed line in the figure represents an imaginary barrier separating the two regions. Because the molecules are moving with high speeds in random directions, many of them will cross the imaginary barrier moving from left to right. Very few molecules will pass through moving from right to left, simply because there are very few of them on the right side of the container at any instant. As a result, there will always be a *net* movement from the region with many molecules to the region with fewer molecules. For this reason, the concentration on the left side of the container will decrease, and that on the right side will increase with time. Once a concentration

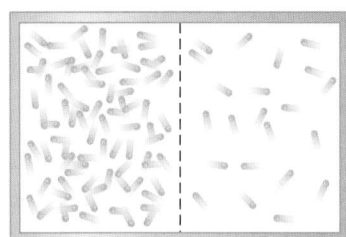

Figure 9.51 When the concentration of gas molecules on the left side of the container exceeds the concentration on the right side, there will be a net motion (diffusion) of molecules from left to right.

equilibrium has been reached, there will be no *net* movement across the cross-sectional area: The rate of movement of molecules from left to right will equal the rate from right to left.

The basic equation for diffusion is **Fick's law,**

Fick's law ▶

$$\text{Diffusion rate} = \frac{\text{mass}}{\text{time}} = \frac{\Delta M}{\Delta t} = DA\left(\frac{C_2 - C_1}{L}\right) \qquad [9.27]$$

where D is a constant of proportionality. The left side of this equation is called the *diffusion rate* and is a measure of the mass being transported per unit time. The equation says that the rate of diffusion is proportional to the cross-sectional area A and to the change in concentration per unit distance, $(C_2 - C_1)/L$, which is called the *concentration gradient*. The concentrations C_1 and C_2 are measured in kilograms per cubic meter. The proportionality constant D is called the **diffusion coefficient** and has units of square meters per second. Table 9.6 lists diffusion coefficients for a few substances.

Table 9.6 Diffusion Coefficients of Various Substances at 20°C

Substance	D (m²/s)
Oxygen through air	6.4×10^{-5}
Oxygen through tissue	1×10^{-11}
Oxygen through water	1×10^{-9}
Sucrose through water	5×10^{-10}
Hemoglobin through water	76×10^{-11}

The Size of Cells and Osmosis

Diffusion through cell membranes is vital in carrying oxygen to the cells of the body and in removing carbon dioxide and other waste products from them. Cells require oxygen for those metabolic processes in which substances are either synthesized or broken down. In such processes, the cell uses up oxygen and produces carbon dioxide as a by-product. A fresh supply of oxygen diffuses from the blood, where its concentration is high, into the cell, where its concentration is low. Likewise, carbon dioxide diffuses from the cell into the blood, where it is in lower concentration. Water, ions, and other nutrients also pass into and out of cells by diffusion.

A cell can function properly only if it can transport nutrients and waste products rapidly across the cell membrane. The surface area of the cell should be large enough so that the exposed membrane area can exchange materials effectively while the volume should be small enough so that materials can reach or leave particular locations rapidly. This requires a large surface-area-to-volume ratio.

Model a cell as a cube, each side with length L. The total surface area is $6L^2$ and the volume is L^3. The surface area to volume is then

$$\frac{\text{surface area}}{\text{volume}} = \frac{6L^2}{L^3} = \frac{6}{L}$$

Because L is in the denominator, a smaller L means a larger ratio. This shows that the smaller the size of a body, the more efficiently it can transport nutrients and waste products across the cell membrane. Cells range in size from a millionth of a meter to several millionths, so a good estimate of a typical cell's surface-to-volume ratio is 10^6.

The diffusion of material through a membrane is partially determined by the size of the pores (holes) in the membrane wall. Small molecules, such as water, may pass through the pores easily, while larger molecules, such as sugar, may pass through only with difficulty or not at all. A membrane that allows passage of some molecules but not others is called a **selectively permeable** membrane.

Osmosis is the diffusion of water across a selectively permeable membrane from a high water concentration to a low water concentration. As in the case of diffusion, osmosis continues until the concentrations on the two sides of the membrane are equal.

BIO APPLICATION
Effect of Osmosis on Living Cells

To understand the effect of osmosis on living cells, consider a particular cell in the body that contains a sugar concentration of 1%. (A 1% solution is 1 g of sugar dissolved in enough water to make 100 ml of solution; "ml" is the abbreviation for milliliters, so 10^{-3} L = 1 cm³.) Assume this cell is immersed in a 5% sugar solution (5 g of sugar dissolved in enough water to make 100 ml). Compared to the 1% solution, there are five times as many sugar molecules per unit volume in the 5% sugar solution, so there must be fewer water molecules. Accordingly, water will diffuse from inside the cell, where its concentration is higher, across the cell membrane to the outside solution, where the concentration of water is lower. This loss of water from the cell would cause it to shrink and perhaps become damaged through dehydration. If the concentrations were reversed, water would diffuse *into* the cell, causing it to swell and perhaps burst. If solutions are introduced into the body intravenously, care must be taken to ensure that they don't disturb the osmotic balance of the body, else cell damage can occur. For example, if a 9% saline solution surrounds a red blood cell, the cell will shrink. By contrast, if the solution is about 1%, the cell will eventually burst.

In the body, blood is cleansed of impurities by osmosis as it flows through the kidneys. (See Fig. 9.52a.) Arterial blood first passes through a bundle of capillaries known as a *glomerulus*, where most of the waste products and some essential salts and minerals are removed. From the glomerulus, a narrow tube emerges that is in intimate contact with other capillaries throughout its length. As blood passes through the tubules, most of the essential elements are returned to it; waste products are not allowed to reenter and are eventually removed in urine.

If the kidneys fail, an artificial kidney or a dialysis machine can filter the blood. Figure 9.52b shows how this is done. Blood from an artery in the arm is mixed with heparin, a blood thinner, and allowed to pass through a tube covered with a semi-permeable membrane. The tubing is immersed in a bath of a dialysate fluid with the same chemical composition as purified blood. Waste products from the blood enter the dialysate by diffusion through the membrane. The filtered blood is then returned to a vein.

APPLICATION

Kidney Function and Dialysis

Motion Through a Viscous Medium

When an object falls through air, its motion is impeded by the force of air resistance. In general, this force is dependent on the shape of the falling object and on its velocity. The force of air resistance acts on all falling objects, but the exact details of the motion can be calculated only for a few cases in which the object has a simple shape, such as a sphere. In this section we will examine the motion of a tiny spherical object falling slowly through a viscous medium.

In 1845 a scientist named George Stokes found that the magnitude of the resistive force on a very small spherical object of radius r falling slowly through a fluid of viscosity η with speed v is given by

$$F_r = 6\pi\eta rv \qquad \text{[9.28]}$$

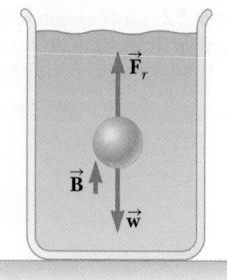

Figure 9.53 A sphere falling through a viscous medium. The forces acting on the sphere are the resistive frictional force $\vec{F}_r$, the buoyant force $\vec{B}$, and the force of gravity $\vec{w}$ acting on the sphere.

This equation, called **Stokes's law,** has many important applications. For example, it describes the sedimentation of particulate matter in blood samples. It was used by Robert Millikan (1886–1953) to calculate the radius of charged oil droplets falling through air. From this, Millikan was ultimately able to determine the charge on the electron, and was awarded the Nobel Prize in 1923 for his pioneering work on elemental charges.

As a sphere falls through a viscous medium, three forces act on it, as shown in Figure 9.53: $\vec{F}_r$, the force of friction; $\vec{B}$, the buoyant force of the fluid; and $\vec{w}$, the force of gravity acting on the sphere. The magnitude of $\vec{w}$ is given by

$$w = \rho g V = \rho g \left(\frac{4}{3} \pi r^3 \right)$$

where ρ is the density of the sphere and $\frac{4}{3} \pi r^3$ is its volume. According to Archimedes's principle, the magnitude of the buoyant force is equal to the weight of the fluid displaced by the sphere,

$$B = \rho_f g V = \rho_f g \left(\frac{4}{3} \pi r^3 \right)$$

where ρ_f is the density of the fluid.

At the instant the sphere begins to fall, the force of friction is zero because the speed of the sphere is zero. As the sphere accelerates, its speed increases and so does $\vec{F}_r$. Finally, **at a speed called the terminal speed v_t, the net force goes to zero.** This occurs when the net upward force balances the downward force of gravity. Therefore, the sphere reaches terminal speed when

$$F_r + B = w$$

or

$$6\pi\eta r v_t + \rho_f g \left(\frac{4}{3} \pi r^3 \right) = \rho g \left(\frac{4}{3} \pi r^3 \right)$$

When this equation is solved for v_t, we get

Terminal speed ▶

$$v_t = \frac{2r^2 g}{9\eta} (\rho - \rho_f)$$

[9.29]

Sedimentation and Centrifugation

If an object isn't spherical, we can still use the basic approach just described to determine its terminal speed. The only difference is that we can't use Stokes's law for the resistive force. Instead, we assume that the resistive force has a magnitude given by $F_r = kv$, where k is a coefficient that must be determined experimentally. As discussed previously, the object reaches its terminal speed when the downward force of gravity is balanced by the net upward force, or

$$w = B + F_r$$

[9.30]

where $B = \rho_f g V$ is the buoyant force. The volume V of the displaced fluid is related to the density ρ of the falling object by $V = m/\rho$. Hence, we can express the buoyant force as

$$B = \frac{\rho_f}{\rho} mg$$

We substitute this expression for B and $F_r = kv_t$ into Equation 9.30 (terminal speed condition):

$$mg = \frac{\rho_f}{\rho} mg + kv_t$$

or

$$v_t = \frac{mg}{k} \left(1 - \frac{\rho_f}{\rho} \right)$$

[9.31]

The terminal speed for particles in biological samples is usually quite small. For example, the terminal speed for blood cells falling through plasma is about 5 cm/h in the gravitational field of the Earth. The terminal speeds for the molecules that make up a cell are many orders of magnitude smaller than this because of their much smaller mass. The speed at which materials fall through a fluid is called the **sedimentation rate** and is important in clinical analysis.

The sedimentation rate in a fluid can be increased by increasing the effective acceleration g that appears in Equation 9.31. A fluid containing various biological molecules is placed in a centrifuge and whirled at very high angular speeds (Fig. 9.54). Under these conditions, the particles gain a large radial acceleration $a_c = v^2/r = \omega^2 r$ that is much greater than the free-fall acceleration, so we can replace g in Equation 9.31 by $\omega^2 r$ and obtain

$$v_t = \frac{m\omega^2 r}{k}\left(1 - \frac{\rho_f}{\rho}\right) \qquad [9.32]$$

This equation indicates that the sedimentation rate is enormously speeded up in a centrifuge ($\omega^2 r \gg g$) and that those particles with the greatest mass will have the largest terminal speed. Consequently the most massive particles will settle out on the bottom of a test tube first.

Figure 9.54 Simplified diagram of a centrifuge (top view).

BIO APPLICATION
Separating biological molecules with centrifugation

■ SUMMARY

9.1 States of Matter
Matter is normally classified as being in one of three states: solid, liquid, or gaseous. The fourth state of matter is called a plasma, which consists of a neutral system of charged particles interacting electromagnetically.

9.2 Density and Pressure
The **density** ρ of a substance of uniform composition is its mass per unit volume—kilograms per cubic meter (kg/m^3) in the SI system:

$$\rho \equiv \frac{M}{V} \qquad [9.1]$$

The **pressure** P in a fluid, measured in pascals (Pa), is the force per unit area that the fluid exerts on an object immersed in it:

$$P \equiv \frac{F}{A} \qquad [9.2]$$

9.3 The Deformation of Solids
The elastic properties of a solid can be described using the concepts of stress and strain. **Stress** is related to the force per unit area producing a deformation; **strain** is a measure of the amount of deformation. Stress is proportional to strain, and the constant of proportionality is the **elastic modulus:**

$$\text{Stress} = \text{elastic modulus} \times \text{strain} \qquad [9.3]$$

Three common types of deformation are (1) the resistance of a solid to elongation or compression, characterized by **Young's modulus** Y; (2) the resistance to displacement of the faces of a solid sliding past each other, characterized by the shear modulus S; and (3) the resistance of a solid or liquid to a change in volume, characterized by the bulk modulus B.

All three types of deformation obey laws similar to Hooke's law for springs. Solving problems is usually a matter of identifying the given physical variables and solving for the unknown variable.

9.4 Variation of Pressure with Depth
The pressure in an incompressible fluid varies with depth h according to the expression

$$P = P_0 + \rho g h \qquad [9.11]$$

where P_0 is atmospheric pressure (1.013×10^5 Pa) and ρ is the density of the fluid.

Pascal's principle states that when pressure is applied to an enclosed fluid, the pressure is transmitted undiminished to every point of the fluid and to the walls of the containing vessel.

9.6 Buoyant Forces and Archimedes' Principle
When an object is partially or fully submerged in a fluid, the fluid exerts an upward force, called the **buoyant force,** on the object. This force is, in fact, just the net difference in pressure between the top and bottom of the object. It can be shown that the magnitude of the buoyant force B is equal to the weight of the fluid displaced by the object, or

$$B = \rho_{\text{fluid}} V_{\text{fluid}} g \qquad [9.12b]$$

Equation 9.12b is known as **Archimedes' principle.**

Solving a buoyancy problem usually involves putting the buoyant force into Newton's second law and then proceeding as in Chapter 4.

9.7 Fluids in Motion

Certain aspects of a fluid in motion can be understood by assuming the fluid is nonviscous and incompressible and that its motion is in a steady state with no turbulence:

1. The flow rate through the pipe is a constant, which is equivalent to stating that the product of the cross-sectional area A and the speed v at any point is constant. At any two points, therefore, we have

$$A_1 v_1 = A_2 v_2 \qquad \text{[9.15]}$$

This relation is referred to as the **equation of continuity.**

2. The sum of the pressure, the kinetic energy per unit volume, and the potential energy per unit volume is the same at any two points along a streamline:

$$P_1 + \tfrac{1}{2}\rho v_1^{\,2} + \rho g y_1 = P_2 + \tfrac{1}{2}\rho v_2^{\,2} + \rho g y_2 \qquad \text{[9.16]}$$

Equation 9.16 is known as **Bernoulli's equation.** Solving problems with Bernoulli's equation is similar to solving problems with the work–energy theorem, whereby two points are chosen, one point where a quantity is unknown and another where all quantities are known. Equation 9.16 is then solved for the unknown quantity.

■ MULTIPLE-CHOICE QUESTIONS

WebAssign The multiple-choice questions in this chapter may be assigned online in Enhanced WebAssign.

1. A hydraulic jack has an input piston of area 0.050 m² and an output piston of area 0.70 m². How much force on the input piston is required to lift a car weighing 1.2×10^3 N? (a) 42 N (b) 68 N (c) 86 N (d) 110 N (e) 130 N

2. A 66.0-kg man lies on his back on a bed of nails, with 1 208 of the nails in contact with his body. The end of each nail has area 1.00×10^{-6} m². What average pressure is exerted by one nail on the man's body? (a) 2.21×10^5 Pa (b) 3.09×10^5 Pa (c) 1.65×10^6 Pa (d) 5.35×10^5 Pa (e) 4.11×10^4 Pa

3. What is the mass of a solid gold rectangular bar that has dimensions of 4.50 cm × 11.0 cm × 26.0 cm? (a) 24.8 kg (b) 45.6 kg (c) 11.4 kg (d) 33.2 kg (e) 19.5 kg

4. A lead bullet is placed in a pool of mercury. What fractional part of the volume of the bullet is submerged? (a) 0.455 (b) 0.622 (c) 0.714 (d) 0.831 (e) 0.930

5. What is the pressure at the bottom of Loch Ness, which is as much as 754 ft deep? (The surface of the lake is only 15.8 m above sea level; hence, the pressure there can be taken to be 1.013×10^5 Pa.) (a) 1.52×10^5 Pa (b) 2.74×10^5 Pa (c) 2.35×10^6 Pa (d) 7.01×10^5 Pa (e) 3.15×10^5 Pa

6. A wooden block floats in water, and a solid steel object is attached to the bottom of the block by a string as in Figure MCQ9.6. If the block remains floating, which of the following statements is valid? (Choose all correct statements.) (a) The buoyant force on the steel object is equal to its weight. (b) The buoyant force on the block is equal to its weight. (c) The tension in the string is equal to the weight of the steel object. (d) The tension in the string is less than the weight of the steel object. (e) The buoy-

Figure MCQ9.6

ant force on the block is equal to the weight of the volume of water it displaces.

7. A horizontal pipe narrows from a radius of 0.250 m to 0.100 m. If the speed of the water in the pipe is 1.00 m/s in the larger-radius pipe, what is the speed in the smaller pipe? (a) 4.50 m/s (b) 2.50 m/s (c) 3.75 m/s (d) 6.25 m/s (e) 5.13 m/s

8. A beach ball filled with air is pushed about 1 m below the surface of a swimming pool and released from rest. Which of the following statements is valid, assuming the size of the ball remains the same? (Choose all correct statements.) (a) As the ball rises in the pool, the buoyant force on it increases. (b) When the ball is released, the buoyant force exceeds the gravitational force, and the ball accelerates upwards. (c) The buoyant force on the ball decreases as the ball approaches the surface of the pool. (d) The buoyant force on the ball equals its weight and remains constant as the ball rises. (e) The buoyant force on the ball while it is submerged is equal to the weight of the volume of water the ball displaces.

9. A boat develops a leak and, after its passengers are rescued, eventually sinks to the bottom of a lake. When the boat is at the bottom, the force of the lake bottom on the boat is (a) greater than the weight of the boat, (b) equal to the weight of the boat, (c) less than the weight of the boat, (d) equal to the weight of the displaced water, or (e) equal to the buoyant force on the boat.

10. Three vessels of different shapes are filled to the same level with water as in Figure MCQ9.10. The area of the base is the same for all three vessels. Which of the following statements is valid? (a) The pressure at the top surface of vessel A is greatest because it has the largest surface area. (b) The pressure at the bottom of vessel A is greatest because it contains the most water. (c) The

pressure at the bottom of each vessel is the same. (d) The force on the bottom of each vessel is not the same. (e) At a given depth below the surface of each vessel, the pressure on the side of vessel A is greatest because of its slope.

Figure MCQ9.10

11. A solid iron sphere and a solid lead sphere of the same size are each suspended by strings and are submerged in a tank of water. (Note that density of lead is greater than that of iron.) Which of the following statements are valid? (Choose all correct statements.) (a) The buoyant force on each is the same. (b) The buoyant force on the lead sphere is greater than the buoyant force on the iron sphere because lead has the greater density. (c) The tension in the string supporting the lead sphere is greater than the tension in the string supporting the iron sphere. (d) The buoyant force on the iron sphere is greater than the buoyant force on the lead sphere because lead displaces more water. (e) None of those statements is true.

12. A beach ball is made of thin plastic. It has been inflated with air, but the plastic is not stretched. By swimming with fins on, you manage to take the ball from the surface of a pool to the bottom. Once the ball is completely submerged, what happens to the buoyant force exerted on the beach ball as you take it deeper? (a) It increases. (b) It remains constant. (c) It decreases. (d) It is impossible to determine.

13. A person in a boat floating in a small pond throws an anchor overboard. What happens to the level of the pond? (a) It rises. (b) It falls. (c) It remains the same.

14. One of the predicted problems due to global warming is that ice in the polar ice caps will melt and raise sea level everywhere in the world. Is that more of a worry for ice (a) at the north pole, where most of the ice floats on water; (b) at the south pole, where most of the ice sits on land; (c) both at the north and south poles equally; or (d) at neither pole?

▪ CONCEPTUAL QUESTIONS

WebAssign The conceptual questions in this chapter may be assigned online in Enhanced WebAssign.

1. A woman wearing high-heeled shoes is invited into a home in which the kitchen has vinyl floor covering. Why should the homeowner be concerned?

2. The density of air is 1.3 kg/m³ at sea level. From your knowledge of air pressure at ground level, estimate the height of the atmosphere. As a simplifying assumption, take the atmosphere to be of uniform density up to some height, after which the density rapidly falls to zero. (In reality, the density of the atmosphere decreases as we go up.) (This question is courtesy of Edward F. Redish. For more questions of this type, see http://www.physics.umd.edu/perg/.)

3. Why do baseball home run hitters like to play in Denver, but curveball pitchers do not?

4. Figure CQ9.4 shows aerial views from directly above two dams. Both dams are equally long (the vertical dimension in the diagram) and equally deep (into the page in the diagram). The dam on the left holds back a very large lake, while the dam on the right holds back a narrow river. Which dam has to be built more strongly?

5. A typical silo on a farm has many bands wrapped around its perimeter, as shown in Figure CQ9.5. Why is the spacing between successive bands smaller at the lower portions of the silo?

6. Many people believe that a vacuum created inside a vacuum cleaner causes particles of dirt to be drawn in. Actually, the dirt is pushed in. Explain.

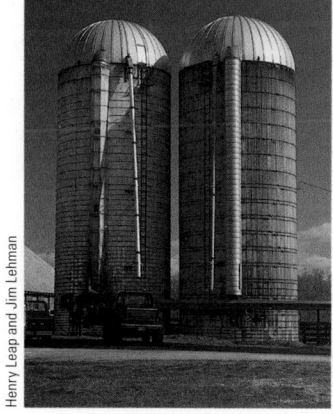

Henry Leap and Jim Lehman

Figure CQ9.5

7. Suppose a damaged ship just barely floats in the ocean after a hole in its hull has been sealed. It is pulled by a tugboat toward shore and into a river, heading toward a dry dock for repair. As the boat is pulled up the river, it sinks. Why?

8. **BIO** During inhalation, the pressure in the lungs is slightly less than external pressure and the muscles

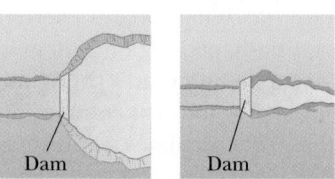

Figure CQ9.4

controlling exhalation are relaxed. Under water, the body equalizes internal and external pressures. Discuss the condition of the muscles if a person under water is breathing through a snorkel. Would a snorkel work in deep water?

9. The water supply for a city is often provided from reservoirs built on high ground. Water flows from the reservoir, through pipes, and into your home when you turn the tap on your faucet. Why is the water flow more rapid out of a faucet on the first floor of a building than in an apartment on a higher floor?

10. An ice cube is placed in a glass of water. What happens to the level of the water as the ice melts?

11. Place two cans of soft drinks, one regular and one diet, in a container of water. You will find that the diet drink floats while the regular one sinks. Use Archimedes' principle to devise an explanation. *Broad Hint:* The artificial sweetener used in diet drinks is less dense than sugar.

12. Will an ice cube float higher in water or in an alcoholic beverage?

13. Tornadoes and hurricanes often lift the roofs of houses. Use the Bernoulli effect to explain why. Why should you keep your windows open under these conditions?

14. Once ski jumpers are airborne (Fig. CQ9.14), why do they bend their bodies forward and keep their hands at their sides?

© iStockPhoto/technotr

Figure CQ9.14

■ PROBLEMS

9.1 States of Matter

9.2 Density and Pressure

1. **S** Suppose two worlds, each having mass M and radius R, coalesce into a single world. Due to gravitational contraction, the combined world has a radius of only $\frac{3}{4}R$. What is the average density of the combined world as a multiple of ρ_0, the average density of the original two worlds?

2. The British gold sovereign coin is an alloy of gold and copper having a total mass of 7.988 g, and is 22-karat gold. (a) Find the mass of gold in the sovereign in kilograms using the fact that the number of karats = 24 × (mass of gold)/(total mass). (b) Calculate the volumes of gold and copper, respectively, used to manufacture the coin. (c) Calculate the density of the British sovereign coin.

3. **Q|C** Four acrobats of mass 75.0 kg, 68.0 kg, 62.0 kg, and 55.0 kg form a human tower, with each acrobat standing on the shoulders of another acrobat. The 75.0-kg acrobat is at the bottom of the tower. (a) What is the normal force acting on the 75-kg acrobat? (b) If the area of each of the 75.0-kg acrobat's shoes is 425 cm², what average pressure (not including atmospheric pressure) does the column of acrobats exert on

the floor? (c) Will the pressure be the same if a different acrobat is on the bottom?

4. **M** Calculate the mass of a solid gold rectangular bar that has dimensions of 4.50 cm × 11.0 cm × 26.0 cm.

5. **Q|C** The nucleus of an atom can be modeled as several protons and neutrons closely packed together. Each particle has a mass of 1.67×10^{-27} kg and radius on the order of 10^{-15} m. (a) Use this model and the data provided to estimate the density of the nucleus of an atom. (b) Compare your result with the density of a material such as iron. What do your result and comparison suggest about the structure of matter?

6. The four tires of an automobile are inflated to a gauge pressure of 2.0×10^5 Pa. Each tire has an area of 0.024 m² in contact with the ground. Determine the weight of the automobile.

7. Suppose a distant world with surface gravity of 7.44 m/s² has an atmospheric pressure of 8.04×10^4 Pa at the surface. (a) What force is exerted by the atmosphere on a disk-shaped region 2.00 m in radius at the surface of a methane ocean? (b) What is the weight of a 10.0-m deep cylindrical column of methane with radius 2.00 m? (c) Calculate the pressure at a depth of 10.0 m in the methane ocean. *Note:* The density of liquid methane is 415 kg/m³.

9.3 The Deformation of Solids

8. Evaluate Young's modulus for the material whose stress-strain curve is shown in Figure 9.8.

9. ⓜ A 200-kg load is hung on a wire of length 4.00 m, cross-sectional area 0.200×10^{-4} m², and Young's modulus 8.00×10^{10} N/m². What is its increase in length?

10. ⓠⓒ Comic-book superheroes are sometimes able to punch holes through steel walls. (a) If the ultimate shear strength of steel is taken to be 2.50×10^8 Pa, what force is required to punch through a steel plate 2.00 cm thick? Assume the superhero's fist has cross-sectional area of 1.00×10^2 cm² and is approximately circular. (b) Qualitatively, what would happen to the superhero on delivery of the punch? What physical law applies?

11. A plank 2.00 cm thick and 15.0 cm wide is firmly attached to the railing of a ship by clamps so that the rest of the board extends 2.00 m horizontally over the sea below. A man of mass 80.0 kg is forced to stand on the very end. If the end of the board drops by 5.00 cm because of the man's weight, find the shear modulus of the wood.

12. ⓜ Assume that if the shear stress in steel exceeds about 4.00×10^8 N/m², the steel ruptures. Determine the shearing force necessary to (a) shear a steel bolt 1.00 cm in diameter and (b) punch a 1.00-cm-diameter hole in a steel plate 0.500 cm thick.

13. For safety in climbing, a mountaineer uses a nylon rope that is 50 m long and 1.0 cm in diameter. When supporting a 90-kg climber, the rope elongates 1.6 m. Find its Young's modulus.

14. ⒷⒾⓄ A stainless-steel orthodontic wire is applied to a tooth, as in Figure P9.14. The wire has an unstretched length of 3.1 cm and a radius of 0.11 mm. If the wire is stretched 0.10 mm, find the magnitude and direction of the force on the tooth. Disregard the width of the tooth and assume Young's modulus for stainless steel is 18×10^{10} Pa.

Figure P9.14

15. ⒷⒾⓄ Bone has a Young's modulus of 18×10^9 Pa. Under compression, it can withstand a stress of about 160×10^6 Pa before breaking. Assume that a femur (thigh bone) is 0.50 m long, and calculate the amount of compression this bone can withstand before breaking.

16. A high-speed lifting mechanism supports an 800-kg object with a steel cable that is 25.0 m long and 4.00 cm² in cross-sectional area. (a) Determine the elongation of the cable. (b) By what additional amount does the cable increase in length if the object is

accelerated upward at a rate of 3.0 m/s²? (c) What is the greatest mass that can be accelerated upward at 3.0 m/s² if the stress in the cable is not to exceed the elastic limit of the cable, which is 2.2×10^8 Pa?

17. A walkway suspended across a hotel lobby is supported at numerous points along its edges by a vertical cable above each point and a vertical column underneath. The steel cable is 1.27 cm in diameter and is 5.75 m long before loading. The aluminum column is a hollow cylinder with an inside diameter of 16.14 cm, an outside diameter of 16.24 cm, and unloaded length of 3.25 m. When the walkway exerts a load force of 8 500 N on one of the support points, how much does the point move down?

18. ⒷⒾⓄ The total cross-sectional area of the load-bearing calcified portion of the two forearm bones (radius and ulna) is approximately 2.4 cm². During a car crash, the forearm is slammed against the dashboard. The arm comes to rest from an initial speed of 80 km/h in 5.0 ms. If the arm has an effective mass of 3.0 kg and bone material can withstand a maximum compressional stress of 16×10^7 Pa, is the arm likely to withstand the crash?

19. Determine the elongation of the rod in Figure P9.19 if it is under a tension of 5.8×10^3 N.

Figure P9.19

9.4 Variation of Pressure with Depth

9.5 Pressure Measurements

20. The spring of the pressure gauge shown in Figure P9.20 has a force constant of 1 250 N/m, and the piston has a radius of 1.20 cm. As the gauge is lowered into water, what change in depth causes the piston to move in by 0.750 cm?

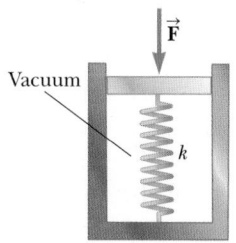

Figure P9.20

21. (a) Calculate the absolute pressure at the bottom of a fresh-water lake at a depth of 27.5 m. Assume the density of the water is 1.00×10^3 kg/m³ and the air above is at a pressure of 101.3 kPa. (b) What force is exerted by the water on the window of an underwater vehicle at this depth if the window is circular and has a diameter of 35.0 cm?

22. Mercury is poured into a U-tube as shown in Figure P9.22a on page 324. The left arm of the tube has cross-sectional area A_1 of 10.0 cm², and the right arm has a cross-sectional area A_2 of 5.00 cm². One hundred grams of water are then poured into the right arm as shown in Figure P9.22b. (a) Determine the length of the water column in the right arm of the U-tube. (b) Given that the density of mercury is 13.6 g/cm^3, what distance h does the mercury rise in the left arm?

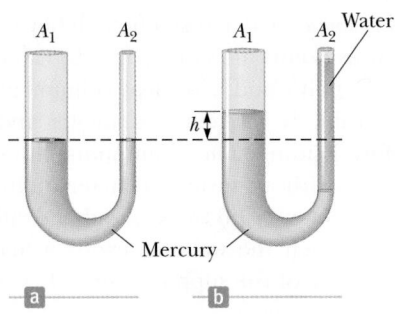

Figure P9.22

23. **BIO** A collapsible plastic bag (Figure P9.23) contains a glucose solution. If the average gauge pressure in the vein is 1.33×10^3 Pa, what must be the minimum height h of the bag in order to infuse glucose into the vein? Assume the specific gravity of the solution is 1.02.

Figure P9.23

24. The deepest point in the ocean is in the Mariana Trench, about 11 km deep. The pressure at the ocean floor is huge, about 1.13×10^8 N/m^2. (a) Calculate the change in volume of 1.00 m^3 of water carried from the surface to the bottom of the Pacific. (b) The density of water at the surface is 1.03×10^3 kg/m^3. Find its density at the bottom. (c) Explain whether or when it is a good approximation to think of water as incompressible.

25. A container is filled to a depth of 20.0 cm with water. On top of the water floats a 30.0-cm-thick layer of oil with specific gravity 0.700. What is the absolute pressure at the bottom of the container?

26. Blaise Pascal duplicated Torricelli's barometer using a red Bordeaux wine, of density 984 kg/m^3 as the working liquid (Fig. P9.26). (a) What was the height h of the wine column for normal atmospheric pressure? (b) Would you expect the vacuum above the column to be as good as for mercury?

Figure P9.26

27. Figure P9.27 shows the essential parts of a hydraulic brake system. The area of the piston in the master cylinder is 1.8 cm^2 and that of the piston in the brake cylinder is 6.4 cm^2. The coefficient of friction between shoe and wheel drum is 0.50. If the wheel has a radius of 34 cm,

Figure P9.27

determine the frictional torque about the axle when a force of 44 N is exerted on the brake pedal.

28. Piston ① in Figure P9.28 has a diameter of 0.25 in.; piston ② has a diameter of 1.5 in. In the absence of friction, determine the force $\vec{\mathbf{F}}$ necessary to support the 500-lb weight.

Figure P9.28

9.6 Buoyant Forces and Archimedes' Principle

29. A table-tennis ball has a diameter of 3.80 cm and average density of 0.084 0 g/cm^3. What force is required to hold it completely submerged under water?

30. **BIO** **Q|C** The average human has a density of 945 kg/m^3 after inhaling and 1 020 kg/m^3 after exhaling. (a) Without making any swimming movements, what percentage of the human body would be above the surface in the Dead Sea (a body of water with a density of about 1 230 kg/m^3) in each of these cases? (b) Given that bone and muscle are denser than fat, what physical characteristics differentiate "sinkers" (those who tend to sink in water) from "floaters" (those who readily float)?

31. A small ferryboat is 4.00 m wide and 6.00 m long. When a loaded truck pulls onto it, the boat sinks an additional 4.00 cm into the river. What is the weight of the truck?

32. **GP** A 62.0-kg survivor of a cruise line disaster rests atop a block of Styrofoam insulation, using it as a raft. The Styrofoam has dimensions 2.00 m × 2.00 m × 0.090 0 m. The bottom 0.024 m of the raft is submerged. (a) Draw a force diagram of the system consisting of the survivor and raft. (b) Write Newton's second law for the system in one dimension, using B for buoyancy, w for the weight of the survivor, and w_r for the weight of the raft. (Set $a = 0$.) (c) Calculate the numeric value for the buoyancy, B. (Seawater has density 1 025 kg/m^3.) (d) Using the value of B and the weight w of the survivor, calculate the weight w_r of the Styrofoam. (e) What is the density of the Styrofoam? (f) What is the maximum buoyant force, corresponding to the raft being submerged up to its top surface? (g) What total mass of survivors can the raft support?

33. QC A wooden block of volume 5.24×10^{-4} m³ floats in water, and a small steel object of mass m is placed on top of the block. When $m = 0.310$ kg, the system is in equilibrium, and the top of the wooden block is at the level of the water. (a) What is the density of the wood? (b) What happens to the block when the steel object is replaced by a second steel object with a mass less than 0.310 kg? What happens to the block when the steel object is replaced by yet another steel object with a mass greater than 0.310 kg?

34. GP A large balloon of mass 226 kg is filled with helium gas until its volume is 325 m³. Assume the density of air is 1.29 kg/m³ and the density of helium is 0.179 kg/m³. (a) Draw a force diagram for the balloon. (b) Calculate the buoyant force acting on the balloon. (c) Find the net force on the balloon and determine whether the balloon will rise or fall after it is released. (d) What maximum additional mass can the balloon support in equilibrium? (e) What happens to the balloon if the mass of the load is *less* than the value calculated in part (d)? (f) What limits the height to which the balloon can rise?

35. QC A spherical weather balloon is filled with hydrogen until its radius is 3.00 m. Its total mass including the instruments it carries is 15.0 kg. (a) Find the buoyant force acting on the balloon, assuming the density of air is 1.29 kg/m³. (b) What is the net force acting on the balloon and its instruments after the balloon is released from the ground? (c) Why does the radius of the balloon tend to increase as it rises to higher altitude?

36. S A man of mass $m = 70.0$ kg and having a density of $\rho = 1\,050$ kg/m³ (while holding his breath) is completely submerged in water. (a) Write Newton's second law for this situation in terms of the man's mass m, the density of water ρ_w, his volume V, and g. Neglect any viscous drag of the water. (b) Substitute $m = \rho V$ into Newton's second law and solve for the acceleration a, canceling common factors. (c) Calculate the numeric value of the man's acceleration. (d) How long does it take the man to sink 8.00 m to the bottom of the lake?

37. QC On October 21, 2001, Ian Ashpole of the United Kingdom achieved a record altitude of 3.35 km (11 000 ft) powered by 600 toy balloons filled with helium. Each filled balloon had a radius of about 0.50 m and an estimated mass of 0.30 kg. (a) Estimate the total buoyant force on the 600 balloons. (b) Estimate the net upward force on all 600 balloons. (c) Ashpole parachuted to Earth after the balloons began to burst at the high altitude and the system lost buoyancy. Why did the balloons burst?

38. The gravitational force exerted on a solid object is 5.00 N as measured when the object is suspended from a spring scale as in Figure P9.38a. When the suspended object is submerged in water, the scale reads 3.50 N (Figure P9.38b). Find the density of the object.

Figure P9.38

39. M A cube of wood having an edge dimension of 20.0 cm and a density of 650 kg/m³ floats on water. (a) What is the distance from the horizontal top surface of the cube to the water level? (b) What mass of lead should be placed on the cube so that the top of the cube will be just level with the water surface?

40. A light spring of force constant $k = 160$ N/m rests vertically on the bottom of a large beaker of water (Fig. P9.40a). A 5.00-kg block of wood (density = 650 kg/m³) is connected to the spring, and the block–spring system is allowed to come to static equilibrium (Fig. P9.40b). What is the elongation ΔL of the spring?

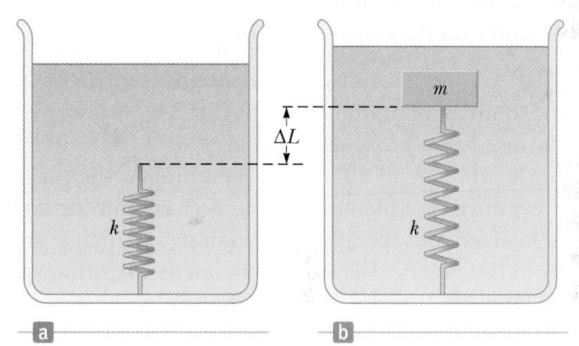

Figure P9.40

41. A sample of an unknown material appears to weigh 300 N in air and 200 N when immersed in alcohol of specific gravity 0.700. What are (a) the volume and (b) the density of the material?

42. An object weighing 300 N in air is immersed in water after being tied to a string connected to a balance. The scale now reads 265 N. Immersed in oil, the object appears to weigh 275 N. Find (a) the density of the object and (b) the density of the oil.

43. A 1.00-kg beaker containing 2.00 kg of oil (density = 916 kg/m³) rests on a scale. A 2.00-kg block of iron is suspended from a spring scale and is completely submerged in the oil (Fig. P9.43). Find the equilibrium readings of both scales.

Figure P9.43

9.7 Fluids in Motion

9.8 Other Applications of Fluid Dynamics

44. Water flowing through a garden hose of diameter 2.74 cm fills a 25.0-L bucket in 1.50 min. (a) What is the speed of the water leaving the end of the hose? (b) A nozzle is now attached to the end of the hose. If the nozzle diameter is one-third the diameter of the hose, what is the speed of the water leaving the nozzle?

45. **BIO** (a) Calculate the mass flow rate (in grams per second) of blood ($\rho = 1.0$ g/cm^3) in an aorta with a cross-sectional area of 2.0 cm^2 if the flow speed is 40 cm/s. (b) Assume that the aorta branches to form a large number of capillaries with a combined cross-sectional area of 3.0×10^3 cm^2. What is the flow speed in the capillaries?

46. A liquid ($\rho = 1.65$ g/cm^3) flows through a horizontal pipe of varying cross section as in Figure P9.46. In the first section, the cross-sectional area is 10.0 cm^2, the flow speed is 275 cm/s, and the pressure is 1.20×10^5 Pa. In the second section, the cross-sectional area is 2.50 cm^2. Calculate the smaller section's (a) flow speed and (b) pressure.

Figure P9.46

47. **BIO** A hypodermic syringe contains a medicine with the density of water (Fig. P9.47). The barrel of the syringe has a cross-sectional area of 2.50×10^{-5} m^2. In the absence of a force on the plunger, the pressure everywhere is 1.00 atm. A force $\vec{F}$ of magnitude 2.00 N is exerted on the plunger, making medicine squirt from the needle. Determine the medicine's flow speed through the needle. Assume the pressure in the needle remains equal to 1.00 atm and that the syringe is horizontal.

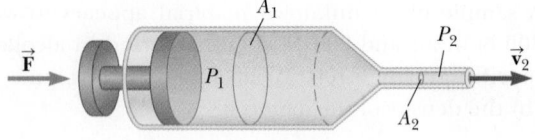

Figure P9.47

48. **BIO** When a person inhales, air moves down the bronchus (windpipe) at 15 cm/s. The average flow speed of the air doubles through a constriction in the bronchus. Assuming incompressible flow, determine the pressure drop in the constriction.

49. **QC** A jet airplane in level flight has a mass of 8.66×10^4 kg, and the two wings have an estimated total area of 90.0 m^2. (a) What is the pressure difference between the lower and upper surfaces of the wings? (b) If the speed of air under the wings is 225 m/s, what is the

speed of the air over the wings? Assume air has a density of 1.29 kg/m^3. (c) Explain why all aircraft have a "ceiling," a maximum operational altitude.

50. **S** An airplane has a mass M, and the two wings have a total area A. During level flight, the pressure on the lower wing surface is P_1. Determine the pressure P_2 on the upper wing surface.

51. **GP** In a water pistol, a piston drives water through a larger tube of radius 1.00 cm into a smaller tube of radius 1.00 mm as in Figure P9.51. (a) If the pistol is fired horizontally at a height of 1.50 m, use ballistics to determine the time it takes water to travel from the nozzle to the ground. (Neglect air resistance and assume atmospheric pressure is 1.00 atm.) (b) If the range of the stream is to be 8.00 m, with what speed must the stream leave the nozzle? (c) Given the areas of the nozzle and cylinder, use the equation of continuity to calculate the speed at which the plunger must be moved. (d) What is the pressure at the nozzle? (e) Use Bernoulli's equation to find the pressure needed in the larger cylinder. Can gravity terms be neglected? (f) Calculate the force that must be exerted on the trigger to achieve the desired range. (The force that must be exerted is due to pressure over and above atmospheric pressure.)

Figure P9.51

52. Water moves through a constricted pipe in steady, ideal flow. At the lower point shown in Figure P9.52, the pressure is 1.75×10^5 Pa and the pipe radius is 3.00 cm. At the higher point located at $y = 2.50$ m, the pressure is 1.20×10^5 Pa and the pipe radius is 1.50 cm. Find the speed of flow (a) in the lower section and (b) in the upper section. (c) Find the volume flow rate through the pipe.

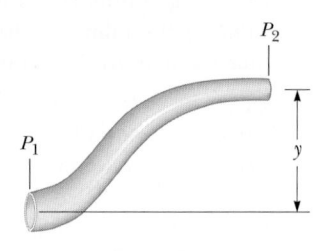

Figure P9.52

53. **M** A jet of water squirts out horizontally from a hole near the bottom of the tank shown in Figure P9.53. If the hole has a diameter of 3.50 mm, what is the height h of the water level in the tank?

Figure P9.53

54. A large storage tank, open to the atmosphere at the top and filled with water, develops a small hole in its side at a point 16.0 m below the water level. If the rate of flow from the leak is 2.50×10^{-3} m³/min, determine (a) the speed at which the water leaves the hole and (b) the diameter of the hole.

55. The inside diameters of the larger portions of the horizontal pipe depicted in Figure P9.55 are 2.50 cm. Water flows to the right at a rate of 1.80×10^{-4} m³/s. Determine the inside diameter of the constriction.

Figure P9.55

56. Water is pumped through a pipe of diameter 15.0 cm from the Colorado River up to Grand Canyon Village, on the rim of the canyon. The river is at 564 m elevation and the village is at 2 096 m. (a) At what minimum pressure must the water be pumped to arrive at the village? (b) If 4 500 m³ are pumped per day, what is the speed of the water in the pipe? (c) What additional pressure is necessary to deliver this flow? *Note:* You may assume the free-fall acceleration and the density of air are constant over the given range of elevations.

57. Old Faithful geyser in Yellowstone Park erupts at approximately 1-hour intervals, and the height of the fountain reaches 40.0 m (Fig. P9.57). (a) Consider the rising stream as a series of separate drops. Analyze the free-fall motion of one of the drops to determine the speed at which the water leaves the ground. (b) Treat the rising stream as an ideal fluid in streamline flow. Use Bernoulli's equation to determine the speed of the water as it leaves ground level. (c) What is the pressure (above atmospheric pressure) in the

heated underground chamber 175 m below the vent? You may assume the chamber is large compared with the geyser vent.

Bildagentur Rm/Photolibrary

Figure P9.57

58. The Venturi tube shown in Figure P9.58 may be used as a fluid flowmeter. Suppose the device is used at a service station to measure the flow rate of gasoline ($\rho = 7.00 \times 10^2$ kg/m³) through a

Figure P9.58

hose having an outlet radius of 1.20 cm. If the difference in pressure is measured to be $P_1 - P_2 = 1.20$ kPa and the radius of the inlet tube to the meter is 2.40 cm, find (a) the speed of the gasoline as it leaves the hose and (b) the fluid flow rate in cubic meters per second.

9.9 Surface Tension, Capillary Action, and Viscous Fluid Flow

59. A square metal sheet 3.0 cm on a side and of negligible thickness is attached to a balance and inserted into a container of fluid. The contact angle is found to be zero, as shown in Figure P9.59a, and the balance to which the metal sheet is attached reads 0.40 N. A thin veneer of oil is then spread over the sheet, and the contact angle becomes 180°, as shown in Figure P9.59b. The balance now reads 0.39 N. What is the surface tension of the fluid?

Figure P9.59

60. **BIO** To lift a wire ring of radius 1.75 cm from the surface of a container of blood plasma, a vertical force of 1.61×10^{-2} N greater than the weight of the ring is required. Calculate the surface tension of blood plasma from this information.

61. A certain fluid has a density of 1 080 kg/m^3 and is observed to rise to a height of 2.1 cm in a 1.0-mm-diameter tube. The contact angle between the wall and the fluid is zero. Calculate the surface tension of the fluid.

62. **BIO** Whole blood has a surface tension of 0.058 N/m and a density of 1 050 kg/m^3. To what height can whole blood rise in a capillary blood vessel that has a radius of 2.0×10^{-6} m if the contact angle is zero?

63. The block of ice (temperature 0°C) shown in Figure P9.63 is drawn over a level surface lubricated by a layer of water 0.10 mm thick. Determine the magnitude of the force $\vec{F}$ needed to pull the block with a constant speed of 0.50 m/s. At 0°C, the viscosity of water has the value $\eta = 1.79 \times 10^{-3}$ N · s/m^2.

1.20 m

0.800 m

$\vec{F}$

0.10 m

Figure P9.63

64. A thin 1.5-mm coating of glycerine has been placed between two microscope slides of width 1.0 cm and length 4.0 cm. Find the force required to pull one of the microscope slides at a constant speed of 0.30 m/s relative to the other slide.

65. A straight horizontal pipe with a diameter of 1.0 cm and a length of 50 m carries oil with a coefficient of viscosity of 0.12 N · s/m^2. At the output of the pipe, the flow rate is 8.6×10^{-5} m^3/s and the pressure is 1.0 atm. Find the *gauge* pressure at the pipe input.

66. **BIO** The pulmonary artery, which connects the heart to the lungs, has an inner radius of 2.6 mm and is 8.4 cm long. If the pressure drop between the heart and lungs is 400 Pa, what is the average speed of blood in the pulmonary artery?

67. Spherical particles of a protein of density 1.8 g/cm^3 are shaken up in a solution of 20°C water. The solution is allowed to stand for 1.0 h. If the depth of water in the tube is 5.0 cm, find the radius of the largest particles that remain in solution at the end of the hour.

68. **BIO** A hypodermic needle is 3.0 cm in length and 0.30 mm in diameter. What pressure difference between the input and output of the needle is required so that the flow rate of water through it will be 1 g/s? (Use 1.0×10^{-3} Pa · s as the viscosity of water.)

69. **BIO** What radius needle should be used to inject a volume of 500 cm^3 of a solution into a patient in 30 min? Assume the length of the needle is 2.5 cm and the solution is elevated 1.0 m above the point of injection. Further, assume the viscosity and density of the solution

are those of pure water, and that the pressure inside the vein is atmospheric.

70. Water is forced out of a fire extinguisher by air pressure, as shown in Figure P9.70. What gauge air pressure in the tank (above atmospheric pressure) is required for the water to have a jet speed of 30.0 m/s when the water level in the tank is 0.500 m below the nozzle?

$\vec{v}$

0.500 m

Figure P9.70

71. **BIO** The aorta in humans has a diameter of about 2.0 cm, and at certain times the blood speed through it is about 55 cm/s. Is the blood flow turbulent? The density of whole blood is 1 050 kg/m^3, and its coefficient of viscosity is 2.7×10^{-3} N · s/m^2.

72. A pipe carrying 20°C water has a diameter of 2.5 cm. Estimate the maximum flow speed if the flow must be streamline.

9.10 Transport Phenomena

73. **BIO** Sucrose is allowed to diffuse along a 10-cm length of tubing filled with water. The tube is 6.0 cm^2 in cross-sectional area. The diffusion coefficient is equal to 5.0×10^{-10} m^2/s, and 8.0×10^{-14} kg is transported along the tube in 15 s. What is the difference in the concentration levels of sucrose at the two ends of the tube?

74. **BIO** Glycerin in water diffuses along a horizontal column that has a cross-sectional area of 2.0 cm^2. The concentration gradient is 3.0×10^{-2} kg/m^4, and the diffusion rate is found to be 5.7×10^{-15} kg/s. Determine the diffusion coefficient.

75. The viscous force on an oil drop is measured to be equal to 3.0×10^{-13} N when the drop is falling through air with a speed of 4.5×10^{-4} m/s. If the radius of the drop is 2.5×10^{-6} m, what is the viscosity of air?

76. Small spheres of diameter 1.00 mm fall through 20°C water with a terminal speed of 1.10 cm/s. Calculate the density of the spheres.

Additional Problems

77. An iron block of volume 0.20 m^3 is suspended from a spring scale and immersed in a flask of water. Then the iron block is removed, and an aluminum block of the same volume replaces it. (a) In which case is the buoyant force the greatest, for the iron block or the aluminum block? (b) In which case does the spring scale read the largest value? (c) Use the known densities of these materials to calculate the quantities requested in parts (a) and (b). Are your calculations consistent with your previous answers to parts (a) and (b)?

78. **S** The true weight of an object can be measured in a vacuum, where buoyant forces are absent. A measurement in air, however, is disturbed by buoyant forces. An object of volume V is weighed in air on an equal-arm balance with the use of counterweights of density ρ. Representing the density of air as ρ_{air} and the balance reading as F_g', show that the true weight F_g is

$$F_g = F_g' + \left(V - \frac{F_g'}{\rho g} \right)\rho_{air}g$$

79. As a first approximation, Earth's continents may be thought of as granite blocks floating in a denser rock (called peridotite) in the same way that ice floats in water. (a) Show that a formula describing this phenomenon is

$$\rho_g t = \rho_p d$$

where ρ_g is the density of granite (2.8×10^3 kg/m^3), ρ_p is the density of peridotite (3.3×10^3 kg/m^3), t is the thickness of a continent, and d is the depth to which a continent floats in the peridotite. (b) If a continent sinks 5.0 km into the peridotite layer (this surface may be thought of as the ocean floor), what is the thickness of the continent?

80. **BIO** Take the density of blood to be ρ and the distance between the feet and the heart to be h_H. Ignore the flow of blood. (a) Show that the difference in blood pressure between the feet and the heart is given by $P_F - P_H = \rho g h_H$. (b) Take the density of blood to be 1.05×10^3 kg/m^3 and the distance between the heart and the feet to be 1.20 m. Find the difference in blood pressure between these two points. This problem indicates that pumping blood from the extremities is very difficult for the heart. The veins in the legs have valves in them that open when blood is pumped toward the heart and close when blood flows away from the heart. Also, pumping action produced by physical activities such as walking and breathing assists the heart.

81. **BIO** The approximate inside diameter of the aorta is 0.50 cm; that of a capillary is 10 μm. The approximate average blood flow speed is 1.0 m/s in the aorta and 1.0 cm/s in the capillaries. If all the blood in the aorta eventually flows through the capillaries, estimate the number of capillaries in the circulatory system.

82. Superman attempts to drink water through a very long vertical straw as in Figure P9.82. With his great strength, he achieves maximum possible suction. The walls of the straw don't collapse. (a) Find the maximum height through which he can lift the water. (b) Still thirsty, the Man of Steel repeats his attempt on the Moon, which has no atmosphere. Find the difference between the water levels inside and outside the straw.

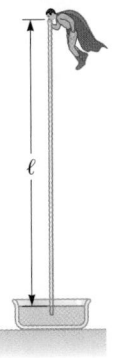

Figure P9.82

83. **BIO** The human brain and spinal cord are immersed in the cerebrospinal fluid. The fluid is normally continuous between the cranial and spinal cavities and exerts a pressure of 100 to 200 mm of H$_2$O above the prevailing

Figure P9.83

atmospheric pressure. In medical work, pressures are often measured in units of mm of H$_2$O because body fluids, including the cerebrospinal fluid, typically have nearly the same density as water. The pressure of the cerebrospinal fluid can be measured by means of a *spinal tap*. A hollow tube is inserted into the spinal column, and the height to which the fluid rises is observed, as shown in Figure P9.83. If the fluid rises to a height of 160 mm, we write its gauge pressure as 160 mm H$_2$O. (a) Express this pressure in pascals, in atmospheres, and in millimeters of mercury. (b) Sometimes it is necessary to determine whether an accident victim has suffered a crushed vertebra that is blocking the flow of cerebrospinal fluid in the spinal column. In other cases, a physician may suspect that a tumor or other growth is blocking the spinal column and inhibiting the flow of cerebrospinal fluid. Such conditions can be investigated by means of the *Queckensted test*. In this procedure the veins in the patient's neck are compressed, to make the blood pressure rise in the brain. The increase in pressure in the blood vessels is transmitted to the cerebrospinal fluid. What should be the normal effect on the height of the fluid in the spinal tap? (c) Suppose compressing the veins had no effect on the level of the fluid. What might account for this phenomenon?

84. **BIO** **S** A *hydrometer* is an instrument used to determine liquid density. A simple one is sketched in Figure P9.84. The bulb of a syringe is squeezed and released to lift a sample of the liquid of interest into a tube containing a calibrated rod of known density. (Assume the rod is cylindrical.) The rod, of length L and average density ρ_0, floats partially immersed in the liquid of density ρ. A length h of the rod protrudes above the surface of the liquid. Show that the density of the liquid is given by

Figure P9.84

$$\rho = \frac{\rho_0 L}{L - h}$$

85. Figure P9.85 (page 330) shows a water tank with a valve. If the valve is opened, what is the maximum

height attained by the stream of water coming out of the right side of the tank? Assume $h = 10.0$ m, $L = 2.00$ m, and $\theta = 30.0°$, and that the cross-sectional area at A is very large compared with that at B.

Figure P9.85

86. A helium-filled balloon, whose envelope has a mass of 0.25 kg, is tied to a 2.0-m-long, 0.050-kg string. The balloon is spherical with a radius of 0.40 m. When released, it lifts a length h of the string and then remains in equilibrium, as in Figure P9.86. Determine the value of h. *Hint:* Only that part of the string above the floor contributes to the load being supported by the balloon.

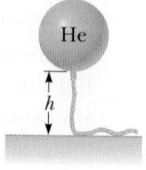

Figure P9.86

87. A light spring of constant $k = 90.0$ N/m is attached vertically to a table (Fig. P9.87a). A 2.00-g balloon is filled with helium (density = 0.179 kg/m³) to a volume of 5.00 m³ and is then connected to the spring, causing the spring to stretch as shown in Figure P89.87b. Determine the extension distance L when the balloon is in equilibrium.

Figure P9.87

88. A U-tube open at both ends is partially filled with water (Fig. P9.88a). Oil ($\rho = 750$ kg/m³) is then poured into the right arm and forms a column $L = 5.00$ cm high (Fig. P9.88b). (a) Determine the difference h in the heights of the two liquid surfaces. (b) The right arm is then shielded from any air motion while air is blown across the top of the left arm until the surfaces of the two liquids are at the same height (Fig. P9.88c). Determine the speed of the air being blown across the left arm. Assume the density of air is 1.29 kg/m³.

Figure P9.88

89. **S** In about 1657, Otto von Guericke, inventor of the air pump, evacuated a sphere made of two brass hemispheres (Fig. P9.89). Two teams of eight horses each could pull the hemispheres apart only on some trials and then "with greatest difficulty," with the resulting sound likened to a cannon firing. Find the force F required to pull the thin-walled evacuated hemispheres apart in terms of R, the radius of the hemispheres, P the pressure inside the hemispheres, and atmospheric pressure P_0.

Figure P9.89

90. Oil having a density of 930 kg/m³ floats on water. A rectangular block of wood 4.00 cm high and with a density of 960 kg/m³ floats partly in the oil and partly in the water. The oil completely covers the block. How far below the interface between the two liquids is the bottom of the block?

91. A water tank open to the atmosphere at the top has two small holes punched in its side, one above the other. The holes are 5.00 cm and 12.0 cm above the floor. How high does water stand in the tank if the two streams of water hit the floor at the same place?

■ AP* REVIEW QUESTIONS

1. Fluids

   (A) tend to move from regions of high pressure to regions of low pressure.

   (B) naturally move from any region of pressure to another, depending on the temperature.

   (C) tend to move from regions of low pressure to regions of high pressure.

   (D) naturally move from any region of pressure to another, depending on the volume.

   (E) None of the above is correct.

2. The equation of continuity for fluid dynamics $A_1v_1 = A_2v_2$ is based on the idea that for an enclosed fluid,

   (A) the pressure varies inversely with the speed of the fluid.

   (B) energy is conserved in the system.

   (C) the speed of the fluid varies directly with the cross-sectional area.

   (D) the volume flow rate is constant.

   (E) the pressure is higher at greater depths.

Note: Figure not drawn to scale

3. In the diagram above, the plunger cylinder in a hydraulic lift has a cross-sectional area of 1.5×10^{-3} m^2. If the lift cylinder has a cross-sectional area of 0.75 m^2, what force is required at the plunger to lift a car that weighs 10,000 N?

   (A) 11.25 N   (D) 13,333 N

   (B) 20 N   (E) 5,000,000 N

   (C) 10,000 N

4. Which of the following statements is true?

    I. The forces a fluid at rest exerts on the walls of its container act perpendicular to the walls.

    II. The pressure in a fluid is the same everywhere throughout the fluid.

    III. The pressure on a small surface in a fluid is the same regardless of the orientation of the surface.

   (A) I only   (D) I and II only

   (B) II only   (E) I and III only

   (C) III only

5. In the diagram above, water is poured into the open tube all the way up to the dashed line, and then is allowed to leave out of the three spouts. Which of the following best describes the spout through which water leaves the fastest, and the spout that allows the water to travel the greatest distance x?

	Fastest	**Greatest x**
(A)	I	I
(B)	I	II
(C)	III	I
(D)	III	II
(E)	III	III

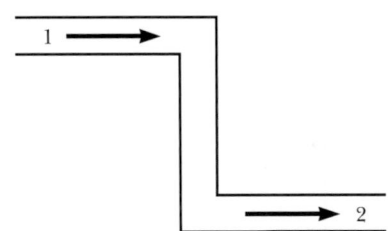

6. Water fills a pipe and flows at a steady rate, as shown in the diagram above. The diameter of the pipe is constant throughout the pipe, and point 1 is at a higher elevation than point 2. How do the velocity of flow and the pressure at points 1 and 2 compare?

	Velocity	**Pressure**
(A)	$v_1 = v_2$	$P_1 < P_2$
(B)	$v_1 < v_2$	$P_1 > P_2$
(C)	$v_1 = v_2$	$P_1 = P_2$
(D)	$v_1 > v_2$	$P_1 < P_2$
(E)	$v_1 = v_2$	$P_1 > P_2$

Questions 7–8
Use the graphs below to answer questions 7 and 8.

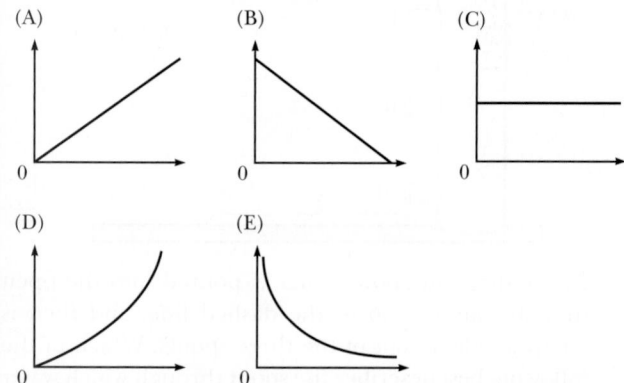

7. Which graph represents the gauge pressure of an ideal fluid as a function of depth in the fluid?

8. Assuming a steady flow, which graph represents the rate of fluid flow through a horizontal pipe as a function of the diameter of the pipe?

Questions 9–10
The absolute pressure P is measured as a function of depth h beneath the surface of a pool. Use the graph below to answer questions 9 and 10.

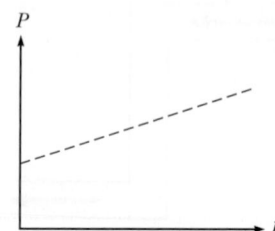

9. In terms of the density ρ of the water in the pool and the acceleration due to gravity g, what does the slope of the line on the graph represent?

(A) ρ

(B) g

(C) ρg

(D) $\dfrac{\rho}{g}$

(E) $\dfrac{g}{\rho}$

10. What does the y-intercept of the graph represent?
   (A) The density of the water
   (B) The acceleration due to gravity
   (C) The atmospheric pressure at the surface of the water
   (D) The total depth of the pool
   (E) The gauge pressure at the bottom of the pool

11. Which of the following statements is true regarding a fluid at rest in a container?
   I. All portions of the fluid must be in equilibrium.
   II. All points at the same depth must be at the same pressure.
   III. The pressure P at a depth h must be greater than atmospheric pressure.

   (A) I only
   (B) I and III only
   (C) I and II only
   (D) II and III only
   (E) I, II, and III

12. Bernoulli's equation is essentially an expression of
   (A) Conservation of energy
   (B) Conservation of time
   (C) Conservation of linear momentum
   (D) Conservation of angular momentum
   (E) Conservation of mass

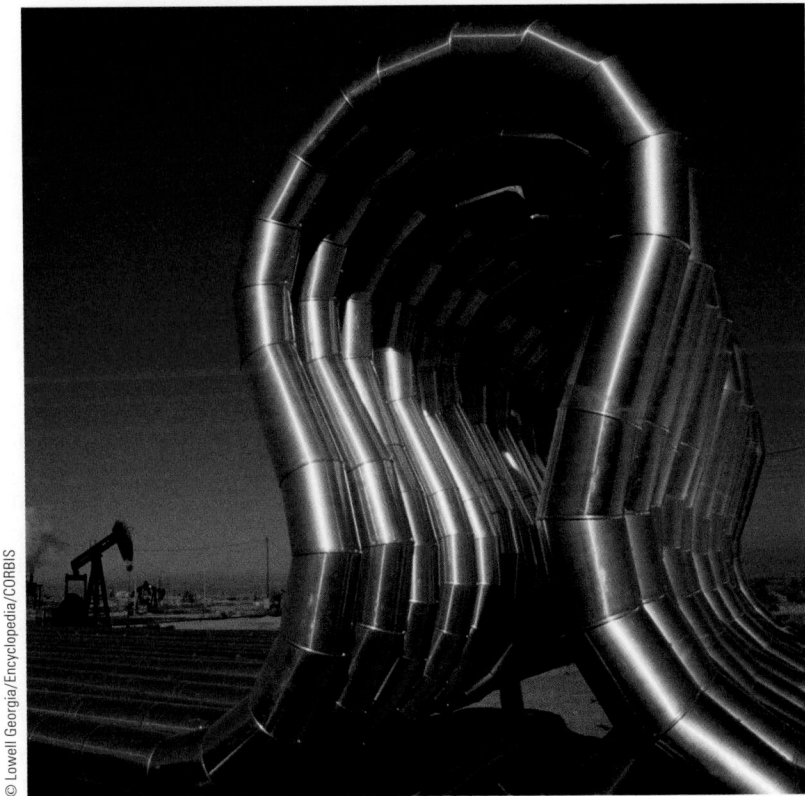

© Lowell Georgia/Encyclopedia/CORBIS

Pipelines carrying liquids often have loops to allow for expansion and contraction due to temperature changes. Without the loops, the pipes could buckle and burst.

Thermal Physics 10

How can trapped water blow off the top of a volcano in a giant explosion? What causes a sidewalk or road to fracture and buckle spontaneously when the temperature changes? How can thermal energy be harnessed to do work, running the engines that make everything in modern living possible?

Answering these and related questions is the domain of **thermal physics,** the study of temperature, heat, and how they affect matter. Quantitative descriptions of thermal phenomena require careful definitions of the concepts of temperature, heat, and internal energy. Heat leads to changes in internal energy and thus to changes in temperature, which cause the expansion or contraction of matter. Such changes can damage roadways and buildings, create stress fractures in metal, and render flexible materials stiff and brittle, the latter resulting in compromised O-rings and the *Challenger* disaster. Changes in internal energy can also be harnessed for transportation, construction, and food preservation.

Gases are critical in the harnessing of thermal energy to do work. Within normal temperature ranges, a gas acts like a large collection of non-interacting point particles, called an ideal gas. Such gases can be studied on either a macroscopic or microscopic scale. On the macroscopic scale, the pressure, volume, temperature, and number of particles associated with a gas can be related in a single equation known as the ideal gas law. On the microscopic scale, a model called the kinetic theory of gases pictures the components of a gas as small particles. That model will enable us to understand how processes on the atomic scale affect macroscopic properties like pressure, temperature, and internal energy.

10.1 Temperature and the Zeroth Law of Thermodynamics

Temperature is commonly associated with how hot or cold an object feels when we touch it. While our senses provide us with qualitative indications of temperature, they are unreliable and often misleading. A metal ice tray feels colder to the hand, for example, than a package of frozen vegetables at the same temperature, because metals conduct thermal energy more rapidly than a cardboard package. What we need is a reliable and reproducible method of making quantitative measurements that establish the relative "hotness" or "coldness" of objects—a method related solely to temperature. Scientists have developed a variety of thermometers for making such measurements.

When placed in contact with each other, two objects at different initial temperatures will eventually reach a common intermediate temperature. If a cup of hot coffee is cooled with an ice cube, for example, the ice rises in temperature and eventually melts while the temperature of the coffee decreases.

Understanding the concept of temperature requires understanding *thermal contact* and *thermal equilibrium*. Two objects are in **thermal contact** if energy can be exchanged between them. Two objects are in **thermal equilibrium** if they are in thermal contact and there is no net exchange of energy.

The exchange of energy between two objects because of differences in their temperatures is called **heat,** a concept examined in more detail in Chapter 11.

Using these ideas, we can develop a formal definition of temperature. Consider two objects A and B that are not in thermal contact with each other, and a third object C that acts as a **thermometer**—a device calibrated to measure the temperature of an object. We wish to determine whether A and B would be in thermal equilibrium if they were placed in thermal contact. The thermometer (object C) is first placed in thermal contact with A until thermal equilibrium is reached, as in Figure 10.1a, whereupon the reading of the thermometer is recorded. The thermometer is then placed in thermal contact with B, and its reading is again recorded at equilibrium (Fig. 10.1b). If the two readings are the same, then A and B are in thermal equilibrium with each other. If A and B are placed in thermal contact with each other, as in Figure 10.1c, there is no net transfer of energy between them.

We can summarize these results in a statement known as the **zeroth law of thermodynamics (the law of equilibrium):**

Zeroth law of ▶
thermodynamics

> If objects A and B are separately in thermal equilibrium with a third object C, then A and B are in thermal equilibrium with each other.

This statement is important because it makes it possible to define **temperature.** We can think of temperature as the property that determines whether or not an

Figure 10.1 The zeroth law of thermodynamics.

The temperatures of A and B are measured to be the same by placing them in thermal contact with a thermometer (object C).

No energy will be exchanged between A and B when they are placed in thermal contact with each other.

C   22.5   C   22.5

A   B   A   B

a   b   c

object is in thermal equilibrium with other objects. **Two objects in thermal equilibrium with each other are at the same temperature.**

■ Quick Quiz

10.1 Two objects with different sizes, masses, and temperatures are placed in thermal contact. Choose the best answer: Energy travels (a) from the larger object to the smaller object (b) from the object with more mass to the one with less mass (c) from the object at higher temperature to the object at lower temperature.

10.2 Thermometers and Temperature Scales

Thermometers are devices used to measure the temperature of an object or a system. When a thermometer is in thermal contact with a system, energy is exchanged until the thermometer and the system are in thermal equilibrium with each other. For accurate readings, the thermometer must be much smaller than the system, so that the energy the thermometer gains or loses doesn't significantly alter the energy content of the system. All thermometers make use of some physical property that changes with temperature and can be calibrated to make the temperature measurable. Some of the physical properties used are (1) the volume of a liquid, (2) the length of a solid, (3) the pressure of a gas held at constant volume, (4) the volume of a gas held at constant pressure, (5) the electric resistance of a conductor, and (6) the color of a very hot object.

Figure 10.2 Schematic diagram of a mercury thermometer. Because of thermal expansion, the level of the mercury rises as the temperature of the mercury changes from 0°C (the ice point) to 100°C (the steam point).

One common thermometer in everyday use consists of a mass of liquid—-usually mercury or alcohol—that expands into a glass capillary tube when its temperature rises (Fig. 10.2). In this case the physical property that changes is the volume of a liquid. To serve as an effective thermometer, the change in volume of the liquid with change in temperature must be very nearly constant over the temperature ranges of interest. When the cross-sectional area of the capillary tube is constant as well, the change in volume of the liquid varies linearly with its length along the tube. We can then define a temperature in terms of the length of the liquid column. The thermometer can be calibrated by placing it in thermal contact with environments that remain at constant temperature. One such environment is a mixture of water and ice in thermal equilibrium at atmospheric pressure. Another commonly used system is a mixture of water and steam in thermal equilibrium at atmospheric pressure.

Once we have marked the ends of the liquid column for our chosen environment on our thermometer, we need to define a scale of numbers associated with various temperatures. An example of such a scale is the **Celsius temperature scale,** formerly called the centigrade scale. On the Celsius scale, the temperature of the ice–water mixture is defined to be zero degrees Celsius, written 0°C and called the **ice point** or **freezing point** of water. The temperature of the water–steam mixture is defined as 100°C, called the **steam point** or **boiling point** of water. Once the ends of the liquid column in the thermometer have been marked at these two points, the distance between marks is divided into 100 equal segments, each corresponding to a change in temperature of one degree Celsius.

Thermometers calibrated in this way present problems when extremely accurate readings are needed. For example, an alcohol thermometer calibrated at the ice and steam points of water might agree with a mercury thermometer only at the calibration points. Because mercury and alcohol have different thermal expansion properties, when one indicates a temperature of 50°C, say, the other may indicate a slightly different temperature. The discrepancies between different types of thermometers are especially large when the temperatures to be measured are far from the calibration points.

The volume of gas in the flask is kept constant by raising or lowering reservoir *B* to keep the mercury level in column *A* constant.

Figure 10.3 A constant-volume gas thermometer measures the pressure of the gas contained in the flask immersed in the bath.

The Constant-Volume Gas Thermometer and the Kelvin Scale

We can construct practical thermometers such as the mercury thermometer, but these types of thermometers don't define temperature in a fundamental way. One thermometer, however, *is* more fundamental, and offers a way to define temperature and relate it directly to internal energy: the **gas thermometer.** In a gas thermometer, the temperature readings are nearly independent of the substance used in the thermometer. One type of gas thermometer is the constant-volume unit shown in Figure 10.3. The behavior observed in this device is the variation of pressure with temperature of a fixed volume of gas. When the constant-volume gas thermometer was developed, it was calibrated using the ice and steam points of water as follows (a different calibration procedure, to be discussed shortly, is now used): The gas flask is inserted into an ice–water bath, and mercury reservoir B is raised or lowered until the volume of the confined gas is at some value, indicated by the zero point on the scale. The height *h*, the difference between the levels in the reservoir and column A, indicates the pressure in the flask at 0°C. The flask is inserted into water at the steam point, and reservoir B is readjusted until the height in column A is again brought to zero on the scale, ensuring that the gas volume is the same as it had been in the ice bath (hence the designation "constant-volume"). A measure of the new value for *h* gives a value for the pressure at 100°C. These pressure and temperature values are then plotted on a graph, as in Figure 10.4. The line connecting the two points serves as a calibration curve for measuring unknown temperatures. If we want to measure the temperature of a substance, we place the gas flask in thermal contact with the substance and adjust the column of mercury until the level in column A returns to zero. The height of the mercury column tells us the pressure of the gas, and we could then find the temperature of the substance from the calibration curve.

Now suppose that temperatures are measured with various gas thermometers containing different gases. Experiments show that the thermometer readings are nearly independent of the type of gas used, as long as the gas pressure is low and the temperature is well above the point at which the gas liquefies.

We can also perform the temperature measurements with the gas in the flask at different starting pressures at 0°C. As long as the pressure is low, we will generate straight-line calibration curves for each starting pressure, as shown for three experimental trials (solid lines) in Figure 10.5.

If the curves in Figure 10.5 are extended back toward negative temperatures, we find a startling result: In every case, regardless of the type of gas or the value of the low starting pressure, **the pressure extrapolates to zero when the temperature is −273.15°C.** This fact suggests that this particular temperature is universal in its importance, because it doesn't depend on the substance used in the thermometer. In addition, because the lowest possible pressure is P = 0, a perfect vacuum, the temperature −273.15°C must represent a lower bound for physical processes. We define this temperature as **absolute zero.**

Absolute zero is used as the basis for the **Kelvin temperature scale,** which sets −273.15°C as its zero point (0 K). The size of a "degree" on the Kelvin scale is chosen to be identical to the size of a degree on the Celsius scale. The relationship between these two temperature scales is

$$T_C = T - 273.15 \qquad \text{[10.1]}$$

where T_C is the Celsius temperature and T is the Kelvin temperature (sometimes called the **absolute temperature**).

Technically, Equation 10.1 should have units on the right-hand side so that it reads $T_C = T °C/K - 273.15°C$. The units are rather cumbersome in this context, so we will usually suppress them in such calculations except in the final answer. (This will also be the case when discussing the Celsius and Fahrenheit scales.)

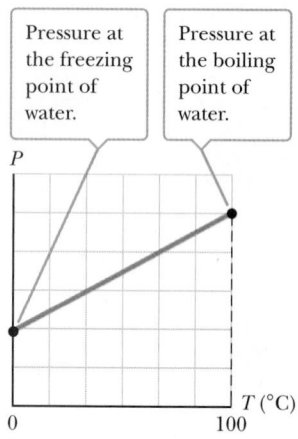

Pressure at the freezing point of water.

Pressure at the boiling point of water.

Figure 10.4 A typical graph of pressure versus temperature taken with a constant-volume gas thermometer.

Early gas thermometers made use of ice and steam points according to the procedure just described. These points are experimentally difficult to duplicate, however, because they are pressure-sensitive. Consequently, a procedure based on two new points was adopted in 1954 by the International Committee on Weights and Measures. The first point is absolute zero. The second point is **the triple point of water, which is the single temperature and pressure at which water, water vapor, and ice can coexist in equilibrium.** This point is a convenient and reproducible reference temperature for the Kelvin scale; it occurs at a temperature of 0.01°C and a pressure of 4.58 mm of mercury. The temperature at the triple point of water on the Kelvin scale occurs at 273.16 K. Therefore, **the SI unit of temperature, the kelvin, is defined as 1/273.16 of the temperature of the triple point of water.** Figure 10.6 shows the Kelvin temperatures for various physical processes and structures. Absolute zero has been closely approached but never achieved.

What would happen to a substance if its temperature could reach 0 K? As Figure 10.5 indicates, the substance would exert zero pressure on the walls of its container (assuming the gas doesn't liquefy or solidify on the way to absolute zero). In Section 10.5 we show that the pressure of a gas is proportional to the kinetic energy of the molecules of that gas. According to classical physics, therefore, the kinetic energy of the gas would go to zero and there would be no motion at all of the individual components of the gas. According to quantum theory, however (to be discussed in Chapter 27), the gas would always retain some residual energy, called the *zero-point energy*, at that low temperature.

> For all three trials, the pressure extrapolates to zero at the temperature −273.15°C.

Figure 10.5 Pressure versus temperature for experimental trials in which gases have different pressures in a constant-volume gas thermometer.

The Celsius, Kelvin, and Fahrenheit Temperature Scales

Equation 10.1 shows that the Celsius temperature T_C is shifted from the absolute (Kelvin) temperature T by 273.15. Because the size of a Celsius degree is the same as a kelvin, a temperature difference of 5°C is equal to a temperature difference of 5 K. The two scales differ only in the choice of zero point. The ice point (273.15 K) corresponds to 0.00°C, and the steam point (373.15 K) is equivalent to 100.00°C.

The most common temperature scale in use in the United States is the Fahrenheit scale. It sets the temperature of the ice point at 32°F and the temperature of the steam point at 212°F. The relationship between the Celsius and Fahrenheit temperature scales is

$$T_F = \tfrac{9}{5}T_C + 32 \qquad \text{[10.2a]}$$

For example, a temperature of 50.0°F corresponds to a Celsius temperature of 10.0°C and an absolute temperature of 283 K.

Equation 10.2a can be inverted to give Celsius temperatures in terms of Fahrenheit temperatures:

$$T_C = \tfrac{5}{9}(T_F - 32) \qquad \text{[10.2b]}$$

Equation 10.2 can also be used to find a relationship between changes in temperature on the Celsius and Fahrenheit scales. In a problem at the end of the chapter you will be asked to show that if the Celsius temperature changes by ΔT_C, the Fahrenheit temperature changes by the amount

$$\Delta T_F = \tfrac{9}{5}\Delta T_C \qquad \text{[10.3]}$$

Figure 10.7 on page 336 compares the Celsius, Fahrenheit, and Kelvin scales. Although less commonly used, other scales do exist, such as the Rankine scale. That scale has Fahrenheit degrees and a zero point at absolute zero.

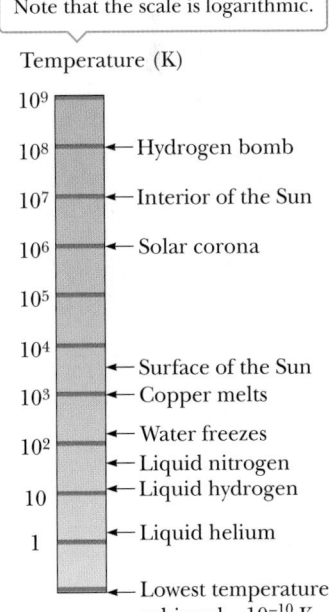

> Note that the scale is logarithmic.

Temperature (K)

10^9	
10^8	← Hydrogen bomb
10^7	← Interior of the Sun
10^6	← Solar corona
10^5	
10^4	
10^3	← Surface of the Sun
	← Copper melts
10^2	← Water freezes
	← Liquid nitrogen
10	← Liquid hydrogen
1	← Liquid helium
	← Lowest temperature achieved ~ 10^{-10} K

Figure 10.6 Absolute temperatures at which various selected physical processes take place.

Figure 10.7 A comparison of the Celsius, Fahrenheit, and Kelvin temperature scales.

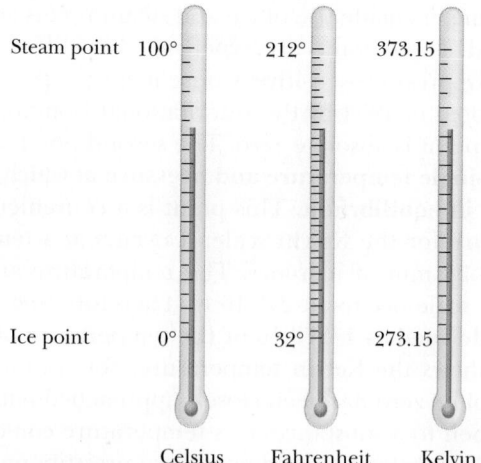

Steam point   100°   212°   373.15

Ice point   0°   32°   273.15

Celsius   Fahrenheit   Kelvin

■ **EXAMPLE 10.1** | **Skin Temperature** BIO

GOAL Apply the temperature conversion formulas.

PROBLEM The temperature gradient between the skin and the air is regulated by cutaneous (skin) blood flow. If the cutaneous blood vessels are constricted, the skin temperature and the temperature of the environment will be about the same. When the vessels are dilated, more blood is brought to the surface. Suppose during dilation the skin warms from 72.0°F to 84.0°F. **(a)** Convert these temperatures to Celsius and find the difference. **(b)** Convert the temperatures to Kelvin, again finding the difference.

STRATEGY This is a matter of applying the conversion formulas, Equations 10.1 and 10.2. For part (b) it's easiest to use the answers for Celsius rather than develop another set of conversion equations.

SOLUTION

(a) Convert the temperatures from Fahrenheit to Celsius and find the difference.

Convert the lower temperature, using Equation 10.2b:

$$T_C = \tfrac{5}{9}(T_F - 32.0) = \tfrac{5}{9}(72.0 - 32.0) = \boxed{22.2°C}$$

Convert the upper temperature:

$$T_C = \tfrac{5}{9}(T_F - 32.0) = \tfrac{5}{9}(84.0 - 32.0) = \boxed{28.9°C}$$

Find the difference of the two temperatures:

$$\Delta T_C = 28.9°C - 22.2°C = \boxed{6.7°C}$$

(b) Convert the temperatures from Fahrenheit to Kelvin and find their difference.

Convert the lower temperature, using the answers for Celsius found in part (a):

$$T_C = T - 273.15 \quad \rightarrow \quad T = T_C + 273.15$$
$$T = 22.2 + 273.15 = \boxed{295\ K}$$

Convert the upper temperature:

$$T = 28.9 + 273.15 = \boxed{302\ K}$$

Find the difference of the two temperatures:

$$\Delta T = 302\ K - 295\ K = \boxed{7\ K}$$

REMARKS The change in temperature in Kelvin and Celsius is the same, as it should be.

QUESTION 10.1 Which represents a larger temperature change, a Celsius degree or a Fahrenheit degree?

EXERCISE 10.1 Core body temperature can rise from 98.6°F to 107°F during extreme exercise, such as a marathon run. Such elevated temperatures can also be caused by viral or bacterial infections or tumors and are dangerous if sustained. (a) Convert the given temperatures to Celsius and find the difference. (b) Convert the temperatures to Kelvin, again finding the difference.

ANSWERS (a) 37.0°C, 41.7°C, 4.7°C   (b) 310.2 K, 314.9 K, 4.7 K

■ EXAMPLE 10.2 | Extraterrestrial Temperature Scale

GOAL Understand how to relate different temperature scales.

PROBLEM An extraterrestrial scientist invents a temperature scale such that water freezes at −75°E and boils at 325°E, where E stands for an extraterrestrial scale. Find an equation that relates temperature in °E to temperature in °C.

STRATEGY Using the given data, find the ratio of the number of °E between the two temperatures to the number of °C. This ratio will be the same as a similar ratio for any other such process—say, from the freezing point to an unknown temperature—corresponding to T_E and T_C. Setting the two ratios equal and solving for T_E in terms of T_C yields the desired relationship. For clarity, the rules of significant figures will not be applied here.

....

SOLUTION

Find the change in temperature in °E between the freezing and boiling points of water:

$$\Delta T_E = 325°E - (-75°E) = 400°E$$

Find the change in temperature in °C between the freezing and boiling points of water:

$$\Delta T_C = 100°C - 0°C = 100°C$$

Form the ratio of these two quantities.

$$\frac{\Delta T_E}{\Delta T_C} = \frac{400°E}{100°C} = 4\,\frac{°E}{°C}$$

This ratio is the same between any other two temperatures—say, from the freezing point to an unknown final temperature. Set the two ratios equal to each other:

$$\frac{\Delta T_E}{\Delta T_C} = \frac{T_E - (-75°E)}{T_C - 0°C} = 4\,\frac{°E}{°C}$$

Solve for T_E:

$$T_E - (-75°E) = 4(°E/°C)(T_C - 0°C)$$
$$T_E = \boxed{4T_C - 75}$$

....

REMARKS The relationship between any other two temperatures scales can be derived in the same way.

QUESTION 10.2 True or False: Finding the relationship between two temperature scales using knowledge of the freezing and boiling point of water in each system is equivalent to finding the equation of a straight line.

EXERCISE 10.2 Find the equation converting °F to °E.

ANSWER $T_E = \frac{20}{9}T_F - 146$

10.3 Thermal Expansion of Solids and Liquids

Our discussion of the liquid thermometer made use of one of the best-known changes that occur in most substances: As temperature of the substance increases, its volume increases. This phenomenon, known as **thermal expansion,** plays an important role in numerous applications. Thermal expansion joints, for example, must be included in buildings, concrete highways, and bridges to compensate for changes in dimensions with variations in temperature (Fig. 10.8 on page 338).

The overall thermal expansion of an object is a consequence of the change in the average separation between its constituent atoms or molecules. To understand this idea, consider how the atoms in a solid substance behave. These atoms are located at fixed equilibrium positions; if an atom is pulled away from its position, a restoring force pulls it back. We can imagine that the atoms are particles connected by springs to their neighboring atoms. (See Fig. 9.1 in the previous chapter.) If an atom is pulled away from its equilibrium position, the distortion of the springs provides a restoring force.

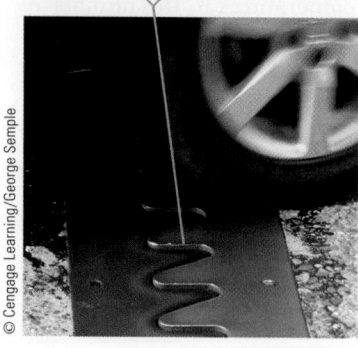

Without these joints to separate sections of roadway on bridges, the surface would buckle due to thermal expansion on very hot days or crack due to contraction on very cold days.

a

The long, vertical joint is filled with a soft material that allows the wall to expand and contract as the temperature of the bricks changes.

b

Figure 10.8 Thermal expansion joints in (a) bridges and (b) walls.

At ordinary temperatures, the atoms vibrate around their equilibrium positions with an amplitude (maximum distance from the center of vibration) of about 10^{-11} m, with an average spacing between the atoms of about 10^{-10} m. As the temperature of the solid increases, the atoms vibrate with greater amplitudes and the average separation between them increases. Consequently, the solid as a whole expands.

If the thermal expansion of an object is sufficiently small compared with the object's initial dimensions, then the change in any dimension is, to a good approximation, proportional to the first power of the temperature change. Suppose an object has an initial length L_0 along some direction at some temperature T_0. Then the length increases by ΔL for a change in temperature ΔT. So for small changes in temperature,

$$\Delta L = \alpha L_0 \, \Delta T \qquad \text{[10.4]}$$

or

$$L - L_0 = \alpha L_0 (T - T_0)$$

where L is the object's final length, T is its final temperature, and the proportionality constant α is called the **coefficient of linear expansion** for a given material and has units of $(°C)^{-1}$.

Table 10.1 lists the coefficients of linear expansion for various materials. Note that for these materials α is positive, indicating an increase in length with increasing temperature.

Thermal expansion affects the choice of glassware used in kitchens and laboratories. If hot liquid is poured into a cold container made of ordinary glass, the container may well break due to thermal stress. The inside surface of the glass becomes hot and expands, while the outside surface is at room temperature, and ordinary glass may not withstand the difference in expansion without breaking. Pyrex® glass has a coefficient of linear expansion of about one-third that of ordinary glass, so the thermal stresses are smaller. Kitchen measuring cups and laboratory beakers are often made of Pyrex so they can be used with hot liquids.

APPLICATION
Pyrex Glass

Tip 10.1 Coefficients of Expansion Are Not Constants

The coefficients of expansion can vary somewhat with temperature, so the given coefficients are actually averages.

Table 10.1 Average Coefficients of Expansion for Some Materials Near Room Temperature

Material	Average Coefficient of Linear Expansion $[(°C)^{-1}]$	Material	Average Coefficient of Volume Expansion $[(°C)^{-1}]$
Aluminum	24×10^{-6}	Acetone	1.5×10^{-4}
Brass and bronze	19×10^{-6}	Benzene	1.24×10^{-4}
Concrete	12×10^{-6}	Ethyl alcohol	1.12×10^{-4}
Copper	17×10^{-6}	Gasoline	9.6×10^{-4}
Glass (ordinary)	9×10^{-6}	Glycerin	4.85×10^{-4}
Glass (Pyrex®)	3.2×10^{-6}	Mercury	1.82×10^{-4}
Invar (Ni-Fe alloy)	0.9×10^{-6}	Turpentine	9.0×10^{-4}
Lead	29×10^{-6}	Air[a] at 0°C	3.67×10^{-3}
Steel	11×10^{-6}	Helium	3.665×10^{-3}

[a]Gases do not have a specific value for the volume expansion coefficient because the amount of expansion depends on the type of process through which the gas is taken. The values given here assume the gas undergoes an expansion at constant pressure.

■ EXAMPLE 10.3 | Expansion of a Railroad Track

GOAL Apply the concept of linear expansion and relate it to stress.

PROBLEM **(a)** A steel railroad track has a length of 30.000 m when the temperature is 0°C. What is its length on a hot day when the temperature is 40.0°C? **(b)** Suppose the track is nailed down so that it can't expand. What stress results in the track due to the temperature change?

STRATEGY **(a)** Apply the linear expansion equation, using Table 10.1 and Equation 10.4. **(b)** A track that cannot expand by ΔL due to external constraints is equivalent to compressing the track by ΔL, creating a stress in the track. Using the equation relating tensile stress to tensile strain together with the linear expansion equation, the amount of (compressional) stress can be calculated using Equation 9.5.

(Example 10.3) Thermal expansion: The extreme heat of a July day in Asbury Park, New Jersey, caused these railroad tracks to buckle.

AP/Wide World Photos

SOLUTION

(a) Find the length of the track at 40.0°C.

Substitute given quantities into Equation 10.4, finding the change in length:

$$\Delta L = \alpha L_0 \Delta T = [11 \times 10^{-6} (°C)^{-1}](30.000 \text{ m})(40.0°C)$$
$$= 0.013 \text{ m}$$

Add the change to the original length to find the final length:

$$L = L_0 + \Delta L = \boxed{30.013 \text{ m}}$$

(b) Find the stress if the track cannot expand.

Substitute into Equation 9.5 to find the stress:

$$\frac{F}{A} = Y\frac{\Delta L}{L} = (2.00 \times 10^{11} \text{ Pa})\left(\frac{0.013 \text{ m}}{30.0 \text{ m}}\right)$$
$$= \boxed{8.7 \times 10^7 \text{ Pa}}$$

REMARKS Repeated heating and cooling is an important part of the weathering process that gradually wears things out, weakening structures over time.

QUESTION 10.3 What happens to the tension of wires in a piano when the temperature decreases?

EXERCISE 10.3 What is the length of the same railroad track on a cold winter day when the temperature is 0°F?

ANSWER 29.994 m

■ APPLYING PHYSICS 10.1 | Bimetallic Strips and Thermostats

How can different coefficients of expansion for metals be used as a temperature gauge and control electronic devices such as air conditioners?

EXPLANATION When the temperatures of a brass rod and a steel rod of equal length are raised by the same amount from some common initial value, the brass rod expands more than the steel rod because brass has a larger coefficient of expansion than steel. A simple device that uses this principle is a **bimetallic strip.** Such strips can be found in the thermostats of certain home heating systems. The strip is made by securely bonding two different metals together. As the temperature of the strip increases, the two metals expand by different amounts and the strip bends, as in Figure 10.9 on page 340. The change in shape can make or break an electrical connection. ■

It may be helpful to picture a thermal expansion as a magnification or a photographic enlargement. For example, as the temperature of a metal washer increases (Active Fig. 10.10 on page 340), all dimensions, including the radius of the hole, increase according to Equation 10.4.

One practical application of thermal expansion is the common technique of using hot water to loosen a metal lid stuck on a glass jar. This works because the circumference of the lid expands more than the rim of the jar.

Figure 10.9 (Applying Physics 10.1) (a) A bimetallic strip bends as the temperature changes because the two metals have different coefficients of expansion. (b) A bimetallic strip used in a thermostat to break or make electrical contact. (c) The interior of a thermostat, showing the coiled bimetallic strip. Why do you suppose the strip is coiled?

Steel
Room temperature   Brass   Higher temperature

Bimetallic strip

On   25°C   Off   30°C

© Cengage Learning/George Sample

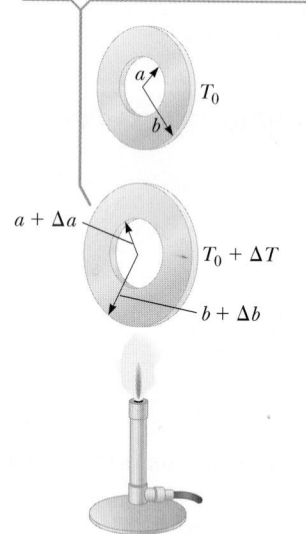

As the washer is heated, all dimensions increase, including the radius of the hole.

a T_0
b

$a + \Delta a$ $T_0 + \Delta T$
$b + \Delta b$

Active Figure 10.10
Thermal expansion of a homogeneous metal washer. (Note that the expansion is exaggerated in this figure.)

Because the linear dimensions of an object change due to variations in temperature, it follows that surface area and volume of the object also change. Consider a square of material having an initial length L_0 on a side and therefore an initial area $A_0 = L_0^2$. As the temperature is increased, the length of each side increases to

$$L = L_0 + \alpha L_0 \Delta T$$

The new area A is

$$A = L^2 = (L_0 + \alpha L_0 \Delta T)(L_0 + \alpha L_0 \Delta T) = L_0^2 + 2\alpha L_0^2 \Delta T + \alpha^2 L_0^2 (\Delta T)^2$$

The last term in this expression contains the quantity $\alpha \Delta T$ raised to the second power. Because $\alpha \Delta T$ is much less than one, squaring it makes it even smaller. Consequently, we can neglect this term to get a simpler expression:

$$A = L_0^2 + 2\alpha L_0^2 \Delta T$$
$$A = A_0 + 2\alpha A_0 \Delta T$$

so that

$$\Delta A = A - A_0 = \gamma A_0 \Delta T \qquad [10.5]$$

where $\gamma = 2\alpha$. The quantity γ (Greek letter gamma) is called the **coefficient of area expansion.**

■ EXAMPLE 10.4 | **Rings and Rods**

GOAL Apply the equation of area expansion.

PROBLEM (a) A circular copper ring at 20.0°C has a hole with an area of 9.980 cm². What minimum temperature must it have so that it can be slipped onto a steel metal rod having a cross-sectional area of 10.000 cm²? (b) Suppose the ring and the rod are heated simultaneously. What minimum change in temperature of both will allow the ring to be slipped onto the end of the rod? (Assume no significant change in the coefficients of linear expansion over this temperature range.)

STRATEGY In part (a), finding the necessary temperature change is just a matter of substituting given values into Equation 10.5, the equation of area expansion. Remember that $\gamma = 2\alpha$. Part (b) is a little harder because now the rod is also expanding. If the ring is to slip onto the rod, however, the final cross-sectional areas of both ring and rod must be equal. Write this condition in mathematical terms, using Equation 10.5 on both sides of the equation, and solve for ΔT.

SOLUTION

(a) Find the temperature of the ring that will allow it to slip onto the rod.

Write Equation 10.5 and substitute known values, leaving ΔT as the sole unknown:

$$\Delta A = \gamma A_0 \Delta T$$
$$0.020 \text{ cm}^2 = [34 \times 10^{-6} \text{ (°C)}^{-1}](9.980 \text{ cm}^2)(\Delta T)$$

Solve for ΔT, then add this change to the initial temperature to get the final temperature:

$$\Delta T = 59°C$$
$$T = T_0 + \Delta T = 20.0°C + 59°C = \boxed{79°C}$$

(b) If both ring and rod are heated, find the minimum change in temperature that will allow the ring to be slipped onto the rod.

Set the final areas of the copper ring and steel rod equal to each other:

$$A_C + \Delta A_C = A_S + \Delta A_S$$

Substitute for each change in area, ΔA:

$$A_C + \gamma_C A_C \Delta T = A_S + \gamma A_S \Delta T$$

Rearrange terms to get ΔT on one side only, factor it out, and solve:

$$\gamma_C A_C \Delta T - \gamma_S A_S \Delta T = A_S - A_C$$
$$(\gamma_C A_C - \gamma_S A_S)\, \Delta T = A_S - A_C$$
$$\Delta T = \frac{A_S - A_C}{\gamma_C A_C - \gamma_S A_S}$$
$$= \frac{10.000\ \text{cm}^2 - 9.980\ \text{cm}^2}{(34 \times 10^{-6}\ °C^{-1})(9.980\ \text{cm}^2) - (22 \times 10^{-6}\ °C^{-1})(10.000\ \text{cm}^2)}$$
$$\Delta T = \boxed{170°C}$$

REMARKS Warming and cooling strategies are sometimes useful for separating glass parts in a chemistry lab, such as the glass stopper in a bottle of reagent.

QUESTION 10.4 If instead of heating the copper ring in part (a) the steel rod is cooled, would the magnitude of the required temperature change be larger, smaller, or the same? Why? (Don't calculate it!)

EXERCISE 10.4 A steel ring with a hole having area of 3.990 cm² is to be placed on an aluminum rod with cross-sectional area of 4.000 cm². Both rod and ring are initially at a temperature of 35.0°C. At what common temperature can the steel ring be slipped onto one end of the aluminum rod?

ANSWER −61°C

We can also show that the *increase in volume* of an object accompanying a change in temperature is

$$\Delta V = \beta V_0\, \Delta T \qquad\qquad \text{[10.6]}$$

where β, the **coefficient of volume expansion,** is equal to 3α. (Note that $\gamma = 2\alpha$ and $\beta = 3\alpha$ only if the coefficient of linear expansion of the object is the same in all directions.) The proof of Equation 10.6 is similar to the proof of Equation 10.5.

As Table 10.1 indicates, each substance has its own characteristic coefficients of expansion.

The thermal expansion of water has a profound influence on rising ocean levels. At current rates of global warming, scientists predict that about one-half of the expected rise in sea level will be caused by thermal expansion; the remainder will be due to the melting of polar ice.

APPLICATION
Rising Sea Levels

■ Quick Quiz

10.2 If you quickly plunge a room-temperature mercury thermometer into very hot water, the mercury level will (a) go up briefly before reaching a final reading, (b) go down briefly before reaching a final reading, or (c) not change.

10.3 If you are asked to make a very sensitive glass thermometer, which of the following working fluids would you choose? (a) mercury (b) alcohol (c) gasoline (d) glycerin

10.4 Two spheres are made of the same metal and have the same radius, but one is hollow and the other is solid. The spheres are taken through the same temperature increase. Which sphere expands more? (a) solid sphere, (b) hollow sphere, (c) they expand by the same amount, or (d) not enough information to say.

▪EXAMPLE 10.5 │ Global Warming and Coastal Flooding   BIO

GOAL Apply the volume expansion equation together with linear expansion.

PROBLEM (a) Estimate the fractional change in the volume of Earth's oceans due to an average temperature change of 1°C. (b) Use the fact that the average depth of the ocean is 4.00×10^3 m to estimate the change in depth. Note that $\beta_{water} = 2.07 \times 10^{-4}(°C)^{-1}$.

STRATEGY In part (a) solve the volume expansion expression, Equation 10.6, for $\Delta V/V$. For part (b) use linear expansion to estimate the increase in depth. Neglect the expansion of landmasses, which would reduce the rise in sea level only slightly.

SOLUTION

(a) Find the fractional change in volume.

Divide the volume expansion equation by V_0 and substitute:

$$\Delta V = \beta V_0 \Delta T$$

$$\frac{\Delta V}{V_0} = \beta \Delta T = (2.07 \times 10^{-4}(°C)^{-1})(1°C) = \boxed{2 \times 10^{-4}}$$

(b) Find the approximate increase in depth.

Use the linear expansion equation. Divide the volume expansion coefficient of water by 3 to get the equivalent linear expansion coefficient:

$$\Delta L = \alpha L_0 \Delta T = \left(\frac{\beta}{3}\right) L_0 \Delta T$$

$$\Delta L = (6.90 \times 10^{-5}(°C)^{-1})(4\,000 \text{ m})(1°C) \approx \boxed{0.3 \text{ m}}$$

REMARKS Three-tenths of a meter may not seem significant, but combined with increased melting of land-based polar ice, some coastal areas could experience flooding. An increase of several degrees increases the value of ΔL several times and could significantly reduce the value of waterfront property.

QUESTION 10.5 Assuming all have the same initial volume, rank the following substances by the amount of volume expansion due to an increase in temperature, from least to most: glass, mercury, aluminum, ethyl alcohol.

EXERCISE 10.5 A 1.00-liter aluminum cylinder at 5.00°C is filled to the brim with gasoline at the same temperature. If the aluminum and gasoline are warmed to 65.0°C, how much of the gasoline spills out? *Hint:* Be sure to account for the expansion of the container. Also, ignore the possibility of evaporation, and assume the volume coefficients are good to three digits.

ANSWER The volume spilled is 53.3 cm³. Forgetting to take into account the expansion of the cylinder results in a (wrong) answer of 57.6 cm³.

▪*Quick Quiz*

10.5 Why doesn't the melting of ocean-based ice raise as much concern as the melting of land-based ice?

The Unusual Behavior of Water

Liquids generally increase in volume with increasing temperature and have volume expansion coefficients about ten times greater than those of solids. Over a small temperature range, water is an exception to this rule, as we can see from its density-versus-temperature curve in Figure 10.11. As the temperature increases from 0°C to 4°C, water contracts, so its density increases. Above 4°C, water exhibits the expected expansion with increasing temperature. The density of water reaches its maximum value of 1 000 kg/m³ at 4°C.

We can use this unusual thermal expansion behavior of water to explain why a pond freezes slowly from the top down. When the atmospheric temperature drops from 7°C to 6°C, say, the water at the surface of the pond also cools and consequently decreases in volume. This means the surface water is more dense than the water below it, which has not yet cooled nor decreased in volume. As a result, the surface water sinks and warmer water from below is forced to the surface to be

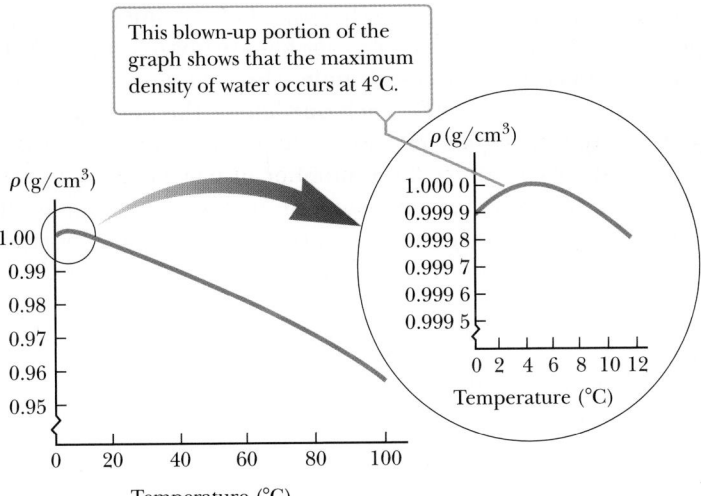

Figure 10.11 The density of water as a function of temperature.

This blown-up portion of the graph shows that the maximum density of water occurs at 4°C.

cooled, a process called *upwelling*. When the atmospheric temperature is between 4°C and 0°C, however, the surface water expands as it cools, becoming less dense than the water below it. The sinking process stops, and eventually the surface water freezes. As the water freezes, the ice remains on the surface because ice is less dense than water. The ice continues to build up on the surface, and water near the bottom of the pool remains at 4°C. Further, the ice forms an insulating layer that slows heat loss from the underlying water, offering thermal protection for marine life.

Without buoyancy and the expansion of water upon freezing, life on Earth may not have been possible. If ice had been more dense than water, it would have sunk to the bottom of the ocean and built up over time. This could have led to a freezing of the oceans, turning Earth into an icebound world similar to Hoth in the Star Wars epic *The Empire Strikes Back*.

The same peculiar thermal expansion properties of water sometimes cause pipes to burst in winter. As energy leaves the water through the pipe by heat and is transferred to the outside cold air, the outer layers of water in the pipe freeze first. The continuing energy transfer causes ice to form ever closer to the center of the pipe. As long as there is still an opening through the ice, the water can expand as its temperature approaches 0°C or as it freezes into more ice, pushing itself into another part of the pipe. Eventually, however, the ice will freeze to the center somewhere along the pipe's length, forming a plug of ice at that point. If there is still liquid water between this plug and some other obstruction, such as another ice plug or a spigot, then no additional volume is available for further expansion and freezing. The pressure in the pipe builds and can rupture the pipe.

BIO APPLICATION

The Expansion of Water on Freezing and Life on Earth

APPLICATION

Bursting Water Pipes in Winter

10.4 Macroscopic Description of an Ideal Gas

The properties of gases are important in a number of thermodynamic processes. Our weather is a good example of the types of processes that depend on the behavior of gases.

If we introduce a gas into a container, it expands to fill the container uniformly, with its pressure depending on the size of the container, the temperature, and the amount of gas. A larger container results in a lower pressure, whereas higher temperatures or larger amounts of gas result in a higher pressure. The pressure P, volume V, temperature T, and amount n of gas in a container are related to each other by an *equation of state*.

The equation of state can be very complicated, but is found experimentally to be relatively simple if the gas is maintained at a low pressure (or a low density).

Such a low-density gas approximates what is called an **ideal gas.** Most gases at room temperature and atmospheric pressure behave approximately as ideal gases. **An ideal gas is a collection of atoms or molecules that move randomly and exert no long-range forces on each other. Each particle of the ideal gas is individually pointlike, occupying a negligible volume.**

A gas usually consists of a very large number of particles, so it's convenient to express the amount of gas in a given volume in terms of the number of **moles,** n. A mole is a number. The same number of particles is found in a mole of helium as in a mole of iron or aluminum. This number is known as *Avogadro's number* and is given by

Avogadro's number ▶

$$N_A = 6.02 \times 10^{23} \text{ particles/mole}$$

Avogadro's number and the definition of a mole are fundamental to chemistry and related branches of physics. The number of moles of a substance is related to its mass m by the expression

$$n = \frac{m}{\text{molar mass}} \qquad [10.7]$$

where the molar mass of the substance is defined as the mass of one mole of that substance, usually expressed in grams per mole.

There are lots of atoms in the world, so it's natural and convenient to choose a very large number like Avogadro's number when describing collections of atoms. At the same time, Avogadro's number must be special in some way because otherwise why not just count things in terms of some large power of ten, like 10^{24}?

It turns out that Avogadro's number was chosen so that the mass in grams of one Avogadro's number of an element is numerically the same as the mass of one atom of the element, expressed in atomic mass units (u).

This relationship is very convenient. Looking at the periodic table of the elements in the back of the book, we find that carbon has an atomic mass of 12 u, so 12 g of carbon consists of exactly 6.02×10^{23} atoms of carbon. The atomic mass of oxygen is 16 u, so in 16 g of oxygen there are again 6.02×10^{23} atoms of oxygen. The same holds true for molecules: The molecular mass of molecular hydrogen, H_2, is 2 u, and there is an Avogadro's number of molecules in 2 g of molecular hydrogen.

The technical definition of a mole is as follows: **One mole (mol) of any substance is that amount of the substance that contains as many particles (atoms, molecules, or other particles) as there are atoms in 12 g of the isotope carbon-12.**

Taking carbon-12 as a test case, let's find the mass of an Avogadro's number of carbon-12 atoms. A carbon-12 atom has an atomic mass of 12 u, or 12 atomic mass units. One atomic mass unit is equal to 1.66×10^{-24} g, about the same as the mass of a neutron or proton—particles that make up atomic nuclei. The mass m of an Avogadro's number of carbon-12 atoms is then given by

$$m = N_A(12 \text{ u}) = 6.02 \times 10^{23}(12 \text{ u})\left(\frac{1.66 \times 10^{-24} \text{ g}}{\text{u}}\right) = 12.0 \text{ g}$$

So we see that Avogadro's number is deliberately chosen to be the inverse of the number of grams in an atomic mass unit. In this way the atomic mass of an atom expressed in atomic mass units is numerically the same as the mass of an Avogadro's number of that kind of atom expressed in grams. Because there are 6.02×10^{23} particles in one mole of *any* element, the mass per atom for a given element is

$$m_{\text{atom}} = \frac{\text{molar mass}}{N_A}$$

For example, the mass of a helium atom is

$$m_{\text{He}} = \frac{4.00 \text{ g/mol}}{6.02 \times 10^{23} \text{ atoms/mol}} = 6.64 \times 10^{-24} \text{ g/atom}$$

Now suppose an ideal gas is confined to a cylindrical container with a volume that can be changed by moving a piston, as in Active Figure 10.12. Assume that the

Active Figure 10.12
A gas confined to a cylinder whose volume can be varied with a movable piston.

cylinder doesn't leak, so the number of moles remains constant. Experiments yield the following observations: First, when the gas is kept at a constant temperature, its pressure is inversely proportional to its volume (Boyle's law). Second, when the pressure of the gas is kept constant, the volume of the gas is directly proportional to the temperature (Charles's law). Third, when the volume of the gas is held constant, the pressure is directly proportional to the temperature (Gay-Lussac's law). These observations can be summarized by the following equation of state, known as the **ideal gas law:**

$$PV = nRT \qquad [10.8]$$

◀ Equation of state for an ideal gas

In this equation R is a constant for a specific gas that must be determined from experiments, whereas T is the temperature in kelvins. Each point on a P versus V diagram would represent a different state of the system. Experiments on several gases show that, as the pressure approaches zero, the quantity PV/nT approaches the same value of R for all gases. For this reason, R is called the **universal gas constant.** In SI units, where pressure is expressed in pascals and volume in cubic meters,

$$R = 8.31 \text{ J/mol} \cdot \text{K} \qquad [10.9]$$

◀ The universal gas constant

If the pressure is expressed in atmospheres and the volume is given in liters (recall that $1 \text{ L} = 10^3 \text{ cm}^3 = 10^{-3} \text{ m}^3$), then

$$R = 0.082\ 1 \text{ L} \cdot \text{atm/mol} \cdot \text{K}$$

Using this value of R and Equation 10.8, the volume occupied by 1 mol of any ideal gas at atmospheric pressure and at 0°C (273 K) is 22.4 L.

> **Tip 10.2 Only Kelvin Works!**
>
> Temperatures used in the ideal gas law must always be in kelvins.

> **Tip 10.3 Standard Temperature and Pressure**
>
> Chemists often define standard temperature and pressure (STP) to be 20°C and 1.0 atm. We choose STP to be 0°C and 1.0 atm.

▪ EXAMPLE 10.6 | An Expanding Gas

GOAL Use the ideal gas law to analyze a system of gas.

PROBLEM An ideal gas at 20.0°C and a pressure of 1.50×10^5 Pa is in a container having a volume of 1.00 L. **(a)** Determine the number of moles of gas in the container. **(b)** The gas pushes against a piston, expanding to twice its original volume, while the pressure falls to atmospheric pressure. Find the final temperature.

STRATEGY In part (a) solve the ideal gas equation of state for the number of moles, n, and substitute the known quantities. Be sure to convert the temperature from Celsius to Kelvin! When comparing two states of a gas as in part (b) it's often most convenient to divide the ideal gas equation of the final state by the equation of the initial state. Then quantities that don't change can immediately be cancelled, simplifying the algebra.

· ·

SOLUTION
(a) Find the number of moles of gas.

Convert the temperature to kelvins:

$$T = T_C + 273 = 20.0 + 273 = 293 \text{ K}$$

Solve the ideal gas law for n and substitute:

$$PV = nRT$$
$$n = \frac{PV}{RT} = \frac{(1.50 \times 10^5 \text{ Pa})(1.00 \times 10^{-3} \text{ m}^3)}{(8.31 \text{ J/mol} \cdot \text{K})(293 \text{ K})}$$
$$= \boxed{6.16 \times 10^{-2} \text{ mol}}$$

(b) Find the temperature after the gas expands to 2.00 L.

Divide the ideal gas law for the final state by the ideal gas law for the initial state:

$$\frac{P_f V_f}{P_i V_i} = \frac{nRT_f}{nRT_i}$$

(Continued)

Cancel the number of moles n and the gas constant R, and solve for T_f:

$$\frac{P_f V_f}{P_i V_i} = \frac{T_f}{T_i}$$

$$T_f = \frac{P_f V_f}{P_i V_i} T_i = \frac{(1.01 \times 10^5 \text{ Pa})(2.00 \text{ L})}{(1.50 \times 10^5 \text{ Pa})(1.00 \text{ L})} (293 \text{ K})$$

$$= \boxed{395 \text{ K}}$$

REMARKS Remember the trick used in part (b); it's often useful in ideal gas problems. Notice that it wasn't necessary to convert units from liters to cubic meters because the units were going to cancel anyway.

QUESTION 10.6 Assuming constant temperature, does a helium balloon expand, contract, or remain at constant volume as it rises through the air?

EXERCISE 10.6 Suppose the temperature of 4.50 L of ideal gas drops from 375 K to 275 K. (a) If the volume remains constant and the initial pressure is atmospheric pressure, find the final pressure. (b) Find the number of moles of gas.

ANSWERS (a) 7.41×10^4 Pa (b) 0.146 mol

▪ EXAMPLE 10.7 | Message in a Bottle

GOAL Apply the ideal gas law in tandem with Newton's second law.

PROBLEM A beachcomber finds a corked bottle containing a message. The air in the bottle is at atmospheric pressure and a temperature of 30.0°C. The cork has a cross-sectional area of 2.30 cm². The beachcomber places the bottle over a fire, figuring the increased pressure will push out the cork. At a temperature of 99°C the cork is ejected from the bottle. **(a)** What was the pressure in the bottle just before the cork left it? **(b)** What force of friction held the cork in place? Neglect any change in volume of the bottle.

STRATEGY In part (a) the number of moles of air in the bottle remains the same as it warms over the fire. Take the ideal gas equation for the final state and divide by the ideal gas equation for the initial state. Solve for the final pressure. In part (b) there are three forces acting on the cork: a friction force, the exterior force of the atmosphere pushing in, and the force of the air inside the bottle pushing out. Apply Newton's second law. Just before the cork begins to move, the three forces are in equilibrium and the static friction force has its maximum value.

SOLUTION

(a) Find the final pressure.

Divide the ideal gas law at the final point by the ideal gas law at the initial point:

$$(1) \quad \frac{P_f V_f}{P_i V_i} = \frac{nRT_f}{nRT_i}$$

Cancel n, R, and V, which don't change, and solve for P_f:

$$\frac{P_f}{P_i} = \frac{T_f}{T_i} \quad \rightarrow \quad P_f = P_i \frac{T_f}{T_i}$$

Substitute known values, obtaining the final pressure:

$$P_f = (1.01 \times 10^5 \text{ Pa}) \frac{372 \text{ K}}{303 \text{ K}} = \boxed{1.24 \times 10^5 \text{ Pa}}$$

(b) Find the magnitude of the friction force acting on the cork.

Apply Newton's second law to the cork just before it leaves the bottle. P_{in} is the pressure inside the bottle, and P_{out} is the pressure outside.

$$\sum F = 0 \quad \rightarrow \quad P_{in}A - P_{out}A - F_{friction} = 0$$

$$F_{friction} = P_{in}A - P_{out}A = (P_{in} - P_{out})A$$

$$= (1.24 \times 10^5 \text{ Pa} - 1.01 \times 10^5 \text{ Pa})(2.30 \times 10^{-4} \text{ m}^2)$$

$$F_{friction} = \boxed{5.29 \text{ N}}$$

REMARKS Notice the use, once again, of the ideal gas law in Equation (1). Whenever comparing the state of a gas at two different points, this is the best way to do the math. One other point: Heating the gas blasted the cork out of the bottle, which meant the gas did work on the cork. The work done by an expanding gas—driving pistons and generators—is one of the foundations of modern technology and will be studied extensively in Chapter 12.

QUESTION 10.7 As the cork begins to move, what happens to the pressure inside the bottle?

EXERCISE 10.7 A tire contains air at a gauge pressure of 5.00×10^4 Pa at a temperature of 30.0°C. After nightfall, the temperature drops to −10.0°C. Find the new gauge pressure in the tire. (Recall that gauge pressure is absolute pressure minus atmospheric pressure. Assume constant volume.)

ANSWER 3.01×10^4 Pa

■ EXAMPLE 10.8 | **Submerging a Balloon**

GOAL Combine the ideal gas law with the equation of hydrostatic equilibrium and buoyancy.

PROBLEM A sturdy balloon with volume 0.500 m³ is attached to a 2.50×10^2-kg iron weight and tossed overboard into a freshwater lake. The balloon is made of a light material of negligible mass and elasticity (although it can be compressed). The air in the balloon is initially at atmospheric pressure. The system fails to sink and there are no more weights, so a skin diver decides to drag it deep enough so that the balloon will remain submerged. **(a)** Find the volume of the balloon at the point where the system will remain submerged, in equilibrium. **(b)** What's the balloon's pressure at that point? **(c)** Assuming constant temperature, to what minimum depth must the balloon be dragged?

STRATEGY As the balloon and weight are dragged deeper into the lake, the air in the balloon is compressed and the volume is reduced along with the buoyancy. At some depth h the total buoyant force acting on the balloon and weight, $B_{bal} + B_{Fe}$, will equal the total weight, $w_{bal} + w_{Fe}$, and the balloon will remain at that depth. Substitute these forces into Newton's second law and solve for the unknown volume of the balloon, answering part (a). Then use the ideal gas law to find the pressure, and the equation of hydrostatic equilibrium to find the depth.

· ·

SOLUTION

(a) Find the volume of the balloon at the equilibrium point.

Find the volume of the iron, V_{Fe}:

$$V_{Fe} = \frac{m_{Fe}}{\rho_{Fe}} = \frac{2.50 \times 10^2 \text{ kg}}{7.86 \times 10^3 \text{ kg/m}^3} = 0.031\ 8 \text{ m}^3$$

Find the mass of the balloon, which is equal to the mass of the air if we neglect the mass of the balloon's material:

$$m_{bal} = \rho_{air} V_{bal} = (1.29 \text{ kg/m}^3)(0.500 \text{ m}^3) = 0.645 \text{ kg}$$

Apply Newton's second law to the system when it's in equilibrium:

$$B_{Fe} - w_{Fe} + B_{bal} - w_{bal} = 0$$

Substitute the appropriate expression for each term:

$$\rho_{wat} V_{Fe}\, g - m_{Fe}\, g + \rho_{wat} V_{bal}\, g - m_{bal}\, g = 0$$

Cancel the g's and solve for the volume of the balloon, V_{bal}:

$$V_{bal} = \frac{m_{bal} + m_{Fe} - \rho_{wat} V_{Fe}}{\rho_{wat}}$$

$$= \frac{0.645 \text{ kg} + 2.50 \times 10^2 \text{ kg} - (1.00 \times 10^3 \text{ kg/m}^3)(0.031\ 8 \text{ m}^3)}{1.00 \times 10^3 \text{kg/m}^3}$$

$$V_{bal} = \boxed{0.219 \text{ m}^3}$$

(b) What's the balloon's pressure at the equilibrium point?

Now use the ideal gas law to find the pressure, assuming constant temperature, so that $T_i = T_f$.

$$\frac{P_f V_f}{P_i V_i} = \frac{nRT_f}{nRT_i} = 1$$

$$P_f = \frac{V_i}{V_f} P_i = \frac{0.500 \text{ m}^3}{0.219 \text{ m}^3} (1.01 \times 10^5 \text{ Pa})$$

$$= \boxed{2.31 \times 10^5 \text{ Pa}}$$

(Continued)

(c) To what minimum depth must the balloon be dragged?

Use the equation of hydrostatic equilibrium to find the depth:

$$P_f = P_{atm} + \rho g h$$

$$h = \frac{P_f - P_{atm}}{\rho g} = \frac{2.31 \times 10^5 \text{ Pa} - 1.01 \times 10^5 \text{ Pa}}{(1.00 \times 10^3 \text{ kg/m}^3)(9.80 \text{ m/s}^2)}$$

$$= \boxed{13.3 \text{ m}}$$

REMARKS Once again, the ideal gas law was used to good effect. This problem shows how even answering a fairly simple question can require the application of several different physical concepts: density, buoyancy, the ideal gas law, and hydrostatic equilibrium.

QUESTION 10.8 If a glass is turned upside down and then submerged in water, what happens to the volume of the trapped air as the glass is pushed deeper under water?

EXERCISE 10.8 A boy takes a 30.0-cm^3 balloon holding air at 1.00 atm at the surface of a freshwater lake down to a depth of 4.00 m. Find the volume of the balloon at this depth. Assume the balloon is made of light material of little elasticity (although it can be compressed) and the temperature of the trapped air remains constant.

ANSWER 21.6 cm^3

As previously stated, the number of molecules contained in one mole of any gas is Avogadro's number, $N_A = 6.02 \times 10^{23}$ particles/mol, so

$$n = \frac{N}{N_A} \qquad [10.10]$$

where n is the number of moles and N is the number of molecules in the gas. With Equation 10.10, we can rewrite the ideal gas law in terms of the total number of molecules as

$$PV = nRT = \frac{N}{N_A} RT$$

or

Ideal gas law ▶

$$PV = Nk_B T \qquad [10.11]$$

where

Boltzmann's constant ▶

$$k_B = \frac{R}{N_A} = 1.38 \times 10^{-23} \text{ J/K} \qquad [10.12]$$

is **Boltzmann's constant.** This reformulation of the ideal gas law will be used in the next section to relate the temperature of a gas to the average kinetic energy of particles in the gas.

10.5 The Kinetic Theory of Gases

In Section 10.4 we discussed the macroscopic properties of an ideal gas, including pressure, volume, number of moles, and temperature. In this section we consider the ideal gas model from the microscopic point of view. We will show that the macroscopic properties can be understood on the basis of what is happening on the atomic scale. In addition, we reexamine the ideal gas law in terms of the behavior of the individual molecules that make up the gas.

Using the model of an ideal gas, we will describe the **kinetic theory of gases.** With this theory we can interpret the pressure and temperature of an ideal gas in terms of microscopic variables. The kinetic theory of gases model makes the following assumptions:

1. **The number of molecules in the gas is large, and the average separation between them is large compared with their dimensions.** Because the number of molecules is large, we can analyze their behavior statistically. The large separation between molecules means that the molecules occupy a negligible volume in the container. This assumption is consistent with the ideal gas model, in which we imagine the molecules to be pointlike.

2. **The molecules obey Newton's laws of motion, but as a whole they move randomly.** By "randomly" we mean that any molecule can move in any direction with equal probability, with a wide distribution of speeds.

3. **The molecules interact only through short-range forces during elastic collisions.** This assumption is consistent with the ideal gas model, in which the molecules exert no long-range forces on each other.

4. **The molecules make elastic collisions with the walls.**

5. **All molecules in the gas are identical.**

◀ Assumptions of kinetic theory for an ideal gas

Although we often picture an ideal gas as consisting of single atoms, *molecular* gases exhibit ideal behavior at low pressures. On average, effects associated with molecular structure have no effect on the motions considered, so we can apply the results of the following development to molecular gases as well as to monatomic gases.

Molecular Model for the Pressure of an Ideal Gas

As a first application of kinetic theory, we derive an expression for the pressure of an ideal gas in a container in terms of microscopic quantities. The pressure of the gas is the result of collisions between the gas molecules and the walls of the container. During these collisions, the gas molecules undergo a change of momentum as a result of the force exerted on them by the walls.

We now derive an expression for the pressure of an ideal gas consisting of N molecules in a container of volume V. In this section we use m to represent the mass of one molecule. The container is a cube with edges of length d (Fig. 10.13). Consider the collision of one molecule moving with a velocity $-v_x$ toward the left-hand face of the box (Fig. 10.14). After colliding elastically with the wall, the molecule moves in the positive x-direction with a velocity $+v_x$. Because the momentum of the molecule is $-mv_x$ before the collision and $+mv_x$ afterward, the change in its momentum is

$$\Delta p_x = mv_x - (-mv_x) = 2mv_x$$

If F_1 is the magnitude of the average force exerted by a molecule on the *wall* in the time Δt, then applying Newton's second law to the wall gives

$$F_1 = \frac{\Delta p_x}{\Delta t} = \frac{2mv_x}{\Delta t}$$

For the molecule to make two collisions with the same wall, it must travel a distance $2d$ along the x-direction in a time Δt. Therefore, the time interval between two collisions with the same wall is $\Delta t = 2d/v_x$, and the force imparted to the wall by a single molecule is

$$F_1 = \frac{2mv_x}{\Delta t} = \frac{2mv_x}{2d/v_x} = \frac{mv_x^{\,2}}{d}$$

The total force F exerted by all the molecules on the wall is found by adding the forces exerted by the individual molecules:

$$F = \frac{m}{d}\left(v_{1x}^{\,2} + v_{2x}^{\,2} + \cdots\right)$$

In this equation v_{1x} is the x-component of velocity of molecule 1, v_{2x} is the x-component of velocity of molecule 2, and so on. The summation terminates when we reach N molecules in the container because there are N molecules in the container.

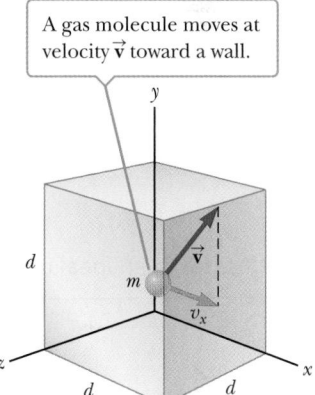

A gas molecule moves at velocity $\vec{v}$ toward a wall.

Figure 10.13 A cubical box with sides of length d containing an ideal gas.

Before collision

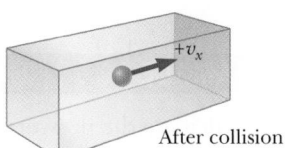

After collision

Figure 10.14 A molecule moving along the x-axis in a container collides elastically with a wall, reversing its momentum and exerting a force on the wall.

The glass vessel contains dry ice (solid carbon dioxide). Carbon dioxide gas is denser than air, hence falls when poured from the cylinder. The gas is colorless, but is made visible by the formation of tiny ice crystals from water vapor.

Note that the average value of the square of the velocity in the x-direction for N molecules is

$$\overline{v_x^2} = \frac{v_{1x}^2 + v_{2x}^2 + \cdots + v_{Nx}^2}{N}$$

where $\overline{v_x^2}$ is the average value of v_x^2. The total force on the wall can then be written

$$F = \frac{Nm}{d}\,\overline{v_x^2}$$

Now we focus on one molecule in the container traveling in some arbitrary direction with velocity $\vec{v}$ and having components v_x, v_y, and v_z. In this case we must express the total force on the wall in terms of the speed of the molecules rather than just a single component. The Pythagorean theorem relates the square of the speed to the square of these components according to the expression $v^2 = v_x^2 + v_y^2 + v_z^2$. Hence, the average value of v^2 for all the molecules in the container is related to the average values $\overline{v_x^2}$, $\overline{v_y^2}$, and $\overline{v_z^2}$ according to the expression $\overline{v^2} = \overline{v_x^2} + \overline{v_y^2} + \overline{v_z^2}$. Because the motion is completely random, the average values $\overline{v_x^2}$, $\overline{v_y^2}$, and $\overline{v_z^2}$ are equal to each other. Using this fact and the earlier equation for $\overline{v_x^2}$, we find that

$$\overline{v_x^2} = \tfrac{1}{3}\,\overline{v^2}$$

The total force on the wall, then, is

$$F = \frac{N}{3}\left(\frac{m\overline{v^2}}{d}\right)$$

This expression allows us to find the total pressure exerted on the wall by dividing the force by the area:

$$P = \frac{F}{A} = \frac{F}{d^2} = \tfrac{1}{3}\left(\frac{N}{d^3}\,m\overline{v^2}\right) = \tfrac{1}{3}\left(\frac{N}{V}\right)m\overline{v^2}$$

Pressure of an ideal gas ▶

$$P = \tfrac{2}{3}\left(\frac{N}{V}\right)\left(\tfrac{1}{2}m\overline{v^2}\right) \qquad [10.13]$$

Equation 10.13 says that **the pressure is proportional to the number of molecules per unit volume and to the average translational kinetic energy of a molecule,** $\tfrac{1}{2}m\overline{v^2}$. With this simplified model of an ideal gas, we have arrived at an important result that relates the large-scale quantity of pressure to an atomic quantity: the average value of the square of the molecular speed. This relationship provides a key link between the atomic world and the large-scale world.

Equation 10.13 captures some familiar features of pressure. One way to increase the pressure inside a container is to increase the number of molecules per unit volume in the container. You do this when you add air to a tire. The pressure in the tire can also be increased by increasing the average translational kinetic energy of the molecules in the tire. As we will see shortly, this can be accomplished by increasing the temperature of the gas inside the tire. That's why the pressure inside a tire increases as the tire warms up during long trips. The continuous flexing of the tires as they move along the road transfers energy to the air inside them, increasing the air's temperature, which in turn raises the pressure.

■ EXAMPLE 10.9 | High-Energy Electron Beam

GOAL Calculate the pressure of an electron particle beam.

PROBLEM A beam of electrons moving in the positive x-direction impacts a target in a vacuum chamber. **(a)** If 1.25×10^{14} electrons traveling at a speed of 3.00×10^7 m/s strike the target during each brief pulse lasting 5.00×10^{-8} s, what average force is exerted on the target during the pulse? Assume all the electrons penetrate the target and are absorbed. **(b)** What average pressure is exerted on the beam spot, which has radius 4.00 mm? *Note*: The beam spot is the region of the target struck by the beam.

STRATEGY The average force exerted by the target on an electron is the change in electron's momentum divided by the time required to bring the electron to rest. By the third law, an equal and opposite force is exerted on the target. During the pulse, N such collisions take place in a total time Δt, so multiplying the negative of a single electron's change in momentum by N and dividing by the pulse duration Δt gives the average force exerted on the target during the pulse. Dividing that force by the area of the beam spot yields the average pressure on the beam spot.

SOLUTION

(a) The force on the target is equal to the negative of the change in momentum of each electron multiplied by the number N of electrons and divided by the pulse duration:

$$F = -\frac{N\Delta p}{\Delta t}$$

Substitute the expression $\Delta p = mv_f - mv_i$ and note that $v_f = 0$ by assumption:

$$F = -\frac{N(mv_f - mv_i)}{\Delta t} = -\frac{Nm(0 - v_i)}{\Delta t}$$

Substitute values:

$$F = -\frac{(1.25 \times 10^{14})(9.11 \times 10^{-31}\text{ kg})(0 - 3.00 \times 10^7\text{ m/s})}{(5.00 \times 10^{-8}\text{ s})}$$

$$= \boxed{0.068\ 3\ N}$$

(b) Calculate the pressure of the beam.

Use the definition of average pressure, the force divided by area:

$$P = \frac{F}{A} = \frac{F}{\pi r^2} = \frac{0.068\ 3\text{ N}}{\pi(0.004\ 00\text{ m})^2}$$

$$= \boxed{1.36 \times 10^3\text{ Pa}}$$

REMARKS High-energy electron beams can be used for welding and shock strengthening of materials. Relativistic effects (see Chapter 26) were neglected in this calculation, and would be relatively small in any case at a tenth the speed of light. This example illustrates how numerous collisions by atomic or, in this case, subatomic particles can result in macroscopic physical effects such as forces and pressures.

QUESTION 10.9 If the same beam were directed at a material that reflected all the electrons, how would the final pressure be affected?

EXERCISE 10.9 A beam of protons traveling at 2.00×10^6 m/s strikes a target during a brief pulse that lasts 7.40×10^{-9} s. (a) If there are 4.00×10^9 protons in the beam and all are reflected elastically, what force is exerted on the target? (b) What average pressure is exerted on the beam spot, which has radius of 2.00 mm?

ANSWERS (a) 0.003 61 N (b) 287 Pa

Molecular Interpretation of Temperature

Having related the pressure of a gas to the average kinetic energy of the gas molecules, we now relate temperature to a microscopic description of the gas. We can obtain some insight into the meaning of temperature by multiplying Equation 10.13 by the volume:

$$PV = \tfrac{2}{3} N \left(\tfrac{1}{2}mv^2\right)$$

Comparing this equation with the equation of state for an ideal gas in the form of Equation 10.11, $PV = Nk_B T$, we note that the left-hand sides of the two equations are identical. Equating the right-hand sides, we obtain

$$T = \frac{2}{3k_B}\left(\tfrac{1}{2}m\overline{v^2}\right) \qquad \text{[10.14]}$$

◄ Temperature is proportional to average kinetic energy

This means that **the temperature of a gas is a direct measure of the average molecular kinetic energy of the gas.** As the temperature of a gas increases, the molecules move with higher average kinetic energy.

Rearranging Equation 10.14, we can relate the translational molecular kinetic energy to the temperature:

$$\tfrac{1}{2}m\overline{v^2} = \tfrac{3}{2}k_B T \qquad \text{[10.15]}$$

◄ Average kinetic energy per molecule

So the average translational kinetic energy per molecule is $\frac{3}{2}k_BT$. The total translational kinetic energy of N molecules of gas is simply N times the average energy per molecule,

Total kinetic energy of ▶
N molecules

$$KE_{total} = N\left(\tfrac{1}{2}mv^2\right) = \tfrac{3}{2}Nk_BT = \tfrac{3}{2}nRT \qquad [10.16]$$

where we have used $k_B = R/N_A$ for Boltzmann's constant and $n = N/N_A$ for the number of moles of gas. From this result, we see that **the total translational kinetic energy of a system of molecules is proportional to the absolute temperature of the system.**

For a monatomic gas, translational kinetic energy is the only type of energy the molecules can have, so Equation 10.16 gives the **internal energy U for a monatomic gas:**

$$U = \tfrac{3}{2}nRT \quad \text{(monatomic gas)} \qquad [10.17]$$

For diatomic and polyatomic molecules, additional possibilities for energy storage are available in the vibration and rotation of the molecule.

The square root of $\overline{v^2}$ is called the **root-mean-square (rms) speed** of the molecules. From Equation 10.15, we get, for the rms speed,

Root-mean-square speed ▶

$$v_{rms} = \sqrt{\overline{v^2}} = \sqrt{\frac{3k_BT}{m}} = \sqrt{\frac{3RT}{M}} \qquad [10.18]$$

Tip 10.4 Kilograms Per Mole, Not Grams Per Mole

In the equation for the rms speed, the units of molar mass M must be consistent with the units of the gas constant R. In particular, if R is in SI units, M must be expressed in kilograms per mole, not grams per mole.

where M is the molar mass in *kilograms per mole*, if R is given in SI units. Equation 10.18 shows that, at a given temperature, lighter molecules tend to move faster than heavier molecules. For example, if gas in a vessel consists of a mixture of hydrogen and oxygen, the hydrogen (H_2) molecules, with a molar mass of 2.0×10^{-3} kg/mol, move four times faster than the oxygen (O_2) molecules, with molar mass 32×10^{-3} kg/mol. If we calculate the rms speed for hydrogen at room temperature (~300 K), we find

$$v_{rms} = \sqrt{\frac{3RT}{M}} = \sqrt{\frac{3(8.31\ \text{J/mol}\cdot\text{K})(300\ \text{K})}{2.0 \times 10^{-3}\ \text{kg/mol}}} = 1.9 \times 10^3\ \text{m/s}$$

This speed is about 17% of the escape speed for Earth, as calculated in Chapter 7. Because it is an average speed, a large number of molecules have much higher speeds and can therefore escape from Earth's atmosphere. This is why Earth's atmosphere doesn't currently contain hydrogen: it has all bled off into space.

Table 10.2 lists the rms speeds for various molecules at 20°C. A system of gas at a given temperature will exhibit a variety of speeds. This distribution of speeds is known as the *Maxwell velocity distribution*. An example of such a distribution for nitrogen gas at two different temperatures is given in Active Figure 10.15. The horizontal axis is speed, and the vertical axis is the number of molecules per unit speed. Notice that three speeds are of special interest: the most probable speed, corresponding to the peak in the graph; the average speed, which is found by averaging over all the possible speeds; and the rms speed. For every gas, note that $v_{mp} < v_{av} < v_{rms}$. As the temperature rises, these three speeds shift to the right.

Table 10.2 Some rms Speeds

Gas	Molar Mass (kg/mol)	v_{rms} at 20°C (m/s)
H_2	2.02×10^{-3}	1 902
He	4.0×10^{-3}	1 352
H_2O	18×10^{-3}	637
Ne	20.2×10^{-3}	602
N_2 and CO	28.0×10^{-3}	511
NO	30.0×10^{-3}	494
O_2	32.0×10^{-3}	478
CO_2	44.0×10^{-3}	408
SO_2	64.1×10^{-3}	338

■ Quick Quiz

10.6 One container is filled with argon gas and another with helium gas. Both containers are at the same temperature. Which atoms have the higher rms speed? (a) argon, (b) helium, (c) they have the same speed, or (d) not enough information to say.

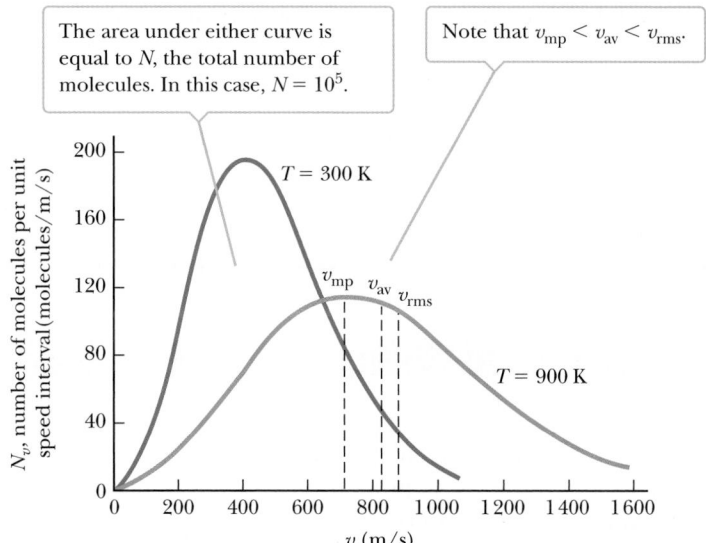

The area under either curve is equal to N, the total number of molecules. In this case, $N = 10^5$.

Note that $v_{mp} < v_{av} < v_{rms}$.

Active Figure 10.15
The Maxwell speed distribution for 10^5 nitrogen molecules at 300 K and 900 K.

■ APPLYING PHYSICS 10.2 | Expansion and Temperature

Imagine a gas in an insulated cylinder with a movable piston. The piston has been pushed inward, compressing the gas, and is now released. As the molecules of the gas strike the piston, they move it outward. Explain, from the point of view of the kinetic theory, how the expansion of this gas causes its temperature to drop.

EXPLANATION From the point of view of kinetic theory, a molecule colliding with the piston causes the piston to move with some velocity. According to the conservation of momentum, the molecule must rebound with less speed than it had before the collision. As these collisions occur, the average speed of the collection of molecules is therefore reduced. Because temperature is related to the average speed of the molecules, the temperature of the gas drops. ■

■ EXAMPLE 10.10 | A Cylinder of Helium

GOAL Calculate the internal energy of a system and the average kinetic energy per molecule.

PROBLEM A cylinder contains 2.00 mol of helium gas at 20.0°C. Assume the helium behaves like an ideal gas. **(a)** Find the total internal energy of the system. **(b)** What is the average kinetic energy per molecule? **(c)** How much energy would have to be added to the system to double the rms speed? The molar mass of helium is equal to 4.00×10^{-3} kg/mol.

STRATEGY This problem requires substitution of given information into the appropriate equations: Equation 10.17 for part (a) and Equation 10.15 for part (b). In part (c) use the equations for the rms speed and internal energy together. A *change* in the internal energy must be computed.

SOLUTION

(a) Find the total internal energy of the system.

Substitute values into Equation 10.17 with $n = 2.00$ and $T = 293$ K:

$$U = \tfrac{3}{2}(2.00 \text{ mol})(8.31 \text{ J/mol} \cdot \text{K})(293 \text{ K}) = \boxed{7.30 \times 10^3 \text{ J}}$$

(b) What is the average kinetic energy per molecule?

Substitute given values into Equation 10.15:

$$\tfrac{1}{2}m\overline{v^2} = \tfrac{3}{2}k_B T = \tfrac{3}{2}(1.38 \times 10^{-23} \text{ J/K})(293 \text{ K})$$
$$= \boxed{6.07 \times 10^{-21} \text{ J}}$$

(c) How much energy must be added to double the rms speed?

From Equation 10.18, doubling the rms speed requires quadrupling T. Calculate the required change of internal energy, which is the energy that must be put into the system:

$$\Delta U = U_f - U_i = \tfrac{3}{2}nRT_f - \tfrac{3}{2}nRT_i = \tfrac{3}{2}nR(T_f - T_i)$$
$$\Delta U = \tfrac{3}{2}(2.00 \text{ mol})(8.31 \text{ J/mol} \cdot \text{K})[(4.00 \times 293 \text{ K}) - 293 \text{ K}]$$
$$= \boxed{2.19 \times 10^4 \text{ J}}$$

(Continued)

REMARKS Computing changes in internal energy will be important in understanding engine cycles in Chapter 12.

QUESTION 10.10 True or False: At the same temperature, 1 mole of helium gas has the same internal energy as 1 mole of argon gas.

EXERCISE 10.10 The temperature of 5.00 moles of argon gas is lowered from 3.00×10^2 K to 2.40×10^2 K. (a) Find the change in the internal energy, ΔU, of the gas. (b) Find the change in the average kinetic energy per atom.

ANSWERS (a) $\Delta U = -3.74 \times 10^3$ J (b) -1.24×10^{-21} J

SUMMARY

10.1 Temperature and the Zeroth Law of Thermodynamics

Two systems are in **thermal contact** if energy can be exchanged between them, and in **thermal equilibrium** if they're in contact and there is no net exchange of energy. The exchange of energy between two objects because of differences in their temperatures is called **heat.**

The **zeroth law of thermodynamics** states that if two objects A and B are separately in thermal equilibrium with a third object, then A and B are in thermal equilibrium with each other. Equivalently, if the third object is a **thermometer,** then the **temperature** it measures for A and B will be the same. Two objects in thermal equilibrium are at the same temperature.

10.2 Thermometers and Temperature Scales

Thermometers measure temperature and are based on physical properties, such as the temperature-dependent expansion or contraction of a solid, liquid, or gas. These changes in volume are related to a linear scale, the most common being the **Fahrenheit, Celsius,** and **Kelvin scales.** The Kelvin temperature scale takes its zero point as **absolute zero** (0 K = $-273.15°$C), the point at which, by extrapolation, the pressure of all gases falls to zero.

The relationship between the Celsius temperature T_C and the Kelvin (absolute) temperature T is

$$T_C = T - 273.15 \qquad [10.1]$$

The relationship between the Fahrenheit and Celsius temperatures is

$$T_F = \tfrac{9}{5}T_C + 32 \qquad [10.2a]$$

10.3 Thermal Expansion of Solids and Liquids

Ordinarily a substance expands when heated. If an object has an initial length L_0 at some temperature and undergoes a change in temperature ΔT, its linear dimension changes by the amount ΔL, which is proportional to the object's initial length and the temperature change:

$$\Delta L = \alpha L_0 \Delta T \qquad [10.4]$$

The parameter α is called the **coefficient of linear expansion.** The change in area of a substance with change in temperature is given by

$$\Delta A = \gamma A_0 \Delta T \qquad [10.5]$$

where $\gamma = 2\alpha$ is the **coefficient of area expansion.** Similarly, the change in volume with temperature of most substances is proportional to the initial volume V_0 and the temperature change ΔT:

$$\Delta V = \beta V_0 \Delta T \qquad [10.6]$$

where $\beta = 3\alpha$ is the **coefficient of volume expansion.**

The expansion and contraction of material due to changes in temperature create stresses and strains, sometimes sufficient to cause fracturing.

10.4 Macroscopic Description of an Ideal Gas

Avogadro's number is $N_A = 6.02 \times 10^{23}$ particles/mol. A mole of anything, by definition, consists of an Avogadro's number of particles. The number is defined so that one mole of carbon-12 atoms has a mass of exactly 12 g. The mass of one mole of a pure substance in grams is the same, numerically, as that substance's atomic (or molecular) mass.

An **ideal gas** obeys the equation

$$PV = nRT \qquad [10.8]$$

where P is the pressure of the gas, V is its volume, n is the number of moles of gas, R is the universal gas constant (8.31 J/mol · K), and T is the absolute temperature in kelvins. A real gas at very low pressures behaves approximately as an ideal gas.

Solving problems usually entails comparing two different states of the same system of gas, dividing the ideal gas equation for the final state by the ideal gas equation for the initial state, canceling factors that don't change, and solving for the unknown quantity.

10.5 The Kinetic Theory of Gases

The **pressure** of N molecules of an ideal gas contained in a volume V is given by

$$P = \tfrac{2}{3}\left(\frac{N}{V}\right)\left(\tfrac{1}{2}m\overline{v^2}\right) \qquad [10.13]$$

where $\tfrac{1}{2}m\overline{v^2}$ is the **average kinetic energy per molecule.**

The average kinetic energy of the molecules of a gas is directly proportional to the absolute temperature of the gas:

$$\tfrac{1}{2}m\overline{v^2} = \tfrac{3}{2}k_B T \qquad [10.15]$$

The quantity k_B is **Boltzmann's constant** (1.38×10^{-23} J/K).

The internal energy of n moles of a monatomic ideal gas is

$$U = \tfrac{3}{2}nRT \qquad [10.17]$$

The **root-mean-square (rms) speed** of the molecules of a gas is

$$v_{\text{rms}} = \sqrt{\frac{3k_B T}{m}} = \sqrt{\frac{3RT}{M}} \qquad [10.18]$$

■ MULTIPLE-CHOICE QUESTIONS

WebAssign The multiple-choice questions in this chapter may be assigned online in Enhanced WebAssign.

1. On a very cold day in upstate New York, the temperature is $-25°C$, which is equivalent to what temperature in Fahrenheit? (a) $-46°F$ (b) $-77°F$ (c) $18°F$ (d) 298 K (e) $-13°F$

2. A hole is drilled in a metal plate. When the metal is heated, what happens to the diameter of the hole? (a) It decreases. (b) It increases. (c) It remains the same. (d) The answer depends on the initial temperature of the metal. (e) None of these

3. The average coefficient of linear expansion of copper is 17×10^{-6} $(°C)^{-1}$. The Statue of Liberty is 93 m tall on a summer morning when the temperature is $25°C$. Assume the copper plates covering the statue are mounted edge to edge without expansion joints and do not buckle or bind on the framework supporting them as the day grows hot. What is the order of magnitude of the statue's increase in height if the temperature increases by $5°C$? (a) 0.1 mm (b) 1 mm (c) 1 cm (d) 10 cm (e) 1 m

4. Convert $162°F$ to the equivalent temperature in Kelvin. (a) 373 K (b) 288 K (c) 345 K (d) 201 K (e) 308 K

5. One way to cool a gas is to let it expand. When a certain gas under a pressure of 5.00×10^6 Pa at $25.0°C$ is allowed to expand to 3.00 times its original volume, its final pressure is 1.07×10^6 Pa. What is its final temperature? (a) $177°C$ (b) 233 K (c) 212 K (d) 191 K (e) 115 K

6. If the volume of an ideal gas is doubled while its temperature is quadrupled, does the pressure (a) remain the same, (b) decrease by a factor of 2, (c) decrease by a factor of 4, (d) increase by a factor of 2, or (e) increase by a factor of 4?

7. A container holds 0.50 m^3 of oxygen at an absolute pressure of 4.0 atm. A valve is opened, allowing the gas to drive a piston, increasing the volume of the gas until the pressure drops to 1.0 atm. If the temperature remains constant, what new volume does the gas occupy? (a) 1.0 m^3 (b) 1.5 m^3 (c) 2.0 m^3 (d) 0.12 m^3 (e) 2.5 m^3

8. What is the internal energy of 26.0 g of neon gas at a temperature of $152°C$? (a) 2 440 J (b) 6 830 J (c) 3 140 J (d) 5 870 J (e) 5 020 J

9. Suppose you empty a tray of ice cubes into a bowl partly full of water and cover the bowl. After one-half hour, the contents of the bowl come to thermal equilibrium, with more liquid water and less ice than you started with. Which of the following is true? (a) The temperature of the liquid water is higher than the temperature of the remaining ice. (b) The temperature of the liquid water is the same as that of the ice. (c) The temperature of the liquid water is less than that of the ice. (d) The comparative temperatures of the liquid water and ice depend on the amounts present.

10. Which of the assumptions below is *not* made in the kinetic theory of gases? (a) The number of molecules is very small. (b) The molecules obey Newton's laws of motion. (c) The collisions between molecules are elastic. (d) The gas is a pure substance. (e) The average separation between molecules is large compared with their dimensions.

11. Suppose for a brief moment the gas molecules hitting a wall stuck to the wall instead of bouncing off the wall. How would the pressure on the wall be affected during that brief time? (a) The pressure would be zero. (b) The pressure would be halved. (c) The pressure would remain unchanged. (d) The pressure would double. (e) The answer would depend on the area of the wall.

12. If the temperature of an ideal gas is increased from 200 K to 600 K, what happens to the rms speed of the molecules? (a) It increases by a factor of 3. (b) It remains the same. (c) It is one-third of the original speed. (d) It is $\sqrt{3}$ times the original speed. (e) It increases by a factor of 6.

13. A rubber balloon is filled with 1 L of air at 1 atm and 300 K and is then cooled to 100 K. The rubber remains flexible as it cools. **(i)** What happens to the volume of the balloon? (a) It decreases to $\tfrac{1}{6}$ L. (b) It decreases to $\tfrac{1}{3}$ L. (c) It decreases to $L/\sqrt{3}$. (d) It is constant. (e) It increases. **(ii)** What happens to the pressure of the air in the balloon? (a) It decreases to $\tfrac{1}{6}$ atm. (b) It decreases to $\tfrac{1}{3}$ atm. (c) It decreases to $1/\sqrt{3}$ atm. (d) It is constant. (e) It increases.

14. Two cylinders A and B at the same temperature contain the same quantity of the same kind of gas. Cylinder A has three times the volume of cylinder B. What can you conclude about the pressures the gases exert? (a) We can conclude nothing about the pressures. (b) The pressure in A is three times the pressure in B. (c) The pressures must be equal. (d) The pressure in A must be one-third the pressure in B.

■ CONCEPTUAL QUESTIONS

WebAssign The conceptual questions in this chapter may be assigned online in Enhanced WebAssign.

1. (a) Why does an ordinary glass dish usually break when placed on a hot stove? (b) Dishes made of Pyrex glass don't break as easily. What characteristic of Pyrex prevents breakage?

2. Why is a power line more likely to break in winter than in summer, even if it is loaded with the same weight?

3. Some thermometers are made of a mercury column in a glass tube. Based on the operation of these common thermometers, which has the larger coefficient of linear expansion, glass or mercury? (Don't answer this question by looking in a table.)

4. A rubber balloon is blown up and the end tied. Is the pressure inside the balloon greater than, less than, or equal to the ambient atmospheric pressure? Explain.

5. Objects deep beneath the surface of the ocean are subjected to extremely high pressures, as we saw in Chapter 9. Some bacteria in these environments have adapted to pressures as much as a thousand times atmospheric pressure. How might such bacteria be affected if they were rapidly moved to the surface of the ocean?

6. After food is cooked in a pressure cooker, why is it very important to cool the container with cold water before attempting to remove the lid?

7. Why do vapor bubbles in a pot of boiling water get larger as they approach the surface?

8. Markings to indicate length are placed on a steel tape in a room that is at a temperature of 22°C. Measurements are then made with the same tape on a day when the temperature is 27°C. Are the measurements too long, too short, or accurate?

9. Some picnickers stop at a convenience store to buy food, including bags of potato chips. They then drive up into the mountains to their picnic site. When they unload the food, they notice that the bags of chips are puffed up like balloons. Why did this happen?

10. Why do small planets tend to have little or no atmosphere?

11. Metal lids on glass jars can often be loosened by running hot water over them. Why does that work?

12. Suppose the volume of an ideal gas is doubled while the pressure is reduced by half. Does the internal energy of the gas increase, decrease, or remain the same? Explain.

13. An automobile radiator is filled to the brim with water when the engine is cool. What happens to the water when the engine is running and the water has been raised to a high temperature?

14. When the metal ring and metal sphere in Figure CQ10.14 are both at room temperature, the sphere can barely be passed through the ring. (a) After the sphere is warmed in a flame, it cannot be passed through the ring. Explain. (b) What if the ring is warmed and the sphere is left at room temperature? Does the sphere pass through the ring?

© Charles D. Winters/Cengage Learning

Figure CQ10.14

■ PROBLEMS

WebAssign The problems in this chapter may be assigned online in Enhanced WebAssign. Selected problems also have Watch It video solutions.

1. denotes straightforward problem; 2. denotes intermediate problem;

3. denotes challenging problem

1. denotes full solution available in *Student Solutions Manual/Study Guide*

1. denotes problems most often assigned in Enhanced WebAssign

BIO denotes biomedical problems

GP denotes guided problems

M denotes Master It tutorial available in Enhanced WebAssign

Q|C denotes asking for quantitative and conceptual reasoning

S denotes symbolic reasoning problem

10.1 Temperature and the Zeroth Law of Thermodynamics

10.2 Thermometers and Temperature Scales

1. For each of the following temperatures, find the equivalent temperature on the indicated scale: (a) −273.15°C on the Fahrenheit scale, (b) 98.6°F on the Celsius scale, and (c) 100 K on the Fahrenheit scale.

2. The pressure in a constant-volume gas thermometer is 0.700 atm at 100°C and 0.512 atm at 0°C. (a) What is the temperature when the pressure is 0.040 0 atm? (b) What is the pressure at 450°C?

3. The boiling point of liquid hydrogen is 20.3 K at atmospheric pressure. What is this temperature on (a) the Celsius scale and (b) the Fahrenheit scale?

4. Death Valley holds the record for the highest recorded temperature in the United States. On July 10, 1913, at a place called Furnace Creek Ranch, the temperature rose to 134°F. The lowest U.S. temperature ever recorded occurred at Prospect Creek Camp in Alaska on January 23, 1971, when the temperature plummeted to −79.8° F. (a) Convert these temperatures to the Celsius scale. (b) Convert the Celsius temperatures to Kelvin.

5. Show that the temperature −40° is unique in that it has the same numerical value on the Celsius and Fahrenheit scales.

6. **M** In a student experiment, a constant-volume gas thermometer is calibrated in dry ice (−78.5°C) and in boiling ethyl alcohol (78.0°C). The separate pressures are 0.900 atm and 1.635 atm. (a) What value of absolute zero in degrees Celsius does the calibration yield? (b) What pressures would be found at (b) the freezing and (c) boiling points of water? *Hint*: Use the linear relationship $P = A + BT$, where A and B are constants.

7. Show that if the temperature on the Celsius scale changes by ΔT_C, the Fahrenheit temperature changes by $\Delta T_F = \frac{9}{5}\Delta T_C$.

8. The temperature difference between the inside and the outside of a home on a cold winter day is 57.0°F. Express this difference on (a) the Celsius scale and (b) the Kelvin scale.

9. **Q|C** A nurse measures the temperature of a patient to be 41.5°C. (a) What is this temperature on the Fahrenheit scale? (b) Do you think the patient is seriously ill? Explain.

10. **S** Temperature differences on the Rankine scale are identical to differences on the Fahrenheit scale, but absolute zero is given as 0°R. (a) Find a relationship converting the temperatures T_F of the Fahrenheit scale to the corresponding temperatures T_R of the Rankine scale. (b) Find a second relationship converting temperatures T_R of the Rankine scale to the temperatures T_K of the Kelvin scale.

10.3 Thermal Expansion of Solids and Liquids

11. The New River Gorge bridge in West Virginia is a 518-m-long steel arch. How much will its length change between temperature extremes of −20°C and 35°C?

12. **Q|C** A grandfather clock is controlled by a swinging brass pendulum that is 1.3 m long at a temperature of 20°C. (a) What is the length of the pendulum rod when the temperature drops to 0.0°C? (b) If a pendulum's period is given by $T = 2\pi\sqrt{L/g}$, where L is its length, does the change in length of the rod cause the clock to run fast or slow?

13. A pair of eyeglass frames are made of epoxy plastic (coefficient of linear expansion = 1.30×10^{-4} °C^{-1}). At room temperature (20.0°C), the frames have circular lens holes 2.20 cm in radius. To what temperature must the frames be heated if lenses 2.21 cm in radius are to be inserted into them?

14. A spherical steel ball bearing has a diameter of 2.540 cm at 25.00°C. (a) What is its diameter when its temperature is raised to 100.0°C? (b) What temperature change is required to increase its volume by 1.000%?

15. A brass ring of diameter 10.00 cm at 20.0°C is heated and slipped over an aluminum rod of diameter 10.01 cm at 20.0°C. Assuming the average coefficients of linear expansion are constant, (a) to what temperature must the combination be cooled to separate the two metals? Is that temperature attainable? (b) What if the aluminum rod were 10.02 cm in diameter?

16. **S** A solid substance has a density ρ_0 at a temperature T_0. If its temperature is increased by an amount ΔT, show that its density at the higher temperature is given by

$$\rho = \frac{\rho_0}{1 + \beta\Delta T}$$

17. **Q|C** Lead has a density of 11.3×10^3 kg/m^3 at 0°C. (a) What is the density of lead at 90°C? (b) Based on your answer to part (a), now consider a situation in which you plan to invest in a gold bar. Would you be better off buying it on a warm day? Explain.

18. **Q|C** The Golden Gate Bridge in San Francisco has a main span of length 1.28 km, one of the longest in the world. Imagine that a steel wire with this length and a cross-sectional area of 4.00×10^{-6} m^2 is laid on the bridge deck with its ends attached to the towers of the bridge, on a summer day when the temperature of the wire is 35.0°C. (a) When winter arrives, the towers stay the same distance apart and the bridge deck keeps the same shape as its expansion joints open. When the temperature drops to −10.0°C, what is the tension in the wire? Take Young's modulus for steel to be 20.0×10^{10} N/m^2. (b) Permanent deformation occurs if the stress in the steel exceeds its elastic limit of 3.00×10^8 N/m^2. At what temperature would the wire reach its elastic limit? (c) Explain how your answers to (a) and (b) would change if the Golden Gate Bridge were twice as long.

19. **M** An underground gasoline tank can hold 1.00×10^3 gallons of gasoline at 52.0°F. If the tank is being filled on a day when the outdoor temperature (and the gasoline in a tanker truck) is 95.0°F, how many gallons from the truck can be poured into the tank? Assume the temperature of the gasoline quickly cools from 95.0°F to 52.0°F upon entering the tank.

20. **S** Show that the coefficient of volume expansion, β, is related to the coefficient of linear expansion, α, through the expression $\beta = 3\alpha$.

21. A hollow aluminum cylinder 20.0 cm deep has an internal capacity of 2.000 L at 20.0°C. It is completely filled with turpentine at 20.0°C. The turpentine and the aluminum cylinder are then slowly warmed together to 80.0°C. (a) How much turpentine overflows? (b) What is the volume of the turpentine remaining in the cylinder at 80.0°C? (c) If the combination with this amount of turpentine is then cooled back to 20.0°C, how far below the cylinder's rim does the turpentine's surface recede?

22. A construction worker uses a steel tape to measure the length of an aluminum support column. If the measured length is 18.700 m when the temperature is 21.2°C, what is the measured length when the temperature rises to 29.4°C? *Note*: Don't neglect the expansion of the tape.

23. The band in Figure P10.23 is stainless steel (coefficient of linear expansion = 17.3×10^{-6} °C^{-1}; Young's modulus = 18×10^{10} N/m^2). It is essentially circular with an initial mean radius of 5.0 mm, a height of 4.0 mm, and a thickness of 0.50 mm. If the band just fits snugly over the tooth when heated to a temperature of 80°C, what is the tension in the band when it cools to a temperature of 37°C?

Figure P10.23

24. **QC** The Trans-Alaskan pipeline is 1 300 km long, reaching from Prudhoe Bay to the port of Valdez, and is subject to temperatures ranging from −73°C to +35°C. (a) How much does the steel pipeline expand due to the difference in temperature? (b) How can one compensate for this expansion?

25. The average coefficient of volume expansion for carbon tetrachloride is 5.81×10^{-4} (°C)$^{-1}$. If a 50.0-gal steel container is filled completely with carbon tetrachloride when the temperature is 10.0°C, how much will spill over when the temperature rises to 30.0°C?

26. **GP** The density of gasoline is 7.30×10^2 kg/m^3 at 0°C. Its average coefficient of volume expansion is 9.60×10^{-4}(°C)$^{-1}$, and note that 1.00 gal = 0.003 80 m^3. (a) Calculate the mass of 10.0 gal of gas at 0°C. (b) If 1.000 m^3 of gasoline at 0°C is warmed by 20.0°C, calculate its new volume. (c) Using the answer to part (b), calculate the density of gasoline at 20.0°C. (d) Calculate the mass of 10.0 gal of gas at 20.0°C. (e) How many extra kilograms of gasoline would you get if you bought 10.0 gal of gasoline at 0°C rather than at 20.0°C from a pump that is not temperature compensated?

27. Figure P10.27 shows a circular steel casting with a gap. If the casting is heated, (a) does the

Figure P10.27

width of the gap increase or decrease? (b) The gap width is 1.600 cm when the temperature is 30.0°C. Determine the gap width when the temperature is 190°C.

28. The concrete sections of a certain superhighway are designed to have a length of 25.0 m. The sections are poured and cured at 10.0°C. What minimum spacing should the engineer leave between the sections to eliminate buckling if the concrete is to reach a temperature of 50.0°C?

10.4 Macroscopic Description of an Ideal Gas

29. One mole of oxygen gas is at a pressure of 6.00 atm and a temperature of 27.0°C. (a) If the gas is heated at constant volume until the pressure triples, what is the final temperature? (b) If the gas is heated so that both the pressure and volume are doubled, what is the final temperature?

30. **GP** A 20.0-L tank of carbon dioxide gas (CO_2) is at a pressure of 9.50×10^5 Pa and temperature of 19.0°C. (a) Calculate the temperature of the gas in Kelvin. (b) Use the ideal gas law to calculate the number of moles of gas in the tank. (c) Use the periodic table to compute the molecular weight of carbon dioxide, expressing it in grams per mole. (d) Obtain the number of grams of carbon dioxide in the tank. (e) A fire breaks out, raising the ambient temperature by 224.0 K while 82.0 g of gas leak out of the tank. Calculate the new temperature and the number of moles of gas remaining in the tank. (f) Using a technique analogous to that in Example 10.6b, find a symbolic expression for the final pressure, neglecting the change in volume of the tank. (g) Calculate the final pressure in the tank as a result of the fire and leakage.

31. (a) An ideal gas occupies a volume of 1.0 cm^3 at 20°C and atmospheric pressure. Determine the number of molecules of gas in the container. (b) If the pressure of the 1.0-cm^3 volume is reduced to 1.0×10^{-11} Pa (an extremely good vacuum) while the temperature remains constant, how many moles of gas remain in the container?

32. **M** An automobile tire is inflated with air originally at 10.0°C and normal atmospheric pressure. During the process, the air is compressed to 28.0% of its original volume and the temperature is increased to 40.0°C. (a) What is the tire pressure in pascals? (b) After the car is driven at high speed, the tire's air temperature rises to 85.0°C and the tire's interior volume increases by 2.00%. What is the new tire pressure (absolute) in pascals?

33. Gas is confined in a tank at a pressure of 11.0 atm and a temperature of 25.0°C. If two-thirds of the gas is withdrawn and the temperature is raised to 75.0°C, what is the new pressure of the gas remaining in the tank?

34. Gas is contained in an 8.00-L vessel at a temperature of 20.0°C and a pressure of 9.00 atm. (a) Determine the

number of moles of gas in the vessel. (b) How many molecules are in the vessel?

35. A weather balloon is designed to expand to a maximum radius of 20 m at its working altitude, where the air pressure is 0.030 atm and the temperature is 200 K. If the balloon is filled at atmospheric pressure and 300 K, what is its radius at liftoff?

36. The density of helium gas at 0°C is $\rho_0 = 0.179$ kg/m^3. The temperature is then raised to $T = 100$°C, but the pressure is kept constant. Assuming the helium is an ideal gas, calculate the new density ρ_f of the gas.

37. An air bubble has a volume of 1.50 cm^3 when it is released by a submarine 100 m below the surface of a lake. What is the volume of the bubble when it reaches the surface? Assume the temperature and the number of air molecules in the bubble remain constant during its ascent.

38. **Q|C** **S** The ideal gas law can be recast in terms of the density of a gas. (a) Use dimensional analysis to find an expression for the density ρ of a gas in terms of the number of moles n, the volume V, and the molecular weight M in kilograms per mole. (b) With the expression found in part (a), show that

$$P = \frac{\rho}{M} RT$$

for an ideal gas. (c) Find the density of the carbon dioxide atmosphere at the surface of Venus, where the pressure is 90.0 atm and the temperature is 7.00×10^2 K. (d) Would an evacuated steel shell of radius 1.00 m and mass 2.00×10^2 kg rise or fall in such an atmosphere? Why?

10.5 The Kinetic Theory of Gases

39. What is the average kinetic energy of a molecule of oxygen at a temperature of 300 K?

40. A sealed cubical container 20.0 cm on a side contains three times Avogadro's number of molecules at a temperature of 20.0°C. Find the force exerted by the gas on one of the walls of the container.

41. Use Avogadro's number to find the mass of a helium atom.

42. Two gases in a mixture pass through a filter at rates proportional to the gases' rms speeds. (a) Find the ratio of speeds for the two isotopes of chlorine, ^{35}Cl and ^{37}Cl, as they pass through the air. (b) Which isotope moves faster?

43. At what temperature would the rms speed of helium atoms equal (a) the escape speed from Earth, 1.12×10^4 m/s and (b) the escape speed from the Moon, 2.37×10^3 m/s? (See Chapter 7 for a discussion of escape speed.) *Note*: The mass of a helium atom is 6.64×10^{-27} kg.

44. **Q|C** A 7.00-L vessel contains 3.50 moles of ideal gas at a pressure of 1.60×10^6 Pa. Find (a) the temperature of the gas and (b) the average kinetic energy of a gas molecule in the vessel. (c) What additional information would you need if you were asked to find the average speed of a gas molecule?

45. Superman leaps in front of Lois Lane to save her from a volley of bullets. In a 1-minute interval, an automatic weapon fires 150 bullets, each of mass 8.0 g, at 400 m/s. The bullets strike his mighty chest, which has an area of 0.75 m^2. Find the average force exerted on Superman's chest if the bullets bounce back after an elastic, head-on collision.

46. **M** In a period of 1.0 s, 5.0×10^{23} nitrogen molecules strike a wall of area 8.0 cm^2. If the molecules move at 300 m/s and strike the wall head on in a perfectly elastic collision, find the pressure exerted on the wall. (The mass of one N$_2$ molecule is 4.68×10^{-26} kg.)

Additional Problems

47. Inside the wall of a house, an L-shaped section of hot-water pipe consists of three parts: a straight horizontal piece $h = 28.0$ cm long, an elbow, and a straight, vertical piece $\ell = 134$ cm long (Fig. P10.47). A stud and a second-story floorboard hold the ends of this section of copper pipe stationary. Find the magnitude and direction of the displacement of the pipe elbow when the water flow is turned on, raising the temperature of the pipe from 18.0°C to 46.5°C.

Figure P10.47

48. **M** The active element of a certain laser is made of a glass rod 30.0 cm long and 1.50 cm in diameter. Assume the average coefficient of linear expansion of the glass is 9.00×10^{-6} (°C)$^{-1}$. If the temperature of the rod increases by 65.0°C, what is the increase in (a) its length, (b) its diameter, and (c) its volume?

49. A popular brand of cola contains 6.50 g of carbon dioxide dissolved in 1.00 L of soft drink. If the evaporating carbon dioxide is trapped in a cylinder at 1.00 atm and 20.0°C, what volume does the gas occupy?

50. **Q|C** Consider an object with any one of the shapes displayed in Table 8.1. What is the percentage increase in the moment of inertia of the object when it is warmed from 0°C to 100°C if it is composed of (a) copper or (b) aluminum? Assume the average linear expansion coefficients shown in Table 10.1 do not vary between 0°C and 100°C. (c) Why are the answers for parts (a) and (b) the same for all the shapes?

51. A steel beam being used in the construction of a skyscraper has a length of 35.000 m when delivered on a cold day at a temperature of 15.000°F. What is the

length of the beam when it is being installed later on a warm day when the temperature is 90.000°F?

52. A 1.5-m-long glass tube that is closed at one end is weighted and lowered to the bottom of a freshwater lake. When the tube is recovered, an indicator mark shows that water rose to within 0.40 m of the closed end. Determine the depth of the lake. Assume constant temperature.

53. Long-term space missions require reclamation of the oxygen in the carbon dioxide exhaled by the crew. In one method of reclamation, 1.00 mol of carbon dioxide produces 1.00 mol of oxygen, with 1.00 mol of methane as a by-product. The methane is stored in a tank under pressure and is available to control the attitude of the spacecraft by controlled venting. A single astronaut exhales 1.09 kg of carbon dioxide each day. If the methane generated in the recycling of three astronauts' respiration during one week of flight is stored in an originally empty 150-L tank at −45.0°C, what is the final pressure in the tank?

54. **QC** **S** A vertical cylinder of cross-sectional area A is fitted with a tight-fitting, frictionless piston of mass m (Fig. P10.54). (a) If n moles of an ideal gas are in the cylinder at a temperature of T, use Newton's second law for equilibrium to show that the height h at which the piston is in equilibrium under its own weight is given by

$$h = \frac{nRT}{mg + P_0 A}$$

where P_0 is atmospheric pressure. (b) Is the pressure inside the cylinder less than, equal to, or greater than atmospheric pressure? (c) If the gas in the cylinder is warmed, how would the answer for h be affected?

Figure P10.54

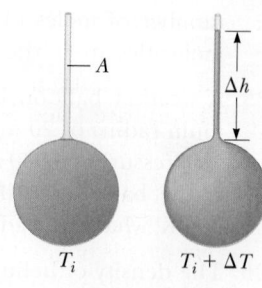

55. A flask made of Pyrex is calibrated at 20.0°C. It is filled to the 100-mL mark on the flask with 35.0°C acetone. (a) What is the volume of the acetone when both it and the flask cool to 20.0°C? (b) Would the temporary increase in the Pyrex flask's volume make an appreciable difference in the answer? Why or why not?

56. **S** The pressure gauge on a cylinder of gas registers the gauge pressure, which is the difference between the interior and exterior pressure, P_0. When the cylinder is full, the mass of the gas in it is m_i at a gauge pressure of P_i. Assuming the temperature of the cylinder remains constant, use the ideal gas law and a relationship between moles and mass to show that the mass of the gas *remaining* in the cylinder when the gauge pressure reading is P_f is given by

$$m_f = m_i \left(\frac{P_f + P_0}{P_i + P_0} \right)$$

57. **QC** **S** A liquid with a coefficient of volume expansion of β just fills a spherical flask of volume V_0 at temperature T_i (Fig. P10.57). The flask is made of a material that has a coefficient of linear expansion of α. The liquid is free to expand into a capillary of cross-sectional area A at the top. (a) Show that if the temperature increases by ΔT, the liquid rises in the capillary by the amount $\Delta h = (V_0/A)(\beta - 3\alpha)\Delta T$. (b) For a typical system, such as a mercury thermometer, why is it a good approximation to neglect the expansion of the flask?

Figure P10.57

58. Before beginning a long trip on a hot day, a driver inflates an automobile tire to a gauge pressure of 1.80 atm at 300 K. At the end of the trip, the gauge pressure has increased to 2.20 atm. (a) Assuming the volume has remained constant, what is the temperature of the air inside the tire? (b) What percentage of the original mass of air in the tire should be released so the pressure returns to its original value? Assume the temperature remains at the value found in part (a) and the volume of the tire remains constant as air is released.

59. Two concrete spans of a 250-m-long bridge are placed end to end so that no room is allowed for expansion (Fig. P10.59a). If the temperature increases by 20.0°C, what is the height y to which the spans rise when they buckle (Fig. P10.59b)?

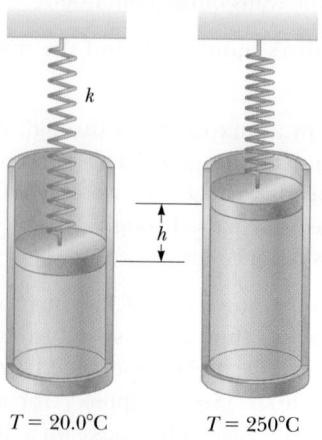

Figure P10.59

60. An expandable cylinder has its top connected to a spring with force constant 2.00×10^3 N/m (Fig. P10.60). The cylinder is filled with 5.00 L of gas with

Figure P10.60

the spring relaxed at a pressure of 1.00 atm and a temperature of 20.0°C. (a) If the lid has a cross-sectional area of 0.010 0 m² and negligible mass, how high will the lid rise when the temperature is raised to 250°C? (b) What is the pressure of the gas at 250°C?

61. **QC** **S** A bimetallic strip of length L is made of two ribbons of different metals bonded together. (a) First assume the strip is originally straight. As the strip is warmed, the metal with the greater average coefficient of expansion expands more than the other, forcing the strip into an arc, with the outer radius having a greater circumference (Fig. P10.61). Derive an expression for the angle of bending, θ, as a function of the initial length of the strips, their average coefficients of linear expansion, the change in temperature, and the separation of the centers of the strips ($\Delta r = r_2 - r_1$). (b) Show that the angle of bending goes to zero when ΔT goes to zero and also when the two average coefficients of expansion become equal. (c) What happens if the strip is cooled?

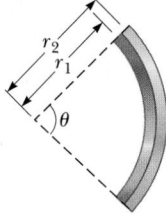

Figure P10.61

62. A 250-m-long bridge is improperly designed so that it cannot expand with temperature. It is made of concrete with $\alpha = 12 \times 10^{-6}$ °C⁻¹. (a) Assuming the maximum change in temperature at the site is expected to be 20°C, find the change in length the span would undergo if it were free to expand. (b) Show that the stress on an object with Young's modulus Y when raised by ΔT with its ends firmly fixed is given by $\alpha Y \Delta T$. (c) If the maximum stress the bridge can withstand without crumbling is 2.0×10^7 Pa, will it crumble because of this temperature increase? Young's modulus for concrete is about 2.0×10^{10} Pa.

63. **QC** Following a collision in outer space, a copper disk at 850°C is rotating about its axis with an angular speed of 25.0 rad/s. As the disk radiates infrared light, its temperature falls to 20.0°C. No external torque acts on the disk. (a) Does the angular speed change as the disk cools? Explain how it changes or why it does not. (b) What is its angular speed at the lower temperature?

64. Two small containers, each with a volume of 100 cm³, contain helium gas at 0°C and 1.00 atm pressure. The two containers are joined by a small open tube of negligible volume, allowing gas to flow from one container to the other. What common pressure will exist in the two containers if the temperature of one container is raised to 100°C while the other container is kept at 0°C?

■ AP* REVIEW QUESTIONS

1. A length of 1.2 cm is added to a material's original length of 10 m as it expands while being heated from 0°C to 100°C. Using the following table, identify the material.

Material	Coefficient of linear expansion α $[(°C)^{-1}]$
Aluminum	24×10^{-6}
Glass (ordinary)	9×10^{-6}
Invar (Ni + Fe alloy)	0.9×10^{-6}
Lead	29×10^{-6}
Concrete	12×10^{-6}

   (A) Aluminum

   (B) Concrete

   (C) Glass (ordinary)

   (D) Invar (Ni + Fe alloy)

   (E) Lead

2. A 10 m sample of Invar ($\alpha = 0.9 \times 10^{-6}/°C$) is cooled from 400 K to 300 K. What is the new length?

   (A) 0.009 m

   (B) 9.0 mm

   (C) 10.009 m

   (D) 9.991 m

   (E) More information is needed

3. A circle with an area of 2 cm^2 needs to fit into an area of 2.48 cm^2. If its coefficient of linear expansion, α, is $30 \times 10^{-6}/°C$, what change in temperature is required for the circle to expand to its required size?

   (A) 40°C

   (B) 400°C

   (C) 4000°C

   (D) 40,000°C

   (E) More information is needed

4. A metal lid is stuck on a glass jar. Mary runs it under hot water to try and loosen it. Will it work and why or why not?

   (A) No. Both the glass jar rim and the metal lid will expand the same amount.

   (B) No. The glass jar rim expands more than the metal lid.

   (C) No. The water is not hot enough to make a difference on either the glass jar rim or the metal lid.

   (D) Yes. The hot water lubricates the joint between the glass jar rim and the metal lid.

   (E) Yes. The metal lid expands more than the glass jar rim.

5. Which of the following is NOT a basic assumption of the kinetic theory of gases?

   (A) All molecules in the gas are identical.

   (B) The number of molecules is large and the molecules are closely spaced.

   (C) The molecules move randomly.

   (D) The molecules interact via short-range forces.

   (E) The molecules make elastic collisions with the walls.

6. The average v_{rms} (root-mean-square) speed of neon gas at 27°C is about 600 m/s. What will its v_{rms} be if its temperature is increased to 927°C?

   (A) 600 m/s

   (B) 1200 m/s

   (C) 2400 m/s

   (D) 5400 m/s

   (E) 20,600 m/s

7. At 20°C, water vapor has a $v_{rms} = 640$ m/s. If sulfur dioxide has a molar mass, M, that is quadruple that of water vapor, what will be the v_{rms} for the sulfur dioxide at 20°C?

(A) 2560 m/s

(B) 1280 m/s

(C) 640 m/s

(D) 320 m/s

(E) 160 m/s

8. If a gas is heated from 127°C to 1327°C, what will happen to the kinetic energy of its molecules?

(A) Cut in half

(B) Stays the same

(C) 2 times greater

(D) 4 times greater

(E) 11 times greater

9. A gas is at a pressure P_1, temperature T_1, and volume V_1. If the gas is heated to twice its original temperature AND pressure, what is the new volume of the gas?

(A) $\dfrac{V_1}{4}$

(B) $\dfrac{V_1}{2}$

(C) V_1

(D) $2V_1$

(E) $4V_1$

10. A gas is at a pressure P_1, temperature T_1, and volume V_1. If the number of moles of the gas is cut in half, while the temperature is doubled and the volume is cut in half, what is the new pressure P_2 for the gas?

(A) $\dfrac{P_1}{4}$

(B) $\dfrac{P_1}{2}$

(C) P_1

(D) $2P_1$

(E) $4P_1$

11. The number of moles of a gas is tripled. If the temperature remains constant, but the pressure becomes 9 times the original, what has happened to its volume?

(A) $\dfrac{V_1}{9}$

(B) $\dfrac{V_1}{3}$

(C) V_1

(D) $3V_1$

(E) $9V_1$

12. A gas is held at a constant pressure. If the number of moles is doubled and the volume is cut in half, what is the new temperature of the gas if the original temperature was 527°C?

(A) −73°C

(B) 132°C

(C) 200°C

(D) 1327°C

(E) 1600°C

Energy transferred to water through radiation, convection, and conduction results in evaporation, a change of phase in which liquid water becomes a gas. Through convection this vapor is carried upward, where it changes phase again, condensing into extremely small droplets or ice crystals, visible as clouds.

John Short/Design Pics/Jupiter Images

11 Energy in Thermal Processes

When two objects with different temperatures are placed in thermal contact, the temperature of the warmer object decreases while the temperature of the cooler object increases. With time they reach a common equilibrium temperature somewhere in between their initial temperatures. During this process, we say that energy is transferred from the warmer object to the cooler one.

Until about 1850 the subjects of thermodynamics and mechanics were considered two distinct branches of science, and the principle of conservation of energy seemed to describe only certain kinds of mechanical systems. Experiments performed by English physicist James Joule (1818–1889) and others showed that the decrease in mechanical energy (kinetic plus potential) of an isolated system was equal to the increase in internal energy of the system. Today, internal energy is treated as a form of energy that can be transformed into mechanical energy and vice versa. Once the concept of energy was broadened to include internal energy, the law of conservation of energy emerged as a universal law of nature.

This chapter focuses on some of the processes of energy transfer between a system and its surroundings.

11.1 Heat and Internal Energy

A major distinction must be made between heat and internal energy. These terms are not interchangeable: Heat involves a *transfer* of internal energy from one location to another. The following formal definitions will make the distinction precise.

Internal energy U is the energy associated with the atoms and molecules of the system. The internal energy includes kinetic and potential energy associated with the random translational, rotational, and vibrational motion of the particles that make up the system, and any potential energy bonding the particles together.

◀ Internal energy

In Chapter 10 we showed that the internal energy of a monatomic ideal gas is associated with the translational motion of its atoms. In this special case, the internal energy is the total translational kinetic energy of the atoms; the higher the temperature of the gas, the greater the kinetic energy of the atoms and the greater the internal energy of the gas. For more complicated diatomic and polyatomic gases, internal energy includes other forms of molecular energy, such as rotational kinetic energy and the kinetic and potential energy associated with molecular vibrations. Internal energy is also associated with the intermolecular potential energy ("bond energy") between molecules in a liquid or solid.

Heat was introduced in Chapter 5 as one possible method of transferring energy between a system and its environment, and we provide a formal definition here:

Heat is the transfer of energy between a system and its environment due to a temperature difference between them.

James Prescott Joule
British physicist (1818–1889)
Joule received some formal education in mathematics, philosophy, and chemistry from John Dalton, but was in large part self-educated. Joule's most active research period, from 1837 through 1847, led to the establishment of the principle of conservation of energy and the relationship between heat and other forms of energy transfer. His study of the quantitative relationship among electrical, mechanical, and chemical effects of heat culminated in his announcement in 1843 of the amount of work required to produce a unit of internal energy.

The symbol Q is used to represent the amount of energy transferred by heat between a system and its environment. For brevity, we will often use the phrase "the energy Q transferred to a system . . ." rather than "the energy Q transferred by heat to a system . . ."

If a pan of water is heated on the burner of a stove, it's incorrect to say more heat is in the water. Heat is the *transfer* of thermal energy, just as work is the transfer of mechanical energy. When an object is pushed, it doesn't have more work; rather, it has more mechanical energy transferred *by* work. Similarly, the pan of water has more thermal energy transferred by heat.

Units of Heat

Early in the development of thermodynamics, before scientists realized the connection between thermodynamics and mechanics, heat was defined in terms of the temperature changes it produced in an object, and a separate unit of energy, the **calorie,** was used for heat. The calorie (cal) is defined as **the energy necessary to raise the temperature of 1 g of water from 14.5°C to 15.5°C.** (The "Calorie," with a capital "C," used in describing the energy content of foods, is actually a kilocalorie.) Likewise, the unit of heat in the U.S. customary system, the **British thermal unit** (Btu), was defined as **the energy required to raise the temperature of 1 lb of water from 63°F to 64°F.**

◀ Definition of the calorie

In 1948 scientists agreed that because heat (like work) is a measure of the transfer of energy, its SI unit should be the joule. The calorie is now defined to be exactly 4.186 J:

$$1 \text{ cal} \equiv 4.186 \text{ J} \qquad \text{[11.1]}$$

◀ The mechanical equivalent of heat

This definition makes no reference to raising the temperature of water. The calorie is a general energy unit, introduced here for historical reasons, although we will make little use of it. The definition in Equation 11.1 is known, from the historical background we have discussed, as the **mechanical equivalent of heat.**

■ **EXAMPLE 11.1** | **Working Off Breakfast** BIO

GOAL Relate caloric energy to mechanical energy.

PROBLEM A student eats a breakfast consisting of a bowl of cereal and milk, containing a total of 3.20×10^2 Calories of energy. He wishes to do an equivalent amount of work in the gymnasium by performing curls with a 25.0-kg barbell (Fig. 11.1). How many times must he raise the weight to expend that much energy? Assume he raises it through a vertical displacement of 0.400 m each time, the distance from his lap to his upper chest.

STRATEGY Convert the energy in Calories to joules, then equate that energy to the work necessary to do n repetitions of the barbell exercise. The work he does lifting the barbell can be found from the work-energy theorem and the change in potential energy of the barbell. He does negative work on the barbell going down, to keep it from speeding up. The net work on the barbell during one repetition is zero, but his muscles expend the same energy both in raising and lowering.

Figure 11.1 (Example 11.1)

SOLUTION

Convert his breakfast Calories, E, to joules:

$$E = (3.20 \times 10^2 \text{Cal}) \left(\frac{1.00 \times 10^3 \text{cal}}{1.00 \text{ Cal}} \right) \left(\frac{4.186 \text{ J}}{\text{cal}} \right)$$
$$= 1.34 \times 10^6 \text{ J}$$

Use the work–energy theorem to find the work necessary to lift the barbell up to its maximum height:

$$W = \Delta KE + \Delta PE = (0 - 0) + (mgh - 0) = mgh$$

The student must expend the same amount of energy lowering the barbell, making $2mgh$ per repetition. Multiply this amount by n repetitions and set it equal to the food energy E:

$$n(2mgh) = E$$

Solve for n, substituting the food energy for E:

$$n = \frac{E}{2mgh} = \frac{1.34 \times 10^6 \text{ J}}{2(25.0 \text{ kg})(9.80 \text{ m/s}^2)(0.400 \text{ m})}$$
$$= \boxed{6.84 \times 10^3 \text{ times}}$$

REMARKS If the student does one repetition every 5 seconds, it will take him 9.5 hours to work off his breakfast! In exercising, a large fraction of energy is lost through heat, however, due to the inefficiency of the body in doing work. This transfer of energy dramatically reduces the exercise requirement by at least three-quarters, a little over two hours. Further, some small fraction of the energy content of the cereal may not actually be absorbed. All the same, it might be best to forgo a second bowl of cereal!

QUESTION 11.1 From the point of view of physics, does the answer depend on how fast the repetitions are performed? How do faster repetitions affect human metabolism?

EXERCISE 11.1 How many sprints from rest to a speed of 5.0 m/s would a 65-kg woman have to complete to burn off 5.0×10^2 Calories? (Assume 100% efficiency in converting food energy to mechanical energy.)

ANSWER 2.6×10^3 sprints

BIO **APPLICATION**

Physiology of Exercise

Getting proper exercise is an important part of staying healthy and keeping weight under control. As seen in the preceding example, the body expends energy when doing mechanical work, and these losses are augmented by the inefficiency of converting the body's internal stores of energy into useful work, with three-quarters or more leaving the body through heat. In addition, exercise tends to elevate the body's general metabolic rate, which persists even after the exercise is over. The increase in metabolic rate due to exercise, more so than the exercise itself, is helpful in weight reduction.

11.2 Specific Heat

The historical definition of the calorie is the amount of energy necessary to raise the temperature of one gram of a specific substance—water—by one degree. That amount is 4.186 J. Raising the temperature of one kilogram of water by 1°C requires 4 186 J of energy. The amount of energy required to raise the temperature of one kilogram of an arbitrary substance by 1°C varies with the substance. For example, the energy required to raise the temperature of one kilogram of copper by 1.0°C is 387 J. Every substance requires a unique amount of energy per unit mass to change the temperature of that substance by 1.0°C.

If a quantity of energy Q is transferred to a substance of mass m, changing its temperature by $\Delta T = T_f - T_i$, the **specific heat** c of the substance is defined by

$$c \equiv \frac{Q}{m\,\Delta T} \qquad [11.2]$$

SI unit: Joule per kilogram-degree Celsius (J/kg · °C)

Table 11.1 lists specific heats for several substances. From the definition of the calorie, the specific heat of water is 4 186 J/kg·°C. The values quoted are typical, but vary depending on the temperature and whether the matter is in a solid, liquid, or gaseous state.

From the definition of specific heat, we can express the energy Q needed to raise the temperature of a system of mass m by ΔT as

$$Q = mc\,\Delta T \qquad [11.3]$$

The energy required to raise the temperature of 0.500 kg of water by 3.00°C, for example, is $Q = (0.500 \text{ kg})(4\,186 \text{ J/kg·°C})(3.00°C) = 6.28 \times 10^3$ J. Note that when the temperature increases, ΔT and Q are *positive*, corresponding to energy flowing *into* the system. When the temperature decreases, ΔT and Q are *negative*, and energy flows *out* of the system.

Table 11.1 shows that water has the highest specific heat relative to most other common substances. This high specific heat is responsible for the moderate temperatures found in regions near large bodies of water. As the temperature of a body of water decreases during winter, the water transfers energy to the air, which carries the energy landward when prevailing winds are toward the land. Off the western coast of the United States, the energy liberated by the Pacific Ocean is carried to the east, keeping coastal areas much warmer than they would otherwise be. Winters are generally colder in the eastern coastal states, because the prevailing winds tend to carry the energy away from land.

The fact that the specific heat of water is higher than the specific heat of sand is responsible for the pattern of airflow at a beach. During the day, the Sun adds roughly equal amounts of energy to the beach and the water, but the lower specific heat of sand causes the beach to reach a higher temperature than the water. As a result, the air above the land reaches a higher temperature than the air above the water. The denser cold air pushes the less dense hot air upward (due to Archimedes' principle), resulting in a breeze from ocean to land during the day. Because the hot air gradually cools as it rises, it subsequently sinks, setting up the circulation pattern shown in Figure 11.2.

A similar effect produces rising layers of air called *thermals* that can help eagles soar higher and hang gliders stay in flight longer. A thermal is created when a portion of the Earth reaches a higher temperature than neighboring regions. Thermals often occur in plowed fields, which are warmed by the Sun to higher temperatures than nearby fields shaded by vegetation. The cooler, denser air over the vegetation-covered fields pushes the expanding air over the plowed field upward, and a thermal is formed.

Table 11.1 Specific Heats of Some Materials at Atmospheric Pressure

Substance	J/kg · °C	cal/g · °C
Aluminum	900	0.215
Beryllium	1 820	0.436
Cadmium	230	0.055
Copper	387	0.092 4
Ethyl Alcohol	2 430	0.581
Germanium	322	0.077
Glass	837	0.200
Gold	129	0.030 8
Human tissue	3 470	0.829
Ice	2 090	0.500
Iron	448	0.107
Lead	128	0.030 5
Mercury	138	0.033
Silicon	703	0.168
Silver	234	0.056
Steam	2 010	0.480
Tin	227	0.054 2
Water	4 186	1.00

Tip 11.1 Finding ΔT

In Equation 11.3, be sure to remember that ΔT is always the final temperature minus the initial temperature: $\Delta T = T_f - T_i$.

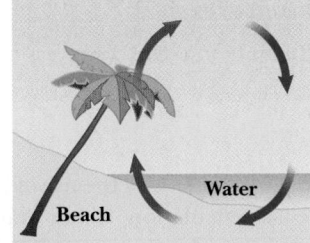

Figure 11.2 Circulation of air at the beach. On a hot day, the air above the sand warms faster than the air above the cooler water. The warmer air floats upward due to Archimedes's principle, resulting in the movement of cooler air toward the beach.

APPLICATION

Sea Breezes and Thermals

11.1 Suppose you have 1 kg each of iron, glass, and water, and all three samples are at 10°C. (a) Rank the samples from lowest to highest temperature after 100 J of energy is added to each by heat. (b) Rank them from least to greatest amount of energy transferred by heat if enough energy is transferred so that each increases in temperature by 20°C.

■ EXAMPLE 11.2 | Stressing a Strut

GOAL Use the energy transfer equation in the context of linear expansion and compressional stress.

PROBLEM A steel strut near a ship's furnace is 2.00 m long, with a mass of 1.57 kg and cross-sectional area of 1.00×10^{-4} m². During operation of the furnace, the strut absorbs a net thermal energy of 2.50×10^5 J. (a) Find the change in temperature of the strut. (b) Find the increase in length of the strut. (c) If the strut is not allowed to expand because it's bolted at each end, find the compressional stress developed in the strut.

STRATEGY This problem can be solved by substituting given quantities into three different equations. In part (a),

the change in temperature can be computed by substituting into Equation 11.3, which relates temperature change to the energy transferred by heat. In part (b), substituting the result of part (a) into the linear expansion equation yields the change in length. If that change of length is thwarted by poor design, as in part (c), the result is compressional stress, found with the compressional stress–strain equation. *Note:* The specific heat of steel may be taken to be the same as that of iron.

SOLUTION

(a) Find the change in temperature.

Solve Equation 11.3 for the change in temperature and substitute:

$$Q = m_s c_s \Delta T \quad \rightarrow \quad \Delta T = \frac{Q}{m_s c_s}$$

$$\Delta T = \frac{(2.50 \times 10^5 \text{ J})}{(1.57 \text{ kg})(448 \text{ J/kg} \cdot \text{°C})} = \boxed{355\text{°C}}$$

(b) Find the change in length of the strut if it's allowed to expand.

Substitute into the linear expansion equation:

$$\Delta L = \alpha L_0 \Delta T = (11 \times 10^{-6} \text{ °C}^{-1})(2.00 \text{ m})(355\text{°C})$$
$$= \boxed{7.8 \times 10^{-3} \text{ m}}$$

(c) Find the compressional stress in the strut if it is not allowed to expand.

Substitute into the compressional stress-strain equation:

$$\frac{F}{A} = Y \frac{\Delta L}{L} = (2.00 \times 10^{11} \text{ Pa}) \frac{7.8 \times 10^{-3} \text{ m}}{2.01 \text{ m}}$$
$$= \boxed{7.8 \times 10^8 \text{ Pa}}$$

REMARKS Notice the use of 2.01 m in the denominator of the last calculation, rather than 2.00 m. This is because, in effect, the strut was compressed back to the original length from the length to which it would have expanded. (The difference is negligible, however.) The answer exceeds the ultimate compressive strength of steel and underscores the importance of allowing for thermal expansion. Of course, it's likely the strut would bend, relieving some of the stress (creating some shear stress in the process). Finally, if the strut is attached at both ends by bolts, thermal expansion and contraction would exert sheer stresses on the bolts, possibly weakening or loosening them over time.

QUESTION 11.2 Which of the following combinations of properties will result in the smallest expansion of a sub-

stance due to the absorption of a given amount Q of thermal energy? (a) small specific heat, large coefficient of expansion (b) small specific heat, small coefficient of expansion (c) large specific heat, small coefficient of expansion (d) large specific heat, large coefficient of expansion

EXERCISE 11.2 Suppose a steel strut having a cross-sectional area of 5.00×10^{-4} m² and length 2.50 m is bolted between two rigid bulkheads in the engine room of a submarine. Assume the density of the steel is the same as that of iron. (a) Calculate the change in temperature of the strut if it absorbs 3.00×10^5 J of thermal energy. (b) Calculate the compressional stress in the strut.

ANSWERS (a) 68.2°C (b) 1.50×10^8 Pa

11.3 Calorimetry

One technique for measuring the specific heat of a solid or liquid is to raise the temperature of the substance to some value, place it into a vessel containing cold water of known mass and temperature, and measure the temperature of the combination after equilibrium is reached. Define the system as the substance and the water. If the vessel is assumed to be a good insulator, so that energy doesn't leave the system, then we can assume the system is isolated. Vessels having this property are called **calorimeters,** and analysis performed using such vessels is called **calorimetry.**

The principle of conservation of energy for this isolated system requires that the net result of all energy transfers is zero. If one part of the system loses energy, another part has to gain the energy because the system is isolated and the energy has nowhere else to go. When a warm object is placed in the cooler water of a calorimeter, the warm object becomes cooler while the water becomes warmer. This principle can be written

$$Q_{cold} = -Q_{hot} \qquad \text{[11.4]}$$

Q_{cold} is positive because energy is flowing into cooler objects, and Q_{hot} is negative because energy is leaving the hot object. The negative sign on the right-hand side of Equation 11.4 ensures that the right-hand side is a positive number, consistent with the left-hand side. The equation is valid only when the system it describes is isolated.

Calorimetry problems involve solving Equation 11.4 for an unknown quantity, usually either a specific heat or a temperature.

■ EXAMPLE 11.3 | Finding a Specific Heat

GOAL Solve a calorimetry problem involving only two substances.

PROBLEM A 125-g block of an unknown substance with a temperature of 90.0°C is placed in a Styrofoam cup containing 0.326 kg of water at 20.0°C. The system reaches an equilibrium temperature of 22.4°C. What is the specific heat, c_x, of the unknown substance if the heat capacity of the cup is neglected?

STRATEGY The water gains thermal energy Q_{cold} while the block loses thermal energy Q_{hot}. Using Equation 11.3, substitute expressions into Equation 11.4 and solve for the unknown specific heat, c_x.

SOLUTION

Let T be the final temperature, and let T_w and T_x be the initial temperatures of the water and block, respectively. Apply Equations 11.3 and 11.4:

$$Q_{cold} = -Q_{hot}$$
$$m_w c_w (T - T_w) = -m_x c_x (T - T_x)$$

Solve for c_x and substitute numerical values:

$$c_x = \frac{m_w c_w (T - T_w)}{m_x (T_x - T)}$$

$$= \frac{(0.326 \text{ kg})(4\,190 \text{ J/kg} \cdot {}^\circ\text{C})(22.4{}^\circ\text{C} - 20.0{}^\circ\text{C})}{(0.125 \text{ kg})(90.0{}^\circ\text{C} - 22.4{}^\circ\text{C})}$$

$$c_x = 388 \text{ J/kg} \cdot {}^\circ\text{C} \quad \rightarrow \quad \boxed{390 \text{ J/kg} \cdot {}^\circ\text{C}}$$

REMARKS Comparing our results to values given in Table 11.1, the unknown substance is probably copper. Note that because the factor $(22.4{}^\circ\text{C} - 20.0{}^\circ\text{C}) = 2.4{}^\circ\text{C}$ has only two significant figures, the final answer must similarly be rounded to two figures, as indicated.

QUESTION 11.3 Objects A, B, and C are at different temperatures, A lowest and C highest. The three objects are put in thermal contact with each other simultaneously. Without doing a calculation, is it possible to determine whether object B will gain or lose thermal energy?

(Continued)

EXERCISE 11.3 A 255-g block of gold at 85.0°C is immersed in 155 g of water at 25.0°C. Find the equilibrium temperature, assuming the system is isolated and the heat capacity of the cup can be neglected.

ANSWER 27.9°C

> ### Tip 11.2 Celsius Versus Kelvin
>
> In equations in which T appears, such as the ideal gas law, the Kelvin temperature must be used. In equations involving ΔT, such as calorimetry equations, it's possible to use either Celsius or Kelvin temperatures because a change in temperature is the same on both scales. When in doubt, use Kelvin.

As long as there are no more than two substances involved, Equation 11.4 can be used to solve elementary calorimetry problems. Sometimes, however, there may be three (or more) substances exchanging thermal energy, each at a different temperature. If the problem requires finding the final temperature, it may not be clear whether the substance with the middle temperature gains or loses thermal energy. In such cases, Equation 11.4 can't be used reliably.

For example, suppose we want to calculate the final temperature of a system consisting initially of a glass beaker at 25°C, hot water at 40°C, and a block of aluminum at 37°C. We know that after the three are combined, the glass beaker warms up and the hot water cools, but we don't know for sure whether the aluminum block gains or loses energy because the final temperature is unknown.

Fortunately, we can still solve such a problem as long as it's set up correctly. With an unknown final temperature T_f, the expression $Q = mc(T_f - T_i)$ will be positive if $T_f > T_i$ and negative if $T_f < T_i$. Equation 11.4 can be written as

$$\sum Q_k = 0 \qquad\qquad [11.5]$$

where Q_k is the energy change in the kth object. Equation 11.5 says that the sum of all the gains and losses of thermal energy must add up to zero, as required by the conservation of energy for an isolated system. Each term in Equation 11.5 will have the correct sign automatically. Applying Equation 11.5 to the water, aluminum, and glass problem, we get

$$Q_w + Q_{al} + Q_g = 0$$

There's no need to decide in advance whether a substance in the system is gaining or losing energy. This equation is similar in style to the conservation of mechanical energy equation, where the gains and losses of kinetic and potential energies sum to zero for an isolated system: $\Delta K + \Delta PE = 0$. As will be seen, changes in thermal energy can be included on the left-hand side of this equation.

When more than two substances exchange thermal energy, it's easy to make errors substituting numbers, so it's a good idea to construct a table to organize and assemble all the data. This strategy is illustrated in the next example.

■ EXAMPLE 11.4   Calculate an Equilibrium Temperature

GOAL Solve a calorimetry problem involving three substances at three different temperatures.

PROBLEM Suppose 0.400 kg of water initially at 40.0°C is poured into a 0.300-kg glass beaker having a temperature of 25.0°C. A 0.500-kg block of aluminum at 37.0°C is placed in the water and the system insulated. Calculate the final equilibrium temperature of the system.

STRATEGY The energy transfer for the water, aluminum, and glass will be designated Q_w, Q_{al}, and Q_g, respectively. The sum of these transfers must equal zero, by conservation of energy. Construct a table, assemble the three terms from the given data, and solve for the final equilibrium temperature, T.

· ·

SOLUTION

Apply Equation 11.5 to the system:

(1) $\quad Q_w + Q_{al} + Q_g = 0$

(2) $\quad m_w c_w (T - T_w) + m_{al} c_{al} (T - T_{al}) + m_g c_g (T - T_g) = 0$

Construct a data table:

Q (J)	m (kg)	c (J/kg · °C)	T_f	T_i
Q_w	0.400	4 190	T	40.0°C
Q_{al}	0.500	9.00×10^2	T	37.0°C
Q_g	0.300	837	T	25.0°C

Using the table, substitute into Equation (2):

$$(1.68 \times 10^3 \, \text{J/°C})(T - 40.0°C)$$
$$+ (4.50 \times 10^2 \, \text{J/°C})(T - 37.0°C)$$
$$+ (2.51 \times 10^2 \, \text{J/°C})(T - 25.0°C) = 0$$
$$(1.68 \times 10^3 \, \text{J/°C} + 4.50 \times 10^2 \, \text{J/°C} + 2.51 \times 10^2 \, \text{J/°C})T$$
$$= 9.01 \times 10^4 \, \text{J}$$

$$T = \boxed{37.9°C}$$

REMARKS The answer turned out to be very close to the aluminum's initial temperature, so it would have been impossible to guess in advance whether the aluminum would lose or gain energy. Notice the way the table was organized, mirroring the order of factors in the different terms. This kind of organization helps prevent substitution errors, which are common in these problems.

QUESTION 11.4 Suppose thermal energy Q leaked from the system. How should the right side of Equation (1) be adjusted? (a) No change is needed. (b) $+Q$ (c) $-Q$.

EXERCISE 11.4 A 20.0-kg gold bar at 35.0°C is placed in a large, insulated 0.800-kg glass container at 15.0°C and 2.00 kg of water at 25.0°C. Calculate the final equilibrium temperature.

ANSWER 26.6°C

11.4 Latent Heat and Phase Change

A substance usually undergoes a change in temperature when energy is transferred between the substance and its environment. In some cases, however, the transfer of energy doesn't result in a change in temperature. This can occur when the physical characteristics of the substance change from one form to another, commonly referred to as a **phase change.** Some common phase changes are solid to liquid (melting), liquid to gas (boiling), and a change in the crystalline structure of a solid. Any such phase change involves a change in the internal energy, but *no change in the temperature.*

The energy Q needed to change the phase of a given pure substance is

$$Q = \pm mL \qquad \text{[11.6]}$$

where L, called the **latent heat** of the substance, depends on the nature of the phase change as well as on the substance.

◀ Latent heat

The unit of latent heat is the joule per kilogram (J/kg). The word *latent* means "lying hidden within a person or thing." The positive sign in Equation 11.6 is chosen when energy is absorbed by a substance, as when ice is melting. The negative sign is chosen when energy is removed from a substance, as when steam condenses to water.

The **latent heat of fusion** L_f is used when a phase change occurs during melting or freezing, whereas the **latent heat of vaporization** L_v is used when a phase change occurs during boiling or condensing.[1] For example, at atmospheric pressure the latent heat of fusion for water is 3.33×10^5 J/kg and the latent heat of

Tip 11.3 Signs Are Critical

For phase changes, use the correct explicit sign in Equation 11.6, positive if you are adding energy to the substance, negative if you're taking it away.

---

[1] When a gas cools, it eventually returns to the liquid phase, or *condenses.* The energy per unit mass given up during the process is called the *heat of condensation,* and it equals the heat of vaporization. When a liquid cools, it eventually solidifies, and the *heat of solidification* equals the heat of fusion.

Table 11.2 Latent Heats of Fusion and Vaporization

Substance	Melting Point (°C)	Latent Heat of Fusion		Boiling Point (°C)	Latent Heat of Vaporization	
		(J/kg)	**cal/g**		**(J/kg)**	**cal/g**
Helium	−269.65	5.23×10^3	1.25	−268.93	2.09×10^4	4.99
Nitrogen	−209.97	2.55×10^4	6.09	−195.81	2.01×10^5	48.0
Oxygen	−218.79	1.38×10^4	3.30	−182.97	2.13×10^5	50.9
Ethyl alcohol	−114	1.04×10^5	24.9	78	8.54×10^5	204
Water	0.00	3.33×10^5	79.7	100.00	2.26×10^6	540
Sulfur	119	3.81×10^4	9.10	444.60	3.26×10^5	77.9
Lead	327.3	2.45×10^4	5.85	1 750	8.70×10^5	208
Aluminum	660	3.97×10^5	94.8	2 450	1.14×10^7	2 720
Silver	960.80	8.82×10^4	21.1	2 193	2.33×10^6	558
Gold	1 063.00	6.44×10^4	15.4	2 660	1.58×10^6	377
Copper	1 083	1.34×10^5	32.0	1 187	5.06×10^6	1 210

vaporization for water is 2.26×10^6 J/kg. The latent heats of different substances vary considerably, as can be seen in Table 11.2.

Another process, sublimation, is the passage from the solid to the gaseous phase without going through a liquid phase. The fuming of dry ice (frozen carbon dioxide) illustrates this process, which has its own latent heat associated with it, the heat of sublimation.

To better understand the physics of phase changes, consider the addition of energy to a 1.00-g cube of ice at −30.0°C in a container held at constant pressure. Suppose this input of energy turns the ice to steam (water vapor) at 120.0°C. Figure 11.3 is a plot of the experimental measurement of temperature as energy is added to the system. We examine each portion of the curve separately.

Part A During this portion of the curve, the temperature of the ice changes from −30.0°C to 0.0°C. Because the specific heat of ice is 2 090 J/kg · °C, we can calculate the amount of energy added from Equation 11.3:

$$Q = mc_{ice} \, \Delta T = (1.00 \times 10^{-3} \text{ kg})(2\,090 \text{ J/kg} \cdot °C)(30.0°C) = 62.7 \text{ J}$$

Part B When the ice reaches 0°C, the ice–water mixture remains at that temperature—even though energy is being added—until all the ice melts to become water at 0°C. According to Equation 11.6, the energy required to melt 1.00 g of ice at 0°C is

$$Q = mL_f = (1.00 \times 10^{-3} \text{ kg})(3.33 \times 10^5 \text{ J/kg}) = 333 \text{ J}$$

Figure 11.3 A plot of temperature versus energy added when 1.00 g of ice, initially at −30.0°C, is converted to steam at 120°C.

Part C   Between 0°C and 100°C, no phase change occurs. The energy added to the water is used to increase its temperature, as in part A. The amount of energy necessary to increase the temperature from 0°C to 100°C is

$$Q = mc_{\text{water}} \Delta T = (1.00 \times 10^{-3} \text{ kg})(4.19 \times 10^3 \text{ J/kg} \cdot \text{°C})(1.00 \times 10^2 \text{ °C})$$

$$Q = 4.19 \times 10^2 \text{ J}$$

Part D   At 100°C, another phase change occurs as the water changes to steam at 100°C. As in Part B, the water–steam mixture remains at constant temperature, this time at 100°C—even though energy is being added—until all the liquid has been converted to steam. The energy required to convert 1.00 g of water at 100°C to steam at 100°C is

$$Q = mL_v = (1.00 \times 10^{-3} \text{ kg})(2.26 \times 10^6 \text{ J/kg}) = 2.26 \times 10^3 \text{ J}$$

Part E   During this portion of the curve, as in parts A and C, no phase change occurs, so all the added energy goes into increasing the temperature of the steam. The energy that must be added to raise the temperature of the steam to 120.0°C is

$$Q = mc_{\text{steam}} \Delta T = (1.00 \times 10^{-3} \text{ kg})(2.01 \times 10^3 \text{ J/kg} \cdot \text{°C})(20.0°C) = 40.2 \text{ J}$$

The total amount of energy that must be added to change 1.00 g of ice at −30.0°C to steam at 120.0°C is the sum of the results from all five parts of the curve, 3.11×10^3 J. Conversely, to cool 1.00 g of steam at 120.0°C to the point at which it becomes ice at −30.0°C, 3.11×10^3 J of energy must be removed.

Phase changes can be described in terms of rearrangements of molecules when energy is added to or removed from a substance. Consider first the liquid-to-gas phase change. The molecules in a liquid are close together, and the forces between them are stronger than the forces between the more widely separated molecules of a gas. Work must therefore be done on the liquid against these attractive molecular forces so as to separate the molecules. The latent heat of vaporization is the amount of energy that must be added to the one kilogram of liquid to accomplish this separation.

Similarly, at the melting point of a solid, the amplitude of vibration of the atoms about their equilibrium positions becomes great enough to allow the atoms to pass the barriers of adjacent atoms and move to their new positions. On average, these new positions are less symmetrical than the old ones and therefore have higher energy. The latent heat of fusion is equal to the work required at the molecular level to transform the mass from the ordered solid phase to the disordered liquid phase.

The average distance between atoms is much greater in the gas phase than in either the liquid or the solid phase. Each atom or molecule is removed from its neighbors, overcoming the attractive forces of nearby neighbors. Therefore, more work is required at the molecular level to vaporize a given mass of a substance than to melt it, so in general the latent heat of vaporization is much greater than the latent heat of fusion (see Table 11.2).

■ *Quick Quiz*

11.2 Calculate the slopes for the A, C, and E portions of Figure 11.3. Rank the slopes from least to greatest and explain what your ranking means. (a) A, C, E (b) C, A, E (c) E, A, C (d) E, C, A

■ PROBLEM-SOLVING STRATEGY

Calorimetry with Phase Changes

1. **Make a table for all data.** Include separate rows for different phases and for any transition between phases. Include columns for each quantity used and a final column for the combination of the quantities. Transfers of thermal

energy in this last column are given by $Q = mc\Delta T$, whereas phase changes are given by $Q = \pm mL_f$ for changes between liquid and solid and by $Q = \pm mL_v$ for changes between liquid and gas.

2. **Apply conservation of energy.** If the system is isolated, use $\Sigma Q_k = 0$ (Eq. 11.5). For a nonisolated system, the net energy change should replace the zero on the right-hand side of that equation. Here, ΣQ_k is just the sum of all the terms in the last column of the table.

3. **Solve** for the unknown quantity.

▪EXAMPLE 11.5 | Ice Water

GOAL Solve a problem involving heat transfer and a phase change from solid to liquid.

PROBLEM At a party, 6.00 kg of ice at $-5.00°C$ is added to a cooler holding 30 liters of water at $20.0°C$. What is the temperature of the water when it comes to equilibrium?

STRATEGY In this problem, it's best to make a table. With the addition of thermal energy Q_{ice} the ice will warm to $0°C$, then melt at $0°C$ with the addition of energy Q_{melt}. Next, the melted ice will warm to some final temperature T by absorbing energy $Q_{ice-water}$, obtained from the energy change of the original liquid water, Q_{water}. By conservation of energy, these quantities must sum to zero.

SOLUTION

Calculate the mass of liquid water:

$$m_{water} = \rho_{water}V$$
$$= (1.00 \times 10^3 \text{ kg/m}^3)(30.0 \text{ L})\frac{1.00 \text{ m}^3}{1.00 \times 10^3 \text{ L}}$$
$$= 30.0 \text{ kg}$$

Write the equation of thermal equilibrium:

(1) $Q_{ice} + Q_{melt} + Q_{ice-water} + Q_{water} = 0$

Construct a comprehensive table:

Q	m (kg)	c (J/kg · °C)	L (J/kg)	T_f (°C)	T_i (°C)	Expression
Q_{ice}	6.00	2 090		0	-5.00	$m_{ice}c_{ice}(T_f - T_i)$
Q_{melt}	6.00		3.33×10^5	0	0	$m_{ice}L_f$
$Q_{ice-water}$	6.00	4 190		T	0	$m_{ice}c_{water}(T_f - T_i)$
Q_{water}	30.0	4 190		T	20.0	$m_{water}c_{water}(T_f - T_i)$

Substitute all quantities in the second through sixth columns into the last column and sum, which is the evaluation of Equation (1), and solve for T:

$6.27 \times 10^4 \text{ J} + 2.00 \times 10^6 \text{ J}$
$\quad + (2.51 \times 10^4 \text{ J/°C})(T - 0°C)$
$\quad\quad + (1.26 \times 10^5 \text{ J/°C})(T - 20.0°C) = 0$

$T = \boxed{3.03°C}$

REMARKS Making a table is optional. However, simple substitution errors are extremely common, and the table makes such errors less likely.

QUESTION 11.5 Can a closed system containing different substances at different initial temperatures reach an equilibrium temperature that is lower than all the initial temperatures?

EXERCISE 11.5 What mass of ice at $-10.0°C$ is needed to cool a whale's water tank, holding $1.20 \times 10^3 \text{ m}^3$ of water, from $20.0°C$ to a more comfortable $10.0°C$?

ANSWER $1.27 \times 10^5 \text{ kg}$

▪EXAMPLE 11.6 | Partial Melting

GOAL Understand how to handle an incomplete phase change.

PROBLEM A 5.00-kg block of ice at $0°C$ is added to an insulated container partially filled with 10.0 kg of water at $15.0°C$. **(a)** Find the final temperature, neglecting the heat capacity of the container. **(b)** Find the mass of the ice that was melted.

STRATEGY Part (a) is tricky because the ice does not entirely melt in this example. When there is any doubt concerning whether there will be a complete phase change, some preliminary calculations are necessary. First, find the total energy required to melt the ice, Q_{melt}, and then find Q_{water}, the maximum energy that can be delivered by the water above 0°C. If the energy delivered by the water is high enough, all the ice melts. If not, there will usually be a final mixture of ice and water at 0°C, unless the ice starts at a temperature far below 0°C, in which case all the liquid water freezes.

SOLUTION

(a) Find the equilibrium temperature.

First, compute the amount of energy necessary to completely melt the ice:

$$Q_{melt} = m_{ice}L_f = (5.00 \text{ kg})(3.33 \times 10^5 \text{ J/kg})$$
$$= 1.67 \times 10^6 \text{ J}$$

Next, calculate the maximum energy that can be lost by the initial mass of liquid water without freezing it:

$$Q_{water} = m_{water}c\Delta T$$
$$= (10.0 \text{ kg})(4\,190 \text{ J/kg} \cdot °\text{C})(0°\text{C} - 15.0°\text{C})$$
$$= -6.29 \times 10^5 \text{ J}$$

This result is less than half the energy necessary to melt all the ice, so the final state of the system is a mixture of water and ice at the freezing point:

$$T = \boxed{0°\text{C}}$$

(b) Compute the mass of ice melted.

Set the total available energy equal to the heat of fusion of m grams of ice, mL_f, and solve for m:

$$6.29 \times 10^5 \text{ J} = mL_f = m(3.33 \times 10^5 \text{ J/kg})$$
$$m = \boxed{1.89 \text{ kg}}$$

REMARKS If this problem is solved assuming (wrongly) that all the ice melts, a final temperature of $T = -16.5°\text{C}$ is obtained. The only way that could happen is if the system were not isolated, contrary to the statement of the problem. In Exercise 11.6, you must also compute the thermal energy needed to warm the ice to its melting point.

QUESTION 11.6 What effect would doubling the initial amount of liquid water have on the amount of ice melted?

EXERCISE 11.6 If 8.00 kg of ice at −5.00°C is added to 12.0 kg of water at 20.0°C, compute the final temperature. How much ice remains, if any?

ANSWER $T = 0°\text{C}$, 5.23 kg

Sometimes problems involve changes in mechanical energy. During a collision, for example, some kinetic energy can be transformed to the internal energy of the colliding objects. This kind of transformation is illustrated in Example 11.7, which involves a possible impact of a comet on Earth. In this example, a number of liberties will be taken in order to estimate the magnitude of the destructive power of such a catastrophic event. The specific heats depend on temperature and pressure, for example, but that will be ignored. Also, the ideal gas law doesn't apply at the temperatures and pressures attained, and the result of the collision wouldn't be superheated steam, but a plasma of charged particles. Despite all these simplifications, the example yields good order-of-magnitude results.

▪ EXAMPLE 11.7 | Armageddon!

GOAL Link mechanical energy to thermal energy, phase changes, and the ideal gas law to create an estimate.

PROBLEM A comet half a kilometer in radius consisting of ice at 273 K hits Earth at a speed of 4.00×10^4 m/s. For simplicity, assume all the kinetic energy converts to thermal energy on impact and that all the thermal energy goes into warming the comet. **(a)** Calculate the volume and mass of the ice. **(b)** Use conservation of energy to find the final temperature of the comet material. Assume, contrary to fact, that the result is superheated steam and that the usual specific heats are valid, although in fact they depend on both temperature and pressure. **(c)** Assuming the steam retains a spherical shape and has the same initial volume as the comet, calculate the pressure of the steam using the ideal gas law. This law actually doesn't apply to a system at such high pressure and temperature, but can be used to get an estimate.

STRATEGY Part (a) requires the volume formula for a sphere and the definition of density. In part (b) conservation of energy can be applied. There are four processes

involved: (1) melting the ice, (2) warming the ice water to the boiling point, (3) converting the boiling water to steam, and (4) warming the steam. The energy needed for these processes will be designated Q_{melt}, Q_{water}, Q_{vapor}, and Q_{steam}, respectively. These quantities plus the change in kinetic energy ΔK sum to zero because they are assumed to be internal to the system. In this case, the first three Q's can be neglected compared to the (extremely large) kinetic energy term. Solve for the unknown temperature and substitute it into the ideal gas law in part (c).

SOLUTION

(a) Find the volume and mass of the ice.

Apply the volume formula for a sphere:

$$V = \frac{4}{3}\pi r^3 = \frac{4}{3}(3.14)(5.00 \times 10^2 \text{ m})^3$$
$$= \boxed{5.23 \times 10^8 \text{ m}^3}$$

Apply the density formula to find the mass of the ice:

$$m = \rho V = (917 \text{ kg/m}^3)(5.23 \times 10^8 \text{ m}^3)$$
$$= \boxed{4.80 \times 10^{11} \text{ kg}}$$

(b) Find the final temperature of the cometary material.

Use conservation of energy:

(1) $Q_{melt} + Q_{water} + Q_{vapor} + Q_{steam} + \Delta K = 0$

(2) $mL_f + mc_{water}\Delta T_{water} + mL_v + mc_{steam}\Delta T_{steam}$
$$+ (0 - \tfrac{1}{2}mv^2) = 0$$

The first three terms are negligible compared to the kinetic energy. The steam term involves the unknown final temperature, so retain only it and the kinetic energy, canceling the mass and solving for T:

$$mc_{steam}(T - 373 \text{ K}) - \tfrac{1}{2}mv^2 = 0$$

$$T = \frac{\tfrac{1}{2}v^2}{c_{steam}} + 373 \text{ K} = \frac{\tfrac{1}{2}(4.00 \times 10^4 \text{ m/s})^2}{2\,010 \text{ J/kg} \cdot \text{K}} + 373 \text{ K}$$

$$T = \boxed{3.98 \times 10^5 \text{ K}}$$

(c) Estimate the pressure of the gas, using the ideal gas law.

First, compute the number of moles of steam:

$$n = (4.80 \times 10^{11} \text{kg})\left(\frac{1 \text{ mol}}{0.018 \text{ kg}}\right) = 2.67 \times 10^{13} \text{ mol}$$

Solve for the pressure, using $PV = nRT$:

$$P = \frac{nRT}{V}$$

$$= \frac{(2.67 \times 10^{13} \text{ mol})(8.31 \text{ J/mol} \cdot \text{K})(3.98 \times 10^5 \text{ K})}{5.23 \times 10^8 \text{ m}^3}$$

$$P = \boxed{1.69 \times 10^{11} \text{ Pa}}$$

REMARKS The estimated pressure is several hundred times greater than the ultimate shear stress of steel! This high-pressure region would expand rapidly, destroying everything within a very large radius. Fires would ignite across a continent-sized region, and tidal waves would wrap around the world, wiping out coastal regions everywhere. The Sun would be obscured for at least a decade, and numerous species, possibly including *Homo sapiens,* would become extinct. Such extinction events are rare, but in the long run represent a significant threat to life on Earth.

QUESTION 11.7 Why would a nickel-iron asteroid be more dangerous than an asteroid of the same size made mainly of ice?

EXERCISE 11.7 Suppose a lead bullet with mass 5.00 g and an initial temperature of 65.0°C hits a wall and completely liquefies. What minimum speed did it have before impact? (*Hint:* The minimum speed corresponds to the case where all the kinetic energy becomes internal energy of the lead and the final temperature of the lead is at its melting point. Don't neglect any terms here!)

ANSWER 341 m/s

11.5 Energy Transfer

For some applications it's necessary to know the rate at which energy is transferred between a system and its surroundings and the mechanisms responsible for the transfer. This information is particularly important when weatherproofing buildings or in medical applications, such as human survival time when exposed to the elements.

Earlier in this chapter we defined heat as a transfer of energy between a system and its surroundings due to a temperature difference between them. In this section we take a closer look at heat as a means of energy transfer and consider the processes of thermal conduction, convection, and radiation.

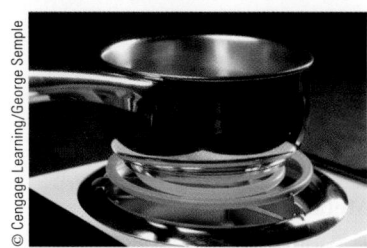

Figure 11.4 Conduction makes the metal handle of a cooking pan hot.

Thermal Conduction

The energy transfer process most closely associated with a temperature difference is called **thermal conduction** or simply **conduction.** In this process the transfer can be viewed on an atomic scale as an exchange of kinetic energy between microscopic particles—molecules, atoms, and electrons—with less energetic particles gaining energy as they collide with more energetic particles. An inexpensive pot, as in Figure 11.4, may have a metal handle with no surrounding insulation. As the pot is warmed, the temperature of the metal handle increases, and the cook must hold it with a cloth potholder to avoid being burned.

The way the handle warms up can be understood by looking at what happens to the microscopic particles in the metal. Before the pot is placed on the stove, the particles are vibrating about their equilibrium positions. As the stove coil warms up, those particles in contact with it begin to vibrate with larger amplitudes. These particles collide with their neighbors and transfer some of their energy in the collisions. Metal atoms and electrons farther and farther from the flame gradually increase the amplitude of their vibrations, until eventually those in the metal near your hand are affected. This increased vibration represents an increase in temperature of the metal (and possibly a burned hand!).

Although the transfer of energy through a substance can be partly explained by atomic vibrations, the rate of conduction depends on the properties of the substance. For example, it's possible to hold a piece of asbestos in a flame indefinitely, which implies that very little energy is conducted through the asbestos. In general, metals are good thermal conductors because they contain large numbers of electrons that are relatively free to move through the metal and can transport energy from one region to another. In a good conductor such as copper, conduction takes place via the vibration of atoms and the motion of free electrons. Materials such as asbestos, cork, paper, and fiberglass are poor thermal conductors. Gases are also poor thermal conductors because of the large distance between their molecules.

Conduction occurs only if there is a difference in temperature between two parts of the conducting medium. The temperature difference drives the flow of energy. Consider a slab of material of thickness Δx and cross-sectional area A with its opposite faces at different temperatures T_c and T_h, where $T_h > T_c$ (Fig. 11.5). The slab allows energy to transfer from the region of higher temperature to the region of lower temperature by thermal conduction. The rate of energy transfer, $P = Q/\Delta t$, is proportional to the cross-sectional area of the slab and the temperature difference and is inversely proportional to the thickness of the slab:

$$P = \frac{Q}{\Delta t} \propto A \frac{\Delta T}{\Delta x}$$

Note that P has units of watts when Q is in joules and Δt is in seconds.

Suppose a substance is in the shape of a long, uniform rod of length L, as in Figure 11.6. We assume the rod is insulated, so thermal energy can't escape by conduction from its surface except at the ends. One end is in thermal contact with an energy reservoir at temperature T_c and the other end is in thermal contact with a

---

Tip 11.4 Blankets and Coats in Cold Weather

When you sleep under a blanket in the winter or wear a warm coat outside, the blanket or coat serves as a layer of material with low thermal conductivity that reduces the transfer of energy away from your body by heat. The primary insulating medium is the air trapped in small pockets within the material.

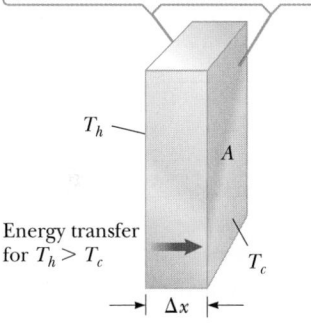

The opposite faces are at different temperatures, with $T_h > T_c$.

Figure 11.5 Energy transfer through a conducting slab of cross-sectional area A and thickness Δx.

The opposite ends of the rod are in thermal contact with energy reservoirs at different temperatures.

Figure 11.6 Conduction of energy through a uniform, insulated rod of length L.

Table 11.3 Thermal Conductivities

Substance	Thermal Conductivity $(J/s \cdot m \cdot °C)$
Metals (at 25°C)	
Aluminum	238
Copper	397
Gold	314
Iron	79.5
Lead	34.7
Silver	427
Gases (at 20°C)	
Air	0.023 4
Helium	0.138
Hydrogen	0.172
Nitrogen	0.023 4
Oxygen	0.023 8
Nonmetals	
(approximate values)	
Asbestos	0.08
Concrete	0.8
Glass	0.8
Ice	2
Rubber	0.2
Water	0.6
Wood	0.08

reservoir at temperature $T_h > T_c$. When a steady state is reached, the temperature at each point along the rod is constant in time. In this case $\Delta T = T_h - T_c$ and $\Delta x = L$, so

$$\frac{\Delta T}{\Delta x} = \frac{T_h - T_c}{L}$$

The rate of energy transfer by conduction through the rod is given by

$$P = kA\frac{(T_h - T_c)}{L} \qquad \text{[11.7]}$$

where k, a proportionality constant that depends on the material, is called the **thermal conductivity.** Substances that are good conductors have large thermal conductivities, whereas good insulators have low thermal conductivities. Table 11.3 lists the thermal conductivities for various substances.

■ Quick Quiz

11.3 Will an ice cube wrapped in a wool blanket remain frozen for (a) less time, (b) the same length of time, or (c) a longer time than an identical ice cube exposed to air at room temperature?

11.4 Two rods of the same length and diameter are made from different materials. The rods are to connect two regions of different temperature so that energy will transfer through the rods by heat. They can be connected in series, as in Figure 11.7a, or in parallel, as in Figure 11.7b. In which case is the rate of energy transfer by heat larger? (a) When the rods are in series (b) When the rods are in parallel (c) The rate is the same in both cases.

Figure 11.7 (Quick Quiz 11.4) In which case is the rate of energy transfer larger?

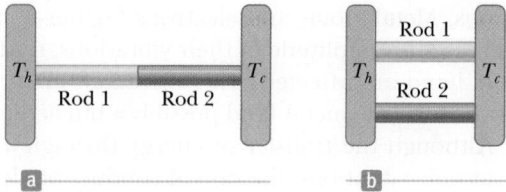

■ **EXAMPLE 11.8** | **Conductive Losses from the Human Body** BIO

GOAL Apply the conduction equation to a human being.

PROBLEM In a human being, a layer of fat and muscle lies under the skin having various thicknesses depending on location. In response to a cold environment, capillaries near the surface of the body constrict, reducing blood flow and thereby reducing the conductivity of the tissues. These tissues form a shell up to an inch thick having a thermal conductivity of about 0.21 W/m · K, the same as skin or fat. **(a)** Estimate the rate of loss of thermal energy due to conduction from the human core region to the skin surface, assuming a shell thickness of 2.0 cm and a skin temperature of 33.0°C. (Skin temperature varies, depending on external conditions.) **(b)** Calculate the thermal energy

lost due to conduction in 1.0 h. **(c)** Estimate the change in body temperature in 1.0 h if the energy is not replenished. Assume a body mass of 75 kg and a skin surface area of 1.73 m².

STRATEGY The solution to part (a) requires applying Equation 11.7 for the rate of energy transfer due to conduction. Multiplying the power found in part (a) by the elapsed time yields the total thermal energy transfer in the given time. In part (c), an estimate for the change in temperature if the energy is not replenished can be developed using Equation 11.3, $Q = mc\Delta T$.

SOLUTION

(a) Estimate the rate of loss of thermal energy due to conduction.

Write the thermal conductivity equation:

$$P = \frac{kA(T_h - T_c)}{L}$$

Substitute values:

$$P = \frac{(0.21 \text{ J/m} \cdot \text{K})(1.73 \text{ m}^2)(37.0°\text{C} - 33.0°\text{C})}{2.0 \times 10^{-2} \text{ m}} = \boxed{73 \text{ W}}$$

(b) Calculate the thermal energy lost due to conduction in 1.0 h.

Multiply the power P by the time Δt:

$$Q = P\Delta t = (73 \text{ W})(3\ 600 \text{ s}) = \boxed{2.6 \times 10^5 \text{ J}}$$

(c) Estimate the change in body temperature in 1.0 h if the energy is not replenished.

Write Equation 11.3 and solve it for ΔT:

$$Q = mc\Delta T$$

$$\Delta T = \frac{Q}{mc} = \frac{2.6 \times 10^5 \text{ J}}{(75 \text{ kg})(3\ 470 \text{ J/kg} \cdot \text{K})} = \boxed{1.0°\text{C}}$$

....

REMARKS The calculation doesn't take into account the thermal gradient, which further reduces the rate of conduction through the shell. Whereas thermal energy transfers through the shell by conduction, other mechanisms remove that energy from the body's surface because air is a poor conductor of thermal energy. Convection, radiation, and evaporation of sweat are the primary mechanisms that remove thermal energy from the skin. The calculation shows that even under mild conditions the body must constantly replenish its internal energy. It's possible to die of exposure even in temperatures well above freezing.

QUESTION 11.8 Why does a long distance runner require very little in the way of warm clothing when run-

ning in cold weather, but puts on a sweater after finishing the run?

EXERCISE 11.8 BIO A female minke whale has a core body temperature of 35°C and a core/blubber interface temperature of 29°C, with an average blubber thickness of 4.0 cm and thermal conductivity of 0.25 W/m·K. (a) At what rate is energy lost from the whale's core by conduction through blubber in water at 5.0°C? Assume a skin temperature of 12°C and a total body area of 22 m². (b) What percent of the daily energy budget is this number? (The average female minke whale requires 8.0×10^8 J of energy per day—that's a lot of plankton and krill.)

ANSWERS (a) 2.3×10^3 W (b) 25%

Home Insulation

To determine whether to add insulation to a ceiling or some other part of a building, the preceding discussion of conduction must be extended for two reasons:

1. The insulating properties of materials used in buildings are usually expressed in engineering (U.S. customary) rather than SI units. Measurements stamped on a package of fiberglass insulating board will be in units such as British thermal units, feet, and degrees Fahrenheit.
2. In dealing with the insulation of a building, conduction through a compound slab must be considered, with each portion of the slab having a certain thickness and a specific thermal conductivity. A typical wall in a house consists of an array of materials, such as wood paneling, drywall, insulation, sheathing, and wood siding.

The rate of energy transfer by conduction through a compound slab is

$$\frac{Q}{\Delta t} = \frac{A(T_h - T_c)}{\sum_i L_i/k_i} \qquad \textbf{[11.8]}$$

where T_h and T_c are the temperatures of the *outer extremities* of the slab and the summation is over all portions of the slab. This formula can be derived algebraically, using the facts that the temperature at the interface between two insulating materials must be the same and that the rate of energy transfer through one insulator must be the same as through all the other insulators. If the slab consists of three different materials, the denominator is the sum of three terms. In engineering

Table 11.4 R-Values for Some Common Building Materials

Material	R value[a] (ft^2 · °F · h/Btu)
Hardwood siding (1.0 in. thick)	0.91
Wood shingles (lapped)	0.87
Brick (4.0 in. thick)	4.00
Concrete block (filled cores)	1.93
Styrofoam (1.0 in. thick)	5.0
Fiberglass batting (3.5 in. thick)	10.90
Fiberglass batting (6.0 in. thick)	18.80
Fiberglass board (1.0 in. thick)	4.35
Cellulose fiber (1.0 in. thick)	3.70
Flat glass (0.125 in. thick)	0.89
Insulating glass (0.25-in. space)	1.54
Vertical air space (3.5 in. thick)	1.01
Stagnant layer of air	0.17
Drywall (0.50 in. thick)	0.45
Sheathing (0.50 in. thick)	1.32

[a]The values in this table can be converted to SI units by multiplying the values by 0.1761.

A worker installing fiberglass insulation in a home. The mask protects the worker against the inhalation of microscopic fibers, which could be hazardous to his health.

practice, the term L/k for a particular substance is referred to as the R-value of the material, so Equation 11.8 reduces to

$$\frac{Q}{\Delta t} = \frac{A(T_h - T_c)}{\sum_i R_i}$$ [11.9]

The R-values for a few common building materials are listed in Table 11.4. Note the unit of R and the fact that the R-values are defined for specific thicknesses.

Next to any vertical outside surface is a very thin, stagnant layer of air that must be considered when the total R-value for a wall is computed. The thickness of this stagnant layer depends on the speed of the wind. As a result, energy loss by conduction from a house on a day when the wind is blowing is greater than energy loss on a day when the wind speed is zero. A representative R-value for a stagnant air layer is given in Table 11.4. The values are typically given in British units, but they can be converted to the equivalent metric units by multiplying the values in the table by 0.1761.

■ EXAMPLE 11.9 | Construction and Thermal Insulation

GOAL Calculate the R-value of several layers of insulating material and its effect on thermal energy transfer.

PROBLEM (a) Find the energy transferred in 1.00 h by conduction through a concrete wall 2.0 m high, 3.65 m long, and 0.20 m thick if one side of the wall is held at 5.00°C and the other side is at 20.0°C (Fig. 11.8). Assume the concrete has a thermal conductivity of 0.80 J/s · m · °C. (b) The owner of the home decides to increase the insulation, so he installs 0.50 in of thick sheathing, 3.5 in of fiberglass batting, and a drywall 0.50 in thick. Calculate the R-factor. (c) Calculate the energy transferred in 1.00 h by conduction. (d) What is the temperature between the concrete wall and the sheathing? Assume there is an air layer on the exterior of the concrete wall but not between the concrete and the sheathing.

STRATEGY The R-value of the concrete wall is given by L/k. Add this to the R-value of two air layers and then substitute

Figure 11.8 (Example 11.9) A cross-sectional view of (a) a concrete wall with two air spaces and (b) the same wall with sheathing, fiberglass batting, drywall, and two air layers.

into Equation 11.8, multiplying by the seconds in an hour to get the total energy transferred through the wall in an hour. Repeat this process, with different materials, for parts (b) and (c). Part (d) requires finding the R-value for an air layer and the concrete wall and then substituting into the thermal conductivity equation. In this problem metric units are used, so be sure to convert the R-values in the table. (Converting to SI requires multiplication of the British units by 0.1761.)

SOLUTION

(a) Find the energy transferred in 1.00 h by conduction through a concrete wall.

Calculate the R-value of concrete plus two air layers:

$$\sum R = \frac{L}{k} + 2R_{\text{air layer}} = \frac{0.20 \text{ m}}{0.80 \text{ J/s} \cdot \text{m} \cdot {}^{\circ}\text{C}} + 2\left(0.030 \frac{\text{m}^2}{\text{J/s} \cdot {}^{\circ}\text{C}}\right)$$

$$= 0.31 \frac{\text{m}^2}{\text{J/s} \cdot {}^{\circ}\text{C}}$$

Write the thermal conduction equation:

$$P = \frac{A(T_h - T_c)}{\sum R}$$

Substitute values:

$$P = \frac{(7.3 \text{ m}^2)(20.0{}^{\circ}\text{C} - 5.00{}^{\circ}\text{C})}{0.31 \text{ m}^2 \cdot \text{s} \cdot {}^{\circ}\text{C/J}} = 353 \text{ W} \quad \rightarrow \quad 350 \text{ W}$$

Multiply the power in watts times the seconds in an hour:

$$Q = P\Delta t = (350 \text{ W})(3\,600 \text{ s}) = \boxed{1.3 \times 10^6 \text{ J}}$$

(b) Calculate the R-factor of the newly insulated wall.

Refer to Table 11.4 and sum the appropriate quantities after converting them to SI units:

$$R_{\text{total}} = R_{\text{outside air layer}} + R_{\text{concrete}} + R_{\text{sheath}}$$
$$+ R_{\text{fiberglass}} + R_{\text{drywall}} + R_{\text{inside air layer}}$$
$$= (0.030 + 0.25 + 0.233 + 1.92 + 0.079 + 0.030)$$
$$= \boxed{2.5 \text{ m}^2 \cdot {}^{\circ}\text{C} \cdot \text{s/J}}$$

(c) Calculate the energy transferred in 1.00 h by conduction.

Write the thermal conduction equation:

$$P = \frac{A(T_h - T_c)}{\sum R}$$

Substitute values:

$$P = \frac{(7.3 \text{ m}^2)(20.0{}^{\circ}\text{C} - 5.00{}^{\circ}\text{C})}{2.5 \text{ m}^2 \cdot \text{s} \cdot {}^{\circ}\text{C/J}} = 44 \text{ W}$$

Multiply the power in watts times the seconds in an hour:

$$Q = P\Delta t = (44 \text{ W})(3\,600 \text{ s}) = \boxed{1.6 \times 10^5 \text{ J}}$$

(d) Calculate the temperature between the concrete and the sheathing.

Write the thermal conduction equation:

$$P = \frac{A(T_h - T_c)}{\sum R}$$

Solve algebraically for T_h by multiplying both sides by $\sum R$ and dividing both sides by area A:

$$P\sum R = A(T_h - T_c) \quad \rightarrow \quad (T_h - T_c) = \frac{P\sum R}{A}$$

Add T_c to both sides:

$$T_h = \frac{P\sum R}{A} + T_c$$

Substitute the R-value for the concrete wall from part (a), but subtract the R-value of one air layer from that calculated in part (a):

$$T_h = \frac{(44 \text{ W})(0.31 \text{ m}^2 \cdot \text{s} \cdot {}^{\circ}\text{C/J} - 0.03 \text{ m}^2 \cdot \text{s} \cdot {}^{\circ}\text{C/J})}{7.3 \text{ m}^2} + 5.00{}^{\circ}\text{C}$$

$$= \boxed{6.7{}^{\circ}\text{C}}$$

REMARKS Notice the enormous energy savings that can be realized with good insulation!

(Continued)

QUESTION 11.9 Which of the following choices results in the best possible *R*-value? (a) Use material with a small thermal conductivity and large thickness. (b) Use thin material with a large thermal conductivity. (c) Use material with a small thermal conductivity and small thickness.

EXERCISE 11.9 Instead of the layers of insulation, the owner installs a brick wall on the exterior of the concrete wall. (a) Calculate the *R*-factor, including the two stagnant air layers on the inside and outside of the wall. (b) Calculate the energy transferred in 1.00 h by conduction, under the same conditions as in the example. (c) What is the temperature between the concrete and the brick?

ANSWERS (a) $1.02 \text{ m}^2 \cdot {}^{\circ}\text{C} \cdot \text{s/J}$ (b) $3.9 \times 10^5 \text{ J}$ (c) $16{}^{\circ}\text{C}$

Convection

Figure 11.9 Warming a hand by convection.

When you warm your hands over an open flame, as illustrated in Figure 11.9, the air directly above the flame, being warmed, expands. As a result, the density of this air decreases and the air rises, warming your hands as it flows by. **The transfer of energy by the movement of a substance is called convection.** When the movement results from differences in density, as with air around a fire, it's referred to as *natural convection*. Airflow at a beach is an example of natural convection, as is the mixing that occurs as surface water in a lake cools and sinks. When the substance is forced to move by a fan or pump, as in some hot air and hot water heating systems, the process is called *forced convection*.

Convection currents assist in the boiling of water. In a teakettle on a hot stovetop, the lower layers of water are warmed first. The warmed water has a lower density and rises to the top, while the denser, cool water at the surface sinks to the bottom of the kettle and is warmed.

The same process occurs when a radiator raises the temperature of a room. The hot radiator warms the air in the lower regions of the room. The warm air expands and, because of its lower density, rises to the ceiling. The denser, cooler air from above sinks, setting up the continuous air current pattern shown in Figure 11.10.

APPLICATION
Cooling Automobile Engines

An automobile engine is maintained at a safe operating temperature by a combination of conduction and forced convection. Water (actually, a mixture of water and antifreeze) circulates in the interior of the engine. As the metal of the engine block increases in temperature, energy passes from the hot metal to the cooler water by thermal conduction. The water pump forces water out of the engine and into the radiator, carrying energy along with it (by forced convection). In the radiator the hot water passes through metal pipes that are in contact with the cooler outside air, and energy passes into the air by conduction. The cooled water is then returned to the engine by the water pump to absorb more energy. The process of air being pulled past the radiator by the fan is also forced convection.

BIO APPLICATION
Algal Blooms in Ponds and Lakes

The algal blooms often seen in temperate lakes and ponds during the spring or fall are caused by convection currents in the water. To understand this process,

Photograph of a teakettle, showing steam and turbulent convection air currents.

Figure 11.10 Convection currents are set up in a room warmed by a radiator.

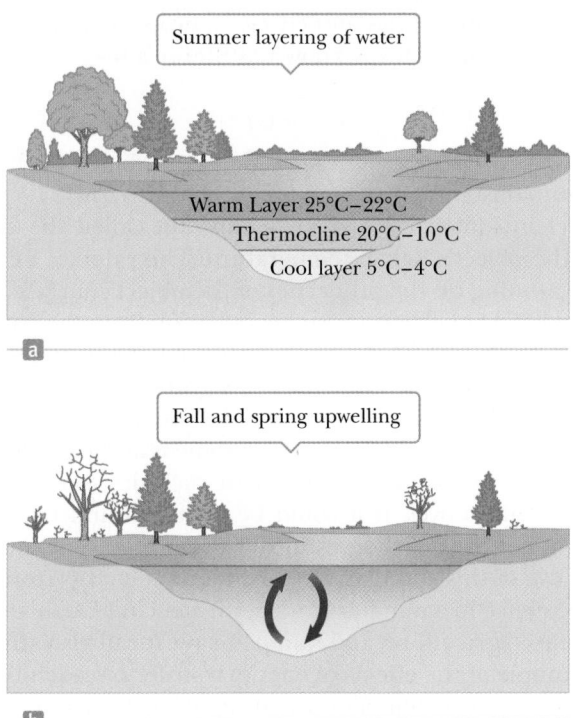

Summer layering of water

Warm Layer 25°C–22°C
Thermocline 20°C–10°C
Cool layer 5°C–4°C

a

Fall and spring upwelling

b

Figure 11.11 (a) During the summer, a warm upper layer of water is separated from a cooler lower layer by a thermocline. (b) Convection currents during the spring and fall mix the water and can cause algal blooms.

consider Figure 11.11. During the summer, bodies of water develop temperature gradients, with a warm upper layer of water separated from a cold lower layer by a buffer zone called a thermocline. In the spring and fall temperature changes in the water break down this thermocline, setting up convection currents that mix the water. The mixing process transports nutrients from the bottom to the surface. The nutrient-rich water forming at the surface can cause a rapid, temporary increase in the algae population.

■ APPLYING PHYSICS 11.1 | Body Temperature BIO

The body temperature of mammals ranges from about 35°C to 38°C, whereas that of birds ranges from about 40°C to 43°C. How can these narrow ranges of body temperature be maintained in cold weather?

EXPLANATION A natural method of maintaining body temperature is via layers of fat beneath the skin. Fat protects against both conduction and convection because of its low thermal conductivity and because there are few blood vessels in fat to carry blood to the surface, where energy losses by convection can occur. Birds ruffle their feathers in cold weather to trap a layer of air with a low thermal conductivity between the feathers and the skin. Bristling the fur produces the same effect in fur-bearing animals.

Humans keep warm with wool sweaters and down jackets that trap the warmer air in regions close to their bodies, reducing energy loss by convection and conduction. ■

Radiation

Another process of transferring energy is through **radiation.** Figure 11.12 shows how your hands can be warmed by a lamp through radiation. Because your hands aren't in physical contact with the lamp and the conductivity of air is very low, conduction can't account for the energy transfer. Nor can convection be responsible for any transfer of energy because your hands aren't above the lamp in the path of convection currents. The warmth felt in your hands must therefore come from the transfer of energy by radiation.

All objects radiate energy continuously in the form of electromagnetic waves due to thermal vibrations of their molecules. These vibrations create the orange glow of an electric stove burner, an electric space heater, and the coils of a toaster.

Figure 11.12 Warming hands by radiation.

The rate at which an object radiates energy is proportional to the fourth power of its absolute temperature. This is known as **Stefan's law,** expressed in equation form as

Stefan's law ▶

$$P = \sigma A e T^4 \qquad \text{[11.10]}$$

where P is the power in watts (or joules per second) radiated by the object, σ is the Stefan–Boltzmann constant, equal to $5.669\ 6 \times 10^{-8}\ \text{W/m}^2 \cdot \text{K}^4$, A is the surface area of the object in square meters, e is a constant called the **emissivity** of the object, and T is the object's Kelvin temperature. The value of e can vary between zero and one, depending on the properties of the object's surface.

Approximately 1 370 J of electromagnetic radiation from the Sun passes through each square meter at the top of the Earth's atmosphere every second. This radiation is primarily visible light, accompanied by significant amounts of infrared and ultraviolet light. We will study these types of radiation in detail in Chapter 21. Some of this energy is reflected back into space, and some is absorbed by the atmosphere, but enough arrives at the surface of the Earth each day to supply all our energy needs hundreds of times over, if it could be captured and used efficiently. The growth in the number of solar houses in the United States is one example of an attempt to make use of this abundant energy. Radiant energy from the Sun affects our day-to-day existence in a number of ways, influencing Earth's average temperature, ocean currents, agriculture, and rain patterns. It can also affect behavior.

As another example of the effects of energy transfer by radiation, consider what happens to the atmospheric temperature at night. If there is a cloud cover above the Earth, the water vapor in the clouds absorbs part of the infrared radiation emitted by the Earth and re-emits it back to the surface. Consequently, the temperature at the surface remains at moderate levels. In the absence of cloud cover, there is nothing to prevent the radiation from escaping into space, so the temperature drops more on a clear night than on a cloudy night.

As an object radiates energy at a rate given by Equation 11.10, it also absorbs radiation. If it didn't, the object would eventually radiate all its energy and its temperature would reach absolute zero. The energy an object absorbs comes from its environment, which consists of other bodies that radiate energy. If an object is at a temperature T and its surroundings are at a temperature T_0, the net energy gained or lost each second by the object as a result of radiation is

$$P_{\text{net}} = \sigma A e (T^4 - T_0^4) \qquad \text{[11.11]}$$

When an object is in equilibrium with its surroundings, it radiates and absorbs energy at the same rate, so its temperature remains constant. When an object is hotter than its surroundings, it radiates more energy than it absorbs and therefore cools.

An **ideal absorber** is an object that absorbs all the light radiation incident on it, including invisible infrared and ultraviolet light. Such an object is called a **black body** because a room-temperature black body would look black. Because a black body doesn't reflect radiation at any wavelength, any light coming from it is due to atomic and molecular vibrations alone. A perfect black body has emissivity $e = 1$. An ideal absorber is also an ideal radiator of energy. The Sun, for example, is nearly a perfect black body. This statement may seem contradictory because the Sun is bright, not dark; the light that comes from the Sun, however, is emitted, not reflected. Black bodies are perfect absorbers that look black at room temperature because they don't reflect any light. All black bodies, except those at absolute zero, emit light that has a characteristic spectrum, discussed in Chapter 27. In contrast to black bodies, an object for which $e = 0$ absorbs none of the energy incident on it, reflecting it all. Such a body is an **ideal reflector.**

White clothing is more comfortable to wear in the summer than black clothing. Black fabric acts as a good absorber of incoming sunlight and as a good emitter of this absorbed energy. About half of the emitted energy, however, travels toward the body, causing the person wearing the garment to feel uncomfortably warm. White or light-colored clothing reflects away much of the incoming energy.

APPLICATION
Light-Colored Summer Clothing

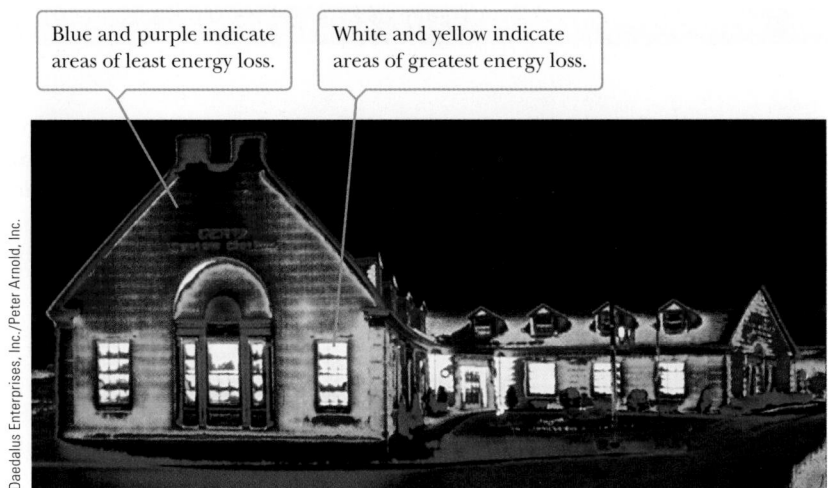

Blue and purple indicate areas of least energy loss.

White and yellow indicate areas of greatest energy loss.

Figure 11.13 This thermogram of a house, made during cold weather.

Thermogram of a woman's breasts. Her left breast is diseased (red and orange) and her right breast (blue) is healthy.

The amount of energy radiated by an object can be measured with temperature-sensitive recording equipment via a technique called **thermography.** An image of the pattern formed by varying radiation levels, called a **thermogram,** is brightest in the warmest areas. Figure 11.13 reproduces a thermogram of a house. More energy escapes in the lighter regions, such as the door and windows. The owners of this house could conserve energy and reduce their heating costs by adding insulation to the attic area and by installing thermal draperies over the windows. Thermograms have also been used to image injured or diseased tissue in medicine, because such areas are often at a different temperature than surrounding healthy tissue, although many radiologists consider thermograms inadequate as a diagnostic tool.

Figure 11.14 shows a recently developed radiation thermometer that has removed most of the risk of taking the temperature of young children or the aged with a rectal thermometer, risks such as bowel perforation or bacterial contamination. The instrument measures the intensity of the infrared radiation leaving the eardrum and surrounding tissues and converts this information to a standard numerical reading. The eardrum is a particularly good location to measure body temperature because it's near the hypothalamus, the body's temperature control center.

BIO APPLICATION

Thermography

BIO APPLICATION

Radiation Thermometers for Measuring Body Temperature

■ Quick Quiz

11.5 Stars A and B have the same temperature, but star A has twice the radius of star B. (a) What is the ratio of star A's power output to star B's output due to electromagnetic radiation? The emissivity of both stars can be assumed to be 1. (b) Repeat the question if the stars have the same radius, but star A has twice the absolute temperature of star B. (c) What's the ratio if star A has both twice the radius and twice the absolute temperature of star B?

Figure 11.14 A radiation thermometer measures a patient's temperature by monitoring the intensity of infrared radiation leaving the ear.

■ APPLYING PHYSICS 11.2 | Thermal Radiation and Night Vision

How can thermal radiation be used to see objects in near total darkness?

EXPLANATION There are two methods of night vision, one enhancing a combination of very faint visible light and infrared light, and another using infrared light only. The latter is valuable for creating images in absolute darkness. Because all objects above absolute zero emit thermal radia-

tion due to the vibrations of their atoms, the infrared (invisible) light can be focused by a special lens and scanned by an array of infrared detector elements. These elements create a thermogram. The information from thousands of separate points in the field of view is converted to electrical impulses and translated by a microchip into a form suitable for display. Different temperature areas are assigned different colors, which can then be easily discerned on the display. ■

■ EXAMPLE 11.10 | Polar Bear Club   BIO

GOAL Apply Stefan's law.

PROBLEM A member of the Polar Bear Club, dressed only in bathing trunks of negligible size, prepares to plunge into the Baltic Sea from the beach in St. Petersburg, Russia. The air is calm, with a temperature of 5°C. If the swimmer's surface body temperature is 25°C, compute the net rate of energy loss from his skin due to radiation. How much energy is lost in 10.0 min? Assume his emissivity is 0.900 and his surface area is 1.50 m².

STRATEGY Use Equation 11.11, the thermal radiation equation, substituting the given information. Remember to convert temperatures to Kelvin by adding 273 to each value in degrees Celsius!

SOLUTION

Convert temperatures from Celsius to Kelvin:

$$T_{5°C} = T_C + 273 = 5 + 273 = 278 \text{ K}$$
$$T_{25°C} = T_C + 273 = 25 + 273 = 298 \text{ K}$$

Compute the net rate of energy loss, using Equation 11.11:

$$P_{net} = \sigma A e(T^4 - T_0^4)$$
$$= (5.67 \times 10^{-8} \text{ W/m}^2 \cdot \text{K}^4)(1.50 \text{ m}^2)$$
$$\times (0.900)[(298 \text{ K})^4 - (278 \text{ K})^4]$$
$$P_{net} = \boxed{146 \text{ W}}$$

Multiply the preceding result by the time, 10 minutes, to get the energy lost in that time due to radiation:

$$Q = P_{net} \times \Delta t = (146 \text{ J/s})(6.00 \times 10^2 \text{ s}) = \boxed{8.76 \times 10^4 \text{ J}}$$

REMARKS Energy is also lost from the body through convection and conduction. Clothing traps layers of air next to the skin, which are warmed by radiation and conduction. In still air these warm layers are more readily retained. Even a Polar Bear Club member enjoys some benefit from the still air, better retaining a stagnant air layer next to the surface of his skin.

QUESTION 11.10 Suppose that at a given temperature the rate of an object's energy loss due to radiation is equal to its loss by conduction. When the object's temperature is raised, is the energy loss due to radiation (a) greater than, (b) equal to, or (c) less than the rate of energy loss due to conduction? (Assume the temperature of the environment is constant.)

EXERCISE 11.10 Repeat the calculation when the man is standing in his bedroom, with an ambient temperature of 20.0°C. Assume his body surface temperature is 27.0°C, with emissivity of 0.900.

ANSWER 55.9 W, 3.35 × 10⁴ J

The Dewar Flask

Figure 11.15 A cross-sectional view of a Thermos bottle designed to store hot or cold liquids.

The Thermos bottle, also called a **Dewar flask** (after its inventor), is designed to minimize energy transfer by conduction, convection, and radiation. The insulated bottle can store either cold or hot liquids for long periods. The standard vessel (Fig. 11.15) is a double-walled Pyrex glass with silvered walls. The space between the walls is evacuated to minimize energy transfer by conduction and convection. The silvered surface minimizes energy transfer by radiation because silver is a very good reflector and has very low emissivity. A further reduction in energy loss is achieved by reducing the size of the neck. Dewar flasks are commonly used to store liquid nitrogen (boiling point 77 K) and liquid oxygen (boiling point 90 K).

To confine liquid helium (boiling point 4.2 K), which has a very low heat of vaporization, it's often necessary to use a double Dewar system in which the Dewar flask containing the liquid is surrounded by a second Dewar flask. The space between the two flasks is filled with liquid nitrogen.

Some of the principles of the Thermos bottle are used in the protection of sensitive electronic instruments in orbiting space satellites. In half of its orbit around the Earth a satellite is exposed to intense radiation from the Sun, and in the other half it lies in the Earth's cold shadow. Without protection, its interior would be subjected to tremendous extremes of temperature. The interior of the satellite is wrapped with blankets of highly reflective aluminum foil. The foil's shiny surface reflects

11.6 | Global Warming and Greenhouse Gases   385

away much of the Sun's radiation while the satellite is in the unshaded part of the orbit and helps retain interior energy while the satellite is in the Earth's shadow.

APPLICATION

Thermos Bottles

11.6 Global Warming and Greenhouse Gases BIO

Many of the principles of energy transfer, and opposition to it, can be understood by studying the operation of a glass greenhouse. During the day, sunlight passes into the greenhouse and is absorbed by the walls, soil, plants, and so on. This absorbed visible light is subsequently reradiated as infrared radiation, causing the temperature of the interior to rise.

In addition, convection currents are inhibited in a greenhouse. As a result, warmed air can't rapidly pass over the surfaces of the greenhouse that are exposed to the outside air and thereby cause an energy loss by conduction through those surfaces. Most experts now consider this restriction to be a more important warming effect than the trapping of infrared radiation. In fact, experiments have shown that when the glass over a greenhouse is replaced by a special glass known to transmit infrared light, the temperature inside is lowered only slightly. On the basis of this evidence, the primary mechanism that raises the temperature of a greenhouse is not the trapping of infrared radiation, but the inhibition of airflow that occurs under any roof (in an attic, for example).

A phenomenon commonly known as the **greenhouse effect** can also play a major role in determining the Earth's temperature. First, note that the Earth's atmosphere is a good transmitter (and hence a poor absorber) of visible radiation and a good absorber of infrared radiation. The visible light that reaches the Earth's surface is absorbed and reradiated as infrared light, which in turn is absorbed (trapped) by the Earth's atmosphere. An extreme case is the warmest planet, Venus, which has a carbon dioxide (CO_2) atmosphere and temperatures approaching 850°F.

As fossil fuels (coal, oil, and natural gas) are burned, large amounts of carbon dioxide are released into the atmosphere, causing it to retain more energy. These emissions are of great concern to scientists and governments throughout the world. Many scientists are convinced that the 10% increase in the amount of atmospheric carbon dioxide since 1970 could lead to drastic changes in world climate. The increase in concentration of atmospheric carbon dioxide in the latter part of the 20th century is shown in Figure 11.16. According to one estimate, doubling the carbon dioxide content in the atmosphere will cause temperatures to increase by 2°C. In temperate regions such as Europe and the United States, a 2°C temperature rise would save billions of dollars per year in fuel costs. Unfortunately, it would also melt a large amount of land-based ice from Greenland and Antarctica, raising the level of the oceans and destroying many coastal regions. A 2°C rise

Figure 11.16 The concentration of atmospheric carbon dioxide in parts per million (ppm) of dry air as a function of time during the latter part of the 20th century. These data were recorded at Mauna Loa Observatory in Hawaii. The yearly variations (rust-colored curve) coincide with growing seasons because vegetation absorbs carbon dioxide from the air. The steady increase (black curve) is of concern to scientists.

Figure 11.17 *Death of an ice shelf.* The image in (a), taken on January 9, 1995 in the near-visible part of the spectrum, shows James Ross Island (spidery-shaped, just off center) before the iceberg calved, but after the disintegration of the ice shelf between James Ross Island and the Antarctic peninsula. In the image in part (b), taken on February 12, 1995, the iceberg has calved and begun moving away from land. The iceberg is about 78 km by 27 km and 200 m thick. A century ago James Ross Island was completely surrounded in ice that joined it to Antarctica.

British Antarctic Survey

a   b

would also increase the frequency of droughts and consequently decrease already low crop yields in tropical and subtropical countries. Even slightly higher average temperatures might make it impossible for certain plants and animals to survive in their customary ranges.

At present, about 3.5×10^{11} tons of CO_2 are released into the atmosphere each year. Most of this gas results from human activities such as the burning of fossil fuels, the cutting of forests, and manufacturing processes. Another greenhouse gas is methane (CH_4), which is released in the digestive process of cows and other ruminants. This gas originates from that part of the animal's stomach called the *rumen,* where cellulose is digested. Termites are also major producers of this gas. Finally, greenhouse gases such as nitrous oxide (N_2O) and sulfur dioxide (SO_2) are increasing due to automobile and industrial pollution.

Whether the increasing greenhouse gases are responsible or not, there is convincing evidence that global warming is under way. The evidence comes from the melting of ice in Antarctica and the retreat of glaciers at widely scattered sites throughout the world (see Fig. 11.17). For example, satellite images of Antarctica show James Ross Island completely surrounded by water for the first time since maps were made, about 100 years ago. Previously, the island was connected to the mainland by an ice bridge. In addition, at various places across the continent, ice shelves are retreating, some at a rapid rate.

Perhaps at no place in the world are glaciers monitored with greater interest than in Switzerland. There, it is found that the Alps have lost about 50% of their glacial ice compared to 130 years ago. The retreat of glaciers on high-altitude peaks in the tropics is even more severe than in Switzerland. The Lewis glacier on Mount Kenya and the snows of Kilimanjaro are two examples. In certain regions of the planet where glaciers are near large bodies of water and are fed by large and frequent snows, however, glaciers continue to advance, so the overall picture of a catastrophic global-warming scenario may be premature. In about 50 years, though, the amount of carbon dioxide in the atmosphere is expected to be about twice what it was in the preindustrial era. Because of the possible catastrophic consequences, most scientists voice the concern that reductions in greenhouse gas emissions need to be made now.

■ SUMMARY

11.1 Heat and Internal Energy

Internal energy is associated with a system's microscopic components. Internal energy includes the kinetic energy of translation, rotation, and vibration of molecules, as well as potential energy.

Heat is the transfer of energy across the boundary of a system resulting from a temperature difference between the system and its surroundings. The symbol Q represents the amount of energy transferred.

The **calorie** is the amount of energy necessary to raise the temperature of 1 g of water from 14.5°C to 15.5°C. The **mechanical equivalent of heat** is 4.186 J/cal.

11.2 Specific Heat

11.3 Calorimetry

The energy required to change the temperature of a substance of mass m by an amount ΔT is

$$Q = mc\Delta T \qquad [11.3]$$

where c is the **specific heat** of the substance. In calorimetry problems the specific heat of a substance can be determined by placing it in water of known temperature, isolating the system, and measuring the temperature at equilibrium. The sum of all energy gains and losses for all the objects in an isolated system is given by

$$\sum Q_k = 0 \qquad [11.5]$$

where Q_k is the energy change in the kth object in the system. This equation can be solved for the unknown specific heat, or used to determine an equilibrium temperature.

11.4 Latent Heat and Phase Change

The energy required to change the phase of a pure substance of mass m is

$$Q = \pm mL \qquad [11.6]$$

where L is the **latent heat** of the substance. The latent heat of fusion, L_f, describes an energy transfer during a change from a solid phase to a liquid phase (or vice versa), while the latent heat of vaporization, L_v, describes an energy transfer during a change from a liquid phase to a gaseous phase (or vice versa). Calorimetry problems involving phase changes are handled with Equation 11.5, with latent heat terms added to the specific heat terms.

11.5 Energy Transfer

Energy can be transferred by several different processes, including work, discussed in Chapter 5, and by conduction, convection, and radiation. **Conduction** can be viewed as an exchange of kinetic energy between colliding molecules or electrons. The rate at which energy transfers by conduction through a slab of area A and thickness L is

$$P = kA\frac{(T_h - T_c)}{L} \qquad [11.7]$$

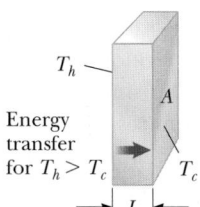

Energy transfer through a slab is proportional to the cross-sectional area and temperature difference, and inversely proportional to the thickness.

where k is the **thermal conductivity** of the material making up the slab.

Energy is transferred by **convection** as a substance moves from one place to another.

All objects emit **radiation** from their surfaces in the form of electromagnetic waves at a net rate of

$$P_{\text{net}} = \sigma Ae(T^4 - T_0^4) \qquad [11.11]$$

where T is the temperature of the object and T_0 is the temperature of the surroundings. An object that is hotter than its surroundings radiates more energy than it absorbs, whereas a body that is cooler than its surroundings absorbs more energy than it radiates.

■ MULTIPLE-CHOICE QUESTIONS

WebAssign The multiple-choice questions in this chapter may be assigned online in Enhanced WebAssign.

1. Convert 3.50×10^3 cal to an equivalent number of joules. (a) 2.74×10^4 J (b) 1.47×10^4 J (c) 3.24×10^4 J (d) 5.33×10^4 J (e) 7.20×10^5 J

2. Ethyl alcohol has about one-half the specific heat of water. Assume equal amounts of energy are transferred by heat into equal-mass liquid samples of alcohol and water in separate insulated containers. The water rises in temperature by 25°C. How much will the alcohol rise in temperature? (a) It will rise by 12°C. (b) It will rise by 25°C. (c) It will rise by 50°C. (d) It depends on the rate of energy transfer. (e) It will not rise in temperature.

3. A wall made of wood 4.00 cm thick has area of 48.0 m². If the temperature inside is 25°C and the temperature outside is 14°C, at what rate is thermal energy transported through the wall by conduction? (a) 82 W (b) 210 W (c) 690 W (d) 1.1×10^3 W (e) 2.1×10^3 W

4. If 9.30×10^5 J of energy are transferred to 2.00 kg of ice at 0°C, what is the final temperature of the system? (a) 22.4°C (b) 14.2°C (c) 31.5°C (d) 18.0°C (e) 0°C

5. How much energy is required to raise the temperature of 5.00 kg of lead from 20.0°C to its melting point of 327°C? (a) 4.04×10^5 J (b) 1.07×10^5 J (c) 8.15×10^4 J (d) 2.13×10^4 J (e) 1.96×10^5 J

6. A granite ball of radius 2.00 m and emissivity 0.450 is heated to 135°C, whereas the ambient temperature is 25.0°C. What is the net power radiated from the ball? (a) 425 W (b) 3.55×10^4 W (c) 145 W (d) 2.01×10^3 W (e) 2.54×10^4 W

7. How long would it take a 1.00×10^3 W heating element to melt 2.00 kg of ice at −20.0°C, assuming all the energy is absorbed by the ice? (a) 4.19 s (b) 419 s (c) 555 min (d) 12.5 min (e) 2.00 h

8. Assume you are measuring the specific heat of a sample of hot metal by using a calorimeter containing water. Because your calorimeter is not perfectly insulating, energy can transfer by heat between the contents of the calorimeter and the room. To obtain the most accurate result for the specific heat of the metal, you should use water with which initial temperature? (a) slightly lower than room temperature (b) the same as room temperature (c) slightly higher than room temperature (d) whatever you like because the initial temperature makes no difference

9. An amount of energy is added to ice, raising its temperature from $-10°C$ to $-5°C$. A larger amount of energy is added to the same mass of water, raising its temperature from $15°C$ to $20°C$. From these results, what can we conclude? (a) Overcoming the latent heat of fusion of ice requires an input of energy. (b) The latent heat of fusion of ice delivers some energy to the system. (c) The specific heat of ice is less than that of water. (d) The specific heat of ice is greater than that of water. (e) More information is needed to draw any conclusion.

10. A poker is a stiff, nonflammable rod used to push burning logs around in a fireplace. Suppose it is to be made of a single material. For best functionality and safety, should the poker be made from a material with (a) high specific heat and high thermal conductivity, (b) low specific heat and low thermal conductivity, (c) low specific heat and high thermal conductivity, (d) high specific heat and low thermal conductivity, or (e) low specific heat and low density?

11. Star A has twice the radius and twice the absolute temperature of star B. What is the ratio of the power output of star A to that of star B? The emissivity of both stars can be assumed to be 1. (a) 4 (b) 8 (c) 16 (d) 32 (e) 64

12. A person shakes a sealed, insulated bottle containing coffee for a few minutes. What is the change in the temperature of the coffee? (a) a large decrease (b) a slight decrease (c) no change (d) a slight increase (e) a large increase

■ CONCEPTUAL QUESTIONS

ENHANCED
WebAssign The conceptual questions in this chapter may be assigned online in Enhanced WebAssign.

1. Rub the palm of your hand on a metal surface for 30 to 45 seconds. Place the palm of your other hand on an unrubbed portion of the surface and then on the rubbed portion. The rubbed portion will feel warmer. Now repeat this process on a wooden surface. Why does the temperature difference between the rubbed and unrubbed portions of the wood surface seem larger than for the metal surface?

2. In winter, why did the pioneers store an open barrel of water alongside their produce?

3. In usually warm climates that experience an occasional hard freeze, fruit growers will spray the fruit trees with water, hoping that a layer of ice will form on the fruit. Why would such a layer be advantageous?

4. It is the morning of a day that will become hot. You just purchased drinks for a picnic and are loading them, with ice, into a chest in the back of your car. (a) You wrap a wool blanket around the chest. Does doing so help to keep the beverages cool, or should you expect the wool blanket to warm them up? Explain your answer. (b) Your younger sister suggests you wrap her up in another wool blanket to keep her cool on the hot day like the ice chest. Explain your response to her.

5. On a clear, cold night, why does frost tend to form on the tops, rather than the sides, of mailboxes and cars?

6. The U.S. penny is now made of copper-coated zinc. Can a calorimetric experiment be devised to test for the metal content in a collection of pennies? If so, describe the procedure.

7. Cups of water for coffee or tea can be warmed with a coil that is immersed in the water and raised to a high temperature by means of electricity. (a) Why do the instructions warn users not to operate the coils in the absence of water? (b) Can the immersion coil be used to warm up a cup of stew?

8. The air temperature above coastal areas is profoundly influenced by the large specific heat of water. One reason is that the energy released when 1 cubic meter of water cools by $1.0°C$ will raise the temperature of an enormously larger volume of air by $1.0°C$. Estimate that volume of air. The specific heat of air is approximately $1.0 \text{ kJ/kg} \cdot °C$. Take the density of air to be 1.3 kg/m^3.

9. A tile floor may feel uncomfortably cold to your bare feet, but a carpeted floor in an adjoining room at the same temperature feels warm. Why?

10. On a very hot day, it's possible to cook an egg on the hood of a car. Would you select a black car or a white car on which to cook your egg? Why?

11. Concrete has a higher specific heat than does soil. Use this fact to explain (partially) why a city has a higher average temperature than the surrounding countryside. Would you expect evening breezes to blow from city to country or from country to city? Explain.

12. You need to pick up a very hot cooking pot in your kitchen. You have a pair of hot pads. Should you soak them in cold water or keep them dry in order to pick up the pot most comfortably?

■ PROBLEMS

WebAssign The problems in this chapter may be assigned online in Enhanced WebAssign. Selected problems also have Watch It video solutions.

1. denotes straightforward problem; **2.** denotes intermediate problem;

3. denotes challenging problem

1. denotes full solution available in *Student Solutions Manual/ Study Guide*

1. denotes problems most often assigned in Enhanced WebAssign

BIO denotes biomedical problems

GP denotes guided problems

M denotes Master It tutorial available in Enhanced WebAssign

QC denotes asking for quantitative and conceptual reasoning

S denotes symbolic reasoning problem

11.1 Heat and Internal Energy

11.2 Specific Heat

1. The highest recorded waterfall in the world is found at Angel Falls in Venezuela. Its longest single waterfall has a height of 807 m. If water at the top of the falls is at 15.0°C, what is the maximum temperature of the water at the bottom of the falls? Assume all the kinetic energy of the water as it reaches the bottom goes into raising the water's temperature.

2. **M** The temperature of a silver bar rises by 10.0°C when it absorbs 1.23 kJ of energy by heat. The mass of the bar is 525 g. Determine the specific heat of silver from these data.

3. Lake Erie contains roughly 4.00×10^{11} m^3 of water. (a) How much energy is required to raise the temperature of that volume of water from 11.0°C to 12.0°C? (b) How many years would it take to supply this amount of energy by using the 1 000-MW exhaust energy of an electric power plant?

4. An aluminum rod is 20.0 cm long at 20°C and has a mass of 350 g. If 10 000 J of energy is added to the rod by heat, what is the change in length of the rod?

5. **QC** A 3.00-g copper coin at 25.0°C drops 50.0 m to the ground. (a) Assuming 60.0% of the change in gravitational potential energy of the coin–Earth system goes into increasing the internal energy of the coin, determine the coin's final temperature. (b) Does the result depend on the mass of the coin? Explain.

6. **BIO** A 55-kg woman cheats on her diet and eats a 540-Calorie (540 kcal) jelly doughnut for breakfast. (a) How many joules of energy are the equivalent of one jelly doughnut? (b) How many stairs must the woman climb to perform an amount of mechanical work equivalent to the food energy in one jelly doughnut? Assume the height of a single stair is 15 cm. (c) If the human body is only 25% efficient in converting chemical energy to mechanical energy, how many stairs must the woman climb to work off her breakfast?

7. **BIO** **QC** A 75-kg sprinter accelerates from rest to a speed of 11.0 m/s in 5.0 s. (a) Calculate the mechanical work done by the sprinter during this time. (b) Calculate the average power the sprinter must generate. (c) If the sprinter converts food energy to mechanical energy with an efficiency of 25%, at what average rate is he burning Calories? (d) What happens to the other 75% of the food energy being used?

8. **BIO** **S** A sprinter of mass m accelerates uniformly from rest to velocity v in t seconds. (a) Write a symbolic expression for the instantaneous mechanical power P required by the sprinter in terms of force F and velocity v. (b) Use Newton's second law and a kinematics equation for the velocity at any time to obtain an expression for the instantaneous power in terms of m, a, and t only. (c) If a 75.0-kg sprinter reaches a speed of 11.0 m/s in 5.00 s, calculate the sprinter's acceleration, assuming it to be constant. (d) Calculate the 75.0-kg sprinter's instantaneous mechanical power as a function of time t and (e) give the maximum rate at which he burns Calories during the sprint, assuming 25% efficiency of conversion form food energy to mechanical energy.

9. A 5.00-g lead bullet traveling at 300 m/s is stopped by a large tree. If half the kinetic energy of the bullet is transformed into internal energy and remains with the bullet while the other half is transmitted to the tree, what is the increase in temperature of the bullet?

10. The apparatus shown in Figure P11.10 was used by Joule to measure the mechanical equivalent of heat. Work is done on the water by a rotating paddle wheel, which is driven by two blocks falling at a constant speed. The temperature of the stirred water increases due to the friction between the water and the paddles. If the energy lost in the bearings and through the walls is neglected, then the loss in potential energy associated with the blocks equals the work done by the paddle wheel on the water. If each block has a mass of 1.50 kg and the insulated tank is filled with 200 g of water, what is the increase in temperature of the water after the blocks fall through a distance of 3.00 m?

Figure P11.10 The falling weights rotate the paddles, causing the temperature of the water to increase.

11. A 200-g aluminum cup contains 800 g of water in thermal equilibrium with the cup at 80°C. The combination of cup and water is cooled uniformly so that the temperature decreases by 1.5°C per minute. At what

rate is energy being removed? Express your answer in watts.

12. A 1.5-kg copper block is given an initial speed of 3.0 m/s on a rough horizontal surface. Because of friction, the block finally comes to rest. (a) If the block absorbs 85% of its initial kinetic energy as internal energy, calculate its increase in temperature. (b) What happens to the remaining energy?

13. A certain steel railroad rail is 13 yd in length and weighs 70.0 lb/yd. How much thermal energy is required to increase the length of such a rail by 3.0 mm? *Note:* Assume the steel has the same specific heat as iron.

14. **GP** In the summer of 1958 in St. Petersburg, Florida, a new sidewalk was poured near the childhood home of one of the authors. No expansion joints were supplied, and by mid-July the sidewalk had been completely destroyed by thermal expansion and had to be replaced, this time with the important addition of expansion joints! This event is modeled here.

A slab of concrete 4.00 cm thick, 1.00 m long, and 1.00 m wide is poured for a sidewalk at an ambient temperature of 25.0°C and allowed to set. The slab is exposed to direct sunlight and placed in a series of such slabs without proper expansion joints, so linear expansion is prevented. (a) Using the linear expansion equation (Eq. 10.4), eliminate ΔL from the equation for compressive stress and strain (Eq. 9.3). (b) Use the expression found in part (a) to eliminate ΔT from Equation 11.3, obtaining a symbolic equation for thermal energy transfer Q. (c) Compute the mass of the concrete slab given that its density is 2.40×10^3 kg/m³. (d) Concrete has an ultimate compressive strength of 2.00×10^7 Pa, specific heat of 880 J/kg · °C, and Young's modulus of 2.1×10^{10} Pa. How much thermal energy must be transferred to the slab to reach this compressive stress? (e) What temperature change is required? (f) If the Sun delivers 1.00×10^3 W of power to the top surface of the slab and if half the energy, on the average, is absorbed and retained, how long does it take the slab to reach the point at which it is in danger of cracking due to compressive stress?

11.3 Calorimetry

15. What mass of water at 25.0°C must be allowed to come to thermal equilibrium with a 1.85-kg cube of aluminum initially at 1.50×10^2°C to lower the temperature of the aluminum to 65.0°C? Assume any water turned to steam subsequently recondenses.

16. Lead pellets, each of mass 1.00 g, are heated to 200°C. How many pellets must be added to 500 g of water that is initially at 20.0°C to make the equilibrium temperature 25.0°C? Neglect any energy transfer to or from the container.

17. An aluminum cup contains 225 g of water and a 40-g copper stirrer, all at 27°C. A 400-g sample of silver at an initial temperature of 87°C is placed in the water.

The stirrer is used to stir the mixture until it reaches its final equilibrium temperature of 32°C. Calculate the mass of the aluminum cup.

18. In a showdown on the streets of Laredo, the good guy drops a 5.00-g silver bullet at a temperature of 20.0°C into a 100-cm³ cup of water at 90.0°C. Simultaneously, the bad guy drops a 5.00-g copper bullet at the same initial temperature into an identical cup of water. Which one ends the showdown with the coolest cup of water in the West? Neglect any energy transfer into or away from the container.

19. **QC** An aluminum calorimeter with a mass of 100 g contains 250 g of water. The calorimeter and water are in thermal equilibrium at 10.0°C. Two metallic blocks are placed into the water. One is a 50.0-g piece of copper at 80.0°C. The other has a mass of 70.0 g and is originally at a temperature of 100°C. The entire system stabilizes at a final temperature of 20.0°C. (a) Determine the specific heat of the unknown sample. (b) Using the data in Table 11.1, can you make a positive identification of the unknown material? Can you identify a possible material? (c) Explain your answers for part (b).

20. **M** A 1.50-kg iron horseshoe initially at 600°C is dropped into a bucket containing 20.0 kg of water at 25.0°C. What is the final temperature of the water–horseshoe system? Ignore the heat capacity of the container and assume a negligible amount of water boils away.

21. A student drops two metallic objects into a 120-g steel container holding 150 g of water at 25°C. One object is a 200-g cube of copper that is initially at 85°C, and the other is a chunk of aluminum that is initially at 5.0°C. To the surprise of the student, the water reaches a final temperature of 25°C, precisely where it started. What is the mass of the aluminum chunk?

22. When a driver brakes an automobile, the friction between the brake drums and the brake shoes converts the car's kinetic energy to thermal energy. If a 1 500-kg automobile traveling at 30 m/s comes to a halt, how much does the temperature rise in each of the four 8.0-kg iron brake drums? (The specific heat of iron is 448 J/kg · °C.)

23. **QC** Equal 0.400-kg masses of lead and tin at 60.0°C are placed in 1.00 kg of water at 20.0°C. (a) What is the equilibrium temperature of the system? (b) If an alloy is half lead and half tin by mass, what specific heat would you anticipate for the alloy? (c) How many atoms of tin N_{Sn} are in 0.400 kg of tin, and how many atoms of lead N_{Pb} are in 0.400 kg of lead? (d) Divide the number N_{Sn} of tin atoms by the number N_{Pb} of lead atoms and compare this ratio with the specific heat of tin divided by the specific heat of lead. What conclusion can be drawn?

24. An unknown substance has a mass of 0.125 kg and an initial temperature of 95.0°C. The substance is then

dropped into a calorimeter made of aluminum containing 0.285 kg of water initially at 25.0°C. The mass of the aluminum container is 0.150 kg, and the temperature of the calorimeter increases to a final equilibrium temperature of 32.0°C. Assuming no thermal energy is transferred to the environment, calculate the specific heat of the unknown substance.

11.4 Latent Heat and Phase Change

25. A 75-g ice cube at 0°C is placed in 825 g of water at 25°C. What is the final temperature of the mixture?

26. A 50-g ice cube at 0°C is heated until 45 g has become water at 100°C and 5.0 g has become steam at 100°C. How much energy was added to accomplish the transformation?

27. A 100-g cube of ice at 0°C is dropped into 1.0 kg of water that was originally at 80°C. What is the final temperature of the water after the ice has melted?

28. How much energy is required to change a 40-g ice cube from ice at −10°C to steam at 110°C?

29. **M** A 75-kg cross-country skier glides over snow as in Figure P11.29. The coefficient of friction between skis and snow is 0.20. Assume all the snow beneath her skis is at 0°C and that all the internal energy generated by friction is added to snow, which sticks to her skis until it melts. How far would she have to ski to melt 1.0 kg of snow?

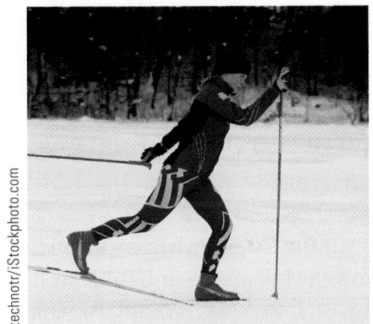

Figure P11.29

30. **GP** Into a 0.500-kg aluminum container at 20.0°C is placed 6.00 kg of ethyl alcohol at 30.0°C and 1.00 kg ice at −10.0°C. Assume the system is insulated from its environment. (a) Identify all five thermal energy transfers that occur as the system goes to a final equilibrium temperature T. Use the form "substance at X°C to substance at Y°C." (b) Construct a table similar to the table in Example 11.5. (c) Sum all terms in the right-most column of the table and set the sum equal to zero. (d) Substitute information from the table into the equation found in part (c) and solve for the final equilibrium temperature, T.

31. A 40-g block of ice is cooled to −78°C and is then added to 560 g of water in an 80-g copper calorimeter at a temperature of 25°C. Determine the final temperature of the system consisting of the ice, water, and calorimeter. (If not all the ice melts, determine how much ice

is left.) Remember that the ice must first warm to 0°C, melt, and then continue warming as water. (The specific heat of ice is 0.500 cal/g · °C = 2 090 J/kg · °C.)

32. **BIO** When you jog, most of the food energy you burn above your basal metabolic rate (BMR) ends up as internal energy that would raise your body temperature if it were not eliminated. The evaporation of perspiration is the primary mechanism for eliminating this energy. Determine the amount of water you lose to evaporation when running for 30 minutes at a rate that uses 400 kcal/h above your BMR. (That amount is often considered to be the "maximum fat-burning" energy output.) The metabolism of 1 gram of fat generates approximately 9.0 kcal of energy and produces approximately 1 gram of water. (The hydrogen atoms in the fat molecule are transferred to oxygen to form water.) What fraction of your need for water will be provided by fat metabolism? (The latent heat of vaporization of water at room temperature is 2.5×10^6 J/kg.)

33. A high-end gas stove usually has at least one burner rated at 14 000 Btu/h. (a) If you place a 0.25-kg aluminum pot containing 2.0 liters of water at 20°C on this burner, how long will it take to bring the water to a boil, assuming all the heat from the burner goes into the pot? (b) Once boiling begins, how much time is required to boil all the water out of the pot?

34. **BIO** A 60.0-kg runner expends 300 W of power while running a marathon. Assuming 10.0% of the energy is delivered to the muscle tissue and that the excess energy is removed from the body primarily by sweating, determine the volume of bodily fluid (assume it is water) lost per hour. (At 37.0°C, the latent heat of vaporization of water is 2.41×10^6 J/kg.)

35. Steam at 100°C is added to ice at 0°C. (a) Find the amount of ice melted and the final temperature when the mass of steam is 10 g and the mass of ice is 50 g. (b) Repeat with steam of mass 1.0 g and ice of mass 50 g.

36. **BIO** The excess internal energy of metabolism is exhausted through a variety of channels, such as through radiation and evaporation of perspiration. Consider another pathway for energy loss: moisture in exhaled breath. Suppose you breathe out 22.0 breaths per minute, each with a volume of 0.600 L. Suppose also that you inhale dry air and exhale air at 37°C containing water vapor with a vapor pressure of 3.20 kPa. The vapor comes from the evaporation of liquid water in your body. Model the water vapor as an ideal gas. Assume its latent heat of evaporation at 37°C is the same as its heat of vaporization at 100°C. Calculate the rate at which you lose energy by exhaling humid air.

37. **QC** A 3.00-g lead bullet at 30.0°C is fired at a speed of 2.40×10^2 m/s into a large, fixed block of ice at 0°C, in which it becomes embedded. (a) Describe the energy transformations that occur as the bullet is cooled. What is the final temperature of the bullet? (b) What quantity of ice melts?

11.5 Energy Transfer

38. A glass windowpane in a home is 0.62 cm thick and has dimensions of 1.0 m × 2.0 m. On a certain day, the indoor temperature is 25°C and the outdoor temperature is 0°C. (a) What is the rate at which energy is transferred by heat through the glass? (b) How much energy is lost through the window in one day, assuming the temperatures inside and outside remain constant?

39. A pond with a flat bottom has a surface area of 820 m² and a depth of 2.0 m. On a warm day, the surface water is at a temperature of 25°C, while the bottom of the pond is at 12°C. Find the rate at which energy is transferred by conduction from the surface to the bottom of the pond.

40. **BIO** The thermal conductivities of human tissues vary greatly. Fat and skin have conductivities of about 0.20 W/m·K and 0.020 W/m·K, respectively, while other tissues inside the body have conductivities of about 0.50 W/m·K. Assume that between the core region of the body and the skin surface lies a skin layer of 1.0 mm, fat layer of 0.50 cm, and 3.2 cm of other tissues. (a) Find the R-factor for each of these layers, and the equivalent R-factor for all layers taken together, retaining two digits. (b) Find the rate of energy loss when the core temperature is 37°C and the exterior temperature is 0°C. Assume that both a protective layer of clothing and an insulating layer of unmoving air are absent, and a body area of 2.0 m².

41. A steam pipe is covered with 1.50-cm-thick insulating material of thermal conductivity 0.200 cal/cm·°C·s. How much energy is lost every second when the steam is at 200°C and the surrounding air is at 20.0°C? The pipe has a circumference of 800 cm and a length of 50.0 m. Neglect losses through the ends of the pipe.

42. The average thermal conductivity of the walls (including windows) and roof of a house in Figure P11.42 is 4.8×10^{-4} kW/m·°C, and their average thickness is 21.0 cm. The house is heated with natural gas, with a heat of combustion (energy released per cubic meter of gas burned) of 9 300 kcal/m³. How many cubic meters of gas must be burned each day to maintain an inside temperature of 25.0°C if the outside temperature is 0.0°C? Disregard surface air layers, radiation, and energy loss by heat through the ground.

Figure P11.42

43. Consider two cooking pots of the same dimensions, each containing the same amount of water at the same initial temperature. The bottom of the first pot is made of copper, while the bottom of the second pot is made of aluminum. Both pots are placed on a hot surface having a temperature of 145°C. The water in the copper-bottomed pot boils away completely in 425 s. How long does it take the water in the aluminum-bottomed pot to boil away completely?

44. A thermopane window consists of two glass panes, each 0.50 cm thick, with a 1.0-cm-thick sealed layer of air in between. (a) If the inside surface temperature is 23°C and the outside surface temperature is 0.0°C, determine the rate of energy transfer through 1.0 m² of the window. (b) Compare your answer to (a) with the rate of energy transfer through 1.0 m² of a single 1.0-cm-thick pane of glass. Disregard surface air layers.

45. **M** A copper rod and an aluminum rod of equal diameter are joined end to end in good thermal contact. The temperature of the free end of the copper rod is held constant at 100°C and that of the far end of the aluminum rod is held at 0°C. If the copper rod is 0.15 m long, what must be the length of the aluminum rod so that the temperature at the junction is 50°C?

46. A Styrofoam box has a surface area of 0.80 m² and a wall thickness of 2.0 cm. The temperature of the inner surface is 5.0°C, and the outside temperature is 25°C. If it takes 8.0 h for 5.0 kg of ice to melt in the container, determine the thermal conductivity of the Styrofoam.

47. A rectangular glass window pane on a house has a width of 1.0 m, a height of 2.0 m, and a thickness of 0.40 cm. Find the energy transferred through the window by conduction in 12 hours on a day when the inside temperature of the house is 22°C and the outside temperature is 2.0°C. Take surface air layers into consideration.

48. A solar sail is made of aluminized Mylar having an emissivity of 0.03 and reflecting 97% of the light that falls on it. Suppose a sail with area 1.00 km² is oriented so that sunlight falls perpendicular to its surface with an intensity of 1.40×10^3 W/m². To what temperature will it warm before it emits as much energy (from both sides) by radiation as it absorbs on the sunny side? Assume the sail is so thin that the temperature is uniform and no energy is emitted from the edges. Take the environment temperature to be 0 K.

49. Measurements on two stars indicate that Star X has a surface temperature of 5 727°C and Star Y has a surface temperature of 11 727°C. If both stars have the same radius, what is the ratio of the luminosity (total power output) of Star Y to the luminosity of Star X? Both stars can be considered to have an emissivity of 1.0.

50. The filament of a 75-W light bulb is at a temperature of 3 300 K. Assuming the filament has an emissivity $e = 1.0$, find its surface area.

Additional Problems

51. The bottom of a copper kettle has a 10-cm radius and is 2.0 mm thick. The temperature of the outside surface is 102°C, and the water inside the kettle is boiling at 1 atm of pressure. Find the rate at which energy is being transferred through the bottom of the kettle.

52. A family comes home from a long vacation with laundry to do and showers to take. The water heater has been turned off during the vacation. If the heater has a capacity of 50.0 gallons and a 4 800-W heating element, how much time is required to raise the temperature of the water from 20.0°C to 60.0°C? Assume the heater is well insulated and no water is withdrawn from the tank during that time.

53. **M** A 40-g ice cube floats in 200 g of water in a 100-g copper cup; all are at a temperature of 0°C. A piece of lead at 98°C is dropped into the cup, and the final equilibrium temperature is 12°C. What is the mass of the lead?

54. **BIO** The surface area of an unclothed person is 1.50 m², and his skin temperature is 33.0°C. The person is located in a dark room with a temperature of 20.0°C, and the emissivity of the skin is $e = 0.95$. (a) At what rate is energy radiated by the body? (b) What is the significance of the sign of your answer?

55. A 200-g block of copper at a temperature of 90°C is dropped into 400 g of water at 27°C. The water is contained in a 300-g glass container. What is the final temperature of the mixture?

56. **QC** Liquid nitrogen has a boiling point of 77 K and a latent heat of vaporization of 2.01×10^5 J/kg. A 25-W electric heating element is immersed in an insulated vessel containing 25 L of liquid nitrogen at its boiling point. (a) Describe the energy transformations that occur as power is supplied to the heating element. (b) How many kilograms of nitrogen are boiled away in a period of 4.0 hours?

57. **QC** A student measures the following data in a calorimetry experiment designed to determine the specific heat of aluminum:

Initial temperature of water and calorimeter:	70.0°C
Mass of water:	0.400 kg
Mass of calorimeter:	0.040 kg
Specific heat of calorimeter:	0.63 kJ/kg · °C
Initial temperature of aluminum:	27.0°C
Mass of aluminum:	0.200 kg
Final temperature of mixture:	66.3°C

Use these data to determine the specific heat of aluminum. Explain whether your result is within 15% of the value listed in Table 11.1.

58. **BIO** Overall, 80% of the energy used by the body must be eliminated as excess thermal energy and needs to be dissipated. The mechanisms of elimination are radiation, evaporation of sweat (2 430 kJ/kg), evaporation from the lungs (38 kJ/h), conduction, and convection.

A person working out in a gym has a metabolic rate of 2 500 kJ/h. His body temperature is 37°C, and the outside temperature 24°C. Assume the skin has an area of 2.0 m² and emissivity of 0.97. (a) At what rate is his excess thermal energy dissipated by radiation? (b) If he eliminates 0.40 kg of perspiration during that hour, at what rate is thermal energy dissipated by evaporation of sweat? (c) At what rate is energy eliminated by evaporation from the lungs? (d) At what rate must the remaining excess energy be eliminated through conduction and convection?

59. Liquid helium has a very low boiling point, 4.2 K, as well as a very low latent heat of vaporization, 2.00×10^4 J/kg. If energy is transferred to a container of liquid helium at the boiling point from an immersed electric heater at a rate of 10.0 W, how long does it take to boil away 2.00 kg of the liquid?

60. A class of 10 students taking an exam has a power output per student of about 200 W. Assume the initial temperature of the room is 20°C and that its dimensions are 6.0 m by 15.0 m by 3.0 m. What is the temperature of the room at the end of 1.0 h if all the energy remains in the air in the room and none is added by an outside source? The specific heat of air is 837 J/kg · °C, and its density is about 1.3×10^{-3} g/cm³.

61. A bar of gold (Au) is in thermal contact with a bar of silver (Ag) of the same length and area (Fig. P11.61). One end of the compound bar is maintained at 80.0°C, and the opposite end is at 30.0°C. Find the temperature at the junction when the energy flow reaches a steady state.

Figure P11.61

62. An iron plate is held against an iron wheel so that a sliding frictional force of 50 N acts between the two pieces of metal. The relative speed at which the two surfaces slide over each other is 40 m/s. (a) Calculate the rate at which mechanical energy is converted to internal energy. (b) The plate and the wheel have masses of 5.0 kg each, and each receives 50% of the internal energy. If the system is run as described for 10 s and each object is then allowed to reach a uniform internal temperature, what is the resultant temperature increase?

63. An automobile has a mass of 1 500 kg, and its aluminum brakes have an overall mass of 6.00 kg. (a) Assuming all the internal energy transformed by friction when the car stops is deposited in the brakes and neglecting energy transfer, how many times could the car be braked to rest starting from 25.0 m/s before the brakes would begin to melt? (Assume an initial temperature of 20.0°C.) (b) Identify some effects that are neglected in part (a), but are likely to be important in a more realistic assessment of the temperature increase of the brakes.

64. Three liquids are at temperatures of 10°C, 20°C, and 30°C, respectively. Equal masses of the first two liquids

are mixed, and the equilibrium temperature is 17°C. Equal masses of the second and third are then mixed, and the equilibrium temperature is 28°C. Find the equilibrium temperature when equal masses of the first and third are mixed.

65. **QC** A *flow calorimeter* is an apparatus used to measure the specific heat of a liquid. The technique is to measure the temperature difference between the input and output points of a flowing stream of the liquid while adding energy at a known rate. (a) Start with the equations $Q = mc(\Delta T)$ and $m = \rho V$, and show that the rate at which energy is added to the liquid is given by the expression $\Delta Q / \Delta t = \rho c(\Delta T)(\Delta V / \Delta t)$. (b) In a particular experiment, a liquid of density 0.72 g/cm³ flows through the calorimeter at the rate of 3.5 cm³/s. At steady state, a temperature difference of 5.8°C is established between the input and output points when energy is supplied at the rate of 40 J/s. What is the specific heat of the liquid?

66. A wood stove is used to heat a single room. The stove is cylindrical in shape, with a diameter of 40.0 cm and a length of 50.0 cm, and operates at a temperature of 400°F. (a) If the temperature of the room is 70.0°F, determine the amount of radiant energy delivered to the room by the stove each second if the emissivity is 0.920. (b) If the room is a square with walls that are 8.00 ft high and 25.0 ft wide, determine the R-value needed in the walls and ceiling to maintain the inside temperature at 70.0°F if the outside temperature is 32.0°F. Note that we are ignoring any heat conveyed by the stove via convection and any energy lost through the walls (and windows!) via convection or radiation.

67. A "solar cooker" consists of a curved reflecting mirror that focuses sunlight onto the object to be heated (Fig. P11.67). The solar power per unit area reaching the Earth at the location of a 0.50-m-diameter solar cooker is 600 W/m². Assuming 50% of the incident energy is converted to thermal energy, how long would it take to boil away 1.0 L of water initially at 20°C? (Neglect the specific heat of the container.)

0.50 m

Figure P11.67

68. **BIO** For bacteriological testing of water supplies and in medical clinics, samples must routinely be incubated for 24 h at 37°C. A standard constant-temperature bath with electric heating and thermostatic control is not suitable in developing nations without continuously operating electric power lines. Peace Corps volunteer and MIT engineer Amy Smith invented a low-cost, low-maintenance incubator to fill the need. The device consists of a foam-insulated box containing several packets of a waxy material that melts at 37.0°C, interspersed among tubes, dishes, or bottles containing the test samples and growth medium (food for bacteria). Outside the box, the waxy material is first melted by a stove or solar energy collector. Then it is put into the box to keep the test samples warm as it solidifies. The heat of fusion of the phase-change material is 205 kJ/kg. Model the insulation as a panel with surface area 0.490 m², thickness 9.50 cm, and conductivity 0.012 0 W/m°C. Assume the exterior temperature is 23.0°C for 12.0 h and 16.0°C for 12.0 h. (a) What mass of the waxy material is required to conduct the bacteriological test? (b) Explain why your calculation can be done without knowing the mass of the test samples or of the insulation.

69. The surface of the Sun has a temperature of about 5 800 K. The radius of the Sun is 6.96×10^8 m. Calculate the total energy radiated by the Sun each second. Assume the emissivity of the Sun is 0.986.

70. **BIO** The evaporation of perspiration is the primary mechanism for cooling the human body. Estimate the amount of water you will lose when you bake in the sun on the beach for an hour. Use a value of 1 000 W/m² for the intensity of sunlight and note that the energy required to evaporate a liquid at a particular temperature is approximately equal to the sum of the energy required to raise its temperature to the boiling point and the latent heat of vaporization (determined at the boiling point).

71. At time $t = 0$, a vessel contains a mixture of 10 kg of water and an unknown mass of ice in equilibrium at 0°C. The temperature of the mixture is measured over a period of an hour, with the following results: During the first 50 min, the mixture remains at 0°C; from 50 min to 60 min, the temperature increases steadily from 0°C to 2°C. Neglecting the heat capacity of the vessel, determine the mass of ice that was initially placed in it. Assume a constant power input to the container.

72. **QC** An ice-cube tray is filled with 75.0 g of water. After the filled tray reaches an equilibrium temperature 20.0°C, it is placed in a freezer set at −8.00°C to make ice cubes. (a) Describe the processes that occur as energy is being removed from the water to make ice. (b) Calculate the energy that must be removed from the water to make ice cubes at −8.00°C.

73. An aluminum rod and an iron rod are joined end to end in good thermal contact. The two rods have equal lengths and radii. The free end of the aluminum rod is maintained at a temperature of 100°C, and the free end of the iron rod is maintained at 0°C. (a) Determine the temperature of the interface between the two rods. (b) If each rod is 15 cm long and each has a cross-sectional area of 5.0 cm², what quantity of energy is conducted across the combination in 30 min?

AP* REVIEW QUESTIONS

1. Tom, 70 kg, needs to burn off 7000 J by doing chin-ups. How many does he need to do if he lifts his body weight a distance of 0.5 m each time?

   (A) 2

   (B) 5

   (C) 20

   (D) 50

   (E) 200

2. Every year, there is a race to the top of the 350 m tall Empire State Building. How many joules are burned by a 100 kg man in this race?

   (A) 350 J

   (B) 3.5×10^3 J

   (C) 3.5×10^4 J

   (D) 3.5×10^5 J

   (E) 3.5×10^6 J

3. How much heat is produced when a 100 kg bodybuilder lifts a 200 kg weight a distance of 1.0 m for 15 reps?

   (A) 200 J

   (B) 2000 J

   (C) 3000 J

   (D) 30,000 J

   (E) More information is needed

4. Glass has a thermal conductivity, k, that is 10 times greater than wood. If the area of a wooden wall is 15 times larger than the area of a glass window, how thick would the glass window have to be to have the same rate of energy transfer by conduction as a 3 cm thick wooden wall?

   (A) 0.7 cm

   (B) 1.0 cm

   (C) 2.0 cm

   (D) 3.0 cm

   (E) 4.5 cm

5. Ice has a thermal conductivity of $k = 2$ J/s · m · °C. The area inside an igloo is 15 m² and the walls are 20 cm thick. If the temperature outside is −10°C and the inside temperature is 30°C, what is the rate of energy transfer by conduction through the walls of the igloo?

   (A) 6000 W

   (B) 6000 J

   (C) 240 W

   (D) 240 J

   (E) More information is needed

6. Assuming the same temperature difference ΔT and area A, what would the ratio of thicknesses L have to be for ice versus air to have the same rate of energy transfer?

   $$\left(\text{Note: } k_{\text{ice}} = 2 \, \frac{\text{J}}{\text{s} \cdot \text{m} \cdot \text{°C}} \text{ and } k_{\text{air}} = 0.02 \, \frac{\text{J}}{\text{s} \cdot \text{m} \cdot \text{°C}} \right)$$

   (A) Air needs to be 10 times thicker

   (B) Ice needs to be 10 times thicker

   (C) Air needs to be 100 times thicker

   (D) Ice needs to be 100 times thicker

   (E) Ice and air are the same thickness

7. Rank the following materials A–E from best insulators to worst insulators, based on their k values.

Material	k value $\left(\dfrac{\text{J}}{\text{s} \cdot \text{m} \cdot \text{°C}} \right)$
A	35
B	0.024
C	0.2
D	2
E	238

   (A) B, C, D, A, E

   (B) C, B, A, D, E

   (C) E, A, D, C, B

   (D) E, B, A, C, D

   (E) More information is needed

8. Look at the table below. Rank materials A, B, and C from largest to smallest thermal conductivity, k.

Material	Length L	Area A	ΔT	H
A	0.1 m	10 m^2	10°C	10,000 W
B	0.2 m	10 m^2	10°C	300 W
C	0.1 m	20 m^2	40°C	8000 W

(A) A, B, C

(B) B, C, A

(C) C, A, B

(D) C, B, A

(E) A, C, B

9. Look at the table below. Rank materials A, B, and C from thickest to thinnest (L).

Material	k	Area A	ΔT	H
A	$1 \dfrac{J}{s \cdot m \cdot °C}$	10 m^2	80°C	400 W
B	$0.1 \dfrac{J}{s \cdot m \cdot °C}$	20 m^2	40°C	100 W
C	$2 \dfrac{J}{s \cdot m \cdot °C}$	30 m^2	10°C	400 W

(A) A, B, C

(B) B, C, A

(C) C, A, B

(D) C, B, A

(E) A, C, B

10. After coming in from the cold, Mary attempts to warm up by holding a warm cup of coffee, standing by a fire, and turning on the forced air furnace. In the order listed, what methods of heat transfer did Mary use?

(A) Convection, radiation, conduction

(B) Conduction, radiation, convection

(C) Radiation, conduction, convection

(D) Radiation, convection, conduction

(E) Conduction, convection, radiation

11. One potential consequence of global warming is the melting of Greenland's ice and the subsequent shutting off of the North Atlantic Ocean current. What type of heat transfer would be lost if this current were to shut down?

(A) Conduction

(B) Radiation

(C) Convection

(D) Both (A) and (B)

(E) Both (A) and (C)

12. On a sunny summer day, a teenager walks across a black asphalt driveway and his feet get hot. How did the heat transfer to the driveway and then to his feet?

(A) Conduction, radiation

(B) Radiation, convection

(C) Convection, radiation

(D) Convection, conduction

(E) Radiation, conduction

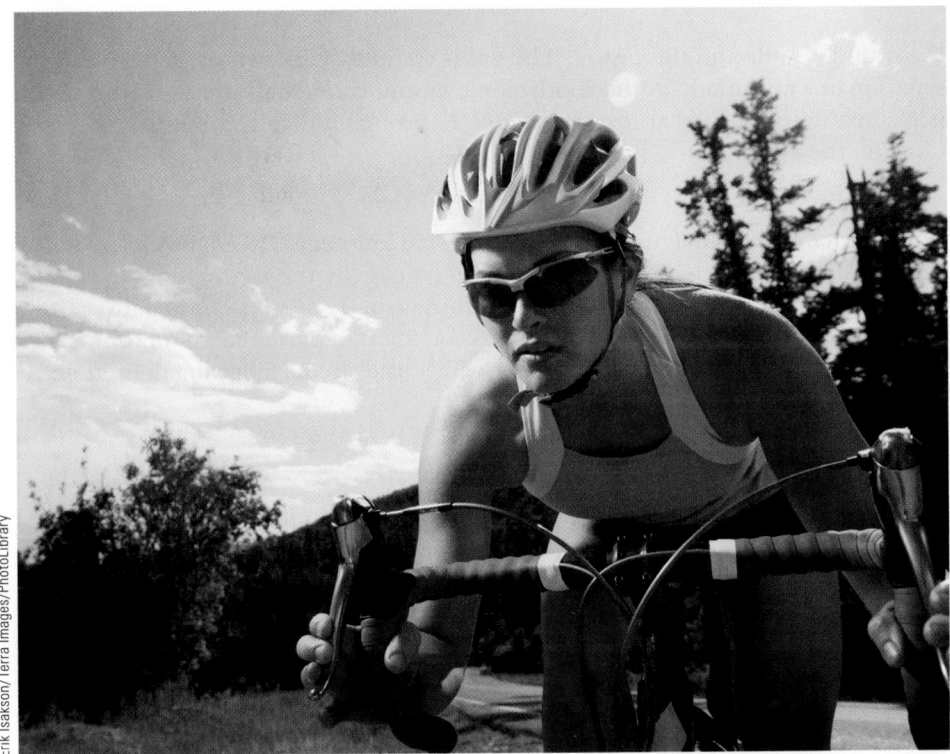

Erik Isakson/Terra Images/PhotoLibrary

A cyclist is an engine: she requires fuel and oxygen to burn it, and the result is work that drives her forward as her excess waste energy is expelled in her evaporating sweat.

The Laws of Thermodynamics 12

According to the first law of thermodynamics, the internal energy of a system can be increased either by adding energy to the system or by doing work on it. That means the internal energy of a system, which is just the sum of the molecular kinetic and potential energies, can change as a result of two separate types of energy transfer across the boundary of the system. Although the first law imposes conservation of energy for both energy added by heat and work done on a system, it doesn't predict which of several possible energy-conserving processes actually occur in nature.

The second law of thermodynamics constrains the first law by establishing which processes allowed by the first law actually occur. For example, the second law tells us that energy never flows by heat spontaneously from a cold object to a hot object. One important application of this law is in the study of heat engines (such as the internal combustion engine) and the principles that limit their efficiency.

12.1 Work in Thermodynamic Processes

Energy can be transferred to a system by heat and by work done on the system. In most cases of interest treated here, the system is a volume of gas, which is important in understanding engines. All such systems of gas will be assumed to be in thermodynamic equilibrium, so that every part of the gas is at the same temperature and pressure. If that were not the case, the ideal gas law wouldn't apply and most of the results presented here wouldn't be valid. Consider a gas contained by a cylinder fitted with a movable piston (Active Fig. 12.1a on page 396) and in equilibrium. The gas occupies a volume V and exerts a uniform pressure P on

Active Figure 12.1
(a) A gas in a cylinder occupying a volume V at a pressure P. (b) Pushing the piston down compresses the gas.

the cylinder walls and the piston. The gas is compressed slowly enough so the system remains essentially in thermodynamic equilibrium at all times. As the piston is pushed downward by an external force F through a displacement Δy, the work done on the gas is

$$W = -F\,\Delta y = -PA\,\Delta y$$

where we have set the magnitude F of the external force equal to PA, possible because the pressure is the same everywhere in the system (by the assumption of equilibrium). Note that if the piston is pushed downward, $\Delta y = y_f - y_i$ is negative, so we need an explicit negative sign in the expression for W to make the work positive. The change in volume of the gas is $\Delta V = A\,\Delta y$, which leads to the following definition:

The **work W done on a gas** at constant pressure is given by

$$W = -P\,\Delta V \qquad\qquad [12.1]$$

where P is the pressure throughout the gas and ΔV is the change in volume of the gas during the process.

If the gas is compressed as in Active Figure 12.1b, ΔV is negative and the work done on the gas is positive. If the gas expands, ΔV is positive and the work done on the gas is negative. The work done by the gas on its environment, W_{env}, is simply the negative of the work done on the gas. In the absence of a change in volume, the work is zero.

The definition of work W in Equation 12.1 specifies **work done on** a gas. In many texts, work W is defined as **work done by** a gas. In this text, work done by a gas is denoted by W_{env}. In every case, $W = -W_{env}$, so the two definitions differ by a minus sign. The reason it's important to define work W as work done *on* a gas is to make the concept of work in thermodynamics consistent with the concept of work in mechanics. In mechanics, the system is some object, and when positive work is done on that object, its energy increases. When work W done on a gas as defined in Equation 12.1 is positive, the internal energy of the gas increases, which is consistent with the mechanics definition.

In Figure 12.2a the man pushes a crate, doing positive work on it, so the crate's speed and therefore its kinetic energy both increase. In Figure 12.2b a man pushes a piston to the right, compressing the gas in the container and doing positive work on the gas. The average speed of the molecules of gas increases, so the temperature and therefore the internal energy of the gas increase. Consequently, just as doing work on a crate increases its kinetic energy, doing work on a system of gas increases its internal energy.

Tip 12.1 Work Done *on* Versus Work Done *by*

Work done *on* the gas is labeled W. That definition focuses on the internal energy of the system. Work done *by* the gas, say on a piston, is labeled W_{env}, where the focus is on harnessing a system's internal energy to do work on something external to the gas. W and W_{env} are two different ways of looking at the same thing. It's always true that $W = -W_{env}$.

Figure 12.2 (a) When a force is exerted on a crate, the work done by that force increases the crate's mechanical energy. (b) When a piston is pushed, the gas in the container is compressed, increasing the gas's thermal energy.

EXAMPLE 12.1 | **Work Done by an Expanding Gas**

GOAL Apply the definition of work at constant pressure.

PROBLEM In a system similar to that shown in Active Figure 12.1, the gas in the cylinder is at a pressure equal to 1.01×10^5 Pa and the piston has an area of 0.100 m^2. As energy is slowly added to the gas by heat, the piston is pushed up a distance of 4.00 cm. Calculate the work done by the expanding gas on the surroundings, W_{env}, assuming the pressure remains constant.

STRATEGY The work done on the environment is the negative of the work done on the gas given in Equation 12.1. Compute the change in volume and multiply by the pressure.

SOLUTION

Find the change in volume of the gas, ΔV, which is the cross-sectional area times the displacement:

$$\Delta V = A\,\Delta y = (0.100\ \text{m}^2)(4.00 \times 10^{-2}\ \text{m})$$
$$= 4.00 \times 10^{-3}\ \text{m}^3$$

Multiply this result by the pressure, getting the work the gas does on the environment, W_{env}:

$$W_{\text{env}} = P\,\Delta V = (1.01 \times 10^5\ \text{Pa})(4.00 \times 10^{-3}\ \text{m}^3)$$
$$= \boxed{404\ \text{J}}$$

REMARKS The volume of the gas increases, so the work done on the environment is positive. The work done on the system during this process is $W = -404\ \text{J}$. The energy required to perform positive work on the environment must come from the energy of the gas.

QUESTION 12.1 If no energy were added to the gas during the expansion, could the pressure remain constant?

EXERCISE 12.1 Gas in a cylinder similar to Active Figure 12.1 moves a piston with area 0.200 m² as energy is slowly added to the system. If 2.00×10^3 J of work is done on the environment and the pressure of the gas in the cylinder remains constant at 1.01×10^5 Pa, find the displacement of the piston.

ANSWER 9.90×10^{-2} m

Equation 12.1 can be used to calculate the work done on the system *only* when the pressure of the gas remains constant during the expansion or compression. A process in which the pressure remains constant is called an **isobaric process.** The pressure vs. volume graph, or ***PV* diagram,** of an isobaric process is shown in Figure 12.3. The curve on such a graph is called the *path* taken between the initial and final states, with the arrow indicating the direction the process is going, in this case from smaller to larger volume. The area under the graph is

$$\text{Area} = P(V_f - V_i) = P\,\Delta V$$

The area under the graph in a *PV* diagram is equal in magnitude to the work done on the gas.

That statement is true in general, whether or not the process proceeds at constant pressure. Just draw the *PV* diagram of the process, find the area underneath the graph (and above the horizontal axis), and that area will be the equal to the magnitude of the work done on the gas. If the arrow on the graph points toward larger volumes, the work done on the gas is negative. If the arrow on the graph points toward smaller volumes, the work done on the gas is positive.

Whenever negative work is done on a system, positive work is done by the system on its environment. The negative work done on the system represents a loss of energy from the system—the cost of doing positive work on the environment.

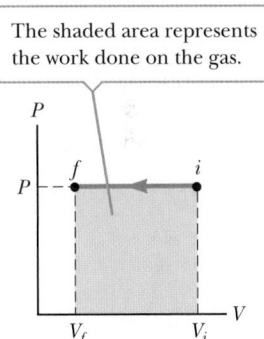

The shaded area represents the work done on the gas.

Figure 12.3 The *PV* diagram for a gas being compressed at constant pressure.

■ *Quick Quiz*

12.1 By visual inspection, order the *PV* diagrams shown in Figure 12.4 from the most negative work done on the system to the most positive work done on the system. (a) a, b, c, d (b) a, c, b, d (c) d, b, c, a (d) d, a, c, b

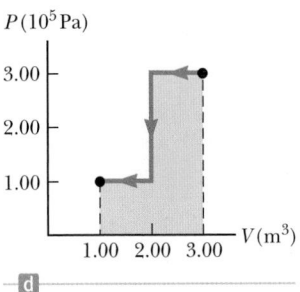

Figure 12.4 (Quick Quiz 12.1 and Example 12.2)

Notice that the graphs in Figure 12.4 all have the same endpoints, but the areas beneath the curves are different. The work done on a system depends on the path taken in the *PV* diagram.

■ EXAMPLE 12.2 | Work and *PV* Diagrams

GOAL Calculate work from a *PV* diagram.

PROBLEM Find the numeric value of the work done on the gas in **(a)** Figure 12.4a and **(b)** Figure 12.4b.

STRATEGY The regions in question are composed of rectangles and triangles. Use basic geometric formulas to find the area underneath each curve. Check the direction of the arrow to determine signs.

SOLUTION

(a) Find the work done on the gas in Figure 12.4a.

Compute the areas A_1 and A_2 in Figure 12.4a. A_1 is a rectangle and A_2 is a triangle.

$$A_1 = \text{height} \times \text{width} = (1.00 \times 10^5 \text{ Pa})(2.00 \text{ m}^3)$$
$$= 2.00 \times 10^5 \text{ J}$$
$$A_2 = \tfrac{1}{2} \text{ base} \times \text{height}$$
$$= \tfrac{1}{2}(2.00 \text{ m}^3)(2.00 \times 10^5 \text{ Pa}) = 2.00 \times 10^5 \text{ J}$$

Sum the areas (the arrows point to increasing volume, so the work done on the gas is negative):

$$\text{Area} = A_1 + A_2 = 4.00 \times 10^5 \text{ J}$$
$$W = \boxed{-4.00 \times 10^5 \text{ J}}$$

(b) Find the work done on the gas in Figure 12.4b.

Compute the areas of the two rectangular regions:

$$A_1 = \text{height} \times \text{width} = (1.00 \times 10^5 \text{ Pa})(1.00 \text{ m}^3)$$
$$= 1.00 \times 10^5 \text{ J}$$
$$A_2 = \text{height} \times \text{width} = (2.00 \times 10^5 \text{ Pa})(1.00 \text{ m}^3)$$
$$= 2.00 \times 10^5 \text{ J}$$

Sum the areas (the arrows point to decreasing volume, so the work done on the gas is positive):

$$\text{Area} = A_1 + A_2 = 3.00 \times 10^5 \text{ J}$$
$$W = \boxed{+3.00 \times 10^5 \text{ J}}$$

REMARKS Notice that in both cases the paths in the *PV* diagrams start and end at the same points, but the answers are different.

QUESTION 12.2 Is work done on a system during a process in which its volume remains constant?

EXERCISE 12.2 Compute the work done on the system in Figures 12.4c and 12.4d.

ANSWERS $-3.00 \times 10^5 \text{ J}$, $+4.00 \times 10^5 \text{ J}$

12.2 The First Law of Thermodynamics

The **first law of thermodynamics** is another energy conservation law that relates changes in internal energy—the energy associated with the position and jiggling of all the molecules of a system—to energy transfers due to heat and work. The first law is universally valid, applicable to all kinds of processes, providing a connection between the microscopic and macroscopic worlds.

There are two ways energy can be transferred between a system and its surrounding environment: by doing work, which requires a macroscopic displacement of an object through the application of a force, and by a direct exchange of energy across the system boundary, often by heat. Heat is the transfer of energy between a system and its environment due to a temperature difference and usually occurs through one or more of the mechanisms of radiation, conduction, and convection. For example, in Figure 12.5 hot gases and radiation impinge on the cylinder, raising its temperature, and energy Q is transferred by conduction to the gas, where it is distributed mainly through convection. Other processes for transferring energy into a system are possible, such as a chemical reaction or an electrical discharge. Any energy Q exchanged between the system and the environment and any work done through the expansion or compression of the system results in a *change in the internal energy,* ΔU, of the system. A change in internal energy results in measurable changes in the macroscopic variables of the system such as the pressure, temperature, and volume. The relationship between the change in internal energy, ΔU, energy Q, and the work W done on the system is given by the **first law of thermodynamics:**

◀ First law of thermodynamics

> If a system undergoes a change from an initial state to a final state, then the change in the internal energy ΔU is given by
>
> $$\Delta U = U_f - U_i = Q + W \qquad \text{[12.2]}$$
>
> where Q is the energy exchanged between the system and the environment, and W is the work done on the system.

The quantity Q is positive when energy is transferred into the system and negative when energy is removed from the system.

Figure 12.5 illustrates the first law for a cylinder of gas and how the system interacts with the environment. The gas cylinder contains a frictionless piston, and the block is initially at rest. Energy Q is introduced into the gas as the gas expands against the piston with constant pressure P. Until the piston hits the stops, it exerts a force on the block, which accelerates on a frictionless surface. Negative work W is done on the gas, and at the same time positive work $W_{env} = -W$ is done by the gas on the block. Adding the work done on the environment, W_{env}, to the work done on the gas, W, gives zero net work, as it must because energy must be conserved.

From Equation 12.2 we also see that the internal energy of any isolated system must remain constant, so that $\Delta U = 0$. Even when a system isn't isolated, the change in internal energy will be zero if the system goes through a cyclic process in which all the thermodynamic variables—pressure, volume, temperature, and moles of gas—return to their original values.

It's important to remember that the quantities in Equation 12.2 concern a *system,* not the effect on the system's environment through work. If the system is hot gas expanding against a piston, as in Figure 12.5, the system work W is *negative* because the piston can only expand at the expense of the internal energy of the gas. The work W_{env} done by the hot gas on the *environment*—in this case, moving a piston which moves the block—is positive, but that's not the work W in Equation 12.2. This way of defining work in the first law makes it consistent with the concept of work defined in Chapter 5. In both the mechanical and thermal cases, the effect on the system is the same: positive work increases the system's energy, and negative work decreases the system's energy.

Figure 12.5 Thermal energy Q is transferred to the gas, increasing its internal energy. The gas presses against the piston, displacing it and performing mechanical work on the environment or, equivalently, doing negative work on the gas, reducing the internal energy.

Some textbooks identify W as the work done by the gas on its environment. This is an equivalent formulation, but it means that W must carry a minus sign in the first law. That convention isn't consistent with previous discussions of the energy of a system, because when W is positive the system *loses* energy, whereas in Chapter 5 positive W means that the system *gains* energy. For that reason, the old convention is not used in this book.

■**EXAMPLE 12.3** | Heating a Gas

GOAL Combine the first law of thermodynamics with work done during a constant pressure process.

PROBLEM An ideal gas absorbs 5.00×10^3 J of energy while doing 2.00×10^3 J of work on the environment during a constant pressure process. **(a)** Compute the change in the internal energy of the gas. **(b)** If the internal energy now drops by 4.50×10^3 J and 7.50×10^3 J is expelled from the system, find the change in volume, assuming a constant pressure process at 1.01×10^5 Pa.

STRATEGY Part (a) requires substitution of the given information into the first law, Equation 12.2. Notice, however, that the given work is done on the *environment*. The negative of this amount is the work done on the *system,* representing a loss of internal energy. Part (b) is a matter of substituting the equation for work at constant pressure into the first law and solving for the change in volume.

. . . .

SOLUTION

(a) Compute the change in internal energy of the gas.

Substitute values into the first law, noting that the work done on the gas is negative:

$$\Delta U = Q + W = 5.00 \times 10^3 \text{ J} - 2.00 \times 10^3 \text{ J}$$
$$= \boxed{3.00 \times 10^3 \text{ J}}$$

(b) Find the change in volume, noting that ΔU and Q are both negative in this case.

Substitute the equation for work done at constant pressure into the first law:

$$\Delta U = Q + W = Q - P\Delta V$$
$$-4.50 \times 10^3 \text{ J} = -7.50 \times 10^3 \text{ J} - (1.01 \times 10^5 \text{ Pa})\Delta V$$

Solve for the change in volume, ΔV:

$$\Delta V = \boxed{-2.97 \times 10^{-2} \text{ m}^3}$$

. . . .

REMARKS The change in volume is negative, so the system contracts, doing negative work on the environment, whereas the work W on the system is positive.

QUESTION 12.3 True or False: When an ideal gas expands at constant pressure, the change in the internal energy must be positive.

EXERCISE 12.3 Suppose the internal energy of an ideal gas rises by 3.00×10^3 J at a constant pressure of 1.00×10^5 Pa, while the system gains 4.20×10^3 J of energy by heat. Find the change in volume of the system.

ANSWER 1.20×10^{-2} m^3

Recall that an expression for the internal energy of an ideal gas is

$$U = \tfrac{3}{2}nRT \qquad\qquad \text{[12.3a]}$$

This expression is valid only for a *monatomic* ideal gas, which means the particles of the gas consist of single atoms. The change in the internal energy, ΔU, for such a gas is given by

$$\Delta U = \tfrac{3}{2}nR\Delta T \qquad\qquad \text{[12.3b]}$$

The **molar specific heat at constant volume** of a monatomic ideal gas, C_v, is defined by

$$C_v \equiv \tfrac{3}{2}R \qquad\qquad \text{[12.4]}$$

Table 12.1 Molar Specific Heats of Various Gases

Gas	Molar Specific Heat (J/mol · K)[a]			
	C_p	C_v	$C_p - C_v$	$\gamma = C_p/C_v$
Monatomic Gases				
He	20.8	12.5	8.33	1.67
Ar	20.8	12.5	8.33	1.67
Ne	20.8	12.7	8.12	1.64
Kr	20.8	12.3	8.49	1.69
Diatomic Gases				
H_2	28.8	20.4	8.33	1.41
N_2	29.1	20.8	8.33	1.40
O_2	29.4	21.1	8.33	1.40
CO	29.3	21.0	8.33	1.40
Cl_2	34.7	25.7	8.96	1.35
Polyatomic Gases				
CO_2	37.0	28.5	8.50	1.30
SO_2	40.4	31.4	9.00	1.29
H_2O	35.4	27.0	8.37	1.30
CH_4	35.5	27.1	8.41	1.31

[a]All values except that for water were obtained at 300 K.

The change in internal energy of an ideal gas can then be written

$$\Delta U = nC_v \Delta T \qquad\qquad [12.5]$$

For ideal gases, this expression is always valid, even when the volume isn't constant. The value of the molar specific heat, however, depends on the gas and can vary under different conditions of temperature and pressure.

A gas with a larger molar specific heat requires more energy to realize a given temperature change. The size of the molar specific heat depends on the structure of the gas molecule and how many different ways it can store energy. A monatomic gas such as helium can store energy as motion in three different directions. A gas such as hydrogen, on the other hand, is diatomic in normal temperature ranges, and aside from moving in three directions, it can also tumble, rotating in two different directions. So hydrogen molecules can store energy in the form of translational motion and in addition can store energy through tumbling. Further, molecules can also store energy in the vibrations of their constituent atoms. A gas composed of molecules with more ways to store energy will have a larger molar specific heat.

Each different way a gas molecule can store energy is called a *degree of freedom*. Each degree of freedom contributes $\frac{1}{2}R$ to the molar specific heat. Because an atomic ideal gas can move in three directions, it has a molar specific heat capacity $C_v = 3\left(\frac{1}{2}R\right) = \frac{3}{2}R$. A diatomic gas like molecular oxygen, O_2, can also tumble in two different directions. This adds $2 \times \frac{1}{2}R = R$ to the molar heat specific heat, so $C_v = \frac{5}{2}R$ for diatomic gases. The spinning about the long axis connecting the two atoms is generally negligible. Vibration of the atoms in a molecule can also contribute to the heat capacity. A full analysis of a given system is often complex, so in general, molar specific heats must be determined by experiment. Some representative values of C_v can be found in Table 12.1.

12.3 Thermal Processes

Engine cycles can be complex. Fortunately, they can often be broken down into a series of simple processes. In this section the four most common processes will be studied and illustrated by their effect on an ideal gas. Each process corresponds to making one of the variables in the ideal gas law a constant or assuming one of the three quantities in the first law of thermodynamics is zero. The four processes are called isobaric (constant pressure), adiabatic (no thermal energy transfer, or $Q = 0$), isovolumetric (constant volume, corresponding to $W = 0$) and isothermal (constant temperature, corresponding to $\Delta U = 0$). Naturally, many other processes don't fall into one of these four categories, so they will be covered in a fifth category, called a general process. What is essential in each case is to be able to calculate the three thermodynamic quantities in the first law: the work W, the thermal energy transfer Q, and the change in the internal energy ΔU.

Isobaric Processes

Recall from Section 12.1 that in an isobaric process the pressure remains constant as the gas expands or is compressed. An expanding gas does work on its environment, given by $W_{env} = P\,\Delta V$. The PV diagram of an isobaric expansion is given in Figure 12.3. As previously discussed, the magnitude of the work done on the gas is just the area under the path in its PV diagram: height times length, or $P\,\Delta V$. The negative of this quantity, $W = -P\,\Delta V$, is the energy lost by the gas because the gas does work as it expands. This is the quantity that should be substituted into the first law.

The work done by the gas on its environment must come at the expense of the change in its internal energy, ΔU. Because the change in the internal energy of an ideal gas is given by $\Delta U = nC_v\,\Delta T$, the temperature of an expanding gas must decrease as the internal energy decreases. Expanding volume and decreasing temperature means the pressure must also decrease, in conformity with the ideal gas law, $PV = nRT$. Consequently, the only way such a process can remain at constant pressure is if thermal energy Q is transferred into the gas by heat. Rearranging the first law, we obtain

$$Q = \Delta U - W = \Delta U + P\,\Delta V$$

Now we can substitute the expression in Equation 12.3b for ΔU and use the ideal gas law to substitute $P\,\Delta V = nR\,\Delta T$:

$$Q = \tfrac{3}{2}nR\,\Delta T + nR\,\Delta T = \tfrac{5}{2}nR\,\Delta T$$

Another way to express this transfer by heat is

$$Q = nC_p\,\Delta T \qquad [12.6]$$

where $C_p = \tfrac{5}{2}R$. For ideal gases, the molar heat capacity at constant pressure, C_p, is the sum of the molar heat capacity at constant volume, C_v, and the gas constant R:

$$C_p = C_v + R \qquad [12.7]$$

This can be seen in the fourth column of Table 12.1, where $C_p - C_v$ is calculated for a number of different gases. The difference works out to be approximately R in virtually every case.

▪ EXAMPLE 12.4 | Expanding Gas

GOAL Use molar specific heats and the first law in a constant pressure process.

PROBLEM Suppose a system of monatomic ideal gas at 2.00×10^5 Pa and an initial temperature of 293 K slowly expands at constant pressure from a volume of 1.00 L to 2.50 L. **(a)** Find the work done on the environment. **(b)** Find the change in internal energy of the gas. **(c)** Use the first law of thermodynamics to obtain the thermal energy absorbed by the gas during the process. **(d)** Use the molar heat capacity at constant pressure to find the thermal energy absorbed. **(e)** How would the answers change for a diatomic ideal gas?

STRATEGY This problem mainly involves substituting values into the appropriate equations. Substitute into the equation for work at constant pressure to obtain the answer to part (a). In part (b) use the ideal gas law twice: to find the temperature when $V = 2.00$ L and to find the number of moles of the gas. These quantities can then be used to obtain the change in internal energy, ΔU. Part (c) can then be solved by substituting into the first law, yielding Q, the answer checked in part (d) with Equation 12.6. Repeat these steps for part (e) after increasing the molar specific heats by R because of the extra two degrees of freedom associated with a diatomic gas.

SOLUTION

(a) Find the work done on the environment.

Apply the definition of work at constant pressure:

$$W_{env} = P \Delta V = (2.00 \times 10^5 \text{ Pa})(2.50 \times 10^{-3} \text{ m}^3$$
$$- 1.00 \times 10^{-3} \text{ m}^3)$$
$$W_{env} = \boxed{3.00 \times 10^2 \text{ J}}$$

(b) Find the change in the internal energy of the gas.

First, obtain the final temperature, using the ideal gas law, noting that $P_i = P_f$:

$$\frac{P_f V_f}{P_i V_i} = \frac{T_f}{T_i} \rightarrow T_f = T_i \frac{V_f}{V_i} = (293 \text{ K}) \frac{(2.50 \times 10^{-3} \text{ m}^3)}{(1.00 \times 10^{-3} \text{ m}^3)}$$
$$T_f = 733 \text{ K}$$

Again using the ideal gas law, obtain the number of moles of gas:

$$n = \frac{P_i V_i}{R T_i} = \frac{(2.00 \times 10^5 \text{ Pa})(1.00 \times 10^{-3} \text{ m}^3)}{(8.31 \text{ J/K} \cdot \text{mol})(293 \text{ K})}$$
$$= 8.21 \times 10^{-2} \text{ mol}$$

Use these results and given quantities to calculate the change in internal energy, ΔU:

$$\Delta U = n C_v \Delta T = \tfrac{3}{2} n R \Delta T$$
$$= \tfrac{3}{2}(8.21 \times 10^{-2} \text{ mol})(8.31 \text{ J/K} \cdot \text{mol})(733 \text{ K} - 293 \text{ K})$$
$$\Delta U = \boxed{4.50 \times 10^2 \text{ J}}$$

(c) Use the first law to obtain the energy transferred by heat.

Solve the first law for Q, and substitute ΔU and $W = -W_{env} = -3.00 \times 10^2$ J:

$$\Delta U = Q + W \rightarrow Q = \Delta U - W$$
$$Q = 4.50 \times 10^2 \text{ J} - (-3.00 \times 10^2 \text{ J}) = \boxed{7.50 \times 10^2 \text{ J}}$$

(d) Use the molar heat capacity at constant pressure to obtain Q.

Substitute values into Equation 12.6:

$$Q = n C_p \Delta T = \tfrac{5}{2} n R \Delta T$$
$$= \tfrac{5}{2}(8.21 \times 10^{-2} \text{ mol})(8.31 \text{ J/K} \cdot \text{mol})(733 \text{ K} - 293 \text{ K})$$
$$= \boxed{7.50 \times 10^2 \text{ J}}$$

(e) How would the answers change for a diatomic gas?

Obtain the new change in internal energy, ΔU, noting that $C_v = \tfrac{5}{2}R$ for a diatomic gas:

$$\Delta U = n C_v \Delta T = \left(\tfrac{3}{2} + 1\right) n R \Delta T$$
$$= \tfrac{5}{2}(8.21 \times 10^{-2} \text{ mol})(8.31 \text{ J/K} \cdot \text{mol})(733 \text{ K} - 293 \text{ K})$$
$$\Delta U = \boxed{7.50 \times 10^2 \text{ J}}$$

Obtain the new energy transferred by heat, Q:

$$Q = n C_p \Delta T = \left(\tfrac{5}{2} + 1\right) n R \Delta T$$
$$= \tfrac{7}{2}(8.21 \times 10^{-2} \text{ mol})(8.31 \text{ J/K} \cdot \text{mol})(733 \text{ K} - 293 \text{ K})$$
$$Q = \boxed{1.05 \times 10^3 \text{ J}}$$

REMARKS Part (b) could also be solved with fewer steps by using the ideal gas equation $PV = nRT$ once the work is known. The pressure and number of moles are constant, and the gas is ideal, so $P\Delta V = nR\Delta T$. Given that $C_v = \tfrac{3}{2}R$, the change in the internal energy ΔU can then be calculated in terms of the expression for work:

$$\Delta U = n C_v \Delta T = \tfrac{3}{2} n R \Delta T = \tfrac{3}{2} P \Delta V = \tfrac{3}{2} W$$

Similar methods can be used in other processes.

(Continued)

QUESTION 12.4 True or False: During a constant pressure compression, the temperature of an ideal gas must always decrease, and the gas must always exhaust thermal energy ($Q < 0$).

EXERCISE 12.4 Suppose an ideal monatomic gas at an initial temperature of 475 K is compressed from 3.00 L to 2.00 L while its pressure remains constant at 1.00×10^5 Pa. Find (a) the work done on the gas, (b) the change in internal energy, and (c) the energy transferred by heat, Q.

ANSWERS (a) 1.00×10^2 J (b) -150 J (c) -250 J

Adiabatic Processes

In an adiabatic process, no energy enters or leaves the system by heat. Such a system is insulated, thermally isolated from its environment. In general, however, the system isn't mechanically isolated, so it can still do work. A sufficiently rapid process may be considered approximately adiabatic because there isn't time for any significant transfer of energy by heat.

For adiabatic processes $Q = 0$, so the first law becomes

$$\Delta U = W \quad \text{(adiabatic processes)}$$

The work done during an adiabatic process can be calculated by finding the change in the internal energy. Alternately, the work can be computed from a PV diagram. For an ideal gas undergoing an adiabatic process, it can be shown that

$$PV^\gamma = \text{constant} \qquad \text{[12.8a]}$$

where

$$\gamma = \frac{C_p}{C_v} \qquad \text{[12.8b]}$$

is called the *adiabatic index* of the gas. Values of the adiabatic index for several different gases are given in Table 12.1. After computing the constant on the right-hand side of Equation 12.8a and solving for the pressure P, the area under the curve in the PV diagram can be found by counting boxes, yielding the work.

If a hot gas is allowed to expand so quickly that there is no time for energy to enter or leave the system by heat, the work done on the gas is negative and the internal energy decreases. This decrease occurs because kinetic energy is transferred from the gas molecules to the moving piston. Such an adiabatic expansion is of practical importance and is nearly realized in an internal combustion engine when a gasoline–air mixture is ignited and expands rapidly against a piston. The following example illustrates this process.

■ EXAMPLE 12.5 | **Work and an Engine Cylinder**

GOAL Use the first law to find the work done in an adiabatic expansion.

PROBLEM In a car engine operating at a frequency of 1.80×10^3 rev/min, the expansion of hot, high-pressure gas against a piston occurs in about 10 ms. Because energy transfer by heat typically takes a time on the order of minutes or hours, it's safe to assume little energy leaves the hot gas during the expansion. Find the work done by the gas on the piston during this adiabatic expansion by assuming the engine cylinder contains 0.100 moles of an ideal monatomic gas that goes from 1.200×10^3 K to 4.00×10^2 K, typical engine temperatures, during the expansion.

STRATEGY Find the change in internal energy using the given temperatures. For an adiabatic process, this equals the work done on the gas, which is the negative of the work done on the environment—in this case, the piston.

SOLUTION

Start with the first law, taking $Q = 0$:

$W = \Delta U - Q = \Delta U - 0 = \Delta U$

Find ΔU from the expression for the internal energy of an ideal monatomic gas:

$$\Delta U = U_f - U_i = \tfrac{3}{2}nR(T_f - T_i)$$
$$= \tfrac{3}{2}(0.100 \text{ mol})(8.31 \text{ J/mol} \cdot \text{K})(4.00 \times 10^2 \text{ K} - 1.20 \times 10^3 \text{ K})$$
$$\Delta U = -9.97 \times 10^2 \text{ J}$$

The change in internal energy equals the work done on the system, which is the negative of the work done on the piston:

$$W_{\text{piston}} = -W = -\Delta U = \boxed{9.97 \times 10^2 \text{ J}}$$

REMARKS The work done on the piston comes at the expense of the internal energy of the gas. In an ideal adiabatic expansion, the loss of internal energy is completely converted into useful work. In a real engine, there are always losses.

QUESTION 12.5 In an adiabatic expansion of an ideal gas, why must the change in temperature always be negative?

EXERCISE 12.5 A monatomic ideal gas with volume 0.200 L is rapidly compressed, so the process can be considered adiabatic. If the gas is initially at 1.01×10^5 Pa and 3.00×10^2 K and the final temperature is 477 K, find the work done by the gas on the environment, W_{env}.

ANSWER -17.9 J

■ EXAMPLE 12.6 | An Adiabatic Expansion

GOAL Use the adiabatic pressure vs. volume relation to find a change in pressure and the work done on a gas.

PROBLEM A monatomic ideal gas at an initial pressure of 1.01×10^5 Pa expands adiabatically from an initial volume of 1.50 m^3, doubling its volume (Figure 12.6). **(a)** Find the new pressure. **(b)** Sketch the PV diagram and estimate the work done on the gas.

STRATEGY There isn't enough information to solve this problem with the ideal gas law. Instead, use Equation 12.8a,b and the given information to find the adiabatic index and the constant C for the process. For part **(b)**, sketch the PV diagram and count boxes to estimate the area under the graph, which gives the work.

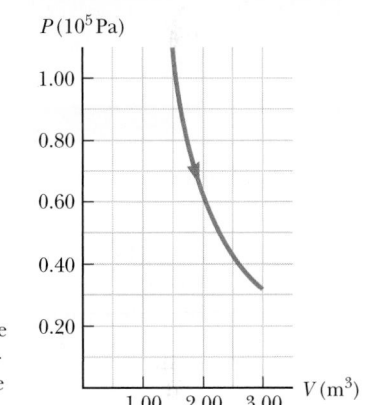

Figure 12.6 (Example 12.6) The PV diagram of an adiabatic expansion: the graph of $P = CV^{-\gamma}$, where C is a constant and $\gamma = C_p/C_v$.

SOLUTION

(a) Find the new pressure.

First, calculate the adiabatic index:

$$\gamma = \frac{C_p}{C_v} = \frac{\tfrac{5}{2}R}{\tfrac{3}{2}R} = \frac{5}{3}$$

Use Equation 12.8a to find the constant C:

$$C = P_1 V_1^{\gamma} = (1.01 \times 10^5 \text{ Pa})(1.50 \text{ m}^3)^{5/3}$$
$$= 1.99 \times 10^5 \text{ Pa} \cdot \text{m}^5$$

The constant C is fixed for the entire process and can be used to find P_2:

$$C = P_2 V_2^{\gamma} = P_2(3.00 \text{ m}^3)^{5/3}$$
$$1.99 \times 10^5 \text{ Pa} \cdot \text{m}^5 = P_2 \ (6.24 \text{ m}^5)$$
$$P_2 = \boxed{3.19 \times 10^4 \text{ Pa}}$$

(b) Estimate the work done on the gas from a PV diagram.

Count the boxes between $V_1 = 1.50$ m^3 and $V_2 = 3.00$ m^3 in the graph of $P = (1.99 \times 10^5 \text{ Pa} \cdot \text{m}^5)V^{-5/3}$ in the PV diagram shown in Figure 12.6:

Number of boxes ≈ 17

Each box has an 'area' of 5.00×10^3 J.

$$W \approx -17 \cdot 5.00 \times 10^3 \text{ J} = \boxed{-8.5 \times 10^4 \text{ J}}$$

(Continued)

REMARKS The exact answer, obtained with calculus, is -8.43×10^4 J, so our result is a very good estimate. The answer is negative because the gas is expanding, doing positive work on the environment, thereby reducing its own internal energy.

QUESTION 12.6 For an adiabatic expansion between two given volumes and an initial pressure, which gas does more work, a monatomic gas or a diatomic gas?

EXERCISE 12.6 Repeat the preceding calculations for an ideal diatomic gas expanding adiabatically from an initial volume of 0.500 m³ to a final volume of 1.25 m³, starting at a pressure of $P_1 = 1.01 \times 10^5$ Pa. Use the same techniques as in the example.

ANSWERS $P_2 = 2.80 \times 10^4$ Pa, $W \approx -4 \times 10^4$ J

Isovolumetric Processes

An **isovolumetric process,** sometimes called an *isochoric* process (which is harder to remember), proceeds at constant volume, corresponding to vertical lines in a *PV* diagram. If the volume doesn't change, no work is done on or by the system, so $W = 0$ and the first law of thermodynamics reads

$$\Delta U = Q \quad \text{(isovolumetric process)}$$

This result tells us that **in an isovolumetric process, the change in internal energy of a system equals the energy transferred to the system by heat.** From Equation 12.5, the energy transferred by heat in constant volume processes is given by

$$Q = nC_v \Delta T \qquad [12.9]$$

■ EXAMPLE 12.7 | An Isovolumetric Process

GOAL Apply the first law to a constant-volume process.

PROBLEM A monatomic ideal gas has a temperature $T = 3.00 \times 10^2$ K and a constant volume of 1.50 L. If there are 5.00 moles of gas, **(a)** how much thermal energy must be added in order to raise the temperature of the gas to 3.80×10^2 K? **(b)** Calculate the change in pressure of the gas, ΔP. **(c)** How much thermal energy would be required if the gas were ideal and diatomic? **(d)** Calculate the change in the pressure for the diatomic gas.

....

SOLUTION

(a) How much thermal energy must be added in order to raise the temperature of the gas to 3.80×10^2 K?

Apply Equation 12.9, using the fact that $C_v = 3R/2$ for an ideal monatomic gas:

$$\begin{aligned}\text{(1)} \quad Q &= \Delta U = nC_v\Delta T = \tfrac{3}{2}nR\Delta T \\ &= \tfrac{3}{2}(5.00 \text{ mol})(8.31 \text{ J/K} \cdot \text{mol})(80.0 \text{ K}) \\ Q &= \boxed{4.99 \times 10^3 \text{ J}}\end{aligned}$$

(b) Calculate the change in pressure, ΔP.

Use the ideal gas equation $PV = nRT$ and Equation (1) to relate ΔP to Q:

$$\Delta(PV) = (\Delta P)V = nR\Delta T = \tfrac{2}{3}Q$$

Solve for ΔP:

$$\Delta P = \frac{2}{3}\frac{Q}{V} = \frac{2}{3}\frac{4.99 \times 10^3 \text{ J}}{1.50 \times 10^{-3} \text{ m}^3}$$

$$= \boxed{2.22 \times 10^6 \text{ Pa}}$$

(c) How much thermal energy would be required if the gas were ideal and diatomic?

Repeat the calculation with $C_v = 5R/2$:

$$Q = \Delta U = nC_v\Delta T = \frac{5}{2}nR\Delta T = 8.31 \times 10^3 \text{ J}$$

(d) Calculate the change in the pressure for the diatomic gas.

Use the result of part (c) and repeat the calculation of part (b), with 2/3 replaced by 2/5 because the gas is diatomic:

$$\Delta P = \frac{2}{5}\frac{Q}{V} = \frac{2}{5}\frac{8.31 \times 10^3 \text{ J}}{1.50 \times 10^{-3} \text{ m}^3}$$

$$= \boxed{2.22 \times 10^6 \text{ Pa}}$$

....

REMARKS The constant volume diatomic gas, under the same conditions, requires more thermal energy per degree of temperature change because there are more ways for the diatomic molecules to store energy. Despite the extra energy added, the diatomic gas reaches the same final pressure as the monatomic gas.

QUESTION 12.7 If the same amount of energy as found in part (a) were transferred to 5.00 moles of carbon dioxide at the same initial temperature, how would the final temperature compare?

EXERCISE 12.7 (a) Find the change in temperature ΔT of 22.0 mol of a monatomic ideal gas if it absorbs 9 750 J at a constant volume of 2.40 L. (b) What is the change in pressure, ΔP? (c) If the system is an ideal diatomic gas, find the change in its temperature. (d) Find the change in pressure of the diatomic gas.

ANSWERS (a) 35.6 K (b) 2.71×10^6 Pa (c) 21.3 K (d) 1.63×10^6 Pa

Isothermal Processes

During an isothermal process, the temperature of a system doesn't change. In an ideal gas the internal energy U depends only on the temperature, so it follows that $\Delta U = 0$ because $\Delta T = 0$. In this case, the first law of thermodynamics gives

$$W = -Q \quad \text{(isothermal process)}$$

We see that if the system is an ideal gas undergoing an isothermal process, the work done on the system is equal to the negative of the thermal energy transferred to the system. Such a process can be visualized in Figure 12.7. A cylinder filled with gas is in contact with a large energy reservoir that can exchange energy with the gas without changing its temperature. For a constant temperature ideal gas,

$$P = \frac{nRT}{V}$$

where the numerator on the right-hand side is constant. The PV diagram of a typical isothermal process is graphed in Figure 12.8, contrasted with an adiabatic process. The pressure falls off more rapidly for an adiabatic expansion because thermal energy can't be transferred into the system. In an isothermal expansion, the system loses energy by doing work on the environment but regains an equal amount of energy across the boundary.

Using methods of calculus, it can be shown that the work done on the environment during an isothermal process is given by

$$W_{\text{env}} = nRT \ln \left(\frac{V_f}{V_i} \right) \qquad \text{[12.10]}$$

The symbol "ln" in Equation 12.10 is an abbreviation for the natural logarithm, discussed in Appendix A. The work W done on the gas is just the negative of W_{env}.

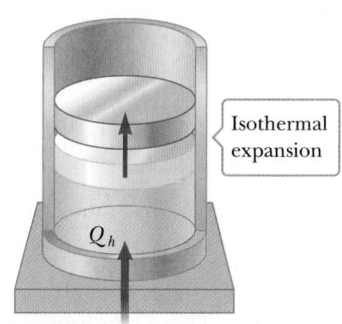

Isothermal expansion

Q_h

Energy reservoir at T_h

Figure 12.7 The gas in the cylinder expands isothermally while in contact with a reservoir at temperature T_h.

$P(10^5 \text{ Pa})$

Isothermal

Adiabatic

$V(\text{m}^3)$

Figure 12.8 The PV diagram of an isothermal expansion, graph of $P = CV^{-1}$, where C is a constant, compared to an adiabatic expansion, $P = C_A V^{-\gamma}$. C_A is a constant equal in magnitude to C in this case but carrying different units.

■ **EXAMPLE 12.8** | **An Isothermally Expanding Balloon**

GOAL Find the work done during an isothermal expansion.

PROBLEM A balloon contains 5.00 moles of a monatomic ideal gas. As energy is added to the system by heat (say, by absorption from the Sun), the volume increases by 25% at a constant temperature of 27.0°C. Find the work W_{env} done by the gas in expanding the balloon, the thermal energy Q transferred to the gas, and the work W done on the gas.

STRATEGY Be sure to convert temperatures to kelvins. Use Equation 12.10 for isothermal work W_{env} done on the environment to find the work W done on the balloon, which satisfies $W = -W_{env}$. Further, for an isothermal process, the thermal energy Q transferred to the system equals the work W_{env} done by the system on the environment.

SOLUTION

Substitute into Equation 12.10, finding the work done during the isothermal expansion. Note that $T = 27.0°C = 3.00 \times 10^2$ K.

$$W_{env} = nRT \ln\left(\frac{V_f}{V_i}\right)$$

$$= (5.00 \text{ mol})(8.31 \text{ J/K} \cdot \text{mol})(3.00 \times 10^2 \text{ K})$$

$$\times \ln\left(\frac{1.25 V_0}{V_0}\right)$$

$$W_{env} = \boxed{2.78 \times 10^3 \text{ J}}$$

$$Q = W_{env} = \boxed{2.78 \times 10^3 \text{ J}}$$

The negative of this amount is the work done on the gas:

$$W = -W_{env} = \boxed{-2.78 \times 10^3 \text{ J}}$$

REMARKS Notice the relationship between the work done on the gas, the work done on the environment, and the energy transferred. These relationships are true of all isothermal processes.

QUESTION 12.8 True or False: In an isothermal process no thermal energy transfer takes place.

EXERCISE 12.8 Suppose that subsequent to this heating, 1.50×10^4 J of thermal energy is removed from the gas isothermally. Find the final volume in terms of the initial volume of the example, V_0. (*Hint:* Follow the same steps as in the example, but in reverse. Also note that the initial volume in this exercise is $1.25V_0$.)

ANSWER $0.375V_0$

General Case

When a process follows none of the four given models, it's still possible to use the first law to get information about it. The work can be computed from the area under the curve of the PV diagram, and if the temperatures at the endpoints can be found, ΔU follows from Equation 12.5, as illustrated in the following example.

■ **EXAMPLE 12.9** | **A General Process**

GOAL Find thermodynamic quantities for a process that doesn't fall into any of the four previously discussed categories.

PROBLEM A quantity of 4.00 moles of a monatomic ideal gas expands from an initial volume of 0.100 m³ to a final volume of 0.300 m³ and pressure of 2.5×10^5 Pa (Fig. 12.9a). Compute **(a)** the work done on the gas, **(b)** the change in internal energy of the gas, and **(c)** the thermal energy transferred to the gas.

STRATEGY The work done on the gas is equal to the negative of the area under the curve in the PV diagram. Use the ideal gas law to get the temperature change and, subsequently, the change in internal energy. Finally, the first law gives the thermal energy transferred by heat.

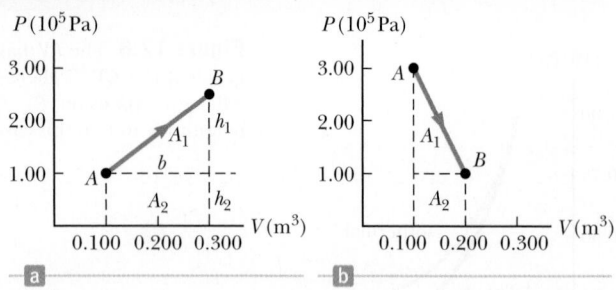

Figure 12.9 (a) (Example 12.9) (b) (Exercise 12.9)

SOLUTION

(a) Find the work done on the gas by computing the area under the curve in Figure 12.9a.

Find A_1, the area of the triangle:

$$A_1 = \tfrac{1}{2}bh_1 = \tfrac{1}{2}(0.200 \text{ m}^3)(1.50 \times 10^5 \text{ Pa}) = 1.50 \times 10^4 \text{ J}$$

Find A_2, the area of the rectangle:

$$A_2 = bh_2 = (0.200 \text{ m}^3)(1.00 \times 10^5 \text{ Pa}) = 2.00 \times 10^4 \text{ J}$$

Sum the two areas (the gas is expanding, so the work done on the gas is negative and a minus sign must be supplied):

$$W = -(A_1 + A_2) = \boxed{-3.50 \times 10^4 \text{ J}}$$

(b) Find the change in the internal energy during the process.

Compute the temperature at points A and B with the ideal gas law:

$$T_A = \frac{P_A V_A}{nR} = \frac{(1.00 \times 10^5 \text{ Pa})(0.100 \text{ m}^3)}{(4.00 \text{ mol})(8.31 \text{ J/K} \cdot \text{mol})} = 301 \text{ K}$$

$$T_B = \frac{P_B V_B}{nR} = \frac{(2.50 \times 10^5 \text{ Pa})(0.300 \text{ m}^3)}{(4.00 \text{ mol})(8.31 \text{ J/K} \cdot \text{mol})} = 2.26 \times 10^3 \text{ K}$$

Compute the change in internal energy:

$$\Delta U = \tfrac{3}{2}nR\,\Delta T$$

$$= \tfrac{3}{2}(4.00 \text{ mol})(8.31 \text{ J/K} \cdot \text{mol})(2.26 \times 10^3 \text{ K} - 301 \text{ K})$$

$$\Delta U = \boxed{9.77 \times 10^4 \text{ J}}$$

(c) Compute Q with the first law:

$$Q = \Delta U - W = 9.77 \times 10^4 \text{ J} - (-3.50 \times 10^4 \text{ J})$$

$$= \boxed{1.33 \times 10^5 \text{ J}}$$

REMARKS As long as it's possible to compute the work, cycles involving these more exotic processes can be completely analyzed. Usually, however, it's necessary to use calculus. Note that the solution to part (b) could have been facilitated by yet another application of $PV = nRT$:

$$\Delta U = \tfrac{3}{2}nR\Delta T = \tfrac{3}{2}\Delta(PV) = \tfrac{3}{2}(P_B V_B - P_A V_A)$$

This result means that even in the absence of information about the number of moles or the temperatures, the problem could be solved knowing the initial and final pressures and volumes.

QUESTION 12.9 For a curve with lower pressures but the same endpoints as in Figure 12.9a, would the thermal energy transferred be (a) smaller than, (b) equal to, or (c) greater than the thermal energy transfer of the straight-line path?

EXERCISE 12.9 Figure 12.9b represents a process involving 3.00 moles of a monatomic ideal gas expanding from 0.100 m^3 to 0.200 m^3. Find the work done on the system, the change in the internal energy of the system, and the thermal energy transferred in the process.

ANSWERS $W = -2.00 \times 10^4$ J, $\Delta U = -1.50 \times 10^4$ J, $Q = 5.00 \times 10^3$ J

Given all the different processes and formulas, it's easy to become confused when approaching one of these ideal gas problems, although most of the time only substitution into the correct formula is required. The essential facts and formulas are compiled in Table 12.2, both for easy reference and also to display the similarities and differences between the processes.

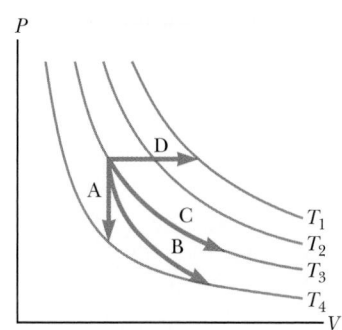

Figure 12.10 (Quick Quiz 12.2) Identify the nature of paths A, B, C, and D.

■ Quick Quiz

12.2 Identify the paths A, B, C, and D in Figure 12.10 as isobaric, isothermal, isovolumetric, or adiabatic. For path B, $Q = 0$.

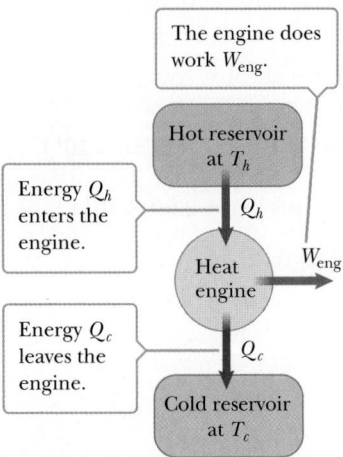

The engine does work W_{eng}.

Hot reservoir at T_h

Energy Q_h enters the engine.

Q_h

Heat engine

W_{eng}

Energy Q_c leaves the engine.

Q_c

Cold reservoir at T_c

Active Figure 12.11
In this schematic representation of a heat engine, part of the thermal energy from the hot reservoir is turned into work while the rest is expelled to the cold reservoir.

Table 12.2 The First Law and Thermodynamic Processes (Ideal Gases)

Process	ΔU	Q	W
Isobaric	$nC_v \Delta T$	$nC_p \Delta T$	$-P \Delta V$
Adiabatic	$nC_v \Delta T$	0	ΔU
Isovolumetric	$nC_v \Delta T$	ΔU	0
Isothermal	0	$-W$	$-nRT \ln \left(\dfrac{V_f}{V_i} \right)$
General	$nC_v \Delta T$	$\Delta U - W$	(PV Area)

12.4 Heat Engines and the Second Law of Thermodynamics

A **heat engine** takes in energy by heat and partially converts it to other forms, such as electrical and mechanical energy. In a typical process for producing electricity in a power plant, for instance, coal or some other fuel is burned, and the resulting internal energy is used to convert water to steam. The steam is then directed at the blades of a turbine, setting it rotating. Finally, the mechanical energy associated with this rotation is used to drive an electric generator. In another heat engine—the internal combustion engine in an automobile—energy enters the engine as fuel is injected into the cylinder and combusted, and a fraction of this energy is converted to mechanical energy.

▶ Cyclic process

In general, a heat engine carries some working substance through a **cyclic process**[1] during which (1) energy is transferred by heat from a source at a high temperature, (2) work is done by the engine, and (3) energy is expelled by the engine by heat to a source at lower temperature. As an example, consider the operation of a steam engine in which the working substance is water. The water in the engine is carried through a cycle in which it first evaporates into steam in a boiler and then expands against a piston. After the steam is condensed with cooling water, it returns to the boiler, and the process is repeated.

It's useful to draw a heat engine schematically, as in Active Figure 12.11. The engine absorbs energy Q_h from the hot reservoir, does work W_{eng}, then gives up energy Q_c to the cold reservoir. (Note that *negative* work is done *on* the engine, so that $W = -W_{eng}$.) Because the working substance goes through a cycle, always returning to its initial thermodynamic state, its initial and final internal energies are equal, so $\Delta U = 0$. From the first law of thermodynamics, therefore,

$$\Delta U = 0 = Q + W \quad \rightarrow \quad Q_{net} = -W = W_{eng}$$

The last equation shows that **the work W_{eng} done by a heat engine equals the net energy absorbed by the engine.** As we can see from Active Figure 12.11, $Q_{net} = |Q_h| - |Q_c|$. Therefore,

$$W_{eng} = |Q_h| - |Q_c| \qquad \text{[12.11]}$$

Ordinarily, a transfer of thermal energy Q can be either positive or negative, so the use of absolute value signs makes the signs of Q_h and Q_c explicit.

If the working substance is a gas, then **the work done by the engine for a cyclic process is the area enclosed by the curve representing the process on a PV diagram.** This area is shown for an arbitrary cyclic process in Figure 12.12.

The **thermal efficiency** e of a heat engine is defined as the work done by the engine, W_{eng}, divided by the energy absorbed during one cycle:

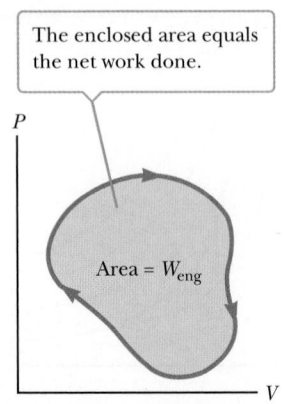

The enclosed area equals the net work done.

P

Area = W_{eng}

V

Figure 12.12 The PV diagram for an arbitrary cyclic process.

[1]Strictly speaking, the internal combustion engine is not a heat engine according to the description of the cyclic process, because the air–fuel mixture undergoes only one cycle and is then expelled through the exhaust system.

$$e \equiv \frac{W_{eng}}{|Q_h|} = \frac{|Q_h| - |Q_c|}{|Q_h|} = 1 - \frac{|Q_c|}{|Q_h|} \qquad [12.12]$$

We can think of thermal efficiency as the ratio of the benefit received (work) to the cost incurred (energy transfer at the higher temperature). Equation 12.12 shows that a heat engine has 100% efficiency ($e = 1$) only if $Q_c = 0$, meaning no energy is expelled to the cold reservoir. In other words, a heat engine with perfect efficiency would have to use all the input energy for doing mechanical work. That isn't possible, as will be seen in Section 12.5.

EXAMPLE 12.10 | The Efficiency of an Engine

GOAL Apply the efficiency formula to a heat engine.

PROBLEM During one cycle, an engine extracts 2.00×10^3 J of energy from a hot reservoir and transfers 1.50×10^3 J to a cold reservoir. **(a)** Find the thermal efficiency of the engine. **(b)** How much work does this engine do in one cycle? **(c)** What average power does the engine generate if it goes through four cycles in 2.50 s?

STRATEGY Apply Equation 12.12 to obtain the thermal efficiency, then use the first law, adapted to engines (Eq. 12.11), to find the work done in one cycle. To obtain the power generated, divide the work done in four cycles by the time it takes to run those cycles.

SOLUTION

(a) Find the engine's thermal efficiency.

Substitute Q_c and Q_h into Equation 12.12:

$$e = 1 - \frac{|Q_c|}{|Q_h|} = 1 - \frac{1.50 \times 10^3 \text{ J}}{2.00 \times 10^3 \text{ J}} = \boxed{0.250, \text{ or } 25.0\%}$$

(b) How much work does this engine do in one cycle?

Apply the first law in the form of Equation 12.11 to find the work done by the engine:

$$W_{eng} = |Q_h| - |Q_c| = 2.00 \times 10^3 \text{ J} - 1.50 \times 10^3 \text{ J}$$
$$= \boxed{5.00 \times 10^2 \text{ J}}$$

(c) Find the average power output of the engine.

Multiply the answer of part (b) by four and divide by time:

$$P = \frac{W}{\Delta t} = \frac{4.00 \times (5.00 \times 10^2 \text{ J})}{2.50 \text{ s}} = \boxed{8.00 \times 10^2 \text{ W}}$$

REMARKS Problems like this usually reduce to solving two equations and two unknowns, as here, where the two equations are the efficiency equation and the first law and the unknowns are the efficiency and the work done by the engine.

QUESTION 12.10 Can the efficiency of an engine always be improved by increasing the thermal energy put into the system during a cycle? Explain.

EXERCISE 12.10 The energy absorbed by an engine is three times as great as the work it performs. **(a)** What is its thermal efficiency? **(b)** What fraction of the energy absorbed is expelled to the cold reservoir? **(c)** What is the average power output of the engine if the energy input is 1 650 J each cycle and it goes through two cycles every 3 seconds?

ANSWERS (a) $\frac{1}{3}$ (b) $\frac{2}{3}$ (c) 367 W

EXAMPLE 12.11 | Analyzing an Engine Cycle

GOAL Combine several concepts to analyze an engine cycle.

PROBLEM A heat engine contains an ideal monatomic gas confined to a cylinder by a movable piston. The gas starts at A, where $T = 3.00 \times 10^2$ K. (See Fig. 12.13a on page 412.) The process $B \rightarrow C$ is an isothermal expansion.

(a) Find the number n of moles of gas and the temperature at B. **(b)** Find ΔU, Q, and W for the isovolumetric process $A \rightarrow B$. **(c)** Repeat for the isothermal process $B \rightarrow C$. **(d)** Repeat for the isobaric process $C \rightarrow A$. **(e)** Find the net

(Continued)

change in the internal energy for the complete cycle. **(f)** Find the thermal energy Q_h transferred into the system, the thermal energy rejected, Q_c, the thermal efficiency, and net work on the environment performed by the engine.

STRATEGY In part (a) n, T, and V can be found from the ideal gas law, which connects the equilibrium values of P, V, and T. Once the temperature T is known at the points A, B, and C, the change in internal energy, ΔU, can be computed from the formula in Table 12.2 for each process. Q and W can be similarly computed, or deduced from the first law, using the techniques applied in the single-process examples.

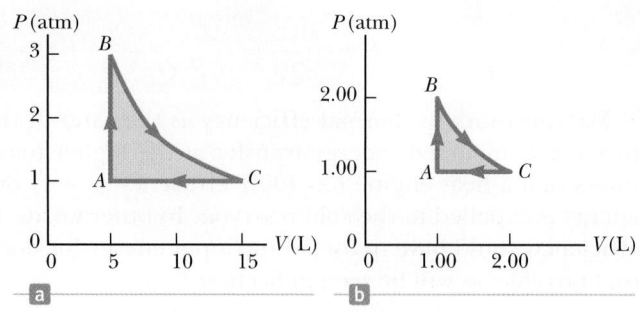

Figure 12.13 (a) (Example 12.11) (b) (Exercise 12.11)

SOLUTION

(a) Find n and T_B with the ideal gas law:

$$n = \frac{P_A V_A}{R T_A} = \frac{(1.00 \text{ atm})(5.00 \text{ L})}{(0.082\ 1 \text{ L} \cdot \text{atm}/\text{mol} \cdot \text{K})(3.00 \times 10^2 \text{ K})}$$

$$= \boxed{0.203 \text{ mol}}$$

$$T_B = \frac{P_B V_B}{nR} = \frac{(3.00 \text{ atm})(5.00 \text{ L})}{(0.203 \text{ mol})(0.082\ 1 \text{ L} \cdot \text{atm}/\text{mol} \cdot \text{K})}$$

$$= \boxed{9.00 \times 10^2 \text{ K}}$$

(b) Find ΔU_{AB}, Q_{AB}, and W_{AB} for the constant volume process $A \rightarrow B$.

Compute ΔU_{AB}, noting that $C_v = \frac{3}{2}R = 12.5 \text{ J/mol} \cdot \text{K}$:

$$\Delta U_{AB} = nC_v \Delta T = (0.203 \text{ mol})(12.5 \text{ J/mol} \cdot \text{K})$$
$$\times (9.00 \times 10^2 \text{ K} - 3.00 \times 10^2 \text{ K})$$

$$\Delta U_{AB} = \boxed{1.52 \times 10^3 \text{ J}}$$

$\Delta V = 0$ for isovolumetric processes, so no work is done:

$$W_{AB} = \boxed{0}$$

We can find Q_{AB} from the first law:

$$Q_{AB} = \Delta U_{AB} = \boxed{1.52 \times 10^3 \text{ J}}$$

(c) Find ΔU_{BC}, Q_{BC}, and W_{BC} for the isothermal process $B \rightarrow C$.

This process is isothermal, so the temperature doesn't change, and the change in internal energy is zero:

$$\Delta U_{BC} = nC_v \Delta T = \boxed{0}$$

Compute the work done on the system, using the negative of Equation 12.10:

$$W_{BC} = -nRT \ln\left(\frac{V_C}{V_B}\right)$$

$$= -(0.203 \text{ mol})(8.31 \text{ J/mol} \cdot \text{K})(9.00 \times 10^2 \text{ K})$$

$$\times \ln\left(\frac{1.50 \times 10^{-2} \text{ m}^3}{5.00 \times 10^{-3} \text{ m}^3}\right)$$

$$W_{BC} = \boxed{-1.67 \times 10^3 \text{ J}}$$

Compute Q_{BC} from the first law:

$$0 = Q_{BC} + W_{BC} \quad \rightarrow \quad Q_{BC} = -W_{BC} = \boxed{1.67 \times 10^3 \text{ J}}$$

(d) Find ΔU_{CA}, Q_{CA}, and W_{CA} for the isobaric process $C \rightarrow A$.

Compute the work on the system, with pressure constant:

$$W_{CA} = -P \Delta V = -(1.01 \times 10^5 \text{ Pa})(5.00 \times 10^{-3} \text{ m}^3$$
$$- 1.50 \times 10^{-2} \text{ m}^3)$$

$$W_{CA} = \boxed{1.01 \times 10^3 \text{ J}}$$

Find the change in internal energy, ΔU_{CA}:

$$\Delta U_{CA} = \tfrac{3}{2}nR\Delta T = \tfrac{3}{2}(0.203 \text{ mol})(8.31 \text{ J/K} \cdot \text{mol})$$
$$\times (3.00 \times 10^2 \text{ K} - 9.00 \times 10^2 \text{ K})$$

$$\Delta U_{CA} = \boxed{-1.52 \times 10^3 \text{ J}}$$

Compute the thermal energy, Q_{CA}, from the first law:

$$Q_{CA} = \Delta U_{CA} - W_{CA} = -1.52 \times 10^3\,\text{J} - 1.01 \times 10^3\,\text{J}$$
$$= \boxed{-2.53 \times 10^3\,\text{J}}$$

(e) Find the net change in internal energy, ΔU_{net}, for the cycle:

$$\Delta U_{net} = \Delta U_{AB} + \Delta U_{BC} + \Delta U_{CA}$$
$$= 1.52 \times 10^3\,\text{J} + 0 - 1.52 \times 10^3\,\text{J} = \boxed{0}$$

(f) Find the energy input, Q_h; the energy rejected, Q_c; the thermal efficiency; and the net work performed by the engine:

Sum all the positive contributions to find Q_h:

$$Q_h = Q_{AB} + Q_{BC} = 1.52 \times 10^3\,\text{J} + 1.67 \times 10^3\,\text{J}$$
$$= \boxed{3.19 \times 10^3\,\text{J}}$$

Sum any negative contributions (in this case, there is only one):

$$Q_c = \boxed{-2.53 \times 10^3\,\text{J}}$$

Find the engine efficiency and the net work done by the engine:

$$e = 1 - \frac{|Q_c|}{|Q_h|} = 1 - \frac{2.53 \times 10^3\,\text{J}}{3.19 \times 10^3\,\text{J}} = \boxed{0.207}$$
$$W_{eng} = -(W_{AB} + W_{BC} + W_{CA})$$
$$= -(0 - 1.67 \times 10^3\,\text{J} + 1.01 \times 10^3\,\text{J})$$
$$= \boxed{6.60 \times 10^2\,\text{J}}$$

REMARKS Cyclic problems are rather lengthy, but the individual steps are often short substitutions. Notice that the change in internal energy for the cycle is zero and that the net work done on the environment is identical to the net thermal energy transferred, both as they should be.

QUESTION 12.11 If BC were a straight-line path, would the work done by the cycle be affected? How?

EXERCISE 12.11 4.05×10^{-2} mol of monatomic ideal gas goes through the process shown in Figure 12.13b. The temperature at point A is 3.00×10^2 K and is 6.00×10^2 K during the isothermal process $B \to C$. (a) Find Q, ΔU, and W for the constant volume process $A \to B$. (b) Do the same for the isothermal process $B \to C$. (c) Repeat, for the constant pressure process $C \to A$. (d) Find Q_h, Q_c, and the efficiency. (e) Find W_{eng}.

ANSWERS (a) $Q_{AB} = \Delta U_{AB} = 151$ J, $W_{AB} = 0$ (b) $\Delta U_{BC} = 0$, $Q_{BC} = -W_{BC} = 1.40 \times 10^2$ J (c) $Q_{CA} = -252$ J, $\Delta U_{CA} = -151$ J, $W_{CA} = 101$ J (d) $Q_h = 291$ J, $Q_c = -252$ J, $e = 0.134$ (e) $W_{eng} = 39$ J

Refrigerators and Heat Pumps

Heat engines can operate in reverse. In this case, energy is injected into the engine, modeled as work W in Active Figure 12.14, resulting in energy being extracted from the cold reservoir and transferred to the hot reservoir. The system now operates as a heat pump, a common example being a refrigerator (Fig. 12.15 on page 414). Energy Q_c is extracted from the interior of the refrigerator and delivered as energy Q_h to the warmer air in the kitchen. The work is done in the compressor unit of the refrigerator, compressing a refrigerant such as freon, causing its temperature to increase.

A household air conditioner is another example of a heat pump. Some homes are both heated and cooled by heat pumps. In winter, the heat pump extracts energy Q_c from the cool outside air and delivers energy Q_h to the warmer air inside. In summer, energy Q_c is removed from the cool inside air, while energy Q_h is ejected to the warm air outside.

For a refrigerator or an air conditioner—a heat pump operating in cooling mode—work W is what you pay for, in terms of electrical energy running the compressor, whereas Q_c is the desired benefit. The most efficient refrigerator or air conditioner is one that removes the greatest amount of energy from the cold reservoir in exchange for the least amount of work.

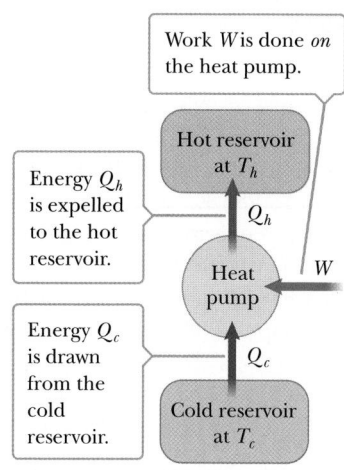

Active Figure 12.14
In this schematic representation of a heat pump, thermal energy is extracted from the cold reservoir and "pumped" to the hot reservoir.

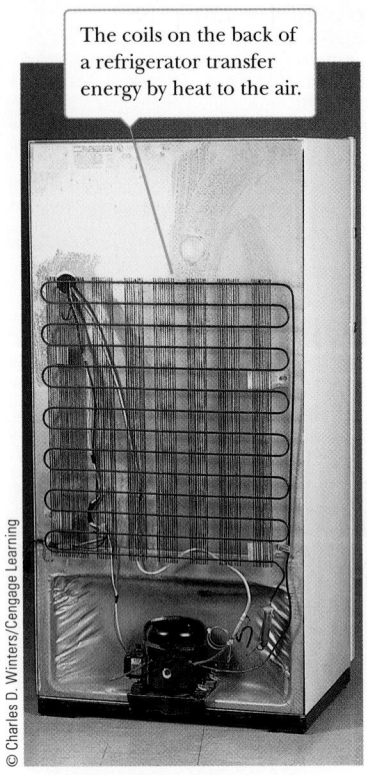

The coils on the back of a refrigerator transfer energy by heat to the air.

© Charles D. Winters/Cengage Learning

Figure 12.15 The back of a household refrigerator. The air surrounding the coils is the hot reservoir.

The coefficient of performance (COP) for a refrigerator or an air conditioner is the magnitude of the energy extracted from the cold reservoir, $|Q_c|$, divided by the work W performed by the device:

$$\text{COP(cooling mode)} = \frac{|Q_c|}{W} \qquad [12.13]$$

SI unit: dimensionless

The larger this ratio, the better the performance, because more energy is being removed for a given amount of work. A good refrigerator or air conditioner will have a COP of 5 or 6.

A heat pump operating in heating mode warms the inside of a house in winter by extracting energy from the colder outdoor air. This statement may seem paradoxical, but recall that this process is equivalent to a refrigerator removing energy from its interior and ejecting it into the kitchen.

The coefficient of performance of a heat pump operating in the heating mode is the magnitude of the energy rejected to the hot reservoir, $|Q_h|$, divided by the work W done by the pump:

$$\text{COP(heating mode)} = \frac{|Q_h|}{W} \qquad [12.14]$$

SI unit: dimensionless

In effect, the COP of a heat pump in the heating mode is the ratio of what you gain (energy delivered to the interior of your home) to what you give (work input). Typical values for this COP are greater than 1, because $|Q_h|$ is usually greater than W.

In a groundwater heat pump, energy is extracted in the winter from water deep in the ground rather than from the outside air, while energy is delivered to that water in the summer. This strategy increases the year-round efficiency of the heating and cooling unit because the groundwater is at a higher temperature than the air in winter and at a cooler temperature than the air in summer.

■ EXAMPLE 12.12 | Cooling the Leftovers

GOAL Apply the coefficient of performance of a refrigerator.

PROBLEM A 2.00-L container of leftover soup at a temperature of 323 K is placed in a refrigerator. Assume the specific heat of the soup is the same as that of water and the density is 1.25×10^3 kg/m³. The refrigerator cools the soup to 283 K. **(a)** If the COP of the refrigerator is 5.00, find the energy needed, in the form of work, to cool the soup. **(b)** If the compressor has a power rating of 0.250 hp, for what minimum length of time must it operate to cool the soup to 283 K? (The minimum time assumes the soup cools at the same rate that the heat pump ejects thermal energy from the refrigerator.)

STRATEGY The solution to this problem requires three steps. First, find the total mass m of the soup. Second, using $Q = mc\,\Delta T$, where $Q = Q_c$, find the energy transfer required to cool the soup. Third, substitute Q_c and the COP into Equation 12.13, solving for W. Divide the work by the power to get an estimate of the time required to cool the soup.

SOLUTION

(a) Find the work needed to cool the soup.

Calculate the mass of the soup:

$$m = \rho V = (1.25 \times 10^3 \text{ kg/m}^3)(2.00 \times 10^{-3} \text{ m}^3) = 2.50 \text{ kg}$$

Find the energy transfer required to cool the soup:

$$Q_c = Q = mc\,\Delta T$$
$$= (2.50 \text{ kg})(4\,190 \text{ J/kg} \cdot \text{K})(283 \text{ K} - 323 \text{ K})$$
$$= -4.19 \times 10^5 \text{ J}$$

Substitute Q_c and the COP into Equation 12.13:

$$\text{COP} = \frac{|Q_c|}{W} = \frac{4.19 \times 10^5 \, \text{J}}{W} = 5.00$$

$$W = \boxed{8.38 \times 10^4 \, \text{J}}$$

(b) Find the time needed to cool the soup.

Convert horsepower to watts:

$$P = (0.250 \, \text{hp})(746 \, \text{W}/1 \, \text{hp}) = 187 \, \text{W}$$

Divide the work by the power to find the elapsed time:

$$\Delta t = \frac{W}{P} = \frac{8.38 \times 10^4 \, \text{J}}{187 \, \text{W}} = \boxed{448 \, \text{s}}$$

REMARKS This example illustrates how cooling different substances requires differing amounts of work due to differences in specific heats. The problem doesn't take into account the insulating properties of the soup container and of the soup itself, which retard the cooling process.

QUESTION 12.12 If the refrigerator door is left open, does the kitchen become cooler? Why or why not?

EXERCISE 12.12 (a) How much work must a heat pump with a COP of 2.50 do to extract 1.00 MJ of thermal energy from the outdoors (the cold reservoir)? (b) If the unit operates at 0.500 hp, how long will the process take? (Be sure to use the correct COP!)

ANSWERS (a) $6.67 \times 10^5 \, \text{J}$ (b) $1.79 \times 10^3 \, \text{s}$

The Second Law of Thermodynamics

There are limits to the efficiency of heat engines. The ideal engine would convert all input energy into useful work, but it turns out that such an engine is impossible to construct. The Kelvin-Planck formulation of the **second law of thermodynamics** can be stated as follows:

> No heat engine operating in a cycle can absorb energy from a reservoir and use it entirely for the performance of an equal amount of work.

This form of the second law means that the efficiency $e = W_{\text{eng}}/|Q_h|$ of engines must always be less than 1. Some energy $|Q_c|$ must always be lost to the environment. In other words, it's theoretically impossible to construct a heat engine with an efficiency of 100%.

To summarize, the first law says **we can't get a greater amount of energy out of a cyclic process than we put in,** and the second law says **we can't break even.** No matter what engine is used, some energy must be transferred by heat to the cold reservoir. In Equation 12.11, the second law simply means $|Q_c|$ is always greater than zero.

There is another equivalent statement of the second law:

> If two systems are in thermal contact, net thermal energy transfers spontaneously by heat from the hotter system to the colder system.

Here, spontaneous means the energy transfer occurs naturally, with no work being done. Thermal energy naturally transfers from hotter systems to colder systems. Work must be done to transfer thermal energy from a colder system to a hotter system, however. An example is the refrigerator, which transfers thermal energy from inside the refrigerator to the warmer kitchen.

Reversible and Irreversible Processes

No engine can operate with 100% efficiency, but different designs yield different efficiencies, and it turns out that one design in particular delivers the maximum possible efficiency. This design is the Carnot cycle, discussed in the next

Lord Kelvin
British Physicist and Mathematician
(1824–1907)
Born William Thomson in Belfast, Kelvin was the first to propose the use of an absolute scale of temperature. His study of Carnot's theory led to the idea that energy cannot pass spontaneously from a colder object to a hotter object; this principle is known as the second law of thermodynamics.

J.-L. Charmet/SPL/Photo Researchers, Inc.

Individual grains of sand drop onto the piston, slowly compressing the gas.

Energy reservoir

Figure 12.16 A method for compressing a gas in a reversible isothermal process.

Sadi Carnot
French Engineer (1796–1832)
Carnot is considered to be the founder of the science of thermodynamics. Some of his notes found after his death indicate that he was the first to recognize the relationship between work and heat.

subsection. Understanding it requires the concepts of reversible and irreversible processes. In a **reversible** process, every state along the path is an equilibrium state, so the system can return to its initial conditions by going along the same path in the reverse direction. A process that doesn't satisfy this requirement is **irreversible.**

Most natural processes are known to be irreversible; the reversible process is an idealization. Although real processes are always irreversible, some are *almost* reversible. If a real process occurs so slowly that the system is virtually always in equilibrium, the process can be considered reversible. Imagine compressing a gas very slowly by dropping grains of sand onto a frictionless piston, as in Figure 12.16. The temperature can be kept constant by placing the gas in thermal contact with an energy reservoir. The pressure, volume, and temperature of the gas are well defined during this isothermal compression. Each added grain of sand represents a change to a new equilibrium state. The process can be reversed by slowly removing grains of sand from the piston.

The Carnot Engine

In 1824, in an effort to understand the efficiency of real engines, a French engineer named Sadi Carnot (1796–1832) described a theoretical engine now called a *Carnot engine* that is of great importance from both a practical and a theoretical viewpoint. He showed that a heat engine operating in an ideal, reversible cycle—now called a **Carnot cycle**—between two energy reservoirs is the most efficient engine possible. Such an engine establishes an upper limit on the efficiencies of all real engines. **Carnot's theorem** can be stated as follows:

> No real engine operating between two energy reservoirs can be more efficient than a Carnot engine operating between the same two reservoirs.

In a Carnot cycle, an ideal gas is contained in a cylinder with a movable piston at one end. The temperature of the gas varies between T_c and T_h. The cylinder walls and the piston are thermally nonconducting. Active Figure 12.17 shows the four stages of the Carnot cycle, and Active Figure 12.18 is the *PV* diagram for the cycle. The cycle consists of two adiabatic and two isothermal processes, all reversible:

1. The process $A \rightarrow B$ is an isothermal expansion at temperature T_h in which the gas is placed in thermal contact with a hot reservoir (a large oven, for example) at temperature T_h (Active Fig. 12.17a). During the process, the gas absorbs energy Q_h from the reservoir and does work W_{AB} in raising the piston.
2. In the process $B \rightarrow C$, the base of the cylinder is replaced by a thermally nonconducting wall and the gas expands adiabatically, so no energy enters or leaves the system by heat (Active Fig. 12.17b). During the process, the temperature falls from T_h to T_c and the gas does work W_{BC} in raising the piston.
3. In the process $C \rightarrow D$, the gas is placed in thermal contact with a cold reservoir at temperature T_c (Active Fig. 12.17c) and is compressed isothermally at temperature T_c. During this time, the gas expels energy Q_c to the reservoir and the work done on the gas is W_{CD}.
4. In the final process, $D \rightarrow A$, the base of the cylinder is again replaced by a thermally nonconducting wall (Active Fig. 12.17d), and the gas is compressed adiabatically. The temperature of the gas increases to T_h, and the work done on the gas is W_{DA}.

For a Carnot engine, the following relationship between the thermal energy transfers and the absolute temperatures can be derived:

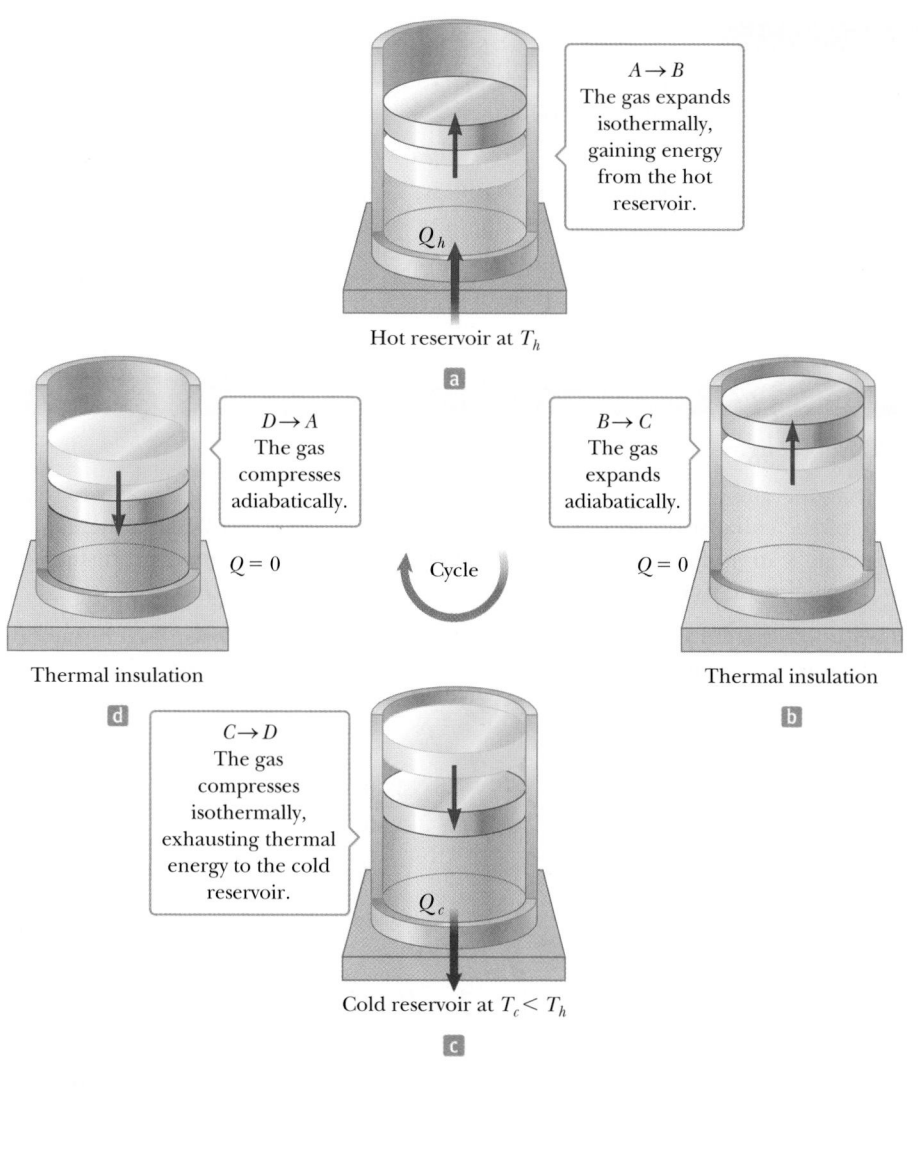

> **Tip 12.3 Don't Shop for a Carnot Engine**
>
> The Carnot engine is only an idealization. If a Carnot engine were developed in an effort to maximize efficiency, it would have zero power output because for all of the processes to be reversible, the engine would have to run infinitely slowly.

$$\frac{|Q_c|}{|Q_h|} = \frac{T_c}{T_h} \qquad [12.15]$$

Substituting this expression into Equation 12.12, we find that the thermal efficiency of a Carnot engine is

$$e_C = 1 - \frac{T_c}{T_h} \qquad [12.16]$$

where T must be in kelvins. From this result, we see that **all Carnot engines operating reversibly between the same two temperatures have the same efficiency.**

Equation 12.16 can be applied to any working substance operating in a Carnot cycle between two energy reservoirs. According to that equation, the efficiency is zero if $T_c = T_h$. The efficiency increases as T_c is lowered and as T_h is increased. The efficiency can be one (100%), however, only if $T_c = 0$ K. According to the **third law of thermodynamics,** it's impossible to lower the temperature of a system to absolute zero in a finite number of steps, so such reservoirs are not available and the maximum efficiency is always less than 1. In most practical cases, the cold reservoir is near room temperature, about 300 K, so increasing the efficiency requires raising the temperature of the hot reservoir. **All real engines operate irreversibly, due to friction and the brevity of their cycles, and are therefore *less* efficient than the Carnot engine.**

◀ Third law of thermodynamics

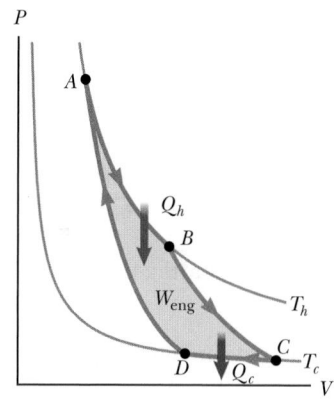

Active Figure 12.18
The PV diagram for the Carnot cycle. The net work done, W_{eng}, equals the net energy transferred into the Carnot engine in one cycle, $|Q_h| - |Q_c|$.

■ *Quick Quiz*

12.3 Three engines operate between reservoirs separated in temperature by 300 K. The reservoir temperatures are as follows:

$$\text{Engine A: } T_h = 1\,000 \text{ K, } T_c = 700 \text{ K}$$
$$\text{Engine B: } T_h = 800 \text{ K, } T_c = 500 \text{ K}$$
$$\text{Engine C: } T_h = 600 \text{ K, } T_c = 300 \text{ K}$$

Rank the engines in order of their theoretically possible efficiency, from highest to lowest. (a) A, B, C (b) B, C, A (c) C, B, A (d) C, A, B

■ **EXAMPLE 12.13** | **The Steam Engine**

GOAL Apply the equations of an ideal (Carnot) engine.

PROBLEM A steam engine has a boiler that operates at 5.00×10^2 K. The energy from the boiler changes water to steam, which drives the piston. The temperature of the exhaust is that of the outside air, 3.00×10^2 K. **(a)** What is the engine's efficiency if it's an ideal engine? **(b)** If the 3.50×10^3 J of energy is supplied from the boiler, find the energy transferred to the cold reservoir and the work done by the engine on its environment.

STRATEGY This problem requires substitution into Equations 12.15 and 12.16, both applicable to a Carnot engine. The first equation relates the ratio Q_c/Q_h to the ratio T_c/T_h, and the second gives the Carnot engine efficiency.

SOLUTION

(a) Find the engine's efficiency, assuming it's ideal.

Substitute into Equation 12.16, the equation for the efficiency of a Carnot engine:

$$e_C = 1 - \frac{T_c}{T_h} = 1 - \frac{3.00 \times 10^2 \text{ K}}{5.00 \times 10^2 \text{ K}} = \boxed{0.400, \text{ or } 40.0\%}$$

(b) Find the energy transferred to the cold reservoir and the work done on the environment if 3.50×10^3 J is delivered to the engine during one cycle.

Equation 12.15 shows that the ratio of energies equals the ratio of temperatures:

$$\frac{|Q_c|}{|Q_h|} = \frac{T_c}{T_h} \quad \rightarrow \quad |Q_c| = |Q_h|\frac{T_c}{T_h}$$

Substitute, finding the energy transferred to the cold reservoir:

$$|Q_c| = (3.50 \times 10^3 \text{ J})\left(\frac{3.00 \times 10^2 \text{ K}}{5.00 \times 10^2 \text{ K}}\right) = \boxed{2.10 \times 10^3 \text{ J}}$$

Use Equation 12.11 to find the work done by the engine:

$$W_{\text{eng}} = |Q_h| - |Q_c| = 3.50 \times 10^3 \text{ J} - 2.10 \times 10^3 \text{ J}$$
$$= \boxed{1.40 \times 10^3 \text{ J}}$$

REMARKS This problem differs from the earlier examples on work and efficiency because we used the special Carnot relationships, Equations 12.15 and 12.16. Remember that these equations can only be used when the cycle is identified as ideal or a Carnot.

QUESTION 12.13 True or False: A nonideal engine operating between the same temperature extremes as a Carnot engine and having the same input thermal energy will perform the same amount of work as the Carnot engine.

EXERCISE 12.13 The highest theoretical efficiency of a gasoline engine based on the Carnot cycle is 0.300, or 30.0%. (a) If this engine expels its gases into the atmosphere, which has a temperature of 3.00×10^2 K, what is the temperature in the cylinder immediately after combustion? (b) If the heat engine absorbs 837 J of energy from the hot reservoir during each cycle, how much work can it perform in each cycle?

ANSWERS (a) 429 K (b) 251 J

12.5 Entropy

Temperature and internal energy, associated with the zeroth and first laws of thermodynamics, respectively, are both state variables, meaning they can be used to describe the thermodynamic state of a system. A state variable called the **entropy** S is related to the second law of thermodynamics. We define entropy on a macroscopic scale as German physicist Rudolf Clausius (1822–1888) first expressed it in 1865:

Let Q_r be the energy absorbed or expelled during a reversible, constant temperature process between two equilibrium states. Then the change in entropy during any constant temperature process connecting the two equilibrium states is defined as

$$\Delta S \equiv \frac{Q_r}{T} \qquad\qquad [12.17]$$

SI unit: joules/kelvin (J/K)

A similar formula holds when the temperature isn't constant, but its derivation entails calculus and won't be considered here. Calculating the change in entropy, ΔS, during a transition between two equilibrium states requires finding a reversible path that connects the states. The entropy change calculated on that reversible path is taken to be ΔS for the *actual* path. This approach is necessary because quantities such as the temperature of a system can be defined only for systems in equilibrium, and a reversible path consists of a sequence of equilibrium states. The subscript r on the term Q_r emphasizes that the path chosen for the calculation must be reversible. The change in entropy ΔS, like changes in internal energy ΔU and changes in potential energy, depends only on the endpoints, and not on the path connecting them.

The concept of entropy gained wide acceptance in part because it provided another variable to describe the state of a system, along with pressure, volume, and temperature. Its significance was enhanced when it was found that **the entropy of the Universe increases in all natural processes.** This is yet another way of stating the second law of thermodynamics.

Although the entropy of the *Universe* increases in all natural processes, the entropy of a *system* can decrease. For example, if system A transfers energy Q to system B by heat, the entropy of system A decreases. This transfer, however, can only occur if the temperature of system B is less than the temperature of system A. Because temperature appears in the denominator in the definition of entropy, system B's increase in entropy will be greater than system A's decrease, so taken together, the entropy of the Universe increases.

For centuries, individuals have attempted to build perpetual motion machines that operate continuously without any input of energy or increase in entropy. The laws of thermodynamics preclude the invention of any such machines.

The concept of entropy is satisfying because it enables us to present the second law of thermodynamics in the form of a mathematical statement. In the next section we find that entropy can also be interpreted in terms of probabilities, a relationship that has profound implications.

Rudolf Clausius
German Physicist (1822–1888)
Born with the name Rudolf Gottlieb, he adopted the classical name of Clausius, which was a popular thing to do in his time. "I propose . . . to call S the entropy of a body, after the Greek word 'transformation.' I have designedly coined the word 'entropy' to be similar to energy, for these two quantities are so analogous in their physical significance, that an analogy of denominations seems to be helpful."

Tip 12.4 Entropy ≠ Energy

Don't confuse energy and entropy. Although the names sound similar the concepts are different.

■ *Quick Quiz*

12.4 Which of the following is true for the entropy change of a system that undergoes a reversible, adiabatic process? (a) $\Delta S < 0$ (b) $\Delta S = 0$ (c) $\Delta S > 0$

■ **EXAMPLE 12.14**   **Melting a Piece of Lead**

GOAL Calculate the change in entropy due to a phase change.

PROBLEM (a) Find the change in entropy of 3.00×10^2 g of lead when it melts at 327°C. Lead has a latent heat of fusion of 2.45×10^4 J/kg. (b) Suppose the same amount of energy is used to melt part of a piece of silver, which is already at its melting point of 961°C. Find the change in the entropy of the silver.

(Continued)

STRATEGY This problem can be solved by substitution into Equation 12.17. Be sure to use the Kelvin temperature scale.

SOLUTION

(a) Find the entropy change of the lead.

Find the energy necessary to melt the lead:

$$Q = mL_f = (0.300 \text{ kg})(2.45 \times 10^4 \text{ J/kg}) = 7.35 \times 10^3 \text{ J}$$

Convert the temperature in degrees Celsius to kelvins:

$$T = T_C + 273 = 327 + 273 = 6.00 \times 10^2 \text{ K}$$

Substitute the quantities found into the entropy equation:

$$\Delta S = \frac{Q}{T} = \frac{7.35 \times 10^3 \text{ J}}{6.00 \times 10^2 \text{ K}} = \boxed{12.3 \text{ J/K}}$$

(b) Find the entropy change of the silver.

The added energy is the same as in part (a), by supposition. Substitute into the entropy equation, after first converting the melting point of silver to kelvins:

$$T = T_C + 273 = 961 + 273 = 1.234 \times 10^3 \text{ K}$$

$$\Delta S = \frac{Q}{T} = \frac{7.35 \times 10^3 \text{ J}}{1.234 \times 10^3 \text{ K}} = \boxed{5.96 \text{ J/K}}$$

REMARKS This example shows that adding a given amount of energy to a system increases its entropy, but adding the same amount of energy to another system at higher temperature results in a smaller increase in entropy. This is because the change in entropy is inversely proportional to the temperature.

QUESTION 12.14 If the same amount of energy were used to melt ice at 0°C to water at 0°C, rank the entropy changes for ice, silver, and lead, from smallest to largest.

EXERCISE 12.14 Find the change in entropy of a 2.00-kg block of gold at 1 063°C when it melts to become liquid gold at 1 063°C. (The latent heat of fusion for gold is 6.44×10^4 J/kg.)

ANSWER 96.4 J/K

■ EXAMPLE 12.15 | Ice, Steam, and the Entropy of the Universe

GOAL Calculate the change in entropy for a system and its environment.

PROBLEM A block of ice at 273 K is put in thermal contact with a container of steam at 373 K, converting 25.0 g of ice to water at 273 K while condensing some of the steam to water at 373 K. **(a)** Find the change in entropy of the ice. **(b)** Find the change in entropy of the steam. **(c)** Find the change in entropy of the Universe.

STRATEGY First, calculate the energy transfer necessary to melt the ice. The amount of energy gained by the ice is lost by the steam. Compute the entropy change for each process and sum to get the entropy change of the Universe.

SOLUTION

(a) Find the change in entropy of the ice.

Use the latent heat of fusion, L_f, to compute the thermal energy needed to melt 25.0 g of ice:

$$Q_{ice} = mL_f = (0.025 \text{ kg})(3.33 \times 10^5 \text{ J}) = 8.33 \times 10^3 \text{ J}$$

Calculate the change in entropy of the ice:

$$\Delta S_{ice} = \frac{Q_{ice}}{T_{ice}} = \frac{8.33 \times 10^3 \text{ J}}{273 \text{ K}} = \boxed{30.5 \text{ J/K}}$$

(b) Find the change in entropy of the steam.

By supposition, the thermal energy lost by the steam is equal to the thermal energy gained by the ice:

$$\Delta S_{steam} = \frac{Q_{steam}}{T_{steam}} = \frac{-8.33 \times 10^3 \text{ J}}{373 \text{ K}} = \boxed{-22.3 \text{ J/K}}$$

(c) Find the change in entropy of the Universe.

Sum the two changes in entropy:

$$\Delta S_{universe} = \Delta S_{ice} + \Delta S_{steam} = 30.5 \text{ J/k} - 22.3 \text{ J/K}$$
$$= \boxed{+ 8.2 \text{ J/K}}$$

REMARKS Notice that the entropy of the Universe increases, as it must in all natural processes.

QUESTION 12.15 True or False: For a given magnitude of thermal energy transfer, the change in entropy is smaller for processes that proceed at lower temperature.

EXERCISE 12.15 A 4.00-kg block of ice at 273 K encased in a thin plastic shell of negligible mass melts in a large lake at 293 K. At the instant the ice has completely melted in the shell and is still at 273 K, calculate the change in entropy of (a) the ice, (b) the lake (which essentially remains at 293 K), and (c) the Universe.

ANSWERS (a) 4.88×10^3 J/K (b) -4.55×10^3 J/K (c) $+3.3 \times 10^2$ J/K

EXAMPLE 12.16 | A Falling Boulder

GOAL Combine mechanical energy and entropy.

PROBLEM A chunk of rock of mass 1.00×10^3 kg at 293 K falls from a cliff of height 125 m into a large lake, also at 293 K. Find the change in entropy of the lake, assuming all the rock's kinetic energy upon entering the lake converts to thermal energy absorbed by the lake.

STRATEGY Gravitational potential energy when the rock is at the top of the cliff converts to kinetic energy of the rock before it enters the lake, then is transferred to the lake as thermal energy. The change in the lake's temperature is negligible (due to its mass). Divide the mechanical energy of the rock by the temperature of the lake to estimate the lake's change in entropy.

SOLUTION

Calculate the gravitational potential energy associated with the rock at the top of the cliff:

$$PE = mgh = (1.00 \times 10^3 \text{ kg})(9.80 \text{ m/s}^2)(125 \text{ m})$$
$$= 1.23 \times 10^6 \text{ J}$$

This energy is transferred to the lake as thermal energy, resulting in an entropy increase of the lake:

$$\Delta S = \frac{Q}{T} = \frac{1.23 \times 10^6 \text{ J}}{293 \text{ K}} = \boxed{4.20 \times 10^3 \text{ J/K}}$$

REMARKS This example shows how even simple mechanical processes can bring about increases in the Universe's entropy.

QUESTION 12.16 If you carefully remove your physics book from a shelf and place it on the ground, what happens to the entropy of the Universe? Does it increase, decrease, or remain the same? Explain.

EXERCISE 12.16 Estimate the change in entropy of a tree trunk at 15.0°C when a bullet of mass 5.00 g traveling at 1.00×10^3 m/s embeds itself in it. (Assume the kinetic energy of the bullet transforms to thermal energy, all of which is absorbed by the tree.)

ANSWER 8.68 J/K

Entropy and Disorder

A large element of chance is inherent in natural processes. The spacing between trees in a natural forest, for example, is random; if you discovered a forest where all the trees were equally spaced, you would conclude that it had been planted. Likewise, leaves fall to the ground with random arrangements. It would be highly unlikely to find the leaves laid out in perfectly straight rows. We can express the results of such observations by saying that **a disorderly arrangement is much more probable than an orderly one if the laws of nature are allowed to act without interference.**

Entropy originally found its place in thermodynamics, but its importance grew tremendously as the field of statistical mechanics developed. This analytical approach employs an alternate interpretation of entropy. In statistical mechanics, the behavior of a substance is described by the statistical behavior of the atoms and molecules contained in it. One of the main conclusions of the statistical mechanical approach is that **isolated systems tend toward greater disorder, and entropy is a measure of that disorder.**

Tip 12.5 Don't Confuse the W's

The symbol W used here is a *probability*, not to be confused with the same symbol used for work.

In light of this new view of entropy, Boltzmann found another method for calculating entropy through use of the relation

$$S = k_B \ln W \qquad [12.18]$$

where $k_B = 1.38 \times 10^{-23}$ J/K is Boltzmann's constant and W is a number proportional to the probability that the system has a particular configuration. The symbol "ln" again stands for natural logarithm, discussed in Appendix A.

Equation 12.18 could be applied to a bag of marbles. Imagine that you have 100 marbles—50 red and 50 green—stored in a bag. You are allowed to draw four marbles from the bag according to the following rules: Draw one marble, record its color, return it to the bag, and draw again. Continue this process until four marbles have been drawn. Note that because each marble is returned to the bag before the next one is drawn, the probability of drawing a red marble is always the same as the probability of drawing a green one.

The results of all possible drawing sequences are shown in Table 12.3. For example, the result RRGR means that a red marble was drawn first, a red one second, a green one third, and a red one fourth. The table indicates that there is only one possible way to draw four red marbles. There are four possible sequences that produce one green and three red marbles, six sequences that produce two green and two red, four sequences that produce three green and one red, and one sequence that produces all green. From Equation 12.18, we see that the state with the greatest disorder (two red and two green marbles) has the highest entropy because it is most probable. In contrast, the most ordered states (all red marbles and all green marbles) are least likely to occur and are states of lowest entropy.

The outcome of the draw can range between these highly ordered (lowest-entropy) and highly disordered (highest-entropy) states. Entropy can be regarded as an index of how far a system has progressed from an ordered to a disordered state.

The second law of thermodynamics is really a statement of what is most probable rather than of what must be. Imagine placing an ice cube in contact with a hot piece of pizza. There is nothing in nature that absolutely forbids the transfer of energy by heat from the ice to the much warmer pizza. Statistically, it's possible for a slow-moving molecule in the ice to collide with a faster-moving molecule in the pizza so that the slow one transfers some of its energy to the faster one. When the great number of molecules present in the ice and pizza are considered, however, the odds are overwhelmingly in favor of the transfer of energy from the faster-moving molecules to the slower-moving molecules. Furthermore, this example demonstrates that a system naturally tends to move from a state of order to a state of disorder. The initial state, in which all the pizza molecules have high kinetic energy and all the ice molecules have lower kinetic energy, is much more ordered than the final state after energy transfer has taken place and the ice has melted.

APPLICATION
The Direction of Time

Even more generally, the second law of thermodynamics defines the direction of time for all events as the direction in which the entropy of the universe increases. Although conservation of energy isn't violated if energy flows spontaneously from a cold object (the ice cube) to a hot object (the pizza slice), that event

Table 12.3 Possible Results of Drawing Four Marbles from a Bag

End Result	Possible Draws	Total Number of Same Results
All R	RRRR	1
1G, 3R	RRRG, RRGR, RGRR, GRRR	4
2G, 2R	RRGG, RGRG, GRRG, RGGR, GRGR, GGRR	6
3G, 1R	GGGR, GGRG, GRGG, RGGG	4
All G	GGGG	1

violates the second law because it represents a spontaneous increase in order. Of course, such an event also violates everyday experience. If the melting ice cube is filmed and the film speeded up, the difference between running the film in forward and reverse directions would be obvious to an audience. The same would be true of filming any event involving a large number of particles, such as a dish dropping to the floor and shattering.

As another example, suppose you were able to measure the velocities of all the air molecules in a room at some instant. It's very unlikely that you would find all molecules moving in the same direction with the same speed; that would be a highly ordered state, indeed. The most probable situation is a system of molecules moving haphazardly in all directions with a wide distribution of speeds, a highly disordered state. This physical situation can be compared to the drawing of marbles from a bag: If a container held 10^{23} molecules of a gas, the probability of finding all the molecules moving in the same direction with the same speed at some instant would be similar to that of drawing a marble from the bag 10^{23} times and getting a red marble on every draw, clearly an unlikely set of events.

The tendency of nature to move toward a state of disorder affects the ability of a system to do work. Consider a ball thrown toward a wall. The ball has kinetic energy, and its state is an ordered one, which means that all the atoms and molecules of the ball move in unison at the same speed and in the same direction (apart from their random internal motions). When the ball hits the wall, however, part of the ball's kinetic energy is transformed into the random, disordered, internal motion of the molecules in the ball and the wall, and the temperatures of the ball and the wall both increase slightly. Before the collision, the ball was capable of doing work. It could drive a nail into the wall, for example. With the transformation of part of the ordered energy into disordered internal energy, this capability of doing work is reduced. The ball rebounds with less kinetic energy than it originally had, because the collision is inelastic.

Various forms of energy can be converted to internal energy, as in the collision between the ball and the wall, but the reverse transformation is never complete. In general, given two kinds of energy, A and B, if A can be completely converted to B and vice versa, we say that A and B are of the *same grade*. However, if A can be completely converted to B and the reverse is never complete, then A is of a *higher grade* of energy than B. In the case of a ball hitting a wall, the kinetic energy of the ball is of a higher grade than the internal energy contained in the ball and the wall after the collision. When high-grade energy is converted to internal energy, it can never be fully recovered as high-grade energy.

This conversion of high-grade energy to internal energy is referred to as the **degradation of energy.** The energy is said to be degraded because it takes on a form that is less useful for doing work. In other words, **in all real processes, the energy available for doing work decreases.**

Finally, note once again that the statement that entropy must increase in all natural processes is true only for isolated systems. There are instances in which the entropy of some system decreases, but with a corresponding net increase in entropy for some other system. When all systems are taken together to form the Universe, **the entropy of the Universe always increases.**

Ultimately, the entropy of the Universe should reach a maximum. When it does, the Universe will be in a state of uniform temperature and density. All physical, chemical, and biological processes will cease, because a state of perfect disorder implies no available energy for doing work. This gloomy state of affairs is sometimes referred to as the ultimate "heat death" of the Universe.

(a) A royal flush is a highly ordered poker hand with a low probability of occurrence. (b) A disordered and worthless poker hand. The probability of this *particular* hand occurring is the same as that of the royal flush. There are so many worthless hands, however, that the probability of being dealt a worthless hand is much higher than that of being dealt a royal flush. Can you calculate the probability of being dealt a full house (a pair and three of a kind) from a standard deck of 52 cards?

■ Quick Quiz

12.5 Suppose you are throwing two dice in a friendly game of craps. For any given throw, the two numbers that are faceup can have a sum of 2, 3, 4, 5, 6, 7, 8, 9, 10, 11, or 12. Which outcome is most probable? Which is least probable?

12.6 Human Metabolism BIO

Animals do work and give off energy by heat, leading us to believe the first law of thermodynamics can be applied to living organisms to describe them in a general way. The internal energy stored in humans goes into other forms needed for maintaining and repairing the major body organs and is transferred out of the body by work as a person walks or lifts a heavy object, and by heat when the body is warmer than its surroundings. Because the rates of change of internal energy, energy loss by heat, and energy loss by work vary widely with the intensity and duration of human activity, it's best to measure the time rates of change of ΔU, Q, and W. Rewriting the first law, these time rates of change are related by

$$\frac{\Delta U}{\Delta t} = \frac{Q}{\Delta t} + \frac{W}{\Delta t}$$ [12.19]

On average, energy Q flows *out* of the body, and work is done *by* the body on its surroundings, so both $Q/\Delta t$ and $W/\Delta t$ are negative. This means that $\Delta U/\Delta t$ would be negative and the internal energy and body temperature would decrease with time if a human were a closed system with no way of ingesting matter or replenishing internal energy stores. Because all animals are actually open systems, they acquire internal energy (chemical potential energy) by eating and breathing, so their internal energy and temperature are kept constant. Overall, the energy from the oxidation of food ultimately supplies the work done by the body and energy lost from the body by heat, and this is the interpretation we give Equation 12.19. That is, $\Delta U/\Delta t$ is the rate at which internal energy is added to our bodies by food, and this term just balances the rate of energy loss by heat, $Q/\Delta t$, and by work, $W/\Delta t$. Finally, if we have a way of measuring $\Delta U/\Delta t$ and $W/\Delta t$ for a human, we can calculate $Q/\Delta t$ from Equation 12.19 and gain useful information on the efficiency of the body as a machine.

Measuring the Metabolic Rate $\Delta U/\Delta t$

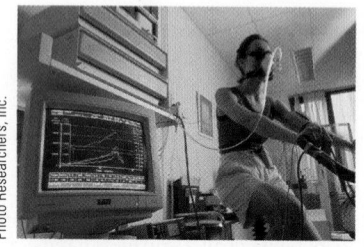

Figure 12.19 This bike rider is being monitored for oxygen consumption.

The value of $W/\Delta t$, the work done by a person per unit time, can easily be determined by measuring the power output supplied by the person (in pedaling a bike, for example). **The metabolic rate $\Delta U/\Delta t$ is the rate at which chemical potential energy in food and oxygen are transformed into internal energy to just balance the body losses of internal energy by work and heat.** Although the mechanisms of food oxidation and energy release in the body are complicated, involving many intermediate reactions and enzymes (organic compounds that speed up the chemical reactions taking place at "low" body temperatures), an amazingly simple rule summarizes these processes: **The metabolic rate is directly proportional to the rate of oxygen consumption by volume.** It is found that for an average diet, the consumption of one liter of oxygen releases 4.8 kcal, or 20 kJ, of energy. We may write this important summary rule as

Metabolic rate equation ▶

$$\frac{\Delta U}{\Delta t} = 4.8 \frac{\Delta V_{O_2}}{\Delta t}$$ [12.20]

where the metabolic rate $\Delta U/\Delta t$ is measured in kcal/s and $\Delta V_{O_2}/\Delta t$, the volume rate of oxygen consumption, is in L/s. Measuring the rate of oxygen consumption during various activities ranging from sleep to intense bicycle racing effectively measures the variation of metabolic rate or the variation in the total power the body generates. A simultaneous measurement of the work per unit time done by a person along with the metabolic rate allows the efficiency of the body as a machine to be determined. Figure 12.19 shows a person monitored for oxygen consumption while riding a bike attached to a dynamometer, a device for measuring power output.

Table 12.4 Oxygen Consumption and Metabolic Rates for Various Activities for a 65-kg Male[a]

Activity	O_2 Use Rate (mL/min · kg)	Metabolic Rate (kcal/h)	Metabolic Rate (W)
Sleeping	3.5	70	80
Light activity (dressing, walking slowly, desk work)	10	200	230
Moderate activity (walking briskly)	20	400	465
Heavy activity (basketball, swimming a fast breaststroke)	30	600	700
Extreme activity (bicycle racing)	70	1 400	1 600

[a]Source: A Companion to Medical Studies, 2/e, R. Passmore, Philadelphia, F. A. Davis, 1968.

Metabolic Rate, Activity, and Weight Gain

Table 12.4 shows the measured rate of oxygen consumption in milliliters per minute per kilogram of body mass and the calculated metabolic rate for a 65-kg male engaged in various activities. A sleeping person uses about 80 W of power, the **basal metabolic rate,** just to maintain and run different body organs such as the heart, lungs, liver, kidneys, brain, and skeletal muscles. More intense activity increases the metabolic rate to a maximum of about 1 600 W for a superb racing cyclist, although such a high rate can only be maintained for periods of a few seconds. When we sit watching a riveting film, we give off about as much energy by heat as a bright (250-W) lightbulb.

Regardless of level of activity, the daily food intake should just balance the loss in internal energy if a person is not to gain weight. Further, exercise is a poor substitute for dieting as a method of losing weight. For example, the loss of 1 pound of body fat requires the muscles to expend 4 100 kcal of energy. If the goal is to lose 1 pound of fat in 35 days, a jogger could run an extra mile a day, because a 65-kg jogger uses about 120 kcal to jog 1 mile (35 days × 120 kcal/day = 4 200 kcal). An easier way to lose the pound of fat would be to diet and eat two fewer slices of bread per day for 35 days, because bread has a calorie content of 60 kcal/slice (35 days × 2 slices/day × 60 kcal/slice = 4 200 kcal).

■ EXAMPLE 12.17 | Fighting Fat

GOAL Estimate human energy usage during a typical day.

PROBLEM In the course of 24 hours, a 65-kg person spends 8 h at a desk, 2 h puttering around the house, 1 h jogging 5 miles, 5 h in moderate activity, and 8 h sleeping. What is the change in her internal energy during this period?

STRATEGY The time rate of energy usage—or power—multiplied by time gives the amount of energy used during a given activity. Use Table 12.4 to find the power P_i needed for each activity, multiply each by the time, and sum them all up.

SOLUTION

$$\Delta U = -\sum P_i \Delta t_i = -(P_1 \Delta t_1 + P_2 \Delta t_2 + \cdots + P_n \Delta t_n)$$

$$= -(200 \text{ kcal/h})(10 \text{ h}) - (5 \text{ mi/h})(120 \text{ kcal/mi})(1 \text{ h}) - (400 \text{ kcal/h})(5 \text{ h}) - (70 \text{ kcal/h})(8 \text{ h})$$

$$\Delta U = \boxed{-5\,000 \text{ kcal}}$$

REMARKS If this is a typical day in the woman's life, she will have to consume less than 5 000 kilocalories on a daily basis in order to lose weight. A complication lies in the fact that human metabolism tends to drop when food intake is reduced.

QUESTION 12.17 How could completely skipping meals lead to weight gain?

(Continued)

EXERCISE 12.17 If a 60.0-kg woman ingests 3 000 kcal a day and spends 6 h sleeping, 4 h walking briskly, 8 h sitting at a desk job, 1 h swimming a fast breaststroke, and 5 h watching action movies on TV, about how much weight will the woman gain or lose every day? (*Note:* Recall that using about 4 100 kcal of energy will burn off a pound of fat.)

ANSWER She'll lose a little more than one-half a pound of fat a day.

Physical Fitness and Efficiency of the Human Body as a Machine

Table 12.5 Physical Fitness and Maximum Oxygen Consumption Rate[a]

Fitness Level	Maximum Oxygen Consumption Rate (mL/min · kg)
Very poor	28
Poor	34
Fair	42
Good	52
Excellent	70

[a]*Source: Aerobics*, K. H. Cooper, Bantam Books, New York, 1968.

One measure of a person's physical fitness is his or her maximum capacity to use or consume oxygen. This "aerobic" fitness can be increased and maintained with regular exercise, but falls when training stops. Typical maximum rates of oxygen consumption and corresponding fitness levels are shown in Table 12.5; we see that the maximum oxygen consumption rate varies from 28 mL/min·kg of body mass for poorly conditioned subjects to 70 mL/min·kg for superb athletes.

We have already pointed out that the first law of thermodynamics can be rewritten to relate the metabolic rate $\Delta U/\Delta t$ to the rate at which energy leaves the body by work and by heat:

$$\frac{\Delta U}{\Delta t} = \frac{Q}{\Delta t} + \frac{W}{\Delta t}$$

Now consider the body as a machine capable of supplying mechanical power to the outside world and ask for its efficiency. The body's efficiency *e* is defined as the ratio of the mechanical power supplied by a human to the metabolic rate or the total power input to the body:

$$e = \text{body's efficiency} = \frac{\left|\dfrac{W}{\Delta t}\right|}{\left|\dfrac{\Delta U}{\Delta t}\right|} \qquad \text{[12.21]}$$

In this definition, absolute value signs are used to show that *e* is a positive number and to avoid explicitly using minus signs required by our definitions of *W* and *Q* in the first law. Table 12.6 shows the efficiency of workers engaged in different activities for several hours. These values were obtained by measuring the power output and simultaneous oxygen consumption of mine workers and calculating the metabolic rate from their oxygen consumption. The table shows that a person can steadily supply mechanical power for several hours at about 100 W with an efficiency of about 17%. It also shows the dependence of efficiency on activity, and that *e* can drop to values as low as 3% for highly inefficient activities like shoveling, which involves many starts and stops. Finally, it is interesting in comparison to the average results of Table 12.6 that a superbly conditioned athlete, efficiently coupled to a mechanical device for extracting power (a bike!), can supply a power of around 300 W for about 30 minutes at a peak efficiency of 22%.

Table 12.6 Metabolic Rate, Power Output, and Efficiency for Different Activities[a]

Activity	Metabolic Rate $\dfrac{\Delta U}{\Delta t}$ (watts)	Power Output $\dfrac{W}{\Delta t}$ (watts)	Efficiency *e*
Cycling	505	96	0.19
Pushing loaded coal cars in a mine	525	90	0.17
Shoveling	570	17.5	0.03

[a]*Source:* "Inter- and Intra-Individual Differences in Energy Expenditure and Mechanical Efficiency," C. H. Wyndham et al., *Ergonomics* **9**, 17 (1966).

■ SUMMARY

12.1 Work in Thermodynamic Processes

The work done on a gas at a constant pressure is

$$W = -P\Delta V \qquad [12.1]$$

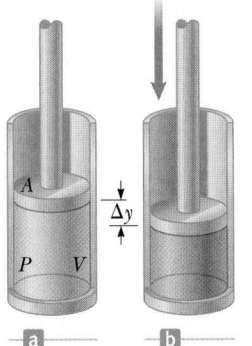

Positive work is done on a gas by compressing it.

The work done on the gas is positive if the gas is compressed (ΔV is negative) and negative if the gas expands (ΔV is positive). In general, the work done on a gas that takes it from some initial state to some final state is the negative of the area under the curve on a PV diagram.

12.2 The First Law of Thermodynamics

According to the first law of thermodynamics, when a system undergoes a change from one state to another, the **change in its internal energy** ΔU is

$$\Delta U = U_f - U_i = Q + W \qquad [12.2]$$

where Q is the energy exchanged across the boundary between the system and the environment and W is the work done on the system. The quantity Q is positive when energy is transferred into the system by heating and negative when energy is removed from the system by cooling. W is positive when work is done on the system (for example, by compression) and negative when the system does positive work on its environment.

$$W = -P\Delta V \qquad W_{\text{env}} = -W = P\Delta V = P(A\Delta x) = F\Delta x$$

Illustration of the first law of thermodynamics.

The change of the internal energy, ΔU, of an ideal gas is given by

$$\Delta U = nC_v\Delta T \qquad [12.5]$$

where C_v is the molar specific heat at constant volume.

12.3 Thermal Processes

An **isobaric process** is one that occurs at constant pressure. The work done on the system in such a process is $-P\,\Delta V$, whereas the thermal energy transferred by heat is given by

$$Q = nC_p\Delta T \qquad [12.6]$$

with the molar heat capacity at constant pressure given by $C_p = C_v + R$.

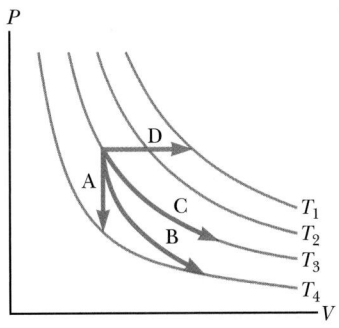

Four gas processes: A is an isochoric process (constant volume); B is an adiabatic expansion (no thermal energy transfer); C is an isothermal process (constant temperature); D is an isobaric process (constant pressure).

In an **adiabatic process** no energy is transferred by heat between the system and its surroundings ($Q = 0$). In this case the first law gives $\Delta U = W$, which means the internal energy changes solely as a consequence of work being done on the system. The pressure and volume in adiabatic processes are related by

$$PV^\gamma = \text{constant} \qquad [12.8a]$$

where $\gamma = C_p/C_v$ is the adiabatic index.

In an **isovolumetric process** the volume doesn't change and no work is done. For such processes, the first law gives $\Delta U = Q$.

An **isothermal process** occurs at constant temperature. The work done by an ideal gas on the environment is

$$W_{\text{env}} = nRT \ln\left(\frac{V_f}{V_i}\right) \qquad [12.10]$$

12.4 Heat Engines and the Second Law of Thermodynamics

In a **cyclic process** (in which the system returns to its initial state), $\Delta U = 0$ and therefore $Q = W_{\text{eng}}$, meaning the energy transferred into the system by heat equals the work done on the system during the cycle.

A **heat engine** takes in energy by heat and partially converts it to other forms of energy, such as mechanical and electrical energy. The work W_{eng} done by a heat engine in carrying a working substance through a cyclic process ($\Delta U = 0$) is

$$W_{\text{eng}} = |Q_h| - |Q_c| \qquad [12.11]$$

where Q_h is the energy absorbed from a hot reservoir and Q_c is the energy expelled to a cold reservoir.

The **thermal efficiency** of a heat engine is defined as the ratio of the work done by the engine to the energy transferred into the engine per cycle:

$$e \equiv \frac{W_{\text{eng}}}{|Q_h|} = 1 - \frac{|Q_c|}{|Q_h|} \qquad [12.12]$$

The engine does work W_{eng}.

Schematic diagram of a heat engine.

Energy Q_h enters the engine.

Energy Q_c leaves the engine.

Heat pumps are heat engines in reverse. In a refrigerator the heat pump removes thermal energy from inside the refrigerator. Heat pumps operating in cooling mode have coefficient of performance given by

$$\text{COP(cooling mode)} = \frac{|Q_c|}{W} \qquad \textbf{[12.13]}$$

A heat pump in heating mode has coefficient of performance

$$\text{COP(heating mode)} = \frac{|Q_h|}{W} \qquad \textbf{[12.14]}$$

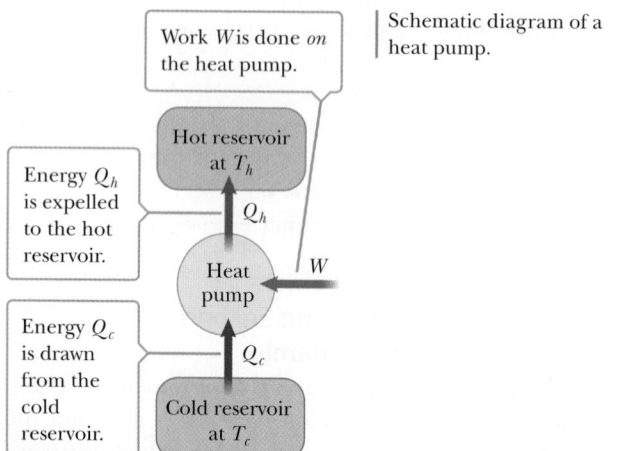

Work W is done *on* the heat pump.

Schematic diagram of a heat pump.

Energy Q_h is expelled to the hot reservoir.

Energy Q_c is drawn from the cold reservoir.

Real processes proceed in an order governed by the **second law of thermodynamics,** which can be stated in two ways:

1. Energy will not flow spontaneously by heat from a cold object to a hot object.

2. No heat engine operating in a cycle can absorb energy from a reservoir and perform an equal amount of work.

No real heat engine operating between the Kelvin temperatures T_h and T_c can exceed the efficiency of an engine operating between the same two temperatures in a **Carnot cycle,** given by

$$e_C = 1 - \frac{T_c}{T_h} \qquad \textbf{[12.16]}$$

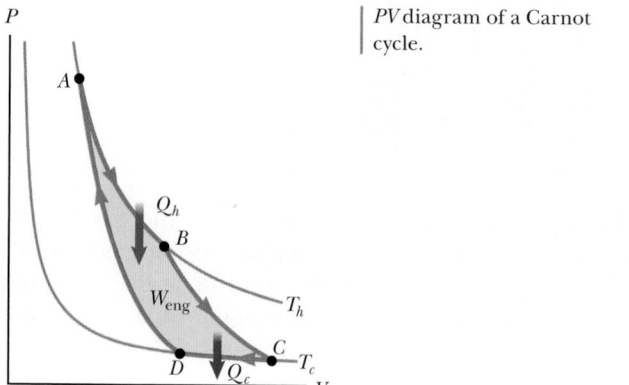

PV diagram of a Carnot cycle.

Perfect efficiency of a Carnot engine requires a cold reservoir of 0 K, absolute zero. According to the **third law of thermodynamics,** however, it is impossible to lower the temperature of a system to absolute zero in a finite number of steps.

12.5 Entropy

The second law can also be stated in terms of a quantity called **entropy** (S). The **change in entropy** of a system is equal to the energy Q_r flowing by heat into (or out of) the system as the system changes from one state to another by a reversible process, divided by the absolute temperature:

$$\Delta S \equiv \frac{Q_r}{T} \qquad \textbf{[12.17]}$$

One of the primary findings of statistical mechanics is that systems tend toward disorder, and entropy is a measure of that disorder. An alternate statement of the second law is that the entropy of the Universe increases in all natural processes.

■ MULTIPLE-CHOICE QUESTIONS

WebAssign The multiple-choice questions in this chapter may be assigned online in Enhanced WebAssign.

1. A monatomic ideal gas expands from 1.00 m³ to 2.50 m³ at a constant pressure of 2.00×10^5 Pa. Find the change in the internal energy of the gas. (a) 7.50×10^5 J (b) 1.05×10^6 J (c) 4.50×10^5 J (d) 3.00×10^5 J (e) -4.50×10^5 J

2. A 2.0-mole ideal gas system is maintained at a constant volume of 4.0 liters. If 100 J of thermal energy is transferred to the system, what is the change in the internal energy of the system? (a) 0 (b) 400 J (c) 70 J (d) 100 J (e) -0.100 J

3. An ideal gas is maintained at a constant pressure of 70.0 kPa during an isobaric process while its volume decreases by 0.20 m³. What is the work done by the system on its environment? (a) 14 kJ (b) 35 kJ (c) −14 kJ (d) −35 kJ (e) −72 kJ

4. How much net work is done by the gas undergoing the cyclic process illustrated in Figure MCQ12.4? Choose the best estimate. (a) 1×10^5 J (b) 2×10^5 J (c) 3×10^5 J (d) 4×10^5 J (e) 5×10^5 Pa

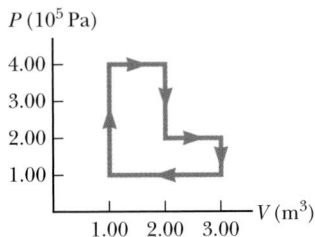

$P\,(10^5\,\text{Pa})$

4.00
3.00
2.00
1.00

1.00 2.00 3.00 $V\,(\text{m}^3)$

Figure MCQ12.4

5. A diatomic ideal gas expands adiabatically from a volume of 1.00 m³ to a final volume of 3.50 m³. If the initial pressure is 1.00×10^5 Pa, what is the final pressure? (a) 6.62×10^4 Pa (b) 1.24×10^5 Pa (c) 3.54×10^4 Pa (d) 2.33×10^4 Pa (e) 1.73×10^4 Pa

6. An ideal gas drives a piston as it expands from 1.00 m³ to 2.00 m³ at a constant temperature of 850 K. If there are 390 moles of gas in the piston, how much work does the gas do in displacing the piston? (a) 1.9×10^6 J (b) 2.5×10^6 J (c) 4.7×10^6 J (d) 2.1×10^5 J (e) 3.5×10^6 J

7. An engine does 15 kJ of work while rejecting 37 kJ to the cold reservoir. What is the efficiency of the engine? (a) 0.15 (b) 0.29 (c) 0.33 (d) 0.45 (e) 1.2

8. A refrigerator does 18 kJ of work while moving 115 kJ of thermal energy from inside the refrigerator. What is its coefficient of performance? (a) 3.4 (b) 2.8 (c) 8.9 (d) 6.4 (e) 5.2

9. If an ideal gas is compressed isothermally, which of the following statements is true? (a) Energy is transferred to the gas by heat. (b) No work is done on the gas. (c) The temperature of the gas increases. (d) The internal energy of the gas remains constant. (e) None of those statements is true.

10. A 1.00-kg block of ice at 0°C and 1.0 atm melts completely to water at 0°C. Calculate the change of the entropy of the ice during the melting process. (For ice, $L_f = 3.33 \times 10^5$ J/kg.) (a) 3 340 J/K (b) 2 170 J/K (c) −3 340 J/K (d) 1 220 J/K (e) −1 220 J/K

11. A steam turbine operates at a boiler temperature of 450 K and an exhaust temperature of 3.0×10^2 K.

What is the maximum theoretical efficiency of this system? (a) 0.24 (b) 0.50 (c) 0.33 (d) 0.67 (e) 0.15

12. When an ideal gas undergoes an adiabatic expansion, which of the following statements is true? (a) The temperature of the gas doesn't change. (b) No work is done by the gas. (c) No energy is delivered to the gas by heat. (d) The internal energy of the gas doesn't change. (e) The pressure increases.

13. If an ideal gas undergoes an isobaric process, which of the following statements is true? (a) The temperature of the gas doesn't change. (b) Work is done on or by the gas. (c) No energy is transferred by heat to or from the gas. (d) The volume of the gas remains the same. (e) The pressure of the gas decreases uniformly.

14. Two different ideal gases, designated A and B, occupy flasks with identical volumes. They have the same initial pressures and temperatures. The same amount of thermal energy Q is transferred to each of them. The final pressure of gas A is greater than the final pressure of gas B. Which of the following statements could explain the discrepancy? (a) Gas A is monatomic; gas B is diatomic. (b) Gas A is diatomic; gas B is monatomic. (c) There are more moles of gas A than gas B. (d) There are more moles of gas B than of gas A. (e) The molar specific heat of gas A is less than that of gas B.

15. An ideal gas is compressed to half its initial volume by means of several possible processes. Which of the following processes results in the most work done on the gas? (a) isothermal (b) adiabatic (c) isobaric (d) The work done is independent of the process.

16. A thermodynamic process occurs in which the entropy of a system changes by −6 J/K. According to the second law of thermodynamics, what can you conclude about the entropy change of the environment? (a) It must be +6 J/K or less. (b) It must be equal to 6 J/K. (c) It must be between 6 J/K and 0. (d) It must be 0. (e) It must be +6 J/K or more.

17. When sufficient thermal energy is added to a substance such as lead, it melts. What happens to the entropy of the substance as it melts? (a) It remains the same. (b) It increases. (c) It decreases. (d) It may increase or decrease, depending on the mass of the substance. (e) It may increase or decrease depending on the process used.

18. A window air conditioner is placed on a table inside a well-insulated apartment, plugged in and turned on. What happens to the average temperature of the apartment? (a) It increases. (b) It decreases. (c) It remains constant. (d) It increases until the unit warms up and then decreases. (e) The answer depends on the initial temperature of the apartment.

■ CONCEPTUAL QUESTIONS

WebAssign The conceptual questions in this chapter may be assigned online in Enhanced WebAssign.

1. What are some factors that affect the efficiency of automobile engines?

2. If you shake a jar full of jelly beans of different sizes, the larger beans tend to appear near the top and the smaller ones tend to fall to the bottom. (a) Why does that occur? (b) Does this process violate the second law of thermodynamics?

3. **BIO** Consider the human body performing a strenuous exercise, such as lifting weights or riding a bicycle. Work is being done by the body, and energy is leaving by conduction from the skin into the surrounding air. According to the first law of thermodynamics, the temperature of the body should be steadily decreasing during the exercise. That isn't what happens, however. Is the first law invalid for this situation? Explain.

4. Clearly distinguish among temperature, heat, and internal energy.

5. For an ideal gas in an isothermal process, there is no change in internal energy. Suppose the gas does work W during such a process. How much energy is transferred by heat?

6. A steam-driven turbine is one major component of an electric power plant. Why is it advantageous to increase the temperature of the steam as much as possible?

7. Is it possible to construct a heat engine that creates no thermal pollution?

8. In solar ponds constructed in Israel, the Sun's energy is concentrated near the bottom of a salty pond. With the proper layering of salt in the water, convection is prevented and temperatures of $100°C$ may be reached. Can you guess the maximum efficiency with which useful mechanical work can be extracted from the pond?

9. When a sealed Thermos bottle full of hot coffee is shaken, what changes, if any, take place in (a) the temperature of the coffee and (b) its internal energy?

10. Give some examples of irreversible processes that occur in nature. Give an example of a process in nature that is nearly reversible.

11. The first law of thermodynamics says we can't get more out of a process than we put in, but the second law says that we can't break even. Explain this statement.

12. If a supersaturated sugar solution is allowed to evaporate slowly, sugar crystals form in the container. Hence, sugar molecules go from a disordered form (in solution) to a highly ordered, crystalline form. Does this process violate the second law of thermodynamics? Explain.

13. Using the first law of thermodynamics, explain why the *total* energy of an isolated system is always constant.

14. What is wrong with the following statement: "Given any two bodies, the one with the higher temperature contains more heat."

■ PROBLEMS

WebAssign The problems in this chapter may be assigned online in Enhanced WebAssign. Selected problems also have Watch It video solutions.

1. denotes straightforward problem; 2. denotes intermediate problem;

3. denotes challenging problem

[1.] denotes full solution available in *Student Solutions Manual/ Study Guide*

1. denotes problems most often assigned in Enhanced WebAssign

BIO denotes biomedical problems

GP denotes guided problems

M denotes Master It tutorial available in Enhanced WebAssign

Q|C denotes asking for quantitative and conceptual reasoning

S denotes symbolic reasoning problem

12.1 Work in Thermodynamic Processes

1. **Q|C** An ideal gas is enclosed in a cylinder with a movable piston on top of it. The piston has a mass of 8 000 g and an area of 5.00 cm^2 and is free to slide up and down, keeping the pressure of the gas constant. (a) How much work is done on the gas as the temperature of 0.200 mol of the gas is raised from $20.0°C$ to $300°C$? (b) What does the sign of your answer to part (a) indicate?

2. Sketch a *PV* diagram and find the work done by the gas during the following stages. (a) A gas is expanded from a volume of 1.0 L to 3.0 L at a constant pressure of 3.0 atm. (b) The gas is then cooled at constant volume until the pressure falls to 2.0 atm. (c) The gas is then compressed at a constant pressure of 2.0 atm from a volume of 3.0 L to 1.0 L. *Note:* Be careful of signs. (d) The gas is heated until its pressure increases from 2.0 atm to 3.0 atm at a constant volume. (e) Find the net work done during the complete cycle.

3. **M** Gas in a container is at a pressure of 1.5 atm and a volume of 4.0 m^3. What is the work done *on* the gas (a) if it expands at constant pressure to twice its initial volume, and (b) if it is compressed at constant pressure to one-quarter its initial volume?

4. A 40.0-g projectile is launched by the expansion of hot gas in an arrangement shown in Figure P12.4a. The cross-sectional area of the launch tube is 1.0 cm², and the length that the projectile travels down the tube after starting from rest is 32 cm. As the gas expands, the pressure varies as shown in Figure P12.4b. The values for the initial pressure and volume are $P_i = 11 \times 10^5$ Pa and $V_i = 8.0$ cm³ while the final values are $P_f = 1.0 \times 10^5$ Pa and $V_f = 40.0$ cm³. Friction between the projectile and the launch tube is negligible. (a) If the projectile is launched into a vacuum, what is the speed of the projectile as it leaves the launch tube? (b) If instead the projectile is launched into air at a pressure of 1.0×10^5 Pa, what fraction of the work done by the expanding gas in the tube is spent by the projectile pushing air out of the way as it proceeds down the tube?

Figure P12.4

5. A gas expands from *I* to *F* along the three paths indicated in Figure P12.5. Calculate the work done *on* the gas along paths (a) *IAF*, (b) *IF*, and (c) *IBF*.

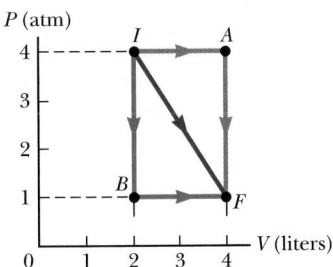

Figure P12.5 Problems 5 and 13.

6. Sketch a *PV* diagram of the following processes: (a) A gas expands at constant pressure P_1 from volume V_1 to volume V_2. It is then kept at constant volume while the pressure is reduced to P_2. (b) A gas is reduced in pressure from P_1 to P_2 while its volume is held constant at V_1. It is then expanded at constant pressure P_2 to a final volume V_2. (c) In which of the processes is more work done *by* the gas? Why?

7. A sample of helium behaves as an ideal gas as it is heated at constant pressure from 273 K to 373 K. If 20.0 J of work is done by the gas during this process, what is the mass of helium present?

8. (a) Find the work done *by* an ideal gas as it expands from point *A* to point *B* along the path shown in Figure P12.8. (b) How much work is done by the gas if it compressed from *B* to *A* along the same path?

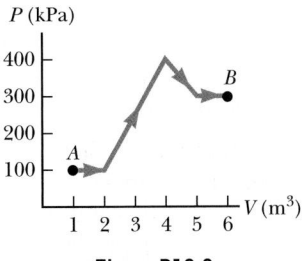

Figure P12.8

9. One mole of an ideal gas initially at a temperature of $T_i = 0°C$ undergoes an expansion at a constant pressure of 1.00 atm to four times its original volume. (a) Calculate the new temperature T_f of the gas. (b) Calculate the work done *on* the gas during the expansion.

10. (a) Determine the work done *on* a fluid that expands from *i* to *f* as indicated in Figure P12.10. (b) How much work is done *on* the fluid if it is compressed from *f* to *i* along the same path?

Figure P12.10

12.2 The First Law of Thermodynamics

12.3 Thermal Processes

11. **S** The only form of energy possessed by molecules of a monatomic ideal gas is translational kinetic energy. Using the results from the discussion of kinetic theory in Section 10.5, show that the internal energy of a monatomic ideal gas at pressure *P* and occupying volume *V* may be written as $U = \frac{3}{2}PV$.

12. **GP** A cylinder of volume 0.300 m³ contains 10.0 mol of neon gas at 20.0°C. Assume neon behaves as an ideal gas. (a) What is the pressure of the gas? (b) Find the internal energy of the gas. (c) Suppose the gas expands at constant pressure to a volume of 1.000 m³. How much work is done on the gas? (d) What is the temperature of the gas at the new volume? (e) Find the internal energy of the gas when its volume is 1.000 m³. (f) Compute the change in the internal energy during the expansion. (g) Compute $\Delta U - W$. (h) Must thermal energy be transferred to the gas during the constant pressure expansion or be taken away? (i) Compute *Q*, the thermal energy transfer. (j) What symbolic relationship between *Q*, ΔU, and *W* is suggested by the values obtained?

13. **M** A gas expands from *I* to *F* in Figure P12.5. The energy added to the gas by heat is 418 J when the gas

goes from I to F along the diagonal path. (a) What is the change in internal energy of the gas? (b) How much energy must be added to the gas by heat for the indirect path IAF to give the same change in internal energy?

14. **Q|C** In a running event, a sprinter does 4.8×10^5 J of work and her internal energy decreases by 7.5×10^5 J. (a) Determine the heat transferred between her body and surroundings during this event. (b) What does the sign of your answer to part (a) indicate?

15. A gas is compressed at a constant pressure of 0.800 atm from 9.00 L to 2.00 L. In the process, 400 J of energy leaves the gas by heat. (a) What is the work done *on* the gas? (b) What is the change in its internal energy?

16. A quantity of a monatomic ideal gas undergoes a process in which both its pressure and volume are doubled as shown in Figure P12.16. What is the energy absorbed by heat into the gas during this process? *Hint:* The internal energy of a monatomic ideal gas at pressure P and occupying volume V is given by $U = \frac{3}{2}PV$.

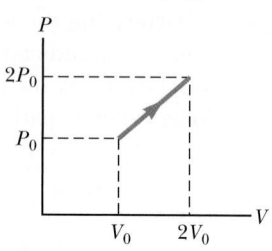
Figure P12.16

17. A gas is enclosed in a container fitted with a piston of cross-sectional area 0.150 m². The pressure of the gas is maintained at 6 000 Pa as the piston moves inward 20.0 cm. (a) Calculate the work done by the gas. (b) If the internal energy of the gas decreases by 8.00 J, find the amount of energy removed from the system by heat during the compression.

18. A monatomic ideal gas undergoes the thermodynamic process shown in the *PV* diagram of Figure P12.18. Determine whether each of the values ΔU, Q, and W for the gas is positive, negative, or zero. *Hint:* The internal energy of a monatomic ideal gas at pressure P and occupying volume V is given by $U = \frac{3}{2}PV$.

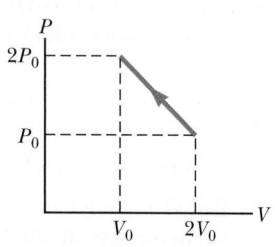
Figure P12.18

19. **Q|C** An ideal gas is compressed from a volume of $V_i = 5.00$ L to a volume of $V_f = 3.00$ L while in thermal contact with a heat reservoir at $T = 295$ K as in Figure P12.19. During the compression process, the piston moves down a distance of $d = 0.130$ m under the action of an average external force of

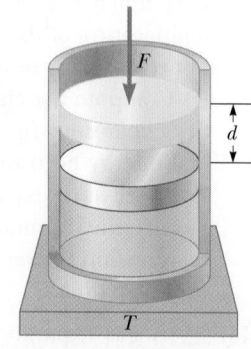
Figure P12.19

$F = 25.0$ kN. Find (a) the work done on the gas, (b) the change in internal energy of the gas, and (c) the thermal energy exchanged between the gas and the reservoir. (d) If the gas is thermally insulated so no thermal energy could be exchanged, what would happen to the temperature of the gas during the compression?

20. A system consisting of 0.025 6 moles of a diatomic ideal gas is taken from state A to state C along the path in Figure P12.20. (a) How much work is done *on* the gas during this process? (b) What is the lowest temperature of the gas during this process, and where does it occur? (c) Find the change in internal energy of the gas and (d) the energy delivered to the gas in going from A to C. *Hint:* For part (c), adapt the equation in the remarks of Example 12.9 to a diatomic ideal gas.

Figure P12.20

21. An ideal monatomic gas expands isothermally from 0.500 m³ to 1.25 m³ at a constant temperature of 675 K. If the initial pressure is 1.00×10^5 Pa, find (a) the work done on the gas, (b) the thermal energy transfer Q, and (c) the change in the internal energy.

22. **S** An ideal gas expands at constant pressure. (a) Show that $P\Delta V = nR\Delta T$. (b) If the gas is monatomic, start from the definition of internal energy and show that $\Delta U = \frac{3}{2}W_{env}$, where W_{env} is the work done by the gas on its environment. (c) For the same monatomic ideal gas, show with the first law that $Q = \frac{5}{2}W_{env}$. (d) Is it possible for an ideal gas to expand at constant pressure while exhausting thermal energy? Explain.

23. **GP** An ideal monatomic gas is contained in a vessel of *constant* volume 0.200 m³. The initial temperature and pressure of the gas are 300 K and 5.00 atm, respectively. The goal of this problem is to find the temperature and pressure of the gas after 16.0 kJ of thermal energy is supplied to the gas. (a) Use the ideal gas law and initial conditions to calculate the number of moles of gas in the vessel. (b) Find the specific heat of the gas. (c) What is the work done by the gas during this process? (d) Use the first law of thermodynamics to find the change in internal energy of the gas. (e) Find the change in temperature of the gas. (f) Calculate the final temperature of the gas. (g) Use the ideal gas expression to find the final pressure of the gas.

24. Consider the cyclic process described by Figure P12.24. If Q is negative for the process BC and ΔU is negative

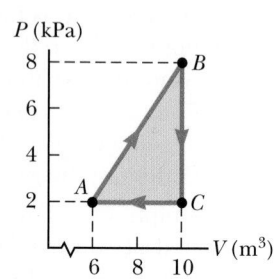
Figure P12.24

for the process *CA*, determine the signs of *Q*, *W*, and Δ*U* associated with each process.

25. A 5.0-kg block of aluminum is heated from 20°C to 90°C at atmospheric pressure. Find (a) the work done by the aluminum, (b) the amount of energy transferred to it by heat, and (c) the increase in its internal energy.

26. One mole of gas initially at a pressure of 2.00 atm and a volume of 0.300 L has an internal energy equal to 91.0 J. In its final state, the gas is at a pressure of 1.50 atm and a volume of 0.800 L, and its internal energy equals 182 J. For the paths *IAF*, *IBF*, and *IF* in Figure P12.26, calculate (a) the work done *on* the gas and (b) the net energy transferred to the gas by heat in the process.

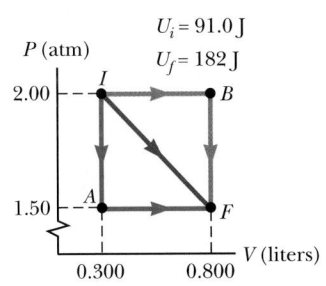

Figure P12.26

27. **S** Consider the Universe to be an adiabatic expansion of atomic hydrogen gas. (a) Use the ideal gas law and Equation 12.8a to show that $TV^{\gamma-1} = C$, where *C* is a constant. (b) The current Universe extends at least 15 billion light-years in all directions (1.4×10^{26} m), and the current temperature of the Universe is 2.7 K. Estimate the temperature of the Universe when it was the size of a nutshell, with a radius of 2 cm. (For this calculation, assume the Universe is spherical.)

28. Suppose the Universe is considered to be an ideal gas of hydrogen atoms expanding adiabatically. (a) If the density of the gas in the Universe is one hydrogen atom per cubic meter, calculate the number of moles per unit volume (n/V). (b) Calculate the pressure of the Universe, taking the temperature of the Universe as 2.7 K. (c) If the current radius of the Universe is 15 billion light-years (1.4×10^{26} m), find the pressure of the Universe when it was the size of a nutshell, with radius 2.0×10^{-2} m. Be careful: Calculator overflow can occur.

12.4 Heat Engines and the Second Law of Thermodynamics

29. A gas increases in pressure from 2.00 atm to 6.00 atm at a constant volume of 1.00 m³ and then expands at constant pressure to a volume of 3.00 m³ before returning to its initial state as shown in Figure P12.29. How much work is done in one cycle?

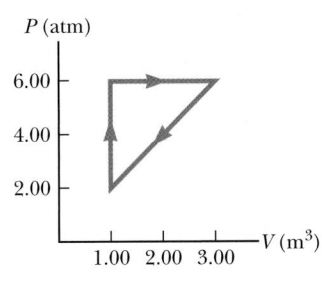

Figure P12.29

30. An ideal gas expands at a constant pressure of 6.00×10^5 Pa from a volume of 1.00 m³ to a volume of 4.00 m³

and then is compressed to one-third that pressure and a volume of 2.50 m³ as shown in Figure P12.30 before returning to its initial state. How much work is done in taking a gas through one cycle of the process shown in the figure?

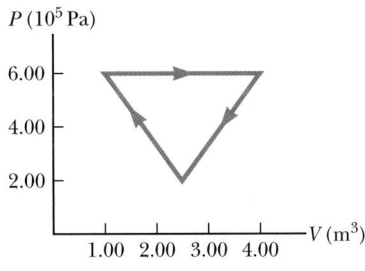

Figure P12.30

31. A heat engine operates between a reservoir at 25°C and one at 375°C. What is the maximum efficiency possible for this engine?

32. **QC** A heat engine is being designed to have a Carnot efficiency of 65% when operating between two heat reservoirs. (a) If the temperature of the cold reservoir is 20°C, what must be the temperature of the hot reservoir? (b) Can the actual efficiency of the engine be equal to 65%? Explain.

33. The work done by an engine equals one-fourth the energy it absorbs from a reservoir. (a) What is its thermal efficiency? (b) What fraction of the energy absorbed is expelled to the cold reservoir?

34. In each cycle of its operation, a heat engine expels 2 400 J of energy and performs 1 800 J of mechanical work. (a) How much thermal energy must be added to the engine in each cycle? (b) Find the thermal efficiency of the engine.

35. One of the most efficient engines ever built is a coal-fired steam turbine engine in the Ohio River valley, driving an electric generator as it operates between 1 870°C and 430°C. (a) What is its maximum theoretical efficiency? (b) Its actual efficiency is 42.0%. How much mechanical power does the engine deliver if it absorbs 1.40×10^5 J of energy each second from the hot reservoir.

36. A gun is a heat engine. In particular, it is an internal combustion piston engine that does not operate in a cycle, but comes apart during its adiabatic expansion process. A certain gun consists of 1.80 kg of iron. It fires one 2.40-g bullet at 320 m/s with an energy efficiency of 1.10%. Assume the body of the gun absorbs all the energy exhaust and increases uniformly in temperature for a short time before it loses any energy by heat into the environment. Find its temperature increase.

37. An engine absorbs 1.70 kJ from a hot reservoir at 277°C and expels 1.20 kJ to a cold reservoir at 27°C in each

cycle. (a) What is the engine's efficiency? (b) How much work is done by the engine in each cycle? (c) What is the power output of the engine if each cycle lasts 0.300 s?

38. A heat pump has a coefficient of performance of 3.80 and operates with a power consumption of 7.03×10^3 W. (a) How much energy does the heat pump deliver into a home during 8.00 h of continuous operation? (b) How much energy does it extract from the outside air in 8.00 h?

39. A freezer has a coefficient of performance of 6.30. The freezer is advertised as using 457 kW-h/y. (a) On average, how much energy does the freezer use in a single day? (b) On average, how much thermal energy is removed from the freezer each day? (c) What maximum mass of water at 20.0°C could the freezer freeze in a single day? *Note:* One kilowatt-hour (kW-h) is an amount of energy equal to operating a 1-kW appliance for one hour.

40. **Q|C** Suppose an ideal (Carnot) heat pump could be constructed. (a) Using Equation 12.15, obtain an expression for the coefficient of performance for such a heat pump in terms of T_h and T_c. (b) Would such a heat pump work better if the difference in the operating temperatures were greater or were smaller? (c) Compute the coefficient of performance for such a heat pump if the cold reservoir is 50.0°C and indoor temperature is 70.0°C.

41. In one cycle a heat engine absorbs 500 J from a high-temperature reservoir and expels 300 J to a low-temperature reservoir. If the efficiency of this engine is 60% of the efficiency of a Carnot engine, what is the ratio of the low temperature to the high temperature in the Carnot engine?

42. **Q|C** A power plant has been proposed that would make use of the temperature gradient in the ocean. The system is to operate between 20.0°C (surface water temperature) and 5.00°C (water temperature at a depth of about 1 km). (a) What is the maximum efficiency of such a system? (b) If the useful power output of the plant is 75.0 MW, how much energy is absorbed per hour? (c) In view of your answer to part (a), do you think such a system is worthwhile (considering that there is no charge for fuel)?

43. A certain nuclear power plant has an electrical power output of 435 MW. The rate at which energy must be supplied to the plant is 1 420 MW. (a) What is the thermal efficiency of the power plant? (b) At what rate is thermal energy expelled by the plant?

44. **M** A heat engine operates in a Carnot cycle between 80.0°C and 350°C. It absorbs 21 000 J of energy per cycle from the hot reservoir. The duration of each cycle is 1.00 s. (a) What is the mechanical power output of this engine? (b) How much energy does it expel in each cycle by heat?

12.5 Entropy

45. A Styrofoam cup holding 125 g of hot water at 1.00×10^2°C cools to room temperature, 20.0°C. What is the change in entropy of the room? (Neglect the specific heat of the cup and any change in temperature of the room.)

46. A 65-g ice cube is initially at 0.0°C. (a) Find the change in entropy of the cube after it melts completely at 0.0°C. (b) What is the change in entropy of the environment in this process? *Hint:* The latent heat of fusion for water is 3.33×10^5 J/kg.

47. A freezer is used to freeze 1.0 L of water completely into ice. The water and the freezer remain at a constant temperature of $T = 0$°C. Determine (a) the change in the entropy of the water and (b) the change in the entropy of the freezer.

48. What is the change in entropy of 1.00 kg of liquid water at 100°C as it changes to steam at 100°C?

49. A 70.0-kg log falls from a height of 25.0 m into a lake. If the log, the lake, and the air are all at 300 K, find the change in entropy of the Universe during this process.

50. If you roll a pair of dice, what is the total number of ways in which you can obtain (a) a 12? (b) a 7?

51. **M** The surface of the Sun is approximately at 5 700 K, and the temperature of the Earth's surface is approximately 290 K. What entropy change occurs when 1 000 J of energy is transferred by heat from the Sun to the Earth?

52. **Q|C** When an aluminum bar is temporarily connected between a hot reservoir at 725 K and a cold reservoir at 310 K, 2.50 kJ of energy is transferred by heat from the hot reservoir to the cold reservoir. In this irreversible process, calculate the change in entropy of (a) the hot reservoir, (b) the cold reservoir, and (c) the Universe, neglecting any change in entropy of the aluminum rod. (d) Mathematically, why did the result for the Universe in part (c) have to be positive?

53. Prepare a table like Table 12.3 for the following occurrence: You toss four coins into the air simultaneously and record all the possible results of the toss in terms of the numbers of heads and tails that can result. (For example, HHTH and HTHH are two possible ways in which three heads and one tail can be achieved.) (a) On the basis of your table, what is the most probable result of a toss? In terms of entropy, (b) what is the most ordered state, and (c) what is the most disordered?

54. **S** *This is a symbolic version of Problem 52.* When a metal bar is temporarily connected between a hot reservoir at T_h and a cold reservoir at T_c, the energy transferred by heat from the hot reservoir to the cold reservoir is Q_h. In this irreversible process, find expressions for the change in entropy of (a) the hot reservoir, (b) the cold reservoir, and (c) the Universe.

12.6 Human Metabolism

55. On a typical day, a 65-kg man sleeps for 8.0 h, does light chores for 3.0 h, walks slowly for 1.0 h, and jogs at moderate pace for 0.5 h. What is the change in his internal energy for all these activities?

56. **BIO** **QC** A weightlifter has a basal metabolic rate of 80.0 W. As he is working out, his metabolic rate increases by about 650 W. (a) How many hours does it take him to work off a 450-Calorie bagel if he stays in bed all day? (b) How long does it take him if he's working out? (c) Calculate the amount of mechanical work necessary to lift a 120-kg barbell 2.00 m. (d) He drops the barbell to the floor and lifts it repeatedly. How many times per minute must he repeat this process to do an amount of mechanical work equivalent to his metabolic rate increase of 650 W during exercise? (e) Could he actually do repetitions at the rate found in part (d) at the given metabolic level? Explain.

57. **BIO** Sweating is one of the main mechanisms with which the body dissipates heat. Sweat evaporates with a latent heat of 2 430 kJ/kg at body temperature, and the body can produce as much as 1.5 kg of sweat per hour. If sweating were the only heat dissipation mechanism, what would be the maximum sustainable metabolic rate, in watts, if 80% of the energy used by the body goes into waste heat?

Additional Problems

58. A Carnot engine operates between the temperatures $T_h = 100°C$ and $T_c = 20°C$. By what factor does the theoretical efficiency increase if the temperature of the hot reservoir is increased to 550°C?

59. A 1 500-kW heat engine operates at 25% efficiency. The heat energy expelled at the low temperature is absorbed by a stream of water that enters the cooling coils at 20°C. If 60 L flows across the coils per second, determine the increase in temperature of the water.

60. A Carnot engine operates between 100°C and 20°C. How much ice can the engine melt from its exhaust after it has done 5.0×10^4 J of work?

61. A substance undergoes the cyclic process shown in Figure P12.61. Work output occurs along path AB while work input is required along path BC, and no work is involved in the constant volume process CA. Energy transfers by heat occur during each process involved in

the cycle. (a) What is the work output during process AB? (b) How much work input is required during process BC? (c) What is the net energy input Q during this cycle?

62. When a gas follows path 123 on the PV diagram in Figure P12.62, 418 J of energy flows into the system by heat and -167 J of work is done *on the gas*. (a) What is the change in the internal energy of the system? (b) How much energy Q flows into the system if the gas follows path 143? The work done on the gas along this path is -63.0 J. What net work would be done on or by the system if the system followed (c) path 12341 and (d) path 14321? (e) What is the change in internal energy of the system in the processes described in parts (c) and (d)?

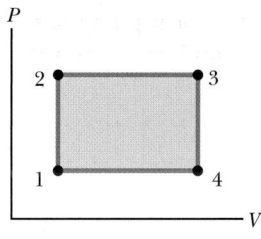

Figure P12.62

63. A 100-kg steel support rod in a building has a length of 2.0 m at a temperature of 20°C. The rod supports a hanging load of 6 000 kg. Find (a) the work done *on* the rod as the temperature increases to 40°C, (b) the energy Q added to the rod (assume the specific heat of steel is the same as that for iron), and (c) the change in internal energy of the rod.

64. **S** An ideal gas initially at pressure P_0, volume V_0, and temperature T_0 is taken through the cycle described in Figure P12.64. (a) Find the net work done *by* the gas per cycle in terms of P_0 and V_0. (b) What is the net energy Q added to the system per cycle? (c) Obtain a numerical value for the net work done per cycle for 1.00 mol of gas initially at 0°C. *Hint:* Recall that the work done by the system equals the area under a PV curve.

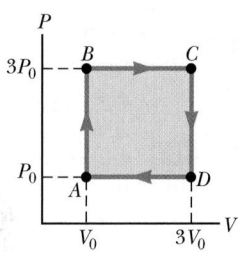

Figure P12.64

65. **M** One mole of neon gas is heated from 300 K to 420 K at constant pressure. Calculate (a) the energy Q transferred to the gas, (b) the change in the internal energy of the gas, and (c) the work done *on* the gas. Note that neon has a molar specific heat of $c = 20.79$ J/mol·K for a constant-pressure process.

66. Every second at Niagara Falls, approximately 5 000 m³ of water falls a distance of 50.0 m. What is the increase in entropy per second due to the falling water? Assume the mass of the surroundings is so great that its temperature and that of the water stay nearly constant at 20.0°C. Also assume a negligible amount of water evaporates.

67. A cylinder containing 10.0 moles of a monatomic ideal gas expands from Ⓐ to Ⓑ along the path shown in Figure P12.67. (a) Find the temperature of the gas at point

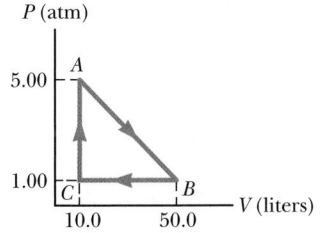

Figure P12.61

A and the temperature at point Ⓑ. (b) How much work is done by the gas during this expansion? (c) What is the change in internal energy of the gas? (d) Find the energy transferred to the gas by heat in this process.

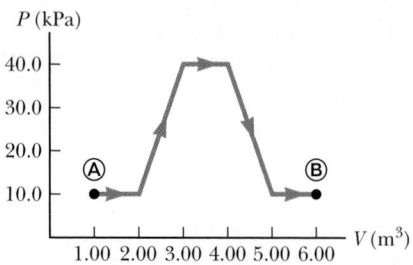

Figure P12.67

68. **GP** Two moles of molecular hydrogen (H_2) react with 1 mole of molecular oxygen (O_2) to produce 2 moles of water (H_2O) together with an energy release of 241.8 kJ/mole of water. Suppose a spherical vessel of radius 0.500 m contains 14.4 moles of H_2 and 7.2 moles of O_2 at 20.0°C. (a) What is the initial pressure in the vessel? (b) What is the initial internal energy of the gas? (c) Suppose a spark ignites the mixture and the gases burn completely into water vapor. How much energy is produced? (d) Find the temperature and pressure of the steam, assuming it's an ideal gas. (e) Find the mass of steam and then calculate the steam's density. (f) If a small hole were put in the sphere, what would be the initial exhaust velocity of the exhausted steam if spewed out into a vacuum? (Use Bernoulli's equation.)

69. **BIO** Suppose you spend 30.0 minutes on a stair-climbing machine, climbing at a rate of 90.0 steps per minute, with each step 8.00 inches high. If you weigh 150 lb and the machine reports that 600 kcal have been burned at the end of the workout, what efficiency is the machine using in obtaining this result? If your actual efficiency is 0.18, how many kcal did you actually burn?

70. **BIO** Hydrothermal vents deep on the ocean floor spout water at temperatures as high as 570°C. This temperature is below the boiling point of water because of the immense pressure at that depth. Because the surrounding ocean temperature is at 4.0°C, an organism could use the temperature gradient as a source of energy. (a) Assuming the specific heat of water under these conditions is 1.0 cal/g · °C, how much energy is released when 1.0 liter of water is cooled from 570°C to 4.0°C? (b) What is the maximum usable energy an organism can extract from this energy source? (Assume the organism has some internal type of heat engine acting between the two temperature extremes.) (c) Water from these vents contains hydrogen sulfide (H_2S) at a concentration of 0.90 mmole/liter. Oxidation of 1.0 mole of H_2S produces 310 kJ of energy. How much energy is available through H_2S oxidation of 1.0 L of water?

71. An electrical power plant has an overall efficiency of 15%. The plant is to deliver 150 MW of electrical power to a city, and its turbines use coal as fuel. The burning coal produces steam at 190°C, which drives the turbines. The steam is condensed into water at 25°C by passing through coils that are in contact with river water. (a) How many metric tons of coal does the plant consume each day (1 metric ton = 1×10^3 kg)? (b) What is the total cost of the fuel per year if the delivery price is $8 per metric ton? (c) If the river water is delivered at 20°C, at what minimum rate must it flow over the cooling coils so that its temperature doesn't exceed 25°C? *Note:* The heat of combustion of coal is 7.8×10^3 cal/g.

72. A diatomic ideal gas expands from a volume of $V_A = 1.00$ m^3 to $V_B = 3.00$ m^3 along the path shown in Figure P12.72. If the initial pressure is $P_A = 2.00 \times 10^5$ Pa and there are 87.5 mol of gas, calculate (a) the work done on the gas during this process, (b) the change in temperature of the gas, and (c) the change in internal energy of the gas. (d) How much thermal energy is transferred to the system?

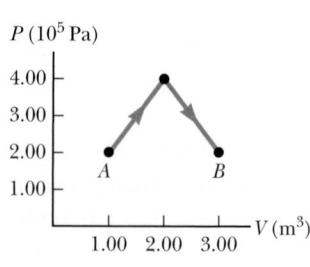

Figure P12.72

■ AP* REVIEW QUESTIONS

(A)

(B)

(C)

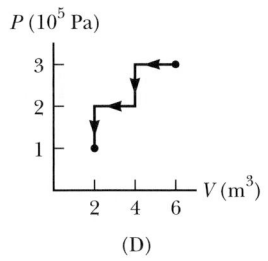

(D)

1. Rank the above *PV* diagrams in order of most negative work to most positive work.

(A) B, C = D, A

(B) B, C, A, D

(C) D, A, C, B

(D) A, C = D, B

(E) A = B = C = D

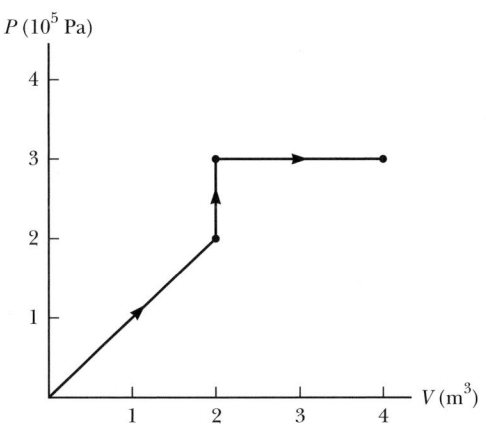

2. How much work is shown in the above *PV* diagram?

(A) -8.0×10^5 J

(B) $+8.0 \times 10^5$ J

(C) -10×10^5 J

(D) $+10 \times 10^5$ J

(E) More information is needed

3. An ideal gas undergoes an isobaric process while absorbing a small amount of heat. If the change in internal energy is large and positive, will work and change in volume be positive or negative?

(A) ΔV is positive, work is positive

(B) ΔV is positive, work is negative

(C) ΔV is negative, work is positive

(D) ΔV is negative, work is negative

(E) More information is needed

4. An ideal gas is held at a constant pressure of 2×10^5 Pa while 3000 J of heat is removed. If 5000 J of internal energy is lost during this process, what is the change in volume of the gas?

(A) $+0.04$ m^3

(B) -0.04 m^3

(C) $+0.01$ m^3

(D) -0.01 m^3

(E) More information is needed

5. An ideal gas undergoes an isovolumetric heating where 4000 J of heat is absorbed. What is the change in internal energy of the gas?

(A) -2000 J

(B) $+2000$ J

(C) -4000 J

(D) $+4000$ J

(E) More information is needed

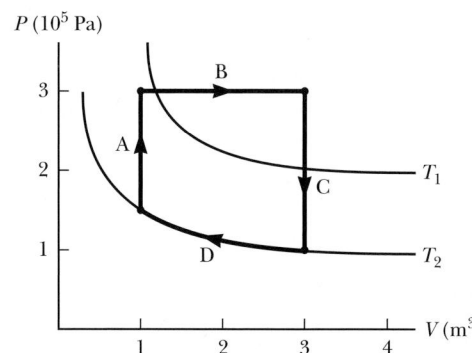

6. For the above diagram, identify what type of process is occurring for sections A, B, C and D.

(A) Isovolumetric, isothermal, isochoric, isothermal

(B) Isobaric, isovolumetric, isobaric, adiabatic

(C) Isovolumetric, isobaric, isovolumetric, adiabatic

(D) Isobaric, isovolumetric, isobaric, isothermal

(E) Isovolumetric, isobaric, isovolumetric, isothermal

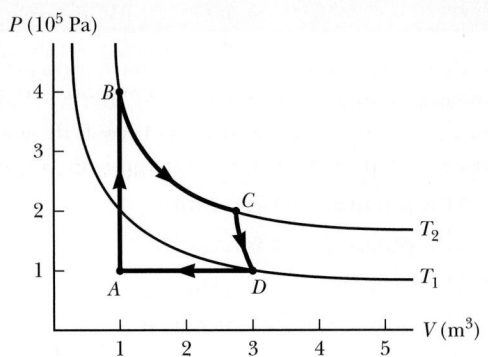

7. For the above *PV* diagram, what is the ratio of temperatures T_B to T_D?

(A) $\dfrac{2}{3}$

(B) $\dfrac{3}{4}$

(C) 1

(D) $\dfrac{4}{3}$

(E) More information is needed

8. An ideal gas, at a pressure of 1×10^5 Pa, a temperature of 20°C, and a volume of 2 m³ has its volume cut in half. If the gas gains 1×10^5 J of internal energy, what type of process occurred?

(A) Adiabatic

(B) Isobaric

(C) Isovolumetric

(D) Isothermal

(E) Isochoric

9. Most car engines operate with 27% efficiency. If during one cycle, the engine extracts 3000 J from the hot gas in the piston, how much work is done by the engine in each cycle?

(A) 111 J

(B) 810 J

(C) 11,000 J

(D) 81,000 J

(E) More information is needed

10. A power plant, operating with a Carnot efficiency of 40%, heats its steam to a temperature of 400°C. At what approximate temperature is the steam exhausted?

(A) −33°C

(B) 131°C

(C) 240°C

(D) 404°C

(E) 560°C

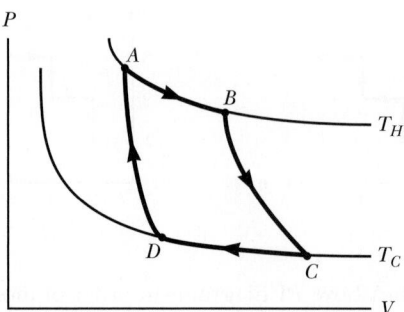

11. The above *PV* diagram shows a Carnot cycle. Where is the heat added to the engine in this cycle?

(A) *AB*

(B) *BC*

(C) *CD*

(D) *DA*

(E) More information is needed

12. One mole of ideal gas *A* has a pressure P_A, volume V_A, and temperature T_A. Five moles of ideal gas *B* has a pressure five times that of gas *A* and a temperature twice that of gas *A*. What is the ratio of V_A to V_B?

(A) $\dfrac{1}{40}$

(B) $\dfrac{2}{5}$

(C) $\dfrac{5}{2}$

(D) 40

(E) More information is needed

Image copyright Epic Stock. Used under license from Shutterstock.com

Ocean waves combine properties of both transverse and longitudinal waves. With proper balance and timing, a surfer can capture some of the wave's energy and take it for a ride.

Vibrations and Waves 13

Periodic motion, from masses on springs to vibrations of atoms, is one of the most important kinds of physical behavior. In this chapter we take a more detailed look at Hooke's law, where the force is proportional to the displacement, tending to restore objects to some equilibrium position. A large number of physical systems can be successfully modeled with this simple idea, including the vibrations of strings, the swinging of a pendulum, and the propagation of waves of all kinds. All these physical phenomena involve periodic motion.

Periodic vibrations can cause disturbances that move through a medium in the form of waves. Many kinds of waves occur in nature, such as sound waves, water waves, seismic waves, and electromagnetic waves. These very different physical phenomena are described by common terms and concepts introduced here.

◄ Hooke's law

13.1 Hooke's Law

One of the simplest types of vibrational motion is that of an object attached to a spring, previously discussed in the context of energy in Chapter 5. We assume the object moves on a frictionless horizontal surface. If the spring is stretched or compressed a small distance x from its unstretched or equilibrium position and then released, it exerts a force on the object as shown in Active Figure 13.1 (page 438). From experiment the spring force F_s is found to obey the equation

$$F_s = -kx \qquad [13.1]$$

where x is the displacement of the object from its equilibrium position ($x = 0$) and k is a positive constant called the **spring constant.** This force law for springs was

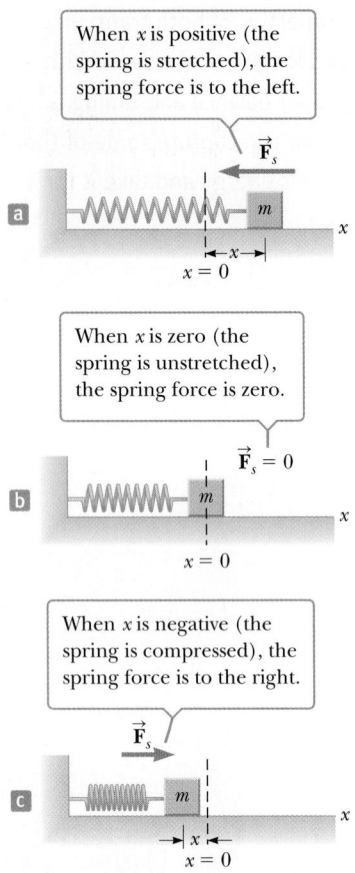

When x is positive (the spring is stretched), the spring force is to the left.

$\vec{F}_s$

a

$x = 0$

When x is zero (the spring is unstretched), the spring force is zero.

$\vec{F}_s = 0$

b

$x = 0$

When x is negative (the spring is compressed), the spring force is to the right.

$\vec{F}_s$

c

$x = 0$

Active Figure 13.1

The force exerted by a spring on an object varies with the displacement of the object from the equilibrium position, $x = 0$.

discovered by Robert Hooke in 1678 and is known as **Hooke's law.** The value of k is a measure of the stiffness of the spring. Stiff springs have large k values, and soft springs have small k values.

The negative sign in Equation 13.1 means that the force exerted by the spring is always directed *opposite* the displacement of the object. When the object is to the right of the equilibrium position, as in Active Figure 13.1a, x is positive and F_s is negative. This means that the force is in the negative direction, to the left. When the object is to the left of the equilibrium position, as in Active Figure 13.1c, x is negative and F_s is positive, indicating that the direction of the force is to the right. Of course, when $x = 0$, as in Active Figure 13.1b, the spring is unstretched and $F_s = 0$. Because the spring force always acts toward the equilibrium position, it is sometimes called a restoring force. **A restoring force always pushes or pulls the object toward the equilibrium position.**

Suppose the object is initially pulled a distance A to the right and released from rest. The force exerted by the spring on the object pulls it back toward the equilibrium position. As the object moves toward $x = 0$, the magnitude of the force decreases (because x decreases) and reaches zero at $x = 0$. The object gains speed as it moves toward the equilibrium position, however, reaching its maximum speed when $x = 0$. The momentum gained by the object causes it to overshoot the equilibrium position and compress the spring. As the object moves to the left of the equilibrium position (negative x-values), the spring force acts on it to the right, steadily increasing in strength, and the speed of the object decreases. The object finally comes briefly to rest at $x = -A$ before accelerating back towards $x = 0$ and ultimately returning to the original position at $x = A$. The process is then repeated, and the object continues to oscillate back and forth over the same path. This type of motion is called **simple harmonic motion. Simple harmonic motion occurs when the net force along the direction of motion obeys Hooke's law—when the net force is proportional to the displacement from the equilibrium point and is always directed toward the equilibrium point.**

Not all periodic motions over the same path can be classified as simple harmonic motion. A ball being tossed back and forth between a parent and a child moves repetitively, but the motion isn't simple harmonic motion because the force acting on the ball doesn't take the form of Hooke's law, Equation 13.1.

The motion of an object suspended from a vertical spring is also simple harmonic. In this case the force of gravity acting on the attached object stretches the spring until equilibrium is reached and the object is suspended at rest. By definition, the equilibrium position of the object is $x = 0$. When the object is moved away from equilibrium by a distance x and released, a net force acts toward the equilibrium position. Because the net force is proportional to x, the motion is simple harmonic.

The following three concepts are important in discussing any kind of periodic motion:

- The **amplitude** A is the maximum distance of the object from its equilibrium position. In the absence of friction, an object in simple harmonic motion oscillates between the positions $x = -A$ and $x = +A$.
- The **period** T is the time it takes the object to move through one complete cycle of motion, from $x = A$ to $x = -A$ and back to $x = A$.
- The **frequency** f is the number of complete cycles or vibrations per unit of time, and is the reciprocal of the period ($f = 1/T$).

The acceleration of an object moving with simple harmonic motion can be found by using Hooke's law in the equation for Newton's second law, $F = ma$. This gives

$$ma = F = -kx$$

Acceleration in simple ▶
harmonic motion

$$\boxed{a = -\frac{k}{m}x}$$ [13.2]

Equation 13.2, an example of a *harmonic oscillator equation,* gives the acceleration as a function of position. Because the maximum value of x is defined to be the amplitude A, the acceleration ranges over the values $-kA/m$ to $+kA/m$. In the next section we will find equations for velocity as a function of position and for position as a function of time. Springs satisfying Hooke's law are also called *ideal* springs. In real springs, spring mass, internal friction, and varying elasticity affect the force law and motion.

> **Tip 13.1 Constant-Acceleration Equations Don't Apply**
>
> The acceleration a of a particle in simple harmonic motion is *not* constant; it changes, varying with x, so we can't apply the constant acceleration kinematic equations of Chapter 2.

■ *Quick Quiz*

13.1 A block on the end of a horizontal spring is pulled from equilibrium at $x = 0$ to $x = A$ and released. Through what total distance does it travel in one full cycle of its motion? (a) $A/2$ (b) A (c) $2A$ (d) $4A$

13.2 For a simple harmonic oscillator, which of the following pairs of vector quantities can't both point in the same direction? (The position vector is the displacement from equilibrium.) (a) position and velocity (b) velocity and acceleration (c) position and acceleration

---

■ EXAMPLE 13.1 | Simple Harmonic Motion on a Frictionless Surface

GOAL Calculate forces and accelerations for a horizontal spring system.

PROBLEM A 0.350-kg object attached to a spring of force constant 1.30×10^2 N/m is free to move on a frictionless horizontal surface, as in Active Figure 13.1. If the object is released from rest at $x = 0.100$ m, find the force on it and its acceleration at $x = 0.100$ m, $x = 0.050\ 0$ m, $x = 0$ m, $x = -0.050\ 0$ m, and $x = -0.100$ m.

STRATEGY Substitute given quantities into Hooke's law to find the forces, then calculate the accelerations with Newton's second law. The amplitude A is the same as the point of release from rest, $x = 0.100$ m.

....

SOLUTION

Write Hooke's force law:

$$F_s = -kx$$

Substitute the value for k and take $x = A = 0.100$ m, finding the spring force at that point:

$$F_{max} = -kA = -(1.30 \times 10^2 \text{ N/m})(0.100 \text{ m})$$
$$= \boxed{-13.0 \text{ N}}$$

Solve Newton's second law for a and substitute to find the acceleration at $x = A$:

$$ma = F_{max}$$
$$a = \frac{F_{max}}{m} = \frac{-13.0 \text{ N}}{0.350 \text{ kg}} = \boxed{-37.1 \text{ m/s}^2}$$

Repeat the same process for the other four points, assembling a table:

Position (m)	Force (N)	Acceleration (m/s^2)
0.100	−13.0	−37.1
0.050	−6.50	−18.6
0	0	0
−0.050	+6.50	+18.6
−0.100	+13.0	+37.1

....

REMARKS The table above shows that when the initial position is halved, the force and acceleration are also halved. Further, positive values of x give negative values of the force and acceleration, whereas negative values of x give positive values of the force and acceleration. As the object moves to the left and passes the equilibrium point, the spring force becomes positive (for negative values of x), slowing the object down.

QUESTION 13.1 Will doubling a given displacement always result in doubling the magnitude of the spring force? Explain.

EXERCISE 13.1 For the same spring and mass system, find the force exerted by the spring and the position x when the object's acceleration is $+9.00$ m/s^2.

ANSWERS 3.15 N, −2.42 cm

■ EXAMPLE 13.2 | Mass on a Vertical Spring

GOAL Apply Newton's second law together with the force of gravity and Hooke's law.

PROBLEM A spring is hung vertically (Fig. 13.2a), and an object of mass m attached to the lower end is then slowly lowered a distance d to the equilibrium point (Fig. 13.2b). **(a)** Find the value of the spring constant if the spring is displaced by 2.0 cm and the mass is 0.55 kg. **(b)** If a second identical spring is attached to the object in parallel with the first spring (Fig. 13.2d), where is the new equilibrium point of the system? **(c)** What is the effective spring constant of the two springs acting as one?

STRATEGY This example is an application of Newton's second law. The spring force is upward, balancing the downward force of gravity mg when the system is in equilibrium. (See Fig. 13.2c.) Because the suspended object is in equilibrium, the forces on the object sum to zero, and it's possible to solve for the spring constant k. Part (b) is solved the same way, but has two spring forces balancing the force of gravity. The spring constants are known, so the second law for equilibrium can be solved for the displacement of the spring. Part (c) involves using the displacement found in part (b). Treating the two springs as one equivalent spring, the second law then leads to the effective spring constant of the two-spring system.

The elongation d is caused by the weight mg of the attached object.

Figure 13.2 (Example 13.2) (a)–(c) Determining the spring constant. Because the upward spring force balances the weight when the system is in equilibrium, it follows that $k = mg/d$. (d) A system involving two springs in parallel.

SOLUTION

(a) Find the value of the spring constant if the spring is displaced by 2.0 cm and the mass of the object is 0.55 kg.

Apply Newton's second law to the object (with $a = 0$) and solve for the spring constant k:

$$\sum F = F_g + F_s = -mg + kd = 0$$

$$k = \frac{mg}{d} = \frac{(0.55\ \text{kg})(9.80\ \text{m/s}^2)}{2.0 \times 10^{-2}\ \text{m}} = \boxed{2.7 \times 10^2\ \text{N/m}}$$

(b) If a second identical spring is attached to the object in parallel with the first spring (Fig. 13.2d), find the new equilibrium point of the system.

Apply Newton's second law, but with two springs acting on the object:

$$\sum F = F_g + F_{s1} + F_{s2} = -mg + kd_2 + kd_2 = 0$$

Solve for d_2:

$$d_2 = \frac{mg}{2k} = \frac{(0.55\ \text{kg})(9.80\ \text{m/s}^2)}{2(2.7 \times 10^2\ \text{N/m})} = \boxed{1.0 \times 10^{-2}\ \text{m}}$$

(c) What is the effective spring constant of the two springs acting as one?

Write the second law for the system, with an effective spring constant k_{eff}:

$$\sum F = F_g + F_s = -mg + k_{\text{eff}}d_2 = 0$$

Solve for k_{eff}:

$$k_{\text{eff}} = \frac{mg}{d_2} = \frac{(0.55\ \text{kg})(9.80\ \text{m/s}^2)}{1.0 \times 10^{-2}\ \text{m}} = 5.4 \times 10^2\ \text{N/m}$$

REMARKS In this example, the spring force is positive because it's directed upward. Once the object is displaced from the equilibrium position and released, it oscillates around the equilibrium position, just like the horizontal spring. Notice that attaching an extra identical spring in parallel is equivalent to having a single spring with twice the force constant. When the springs are attached end to end in series, however, the exercise illustrates that, all other things being equal, longer springs have smaller force constants than shorter springs.

QUESTION 13.2 Generalize: When two springs with force constants k_1 and k_2 act in parallel on an object, what is the spring constant k_{eq} of the single spring that would be equivalent to the two springs, in terms of k_1 and k_2?

EXERCISE 13.2 When a 75.0-kg man slowly adds his weight to a vertical spring attached to the ceiling, he reaches equilibrium when the spring is stretched by 6.50 cm. (a) Find the spring constant. (b) If a second, identical spring is hung on the first, and the man again adds his weight to the system, by how much does the system of springs stretch? (c) What would be the spring constant of a single, equivalent spring?

ANSWERS (a) 1.13×10^4 N/kg (b) 13.0 cm (c) 5.65×10^3 N/m

13.2 Elastic Potential Energy

In this section we review the material covered in Section 4 of Chapter 5.

A system of interacting objects has potential energy associated with the configuration of the system. A compressed spring has potential energy that, when allowed to expand, can do work on an object, transforming spring potential energy into the object's kinetic energy. As an example, Figure 13.3 shows a ball being projected from a spring-loaded toy gun, where the spring is compressed a distance x. As the gun is fired, the compressed spring does work on the ball and imparts kinetic energy to it.

Recall that the energy stored in a stretched or compressed spring or some other elastic material is called elastic potential energy, PE_s, given by

$$PE_s \equiv \tfrac{1}{2}kx^2 \qquad \text{[13.3]}$$

◀ Elastic potential energy

Recall also that the law of conservation of energy, including both gravitational and spring potential energy, is given by

$$(KE + PE_g + PE_s)_i = (KE + PE_g + PE_s)_f \qquad \text{[13.4]}$$

If nonconservative forces such as friction are present, then the change in mechanical energy must equal the work done by the nonconservative forces:

$$W_{nc} = (KE + PE_g + PE_s)_f - (KE + PE_g + PE_s)_i \qquad \text{[13.5]}$$

Rotational kinetic energy must be included in both Equation 13.4 and Equation 13.5 for systems involving torques.

As an example of the energy conversions that take place when a spring is included in a system, consider Figure 13.4 (page 442). A block of mass m slides on a frictionless horizontal surface with constant velocity $\vec{v}_i$ and collides with a coiled spring. The description that follows is greatly simplified by assuming the spring is very light (an ideal spring) and therefore has negligible kinetic energy. As the spring is compressed, it exerts a force to the left on the block. At maximum compression, the block comes to rest for just an instant (Fig. 13.4c). The initial total energy in the system (block plus spring) before the collision is the kinetic energy of the block. After the block collides with the spring and the spring is partially compressed, as in Figure 13.4b, the block has kinetic energy $\tfrac{1}{2}mv^2$ (where $v < v_i$) and the spring has potential energy $\tfrac{1}{2}kx^2$. When the block stops for an instant at the point of maximum compression, the kinetic energy is zero. Because the spring force is conservative and because there are no external forces that can do work on the system, **the total mechanical energy of the system consisting of the block**

Energy = elastic PE_s

x

Energy = KE

Figure 13.3 A ball projected from a spring-loaded gun. The elastic potential energy stored in the spring is transformed into the kinetic energy of the ball.

Figure 13.4 A block sliding on a frictionless horizontal surface collides with a light spring. In the absence of friction, the mechanical energy in this process remains constant.

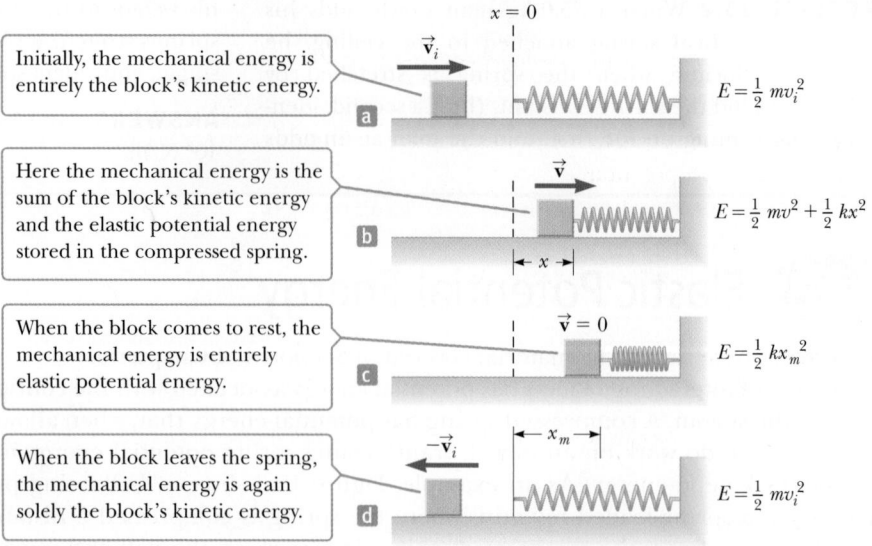

Initially, the mechanical energy is entirely the block's kinetic energy.

$E = \frac{1}{2}mv_i^2$

Here the mechanical energy is the sum of the block's kinetic energy and the elastic potential energy stored in the compressed spring.

$E = \frac{1}{2}mv^2 + \frac{1}{2}kx^2$

When the block comes to rest, the mechanical energy is entirely elastic potential energy.

$E = \frac{1}{2}kx_m^2$

When the block leaves the spring, the mechanical energy is again solely the block's kinetic energy.

$E = \frac{1}{2}mv_i^2$

APPLICATION
Archery

Figure 13.5 Elastic potential energy is stored in this drawn bow.

and spring remains constant. Energy is transformed from the kinetic energy of the block to the potential energy stored in the spring. As the spring expands, the block moves in the opposite direction and regains all its initial kinetic energy, as in Figure 13.4d.

When an archer pulls back on a bowstring, elastic potential energy is stored in both the bent bow and stretched bowstring (Fig. 13.5). When the arrow is released, the potential energy stored in the system is transformed into the kinetic energy of the arrow. Devices such as crossbows and slingshots work the same way.

■ Quick Quiz

13.3 When an object moving in simple harmonic motion is at its maximum displacement from equilibrium, which of the following is at a maximum? (a) velocity, (b) acceleration, or (c) kinetic energy

■ EXAMPLE 13.3 | **Stop That Car!**

GOAL Apply conservation of energy and the work–energy theorem with spring and gravitational potential energy.

PROBLEM A 13 000-N car starts at rest and rolls down a hill from a height of 10.0 m (Fig. 13.6). It then moves across a level surface and collides with a light spring-loaded guardrail. (a) Neglecting any losses due to friction, and ignoring the rotational kinetic energy of the wheels, find the maximum distance the spring is compressed. Assume a spring constant of 1.0×10^6 N/m. (b) Calculate the maximum acceleration of the car after contact with the spring, assuming no frictional losses. (c) If the spring is compressed by only 0.30 m, find the change in the mechanical energy due to friction.

Figure 13.6 (Example 13.3) A car starts from rest on a hill at the position shown. When the car reaches the bottom of the hill, it collides with a spring-loaded guardrail.

STRATEGY Because friction losses are neglected, use conservation of energy in the form of Equation 13.4 to solve for the spring displacement in part (a). The initial and final values of the car's kinetic energy are zero, so the initial potential energy of the car–spring–Earth system is completely converted to elastic potential energy in the spring at the end of the ride. In part (b) apply Newton's second law, substituting the answer to part (a) for *x* because the maximum compression will give the maximum acceleration. In part (c) friction is no longer neglected, so use the work–energy theorem, Equation 13.5. The change in mechanical energy must equal the mechanical energy lost due to friction.

SOLUTION

(a) Find the maximum spring compression, assuming no energy losses due to friction.

Apply conservation of mechanical energy. Initially, there is only gravitational potential energy, and at maximum compression of the guardrail, there is only spring potential energy.

$$(KE + PE_g + PE_s)_i = (KE + PE_g + PE_s)_f$$
$$0 + mgh + 0 = 0 + 0 + \tfrac{1}{2}kx^2$$

Solve for x:

$$x = \sqrt{\frac{2mgh}{k}} = \sqrt{\frac{2(13\,000\text{ N})(10.0\text{ m})}{1.0 \times 10^6\text{ N/m}}} = \boxed{0.51\text{ m}}$$

(b) Calculate the maximum acceleration of the car by the spring, neglecting friction.

Apply Newton's second law to the car:

$$ma = -kx \quad \rightarrow \quad a = -\frac{kx}{m} = -\frac{kxg}{mg} = -\frac{kxg}{w}$$

Substitute values:

$$a = -\frac{(1.0 \times 10^6\text{ N/m})(0.51\text{ m})(9.8\text{ m/s}^2)}{13\,000\text{ N}}$$
$$= \boxed{-380\text{ m/s}^2}$$

(c) If the compression of the guardrail is only 0.30 m, find the change in the mechanical energy due to friction.

Use the work–energy theorem:

$$W_{nc} = (KE + PE_g + PE_s)_f - (KE + PE_g + PE_s)_i$$
$$= (0 + 0 + \tfrac{1}{2}kx^2) - (0 + mgh + 0)$$
$$= \tfrac{1}{2}(1.0 \times 10^6\text{ N/m})(0.30)^2 - (13\,000\text{ N})(10.0\text{ m})$$
$$W_{nc} = \boxed{-8.5 \times 10^4\text{ J}}$$

REMARKS The answer to part (b) is about 40 times greater than the acceleration of gravity, so we'd better be wearing our seat belts. Note that the solution didn't require calculation of the velocity of the car.

QUESTION 13.3 True or False: In the absence of energy losses due to friction, doubling the height of the hill doubles the maximum acceleration delivered by the spring.

EXERCISE 13.3 A spring-loaded gun fires a 0.100-kg puck along a tabletop. The puck slides up a curved ramp and flies straight up into the air. If the spring is displaced 12.0 cm from equilibrium and the spring constant is 875 N/m, how high does the puck rise, neglecting friction? (b) If instead it only rises to a height of 5.00 m because of friction, what is the change in mechanical energy?

ANSWERS (a) 6.43 m (b) −1.40 J

In addition to studying the preceding example, it's a good idea to review those given in Section 5.4.

Velocity as a Function of Position

Conservation of energy provides a simple method of deriving an expression for the velocity of an object undergoing periodic motion as a function of position. The object in question is initially at its maximum extension A (Fig. 13.7a on page 444) and is then released from rest. The initial energy of the system is entirely elastic potential energy stored in the spring, $\tfrac{1}{2}kA^2$. As the object moves toward the origin to some new position x (Fig. 13.7b), part of this energy is transformed into kinetic energy, and the potential energy stored in the spring is reduced to $\tfrac{1}{2}kx^2$. Because the total energy of the system is equal to $\tfrac{1}{2}kA^2$ (the initial energy stored

Figure 13.7 (a) An object attached to a spring on a frictionless surface is released from rest with the spring extended a distance A. Just before the object is released, the total energy is the elastic potential energy $\frac{1}{2}kA^2$. (b) When the object reaches position x, it has kinetic energy $\frac{1}{2}mv^2$ and the elastic potential energy has decreased to $\frac{1}{2}kx^2$.

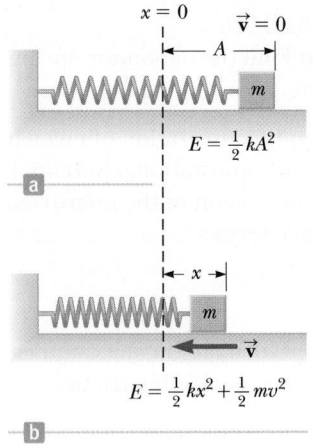

in the spring), we can equate this quantity to the sum of the kinetic and potential energies at the position x:

$$\tfrac{1}{2}kA^2 = \tfrac{1}{2}mv^2 + \tfrac{1}{2}kx^2$$

Solving for v, we get

$$v = \pm\sqrt{\frac{k}{m}(A^2 - x^2)} \qquad \text{[13.6]}$$

This expression shows that the object's speed is a maximum at $x = 0$ and is zero at the extreme positions $x = \pm A$.

The right side of Equation 13.6 is preceded by the $\pm$ sign because the square root of a number can be either positive or negative. If the object in Figure 13.7 is moving to the right, v is positive; if the object is moving to the left, v is negative.

■ EXAMPLE 13.4 | The Object–Spring System Revisited

GOAL Apply the time-independent velocity expression, Equation 13.6, to an object-spring system.

PROBLEM A 0.500-kg object connected to a light spring with a spring constant of 20.0 N/m oscillates on a frictionless horizontal surface. **(a)** Calculate the total energy of the system and the maximum speed of the object if the amplitude of the motion is 3.00 cm. **(b)** What is the velocity of the object when the displacement is 2.00 cm? **(c)** Compute the kinetic and potential energies of the system when the displacement is 2.00 cm.

STRATEGY The total energy of the system can be found most easily at $x = A$, where the kinetic energy is zero. There, the potential energy alone is equal to the total energy. Conservation of energy then yields the speed at $x = 0$. For part (b), obtain the velocity by substituting the given value of x into the time-independent velocity equation. Using this result, the kinetic energy asked for in part (c) can be found by substitution, and the potential energy can be found by substitution into Equation 13.3.

. . . .

SOLUTION

(a) Calculate the total energy and maximum speed if the amplitude is 3.00 cm.

Substitute $x = A = 3.00$ cm and $k = 20.0$ N/m into the equation for the total mechanical energy E:

$$E = KE + PE_g + PE_s$$
$$= 0 + 0 + \tfrac{1}{2}kA^2 = \tfrac{1}{2}(20.0 \text{ N/m})(3.00 \times 10^{-2} \text{ m})^2$$
$$= \boxed{9.00 \times 10^{-3} \text{ J}}$$

Use conservation of energy with $x_i = A$ and $x_f = 0$ to compute the speed of the object at the origin:

$$(KE + PE_g + PE_s)_i = (KE + PE_g + PE_s)_f$$
$$0 + 0 + \tfrac{1}{2}kA^2 = \tfrac{1}{2}mv_{max}^2 + 0 + 0$$
$$\tfrac{1}{2}mv_{max}^2 = 9.00 \times 10^{-3}\,\text{J}$$
$$v_{max} = \sqrt{\frac{18.0 \times 10^{-3}\,\text{J}}{0.500\,\text{kg}}} = \boxed{0.190\,\text{m/s}}$$

(b) Compute the velocity of the object when the displacement is 2.00 cm.

Substitute known values directly into Equation 13.6:

$$v = \pm\sqrt{\frac{k}{m}\left(A^2 - x^2\right)}$$
$$= \pm\sqrt{\frac{20.0\,\text{N/m}}{0.500\,\text{kg}}\left[(0.030\,0\,\text{m})^2 - (0.020\,0\,\text{m})^2\right]}$$
$$= \boxed{\pm 0.141\,\text{m/s}}$$

(c) Compute the kinetic and potential energies when the displacement is 2.00 cm.

Substitute into the equation for kinetic energy:

$$KE = \tfrac{1}{2}mv^2 = \tfrac{1}{2}(0.500\,\text{kg})(0.141\,\text{m/s})^2 = \boxed{4.97 \times 10^{-3}\,\text{J}}$$

Substitute into the equation for spring potential energy:

$$PE_s = \tfrac{1}{2}kx^2 = \tfrac{1}{2}(20.0\,\text{N/m})(2.00 \times 10^{-2}\,\text{m})^2$$
$$= \boxed{4.00 \times 10^{-3}\,\text{J}}$$

REMARKS With the given information, it is impossible to choose between the positive and negative solutions in part (b). Notice that the sum $KE + PE_s$ in part (c) equals the total energy E found in part (a), as it should (except for a small discrepancy due to rounding).

QUESTION 13.4 True or False: Doubling the initial displacement doubles the speed of the object at the equilibrium point.

EXERCISE 13.4 For what values of x is the speed of the object 0.10 m/s?   **ANSWER** ± 2.55 cm

13.3 Comparing Simple Harmonic Motion with Uniform Circular Motion

We can better understand and visualize many aspects of simple harmonic motion along a straight line by looking at its relationship to uniform circular motion. Active Figure 13.8 is a top view of an experimental arrangement that is useful for this purpose. A ball is attached to the rim of a turntable of radius A, illuminated from the side by a lamp. We find that **as the turntable rotates with constant angular speed, the shadow of the ball moves back and forth with simple harmonic motion.**

This fact can be understood from Equation 13.6, which says that the velocity of an object moving with simple harmonic motion is related to the displacement by

$$v = C\sqrt{A^2 - x^2}$$

where C is a constant. To see that the shadow also obeys this relation, consider Figure 13.9 (page 446), which shows the ball moving with a constant speed v_0 in a direction tangent to the circular path. At this instant, the velocity of the ball in the x-direction is given by $v = v_0 \sin\theta$, or

$$\sin\theta = \frac{v}{v_0}$$

As the ball rotates like a particle in uniform circular motion...

Lamp

Q

P

A

Turntable

A

Screen

...the ball's shadow on the screen moves back and forth with simple harmonic motion.

Active Figure 13.8
An experimental setup for demonstrating the connection between simple harmonic motion and uniform circular motion.

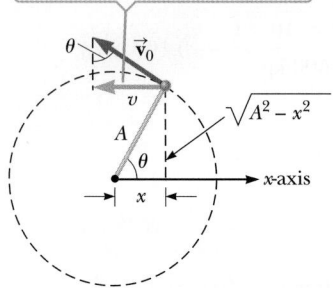

The x-component of the ball's velocity equals the projection of $\vec{v}_0$ on the x-axis.

Figure 13.9 The ball rotates with constant speed v_0.

From the larger triangle in Figure 13.9 we can obtain a second expression for $\sin \theta$:

$$\sin \theta = \frac{\sqrt{A^2 - x^2}}{A}$$

Equating the right-hand sides of the two expressions for $\sin \theta$, we find the following relationship between the velocity v and the displacement x:

$$\frac{v}{v_0} = \frac{\sqrt{A^2 - x^2}}{A}$$

or

$$v = \frac{v_0}{A}\sqrt{A^2 - x^2} = C\sqrt{A^2 - x^2}$$

The velocity of the ball in the x-direction is related to the displacement x in exactly the same way as the velocity of an object undergoing simple harmonic motion. The shadow therefore moves with simple harmonic motion.

A valuable example of the relationship between simple harmonic motion and circular motion can be seen in vehicles and machines that use the back-and-forth motion of a piston to create rotational motion in a wheel. Consider the drive wheel of a locomotive. In Figure 13.10, the rods are connected to a piston that moves back and forth in simple harmonic motion. The rods transform the back-and-forth motion of the piston into rotational motion of the wheels. A similar mechanism in an automobile engine transforms the back-and-forth motion of the pistons to rotational motion of the crankshaft.

Period and Frequency

APPLICATION
Pistons and Drive Wheels

The period T of the shadow in Active Figure 13.8, which represents the time required for one complete trip back and forth, is also the time it takes the ball to make one complete circular trip on the turntable. Because the ball moves through the distance $2\pi A$ (the circumference of the circle) in the time T, the speed v_0 of the ball around the circular path is

$$v_0 = \frac{2\pi A}{T}$$

and the period is

$$T = \frac{2\pi A}{v_0} \qquad [13.7]$$

Figure 13.10 The drive wheel mechanism of an old locomotive.

Imagine that the ball moves from P to Q, a quarter of a revolution, in Active Figure 13.8. The motion of the shadow is equivalent to the horizontal motion of an object on the end of a spring. For this reason, the radius A of the circular motion is the same as the amplitude A of the simple harmonic motion of the shadow. During the quarter of a cycle shown, the shadow moves from a point where the energy of the system (ball and spring) is solely elastic potential energy to a point where the energy is solely kinetic energy. By conservation of energy, we have

$$\tfrac{1}{2}kA^2 = \tfrac{1}{2}mv_0^2$$

which can be solved for A/v_0:

$$\frac{A}{v_0} = \sqrt{\frac{m}{k}}$$

Substituting this expression for A/v_0 in Equation 13.7, we find that the period is

The period of an object– ▶
spring system moving with
simple harmonic motion

$$T = 2\pi\sqrt{\frac{m}{k}} \qquad [13.8]$$

Equation 13.8 represents the time required for an object of mass m attached to a spring with spring constant k to complete one cycle of its motion. The square root of the mass is in the numerator, so a large mass will mean a large period, in agreement with intuition. The square root of the spring constant k is in the denominator, so a large spring constant will yield a small period, again agreeing with intuition. It's also interesting that the period doesn't depend on the amplitude A.

The inverse of the period is the frequency of the motion:

$$f = \frac{1}{T} \qquad [13.9]$$

Therefore, the frequency of the periodic motion of a mass on a spring is

$$f = \frac{1}{2\pi}\sqrt{\frac{k}{m}} \qquad [13.10]$$

◀ Frequency of an object–spring system

The units of frequency are cycles per second (s^{-1}), or **hertz** (Hz). The **angular frequency** ω is

$$\omega = 2\pi f = \sqrt{\frac{k}{m}} \qquad [13.11]$$

◀ Angular frequency of an object–spring system

The frequency and angular frequency are actually closely related concepts. The unit of frequency is cycles per second, where a cycle may be thought of as a unit of angular measure corresponding to 2π radians, or $360°$. Viewed in this way, angular frequency is just a unit conversion of frequency. Radian measure is used for angles mainly because it provides a convenient and natural link between linear and angular quantities.

Although an ideal mass–spring system has a period proportional to the square root of the object's mass m, experiments show that a graph of T^2 versus m doesn't pass through the origin. This is because the spring itself has a mass. The coils of the spring oscillate just like the object, except the amplitudes are smaller for all coils but the last. For a cylindrical spring, energy arguments can be used to show that the *effective* additional mass of a light spring is one-third the mass of the spring. The square of the period is proportional to the total oscillating mass, so a graph of T^2 versus total mass (the mass hung on the spring plus the effective oscillating mass of the spring) would pass through the origin.

> **Tip 13.2 Twin Frequencies**
>
> The *frequency* gives the number of cycles per second, whereas the *angular frequency* gives the number of radians per second. These two physical concepts are nearly identical and are linked by the conversion factor 2π rad/cycle.

■ Quick Quiz

13.4 An object of mass m is attached to a horizontal spring, stretched to a displacement A from equilibrium and released, undergoing harmonic oscillations on a frictionless surface with period T_0. The experiment is then repeated with a mass of $4m$. What's the new period of oscillation? (a) $2T_0$ (b) T_0 (c) $T_0/2$ (d) $T_0/4$

13.5 Consider the situation in Quick Quiz 13.4. Is the subsequent total mechanical energy of the object with mass $4m$ (a) greater than, (b) less than, or (c) equal to the original total mechanical energy?

■ APPLYING PHYSICS 13.1 | Bungee Jumping

A bungee cord can be modeled as a spring. If you go bungee jumping, you will bounce up and down at the end of the elastic cord after your dive off a bridge (Fig. 13.11 on page 448). Suppose you perform a dive and measure the frequency of your bouncing. You then move to another bridge, but find that the bungee cord is too long for dives off this bridge. What possible solutions might be applied? In terms of the original frequency, what is the frequency of vibration associated with the solution?

EXPLANATION There are two possible solutions: Make the bungee cord smaller or fold it in half. The latter would be the safer of the two choices, as we'll see. The force exerted by the bungee cord, modeled as a spring, is proportional to the separation of the coils as the spring is extended. First, we extend the spring by a given distance and measure the distance between coils. We then cut the spring in half. If one of the half-springs is now extended by the same distance, the coils will be twice as far apart as they were for the complete spring. Therefore, it takes twice as much force to stretch the half-spring through the same displacement, so the half-spring has a spring constant twice that of the complete spring. The folded bungee cord can then be modeled as two half-springs in parallel. Each half has a spring constant that is twice the original spring constant of the bungee cord. In addition, an object hanging on the folded bungee cord will experience two forces, one from each half-spring. As a result, the required force for a given extension will be four times as much as for the original bungee cord. The effective spring constant of the folded bungee cord is therefore four times as large as the original spring constant. Because the frequency of oscillation is proportional to the square root of the spring constant, your bouncing frequency on the folded cord will be twice what it was on the original cord.

This discussion neglects the fact that the coils of a spring have an initial separation. It's also important to remember that a shorter coil may lose elasticity more readily, possibly even going beyond the elastic limit for the material, with disastrous results. Bungee jumping is dangerous; discretion is advised! ∎

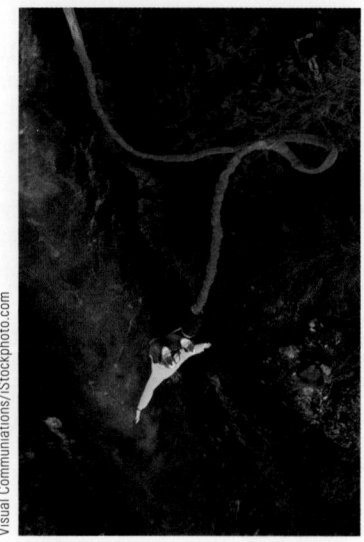

Figure 13.11 (Applying Physics 13.1) A bungee jumper relies on elastic forces to pull him up short of a deadly impact.

EXAMPLE 13.5 | **That Car Needs Shock Absorbers!**

GOAL Understand the relationships between period, frequency, and angular frequency.

PROBLEM A 1.30×10^3-kg car is constructed on a frame supported by four springs. Each spring has a spring constant of 2.00×10^4 N/m. If two people riding in the car have a combined mass of 1.60×10^2 kg, find the frequency of vibration of the car when it is driven over a pothole in the road. Find also the period and the angular frequency. Assume the weight is evenly distributed.

STRATEGY Because the weight is evenly distributed, each spring supports one-fourth of the mass. Substitute this value and the spring constant into Equation 13.10 to get the frequency. The reciprocal is the period, and multiplying the frequency by 2π gives the angular frequency.

....

SOLUTION

Compute one-quarter of the total mass:

$$m = \tfrac{1}{4}(m_{car} + m_{pass}) = \tfrac{1}{4}(1.30 \times 10^3 \text{ kg} + 1.60 \times 10^2 \text{ kg})$$
$$= 365 \text{ kg}$$

Substitute into Equation 13.10 to find the frequency:

$$f = \frac{1}{2\pi}\sqrt{\frac{k}{m}} = \frac{1}{2\pi}\sqrt{\frac{2.00 \times 10^4 \text{ N/m}}{365 \text{ kg}}} = \boxed{1.18 \text{ Hz}}$$

Invert the frequency to get the period:

$$T = \frac{1}{f} = \frac{1}{1.18 \text{ Hz}} = \boxed{0.847 \text{ s}}$$

Multiply the frequency by 2π to get the angular frequency:

$$\omega = 2\pi f = 2\pi(1.18 \text{ Hz}) = \boxed{7.41 \text{ rad/s}}$$

....

REMARKS Solving this problem didn't require any knowledge of the size of the pothole because the frequency doesn't depend on the amplitude of the motion.

QUESTION 13.5 True or False: The frequency of vibration of a heavy vehicle is greater than that of a lighter vehicle, assuming the two vehicles are supported by the same set of springs.

EXERCISE 13.5 A 45.0-kg boy jumps on a 5.00-kg pogo stick with spring constant 3 650 N/m. Find (a) the angular frequency, (b) the frequency, and (c) the period of the boy's motion.

ANSWERS (a) 8.54 rad/s (b) 1.36 Hz (c) 0.735 s

Position, Velocity, and Acceleration as a Function of Time

We can obtain an expression for the position of an object moving with simple harmonic motion as a function of time by returning to the relationship between simple harmonic motion and uniform circular motion. Again, consider a ball on the rim of a rotating turntable of radius A, as in Figure 13.12. We refer to the circle made by the ball as the *reference circle* for the motion. We assume the turntable revolves at a *constant* angular speed ω. As the ball rotates on the reference circle, the angle θ made by the line OP with the x-axis changes with time. Meanwhile, the projection of P on the x-axis, labeled point Q, moves back and forth along the axis with simple harmonic motion.

From the right triangle OPQ, we see that $\cos \theta = x/A$. Therefore, the x-coordinate of the ball is

$$x = A \cos \theta$$

Because the ball rotates with constant angular speed, it follows that $\theta = \omega t$ (see Chapter 7), so we have

$$x = A \cos (\omega t) \qquad \text{[13.12]}$$

In one complete revolution, the ball rotates through an angle of 2π rad in a time equal to the period T. In other words, the motion repeats itself every T seconds. Therefore,

$$\omega = \frac{\Delta\theta}{\Delta t} = \frac{2\pi}{T} = 2\pi f \qquad \text{[13.13]}$$

where f is the frequency of the motion. The angular speed of the ball as it moves around the reference circle is the same as the angular frequency of the projected simple harmonic motion. Consequently, Equation 13.12 can be written

$$x = A \cos (2\pi ft) \qquad \text{[13.14a]}$$

This cosine function represents the position of an object moving with simple harmonic motion as a function of time, and is graphed in Figure 13.13a. Because the cosine function varies between 1 and -1, x varies between A and $-A$. The shape of the graph is called *sinusoidal*.

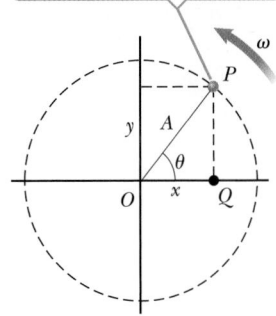

As the ball at P rotates in a circle with uniform angular speed, its projection Q along the x-axis moves with simple harmonic motion.

Figure 13.12 A reference circle.

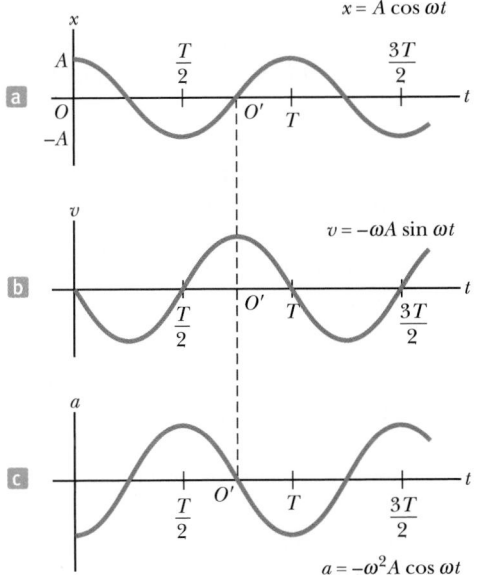

Figure 13.13 (a) Displacement, (b) velocity, and (c) acceleration versus time for an object moving with simple harmonic motion under the initial conditions $x_0 = A$ and $v_0 = 0$ at $t = 0$.

Figure 13.14 An experimental apparatus for demonstrating simple harmonic motion. A pen attached to the oscillating object traces out a sinusoidal wave on the moving chart paper.

Figures 13.13b and 13.13c represent curves for velocity and acceleration as a function of time. To find the equation for the velocity, use Equations 13.6 and 13.14a together with the identity $\cos^2 \theta + \sin^2 \theta = 1$, obtaining

$$v = -A\omega \sin(2\pi ft) \qquad [13.14b]$$

where we have used the fact that $\omega = \sqrt{k/m}$. The $\pm$ sign is no longer needed, because sine can take both positive and negative values. Deriving an expression for the acceleration involves substituting Equation 13.14a into Equation 13.2, Newton's second law for springs:

$$a = -A\omega^2 \cos(2\pi ft) \qquad [13.14c]$$

The detailed steps of these derivations are left as an exercise for the student. Notice that when the displacement x is at a maximum, at $x = A$ or $x = -A$, the velocity is zero, and when x is zero, the magnitude of the velocity is a maximum. Further, when $x = +A$, its most positive value, the acceleration is a maximum but in the negative x-direction, and when x is at its most negative position, $x = -A$, the acceleration has its maximum value in the positive x-direction. These facts are consistent with our earlier discussion of the points at which v and a reach their maximum, minimum, and zero values.

The maximum values of the position, velocity, and acceleration are always equal to the magnitude of the expression in front of the trigonometric function in each equation because the largest value of either cosine or sine is 1.

Figure 13.14 illustrates one experimental arrangement that demonstrates the sinusoidal nature of simple harmonic motion. An object connected to a spring has a marking pen attached to it. While the object vibrates vertically, a sheet of paper is moved horizontally with constant speed. The pen traces out a sinusoidal pattern.

■ **Quick Quiz**

13.6 If the amplitude of a system moving in simple harmonic motion is doubled, which of the following quantities *doesn't* change? (a) total energy (b) maximum speed (c) maximum acceleration (d) period

---

■ **EXAMPLE 13.6** | **The Vibrating Object–Spring System**

GOAL Identify the physical parameters of a harmonic oscillator from its mathematical description.

PROBLEM (a) Find the amplitude, frequency, and period of motion for an object vibrating at the end of a horizontal spring if the equation for its position as a function of time is

$$x = (0.250 \text{ m}) \cos\left(\frac{\pi}{8.00} t\right)$$

(b) Find the maximum magnitude of the velocity and acceleration. (c) What are the position, velocity, and acceleration of the object after 1.00 s has elapsed?

STRATEGY In part (a) the amplitude and frequency can be found by comparing the given equation with the standard form in Equation 13.14a, matching up the numerical values with the corresponding terms in the standard form. In part (b) the maximum speed will occur when the sine function in Equation 13.14b equals 1 or −1, the extreme values of the sine function (and similarly for the acceleration and the cosine function). In each case, find the magnitude of the expression in front of the trigonometric function. Part (c) is just a matter of substituting values into Equations 13.14a–13.14c.

....

SOLUTION

(a) Find the amplitude, frequency, and period.

Write the standard form given by Equation 13.14a and underneath it write the given equation:

(1) $x = A \cos(2\pi ft)$

(2) $x = (0.250 \text{ m}) \cos\left(\dfrac{\pi}{8.00} t\right)$

Equate the factors in front of the cosine functions to find the amplitude:

$A = \boxed{0.250 \text{ m}}$

The angular frequency ω is the factor in front of t in Equations (1) and (2). Equate these factors:

$$\omega = 2\pi f = \frac{\pi}{8.00} \text{ rad/s} = 0.393 \text{ rad/s}$$

Divide ω by 2π to get the frequency f:

$$f = \frac{\omega}{2\pi} = \boxed{0.062\ 5 \text{ Hz}}$$

The period T is the reciprocal of the frequency:

$$T = \frac{1}{f} = \boxed{16.0 \text{ s}}$$

(b) Find the maximum magnitudes of the velocity and the acceleration.

Calculate the maximum speed from the factor in front of the sine function in Equation 13.14b:

$$v_{max} = A\omega = (0.250 \text{ m})(0.393 \text{ rad/s}) = \boxed{0.098\ 3 \text{ m/s}}$$

Calculate the maximum acceleration from the factor in front of the cosine function in Equation 13.14c:

$$a_{max} = A\omega^2 = (0.250 \text{ m})(0.393 \text{ rad/s})^2 = \boxed{0.038\ 6 \text{ m/s}^2}$$

(c) Find the position, velocity, and acceleration of the object after 1.00 s.

Substitute $t = 1.00$ s in the given equation:

$$x = (0.250 \text{ m}) \cos (0.393 \text{ rad}) = \boxed{0.231 \text{ m}}$$

Substitute values into the velocity equation:

$$v = -A\omega \sin (\omega t)$$
$$= -(0.250 \text{ m})(0.393 \text{ rad/s}) \sin (0.393 \text{ rad/s} \cdot 1.00 \text{ s})$$
$$v = \boxed{-0.037\ 6 \text{ m/s}}$$

Substitute values into the acceleration equation:

$$a = -A\omega^2 \cos (\omega t)$$
$$= -(0.250 \text{ m})(0.393 \text{ rad/s}^2)^2 \cos (0.393 \text{ rad/s} \cdot 1.00 \text{ s})$$
$$a = \boxed{-0.035\ 7 \text{ m/s}^2}$$

REMARKS In evaluating the sine or cosine function, the angle is in radians, so you should either set your calculator to evaluate trigonometric functions based on radian measure or convert from radians to degrees.

QUESTION 13.6 If the mass is doubled, is the magnitude of the acceleration of the system at any position (a) doubled, (b) halved, or (c) unchanged?

EXERCISE 13.6 If the object–spring system is described by $x = (0.330 \text{ m}) \cos (1.50t)$, find (a) the amplitude, the angular frequency, the frequency, and the period, (b) the maximum magnitudes of the velocity and acceleration, and (c) the position, velocity, and acceleration when $t = 0.250$ s.

ANSWERS (a) $A = 0.330$ m, $\omega = 1.50$ rad/s, $f = 0.239$ Hz, $T = 4.18$ s (b) $v_{max} = 0.495$ m/s, $a_{max} = 0.743$ m/s^2 (c) $x = 0.307$ m, $v = -0.181$ m/s, $a = -0.691$ m/s^2

13.5 Motion of a Pendulum

A simple pendulum is another mechanical system that exhibits periodic motion. It consists of a small bob of mass m suspended by a light string of length L fixed at its upper end, as in Active Figure 13.15 (page 452). (By a light string, we mean that the string's mass is assumed to be very small compared with the mass of the bob and hence can be ignored.) When released, the bob swings to and fro over the same path, but is its motion simple harmonic?

Answering this question requires examining the restoring force—the force of gravity—that acts on the pendulum. The pendulum bob moves along a circular arc, rather than back and forth in a straight line. When the oscillations are small, however, the motion of the bob is nearly straight, so Hooke's law may apply approximately.

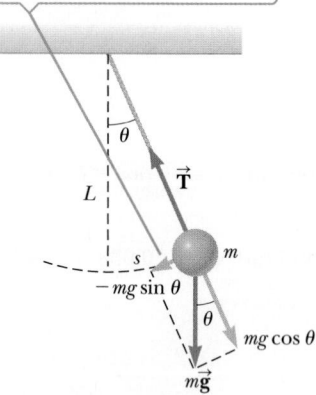

The restoring force causing the pendulum to oscillate harmonically is the tangential component of the gravity force $-mg \sin \theta$.

Active Figure 13.15

A simple pendulum consists of a bob of mass m suspended by a light string of length L. (L is the distance from the pivot to the center of mass of the bob.)

Tip 13.3 Pendulum Motion Is Not Harmonic

Remember that the pendulum *does not* exhibit true simple harmonic motion for *any* angle. If the angle is less than about 15°, the motion can be *modeled* as approximately simple harmonic.

The period of a simple ▶ pendulum depends only on L and g

APPLICATION

Pendulum Clocks

In Active Figure 13.15, s is the displacement of the bob from equilibrium along the arc. Hooke's law is $F = -kx$, so we are looking for a similar expression involving s, $F_t = -ks$, where F_t is the force acting in a direction tangent to the circular arc. From the figure, the restoring force is

$$F_t = -mg \sin \theta$$

Since $s = L\theta$, the equation for F_t can be written as

$$F_t = -mg \sin \left(\frac{s}{L} \right)$$

This expression isn't of the form $F_t = -ks$, so in general, the motion of a pendulum is *not* simple harmonic. For small angles less than about 15 degrees, however, the angle θ measured in radians and the sine of the angle are approximately equal. For example, $\theta = 10.0° = 0.175$ rad, and sin $(10.0°) = 0.174$. Therefore, if we restrict the motion to *small* angles, the approximation $\sin \theta \approx \theta$ is valid, and the restoring force can be written

$$F_t = -mg \sin \theta \approx -mg \theta$$

Substituting $\theta = s/L$, we obtain

$$F_t = -\left(\frac{mg}{L} \right) s$$

This equation follows the general form of Hooke's force law $F_t = -ks$, with $k = mg/L$. We are justified in saying that a pendulum undergoes simple harmonic motion only when it swings back and forth at small amplitudes (or, in this case, small values of θ, so that $\sin \theta \cong \theta$).

Recall that for the object–spring system, the angular frequency is given by Equation 13.11:

$$\omega = 2\pi f = \sqrt{\frac{k}{m}}$$

Substituting the expression of k for a pendulum, we obtain

$$\omega = \sqrt{\frac{mg/L}{m}} = \sqrt{\frac{g}{L}}$$

This angular frequency can be substituted into Equation 13.12, which then mathematically describes the motion of a pendulum. The frequency is just the angular frequency divided by 2π, while the period is the reciprocal of the frequency, or

$$T = 2\pi \sqrt{\frac{L}{g}} \qquad [13.15]$$

This equation reveals the somewhat surprising result that the period of a simple pendulum doesn't depend on the mass, but only on the pendulum's length and on the free-fall acceleration. Further, the amplitude of the motion isn't a factor as long as it's relatively small. The analogy between the motion of a simple pendulum and the object–spring system is illustrated in Active Figure 13.16.

Galileo first noted that the period of a pendulum was independent of its amplitude. He supposedly observed this while attending church services at the cathedral in Pisa. The pendulum he studied was a swinging chandelier that was set in motion when someone bumped it while lighting candles. Galileo was able to measure its period by timing the swings with his pulse.

The dependence of the period of a pendulum on its length and on the free-fall acceleration allows us to use a pendulum as a timekeeper for a clock. A number of clock designs employ a pendulum, with the length adjusted so that its period serves as the basis for the rate at which the clock's hands turn. Of course, these

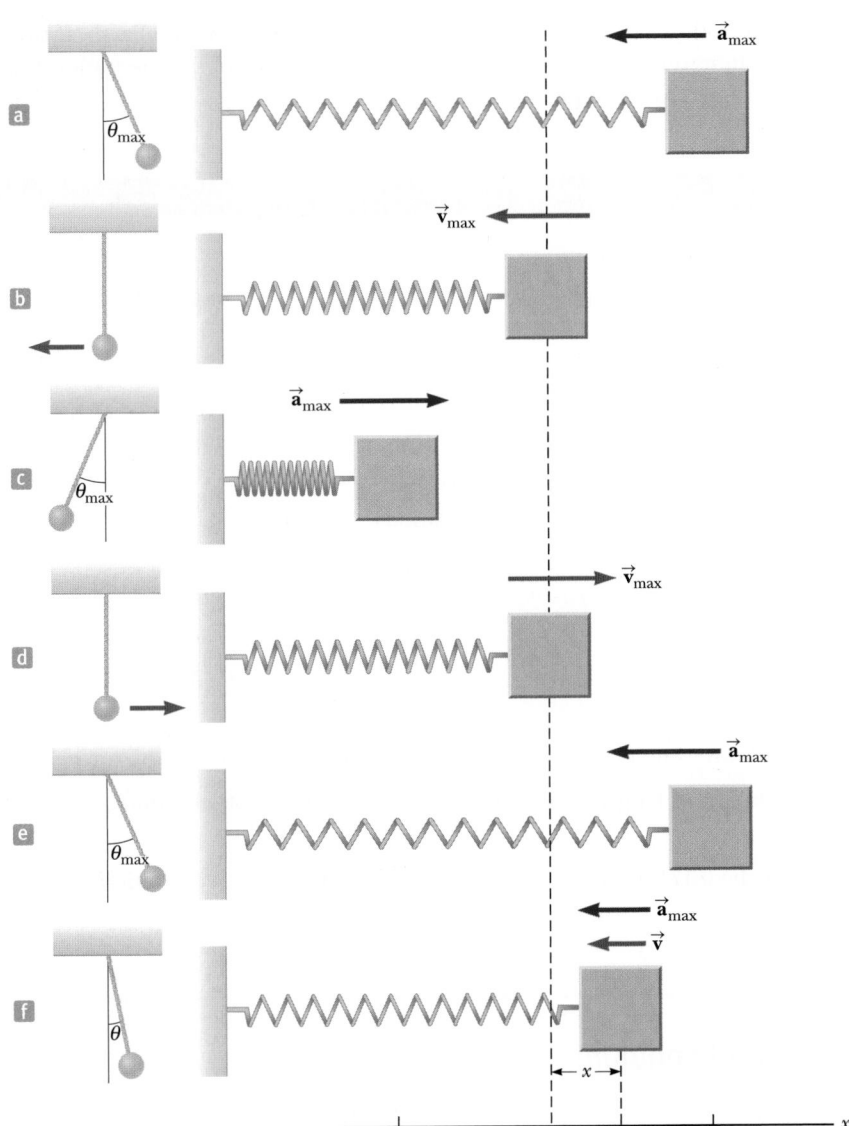

Active Figure 13.16
Simple harmonic motion for an
object–spring system, and its
analogy, the motion of a simple
pendulum.

clocks are used at different locations on the Earth, so there will be some variation
of the free-fall acceleration. To compensate for this variation, the pendulum of a
clock should have some movable mass so that the effective length can be adjusted.

Geologists often make use of the simple pendulum and Equation 13.15 when
prospecting for oil or minerals. Deposits beneath the Earth's surface can produce
irregularities in the free-fall acceleration over the region being studied. A specially
designed pendulum of known length is used to measure the period, which in turn
is used to calculate g. Although such a measurement in itself is inconclusive, it's an
important tool for geological surveys.

APPLICATION

Use of Pendulum in Prospecting

■ Quick Quiz

13.7 A simple pendulum is suspended from the ceiling of a stationary elevator,
and the period is measured. If the elevator moves with constant velocity, does the
period (a) increase, (b) decrease, or (c) remain the same? If the elevator accelerates
upward, does the period (a) increase, (b) decrease, or (c) remain the same?

13.8 A pendulum clock depends on the period of a pendulum to keep correct time.
Suppose a pendulum clock is keeping correct time and then Dennis the Menace
slides the bob of the pendulum downward on the oscillating rod. Does the clock run
(a) slow, (b) fast, or (c) correctly?

13.9 The period of a simple pendulum is measured to be *T* on the Earth. If the same pendulum were set in motion on the Moon, would its period be (a) less than *T*, (b) greater than *T*, or (c) equal to *T*?

■ EXAMPLE 13.7 | Measuring the Value of *g*

GOAL Determine *g* from pendulum motion.

PROBLEM Using a small pendulum of length 0.171 m, a geophysicist counts 72.0 complete swings in a time of 60.0 s. What is the value of *g* in this location?

STRATEGY First calculate the period of the pendulum by dividing the total time by the number of complete swings. Solve Equation 13.15 for *g* and substitute values.

SOLUTION

Calculate the period by dividing the total elapsed time by the number of complete oscillations:

$$T = \frac{\text{time}}{\text{\# of oscillations}} = \frac{60.0 \text{ s}}{72.0} = 0.833 \text{ s}$$

Solve Equation 13.15 for *g* and substitute values:

$$T = 2\pi \sqrt{\frac{L}{g}} \quad \rightarrow \quad T^2 = 4\pi^2 \frac{L}{g}$$

$$g = \frac{4\pi^2 L}{T^2} = \frac{(39.5)(0.171 \text{ m})}{(0.833 \text{ s})^2} = \boxed{9.73 \text{ m/s}^2}$$

REMARKS Measuring such a vibration is a good way of determining the local value of the acceleration of gravity.

QUESTION 13.7 True or False: A simple pendulum of length 0.50 m has a larger frequency of vibration than a simple pendulum of length 1.0 m.

EXERCISE 13.7 What would be the period of the 0.171-m pendulum on the Moon, where the acceleration of gravity is 1.62 m/s²?

ANSWER 2.04 s

The Physical Pendulum

The simple pendulum discussed thus far consists of a mass attached to a string. A pendulum, however, can be made from an object of any shape. The general case is called the *physical pendulum*.

In Figure 13.17 a rigid object is pivoted at point *O*, which is a distance *L* from the object's center of mass. The center of mass oscillates along a circular arc, just like the simple pendulum. The period of a physical pendulum is given by

$$T = 2\pi \sqrt{\frac{I}{mgL}} \qquad [13.16]$$

where *I* is the object's moment of inertia and *m* is the object's mass. As a check, notice that in the special case of a simple pendulum with an arm of length *L* and negligible mass, the moment of inertia is $I = mL^2$. Substituting into Equation 13.16 results in

$$T = 2\pi \sqrt{\frac{mL^2}{mgL}} = 2\pi \sqrt{\frac{L}{g}}$$

which is the correct period for a simple pendulum.

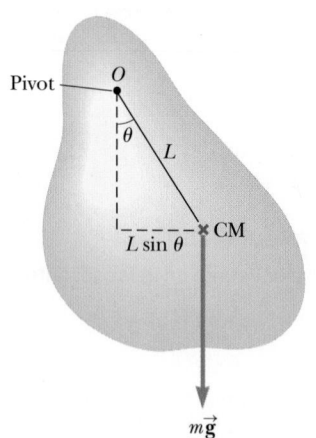

Figure 13.17 A physical pendulum pivoted at *O*.

13.6 Damped Oscillations

The vibrating motions we have discussed so far have taken place in ideal systems that *oscillate indefinitely* under the action of a linear restoring force. In all real

Figure 13.18 (a) A shock absorber consists of a piston oscillating in a chamber filled with oil. As the piston oscillates, the oil is squeezed through holes between the piston and the chamber, causing a damping of the piston's oscillations. (b) One type of automotive suspension system, in which a shock absorber is placed inside a coil spring at each wheel.

mechanical systems, forces of friction retard the motion, so the systems don't oscillate indefinitely. The friction reduces the mechanical energy of the system as time passes, and the motion is said to be **damped.**

Shock absorbers in automobiles (Fig. 13.18) are one practical application of damped motion. A shock absorber consists of a piston moving through a liquid such as oil. The upper part of the shock absorber is firmly attached to the body of the car. When the car travels over a bump in the road, holes in the piston allow it to move up and down in the fluid in a damped fashion.

Damped motion varies with the fluid used. For example, if the fluid has a relatively low viscosity, the vibrating motion is preserved but the amplitude of vibration decreases in time and the motion ultimately ceases. This process is known as *underdamped* oscillation. The position vs. time curve for an object undergoing such oscillation appears in Active Figure 13.19. Figure 13.20 compares three types of damped motion, with curve (a) representing underdamped oscillation. If the fluid viscosity is increased, the object returns rapidly to equilibrium after it's released and doesn't oscillate. In this case the system is said to be *critically damped,* and is shown as curve (b) in Figure 13.20. The piston returns to the equilibrium position in the shortest time possible without once overshooting the equilibrium position. If the viscosity is made greater still, the system is said to be *overdamped.* In this case the piston returns to equilibrium without ever passing through the equilibrium point, but the time required to reach equilibrium is greater than in critical damping, as illustrated by curve (c) in Figure 13.20.

To make automobiles more comfortable to ride in, shock absorbers are designed to be slightly underdamped. This can be demonstrated by a sharp downward push on the hood of a car. After the applied force is removed, the body of the car oscillates a few times about the equilibrium position before returning to its fixed position.

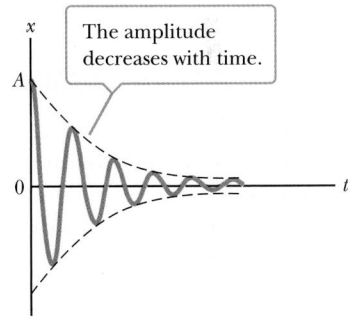

The amplitude decreases with time.

Active Figure 13.19
A graph of displacement versus time for an underdamped oscillator.

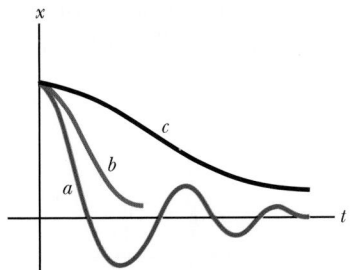

Figure 13.20 Plots of displacement versus time for (a) an underdamped oscillator, (b) a critically damped oscillator, and (c) an overdamped oscillator.

13.7 Waves

The world is full of waves: sound waves, waves on a string, seismic waves, and electromagnetic waves, such as visible light, radio waves, television signals, and x-rays. All these waves have as their source a vibrating object, so we can apply the concepts of simple harmonic motion in describing them.

In the case of sound waves, the vibrations that produce waves arise from sources such as a person's vocal chords or a plucked guitar string. The vibrations of electrons in an antenna produce radio or television waves, and the simple up-and-down motion of a hand can produce a wave on a string. Certain concepts are common to all waves, regardless of their nature. In the remainder of this chapter, we focus our attention on the general properties of waves. In later chapters we will study specific types of waves, such as sound waves and electromagnetic waves.

What Is a Wave?

When you drop a pebble into a pool of water, the disturbance produces water waves, which move away from the point where the pebble entered the water. A leaf floating near the disturbance moves up and down and back and forth about its original position, but doesn't undergo any net displacement attributable to the disturbance. This means that the water wave (or disturbance) moves from one place to another, *but the water isn't carried with it.*

When we observe a water wave, we see a rearrangement of the water's surface. Without the water, there wouldn't be a wave. Similarly, a wave traveling on a string wouldn't exist without the string. Sound waves travel through air as a result of pressure variations from point to point. Therefore, we can consider a wave to be *the motion of a disturbance.* In Chapter 21 we discuss electromagnetic waves, which don't require a medium.

The mechanical waves discussed in this chapter require (1) some source of disturbance, (2) a medium that can be disturbed, and (3) some physical connection or mechanism through which adjacent portions of the medium can influence each other. All waves carry energy and momentum. The amount of energy transmitted through a medium and the mechanism responsible for the transport of energy differ from case to case. The energy carried by ocean waves during a storm, for example, is much greater than the energy carried by a sound wave generated by a single human voice.

■ APPLYING PHYSICS 11.2 | Burying Bond

At one point in *On Her Majesty's Secret Service,* a James Bond film from the 1960s, Bond was escaping on skis. He had a good lead and was a hard-to-hit moving target. There was no point in wasting bullets shooting at him, so why did the bad guys open fire?

EXPLANATION These misguided gentlemen had a good understanding of the physics of waves. An impulsive sound, like a gunshot, can cause an acoustical disturbance that propagates through the air. If it impacts a ledge of snow that is ready to break free, an avalanche can result. Such a disaster occurred in 1916 during World War I when Austrian soldiers in the Alps were smothered by an avalanche caused by cannon fire. So the bad guys, who have never been able to hit Bond with a bullet, decided to use the sound of gunfire to start an avalanche. ■

Types of Waves

One of the simplest ways to demonstrate wave motion is to flip one end of a long string that is under tension and has its opposite end fixed, as in Active Figure 13.21. The bump (called a pulse) travels to the right with a definite speed. A disturbance of this type is called a **traveling wave.** The figure shows the shape of the string at three closely spaced times.

As such a wave pulse travels along the string, **each segment of the string that is disturbed moves in a direction perpendicular to the wave motion.** Figure 13.22 illustrates this point for a particular tiny segment P. The string never moves in the direction of the wave. A traveling wave in which the particles of the disturbed medium move in a direction perpendicular to the wave velocity is called a **transverse wave.** Figure 13.23a illustrates the formation of transverse waves on a long spring.

In another class of waves, called **longitudinal waves, the elements of the medium undergo displacements parallel to the direction of wave motion.** Sound waves in air are longitudinal. Their disturbance corresponds to a series of high- and low-pressure regions that may travel through air or through any material medium with a certain speed. A longitudinal pulse can easily be produced in a stretched spring, as in Figure 13.23b. The free end is pumped back and forth along the length of the spring. This action produces compressed and stretched regions of the coil that travel along the spring, parallel to the wave motion.

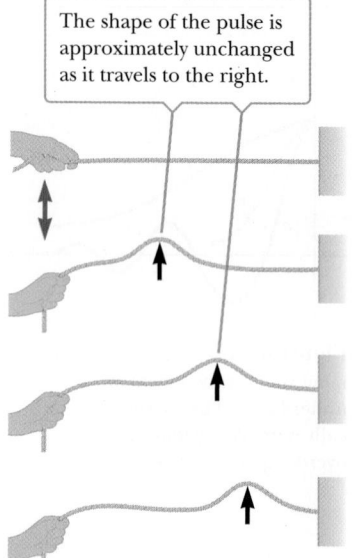

The shape of the pulse is approximately unchanged as it travels to the right.

Active Figure 13.21 A hand moves the end of a stretched string up and down once (red arrow), causing a pulse to travel along the string.

Waves need not be purely transverse or purely longitudinal: ocean waves exhibit a superposition of both types. When an ocean wave encounters a cork, the cork executes a circular motion, going up and down while going forward and back.

Another type of wave, called a **soliton,** consists of a solitary wave front that propagates in isolation. Ordinary water waves generally spread out and dissipate, but solitons tend to maintain their form. The study of solitons began in 1849, when Scottish engineer John Scott Russell noticed a solitary wave leaving the turbulence in front of a barge and propagating forward all on its own. The wave maintained its shape and traveled down a canal at about 10 mi/h. Russell chased the wave two miles on horseback before losing it. Only in the 1960s did scientists take solitons seriously; they are now widely used to model physical phenomena, from elementary particles to the Giant Red Spot of Jupiter.

Picture of a Wave

Active Figure 13.24 shows the curved shape of a vibrating string. This pattern is a sinusoidal curve, the same as in simple harmonic motion. The brown curve can be thought of as a snapshot of a traveling wave taken at some instant of time, say, $t = 0$; the blue curve is a snapshot of the same traveling wave at a later time. This picture can also be used to represent a wave on water. In such a case, a high point would correspond to the *crest* of the wave and a low point to the *trough* of the wave.

The same waveform can be used to describe a longitudinal wave, even though no up-and-down motion is taking place. Consider a longitudinal wave traveling on a spring. Figure 13.25a is a snapshot of this wave at some instant, and Figure 13.25b shows the sinusoidal curve that represents the wave. Points where the coils of the spring are compressed correspond to the crests of the waveform, and stretched regions correspond to troughs.

The type of wave represented by the curve in Figure 13.25b is often called a *density wave* or *pressure wave,* because the crests, where the spring coils are compressed, are regions of high density, and the troughs, where the coils are stretched, are regions of low density. Sound waves are longitudinal waves, propagating as a series of high- and low-density regions.

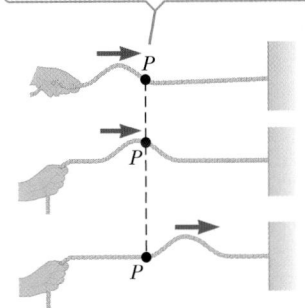

Any element P (black dot) on the rope moves in a direction perpendicular to the direction of propagation of the wave motion (red arrows).

Figure 13.22 A pulse traveling on a stretched string is a transverse wave.

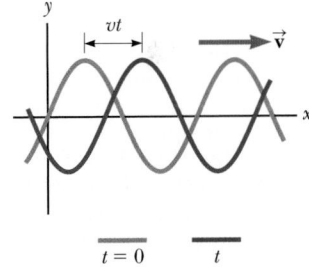

Active Figure 13.24
A one-dimensional sinusoidal wave traveling to the right with a speed v. The brown curve is a snapshot of the wave at $t = 0$, and the blue curve is another snapshot at some later time t.

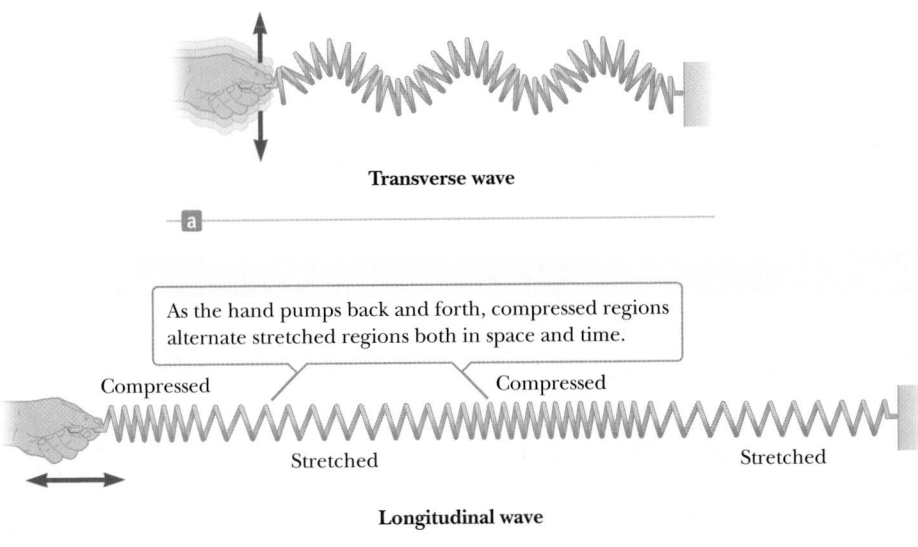

Transverse wave

As the hand pumps back and forth, compressed regions alternate stretched regions both in space and time.

Compressed   Compressed

Stretched   Stretched

Longitudinal wave

Figure 13.23 (a) A transverse wave is set up in a spring by moving one end of the spring perpendicular to its length. (b) A longitudinal wave along a stretched spring.

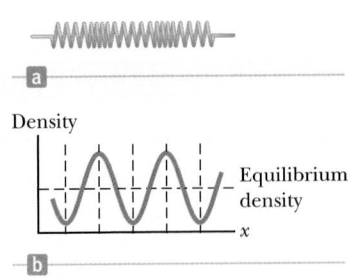

Density

Equilibrium density

Figure 13.25 (a) A longitudinal wave on a spring. (b) The crests of the waveform correspond to compressed regions of the spring, and the troughs correspond to stretched regions of the spring.

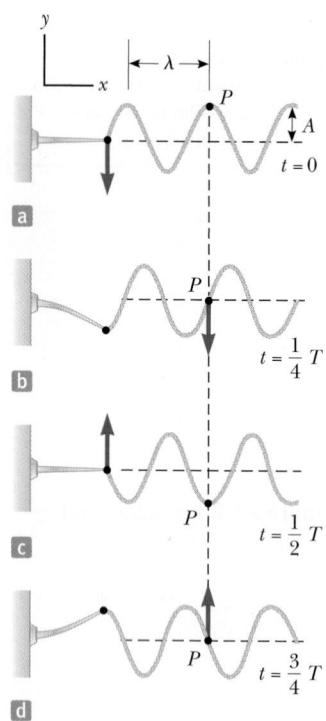

a

b

c

d

Active Figure 13.26
One method for producing traveling waves on a continuous string. The left end of the string is connected to a blade that is set vibrating. Every part of the string, such as point P, oscillates vertically with simple harmonic motion.

13.8 Frequency, Amplitude, and Wavelength

Active Figure 13.26 illustrates a method of producing a continuous wave or a steady stream of pulses on a very long string. One end of the string is connected to a blade that is set vibrating. As the blade oscillates vertically with simple harmonic motion, a traveling wave moving to the right is set up in the string. Active Figure 13.26 consists of views of the wave at intervals of one-quarter of a period. Note that **each small segment of the string, such as P, oscillates vertically in the y-direction with simple harmonic motion.** That must be the case because each segment follows the simple harmonic motion of the blade. Every segment of the string can therefore be treated as a simple harmonic oscillator vibrating with the same frequency as the blade that drives the string.

The frequencies of the waves studied in this course will range from rather low values for waves on strings and waves on water, to values for sound waves between 20 Hz and 20 000 Hz (recall that 1 Hz = 1 s^{-1}), to much higher frequencies for electromagnetic waves. These waves have different physical sources, but can be described with the same concepts.

The horizontal dashed line in Active Figure 13.26 represents the position of the string when no wave is present. The maximum distance the string moves above or below this equilibrium value is called the **amplitude** A of the wave. For the waves we work with, the amplitudes at the crest and the trough will be identical.

Active Figure 13.26a illustrates another characteristic of a wave. The horizontal arrows show the distance between two successive points that behave identically. This distance is called the **wavelength** λ (the Greek letter lambda).

We can use these definitions to derive an expression for the speed of a wave. We start with the defining equation for the **wave speed v**:

$$v = \frac{\Delta x}{\Delta t}$$

The wave speed is the speed at which a particular part of the wave—say, a crest—moves through the medium.

A wave advances a distance of one wavelength in a time interval equal to one period of the vibration. Taking $\Delta x = \lambda$ and $\Delta t = T$, we see that

$$v = \frac{\lambda}{T}$$

Because the frequency is the reciprocal of the period, we have

Wave speed ▶

$$\boxed{v = f\lambda}$$ [13.17]

This important general equation applies to many different types of waves, such as sound waves and electromagnetic waves.

■ EXAMPLE 13.8 | A Traveling Wave

GOAL Obtain information about a wave directly from its graph.

PROBLEM A wave traveling in the positive x-direction is pictured in Figure 13.27a. Find the amplitude, wavelength, speed, and period of the wave if it has a frequency of 8.00 Hz. In Figure 13.27a, $\Delta x = 40.0$ cm and $\Delta y = 15.0$ cm.

STRATEGY The amplitude and wavelength can be read directly from the figure: The maximum vertical displacement is the amplitude, and the distance from one crest to the next is the wavelength. Multiplying the wavelength by the frequency gives the speed, whereas the period is the reciprocal of the frequency.

Figure 13.27 (a) (Example 13.8) (b) (Exercise 13.8)

SOLUTION

The maximum wave displacement is the amplitude A:	$A = \Delta y = 15.0$ cm = $\boxed{0.150 \text{ m}}$
The distance from crest to crest is the wavelength:	$\lambda = \Delta x = 40.0$ cm = $\boxed{0.400 \text{ m}}$
Multiply the wavelength by the frequency to get the speed:	$v = f\lambda = (8.00 \text{ Hz})(0.400 \text{ m}) = \boxed{3.20 \text{ m/s}}$
Take the reciprocal of the frequency to get the period:	$T = \dfrac{1}{f} = \dfrac{1}{8.00 \text{ Hz}} = \boxed{0.125 \text{ s}}$

REMARKS It's important not to confuse the wave with the medium it travels in. A wave is energy transmitted through a medium; some waves, such as light waves, don't require a medium.

QUESTION 13.8 Is the frequency of a wave affected by the wave's amplitude?

EXERCISE 13.8 A wave traveling in the positive x-direction is pictured in Figure 13.27b. Find the amplitude, wavelength, speed, and period of the wave if it has a frequency of 15.0 Hz. In the figure, $\Delta x = 72.0$ cm and $\Delta y = 25.0$ cm.

ANSWERS $A = 0.250$ m, $\lambda = 0.720$ m, $v = 10.8$ m/s, $T = 0.0667$ s

---

■ EXAMPLE 13.9 | Sound and Light

GOAL Perform elementary calculations using speed, wavelength, and frequency.

PROBLEM A wave has a wavelength of 3.00 m. Calculate the frequency of the wave if it is **(a)** a sound wave and **(b)** a light wave. Take the speed of sound as 343 m/s and the speed of light as 3.00×10^8 m/s.

SOLUTION

(a) Find the frequency of a sound wave with $\lambda = 3.00$ m.

Solve Equation 3.17 for the frequency and substitute: **(1)** $\quad f = \dfrac{v}{\lambda} = \dfrac{343 \text{ m/s}}{3.00 \text{ m}} = \boxed{114 \text{ Hz}}$

(b) Find the frequency of a light wave with $\lambda = 3.00$ m.

Substitute into Equation (1), using the speed of light for c: $f = \dfrac{c}{\lambda} = \dfrac{3.00 \times 10^8 \text{ m/s}}{3.00 \text{ m}} = \boxed{1.00 \times 10^8 \text{ Hz}}$

REMARKS The same equation can be used to find the frequency in each case, despite the great difference between the physical phenomena. Notice how much larger frequencies of light waves are than frequencies of sound waves.

QUESTION 13.9 A wave in one medium encounters a new medium and enters it. Which of the following wave properties will be affected in this process? (a) wavelength (b) frequency (c) speed

EXERCISE 13.9 **(a)** Find the wavelength of an electromagnetic wave with frequency 9.00 GHz = 9.00×10^9 Hz (G = giga = 10^9), which is in the microwave range. **(b)** Find the speed of a sound wave in an unknown fluid medium if a frequency of 567 Hz has a wavelength of 2.50 m.

ANSWERS (a) 0.033 3 m (b) 1.42×10^3 m/s

13.9 The Speed of Waves on Strings

In this section we focus our attention on the speed of a transverse wave on a stretched string.

For a vibrating string, there are two speeds to consider. One is the speed of the physical string that vibrates up and down, transverse to the string, in the y-direction. The other is the *wave speed*, which is the rate at which the disturbance propagates along the length of the string in the x-direction. We wish to find an expression for the wave speed.

If a horizontal string under tension is pulled vertically and released, it starts at its maximum displacement, $y = A$, and takes a certain amount of time to go to $y = -A$ and back to A again. This amount of time is the period of the wave, and is the same as the time needed for the wave to advance *horizontally* by one wavelength. Dividing the wavelength by the period of one transverse oscillation gives the wave speed.

For a fixed wavelength, a string under greater tension F has a greater wave speed because the period of vibration is shorter, and the wave advances one wavelength during one period. It also makes sense that a string with greater mass per unit length, μ, vibrates more slowly, leading to a longer period and a slower wave speed. The wave speed is given by

$$v = \sqrt{\frac{F}{\mu}}$$ [13.18]

where F is the tension in the string and μ is the mass of the string per unit length, called the *linear density*. From Equation 13.18, it's clear that a larger tension F results in a larger wave speed, whereas a larger linear density μ gives a slower wave speed, as expected.

According to Equation 13.18, the propagation speed of a mechanical wave, such as a wave on a string, depends only on the properties of the string through which the disturbance travels. It doesn't depend on the amplitude of the vibration. This turns out to be generally true of waves in various media.

A proof of Equation 13.18 requires calculus, but dimensional analysis can easily verify that the expression is dimensionally correct. Note that the dimensions of F are ML/T^2, and the dimensions of μ are M/L. The dimensions of F/μ are therefore L^2/T^2, so those of $\sqrt{F/\mu}$ are L/T, giving the dimensions of speed. No other combination of F and μ is dimensionally correct, so in the case in which the tension and mass density are the only relevant physical factors, we have verified Equation 13.18 up to an overall constant.

APPLICATION
Bass Guitar Strings

According to Equation 13.18, we can increase the speed of a wave on a stretched string by increasing the tension in the string. Increasing the mass per unit length, on the other hand, decreases the wave speed. These physical facts lie behind the metallic windings on the bass strings of pianos and guitars. The windings increase the mass per unit length, μ, decreasing the wave speed and hence the frequency, resulting in a lower tone. Tuning a string to a desired frequency is a simple matter of changing the tension in the string.

■ EXAMPLE 13.10 │ A Pulse Traveling on a String

GOAL Calculate the speed of a wave on a string.

PROBLEM A uniform string has a mass M of 0.030 0 kg and a length L of 6.00 m. Tension is maintained in the string by suspending a block of mass $m = 2.00$ kg from one end (Fig. 13.28). **(a)** Find the speed of a transverse wave pulse on this string. **(b)** Find the time it takes the pulse to travel from the wall to the pulley. Neglect the mass of the hanging part of the string.

STRATEGY The tension F can be obtained from Newton's second law for equilibrium applied to the block, and the mass per unit length of the string is $\mu = M/L$. With these quantities, the speed of the transverse pulse can be found by substitution into Equation 13.18. Part (b) requires the formula $d = vt$.

Figure 13.28 (Example 13.10) The tension F in the string is maintained by the suspended block. The wave speed is given by the expression $v = \sqrt{F/\mu}$.

SOLUTION

(a) Find the speed of the wave pulse.

Apply the second law to the block: the tension F is equal and opposite to the force of gravity.

$$\Sigma F = F - mg = 0 \quad \rightarrow \quad F = mg$$

Substitute expressions for F and μ into Equation 13.18:

$$v = \sqrt{\frac{F}{\mu}} = \sqrt{\frac{mg}{M/L}}$$

$$= \sqrt{\frac{(2.00 \text{ kg})(9.80 \text{ m/s}^2)}{(0.030\ 0 \text{ kg})/(6.00 \text{ m})}} = \sqrt{\frac{19.6 \text{ N}}{0.005\ 00 \text{ kg/m}}}$$

$$= \boxed{62.6 \text{ m/s}}$$

(b) Find the time it takes the pulse to travel from the wall to the pulley.

Solve the distance formula for time:

$$t = \frac{d}{v} = \frac{5.00 \text{ m}}{62.6 \text{ m/s}} = \boxed{0.079\ 9 \text{ s}}$$

REMARKS Don't confuse the speed of the wave on the string with the speed of the sound wave produced by the vibrating string. (See Chapter 14.)

QUESTION 13.10 If the mass of the block is quadrupled, what happens to the speed of the wave?

EXERCISE 13.10 To what tension must a string with mass 0.010 0 kg and length 2.50 m be tightened so that waves will travel on it at a speed of 125 m/s?

ANSWER 62.5 N

13.10 Interference of Waves

Many interesting wave phenomena in nature require two or more waves passing through the same region of space at the same time. **Two traveling waves can meet and pass through each other without being destroyed or even altered.** For instance, when two pebbles are thrown into a pond, the expanding circular waves don't destroy each other. In fact, the ripples pass through each other. Likewise, when sound waves from two sources move through air, they pass through each other. In the region of overlap, the resultant wave is found by adding the displacements of the individual waves. For such analyses, the **superposition principle** applies:

> When two or more traveling waves encounter each other while moving through a medium, the resultant wave is found by adding together the displacements of the individual waves point by point.

Experiments show that the superposition principle is valid only when the individual waves have small amplitudes of displacement, which is an assumption we make in all our examples.

Figures 13.29a and 13.29b show two waves of the same amplitude and frequency. If at some instant of time these two waves were traveling through the same region of space, the resultant wave at that instant would have a shape like that shown in Figure 13.29c. For example, suppose the waves are water waves of amplitude 1 m. At the instant they overlap so that crest meets crest and trough meets trough, the resultant wave has an amplitude of 2 m. Waves coming together like that are said to be *in phase* and to exhibit **constructive interference.**

Figures 13.30a (page 462) and 13.30b show two similar waves. In this case, however, the crest of one coincides with the trough of the other, so one wave is *inverted* relative to the other. The resultant wave, shown in Figure 13.30c, is seen to be a

Combining the two waves in parts (a) and (b) results in a wave with twice the amplitude.

Figure 13.29 Constructive interference. If two waves having the same frequency and amplitude are in phase, as in (a) and (b), the resultant wave when they combine (c) has the same frequency as the individual waves, but twice their amplitude.

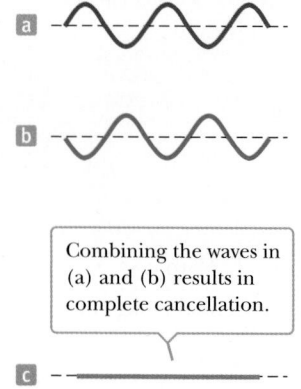

Figure 13.30 Destructive interference. The two waves in (a) and (b) have the same frequency and amplitude but are 180° out of phase.

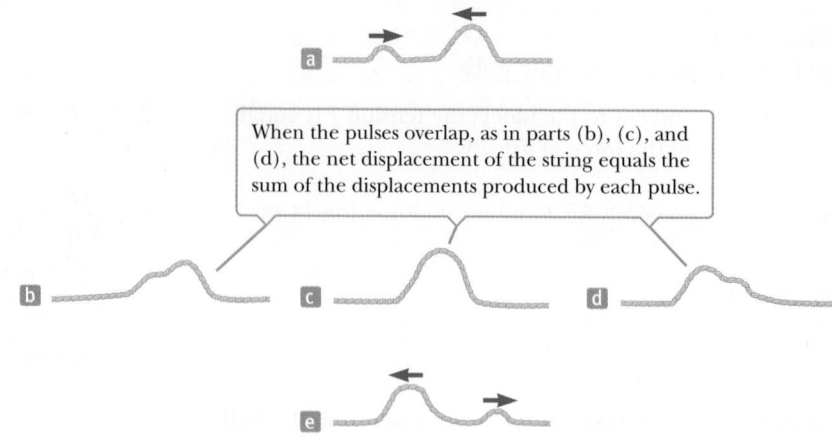

When the pulses overlap, as in parts (b), (c), and (d), the net displacement of the string equals the sum of the displacements produced by each pulse.

Active Figure 13.32
Two wave pulses traveling on a stretched string in opposite directions pass through each other.

Figure 13.31 Interference patterns produced by outward-spreading waves from many drops of liquid falling into a body of water.

state of complete cancellation. If these were water waves coming together, one of the waves would exert an upward force on an individual drop of water at the same instant the other wave was exerting a downward force. The result would be no motion of the water at all. In such a situation the two waves are said to be 180° out of phase and to exhibit **destructive interference.** Figure 13.31 illustrates the interference of water waves produced by drops of water falling into a pond.

Active Figure 13.32 shows constructive interference in two pulses moving toward each other along a stretched string; Active Figure 13.33 shows destructive interference in two pulses. Notice in both figures that when the two pulses separate, their shapes are unchanged, as if they had never met!

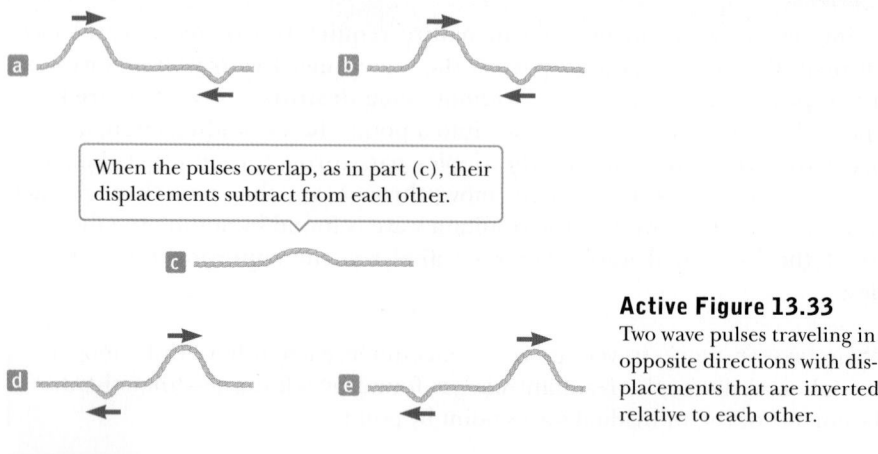

When the pulses overlap, as in part (c), their displacements subtract from each other.

Active Figure 13.33
Two wave pulses traveling in opposite directions with displacements that are inverted relative to each other.

Active Figure 13.34
The reflection of a traveling wave at the fixed end of a stretched string. Note that the reflected pulse is inverted, but its shape remains the same.

13.11 Reflection of Waves

In our discussion so far, we have assumed waves could travel indefinitely without striking anything. Often, such conditions are not realized in practice. Whenever a traveling wave reaches a boundary, part or all of the wave is reflected. For example, consider a pulse traveling on a string that is fixed at one end (Active Fig. 13.34). When the pulse reaches the wall, it is reflected.

Note that the reflected pulse is inverted. This can be explained as follows: When the pulse meets the wall, the string exerts an upward force on the wall. According to Newton's third law, the wall must exert an equal and opposite (downward) reaction force on the string. This downward force causes the pulse to invert on reflection.

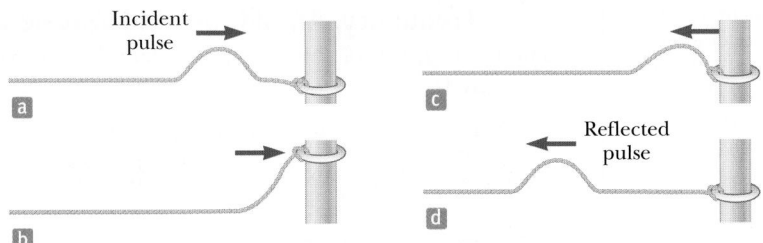

Active Figure 13.35
The reflection of a traveling wave at the free end of a stretched string. In this case the reflected pulse is not inverted.

Now suppose the pulse arrives at the string's end, and the end is attached to a ring of negligible mass that is free to slide along the post without friction (Active Fig. 13.35). Again the pulse is reflected, but this time it is not inverted. On reaching the post, the pulse exerts a force on the ring, causing it to accelerate upward. The ring is then returned to its original position by the downward component of the tension in the string.

An alternate method of showing that a pulse is reflected without inversion when it strikes a free end of a string is to send the pulse down a string hanging vertically. When the pulse hits the free end, it's reflected without inversion, just as is the pulse in Active Figure 13.35.

Finally, when a pulse reaches a boundary, it's partly reflected and partly transmitted past the boundary into the new medium. This effect is easy to observe in the case of two ropes of different density joined at some boundary.

■ SUMMARY

13.1 Hooke's Law
Simple harmonic motion occurs when the net force on an object along the direction of motion is proportional to the object's displacement and in the opposite direction:

$$F_s = -kx \qquad \text{[13.1]}$$

This equation is called Hooke's law. The time required for one complete vibration is called the **period** of the motion. The reciprocal of the period is the **frequency** of the motion, which is the number of oscillations per second.

When an object moves with simple harmonic motion, its **acceleration** as a function of position is

$$a = -\frac{k}{m}x \qquad \text{[13.2]}$$

13.2 Elastic Potential Energy
The energy stored in a stretched or compressed spring or in some other elastic material is called **elastic potential energy:**

$$PE_s \equiv \tfrac{1}{2}kx^2 \qquad \text{[13.3]}$$

The **velocity** of an object as a function of position, when the object is moving with simple harmonic motion, is

$$v = \pm\sqrt{\frac{k}{m}(A^2 - x^2)} \qquad \text{[13.6]}$$

13.3 Comparing Simple Harmonic Motion with Uniform Circular Motion
The **period** of an object of mass m moving with simple harmonic motion while attached to a spring of spring constant k is

$$T = 2\pi\sqrt{\frac{m}{k}} \qquad \text{[13.8]}$$

where T is independent of the amplitude A.

The **frequency** of an object–spring system is $f = 1/T$. The **angular frequency** ω of the system in rad/s is

$$\omega = 2\pi f = \sqrt{\frac{k}{m}} \qquad \text{[13.11]}$$

13.4 Position, Velocity, and Acceleration as a Function of Time
When an object is moving with simple harmonic motion, the **position, velocity,** and **acceleration** of the object as a function of time are given by

$$x = A\cos(2\pi f t) \qquad \text{[13.14a]}$$

$$v = -A\omega\sin(2\pi f t) \qquad \text{[13.14b]}$$

$$a = -A\omega^2\cos(2\pi f t) \qquad \text{[13.14c]}$$

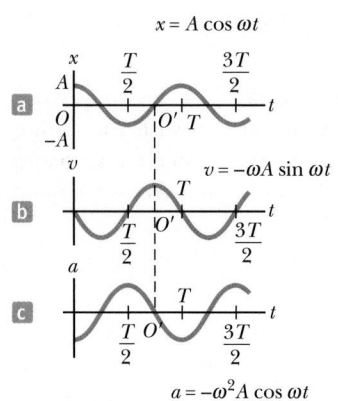

$x = A \cos \omega t$

$v = -\omega A \sin \omega t$

$a = -\omega^2 A \cos \omega t$

(a) Displacement, (b) velocity, and (c) acceleration versus time for an object moving with simple harmonic motion under the initial conditions $x_0 = A$ and $v_0 = 0$ at $t = 0$.

13.5 Motion of a Pendulum

A **simple pendulum** of length L moves with simple harmonic motion for small angular displacements from the vertical, with a period of

$$T = 2\pi \sqrt{\frac{L}{g}} \qquad [13.15]$$

13.7 Waves

In a **transverse wave** the elements of the medium move in a direction perpendicular to the direction of the wave. An example is a wave on a stretched string.

In a **longitudinal wave** the elements of the medium move parallel to the direction of the wave velocity. An example is a sound wave.

13.8 Frequency, Amplitude, and Wavelength

The relationship of the speed, wavelength, and frequency of a wave is

$$v = f\lambda \qquad [13.17]$$

This relationship holds for a wide variety of different waves.

13.9 The Speed of Waves on Strings

The speed of a wave traveling on a stretched string of mass per unit length μ and under tension F is

$$v = \sqrt{\frac{F}{\mu}} \qquad [13.18]$$

13.10 Interference of Waves

The **superposition principle** states that if two or more traveling waves are moving through a medium, the resultant wave is found by adding the individual waves together point by point. When waves meet crest to crest and trough to trough, they undergo **constructive interference.** When crest meets trough, the waves undergo **destructive interference.**

13.11 Reflection of Waves

When a wave pulse reflects from a rigid boundary, the pulse is inverted. When the boundary is free, the reflected pulse is not inverted.

■ MULTIPLE-CHOICE QUESTIONS

WebAssign The multiple-choice questions in this chapter may be assigned online in Enhanced WebAssign.

---

1. The distance between the crest of a water wave and the next trough is 2 m. If the frequency of a particular wave is 2 Hz, what is the speed of the wave? (a) 4 m/s (b) 1 m/s (c) 8 m/s (d) 2 m/s (e) impossible to determine from the information given

2. The position of an object moving with simple harmonic motion is given by $x = 4 \cos (6\pi t)$, where x is in meters and t is in seconds. What is the period of the oscillating system? (a) 4 s (b) $\frac{1}{6}$ s (c) $\frac{1}{3}$ s (d) 6π s (e) impossible to determine from the information given

3. A block-spring system vibrating on a frictionless, horizontal surface with an amplitude of 6.0 cm has a total energy of 12 J. If the block is replaced by one having twice the mass of the original block and the amplitude of the motion is again 6.0 cm, what is the energy of the more massive system? (a) 12 J (b) 24 J (c) 6 J (d) 48 J (e) none of those answers

4. A mass of 0.40 kg, hanging from a spring with a spring constant of 80.0 N/m, is set into an up-and-down simple harmonic motion. If the mass is displaced from equilibrium by 0.10 m and released from rest, what is

its speed when moving through the equilibrium point? (a) 0 (b) 1.4 m/s (c) 2.0 m/s (d) 3.4 m/s (e) 4.2 m/s

5. If an object of mass m attached to a light spring is replaced by one of mass $9m$, the frequency of the vibrating system changes by what multiplicative factor? (a) $\frac{1}{9}$ (b) $\frac{1}{3}$ (c) 3.0 (d) 9.0 (e) 6.0

6. An object of mass 0.40 kg, hanging from a spring with a spring constant of 8.0 N/m, is set into an up-and-down simple harmonic motion. What is the magnitude of the acceleration of the object when it is at its maximum displacement of 0.10 m? (a) 0 (b) 0.45 m/s² (c) 1.0 m/s² (d) 2.0 m/s² (e) 2.40 m/s²

7. A runaway railroad car with mass 3.0×10^5 kg coasts across a level track at 2.0 m/s when it collides elastically with a spring-loaded bumper at the end of the track. If the spring constant of the bumper is 2.0×10^6 N/m, what is the maximum compression of the spring during the collision? (a) 0.77 m (b) 0.58 m (c) 0.34 m (d) 1.07 m (e) 1.24 m

8. If a simple pendulum oscillates with a small amplitude and its length is doubled, what happens to the

frequency of its motion? (a) It doubles. (b) It becomes $\sqrt{2}$ times as large. (c) It becomes half as large. (d) It becomes $1/\sqrt{2}$ as large. (e) It remains the same.

9. A simple pendulum has a period of 2.5 s. What is its period if its length is made four times as large? (a) 0.625 s (b) 1.25 s (c) 2.5 s (d) 3.54 s (e) 5.0 s

10. A particle on a spring moves in simple harmonic motion along the x-axis between turning points at $x_1 = 100$ cm and $x_2 = 140$ cm. At which of the following positions does the particle have its maximum kinetic energy? (a) 100 cm (b) 110 cm (c) 120 cm (d) 130 cm (e) 140 cm

11. Which of the following statements is *not* true regarding a mass–spring system that moves with simple harmonic motion in the absence of friction? (a) The total energy of the system remains constant. (b) The energy of the system is continually transformed between kinetic and potential energy. (c) The total energy of the system is proportional to the square of the amplitude. (d) The potential energy stored in the system is greatest when the mass passes through the equilibrium position. (e) The velocity of the oscillating mass has its maximum value when the mass passes through the equilibrium position.

12. A block is attached to a spring hanging vertically. After being slowly lowered, it hangs at rest with the spring stretched by 15.0 cm. If the block is raised back up and released from rest with the spring unstretched, what maximum distance does it fall? (a) 7.5 cm (b) 15.0 cm (c) 30.0 cm (d) 60.0 cm (e) impossible to determine without knowing the mass and spring constant

13. An object–spring system moving with simple harmonic motion has an amplitude A. When the kinetic energy of the object equals twice the potential energy stored in the spring, what is the position x of the object? (a) A (b) $\frac{1}{3}A$ (c) $A/\sqrt{3}$ (d) 0 (e) none of those answers

14. You stand on the end of a diving board and bounce to set it into oscillation. You find a maximum response in terms of the amplitude of oscillation of the end of the board when you bounce at a frequency f. You now move to the middle of the board and repeat the experiment. Is the resonance frequency of the forced oscillations at this point (a) higher, (b) lower, or (c) the same as f?

CONCEPTUAL QUESTIONS

WebAssign The conceptual questions in this chapter may be assigned online in Enhanced WebAssign.

1. An object–spring system undergoes simple harmonic motion with an amplitude A. Does the total energy change if the mass is doubled but the amplitude isn't changed? Are the kinetic and potential energies at a given point in its motion affected by the change in mass? Explain.

2. If an object–spring system is hung vertically and set into oscillation, why does the motion eventually stop?

3. An object is hung on a spring, and the frequency of oscillation of the system, f, is measured. The object, a second identical object, and the spring are carried to space in the space shuttle. The two objects are attached to the ends of the spring, and the system is taken out into space on a space walk. The spring is extended, and the system is released to oscillate while floating in space. The coils of the spring don't bump into one another. What is the frequency of oscillation for this system in terms of f?

4. If a spring is cut in half, what happens to its spring constant?

5. A pendulum bob is made from a sphere filled with water. What would happen to the frequency of vibration of this pendulum if the sphere had a hole in it that allowed the water to leak out slowly?

6. If a pendulum clock keeps perfect time at the base of a mountain, will it also keep perfect time when it is moved to the top of the mountain? Explain.

7. (a) Is a bouncing ball an example of simple harmonic motion? (b) Is the daily movement of a student from home to school and back simple harmonic motion?

8. If a grandfather clock were running slow, how could we adjust the length of the pendulum to correct the time?

9. What happens to the speed of a wave on a string when the frequency is doubled? Assume the tension in the string remains the same.

10. If you stretch a rubber hose and pluck it, you can observe a pulse traveling up and down the hose. What happens to the speed of the pulse if you stretch the hose more tightly? What happens to the speed if you fill the hose with water?

11. Explain why the kinetic and potential energies of an object–spring system can never be negative.

12. A grandfather clock depends on the period of a pendulum to keep correct time. Suppose such a clock is calibrated correctly and then the temperature of the room in which it resides increases. Does the clock run slow, fast, or correctly? *Hint:* A material expands when its temperature increases.

■ PROBLEMS

WebAssign The problems in this chapter may be assigned online in Enhanced WebAssign. Selected problems also have Watch It video solutions.

1. denotes straightforward problem; **2.** denotes intermediate problem;
3. denotes challenging problem
1. denotes full solution available in *Student Solutions Manual/ Study Guide*

1. denotes problems most often assigned in Enhanced WebAssign
BIO denotes biomedical problems
GP denotes guided problems
M denotes Master It tutorial available in Enhanced WebAssign
Q|C denotes asking for quantitative and conceptual reasoning
S denotes symbolic reasoning problem

13.1 Hooke's Law

1. A block of mass $m =$ 0.60 kg attached to a spring with force constant 130 N/m is free to move on a frictionless, horizontal surface as in Figure P13.1. The block is released from rest after the spring is stretched a distance $A = 0.13$ m. At that instant, find (a) the force on the block and (b) its acceleration.

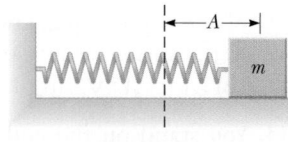
Figure P13.1

2. A spring oriented vertically is attached to a hard horizontal surface as in Figure P13.2. The spring has a force constant of 1.46 kN/m. How much is the spring compressed when a object of mass $m = 2.30$ kg is placed on top of the spring and the system is at rest?

Figure P13.2

3. The force constant of a spring is 137 N/m. Find the magnitude of the force required to (a) compress the spring by 4.80 cm from its unstretched length and (b) stretch the spring by 7.36 cm from its unstretched length.

4. A load of 50 N attached to a spring hanging vertically stretches the spring 5.0 cm. The spring is now placed horizontally on a table and stretched 11 cm. (a) What force is required to stretch the spring by that amount? (b) Plot a graph of force (on the *y*-axis) versus spring displacement from the equilibrium position along the *x*-axis.

5. A spring is hung from a ceiling, and an object attached to its lower end stretches the spring by a distance $d = 5.00$ cm from its unstretched position when the system is in equilibrium as in Figure P13.5. If the spring constant is 47.5 N/m, determine the mass of the object.

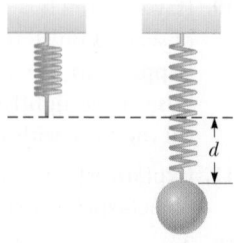
Figure P13.5

6. An archer must exert a force of 375 N on the bowstring shown in Figure P13.6a such that the string makes an angle of $\theta = 35.0°$ with the vertical. (a) Determine the tension in the bowstring. (b) If the applied force is replaced by a stretched spring as in Figure P13.6b and the spring is stretched 30.0 cm from its unstretched length, what is the spring constant?

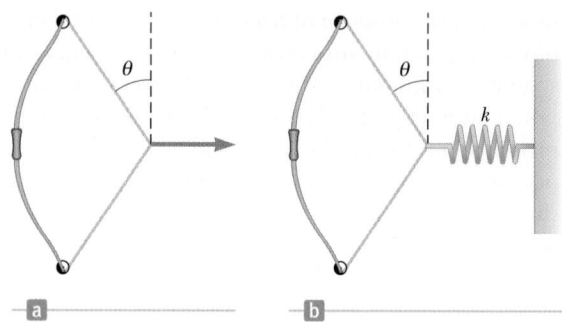
Figure P13.6

7. **Q|C** A spring 1.50 m long with force constant 475 N/m is hung from the ceiling of an elevator, and a block of mass 10.0 kg is attached to the bottom of the spring. (a) By how much is the spring stretched when the block is slowly lowered to its equilibrium point? (b) If the elevator subsequently accelerates upward at 2.00 m/s², what is the position of the block, taking the equilibrium position found in part (a) as $y = 0$ and upwards as the positive *y*-direction. (c) If the elevator cable snaps during the acceleration, describe the subsequent motion of the block relative to the freely falling elevator. What is the amplitude of its motion?

13.2 Elastic Potential Energy

8. A block of mass $m = 2.00$ kg is attached to a spring of force constant $k = 5.00 \times 10^2$ N/m that lies on a horizontal frictionless surface as shown in Figure P13.8. The block is pulled to a position $x_i = 5.00$ cm to the right of equilibrium and released from rest. Find (a) the work required to stretch the spring and (b) the speed the block has as it passes through equilibrium.

Figure P13.8

9. A slingshot consists of a light leather cup containing a stone. The cup is pulled back against two parallel rubber bands. It takes a force of 15 N to stretch either one of these bands 1.0 cm. (a) What is the potential energy stored in the two bands together when a 50-g stone is placed in the cup and pulled back 0.20 m from the equilibrium position? (b) With what speed does the stone leave the slingshot?

10. An archer pulls her bowstring back 0.400 m by exerting a force that increases uniformly from zero to 230 N. (a) What is the equivalent spring constant of the bow? (b) How much work is done in pulling the bow?

11. A child's toy consists of a piece of plastic attached to a spring (Fig. P13.11). The spring is compressed against the floor a distance of 2.00 cm, and the toy is released. If the toy has a mass of 100 g and rises to a maximum height of 60.0 cm, estimate the force constant of the spring.

Figure P13.11

12. An automobile having a mass of 1 000 kg is driven into a brick wall in a safety test. The bumper behaves like a spring with constant 5.00×10^6 N/m and is compressed 3.16 cm as the car is brought to rest. What was the speed of the car before impact, assuming no energy is lost in the collision with the wall?

13. A 10.0-g bullet is fired into, and embeds itself in, a 2.00-kg block attached to a spring with a force constant of 19.6 N/m and whose mass is negligible. How far is the spring compressed if the bullet has a speed of 300 m/s just before it strikes the block and the block slides on a frictionless surface? *Note:* You must use conservation of momentum in this problem because of the inelastic collision between the bullet and block.

14. **S** An object–spring system moving with simple harmonic motion has an amplitude A. (a) What is the total energy of the system in terms of k and A only? (b) Suppose at a certain instant the kinetic energy is twice the elastic potential energy. Write an equation describing this situation, using only the variables for the mass m, velocity v, spring constant k, and position x. (c) Using the results of parts (a) and (b) and the conservation of energy equation, find the positions x of the object when its kinetic energy equals twice the potential energy stored in the spring. (The answer should in terms of A only.)

15. **GP** A horizontal block–spring system with the block on a frictionless surface has total mechanical energy E = 47.0 J and a maximum displacement from equilibrium of 0.240 m. (a) What is the spring constant? (b) What is the kinetic energy of the system at the equilibrium point? (c) If the maximum speed of the block is 3.45 m/s, what is its mass? (d) What is the speed of the block when its displacement is 0.160 m? (e) Find the kinetic energy of the block at x = 0.160 m. (f) Find the potential energy stored in the spring when x = 0.160 m. (g) Suppose the same system is released from rest at x = 0.240 m on a rough surface so that it loses

14.0 J by the time it reaches its first turning point (after passing equilibrium at x = 0). What is its position at that instant?

16. **Q|C** A 0.250-kg block resting on a frictionless, horizontal surface is attached to a spring having force constant 83.8 N/m as in Figure P13.16. A horizontal force $\vec{F}$ causes the spring to stretch a distance of 5.46 cm from its equilibrium position. (a) Find the value of F. (b) What is the total energy stored in the system when the spring is stretched? (c) Find the magnitude of the acceleration of the block immediately after the applied force is removed. (d) Find the speed of the block when it first reaches the equilibrium position. (e) If the surface is not frictionless but the block still reaches the equilibrium position, how would your answer to part (d) change? (f) What other information would you need to know to find the actual answer to part (d) in this case?

Figure P13.16

13.3 Comparing Simple Harmonic Motion with Uniform Circular Motion

13.4 Position, Velocity, and Acceleration as a Function of Time

17. A 0.40-kg object connected to a light spring with a force constant of 19.6 N/m oscillates on a frictionless horizontal surface. If the spring is compressed 4.0 cm and released from rest, determine (a) the maximum speed of the object, (b) the speed of the object when the spring is compressed 1.5 cm, and (c) the speed of the object as it passes the point 1.5 cm from the equilibrium position. (d) For what value of x does the speed equal one-half the maximum speed?

18. An object–spring system oscillates with an amplitude of 3.5 cm. If the spring constant is 250 N/m and the object has a mass of 0.50 kg, determine (a) the mechanical energy of the system, (b) the maximum speed of the object, and (c) the maximum acceleration of the object.

19. **M** At an outdoor market, a bunch of bananas attached to the bottom of a vertical spring of force constant 16.0 N/m is set into oscillatory motion with an amplitude of 20.0 cm. It is observed that the maximum speed of the bunch of bananas is 40.0 cm/s. What is the weight of the bananas in newtons?

20. A 50.0-g object is attached to a horizontal spring with a force constant of 10.0 N/m and released from rest with an amplitude of 25.0 cm. What is the velocity of the object when it is halfway to the equilibrium position if the surface is frictionless?

21. A horizontal spring attached to a wall has a force constant of k = 850 N/m. A block of mass m = 1.00 kg is attached to the spring and rests on a frictionless, horizontal surface as in Figure P13.21 on page 468. (a) The

block is pulled to a position $x_i = 6.00$ cm from equilibrium and released. Find the potential energy stored in the spring when the block is 6.00 cm from equilibrium. (b) Find the speed of the block as it passes through the equilibrium position. (c) What is the speed of the block when it is at a position $x_i/2 = 3.00$ cm?

$x = 0 \quad x = x_i/2 \quad x = x_i$

Figure P13.21

22. An object moves uniformly around a circular path of radius 20.0 cm, making one complete revolution every 2.00 s. What are (a) the translational speed of the object, (b) the frequency of motion in hertz, and (c) the angular speed of the object?

23. Consider the simplified single-piston engine in Figure P13.23. If the wheel rotates at a constant angular speed ω, explain why the piston oscillates in simple harmonic motion.

$x = -A \quad x(t)$
$x = 0$

Figure P13.23

24. The period of motion of an object–spring system is $T = 0.528$ s when an object of mass $m = 238$ g is attached to the spring. Find (a) the frequency of motion in hertz and (b) the force constant of the spring. (c) If the total energy of the oscillating motion is 0.234 J, find the amplitude of the oscillations.

25. **M** A vertical spring stretches 3.9 cm when a 10-g object is hung from it. The object is replaced with a block of mass 25 g that oscillates up and down in simple harmonic motion. Calculate the period of motion.

26. When four people with a combined mass of 320 kg sit down in a 2.0×10^3-kg car, they find that their weight compresses the springs an additional 0.80 cm. (a) What is the effective force constant of the springs? (b) The four people get out of the car and bounce it up and down. What is the frequency of the car's vibration?

27. A cart of mass 250 g is placed on a frictionless horizontal air track. A spring having a spring constant of 9.5 N/m is attached between the cart and the left end of the track. If the cart is displaced 4.5 cm from its equilibrium position, find (a) the period at which it oscillates, (b) its maximum speed, and (c) its speed when it is located 2.0 cm from its equilibrium position.

28. The position of an object connected to a spring varies with time according to the expression $x = (5.2 \text{ cm}) \sin (8.0\pi t)$. Find (a) the period of this motion, (b) the frequency of the motion, (c) the amplitude of the motion, and (d) the first time after $t = 0$ that the object reaches the position $x = 2.6$ cm.

29. A 326-g object is attached to a spring and executes simple harmonic motion with a period of 0.250 s. If the total energy of the system is 5.83 J, find (a) the maximum speed of the object, (b) the force constant of the spring, and (c) the amplitude of the motion.

30. **S** An object executes simple harmonic motion with an amplitude A. (a) At what values of its position does its speed equal half its maximum speed? (b) At what values of its position does its potential energy equal half the total energy?

31. A 2.00-kg object on a frictionless horizontal track is attached to the end of a horizontal spring whose force constant is 5.00 N/m. The object is displaced 3.00 m to the right from its equilibrium position and then released, initiating simple harmonic motion. (a) What is the force (magnitude and direction) acting on the object 3.50 s after it is released? (b) How many times does the object oscillate in 3.50 s?

32. **GP** A spring of negligible mass stretches 3.00 cm from its relaxed length when a force of 7.50 N is applied. A 0.500-kg particle rests on a frictionless horizontal surface and is attached to the free end of the spring. The particle is displaced from the origin to $x = 5.00$ cm and released from rest at $t = 0$. (a) What is the force constant of the spring? (b) What are the angular frequency ω, the frequency, and the period of the motion? (c) What is the total energy of the system? (d) What is the amplitude of the motion? (e) What are the maximum velocity and the maximum acceleration of the particle? (f) Determine the displacement x of the particle from the equilibrium position at $t = 0.500$ s. (g) Determine the velocity and acceleration of the particle when $t = 0.500$ s.

33. Given that $x = A \cos (\omega t)$ is a sinusoidal function of time, show that v (velocity) and a (acceleration) are also sinusoidal functions of time. *Hint:* Use Equations 13.6 and 13.2.

13.5 Motion of a Pendulum

34. A man enters a tall tower, needing to know its height. He notes that a long pendulum extends from the ceiling almost to the floor and that its period is 15.5 s. (a) How tall is the tower? (b) If this pendulum is taken to the Moon, where the free-fall acceleration is 1.67 m/s², what is the period there?

35. A simple pendulum has a length of 52.0 cm and makes 82.0 complete oscillations in 2.00 min. Find (a) the period of the pendulum and (b) the value of g at the location of the pendulum.

36. A "seconds" pendulum is one that moves through its equilibrium position once each second. (The period of the pendulum is 2.000 s.) The length of a seconds pendulum is 0.992 7 m at Tokyo and 0.994 2 m at Cambridge, England. What is the ratio of the free-fall accelerations at these two locations?

37. A pendulum clock that works perfectly on the Earth is taken to the Moon. (a) Does it run fast or slow there? (b) If the clock is started at 12:00 midnight, what will it read after one Earth day (24.0 h)? Assume the free-fall acceleration on the Moon is 1.63 m/s².

38. A coat hanger of mass $m = 0.238$ kg oscillates on a peg as a physical pendulum as shown in Figure P13.38. The distance from the pivot to the center of mass of the coat hanger is $d = 18.0$ cm and the period of the motion is $T = 1.25$ s. Find the moment of inertia of the coat hanger about the pivot.

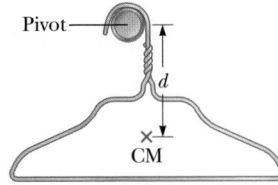

Figure P13.38

39. **M** The free-fall acceleration on Mars is 3.7 m/s². (a) What length of pendulum has a period of 1 s on Earth? (b) What length of pendulum would have a 1-s period on Mars? An object is suspended from a spring with force constant 10 N/m. Find the mass suspended from this spring that would result in a period of 1 s (c) on Earth and (d) on Mars.

40. A simple pendulum is 5.00 m long. (a) What is the period of simple harmonic motion for this pendulum if it is located in an elevator accelerating upward at 5.00 m/s²? (b) What is its period if the elevator is accelerating downward at 5.00 m/s²? (c) What is the period of simple harmonic motion for the pendulum if it is placed in a truck that is accelerating horizontally at 5.00 m/s²?

13.6 Damped Oscillations

13.7 Waves

13.8 Frequency, Amplitude, and Wavelength

41. The sinusoidal wave shown in Figure P13.41 is traveling in the positive x-direction and has a frequency

Figure P13.41

of 18.0 Hz. Find the (a) amplitude, (b) wavelength, (c) period, and (d) speed of the wave.

42. An object attached to a spring vibrates with simple harmonic motion as described by Figure P13.42. For this motion, find (a) the amplitude, (b) the period, (c) the angular frequency, (d) the maximum speed, (e) the maximum acceleration, and (f) an equation for its position x in terms of a sine function.

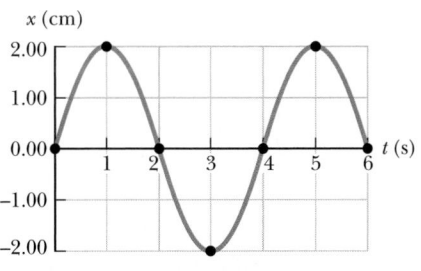

Figure P13.42

43. Light waves are electromagnetic waves that travel at 3.00×10^8 m/s. The eye is most sensitive to light having a wavelength of 5.50×10^{-7} m. Find (a) the frequency of this light wave and (b) its period.

44. The distance between two successive minima of a transverse wave is 2.76 m. Five crests of the wave pass a given point along the direction of travel every 14.0 s. Find (a) the frequency of the wave and (b) the wave speed.

45. A harmonic wave is traveling along a rope. It is observed that the oscillator that generates the wave completes 40.0 vibrations in 30.0 s. Also, a given maximum travels 425 cm along the rope in 10.0 s. What is the wavelength?

46. **BIO** A bat can detect small objects, such as an insect, whose size is approximately equal to one wavelength of the sound the bat makes. If bats emit a chirp at a frequency of 60.0×10^3 Hz and the speed of sound in air is 343 m/s, what is the smallest insect a bat can detect?

47. A cork on the surface of a pond bobs up and down two times per second on ripples having a wavelength of 8.50 cm. If the cork is 10.0 m from shore, how long does it take a ripple passing the cork to reach the shore?

48. Ocean waves are traveling to the east at 4.0 m/s with a distance of 20 m between crests. With what frequency do the waves hit the front of a boat (a) when the boat is at anchor and (b) when the boat is moving westward at 1.0 m/s?

13.9 The Speed of Waves on Strings

49. An ethernet cable is 4.00 m long and has a mass of 0.200 kg. A transverse wave pulse is produced by plucking one end of the taut cable. The pulse makes four trips down and back along the cable in 0.800 s. What is the tension in the cable?

50. A circus performer stretches a tightrope between two towers. He strikes one end of the rope and sends a wave along it toward the other tower. He notes that it takes the wave 0.800 s to reach the opposite tower, 20.0 m away. If a 1.00-m length of the rope has a mass of 0.350 kg, find the tension in the tightrope.

51. A piano string of mass per unit length 5.00×10^{-3} kg/m is under a tension of 1 350 N. Find the speed with which a wave travels on this string.

52. QC S A student taking a quiz finds on a reference sheet the two equations

$$f = \frac{1}{T} \quad \text{and} \quad v = \sqrt{\frac{T}{\mu}}$$

She has forgotten what T represents in each equation. (a) Use dimensional analysis to determine the units required for T in each equation. (b) Explain how you can identify the physical quantity each T represents from the units.

53. Transverse waves with a speed of 50.0 m/s are to be produced on a stretched string. A 5.00-m length of string with a total mass of 0.060 0 kg is used. (a) What is the required tension in the string? (b) Calculate the wave speed in the string if the tension is 8.00 N.

54. An astronaut on the Moon wishes to measure the local value of g by timing pulses traveling down a wire that has a large object suspended from it. Assume a wire of mass 4.00 g is 1.60 m long and has a 3.00-kg object suspended from it. A pulse requires 36.1 ms to traverse the length of the wire. Calculate g_{Moon} from these data. (You may neglect the mass of the wire when calculating the tension in it.)

55. A simple pendulum consists of a ball of mass 5.00 kg hanging from a uniform string of mass 0.060 0 kg and length L. If the period of oscillation of the pendulum is 2.00 s, determine the speed of a transverse wave in the string when the pendulum hangs vertically.

56. A string is 50.0 cm long and has a mass of 3.00 g. A wave travels at 5.00 m/s along this string. A second string has the same length, but half the mass of the first. If the two strings are under the same tension, what is the speed of a wave along the second string?

57. M Tension is maintained in a string as in Figure P13.57. The observed wave speed is $v = 24.0$ m/s when the suspended mass is $m = 3.00$ kg. (a) What is the mass per unit length of the string? (b) What is the wave speed when the suspended mass is $m = 2.00$ kg?

Figure P13.57

58. The elastic limit of a piece of steel wire is 2.70×10^9 Pa. What is the maximum speed at which transverse wave pulses can propagate along the wire without

exceeding its elastic limit? (The density of steel is 7.86×10^3 kg/m³.)

59. QC A 2.65-kg power line running between two towers has a length of 38.0 m and is under a tension of 12.5 N. (a) What is the speed of a transverse pulse set up on the line? (b) If the tension in the line was unknown, describe a procedure a worker on the ground might use to estimate the tension.

60. S A taut clothesline has length L and a mass M. A transverse pulse is produced by plucking one end of the clothesline. If the pulse makes n round trips along the clothesline in t seconds, find expressions for (a) the speed of the pulse in terms of n, L, and t and (b) the tension F in the clothesline in terms of the same variables and mass M.

13.10 Interference of Waves

13.11 Reflection of Waves

61. A wave of amplitude 0.30 m interferes with a second wave of amplitude 0.20 m traveling in the same direction. What are (a) the largest and (b) the smallest resultant amplitudes that can occur, and under what conditions will these maxima and minima arise?

Additional Problems

62. The position of a 0.30-kg object attached to a spring is described by

$$x = (0.25 \text{ m}) \cos (0.4\pi t)$$

Find (a) the amplitude of the motion, (b) the spring constant, (c) the position of the object at $t = 0.30$ s, and (d) the object's speed at $t = 0.30$ s.

63. An object of mass 2.00 kg is oscillating freely on a vertical spring with a period of 0.600 s. Another object of unknown mass on the same spring oscillates with a period of 1.05 s. Find (a) the spring constant k and (b) the unknown mass.

64. A certain tuning fork vibrates at a frequency of 196 Hz while each tip of its two prongs has an amplitude of 0.850 mm. (a) What is the period of this motion? (b) Find the wavelength of the sound produced by the vibrating fork, taking the speed of sound in air to be 343 m/s.

65. A simple pendulum has mass 1.20 kg and length 0.700 m. (a) What is the period of the pendulum near the surface of Earth? (b) If the same mass is attached to a spring, what spring constant would result in the period of motion found in part (a)?

66. A 500-g block is released from rest and slides down a frictionless track that begins 2.00 m above the horizontal, as shown in Figure P13.66. At the bottom of the track, where the surface is horizontal, the block strikes and sticks to a light spring with a spring constant of 20.0 N/m. Find the maximum distance the spring is compressed.

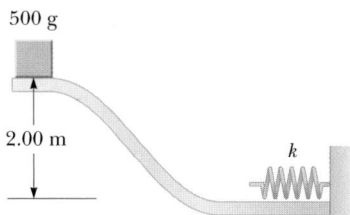

Figure P13.66

67. A 3.00-kg object is fastened to a light spring, with the intervening cord passing over a pulley (Fig. P13.67). The pulley is frictionless, and its inertia may be neglected. The object is released from rest when the spring is unstretched. If the object drops 10.0 cm before stopping, find (a) the spring constant of the spring and (b) the speed of the object when it is 5.00 cm below its starting point.

Figure P13.67

68. A 5.00-g bullet moving with an initial speed of 400 m/s is fired into and passes through a 1.00-kg block, as in Figure P13.68. The block, initially at rest on a frictionless horizontal surface, is connected to a spring with a spring constant of 900 N/m. If the block moves 5.00 cm to the right after impact, find (a) the speed at which the bullet emerges from the block and (b) the mechanical energy lost in the collision.

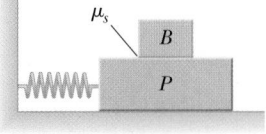

Figure P13.68

69. **M** A large block P executes horizontal simple harmonic motion as it slides across a frictionless surface with a frequency $f = 1.50$ Hz. Block B rests on it, as shown in Figure P13.69, and the coefficient of static friction between the two is $\mu_s = 0.600$. What maximum amplitude of oscillation can the system have if block B is not to slip?

Figure P13.69

70. A spring in a toy gun has a spring constant of 9.80 N/m and can be compressed 20.0 cm beyond the equilibrium position. A 1.00-g pellet resting against the spring is propelled forward when the spring is released. (a) Find the muzzle speed of the pellet. (b) If the pellet is fired horizontally from a height of 1.00 m above the floor, what is its range?

71. **QC** A light balloon filled with helium of density 0.179 kg/m^3 is tied to a light string of length $L = 3.00$ m. The string is tied to the ground, forming an "inverted" simple pendulum (Fig. P13.71a). If the balloon is displaced slightly from equilibrium, as in Figure P13.71b, (a) show that the motion is simple harmonic and (b) determine the period of the motion. Take the density of air to be 1.29 kg/m^3. *Hint:* Use an analogy with the simple pendulum discussed in the text, and see Chapter 9.

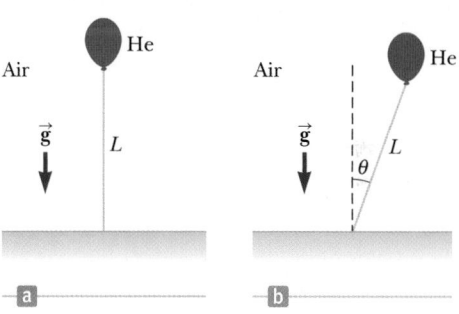

Figure P13.71

72. **S** An object of mass m is connected to two rubber bands of length L, each under tension F, as in Figure P13.72. The object is displaced vertically by a small distance y. Assuming the tension does not change, show that (a) the restoring force is $-(2F/L)y$ and (b) the system exhibits simple harmonic motion with an angular frequency $\omega = \sqrt{2F/mL}$.

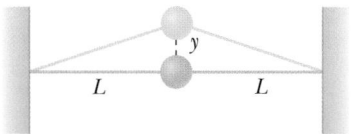

Figure P13.72

73. Assume a hole is drilled through the center of the Earth. It can be shown that an object of mass m at a distance r from the center of the Earth is pulled toward the center only by the material in the shaded portion of Figure P13.73. Assume Earth has a uniform density ρ. Write down Newton's law

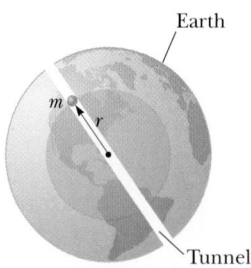

Figure P13.73

of gravitation for an object at a distance r from the center of the Earth and show that the force on it is of the form of Hooke's law, $F = -kr$, with an effective force constant of $k = \left(\frac{4}{3}\right)\pi\rho Gm$, where G is the gravitational constant.

74. **BIO** Figure P13.74 shows a crude model of an insect wing. The mass m represents the entire mass of the wing, which pivots about the fulcrum F. The spring represents the surrounding connective tissue. Motion of the wing corresponds to vibration of the spring. Suppose the mass of the wing is 0.30 g and the effective spring constant of the tissue is 4.7×10^{-4} N/m. If the mass m moves up and down a distance of 2.0 mm from its position of equilibrium, what is the maximum speed of the outer tip of the wing?

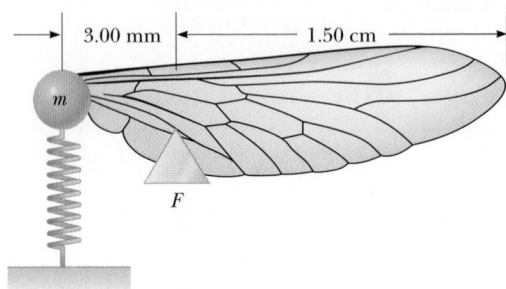

3.00 mm   1.50 cm

m

F

Figure P13.74

75. A 2.00-kg block hangs without vibrating at the end of a spring ($k = 500$ N/m) that is attached to the ceiling of an elevator car. The car is rising with an upward acceleration of $g/3$ when the acceleration suddenly ceases (at $t = 0$). (a) What is the angular frequency of oscillation of the block after the acceleration ceases? (b) By what amount is the spring stretched during the time that the elevator car is accelerating?

76. **QC** **S** A system consists of a vertical spring with force constant $k = 1\,250$ N/m, length $L = 1.50$ m, and object of mass $m = 5.00$ kg attached to the end (Fig. P13.76). The object is placed at the level of the point of attachment with the spring unstretched, at position $y_i = L$, and then it is released so that it swings like a pendulum. (a) Write Newton's second law symbolically for the system as the object passes through its lowest point. (Note that at the lowest point, $r = L - y_f$.) (b) Write the conservation of energy equation symbolically, equating the total mechanical energies at the initial point and lowest point. (c) Find the coordinate position of the lowest point. (d) Will this pendulum's period be greater or less than the period of a simple pendulum with the same mass m and length L? Explain.

y

L

m — $y_i = L$

$L - y_f$

$y = 0$

y_f

$\vec{v}$

Figure P13.76

■ AP* REVIEW QUESTIONS

1. A 0.3 kg mass is hung from a spring and the spring stretches 0.2 m. The spring is then pulled down an additional 0.5 m with a force of 0.2 N and released. As it oscillates, what is the acceleration of the mass when it returns to its starting position?

   (A) 0
   (B) 0.7 m/s^2
   (C) 1.7 m/s^2
   (D) 12.5 m/s^2
   (E) More information needed

2. A 0.5 kg mass is attached to a 200 N/m spring on a horizontal frictionless table. If the spring is pulled back 0.3 m and released, what will be the mass's maximum velocity and where will that occur?

   (A) 6.0 m/s, at maximum compression position
   (B) 6.0 m/s, at maximum stretched position
   (C) 6.0 m/s, at equilibrium position
   (D) 36 m/s, at maximum stretched position
   (E) 36 m/s, at equilibrium position

3. A bow is pulled back a distance x and fires an arrow straight up into the air, where it reaches a height h. The same arrow is now pulled back $3x$ in a new bow with a spring constant half that of the original bow. If this arrow is shot straight up into the air, how high will it go? (Ignore air resistance in both cases.)

   (A) $\frac{2}{9} h$
   (B) $\frac{2}{3} h$
   (C) $\frac{3}{2} h$
   (D) $\frac{9}{2} h$
   (E) More information is needed

4. A 0.5 kg object is attached to a 50 N/m spring and is oscillating back and forth on a frictionless horizontal surface with a maximum kinetic energy of 5 J. What is the velocity of the object at a displacement of 20 cm from equilibrium if this displacement is not the amplitude?

   (A) 2.0 m/s
   (B) 4.0 m/s
   (C) 8.0 m/s
   (D) 16 m/s
   (E) More information needed

5. A mass attached to a spring is pulled down a distance y and released. It oscillates up and down between $+y$ and $-y$. What is true about the velocity, acceleration, and force at $y = 0$?

	velocity	acceleration	force
(A)	0	0	0
(B)	0	maximum	maximum
(C)	maximum	0	0
(D)	0	maximum	0
(E)	maximum	maximum	maximum

6. A mass, m, attached to a spring with a spring constant k oscillates up and down with a period of T_0 and a frequency of f_0. If the mass is changed to be 8 times its original value and the spring is replaced with a new spring that has double the spring constant, what will happen to the frequency of oscillation?

   (A) $\frac{f_0}{4}$
   (B) $\frac{f_0}{2}$
   (C) $2f_0$
   (D) $4f_0$
   (E) $8f_0$

7. A 1000 N bungee jumper oscillates up and down with a frequency of 0.4 Hz. What is the spring constant of the bungee cord?

   (A) $160\pi^2$ N/m
   (B) $320\pi^2$ N/m
   (C) $640\pi^2$ N/m
   (D) $1600\pi^2$ N/m
   (E) $6400\pi^2$ N/m

8. In a new party game, a 25 kg child on a frictionless sled is compressed back onto a 250 N/m spring a distance of 2 m. Once released, the child will first slide horizontally, then smoothly up a frictionless ramp. How high up the ramp will they go?

(A) 0.5 m

(B) 1 m

(C) 2 m

(D) 3 m

(E) 4 m

9. What length does a pendulum on Mars have to be to have the same period as a 10 m long pendulum on Earth, if the acceleration due to gravity on Mars is 40% that of Earth's?

(A) 2π m

(B) 4π m

(C) 2.0 m

(D) 4.0 m

(E) More information is needed

10. A pendulum on Earth has length ℓ_0, period T_0, and frequency f_0. If the pendulum is moved to the Moon (where gravity is one-sixth that on Earth) and made twice as long, what will the new frequency be?

(A) $\dfrac{1}{\sqrt{12}}f_0$

(B) $\dfrac{1}{\sqrt{3}}f_0$

(C) $\sqrt{3}f_0$

(D) $\sqrt{12}f_0$

(E) $12f_0$

11. A person sitting in a 3.0 m long boat notices the crests of waves are hitting the front and back of the boat at the same time. She counts 4.0 waves in a time of 2.0 s. What is the velocity of the waves?

(A) 0.7 m/s

(B) 1.5 m/s

(C) 3.0 m/s

(D) 6.0 m/s

(E) More information needed

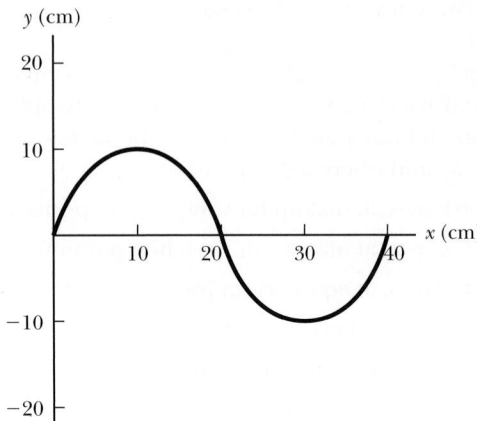

12. A wave traveling in the $+x$ direction is shown in the above diagram. If the wave has a period of 0.2 s, what is the velocity and amplitude of the wave?

(A) 2 m/s, 0.2 m

(B) 2 m/s, 0.4 m

(C) 2 m/s, 0.1 m

(D) 200 m/s, 0.2 m

(E) 200 m/s, 0.1 m

Chris Vuille

Pianist Jamila Tekalli exploits the physics of vibrating strings to produce the great variety of sounds typical of a grand piano. Note that the strings are shorter on the left, where the higher frequencies originate, and longer on the right, where the lower frequencies are produced. The long bass strings are wound with wire to increase their linear density, which further lowers their natural frequencies. When any one string is struck by a hammer, other strings resonate in response, contributing to the piano's characteristic sound.

Sound 14

Sound waves are the most important example of longitudinal waves. In this chapter we discuss the characteristics of sound waves: how they are produced, what they are, and how they travel through matter. We then investigate what happens when sound waves interfere with each other. The insights gained in this chapter will help you understand how we hear.

14.1 Producing a Sound Wave

Whether it conveys the shrill whine of a jet engine or the soft melodies of a crooner, any sound wave has its source in a vibrating object. Musical instruments produce sounds in a variety of ways. The sound of a clarinet is produced by a vibrating reed, the sound of a drum by the vibration of the taut drumhead, the sound of a piano by vibrating strings, and the sound from a singer by vibrating vocal cords.

Sound waves are longitudinal waves traveling through a medium, such as air. In order to investigate how sound waves are produced, we focus our attention on the tuning fork, a common device for producing pure musical notes. A tuning fork consists of two metal prongs, or tines, that vibrate when struck. Their vibration disturbs the air near them, as shown in Figure 14.1 (page 474). (The amplitude of vibration of the tine shown in the figure has been greatly exaggerated for clarity.) When a tine swings to the right, as in Figure 14.1a, the molecules in an element of air in front of its movement are forced closer together than normal. Such a region of high molecular density and high air pressure is called a **compression.** This compression moves away from the fork like a ripple on a pond. When the tine swings to the left, as in Figure 14.1b, the molecules in an element of air to the right of the tine spread apart, and the density and air pressure in this region are then

Figure 14.1 A vibrating tuning fork. (a) As the right tine of the fork moves to the right, a high-density region (compression) of air is formed in front of its movement. (b) As the right tine moves to the left, a low-density region (rarefaction) of air is formed behind it.

Figure 14.2 (a) As the tuning fork vibrates, a series of compressions and rarefactions moves outward, away from the fork. (b) The crests of the wave correspond to compressions, the troughs to rarefactions.

lower than normal. Such a region of reduced density is called a **rarefaction** (pronounced "rare a fak′ shun"). Molecules to the right of the rarefaction in the figure move to the left. The rarefaction itself therefore moves to the right, following the previously produced compression.

As the tuning fork continues to vibrate, a succession of compressions and rarefactions forms and spreads out from it. The resultant pattern in the air is somewhat like that pictured in Figure 14.2a. We can use a sinusoidal curve to represent a sound wave, as in Figure 14.2b. Notice that there are crests in the sinusoidal wave at the points where the sound wave has compressions and troughs where the sound wave has rarefactions. The compressions and rarefactions of the sound waves are superposed on the random thermal motion of the atoms and molecules of the air (discussed in Chapter 10), so sound waves in gases travel at about the molecular rms speed.

14.2 Characteristics of Sound Waves

As already noted, the general motion of elements of air near a vibrating object is back and forth between regions of compression and rarefaction. This back-and-forth motion of elements of the medium in the direction of the disturbance is characteristic of a longitudinal wave. **The motion of the elements of the medium in a longitudinal sound wave is back and forth along the direction in which the wave travels.** By contrast, **in a transverse wave, the vibrations of the elements of the medium are at right angles to the direction of travel of the wave.**

Categories of Sound Waves

Sound waves fall into three categories covering different ranges of frequencies. **Audible waves** are longitudinal waves that lie within the range of sensitivity of the human ear, approximately 20 to 20 000 Hz. **Infrasonic waves** are longitudinal waves with frequencies below the audible range. Earthquake waves are an example. **Ultrasonic waves** are longitudinal waves with frequencies above the audible range for humans and are produced by certain types of whistles. Animals such as dogs can hear the waves emitted by these whistles.

Applications of Ultrasound

BIO APPLICATION
Medical Uses of Ultrasound

Ultrasonic waves are sound waves with frequencies greater than 20 kHz. Because of their high frequency and corresponding short wavelengths, ultrasonic waves can be used to produce images of small objects and are currently in wide use in medical applications, both as a diagnostic tool and in certain treatments. Internal organs can be examined via the images produced by the reflection and absorption of ultrasonic waves. Although ultrasonic waves are far safer than x-rays, their images don't always have as much detail. Certain organs, however, such as the liver and the spleen, are invisible to x-rays but can be imaged with ultrasonic waves.

Medical workers can measure the speed of the blood flow in the body with a device called an ultrasonic flow meter, which makes use of the Doppler effect (discussed in Section 14.6). The flow speed is found by comparing the frequency of the waves scattered by the flowing blood with the incident frequency.

Figure 14.3 illustrates the technique that produces ultrasonic waves for clinical use. Electrical contacts are made to the opposite faces of a crystal, such as quartz or strontium titanate. If an alternating voltage of high frequency is applied to these contacts, the crystal vibrates at the same frequency as the applied voltage, emitting a beam of ultrasonic waves. At one time, a technique like this was used to produce sound in nearly all headphones. This method of transforming electrical energy into mechanical energy, called the **piezoelectric effect,** is reversible: If some external source causes the crystal to vibrate, an alternating voltage is produced across it. A single crystal can therefore be used to both generate and receive ultrasonic waves.

The primary physical principle that makes ultrasound imaging possible is the fact that a sound wave is partially reflected whenever it is incident on a boundary between two materials having different densities. If a sound wave is traveling in a material of density ρ_i and strikes a material of density ρ_t, the percentage of the incident sound wave intensity reflected, PR, is given by

$$PR = \left(\frac{\rho_i - \rho_t}{\rho_i + \rho_t}\right)^2 \times 100$$

This equation assumes that the direction of the incident sound wave is perpendicular to the boundary and that the speed of sound is approximately the same in the two materials. The latter assumption holds very well for the human body because the speed of sound doesn't vary much in the organs of the body.

Physicians commonly use ultrasonic waves to observe fetuses. This technique presents far less risk than do x-rays, which deposit more energy in cells and can produce birth defects. First the abdomen of the mother is coated with a liquid, such as mineral oil. If that were not done, most of the incident ultrasonic waves from the piezoelectric source would be reflected at the boundary between the air and the mother's skin. Mineral oil has a density similar to that of skin, and a very small fraction of the incident ultrasonic wave is reflected when $\rho_i \approx \rho_t$. The ultrasound energy is emitted in pulses rather than as a continuous wave, so the same crystal can be used as a detector as well as a transmitter. An image of the fetus is obtained by using an array of transducers placed on the abdomen. The reflected sound waves picked up by the transducers are converted to an electric signal, which is used to form an image on a fluorescent screen. Difficulties such as the likelihood of spontaneous abortion or of breech birth are easily detected with this technique. Fetal abnormalities such as spina bifida and water on the brain are also readily observed.

A relatively new medical application of ultrasonics is the *cavitron ultrasonic surgical aspirator* (CUSA). This device has made it possible to surgically remove brain tumors that were previously inoperable. The probe of the CUSA emits ultrasonic waves (at about 23 kHz) at its tip. When the tip touches a tumor, the part of the tumor near the probe is shattered and the residue can be sucked up (aspirated) through the hollow probe. Using this technique, neurosurgeons are able to remove brain tumors without causing serious damage to healthy surrounding tissue.

Ultrasound has been used not only for imaging purposes but also in surgery to destroy uterine fibroids and tumors of the prostate gland. A new ultrasound device developed in 2009 allows neurosurgeons to perform brain surgery without opening the skull or cutting the skin. High-intensity focused ultrasound (HIFU) is created with an array of a thousand ultrasound transducers placed on the patient's skull. Each transducer can be individually focused on a selected region

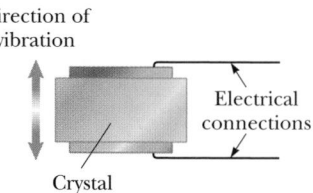

Figure 14.3 An alternating voltage applied to the faces of a piezoelectric crystal causes the crystal to vibrate.

An ultrasound image of a human fetus in the womb.

BIO APPLICATION

Cavitron Ultrasonic Surgical Aspirator

BIO APPLICATION

High-intensity focused ultrasound (HIFU)

of the brain. The ultrasound heats the brain tissue in a small area and destroys it. Patients are conscious during the procedure and report momentary tingling or dizziness, sometimes a mild headache. A cooling system is required to keep the patient's skull from overheating. The device can eliminate tumors and malfunctioning neural tissue, and may have application in the treatment of Parkinson's disease and strokes. It may also be possible to use HIFU to target the delivery of therapeutic drugs in specific brain locations.

Ultrasound is also used to break up kidney stones that are otherwise too large to pass. Previously, invasive surgery was often required.

Another interesting application of ultrasound is the ultrasonic ranging unit used in some cameras to provide an almost instantaneous measurement of the distance between the camera and the object to be photographed. The principal component of this device is a crystal that acts as both a loudspeaker and a microphone. A pulse of ultrasonic waves is transmitted from the transducer to the object, which then reflects part of the signal, producing an echo that is detected by the device. The time interval between the outgoing pulse and the detected echo is electronically converted to a distance, because the speed of sound is a known quantity.

APPLICATION
Ultrasonic Ranging Unit for Cameras

14.3 The Speed of Sound

The speed of a sound wave in a fluid depends on the fluid's compressibility and inertia. If the fluid has a bulk modulus B and an equilibrium density ρ, the speed of sound in it is

Speed of sound in a fluid ▶

$$v = \sqrt{\frac{B}{\rho}} \qquad [14.1]$$

Equation 14.1 also holds true for a gas. Recall from Chapter 9 that the bulk modulus is defined as the ratio of the change in pressure, ΔP, to the resulting fractional change in volume, $\Delta V/V$:

$$B \equiv -\frac{\Delta P}{\Delta V/V} \qquad [14.2]$$

B is always positive because an increase in pressure (positive ΔP) results in a decrease in volume. Hence, the ratio $\Delta P/\Delta V$ is always negative.

It's interesting to compare Equation 14.1 with Equation 13.18 for the speed of transverse waves on a string, $v = \sqrt{F/\mu}$, discussed in Chapter 13. In both cases the wave speed depends on an elastic property of the medium (B or F) and on an inertial property of the medium (ρ or μ). In fact, the speed of all mechanical waves follows an expression of the general form

$$v = \sqrt{\frac{\text{elastic property}}{\text{inertial property}}}$$

Another example of this general form is the **speed of a longitudinal wave in a solid rod,** which is

$$v = \sqrt{\frac{Y}{\rho}} \qquad [14.3]$$

where Y is the Young's modulus of the solid (see Eq. 9.3) and ρ is its density. This expression is valid only for a thin, solid rod.

Table 14.1 lists the speeds of sound in various media. The speed of sound is much higher in solids than in gases because the molecules in a solid interact more strongly with each other than do molecules in a gas. Striking a long steel rail with a hammer, for example, produces two sound waves, one moving through the rail and a slower wave moving through the air. A person with an ear pressed against

Table 14.1 Speeds of Sound in Various Media

Medium	v (m/s)
Gases	
Air (0°C)	331
Air (100°C)	386
Hydrogen (0°C)	1 286
Oxygen (0°C)	317
Helium (0°C)	972
Liquids at 25°C	
Water	1 493
Methyl alcohol	1 143
Sea water	1 533
Solids[a]	
Aluminum	6 420
Copper (rolled)	5 010
Steel	5 950
Lead (rolled)	1 960
Synthetic rubber	1 600

[a]Values given are for propagation of longitudinal waves in bulk media. Speeds for longitudinal waves in thin rods are smaller, and speeds of transverse waves in bulk are smaller yet.

the rail first hears the faster sound moving through the rail, then the sound moving through air. In general, sound travels faster through solids than liquids and faster through liquids than gases, although there are exceptions.

The speed of sound also depends on the temperature of the medium. For sound traveling through air, the relationship between the speed of sound and temperature is

$$v = (331 \text{ m/s}) \sqrt{\frac{T}{273 \text{ K}}} \qquad \text{[14.4]}$$

where 331 m/s is the speed of sound in air at 0°C and T is the absolute (Kelvin) temperature. Using this equation, the speed of sound in air at 293 K (a typical room temperature) is approximately 343 m/s.

■ Quick Quiz

14.1 Which of the following actions will increase the speed of sound in air?
(a) decreasing the air temperature (b) increasing the frequency of the sound
(c) increasing the air temperature (d) increasing the amplitude of the sound wave
(e) reducing the pressure of the air

■ APPLYING PHYSICS 14.1 | The Sounds Heard During a Storm

How does lightning produce thunder, and what causes the extended rumble?

EXPLANATION Assume you're at ground level, and neglect ground reflections. When lightning strikes, a channel of ionized air carries a large electric current from a cloud to the ground. This results in a rapid temperature increase of the air in the channel as the current moves through it, causing a similarly rapid expansion of the air. The expansion is so sudden and so intense that a tremendous disturbance—thunder—is produced in the air. The entire length of the channel produces the sound at essentially the same instant of time. Sound produced at the bottom of the channel reaches you first because that's the point closest to you. Sounds from progressively higher portions of the channel reach you at later times, resulting in an extended roar. If the lightning channel were a perfectly straight line, the roar might be steady, but the zigzag shape of the path results in the rumbling variation in loudness, with different quantities of sound energy from different segments arriving at any given instant. ■

■ EXAMPLE 14.1 | Explosion over an Ice Sheet

GOAL Calculate time of travel for sound through various media.

PROBLEM An explosion occurs 275 m above an 867-m-thick ice sheet that lies over ocean water. If the air temperature is −7.00°C, how long does it take the sound to reach a research vessel 1 250 m below the ice? Neglect any changes in the bulk modulus and density with temperature and depth. (Use $B_{\text{ice}} = 9.2 \times 10^9$ Pa.)

STRATEGY Calculate the speed of sound in air with Equation 14.4, and use $d = vt$ to find the time needed for the sound to reach the surface of the ice. Use Equation 14.1 to compute the speed of sound in ice, again finding the time with the distance equation. Finally, use the speed of sound in salt water to find the time needed to traverse the water and then sum the three times.

. . . .

SOLUTION

Calculate the speed of sound in air at −7.00°C, which is equivalent to 266 K:

$$v_{\text{air}} = (331 \text{ m/s})\sqrt{\frac{T}{273 \text{ K}}} = (331 \text{ m/s})\sqrt{\frac{266 \text{ K}}{273 \text{ K}}} = 327 \text{ m/s}$$

Calculate the travel time through the air:

$$t_{\text{air}} = \frac{d}{v_{\text{air}}} = \frac{275 \text{ m}}{327 \text{ m/s}} = 0.841 \text{ s}$$

Compute the speed of sound in ice, using the bulk modulus and density of ice:

$$v_{\text{ice}} = \sqrt{\frac{B}{\rho}} = \sqrt{\frac{9.2 \times 10^9 \text{ Pa}}{917 \text{ kg/m}^3}} = 3.2 \times 10^3 \text{ m/s}$$

(Continued)

Compute the travel time through the ice:

$$t_{ice} = \frac{d}{v_{ice}} = \frac{867 \text{ m}}{3\ 200 \text{ m/s}} = 0.27 \text{ s}$$

Compute the travel time through the ocean water:

$$t_{water} = \frac{d}{v_{water}} = \frac{1\ 250 \text{ m}}{1\ 533 \text{ m/s}} = 0.815 \text{ s}$$

Sum the three times to obtain the total time of propagation:

$$t_{tot} = t_{air} + t_{ice} + t_{water} = 0.841 \text{ s} + 0.27 \text{ s} + 0.815 \text{ s}$$
$$= \boxed{1.93 \text{ s}}$$

REMARKS Notice that the speed of sound is highest in solid ice, second highest in liquid water, and slowest in air. The speed of sound depends on temperature, so the answer would have to be modified if the actual temperatures of ice and the sea water were known. At 0°C, for example, the speed of sound in sea water falls to 1 449 m/s.

QUESTION 14.1 Is the speed of sound in rubber higher or lower than the speed of sound in aluminum? Explain.

EXERCISE 14.1 Compute the speed of sound in the following substances at 273 K: (a) lead ($Y = 1.6 \times 10^{10}$ Pa), (b) mercury ($B = 2.8 \times 10^{10}$ Pa), and (c) air at −15.0°C.

ANSWERS (a) 1.2×10^3 m/s (b) 1.4×10^3 m/s (c) 322 m/s

14.4 Energy and Intensity of Sound Waves

As the tines of a tuning fork move back and forth through the air, they exert a force on a layer of air and cause it to move. In other words, the tines do work on the layer of air. That the fork pours sound energy into the air is one reason the vibration of the fork slowly dies out. (Other factors, such as the energy lost to friction as the tines bend, are also responsible for the lessening of movement.)

The average **intensity I** of a wave on a given surface is defined as the rate at which energy flows through the surface, $\Delta E / \Delta t$, divided by the surface area A:

$$I \equiv \frac{1}{A}\frac{\Delta E}{\Delta t} \qquad [14.5]$$

where the direction of energy flow is perpendicular to the surface at every point.

SI unit: watt per meter squared (W/m^2)

A rate of energy transfer is power, so Equation 14.5 can be written in the alternate form

Intensity of a wave ▶

$$I \equiv \frac{\text{power}}{\text{area}} = \frac{P}{A} \qquad [14.6]$$

where P is the sound power passing through the surface, measured in watts, and the intensity again has units of watts per square meter.

The faintest sounds the human ear can detect at a frequency of 1 000 Hz have an intensity of about 1×10^{-12} W/m^2. This intensity is called the **threshold of hearing.** The loudest sounds the ear can tolerate have an intensity of about 1 W/m^2 (the **threshold of pain**). At the threshold of hearing, the increase in pressure in the ear is approximately 3×10^{-5} Pa over normal atmospheric pressure. Because atmospheric pressure is about 1×10^5 Pa, this means the ear can detect pressure fluctuations as small as about 3 parts in 10^{10}! The maximum displacement of an air molecule at the threshold of hearing is about 1×10^{-11} m, which is a remarkably small number! If we compare this displacement with the diameter of a molecule (about 10^{-10} m), we see that the ear is an extremely sensitive detector of sound waves.

The loudest sounds the human ear can tolerate at 1 kHz correspond to a pressure variation of about 29 Pa away from normal atmospheric pressure, with a maximum displacement of air molecules of 1×10^{-5} m.

Intensity Level in Decibels

The loudest tolerable sounds have intensities about 1.0×10^{12} times greater than the faintest detectable sounds. The most intense sound, however, isn't perceived as being 1.0×10^{12} times louder than the faintest sound because the sensation of loudness is approximately logarithmic in the human ear. (For a review of logarithms, see Section A.3, heading G, in Appendix A.) The relative intensity of a sound is called the **intensity level** or **decibel level,** defined by

$$\beta \equiv 10 \log \left(\frac{I}{I_0}\right) \qquad\qquad [14.7]$$

◀ Intensity level

The constant $I_0 = 1.0 \times 10^{-12}$ W/m² is the reference intensity, the sound intensity at the threshold of hearing, I is the intensity, and β is the corresponding intensity level measured in decibels (dB). (The word *decibel*, which is one-tenth of a *bel*, comes from the name of the inventor of the telephone, Alexander Graham Bell (1847–1922).)

To get a feel for various decibel levels, we can substitute a few representative numbers into Equation 14.7, starting with $I = 1.0 \times 10^{-12}$ W/m²:

$$\beta = 10 \log \left(\frac{1.0 \times 10^{-12} \text{ W/m}^2}{1.0 \times 10^{-12} \text{ W/m}^2}\right) = 10 \log (1) = 0 \text{ dB}$$

From this result, we see that the lower threshold of human hearing has been chosen to be zero on the decibel scale. Progressing upward by powers of ten yields

$$\beta = 10 \log \left(\frac{1.0 \times 10^{-11} \text{ W/m}^2}{1.0 \times 10^{-12} \text{ W/m}^2}\right) = 10 \log (10) = 10 \text{ dB}$$

$$\beta = 10 \log \left(\frac{1.0 \times 10^{-10} \text{ W/m}^2}{1.0 \times 10^{-12} \text{ W/m}^2}\right) = 10 \log (100) = 20 \text{ dB}$$

Notice the pattern: *Multiplying* a given intensity by ten *adds* 10 db to the intensity level. This pattern holds throughout the decibel scale. For example, a 50-dB sound is 10 times as intense as a 40-dB sound, whereas a 60-dB sound is 100 times as intense as a 40-dB sound.

On this scale, the threshold of pain ($I = 1.0$ W/m²) corresponds to an intensity level of $\beta = 10 \log (1/1 \times 10^{-12}) = 10 \log (10^{12}) = 120$ dB. Nearby jet airplanes can create intensity levels of 150 dB, and subways and riveting machines have levels of 90 to 100 dB. The electronically amplified sound heard at rock concerts can attain levels of up to 120 dB, the threshold of pain. Exposure to such high intensity levels can seriously damage the ear. Earplugs are recommended whenever prolonged intensity levels exceed 90 dB. Recent evidence suggests that noise pollution, which is common in most large cities and in some industrial environments, may be a contributing factor to high blood pressure, anxiety, and nervousness. Table 14.2 gives the approximate intensity levels of various sounds.

Tip 14.1 Intensity Versus Intensity Level

Don't confuse intensity with intensity level. Intensity is a physical quantity with units of watts per meter squared; intensity level, or decibel level, is a convenient mathematical transformation of intensity to a logarithmic scale.

Table 14.2 Intensity Levels in Decibels for Different Sources

Source of Sound	β(dB)
Nearby jet airplane	150
Jackhammer, machine gun	130
Siren, rock concert	120
Subway, power mower	100
Busy traffic	80
Vacuum cleaner	70
Normal conversation	50
Mosquito buzzing	40
Whisper	30
Rustling leaves	10
Threshold of hearing	0

■ EXAMPLE 14.2 | A Noisy Grinding Machine

GOAL Working with watts and decibels.

PROBLEM A noisy grinding machine in a factory produces a sound intensity of 1.00×10^{-5} W/m². Calculate **(a)** the decibel level of this machine and **(b)** the new intensity level when a second, identical machine is added to the factory. **(c)** A

(Continued)

certain number of additional such machines are put into operation alongside these two machines. When all the machines are running at the same time the decibel level is 77.0 dB. Find the sound intensity.

STRATEGY Parts (a) and (b) require substituting into the decibel formula, Equation 14.7, with the intensity in part (b) twice the intensity in part (a). In part (c), the intensity level in decibels is given, and it's necessary to work backwards, using the inverse of the logarithm function, to get the intensity in watts per meter squared.

SOLUTION

(a) Calculate the intensity level of the single grinder.

Substitute the intensity into the decibel formula:

$$\beta = 10 \log \left(\frac{1.00 \times 10^{-5} \text{ W/m}^2}{1.00 \times 10^{-12} \text{ W/m}^2} \right) = 10 \log (10^7)$$

$$= \boxed{70.0 \text{ dB}}$$

(b) Calculate the new intensity level when an additional machine is added.

Substitute twice the intensity of part (a) into the decibel formula:

$$\beta = 10 \log \left(\frac{2.00 \times 10^{-5} \text{ W/m}^2}{1.00 \times 10^{-12} \text{ W/m}^2} \right) = \boxed{73.0 \text{ dB}}$$

(c) Find the intensity corresponding to an intensity level of 77.0 dB.

Substitute 77.0 dB into the decibel formula and divide both sides by 10:

$$\beta = 77.0 \text{ dB} = 10 \log \left(\frac{I}{I_0} \right)$$

$$7.70 = \log \left(\frac{I}{10^{-12} \text{ W/m}^2} \right)$$

Make each side the exponent of 10. On the right-hand side, $10^{\log u} = u$, by definition of base 10 logarithms.

$$10^{7.70} = 5.01 \times 10^7 = \frac{I}{1.00 \times 10^{-12} \text{ W/m}^2}$$

$$I = \boxed{5.01 \times 10^{-5} \text{ W/m}^2}$$

REMARKS The answer is five times the intensity of the single grinder, so in part (c) there are five such machines operating simultaneously. Because of the logarithmic definition of intensity level, large changes in intensity correspond to small changes in intensity level.

QUESTION 14.2 By how many decibels is the sound intensity level raised when the sound intensity is doubled?

EXERCISE 14.2 Suppose a manufacturing plant has an average sound intensity level of 97.0 dB created by 25 identical machines. (a) Find the total intensity created by all the machines. (b) Find the sound intensity created by one such machine. (c) What's the sound intensity level if five such machines are running?

ANSWERS (a) $5.01 \times 10^{-3} \text{ W/m}^2$ (b) $2.00 \times 10^{-4} \text{ W/m}^2$ (c) 90.0 dB

BIO APPLICATION
OSHA Noise-Level Regulations

Federal OSHA regulations now demand that no office or factory worker be exposed to noise levels that average more than 85 dB over an 8-h day. From a management point of view, here's the good news: one machine in the factory may produce a noise level of 70 dB, but a second machine, though doubling the total intensity, increases the noise level by only 3 dB. Because of the logarithmic nature of intensity levels, doubling the intensity doesn't double the intensity level; in fact, it alters it by a surprisingly small amount. This means that equipment can be added to the factory without appreciably altering the intensity level of the environment.

Now here's the bad news: as you remove noisy machinery, the intensity level isn't lowered appreciably. In Exercise 14.2, reducing the intensity level by 7 dB would require the removal of 20 of the 25 machines! To lower the level another 7 dB would require removing 80% of the remaining machines, in which case only one machine would remain.

14.5 Spherical and Plane Waves

If a small spherical object oscillates so that its radius changes periodically with time, a spherical sound wave is produced (Fig. 14.4). The wave moves outward from the source at a constant speed.

Because all points on the vibrating sphere behave in the same way, we conclude that the energy in a spherical wave propagates equally in all directions. This means that no one direction is preferred over any other. If P_{av} is the average power emitted by the source, then at any distance r from the source, this power must be distributed over a spherical surface of area $4\pi r^2$, assuming no absorption in the medium. (Recall that $4\pi r^2$ is the surface area of a sphere.) Hence, the **intensity** of the sound at a distance r from the source is

$$I = \frac{\text{average power}}{\text{area}} = \frac{P_{av}}{A} = \frac{P_{av}}{4\pi r^2} \qquad \text{[14.8]}$$

This equation shows that the intensity of a wave decreases with increasing distance from its source, as you might expect. The fact that I varies as $1/r^2$ is a result of the assumption that the small source (sometimes called a **point source**) emits a spherical wave. (In fact, light waves also obey this so-called inverse-square relationship.) Because the average power is the same through any spherical surface centered at the source, we see that the intensities at distances r_1 and r_2 (Fig. 14.4) from the center of the source are

$$I_1 = \frac{P_{av}}{4\pi r_1^{\,2}} \qquad I_2 = \frac{P_{av}}{4\pi r_2^{\,2}}$$

The ratio of the intensities at these two spherical surfaces is

$$\frac{I_1}{I_2} = \frac{r_2^{\,2}}{r_1^{\,2}} \qquad \text{[14.9]}$$

It's useful to represent spherical waves graphically with a series of circular arcs (lines of maximum intensity) concentric with the source representing part of a spherical surface, as in Figure 14.5. We call such an arc a **wave front.** The distance between adjacent wave fronts equals the wavelength λ. The radial lines pointing outward from the source and perpendicular to the arcs are called **rays.**

Now consider a small portion of a wave front that is at a *great* distance (relative to λ) from the source, as in Figure 14.6. In this case the rays are nearly parallel to each other and the wave fronts are very close to being planes. At distances from the source that are great relative to the wavelength, therefore, we can approximate the wave front with parallel planes, called **plane waves.** Any small portion of a spherical wave that is far from the source can be considered a plane wave. Figure 14.7 illustrates a plane wave propagating along the x-axis. If the positive

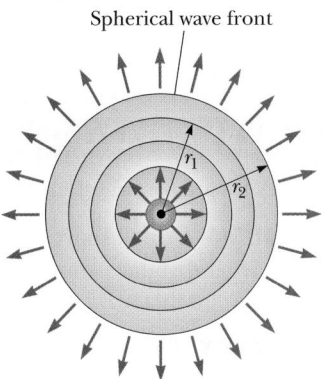

Figure 14.4 A spherical wave propagating radially outward from an oscillating sphere. The intensity of the wave varies as $1/r^2$.

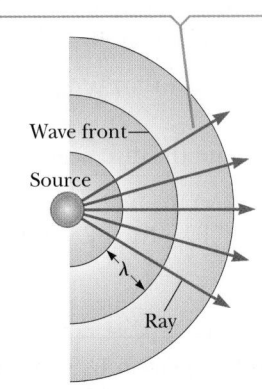

The rays are radial lines pointing outward from the source, perpendicular to the wave fronts.

Figure 14.5 Spherical waves emitted by a point source. The circular arcs represent the spherical wave fronts concentric with the source.

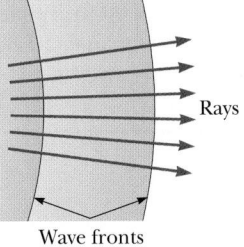

Figure 14.6 Far away from a point source, the wave fronts are nearly parallel planes and the rays are nearly parallel lines perpendicular to the planes. A small segment of a spherical wave front is approximately a plane wave.

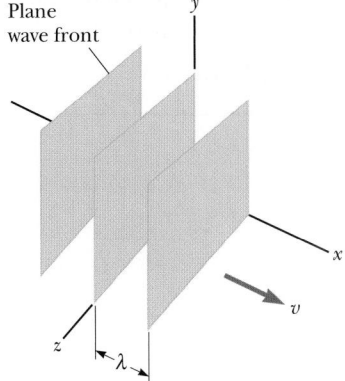

The wave fronts are planes parallel to the yz-plane.

Figure 14.7 A representation of a plane wave moving in the positive x-direction with a speed v.

x-direction is taken to be the direction of the wave motion (or ray) in this figure, then the wave fronts are parallel to the plane containing the *y*- and *z*-axes.

■ EXAMPLE 14.3 | **Intensity Variations of a Point Source**

GOAL Relate sound intensities and their distances from a point source.

PROBLEM A small source emits sound waves with a power output of 80.0 W. **(a)** Find the intensity 3.00 m from the source. **(b)** At what distance would the intensity be one-fourth as much as it is at *r* = 3.00 m? **(c)** Find the distance at which the sound level is 40.0 dB.

STRATEGY The source is small, so the emitted waves are spherical and the intensity in part (a) can be found by substituting values into Equation 14.8. Part (b) involves solving for *r* in Equation 14.8 followed by substitution (although Eq. 14.9 can be used instead). In part (c), convert from the sound intensity level to the intensity in W/m², using Equation 14.7. Then substitute into Equation 14.9 (although Eq. 14.8 could be used instead) and solve for r_2.

....

SOLUTION

(a) Find the intensity 3.00 m from the source.

Substitute P_{av} = 80.0 W and *r* = 3.00 m into Equation 14.8:

$$I = \frac{P_{av}}{4\pi r^2} = \frac{80.0 \text{ W}}{4\pi(3.00 \text{ m})^2} = \boxed{0.707 \text{ W/m}^2}$$

(b) At what distance would the intensity be one-fourth as much as it is at *r* = 3.00 m?

Take *I* = (0.707 W/m²)/4, and solve for *r* in Equation 14.8:

$$r = \left(\frac{P_{av}}{4\pi I}\right)^{1/2} = \left[\frac{80.0 \text{ W}}{4\pi(0.707 \text{ W/m}^2)/4.0}\right]^{1/2} = \boxed{6.00 \text{ m}}$$

(c) Find the distance at which the sound level is 40.0 dB.

Convert the intensity level of 40.0 dB to an intensity in W/m² by solving Equation 14.7 for *I*:

$$40.0 = 10 \log\left(\frac{I}{I_0}\right) \rightarrow 4.00 = \log\left(\frac{I}{I_0}\right)$$

$$10^{4.00} = \frac{I}{I_0} \rightarrow I = 10^{4.00} I_0 = 1.00 \times 10^{-8} \text{ W/m}^2$$

Solve Equation 14.9 for r_2^2, substitute the intensity and the result of part (a), and take the square root:

$$\frac{I_1}{I_2} = \frac{r_2^2}{r_1^2} \rightarrow r_2^2 = r_1^2 \frac{I_1}{I_2}$$

$$r_2^2 = (3.00 \text{ m})^2 \left(\frac{0.707 \text{ W/m}^2}{1.00 \times 10^{-8} \text{ W/m}^2}\right)$$

$$r_2 = \boxed{2.52 \times 10^4 \text{ m}}$$

REMARKS Once the intensity is known at one position a certain distance away from the source, it's easier to use Equation 14.9 rather than Equation 14.8 to find the intensity at any other location. This is particularly true for part (b), where, using Equation 14.9, we can see right away that doubling the distance reduces the intensity to one-fourth its previous value.

QUESTION 14.3 The power output of a sound system is increased by a factor of 25. By what factor should you adjust your distance from the speakers so the sound intensity is the same?

EXERCISE 14.3 Suppose a certain jet plane creates an intensity level of 125 dB at a distance of 5.00 m. What intensity level does it create on the ground directly underneath it when flying at an altitude of 2.00 km?

ANSWER 73.0 dB

14.6 The Doppler Effect

If a car or truck is moving while its horn is blowing, the frequency of the sound you hear is higher as the vehicle approaches you and lower as it moves away from you. This phenomenon is one example of the *Doppler effect*, named for Austrian physicist Christian Doppler (1803–1853), who discovered it. The same effect is heard if you're on a motorcycle and the horn is stationary: the frequency is higher as you approach the source and lower as you move away.

Although the Doppler effect is most often associated with sound, it's common to all waves, including light.

In deriving the Doppler effect, we assume the air is stationary and that all speed measurements are made relative to this stationary medium. In the general case, the speed of the observer v_O, the speed of the source, v_S, and the speed of sound v are all measured relative to the medium in which the sound is propagated.

Case 1: The Observer Is Moving Relative to a Stationary Source

In Active Figure 14.8 an observer is moving with a speed of v_O toward the source (considered a point source), which is at rest ($v_S = 0$).

We take the frequency of the source to be f_S, the wavelength of the source to be λ_S, and the speed of sound in air to be v. If both observer and source are stationary, the observer detects f_S wave fronts per second. (That is, when $v_O = 0$ and $v_S = 0$, the observed frequency f_O equals the source frequency f_S.) When moving toward the source, the observer moves a distance of $v_O t$ in t seconds. During this interval, **the observer detects an additional number of wave fronts.** The number of extra wave fronts is equal to the distance traveled, $v_O t$, divided by the wavelength λ_S:

$$\text{Additional wave fronts detected} = \frac{v_O t}{\lambda_S}$$

Divide this equation by the time t to get the number of additional wave fronts detected *per second*, v_O/λ_S. Hence, the frequency heard by the observer is *increased* to

$$f_O = f_S + \frac{v_O}{\lambda_S}$$

Substituting $\lambda_S = v/f_S$ into this expression for f_O, we obtain

$$f_O = f_S\left(\frac{v + v_O}{v}\right) \qquad \text{[14.10]}$$

When the observer is *moving away* from a stationary source (Fig. 14.9), the observed frequency decreases. A derivation yields the same result as Equation 14.10, but with $v - v_O$ in the numerator. Therefore, when the observer is moving away from the source, substitute $-v_O$ for v_O in Equation 14.10.

Case 2: The Source Is Moving Relative to a Stationary Observer

Now consider a source moving toward an observer at rest, as in Active Figure 14.10. Here, the wave fronts passing observer A are closer together because the source is moving in the direction of the outgoing wave. As a result, the wavelength λ_O

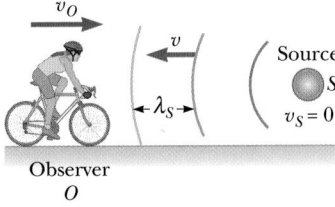

Active Figure 14.8
An observer moving with a speed v_O *toward* a stationary point source (S) hears a frequency f_O that is *greater* than the source frequency f_S.

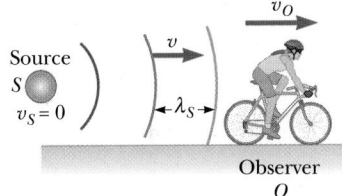

Figure 14.9 An observer moving with a speed of v_O *away* from a stationary source hears a frequency f_O that is *lower* than the source frequency f_S.

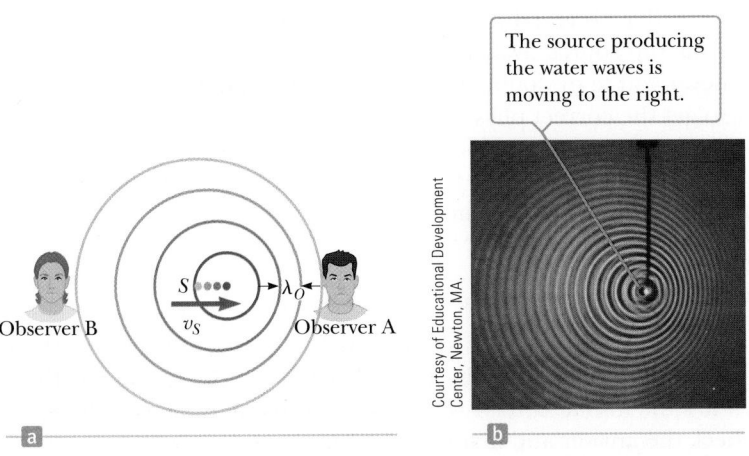

The source producing the water waves is moving to the right.

Observer B   Observer A

v_S λ_O

a   b

Active Figure 14.10
(a) A source S moving with speed v_S toward stationary observer A and away from stationary observer B. Observer A hears an *increased* frequency, and observer B hears a *decreased* frequency. (b) The Doppler effect in water, observed in a ripple tank.

Courtesy of Educational Development Center, Newton, MA.

measured by observer A is shorter than the wavelength λ_S of the source at rest.
During each vibration, which lasts for an interval T (the period), the source moves
a distance $v_S T = v_S/f_S$ and **the wavelength is shortened by that amount.** The
observed wavelength is therefore given by

$$\lambda_O = \lambda_S - \frac{v_S}{f_S}$$

Because $\lambda_S = v/f_S$, the frequency observed by A is

$$f_O = \frac{v}{\lambda_O} = \frac{v}{\lambda_S - \dfrac{v_S}{f_S}} = \frac{v}{\dfrac{v}{f_S} - \dfrac{v_S}{f_S}}$$

or

$$f_O = f_S\left(\frac{v}{v - v_S}\right) \qquad [14.11]$$

As expected, **the observed frequency increases when the source is moving toward
the observer.** When the source is *moving away* from an observer at rest, the minus
sign in the denominator must be replaced with a plus sign, so the factor becomes
$(v + v_S)$.

General Case

When both the source and the observer are in motion relative to Earth, Equations
14.10 and 14.11 can be combined to give

◀ Doppler shift: observer
and source in motion

$$f_O = f_S\left(\frac{v + v_O}{v - v_S}\right) \qquad [14.12]$$

In this expression, the signs for the values substituted for v_O and v_S depend on
the direction of the velocity. When the observer moves *toward* the source, a *positive*
speed is substituted for v_O; when the observer moves *away from* the source, a *negative* speed is substituted for v_O. Similarly, a *positive* speed is substituted for v_S when
the source moves *toward* the observer, a *negative* speed when the source moves away
from the observer.

Choosing incorrect signs is the most common mistake made in working a Doppler effect problem. The following rules may be helpful: The word *toward* is associated with an *increase* in the observed frequency; the words *away from* are associated
with a *decrease* in the observed frequency.

These two rules derive from the physical insight that when the observer is
moving toward the source (or the source toward the observer), there is a smaller
observed period between wave crests, hence a larger frequency, with the reverse
holding—a smaller observed frequency—when the observer is moving away from
the source (or the source away from the observer). Keep the physical insight in
mind whenever you're in doubt about the signs in Equation 14.12: Adjust them as
necessary to get the correct physical result.

The second most common mistake made in applying Equation 14.12 is to accidentally reverse numerator and denominator. Some find it helpful to remember
the equation in the following form:

$$\frac{f_O}{v + v_O} = \frac{f_S}{v - v_S}$$

The advantage of this form is its symmetry: both sides are very nearly the same,
with O's on the left and S's on the right. Forgetting which side has the plus sign
and which has the minus sign is not a serious problem as long as physical insight is
used to check the answer and make adjustments as necessary.

■ *Quick Quiz*

14.2 Suppose you're on a hot air balloon ride, carrying a buzzer that emits a sound of frequency f. If you accidentally drop the buzzer over the side while the balloon is rising at constant speed, what can you conclude about the sound you hear as the buzzer falls toward the ground? (a) The frequency and intensity increase. (b) The frequency decreases and the intensity increases. (c) The frequency decreases and the intensity decreases. (d) The frequency remains the same, but the intensity decreases.

■ APPLYING PHYSICS 14.2 | Out of-Tune Speakers

Suppose you place your stereo speakers far apart and run past them from right to left or left to right. If you run rapidly enough and have excellent pitch discrimination, you may notice that the music playing seems to be out of tune when you're between the speakers. Why?

EXPLANATION When you are between the speakers, you are running away from one of them and toward the other, so there is a Doppler shift downward for the sound from the speaker behind you and a Doppler shift upward for the sound from the speaker ahead of you. As a result, the sound from the two speakers will not be in tune. A calculation shows that a world-class sprinter could run fast enough to generate about a semitone difference in the sound from the two speakers. ■

■ EXAMPLE 14.4 | Listen, but Don't Stand on the Track

GOAL Solve a Doppler shift problem when only the source is moving.

PROBLEM A train moving at a speed of 40.0 m/s sounds its whistle, which has a frequency of 5.00×10^2 Hz. Determine the frequency heard by a stationary observer as the train *approaches* the observer. The ambient temperature is 24.0°C.

STRATEGY Use Equation 14.4 to get the speed of sound at the ambient temperature, then substitute values into Equation 14.12 for the Doppler shift. Because the train approaches the observer, the observed frequency will be larger. Choose the sign of v_S to reflect this fact.

SOLUTION

Use Equation 14.4 to calculate the speed of sound in air at $T = 24.0°C$:

$$v = (331 \text{ m/s})\sqrt{\frac{T}{273 \text{ K}}}$$

$$= (331 \text{ m/s})\sqrt{\frac{(273 + 24.0) \text{ K}}{273 \text{ K}}} = \boxed{345 \text{ m/s}}$$

The observer is stationary, so $v_O = 0$. The train is moving *toward* the observer, so $v_S = +40.0$ m/s (*positive*). Substitute these values and the speed of sound into the Doppler shift equation:

$$f_O = f_S\left(\frac{v + v_O}{v - v_S}\right)$$

$$= (5.00 \times 10^2 \text{ Hz})\left(\frac{345 \text{ m/s}}{345 \text{ m/s} - 40.0 \text{ m/s}}\right)$$

$$= \boxed{566 \text{ Hz}}$$

REMARKS If the train were going away from the observer, $v_S = -40.0$ m/s would have been chosen instead.

QUESTION 14.4 Does the Doppler shift change due to temperature variations? If so, why? For typical daily variations in temperature in a moderate climate, would any change in the Doppler shift be best characterized as (a) nonexistent, (b) small, or (c) large?

EXERCISE 14.4 Determine the frequency heard by the stationary observer as the train *recedes* from the observer.

ANSWER 448 Hz

■ EXAMPLE 14.5 | The Noisy Siren

GOAL Solve a Doppler shift problem when both the source and observer are moving.

PROBLEM An ambulance travels down a highway at a speed of 75.0 mi/h, its siren emitting sound at a frequency of 4.00×10^2 Hz. What frequency is heard by a passenger in a car traveling at 55.0 mi/h in the opposite direction as the car and ambulance **(a)** *approach* each other and **(b)** pass and *move away* from each other? Take the speed of sound in air to be $v = 345$ m/s.

STRATEGY Aside from converting mi/h to m/s, this problem only requires substitution into the Doppler formula, but two signs must be chosen correctly in each part. In part (a) the observer moves toward the source and the source moves toward the observer, so both v_O and v_S should be chosen to be positive. Switch signs after they pass each other.

SOLUTION

Convert the speeds from mi/h to m/s:

$$v_S = (75.0 \text{ mi/h}) \left(\frac{0.447 \text{ m/s}}{1.00 \text{ mi/h}} \right) = 33.5 \text{ m/s}$$

$$v_O = (55.0 \text{ mi/h}) \left(\frac{0.447 \text{ m/s}}{1.00 \text{ mi/h}} \right) = 24.6 \text{ m/s}$$

(a) Compute the observed frequency as the ambulance and car approach each other.

Each vehicle goes toward the other, so substitute $v_O = +24.6$ m/s and $v_S = +33.5$ m/s into the Doppler shift formula:

$$f_O = f_S \left(\frac{v + v_O}{v - v_S} \right)$$

$$= (4.00 \times 10^2 \text{ Hz}) \left(\frac{345 \text{ m/s} + 24.6 \text{ m/s}}{345 \text{ m/s} - 33.5 \text{ m/s}} \right) = \boxed{475 \text{ Hz}}$$

(b) Compute the observed frequency as the ambulance and car recede from each other.

Each vehicle goes away from the other, so substitute $v_O = -24.6$ m/s and $v_S = -33.5$ m/s into the Doppler shift formula:

$$f_O = f_S \left(\frac{v + v_O}{v - v_S} \right)$$

$$= (4.00 \times 10^2 \text{ Hz}) \left(\frac{345 \text{ m/s} + (-24.6 \text{ m/s})}{345 \text{ m/s} - (-33.5 \text{ m/s})} \right)$$

$$= \boxed{339 \text{ Hz}}$$

REMARKS Notice how the signs were handled. In part (b) the negative signs were required on the speeds because both observer and source were moving away from each other. Sometimes, of course, one of the speeds is negative and the other is positive.

QUESTION 14.5 Is the Doppler shift affected by sound intensity level?

EXERCISE 14.5 Repeat this problem, but assume the ambulance and car are going the same direction, with the ambulance initially behind the car. The speeds and the frequency of the siren are the same as in the example. Find the frequency heard by the observer in the car (a) before and (b) after the ambulance passes the car. *Note:* The highway patrol subsequently gives the driver of the car a ticket for not pulling over for an emergency vehicle!

ANSWERS (a) 411 Hz (b) 391 Hz

Shock Waves

What happens when the source speed v_S *exceeds* the wave velocity v? Figure 14.11 describes this situation graphically. The circles represent spherical wave fronts emitted by the source at various times during its motion. At $t = 0$, the source is at point S_0, and at some later time t, the source is at point S_n. In the interval t, the wave front centered at S_0 reaches a radius of vt. In this same interval, the source travels to S_n, a distance of $v_S t$. At the instant the source is at S_n, the waves just begin-

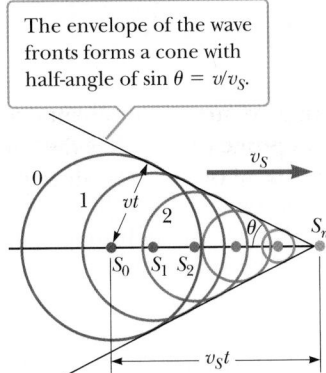

The envelope of the wave fronts forms a cone with half-angle of sin $\theta = v/v_S$.

Figure 14.11 A representation of a shock wave, produced when a source moves from S_0 to S_n with a speed v_S that is *greater* than the wave speed v in that medium.

Figure 14.12 The V-shaped bow wave of a boat is formed because the boat travels at a speed greater than the speed of the water waves. A bow wave is analogous to a shock wave formed by an airplane traveling faster than sound.

ning to be generated at this point have wave fronts of zero radius. The line drawn from S_n to the wave front centered on S_0 is tangent to all other wave fronts generated at intermediate times. All such tangent lines lie on the surface of a cone. The angle θ between one of these tangent lines and the direction of travel is given by

$$\sin \theta = \frac{v}{v_s}$$

The ratio v_S/v is called the **Mach number.** The conical wave front produced when $v_S > v$ (supersonic speeds) is known as a **shock wave.** An interesting example of a shock wave is the V-shaped wave front produced by a boat (the bow wave) when the boat's speed exceeds the speed of the water waves (Fig. 14.12).

Jet aircraft and space shuttles traveling at supersonic speeds produce shock waves that are responsible for the loud explosion, or sonic boom, heard on the ground. A shock wave carries a great deal of energy concentrated on the surface of the cone, with correspondingly great pressure variations. Shock waves are unpleasant to hear and can damage buildings when aircraft fly supersonically at low altitudes. In fact, an airplane flying at supersonic speeds produces a double boom because two shock waves are formed: one from the nose of the plane and one from the tail (Fig. 14.13).

■ Quick Quiz

14.3 As an airplane flying with constant velocity moves from a cold air mass into a warm air mass, does the Mach number (a) increase, (b) decrease, or (c) remain the same?

The large pressure variation in the shock wave condenses water vapor into droplets.

Pressure

Atmospheric pressure

a

b

Figure 14.13 (a) The two shock waves produced by the nose and tail of a jet airplane traveling at supersonic speed. (b) A shock wave due to a jet traveling at the speed of sound is made visible as a fog of water vapor.

A sound wave from the speaker (S) enters the tube and splits into two parts at point P.

Path length r_2

S

P

R

Path length r_1

The two waves combine at the opposite side and are detected at the receiver (R).

Figure 14.14 An acoustical system for demonstrating interference of sound waves. The upper path length is varied by the sliding section.

Condition for destructive ▶
interference

APPLICATION

Connecting Your Stereo Speakers

Tip 14.3 Do Waves Really Interfere?

In popular usage, to *interfere* means "to come into conflict with" or "to intervene to affect an outcome." This differs from its use in physics, where waves pass through each other and interfere, but don't affect each other in any way.

14.7 Interference of Sound Waves

Sound waves can be made to interfere with each other, a phenomenon that can be demonstrated with the device shown in Figure 14.14. Sound from a loudspeaker at S is sent into a tube at P, where there is a T-shaped junction. The sound splits and follows two separate pathways, indicated by the red arrows. Half of the sound travels upward, half downward. Finally, the two sounds merge at an opening where a listener places her ear. If the two paths r_1 and r_2 have the same length, waves that enter the junction will separate into two halves, travel the two paths, and then combine again at the ear. This reuniting of the two waves produces *constructive interference*, and the listener hears a loud sound. If the upper path is adjusted to be one full wavelength longer than the lower path, constructive interference of the two waves occurs again, and a loud sound is detected at the receiver. We have the following result: **If the path difference $r_2 - r_1$ is zero or some integer multiple of wavelengths, then constructive interference occurs and**

$$r_2 - r_1 = n\lambda \qquad (n = 0, 1, 2, \ldots) \qquad \text{[14.13]}$$

Suppose, however, that one of the path lengths, r_2, is adjusted so that the upper path is half a wavelength *longer* than the lower path r_1. In this case an entering sound wave splits and travels the two paths as before, but now the wave along the upper path must travel a distance equivalent to half a wavelength farther than the wave traveling along the lower path. As a result, the crest of one wave meets the trough of the other when they merge at the receiver, causing the two waves to cancel each other. This phenomenon is called *totally destructive interference*, and no sound is detected at the receiver. In general, **if the path difference $r_2 - r_1$ is $\frac{1}{2}$, $1\frac{1}{2}$, $2\frac{1}{2}$ ... wavelengths, destructive interference occurs and**

$$r_2 - r_1 = \left(n + \tfrac{1}{2}\right)\lambda \qquad (n = 0, 1, 2, \ldots) \qquad \text{[14.14]}$$

Nature provides many other examples of interference phenomena, most notably in connection with light waves, described in Chapter 24.

In connecting the wires between your stereo system and loudspeakers, you may notice that the wires are usually color coded and that the speakers have positive and negative signs on the connections. The reason for this is that the speakers need to be connected with the same "polarity." If they aren't, then the same electrical signal fed to both speakers will result in one speaker cone moving outward at the same time that the other speaker cone is moving inward. In this case, the sound leaving the two speakers will be 180° out of phase with each other. If you are sitting midway between the speakers, the sounds from both speakers travel the same distance and preserve the phase difference they had when they left. In an ideal situation, for a 180° phase difference, you would get complete destructive interference and no sound! In reality, the cancellation is not complete and is much more significant for bass notes (which have a long wavelength) than for the shorter wavelength treble notes. Nevertheless, to avoid a significant reduction in the intensity of bass notes, the color-coded wires and the signs on the speaker connections should be carefully noted.

■ EXAMPLE 14.6 | **Two Speakers Driven by the Same Source**

GOAL Use the concept of interference to compute a frequency.

PROBLEM Two speakers placed 3.00 m apart are driven by the same oscillator (Fig. 14.15). A listener is originally at point O, which is located 8.00 m from the center of the line connecting the two speakers. The listener then walks to point P, which is a perpendicular distance 0.350 m from O, before

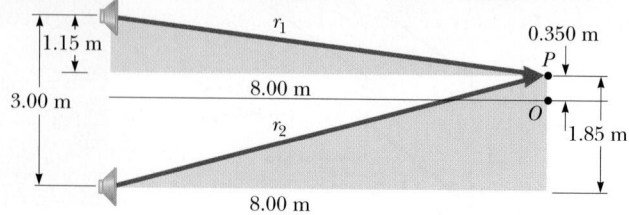

Figure 14.15 (Example 14.6) Two loudspeakers driven by the same source can produce interference.

reaching the *first minimum* in sound intensity. What is the frequency of the oscillator? Take the speed of sound in air to be $v_s = 343$ m/s.

STRATEGY The position of the first minimum in sound intensity is given, which is a point of destructive interference. We can find the path lengths r_1 and r_2 with the Pythagorean theorem and then use Equation 14.14 for destructive interference to find the wavelength λ. Using $v = f\lambda$ then yields the frequency.

SOLUTION

Use the Pythagorean theorem to find the path lengths r_1 and r_2:

$$r_1 = \sqrt{(8.00 \text{ m})^2 + (1.15 \text{ m})^2} = 8.08 \text{ m}$$

$$r_2 = \sqrt{(8.00 \text{ m})^2 + (1.85 \text{ m})^2} = 8.21 \text{ m}$$

Substitute these values and $n = 0$ into Equation 14.14, solving for the wavelength:

$$r_2 - r_1 = (n + \tfrac{1}{2})\lambda$$

$$8.21 \text{ m} - 8.08 \text{ m} = 0.13 \text{ m} = \lambda/2 \quad \rightarrow \quad \lambda = 0.26 \text{ m}$$

Solve $v = \lambda f$ for the frequency f and substitute the speed of sound and the wavelength:

$$f = \frac{v}{\lambda} = \frac{343 \text{ m/s}}{0.26 \text{ m}} = \boxed{1.3 \text{ kHz}}$$

REMARKS For problems involving constructive interference, the only difference is that Equation 14.13, $r_2 - r_1 = n\lambda$, would be used instead of Equation 14.14.

QUESTION 14.6 True or False: In the same context, smaller wavelengths of sound would create more interference maxima and minima than longer wavelengths.

EXERCISE 14.6 If the oscillator frequency is adjusted so that the location of the first minimum is at a distance of 0.750 m from O, what is the new frequency?

ANSWER 0.62 kHz

14.8   Standing Waves

Standing waves can be set up in a stretched string by connecting one end of the string to a stationary clamp and connecting the other end to a vibrating object, such as the end of a tuning fork, or by shaking the hand holding the string up and down at a steady rate (Fig. 14.16). Traveling waves then reflect from the ends and move in both directions on the string. The incident and reflected waves combine according to the **superposition principle.** (See Section 13.10.) If the string vibrates at exactly the right frequency, the wave appears to stand still, hence its name, **standing wave.** A **node** occurs where the two traveling waves always have the same magnitude of displacement but the opposite sign, so the net displacement is zero at that point. There is no motion in the string at the nodes, but midway between two adjacent nodes, at an **antinode,** the string vibrates with the largest amplitude.

Figure 14.17 (page 490) shows snapshots of the oscillation of a standing wave during half of a cycle. The pink arrows indicate the direction of motion of different parts of the string. Notice that **all points on the string oscillate together vertically with the same frequency, but different points have different amplitudes of motion.** The points of attachment to the wall and all other stationary points on the string are called nodes, labeled N in Figure 14.17a. From the figure, observe that the distance between adjacent nodes is one-half the wavelength of the wave:

$$d_{NN} = \tfrac{1}{2}\lambda$$

Consider a string of length L that is fixed at both ends, as in Active Figure 14.18 on page 490. For a string, we can set up standing-wave patterns at many frequencies—the more loops, the higher the frequency. Figure 14.19 (page 490) is a multiflash photograph of a standing wave on a string.

First, **the ends of the string must be nodes, because these points are fixed.** If the string is displaced at its midpoint and released, the vibration shown in Active

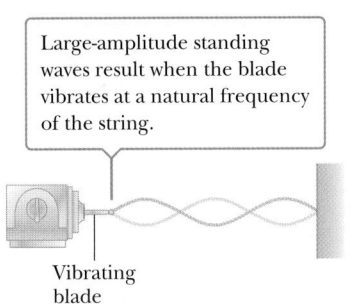

Large-amplitude standing waves result when the blade vibrates at a natural frequency of the string.

Vibrating blade

Figure 14.16 Standing waves can be set up in a stretched string by connecting one end of the string to a vibrating blade.

Figure 14.17 A standing-wave pattern in a stretched string, shown by snapshots of the string during one-half of a cycle. In part (a) N denotes a node.

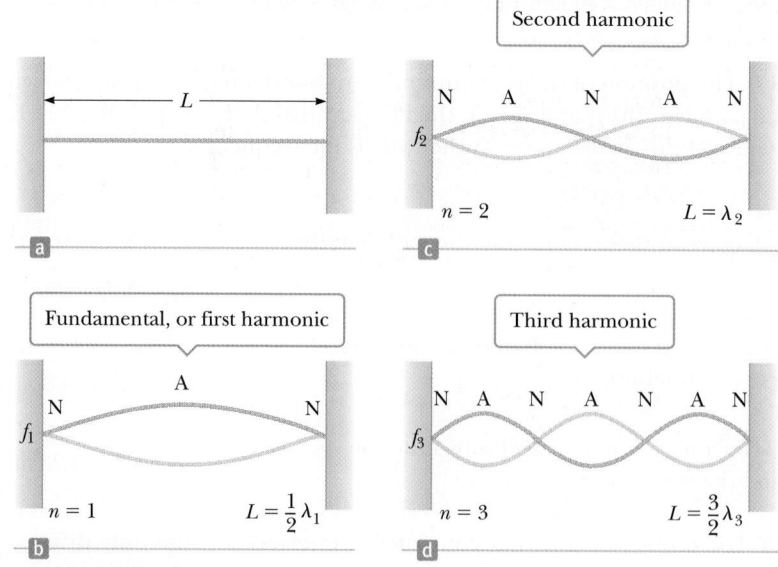

Active Figure 14.18

(a) Standing waves in a stretched string of length L fixed at both ends. The characteristic frequencies of vibration form a harmonic series: (b) the fundamental frequency, or first harmonic; (c) the second harmonic; and (d) the third harmonic. Note that N denotes a node, A an antinode.

Figure 14.18b can be produced, in which case the center of the string is an antinode, labeled A. Note that from end to end, the pattern is N–A–N. The distance from a node to its adjacent antinode, N–A, is always equal to a quarter wavelength, $\lambda_1/4$. There are two such segments, N–A and A–N, so $L = 2(\lambda_1/4) = \lambda_1/2$, and $\lambda_1 = 2L$. The frequency of this vibration is therefore

$$f_1 = \frac{v}{\lambda_1} = \frac{v}{2L} \qquad \text{[14.15]}$$

Recall that the speed of a wave on a string is $v = \sqrt{F/\mu}$, where F is the tension in the string and μ is its mass per unit length (Chapter 13). Substituting into Equation 14.15, we obtain

$$f_1 = \frac{1}{2L}\sqrt{\frac{F}{\mu}} \qquad \text{[14.16]}$$

Figure 14.19 Multiflash photograph of a standing-wave two-loop pattern in a second harmonic ($n = 2$), using a cord driven by a vibrator at the left end.

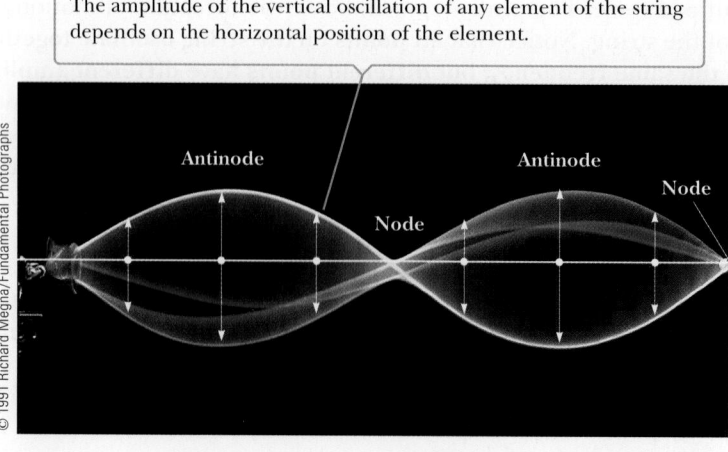

The amplitude of the vertical oscillation of any element of the string depends on the horizontal position of the element.

This lowest frequency of vibration is called the **fundamental frequency** of the vibrating string, or the **first harmonic.**

The first harmonic has nodes only at the ends: the points of attachment, with node-antinode pattern of N–A–N. The next harmonic, called the **second harmonic** (also called the **first overtone**), can be constructed by inserting an additional node–antinode segment between the endpoints. This makes the pattern N–A–N–A–N, as in Active Figure 14.18c. We count the node–antinode pairs: N–A, A–N, N–A, and A–N, four segments in all, each representing a quarter wavelength. We then have $L = 4(\lambda_2/4) = \lambda_2$, and the second harmonic (first overtone) is

$$f_2 = \frac{v}{\lambda_2} = \frac{v}{L} = 2\left(\frac{v}{2L}\right) = 2f_1$$

This frequency is equal to *twice* the fundamental frequency. The **third harmonic** (**second overtone**) is constructed similarly. Inserting one more N–A segment, we obtain Active Figure 14.18d, the pattern of nodes reading N–A–N–A–N–A–N. There are six node–antinode segments, so $L = 6(\lambda_3/4) = 3(\lambda_3/2)$, which means that $\lambda_3 = 2L/3$, giving

$$f_3 = \frac{v}{\lambda_3} = \frac{3v}{2L} = 3f_1$$

All the higher harmonics, it turns out, are positive integer multiples of the fundamental:

$$f_n = nf_1 = \frac{n}{2L}\sqrt{\frac{F}{\mu}} \qquad n = 1, 2, 3, \ldots$$ [14.17]   ◄ Natural frequencies of a string fixed at both ends

The frequencies f_1, $2f_1$, $3f_1$, and so on form a **harmonic series.**

■ **Quick Quiz**

14.4 Which of the following frequencies are higher harmonics of a string with fundamental frequency of 150 Hz? (a) 200 Hz (b) 300 Hz (c) 400 Hz (d) 500 Hz (e) 600 Hz

When a stretched string is distorted to a shape that corresponds to any one of its harmonics, after being released it vibrates only at the frequency of that harmonic. If the string is struck or bowed, however, the resulting vibration includes different amounts of various harmonics, including the fundamental frequency. Waves not in the harmonic series are quickly damped out on a string fixed at both ends. In effect, when disturbed, the string "selects" the standing-wave frequencies. As we'll see later, the presence of several harmonics on a string gives stringed instruments their characteristic sound, which enables us to distinguish one from another even when they are producing identical fundamental frequencies.

The frequency of a string on a musical instrument can be changed by varying either the tension or the length. The tension in guitar and violin strings is varied by turning pegs on the neck of the instrument. As the tension is increased, the frequency of the harmonic series increases according to Equation 14.17. Once the instrument is tuned, the musician varies the frequency by pressing the strings against the neck at a variety of positions, thereby changing the effective lengths of the vibrating portions of the strings. As the length is reduced, the frequency again increases, as follows from Equation 14.17.

APPLICATION
Tuning a Musical Instrument

Finally, Equation 14.17 shows that a string of fixed length can be made to vibrate at a lower fundamental frequency by increasing its mass per unit length. This increase is achieved in the bass strings of guitars and pianos by wrapping the strings with metal windings.

■ EXAMPLE 14.7 | Guitar Fundamentals

GOAL Apply standing-wave concepts to a stringed instrument.

PROBLEM The high E string on a certain guitar measures 64.0 cm in length and has a fundamental frequency of 329 Hz. When a guitarist presses down so that the string is in contact with the first fret (Fig. 14.20a), the string is shortened so that it plays an F note that has a frequency of 349 Hz. **(a)** How far is the fret from the nut? **(b)** Overtones can be produced on a guitar string by gently placing the index finger in the location of a node of a higher harmonic. The string should be touched, but not depressed against a fret. (Given the width of a finger, pressing too hard will damp out higher harmonics as well.) The fundamental frequency is thereby suppressed, making it possible to hear overtones. Where on the guitar string relative to the nut should the finger be lightly placed so as to hear the second harmonic? The fourth harmonic? (This is equivalent to finding the location of the nodes in each case.)

STRATEGY For part (a) use Equation 14.15, corresponding to the fundamental frequency, to find the speed of waves on the string. Shortening the string by playing a higher note doesn't affect the wave speed, which depends only on the tension and linear density of the string (which are unchanged). Solve Equation 14.15 for the new length L, using the new fundamental frequency, and subtract this length from the original length to find the distance from the nut to the first fret. In part (b) remember that the distance from node to node is half a wavelength. Calculate the wavelength, divide it in two, and locate the nodes, which are integral numbers of half-wavelengths from the nut. *Note:* The nut is a small piece of wood or ebony at the top of the fret board. The distance from the nut to the bridge (below the sound hole) is the length of the string. (See Fig. 14.20b.)

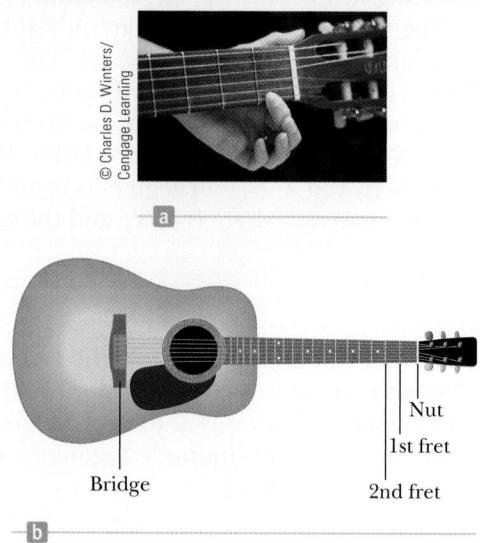

© Charles D. Winters/Cengage Learning

Figure 14.20 (Example 14.7) (a) Playing an F note on a guitar. (b) Some parts of a guitar.

· ·

SOLUTION

(a) Find the distance from the nut to the first fret.

Substitute $L_0 = 0.640$ m and $f_1 = 329$ Hz into Equation 14.15, finding the wave speed on the string:

$$f_1 = \frac{v}{2L_0}$$

$$v = 2L_0 f_1 = 2(0.640 \text{ m})(329 \text{ Hz}) = 421 \text{ m/s}$$

Solve Equation 14.15 for the length L, and substitute the wave speed and the frequency of an F note.

$$L = \frac{v}{2f} = \frac{421 \text{ m/s}}{2(349 \text{ Hz})} = 0.603 \text{ m} = 60.3 \text{ cm}$$

Subtract this length from the original length L_0 to find the distance from the nut to the first fret:

$$\Delta x = L_0 - L = 64.0 \text{ cm} - 60.3 \text{ cm} = \boxed{3.7 \text{ cm}}$$

(b) Find the locations of nodes for the second and fourth harmonics.

The second harmonic has a wavelength $\lambda_2 = L_0 = 64.0$ cm. The distance from nut to node corresponds to half a wavelength.

$$\Delta x = \tfrac{1}{2}\lambda_2 = \tfrac{1}{2}L_0 = 32.0 \text{ cm}$$

The fourth harmonic, of wavelength $\lambda_4 = \tfrac{1}{2}L_0 = 32.0$ cm, has three nodes between the endpoints:

$$\Delta x = \tfrac{1}{2}\lambda_4 = \boxed{16.0 \text{ cm}} \, , \Delta x = 2(\lambda_4/2) = \boxed{32.0 \text{ cm}} \, ,$$

$$\Delta x = 3(\lambda_4/2) = \boxed{48.0 \text{ cm}}$$

· ·

REMARKS Placing a finger at the position $\Delta x = 32.0$ cm damps out the fundamental and odd harmonics, but not all the higher even harmonics. The second harmonic dominates, however, because the rest of the string is free to vibrate. Placing the finger at $\Delta x = 16.0$ cm or 48.0 cm damps out the first through third harmonics, allowing the fourth harmonic to be heard.

QUESTION 14.7 True or False: If a guitar string has length L, gently placing a thin object at the position $\left(\tfrac{1}{2}\right)^n L$ will always result in the sounding of a higher harmonic, where n is a positive integer.

EXERCISE 14.7 Pressing the E string down on the fret board just above the second fret pinches the string firmly against the fret, giving an F-sharp, which has frequency 3.70×10^2 Hz. (a) Where should the second fret be located? (b) Find two locations where you could touch the open E string and hear the third harmonic.

ANSWERS (a) 7.1 cm from the nut and 3.4 cm from the first fret. Note that the distance from the first to the second fret isn't the same as from the nut to the first fret. (b) 21.3 cm and 42.7 cm from the nut

---

EXAMPLE 14.8 | Harmonics of a Stretched Wire

GOAL Calculate string harmonics, relate them to sound, and combine them with tensile stress.

PROBLEM (a) Find the frequencies of the fundamental, second, and third harmonics of a steel wire 1.00 m long with a mass per unit length of 2.00×10^{-3} kg/m and under a tension of 80.0 N. (b) Find the wavelengths of the sound waves created by the vibrating wire for all three modes. Assume the speed of sound in air is 345 m/s. (c) Suppose the wire is carbon steel with a density of 7.80×10^3 kg/m^3, a cross-sectional area $A = 2.56 \times 10^{-7}$ m^2, and an elastic limit of 2.80×10^8 Pa. Find the fundamental frequency if the wire is tightened to the elastic limit. Neglect any stretching of the wire (which would slightly reduce the mass per unit length).

STRATEGY (a) It's easiest to find the speed of waves on the wire then substitute into Equation 14.15 to find the first harmonic. The next two are multiples of the first, given by Equation 14.17. (b) The frequencies of the sound waves are the same as the frequencies of the vibrating wire, but the wavelengths are different. Use $v_s = f\lambda$, where v_s is the speed of sound in air, to find the wavelengths in air. (c) Find the force corresponding to the elastic limit and substitute it into Equation 14.16.

SOLUTION

(a) Find the first three harmonics at the given tension.

Use Equation 13.18 to calculate the speed of the wave on the wire:

$$v = \sqrt{\frac{F}{\mu}} = \sqrt{\frac{80.0 \text{ N}}{2.00 \times 10^{-3} \text{ kg/m}}} = 2.00 \times 10^2 \text{ m/s}$$

Find the wire's fundamental frequency from Equation 14.15:

$$f_1 = \frac{v}{2L} = \frac{2.00 \times 10^2 \text{ m/s}}{2(1.00 \text{ m})} = \boxed{1.00 \times 10^2 \text{ Hz}}$$

Find the next two harmonics by multiplication:

$$f_2 = 2f_1 = \boxed{2.00 \times 10^2 \text{ Hz}}, f_3 = 3f_1 = \boxed{3.00 \times 10^2 \text{ Hz}}$$

(b) Find the wavelength of the sound waves produced.

Solve $v_s = f\lambda$ for the wavelength and substitute the frequencies:

$$\lambda_1 = v_s/f_1 = (345 \text{ m/s})/(1.00 \times 10^2 \text{ Hz}) = \boxed{3.45 \text{ m}}$$

$$\lambda_2 = v_s/f_2 = (345 \text{ m/s})/(2.00 \times 10^2 \text{ Hz}) = \boxed{1.73 \text{ m}}$$

$$\lambda_3 = v_s/f_3 = (345 \text{ m/s})/(3.00 \times 10^2 \text{ Hz}) = \boxed{1.15 \text{ m}}$$

(c) Find the fundamental frequency corresponding to the elastic limit.

Calculate the tension in the wire from the elastic limit:

$$\frac{F}{A} = \text{elastic limit} \quad \rightarrow \quad F = (\text{elastic limit})A$$

$$F = (2.80 \times 10^8 \text{ Pa})(2.56 \times 10^{-7} \text{ m}^2) = 71.7 \text{ N}$$

Substitute the values of F, μ, and L into Equation 14.16:

$$f_1 = \frac{1}{2L}\sqrt{\frac{F}{\mu}}$$

$$f_1 = \frac{1}{2(1.00 \text{ m})}\sqrt{\frac{71.7 \text{ N}}{2.00 \times 10^{-3} \text{ kg/m}}} = \boxed{94.7 \text{ Hz}}$$

REMARKS From the answer to part (c), it appears we need to choose a thicker wire or use a better grade of steel with a higher elastic limit. The frequency corresponding to the elastic limit is smaller than the fundamental!

(Continued)

QUESTION 14.8 A string on a guitar is replaced with one of lower linear density. To obtain the same frequency sound as previously, must the tension of the new string be (a) greater than, (b) less than, or (c) equal to the tension in the old string?

EXERCISE 14.8 (a) Find the fundamental frequency and second harmonic if the tension in the wire is increased to 115 N. (Assume the wire doesn't stretch or break.) (b) Using a sound speed of 345 m/s, find the wavelengths of the sound waves produced.

ANSWERS (a) 1.20×10^2 Hz, 2.40×10^2 Hz (b) 2.88 m, 1.44 m

If pendulum *A* is set in oscillation, only pendulum *C*, with a length matching that of *A*, will eventually oscillate with a large amplitude, or resonate.

Figure 14.21 A demonstration of resonance.

APPLICATION

Shattering Goblets with the Voice

APPLICATION

Structural integrity and resonance

14.9 Forced Vibrations and Resonance

In Chapter 13 we learned that the energy of a damped oscillator decreases over time because of friction. It's possible to compensate for this energy loss by applying an external force that does positive work on the system.

For example, suppose an object–spring system having some natural frequency of vibration f_0 is pushed back and forth by a periodic force with frequency f. The system vibrates at the frequency f of the driving force. This type of motion is referred to as a **forced vibration.** Its amplitude reaches a maximum when the frequency of the driving force equals the natural frequency of the system f_0, called the **resonant frequency** of the system. Under this condition, the system is said to be in **resonance.**

In Section 14.8 we learned that a stretched string can vibrate in one or more of its natural modes. Here again, if a periodic force is applied to the string, the amplitude of vibration increases as the frequency of the applied force approaches one of the string's natural frequencies of vibration.

Resonance vibrations occur in a wide variety of circumstances. Figure 14.21 illustrates one experiment that demonstrates a resonance condition. Several pendulums of different lengths are suspended from a flexible beam. If one of them, such as *A*, is set in motion, the others begin to oscillate because of vibrations in the flexible beam. Pendulum *C*, the same length as *A*, oscillates with the greatest amplitude because its natural frequency matches that of pendulum *A* (the driving force).

Another simple example of resonance is a child being pushed on a swing, which is essentially a pendulum with a natural frequency that depends on its length. The swing is kept in motion by a series of appropriately timed pushes. For its amplitude to increase, the swing must be pushed each time it returns to the person's hands. This corresponds to a frequency equal to the natural frequency of the swing. If the energy put into the system per cycle of motion equals the energy lost due to friction, the amplitude remains constant.

Opera singers have been known to set crystal goblets in audible vibration with their powerful voices. This is yet another example of resonance: The sound waves emitted by the singer can set up large-amplitude vibrations in the glass. If a highly amplified sound wave has the right frequency, the amplitude of forced vibrations in the glass increases to the point where the glass becomes heavily strained and shatters.

The classic example of structural resonance occurred in 1940, when the Tacoma Narrows bridge in the state of Washington was set in oscillation by the wind (Fig. 14.22). The amplitude of the oscillations increased rapidly and reached a high value until the bridge ultimately collapsed (probably because of metal fatigue). In recent years, however, a number of researchers have called this explanation into question. Gusts of wind, in general, don't provide the periodic force necessary for a sustained resonance condition, and the bridge exhibited large twisting oscillations, rather than the simple up-and-down oscillations expected of resonance.

A more recent example of destruction by structural resonance occurred during the Loma Prieta earthquake near Oakland, California, in 1989. In a mile-long section of the double-decker Nimitz Freeway, the upper deck collapsed onto the lower deck, killing several people. The collapse occurred because that particular section

a | b

Figure 14.22 (a) In 1940, turbulent winds set up torsional vibrations in the Tacoma Narrows Bridge, causing it to oscillate at a frequency near one of the natural frequencies of the bridge structure. (b) Once established, this resonance condition led to the bridge's collapse. A number of scientists, however, have challenged the resonance interpretation.

was built on mud fill, whereas other parts were built on bedrock. As seismic waves pass through mud fill or other loose soil, their speed decreases and their amplitude increases. The section of the freeway that collapsed oscillated at the same frequency as other sections, but at a much larger amplitude.

14.10 Standing Waves in Air Columns

Standing longitudinal waves can be set up in a tube of air, such as an organ pipe, as the result of interference between sound waves traveling in opposite directions. The relationship between the incident wave and the reflected wave depends on whether the reflecting end of the tube is open or closed. A portion of the sound wave is reflected back into the tube even at an open end. **If one end is closed, a node must exist at that end because the movement of air is restricted. If the end is open, the elements of air have complete freedom of motion, and an antinode exists.**

Figure 14.23a shows the first three modes of vibration of a pipe open at both ends. When air is directed against an edge at the left, longitudinal standing waves

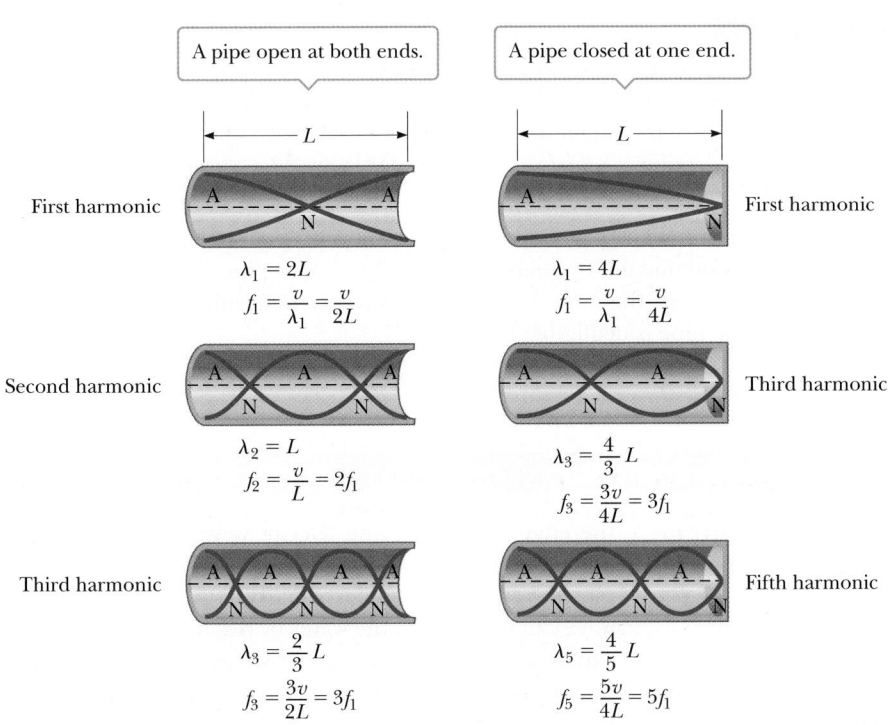

a | b

Figure 14.23 (a) Standing longitudinal waves in an organ pipe open at both ends. The natural frequencies $f_1, 2f_1, 3f_1 \ldots$ form a harmonic series. (b) Standing longitudinal waves in an organ pipe closed at one end. Only *odd* harmonics are present, and the natural frequencies are $f_1, 3f_1, 5f_1$, and so on.

The standing longitudinal waves
in Figure 14.23 are drawn as
transverse waves only because it's
difficult to draw longitudinal displacements: they're in the same
direction as the wave propagation. In the figure, the vertical
axis represents either pressure or
horizontal displacement of the
elements of the medium.

are formed and the pipe vibrates at its natural frequencies. Note that, from end to
end, the pattern is A–N–A, the same pattern as in the vibrating string, except node
and antinode have exchanged positions. As before, an antinode and its adjacent
node, A–N, represent a quarter-wavelength, and there are two, A–N and N–A, so
$L = 2(\lambda_1/4) = \lambda_1/2$ and $\lambda_1 = 2L$. The fundamental frequency of the pipe open at
both ends is then $f_1 = v/\lambda_1 = v/2L$. The next harmonic has an additional node
and antinode between the ends, creating the pattern A–N–A–N–A. We count the
pairs: A–N, N–A, A–N, and N–A, making four segments, each with length $\lambda_2/4$.
We have $L = 4(\lambda_2/4) = \lambda_2$, and the second harmonic (first overtone) is $f_2 = v/\lambda_2 =
v/L = 2(v/2L) = 2f_1$. All higher harmonics, it turns out, are positive integer mul-
tiples of the fundamental:

Pipe open at both ends; ▶
all harmonics are present

$$f_n = n\frac{v}{2L} = nf_1 \qquad n = 1, 2, 3, \ldots \qquad \text{[14.18]}$$

where v is the speed of sound in air. Notice the similarity to Equation 14.17, which
also involves multiples of the fundamental.

If a pipe is open at one end and closed at the other, the open end is an antinode
and the closed end is a node (Fig. 14.23b). In such a pipe, the fundamental frequency consists of a single antinode–node pair, A–N, so $L = \lambda_1/4$ and $\lambda_1 = 4L$. The
fundamental harmonic for a pipe closed at one end is then $f_1 = v/\lambda_1 = v/4L$. The
first overtone has another node and antinode between the open end and closed
end, making the pattern A–N–A–N. There are three antinode–node segments in
this pattern (A–N, N–A, and A–N), so $L = 3(\lambda_3/4)$ and $\lambda_3 = 4L/3$. The first overtone therefore has frequency $f_3 = v/\lambda_3 = 3v/4L = 3f_1$. Similarly, $f_5 = 5f_1$. In contrast to the pipe open at both ends, **there are no even multiples of the fundamental harmonic.** The odd harmonics for a pipe open at one end only are given by

Pipe closed at one end; ▶
**only odd harmonics are
present**

$$f_n = n\frac{v}{4L} = nf_1 \qquad n = 1, 3, 5, \ldots \qquad \text{[14.19]}$$

■ Quick Quiz

14.5 A pipe open at both ends resonates at a fundamental frequency f_{open}. When
one end is covered and the pipe is again made to resonate, the fundamental frequency is f_{closed}. Which of the following expressions describes how these two reso-
nant frequencies compare? (a) $f_{\text{closed}} = f_{\text{open}}$ (b) $f_{\text{closed}} = \frac{3}{2} f_{\text{open}}$ (c) $f_{\text{closed}} = 2 f_{\text{open}}$
(d) $f_{\text{closed}} = \frac{1}{2} f_{\text{open}}$ (e) none of these

14.6 Balboa Park in San Diego has an outdoor organ. When the air temperature
increases, the fundamental frequency of one of the organ pipes (a) increases,
(b) decreases, (c) stays the same, or (d) is impossible to determine. (The thermal
expansion of the pipe is negligible.)

■ APPLYING PHYSICS 14.3 │ Oscillations in a Harbor

Why do passing ocean waves sometimes cause the water in
a harbor to undergo very large oscillations, called a *seiche*
(pronounced *saysh*)?

EXPLANATION Water in a harbor is enclosed and possesses a natural frequency based on the size of the harbor.
This is similar to the natural frequency of the enclosed
air in a bottle, which can be excited by blowing across

the edge of the opening. Ocean waves pass by the opening of the harbor at a certain frequency. If this frequency
matches that of the enclosed harbor, then a large standing
wave can be set up in the water by resonance. This situation
can be simulated by carrying a fish tank filled with water. If
your walking frequency matches the natural frequency of
the water as it sloshes back and forth, a large standing wave
develops in the fish tank. ■

▪ APPLYING PHYSICS 14.4 | Why are Instruments Warmed Up?

Why do the strings go flat and the wind instruments go sharp during a performance if an orchestra doesn't warm up beforehand?

EXPLANATION Without warming up, all the instruments will be at room temperature at the beginning of the concert. As the wind instruments are played, they fill with warm air from the player's exhalation. The increase in temperature of the air in the instruments causes an increase in the speed of sound, which raises the resonance frequencies of the air columns. As a result, the instruments go sharp. The strings on the stringed instruments also increase in temperature due to the friction of rubbing with the bow. This results in thermal expansion, which causes a decrease in tension in the strings. With the decrease in tension, the wave speed on the strings drops and the fundamental frequencies decrease, so the stringed instruments go flat. ▪

▪ APPLYING PHYSICS 14.5 | How Do Bugles Work?

A bugle has no valves, keys, slides, or finger holes. How can it be used to play a song?

EXPLANATION Songs for the bugle are limited to harmonics of the fundamental frequency because there is no control over frequencies without valves, keys, slides, or finger holes. The player obtains different notes by changing the tension in the lips as the bugle is played, exciting different harmonics. The normal playing range of a bugle is among the third, fourth, fifth, and sixth harmonics of the fundamental. "Reveille," for example, is played with just the three notes G, C, and F, and "Taps" is played with these three notes and the G one octave above the lower G. ▪

▪ EXAMPLE 14.9 | Harmonics of a Pipe

GOAL Find frequencies of open and closed pipes.

PROBLEM A pipe is 2.46 m long. **(a)** Determine the frequencies of the first three harmonics if the pipe is open at both ends. Take 343 m/s as the speed of sound in air. **(b)** How many harmonic frequencies of this pipe lie in the audible range, from 20 Hz to 20 000 Hz? **(c)** What are the three lowest possible frequencies if the pipe is closed at one end and open at the other?

STRATEGY Substitute into Equation 14.18 for part (a) and Equation 14.19 for part (c). All harmonics, $n = 1, 2, 3 \ldots$ are available for the pipe open at both ends, but only the harmonics with $n = 1, 3, 5, \ldots$ for the pipe closed at one end. For part (b), set the frequency in Equation 14.18 equal to 2.00×10^4 Hz.

. . . .

SOLUTION

(a) Find the frequencies if the pipe is open at both ends.

Substitute into Equation 14.18, with $n = 1$:

$$f_1 = \frac{v}{2L} = \frac{343 \text{ m/s}}{2(2.46 \text{ m})} = \boxed{69.7 \text{ Hz}}$$

Multiply to find the second and third harmonics:

$$f_2 = 2f_1 = \boxed{139 \text{ Hz}} \qquad f_3 = 3f_1 = \boxed{209 \text{ Hz}}$$

(b) How many harmonics lie between 20 Hz and 20 000 Hz for this pipe?

Set the frequency in Equation 14.18 equal to 2.00×10^4 Hz and solve for n:

$$f_n = n\frac{v}{2L} = n\frac{343 \text{ m/s}}{2 \cdot 2.46 \text{ m}} = 2.00 \times 10^4 \text{ Hz}$$

This works out to $n = 286.88$, which must be truncated down ($n = 287$ gives a frequency over 2.00×10^4 Hz):

$$n = \boxed{286}$$

(c) Find the frequencies for the pipe closed at one end.

Apply Equation 14.19 with $n = 1$:

$$f_1 = \frac{v}{4L} = \frac{343 \text{ m/s}}{4(2.46 \text{ m})} = \boxed{34.9 \text{ Hz}}$$

The next two harmonics are odd multiples of the first:

$$f_3 = 3f_1 = \boxed{105 \text{ Hz}} \qquad f_5 = 5f_1 = \boxed{175 \text{ Hz}}$$

. . . .

(Continued)

QUESTION 14.9 True or False: The fundamental wavelength of a longer pipe is greater than the fundamental wavelength of a shorter pipe.

EXERCISE 14.9 (a) What length pipe open at both ends has a fundamental frequency of 3.70×10^2 Hz? Find the first overtone. (b) If the one end of this pipe is now closed, what is the new fundamental frequency? Find the first overtone. (c) If the pipe is open at one end only, how many harmonics are possible in the normal hearing range from 20 to 20 000 Hz?

ANSWERS (a) 0.464 m, 7.40×10^2 Hz (b) 185 Hz, 555 Hz (c) 54

■ EXAMPLE 14.10 | Resonance in a Tube of Variable Length

GOAL Understand resonance in tubes and perform elementary calculations.

PROBLEM Figure 14.24a shows a simple apparatus for demonstrating resonance in a tube. A long tube open at both ends is partially submerged in a beaker of water, and a vibrating tuning fork of unknown frequency is placed near the top of the tube. The length of the air column, L, is adjusted by moving the tube vertically. The sound waves generated by the fork are reinforced when the length of the air column corresponds to one of the resonant frequencies of the tube. Suppose the smallest value of L for which a peak occurs in the sound intensity is 9.00 cm. **(a)** With this measurement, determine the frequency of the tuning fork. **(b)** Find the wavelength and the next two air-column lengths giving resonance. Take the speed of sound to be 343 m/s.

STRATEGY Once the tube is in the water, the setup is the same as a pipe closed at one end. For part (a), substitute values for v and L into Equation 14.19 with $n = 1$, and find the frequency of the tuning fork.

Figure 14.24 (Example 14.10) (a) Apparatus for demonstrating the resonance of sound waves in a tube closed at one end. The length L of the air column is varied by moving the tube vertically while it is partially submerged in water. (b) The first three resonances of the system.

(b) The next resonance maximum occurs when the water level is low enough to allow a second node (see Fig. 14.24b), which is another half-wavelength in distance. The third resonance occurs when the third node is reached, requiring yet another half-wavelength of distance. The frequency in each case is the same because it's generated by the tuning fork.

· ·

SOLUTION

(a) Find the frequency of the tuning fork.

Substitute $n = 1$, $v = 343$ m/s, and $L_1 = 9.00 \times 10^{-2}$ m into Equation 14.19:

$$f_1 = \frac{v}{4L_1} = \frac{343 \text{ m/s}}{4(9.00 \times 10^{-2} \text{ m})} = \boxed{953 \text{ Hz}}$$

(b) Find the wavelength and the next two water levels giving resonance.

Calculate the wavelength, using the fact that, for a tube open at one end, $\lambda = 4L$ for the fundamental.

$$\lambda = 4L_1 = 4(9.00 \times 10^{-2} \text{ m}) = \boxed{0.360 \text{ m}}$$

Add a half-wavelength of distance to L_1 to get the next resonance position:

$$L_2 = L_1 + \lambda/2 = 0.090\ 0 \text{ m} + 0.180 \text{ m} = \boxed{0.270 \text{ m}}$$

Add another half-wavelength to L_2 to obtain the third resonance position:

$$L_3 = L_2 + \lambda/2 = 0.270 \text{ m} + 0.180 \text{ m} = \boxed{0.450 \text{ m}}$$

· ·

REMARKS This experimental arrangement is often used to measure the speed of sound, in which case the frequency of the tuning fork must be known in advance.

QUESTION 14.10 True or False: The resonant frequency of an air column depends on the length of the column and the speed of sound.

EXERCISE 14.10 An unknown gas is introduced into the aforementioned apparatus using the same tuning fork, and the first resonance occurs when the air column is 5.84 cm long. Find the speed of sound in the gas.

ANSWER 223 m/s

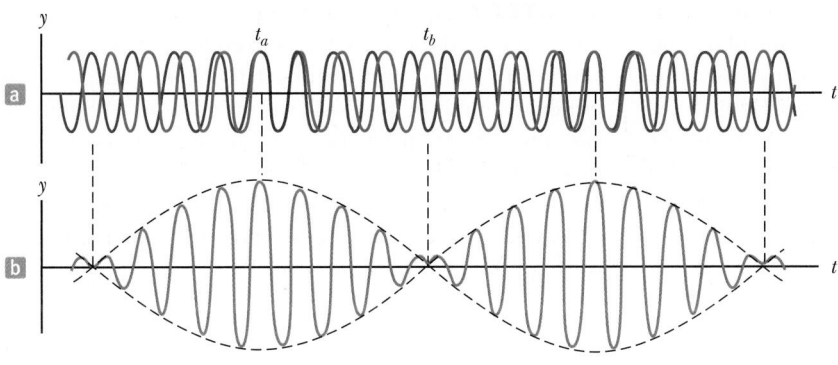

Active Figure 14.25
Beats are formed by the combination of two waves of slightly different frequencies traveling in the same direction. (a) The individual waves heard by an observer at a fixed point in space. (b) The combined wave has an amplitude (dashed line) that oscillates in time.

14.11 Beats

The interference phenomena we have been discussing so far have involved the superposition of two or more waves with the same frequency, traveling in opposite directions. Another type of interference effect results from the superposition of two waves with slightly different frequencies. In such a situation, the waves at some fixed point are periodically in and out of phase, corresponding to an alternation in time between constructive and destructive interference. To understand this phenomenon, consider Active Figure 14.25. The two waves shown in Active Figure 14.25a were emitted by two tuning forks having slightly different frequencies; Active Figure 14.25b shows the superposition of these waves. At some time t_a the waves are in phase and constructive interference occurs, as demonstrated by the resultant curve in Active Figure 14.25b. At some later time, however, the vibrations of the two forks move out of step with each other. At time t_b, one fork emits a compression while the other emits a rarefaction, and destructive interference occurs, as demonstrated by the curve shown. As time passes, the vibrations of the two forks move out of phase, then into phase again, and so on. As a consequence, a listener at some fixed point hears an alternation in loudness, known as **beats.** The number of beats per second, or the *beat frequency,* equals the difference in frequency between the two sources:

$$f_b = |f_2 - f_1| \qquad [14.20]$$

◄ Beat frequency

where f_b is the beat frequency and f_1 and f_2 are the two frequencies. The absolute value is used because the beat frequency is a positive quantity and will occur regardless of the order of subtraction.

A stringed instrument such as a piano can be tuned by beating a note on the instrument against a note of known frequency. The string can then be tuned to the desired frequency by adjusting the tension until no beats are heard.

APPLICATION

Using Beats to Tune a Musical Instrument

▪ Quick Quiz

14.7 You are tuning a guitar by comparing the sound of the string with that of a standard tuning fork. You notice a beat frequency of 5 Hz when both sounds are present. As you tighten the guitar string, the beat frequency rises steadily to 8 Hz. To tune the string exactly to the tuning fork, you should (a) continue to tighten the string, (b) loosen the string, or (c) impossible to determine from the given information.

▪ EXAMPLE 14.11 | Sour Notes

GOAL Apply the beat frequency concept.

PROBLEM A certain piano string is supposed to vibrate at a frequency of 4.40×10^2 Hz. To check its frequency, a tuning fork known to vibrate at a frequency of 4.40×10^2 Hz is sounded at the same time the piano key is struck, and a beat frequency of 4 beats per second is heard. **(a)** Find the two possible frequencies at which the string could be vibrating.

(Continued)

(b) Suppose the piano tuner runs toward the piano, holding the vibrating tuning fork while his assistant plays the note, which is at 436 Hz. At his maximum speed, the piano tuner notices the beat frequency drops from 4 Hz to 2 Hz (without going through a beat frequency of zero). How fast is he moving? Use a sound speed of 343 m/s. **(c)** While the piano tuner is running, what beat frequency is observed by the assistant? *Note:* Assume all numbers are accurate to two decimal places, necessary for this last calculation.

STRATEGY **(a)** The beat frequency is equal to the absolute value of the difference in frequency between the two sources of sound and occurs if the piano string is tuned either too high or too low. Solve Equation 14.20 for these two possible frequencies. **(b)** Moving toward the piano raises the observed piano string frequency. Solve the Doppler shift formula, Equation 14.12, for the speed of the observer. **(c)** The assistant observes a Doppler shift for the tuning fork. Apply Equation 14.12.

SOLUTION
(a) Find the two possible frequencies.

Case 1: $f_2 - f_1$ is already positive, so just drop the absolute-value signs:

$f_b = f_2 - f_1 \rightarrow 4 \text{ Hz} = f_2 - 4.40 \times 10^2 \text{ Hz}$
$f_2 = \boxed{444 \text{ Hz}}$

Case 2: $f_2 - f_1$ is negative, so drop the absolute-value signs, but apply an overall negative sign:

$f_b = -(f_2 - f_1) \rightarrow 4 \text{ Hz} = -(f_2 - 4.40 \times 10^2 \text{ Hz})$
$f_2 = \boxed{436 \text{ Hz}}$

(b) Find the speed of the observer if running toward the piano results in a beat frequency of 2 Hz.

Apply the Doppler shift to the case where frequency of the piano string heard by the running observer is $f_O = 438$ Hz:

$$f_O = f_S\left(\frac{v + v_O}{v - v_S}\right)$$

$$438 \text{ Hz} = (436 \text{ Hz})\left(\frac{343 \text{ m/s} + v_O}{343 \text{ m/s}}\right)$$

$$v_O = \left(\frac{438 \text{ Hz} - 436 \text{ Hz}}{436 \text{ Hz}}\right)(343 \text{ m/s}) = \boxed{1.57 \text{ m/s}}$$

(c) What beat frequency does the assistant observe?

Apply Equation 14.12. Now the source is the tuning fork, so $f_S = 4.40 \times 10^2$ Hz.

$$f_O = f_S\left(\frac{v + v_O}{v - v_S}\right)$$

$$= (4.40 \times 10^2 \text{ Hz})\left(\frac{343 \text{ m/s}}{343 \text{ m/s} - 1.57 \text{ m/s}}\right) = 442 \text{ Hz}$$

Compute the beat frequency:

$f_b = f_2 - f_1 = 442 \text{ Hz} - 436 \text{ Hz} = \boxed{6 \text{ Hz}}$

REMARKS The assistant on the piano bench and the tuner running with the fork observe different beat frequencies. Many physical observations depend on the state of motion of the observer, a subject discussed more fully in Chapter 26, on relativity.

QUESTION 14.11 Why aren't beats heard when two different notes are played on the piano?

EXERCISE 14.11 The assistant adjusts the tension in the same piano string, and a beat frequency of 2.00 Hz is heard when the note and the tuning fork are struck at the same time. **(a)** Find the two possible frequencies of the string. **(b)** Assume the actual string frequency is the higher frequency. If the piano tuner runs away from the piano at 4.00 m/s while holding the vibrating tuning fork, what beat frequency does he hear? **(c)** What beat frequency does the assistant on the bench hear? Use 343 m/s for the speed of sound.

ANSWERS (a) 438 Hz, 442 Hz (b) 3 Hz (c) 7 Hz

14.12 Quality of Sound

The sound-wave patterns produced by most musical instruments are complex. Figure 14.26 shows characteristic waveforms (pressure is plotted on the vertical axis, time on the horizontal axis) produced by a tuning fork, a flute, and a clarinet,

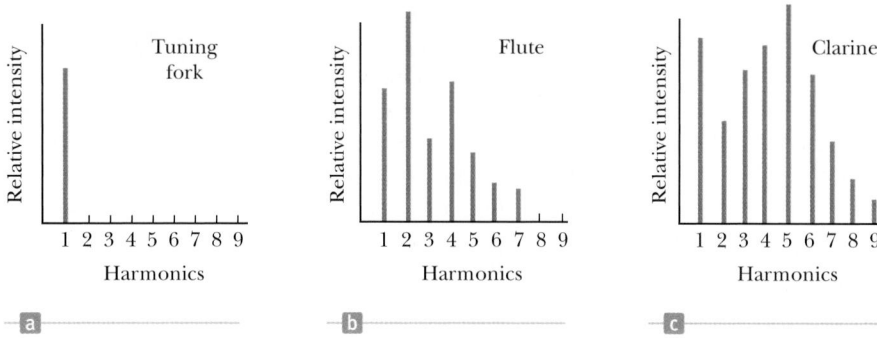

Figure 14.27 Harmonics of the waveforms in Figure 14.26. Note their variation in intensity.

Figure 14.26 Sound wave patterns produced by various instruments.

each playing the same steady note. Although each instrument has its own characteristic pattern, the figure reveals that each of the waveforms is periodic. Note that the tuning fork produces only one harmonic (the fundamental frequency), but the two instruments emit mixtures of harmonics. Figure 14.27 graphs the harmonics of the waveforms of Figure 14.26. When the note is played on the flute (Fig. 14.26b), part of the sound consists of a vibration at the fundamental frequency, an even higher intensity is contributed by the second harmonic, the fourth harmonic produces about the same intensity as the fundamental, and so on. These sounds add together according to the principle of superposition to give the complex waveform shown. The clarinet emits a certain intensity at a frequency of the first harmonic, about half as much intensity at the frequency of the second harmonic, and so forth. The resultant superposition of these frequencies produces the pattern shown in Figure 14.26c. The tuning fork (Figs. 14.26a and 14.27a) emits sound only at the frequency of the first harmonic.

In music, the characteristic sound of any instrument is referred to as the *quality*, or *timbre*, of the sound. The quality depends on the mixture of harmonics in the sound. We say that the note C on a flute differs in quality from the same C on a clarinet. Instruments such as the bugle, trumpet, violin, and tuba are rich in harmonics. A musician playing a wind instrument can emphasize one or another of these harmonics by changing the configuration of the lips, thereby playing different musical notes with the same valve openings.

Tip 14.5 Pitch Is Not the Same as Frequency

Although pitch is related mostly (but not completely) to frequency, the two terms are not the same. A phrase such as "the pitch of the sound" is incorrect because pitch is not a physical property of the sound. Frequency is the physical measurement of the number of oscillations per second of the sound. Pitch is a psychological reaction to sound that enables a human being to place the sound on a scale from high to low or from treble to bass. Frequency is the stimulus and pitch is the response.

■ **APPLYING PHYSICS 14.6** | **Why Does the Professor Sound Like Donald Duck?**

A professor performs a demonstration in which he breathes helium and then speaks with a comical voice. One student explains, "The velocity of sound in helium is higher than in air, so the fundamental frequency of the standing waves in the mouth is increased." Another student says, "No, the fundamental frequency is determined by the vocal folds and cannot be changed. Only the quality of the voice has changed." Which student is correct?

EXPLANATION The second student is correct. The fundamental frequency of the complex tone from the voice is determined by the vibration of the vocal folds and is not changed by substituting a different gas in the mouth. The introduction of the helium into the mouth results in harmonics of higher frequencies being excited more than in the normal voice, but the fundamental frequency of the voice is the same, only the quality has changed. The unusual inclusion of the higher frequency harmonics results in a common description of this effect as a "high-pitched" voice, but that description is incorrect. (It is really a "quacky" timbre.) ■

14.13 The Ear BIO

The human ear is divided into three regions: the outer ear, the middle ear, and the inner ear (Fig. 14.28). The *outer ear* consists of the ear canal (which is open to the atmosphere), terminating at the eardrum (tympanum). Sound waves travel down the ear canal to the eardrum, which vibrates in and out in phase with the pushes and pulls caused by the alternating high and low pressures of the waves. Behind the eardrum are three small bones of the *middle ear,* called the hammer, the anvil, and the stirrup because of their shapes. These bones transmit the vibration to the *inner ear,* which contains the cochlea, a snail-shaped tube about 2 cm long. The cochlea makes contact with the stirrup at the oval window and is divided along its length by the basilar membrane, which consists of small hairs (cilia) and nerve fibers. This membrane varies in mass per unit length and in tension along its length, and different portions of it resonate at different frequencies. (Recall that the natural frequency of a string depends on its mass per unit length and on the tension in it.) Along the basilar membrane are numerous nerve endings, which sense the vibration of the membrane and in turn transmit impulses to the brain. The brain interprets the impulses as sounds of varying frequency, depending on the locations along the basilar membrane of the impulse-transmitting nerves and on the rates at which the impulses are transmitted.

Figure 14.29 shows the frequency response curves of an average human ear for sounds of equal loudness, ranging from 0 to 120 dB. To interpret this series of graphs, take the bottom curve as the threshold of hearing. Compare the intensity level on the vertical axis for the two frequencies 100 Hz and 1 000 Hz. The vertical axis shows that the 100-Hz sound must be about 38 dB greater than the 1 000-Hz sound to be at the threshold of hearing, which means that the threshold of hearing is very strongly dependent on frequency. The easiest frequencies to hear are around 3 300 Hz; those above 12 000 Hz or below about 50 Hz must be relatively intense to be heard.

Now consider the curve labeled 80. This curve uses a 1 000-Hz tone at an intensity level of 80 dB as its reference. The curve shows that a tone of frequency 100 Hz would have to be about 4 dB louder than the 80-dB, 1 000-Hz tone in order to sound as loud. Notice that the curves flatten out as the intensity levels of the sounds increase, so when sounds are loud, all frequencies can be heard equally well.

Figure 14.28 The structure of the human ear. The three tiny bones (ossicles) that connect the eardrum to the window of the cochlea act as a double-lever system to decrease the amplitude of vibration and hence increase the pressure on the fluid in the cochlea.

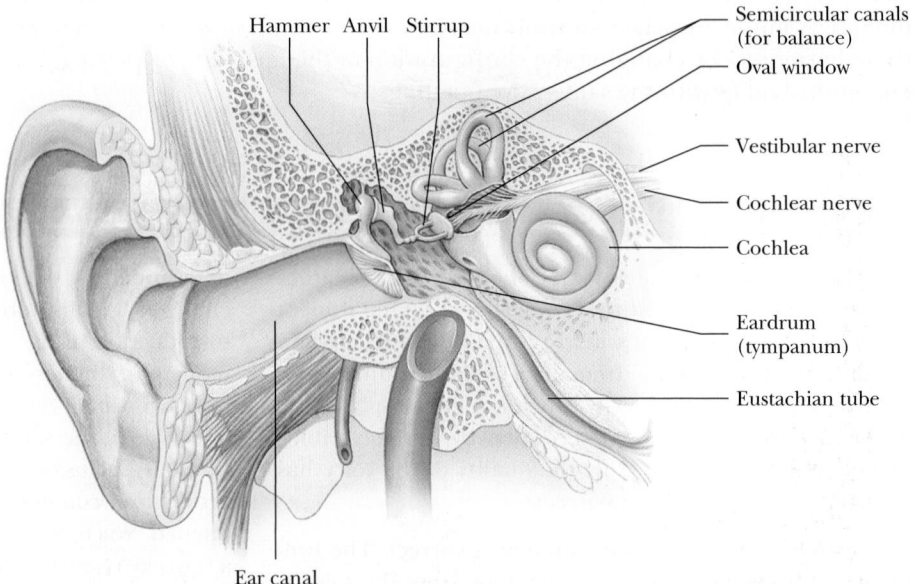

Hammer Anvil Stirrup

Semicircular canals (for balance)

Oval window

Vestibular nerve

Cochlear nerve

Cochlea

Eardrum (tympanum)

Eustachian tube

Ear canal

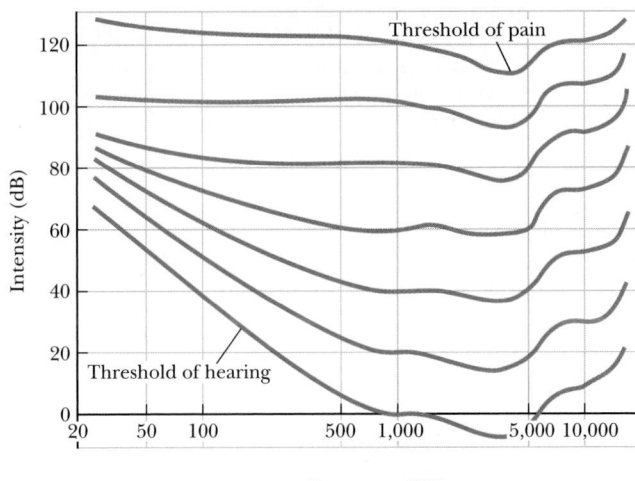

Figure 14.29 Curves of intensity level versus frequency for sounds that are perceived to be of equal loudness. Note that the ear is most sensitive at a frequency of about 3 300 Hz. The lowest curve corresponds to the threshold of hearing for only about 1% of the population.

The small bones in the middle ear represent an intricate lever system that increases the force on the oval window. The pressure is greatly magnified because the surface area of the eardrum is about 20 times that of the oval window (in analogy with a hydraulic press). The middle ear, together with the eardrum and oval window, in effect acts as a matching network between the air in the outer ear and the liquid in the inner ear. The overall energy transfer between the outer ear and the inner ear is highly efficient, with pressure amplification factors of several thousand. In other words, pressure variations in the inner ear are much greater than those in the outer ear.

The ear has its own built-in protection against loud sounds. The muscles connecting the three middle-ear bones to the walls control the volume of the sound by changing the tension on the bones as sound builds up, thus hindering their ability to transmit vibrations. In addition, the eardrum becomes stiffer as the sound intensity increases. These two events make the ear less sensitive to loud incoming sounds. There is a time delay between the onset of a loud sound and the ear's protective reaction, however, so a very sudden loud sound can still damage the ear.

The complex structure of the human ear is believed to be related to the fact that mammals evolved from seagoing creatures. In comparison, insect ears are considerably simpler in design because insects have always been land residents. A typical insect ear consists of an eardrum exposed directly to the air on one side and to an air-filled cavity on the other side. Nerve cells communicate directly with the cavity and the brain, without the need for the complex intermediary of an inner and middle ear. This simple design allows the ear to be placed virtually anywhere on the body. For example, a grasshopper has its ears on its legs. One advantage of the simple insect ear is that the distance and orientation of the ears can be varied so that it is easier to locate sources of sound, such as other insects.

One of the most amazing medical advances in recent decades is the cochlear implant, allowing the deaf to hear. Deafness can occur when the hairlike sensors (cilia) in the cochlea break off over a lifetime or sometimes because of prolonged exposure to loud sounds. Because the cilia don't grow back, the ear loses sensitivity to certain frequencies of sound. The cochlear implant stimulates the nerves in the ear electronically to restore hearing loss that is due to damaged or absent cilia.

BIO APPLICATION
Cochlear Implants

■ SUMMARY

14.2 Characteristics of Sound Waves

Sound waves are longitudinal waves. **Audible waves** are sound waves with frequencies between 20 and 20 000 Hz.

Infrasonic waves have frequencies below the audible range, and **ultrasonic waves** have frequencies above the audible range.

14.3 The Speed of Sound

The speed of sound in a medium of bulk modulus B and density ρ is

$$v = \sqrt{\frac{B}{\rho}} \qquad \text{[14.1]}$$

The speed of sound also depends on the temperature of the medium. The relationship between temperature and the speed of sound in air is

$$v = (331 \text{ m/s}) \sqrt{\frac{T}{273 \text{ K}}} \qquad \text{[14.4]}$$

where T is the absolute (Kelvin) temperature and 331 m/s is the speed of sound in air at 0°C.

14.4 Energy and Intensity of Sound Waves

The **average intensity** of sound incident on a surface is defined by

$$I \equiv \frac{\text{power}}{\text{area}} = \frac{P}{A} \qquad \text{[14.6]}$$

where the power P is the energy per unit time flowing through the surface, which has area A. The **intensity level** of a sound wave is given by

$$\beta \equiv 10 \log \left(\frac{I}{I_0} \right) \qquad \text{[14.7]}$$

The constant $I_0 = 1.0 \times 10^{-12}$ W/m^2 is a reference intensity, usually taken to be at the threshold of hearing, and I is the intensity at level β, measured in **decibels** (dB).

14.5 Spherical and Plane Waves

The **intensity** of a *spherical wave* produced by a point source is proportional to the average power emitted and inversely proportional to the square of the distance from the source:

$$I = \frac{P_{av}}{4\pi r^2} \qquad \text{[14.8]}$$

14.6 The Doppler Effect

The change in frequency heard by an observer whenever there is relative motion between a source of sound and the observer is called the **Doppler effect.** If the observer is moving with speed v_O and the source is moving with speed v_S, the observed frequency is

$$f_O = f_S \left(\frac{v + v_O}{v - v_S} \right) \qquad \text{[14.12]}$$

where v is the speed of sound. A positive speed is substituted for v_O when the observer moves toward the source, a negative speed when the observer moves away from the source. Similarly, a positive speed is substituted for v_S when the sources moves toward the observer, a negative speed when the source moves away. Speeds are measured relative to the medium in which the sound is propagated.

14.7 Interference of Sound Waves

When waves interfere, the resultant wave is found by adding the individual waves together point by point. When crest meets crest and trough meets trough, the waves undergo **constructive interference,** with path length difference

$$r_2 - r_1 = n\lambda \qquad n = 0, 1, 2, \ldots \qquad \text{[14.13]}$$

When crest meets trough, **destructive interference** occurs, with path length difference

$$r_2 - r_1 = (n + \tfrac{1}{2})\lambda \qquad n = 0, 1, 2, \ldots \qquad \text{[14.14]}$$

14.8 Standing Waves

Standing waves are formed when two waves having the same frequency, amplitude, and wavelength travel in opposite directions through a medium. The natural frequencies of vibration of a stretched string of length L, fixed at both ends, are

$$f_n = nf_1 = \frac{n}{2L} \sqrt{\frac{F}{\mu}} \qquad n = 1, 2, 3, \ldots \qquad \text{[14.17]}$$

where F is the tension in the string and μ is its mass per unit length.

14.9 Forced Vibrations and Resonance

A system capable of oscillating is said to be in **resonance** with some driving force whenever the frequency of the driving force matches one of the natural frequencies of the system. When the system is resonating, it oscillates with maximum amplitude.

14.10 Standing Waves in Air Columns

Standing waves can be produced in a tube of air. If the reflecting end of the tube is *open*, all harmonics are present and the natural frequencies of vibration are

$$f_n = n \frac{v}{2L} = nf_1 \qquad n = 1, 2, 3, \ldots \qquad \text{[14.18]}$$

If the tube is *closed* at the reflecting end, only the *odd* harmonics are present and the natural frequencies of vibration are

$$f_n = n \frac{v}{4L} = nf_1 \qquad n = 1, 3, 5, \ldots \qquad \text{[14.19]}$$

14.11 Beats

The phenomenon of **beats** is an interference effect that occurs when two waves with slightly different frequencies combine at a fixed point in space. For sound waves, the intensity of the resultant sound changes periodically with time. The *beat frequency* is

$$f_b = |f_2 - f_1| \qquad \text{[14.20]}$$

where f_2 and f_1 are the two source frequencies.

■ MULTIPLE-CHOICE QUESTIONS

WebAssign The multiple-choice questions in this chapter may be assigned online in Enhanced WebAssign.

1. A sound wave traveling in air has a frequency f and wavelength λ. A second sound wave traveling in air has wavelength $\lambda/2$. What is the frequency of the second sound wave? (a) $4f$ (b) $2f$ (c) f (d) $\frac{1}{2}f$ (e) $\frac{1}{4}f$

2. The temperature at Furnace Creek in Death Valley reached 134°F on July 10, 1913. What is the speed of sound in air at this temperature? (a) 321 m/s (b) 343 m/s (c) 364 m/s (d) 375 m/s (e) 405 m/s

3. Ethyl alcohol has a density of 0.806×10^3 kg/m^3 and a bulk modulus of 1.0×10^9 Pa. Compute the speed of sound in ethyl alcohol. (a) 1 100 m/s (b) 340 m/s (c) 820 m/s (d) 450 m/s (e) 1 300 m/s

4. Considering the footnote following Table 14.1, what is the speed of a longitudinal wave in a thin, solid aluminum rod? (a) 340 m/s (b) 570 m/s (c) 1 400 m/s (d) 3 200 m/s (e) 5 100 m/s

5. The sound intensity level of a jet plane going down the runway as observed from a certain location is 105 dB. What is the intensity of the sound at this location? (a) 2.45×10^{-2} W/m^2 (b) 3.54×10^{-3} W/m^2 (c) 8.25×10^{-3} W/m^2 (d) 3.16×10^{-2} W/m^2 (e) 1.05×10^{-2} W/m^2

6. A point source broadcasts sound into a uniform medium. If the distance from the source is tripled, how does the intensity change? (a) It becomes one-ninth as large. (b) It becomes one-third as large. (c) It is unchanged. (d) It becomes three times larger. (e) It becomes nine times larger.

7. If a 1.00-kHz sound source moves at a speed of 50.0 m/s toward a listener who moves at a speed of 30.0 m/s in a direction away from the source, what is the apparent frequency heard by the listener? (The speed of sound is 343 m/s.) (a) 796 Hz (b) 949 Hz (c) 1 000 Hz (d) 1 070 Hz (e) 1 270 Hz

8. What happens to a sound wave when it travels from air into water? (a) Its intensity increases. (b) Its wavelength decreases. (c) Its frequency increases. (d) Its frequency remains the same. (e) Its velocity decreases.

9. When two tuning forks are sounded at the same time, a beat frequency of 5 Hz occurs. If one of the tuning forks has a frequency of 245 Hz, what is the frequency of the other tuning fork? (a) 240 Hz (b) 242.5 Hz

(c) 247.5 Hz (d) 250 Hz (e) More than one answer could be correct.

10. A flute has a length of 58.0 cm. If the speed of sound in air is 343 m/s, what is the fundamental frequency of the flute, assuming it is a tube closed at one end and open at the other? (a) 148 Hz (b) 296 Hz (c) 444 Hz (d) 591 Hz (e) None of those answers.

11. The fundamental frequency of a resonating pipe is 150 Hz, and the next higher resonant frequencies are 300 Hz and 450 Hz. From this information, what can you conclude? (a) The pipe is open at one end and closed at the other. (b) The pipe could be open at each end or closed at each end. (c) The pipe must be open at each end. (d) The pipe must be closed at each end. (e) The pipe is open at both ends for the lowest frequency, only.

12. As you travel down the highway in your car, an ambulance approaches you from the rear at a high speed sounding its siren at a frequency of 500 Hz. Which statement is correct? (a) You hear a frequency less than 500 Hz. (b) You hear a frequency equal to 500 Hz. (c) You hear a frequency greater than 500 Hz. (d) You hear a frequency greater than 500 Hz, whereas the ambulance driver hears a frequency lower than 500 Hz. (e) You hear a frequency less than 500 Hz, whereas the ambulance driver hears a frequency of 500 Hz.

13. Two sirens A and B are sounding so that the frequency from A is twice the frequency from B. Compared with the speed of sound from A, is the speed of sound from B (a) twice as fast, (b) half as fast, (c) four times as fast, (d) one-fourth as fast, or (e) the same?

14. A hollow pipe (such as an organ pipe open at both ends) is made to go into resonance at frequency f_{open}. One end of the pipe is now covered and the pipe is again made to go into resonance, this time at frequency f_{closed}. Both resonances are first harmonics. How do these two resonances compare? (a) They are the same. (b) $f_{\text{open}} = 2f_{\text{closed}}$ (c) $f_{\text{closed}} = 2f_{\text{open}}$ (d) $f_{\text{open}} = f_{\text{closed}}$ (e) $f_{\text{closed}} = \frac{3}{2}f_{\text{open}}$

15. Doubling the power output from a sound source emitting a single frequency will result in what increase in decibel level? (a) 0.50 dB (b) 2.0 dB (c) 3.0 dB (d) 4 dB (e) above 20 dB

■ CONCEPTUAL QUESTIONS

WebAssign The conceptual questions in this chapter may be assigned online in Enhanced WebAssign.

1. (a) You are driving down the highway in your car when a police car sounding its siren overtakes you and passes you. If its frequency at rest is f_0, is the frequency you

hear while the car is catching up to you higher or lower than f_0? (b) What about the frequency you hear after the car has passed you?

2. A crude model of the human throat is that of a pipe open at both ends with a vibrating source to introduce the sound into the pipe at one end. Assuming the vibrating source produces a range of frequencies, discuss the effect of changing the pipe's length.

3. Older auto-focus cameras sent out a pulse of sound and measured the time interval required for the pulse to reach an object, reflect off of it, and return to be detected. Can air temperature affect the camera's focus? New cameras use a more reliable infrared system.

4. Explain how the distance to a lightning bolt (Fig. CQ14.4) can be determined by counting the seconds between the flash and the sound of thunder.

Figure CQ14.4

5. Secret agents in the movies always want to get to a secure phone with a voice scrambler. How do these devices work?

6. Why does a vibrating guitar string sound louder when placed on the instrument than it would if allowed to vibrate in the air while off the instrument?

7. You are driving toward the base of a cliff and you honk your horn. (a) Is there a Doppler shift of the sound when you hear the echo? If so, is it like a moving source or moving observer? (b) What if the reflection occurs not from a cliff, but from the forward edge of a huge alien spacecraft moving toward you as you drive?

8. The radar systems used by police to detect speeders are sensitive to the Doppler shift of a pulse of radio waves. Discuss how this sensitivity can be used to measure the speed of a car.

9. An archer shoots an arrow from a bow. Does the string of the bow exhibit standing waves after the arrow leaves? If so, and if the bow is perfectly symmetric so that the arrow leaves from the center of the string, what harmonics are excited?

10. A soft drink bottle resonates as air is blown across its top. What happens to the resonant frequency as the level of fluid in the bottle decreases?

11. An airplane mechanic notices that the sound from a twin-engine aircraft varies rapidly in loudness when both engines are running. What could be causing this variation from loud to soft?

■ PROBLEMS

WebAssign The problems in this chapter may be assigned online in Enhanced WebAssign. Selected problems also have Watch It video solutions.

1. denotes straightforward problem; 2. denotes intermediate problem;

3. denotes challenging problem

1. denotes full solution available in *Student Solutions Manual/ Study Guide*

1. denotes problems most often assigned in Enhanced WebAssign

BIO denotes biomedical problems

GP denotes guided problems

M denotes Master It tutorial available in Enhanced WebAssign

Q|C denotes asking for quantitative and conceptual reasoning

S denotes symbolic reasoning problem

14.2 Characteristics of Sound Waves

14.3 The Speed of Sound

Note: Unless otherwise specified, assume the speed of sound in air is 343 m/s, its value at an air temperature of 20.0°C. At any other Celsius temperature T_C, the speed of sound in air is described by Equation 14.4:

$$v = 331\sqrt{1 + \frac{T_C}{273}}$$

where v is in m/s and T is in °C. Use Table 14.1 to find speeds of sound in other media.

1. **Q|C** Suppose you hear a clap of thunder 16.2 s after seeing the associated lightning stroke. The speed of light in air is 3.00×10^8 m/s. (a) How far are you from the lightning stroke? (b) Do you need to know the value of the speed of light to answer? Explain.

2. Earthquakes at fault lines in Earth's crust create seismic waves, which are longitudinal (P-waves) or transverse (S-waves). The P-waves have a speed of about 7 km/s. Estimate the average bulk modulus of Earth's crust given that the density of rock is about 2 500 kg/m³.

3. On a hot summer day, the temperature of air in Arizona reaches 114°F. What is the speed of sound in air at this temperature?

4. **BIO** A dolphin located in seawater at a temperature of 25°C emits a sound directed toward the bottom of the ocean 150 m below. How much time passes before it hears an echo?

5. A group of hikers hears an echo 3.00 s after shouting. How far away is the mountain that reflected the sound wave?

6. **BIO** The range of human hearing extends from approximately 20 Hz to 20 000 Hz. Find the wavelengths of these extremes at a temperature of 27°C.

7. A sound wave propagating in air has a frequency of 4.00 kHz. Calculate the change in wavelength when the wave, initially traveling in a region where $T = 27.0$°C, enters a region where $T = 10.0$°C.

8. A stone is dropped from rest into a well. The sound of the splash is heard exactly 2.00 s later. Find the depth of the well if the air temperature is 10.0°C.

9. **QC** A hammer strikes one end of a thick steel rail of length 8.50 m. A microphone located at the opposite end of the rail detects two pulses of sound, one that travels through the air and a longitudinal wave that travels through the rail. (a) Which pulse reaches the microphone first? (b) Find the separation in time between the arrivals of the two pulses.

14.4 Energy and Intensity of Sound Waves

14.5 Spherical and Plane Waves

10. **QC** The intensity level produced by a jet airplane at a certain location is 150 dB. (a) Calculate the intensity of the sound wave generated by the jet at the given location. (b) Compare the answer to part (a) to the threshold of pain and explain why employees directing jet airplanes at airports must wear hearing protection equipment.

11. One of the loudest sounds in recent history was that made by the explosion of Krakatoa on August 26–27, 1883. According to barometric measurements, the sound had a decibel level of 180 dB at a distance of 161 km. Assuming the intensity falls off as the inverse of the distance squared, what was the decibel level on Rodriguez Island, 4 800 km away?

12. A sound wave from a siren has an intensity of 100.0 W/m² at a certain point, and a second sound wave from a nearby ambulance has an intensity level 10 dB greater than the siren's sound wave at the same point. What is the intensity level of the sound wave due to the ambulance?

13. **BIO** A person wears a hearing aid that uniformly increases the intensity level of all audible frequencies of sound by 30.0 dB. The hearing aid picks up sound having a frequency of 250 Hz at an intensity of $3.0 \times$ 10^{-11} W/m². What is the intensity delivered to the eardrum?

14. **BIO** The area of a typical eardrum is about 5.0×10^{-5} m². Calculate the sound power (the energy per second) incident on an eardrum at (a) the threshold of hearing and (b) the threshold of pain.

15. **BIO** The toadfish makes use of resonance in a closed tube to produce very loud sounds. The tube is its swim bladder, used as an amplifier. The sound level of this creature has been measured as high as 100 dB. (a) Calculate the intensity of the sound wave emitted. (b) What is the intensity level if three of these toadfish try to make a sound at the same time?

16. **GP** A trumpet creates a sound intensity level of 1.15×10^2 dB at a distance of 1.00 m. (a) What is the sound intensity of a trumpet at this distance? (b) What is the sound intensity of five trumpets at this distance? (c) Find the sound intensity of five trumpets at the location of the first row of an audience, 8.00 m away, assuming, for simplicity, the sound energy propagates uniformly in all directions. (d) Calculate the decibel level of the five trumpets in the first row. (e) If the trumpets are being played in an outdoor auditorium, how far away, in theory, can their combined sound be heard? (f) In practice such a sound could not be heard once the listener was 2–3 km away. Why can't the sound be heard at the distance found in part (e)? *Hint:* In a very quiet room the ambient sound intensity level is about 30 dB.

17. There is evidence that elephants communicate via infrasound, generating rumbling vocalizations as low as 14 Hz that can travel up to 10 km. The intensity level of these sounds can reach 103 dB, measured a distance of 5.0 m from the source. Determine the intensity level of the infrasound 10 km from the source, assuming the sound energy radiates uniformly in all directions.

18. A family ice show is held at an enclosed arena. The skaters perform to music playing at a level of 80.0 dB. This intensity level is too loud for your baby, who yells at 75.0 dB. (a) What total sound intensity engulfs you? (b) What is the combined sound level?

19. **M** A train sounds its horn as it approaches an intersection. The horn can just be heard at a level of 50 dB by an observer 10 km away. (a) What is the average power generated by the horn? (b) What intensity level of the horn's sound is observed by someone waiting at an intersection 50 m from the train? Treat the horn as a point source and neglect any absorption of sound by the air.

20. An outside loudspeaker (considered a small source) emits sound waves with a power output of 100 W. (a) Find the intensity 10.0 m from the source. (b) Find the intensity level in decibels at that distance. (c) At what distance would you experience the sound at the threshold of pain, 120 dB?

21. **S** Show that the difference in decibel levels β_1 and β_2 of a sound source is related to the ratio of its distances r_1 and r_2 from the receivers by the formula

$$\beta_2 - \beta_1 = 20 \log\left(\frac{r_1}{r_2}\right)$$

22. A skyrocket explodes 100 m above the ground (Fig. P14.22). Three observers are spaced 100 m apart, with the first (A) directly under the explosion. (a) What is the ratio of the sound intensity heard by observer A to that heard by observer B? (b) What is the ratio of the intensity heard by observer A to that heard by observer C?

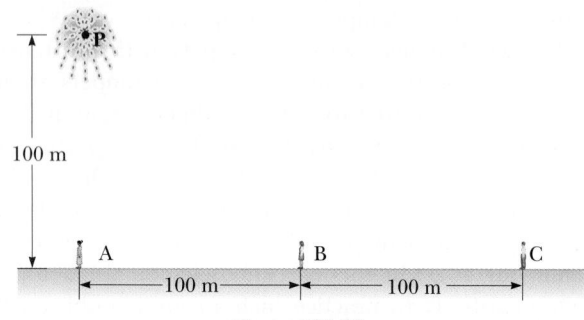

Figure P14.22

14.6 The Doppler Effect

23. A commuter train passes a passenger platform at a constant speed of 40.0 m/s. The train horn is sounded at its characteristic frequency of 320 Hz. (a) What overall change in frequency is detected by a person on the platform as the train moves from approaching to receding? (b) What wavelength is detected by a person on the platform as the train approaches?

24. An airplane traveling at half the speed of sound emits a sound of frequency 5.00 kHz. At what frequency does a stationary listener hear the sound (a) as the plane approaches? (b) After it passes?

25. Two trains on separate tracks move toward each other. Train 1 has a speed of 130 km/h; train 2, a speed of 90.0 km/h. Train 2 blows its horn, emitting a frequency of 500 Hz. What is the frequency heard by the engineer on train 1?

26. At rest, a car's horn sounds the note A (440 Hz). The horn is sounded while the car is moving down the street. A bicyclist moving in the same direction with one-third the car's speed hears a frequency of 415 Hz. (a) Is the cyclist ahead of or behind the car? (b) What is the speed of the car?

27. An alert physics student stands beside the tracks as a train rolls slowly past. He notes that the frequency of the train whistle is 465 Hz when the train is approaching him and 441 Hz when the train is receding from

him. Using these frequencies, he calculates the speed of the train. What value does he find?

28. **BIO** **Q|C** A bat flying at 5.00 m/s is chasing an insect flying in the same direction. If the bat emits a 40.0-kHz chirp and receives back an echo at 40.4 kHz, (a) what is the speed of the insect? (b) Will the bat be able to catch the insect? Explain.

29. A tuning fork vibrating at 512 Hz falls from rest and accelerates at 9.80 m/s². How far below the point of release is the tuning fork when waves of frequency 485 Hz reach the release point?

30. **BIO** Expectant parents are thrilled to hear their unborn baby's heartbeat, revealed by an ultrasonic motion detector. Suppose the fetus's ventricular wall moves in simple harmonic motion with amplitude 1.80 mm and frequency 115 beats per minute. The motion detector in contact with the mother's abdomen produces sound at precisely 2 MHz, which travels through tissue at 1.50 km/s. (a) Find the maximum linear speed of the heart wall. (b) Find the maximum frequency at which sound arrives at the wall of the baby's heart. (c) Find the maximum frequency at which reflected sound is received by the motion detector. (By electronically "listening" for echoes at a frequency different from the broadcast frequency, the motion detector can produce beeps of audible sound in synchrony with the fetal heartbeat.)

31. **M** A supersonic jet traveling at Mach 3.00 at an altitude of $h = 20\ 000$ m is directly over a person at time $t = 0$ as shown in Figure P14.31. Assume the average speed of sound in air is 335 m/s over the path of the sound. (a) At what time will the person encounter the shock wave due to the sound emitted at $t = 0$? (b) Where will the plane be when this shock wave is heard?

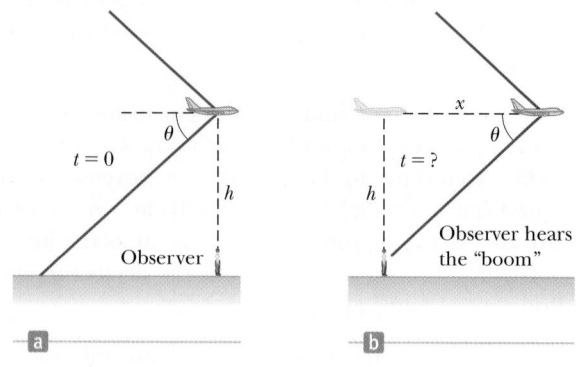

Figure P14.31

32. **GP** A yellow submarine traveling horizontally at 11.0 m/s uses sonar with a frequency of 5.27×10^3 Hz. A red submarine is in front of the yellow submarine and moving 3.00 m/s relative to the water in the same direction. A crewman in the red submarine observes sound waves ("pings") from the yellow submarine. Take the speed of sound in seawater as 1 533 m/s. (a) Write Equation 14.12. (b) Which submarine is the

source of the sound? (c) Which submarine carries the observer? (d) Does the motion of the observer's submarine increase or decrease the time between the pressure maxima of the incoming sound waves? How does that affect the observed period? The observed frequency? (e) Should the sign of v_0 be positive or negative? (f) Does the motion of the source submarine increase or decrease the time observed between the pressure maxima? How does this motion affect the observed period? The observed frequency? (g) What sign should be chosen for v_s? (h) Substitute the appropriate numbers and obtain the frequency observed by the crewman on the red submarine.

14.7 Interference of Sound Waves

33. Two small speakers are driven by a common oscillator at 8.00×10^2 Hz. The speakers face each other and are separated by 1.25 m. Locate the points along a line joining the two speakers where relative minima would be expected. (Use $v = 343$ m/s.)

34. The acoustical system shown in Figure P14.34 is driven by a speaker emitting sound of frequency 756 Hz. (a) If constructive interference occurs at a particular instant, by what minimum amount should the path length in the upper U-shaped tube be increased so that destructive interference occurs instead? (b) What minimum increase in the original length of the upper tube will again result in constructive interference?

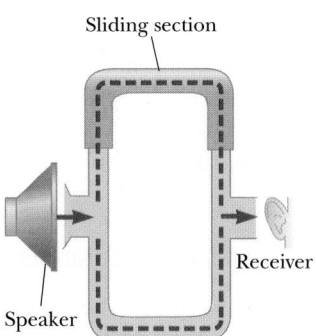

Figure P14.34

35. The ship in Figure P14.35 travels along a straight line parallel to the shore and a distance $d = 600$ m from it. The ship's radio receives simultaneous signals of the same frequency from antennas A and B, separated by

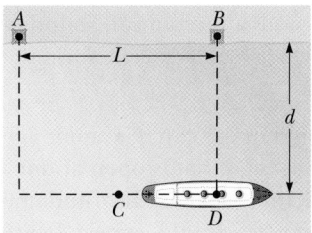

Figure P14.35

a distance $L = 800$ m. The signals interfere constructively at point C, which is equidistant from A and B. The signal goes through the first minimum at point D, which is directly outward from the shore from point B. Determine the wavelength of the radio waves.

36. Two loudspeakers are placed above and below each other, as in Figure P14.36 and driven by the same source at a frequency of 4.50×10^2 Hz. An observer is in front of the speakers (to the right) at point O, at the same distance from each speaker. What minimum vertical distance upward should the top speaker be moved to create destructive interference at point O?

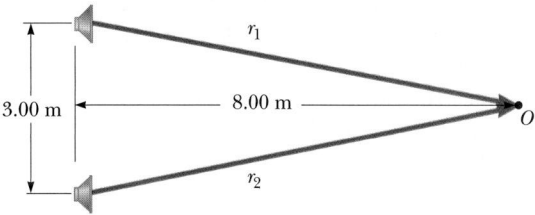

Figure P14.36

37. A pair of speakers separated by a distance $d = 0.700$ m are driven by the same oscillator at a frequency of 686 Hz. An observer originally positioned at one of the speakers begins to walk along a line perpendicular to the line joining the speakers as in Figure P14.37. (a) How far must the observer walk before reaching a relative maximum in intensity? (b) How far will the observer be from the speaker when the first relative minimum is detected in the intensity?

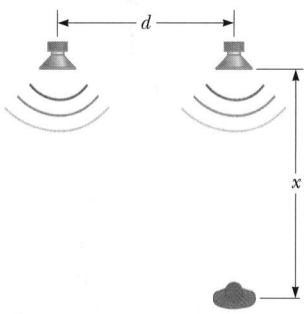

Figure P14.37

14.8 Standing Waves

38. A steel wire in a piano has a length of 0.700 0 m and a mass of 4.300×10^{-3} kg. To what tension must this wire be stretched so that the fundamental vibration corresponds to middle C ($f_C = 261.6$ Hz on the chromatic musical scale)?

39. A stretched string fixed at each end has a mass of 40.0 g and a length of 8.00 m. The tension in the string is 49.0 N. (a) Determine the positions of the nodes and antinodes for the third harmonic. (b) What is the vibration frequency for this harmonic?

40. How far, and in what direction, should a cellist move her finger to adjust a string's tone from an out-of-tune 449 Hz to an in-tune 440 Hz? The string is 68.0 cm long, and the finger is 20.0 cm from the nut for the 449-Hz tone.

41. A stretched string of length L is observed to vibrate in five equal segments when driven by a 630-Hz oscillator. What oscillator frequency will set up a standing wave so that the string vibrates in three segments?

42. Two pieces of steel wire with identical cross sections have lengths of L and $2L$. The wires are each fixed at both ends and stretched so that the tension in the longer wire is four times greater than in the shorter wire. If the fundamental frequency in the shorter wire is 60 Hz, what is the frequency of the second harmonic in the longer wire?

43. A steel wire with mass 25.0 g and length 1.35 m is strung on a bass so that the distance from the nut to the bridge is 1.10 m. (a) Compute the linear density of the string. (b) What velocity wave on the string will produce the desired fundamental frequency of the E_1 string, 41.2 Hz? (c) Calculate the tension required to obtain the proper frequency. (d) Calculate the wavelength of the string's vibration. (e) What is the wavelength of the sound produced in air? (Assume the speed of sound in air is 343 m/s.)

44. **S** A standing wave is set up in a string of variable length and tension by a vibrator of variable frequency. Both ends of the string are fixed. When the vibrator has a frequency f_A, in a string of length L_A and under tension T_A, n_A antinodes are set up in the string. (a) Write an expression for the frequency f_A of a standing wave in terms of the number n_A, length L_A, tension T_A, and linear density μ_A. (b) If the length of the string is doubled to $L_B = 2L_A$, what frequency f_B (written as a multiple of f_A) will result in the same number of antinodes? Assume the tension and linear density are unchanged. *Hint:* Make a ratio of expressions for f_B and f_A. (c) If the frequency and length are held constant, what tension T_B will produce $n_A + 1$ antinodes? (d) If the frequency is tripled and the length of the string is halved, by what factor should the tension be changed so that twice as many antinodes are produced?

45. A 12.0-kg object hangs in equilibrium from a string with total length of $L = 5.00$ m and linear mass density of $\mu = 0.001\ 00$ kg/m. The string is wrapped around two light, frictionless pulleys that are separated by the distance $d = 2.00$ m (Fig. P14.45a). (a) Determine the tension in the string. (b) At what frequency must

the string between the pulleys vibrate in order to form the standing-wave pattern shown in Figure P14.45b?

46. **M** In the arrangement shown in Figure P14.46, an object of mass $m = 5.0$ kg hangs from a cord around a light pulley. The length of the cord between point P and the pulley is $L = 2.0$ m. (a) When the vibrator is set to a frequency of 150 Hz, a standing wave with six loops is formed. What must be the linear mass density of the cord? (b) How many loops (if any) will result if m is changed to 45 kg? (c) How many loops (if any) will result if m is changed to 10 kg?

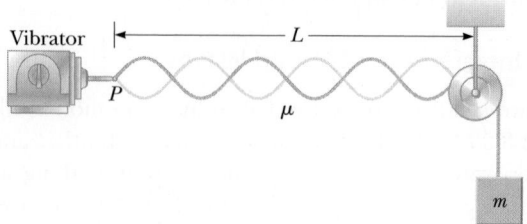

Vibrator

P

L

μ

m

Figure P14.46

47. **BIO** A 60.00-cm guitar string under a tension of 50.000 N has a mass per unit length of 0.100 00 g/cm. What is the highest resonant frequency that can be heard by a person capable of hearing frequencies up to 20 000 Hz?

14.9 Forced Vibrations and Resonance

48. Standing-wave vibrations are set up in a crystal goblet with four nodes and four antinodes equally spaced around the 20.0-cm circumference of its rim. If transverse waves move around the glass at 900 m/s, an opera singer would have to produce a high harmonic with what frequency in order to shatter the glass with a resonant vibration?

14.10 Standing Waves in Air Columns

49. The windpipe of a typical whooping crane is about 5.0 ft. long. What is the lowest resonant frequency of this pipe, assuming it is closed at one end? Assume a temperature of 37°C.

50. The overall length of a piccolo is 32.0 cm. The resonating air column vibrates as in a pipe that is open at both ends. (a) Find the frequency of the lowest note a piccolo can play. (b) Opening holes in the side effectively shortens the length of the resonant column. If the highest note a piccolo can sound is 4 000 Hz, find the distance between adjacent antinodes for this mode of vibration.

51. **BIO** The human ear canal is about 2.8 cm long. If it is regarded as a tube that is open at one end and closed at the eardrum, what is the fundamental frequency around which we would expect hearing to be most sensitive?

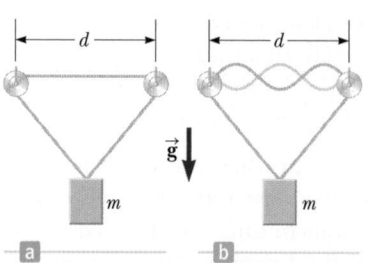

d

d

$\vec{\mathbf{g}}$

m

m

a

b

Figure P14.45

52. **QC** A tunnel under a river is 2.00 km long. (a) At what frequencies can the air in the tunnel resonate? (b) Explain whether it would be good to make a rule against blowing your car horn when you are in the tunnel.

53. **M** A pipe open at both ends has a fundamental frequency of 300 Hz when the temperature is 0°C. (a) What is the length of the pipe? (b) What is the fundamental frequency at a temperature of 30.0°C?

54. Two adjacent natural frequencies of an organ pipe are found to be 550 Hz and 650 Hz. (a) Calculate the fundamental frequency of the pipe. (b) Is the pipe open at both ends or open at only one end? (c) What is the length of the pipe?

14.11 Beats

55. In certain ranges of a piano keyboard, more than one string is tuned to the same note to provide extra loudness. For example, the note at 1.10×10^2 Hz has two strings at this frequency. If one string slips from its normal tension of 6.00×10^2 N to 5.40×10^2 N, what beat frequency is heard when the hammer strikes the two strings simultaneously?

56. The G string on a violin has a fundamental frequency of 196 Hz. It is 30.0 cm long and has a mass of 0.500 g. While this string is sounding, a nearby violinist effectively shortens the G string on her identical violin (by sliding her finger down the string) until a beat frequency of 2.00 Hz is heard between the two strings. When that occurs, what is the effective length of her string?

57. Two train whistles have identical frequencies of 1.80×10^2 Hz. When one train is at rest in the station and the other is moving nearby, a commuter standing on the station platform hears beats with a frequency of 2.00 beats/s when the whistles operate together. What are the two possible speeds and directions that the moving train can have?

58. Two pipes of equal length are each open at one end. Each has a fundamental frequency of 480 Hz at 300 K. In one pipe the air temperature is increased to 305 K. If the two pipes are sounded together, what beat frequency results?

59. A student holds a tuning fork oscillating at 256 Hz. He walks toward a wall at a constant speed of 1.33 m/s. (a) What beat frequency does he observe between the tuning fork and its echo? (b) How fast must he walk away from the wall to observe a beat frequency of 5.00 Hz?

14.13 The Ear

60. **BIO** If a human ear canal can be thought of as resembling an organ pipe, closed at one end, that resonates

at a fundamental frequency of 3 000 Hz, what is the length of the canal? Use a normal body temperature of 37°C for your determination of the speed of sound in the canal.

61. **BIO** Some studies suggest that the upper frequency limit of hearing is determined by the diameter of the eardrum. The wavelength of the sound wave and the diameter of the eardrum are approximately equal at this upper limit. If the relationship holds exactly, what is the diameter of the eardrum of a person capable of hearing 20 000 Hz? (Assume a body temperature of 37.0°C.)

Additional Problems

62. A typical sound level for a buzzing mosquito is 40 dB, and that of a vacuum cleaner is approximately 70 dB. Approximately how many buzzing mosquitoes will produce a sound intensity equal to that of a vacuum cleaner?

63. Assume a 150-W loudspeaker broadcasts sound equally in all directions and produces sound with a level of 103 dB at a distance of 1.60 m from its center. (a) Find its sound power output. If a salesperson claims the speaker is rated at 150 W, he is referring to the maximum electrical power input to the speaker. (b) Find the efficiency of the speaker, that is, the fraction of input power that is converted into useful output power.

64. Two small loudspeakers emit sound waves of different frequencies equally in all directions. Speaker A has an output of 1.00 mW, and speaker B has an output of 1.50 mW. Determine the sound level (in decibels) at point C in Figure P14.64 assuming (a) only speaker A emits sound, (b) only speaker B emits sound, and (c) both speakers emit sound.

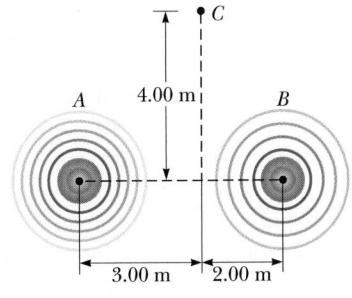

Figure P14.64

65. An interstate highway has been built through a neighborhood in a city. In the afternoon, the sound level in an apartment in the neighborhood is 80.0 dB as 100 cars pass outside the window every minute. Late at night, the traffic flow is only five cars per minute. What is the average late-night sound level?

66. A student uses an audio oscillator of adjustable frequency to measure the depth of a water well. He

reports hearing two successive resonances at 52.0 Hz and 60.0 Hz. How deep is the well?

67. A stereo speaker is placed between two observers who are 36 m apart, along the line connecting them. If one observer records an intensity level of 60 dB, and the other records an intensity level of 80 dB, how far is the speaker from each observer?

68. **M** Two ships are moving along a line due east (Fig. P14.68). The trailing vessel has a speed relative to a land-based observation point of $v_1 = 64.0$ km/h, and the leading ship has a speed of $v_2 = 45.0$ km/h relative to that point. The two ships are in a region of the ocean where the current is moving uniformly due west at $v_{current} = 10.0$ km/h. The trailing ship transmits a sonar signal at a frequency of 1 200.0 Hz through the water. What frequency is monitored by the leading ship?

Figure P14.68

69. A quartz watch contains a crystal oscillator in the form of a block of quartz that vibrates by contracting and expanding. Two opposite faces of the block, 7.05 mm apart, are antinodes, moving alternately toward and away from each other. The plane halfway between these two faces is a node of the vibration. The speed of sound in quartz is 3.70×10^3 m/s. Find the frequency of the vibration. An oscillating electric voltage accompanies the mechanical oscillation, so the quartz is described as *piezoelectric*. An electric circuit feeds in energy to maintain the oscillation and also counts the voltage pulses to keep time.

70. A flowerpot is knocked off a window ledge from a height $d = 20.0$ m above the sidewalk as shown in Figure P14.70. It falls toward an unsuspecting man of height $h = 1.75$ m who is standing below. Assume the man below requires 0.300 s to respond to a warning. How close to the sidewalk can the flowerpot fall before it is too late for a warning shouted from the window to reach the man in time?

Figure P14.70

71. On a workday, the average decibel level of a busy street is 70 dB, with 100 cars passing a given point every minute. If the number of cars is reduced to 25 every minute on a weekend, what is the decibel level of the street?

72. A flute is designed so that it plays a frequency of 261.6 Hz, middle C, when all the holes are covered and the temperature is 20.0°C. (a) Consider the flute to be a pipe open at both ends and find its length, assuming the middle-C frequency is the fundamental frequency. (b) A second player, nearby in a colder room, also attempts to play middle C on an identical flute. A beat frequency of 3.00 beats/s is heard. What is the temperature of the room?

73. A block with a speaker bolted to it is connected to a spring having spring constant $k = 20.0$ N/m, as shown in Figure P14.73. The total mass of the block and speaker is 5.00 kg, and the amplitude of the unit's motion is 0.500 m. If the speaker emits sound waves of frequency 440 Hz, determine the (a) lowest and (b) highest frequencies heard by the person to the right of the speaker.

Figure P14.73

74. A student stands several meters in front of a smooth reflecting wall, holding a board on which a wire is fixed at each end. The wire, vibrating in its third harmonic, is 75.0 cm long, has a mass of 2.25 g, and is under a tension of 400 N. A second student, moving toward the wall, hears 8.30 beats per second. What is the speed of the student approaching the wall?

75. By proper excitation, it is possible to produce both longitudinal and transverse waves in a long metal rod. In a particular case, the rod is 150 cm long and 0.200 cm in radius and has a mass of 50.9 g. Young's modulus for the material is 6.80×10^{10} Pa. Determine the required tension in the rod so that the ratio of the speed of longitudinal waves to the speed of transverse waves is 8.

76. A 0.500-m-long brass pipe open at both ends has a fundamental frequency of 350 Hz. (a) Determine the temperature of the air in the pipe. (b) If the temperature is increased by 20.0°C, what is the new fundamental frequency of the pipe? Be sure to include the effects of temperature on both the speed of sound in air and the length of the pipe.

■ AP* REVIEW QUESTIONS

1. Which of the following will have the highest speed of sound?

   (A) Air, 20°C

   (B) Water, 20°C

   (C) Steel, 20°C

   (D) Air, 30°C

   (E) Air, 40°C

2. Two baseball fans, one sitting 175 m from home plate in the stadium and the other sitting in front of his satellite TV, observe a player hit the ball. If the speed of sound travels at 350 m/s, and the satellite signal travels at the speed of light and up to a satellite 150 km above the Earth, which fan hears the crack of the bat first and how soon do they hear it?

   (A) Fan at home, 0.5 s

   (B) Fan at home, 1×10^{-3} s

   (C) Fan at game, 5.0×10^{-4} s

   (D) Fan at home, 5.0×10^{-4} s

   (E) Fan at game, 0.5 s

3. An open tube pipe of length L plays a fundamental frequency f. How long would a closed tube pipe have to be to play the fourth harmonic?

   (A) $\frac{1}{4} L$

   (B) $\frac{1}{2} L$

   (C) L

   (D) $2L$

   (E) $4L$

4. A person waiting for a bus sees an ambulance coming toward him with its sirens emitting a frequency of 450 Hz. What approximate frequencies will the person hear as the ambulance approaches, then passes?

   (A) 470 Hz, 450 Hz

   (B) 450 Hz, 470 Hz

   (C) 450 Hz, 450 Hz

   (D) 430 Hz, 470 Hz

   (E) 470 Hz, 430 Hz

5. A person is riding her bike on a road running parallel to railroad tracks. Train A, traveling in the same direction as the bike rider, sounds a 400 Hz train whistle as it approaches and passes the bike rider. Train B is traveling in the opposite direction as the bike rider as it also emits a train whistle of 400 Hz as it approaches and passes the bike rider. In which of the following situations will the bike rider hear the highest and lowest frequencies?

   (A) A approaches, A moves away

   (B) B approaches, A moves away

   (C) A approaches, B moves away

   (D) B approaches, B moves away

   (E) More information is needed

6. Astronomers noticed that stars and galaxies have a redshift, as longer wavelengths are observed. What does that mean about how the stars and galaxies are moving in relation to Earth?

   (A) Moving away from us

   (B) Moving toward us

   (C) Not moving

   (D) Coming closer

   (E) Doesn't mean anything and the Doppler effect only applies to sound waves.

7. A wave with a wavelength of 2.0 m travels from 2 speakers (A and B) located 3 m apart. A person is standing 4 m in front of speaker A. What is the difference in the distance the waves have to travel to reach the person and what kind of interference will occur at that point?

   (A) 1.0 m, constructive

   (B) 1.0 m, destructive

   (C) 2.0 m, constructive

   (D) 2.0 m, destructive

   (E) More information is needed

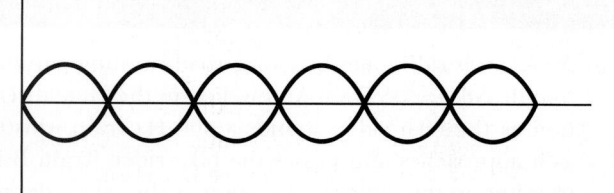

8. The above wave pattern has how many nodes and antinodes?

(A) 7, 6

(B) 6, 7

(C) 5, 6

(D) 6, 5

(E) 6, 6

9. A pipe organ tube that is closed on one end and open on the other has a length L and is playing the first harmonic. What happens to the frequency of the first harmonic if the tube is closed?

(A) cut by 4

(B) cut in half

(C) stays the same

(D) doubles

(E) quadruples

10. A closed pipe, A, has length L. An open pipe, B, has length $L/2$. What is the ratio of the fundamental frequency A to fundamental frequency B?

(A) 1:4

(B) 1:2

(C) 2:1

(D) 4:1

(E) More information is needed

11. When two out-of-tune trumpets attempt to play the same note, a beat frequency of 8 Hz is heard. If one trumpet is playing 260 Hz, what are the possible frequencies of the second trumpet?

(A) 268 Hz, 276 Hz

(B) 252 Hz, 268 Hz

(C) 246 Hz, 252 Hz

(D) 252 Hz, 260 Hz

(E) More information is needed

12. How can the speed of sound in air be increased?

(A) Increase the temperature

(B) Decrease the temperature

(C) Increase the pressure

(D) Decrease the pressure

(E) Increase the wind speed

This is a nighttime view of multiple bolts of lightning striking the Kitt Peak Observatory in Tucson, Arizona. During a thunderstorm, a high concentration of electrical charge in a thundercloud creates a higher-than-normal electric field between the thundercloud and the negatively charged Earth's surface. This strong electric field creates an electric discharge—an enormous spark—between the charged cloud and the ground. Other discharges observed in the sky include cloud-to-cloud discharges and the more frequent intracloud discharges.

Luke Adams/Alamy

Electric Forces and Electric Fields 15

Electricity is the lifeblood of technological civilization and modern society. Without it, we revert to the mid-nineteenth century: no telephones, no television, none of the household appliances that we take for granted. Modern medicine would be a fantasy, and due to the lack of sophisticated experimental equipment and fast computers—and especially the slow dissemination of information—science and technology would grow at a glacial pace.

Instead, with the discovery and harnessing of electric forces and fields, we can view arrangements of atoms, probe the inner workings of the cell, and send spacecraft beyond the limits of the solar system. All this has become possible in just the last few generations of human life, a blink of the eye compared to the million years our kind spent foraging the savannahs of Africa.

Around 700 B.C. the ancient Greeks conducted the earliest known study of electricity. It all began when someone noticed that a fossil material called amber would attract small objects after being rubbed with wool. Since then we have learned that this phenomenon is not restricted to amber and wool, but occurs (to some degree) when almost any two nonconducting substances are rubbed together.

In this chapter we use the effect of charging by friction to begin an investigation of electric forces. We then discuss Coulomb's law, which is the fundamental law of force between any two stationary charged particles. The concept of an electric field associated with charges is introduced and its effects on other charged particles described. We end with discussions of the Van de Graaff generator and Gauss's law.

Benjamin Franklin
(1706–1790)
Franklin was a printer, author, physical scientist, inventor, diplomat, and a founding father of the United States. His work on electricity in the late 1740s changed a jumbled, unrelated set of observations into a coherent science.

Like charges repel; unlike ▶ charges attract.

15.1 Properties of Electric Charges

After running a plastic comb through your hair, you will find that the comb attracts bits of paper. The attractive force is often strong enough to suspend the paper from the comb, defying the gravitational pull of the entire Earth. The same effect occurs with other rubbed materials, such as glass and hard rubber.

Another simple experiment is to rub an inflated balloon against wool (or across your hair). On a dry day, the rubbed balloon will then stick to the wall of a room, often for hours. These materials have become electrically charged. You can give your body an electric charge by vigorously rubbing your shoes on a wool rug or by sliding across a car seat. You can then surprise and annoy a friend or coworker with a light touch on the arm, delivering a slight shock to both yourself and your victim. (If the coworker is your boss, don't expect a promotion!) These experiments work best on a dry day because excessive moisture can facilitate a leaking away of the charge.

Experiments also demonstrate that there are two kinds of electric charge, which Benjamin Franklin (1706–1790) named **positive** and **negative.** Figure 15.1 illustrates the interaction of the two charges. A hard rubber (or plastic) rod that has been rubbed with fur is suspended by a piece of string. When a glass rod that has been rubbed with silk is brought near the rubber rod, the rubber rod is attracted toward the glass rod (Fig. 15.1a). If two charged rubber rods (or two charged glass rods) are brought near each other, as in Figure 15.1b, the force between them is repulsive. These observations may be explained by assuming the rubber and glass rods have acquired different kinds of excess charge. We use the convention suggested by Franklin, where the excess electric charge on the glass rod is called positive and that on the rubber rod is called negative. On the basis of such observations, we conclude that **like charges repel one another and unlike charges attract one another.** Objects usually contain equal amounts of positive and negative charge; electrical forces between objects arise when those objects have net negative or positive charges.

Nature's basic carriers of positive charge are protons, which, along with neutrons, are located in the nuclei of atoms. The nucleus, about 10^{-15} m in radius, is surrounded by a cloud of negatively charged electrons about ten thousand times larger in extent. An electron has the same magnitude charge as a proton, but the opposite sign. In a gram of matter there are approximately 10^{23} positively charged protons and just as many negatively charged electrons, so the net charge is zero.

Figure 15.1 An experimental setup for observing the electrical force between two charged objects.

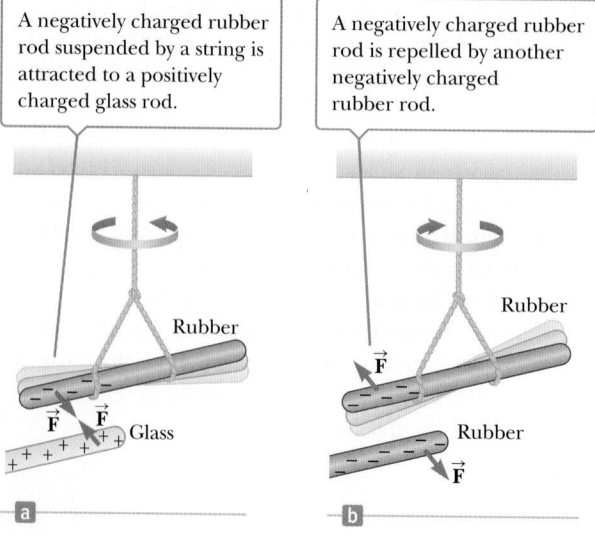

Because the nucleus of an atom is held firmly in place inside a solid, protons never move from one material to another. Electrons are far lighter than protons and hence more easily accelerated by forces. Further, they occupy the outer regions of the atom. Consequently, objects become charged by gaining or losing electrons.

Charge transfers readily from one type of material to another. Rubbing the two materials together serves to increase the area of contact, facilitating the transfer process.

An important characteristic of charge is that **electric charge is always conserved.** Charge isn't *created* when two neutral objects are rubbed together; rather, the objects become charged because **negative charge is transferred from one object to the other.** One object gains a negative charge while the other loses an equal amount of negative charge and hence is left with a net positive charge. When a glass rod is rubbed with silk, as in Figure 15.2, electrons are transferred from the rod to the silk. As a result, the glass rod carries a net positive charge, the silk a net negative charge. Likewise, when rubber is rubbed with fur, electrons are transferred from the fur to the rubber.

In 1909 Robert Millikan (1886–1953) discovered that if an object is charged, its charge is always a multiple of a fundamental unit of charge, designated by the symbol e. In modern terms, the charge is said to be **quantized,** meaning that charge occurs in discrete chunks that can't be further subdivided. An object may have a charge of $\pm e$, $\pm 2e$, $\pm 3e$, and so on, but never[1] a fractional charge of $\pm 0.5e$ or $\pm 0.22e$. Other experiments in Millikan's time showed that the electron has a charge of $-e$ and the proton has an equal and opposite charge of $+e$. Some particles, such as a neutron, have no net charge. A neutral atom (an atom with no net charge) contains as many protons as electrons. The value of e is now known to be $1.602\ 19 \times 10^{-19}$ C. (The SI unit of electric charge is the **coulomb,** or C.)

◀ Charge is conserved

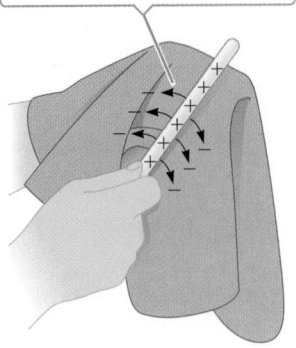

Each (negatively-charged) electron transferred from the rod to the silk leaves an equal positive charge on the rod.

Figure 15.2 When a glass rod is rubbed with silk, electrons are transferred from the glass to the silk. Because the charges are transferred in discrete bundles, the charges on the two objects are $\pm e$, $\pm 2e$, $\pm 3e$, and so on.

15.2 Insulators and Conductors

Substances can be classified in terms of their ability to conduct electric charge.

> In **conductors,** electric charges move freely in response to an electric force. All other materials are called **insulators.**

Glass and rubber are insulators. When such materials are charged by rubbing, only the rubbed area becomes charged, and there is no tendency for the charge to move into other regions of the material. In contrast, materials such as copper, aluminum, and silver are good conductors. When such materials are charged in some small region, the charge readily distributes itself over the entire surface of the material. If you hold a copper rod in your hand and rub the rod with wool or fur, it will not attract a piece of paper. This might suggest that a metal can't be charged. However, if you hold the copper rod with an insulator and then rub it with wool or fur, the rod remains charged and attracts the paper. In the first case, the electric charges produced by rubbing readily move from the copper through your body and finally to ground. In the second case, the insulating handle prevents the flow of charge to ground.

Semiconductors are a third class of materials, and their electrical properties are somewhere between those of insulators and those of conductors. Silicon and germanium are well-known semiconductors that are widely used in the fabrication of a variety of electronic devices.

---

[1]There is strong evidence for the existence of fundamental particles called **quarks** that have charges of $\pm e/3$ or $\pm 2e/3$. The charge is *still* quantized, but in units of $\pm e/3$ rather than $\pm e$. A more complete discussion of quarks and their properties is presented in Chapter 30.

Before contact, the negative rod repels the sphere's electrons, inducing a local positive charge.

a

After contact, electrons from the rod flow onto the sphere, neutralizing the local positive charges.

b

When the rod is removed, negative charge remains on the sphere.

c

Figure 15.3 Charging a metallic object by conduction.

Charging by Conduction

Consider a negatively charged rubber rod brought into contact with an insulated neutral conducting sphere. The excess electrons on the rod repel electrons on the sphere, creating local positive charges on the neutral sphere. On contact, some electrons on the rod are now able to move onto the sphere, as in Figure 15.3, neutralizing the positive charges. When the rod is removed, the sphere is left with a net negative charge. This process is referred to as charging by **conduction.** The object being charged in such a process (the sphere) is always left with a charge having the same sign as the object doing the charging (the rubber rod).

Charging by Induction

An object connected to a conducting wire or copper pipe buried in the Earth is said to be **grounded.** The Earth can be considered an infinite reservoir for electrons; in effect, it can accept or supply an unlimited number of electrons. With this idea in mind, we can understand the charging of a conductor by a process known as **induction.**

Consider a negatively charged rubber rod brought near a neutral (uncharged) conducting sphere that is insulated, so there is no conducting path to ground (Fig. 15.4). Initially the sphere is electrically neutral (Fig. 15.4a). When the negatively charged rod is brought close to the sphere, the repulsive force between the electrons in the rod and those in the sphere causes some electrons to move to the side of the sphere farthest away from the rod (Fig. 15.4b). The region of the sphere nearest the negatively charged rod has an excess of positive charge because of the migration of electrons away from that location. If a grounded conducting wire is then connected to the sphere, as in Figure 15.4c, some of the electrons leave the sphere and travel to ground. If the wire to ground is then removed (Fig. 15.4d), the conducting sphere is left with an excess of induced positive charge. Finally, when the rubber rod is removed from the vicinity of the sphere (Fig. 15.4e), the induced positive charge remains on the ungrounded sphere. Even though the positively charged atomic nuclei remain fixed, this excess positive charge becomes uniformly distributed over the surface of the ungrounded sphere because of the repulsive forces among the like charges and the high mobility of electrons in a metal.

In the process of inducing a charge on the sphere, the charged rubber rod doesn't lose any of its negative charge because it never comes in contact with the sphere. Further, the sphere is left with a charge opposite that of the rubber rod. **Charging an object by induction requires no contact with the object inducing the charge.**

A process similar to charging by induction in conductors also takes place in insulators. In most neutral atoms or molecules, the center of positive charge coincides with the center of negative charge. In the presence of a charged object, however, these centers may separate slightly, resulting in more positive charge on one side of the molecule than on the other. This effect is known as **polarization.** The realignment of charge within individual molecules produces an induced charge on the surface of the insulator, as shown in Figure 15.5a. This property explains why a balloon charged through rubbing will stick to an electrically neutral wall or why the comb you just used on your hair attracts tiny bits of neutral paper.

Quick Quiz

15.1 A suspended object A is attracted to a neutral wall. It's also attracted to a positively charged object B. Which of the following is true about object A? (a) It is uncharged. (b) It has a negative charge. (c) It has a positive charge. (d) It may be either charged or uncharged.

15.3 Coulomb's Law

In 1785 Charles Coulomb (1736–1806) experimentally established the fundamental law of electric force between two stationary charged particles.

> An **electric force** has the following properties:
>
> 1. It is directed along a line joining the two particles and is inversely proportional to the square of the separation distance r, between them.
> 2. It is proportional to the product of the magnitudes of the charges, $|q_1|$ and $|q_2|$, of the two particles.
> 3. It is attractive if the charges are of opposite sign and repulsive if the charges have the same sign.

From these observations, Coulomb proposed the following mathematical form for the electric force between two charges:

> The magnitude of the electric force F between charges q_1 and q_2 separated by a distance r is given by
>
> $$F = k_e \frac{|q_1||q_2|}{r^2} \qquad [15.1]$$
>
> where k_e is a constant called the *Coulomb constant.*

Equation 15.1, known as **Coulomb's law,** applies exactly only to point charges and to spherical distributions of charges, in which case r is the distance between the two centers of charge. Electric forces between unmoving charges are called *electrostatic* forces. Moving charges, in addition, create magnetic forces, studied in Chapter 19.

The value of the Coulomb constant in Equation 15.1 depends on the choice of units. The SI unit of charge is the **coulomb** (C). From experiment, we know that the **Coulomb constant** in SI units has the value

$$k_e = 8.987\ 5 \times 10^9\ \text{N} \cdot \text{m}^2/\text{C}^2 \qquad [15.2]$$

This number can be rounded, depending on the accuracy of other quantities in a given problem. We'll use either two or three significant digits, as usual.

The positively charged balloon induces a migration of negative charges to the wall's surface.

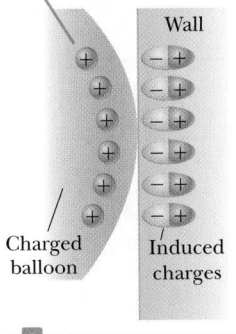

The charged rod attracts the paper because a charge separation is induced in the molecules of the paper.

© Charles D. Winters/Cengage Learning

Figure 15.5 (a) A charged balloon is brought near an insulating wall. (b) A charged rod is brought close to bits of paper.

The neutral sphere has equal numbers of positive and negative charges.

a

Electrons redistribute when a charged rod is brought close.

b

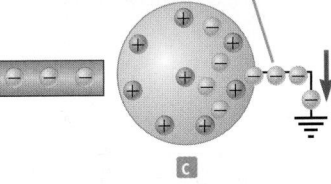

Some electrons leave the grounded sphere through the ground wire.

c

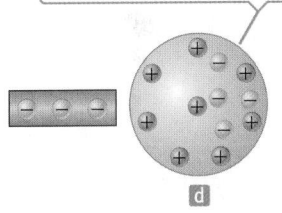

The excess positive charge is nonuniformly distributed.

d

The remaining electrons redistribute uniformly, and there is a net uniform distribution of positive charge on the sphere's surface.

e

Figure 15.4 Charging a metallic object by induction. (a) A neutral metallic sphere. (b) A charged rubber rod is placed near the sphere. (c) The sphere is grounded. (d) The ground connection is removed. (e) The rod is removed.

Charles Coulomb
(1736–1806)
Coulomb's major contribution to science was in the field of electrostatics and magnetism. During his lifetime, he also investigated the strengths of materials and identified the forces that affect objects on beams, thereby contributing to the field of structural mechanics.

Table 15.1 Charge and Mass of the Electron, Proton, and Neutron

Particle	Charge (C)	Mass (kg)
Electron	-1.60×10^{-19}	9.11×10^{-31}
Proton	$+1.60 \times 10^{-19}$	1.67×10^{-27}
Neutron	0	1.67×10^{-27}

The charge on the proton has a magnitude of $e = 1.6 \times 10^{-19}$ C. Therefore, it would take $1/e = 6.3 \times 10^{18}$ protons to create a total charge of $+1.0$ C. Likewise, 6.3×10^{18} electrons would have a total charge of -1.0 C. Compare this charge with the number of free electrons in 1 cm³ of copper, which is on the order of 10^{23}. Even so, 1.0 C is a very large amount of charge. In typical electrostatic experiments in which a rubber or glass rod is charged by friction, there is a net charge on the order of 10^{-6} C ($= 1 \mu$C). Only a very small fraction of the total available charge is transferred between the rod and the rubbing material. Table 15.1 lists the charges and masses of the electron, proton, and neutron.

When using Coulomb's force law, remember that force is a vector quantity and must be treated accordingly. Active Figure 15.6a shows the electric force of repulsion between two positively charged particles. Like other forces, electric forces obey Newton's third law; hence, the forces $\vec{F}_{12}$ and $\vec{F}_{21}$ are equal in magnitude but opposite in direction. (The notation $\vec{F}_{12}$ denotes the force exerted by particle 1 on particle 2; likewise, $\vec{F}_{21}$ is the force exerted by particle 2 on particle 1.) From Newton's third law, F_{12} and F_{21} are always equal regardless of whether q_1 and q_2 have the same magnitude.

■ *Quick Quiz*

15.2 Object A has a charge of $+2 \mu$C, and object B has a charge of $+6 \mu$C. Which statement is true?
(a) $\vec{F}_{AB} = -3\vec{F}_{BA}$ (b) $\vec{F}_{AB} = -\vec{F}_{BA}$ (c) $3\vec{F}_{AB} = -\vec{F}_{BA}$

The Coulomb force is similar to the gravitational force. Both act at a distance without direct contact. Both are inversely proportional to the distance squared, with the force directed along a line connecting the two bodies. The mathematical form is the same, with the masses m_1 and m_2 in Newton's law replaced by q_1 and q_2 in Coulomb's law and with Newton's constant G replaced by Coulomb's constant k_e. There are two important differences: (1) electric forces can be either attractive or repulsive, but gravitational forces are always attractive, and (2) the electric force between charged elementary particles is far stronger than the gravitational force between the same particles, as the next example shows.

Active Figure 15.6
Two point charges separated by a distance r exert a force on each other given by Coulomb's law. The force on q_1 is equal in magnitude and opposite in direction to the force on q_2.

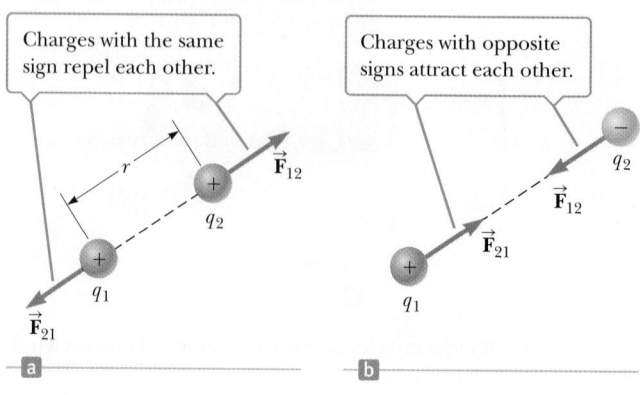

■ EXAMPLE 15.1 | Forces in a Hydrogen Atom

GOAL Contrast the magnitudes of an electric force and a gravitational force.

PROBLEM The electron and proton of a hydrogen atom are separated (on the average) by a distance of about 5.3×10^{-11} m. **(a)** Find the magnitudes of the electric force and the gravitational force that each particle exerts on the other, and the ratio of the electric force F_e to the gravitational force F_g. **(b)** Compute the acceleration caused by the electric force of the proton on the electron. Repeat for the gravitational acceleration.

STRATEGY Solving this problem is just a matter of substituting known quantities into the two force laws and then finding the ratio.

· ·

SOLUTION

(a) Compute the magnitudes of the electric and gravitational forces, and find the ration F_e/F_g.

Substitute $|q_1| = |q_2| = e$ and the distance into Coulomb's law to find the electric force:

$$F_e = k_e \frac{|e|^2}{r^2} = \left(8.99 \times 10^9 \, \frac{\text{N} \cdot \text{m}^2}{\text{C}^2} \right) \frac{(1.6 \times 10^{-19} \, \text{C})^2}{(5.3 \times 10^{-11} \, \text{m})^2}$$

$$= \boxed{8.2 \times 10^{-8} \, \text{N}}$$

Substitute the masses and distance into Newton's law of gravity to find the gravitational force:

$$F_g = G \frac{m_e m_p}{r^2}$$

$$= \left(6.67 \times 10^{-11} \, \frac{\text{N} \cdot \text{m}^2}{\text{kg}^2} \right) \frac{(9.11 \times 10^{-31} \, \text{kg})(1.67 \times 10^{-27} \, \text{kg})}{(5.3 \times 10^{-11} \, \text{m})^2}$$

$$= \boxed{3.6 \times 10^{-47} \, \text{N}}$$

Find the ratio of the two forces:

$$\frac{F_e}{F_g} = \boxed{2.3 \times 10^{39}}$$

(b) Compute the acceleration of the electron caused by the electric force. Repeat for the gravitational acceleration.

Use Newton's second law and the electric force found in part (a):

$$m_e a_e = F_e \quad \rightarrow \quad a_e = \frac{F_e}{m_e} = \frac{8.2 \times 10^{-8} \, \text{N}}{9.11 \times 10^{-31} \, \text{kg}} = \boxed{9.0 \times 10^{22} \, \text{m/s}^2}$$

Use Newton's second law and the gravitational force found in part (a):

$$m_e a_g = F_g \quad \rightarrow \quad a_g = \frac{F_g}{m_e} = \frac{3.6 \times 10^{-47} \, \text{N}}{9.11 \times 10^{-31} \, \text{kg}} = \boxed{4.0 \times 10^{-17} \, \text{m/s}^2}$$

· ·

REMARKS The gravitational force between the charged constituents of the atom is negligible compared with the electric force between them. The electric force is so strong, however, that any net charge on an object quickly attracts nearby opposite charges, neutralizing the object. As a result, gravity plays a greater role in the mechanics of moving objects in everyday life.

QUESTION 15.1 If the distance between two charges is doubled, by what factor is the magnitude of the electric force changed?

EXERCISE 15.1 **(a)** Find the magnitude of the electric force between two protons separated by 1 femtometer (10^{-15} m), approximately the distance between two protons in the nucleus of a helium atom. **(b)** If the protons were not held together by the strong nuclear force, what would be their initial acceleration due to the electric force between them?

ANSWERS (a) 2×10^2 N (b) 1×10^{29} m/s^2

The Superposition Principle

When a number of separate charges act on the charge of interest, each exerts an electric force. These electric forces can all be computed separately, one at a time, then added as vectors. This is another example of the **superposition principle.** The following example illustrates this procedure in one dimension.

■ EXAMPLE 15.2 | Finding Electrostatic Equilibrium

GOAL Apply Coulomb's law in one dimension.

PROBLEM Three charges lie along the x-axis as in Figure 15.7. The positive charge $q_1 = 15$ μC is at $x = 2.0$ m, and the positive charge $q_2 = 6.0$ μC is at the origin. Where must a *negative* charge q_3 be placed on the x-axis so that the resultant electric force on it is zero?

STRATEGY If q_3 is to the right or left of the other two charges, the net force on q_3 can't be zero because then $\vec{F}_{13}$ and $\vec{F}_{23}$ act in the same direction. Consequently, q_3 must lie between the two other charges. Write $\vec{F}_{13}$ and $\vec{F}_{23}$ in terms of the unknown coordinate position x, then sum them and set them equal to zero, solving for the unknown. The solution can be obtained with the quadratic formula.

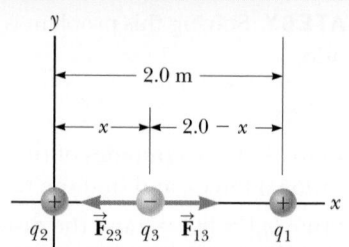

Figure 15.7 (Example 15.2) Three point charges are placed along the x-axis. The charge q_3 is negative, whereas q_1 and q_2 are positive. If the resultant force on q_3 is zero, the force $\vec{F}_{13}$ exerted by q_1 on q_3 must be equal in magnitude and opposite the force $\vec{F}_{23}$ exerted by q_2 on q_3.

SOLUTION

Write the x-component of $\vec{F}_{13}$:

$$F_{13x} = +k_e \frac{(15 \times 10^{-6} \text{ C})|q_3|}{(2.0 \text{ m} - x)^2}$$

Write the x-component of $\vec{F}_{23}$:

$$F_{23x} = -k_e \frac{(6.0 \times 10^{-6} \text{ C})|q_3|}{x^2}$$

Set the sum equal to zero:

$$k_e \frac{(15 \times 10^{-6} \text{ C})|q_3|}{(2.0 \text{ m} - x)^2} - k_e \frac{(6.0 \times 10^{-6} \text{ C})|q_3|}{x^2} = 0$$

Cancel k_e, 10^{-6}, and q_3 from the equation and rearrange terms (explicit significant figures and units are temporarily suspended for clarity):

(1) $6(2 - x)^2 = 15x^2$

Put this equation into standard quadratic form, $ax^2 + bx + c = 0$:

$$6(4 - 4x + x^2) = 15x^2 \quad \rightarrow \quad 2(4 - 4x + x^2) = 5x^2$$

$$3x^2 + 8x - 8 = 0$$

Apply the quadratic formula:

$$x = \frac{-8 \pm \sqrt{64 - (4)(3)(-8)}}{2 \cdot 3} = \frac{-4 \pm 2\sqrt{10}}{3}$$

Only the positive root makes sense:

$$x = \boxed{0.77 \text{ m}}$$

REMARKS Notice that physical reasoning was required to choose between the two possible answers for x, which is nearly always the case when quadratic equations are involved. Use of the quadratic formula could have been avoided by taking the square root of both sides of Equation (1); however, this shortcut is often unavailable.

QUESTION 15.2 If q_1 has the same magnitude as before but is negative, in what region along the x-axis would it be possible for the net electric force on q_3 to be zero? (a) $x < 0$ (b) $0 < x < 2$ m (c) 2 m $< x$

EXERCISE 15.2 Three charges lie along the x-axis. A positive charge $q_1 = 10.0$ μC is at $x = 1.00$ m, and a negative charge $q_2 = -2.00$ μC is at the origin. Where must a positive charge q_3 be placed on the x-axis so that the resultant force on it is zero?

ANSWER $x = -0.809$ m

■ EXAMPLE 15.3 | A Charge Triangle

GOAL Apply Coulomb's law in two dimensions.

PROBLEM Consider three point charges at the corners of a triangle, as shown in Figure 15.8, where $q_1 = 6.00 \times 10^{-9}$ C, $q_2 = -2.00 \times 10^{-9}$ C, and $q_3 = 5.00 \times 10^{-9}$ C. **(a)** Find the components of the force $\vec{F}_{23}$ exerted by q_2 on q_3. **(b)** Find the components of the force $\vec{F}_{13}$ exerted by q_1 on q_3. **(c)** Find the resultant force on q_3, in terms of components and also in terms of magnitude and direction.

STRATEGY Coulomb's law gives the magnitude of each force, which can be split with right-triangle trigonometry into x- and y-components. Sum the vectors componentwise and then find the magnitude and direction of the resultant vector.

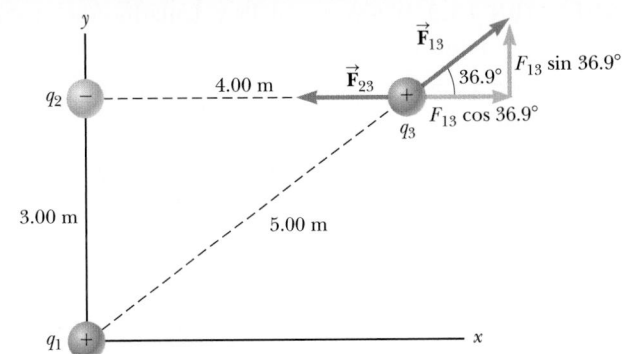

Figure 15.8 (Example 15.3) The force exerted by q_1 on q_3 is $\vec{F}_{13}$. The force exerted by q_2 on q_3 is $\vec{F}_{23}$. The *resultant force* $\vec{F}_3$ exerted on q_3 is the *vector* sum $\vec{F}_{13} + \vec{F}_{23}$.

SOLUTION

(a) Find the components of the force exerted by q_2 on q_3.

Find the magnitude of $\vec{F}_{23}$ with Coulomb's law:

$$F_{23} = k_e \frac{|q_2||q_3|}{r^2}$$

$$= (8.99 \times 10^9 \text{ N} \cdot \text{m}^2/\text{C}^2) \frac{(2.00 \times 10^{-9} \text{ C})(5.00 \times 10^{-9} \text{ C})}{(4.00 \text{ m})^2}$$

$$F_{23} = 5.62 \times 10^{-9} \text{ N}$$

Because $\vec{F}_{23}$ is horizontal and points in the negative x-direction, the negative of the magnitude gives the x-component, and the y-component is zero:

$$F_{23x} = \boxed{-5.62 \times 10^{-9} \text{ N}}$$
$$F_{23y} = \boxed{0}$$

(b) Find the components of the force exerted by q_1 on q_3.

Find the magnitude of $\vec{F}_{13}$:

$$F_{13} = k_e \frac{|q_1||q_3|}{r^2}$$

$$= (8.99 \times 10^9 \text{ N} \cdot \text{m}^2/\text{C}^2)\frac{(6.00 \times 10^{-9} \text{ C})(5.00 \times 10^{-9} \text{ C})}{(5.00 \text{ m})^2}$$

$$F_{13} = 1.08 \times 10^{-8} \text{ N}$$

Use the given triangle to find the components of $\vec{F}_{13}$:

$$F_{13x} = F_{13} \cos \theta = (1.08 \times 10^{-8} \text{ N}) \cos (36.9°)$$
$$= \boxed{8.64 \times 10^{-9} \text{ N}}$$

$$F_{13y} = F_{13} \sin \theta = (1.08 \times 10^{-8} \text{ N}) \sin (36.9°)$$
$$= \boxed{6.48 \times 10^{-9} \text{ N}}$$

(c) Find the components of the resultant vector.

Sum the x-components to find the resultant F_x:

$$F_x = -5.62 \times 10^{-9} \text{ N} + 8.64 \times 10^{-9} \text{ N}$$
$$= \boxed{3.02 \times 10^{-9} \text{ N}}$$

Sum the y-components to find the resultant F_y:

$$F_y = 0 + 6.48 \times 10^{-9} \text{ N} = \boxed{6.48 \times 10^{-9} \text{ N}}$$

Find the magnitude of the resultant force on the charge q_3, using the Pythagorean theorem:

$$|\vec{F}| = \sqrt{F_x{}^2 + F_y{}^2}$$
$$= \sqrt{(3.01 \times 10^{-9} \text{ N})^2 + (6.50 \times 10^{-9} \text{ N})^2}$$
$$= \boxed{7.15 \times 10^{-9} \text{ N}}$$

Find the angle the resultant force makes with respect to the positive x-axis:

$$\theta = \tan^{-1}\left(\frac{F_y}{F_x}\right) = \tan^{-1}\left(\frac{6.48 \times 10^{-9} \text{ N}}{3.02 \times 10^{-9} \text{ N}}\right) = \boxed{65.0°}$$

(Continued)

REMARKS The methods used here are just like those used with Newton's law of gravity in two dimensions.

QUESTION 15.3 Without actually calculating the electric force on q_2, determine the quadrant into which the electric force vector points.

EXERCISE 15.3 Using the same triangle, find the vector components of the electric force on q_1 and the vector's magnitude and direction.

ANSWERS $F_x = -8.64 \times 10^{-9}$ N, $F_y = 5.52 \times 10^{-9}$ N, $F = 1.03 \times 10^{-8}$ N, $\theta = 147°$

15.4 The Electric Field

The gravitational force and the electrostatic force are both capable of acting through space, producing an effect even when there isn't any physical contact between the objects involved. Field forces can be discussed in a variety of ways, but an approach developed by Michael Faraday (1791–1867) is the most practical. In this approach an **electric field** is said to exist in the region of space around a charged object. The electric field exerts an electric force on any other charged object within the field. This differs from the Coulomb's law concept of a force exerted at a distance in that the force is now exerted by something—the field—that is in the same location as the charged object.

Figure 15.9 shows an object with a small positive charge q_0 placed near a second object with a much larger positive charge Q.

The electric field $\vec{\mathbf{E}}$ produced by a charge Q at the location of a small "test" charge q_0 is defined as the electric force $\vec{\mathbf{F}}$ exerted by Q on q_0 divided by the test charge q_0:

$$\vec{\mathbf{E}} \equiv \frac{\vec{\mathbf{F}}}{q_0} \qquad [15.3]$$

SI unit: newton per coulomb (N/C)

Conceptually and experimentally, the test charge q_0 is required to be very small (arbitrarily small, in fact), so it doesn't cause any significant rearrangement of the charge creating the electric field $\vec{\mathbf{E}}$. Mathematically, however, the size of the test charge makes no difference: the calculation comes out the same, regardless. In view of this, using $q_0 = 1$ C in Equation 15.3 can be convenient if not rigorous.

When a positive test charge is used, the electric field always has the same direction as the electric force on the test charge, which follows from Equation 15.3. Hence, in Figure 15.9, the direction of the electric field is horizontal and to the right. The electric field at point A in Figure 15.10a is vertical and downward because at that point a positive test charge would be attracted toward the negatively charged sphere.

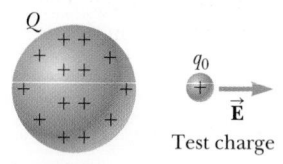

Figure 15.9 A small object with a positive charge q_0 placed near an object with a larger positive charge Q is subject to an electric field $\vec{\mathbf{E}}$ directed as shown. The magnitude of the electric field at the location of q_0 is defined as the electric force on q_0 divided by the charge q_0.

Figure 15.10 (a) The electric field at A due to the negatively charged sphere is downward, toward the negative charge. (b) The electric field at P due to the positively charged conducting sphere is upward, away from the positive charge. (c) A test charge q_0 placed at P will cause a rearrangement of charge on the sphere unless q_0 is negligibly small compared with the charge on the sphere.

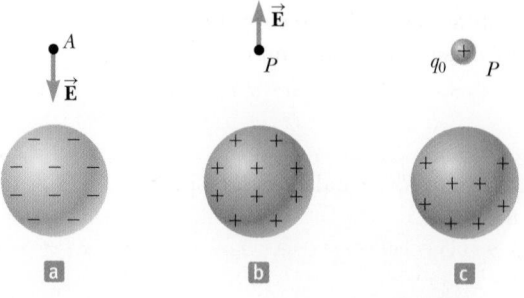

Once the electric field due to a given arrangement of charges is known at some point, the force on *any* particle with charge q placed at that point can be calculated from a rearrangement of Equation 15.3:

$$\vec{\mathbf{F}} = q\vec{\mathbf{E}} \qquad [15.4]$$

Here q_0 has been replaced by q, which need not be a mere test charge.

As shown in Active Figure 15.11, the direction of $\vec{\mathbf{E}}$ is the direction of the force that acts on a positive test charge q_0 placed in the field. We say that **an electric field exists at a point if a test charge at that point is subject to an electric force there.**

Consider a point charge q located a distance r from a test charge q_0. According to Coulomb's law, the *magnitude* of the electric force of the charge q on the test charge is

$$F = k_e \frac{|q||q_0|}{r^2} \qquad [15.5]$$

Because the magnitude of the electric field at the position of the test charge is defined as $E = F/q_0$, we see that the *magnitude* of the electric field due to the charge q at the position of q_0 is

$$E = k_e \frac{|q|}{r^2} \qquad [15.6]$$

Equation 15.6 points out an important property of electric fields that makes them useful quantities for describing electrical phenomena. As the equation indicates, an electric field at a given point depends only on the charge q on the object setting up the field and the distance r from that object to a specific point in space. As a result, we can say that an electric field exists at point P in Active Figure 15.11 whether or not there is a test charge at P.

The principle of superposition holds when the electric field due to a group of point charges is calculated. We first use Equation 15.6 to calculate the electric field produced by each charge individually at a point and then add the electric fields together as vectors.

It's also important to exploit any symmetry of the charge distribution. For example, if equal charges are placed at $x = a$ and at $x = -a$, the electric field is zero at the origin, by symmetry. Similarly, if the x axis has a uniform distribution of positive charge, it can be guessed by symmetry that the electric field points away from the x axis and is zero parallel to that axis.

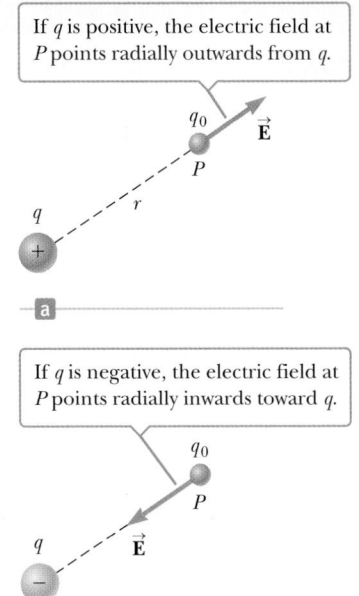

If q is positive, the electric field at P points radially outwards from q.

a

If q is negative, the electric field at P points radially inwards toward q.

b

Active Figure 15.11
A test charge q_0 at P is a distance r from a point charge q.

■ *Quick Quiz*

15.3 A test charge of $+3\ \mu C$ is at a point P where the electric field due to other charges is directed to the right and has a magnitude of 4×10^6 N/C. If the test charge is replaced with a charge of $-3\ \mu C$, the electric field at P (a) has the same magnitude as before, but changes direction, (b) increases in magnitude and changes direction, (c) remains the same, or (d) decreases in magnitude and changes direction.

15.4 A circular ring of charge of radius b has a total charge q uniformly distributed around it. Find the magnitude to the electric field in the center of the ring.

(a) 0   (b) $k_e q/b^2$ (c) $k_e q^2/b^2$ (d) $k_e q^2/b$ (e) None of these answers is correct.

15.5 A "free" electron and a "free" proton are placed in an identical electric field. Which of the following statements are true? (a) Each particle is acted upon by the same electric force and has the same acceleration. (b) The electric force on the proton is greater in magnitude than the electric force on the electron, but in the opposite direction. (c) The electric force on the proton is equal in magnitude to the electric force on the electron, but in the opposite direction. (d) The magnitude of the acceleration of the electron is greater than that of the proton. (e) Both particles have the same acceleration.

▪ EXAMPLE 15.4 | Electrified Oil

GOAL Use electric forces and fields together with Newton's second law in a one-dimensional problem.

PROBLEM Tiny droplets of oil acquire a small negative charge while dropping through a vacuum (pressure = 0) in an experiment. An electric field of magnitude 5.92×10^4 N/C points straight down. **(a)** One particular droplet is observed to remain suspended against gravity. If the mass of the droplet is 2.93×10^{-15} kg, find the charge carried by the droplet. **(b)** Another droplet of the same mass falls 10.3 cm from rest in 0.250 s, again moving through a vacuum. Find the charge carried by the droplet.

STRATEGY We use Newton's second law with both gravitational and electric forces. In both parts the electric field $\vec{E}$ is pointing down, taken as the negative direction, as usual. In part (a) the acceleration is equal to zero. In part (b) the acceleration is uniform, so the kinematic equations yield the acceleration. Newton's law can then be solved for q.

SOLUTION

(a) Find the charge on the suspended droplet.

Apply Newton's second law to the droplet in the vertical direction:

$$(1) \quad ma = \sum F = -mg + Eq$$

E points downward, hence is negative. Set $a = 0$ in Equation (1) and solve for q:

$$q = \frac{mg}{E} = \frac{(2.93 \times 10^{-15}\,\text{kg})(9.80\,\text{m/s}^2)}{-5.92 \times 10^4\,\text{N/C}}$$

$$= \boxed{-4.85 \times 10^{-19}\,\text{C}}$$

(b) Find the charge on the falling droplet.

Use the kinematic displacement equation to find the acceleration:

$$\Delta y = \tfrac{1}{2}at^2 + v_0 t$$

Substitute $\Delta y = -0.103$ m, $t = 0.250$ s, and $v_0 = 0$:

$$-0.103\,\text{m} = \tfrac{1}{2}a(0.250\,\text{s})^2 \quad \rightarrow \quad a = -3.30\,\text{m/s}^2$$

Solve Equation (1) for q and substitute:

$$q = \frac{m(a + g)}{E}$$

$$= \frac{(2.93 \times 10^{-15}\,\text{kg})(-3.30\,\text{m/s}^2 + 9.80\,\text{m/s}^2)}{-5.92 \times 10^4\,\text{N/C}}$$

$$= \boxed{-3.22 \times 10^{-19}\,\text{C}}$$

REMARKS This example exhibits features similar to the Millikan Oil-Drop experiment discussed in Section 15.7, which determined the value of the fundamental electric charge e. Notice that in both parts of the example, the charge is very nearly a multiple of e.

QUESTION 15.4 What would be the acceleration of the oil droplet in part (a) if the electric field suddenly reversed direction without changing in magnitude?

EXERCISE 15.4 Suppose a droplet of unknown mass remains suspended against gravity when $E = -2.70 \times 10^5$ N/C. What is the minimum mass of the droplet?

ANSWER 4.41×10^{-15} kg

▪ PROBLEM-SOLVING STRATEGY

Calculating Electric Forces and Fields

The following procedure is used to calculate electric forces. The same procedure can be used to calculate an electric field, a simple matter of replacing the charge of interest, q, with a convenient test charge and dividing by the test charge at the end:

1. **Draw** a diagram of the charges in the problem.
2. **Identify** the charge of interest, q, and circle it.
3. **Convert all units** to SI, with charges in coulombs and distances in meters, so as to be consistent with the SI value of the Coulomb constant k_e.
4. **Apply Coulomb's law.** For each charge Q, find the electric force on the charge of interest, q. The magnitude of the force can be found using Coulomb's law.

The vector direction of the electric force is along the line of the two charges, directed away from Q if the charges have the same sign, toward Q if the charges have the opposite sign. Find the angle θ this vector makes with the positive x-axis. The x-component of the electric force exerted by Q on q will be $F\cos\theta$, and the y-component will be $F\sin\theta$.

5. **Sum all the x-components,** getting the x-component of the resultant electric force.
6. **Sum all the y-components,** getting the y-component of the resultant electric force.
7. **Use the Pythagorean theorem and trigonometry** to find the magnitude and direction of the resultant force if desired.

▪ EXAMPLE 15.5 | Electric Field Due to Two Point Charges

GOAL Use the superposition principle to calculate the electric field due to two point charges.

PROBLEM Charge $q_1 = 7.00\ \mu C$ is at the origin, and charge $q_2 = -5.00\ \mu C$ is on the x-axis, 0.300 m from the origin (Fig. 15.12). **(a)** Find the magnitude and direction of the electric field at point P, which has coordinates $(0, 0.400)$ m. **(b)** Find the force on a charge of 2.00×10^{-8} C placed at P.

STRATEGY Follow the problem-solving strategy, finding the electric field at point P due to each individual charge in terms of x- and y-components, then adding the components of each type to get the x- and y-components of the resultant electric field at P. The magnitude of the force in part (b) can be found by simply multiplying the magnitude of the electric field by the charge.

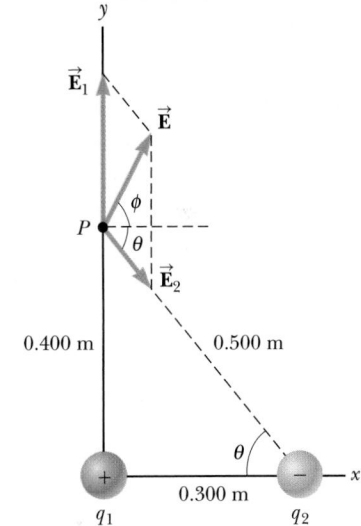

Figure 15.12 (Example 15.5) The resultant electric field $\vec{E}$ at P equals the vector sum $\vec{E}_1 + \vec{E}_2$, where $\vec{E}_1$ is the field due to the positive charge q_1 and $\vec{E}_2$ is the field due to the negative charge q_2.

SOLUTION

(a) Calculate the electric field at P.

Find the magnitude of $\vec{E}_1$ with Equation 15.6:

$$E_1 = k_e\frac{|q_1|}{r_1{}^2} = (8.99 \times 10^9\ \text{N} \cdot \text{m}^2/\text{C}^2)\frac{(7.00 \times 10^{-6}\ \text{C})}{(0.400\ \text{m})^2}$$

$$= 3.93 \times 10^5\ \text{N/C}$$

The vector $\vec{E}_1$ is vertical, making an angle of 90° with respect to the positive x-axis. Use this fact to find its components:

$$E_{1x} = E_1 \cos(90°) = 0$$
$$E_{1y} = E_1 \sin(90°) = 3.93 \times 10^5\ \text{N/C}$$

Next, find the magnitude of $\vec{E}_2$, again with Equation 15.6:

$$E_2 = k_e\frac{|q_2|}{r_2{}^2} = (8.99 \times 10^9\ \text{N} \cdot \text{m}^2/\text{C}^2)\frac{(5.00 \times 10^{-6}\ \text{C})}{(0.500\ \text{m})^2}$$

$$= 1.80 \times 10^5\ \text{N/C}$$

Obtain the x-component of $\vec{E}_2$, using the triangle in Figure 15.12 to find $\cos\theta$:

$$\cos\theta = \frac{\text{adj}}{\text{hyp}} = \frac{0.300}{0.500} = 0.600$$

$$E_{2x} = E_2 \cos\theta = (1.80 \times 10^5\ \text{N/C})(0.600)$$
$$= 1.08 \times 10^5\ \text{N/C}$$

Obtain the y-component in the same way, but a minus sign has to be provided for $\sin\theta$ because this component is directed downwards:

$$\sin\theta = \frac{\text{opp}}{\text{hyp}} = \frac{0.400}{0.500} = 0.800$$

$$E_{2y} = E_2 \sin\theta = (1.80 \times 10^5\ \text{N/C})(-0.800)$$
$$= -1.44 \times 10^5\ \text{N/C}$$

(Continued)

Sum the x-components to get the x-component of the resultant vector:

$$E_x = E_{1x} + E_{2x} = 0 + 1.08 \times 10^5 \text{ N/C} = 1.08 \times 10^5 \text{ N/C}$$

Sum the y-components to get the y-component of the resultant vector:

$$E_y = E_{1y} + E_{2y} = 3.93 \times 10^5 \text{ N/C} - 1.44 \times 10^5 \text{ N/C}$$
$$E_y = 2.49 \times 10^5 \text{ N/C}$$

Use the Pythagorean theorem to find the magnitude of the resultant vector:

$$E = \sqrt{E_x^2 + E_y^2} = \boxed{2.71 \times 10^5 \text{ N/C}}$$

The inverse tangent function yields the direction of the resultant vector:

$$\phi = \tan^{-1}\left(\frac{E_y}{E_x}\right) = \tan^{-1}\left(\frac{2.49 \times 10^5 \text{ N/C}}{1.08 \times 10^5 \text{ N/C}}\right) = \boxed{66.6°}$$

(b) Find the force on a charge of 2.00×10^{-8} C placed at P.

Calculate the magnitude of the force (the direction is the same as that of $\vec{E}$ because the charge is positive):

$$F = Eq = (2.71 \times 10^5 \text{ N/C})(2.00 \times 10^{-8} \text{ C})$$
$$= \boxed{5.42 \times 10^{-3} \text{ N}}$$

REMARKS There were numerous steps to this problem, but each was very short. When attacking such problems, it's important to focus on one small step at a time. The solution comes not from a leap of genius, but from the assembly of a number of relatively easy parts.

QUESTION 15.5 Suppose q_2 were moved slowly to the right. What would happen to the angle ϕ?

EXERCISE 15.5 (a) Place a charge of $-7.00 \ \mu$C at point P and find the magnitude and direction of the electric field at the location of q_2 due to q_1 and the charge at P. (b) Find the magnitude and direction of the force on q_2.

ANSWERS (a) 5.84×10^5 N/C, $\phi = 20.2°$ (b) $F = 2.92$ N, $\phi = 200.°$

15.5 Electric Field Lines

A convenient aid for visualizing electric field patterns is to draw lines pointing in the direction of the electric field vector at any point. These lines, introduced by Michael Faraday and called **electric field lines,** are related to the electric field in any region of space in the following way:

1. The electric field vector $\vec{E}$ is tangent to the electric field lines at each point.
2. The number of lines per unit area through a surface perpendicular to the lines is proportional to the strength of the electric field in a given region.

Note that $\vec{E}$ is large when the field lines are close together and small when the lines are far apart.

Figure 15.13a shows some representative electric field lines for a single positive point charge. This two-dimensional drawing contains only the field lines that lie in the plane containing the point charge. The lines are actually directed radially outward from the charge in *all* directions, somewhat like the quills of an angry porcupine. Because a positive test charge placed in this field would be repelled by the charge q, the lines are directed radially away from the positive charge. The electric field lines for a single negative point charge are directed toward the charge (Fig. 15.13b) because a positive test charge is attracted by a negative charge. In either case the lines are radial and extend all the way to infinity. Note that the lines are

Tip 15.1 Electric Field Lines Aren't Paths of Particles

Electric field lines are *not* material objects. They are used only as a pictorial representation of the electric field at various locations. Except in special cases, they *do not* represent the path of a charged particle released in an electric field.

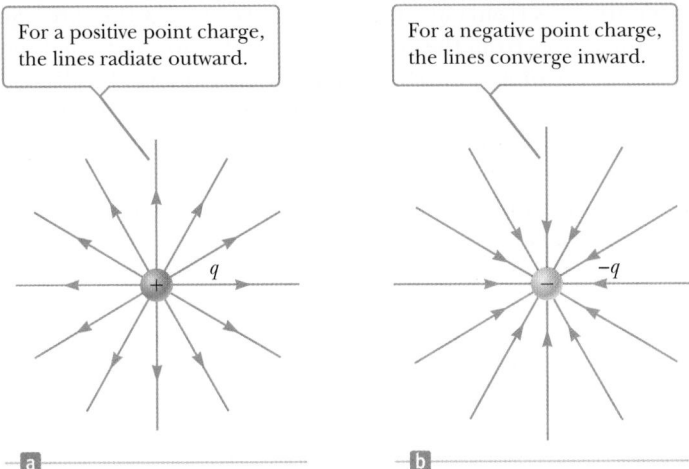

Figure 15.13 (a), (b) The electric field lines for a point charge. Notice that the figures show only those field lines that lie in the plate of the page.

closer together as they get near the charge, indicating that the strength of the field is increasing. Equation 15.6 verifies that this is indeed the case.

The rules for drawing electric field lines for any charge distribution follow directly from the relationship between electric field lines and electric field vectors:

1. The lines for a group of point charges must begin on positive charges and end on negative charges. In the case of an excess of charge, some lines will begin or end infinitely far away.
2. The number of lines drawn leaving a positive charge or ending on a negative charge is proportional to the magnitude of the charge.
3. No two field lines can cross each other.

Figure 15.14 shows the beautifully symmetric electric field lines for two point charges of equal magnitude but opposite sign. This charge configuration is called an **electric dipole.** Note that the number of lines that begin at the positive charge must equal the number that terminate at the negative charge. At points very near either charge, the lines are nearly radial. The high density of lines between the charges indicates a strong electric field in this region.

Figure 15.15 shows the electric field lines in the vicinity of two equal positive point charges. Again, close to either charge the lines are nearly radial. The same

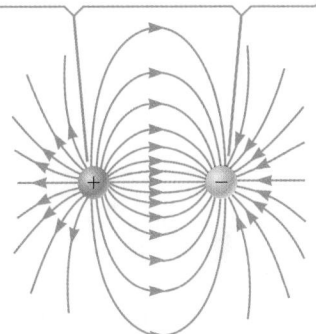

Figure 15.14 The electric field lines for two equal and opposite point charges (an electric dipole).

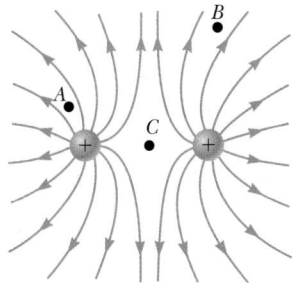

Figure 15.15 The electric field lines for two positive point charges. The points A, B, and C are discussed in Quick Quiz 15.6.

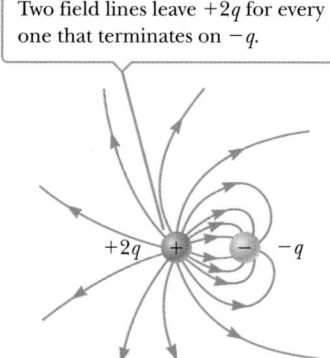

Two field lines leave $+2q$ for every one that terminates on $-q$.

$+2q$ $+$ $-$ $-q$

Active Figure 15.16
The electric field lines for a point charge of $+2q$ and a second point charge of $-q$.

number of lines emerges from each charge because the charges are equal in magnitude. At great distances from the charges, the field is approximately equal to that of a single point charge of magnitude $2q$. The bulging out of the electric field lines between the charges reflects the repulsive nature of the electric force between like charges. Also, the low density of field lines between the charges indicates a weak field in this region, unlike the dipole.

Finally, Active Figure 15.16 is a sketch of the electric field lines associated with the positive charge $+2q$ and the negative charge $-q$. In this case the number of lines leaving charge $+2q$ is twice the number terminating on charge $-q$. Hence, only half of the lines that leave the positive charge end at the negative charge. The remaining half terminate on negative charges that we assume to be located at infinity. At great distances from the charges (great compared with the charge separation), the electric field lines are equivalent to those of a single charge $+q$.

■ Quick Quiz

15.6 Rank the magnitudes of the electric field at points A, B, and C in Figure 15.15, with the largest magnitude first.

(a) A, B, C (b) A, C, B (c) C, A, B (d) The answer can't be determined by visual inspection.

■ APPLYING PHYSICS 15.1 | Measuring Atmospheric Electric Fields

The electric field near the surface of the Earth in fair weather is about 100 N/C downward. Under a thundercloud, the electric field can be very large, on the order of 20 000 N/C. How are these electric fields measured?

EXPLANATION A device for measuring these fields is called the *field mill*. Figure 15.17 shows the fundamental components of a field mill: two metal plates parallel to the ground. Each plate is connected to ground with a wire, with an ammeter (a low-resistance device for measuring the flow of charge, to be discussed in Section 17.3) in one path. Consider first just the lower plate. Because it's connected to ground and the ground carries a negative charge, the plate is negatively charged. The electric field lines are therefore directed downward, ending on the plate

as in Figure 15.17a. Now imagine that the upper plate is suddenly moved over the lower plate, as in Figure 15.17b. This plate is also connected to ground and is also negatively charged, so the field lines now end on the upper plate. The negative charges in the lower plate are repelled by those on the upper plate and must pass through the ammeter, registering a flow of charge. The amount of charge that was on the lower plate is related to the strength of the electric field. In this way, the flow of charge through the ammeter can be calibrated to measure the electric field. The plates are normally designed like the blades of a fan, with the upper plate rotating so that the lower plate is alternately covered and uncovered. As a result, charges flow back and forth continually through the ammeter, and the reading can be related to the electric field strength. ■

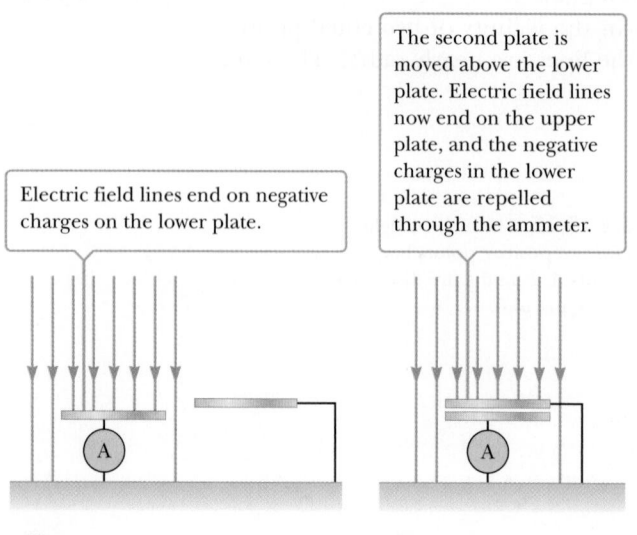

Electric field lines end on negative charges on the lower plate.

The second plate is moved above the lower plate. Electric field lines now end on the upper plate, and the negative charges in the lower plate are repelled through the ammeter.

A

A

a

b

Figure 15.17 Experimental setup for Applying Physics 15.1.

15.6 Conductors in Electrostatic Equilibrium

A good electric conductor like copper, although electrically neutral, contains charges (electrons) that aren't bound to any atom and are free to move about within the material. When no net motion of charge occurs within a conductor, the conductor is said to be in **electrostatic equilibrium.** An isolated conductor (one that is insulated from ground) has the following properties:

1. The electric field is zero everywhere inside the conducting material.
2. Any excess charge on an isolated conductor resides entirely on its surface.
3. The electric field just outside a charged conductor is perpendicular to the conductor's surface.
4. On an irregularly shaped conductor, the charge accumulates at sharp points, where the radius of curvature of the surface is smallest.

◄ Properties of an isolated conductor

The first property can be understood by examining what would happen if it were *not* true. If there were an electric field inside a conductor, the free charge there would move and a flow of charge, or current, would be created. If there were a net movement of charge, however, the conductor would no longer be in electrostatic equilibrium.

Property 2 is a direct result of the $1/r^2$ repulsion between like charges described by Coulomb's law. If by some means an excess of charge is placed inside a conductor, the repulsive forces between the like charges push them as far apart as possible, causing them to quickly migrate to the surface. (We won't prove it here, but the excess charge resides on the surface because Coulomb's law is an inverse-square law. With any other power law, an excess of charge would exist on the surface, but there would be a distribution of charge, of either the same or opposite sign, inside the conductor.)

Property 3 can be understood by again considering what would happen if it were not true. If the electric field in Figure 15.18 were not perpendicular to the surface, it would have a component along the surface, which would cause the free charges of the conductor to move (to the left in the figure). If the charges moved, however, a current would be created and the conductor would no longer be in electrostatic equilibrium. Therefore, $\vec{\mathbf{E}}$ must be perpendicular to the surface.

To see why property 4 must be true, consider Figure 15.19a (page 530), which shows a conductor that is fairly flat at one end and relatively pointed at the other. Any excess charge placed on the object moves to its surface. Figure 15.19b shows the forces between two such charges at the flatter end of the object. These forces

Figure 15.18 This situation is *impossible* if the conductor is in electrostatic equilibrium. If the electric field $\vec{\mathbf{E}}$ had a component parallel to the surface, an electric force would be exerted on the charges along the surface and they would move to the left.

Figure 15.19 (a) A conductor with a flatter end *A* and a relatively sharp end *B*. Excess charge placed on this conductor resides entirely at its surface and is distributed so that (b) there is less charge per unit area on the flatter end and (c) there is a large charge per unit area on the sharper end.

are predominantly directed parallel to the surface, so the charges move apart until repulsive forces from other nearby charges establish an equilibrium. At the sharp end, however, the forces of repulsion between two charges are directed predominantly away from the surface, as in Figure 15.19c. As a result, there is less tendency for the charges to move apart along the surface here, and the amount of charge per unit area is greater than at the flat end. The cumulative effect of many such outward forces from nearby charges at the sharp end produces a large resultant force directed away from the surface that can be great enough to cause charges to leap from the surface into the surrounding air.

Many experiments have shown that the net charge on a conductor resides on its surface. One such experiment was first performed by Michael Faraday and is referred to as *Faraday's ice-pail experiment*. Faraday lowered a metal ball having a negative charge at the end of a silk thread (an insulator) into an uncharged hollow conductor insulated from ground, a metal ice-pail as in Figure 15.20a. As the ball entered the pail, the needle on an electrometer attached to the outer surface of the pail was observed to deflect. (An electrometer is a device used to measure charge.) The needle deflected because the charged ball induced a positive charge on the inner wall of the pail, which left an equal negative charge on the outer wall (Fig. 15.20b).

Faraday next touched the inner surface of the pail with the ball and noted that the deflection of the needle did not change, either when the ball touched the inner surface of the pail (Fig. 15.20c) or when it was removed (Fig. 15.20d). Further, he found that the ball was now uncharged because when it touched the inside of the pail, the excess negative charge on the ball had been drawn off, neutralizing the induced positive charge on the inner surface of the pail. In this way Faraday discovered the useful result that *all* the excess charge on an object can be transferred to an already charged metal shell if the object is touched to the *inside* of the shell. As we will see, this result is the principle of operation of the Van de Graaff generator.

Faraday concluded that because the deflection of the needle in the electrometer didn't change when the charged ball touched the inside of the pail, the positive charge induced on the inside surface of the pail was just enough to neutralize the negative charge on the ball. As a result of his investigations, he concluded that a charged object suspended inside a metal container rearranged the charge on the container so that the sign of the charge on its inside surface was *opposite* the sign of the charge on the suspended object. This produced a charge on the outside surface of the container of the same sign as that on the suspended object.

Faraday also found that if the electrometer was connected to the inside surface of the pail after the experiment had been run, the needle showed no deflection. Thus, the *excess* charge acquired by the pail when contact was made between ball and pail appeared on the outer surface of the pail.

If a metal rod having sharp points is attached to a house, most of any charge on the house passes through these points, eliminating the induced charge on the house produced by storm clouds. In addition, a lightning discharge striking the house passes through the metal rod and is safely carried to the ground through

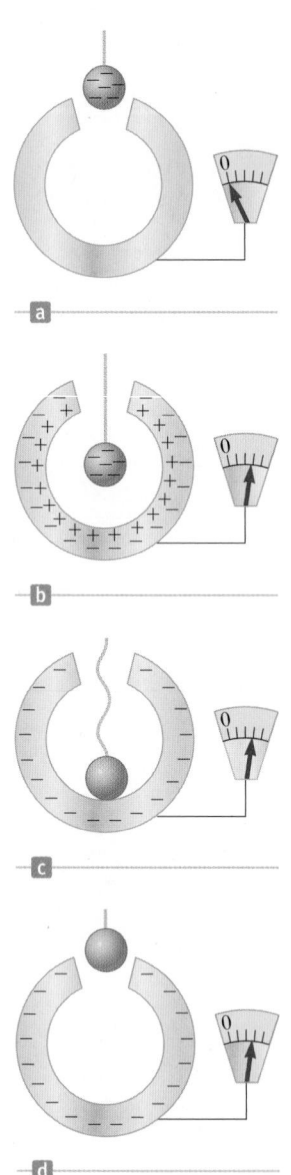

Figure 15.20 An experiment showing that any charge transferred to a conductor resides on its surface in electrostatic equilibrium. The hollow conductor is insulated from ground, and the small metal ball is supported by an insulating thread.

wires leading from the rod to the Earth. Lightning rods using this principle were first developed by Benjamin Franklin. Some European countries couldn't accept the fact that such a worthwhile idea could have originated in the New World, so they "improved" the design by eliminating the sharp points!

APPLICATION

Lightning Rods

■ APPLYING PHYSICS 15.2 | Conductors and Field Lines

Suppose a point charge $+Q$ is in empty space. Wearing rubber gloves, you proceed to surround the charge with a concentric spherical conducting shell. What effect does that have on the field lines from the charge?

EXPLANATION When the spherical shell is placed around the charge, the charges in the shell rearrange to satisfy the rules for a conductor in equilibrium. A net charge of $-Q$ moves to the interior surface of the con-

ductor, so the electric field inside the conductor becomes zero. This means the field lines originating on the $+Q$ charge now terminate on the negative charges. The movement of the negative charges to the inner surface of the sphere leaves a net charge of $+Q$ on the outer surface of the sphere. Then the field lines outside the sphere look just as before: the only change, overall, is the absence of field lines within the conductor. ■

■ APPLYING PHYSICS 15.3 | Driver Safety During Electrical Storms

Why is it safe to stay inside an automobile during a lightning storm?

EXPLANATION Many people believe that staying inside the car is safe because of the insulating characteristics of the rubber tires, but in fact that isn't true. Lightning can travel through several kilometers of air, so it can certainly

penetrate a centimeter of rubber. The safety of remaining in the car is due to the fact that charges on the metal shell of the car will reside on the outer surface of the car, as noted in property 2 discussed earlier. As a result, an occupant in the automobile touching the inner surfaces is not in danger. ■

15.7 The Millikan Oil-Drop Experiment

From 1909 to 1913, Robert Andrews Millikan (1868–1953) performed a brilliant set of experiments at the University of Chicago in which he measured the elementary charge e of the electron and demonstrated the quantized nature of the electronic charge. The apparatus he used, diagrammed in Active Figure 15.21, contains two parallel metal plates. Oil droplets that have been charged by friction in an atomizer are allowed to pass through a small hole in the upper plate. A horizontal light beam is used to illuminate the droplets, which are viewed by a telescope with axis at right angles to the beam. The droplets then appear as shining stars against a dark background, and the rate of fall of individual drops can be determined.

We assume a single drop having a mass of m and carrying a charge of q is being viewed and its charge is negative. If no electric field is present between the plates,

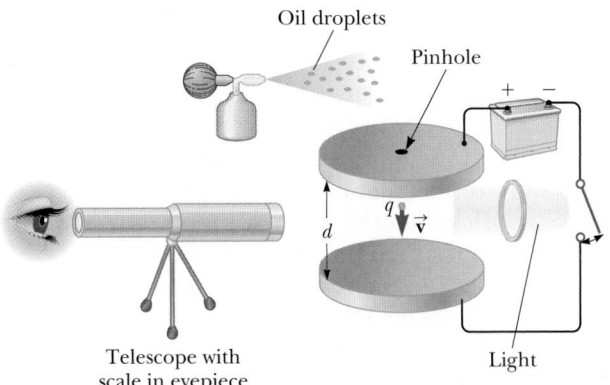

Oil droplets

Pinhole

q $\vec{v}$

d

Telescope with
scale in eyepiece

Light

Active Figure 15.21

A schematic view of Millikan's oil-drop apparatus.

Figure 15.22 The forces on a negatively charged oil droplet in Millikan's experiment.

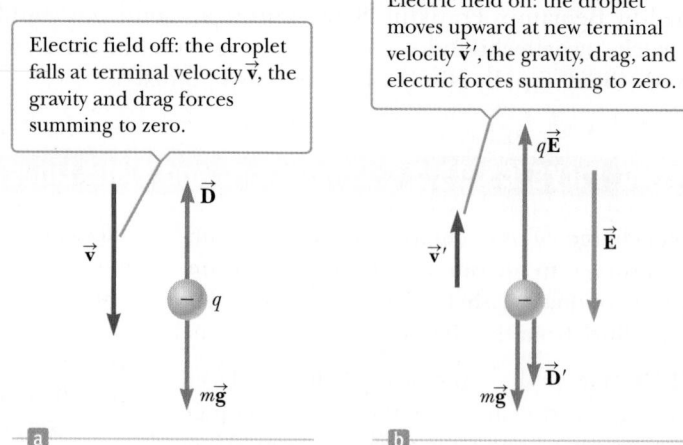

the two forces acting on the charge are the force of gravity, $m\vec{g}$, acting downward, and an upward viscous drag force $\vec{D}$ (Fig. 15.22a). The drag force is proportional to the speed of the drop. When the drop reaches its terminal speed, v, the two forces balance each other ($mg = D$).

Now suppose an electric field is set up between the plates by a battery connected so that the upper plate is positively charged. In this case a third force, $q\vec{E}$, acts on the charged drop. Because q is negative and $\vec{E}$ is downward, the electric force is *upward* as in Figure 15.22b. If this force is great enough, the drop moves upward and the drag force $\vec{D}'$ acts downward. When the upward electric force, $q\vec{E}$, balances the sum of the force of gravity and the drag force, both acting downward, the drop reaches a new terminal speed v'.

With the field turned on, a drop moves slowly upward, typically at a rate of *hundredths* of a centimeter per second. The rate of fall in the absence of a field is comparable. Hence, a single droplet with constant mass and radius can be followed for hours as it alternately rises and falls, simply by turning the electric field on and off.

After making measurements on thousands of droplets, Millikan and his coworkers found that, to within about 1% precision, every drop had a charge equal to some positive or negative integer multiple of the elementary charge e,

$$q = ne \quad n = 0, \pm 1, \pm 2, \pm 3, \dots \qquad [15.7]$$

where $e = 1.60 \times 10^{-19}$ C. It was later established that positive integer multiples of e would arise when an oil droplet had lost one or more electrons. Likewise, negative integer multiples of e would arise when a drop had gained one or more electrons. Gains or losses in integral numbers provide conclusive evidence that charge is quantized. In 1923 Millikan was awarded the Nobel Prize in Physics for this work.

15.8 The Van de Graaff Generator

In 1929 Robert J. Van de Graaff (1901–1967) designed and built an electrostatic generator that has been used extensively in nuclear physics research. The principles of its operation can be understood with knowledge of the properties of electric fields and charges already presented in this chapter. Figure 15.23 shows the basic construction of this device. A motor-driven pulley P moves a belt past positively charged comb-like metallic needles positioned at A. Negative charges are attracted to these needles from the belt, leaving the left side of the belt with a net positive charge. The positive charges attract electrons onto the belt as it moves past a second comb of needles at B, increasing the excess positive charge on the dome. Because the electric field inside the metal dome is negligible, the positive charge on it can easily be increased regardless of how much charge is already present. The result is that the dome is left with a large amount of positive charge.

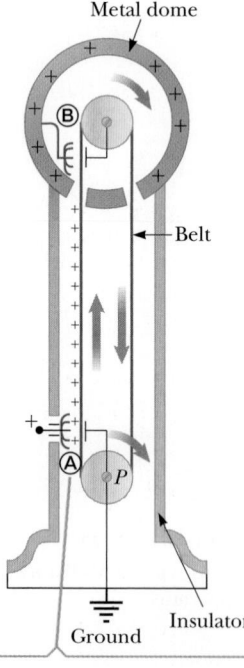

The charge is deposited on the belt at point Ⓐ and transferred to the hollow conductor at point Ⓑ.

Figure 15.23 A schematic diagram of a Van de Graaff generator. Charge is transferred to the dome by means of a rotating belt.

This accumulation of charge on the dome can't continue indefinitely. As more and more charge appears on the surface of the dome, the magnitude of the electric field at that surface is also increasing. Finally, the strength of the field becomes great enough to partially ionize the air near the surface, increasing the conductivity of the air. Charges on the dome now have a pathway to leak off into the air, producing some spectacular "lightning bolts" as the discharge occurs. As noted earlier, charges find it easier to leap off a surface at points where the curvature is great. As a result, one way to inhibit the electric discharge, and to increase the amount of charge that can be stored on the dome, is to increase its radius. Another method for inhibiting discharge is to place the entire system in a container filled with a high-pressure gas, which is significantly more difficult to ionize than air at atmospheric pressure.

If protons (or other charged particles) are introduced into a tube attached to the dome, the large electric field of the dome exerts a repulsive force on the protons, causing them to accelerate to energies high enough to initiate nuclear reactions between the protons and various target nuclei.

15.9 Electric Flux and Gauss's Law

Gauss's law is essentially a technique for calculating the average electric field on a closed surface, developed by Karl Friedrich Gauss (1777–1855). When the electric field, because of its symmetry, is constant everywhere on that surface and perpendicular to it, the exact electric field can be found. In such special cases, Gauss's law is far easier to apply than Coulomb's law.

Gauss's law relates the electric flux through a closed surface and the total charge inside that surface. A *closed surface* has an inside and an outside: an example is a sphere. *Electric flux* is a measure of how much the electric field vectors penetrate through a given surface. If the electric field vectors are tangent to the surface at all points, for example, they don't penetrate the surface and the electric flux through the surface is zero. These concepts will be discussed more fully in the next two subsections. As we'll see, Gauss's law states that the electric flux through a closed surface is proportional to the charge contained *inside* the surface.

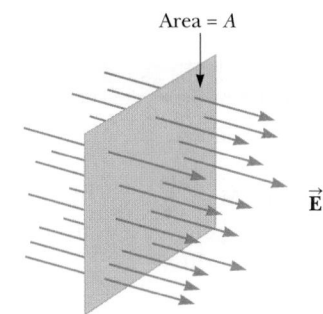

Figure 15.24 Field lines of a uniform electric field penetrating a plane of area A perpendicular to the field. The electric flux Φ_E through this area is equal to EA.

Electric Flux

Consider an electric field that is uniform in both magnitude and direction, as in Figure 15.24. The electric field lines penetrate a surface of area A, which is perpendicular to the field. The technique used for drawing a figure such as Figure 15.24 is that the number of lines per unit area, N/A, is proportional to the magnitude of the electric field, or $E \propto N/A$. We can rewrite this proportion as $N \propto EA$, which means that the number of field lines is proportional to the *product* of E and A, called the **electric flux** and represented by the symbol Φ_E:

$$\Phi_E = EA \qquad \text{[15.8]}$$

Note that Φ_E has SI units of $\text{N} \cdot \text{m}^2/\text{C}$ and is proportional to the number of field lines that pass through some area A oriented perpendicular to the field. (It's called flux by analogy with the term *flux* in fluid flow, which is the volume of liquid flowing through a perpendicular area per second.) If the surface under consideration is not perpendicular to the field, as in Figure 15.25, the expression for the electric flux is

$$\Phi_E = EA \cos \theta \qquad \text{[15.9]}$$

where a vector perpendicular to the area A is at an angle θ with respect to the field. This vector is often said to be *normal* to the surface, and we will refer to it as "the normal vector to the surface." The number of lines that cross this area is equal to the number that cross the projected area A', which is perpendicular to the field.

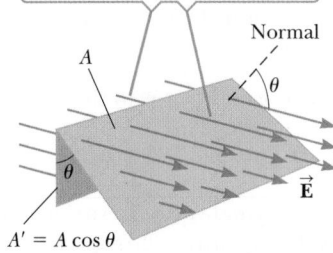

The number of field lines that go through the area A' is the same as the number that go through area A.

$A' = A \cos \theta$

Figure 15.25 Field lines for a uniform electric field through an area A that is at an angle of $(90° - \theta)$ to the field.

◀ Electric flux

We see that the two areas are related by $A' = A \cos \theta$. From Equation 15.9, we see that the flux through a surface of fixed area has the maximum value EA when the surface is perpendicular to the field (when $\theta = 0°$) and that the flux is zero when the surface is parallel to the field (when $\theta = 90°$). **By convention, for a closed surface, the flux lines passing into the interior of the volume are negative and those passing out of the interior of the volume are positive.** This convention is equivalent to requiring the normal vector of the surface to point outward when computing the flux through a closed surface.

■ Quick Quiz

15.7 Calculate the magnitude of the flux of a constant electric field of 5.00 N/C in the z-direction through a rectangle with area 4.00 m^2 in the xy-plane. (a) 0 (b) 10.0 N · m^2/C (c) 20.0 N · m^2/C (d) More information is needed

15.8 Suppose the electric field of Quick Quiz 15.7 is tilted 60° away from the positive z-direction. Calculate the magnitude of the flux through the same area. (a) 0 (b) 10.0 N · m^2/C (c) 20.0 N · m^2/C (d) More information is needed

---

■ EXAMPLE 15.6   Flux Through a Cube

GOAL Calculate the electric flux through a closed surface.

PROBLEM Consider a uniform electric field oriented in the x-direction. Find the electric flux through each surface of a cube with edges L oriented as shown in Figure 15.26, and the net flux.

STRATEGY This problem involves substituting into the definition of electric flux given by Equation 15.9. In each case E and $A = L^2$ are the same; the only difference is the angle θ that the electric field makes with respect to a vector perpendicular to a given surface and pointing outward (the normal vector to the surface). The angles can be determined by inspection. The flux through a surface parallel to the xy-plane will be labeled Φ_{xy} and further designated by position (front, back); others will be labeled similarly: Φ_{xz} top or bottom, and Φ_{yz} left or right.

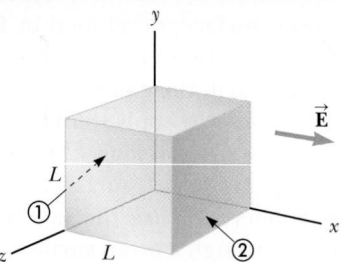

Figure 15.26 (Example 15.6) A hypothetical surface in the shape of a cube in a uniform electric field parallel to the x-axis. The net flux through the surface is zero when the net charge inside the cube is zero.

SOLUTION

The normal vector to the xy-plane points in the negative z-direction. This, in turn, is perpendicular to $\vec{E}$, so $\theta = 90°$. (The opposite side works similarly.)

$\Phi_{xy} = EA \cos (90°) = \boxed{0}$ (back and front surfaces)

The normal vector to the xz-plane points in the negative y-direction. This, in turn, is perpendicular to $\vec{E}$, so again $\theta = 90°$. (The opposite side works similarly.)

$\Phi_{xz} = EA \cos (90°) = \boxed{0}$ (top and bottom surfaces)

The normal vector to surface ① (the yz-plane) points in the negative x-direction. This is antiparallel to $\vec{E}$, so $\theta = 180°$.

$\Phi_{yz} = EA \cos (180°) = \boxed{-EL^2}$ (surface ①)

Surface ② has normal vector pointing in the positive x-direction, so $\theta = 0°$.

$\Phi_{yz} = EA \cos (0°) = \boxed{EL^2}$ (surface ②)

We calculate the net flux by summing:

$\Phi_{net} = 0 + 0 + 0 + 0 - EL^2 + EL^2 = \boxed{0}$

REMARKS In doing this calculation, it is necessary to remember that the angle in the definition of flux is measured from the normal vector to the surface and that this vector must point outwards for a closed surface. As a result, the normal vector for the yz-plane on the left points in the negative x-direction, and the normal vector to the plane parallel to the yz-plane on the right points in the positive x-direction. Notice that there aren't any charges in the box. The net electric flux is always zero for closed surfaces that contain a net charge of zero.

QUESTION 15.6 If the surface in Figure 15.26 were spherical, would the answer be (a) greater than, (b) less than, or (c) the same as the net electric flux found for the cubical surface?

EXERCISE 15.6 Suppose the constant electric field in Example 15.6 points in the positive *y*-direction instead. Calculate the flux through the *xz*-plane and the surface parallel to it. What's the net electric flux through the surface of the cube?

ANSWERS $\Phi_{xz} = -EL^2$ (bottom surface), $\Phi_{xz} = +EL^2$ (top surface). The net flux is still zero.

Gauss's Law

Consider a point charge q surrounded by a spherical surface of radius r centered on the charge, as in Figure 15.27a. The magnitude of the electric field everywhere on the surface of the sphere is

$$E = k_e \frac{q}{r^2}$$

Note that the electric field is perpendicular to the spherical surface at all points on the surface. The electric flux through the surface is therefore EA, where $A = 4\pi r^2$ is the surface area of the sphere:

$$\Phi_E = EA = k_e \frac{q}{r^2}(4\pi r^2) = 4\pi k_e q$$

It's sometimes convenient to express k_e in terms of another constant, ϵ_0, as $k_e = 1/(4\pi\epsilon_0)$. The constant ϵ_0 is called the **permittivity of free space** and has the value

$$\epsilon_0 = \frac{1}{4\pi k_e} = 8.85 \times 10^{-12} \, \text{C}^2/\text{N} \cdot \text{m}^2 \qquad \textbf{[15.10]}$$

The use of k_e or ϵ_0 is strictly a matter of taste. The electric flux through the closed spherical surface that surrounds the charge q can now be expressed as

$$\Phi_E = 4\pi k_e q = \frac{q}{\epsilon_0}$$

This result says that the electric flux through a sphere that surrounds a charge q is equal to the charge divided by the constant ϵ_0. Using calculus, this result can be proven for *any* closed surface that surrounds the charge q. For example, if the surface surrounding q is irregular, as in Figure 15.27b, the flux through that surface is also q/ϵ_0. This leads to the following general result, known as Gauss's law:

The electric flux Φ_E through any closed surface is equal to the net charge inside the surface, Q_{inside}, divided by ϵ_0:

$$\Phi_E = \frac{Q_{\text{inside}}}{\epsilon_0} \qquad \textbf{[15.11]}$$

◀ Gauss's Law

Although it's not obvious, Gauss's law describes how charges create electric fields. In principle it can always be used to calculate the electric field of a system of charges or a continuous distribution of charge. In practice, the technique is useful only in a limited number of cases in which there is a high degree of symmetry, such as spheres, cylinders, or planes. With the symmetry of these special shapes, the charges can be surrounded by an imaginary surface, called a Gaussian surface. This imaginary surface is used strictly for mathematical calculation, and need not be an actual, physical surface. If the imaginary surface is chosen so that the electric field is constant everywhere on it, the electric field can be computed with

$$EA = \Phi_E = \frac{Q_{\text{inside}}}{\epsilon_0} \qquad \textbf{[15.12]}$$

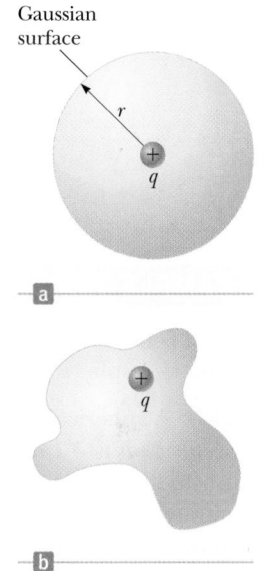

Figure 15.27 (a) The flux through a spherical surface of radius r surrounding a point charge q is $\Phi_E = q/\epsilon_0$. (b) The flux through any arbitrary surface surrounding the charge is also equal to q/ϵ_0.

Tip 15.2 Gaussian Surfaces Aren't Real

A Gaussian surface is an imaginary surface, created solely to facilitate a mathematical calculation. It doesn't necessarily coincide with the surface of a physical object.

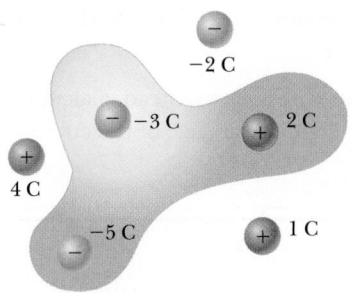

Active Figure 15.28
(Quick Quiz 15.9)

as will be seen in the examples. Although Gauss's law in this form can be used to obtain the electric field only for problems with a lot of symmetry, it can *always* be used to obtain the *average* electric field on *any* surface.

■ *Quick Quiz*

15.9 Find the electric flux through the surface in Active Figure 15.28. (a) $-(3 \text{ C})/\epsilon_0$ (b) $(3 \text{ C})/\epsilon_0$ (c) 0 (d) $-(6 \text{ C})/\epsilon_0$

15.10 For a closed surface through which the net flux is zero, each of the following four statements *could* be true. Which of the statements *must* be true? (There may be more than one.) (a) There are no charges inside the surface. (b) The net charge inside the surface is zero. (c) The electric field is zero everywhere on the surface. (d) The number of electric field lines entering the surface equals the number leaving the surface.

■ **EXAMPLE 15.7** │ **The Electric Field of a Charged Spherical Shell**

GOAL Use Gauss's law to determine electric fields when the symmetry is spherical.

PROBLEM A spherical conducting shell of inner radius a and outer radius b carries a total charge $+Q$ distributed on the surface of a conducting shell (Fig. 15.29a). The quantity Q is taken to be positive. **(a)** Find the electric field in the interior of the conducting shell, for $r < a$, and **(b)** the electric field outside the shell, for $r > b$. **(c)** If an additional charge of $-2Q$ is placed at the center, find the electric field for $r > b$. **(d)** What is the distribution of charge on the sphere in part (c)?

STRATEGY For each part, draw a spherical Gaussian surface in the region of interest. Add up the charge inside the Gaussian surface, substitute it and the area into Gauss's law, and solve for the electric field. To find the distribution of charge in part (c), use Gauss's law in reverse: the charge distribution must be such that the electrostatic field is zero inside a conductor.

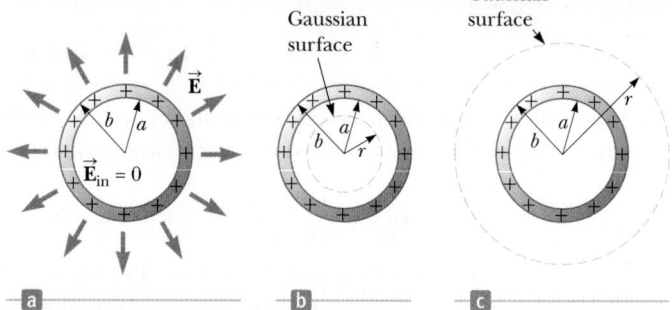

Figure 15.29 (Example 15.7) (a) The electric field inside a uniformly charged spherical shell is *zero*. It is also zero for the conducting material in the region $a < r < b$. The field outside is the same as that of a point charge having a total charge Q located at the center of the shell. (b) The construction of a Gaussian surface for calculating the electric field *inside* a spherical shell. (c) The construction of a Gaussian surface for calculating the electric field *outside* a spherical shell.

SOLUTION

(a) Find the electric field for $r < a$.

Apply Gauss's law, Equation 15.12, to the Gaussian surface illustrated in Figure 15.29b (note that there isn't any charge inside this surface):

$$EA = E(4\pi r^2) = \frac{Q_{inside}}{\epsilon_0} = 0 \quad \rightarrow \quad E = 0$$

(b) Find the electric field for $r > b$.

Apply Gauss's law, Equation 15.12, to the Gaussian surface illustrated in Figure 15.29c:

$$EA = E(4\pi r^2) = \frac{Q_{inside}}{\epsilon_0} = \frac{Q}{\epsilon_0}$$

Divide by the area:

$$E = \frac{Q}{4\pi\epsilon_0 r^2}$$

(c) Now an additional charge of $-2Q$ is placed at the center of the sphere. Compute the new electric field outside the sphere, for $r > b$.

Apply Gauss's law as in part (b), including the new charge in Q_{inside}:

$$EA = E(4\pi r^2) = \frac{Q_{inside}}{\epsilon_0} = \frac{+Q - 2Q}{\epsilon_0}$$

Solve for the electric field:

$$E = -\frac{Q}{4\pi\epsilon_0 r^2}$$

(d) Find the charge distribution on the sphere for part (c).

Write Gauss's law for the interior of the shell:

$$EA = \frac{Q_{inside}}{\epsilon_0} = \frac{Q_{center} + Q_{inner\ surface}}{\epsilon_0}$$

Find the charge on the inner surface of the shell, noting that the electric field in the conductor is zero:

$$Q_{center} + Q_{inner\ surface} = 0$$
$$Q_{inner\ surface} = -Q_{center} = \boxed{+2Q}$$

Find the charge on the outer surface, noting that the inner and outer surface charges must sum to $+Q$:

$$Q_{outer\ surface} + Q_{inner\ surface} = Q$$
$$Q_{outer\ surface} = -Q_{inner\ surface} + Q = \boxed{-Q}$$

. . . .

REMARKS The important thing to notice is that in each case, the charge is spread out over a region with spherical symmetry or is located at the exact center. That is what allows the computation of a value for the electric field.

QUESTION 15.7 If the charge at the center of the sphere is made positive, how is the charge on the inner surface of the sphere affected?

EXERCISE 15.7 Suppose the charge at the center is now increased to $+2Q$, while the surface of the conductor still retains a charge of $+Q$. (a) Find the electric field exterior to the sphere, for $r > b$. (b) What's the electric field inside the conductor, for $a < r < b$? (c) Find the charge distribution on the conductor.

ANSWERS (a) $E = 3Q/4\pi\epsilon_0 r^2$ (b) $E = 0$, which is always the case when charges are not moving in a conductor. (c) Inner surface: $-2Q$; outer surface: $+3Q$

In Example 15.7, not much was said about the distribution of charge on the conductor. Whenever there is a net nonzero charge, the individual charges will try to get as far away from each other as possible. Hence, charge will reside either on the inside surface or on the outside surface. Because the electric field in the conductor is zero, there will always be enough charge on the inner surface to cancel whatever charge is at the center. In part (b) there is no charge on the inner surface and a charge of $+Q$ on the outer surface. In part (c), with a $-Q$ charge at the center, $+Q$ is on the inner surface and 0 C is on the outer surface. Finally, in the exercise, with $-2Q$ in the center, there must be $+2Q$ on the inner surface and $-Q$ on the outer surface. In each case the total charge on the conductor remains the same, $+Q$; it's just arranged differently.

Problems like Example 15.7 are often said to have "thin, nonconducting shells" carrying a uniformly distributed charge. In these cases no distinction need be made between the outer surface and inner surface of the shell. The next example makes that implicit assumption.

■ EXAMPLE 15.8 | A Nonconducting Plane Sheet of Charge

GOAL Apply Gauss's law to a problem with plane symmetry.

PROBLEM Find the electric field above and below a nonconducting infinite plane sheet of charge with uniform positive charge per unit area σ (Fig. 15.30a, page 538).

STRATEGY By symmetry, the electric field must be perpendicular to the plane and directed away from it on either side, as shown in Figure 15.30b. For the Gaussian surface, choose a small cylinder with axis perpendicular to the plane, each end having area A_0. No electric field lines pass through the curved surface of the cylinder, only through the two ends, which have total area $2A_0$. Apply Gauss's law, using Figure 15.30b.

(Continued)

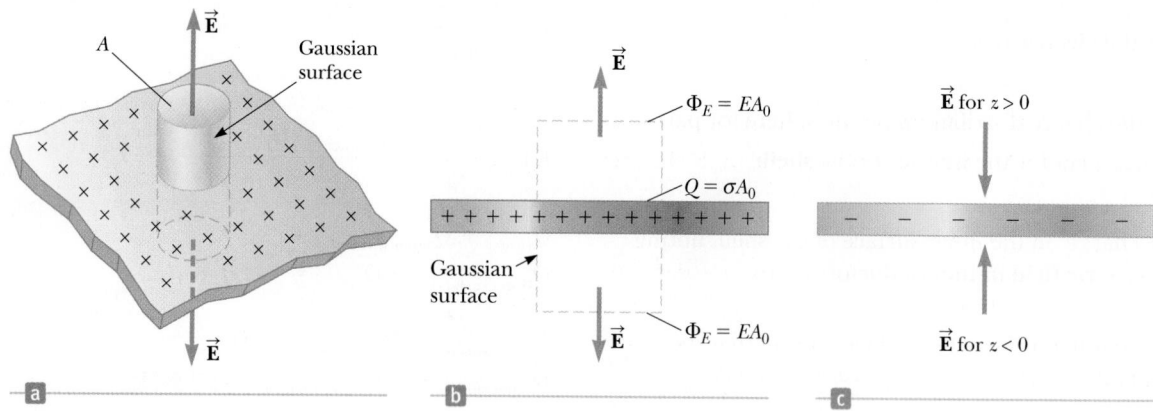

Figure 15.30 (Example 15.8) (a) A cylindrical Gaussian surface penetrating an infinite sheet of charge. (b) A cross section of the same Gaussian cylinder. The flux through each end of the Gaussian surface is EA_0. There is no flux through the cylindrical surface. (c) (Exercise 15.8).

SOLUTION

(a) Find the electric field above and below a plane of uniform charge.

Apply Gauss's law, Equation 15.12:

$$EA = \frac{Q_{inside}}{\epsilon_0}$$

The total charge inside the Gaussian cylinder is the charge density times the cross-sectional area:

$$Q_{inside} = \sigma A_0$$

The electric flux comes entirely from the two ends, each having area A_0. Substitute $A = 2A_0$ and Q_{inside} and solve for E.

$$E = \frac{\sigma A_0}{(2A_0)\epsilon_0} = \boxed{\frac{\sigma}{2\epsilon_0}}$$

This is the *magnitude* of the electric field. Find the z-component of the field above and below the plane. The electric field points away from the plane, so it's positive above the plane and negative below the plane.

$$\boxed{E_z = \frac{\sigma}{2\epsilon_0} \quad z > 0}$$

$$\boxed{E_z = -\frac{\sigma}{2\epsilon_0} \quad z < 0}$$

REMARKS Notice here that the plate was taken to be a thin, nonconducting shell. If it's made of metal, of course, the electric field inside it is zero, with half the charge on the upper surface and half on the lower surface.

QUESTION 15.8 In reality, the sheet carrying charge would likely be metallic and have a small but nonzero thickness. If it carries the same charge per unit area, what is the electric field inside the sheet between the two surfaces?

EXERCISE 15.8 Suppose an infinite nonconducting plane of charge as in Example 15.8 has a uniform negative charge density of $-\sigma$. Find the electric field above and below the plate. Sketch the field.

ANSWERS $E_z = \dfrac{-\sigma}{2\epsilon_0}$, $z > 0$; $E_z = \dfrac{\sigma}{2\epsilon_0}$, $z < 0$. See Figure 15.30c for the sketch.

Figure 15.31 Cross section of an idealized parallel-plate capacitor. Electric field vector contributions sum together in between the plates, but cancel outside.

An important circuit element that will be studied extensively in the next chapter is the parallel-plate capacitor. The device consists of a plate of positive charge, as in Example 15.8, with the negative plate of Exercise 15.8 placed above it. The sum of these two fields is illustrated in Figure 15.31. The result is an electric field with double the magnitude in between the two plates:

$$E = \frac{\sigma}{\epsilon_0} \qquad \text{[15.13]}$$

Outside the plates, the electric fields cancel.

■ SUMMARY

15.1 Properties of Electric Charges

Electric charges have the following properties:

1. Unlike charges attract one another and like charges repel one another.

2. Electric charge is always conserved.

3. Charge comes in discrete packets that are integral multiples of the basic electric charge $e = 1.6 \times 10^{-19}$ C.

4. The force between two charged particles is proportional to the inverse square of the distance between them.

15.2 Insulators and Conductors

Conductors are materials in which charges move freely in response to an electric field. All other materials are called **insulators.**

15.3 Coulomb's Law

Coulomb's law states that the electric force between two stationary charged particles separated by a distance r has the magnitude

$$F = k_e \frac{|q_1||q_2|}{r^2} \quad \text{[15.1]}$$

where $|q_1|$ and $|q_2|$ are the magnitudes of the charges on the particles in coulombs and

$$k_e \approx 8.99 \times 10^9 \text{ N} \cdot \text{m}^2/\text{C}^2 \quad \text{[15.2]}$$

is the **Coulomb constant.**

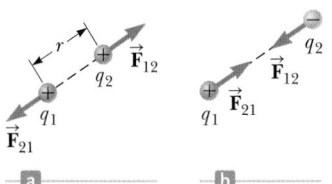

(a) The electric force between two charges with the same sign is repulsive, and (b) it is attractive when the charges have opposite signs.

15.4 The Electric Field

An electric field $\vec{E}$ exists at some point in space if a small test charge q_0 placed at that point is acted upon by an electric force $\vec{F}$. The electric field is defined as

$$\vec{E} \equiv \frac{\vec{F}}{q_0} \quad \text{[15.3]}$$

The **direction** of the electric field at a point in space is defined to be the direction of the electric force that would be exerted on a small positive charge placed at that point.

Source charge   Test charge

The electric force of charge Q on a test charge q_0 divided by q_0 gives the electric field $\vec{E}$ of Q at that point.

The magnitude of the electric field due to a *point charge* q at a distance r from the point charge is

$$E = k_e \frac{|q|}{r^2} \quad \text{[15.6]}$$

15.5 Electric Field Lines

Electric field lines are useful for visualizing the electric field in any region of space. The electric field vector $\vec{E}$ is tangent to the electric field lines at every point. Further, the number of electric field lines per unit area through a surface perpendicular to the lines is proportional to the strength of the electric field at that surface.

15.6 Conductors in Electrostatic Equilibrium

A **conductor in electrostatic equilibrium** has the following properties:

1. The electric field is zero everywhere inside the conducting material.

2. Any excess charge on an isolated conductor must reside entirely on its surface.

3. The electric field just outside a charged conductor is perpendicular to the conductor's surface.

4. On an irregularly shaped conductor, charge accumulates where the radius of curvature of the surface is smallest, at sharp points.

15.9 Electric Flux and Gauss's Law

Gauss's law states that the electric flux through any closed surface is equal to the net charge Q inside the surface divided by the permittivity of free space, ϵ_0:

$$EA = \Phi_E = \frac{Q_{\text{inside}}}{\epsilon_0} \quad \text{[15.12]}$$

For highly symmetric distributions of charge, Gauss's law can be used to calculate electric fields.

The electric flux Φ through any arbitrary surface surrounding a charge q is q/ϵ_0.

■ MULTIPLE-CHOICE QUESTIONS

WebAssign The multiple-choice questions in this chapter may be assigned online in Enhanced WebAssign.

1. A very small ball has a mass of 5.0×10^{-3} kg and a charge of $4.0 \ \mu\text{C}$. What magnitude electric field directed upward will balance the weight of the ball?

(a) 8.2×10^2 N/C (b) 1.2×10^4 N/C (c) 2.0×10^{-2} N/C (d) 5.1×10^6 N/C (e) 3.7×10^3 N/C

2. Estimate the magnitude of the electric field strength due to the proton in a hydrogen atom at a distance of 5.29×10^{-11} m, the expected position of the electron in the atom. (a) 10^{-11} N/C (b) 10^{8} N/C (c) 10^{14} N/C (d) 10^{6} N/C (e) 10^{12} N/C

3. The magnitude of the electric force between two protons is 2.3×10^{-26} N. How far apart are they? (a) 0.10 m (b) 0.022 m (c) 3.1 m (d) 0.005 7 m (e) 0.48 m

4. A uniform electric field of 1.0 N/C is set up by a uniform distribution of charge in the xy-plane. What is the electric field inside a metal ball placed 0.50 m above the xy-plane? (a) 1.0 N/C (b) −1.0 N/C (c) 0 (d) 0.25 N/C (e) It varies depending on the position inside the ball.

5. Charges of 3.0 nC, −2.0 nC, −7.0 nC, and 1.0 nC are contained inside a rectangular box with length 1.0 m, width 2.0 m, and height 2.5 m. Outside the box are charges of 1.0 nC and 4.0 nC. What is the electric flux through the surface of the box? (a) 0 (b) -560 N · m^2/C (c) -340 N · m^2/C (d) 260 N · m^2/C (e) 170 N · m^2/C

6. An electron with a speed of 3.00×10^{6} m/s moves into a uniform electric field of magnitude 1.00×10^{3} N/C. The field lines are parallel to the electron's velocity and pointing in the same direction as the velocity. How far does the electron travel before it is brought to rest? (a) 2.56 cm (b) 5.12 cm (c) 11.2 cm (d) 3.34 m (e) 4.24 m

7. A charge of −4.00 nC is located at (0, 1.00) m. What is the x-component of the electric field at (4.00, −2.00) m? (a) 1.15 N/C (b) −2.24 N/C (c) 3.91 N/C (d) −1.15 N/C (e) 0.863 N/C

8. Two point charges attract each other with an electric force of magnitude F. If one charge is reduced to one-third its original value and the distance between the charges is doubled, what is the resulting magnitude of the electric force between them? (a) $F/12$ (b) $F/3$ (c) $F/6$ (d) $3F/4$ (e) $3F/2$

9. In which of the following contexts can Gauss's law *not* be readily applied to find the electric field? (a) near a long, uniformly charged wire (b) above a large uniformly charged plane (c) inside a uniformly charged ball (d) outside a uniformly charged sphere (e) Gauss's law can be readily applied to find the electric field in all these contexts.

10. What happens when a charged insulator is placed near an uncharged metallic object? (a) They repel each other. (b) They attract each other. (c) They may attract or repel each other, depending on whether the charge on the insulator is positive or negative. (d) They exert no electrostatic force on each other. (e) The charged insulator always spontaneously discharges.

11. What prevents gravity from pulling you through the ground to the center of Earth? Choose the best answer. (a) The density of matter is too great. (b) The positive nuclei of your body's atoms repel the positive nuclei of the atoms of the ground. (c) The density of the ground is greater than the density of your body. (d) Atoms are bound together by chemical bonds. (e) Electrons on the ground's surface and the surface of your feet repel one another.

12. Three charged particles are arranged on corners of a square as shown in Figure MCQ15.12, with charge $-Q$ on both the particle at the upper left corner and the particle at the lower right corner, and charge $+2Q$ on the particle at the lower left corner. What is the direction of the electric field at the upper right corner, which is a point in empty space? (a) upward and to the right (b) to the right (c) downward (d) downward and to the left (e) The field is exactly zero at that point.

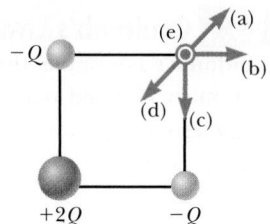

Figure MCQ15.12 Multiple-Choice Questions 12 and 13.

13. Suppose the $+2Q$ charge at the lower left corner of Figure MCQ15.12 is removed. Which statement is true about the magnitude of the electric field at the upper right corner? (a) It becomes larger. (b) It becomes smaller. (c) It stays the same. (d) It changes unpredictably. (e) It is zero.

14. A metallic coin is given a positive electric charge. Does its mass (a) increase measurably, (b) increase by an amount too small to measure directly, (c) stay unchanged, (d) decrease by an amount too small to measure directly, or (e) decrease measurably?

■ CONCEPTUAL QUESTIONS

WebAssign The conceptual questions in this chapter may be assigned online in Enhanced WebAssign.

1. A glass object receives a positive charge of +3 nC by rubbing it with a silk cloth. In the rubbing process, have protons been added to the object or have electrons been removed from it?

2. Explain from an atomic viewpoint why charge is usually transferred by electrons.

3. A person is placed in a large, hollow metallic sphere that is insulated from ground. If a large charge is placed on the sphere, will the person be harmed upon touching the inside of the sphere?

4. Why must hospital personnel wear special conducting shoes while working around oxygen in an operating

room? What might happen if the personnel wore shoes with rubber soles?

5. (a) Would life be different if the electron were positively charged and the proton were negatively charged? (b) Does the choice of signs have any bearing on physical and chemical interactions? Explain your answers.

6. If a suspended object *A* is attracted to a charged object *B*, can we conclude that *A* is charged? Explain.

7. Explain how a positively charged object can be used to leave another metallic object with a net negative charge. Discuss the motion of charges during the process.

8. Consider point *A* in Figure CQ15.8 located an arbitrary distance from two point charges in otherwise empty space. (a) Is it possible for an electric field to exist at point *A* in empty space? (b) Does charge exist at this point? (c) Does a force exist at this point?

Figure CQ15.8

9. A student stands on a thick piece of insulating material, places her hand on top of a Van de Graaff generator, and then turns on the generator. Does she receive a shock?

10. In fair weather, there is an electric field at the surface of the Earth, pointing down into the ground. What is the sign of the electric charge on the ground in this situation?

11. A charged comb often attracts small bits of dry paper that then fly away when they touch the comb. Explain why that occurs.

12. Why should a ground wire be connected to the metal support rod for a television antenna?

13. There are great similarities between electric and gravitational fields. A room can be electrically shielded so that there are no electric fields in the room by surrounding it with a conductor. Can a room be gravitationally shielded? Explain.

14. A spherical surface surrounds a point charge *q*. Describe what happens to the total flux through the surface if (a) the charge is tripled, (b) the volume of the sphere is doubled, (c) the surface is changed to a cube, (d) the charge is moved to another location inside the surface, and (e) the charge is moved outside the surface.

15. If more electric field lines leave a Gaussian surface than enter it, what can you conclude about the net charge enclosed by that surface?

16. A student who grew up in a tropical country and is studying in the United States may have no experience with static electricity sparks and shocks until his or her first American winter. Explain.

■ PROBLEMS

ENHANCED **WebAssign** The problems in this chapter may be assigned online in Enhanced WebAssign. Selected problems also have Watch It video solutions.

1. denotes straightforward problem; **2.** denotes intermediate problem;
3. denotes challenging problem
1. denotes full solution available in *Student Solutions Manual/ Study Guide*

1. denotes problems most often assigned in Enhanced WebAssign
BIO denotes biomedical problems
GP denotes guided problems
M denotes Master It tutorial available in Enhanced WebAssign
Q|C denotes asking for quantitative and conceptual reasoning
S denotes symbolic reasoning problem

15.3 Coulomb's Law

1. **Q|C** A 7.50-nC charge is located 1.80 m from a 4.20-nC charge. (a) Find the magnitude of the electrostatic force that one particle exerts on the other. (b) Is the force attractive or repulsive?

2. A charged particle *A* exerts a force of 2.62 N to the right on charged particle *B* when the particles are 13.7 mm apart. Particle *B* moves straight away from *A* to make the distance between them 17.7 mm. What vector force does particle *B* then exert on *A*?

3. **Q|C** Two metal balls *A* and *B* of negligible radius are floating at rest on Space Station Freedom between two metal bulkheads, connected by a taut nonconducting thread of length 2.00 m. Ball *A* carries charge *q*, and ball *B* carries charge 2*q*. Each ball is 1.00 m away from

a bulkhead. (a) If the tension in the string is 2.50 N, what is the magnitude of *q*? (b) What happens to the system as time passes? Explain.

4. A small sphere of mass $m = 7.50$ g and charge $q_1 = 32.0$ nC is attached to the end of a string and hangs vertically as in Figure P15.4. A second charge of equal mass and charge $q_2 = -58.0$ nC is located below the first charge a distance $d = 2.00$ cm below the first charge as in Figure P15.4. (a) Find the tension in the string. (b) If the string can withstand a maximum tension of 0.180 N, what is the smallest value *d* can have before the string breaks?

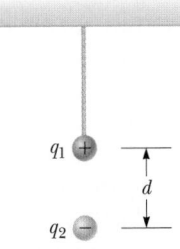

Figure P15.4

5. The nucleus of ^{8}Be, which consists of 4 protons and 4 neutrons, is very unstable and spontaneously breaks into two alpha particles (helium nuclei, each consisting of 2 protons and 2 neutrons). (a) What is the force between the two alpha particles when they are 5.00×10^{-15} m apart, and (b) what is the initial magnitude of the acceleration of the alpha particles due to this force? Note that the mass of an alpha particle is 4.002 6 u.

6. **BIO** A molecule of DNA (deoxyribonucleic acid) is 2.17 μm long. The ends of the molecule become singly ionized: negative on one end, positive on the other. The helical molecule acts like a spring and compresses 1.00% upon becoming charged. Determine the effective spring constant of the molecule.

7. A small sphere of charge 0.800 μC hangs from the end of a spring as in Figure P15.7a. When another small sphere of charge -0.600 μC is held beneath the first sphere as in Figure P15.7b, the spring stretches by $d = 3.50$ cm from its original length and reaches a new equilibrium position with a separation between the charges of $r = 5.00$ cm. What is the force constant of the spring?

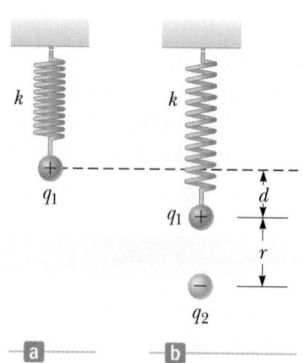

Figure P15.7

8. **S** Four point charges are at the corners of a square of side a as shown in Figure P15.8. Determine the magnitude and direction of the resultant electric force on q, with k_e, q, and a left in symbolic form.

Figure P15.8

9. Two small identical conducting spheres are placed with their centers 0.30 m apart. One is given a charge of 12×10^{-9} C, the other a charge of -18×10^{-9} C. (a) Find the electrostatic force exerted on one sphere by the other. (b) The spheres are connected by a conducting wire. Find the electrostatic force between the two after equilibrium is reached, where both spheres have the same charge.

10. Calculate the magnitude and direction of the Coulomb force on each of the three charges shown in Figure P15.10.

Figure P15.10 Problems 10 and 18.

11. **M** Three charges are arranged as shown in Figure P15.11. Find the magnitude and direction of the electrostatic force on the charge at the origin.

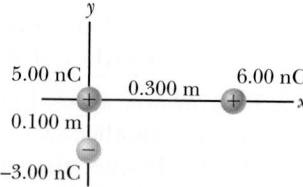

Figure P15.11

12. A positive charge $q_1 = 2.70$ μC on a frictionless horizontal surface is attached to a spring of force constant k as in Figure P15.12. When a charge of $q_2 = -8.60$ μC is placed 9.50 cm away from the positive charge, the spring stretches by 5.00 mm, reducing the distance between charges to $d = 9.00$ cm. Find the value of k.

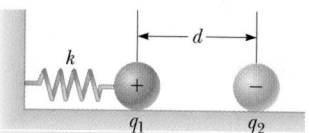

Figure P15.12

13. Three point charges are located at the corners of an equilateral triangle as in Figure P15.13. Find the magnitude and direction of the net electric force on the 2.00 μC charge.

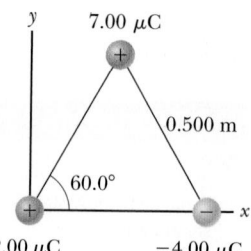

Figure P15.13 Problems 13 and 24.

14. Two identical metal blocks resting on a frictionless horizontal surface are connected by a light metal spring having constant $k = 100$ N/m and unstretched length $L_i = 0.400$ m as in Figure P15.14a. A charge Q is slowly placed on each block causing the spring to stretch to an equilibrium length $L = 0.500$ m as in Figure P15.14b. Determine the value of Q, modeling the blocks as charged particles.

Figure P15.14

15. Two small metallic spheres, each of mass $m = 0.20$ g, are suspended as pendulums by light strings from a common point as shown in Figure P15.15. The spheres are given the same electric charge, and it is found that they come to equilibrium when each string is at an angle of $\theta = 5.0°$ with the vertical. If each string has length $L = 30.0$ cm, what is the magnitude of the charge on each sphere?

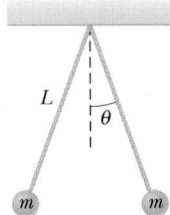

Figure P15.15

16. GP Particle A of charge 3.00×10^{-4} C is at the origin, particle B of charge -6.00×10^{-4} C is at (4.00 m, 0) and particle C of charge 1.00×10^{-4} C is at (0, 3.00 m). (a) What is the x-component of the electric force exerted by A on C? (b) What is the y-component of the force exerted by A on C? (c) Find the magnitude of the force exerted by B on C. (d) Calculate the x-component of the force exerted by B on C. (e) Calculate the y-component of the force exerted by B on C. (f) Sum the two x-components to obtain the resultant x-component of the electric force acting on C. (g) Repeat part (f) for the y-component. (h) Find the magnitude and direction of the resultant electric force acting on C.

15.4 The Electric Field

17. A small object of mass 3.80 g and charge -18 μC is suspended motionless above the ground when immersed in a uniform electric field perpendicular to the ground. What is the magnitude and direction of the electric field?

18. (a) Determine the electric field strength at a point 1.00 cm to the left of the middle charge shown in Figure P15.10. (b) If a charge of -2.00 μC is placed at this point, what are the magnitude and direction of the force on it?

19. An electric field of magnitude 5.25×10^5 N/C points due south at a certain location. Find the magnitude and direction of the force on a -6.00 μC charge at this location.

20. An electron is accelerated by a constant electric field of magnitude 300 N/C. (a) Find the acceleration of the electron. (b) Use the equations of motion with constant acceleration to find the electron's speed after 1.00×10^{-8} s, assuming it starts from rest.

21. A small block of mass m and charge Q is placed on an insulated, frictionless, inclined plane of angle θ as in Figure P15.21. An electric field is applied parallel to the incline. (a) Find an expression for the magnitude of the electric field that enables the block to remain at rest. (b) If $m = 5.40$ g, $Q = -7.00$ μC, and

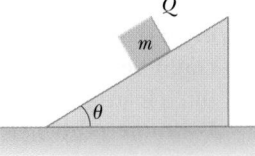

Figure P15.21

$\theta = 25.0°$, determine the magnitude and direction of the electric field that enables the block to remain at rest on the incline.

22. A small sphere of charge $q = +68$ μC and mass $m = 5.8$ g is attached to a light string and placed in a uniform electric field $\vec{E}$ that makes an angle $\theta = 37°$ with the horizontal. The opposite end of the string is attached to a wall and the sphere is in static equilibrium when the string is horizontal as in Figure P15.22. (a) Construct a free body diagram for the sphere. Find (b) the magnitude of the electric field and (c) the tension in the string.

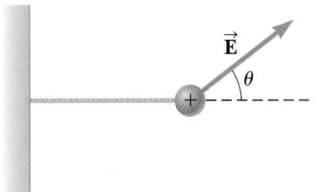

Figure P15.22

23. M A proton accelerates from rest in a uniform electric field of 640 N/C. At some later time, its speed is 1.20×10^6 m/s. (a) Find the magnitude of the acceleration of the proton. (b) How long does it take the proton to reach this speed? (c) How far has it moved in that interval? (d) What is its kinetic energy at the later time?

24. QIC (a) Find the magnitude and direction of the electric field at the position of the 2.00 μC charge in Figure P15.13. (b) How would the electric field at that point be affected if the charge there were doubled? Would the magnitude of the electric force be affected?

25. S Two equal positive charges are at opposite corners of a trapezoid as in Figure P15.25. Find symbolic expressions for the components of the electric field at the point P.

Figure P15.25

26. Three point charges are located on a circular arc as shown in Figure P15.26. (a) What is the total electric field at P, the center of the arc? (b) Find the electric force that would be exerted on a -5.00-nC charge placed at P.

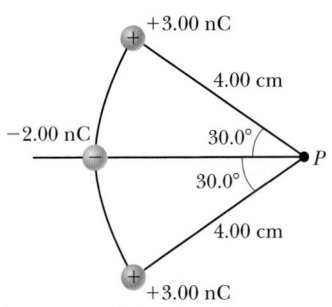

Figure P15.26

27. In Figure P15.27 determine the point (other than infinity) at which the total electric field is zero.

Figure P15.27

28. Three charges are at the corners of an equilateral triangle, as shown in Figure P15.28. Calculate the electric field at a point midway between the two charges on the x-axis.

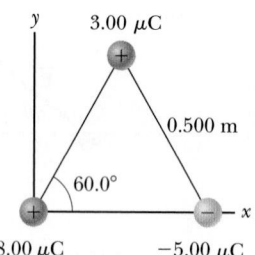

Figure P15.28

29. Three identical charges ($q = -5.0\ \mu C$) lie along a circle of radius 2.0 m at angles of 30°, 150°, and 270°, as shown in Figure P15.29. What is the resultant electric field at the center of the circle?

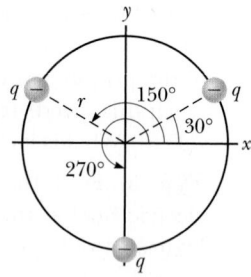

Figure P15.29

15.5 Electric Field Lines

15.6 Conductors in Electrostatic Equilibrium

30. Figure P15.30 shows the electric field lines for two point charges separated by a small distance. (a) Determine the ratio q_1/q_2. (b) What are the signs of q_1 and q_2?

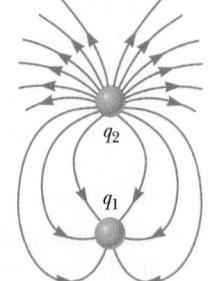

Figure P15.30

31. (a) Sketch the electric field lines around an isolated point charge $q > 0$. (b) Sketch the electric field pattern around an isolated negative point charge of magnitude $-2q$.

32. (a) Sketch the electric field pattern around two positive point charges of magnitude 1 μC placed close together. (b) Sketch the electric field pattern around two negative point charges of $-2\ \mu C$, placed close together. (c) Sketch the pattern around two point charges of $+1\ \mu C$ and $-2\ \mu C$, placed close together.

33. Two point charges are a small distance apart. (a) Sketch the electric field lines for the two if one has a charge four times that of the other and both charges are positive. (b) Repeat for the case in which both charges are negative.

34. **S** Three equal positive charges are at the corners of an equilateral triangle of side a as in Figure P15.34. Assume the three charges together create an electric field. (a) Sketch the electric field lines in the plane of the charges. (b) Find the location of one point (other than ∞) where the electric field is zero. What are (c) the magnitude and (d) the direction of the electric field at P due to the two charges at the base?

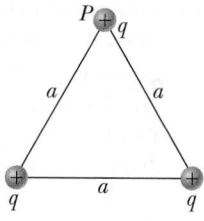

Figure P15.34

35. Refer to Figure 15.20. The charge lowered into the center of the hollow conductor has a magnitude of 5 μC. Find the magnitude and sign of the charge on the inside and outside of the hollow conductor when the charge is as shown in (a) Figure 15.20a, (b) Figure 15.20b, (c) Figure 15.20c, and (d) Figure 15.20d.

15.8 The Van de Graaff Generator

36. The dome of a Van de Graaff generator receives a charge of 2.0×10^{-4} C. Find the strength of the electric field (a) inside the dome, (b) at the surface of the dome, assuming it has a radius of 1.0 m, and (c) 4.0 m from the center of the dome. *Hint:* See Section 15.6 to review properties of conductors in electrostatic equilibrium. Also, use that the points on the surface are outside a spherically symmetric charge distribution; the total charge may be considered to be located at the center of the sphere.

37. If the electric field strength in air exceeds 3.0×10^6 N/C, the air becomes a conductor. Using this fact, determine the maximum amount of charge that can be carried by a metal sphere 2.0 m in radius. (See the hint in Problem 36.)

38. In the Millikan oil-drop experiment illustrated in Figure 15.21, an atomizer (a sprayer with a fine nozzle) is used to introduce many tiny droplets of oil between two oppositely charged parallel metal plates. Some of the droplets pick up one or more excess electrons. The charge on the plates is adjusted so that the electric force on the excess electrons exactly balances the weight of the droplet. The idea is to look for a droplet that has the smallest electric force and assume it has only one excess electron. This strategy lets the observer measure the charge on the electron. Suppose we are using an electric field of 3×10^4 N/C. The charge on one electron is about 1.6×10^{-19} C. Estimate the radius of an oil drop of density 858 kg/m³ for which its weight could be balanced by the electric force of this field on one electron. (Problem 38 is courtesy of E. F. Redish. For more problems of this type, visit www.physics.umd.edu/perg/.)

39. A Van de Graaff generator is charged so that a proton at its surface accelerates radially outward at 1.52×10^{12} m/s². Find (a) the magnitude of the electric force on the proton at that instant and (b) the magnitude and direction of the electric field at the surface of the generator.

15.9 Electric Flux and Gauss's Law

40. A uniform electric field of magnitude $E = 435$ N/C makes an angle of $\theta = 65.0°$ with a plane surface of area $A = 3.50$ m² as in Figure P15.40. Find the electric flux through this surface.

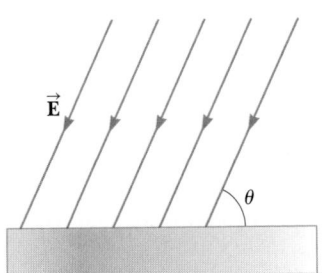

Figure P15.40

41. **M** An electric field of intensity 3.50 kN/C is applied along the x-axis. Calculate the electric flux through a rectangular plane 0.350 m wide and 0.700 m long if (a) the plane is parallel to the yz-plane, (b) the plane is parallel to the xy-plane, and (c) the plane contains the y-axis and its normal makes an angle of 40.0° with the x-axis.

42. **Q|C** The electric field everywhere on the surface of a charged sphere of radius 0.230 m has a magnitude of 575 N/C and points radially outward from the center of the sphere. (a) What is the net charge on the sphere? (b) What can you conclude about the nature and distribution of charge inside the sphere?

43. **S** Four closed surfaces, S_1 through S_4, together with the charges $-2Q$, Q, and $-Q$, are sketched in Figure P15.43. (The colored lines are the intersections of the surfaces with the page.) Find the electric flux through each surface.

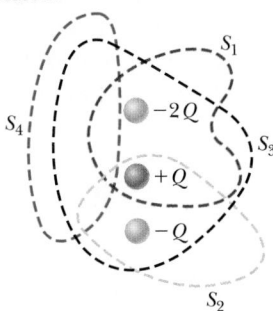

Figure P15.43

44. A charge $q = +5.80$ μC is located at the center of a regular tetrahedron (a four-sided surface) as in Figure P15.44. Find (a) the total electric flux through the tetrahedron and (b) the electric flux through one face of the tetrahedron.

Figure P15.44

45. A point charge q is located at the center of a spherical shell of radius a that has a charge $-q$ uniformly distributed on its surface. Find the electric field (a) for all points outside the spherical shell and (b) for a point inside the shell a distance r from the center.

46. **Q|C** A charge of 1.70×10^2 μC is at the center of a cube of edge 80.0 cm. No other charges are nearby. (a) Find the flux through the whole surface of the cube. (b) Find the flux through each face of the cube. (c) Would your answers to parts (a) or (b) change if the charge were not at the center? Explain.

47. Suppose the conducting spherical shell of Figure 15.29 carries a charge of 3.00 nC and that a charge of -2.00 nC is at the center of the sphere. If $a = 2.00$ m and $b = 2.40$ m, find the electric field at (a) $r = 1.50$ m, (b) $r = 2.20$ m, and (c) $r = 2.50$ m. (d) What is the charge distribution on the sphere?

48. **S** A very large nonconducting plate lying in the xy-plane carries a charge per unit area of σ. A second such plate located at $z = 2.00$ cm and oriented parallel to the xy-plane carries a charge per unit area of -2σ. Find the electric field (a) for $z < 0$, (b) $0 < z < 2.00$ cm, and (c) $z > 2.00$ cm.

Additional Problems

49. In deep space two spheres each of radius 5.00 m are connected by a 3.00×10^2 m nonconducting cord. If a uniformly distributed charge of 35.0 mC resides on the surface of each sphere, calculate the tension in the cord.

50. **Q|C** A nonconducting, thin plane sheet of charge carries a uniform charge per unit area of 5.20 μC/m² as in Figure 15.30. (a) Find the electric field at a distance of 8.70 cm from the plate. (b) Explain whether your result changes as the distance from the sheet is varied.

51. Three point charges are aligned along the x-axis as shown in Figure P15.51. Find the electric field at the position $x = +2.0$ m, $y = 0$.

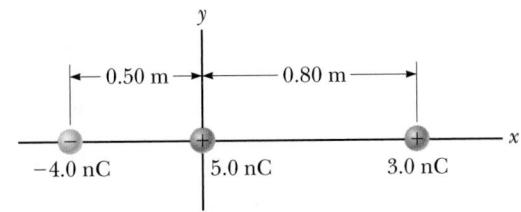

Figure P15.51

52. **M** A small plastic ball of mass $m = 2.00$ g is suspended by a string of length $L = 20.0$ cm in a uniform electric field, as shown in Figure P15.52. If the ball is in

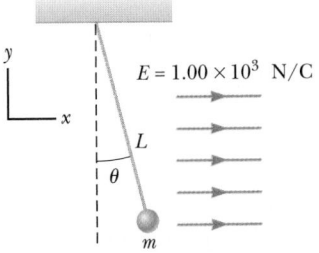

Figure P15.52

equilibrium when the string makes a $\theta = 15.0°$ angle with the vertical as indicated, what is the net charge on the ball?

53. (a) Two identical point charges $+q$ are located on the y-axis at $y = +a$ and $y = -a$. What is the electric field along the x-axis at $x = b$? (b) A circular ring of charge of radius a has a total positive charge Q distributed uniformly around it. The ring is in the $x = 0$ plane with its center at the origin. What is the electric field along the x-axis at $x = b$ due to the ring of charge? *Hint:* Consider the charge Q to consist of many pairs of identical point charges positioned at the ends of diameters of the ring.

54. **S** The electrons in a particle beam each have a kinetic energy K. Find the magnitude of the electric field that will stop these electrons in a distance d, expressing the answer symbolically in terms of K, e, and d. Should the electric field point in the direction of the motion of the electron, or should it point in the opposite direction?

55. **S** A point charge $+2Q$ is at the origin and a point charge $-Q$ is located along the x-axis at $x = d$ as in Figure P15.55. Find symbolic expressions for the components of the net force on a third point charge $+Q$ located along the y-axis at $y = d$.

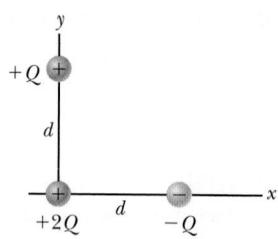

Figure P15.55

56. **Q|C** A 1.00-g cork ball having a positive charge of 2.00 mC is suspended vertically on a 0.500-m-long light string in the presence of a uniform downward-directed electric field of magnitude $E = 1.00 \times 10^5$ N/C as in Figure P15.56. If the ball is displaced slightly from the vertical, it oscillates like a simple pendulum. (a) Determine the period of the ball's oscillation. (b) Should gravity be included in the calculation for part (a)? Explain.

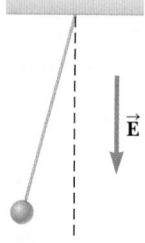

Figure P15.56

57. Two 2.0-g spheres are suspended by 10.0-cm-long light strings (Fig. P15.57). A uniform electric field is applied in the x-direction. If the spheres have charges of -5.0×10^{-8} C and $+5.0 \times 10^{-8}$ C, determine the electric field intensity that enables the spheres to be in equilibrium at $\theta = 10°$.

Figure P15.57

58. **Q|C** A point charge of magnitude 5.00 μC is at the origin of a coordinate system, and a charge of -4.00 μC is

at the point $x = 1.00$ m. There is a point on the x-axis, at x less than infinity, where the electric field goes to zero. (a) Show by conceptual arguments that this point cannot be located between the charges. (b) Show by conceptual arguments that the point cannot be at any location between $x = 0$ and negative infinity. (c) Show by conceptual arguments that the point must be between $x = 1.00$ m and $x = $ positive infinity. (d) Use the values given to find the point and show that it is consistent with your conceptual argument.

59. Two hard rubber spheres, each of mass $m = 15.0$ g, are rubbed with fur on a dry day and are then suspended with two insulating strings of length $L = 5.00$ cm whose support points are a distance $d = 3.00$ cm from each other as shown in Figure P15.59. During the rubbing process, one sphere receives exactly twice the charge of the other. They are observed to hang at equilibrium,

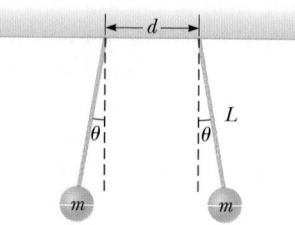

Figure P15.59

each at an angle of $\theta = 10.0°$ with the vertical. Find the amount of charge on each sphere.

60. Two small beads having positive charges $q_1 = 3q$ and $q_2 = q$ are fixed at the opposite ends of a horizontal insulating rod of length $d = 1.50$ m. The bead with charge q_1 is at the origin. As shown in Figure P15.60, a

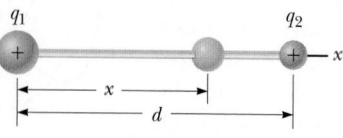

Figure P15.60

third small charged bead is free to slide on the rod. At what position x is the third bead in equilibrium?

61. **M** A solid conducting sphere of radius 2.00 cm has a charge of 8.00 μC. A conducting spherical shell of inner radius 4.00 cm and outer radius 5.00 cm is concentric with the solid sphere and has a charge of -4.00 μC. Find the electric field at (a) $r = 1.00$ cm, (b) $r = 3.00$ cm, (c) $r = 4.50$ cm, and (d) $r = 7.00$ cm from the center of this charge configuration.

62. Three identical point charges, each of mass $m = 0.100$ kg, hang from three strings, as shown in Figure P15.62. If the lengths of the left and right strings are each $L = 30.0$ cm and if the angle θ is $45.0°$, determine the value of q.

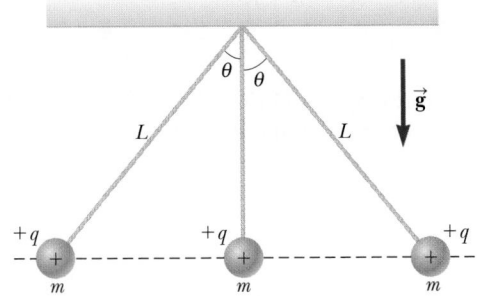

Figure P15.62

63. Each of the electrons in a particle beam has a kinetic energy of 1.60×10^{-17} J. (a) What is the magnitude of the uniform electric field (pointing in the direction of the electrons' movement) that will stop these electrons in a distance of 10.0 cm? (b) How long will it take to stop the electrons? (c) After the electrons stop, what will they do? Explain.

64. Protons are projected with an initial speed $v_0 = 9\,550$ m/s into a region where a uniform electric field of magnitude $E = 720$ N/C is present (Fig. P15.64). The protons are to hit a target that lies a horizontal distance of 1.27 mm from the point where the protons are launched. Find (a) the two projection angles θ that will result in a hit and (b) the total duration of flight for each of the two trajectories.

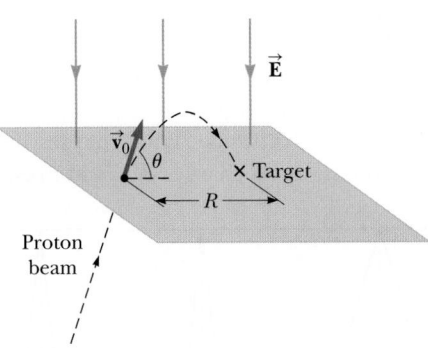

Figure P15.64

■ AP* REVIEW QUESTIONS

1. A rubber rod is rubbed with 2 pieces of fur and then a piece of flannel. If the charges on the fur pieces are $+2\ \mu C$ and $+3\ \mu C$, and the charge on the rubber rod is $-12\ \mu C$, what is the charge on the flannel?

   (A) $+5\ \mu C$

   (B) $-5\ \mu C$

   (C) $+7\ \mu C$

   (D) $-7\ \mu C$

   (E) More information is needed

2. The following diagrams show charges interacting. What are the signs on charges a, b, and c respectively?

   (A) $+, +, +$

   (B) $-, -, -$

   (C) $+, +, -$

   (D) $-, -, +$

   (E) Both (C) and (D) are possible

3. Two negative charges, $q_1 = -4\ \mu C$ and $q_2 = -7\ \mu C$, are placed on the x-axis at 1 cm and 9 cm respectively. In what region does a charge $+q_3$ need to be placed so that it will be in equilibrium?

   (A) $x < 1$ cm

   (B) 1 cm $< x < 5$ cm

   (C) 5 cm $< x < 9$ cm

   (D) $x > 9$ cm

   (E) not possible for q_3 to be in equilibrium

4. Two charges, $q_1 = +14\ \mu C$ and $q_2 = -5\ \mu C$, are placed on the x-axis at 0 m and 4 m respectively, as shown on the diagram above. What is the magnitude and direction of the force on a third charge, $q_3 = +7\ \mu C$, located at 7 m?

   (A) 17 mN right

   (B) 17 mN left

   (C) 53 mN right

   (D) 53 mN left

   (E) 0 N

5. Two charges, $q_1 = +3\ \mu C$ and $q_2 = -5\ \mu C$, are placed on the x-axis at 0 m and 4 m respectively, as shown on the diagram above. What is the magnitude and direction of the electric field at point A?

   (A) 5×10^3 N/C right

   (B) 3.2×10^4 N/C left

   (C) 3.2×10^4 N/C right

   (D) 2.2×10^4 N/C left

   (E) 2.2×10^4 N/C right

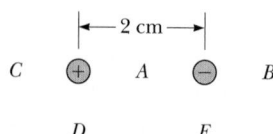

6. A proton and a neutron are placed 2 cm apart. At which location on the diagram would the electric field lines be pointing directly toward the right?

   (A) A

   (B) B

   (C) C

   (D) D

   (E) E

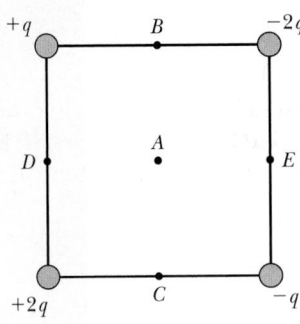

7. Two protons are placed 2 cm apart. At which location is the electric field zero?

(A) *A*

(B) *B*

(C) *C*

(D) *D*

(E) *E*

Questions 8 and 9

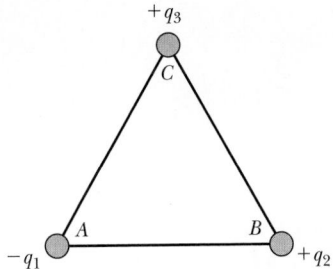

8. Three charges are placed on the corners of an equilateral triangle, as shown in the diagram above. What is the direction of the electric field at point *C*?

(A) ↙

(B) ↖

(C) ←

(D) →

(E) ↘

9. Three charges are placed on the corners of an equilateral triangle, as shown in the diagram above. What is the direction of the electric force at point *A*?

(A) ↗

(B) →

(C) ←

(D) ↗

(E) →

10. Four charges are placed on the corners of a square, as shown above. Where is the electric field zero?

(A) *A* only

(B) *B* and *C*

(C) *C*, *D*, and *E*

(D) *B*, *C*, *D*, and *E*

(E) Electric field is non-zero at all locations *A–E* on the diagram

11. A rod is suspended on a string. It is attracted to a neutral wall and a negatively charged object. What is true about the rod?

(A) It is positive.

(B) It is negative.

(C) It is uncharged.

(D) It may be positive or uncharged.

(E) It may be negative or uncharged.

12. Two negative charges, $q_1 = -8 \ \mu C$ and $q_2 = -6 \mu C$, are located on the *x*-axis at the origin and 8 cm respectively, as shown in the diagram above. In what region would a positive charge $+q_3$ have to be placed to have the net electric field at $q_3 = 0$?

(A) $x < 0$ cm

(B) 0 cm $< x < 4$ cm

(C) $x = 4$ cm

(D) 4 cm $< x < 8$ cm

(E) $x > 8$ cm

The world's largest air-insulated Van de Graaff generator produces bolts of lightning indoors at the Museum of Science in Boston. The discharges occur when the voltage difference gets large enough to ionize the air, an instance of dielectric breakdown.

Yoshiki Hase, Courtesy Museum of Science, Boston

16 Electrical Energy and Capacitance

The concept of potential energy was first introduced in Chapter 5 in connection with the conservative forces of gravity and springs. By using the principle of conservation of energy, we were often able to avoid working directly with forces when solving problems. Here we learn that the potential energy concept is also useful in the study of electricity. Because the Coulomb force is conservative, we can define an electric potential energy corresponding to that force. In addition, we define an electric potential—the potential energy per unit charge—corresponding to the electric field.

With the concept of electric potential in hand, we can begin to understand electric circuits, starting with an investigation of common circuit elements called capacitors. These simple devices store electrical energy and have found uses virtually everywhere, from etched circuits on a microchip to the creation of enormous bursts of power in fusion experiments.

16.1 Potential Difference and Electric Potential

Electric potential energy and electric potential are closely related concepts. The electric potential turns out to be just the electric potential energy per unit charge. This relationship is similar to that between electric force and the electric field, which is the electric force per unit charge.

Work and Electric Potential Energy

Recall from Chapter 5 that the work done by a conservative force $\vec{F}$ on an object depends only on the initial and final positions of the object and not on the path taken between those two points. This, in turn, means that a potential energy function *PE* exists. As we have seen, potential energy is a scalar quantity with the change in potential energy equal by definition to the negative of the work done by the conservative force: $\Delta PE = PE_f - PE_i = -W_F$.

Both the Coulomb force law and the universal law of gravity are proportional to $1/r^2$. Because they have the same mathematical form and because the gravity force is conservative, it follows that **the Coulomb force is also conservative.** As with gravity, an electrical potential energy function can be associated with this force.

To make these ideas more quantitative, imagine a small positive charge placed at point *A* in a *uniform* electric field $\vec{\mathbf{E}}$, as in Figure 16.1. For simplicity, we first consider only constant electric fields and charges that move parallel to that field in one dimension (taken to be the *x*-axis). The electric field between equally and oppositely charged parallel plates is an example of a field that is approximately constant. (See Chapter 15.) As the charge moves from point *A* to point *B* under the influence of the electric field $\vec{\mathbf{E}}$, the work done on the charge by the electric field is equal to the part of the electric force $q\vec{\mathbf{E}}$ acting parallel to the displacement times the displacement $\Delta x = x_f - x_i$:

$$W_{AB} = F_x \Delta x = qE_x(x_f - x_i)$$

In this expression q is the charge and E_x is the vector component of $\vec{\mathbf{E}}$ in the *x*-direction (*not* the magnitude of $\vec{\mathbf{E}}$). Unlike the magnitude of $\vec{\mathbf{E}}$, the component E_x can be positive or negative, depending on the direction of $\vec{\mathbf{E}}$, although in Figure 16.1 E_x is positive. Finally, note that the displacement, like q and E_x, can also be either positive or negative, depending on the direction of the displacement.

The preceding expression for the work done by an electric field on a charge moving in one dimension is valid for both positive and negative charges and for constant electric fields pointing in *any* direction. When numbers are substituted with correct signs, the overall correct sign automatically results. In some books the expression $W = qEd$ is used, instead, where E is the magnitude of the electric field and d is the distance the particle travels. The weakness of this formulation is that it doesn't allow, mathematically, for negative electric work on positive charges, nor for positive electric work on negative charges! Nonetheless, the expression is easy to remember and useful for finding magnitudes: the magnitude of the work done by a constant electric field on a charge moving parallel to the field is always given by $|W| = |q|Ed$.

We can substitute our definition of electric work into the work–energy theorem (assume other forces are absent):

$$W = qE_x \Delta x = \Delta KE$$

The electric force is conservative, so the electric work depends only on the end-points of the path, *A* and *B*, not on the path taken. Therefore, as the charge accelerates to the right in Figure 16.1, it gains kinetic energy and loses an equal amount of potential energy. Recall from Chapter 5 that **the work done by a conservative force can be reinterpreted as the negative of the change in a potential energy associated with that force.** This interpretation motivates the definition of the change in electric potential energy:

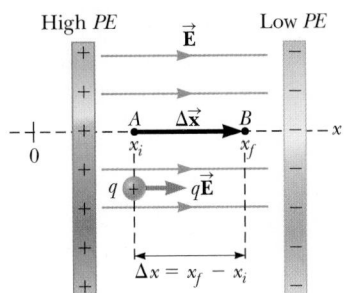

Figure 16.1 When a charge q moves in a uniform electric field $\vec{\mathbf{E}}$ from point *A* to point *B*, the work done on the charge by the electric force is $qE_x \Delta x$.

◀ Change in electric potential energy

The change in the electric potential energy, ΔPE, of a system consisting of an object of charge q moving through a displacement Δx in a constant electric field $\vec{\mathbf{E}}$ is given by

$$\Delta PE = -W_{AB} = -qE_x \Delta x \qquad \text{[16.1]}$$

where E_x is the *x*-component of the electric field and $\Delta x = x_f - x_i$ is the displacement of the charge along the *x*-axis.

SI unit: joule (J)

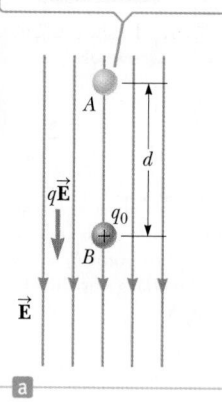

When a positive test charge moves from A to B, the electric potential energy decreases.

a

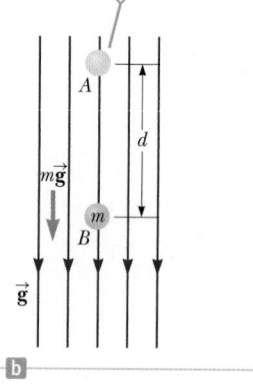

When an object with mass moves from A to B, the gravitational potential energy decreases.

b

Figure 16.2 (a) When the electric field $\vec{E}$ is directed downward, point B is at a lower electric potential than point A. (b) An object of mass m moves in the direction of the gravitational field $\vec{g}$.

Although potential energy can be defined for any electric field, **Equation 16.1 is valid only for the case of a uniform (i.e., constant) electric field, for a particle that undergoes a displacement along a given axis (here called the x-axis).** Because the electric field is conservative, the change in potential energy doesn't depend on the path. Consequently, it's unimportant whether or not the charge remains on the axis at all times during the displacement: the change in potential energy will be the same. In subsequent sections we will examine situations in which the electric field is not uniform.

Electric and gravitational potential energy can be compared in Figure 16.2. In this figure the electric and gravitational fields are both directed downwards. We see that positive charge in an electric field acts very much like mass in a gravity field: a positive charge at point A falls in the direction of the electric field, just as a positive mass falls in the direction of the gravity field. Let point B be the zero point for potential energy in both Figures 16.2a and 16.2b. From conservation of energy, in falling from point A to point B the positive charge gains kinetic energy equal in magnitude to the loss of electric potential energy:

$$\Delta KE + \Delta PE_{el} = \Delta KE + (0 - |q|Ed) = 0 \quad \rightarrow \quad \Delta KE = |q|Ed$$

The absolute-value signs on q are there only to make explicit that the charge is positive in this case. Similarly, the object in Figure 16.2b gains kinetic energy equal in magnitude to the loss of gravitational potential energy:

$$\Delta KE + \Delta PE_{g} = \Delta KE + (0 - mgd) = 0 \quad \rightarrow \quad \Delta KE = mgd$$

So for positive charges, electric potential energy works very much like gravitational potential energy. In both cases moving an object opposite the direction of the field results in a gain of potential energy, and upon release, the potential energy is converted to the object's kinetic energy.

Electric potential energy differs significantly from gravitational potential energy, however, in that there are two kinds of electrical charge—positive and negative—whereas gravity has only positive "gravitational charge" (i.e., mass). A negatively charged particle at rest at point A in Figure 16.2a would have to be *pushed* down to point B. To see why, apply the work–energy theorem to a negative charge at rest at point A and assumed to have some speed v on arriving at point B:

$$W = \Delta KE + \Delta PE_{el} = \left(\tfrac{1}{2}mv^2 - 0\right) + \left[0 - (-|q|Ed)\right]$$
$$W = \tfrac{1}{2}mv^2 + |q|Ed$$

Notice that the negative charge, $-|q|$, unlike the positive charge, had a positive change in electric potential energy in moving from point A to point B. If the negative charge has any speed at point B, the kinetic energy corresponding to that speed is also positive. Because both terms on the right-hand side of the work–energy equation are positive, there is no way of getting the negative charge from point A to point B without doing positive work W on it. In fact, if the negative charge is simply released at point A, it will "fall" upwards against the direction of the field!

■ Quick Quiz

16.1 If an electron is released from rest in a uniform electric field, does the electric potential energy of the charge–field system (a) increase, (b) decrease, or (c) remain the same?

■ **EXAMPLE 16.1** | **Potential Energy Differences in an Electric Field**

GOAL Illustrate the concept of electric potential energy.

PROBLEM A proton is released from rest at $x = -2.00$ cm in a constant electric field with magnitude 1.50×10^3 N/C, pointing in the positive x-direction. **(a)** Calculate the change in the electric potential energy associated with the proton when it reaches $x = 5.00$ cm. **(b)** An electron is now fired in the same direction from the same position. What is the change in electric potential energy associated with the electron if it reaches $x = 12.0$ cm? **(c)** If the direction of the electric field is reversed and an electron is released from rest at $x = 3.00$ cm, by how much has the electric potential energy changed when the electron reaches $x = 7.00$ cm?

STRATEGY This problem requires a straightforward substitution of given values into the definition of electric potential energy, Equation 16.1.

SOLUTION

(a) Calculate the change in the electric potential energy associated with the proton.

Apply Equation 16.1:

$$\Delta PE = -qE_x \Delta x = -qE_x(x_f - x_i)$$
$$= -(1.60 \times 10^{-19}\text{ C})(1.50 \times 10^3\text{ N/C})$$
$$\times [0.050\,0\text{ m} - (-0.020\,0\text{ m})]$$
$$= \boxed{-1.68 \times 10^{-17}\text{ J}}$$

(b) Find the change in electric potential energy associated with an electron fired from $x = -0.020\,0$ m and reaching $x = 0.120$ m.

Apply Equation 16.1, but in this case note that the electric charge q is negative:

$$\Delta PE = -qE_x \Delta x = -qE_x(x_f - x_i)$$
$$= -(-1.60 \times 10^{-19}\text{ C})(1.50 \times 10^3\text{ N/C})$$
$$\times [(0.120\text{ m} - (-0.020\,0\text{ m})]$$
$$= \boxed{+3.36 \times 10^{-17}\text{ J}}$$

(c) Find the change in potential energy associated with an electron traveling from $x = 3.00$ cm to $x = 7.00$ cm if the direction of the electric field is reversed.

Substitute, but now the electric field points in the negative x-direction, hence carries a minus sign:

$$\Delta PE = -qE_x \Delta x = -qE_x (x_f - x_i)$$
$$= -(-1.60 \times 10^{-19}\text{ C})(-1.50 \times 10^3\text{ N/C})$$
$$\times (0.070\text{ m} - 0.030\text{ m})$$
$$= \boxed{-9.60 \times 10^{-18}\text{ J}}$$

REMARKS Notice that the proton (actually the proton–field system) lost potential energy when it moved in the positive x-direction, whereas the electron gained potential energy when it moved in the same direction. Finding changes in potential energy with the field reversed was only a matter of supplying a minus sign, bringing the total number in this case to three! It's important not to drop any of the signs.

QUESTION 16.1 True or False: When an electron is released from rest in a constant electric field, the change in the electric potential energy associated with the electron becomes more negative with time.

EXERCISE 16.1 Find the change in electric potential energy associated with the electron in part (b) as it goes on from $x = 0.120$ m to $x = -0.180$ m. (Note that the electron must turn around and go back at some point. The location of the turning point is unimportant because changes in potential energy depend only on the endpoints of the path.)

ANSWER -7.20×10^{-17} J

■ EXAMPLE 16.2 | Dynamics of Charged Particles

GOAL Use electric potential energy in conservation of energy problems.

PROBLEM **(a)** Find the speed of the proton at $x = 0.050\,0$ m in part (a) of Example 16.1. **(b)** Find the initial speed of the electron (at $x = -2.00$ cm) in part (b) of Example 16.1 given that its speed has fallen by half when it reaches $x = 0.120$ m.

STRATEGY Apply conservation of energy, solving for the unknown speeds. Part (b) involves two equations: the conservation of energy equation and the condition $v_f = \frac{1}{2}v_i$ for the unknown initial and final speeds. The changes in electric potential energy have already been calculated in Example 16.1.

(Continued)

SOLUTION

(a) Calculate the proton's speed at $x = 0.050$ m.

Use conservation of energy, with an initial speed of zero:

$$\Delta KE + \Delta PE = 0 \quad \rightarrow \quad (\tfrac{1}{2}m_p v^2 - 0) + \Delta PE = 0$$

Solve for v and substitute the change in potential energy found in Example 16.1a:

$$v^2 = -\frac{2}{m_p}\Delta PE$$

$$v = \sqrt{-\frac{2}{m_p}\Delta PE}$$

$$= \sqrt{-\frac{2}{(1.67 \times 10^{-27}\text{ kg})}(-1.68 \times 10^{-17}\text{ J})}$$

$$= \boxed{1.42 \times 10^5 \text{ m/s}}$$

(b) Find the electron's initial speed (at $x = -2.00$ cm) given that its speed has fallen by half at $x = 0.120$ m.

Apply conservation of energy once again, substituting expressions for the initial and final kinetic energies:

$$\Delta KE + \Delta PE = 0$$

$$(\tfrac{1}{2}m_e v_f^2 - \tfrac{1}{2}m_e v_i^2) + \Delta PE = 0$$

Substitute the condition $v_f = \tfrac{1}{2}v_i$ and subtract the change in potential energy from both sides:

$$\tfrac{1}{2}m_e(\tfrac{1}{2}v_i)^2 - \tfrac{1}{2}m_e v_i^2 = -\Delta PE$$

Combine terms and solve for v_i, the initial speed, and substitute the change in potential energy found in Example 16.1b:

$$-\tfrac{3}{8}m_e v_i^2 = -\Delta PE$$

$$v_i = \sqrt{\frac{8\Delta PE}{3m_e}} = \sqrt{\frac{8(3.36 \times 10^{-17}\text{ J})}{3(9.11 \times 10^{-31}\text{ kg})}}$$

$$= \boxed{9.92 \times 10^6 \text{ m/s}}$$

REMARKS Although the changes in potential energy associated with the proton and electron were similar in magnitude, the effect on their speeds differed dramatically. The change in potential energy had a proportionately much greater effect on the much lighter electron than on the proton.

QUESTION 16.2 True or False: If a proton and electron both move through the same displacement in an electric field, the change in potential energy associated with the proton must be equal in magnitude and opposite in sign to the change in potential energy associated with the electron.

EXERCISE 16.2 Refer to Exercise 16.1. Find the electron's speed at $x = -0.180$ m. Note: Use the initial velocity from part (b) of Example 16.2.

ANSWER 1.35×10^7 m/s   The answer is 4.5% of the speed of light.

Electric Potential

In Chapter 15 it was convenient to define an electric field $\vec{\mathbf{E}}$ related to the electric force $\vec{\mathbf{F}} = q\vec{\mathbf{E}}$. In this way the properties of fixed collections of charges could be easily studied, and the force on any particle in the electric field could be obtained simply by multiplying by the particle's charge q. For the same reasons, it's useful to define an *electric potential difference* ΔV related to the potential energy by $\Delta PE = q\Delta V$:

The electric potential difference ΔV between points A and B is the change in electric potential energy as a charge q moves from A to B divided by the charge q:

Potential difference ▶
between two points

$$\Delta V = V_B - V_A = \frac{\Delta PE}{q} \qquad\qquad [16.2]$$

SI unit: joule per coulomb, or volt (J/C, or V)

This definition is completely general, although in many cases calculus would be required to compute the change in potential energy of the system. Because electric potential energy is a scalar quantity, **electric potential is also a scalar quantity**. From Equation 16.2, we see that electric potential difference is a measure of the change in electric potential energy per unit charge. Alternately, the electric potential difference is the work per unit charge that would have to be done by some force to move a charge from point A to point B in the electric field. The SI unit of electric potential is the joule per coulomb, called the volt (V). From the definition of that unit, 1 J of work must be done to move a 1-C charge between two points that are at a potential difference of 1 V. In the process of moving through a potential difference of 1 V, the 1-C charge gains 1 J of energy.

For the special case of a uniform electric field such as that between charged parallel plates, dividing Equation 16.1 by q gives

$$\frac{\Delta PE}{q} = -E_x \Delta x$$

Comparing this equation with Equation 16.2, we find that

$$\Delta V = -E_x \Delta x \qquad\qquad [16.3]$$

Equation 16.3 shows that potential difference also has units of electric field times distance. It then follows that the SI unit of the electric field, the newton per coulomb, can also be expressed as volts per meter:

$$1 \text{ N/C} = 1 \text{ V/m}$$

Because Equation 16.3 is directly related to Equation 16.1, remember that it's valid only for the system consisting of a uniform electric field and a charge moving in one dimension.

Released from rest, positive charges accelerate spontaneously from regions of high potential to low potential. If a positive charge is given some initial velocity in the direction of high potential, it can move in that direction, but will slow and finally turn around, just like a ball tossed upwards in a gravity field. Negative charges do exactly the opposite: released from rest, they accelerate from regions of low potential toward regions of high potential. Work must be done on negative charges to make them go in the direction of lower electric potential.

> **Tip 16.1 Potential and Potential Energy**
>
> Electric potential is characteristic of the field only, independent of a test charge that may be placed in that field. On the other hand, potential energy is a characteristic of the charge-field system due to an interaction between the field and a charge placed in the field.

■ Quick Quiz

16.2 If a negatively charged particle is placed at rest in an electric potential field that increases in the positive x-direction, will the particle (a) accelerate in the positive x-direction, (b) accelerate in the negative x-direction, or (c) remain at rest?

16.3 Figure 16.3 is a graph of an electric potential as a function of position. If a positively charged particle is placed at point A, what will its subsequent motion be? Will it (a) go to the right, (b) go to the left, (c) remain at point A, or (d) oscillate around point B?

16.4 If a negatively charged particle is placed at point B in Figure 16.3 and given a very small kick to the right, what will its subsequent motion be? Will it (a) go to the right and not return, (b) go to the left, (c) remain at point B, or (d) oscillate around point B?

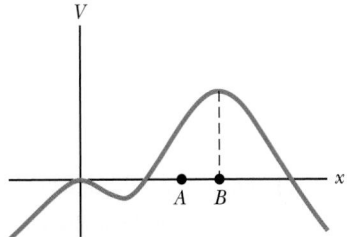

Figure 16.3 (Quick Quizzes 16.3 and 16.4)

APPLICATION
Automobile Batteries

An application of potential difference is the 12-V battery found in an automobile. Such a battery maintains a potential difference across its terminals, with the positive terminal 12 V higher in potential than the negative terminal. In practice the negative terminal is usually connected to the metal body of the car, which can be considered to be at a potential of zero volts. The battery provides the electrical current necessary to operate headlights, a radio, power windows, motors, and so forth. Now consider a charge of +1 C, to be moved around a circuit that contains the battery connected to some of these external devices. As the charge is moved inside the battery from the negative terminal (at 0 V) to the positive terminal (at 12 V), the work done on the charge by the battery is 12 J. Every coulomb of positive charge that leaves the positive terminal of the battery carries an energy of 12 J. As the charge moves through the external circuit toward the negative terminal, it gives up its 12 J of electrical energy to the external devices. When the charge reaches the negative terminal, its electrical energy is zero again. At this point, the battery takes over and restores 12 J of energy to the charge as it is moved from the negative to the positive terminal, enabling it to make another transit of the circuit. The actual amount of charge that leaves the battery each second and traverses the circuit depends on the properties of the external devices, as seen in the next chapter.

■ **EXAMPLE 16.3** | **TV Tubes and Atom Smashers**

GOAL Relate electric potential to an electric field and conservation of energy.

PROBLEM In atom smashers (also known as cyclotrons and linear accelerators) charged particles are accelerated in much the same way they are accelerated in TV tubes: through potential differences. Suppose a proton is injected at a speed of 1.00×10^6 m/s between two plates 5.00 cm apart, as shown in Figure 16.4. The proton subsequently accelerates across the gap and exits through the opening. **(a)** What must the electric potential difference be if the exit speed is to be 3.00×10^6 m/s? **(b)** What is the magnitude of the electric field between the plates, assuming it's constant?

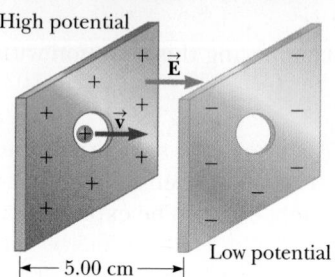

Figure 16.4 (Example 16.3) A proton enters a cavity and accelerates from one charged plate toward the other in an electric field $\vec{E}$.

STRATEGY Use conservation of energy, writing the change in potential energy in terms of the change in electric potential, ΔV, and solve for ΔV. For part (b), solve Equation 16.3 for the electric field.

. . . .

SOLUTION

(a) Find the electric potential yielding the desired exit speed of the proton.

Apply conservation of energy, writing the potential energy in terms of the electric potential:

$$\Delta KE + \Delta PE = \Delta KE + q\,\Delta V = 0$$

Solve the energy equation for the change in potential:

$$\Delta V = -\frac{\Delta KE}{q} = -\frac{\frac{1}{2}m_p v_f^2 - \frac{1}{2}m_p v_i^2}{q} = -\frac{m_p}{2q}\left(v_f^2 - v_i^2\right)$$

Substitute the given values, obtaining the necessary potential difference:

$$\Delta V = -\frac{(1.67 \times 10^{-27}\ \text{kg})}{2(1.60 \times 10^{-19}\ \text{C})}\left[(3.00 \times 10^6\ \text{m/s})^2\right.$$
$$\left. - (1.00 \times 10^6\ \text{m/s})^2\right]$$

$$\Delta V = \boxed{-4.18 \times 10^4\ \text{V}}$$

(b) What electric field must exist between the plates?

Solve Equation 16.3 for the electric field and substitute:

$$E = -\frac{\Delta V}{\Delta x} = \frac{4.18 \times 10^4\ \text{V}}{0.050\ 0\ \text{m}} = \boxed{8.36 \times 10^5\ \text{N/C}}$$

. . . .

REMARKS Systems of such cavities, consisting of alternating positive and negative plates, are used to accelerate charged particles to high speed before smashing them into targets. To prevent a slowing of, say, a positively charged particle after it passes through the negative plate of one cavity and enters the next, the charges on the plates are reversed. Otherwise, the particle would be traveling from the negative plate to a positive plate in the second cavity, and the kinetic energy gained in the previous cavity would be lost in the second.

QUESTION 16.3 True or False: A more massive particle gains less energy in traversing a given potential difference than does a lighter particle.

EXERCISE 16.3 Suppose electrons in a TV tube are accelerated through a potential difference of 2.00×10^4 V from the heated cathode (negative electrode), where they are produced, toward the screen, which also serves as the anode (positive electrode), 25.0 cm away. (a) At what speed would the electrons impact the phosphors on the screen? Assume they accelerate from rest and ignore relativistic effects (Chapter 26). (b) What's the magnitude of the electric field, if it is assumed constant?

ANSWERS   (a) 8.38×10^7 m/s (b) 8.00×10^4 V/m

16.2 Electric Potential and Potential Energy Due to Point Charges

In electric circuits a point of zero electric potential is often defined by grounding (connecting to the Earth) some point in the circuit. For example, if the negative terminal of a 12-V battery were connected to ground, it would be considered to have a potential of zero, whereas the positive terminal would have a potential of +12 V. The potential difference created by the battery, however, is only locally defined. In this section we describe the electric potential of a point charge, which is defined throughout space.

The electric field of a point charge extends throughout space, so its electric potential does, also. The zero point of electric potential could be taken anywhere, but is usually taken to be an infinite distance from the charge, far from its influence and the influence of any other charges. With this choice, the methods of calculus can be used to show that the electric potential created by a point charge q at any distance r from the charge is given by

$$V = k_e \frac{q}{r}$$ [16.4]

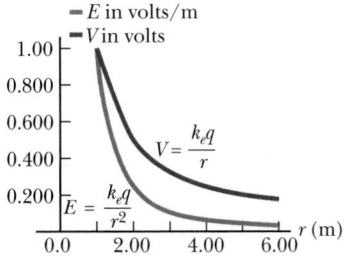

Figure 16.5 Electric field and electric potential versus distance from a point charge of 1.11×10^{-10} C. Note that V is proportional to $1/r$, whereas E is proportional to $1/r^2$.

◀ Electric potential created by a point charge

Equation 16.4 shows that the electric potential, or work per unit charge, required to move a test charge in from infinity to a distance r from a positive point charge q increases as the positive test charge moves closer to q. A plot of Equation 16.4 in Figure 16.5 shows that the potential associated with a point charge decreases as $1/r$ with increasing r, in contrast to the magnitude of the charge's electric field, which decreases as $1/r^2$.

The electric potential of two or more charges is obtained by applying the **superposition principle: the total electric potential at some point P due to several point charges is the algebraic sum of the electric potentials due to the individual charges**. This method is similar to the one used in Chapter 15 to find the resultant electric field at a point in space. Unlike electric field superposition, which involves a sum of vectors, the superposition of electric potentials requires evaluating a sum of scalars. As a result, it's much easier to evaluate the electric potential at some point due to several charges than to evaluate the electric field, which is a vector quantity.

Figure 16.6 is a computer-generated plot of the electric potential associated with an electric dipole, which consists of two charges of equal magnitude but

◀ Superposition principle

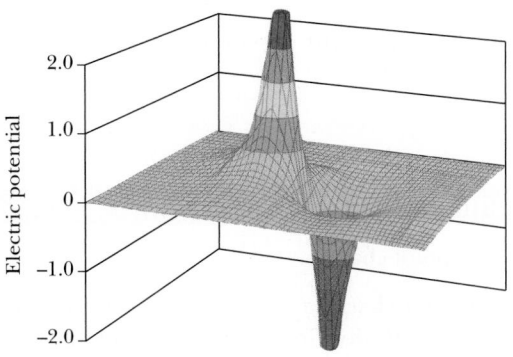

Figure 16.6 The electric potential (in arbitrary units) in the plane containing an electric dipole. Potential is plotted in the vertical dimension.

opposite in sign. The charges lie in a horizontal plane at the center of the potential spikes. The value of the potential is plotted in the vertical dimension. The computer program has added the potential of each charge to arrive at total values of the potential.

Just as in the case of constant electric fields, there is a relationship between electric potential and electric potential energy. If V_1 is the electric potential due to charge q_1 at a point P (Active Fig. 16.7a) the work required to bring charge q_2 from infinity to P without acceleration is $q_2 V_1$. By definition, this work equals the potential energy PE of the two-particle system when the particles are separated by a distance r (Active Fig. 16.7b).

We can therefore express the electrical potential energy of the *pair* of charges as

Potential energy of a pair ▶
of charges

$$PE = q_2 V_1 = k_e \frac{q_1 q_2}{r}$$ [16.5]

If the charges are of the *same* sign, PE is positive. Because like charges repel, positive work must be done on the system by an external agent to force the two charges near each other. Conversely, if the charges are of *opposite* sign, the force is attractive and PE is negative. This means that negative work must be done to prevent unlike charges from accelerating toward each other as they are brought close together.

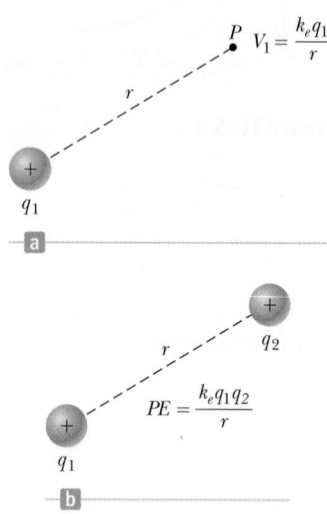

Active Figure 16.7
(a) The electric potential V_1 at P due to the point charge q_1 is $V_1 = k_e q_1/r$.
(b) If a second charge, q_2, is brought from infinity to P, the potential energy of the pair is $PE = k_e q_1 q_2/r$.

■ Quick Quiz

16.5 Consider a collection of charges in a given region and suppose all other charges are distant and have a negligible effect. Further, the electric potential is taken to be zero at infinity. If the electric potential at a given point in the region is zero, which of the following statements must be true? (a) The electric field is zero at that point. (b) The electric potential energy is a minimum at that point. (c) There is no net charge in the region. (d) Some charges in the region are positive, and some are negative. (e) The charges have the same sign and are symmetrically arranged around the given point.

16.6 A spherical balloon contains a positively charged particle at its center. As the balloon is inflated to a larger volume while the charged particle remains at the center, which of the following are true? (a) The electric potential at the surface of the balloon increases. (b) The magnitude of the electric field at the surface of the balloon increases. (c) The electric flux through the balloon remains the same. (d) none of these.

■ PROBLEM-SOLVING STRATEGY

Electric Potential

1. Draw a diagram of all charges and circle the point of interest.
2. Calculate the distance from each charge to the point of interest, labeling it on the diagram.
3. For each charge q, calculate the scalar quantity $V = \dfrac{k_e q}{r}$. *The sign of each charge must be included in your calculations!*
4. Sum all the numbers found in the previous step, obtaining the electric potential at the point of interest.

■ EXAMPLE 16.4 | Finding the Electric Potential

GOAL Calculate the electric potential due to a collection of point charges.

PROBLEM A 5.00-μC point charge is at the origin, and a point charge $q_2 = -2.00\ \mu$C is on the x-axis at (3.00, 0) m, as in Figure 16.8. **(a)** If the electric potential is taken to be zero at infinity, find the electric potential due to these charges at point P with coordinates (0, 4.00) m. **(b)** How much work is required to bring a third point charge of 4.00 μC from infinity to P?

STRATEGY For part (a), the electric potential at P due to each charge can be calculated from $V = k_e q/r$. The electric potential at P is the sum of these two quantities. For part (b), use the work–energy theorem, together with Equation 16.5, recalling that the potential at infinity is taken to be zero.

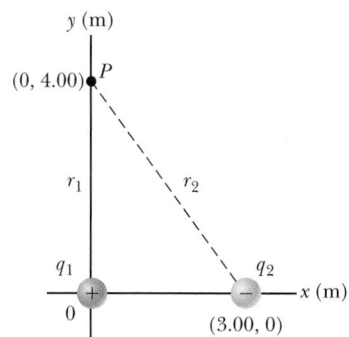

Figure 16.8 (Example 16.4) The electric potential at point P due to the point charges q_1 and q_2 is the algebraic sum of the potentials due to the individual charges.

SOLUTION

(a) Find the electric potential at point P.

Calculate the electric potential at P due to the 5.00-μC charge:

$$V_1 = k_e \frac{q_1}{r_1} = \left(8.99 \times 10^9 \frac{\text{N} \cdot \text{m}^2}{\text{C}^2}\right)\left(\frac{5.00 \times 10^{-6} \text{ C}}{4.00 \text{ m}}\right)$$
$$= 1.12 \times 10^4 \text{ V}$$

Find the electric potential at P due to the -2.00-μC charge:

$$V_2 = k_e \frac{q_2}{r_2} = \left(8.99 \times 10^9 \frac{\text{N} \cdot \text{m}^2}{\text{C}^2}\right)\left(\frac{-2.00 \times 10^{-6} \text{ C}}{5.00 \text{ m}}\right)$$
$$= -0.360 \times 10^4 \text{ V}$$

Sum the two quantities to find the total electric potential at P:

$$V_P = V_1 + V_2 = 1.12 \times 10^4 \text{ V} + (-0.360 \times 10^4 \text{ V})$$
$$= \boxed{7.6 \times 10^3 \text{ V}}$$

(b) Find the work needed to bring the 4.00-μC charge from infinity to P.

Apply the work–energy theorem, with Equation 16.5:

$$W = \Delta PE = q_3 \Delta V = q_3(V_P - V_\infty)$$
$$= (4.00 \times 10^{-6} \text{ C})(7.6 \times 10^3 \text{ V} - 0)$$
$$W = \boxed{3.0 \times 10^{-2} \text{ J}}$$

REMARKS Unlike the electric field, where vector addition is required, the electric potential due to more than one charge can be found with ordinary addition of scalars. Further, notice that the work required to move the charge is equal to the change in electric potential energy. The sum of the work done moving the particle plus the work done by the electric field is zero ($W_{\text{other}} + W_{\text{electric}} = 0$) because the particle starts and ends at rest. Therefore, $W_{\text{other}} = -W_{\text{electric}} = \Delta U_{\text{electric}} = q \Delta V$.

QUESTION 16.4 If q_2 were moved to the right, what would happen to the electric potential V_p at point P? (a) It would increase. (b) It would decrease. (c) It would remain the same.

EXERCISE 16.4 Suppose a charge of -2.00 μC is at the origin and a charge of 3.00 μC is at the point (0, 3.00) m. (a) Find the electric potential at (4.00, 0) m, assuming the electric potential is zero at infinity, and (b) find the work necessary to bring a 4.00 μC charge from infinity to the point (4.00, 0) m.

ANSWERS (a) 8.99×10^2 V (b) 3.60×10^{-3} J

■ EXAMPLE 16.5 | Electric Potential Energy and Dynamics

GOAL Apply conservation of energy and electrical potential energy to a configuration of charges.

PROBLEM Suppose three protons lie on the x-axis, at rest relative to one another at a given instant of time, as in Figure 16.9. If proton q_3 on the right is released while the others are held fixed in place, find a symbolic expression for the proton's speed at infinity and evaluate this speed when $r_0 = 2.00$ fm. (*Note:* 1 fm $= 10^{-15}$ m.)

Figure 16.9 (Example 16.5)

(*Continued*)

STRATEGY First calculate the initial electric potential energy associated with the system of three particles. There will be three terms, one for each interacting pair. Then calculate the final electric potential energy associated with the system when the proton on the right is arbitrarily far away. Because the electric potential energy falls off as $1/r$, two of the terms will vanish. Using conservation of energy then yields the speed of the particle in question.

. . . .

SOLUTION

Calculate the electric potential energy associated with the initial configuration of charges:

$$PE_i = \frac{k_e q_1 q_2}{r_{12}} + \frac{k_e q_1 q_3}{r_{13}} + \frac{k_e q_2 q_3}{r_{23}} = \frac{k_e e^2}{r_0} + \frac{k_e e^2}{2r_0} + \frac{k_e e^2}{r_0}$$

Calculate the electric potential energy associated with the final configuration of charges:

$$PE_f = \frac{k_e q_1 q_2}{r_{12}} = \frac{k_e e^2}{r_0}$$

Write the conservation of energy equation:

$$\Delta KE + \Delta PE = KE_f - KE_i + PE_f - PE_i = 0$$

Substitute appropriate terms:

$$\tfrac{1}{2} m_3 v_3^2 - 0 + \frac{k_e e^2}{r_0} - \left(\frac{k_e e^2}{r_0} + \frac{k_e e^2}{2r_0} + \frac{k_e e^2}{r_0} \right) = 0$$

$$\tfrac{1}{2} m_3 v_3^2 - \left(\frac{k_e e^2}{2r_0} + \frac{k_e e^2}{r_0} \right) = 0$$

Solve for v_3 after combining the two remaining potential energy terms:

$$v_3 = \sqrt{\frac{3 k_e e^2}{m_3 r_0}}$$

Evaluate taking $r_0 = 2.00$ fm:

$$v_3 = \sqrt{\frac{3(8.99 \times 10^9 \ \text{N} \cdot \text{m}^2/\text{C}^2)(1.60 \times 10^{-19} \ \text{C})^2}{(1.67 \times 10^{-27} \ \text{kg})(2.00 \times 10^{-15} \ \text{m})}} = 1.44 \times 10^7 \ \text{m/s}$$

. . . .

REMARKS The difference in the initial and final kinetic energies yields the energy available for motion. This calculation is somewhat contrived because it would be difficult, although not impossible, to arrange such a configuration of protons; it could conceivably occur by chance inside a star.

QUESTION 16.5 If a fourth proton were placed to the right of q_3, how many additional potential energy terms would have to be calculated in the initial configuration?

EXERCISE 16.5 Starting from the initial configuration of three protons, suppose the end two particles are released simultaneously and the middle particle is fixed. Obtain a numerical answer for the speed of the two particles at infinity. (Note that their speeds, by symmetry, must be the same.)

ANSWER $1.31 \times 10^7 \ \text{m/s}$

16.3 Potentials and Charged Conductors

The electric potential at all points on a charged conductor can be determined by combining Equations 16.1 and 16.2. From Equation 16.1, we see that the work done on a charge by electric forces is related to the change in electrical potential energy of the charge by

$$W = -\Delta PE$$

From Equation 16.2, we see that the change in electric potential energy between two points A and B is related to the potential difference between those points by

$$\Delta PE = q(V_B - V_A)$$

Combining these two equations, we find that

$$W = -q(V_B - V_A) \qquad \text{[16.6]}$$

Using this equation, we obtain the following general result: **No net work is required to move a charge between two points that are at the same electric potential.** In mathematical terms this result says that $W = 0$ whenever $V_B = V_A$.

In Chapter 15 we found that when a conductor is in electrostatic equilibrium, a net charge placed on it resides entirely on its surface. Further, we showed that the electric field just outside the surface of a charged conductor in electrostatic equilibrium is perpendicular to the surface and that the field inside the conductor is zero. We now show that **all points on the surface of a charged conductor in electrostatic equilibrium are at the same potential**.

Consider a surface path connecting any points A and B on a charged conductor, as in Figure 16.10. The charges on the conductor are assumed to be in equilibrium with each other, so none are moving. In this case the electric field $\vec{E}$ is always perpendicular to the displacement along this path. This must be so, for otherwise the part of the electric field tangent to the surface would move the charges. Because $\vec{E}$ is perpendicular to the path, no work is done by the electric field if a charge is moved between the given two points. From Equation 16.6 we see that if the work done is zero, the difference in electric potential, $V_B - V_A$, is also zero. It follows that **the electric potential is a constant everywhere on the surface of a charged conductor in equilibrium**. Further, because the electric field inside a conductor is zero, no work is required to move a charge between two points inside the conductor. Again, Equation 16.6 shows that if the work done is zero, the difference in electric potential between any two points inside a conductor must also be zero. We conclude that the electric potential is constant everywhere inside a conductor.

Finally, because one of the points inside the conductor could be arbitrarily close to the surface of the conductor, we conclude that **the electric potential is constant everywhere inside a conductor and equal to that same value at the surface**. As a consequence, no work is required to move a charge from the interior of a charged conductor to its surface. (It's important to realize that the potential inside a conductor is not necessarily zero, even though the interior electric field is zero.)

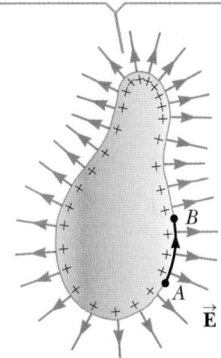

Notice from the spacing of the positive signs that the surface charge density is nonuniform.

Figure 16.10 An arbitrarily shaped conductor with an excess positive charge. When the conductor is in electrostatic equilibrium, all the charge resides at the surface, $\vec{E} = 0$, inside the conductor, and the electric field just outside the conductor is perpendicular to the surface. The potential is constant inside the conductor and is equal to the potential at the surface.

The Electron Volt

An appropriately sized unit of energy commonly used in atomic and nuclear physics is the electron volt (eV). For example, electrons in normal atoms typically have energies of tens of eV's, excited electrons in atoms emitting x-rays have energies of thousands of eV's, and high-energy gamma rays (electromagnetic waves) emitted by the nucleus have energies of millions of eV's.

The **electron volt** is defined as the kinetic energy that an electron gains when accelerated through a potential difference of 1 V.

◄ Definition of the electron volt

Because 1 V = 1 J/C and because the magnitude of the charge on the electron is 1.60×10^{-19} C, we see that the electron volt is related to the joule by

$$1 \text{ eV} = 1.60 \times 10^{-19} \text{ C} \cdot \text{V} = 1.60 \times 10^{-19} \text{ J} \qquad \text{[16.7]}$$

■ Quick Quiz

16.7 An electron initially at rest accelerates through a potential difference of 1 V, gaining kinetic energy KE_e, whereas a proton, also initially at rest, accelerates through a potential difference of −1 V, gaining kinetic energy KE_p. Which of the following relationships holds? (a) $KE_e = KE_p$ (b) $KE_e < KE_p$ (c) $KE_e > KE_p$ (d) The answer can't be determined from the given information.

16.4 Equipotential Surfaces

A surface on which all points are at the same potential is called an **equipotential surface**. The potential difference between any two points on an equipotential surface is zero. Hence, **no work is required to move a charge at constant speed on an equipotential surface**.

Figure 16.11 Equipotentials (dashed blue lines) and electric field lines (orange lines) for (a) a positive point charge and (b) two point charges of equal magnitude and opposite sign. In all cases the equipotentials are *perpendicular* to the electric field lines at every point.

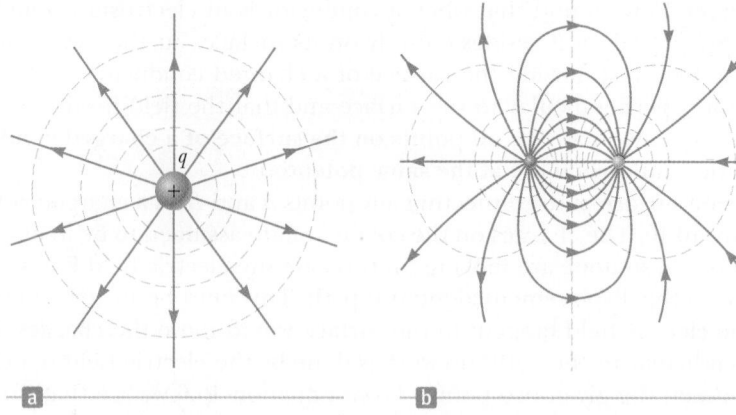

Equipotential surfaces have a simple relationship to the electric field: **The electric field at every point of an equipotential surface is perpendicular to the surface**. If the electric field $\vec{E}$ had a component parallel to the surface, that component would produce an electric force on a charge placed on the surface. This force would do work on the charge as it moved from one point to another, in contradiction to the definition of an equipotential surface.

Equipotential surfaces can be represented on a diagram by drawing equipotential contours, which are two-dimensional views of the intersections of the equipotential surfaces with the plane of the drawing. These equipotential contours are generally referred to simply as **equipotentials.** Figure 16.11a shows the equipotentials (in blue) associated with a positive point charge. Note that the equipotentials are perpendicular to the electric field lines (in orange) at all points. Recall that the electric potential created by a point charge q is given by $V = k_e q/r$. This relation shows that, for a single point charge, the potential is constant on any surface on which r is constant. It follows that the equipotentials of a point charge are a family of spheres centered on the point charge. Figure 16.11b shows the equipotentials associated with two charges of equal magnitude but opposite sign.

16.5 Applications

The Electrostatic Precipitator

APPLICATION
The Electrostatic Precipitator

One important application of electric discharge in gases is a device called an *electrostatic precipitator*. This device removes particulate matter from combustion gases, thereby reducing air pollution. It's especially useful in coal-burning power plants and in industrial operations that generate large quantities of smoke. Systems currently in use can eliminate approximately 90% by mass of the ash and dust from the smoke. Unfortunately, a very high percentage of the lighter particles still escape, and they contribute significantly to smog and haze.

Figure 16.12 illustrates the basic idea of the electrostatic precipitator. A high voltage (typically 40 kV to 100 kV) is maintained between a wire running down the center of a duct and the outer wall, which is grounded. The wire is maintained at a negative electric potential with respect to the wall, so the electric field is directed toward the wire. The electric field near the wire reaches a high enough value to cause a discharge around the wire and the formation of positive ions, electrons, and negative ions, such as O_2^-. As the electrons and negative ions are accelerated toward the outer wall by the nonuniform electric field, the dirt particles in the streaming gas become charged by collisions and ion capture. Because most of the charged dirt particles are negative, they are also drawn to the outer wall by the electric field. When the duct is shaken, the particles fall loose and are collected at the bottom.

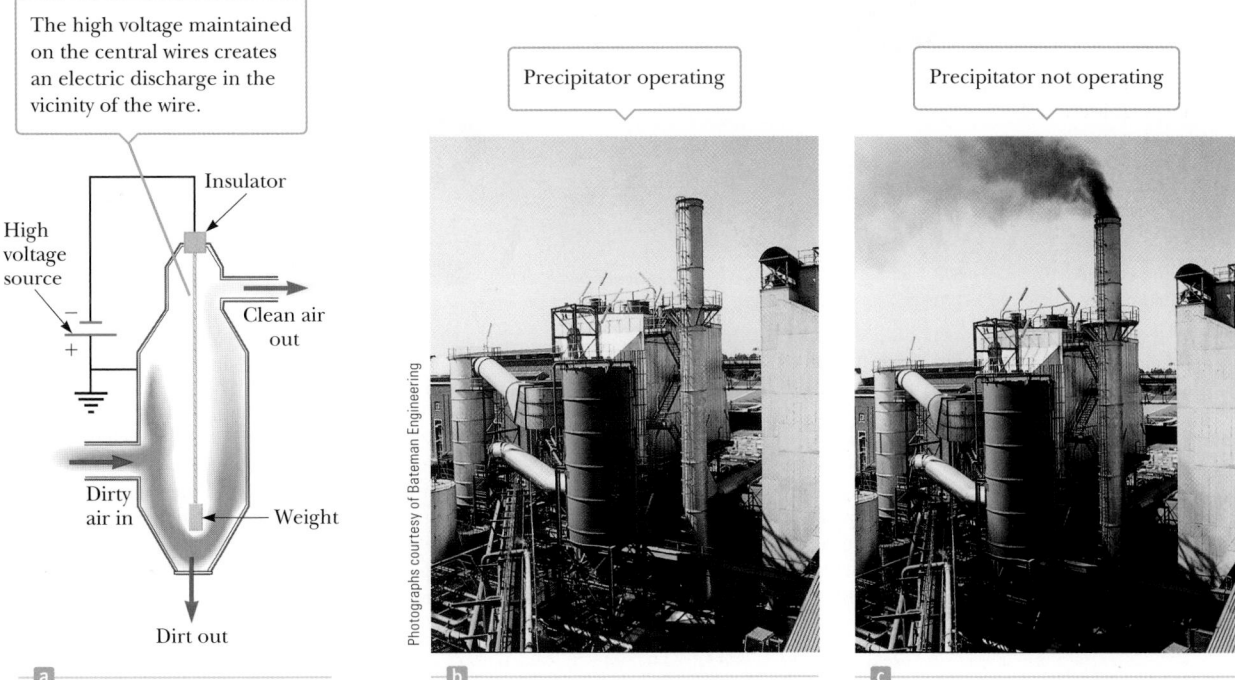

Figure 16.12 (a) A schematic diagram of an electrostatic precipitator. Compare the air pollution when the precipitator is (b) operating and (c) turned off.

In addition to reducing the amounts of harmful gases and particulate matter in the atmosphere, the electrostatic precipitator recovers valuable metal oxides from the stack.

A similar device called an *electrostatic air cleaner* is used in homes to relieve the discomfort of allergy sufferers. Air laden with dust and pollen is drawn into the device across a positively charged mesh screen. The airborne particles become positively charged when they make contact with the screen, and then they pass through a second, negatively charged mesh screen. The electrostatic force of attraction between the positively charged particles in the air and the negatively charged screen causes the particles to precipitate out on the surface of the screen, removing a very high percentage of contaminants from the air stream.

APPLICATION
The Electrostatic Air Cleaner

Xerography and Laser Printers

APPLICATION
Xerographic Copiers

Xerography is widely used to make photocopies of printed materials. The basic idea behind the process was developed by Chester Carlson, who was granted a patent for his invention in 1940. In 1947 the Xerox Corporation launched a full-scale program to develop automated duplicating machines using Carlson's process. The huge success of that development is evident: today, practically all offices and libraries have one or more duplicating machines, and the capabilities of these machines continue to evolve.

Some features of the xerographic process involve simple concepts from electrostatics and optics. The one idea that makes the process unique, however, is the use of photoconductive material to form an image. A photoconductor is a material that is a poor conductor of electricity in the dark, but a reasonably good conductor when exposed to light.

Figure 16.13 (page 562) illustrates the steps in the xerographic process. First, the surface of a plate or drum is coated with a thin film of the photoconductive material (usually selenium or some compound of selenium), and the photoconductive surface is given a positive electrostatic charge in the dark (Fig. 16.13a). The page to be copied is then projected onto the charged surface (Fig. 16.13b). The

a

a Charging the drum   b Imaging the document   c Applying the toner   d Transferring the toner to the paper   e Laser printer drum

Selenium-coated drum

Lens

Negatively charged toner

Interlaced pattern of laser lines

Laser beam

Figure 16.13 The xerographic process. (a) The photoconductive surface is positively charged. (b) Through the use of a light source and a lens, a hidden image is formed on the charged surface in the form of positive charges. (c) The surface containing the image is covered with a negatively charged powder, which adheres only to the image area. (d) A piece of paper is placed over the surface and given a charge. This transfers the image to the paper, which is then heated to "fix" the powder to the paper. (e) The image on the drum of a laser printer is produced by turning a laser beam on and off as it sweeps across the selenium-coated drum.

photoconducting surface becomes conducting only in areas where light strikes; there the light produces charge carriers in the photoconductor that neutralize the positively charged surface. The charges remain on those areas of the photoconductor not exposed to light, however, leaving a hidden image of the object in the form of a positive distribution of surface charge.

Next, a negatively charged powder called a *toner* is dusted onto the photoconducting surface (Fig. 16.13c). The charged powder adheres only to the areas that contain the positively charged image. At this point, the image becomes visible. It is then transferred to the surface of a sheet of positively charged paper. Finally, the toner is "fixed" to the surface of the paper by heat (Fig. 16.13d), resulting in a permanent copy of the original.

APPLICATION

Laser Printers

The steps for producing a document on a laser printer are similar to those used in a photocopy machine in that parts (a), (c), and (d) of Figure 16.13 remain essentially the same. The difference between the two techniques lies in the way the image is formed on the selenium-coated drum. In a laser printer the command to print the letter *O*, for instance, is sent to a laser from the memory of a computer. A rotating mirror inside the printer causes the beam of the laser to sweep across the selenium-coated drum in an interlaced pattern (Fig. 16.13e). Electrical signals generated by the printer turn the laser beam on and off in a pattern that traces out the letter *O* in the form of positive charges on the selenium. Toner is then applied to the drum, and the transfer to paper is accomplished as in a photocopy machine.

16.6 Capacitance

A **capacitor** is a device used in a variety of electric circuits, such as to tune the frequency of radio receivers, eliminate sparking in automobile ignition systems, or store short-term energy for rapid release in electronic flash units. Figure 16.14 shows a typical design for a capacitor. It consists of two parallel metal plates separated by a distance d. Used in an electric circuit, the plates are connected to the positive and negative terminals of a battery or some other voltage source. When this connection is made, electrons are pulled off one of the plates, leaving it with a charge of $+Q$, and are transferred through the battery to the other plate, leaving it with a charge of $-Q$, as shown in the figure. The transfer of charge stops when the potential difference across the plates equals the potential difference of the

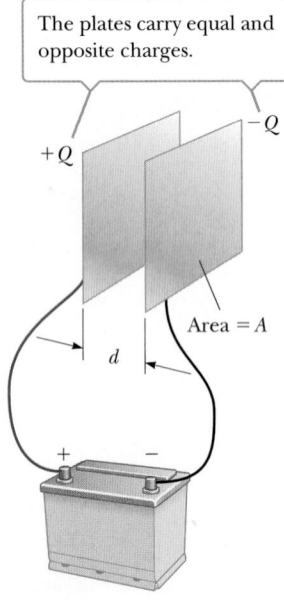

The plates carry equal and opposite charges.

$+Q$

$-Q$

Area = A

d

$+$ $-$

Figure 16.14 A parallel-plate capacitor consists of two parallel plates, each of area A, separated by a distance d.

battery. A charged capacitor is a device that stores energy that can be reclaimed when needed for a specific application.

> The capacitance C of a capacitor is the ratio of the magnitude of the charge on either conductor (plate) to the magnitude of the potential difference between the conductors (plates):
>
> $$C \equiv \frac{Q}{\Delta V}$$
>
> [16.8]
>
> **SI unit: farad (F) = coulomb per volt (C/V)**

◄ Capacitance of a pair of conductors

The quantities Q and ΔV are always taken to be positive when used in Equation 16.8. For example, if a 3.0-μF capacitor is connected to a 12-V battery, the magnitude of the charge on each plate of the capacitor is

$$Q = C \Delta V = (3.0 \times 10^{-6} \text{ F})(12 \text{ V}) = 36 \; \mu\text{C}$$

From Equation 16.8, we see that a large capacitance is needed to store a large amount of charge for a given applied voltage. The farad is a very large unit of capacitance. In practice, most typical capacitors have capacitances ranging from microfarads (1 μF = 1 $\times$ 10^{-6} F) to picofarads (1 pF = 1 $\times$ 10^{-12} F).

Tip 16.2 Potential Difference Is ΔV, Not V

Use the symbol ΔV for the potential difference across a circuit element or a device (many other books use simply V for potential difference). The dual use of V to represent potential in one place and a potential difference in another can lead to unnecessary confusion.

16.7 The Parallel-Plate Capacitor

The capacitance of a device depends on the geometric arrangement of the conductors. The capacitance of a parallel-plate capacitor with plates separated by air (see Fig. 16.14) can be easily calculated from three facts. First, recall from Chapter 15 that the magnitude of the electric field between two plates is given by $E = \sigma/\epsilon_0$, where σ is the magnitude of the charge per unit area on each plate. Second, we found earlier in this chapter that the potential difference between two plates is $\Delta V = Ed$, where d is the distance between the plates. Third, the charge on one plate is given by $Q = \sigma A$, where A is the area of the plate. Substituting these three facts into the definition of capacitance gives the desired result:

$$C = \frac{Q}{\Delta V} = \frac{\sigma A}{Ed} = \frac{\sigma A}{(\sigma/\epsilon_0)d}$$

Canceling the charge per unit area, σ, yields

$$C = \epsilon_0 \frac{A}{d}$$

[16.9]

◄ Capacitance of a parallel-plate capacitor

where A is the area of one of the plates, d is the distance between the plates, and ϵ_0 is the permittivity of free space.

From Equation 16.9, we see that plates with larger area can store more charge. The same is true for a small plate separation d because then the positive charges on one plate exert a stronger force on the negative charges on the other plate, allowing more charge to be held on the plates.

Figure 16.15 shows the electric field lines of a more realistic parallel-plate capacitor. The electric field is very nearly constant in the center between the plates, but

Figure 16.15 The electric field between the plates of a parallel-plate capacitor is uniform near the center, but nonuniform near the edges.

Figure 16.16 When the key of one type of keyboard is pressed, the capacitance of a parallel-plate capacitor increases as the plate spacing decreases. The substance labeled "dielectric" is an insulating material, as described in Section 16.10.

becomes less so when approaching the edges. For most purposes, however, the field may be taken as constant throughout the region between the plates.

APPLICATION
Camera Flash Attachments

One practical device that uses a capacitor is the flash attachment on a camera. A battery is used to charge the capacitor, and the stored charge is then released when the shutter-release button is pressed to take a picture. The stored charge is delivered to a flash tube very quickly, illuminating the subject at the instant more light is needed.

APPLICATION
Computer Keyboards

Computers make use of capacitors in many ways. For example, one type of computer keyboard has capacitors at the bases of its keys, as in Figure 16.16. Each key is connected to a movable plate, which represents one side of the capacitor; the fixed plate on the bottom of the keyboard represents the other side of the capacitor. When a key is pressed, the capacitor spacing decreases, causing an increase in capacitance. External electronic circuits recognize each key by the *change* in its capacitance when it is pressed.

APPLICATION
Electrostatic Confinement

Capacitors are useful for storing a large amount of charge that needs to be delivered quickly. A good example on the forefront of fusion research is electrostatic confinement. In this role capacitors discharge their electrons through a grid. The negatively charged electrons in the grid draw positively charged particles to them and therefore to each other, causing some particles to fuse and release energy in the process.

■ EXAMPLE 16.6 | **A Parallel-Plate Capacitor**

GOAL Calculate fundamental physical properties of a parallel-plate capacitor.

PROBLEM A parallel-plate capacitor has an area $A = 2.00 \times 10^{-4}$ m^2 and a plate separation $d = 1.00 \times 10^{-3}$ m. **(a)** Find its capacitance. **(b)** How much charge is on the positive plate if the capacitor is connected to a 3.00-V battery? Calculate **(c)** the charge density on the positive plate, assuming the density is uniform, and **(d)** the magnitude of the electric field between the plates.

STRATEGY Parts (a) and (b) can be solved by substituting into the basic equations for capacitance. In part (c) use the definition of charge density, and in part (d) use the fact that the voltage difference equals the electric field times the distance.

. . . .

SOLUTION

(a) Find the capacitance.

Substitute into Equation 16.9:

$$C = \epsilon_0 \frac{A}{d} = (8.85 \times 10^{-12}\,\text{C}^2/\text{N} \cdot \text{m}^2)\left(\frac{2.00 \times 10^{-4}\,\text{m}^2}{1.00 \times 10^{-3}\,\text{m}}\right)$$

$$C = \boxed{1.77 \times 10^{-12}\,\text{F} = 1.77\,\text{pF}}$$

(b) Find the charge on the positive plate after the capacitor is connected to a 3.00-V battery.

Substitute into Equation 16.8:

$$C = \frac{Q}{\Delta V} \quad \rightarrow \quad Q = C\,\Delta V = (1.77 \times 10^{-12}\,\text{F})(3.00\,\text{V})$$

$$= \boxed{5.31 \times 10^{-12}\,\text{C}}$$

(c) Calculate the charge density on the positive plate.

Charge density is charge divided by area:

$$\sigma = \frac{Q}{A} = \frac{5.31 \times 10^{-12}\ \text{C}}{2.00 \times 10^{-4}\ \text{m}^2} = \boxed{2.66 \times 10^{-8}\ \text{C/m}^2}$$

(d) Calculate the magnitude of the electric field between the plates.

Apply $\Delta V = Ed$:

$$E = \frac{\Delta V}{d} = \frac{3.00\ \text{V}}{1.00 \times 10^{-3}\ \text{m}} = \boxed{3.00 \times 10^3\ \text{V/m}}$$

REMARKS The answer to part (d) could also have been obtained from the electric field derived for a parallel plate capacitor, Equation 15.13, $E = \sigma/\epsilon_0$.

QUESTION 16.6 How do the answers change if the distance between the plates is doubled?

EXERCISE 16.6 Two plates, each of area $3.00 \times 10^{-4}\ \text{m}^2$, are used to construct a parallel-plate capacitor with capacitance 1.00 pF. (a) Find the necessary separation distance. (b) If the positive plate is to hold a charge of $5.00 \times 10^{-12}\ \text{C}$, find the charge density. (c) Find the electric field between the plates. (d) What voltage battery should be attached to the plate to obtain the preceding results?

ANSWERS (a) $2.66 \times 10^{-3}\ \text{m}$ (b) $1.67 \times 10^{-8}\ \text{C/m}^2$ (c) $1.89 \times 10^3\ \text{N/C}$ (d) 5.00 V

Symbols for Circuit Elements and Circuits

The symbol that is commonly used to represent a capacitor in a circuit is —||— or sometimes —|(—. Don't confuse either of these symbols with the circuit symbol, —|⊢— which is used to designate a battery (or any other source of direct current). The positive terminal of the battery is at the higher potential and is represented by the longer vertical line in the battery symbol. In the next chapter we discuss another circuit element, called a resistor, represented by the symbol —Ʌ/\/—. When wires in a circuit don't have appreciable resistance compared with the resistance of other elements in the circuit, the wires are represented by straight lines.

It's important to realize that a circuit is a collection of real objects, usually containing a source of electrical energy (such as a battery) connected to elements that convert electrical energy to other forms (light, heat, sound) or store the energy in electric or magnetic fields for later retrieval. A real circuit and its schematic diagram are sketched side by side in Figure 16.17. The circuit symbol for a lightbulb shown in Figure 16.17b is —⊗—.

If you are not familiar with circuit diagrams, trace the path of the real circuit with your finger to see that it is equivalent to the geometrically regular schematic diagram.

Figure 16.17 (a) A real circuit and (b) its equivalent circuit diagram.

16.8 Combinations of Capacitors

Two or more capacitors can be combined in circuits in several ways, but most reduce to two simple configurations, called *parallel* and *series*. The idea, then, is to find the single equivalent capacitance due to a combination of several different capacitors that are in parallel or in series with each other. Capacitors are manufactured with a number of different standard capacitances, and by combining them in different ways, any desired value of the capacitance can be obtained.

Capacitors in Parallel

Two capacitors connected as shown in Active Figure 16.18a (page 566) are said to be in *parallel*. The left plate of each capacitor is connected to the positive terminal of the battery by a conducting wire, so the left plates are at the same potential. In

(a) A parallel connection of two capacitors. (b) The circuit diagram for the parallel combination. (c) The potential differences across the capacitors are the same, and the equivalent capacitance is $C_{eq} = C_1 + C_2$.

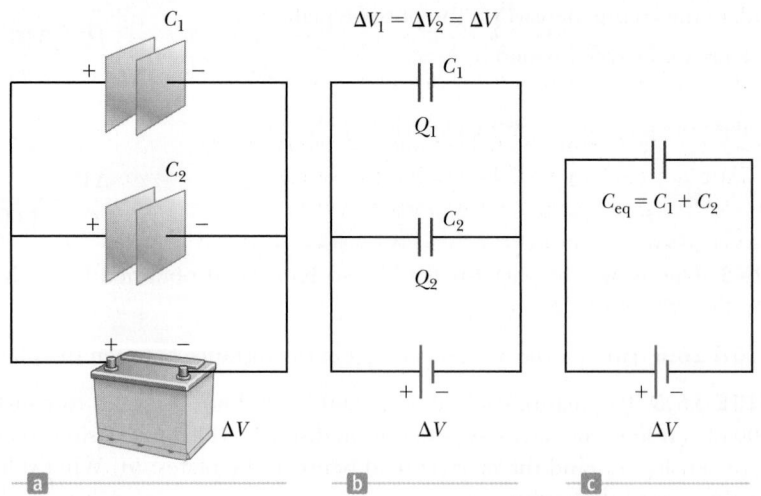

the same way, the right plates, both connected to the negative terminal of the battery, are also at the same potential. This means that **capacitors in parallel both have the same potential difference ΔV across them**. Capacitors in parallel are illustrated in Active Figure 16.18b.

When the capacitors are first connected in the circuit, electrons are transferred from the left plates through the battery to the right plates, leaving the left plates positively charged and the right plates negatively charged. The energy source for this transfer of charge is the internal chemical energy stored in the battery, which is converted to electrical energy. The flow of charge stops when the voltage across the capacitors equals the voltage of the battery, at which time the capacitors have their maximum charges. If the maximum charges on the two capacitors are Q_1 and Q_2, respectively, the *total charge*, Q, stored by the two capacitors is

$$Q = Q_1 + Q_2 \qquad \text{[16.10]}$$

We can replace these two capacitors with one equivalent capacitor having a capacitance of C_{eq}. This equivalent capacitor must have exactly the same external effect on the circuit as the original two, so it must store Q units of charge and have the same potential difference across it. The respective charges on each capacitor are

$$Q_1 = C_1 \, \Delta V \quad \text{and} \quad Q_2 = C_2 \, \Delta V$$

The charge on the equivalent capacitor is

$$Q = C_{eq} \, \Delta V$$

Substituting these relationships into Equation 16.10 gives

$$C_{eq} \, \Delta V = C_1 \, \Delta V + C_2 \, \Delta V$$

or

$$C_{eq} = C_1 + C_2 \quad \left(\begin{array}{l}\text{parallel}\\\text{combination}\end{array}\right) \qquad \text{[16.11]}$$

> **Tip 16.3 Voltage Is the Same as Potential Difference**
>
> A voltage *across* a device, such as a capacitor, has the same meaning as the potential difference across the device. For example, if we say that the voltage across a capacitor is 12 V, we mean that the potential difference between its plates is 12 V.

If we extend this treatment to three or more capacitors connected in parallel, the equivalent capacitance is found to be

$$C_{eq} = C_1 + C_2 + C_3 + \cdots \quad \left(\begin{array}{l}\text{parallel}\\\text{combination}\end{array}\right) \qquad \text{[16.12]}$$

We see that **the equivalent capacitance of a parallel combination of capacitors is larger than any of the individual capacitances.**

■ EXAMPLE 16.7 │ Four Capacitors Connected in Parallel

GOAL Analyze a circuit with several capacitors in parallel.

PROBLEM (a) Determine the capacitance of the single capacitor that is equivalent to the parallel combination of capacitors shown in Figure 16.19. Find (b) the charge on the 12.0-μF capacitor and (c) the total charge contained in the configuration. (d) Derive a symbolic expression for the fraction of the total charge contained on one of the capacitors.

STRATEGY For part (a), add the individual capacitances. For part (b), apply the formula $C = Q/\Delta V$ to the 12.0-μF capacitor. The voltage difference is the same as the difference across the battery. To find the total charge contained in all four capacitors, use the equivalent capacitance in the same formula.

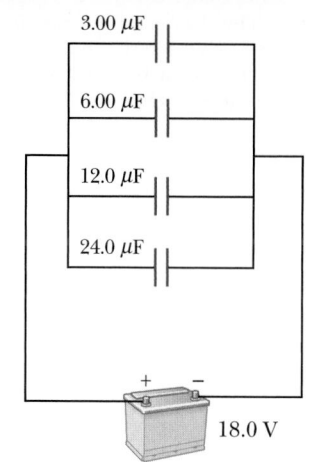

Figure 16.19 (Example 16.7) Four capacitors connected in parallel.

SOLUTION

(a) Find the equivalent capacitance.

Apply Equation 16.12:

$$C_{eq} = C_1 + C_2 + C_3 + C_4$$
$$= 3.00 \ \mu F + 6.00 \ \mu F + 12.0 \ \mu F + 24.0 \ \mu F$$
$$= \boxed{45.0 \ \mu F}$$

(b) Find the charge on the 12-μF capacitor (designated C_3).

Solve the capacitance equation for Q and substitute:

$$Q = C_3 \Delta V = (12.0 \times 10^{-6} \ F)(18.0 \ V) = 216 \times 10^{-6} \ C$$
$$= \boxed{216 \ \mu C}$$

(c) Find the total charge contained in the configuration.

Use the equivalent capacitance:

$$C_{eq} = \frac{Q}{\Delta V} \quad \rightarrow \quad Q = C_{eq} \Delta V = (45.0 \ \mu F)(18.0 \ V) = \boxed{8.10 \times 10^2 \ \mu C}$$

(d) Derive a symbolic expression for the fraction of the total charge contained in one of the capacitors.

Write a symbolic expression for the fractional charge in the ith capacitor and use the capacitor definition:

$$\frac{Q_i}{Q_{tot}} = \frac{C_i \Delta V}{C_{eq} \Delta V} = \frac{C_i}{C_{eq}}$$

REMARKS The charge on any one of the parallel capacitors can be found as in part (b) because the potential difference is the same. Notice that finding the total charge does not require finding the charge on each individual capacitor and adding. It's easier to use the equivalent capacitance in the capacitance definition.

QUESTION 16.7 If all four capacitors had the same capacitance, what fraction of the total charge would be held by each?

EXERCISE 16.7 Find the charge on the 24.0-μF capacitor.

ANSWER 432 μC

Capacitors in Series

Now consider two capacitors connected in *series*, as illustrated in Active Figure 16.20a (page 568). **For a series combination of capacitors, the magnitude of the charge must be the same on all the plates.** To understand this principle, consider the charge transfer process in some detail. When a battery is connected to the

◄ *Q* is the same for all capacitors connected in series

Active Figure 16.20

A series combination of two capacitors. The charges on the capacitors are the same, and the equivalent capacitance can be calculated from the reciprocal relationship $1/C_{eq} = (1/C_1) + (1/C_2)$.

circuit, electrons with total charge $-Q$ are transferred from the left plate of C_1 to the right plate of C_2 through the battery, leaving the left plate of C_1 with a charge of $+Q$. As a consequence, the magnitudes of the charges on the left plate of C_1 and the right plate of C_2 must be the same. Now consider the right plate of C_1 and the left plate of C_2, in the middle. These plates are not connected to the battery (because of the gap across the plates) and, taken together, are electrically neutral. The charge of $+Q$ on the left plate of C_1, however, attracts negative charges to the right plate of C_1. These charges will continue to accumulate until the left and right plates of C_1, taken together, become electrically neutral, which means that the charge on the right plate of C_1 is $-Q$. This negative charge could only have come from the left plate of C_2, so C_2 has a charge of $+Q$.

Therefore, regardless of how many capacitors are in series or what their capacitances are, **all the right plates gain charges of $-Q$ and all the left plates have charges of $+Q$** (a consequence of the conservation of charge).

After an equivalent capacitor for a series of capacitors is fully charged, **the equivalent capacitor must end up with a charge of $-Q$ on its right plate and a charge of $+Q$ on its left plate.** Applying the definition of capacitance to the circuit in Active Figure 16.20b, we have

$$\Delta V = \frac{Q}{C_{eq}}$$

where ΔV is the potential difference between the terminals of the battery and C_{eq} is the equivalent capacitance. Because $Q = C\Delta V$ can be applied to each capacitor, the potential differences across them are given by

$$\Delta V_1 = \frac{Q}{C_1} \qquad \Delta V_2 = \frac{Q}{C_2}$$

From Active Figure 16.20a, we see that

$$\Delta V = \Delta V_1 + \Delta V_2 \qquad \text{[16.13]}$$

where ΔV_1 and ΔV_2 are the potential differences across capacitors C_1 and C_2 (a consequence of the conservation of energy).

The potential difference across any number of capacitors (or other circuit elements) in series equals the sum of the potential differences across the individual capacitors. Substituting these expressions into Equation 16.13 and noting that $\Delta V = Q/C_{eq}$, we have

$$\frac{Q}{C_{eq}} = \frac{Q}{C_1} + \frac{Q}{C_2}$$

Canceling Q, we arrive at the following relationship:

$$\frac{1}{C_{eq}} = \frac{1}{C_1} + \frac{1}{C_2} \quad \begin{pmatrix} \text{series} \\ \text{combination} \end{pmatrix} \qquad \text{[16.14]}$$

If this analysis is applied to three or more capacitors connected in series, the equivalent capacitance is found to be

$$\frac{1}{C_{eq}} = \frac{1}{C_1} + \frac{1}{C_2} + \frac{1}{C_3} + \cdots \quad \left(\begin{array}{c}\text{series}\\\text{combination}\end{array}\right) \qquad [16.15]$$

As we will show in Example 16.8, Equation 16.15 implies that **the equivalent capacitance of a series combination is always smaller than any individual capacitance in the combination**.

■ *Quick Quiz*

16.8 A capacitor is designed so that one plate is large and the other is small. If the plates are connected to a battery, (a) the large plate has a greater charge than the small plate, (b) the large plate has less charge than the small plate, or (c) the plates have equal, but opposite, charge.

■ **EXAMPLE 16.8** │ **Four Capacitors Connected in Series**

GOAL Find an equivalent capacitance of capacitors in series, and the charge and voltage on each capacitor.

PROBLEM Four capacitors are connected in series with a battery, as in Figure 16.21. **(a)** Calculate the capacitance of the equivalent capacitor. **(b)** Compute the charge on the 12-μF capacitor. **(c)** Find the voltage drop across the 12-μF capacitor.

STRATEGY Combine all the capacitors into a single, equivalent capacitor using Equation 16.15. Find the charge on this equivalent capacitor using $C = Q/\Delta V$. This charge is the same as on the individual capacitors. Use this same equation again to find the voltage drop across the 12-μF capacitor.

Figure 16.21 (Example 16.8) Four capacitors connected in series.

....

SOLUTION

(a) Calculate the equivalent capacitance of the series.

Apply Equation 16.15:

$$\frac{1}{C_{eq}} = \frac{1}{3.0\ \mu F} + \frac{1}{6.0\ \mu F} + \frac{1}{12\ \mu F} + \frac{1}{24\ \mu F}$$

$$C_{eq} = \boxed{1.6\ \mu F}$$

(b) Compute the charge on the 12-μF capacitor.

The desired charge equals the charge on the equivalent capacitor:

$$Q = C_{eq}\ \Delta V = (1.6 \times 10^{-6}\ F)(18\ V) = \boxed{29\ \mu C}$$

(c) Find the voltage drop across the 12-μF capacitor.

Apply the basic capacitance equation:

$$C = \frac{Q}{\Delta V} \rightarrow \Delta V = \frac{Q}{C} = \frac{29\ \mu C}{12\ \mu F} = \boxed{2.4\ V}$$

....

REMARKS Notice that the equivalent capacitance is less than that of any of the individual capacitors. The relationship $C = Q/\Delta V$ can be used to find the voltage drops on the other capacitors, just as in part (c).

QUESTION 16.8 Over which capacitor is the voltage drop the smallest? The largest?

EXERCISE 16.8 The 24-μF capacitor is removed from the circuit, leaving only three capacitors in series. Find (a) the equivalent capacitance, (b) the charge on the 6-μF capacitor, and (c) the voltage drop across the 6-μF capacitor.

ANSWERS (a) 1.7 μF (b) 31 μC (c) 5.2 V

■ **PROBLEM-SOLVING STRATEGY**

Complex Capacitor Combinations

1. Combine capacitors that are in series or in parallel, following the derived formulas.

2. **Redraw** the circuit after every combination.
3. **Repeat** the first two steps until there is only a single equivalent capacitor.
4. **Find the charge** on the single equivalent capacitor, using $C = Q/\Delta V$.
5. **Work backwards** through the diagrams to the original one, finding the charge and voltage drop across each capacitor along the way. To do this, use the following collection of facts:
   A. The capacitor equation: $C = Q/\Delta V$
   B. Capacitors in parallel: $C_{eq} = C_1 + C_2$
   C. Capacitors in parallel all have the same voltage difference, ΔV, as does their equivalent capacitor.
   D. Capacitors in series: $\dfrac{1}{C_{eq}} = \dfrac{1}{C_1} + \dfrac{1}{C_2}$
   E. Capacitors in series all have the same charge, Q, as does their equivalent capacitor.

■ EXAMPLE 16.9 | Equivalent Capacitance

GOAL Solve a complex combination of series and parallel capacitors.

PROBLEM (a) Calculate the equivalent capacitance between a and b for the combination of capacitors shown in Figure 16.22a. All capacitances are in microfarads. (b) If a 12-V battery is connected across the system between points a and b, find the charge on the 4.0-μF capacitor in the first diagram and the voltage drop across it.

STRATEGY For part (a), use Equations 16.12 and 16.15 to reduce the combination step by step, as indicated in the figure. For part (b), to find the charge on the 4.0-μF capacitor, start with Figure 16.22c, finding the charge on the 2.0-μF capacitor. This same charge is on each of the 4.0-μF capacitors in the second diagram, by fact 5E of the Problem-Solving Strategy. One of these 4.0-μF capacitors in the second diagram is simply the original 4.0-μF capacitor in the first diagram.

Figure 16.22 (Example 16.9) To find the equivalent capacitance of the circuit in (a), use the series and parallel rules described in the text to successively reduce the circuit as indicated in (b), (c), and (d). All capacitances are in microfarads.

....

SOLUTION

(a) Calculate the equivalent capacitance.

Find the equivalent capacitance of the parallel 1.0-μF and 3.0-μF capacitors in Figure 16.22a:

$$C_{eq} = C_1 + C_2 = 1.0\ \mu\text{F} + 3.0\ \mu\text{F} = 4.0\ \mu\text{F}$$

Find the equivalent capacitance of the parallel 2.0-μF and 6.0-μF capacitors in Figure 16.22a:

$$C_{eq} = C_1 + C_2 = 2.0\ \mu\text{F} + 6.0\ \mu\text{F} = 8.0\ \mu\text{F}$$

Combine the two series 4.0-μF capacitors in Figure 16.22b:

$$\frac{1}{C_{eq}} = \frac{1}{C_1} + \frac{1}{C_2} = \frac{1}{4.0\ \mu\text{F}} + \frac{1}{4.0\ \mu\text{F}}$$

$$= \frac{1}{2.0\ \mu\text{F}} \quad \rightarrow \quad C_{eq} = 2.0\ \mu\text{F}$$

Combine the two series 8.0-μF capacitors in Figure 16.22b:

$$\frac{1}{C_{eq}} = \frac{1}{C_1} + \frac{1}{C_2} = \frac{1}{8.0\ \mu\text{F}} + \frac{1}{8.0\ \mu\text{F}}$$

$$= \frac{1}{4.0\ \mu\text{F}} \quad \rightarrow \quad C_{eq} = 4.0\ \mu\text{F}$$

Finally, combine the two parallel capacitors in Figure 16.22c to find the equivalent capacitance between a and b:

$$C_{eq} = C_1 + C_2 = 2.0\ \mu\text{F} + 4.0\ \mu\text{F} = \boxed{6.0\ \mu\text{F}}$$

(b) Find the charge on the 4.0-μF capacitor and the voltage drop across it.

Compute the charge on the 2.0-μF capacitor in Figure 16.22c, which is the same as the charge on the 4.0-μF capacitor in Figure 16.22a:

$$C = \frac{Q}{\Delta V} \quad \rightarrow \quad Q = C\Delta V = (2.0 \; \mu\text{F})(12 \; \text{V}) = \boxed{24 \; \mu\text{C}}$$

Use the basic capacitance equation to find the voltage drop across the 4.0-μF capacitor in Figure 16.22a:

$$C = \frac{Q}{\Delta V} \quad \rightarrow \quad \Delta V = \frac{Q}{C} = \frac{24 \; \mu\text{C}}{4.0 \; \mu\text{F}} = \boxed{6.0 \; \text{V}}$$

....

REMARKS To find the rest of the charges and voltage drops, it's just a matter of using $C = Q/\Delta V$ repeatedly, together with facts 5C and 5E in the Problem-Solving Strategy. The voltage drop across the 4.0-μF capacitor could also have been found by noticing, in Figure 16.22b, that both capacitors had the same value and so by symmetry would split the total drop of 12 volts between them.

QUESTION 16.9 Which capacitor holds more charge, the 1.0-μF capacitor or the 3.0-μF capacitor?

EXERCISE 16.9 (a) In Example 16.9 find the charge on the 8.0-μF capacitor in Figure 16.22a and the voltage drop across it. (b) Do the same for the 6.0-μF capacitor in Figure 16.22a.

ANSWERS (a) 48 μC, 6.0 V (b) 36 μC, 6.0 V

16.9 Energy Stored in a Charged Capacitor

Almost everyone who works with electronic equipment has at some time verified that a capacitor can store energy. If the plates of a charged capacitor are connected by a conductor such as a wire, charge transfers from one plate to the other until the two are uncharged. The discharge can often be observed as a visible spark. If you accidentally touched the opposite plates of a charged capacitor, your fingers would act as a pathway by which the capacitor could discharge, inflicting an electric shock. The degree of shock would depend on the capacitance and voltage applied to the capacitor. *Where high voltages and large quantities of charge are present, as in the power supply of a television set, such a shock can be fatal.*

Capacitors store electrical energy, and that energy is the same as the work required to move charge onto the plates. If a capacitor is initially uncharged (both plates are neutral) so that the plates are at the same potential, very little work is required to transfer a small amount of charge ΔQ from one plate to the other. Once this charge has been transferred, however, a small potential difference $\Delta V = \Delta Q/C$ appears between the plates, so work must be done to transfer additional charge against this potential difference. From Equation 16.6, if the potential difference at any instant during the charging process is ΔV, the work ΔW required to move more charge ΔQ through this potential difference is given by

$$\Delta W = \Delta V \Delta Q$$

We know that $\Delta V = Q/C$ for a capacitor that has a total charge of Q. Therefore, a plot of voltage versus total charge gives a straight line with a slope of $1/C$, as shown in Figure 16.23. The work ΔW, for a particular ΔV, is the area of the blue rectangle. Adding up all the rectangles gives an approximation of the total work needed to fill the capacitor. In the limit as ΔQ is taken to be infinitesimally small, the total work needed to charge the capacitor to a final charge Q and voltage ΔV is the area under the line. This is just the area of a triangle, one-half the base times the height, so it follows that

$$W = \tfrac{1}{2} Q \Delta V \qquad\qquad [16.16]$$

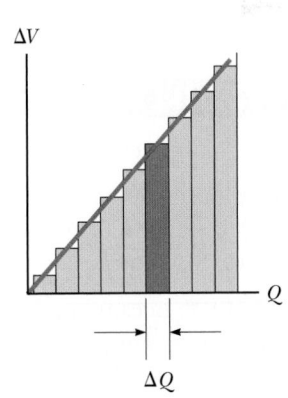

Figure 16.23 A plot of voltage vs. charge for a capacitor is a straight line with slope $1/C$. The work required to move a charge of ΔQ through a potential difference of ΔV across the capacitor plates is $\Delta W = \Delta V \Delta Q$, which equals the area of the blue rectangle. The *total work* required to charge the capacitor to a final charge of Q is the area under the straight line, which equals $Q\Delta V/2$.

As previously stated, W is also the energy stored in the capacitor. From the definition of capacitance, we have $Q = C\,\Delta V$; hence, we can express the energy stored three different ways:

$$\text{Energy stored} = \tfrac{1}{2}Q\Delta V = \tfrac{1}{2}C\,(\Delta V)^2 = \frac{Q^2}{2C} \qquad \textbf{[16.17]}$$

For example, the amount of energy stored in a 5.0-μF capacitor when it is connected across a 120-V battery is

$$\text{Energy stored} = \tfrac{1}{2}C\,(\Delta V)^2 = \tfrac{1}{2}(5.0 \times 10^{-6}\,\text{F})(120\,\text{V})^2 = 3.6 \times 10^{-2}\,\text{J}$$

In practice, there is a limit to the maximum energy (or charge) that can be stored in a capacitor. At some point, the Coulomb forces between the charges on the plates become so strong that electrons jump across the gap, discharging the capacitor. For this reason, capacitors are usually labeled with a maximum operating voltage. (This physical fact can actually be exploited to yield a circuit with a regularly blinking light).

Large capacitors can store enough electrical energy to cause severe burns or even death if they are discharged so that the flow of charge can pass through the heart. Under the proper conditions, however, they can be used to *sustain* life by stopping cardiac fibrillation in heart attack victims. When fibrillation occurs, the heart produces a rapid, irregular pattern of beats. A fast discharge of electrical energy through the heart can return the organ to its normal beat pattern. Emergency medical teams use portable defibrillators that contain batteries capable of charging a capacitor to a high voltage. (The circuitry actually permits the capacitor to be charged to a much higher voltage than the battery.) In this case and others (camera flash units and lasers used for fusion experiments), capacitors serve as energy reservoirs that can be slowly charged and then quickly discharged to provide large amounts of energy in a short pulse. The stored electrical energy is released through the heart by conducting electrodes, called paddles, placed on both sides of the victim's chest. The paramedics must wait between applications of electrical energy because of the time it takes the capacitors to become fully charged. The high voltage on the capacitor can be obtained from a low-voltage battery in a portable machine through the phenomenon of *electromagnetic induction*, to be studied in Chapter 20.

BIO APPLICATION
Defibrillators

■ EXAMPLE 16.10 | Typical Voltage, Energy, and Discharge Time for a Defibrillator

GOAL Apply energy and power concepts to a capacitor.

PROBLEM A fully charged defibrillator contains 1.20 kJ of energy stored in a 1.10×10^{-4} F capacitor. In a discharge through a patient, 6.00×10^2 J of electrical energy is delivered in 2.50 ms. **(a)** Find the voltage needed to store 1.20 kJ in the unit. **(b)** What average power is delivered to the patient?

STRATEGY Because we know the energy stored and the capacitance, we can use Equation 16.17 to find the required voltage in part (a). For part (b), dividing the energy delivered by the time gives the average power.

....

SOLUTION

(a) Find the voltage needed to store 1.20 kJ in the unit.

Solve Equation 16.17 for ΔV:

$$\text{Energy stored} = \tfrac{1}{2}C\Delta V^2$$

$$\Delta V = \sqrt{\frac{2 \times (\text{energy stored})}{C}}$$

$$= \sqrt{\frac{2(1.20 \times 10^3\,\text{J})}{1.10 \times 10^{-4}\,\text{F}}}$$

$$= \boxed{4.67 \times 10^3\,\text{V}}$$

(b) What average power is delivered to the patient?

Divide the energy delivered by the time:

$$P_{av} = \frac{\text{energy delivered}}{\Delta t} = \frac{6.00 \times 10^2 \text{ J}}{2.50 \times 10^{-3} \text{ s}}$$

$$= 2.40 \times 10^5 \text{ W}$$

REMARKS The power delivered by a draining capacitor isn't constant, as we'll find in the study of *RC* circuits in Chapter 18. For that reason, we were able to find only an average power. Capacitors are necessary in defibrillators because they can deliver energy far more quickly than batteries. Batteries provide current through relatively slow chemical reactions, whereas capacitors can quickly release charge that has already been produced and stored.

QUESTION 16.10 If the voltage across the capacitor were doubled, would the energy stored be (a) halved, (b) doubled, or (c) quadrupled?

EXERCISE 16.10 (a) Find the energy contained in a 2.50×10^{-5} F parallel-plate capacitor if it holds 1.75×10^{-3} C of charge. (b) What's the voltage between the plates? (c) What new voltage will result in a doubling of the stored energy?

ANSWERS (a) 6.13×10^{-2} J (b) 70.0 V (c) 99.0 V

■ APPLYING PHYSICS 16.1 Maximum Energy Design

How should three capacitors and two batteries be connected so that the capacitors will store the maximum possible energy?

EXPLANATION The energy stored in the capacitor is proportional to the capacitance and the square of the poten-

tial difference, so we would like to maximize each of these quantities. If the three capacitors are connected in parallel, their capacitances add, and if the batteries are in series, their potential differences, similarly, also add together. ■

■ Quick Quiz

16.9 A parallel-plate capacitor is disconnected from a battery, and the plates are pulled a small distance farther apart. Do the following quantities increase, decrease, or stay the same?
(a) C (b) Q (c) E between the plates (d) ΔV (e) energy stored in the capacitor

16.10 Capacitors with Dielectrics

A **dielectric** is an insulating material, such as rubber, plastic, or waxed paper. When a dielectric is inserted between the plates of a capacitor, the capacitance increases. If the dielectric completely fills the space between the plates, the capacitance is multiplied by the factor κ, called the **dielectric constant**.

The following experiment illustrates the effect of a dielectric in a capacitor. Consider a parallel-plate capacitor of charge Q_0 and capacitance C_0 in the absence of a dielectric. The potential difference across the capacitor plates can be measured, and is given by $\Delta V_0 = Q_0/C_0$ (Fig. 16.24a on page 574). Because the capacitor is not connected to an external circuit, there is no pathway for charge to leave or be added to the plates. If a dielectric is now inserted between the plates as in Figure 16.24b, the voltage across the plates is *reduced* by the factor κ to the value

$$\Delta V = \frac{\Delta V_0}{\kappa}$$

Figure 16.24 When a dielectric with dielectric constant κ is inserted in a charged capacitor that is *not* connected to a battery, the potential difference is reduced to $\Delta V = \Delta V_0/\kappa$ and the capacitance increases to $C = \kappa C_0$.

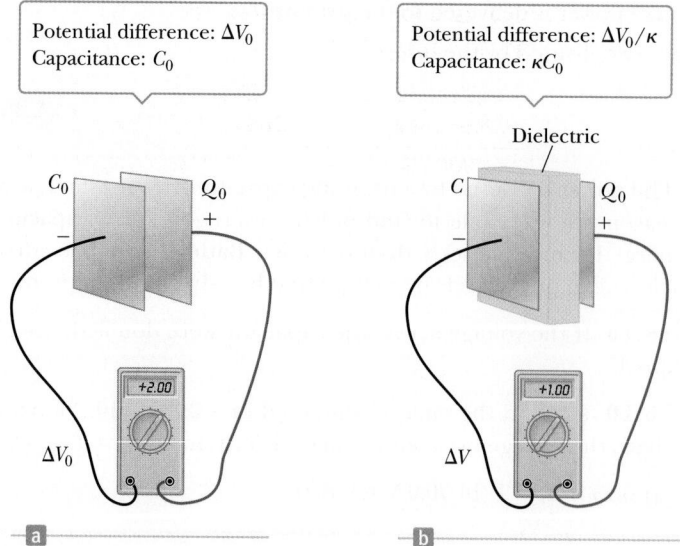

Potential difference: ΔV_0
Capacitance: C_0

Potential difference: $\Delta V_0/\kappa$
Capacitance: κC_0

Dielectric

Because $\kappa > 1$, ΔV is less than ΔV_0. Because the charge Q_0 on the capacitor doesn't change, we conclude that the capacitance in the presence of the dielectric must change to the value

$$C = \frac{Q_0}{\Delta V} = \frac{Q_0}{\Delta V_0/\kappa} = \frac{\kappa Q_0}{\Delta V_0}$$

or

$$C = \kappa C_0 \qquad [16.18]$$

According to this result, the capacitance is *multiplied* by the factor κ when the dielectric fills the region between the plates. For a parallel-plate capacitor, where the capacitance in the absence of a dielectric is $C_0 = \epsilon_0 A/d$, we can express the capacitance in the presence of a dielectric as

$$C = \kappa \epsilon_0 \frac{A}{d} \qquad [16.19]$$

From this result, it appears that the capacitance could be made very large by decreasing d, the separation between the plates. In practice the lowest value of d is limited by the electric discharge that can occur through the dielectric material separating the plates. For any given plate separation, there is a maximum electric field that can be produced in the dielectric before it breaks down and begins to conduct. This maximum electric field is called the **dielectric strength**, and for air its value is about 3×10^6 V/m. Most insulating materials have dielectric strengths greater than that of air, as indicated by the values listed in Table 16.1. Figure 16.25 shows an instance of dielectric breakdown in air.

Commercial capacitors are often made by using metal foil interlaced with thin sheets of paraffin-impregnated paper or Mylar®, which serves as the dielectric material. These alternate layers of metal foil and dielectric are rolled into a small cylinder (Fig. 16.26a). One type of a high-voltage capacitor consists of a number of interwoven metal plates immersed in silicone oil (Fig. 16.26b). Small capacitors are often constructed from ceramic materials. Variable capacitors (typically 10 pF to 500 pF) usually consist of two interwoven sets of metal plates, one fixed and the other movable, with air as the dielectric.

An electrolytic capacitor (Fig. 16.26c) is often used to store large amounts of charge at relatively low voltages. It consists of a metal foil in contact with an electrolyte—a solution that conducts charge by virtue of the motion of the ions contained in it. When a voltage is applied between the foil and the electrolyte, a thin

Figure 16.25 Dielectric breakdown in air. Sparks are produced when a large alternating voltage is applied across the wires by a high-voltage induction coil power supply.

Table 16.1 Dielectric Constants and Dielectric Strengths of Various Materials at Room Temperature

Material	Dielectric Constant κ	Dielectric Strength (V/m)
Air	1.000 59	3×10^6
Bakelite®	4.9	24×10^6
Fused quartz	3.78	8×10^6
Neoprene rubber	6.7	12×10^6
Nylon	3.4	14×10^6
Paper	3.7	16×10^6
Polystyrene	2.56	24×10^6
Pyrex® glass	5.6	14×10^6
Silicone oil	2.5	15×10^6
Strontium titanate	233	8×10^6
Teflon®	2.1	60×10^6
Vacuum	1.000 00	—
Water	80	—

A tubular capacitor consists of alternating metal foil and paper rolled into a cylinder.

Paper

Metal foil

A high-voltage capacitor consisting of many parallel plates separated by insulating oil

Plates

Oil

An electrolytic capacitor

Case

Electrolyte

Contacts

Metallic foil + oxide layer

a

b

c

Figure 16.26 Three commercial capacitor designs.

layer of metal oxide (an insulator) is formed on the foil, and this layer serves as the dielectric. Enormous capacitances can be attained because the dielectric layer is very thin.

Figure 16.27 shows a variety of commercially available capacitors. Variable capacitors are used in radios to adjust the frequency.

When electrolytic capacitors are used in circuits, the polarity (the plus and minus signs on the device) must be observed. If the polarity of the applied voltage is opposite that intended, the oxide layer will be removed and the capacitor will conduct rather than store charge. Further, reversing the polarity can result in such a large current that the capacitor may either burn or produce steam and explode.

Chris Vuille

a

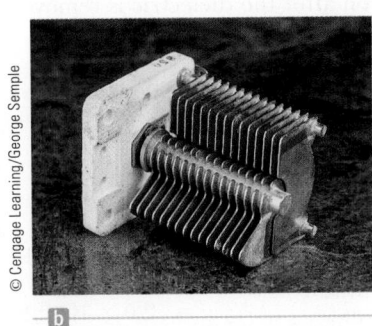

© Cengage Learning/George Semple

b

Figure 16.27 (a) A collection of capacitors used in a variety of applications. (b) A variable capacitor. When one set of metal plates is rotated so as to lie between a fixed set of plates, the capacitance of the device changes.

■ APPLYING PHYSICS 16.2 | Stud Finders

If you have ever tried to hang a picture on a wall securely, you know that it can be difficult to locate a wooden stud in which to anchor your nail or screw. The principles discussed in this section can be used to detect a stud electronically. The primary element of an electronic stud finder is a capacitor with its plates arranged side by side instead of facing one another, as in Figure 16.28. How does this device work?

EXPLANATION As the detector is moved along a wall, its capacitance changes when it passes across a stud because the dielectric constant of the material "between" the plates changes. The change in capacitance can be used to cause a light to come on, signaling the presence of the stud. ■

Figure 16.28 (Applying Physics 16.2) A stud finder produces an electric field that is affected by the dielectric constant of the materials placed in its field. When the device moves across a stud, the change in dielectric constant activates a signal light.

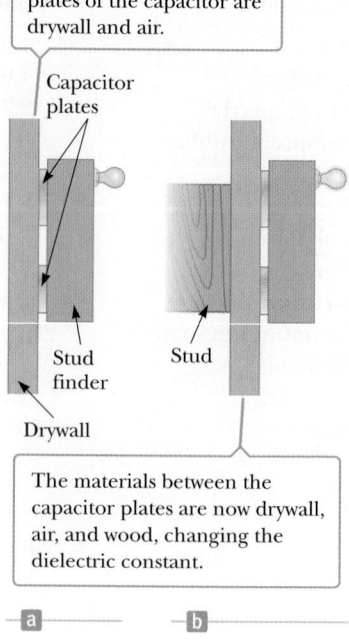

The materials between the plates of the capacitor are drywall and air.

Capacitor plates

Stud finder

Stud

Drywall

The materials between the capacitor plates are now drywall, air, and wood, changing the dielectric constant.

a   b

■ Quick Quiz

16.10 A fully charged parallel-plate capacitor remains connected to a battery while a dielectric is slid between the plates. Do the following quantities increase, decrease, or stay the same? (a) C (b) Q (c) E between the plates (d) ΔV (e) energy stored in the capacitor

■ EXAMPLE 16.11 | A Paper-Filled Capacitor

GOAL Calculate fundamental physical properties of a parallel-plate capacitor with a dielectric.

PROBLEM A parallel-plate capacitor has plates 2.0 cm by 3.0 cm. The plates are separated by a 1.0-mm thickness of paper. Find **(a)** the capacitance of this device and **(b)** the maximum charge that can be placed on the capacitor. **(c)** After the fully charged capacitor is disconnected from the battery, the dielectric is subsequently removed. Find the new electric field across the capacitor. Does the capacitor discharge?

STRATEGY For part (a), obtain the dielectric constant for paper from Table 16.1 and substitute, with other given quantities, into Equation 16.19. For part (b), note that Table 16.1 also gives the dielectric strength of paper, which is the maximum electric field that can be applied before electrical breakdown occurs. Use Equation 16.3, $\Delta V = Ed$, to obtain the maximum voltage and substitute into the basic capacitance equation. For part (c), remember that disconnecting the battery traps the extra charge on the plates, which must remain even after the dielectric is removed. Find the charge density on the plates and use Gauss's law to find the new electric field between the plates.

SOLUTION

(a) Find the capacitance of this device.

Substitute into Equation 16.19:

$$C = \kappa \epsilon_0 \frac{A}{d}$$

$$= 3.7 \left(8.85 \times 10^{-12} \frac{C^2}{N \cdot m^2} \right) \left(\frac{6.0 \times 10^{-4} \text{ m}^2}{1.0 \times 10^{-3} \text{ m}} \right)$$

$$= \boxed{2.0 \times 10^{-11} \text{ F}}$$

(b) Find the maximum charge that can be placed on the capacitor.

Calculate the maximum applied voltage, using the dielectric strength of paper, E_{max}:

$$\Delta V_{max} = E_{max}d = (16 \times 10^6 \text{ V/m})(1.0 \times 10^{-3} \text{ m})$$
$$= 1.6 \times 10^4 \text{ V}$$

Solve the basic capacitance equation for Q_{max} and substitute ΔV_{max} and C:

$$Q_{max} = C \Delta V_{max} = (2.0 \times 10^{-11} \text{ F})(1.6 \times 10^4 \text{ V})$$
$$= \boxed{0.32 \ \mu\text{C}}$$

(c) Suppose the fully charged capacitor is disconnected from the battery and the dielectric is subsequently removed. Find the new electric field between the plates of the capacitor. Does the capacitor discharge?

Compute the charge density on the plates:

$$\sigma = \frac{Q_{max}}{A} = \frac{3.2 \times 10^{-7} \text{ C}}{6.0 \times 10^{-4} \text{ m}^2} = 5.3 \times 10^{-4} \text{ C/m}^2$$

Calculate the electric field from the charge density:

$$E = \frac{\sigma}{\epsilon_0} = \frac{5.3 \times 10^{-4} \text{ C/m}^2}{8.85 \times 10^{-12} \text{ C}^2/\text{m}^2 \cdot \text{N}} = \boxed{6.0 \times 10^7 \text{ N/C}}$$

Because the electric field without the dielectric exceeds the value of the dielectric strength of air, the capacitor discharges across the gap.

REMARKS Dielectrics allow κ times as much charge to be stored on a capacitor for a given voltage. They also allow an increase in the applied voltage by increasing the threshold of electrical breakdown.

QUESTION 16.11 Subsequent to part (c), the capacitor is reconnected to the battery. Is the charge on the plates (a) larger than, (b) smaller than, or (c) the same as found in part (b)?

EXERCISE 16.11 A parallel-plate capacitor has plate area of 2.50×10^{-3} m^2 and distance between the plates of 2.00 mm. (a) Find the maximum charge that can be placed on the capacitor if air is between the plates. (b) Find the maximum charge if the air is replaced by polystyrene.

ANSWERS (a) 7×10^{-8} C (b) 1.4×10^{-6} C

▪ EXAMPLE 16.12 | Capacitors with Two Dielectrics

GOAL Derive a symbolic expression for a parallel-plate capacitor with two dielectrics.

PROBLEM A parallel-plate capacitor has dielectrics with constants κ_1 and κ_2 between the two plates, as shown in Figure 16.29. Each dielectric fills exactly half the volume between the plates. Derive expressions for **(a)** the potential difference between the two plates and **(b)** the resulting capacitance of the system.

STRATEGY The magnitude of the potential difference between the two plates of a capacitor is equal to the electric field multiplied by the plate separation. The electric field in a region is reduced by a factor of $1/\kappa$ when a dielectric is introduced, so $E = \sigma/\epsilon = \sigma/\kappa\epsilon_0$. Add the potential difference across each dielectric to find the total potential difference ΔV between the plates. The voltage difference across each dielectric is given by $\Delta V = Ed$, where E is the electric field and d the displacement. Obtain the capacitance from the relationship $C = Q/\Delta V$.

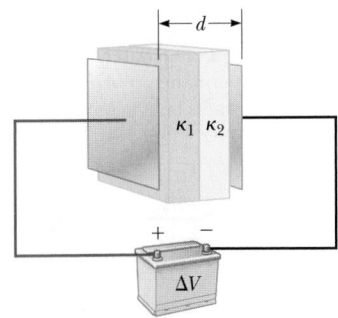

Figure 16.29 (Exercise 16.12)

SOLUTION

(a) Derive an expression for the potential difference between the two plates.

Write a general expression for the potential difference across both slabs:

$$\Delta V = \Delta V_1 + \Delta V_2 = E_1 d_1 + E_2 d_2$$

(Continued)

Substitute expressions for the electric fields and dielectric thicknesses, $d_1 = d_2 = d/2$:

$$\Delta V = \frac{\sigma}{\kappa_1 \epsilon_0} \frac{d}{2} + \frac{\sigma}{\kappa_2 \epsilon_0} \frac{d}{2} = \boxed{\frac{\sigma d}{2 \epsilon_0} \left(\frac{1}{\kappa_1} + \frac{1}{\kappa_2} \right)}$$

(b) Derive an expression for the resulting capacitance of the system.

Write the general expression for capacitance:

$$C = \frac{Q}{\Delta V}$$

Substitute $Q = \sigma A$ and the expression for the potential difference from part (a):

$$C = \frac{\sigma A}{\dfrac{\sigma d}{2 \epsilon_0} \left(\dfrac{1}{\kappa_1} + \dfrac{1}{\kappa_2} \right)} = \boxed{\frac{2 \epsilon_0 A}{d} \frac{\kappa_1 \kappa_2}{\kappa_1 + \kappa_2}}$$

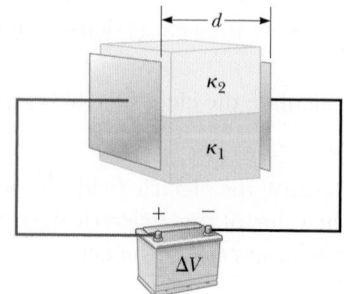

REMARKS The answer is the same as if there had been two capacitors in series with the respective dielectrics. When a capacitor consists of two dielectrics as shown in Figure 16.30, however, it's equivalent to two different capacitors in parallel.

QUESTION 16.12 What answer is obtained when the two dielectrics are removed so there is vacuum between the plates?

EXERCISE 16.12 Suppose a capacitor has two dielectrics arranged as shown in Figure 16.30, each dielectric filling exactly half of the volume between the two plates. Derive an expression for the capacitance if each dielectric fills exactly half the volume between the plates.

ANSWER $C = \dfrac{\kappa_1 + \kappa_2}{2} \dfrac{\epsilon_0 A}{d}$

Figure 16.30 (Exercise 16.12)

Figure 16.31 The water molecule, H_2O, has a permanent polarization resulting from its bent geometry.

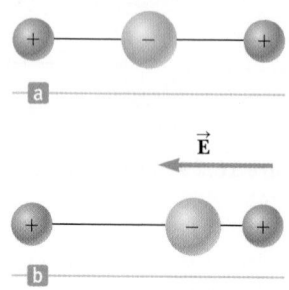

Figure 16.32 (a) A symmetric molecule has no permanent polarization. (b) An external electric field induces a polarization in the molecule.

An Atomic Description of Dielectrics

The explanation of why a dielectric increases the capacitance of a capacitor is based on an atomic description of the material, which in turn involves a property of some molecules called **polarization**. A molecule is said to be polarized when there is a separation between the average positions of its negative charge and its positive charge. In some molecules, such as water, this condition is always present. To see why, consider the geometry of a water molecule (Fig. 16.31).

The molecule is arranged so that the negative oxygen atom is bonded to the positively charged hydrogen atoms with a 105° angle between the two bonds. The center of negative charge is at the oxygen atom, and the center of positive charge lies at a point midway along the line joining the hydrogen atoms (point x in the diagram). Materials composed of molecules that are permanently polarized in this way have large dielectric constants, and indeed, Table 16.1 shows that the dielectric constant of water is large ($\kappa = 80$) compared with other common substances.

A symmetric molecule (Fig. 16.32a) can have no permanent polarization, but a polarization can be induced in it by an external electric field. A field directed to the left, as in Figure 16.32b, would cause the center of positive charge to shift to the left from its initial position and the center of negative charge to shift to the right. This *induced polarization* is the effect that predominates in most materials used as dielectrics in capacitors.

To understand why the polarization of a dielectric can affect capacitance, consider the slab of dielectric shown in Figure 16.33. Before placing the slab between the plates of the capacitor, the polar molecules are randomly oriented (Fig. 16.33a). The polar molecules are dipoles, and each creates a dipole electric field, but because of their random orientation, this field averages to zero.

After insertion of the dielectric slab into the electric field $\vec{E}_0$ between the plates (Fig. 16.33b), the positive plate attracts the negative ends of the dipoles and the negative plate attracts the positive ends of the dipoles. These forces exert a torque

Figure 16.33 (a) Polar molecules are randomly oriented in a dielectric. (b) An electric field is applied to the dielectric. (c) The charged edges of the dielectric act like an additional pair of parallel plates, reducing the overall field between the actual plates. The interior of the dielectric is still neutral.

Polar molecules are randomly oriented in the absence of an external electric field.

When an external electric field is applied, the molecules partially align with the field.

The charged edges create an induced electric field $\vec{E}_{ind}$ pointing in the direction opposite $\vec{E}_0$.

on the molecules making up the dielectric, reorienting them so that on average the negative pole is more inclined toward the positive plate and the positive pole is more aligned toward the negative plate. The positive and negative charges in the middle still cancel each other, but there is a net accumulation of negative charge in the dielectric next to the positive plate and a net accumulation of positive charge next to the negative plate. This configuration can be modeled as an additional pair of charged plates, as in Figure 16.33c, creating an induced electric field $\vec{E}_{ind}$ that partly cancels the original electric field $\vec{E}_0$. If the battery is not connected when the dielectric is inserted, the potential difference ΔV_0 across the plates is reduced to $\Delta V_0/\kappa$.

If the capacitor is still connected to the battery, however, the negative poles push more electrons off the positive plate, making it more positive. Meanwhile, the positive poles attract more electrons onto the negative plate. This situation continues until the potential difference across the battery reaches its original magnitude, equal to the potential gain across the battery. The net effect is an increase in the amount of charge stored on the capacitor. Because the plates can store more charge for a given voltage, it follows from $C = Q\,\Delta V$ that the capacitance must increase.

■ Quick Quiz

16.11 Consider a parallel-plate capacitor with a dielectric material between the plates. If the temperature of the dielectric increases, does the capacitance (a) decrease, (b) increase, or (c) remain the same?

■ SUMMARY

16.1 Potential Difference and Electric Potential

The change in the electric potential energy of a system consisting of an object of charge q moving through a displacement Δx in a constant electric field $\vec{E}$ is given by

$$\Delta PE = -W_{AB} = -qE_x\,\Delta x \qquad [16.1]$$

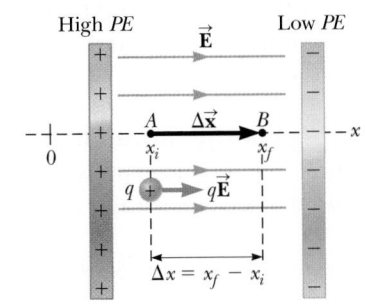

When a charge q moves in a uniform electric field $\vec{E}$ from point A to point B, the work done on the charge by the electric force is $qE_x\,\Delta x$.

where E_x is the component of the electric field in the x-direction and $\Delta x = x_f - x_i$. The **difference in electric potential** between two points A and B is

$$\Delta V = V_B - V_A = \frac{\Delta PE}{q} \qquad [16.2]$$

where ΔPE is the *change* in electrical potential energy as a charge q moves between A and B. The units of potential difference are joules per coulomb, or **volts**; 1 J/C = 1 V.

The **electric potential difference** between two points A and B in a *uniform* electric field $\vec{E}$ is

$$\Delta V = -E_x\,\Delta x \qquad [16.3]$$

where $\Delta x = x_f - x_i$ is the displacement between A and B and E_x is the x-component of the electric field in that region.

16.2 Electric Potential and Potential Energy Due to Point Charges

The **electric potential** due to a point charge q at distance r from the point charge is

$$V = k_e \frac{q}{r} \qquad [16.4]$$

Electric field and electric potential versus distance from a point charge of 1.11×10^{-10} C. Note that V is proportional to $1/r$, whereas E is proportional to $1/r^2$.

The **electric potential energy** of a pair of point charges separated by distance r is

$$PE = k_e \frac{q_1 q_2}{r} \qquad [16.5]$$

These equations can be used in the solution of conservation of energy problems and in the work–energy theorem.

16.3 Potentials and Charged Conductors

16.4 Equipotential Surfaces

Every point on the surface of a charged conductor in electrostatic equilibrium is at the same potential. Further, the potential is constant everywhere inside the conductor and equals its value on the surface.

The **electron volt** is defined as the energy that an electron (or proton) gains when accelerated through a potential difference of 1 V. The conversion between electron volts and joules is

$$1 \text{ eV} = 1.60 \times 10^{-19} \text{ C} \cdot \text{V} = 1.60 \times 10^{-19} \text{ J} \quad [16.7]$$

Any surface on which the potential is the same at every point is called an equipotential surface. The electric field is always oriented perpendicular to an equipotential surface.

16.6 Capacitance

A capacitor consists of two metal plates with charges that are equal in magnitude but opposite in sign. The capacitance C of any capacitor is the ratio of the magnitude of the charge Q on either plate to the magnitude of potential difference ΔV between them:

$$C \equiv \frac{Q}{\Delta V} \qquad [16.8]$$

Capacitance has the units coulombs per volt, or farads; 1 C/V = 1 F.

16.7 The Parallel-Plate Capacitor

The capacitance of two parallel metal plates of area A separated by distance d is

$$C = \epsilon_0 \frac{A}{d} \qquad [16.9]$$

where $\epsilon_0 = 8.85 \times 10^{-12}$ C^2/N $\cdot$ m^2 is a constant called the **permittivity of free space.**

A parallel-plate capacitor consists of two parallel plates, each of area A, separated by a distance d.

16.8 Combinations of Capacitors

The **equivalent capacitance of a parallel combination** of capacitors is

$$C_{eq} = C_1 + C_2 + C_3 + \cdots \qquad [16.12]$$

If two or more capacitors are connected in series, the **equivalent capacitance of the series combination** is

$$\frac{1}{C_{eq}} = \frac{1}{C_1} + \frac{1}{C_2} + \frac{1}{C_3} + \cdots \qquad [16.15]$$

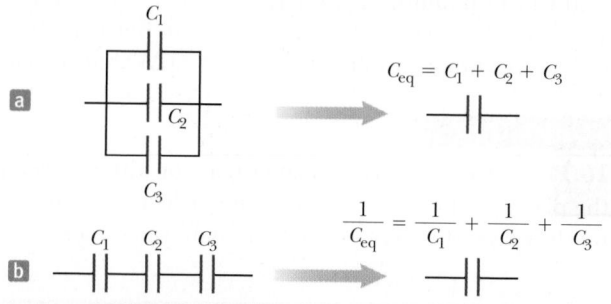

Capacitors in (a) parallel or in (b) series can be written as a single equivalent capacitor.

Problems involving a combination of capacitors can be solved by applying Equations 16.12 and 16.15 repeatedly to a circuit diagram, simplifying it as much as possible. This step is followed by working backwards to the original diagram, applying $C = Q/\Delta V$, that parallel capacitors have the same voltage drop, and that series capacitors have the same charge.

16.9 Energy Stored in a Charged Capacitor

Three equivalent expressions for calculating the **energy stored** in a charged capacitor are

$$\text{Energy stored} = \tfrac{1}{2}Q\,\Delta V = \tfrac{1}{2}C(\Delta V)^2 = \frac{Q^2}{2C} \qquad [16.17]$$

16.10 Capacitors with Dielectrics

When a nonconducting material, called a **dielectric,** is placed between the plates of a capacitor, the capacitance is multiplied by the factor κ, which is called the **dielectric constant**, a property of the dielectric material. The capacitance of a parallel-plate capacitor filled with a dielectric is

$$C = \kappa \epsilon_0 \frac{A}{d} \qquad [16.19]$$

■ MULTIPLE-CHOICE QUESTIONS

WebAssign The multiple-choice questions in this chapter may be assigned online in Enhanced WebAssign.

---

1. A proton is released at the origin in a constant electric field of 850 N/C acting in the positive x-direction. Find the change in the electric potential energy associated with the proton after it travels to $x = 2.5$ m. (a) 3.4×10^{-16} J (b) -3.4×10^{-16} J (c) 2.5×10^{-16} J (d) -2.5×10^{-16} J (e) -1.6×10^{-19} J

2. An electron in an x-ray machine is accelerated through a potential difference of 1.00×10^4 V before it hits the target. What is the kinetic energy of the electron in electron volts? (a) 1.00×10^4 eV (b) 1.60×10^{-15} eV (c) 1.60×10^{-22} eV (d) 6.25×10^{22} eV (e) 1.60×10^{-19} eV

3. The electric potential at $x = 3.0$ m is 120 V, and the electric potential at $x = 5.0$ m is 190 V. What is the electric field in this region, assuming it's constant? (a) 140 N/C (b) -140 N/C (c) 35 N/C (d) -35 N/C (e) 75 N/C

4. A helium nucleus (charge $= 2e$, mass $= 6.63 \times 10^{-27}$ kg) traveling at a speed of 6.20×10^5 m/s enters an electric field, traveling from point Ⓐ, at a potential of 1.50×10^3 V, to point Ⓑ, at 4.00×10^3 V. What is its speed at point Ⓑ (a) 7.91×10^5 m/s (b) 3.78×10^5 m/s (c) 2.13×10^5 m/s (d) 2.52×10^6 m/s (e) 3.01×10^8 m/s

5. If three unequal capacitors, initially uncharged, are connected in series across a battery, which of the following statements is true? (a) The equivalent capacitance is greater than any of the individual capacitances. (b) The largest voltage appears across the capacitor with the smallest capacitance. (c) The largest voltage appears across the capacitor with the largest capacitance. (d) The capacitor with the largest capacitance has the greatest charge. (e) The capacitor with the smallest capacitance has the smallest charge.

6. Four point charges are positioned on the rim of a circle. The charge on each of the four is $+0.5$ μC, $+1.5$ μC, -1.0 μC, and -0.5 μC. If the electrical potential at the center of the circle due to the $+0.5$ μC charge alone is 4.5×10^4 V, what is the total electric potential at the center due to the four charges? (a) 18.0×10^4 V (b) 4.5×10^4 V (c) 0 (d) -4.5×10^4 V (e) 9.0×10^4 V

7. An electronics technician wishes to construct a parallel-plate capacitor using rutile ($\kappa = 1.00 \times 10^2$) as the dielectric. If the cross-sectional area of the plates is 1.00 cm², what is the capacitance if the rutile thickness is 1.00 mm? (a) 88.5 pF (b) 177.0 pF (c) 8.85 μF (d) 100.0 μF (e) 354 μF

8. A parallel-plate capacitor is connected to a battery. What happens to the stored energy if the plate separation is doubled while the capacitor remains connected to the battery? (a) It remains the same. (b) It is doubled. (c) It decreases by a factor of 2. (d) It decreases by a factor of 4. (e) It increases by a factor of 4.

9. A parallel-plate capacitor filled with air carries a charge Q. The battery is disconnected, and a slab of material with dielectric constant $\kappa = 2$ is inserted between the plates. Which of the following statements is correct? (a) The voltage across the capacitor decreases by a factor of 2. (b) The voltage across the capacitor is doubled. (c) The charge on the plates is doubled. (d) The charge on the plates decreases by a factor of 2. (e) The electric field is doubled.

10. After a parallel-plate capacitor is charged by a battery, it is disconnected from the battery and its plate separation is increased. Which of the following statements is correct? (a) The energy stored in the capacitor decreases. (b) The energy stored in the capacitor increases. (c) The electric field between the plates decreases. (d) The potential difference between the plates decreases. (e) The charge on the plates decreases.

11. A battery is attached to several different capacitors connected in parallel. Which of the following statements is true? (a) All the capacitors have the same charge, and the equivalent capacitance is greater than the capacitance of any of the capacitors in the group. (b) The capacitor with the largest capacitance carries the smallest charge. (c) The potential difference across each capacitor is the same, and the equivalent capacitance is greater than any of the capacitors in the group. (d) The capacitor with the smallest capacitance carries the largest charge. (e) The potential differences across the capacitors are the same only if the capacitances are the same.

12. A battery is attached across several different capacitors connected in series. Which of the following statements

are true? (a) All the capacitors have the same charge, and the equivalent capacitance is less than the capacitance of any of the individual capacitors in the group. (b) All the capacitors have the same charge, and the equivalent capacitance is greater than any of the individual capacitors in the group. (c) The capacitor with the largest capacitance carries the largest charge. (d) The potential difference across each capacitor must be the same. (e) The largest potential difference appears across the capacitor having the largest capacitance. (f) The largest potential difference appears across the capacitor with the smallest capacitance.

■ CONCEPTUAL QUESTIONS

WebAssign The conceptual questions in this chapter may be assigned online in Enhanced WebAssign.

1. (a) Describe the motion of a proton after it is released from rest in a uniform electric field. (b) Describe the changes (if any) in its kinetic energy and the electric potential energy associated with the proton.

2. Rank the potential energies of the four systems of particles shown in Figure CQ16.2 from largest to smallest. Include equalities if appropriate.

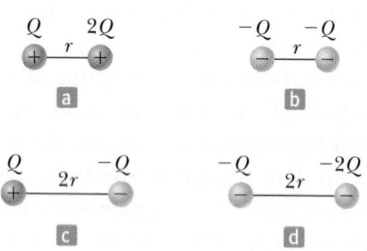

Figure CQ16.2

3. A parallel-plate capacitor is charged by a battery, and the battery is then disconnected from the capacitor. Because the charges on the capacitor plates are opposite in sign, they attract each other. Hence, it takes positive work to increase the plate separation. Show that the external work done when the plate separation is increased leads to an increase in the energy stored in the capacitor.

4. When charged particles are separated by an infinite distance, the electric potential energy of the pair is zero. When the particles are brought close, the electric potential energy of a pair with the same sign is positive, whereas the electric potential energy of a pair with opposite signs is negative. Explain.

5. Suppose you are sitting in a car and a 20-kV power line drops across the car. Should you stay in the car or get out? The power line potential is 20 kV compared to the potential of the ground.

6. Why is it important to avoid sharp edges or points on conductors used in high-voltage equipment?

7. Explain why, under static conditions, all points in a conductor must be at the same electric potential.

8. If you are given three different capacitors C_1, C_2, and C_3, how many different combinations of capacitance can you produce, using all capacitors in your circuits?

9. (a) Why is it dangerous to touch the terminals of a high-voltage capacitor even after the voltage source that charged the battery is disconnected from the capacitor? (b) What can be done to make the capacitor safe to handle after the voltage source has been removed?

10. The plates of a capacitor are connected to a battery. (a) What happens to the charge on the plates if the connecting wires are removed from the battery? (b) What happens to the charge if the wires are removed from the battery and connected to each other?

11. Rank the electric potentials at the four points shown in Figure CQ16.11 from largest to smallest.

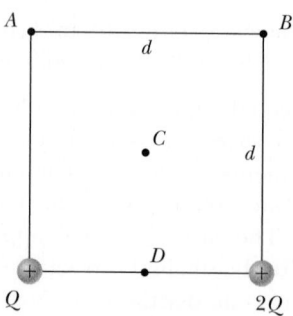

Figure CQ16.11

12. If you were asked to design a capacitor in which small size and large capacitance were required, what would be the two most important factors in your design?

13. Is it always possible to reduce a combination of capacitors to one equivalent capacitor with the rules developed in this chapter? Explain.

14. Explain why a dielectric increases the maximum operating voltage of a capacitor even though the physical size of the capacitor doesn't change.

◼ PROBLEMS

WebAssign The problems in this chapter may be assigned online in Enhanced WebAssign. Selected problems also have Watch It video solutions.

1. denotes straightforward problem; **2.** denotes intermediate problem;

3. denotes challenging problem

1. denotes full solution available in *Student Solutions Manual/Study Guide*

1. denotes problems most often assigned in Enhanced WebAssign

BIO denotes biomedical problems

GP denotes guided problems

M denotes Master It tutorial available in Enhanced WebAssign

Q|C denotes asking for quantitative and conceptual reasoning

S denotes symbolic reasoning problem

16.1 Potential Difference and Electric Potential

1. A uniform electric field of magnitude 375 N/C pointing in the positive *x*-direction acts on an electron, which is initially at rest. After the electron has moved 3.20 cm, what is (a) the work done by the field on the electron, (b) the change in potential energy associated with the electron, and (c) the velocity of the electron?

2. A proton is released from rest in a uniform electric field of magnitude 385 N/C. Find (a) the electric force on the proton, (b) the acceleration of the proton, and (c) the distance it travels in 2.00 μs.

3. **BIO** A potential difference of 90 mV exists between the inner and outer surfaces of a cell membrane. The inner surface is negative relative to the outer surface. How much work is required to eject a positive sodium ion (Na⁺) from the interior of the cell?

4. A metal sphere of radius 5.00 cm is initially uncharged. How many electrons would have to be placed on the sphere to produce an electric field of magnitude 1.50×10^5 N/C at a point 8.00 cm from the center of the sphere?

5. The potential difference between the accelerating plates of a TV set is about 25 kV. If the distance between the plates is 1.5 cm, find the magnitude of the uniform electric field in the region between the plates.

6. A point charge $q = +40.0$ μC moves from *A* to *B* separated by a distance $d = 0.180$ m in the presence of an external electric field $\vec{E}$ of magnitude 275 N/C directed toward the right as in Figure P16.6. Find (a) the electric force exerted on the charge, (b) the work done by the electric force, (c) the change in the electric potential energy of the charge, and (d) the potential difference between *A* and *B*.

Figure P16.6

7. **M** Oppositely charged parallel plates are separated by 5.33 mm. A potential difference of 600 V exists between the plates. (a) What is the magnitude of the electric field between the plates? (b) What is the magnitude of the force on an electron between the plates? (c) How much work must be done on the electron to move it to the negative plate if it is initially positioned 2.90 mm from the positive plate?

8. **Q|C** **S** (a) Find the potential difference ΔV_e required to stop an electron (called a "stopping potential") moving with an initial speed of 2.85×10^7 m/s. (b) Would a proton traveling at the same speed require a greater or lesser magnitude potential difference? Explain. (c) Find a symbolic expression for the ratio of the proton stopping potential and the electron stopping potential, $\Delta V_p / \Delta V_e$. The answer should be in terms of the proton mass m_p and electron mass m_e.

9. **Q|C** A 74.0-g block carrying a charge $Q = 35.0$ μC is connected to a spring for which $k = 78.0$ N/m. The block lies on a frictionless, horizontal surface and is immersed in a uniform electric field of magnitude $E = 4.86 \times 10^4$ N/C directed as shown in Figure P16.9. If the block is released from rest when the spring is unstretched ($x = 0$), (a) by what maximum distance does the block move from its initial position? (b) Find the subsequent equilibrium position of the block and the amplitude of its motion. (c) Using conservation of energy, find a symbolic relationship giving the potential difference between its initial position and the point of maximum extension in terms of the spring constant k, the amplitude A, and the charge Q.

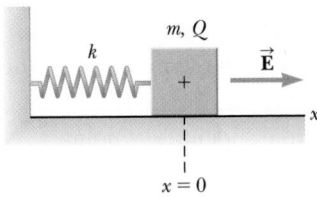

Figure P16.9

10. On planet Tehar, the free-fall acceleration is the same as that on the Earth, but there is also a strong downward electric field that is uniform close to the planet's surface. A 2.00-kg ball having a charge of 5.00 μC is thrown upward at a speed of 20.1 m/s. It hits the ground after an interval of 4.10 s. What is the potential difference between the starting point and the top point of the trajectory?

16.2 Electric Potential and Potential Energy Due to Point Charges

16.3 Potentials and Charged Conductors

16.4 Equipotential Surfaces

11. QC An electron is at the origin. (a) Calculate the electric potential V_A at point A, $x = 0.250$ cm. (b) Calculate the electric potential V_B at point B, $x = 0.750$ cm. What is the potential difference $V_B - V_A$? (c) Would a negatively charged particle placed at point A necessarily go through this same potential difference upon reaching point B? Explain.

12. The two charges in Figure P16.12 are separated by $d = 2.00$ cm. Find the electric potential at (a) point A and (b) point B, which is halfway between the charges.

Figure P16.12

13. (a) Find the electric potential, taking zero at infinity, at the upper right corner (the corner without a charge) of the rectangle in Figure P16.13. (b) Repeat if the 2.00-μC charge is replaced with a charge of -2.00 μC.

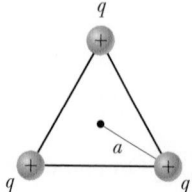

Figure P16.13 Problems 13 and 14.

14. Three charges are situated at corners of a rectangle as in Figure P16.13. How much energy would be expended in moving the 8.00-μC charge to infinity?

15. M QC Two point charges $Q_1 = +5.00$ nC and $Q_2 = -3.00$ nC are separated by 35.0 cm. (a) What is the electric potential at a point midway between the charges? (b) What is the potential energy of the pair of charges? What is the significance of the algebraic sign of your answer?

16. QC S Three identical point charges each of charge q are located at the vertices of an equilateral triangle as in Figure P16.16. The distance from the center of the triangle to each vertex is a. (a) Show that the electric field at the center of the triangle is zero. (b) Find a symbolic expression for the electric potential at the center of the triangle. (c) Give a physical explanation of the fact that the electric potential is not zero, yet the electric field is zero at the center.

Figure P16.16

17. The three charges in Figure P16.17 are at the vertices of an isosceles triangle. Let $q = 7.00$ nC and calculate the electric potential at the midpoint of the base.

Figure P16.17

18. S A positive point charge $q = +2.50$ nC is located at $x = 1.20$ m and a negative charge of $-2q = -5.00$ nC is located at the origin as in Figure P16.18. (a) Sketch the electric potential versus x for points along the x-axis in the range -1.50 m $< x <$ 1.50 m. (b) Find a symbolic expression for the potential on the x-axis at an arbitrary point P between the two charges. (c) Find the electric potential at $x = 0.600$ m. (d) Find the point along the x-axis between the two charges where the electric potential is zero.

Figure P16.18

19. GP A proton is located at the origin, and a second proton is located on the x-axis at $x = 6.00$ fm (1 fm = 10^{-15} m). (a) Calculate the electric potential energy associated with this configuration. (b) An alpha particle (charge = $2e$, mass = 6.64×10^{-27} kg) is now placed at $(x, y) = (3.00, 3.00)$ fm. Calculate the electric potential energy associated with this configuration. (c) Starting with the three-particle system, find the change in electric potential energy if the alpha particle is allowed to escape to infinity while the two protons remain fixed in place. (Throughout, neglect any radiation effects.) (d) Use conservation of energy to calculate the speed of the alpha particle at infinity. (e) If the two protons are released from rest and the alpha particle remains fixed, calculate the speed of the protons at infinity.

20. QC A proton and an alpha particle (charge = $2e$, mass = 6.64×10^{-27} kg) are initially at rest, separated by 4.00×10^{-15} m. (a) If they are both released simultaneously, explain why you can't find their velocities at infinity using only conservation of energy. (b) What other conservation law can be applied in this case? (c) Find the speeds of the proton and alpha particle, respectively, at infinity.

21. A tiny sphere of mass 8.00 μg and charge -2.80 nC is initially at a distance of 1.60 μm from a fixed charge of $+8.50$ nC. If the 8.00-mg sphere is released from rest, find (a) its kinetic energy when it is 0.500 μm from the fixed charge and (b) its speed when it is 0.500 μm from the fixed charge.

22. The metal sphere of a small Van de Graaff generator illustrated in Figure 15.23 has a radius of 18 cm. When the electric field at the surface of the sphere reaches 3.0×10^6 V/m, the air breaks down, and the generator discharges. What is the maximum potential the sphere can have before breakdown occurs?

23. In Rutherford's famous scattering experiments that led to the planetary model of the atom, alpha particles (having charges of $+2e$ and masses of 6.64×10^{-27} kg) were fired toward a gold nucleus with charge $+79e$. An alpha particle, initially very far from the gold nucleus, is fired at 2.00×10^7 m/s directly toward the nucleus, as in Figure P16.23. How close does the alpha particle get to the gold nucleus before turning around? Assume the gold nucleus remains stationary.

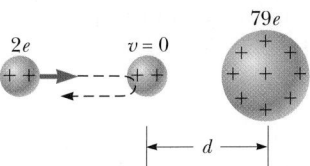

Figure P16.23

24. **S** Four point charges each having charge Q are located at the corners of a square having sides of length a. Find symbolic expressions for (a) the total electric potential at the center of the square due to the four charges and (b) the work required to bring a fifth charge q from infinity to the center of the square.

16.6 Capacitance

16.7 The Parallel-Plate Capacitor

25. Consider the Earth and a cloud layer 800 m above the planet to be the plates of a parallel-plate capacitor. (a) If the cloud layer has an area of 1.0 km^2 = 1.0 $\times$ 10^6 m^2, what is the capacitance? (b) If an electric field strength greater than 3.0×10^6 N/C causes the air to break down and conduct charge (lightning), what is the maximum charge the cloud can hold?

26. (a) When a 9.00-V battery is connected to the plates of a capacitor, it stores a charge of 27.0 μC. What is the value of the capacitance? (b) If the same capacitor is connected to a 12.0-V battery, what charge is stored?

27. An air-filled parallel-plate capacitor has plates of area 2.30 cm^2 separated by 1.50 mm. The capacitor is connected to a 12.0-V battery. (a) Find the value of its capacitance. (b) What is the charge on the capacitor? (c) What is the magnitude of the uniform electric field between the plates?

28. Two conductors having net charges of +10.0 μC and −10.0 μC have a potential difference of 10.0 V between them. (a) Determine the capacitance of the system. (b) What is the potential difference between the two

conductors if the charges on each are increased to +100 μC and −100 μC?

29. **M** An air-filled capacitor consists of two parallel plates, each with an area of 7.60 cm^2 and separated by a distance of 1.80 mm. If a 20.0-V potential difference is applied to these plates, calculate (a) the electric field between the plates, (b) the capacitance, and (c) the charge on each plate.

30. A 1-megabit computer memory chip contains many 60.0×10^{-15}-F capacitors. Each capacitor has a plate area of 21.0×10^{-12} m^2. Determine the plate separation of such a capacitor. (Assume a parallel-plate configuration.) The diameter of an atom is on the order of 10^{-10} m = 1 Å. Express the plate separation in angstroms.

31. **QC** A parallel-plate capacitor with area 0.200 m^2 and plate separation of 3.00 mm is connected to a 6.00-V battery. (a) What is the capacitance? (b) How much charge is stored on the plates? (c) What is the electric field between the plates? (d) Find the magnitude of the charge density on each plate. (e) Without disconnecting the battery, the plates are moved farther apart. Qualitatively, what happens to each of the previous answers?

32. A small object with a mass of 350 μg carries a charge of 30.0 nC and is suspended by a thread between the vertical plates of a parallel-plate capacitor. The plates are separated by 4.00 cm. If the thread makes an angle of 15.0° with the vertical, what is the potential difference between the plates?

16.8 Combinations of Capacitors

33. Given a 2.50-μF capacitor, a 6.25-μF capacitor, and a 6.00-V battery, find the charge on each capacitor if you connect them (a) in series across the battery and (b) in parallel across the battery.

34. Two capacitors, $C_1 = 5.00$ μF and $C_2 = 12.0$ μF, are connected in parallel, and the resulting combination is connected to a 9.00-V battery. Find (a) the equivalent capacitance of the combination, (b) the potential difference across each capacitor, and (c) the charge stored on each capacitor.

35. Find (a) the equivalent capacitance of the capacitors in Figure P16.35, (b) the charge on each capacitor, and (c) the potential difference across each capacitor.

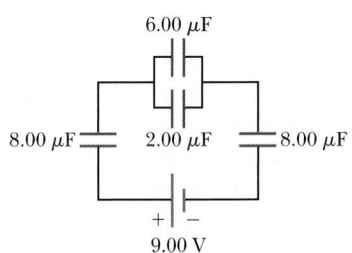

Figure P16.35

36. Two capacitors give an equivalent capacitance of 9.00 pF when connected in parallel and an equivalent capacitance of 2.00 pF when connected in series. What is the capacitance of each capacitor?

37. For the system of capacitors shown in Figure P16.37, find (a) the equivalent capacitance of the system, (b) the charge on each capacitor, and (c) the potential difference across each capacitor.

Figure P16.37 Problems 37 and 56.

38. **GP** Consider the combination of capacitors in Figure P16.38. (a) Find the equivalent single capacitance of the two capacitors in series and redraw the diagram (called diagram 1) with this equivalent capacitance. (b) In diagram 1 find the equivalent capacitance of the three capacitors in parallel and redraw the diagram as a single battery and single capacitor in a loop. (c) Compute the charge on the single equivalent capacitor. (d) Returning to diagram 1, compute the charge on each individual capacitor. Does the sum agree with the value found in part (c)? (e) What is the charge on the 24.0-μF capacitor and on the 8.00-μF capacitor? Compute the voltage drop across (f) the 24.0-μF capacitor and (g) the 8.00-μF capacitor.

Figure P16.38

39. Find the charge on each of the capacitors in Figure P16.39.

Figure P16.39

40. **QC** **S** Three capacitors are connected to a battery as shown in Figure P16.40. Their capacitances are $C_1 = 3C$, $C_2 = C$, and $C_3 = 5C$. (a) What is the equivalent capacitance of this set

Figure P16.40

of capacitors? (b) State the ranking of the capacitors according to the charge they store from largest to smallest. (c) Rank the capacitors according to the potential differences across them from largest to smallest. (d) Assume C_3 is increased. Explain what happens to the charge stored by each capacitor.

41. A 25.0-μF capacitor and a 40.0-μF capacitor are charged by being connected across separate 50.0-V batteries. (a) Determine the resulting charge on each capacitor. (b) The capacitors are then disconnected from their batteries and connected to each other, with each negative plate connected to the other positive plate. What is the final charge of each capacitor? (c) What is the final potential difference across the 40.0-μF capacitor?

42. (a) Find the equivalent capacitance between points a and b for the group of capacitors connected as shown in Figure P16.42 if $C_1 = 5.00$ μF, $C_2 = 10.00$ μF, and $C_3 = 2.00$ μF. (b) If the potential between points a and b is 60.0 V, what charge is stored on C_3?

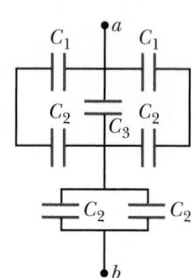

Figure P16.42

43. A 1.00-μF capacitor is charged by being connected across a 10.0-V battery. It is then disconnected from the battery and connected across an uncharged 2.00-μF capacitor. Determine the resulting charge on each capacitor.

44. **M** Four capacitors are connected as shown in Figure P16.44. (a) Find the equivalent capacitance between points a and b. (b) Calculate the charge on each capacitor, taking $\Delta V_{ab} = 15.0$ V.

Figure P16.44

16.9 Energy Stored in a Charged Capacitor

45. A 12.0-V battery is connected to a 4.50-μF capacitor. How much energy is stored in the capacitor?

46. **QC** Two capacitors, $C_1 = 18.0$ μF and $C_2 = 36.0$ μF, are connected in series, and a 12.0-V battery is connected across them. (a) Find the equivalent capacitance, and the energy contained in this equivalent capacitor. (b) Find the energy stored in each individual capacitor. Show that the sum of these two energies is the same as the energy found in part (a). Will this equality always be true, or does it depend on the number of capacitors and their capacitances? (c) If the same capacitors were connected in parallel, what potential difference would be required across them so that the combination stores the same energy as in part (a)? Which capacitor stores more energy in this situation, C_1 or C_2?

47. A parallel-plate capacitor has capacitance 3.00 μF. (a) How much energy is stored in the capacitor if it is connected to a 6.00-V battery? (b) If the battery is disconnected and the distance between the charged plates doubled, what is the energy stored? (c) The battery is subsequently reattached to the capacitor, but the plate separation remains as in part (b). How much energy is stored? (Answer each part in microjoules.)

48. A certain storm cloud has a potential difference of 1.00×10^8 V relative to a tree. If, during a lightning storm, 50.0 C of charge is transferred through this potential difference and 1.00% of the energy is absorbed by the tree, how much water (sap in the tree) initially at 30.0°C can be boiled away? Water has a specific heat of 4 186 J/kg°C, a boiling point of 100°C, and a heat of vaporization of 2.26×10^6 J/kg.

16.10 Capacitors with Dielectrics

49. **Q|C** The voltage across an air-filled parallel-plate capacitor is measured to be 85.0 V. When a dielectric is inserted and completely fills the space between the plates as in Figure P16.49, the voltage drops to 25.0 V. (a) What is the dielectric constant of the inserted material? Can you identify the dielectric? (b) If the dielectric doesn't completely fill the space between the plates, what could you conclude about the voltage across the plates?

Figure P16.49

50. (a) How much charge can be placed on a capacitor with air between the plates before it breaks down if the area of each plate is 5.00 cm²? (b) Find the maximum charge if polystyrene is used between the plates instead of air. Assume the dielectric strength of air is 3.00×10^6 V/m and that of polystyrene is 24.0×10^6 V/m.

51. Determine (a) the capacitance and (b) the maximum voltage that can be applied to a Teflon-filled parallel-plate capacitor having a plate area of 175 cm² and an insulation thickness of 0.040 0 mm.

52. Consider a plane parallel-plate capacitor made of two strips of aluminum foil separated by a layer of paraffin-coated paper. Each strip of foil and paper is 7.00 cm wide. The foil is 0.004 00 mm thick, and the paper is 0.025 0 mm thick and has a dielectric constant of 3.70. What length should the strips be if a capacitance of 9.50×10^{-8} F is desired? (If, after this plane capacitor is formed, a second paper strip can be added below the foil-paper-foil stack and the resulting assembly rolled into a cylindrical form—similar to that shown in Figure 16.26—the capacitance can be doubled because both surfaces of each foil strip would then store charge. Without the second strip of paper, however, rolling the layers would result in a short circuit.)

53. **BIO** A model of a red blood cell portrays the cell as a spherical capacitor, a positively charged liquid sphere of surface area A separated from the surrounding negatively charged fluid by a membrane of thickness t. Tiny electrodes introduced into the interior of the cell show a potential difference of 100 mV across the membrane. The membrane's thickness is estimated to be 100 nm and has a dielectric constant of 5.00. (a) If an average red blood cell has a mass of 1.00×10^{-12} kg, estimate the volume of the cell and thus find its surface area. The density of blood is 1 100 kg/m³. (b) Estimate the capacitance of the cell by assuming the membrane surfaces act as parallel plates. (c) Calculate the charge on the surface of the membrane. How many electronic charges does the surface charge represent?

Additional Problems

54. When a potential difference of 150 V is applied to the plates of an air-filled parallel-plate capacitor, the plates carry a surface charge density of 3.00×10^{-10} C/cm². What is the spacing between the plates?

55. **S** Three parallel-plate capacitors are constructed, each having the same plate area A and with C_1 having plate spacing d_1, C_2 having plate spacing d_2, and C_3 having plate spacing d_3. Show that the total capacitance C of the three capacitors connected in series is the same as a capacitor of plate area A and with plate spacing $d = d_1 + d_2 + d_3$.

56. **Q|C** For the system of four capacitors shown in Figure P16.37, find (a) the total energy stored in the system and (b) the energy stored by each capacitor. (c) Compare the sum of the answers in part (b) with your result to part (a) and explain your observation.

57. **S** A parallel-plate capacitor with a plate separation d has a capacitance C_0 in the absence of a dielectric. A slab of dielectric material of dielectric constant κ and thickness $d/3$ is then inserted between the plates as in

Figure P16.57a. Show that the capacitance of this partially filled capacitor is given by

$$C = \left(\frac{3\kappa}{2\kappa + 1}\right)C_0$$

Hint: Treat the system as two capacitors connected in series as in Figure P16.57b, one with dielectric in it and the other one empty.

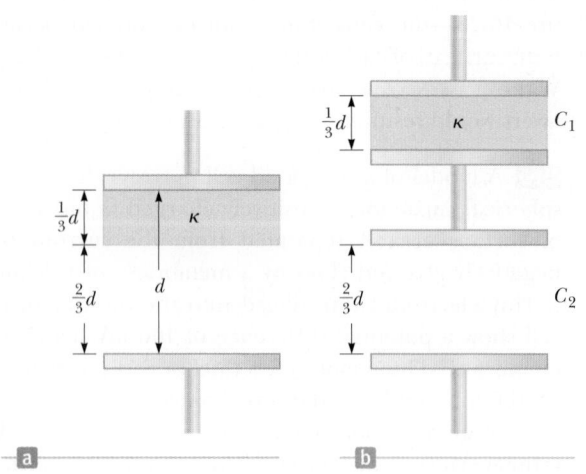

Figure P16.57

58. **S** Two capacitors give an equivalent capacitance of C_p when connected in parallel and an equivalent capacitance of C_s when connected in series. What is the capacitance of each capacitor?

59. **M** A parallel-plate capacitor is constructed using a dielectric material whose dielectric constant is 3.00 and whose dielectric strength is 2.00×10^8 V/m. The desired capacitance is 0.250 μF, and the capacitor must withstand a maximum potential difference of 4.00 kV. Find the minimum area of the capacitor plates.

60. Two charges of 1.0 μC and -2.0 μC are 0.50 m apart at two vertices of an equilateral triangle as in Figure P16.60. (a) What is the electric potential due to the 1.0-μC charge at the third vertex, point P? (b) What is the electric potential due to the -2.0-μC charge at P? (c) Find the total electric potential at P. (d) What is the work required to move a 3.0-μC charge from infinity to P?

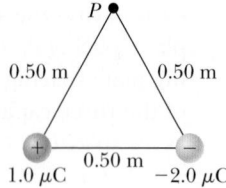

Figure P16.60

61. Find the equivalent capacitance of the group of capacitors shown in Figure P16.61.

Figure P16.61

62. A spherical capacitor consists of a spherical conducting shell of radius b and charge $-Q$ concentric with a smaller conducting sphere of radius a and charge Q. (a) Find the capacitance of this device. (b) Show that as the radius b of the outer sphere approaches infinity, the capacitance approaches the value $a/k_e = 4\pi\epsilon_0 a$.

63. **BIO** The immediate cause of many deaths is ventricular fibrillation, an uncoordinated quivering of the heart, as opposed to proper beating. An electric shock to the chest can cause momentary paralysis of the heart muscle, after which the heart will sometimes start organized beating again. A *defibrillator* is a device that applies a strong electric shock to the chest over a time of a few milliseconds. The device contains a capacitor of a few microfarads, charged to several thousand volts. Electrodes called paddles, about 8 cm across and coated with conducting paste, are held against the chest on both sides of the heart. Their handles are insulated to prevent injury to the operator, who calls "Clear!" and pushes a button on one paddle to discharge the capacitor through the patient's chest. Assume an energy of 300 W · s is to be delivered from a 30.0-μF capacitor. To what potential difference must it be charged?

64. When a certain air-filled parallel-plate capacitor is connected across a battery, it acquires a charge of 150 μC on each plate. While the battery connection is maintained, a dielectric slab is inserted into, and fills, the region between the plates. This results in the accumulation of an additional charge of 200 μC on each plate. What is the dielectric constant of the slab?

65. Capacitors $C_1 = 6.0$ μF and $C_2 = 2.0$ μF are charged as a parallel combination across a 250-V battery. The capacitors are disconnected from the battery and from each other. They are then connected positive plate to negative plate and negative plate to positive plate. Calculate the resulting charge on each capacitor.

66. **S** Two positive charges each of charge q are fixed on the y-axis, one at $y = d$ and the other at $y = -d$ as in Figure P16.66. A third positive charge $2q$ located on the x-axis at $x = 2d$ is released from rest. Find symbolic expressions for (a) the total electric potential due to the first two charges at the location of the charge $2q$, (b) the electric potential energy of the charge $2q$, (c) the kinetic energy of the charge $2q$ after it has moved infinitely far from the other charges, and (d) the speed of the charge $2q$ after it has moved infinitely far from the other charges if its mass is m.

Figure P16.66

67. Metal sphere A of radius 12.0 cm carries 6.00 μC of charge, and metal sphere B of radius 18.0 cm carries -4.00 μC of charge. If the two spheres are attached by a very long conducting thread, what is the final distribution of charge on the two spheres?

68. An electron is fired at a speed $v_0 = 5.6 \times 10^6$ m/s and at an angle $\theta_0 = -45°$ between two parallel conducting plates that are $D = 2.0$ mm apart, as in Figure P16.68. If the voltage difference between the plates is $\Delta V = 100$ V, determine (a) how close, d, the electron will get to the bottom plate and (b) where the electron will strike the top plate.

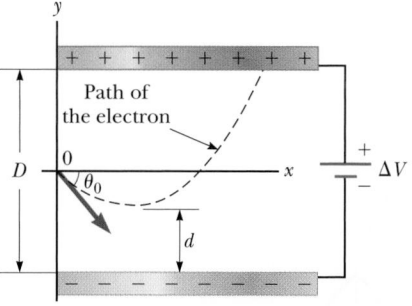

Figure P16.68

■ AP* REVIEW QUESTIONS

1. Two charged metal plates with an electric field E between them are placed a distance d apart. What can be changed to create the largest potential difference between the plates?

   (A) $2E, 2d$

   (B) $3E, d/3$

   (C) $E/2, d/4$

   (D) $E/4, 4d$

   (E) $E/2, 3d$

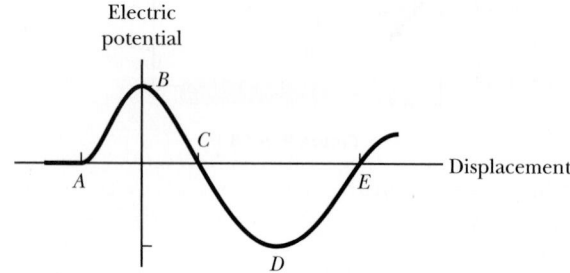

2. A proton is located in a region with the electric potential shown on the graph. If the proton is released at point D, where will the proton move?

   (A) Move to A

   (B) Move to B

   (C) Move to C

   (D) Stay at D

   (E) Move to E

Questions 3 and 4

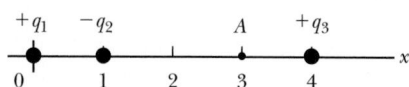

3. Three point charges, $q_1 = +6$ nC, $q_2 = -4$ nC, and $q_3 = +2$ nC, are spaced apart on the x-axis as shown in the diagram above. What is the electric potential at point A?

   (A) 18 V

   (B) 54 V

   (C) 1.8×10^{10} V

   (D) 5.4×10^{10} V

   (E) More information is needed

4. How far away from point A would a new point charge ($q_4 = -10$ nC) need to be placed to have the potential at A be equal to zero?

   (A) 1.7 m to left of A

   (B) 1.7 m to right of A

   (C) 5 m to left of A

   (D) 5 m to right of A

   (E) (C) and (D) are both correct as direction does not matter

5. A capacitor with no dielectric was built with only 50% of the capacitance required in a circuit. How can the capacitor be adjusted to create the 100% capacitance?

   (A) $A, 2d$

   (B) $A, d/2$

   (C) $2A, d/3$

   (D) $3A, 3d$

   (E) $A/2, 2d$

6. A capacitor with capacitance C_0 was built and placed in a circuit. If the distance between the plates is cut in half and the area of the plates is doubled, what is the overall effect on the capacitance?

   (A) $\dfrac{C_0}{2}$

   (B) C_0

   (C) $2C_0$

   (D) $4C_0$

   (E) $8C_0$

7. A capacitor has a capacitance C_0, plate area A, and plate separation d. The capacitor is changed so the new capacitance is $C = 9C_0$. What was changed to make this possible?

   (A) $A, d/3$

   (B) $3A, 3d$

   (C) $9A, d$

   (D) $9A, 3d$

   (E) $3A, d/3$

Questions 8 and 9

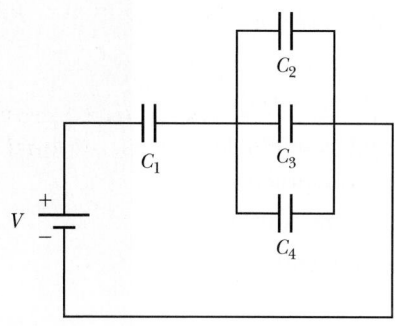

8. In the circuit above, what will happen to the total charge Q stored in the circuit when S_1 is closed and S_2 is left open?

(A) Increases

(B) Decreases

(C) Stays the same

(D) Drops to zero

(E) More information is needed

9. In the circuit above, what will happen to the total charge Q stored in the circuit when S_1 remains closed and S_2 is now closed?

(A) Increases

(B) Decreases

(C) Stays the same

(D) Drops to zero

(E) More information is needed

10. For the circuit above, what is the equivalent capacitance if all capacitors are 2 F?

(A) 0.7 F

(B) 1.5 F

(C) 2.7 F

(D) 3.5 F

(E) 8 F

11. A capacitor currently stores 4 J of energy and needs to double that. What can the engineer do to increase the energy stored in the capacitor?

(A) $V, 2A, 2d$

(B) $3V, A/2, d/2$

(C) $2V, 2A, 2d$

(D) $4V, A/4, 2d$

(E) $2V, A, 3d$

12. A capacitor's area is cut by 1/3, while its plate separation is tripled. If the voltage is doubled, what has happened to the energy stored compared to its original state?

(A) $\dfrac{2}{9} U_C$

(B) $\dfrac{4}{9} U_C$

(C) U_C

(D) $2U_C$

(E) $4U_C$

The blue glow comes from positively-charged xenon atoms that are electrostatically accelerated, then expelled from an ion engine prototype. The current of ions produces ninety millinewtons of thrust continuously for months at a time. Electrons must be fed back into the exhaust to prevent a buildup of negative charge. Such engines are highly efficient and suitable for extended deep space missions.

Courtesy of NASA Jet Propulsion Laboratory/PIA04238

17 Current and Resistance

Many practical applications and devices are based on the principles of static electricity, but electricity was destined to become an inseparable part of our daily lives when scientists learned how to produce a continuous flow of charge for relatively long periods of time using batteries. The battery or voltaic cell was invented in 1800 by Italian physicist Alessandro Volta. Batteries supplied a continuous flow of charge at low potential, in contrast to earlier electrostatic devices that produced a tiny flow of charge at high potential for brief periods. This steady source of electric current allowed scientists to perform experiments to learn how to control the flow of electric charges in circuits. Today, electric currents power our lights, radios, television sets, air conditioners, computers, and refrigerators. They ignite the gasoline in automobile engines, travel through miniature components making up the chips of microcomputers, and provide the power for countless other invaluable tasks.

In this chapter we define current and discuss some of the factors that contribute to the resistance to the flow of charge in conductors. We also discuss energy transformations in electric circuits. These topics will be the foundation for additional work with circuits in later chapters.

17.1 Electric Current

In Figure 17.1 charges move in a direction perpendicular to a surface of area A. (The area could be the cross-sectional area of a wire, for example.) **The current is the rate at which charge flows through this surface.**

Suppose ΔQ is the amount of charge that flows through an area A in a time interval Δt and that the direction of flow is perpendicular to the area. Then the **average current I_{av}** is equal to the amount of charge divided by the time interval:

$$I_{av} \equiv \frac{\Delta Q}{\Delta t}$$

[17.1a]

SI unit: coulomb/second (C/s), or the ampere (A)

Tip 17.1 *Current Flow Is Redundant*

The phrases *flow of current* and *current flow* are commonly used, but here the word *flow* is redundant because current is already defined as a flow (of charge). Avoid this construction!

Current is composed of individual moving charges, so for an extremely low current, it is conceivable that a single charge could pass through area A in one instant and no charge in the next instant. All currents, then, are essentially averages over time. Given the very large number of charges usually involved, however, it makes sense to define an instantaneous current.

The **instantaneous current I** is the limit of the average current as the time interval goes to zero:

$$I = \lim_{\Delta t \to 0} I_{av} = \lim_{\Delta t \to 0} \frac{\Delta Q}{\Delta t}$$

[17.1b]

SI unit: coulomb/second (C/s), or the ampere (A)

When the current is steady, the average and instantaneous currents are the same. Note that one ampere of current is equivalent to one coulomb of charge passing through the cross-sectional area in a time interval of 1 s.

When charges flow through a surface as in Figure 17.1, they can be positive, negative, or both. **The direction of conventional current used in this book is the direction positive charges flow.** (This historical convention originated about 200 years ago, when the ideas of positive and negative charges were introduced.) In a common conductor such as copper, the current is due to the motion of negatively charged electrons, so the direction of the current is opposite the direction of motion of the electrons. On the other hand, for a beam of positively charged protons in an accelerator, the current is in the same direction as the motion of the protons. In some cases—gases and electrolytes, for example—the current is the result of the flows of both positive and negative charges. Moving charges, whether positive or negative, are referred to as *charge carriers*. In a metal, for example, the charge carriers are electrons.

In electrostatics, where charges are stationary, the electric potential is the same everywhere in a conductor. That is no longer true for conductors carrying current: as charges move along a wire, the electric potential is continually decreasing (except in the special case of superconductors). The decreasing electric potential means that the moving charges lose energy according to the relationship $\Delta U_{charges} = q\Delta V$, while an energy $\Delta U_{wire} = -q\Delta V$ is deposited in the current-carrying wire. (Those expressions derive from Equation 16.2.) If q is taken to be positive, corresponding to the convention of positive current, then $\Delta V = V_f - V_i$ is negative because, in a circuit, positive charges move from regions of high potential to regions of low potential. That in turn means $\Delta U_{charges} = q\Delta V$ is negative, as it should be, because the moving charges lose energy. Often only the magnitude is desired, however, in which case absolute values are substituted into q and ΔV. If the current is constant, then dividing the energy by the elapsed time yields the power delivered to the circuit element, such as a lightbulb filament.

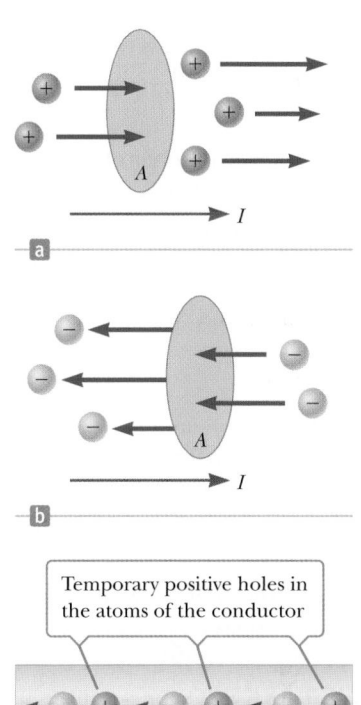

Temporary positive holes in the atoms of the conductor

Figure 17.1 The time rate of flow of charge through area A is the current I. (a) The direction of current is the same as the flow of positive charge. (b) Negative charges flowing to the left is equivalent to an equal amount of positive charge flowing to the right. (c) In a conductor, positive holes open in the lattice of the conductor's atoms as electrons move in response to a potential. Negative electrons moving actively to the left are equivalent to positive holes migrating to the right.

▪ EXAMPLE 17.1 | Turn On the Light

GOAL Apply the concept of current.

PROBLEM The amount of charge that passes through the filament of a certain lightbulb in 2.00 s is 1.67 C. Find **(a)** the average current in the lightbulb and **(b)** the number of electrons that pass through the filament in 5.00 s. **(c)** If the current is supplied by a 12.0-V battery, what total energy is delivered to the lightbulb filament? What is the average power?

STRATEGY Substitute into Equation 17.1a for part (a), then multiply the answer by the time given in part (b) to get the total charge that passes in that time. The total charge equals the number N of electrons going through the circuit times the charge per electron. To obtain the energy delivered to the filament, multiply the potential difference, ΔV, by the total charge. Dividing the energy by time yields the average power.

....

SOLUTION

(a) Compute the average current in the lightbulb.

Substitute the charge and time into Equation 17.1a:

$$I_{av} = \frac{\Delta Q}{\Delta t} = \frac{1.67 \text{ C}}{2.00 \text{ s}} = \boxed{0.835 \text{ A}}$$

(b) Find the number of electrons passing through the filament in 5.00 s.

The total number N of electrons times the charge per electron equals the total charge, $I_{av} \Delta t$:

(1) $\quad Nq = I_{av} \Delta t$

Substitute and solve for N:

$N(1.60 \times 10^{-19} \text{ C/electron}) = (0.835 \text{ A})(5.00 \text{ s})$

$N = \boxed{2.61 \times 10^{19} \text{ electrons}}$

(c) What total energy is delivered to the lightbulb filament? What is the average power?

Multiply the potential difference by the total charge to obtain the energy transferred to the filament:

(2) $\quad \Delta U = q\Delta V = (1.67 \text{ C})(12.0 \text{ V}) = \boxed{20.0 \text{ J}}$

Divide the energy by the elapsed time to calculate the average power:

$$P_{av} = \frac{\Delta U}{\Delta t} = \frac{20.0 \text{ J}}{2.00 \text{ s}} = \boxed{10.0 \text{ W}}$$

....

REMARKS It's important to use units to ensure the correctness of equations such as Equation (1). Notice the enormous number of electrons that pass through a given point in a typical circuit. Magnitudes were used in calculating the energies in Equation (2). Technically, the charge carriers are electrons with negative charge moving from a lower potential to a higher potential, so the change in their energy is $\Delta U_{charge} = q\Delta V = (-1.67 \text{ C})(+12.0 \text{ V}) = -20.0 \text{ J}$, a loss of energy that is delivered to the filament, $\Delta U_{fil} = -\Delta U_{charge} = +20.0 \text{ J}$. The energy and power, calculated here using the definitions of Chapter 16, will be further addressed in Section 17.6.

QUESTION 17.1 Is it possible to have an instantaneous current of $e/2$ per second? Explain. Can the average current take this value?

EXERCISE 17.1 A 9.00-V battery delivers a current of 1.34 A to the lightbulb filament of a pocket flashlight. (a) How much charge passes through the filament in 2.00 min? (b) How many electrons pass through the filament? Calculate (c) the energy delivered to the filament during that time and (d) the power delivered by the battery.

ANSWERS (a) 161 C (b) 1.01×10^{21} electrons (c) 1.45×10^{3} J (d) 12.1 W

▪ Quick Quiz

17.1 Consider positive and negative charges moving horizontally through the four regions in Figure 17.2. Rank the magnitudes of the currents in these four regions from lowest to highest. (I_a is the current in Figure 17.2a, I_b the current in Figure 17.2b, etc.) (a) I_d, I_a, I_c, I_b (b) I_a, I_c, I_b, I_d (c) I_c, I_a, I_d, I_b (d) I_d, I_b, I_c, I_a (e) I_a, I_b, I_c, I_d (f) None of these

a   b   c   d

Figure 17.2
(Quick Quiz 17.1)

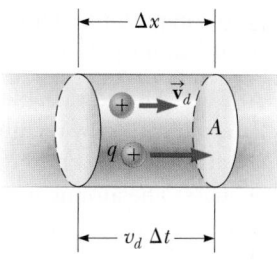

Figure 17.3 A section of a uniform conductor of cross-sectional area A. The charge carriers move with a speed v_d, and the distance they travel in time Δt is given by $\Delta x = v_d \Delta t$. The number of mobile charge carriers in the section of length Δx is given by $nAv_d\Delta t$, where n is the number of mobile carriers per unit volume.

17.2 A Microscopic View: Current and Drift Speed

Macroscopic currents can be related to the motion of the microscopic charge carriers making up the current. It turns out that current depends on the average speed of the charge carriers in the direction of the current, the number of charge carriers per unit volume, and the size of the charge carried by each.

Consider identically charged particles moving in a conductor of cross-sectional area A (Fig. 17.3). The volume of an element of length Δx of the conductor is $A\Delta x$. If n represents the number of mobile charge carriers per unit volume, the number of carriers in the volume element is $nA\,\Delta x$. The mobile charge ΔQ in this element is therefore

$$\Delta Q = \text{number of carriers} \times \text{charge per carrier} = (nA\,\Delta x)q$$

where q is the charge on each carrier. If the carriers move with a constant average speed called the **drift speed** v_d, the distance they move in the time interval Δt is $\Delta x = v_d\,\Delta t$. We can therefore write

$$\Delta Q = (nAv_d\,\Delta t)q$$

If we divide both sides of this equation by Δt and take the limit as Δt goes to zero, we see that the current in the conductor is

$$I = \lim_{\Delta t \to 0} \frac{\Delta Q}{\Delta t} = nqv_dA \qquad \text{[17.2]}$$

To understand the meaning of drift speed, consider a conductor in which the charge carriers are free electrons. If the conductor is isolated, these electrons undergo random motion similar to the motion of the molecules of a gas. The drift speed is normally much smaller than the free electrons' average speed between collisions with the fixed atoms of the conductor. When a potential difference is applied between the ends of the conductor (say, with a battery), an electric field is set up in the conductor, creating an electric force on the electrons and hence a current. In reality, the electrons don't simply move in straight lines along the conductor. Instead, they undergo repeated collisions with the atoms of the metal, and the result is a complicated zigzag motion with only a small average drift speed along the wire (Active Fig. 17.4). The energy transferred from the electrons to the metal atoms during a collision increases the vibrational energy of the atoms and causes a corresponding increase in the temperature of the conductor. Despite the collisions, however, the electrons move slowly along the conductor in a direction opposite $\vec{\mathbf{E}}$ with the drift velocity $\vec{\mathbf{v}}_d$.

> Although electrons move with average velocity $\vec{\mathbf{v}}_d$, collisions with atoms cause sharp, momentary changes of direction.

Active Figure 17.4
A schematic representation of the zigzag motion of a charge carrier in a conductor. Notice that the drift velocity $\vec{\mathbf{v}}_d$ is opposite the direction of the electric field.

■ **EXAMPLE 17.2** | **Drift Speed of Electrons**

GOAL Calculate a drift speed and compare it with the rms speed of an electron gas.

PROBLEM A copper wire of cross-sectional area 3.00×10^{-6} m^2 carries a current of 10.0 A. **(a)** Assuming each copper atom contributes one free electron to the metal, find the drift speed of the electrons in this wire. **(b)** Use the ideal gas

(Continued)

model to compare the drift speed with the random rms speed an electron would have at 20.0°C. The density of copper is 8.92 g/cm³, and its atomic mass is 63.5 u.

STRATEGY All the variables in Equation 17.2 are known except for n, the number of free charge carriers per unit volume. We can find n by recalling that one mole of copper contains an Avogadro's number (6.02×10^{23}) of atoms and each atom contributes one charge carrier to the metal. The volume of one mole can be found from copper's known density and atomic mass. The atomic mass is the same, numerically, as the number of grams in a mole of the substance.

SOLUTION

(a) Find the drift speed of the electrons.

Calculate the volume of one mole of copper from its density and its atomic mass:

$$V = \frac{m}{\rho} = \frac{63.5 \text{ g}}{8.92 \text{ g/cm}^3} = 7.12 \text{ cm}^3$$

Convert the volume from cm³ to m³:

$$7.12 \text{ cm}^3 \left(\frac{1 \text{ m}}{10^2 \text{ cm}} \right)^3 = 7.12 \times 10^{-6} \text{ m}^3$$

Divide Avogadro's number (the number of electrons in one mole) by the volume per mole to obtain the number density:

$$n = \frac{6.02 \times 10^{23} \text{ electrons/mole}}{7.12 \times 10^{-6} \text{ m}^3/\text{mole}}$$

$$= 8.46 \times 10^{28} \text{ electrons/m}^3$$

Solve Equation 17.2 for the drift speed and substitute:

$$v_d = \frac{I}{nqA}$$

$$= \frac{10.0 \text{ C/s}}{(8.46 \times 10^{28} \text{ electrons/m}^3)(1.60 \times 10^{-19} \text{ C})(3.00 \times 10^{-6} \text{ m}^2)}$$

$$v_d = \boxed{2.46 \times 10^{-4} \text{ m/s}}$$

(b) Find the rms speed of a gas of electrons at 20.0°C.

Apply Equation 10.18:

$$v_{\text{rms}} = \sqrt{\frac{3k_B T}{m_e}}$$

Convert the temperature to the Kelvin scale and substitute values:

$$v_{\text{rms}} = \sqrt{\frac{3(1.38 \times 10^{-23} \text{ J/K})(293 \text{ K})}{9.11 \times 10^{-31} \text{ kg}}}$$

$$= \boxed{1.15 \times 10^5 \text{ m/s}}$$

REMARKS The drift speed of an electron in a wire is very small, only about one-billionth of its random thermal speed.

QUESTION 17.2 True or False: The drift velocity in a wire of a given composition is inversely proportional to the number density of charge carriers.

EXERCISE 17.2 What current in a copper wire with a cross-sectional area of 7.50×10^{-7} m² would result in a drift speed equal to 5.00×10^{-4} m/s?

ANSWER 5.08 A

Tip 17.2 Electrons Are Everywhere in the Circuit

Electrons don't have to travel from the light switch to the lightbulb for the lightbulb to operate. Electrons already in the filament of the lightbulb move in response to the electric field set up by the battery. Also, the battery does *not* provide electrons to the circuit; it provides *energy* to the existing electrons.

Example 17.2 shows that drift speeds are typically very small. In fact, the drift speed is much smaller than the average speed between collisions. Electrons traveling at 2.46×10^{-4} m/s, as in the example, would take about 68 min to travel 1 m! In view of this low speed, why does a lightbulb turn on almost instantaneously when a switch is thrown? Think of the flow of water through a pipe. If a drop of water is forced into one end of a pipe that is already filled with water, a drop must be pushed out the other end of the pipe. Although it may take an individual drop a long time to make it through the pipe, a flow initiated at one end produces a similar flow at the other end very quickly. Another familiar analogy is the motion of a bicycle chain. When the sprocket moves one link, the other links all move more or less immediately, even though it takes a given link some time to make a complete rotation. In a conductor, the electric field driving the free electrons travels at a speed close to that of light, so when you flip a light switch, the message for the electrons to start moving through the wire (the electric field) reaches them at a speed on the order of 10^8 m/s!

17.2 Suppose a current-carrying wire has a cross-sectional area that gradually becomes smaller along the wire so that the wire has the shape of a very long, truncated cone. How does the drift speed vary along the wire? (a) It slows down as the cross section becomes smaller. (b) It speeds up as the cross section becomes smaller. (c) It doesn't change. (d) More information is needed.

17.3 Current and Voltage Measurements In Circuits

To study electric current in circuits, we need to understand how to measure currents and voltages.

The circuit shown in Figure 17.5a is a drawing of the actual circuit necessary for measuring the current in Example 17.1. Figure 17.5b shows a stylized figure called a circuit diagram that represents the actual circuit of Figure 17.5a. This circuit consists of only a battery and a lightbulb. The word *circuit* means "a closed loop of some sort around which current circulates." The battery pumps charge through the bulb and around the loop. No charge would flow without a complete conducting path from the positive terminal of the battery into one side of the bulb, out the other side, and through the copper conducting wires back to the negative terminal of the battery. The most important quantities that characterize how the bulb works in different situations are the current I in the bulb and the potential difference ΔV across the bulb. To measure the current in the bulb, we place an ammeter, the device for measuring current, in line with the bulb so there is no path for the current to bypass the meter; all the charge passing through the bulb must also pass through the ammeter. The voltmeter measures the potential difference, or voltage, between the two ends of the bulb's filament. If we use two meters simultaneously as in Figure 17.5a, we can remove the voltmeter and see if its presence affects the current reading. Figure 17.5c shows a digital multimeter, a convenient device, with a digital readout, that can be used to measure voltage, current, or resistance. An advantage of using a digital multimeter as a voltmeter is that it will usually not affect the current because a digital meter has enormous resistance to the flow of charge in the voltmeter mode.

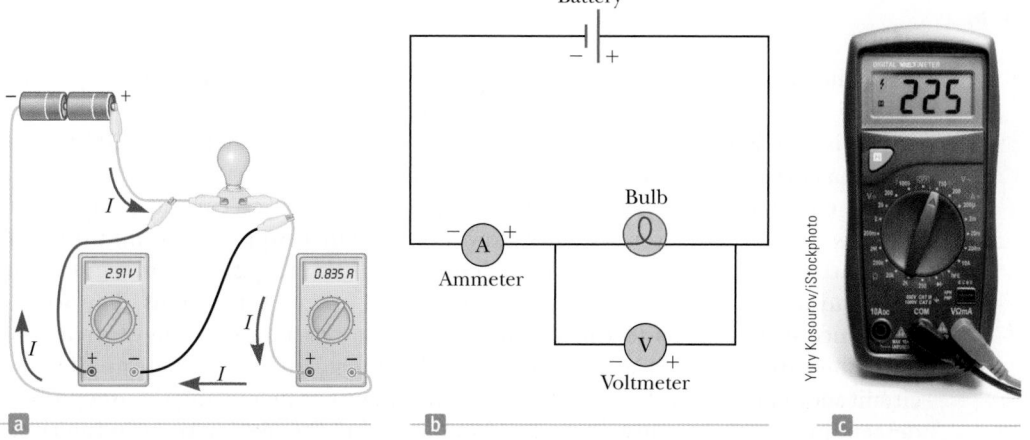

Figure 17.5 (a) A sketch of an actual circuit used to measure the current in a flashlight bulb and the potential difference across it. (b) A schematic diagram of the circuit shown in (a). (c) A digital multimeter can be used to measure both current and potential difference.

At this point, you can measure the current as a function of voltage (an I–ΔV curve) of various devices in the lab. All you need is a variable voltage supply (an adjustable battery) capable of supplying potential differences from about -5 V to $+5$ V, a bulb, a resistor, some wires and alligator clips, and a couple of multimeters. Be sure to always start your measurements using the highest multimeter scales (say, 10 A and 1 000 V), and increase the sensitivity one scale at a time to obtain the highest accuracy without overloading the meters. (Increasing the sensitivity means lowering the maximum current or voltage that the scale reads.) Note that the meters must be connected with the proper polarity with respect to the voltage supply, as shown in Figure 17.5b. Finally, follow your instructor's directions carefully to avoid damaging the meters and incurring a soaring lab fee.

■ Quick Quiz

17.3 Look at the four "circuits" shown in Figure 17.6 and select those that will light the bulb.

a   b   c   d

Figure 17.6 (Quick Quiz 17.3)

17.4 Resistance, Resistivity, and Ohm's Law

Resistance and Ohm's Law

When a voltage (potential difference) ΔV is applied across the ends of a metallic conductor as in Figure 17.7, the current in the conductor is found to be proportional to the applied voltage; $I \propto \Delta V$. If the proportionality holds, we can write $\Delta V = IR$, where the proportionality constant R is called the *resistance* of the conductor. In fact, we define the **resistance** as the ratio of the voltage across the conductor to the current it carries:

Resistance ▶

$$R \equiv \frac{\Delta V}{I} \qquad [17.3]$$

Resistance has SI units of volts per ampere, called **ohms** (Ω). If a potential difference of 1 V across a conductor produces a current of 1 A, the resistance of the conductor is 1 Ω. For example, if an electrical appliance connected to a 120-V source carries a current of 6 A, its resistance is 20 Ω.

The concepts of electric current, voltage, and resistance can be compared to the flow of water in a river. As water flows downhill in a river of constant width and depth, the flow rate (water current) depends on the steepness of descent of the river and the effects of rocks, the riverbank, and other obstructions. The voltage difference is analogous to the steepness, and the resistance to the obstructions. Based on this analogy, it seems reasonable that increasing the voltage applied to a circuit should increase the current in the circuit, just as increasing the steepness of descent increases the water current. Also, increasing the obstructions in the river's path will reduce the water current, just as increasing the resistance in a circuit will lower the electric current. Resistance in a circuit arises due to collisions between the electrons carrying the current with fixed atoms inside the conductor. These

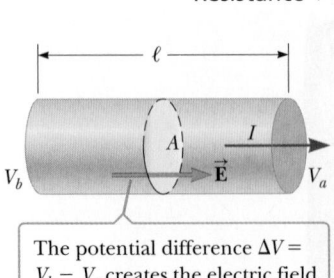

The potential difference $\Delta V = V_b - V_a$ creates the electric field $\vec{E}$ that produces the current I.

Figure 17.7 A uniform conductor of length ℓ and cross-sectional area A. The current I is proportional to the potential difference or, equivalently, to the electric field and length.

collisions inhibit the movement of charges in much the same way as would a force of friction. For many materials, including most metals, experiments show that **the resistance remains constant over a wide range of applied voltages or currents**. This statement is known as **Ohm's law**, after Georg Simon Ohm (1789–1854), who was the first to conduct a systematic study of electrical resistance.

Ohm's law is given by

$$\Delta V = IR \qquad [17.4]$$

where R is understood to be independent of ΔV, the potential drop across the resistor, and I, the current in the resistor. We will continue to use this traditional form of Ohm's law when discussing electrical circuits. A **resistor** is a conductor that provides a specified resistance in an electric circuit. The symbol for a resistor in circuit diagrams is a zigzag line: ——⋀⋀⋀——.

Ohm's law is an empirical relationship valid only for certain materials. Materials that obey Ohm's law, and hence have a constant resistance over a wide range of voltages, are said to be **ohmic**. Materials having resistance that changes with voltage or current are **nonohmic**. Ohmic materials have a linear current–voltage relationship over a large range of applied voltages (Fig. 17.8a). Nonohmic materials have a nonlinear current–voltage relationship (Fig. 17.8b). One common semiconducting device that is nonohmic is the *diode*, a circuit element that acts like a one-way valve for current. Its resistance is small for currents in one direction (positive ΔV) and large for currents in the reverse direction (negative ΔV). Most modern electronic devices, such as transistors, have nonlinear current–voltage relationships; their operation depends on the particular ways in which they violate Ohm's law.

■ Quick Quiz

17.4 In Figure 17.8b does the resistance of the diode (a) increase or (b) decrease as the positive voltage ΔV increases?

17.5 All electric devices are required to have identifying plates that specify their electrical characteristics. The plate on a certain steam iron states that the iron carries a current of 6.00 A when connected to a source of 1.20×10^2 V. What is the resistance of the steam iron? (a) 0.050 0 Ω (b) 20.0 Ω (c) 36.0 Ω

Resistivity

Electrons don't move in straight-line paths through a conductor. Instead, they undergo repeated collisions with the metal atoms. Consider a conductor with a voltage applied across its ends. An electron gains speed as the electric force associated with the internal electric field accelerates it, giving it a velocity in the direction opposite that of the electric field. A collision with an atom randomizes the electron's velocity, reducing it in the direction opposite the field. The process then repeats itself. Together, these collisions affect the electron somewhat as a force of internal friction would. This step is the origin of a material's resistance.

The resistance of an ohmic conductor increases with length, which makes sense because the electrons going through it must undergo more collisions in a longer conductor. A smaller cross-sectional area also increases the resistance of a conductor, just as a smaller pipe slows the fluid moving through it. The resistance, then, is proportional to the conductor's length ℓ and inversely proportional to its cross-sectional area A,

$$R = \rho \frac{\ell}{A} \qquad [17.5]$$

where the constant of proportionality, ρ, is called the **resistivity** of the material. Every material has a characteristic resistivity that depends on its electronic structure and on temperature. Good electric conductors have very low resistivities, and

Georg Simon Ohm
(1787–1854)
A high school teacher in Cologne and later a professor at Munich, Ohm formulated the concept of resistance and discovered the proportionalities expressed in Equation 17.5.

An assortment of resistors used for a variety of applications in electronic circuits.

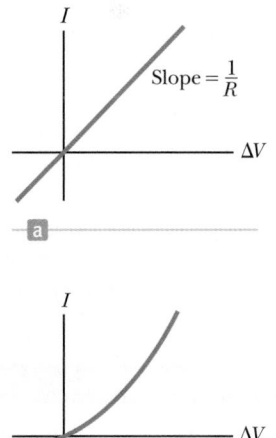

Figure 17.8 (a) The current–voltage curve for an ohmic material. The curve is linear, and the slope gives the resistance of the conductor. (b) A nonlinear current–voltage curve for a semiconducting diode. This device doesn't obey Ohm's law.

Table 17.1 Resistivities and Temperature Coefficients of Resistivity for Various Materials (at 20°C)

Material	Resistivity ($\Omega \cdot$ m)	Temperature Coefficient of Resistivity [(°C)$^{-1}$]
Silver	1.59×10^{-8}	3.8×10^{-3}
Copper	1.7×10^{-8}	3.9×10^{-3}
Gold	2.44×10^{-8}	3.4×10^{-3}
Aluminum	2.82×10^{-8}	3.9×10^{-3}
Tungsten	5.6×10^{-8}	4.5×10^{-3}
Iron	10.0×10^{-8}	5.0×10^{-3}
Platinum	11×10^{-8}	3.92×10^{-3}
Lead	22×10^{-8}	3.9×10^{-3}
Nichrome[a]	150×10^{-8}	0.4×10^{-3}
Carbon	3.5×10^{-5}	-0.5×10^{-3}
Germanium	0.46	-48×10^{-3}
Silicon	640	-75×10^{-3}
Glass	10^{10}–10^{14}	
Hard rubber	$\approx 10^{13}$	
Sulfur	10^{15}	
Quartz (fused)	75×10^{16}	

[a]A nickel-chromium alloy commonly used in heating elements.

good insulators have very high resistivities. Table 17.1 lists the resistivities of various materials at 20°C. Because resistance values are in ohms, resistivity values must be in ohm-meters ($\Omega \cdot$ m).

■ APPLYING PHYSICS 17.1 | Dimming of Aging Lightbulbs

As a lightbulb ages, why does it gives off less light than when new?

EXPLANATION There are two reasons for the light-bulb's behavior, one electrical and one optical, but both are related to the same phenomenon occurring within the bulb. The filament of an old lightbulb is made of a tungsten wire that has been kept at a high temperature for many hours. High temperatures evaporate tungsten from the filament, decreasing its radius. From $R = \rho \ell / A$, we see that a decreased cross-sectional area leads to an increase in the resistance of the filament. This increasing resistance with age means that the filament will carry less current for the same applied voltage. With less current in the filament, there is less light output, and the filament glows more dimly.

At the high operating temperature of the filament, tungsten atoms leave its surface, much as water molecules evaporate from a puddle of water. The atoms are carried away by convection currents in the gas in the bulb and are deposited on the inner surface of the glass. In time, the glass becomes less transparent because of the tungsten coating, which decreases the amount of light that passes through the glass. ■

■ EXAMPLE 17.3 | The Resistance of Nichrome Wire

GOAL Combine the concept of resistivity with Ohm's law.

PROBLEM (a) Calculate the resistance per unit length of a 22-gauge Nichrome wire of radius 0.321 mm. (b) If a potential difference of 10.0 V is maintained across a 1.00-m length of the Nichrome wire, what is the current in the wire? (c) The wire is melted down and recast with twice its original length. Find the new resistance R_N as a multiple of the old resistance R_O.

STRATEGY Part (a) requires substitution into Equation 17.5, after calculating the cross-sectional area, whereas part (b) is a matter of substitution into Ohm's law. Part (c) requires some algebra. The idea is to take the expression for the new resistance and substitute expressions for ℓ_N and A_N, the new length and cross-sectional area, in terms of the old length and cross section. For the area substitution, remember that the volumes of the old and new wires are the same.

SOLUTION

(a) Calculate the resistance per unit length.

Find the cross-sectional area of the wire:

$$A = \pi r^2 = \pi(0.321 \times 10^{-3}\,\text{m})^2 = 3.24 \times 10^{-7}\,\text{m}^2$$

Obtain the resistivity of Nichrome from Table 17.1, solve Equation 17.5 for R/ℓ, and substitute:

$$\frac{R}{\ell} = \frac{\rho}{A} = \frac{1.5 \times 10^{-6}\,\Omega \cdot \text{m}}{3.24 \times 10^{-7}\,\text{m}^2} = \boxed{4.6\,\Omega/\text{m}}$$

(b) Find the current in a 1.00-m segment of the wire if the potential difference across it is 10.0 V.

Substitute given values into Ohm's law:

$$I = \frac{\Delta V}{R} = \frac{10.0\,\text{V}}{4.6\,\Omega} = \boxed{2.2\,\text{A}}$$

(c) If the wire is melted down and recast with twice its original length, find the new resistance as a multiple of the old.

Find the new area A_N in terms of the old area A_O, using the fact the volume doesn't change and $\ell_N = 2\ell_O$:

$$V_N = V_O \;\rightarrow\; A_N\ell_N = A_O\ell_O \;\rightarrow\; A_N = A_O(\ell_O/\ell_N)$$
$$A_N = A_O(\ell_O/2\ell_O) = A_O/2$$

Substitute into Equation 17.5:

$$R_N = \frac{\rho\ell_N}{A_N} = \frac{\rho(2\ell_O)}{(A_O/2)} = 4\frac{\rho\ell_O}{A_O} = \boxed{4R_O}$$

REMARKS From Table 17.1, the resistivity of Nichrome is about 100 times that of copper, a typical good conductor. Therefore, a copper wire of the same radius would have a resistance per unit length of only 0.052 Ω/m, and a 1.00-m length of copper wire of the same radius would carry the same current (2.2 A) with an applied voltage of only 0.115 V.

Because of its resistance to oxidation, Nichrome is often used for heating elements in toasters, irons, and electric heaters.

QUESTION 17.3 Would replacing the Nichrome with copper result in a higher current or lower current?

EXERCISE 17.3 What is the resistance of a 6.0-m length of Nichrome wire that has a radius 0.321 mm? How much current does it carry when connected to a 120-V source?

ANSWERS 28 Ω; 4.3 A

■ *Quick Quiz*

17.6 Suppose an electrical wire is replaced with one having every linear dimension doubled (i.e., the length and radius have twice their original values). Does the wire now have (a) more resistance than before, (b) less resistance, or (c) the same resistance?

17.5 Temperature Variation of Resistance

The resistivity ρ, and hence the resistance, of a conductor depends on a number of factors. One of the most important is the temperature of the metal. For most metals, resistivity increases with increasing temperature. This correlation can be understood as follows: as the temperature of the material increases, its constituent atoms vibrate with greater amplitudes. As a result, the electrons find it more difficult to get by those atoms, just as it is more difficult to weave through a crowded room when the people are in motion than when they are standing still. The increased electron scattering with increasing temperature results in increased resistivity. Technically, thermal expansion also affects resistance; however, this is a very small effect.

Over a limited temperature range, the resistivity of most metals increases linearly with increasing temperature according to the expression

$$\rho = \rho_0[1 + \alpha(T - T_0)]$$ [17.6]

In an old-fashioned carbon filament incandescent lamp, the electrical resistance is typically 10 Ω, but changes with temperature.

where ρ is the resistivity at some temperature T (in Celsius degrees), ρ_0 is the resistivity at some reference temperature T_0 (usually taken to be 20°C), and α is a parameter called the **temperature coefficient of resistivity**. Temperature coefficients for various materials are provided in Table 17.1. The interesting negative values of α for semiconductors arise because these materials possess weakly bound charge carriers that become free to move and contribute to the current as the temperature rises.

Because the resistance of a conductor with a uniform cross section is proportional to the resistivity according to Equation 17.5 ($R = \rho l/A$), the temperature variation of resistance can be written

$$R = R_0[1 + \alpha(T - T_0)] \qquad [17.7]$$

Precise temperature measurements are often made using this property, as shown by the following example.

■ EXAMPLE 17.4   **A Platinum Resistance Thermometer**

GOAL Apply the temperature dependence of resistance.

PROBLEM A resistance thermometer, which measures temperature by measuring the change in resistance of a conductor, is made of platinum and has a resistance of 50.0 Ω at 20.0°C. **(a)** When the device is immersed in a vessel containing melting indium, its resistance increases to 76.8 Ω. From this information, find the melting point of indium. **(b)** The indium is heated further until it reaches a temperature of 235°C. What is the ratio of the new current in the platinum to the current I_{mp} at the melting point?

STRATEGY For part (a), solve Equation 17.7 for $T - T_0$ and get α for platinum from Table 17.1, substituting known quantities. For part (b), use Ohm's law in Equation 17.7.

. . . .

SOLUTION

(a) Find the melting point of indium.

Solve Equation 17.7 for $T - T_0$:

$$T - T_0 = \frac{R - R_0}{\alpha R_0} = \frac{76.8\ \Omega - 50.0\ \Omega}{[3.92 \times 10^{-3}\ (°C)^{-1}][50.0\ \Omega]}$$

$$= 137°\ C$$

Substitute $T_0 = 20.0°C$ and obtain the melting point of indium:

$$T = \boxed{157°C}$$

(b) Find the ratio of the new current to the old when the temperature rises from 157°C to 235°C.

Write Equation 17.7, with R_0 and T_0 replaced by R_{mp} and T_{mp}, the resistance and temperature at the melting point.

$$R = R_{mp}[1 + \alpha(T - T_{mp})]$$

According to Ohm's law, $R = \Delta V/I$ and $R_{mp} = \Delta V/I_{mp}$. Substitute these expressions into Equation 17.7:

$$\frac{\Delta V}{I} = \frac{\Delta V}{I_{mp}}[1 + \alpha(T - T_{mp})]$$

Cancel the voltage differences, invert the two expressions, and then divide both sides by I_{mp}:

$$\frac{I}{I_{mp}} = \frac{1}{1 + \alpha(T - T_{mp})}$$

Substitute $T = 235°C$, $T_{mp} = 157°C$, and the value for α, obtaining the desired ratio:

$$\frac{I}{I_{mp}} = \boxed{0.766}$$

. . . .

REMARKS As the temperature rises, both the rms speed of the electrons in the metal and the resistance increase.

QUESTION 17.4 What happens to the drift speed of the electrons as the temperature rises? (a) It becomes larger. (b) It becomes smaller. (c) It remains unchanged.

EXERCISE 17.4 Suppose a wire made of an unknown alloy and having a temperature of 20.0°C carries a current of 0.450 A. At 52.0°C the current is 0.370 A for the same potential difference. Find the temperature coefficient of resistivity of the alloy.

ANSWER $6.76 \times 10^{-3} \ (°C)^{-1}$

17.6 Electrical Energy and Power

If a battery is used to establish an electric current in a conductor, chemical energy stored in the battery is continuously transformed into kinetic energy of the charge carriers. This kinetic energy is quickly lost as a result of collisions between the charge carriers and fixed atoms in the conductor, causing an increase in the temperature of the conductor. In this way the chemical energy stored in the battery is continuously transformed into thermal energy.

To understand the process of energy transfer in a simple circuit, consider a battery with terminals connected to a resistor (Active Fig. 17.9; remember that the positive terminal of the battery is always at the higher potential). Now imagine following a quantity of positive charge ΔQ around the circuit from point A, through the battery and resistor, and back to A. Point A is a reference point that is grounded (the ground symbol is ⏚), and its potential is taken to be zero. As the charge ΔQ moves from A to B through the battery, the electrical potential energy of the system increases by the amount $\Delta Q \, \Delta V$ and the chemical potential energy in the battery decreases by the same amount. (Recall from Chapter 16 that $\Delta PE = q \, \Delta V$.) As the charge moves from C to D through the resistor, however, it loses this electrical potential energy during collisions with atoms in the resistor. In the process the energy is transformed to internal energy corresponding to increased vibrational motion of those atoms. Because we can ignore the very small resistance of the interconnecting wires, no energy transformation occurs for paths BC and DA. When the charge returns to point A, the net result is that some of the chemical energy in the battery has been delivered to the resistor and has caused its temperature to rise.

The charge ΔQ loses energy $\Delta Q \, \Delta V$ as it passes through the resistor. If Δt is the time it takes the charge to pass through the resistor, the instantaneous rate at which it loses electric potential energy is

$$\lim_{\Delta t \to 0} \frac{\Delta Q}{\Delta t} \Delta V = I \Delta V$$

where I is the current in the resistor and ΔV is the potential difference across it. Of course, the charge regains this energy when it passes through the battery, at the expense of chemical energy in the battery. The rate at which the system loses potential energy as the charge passes through the resistor is equal to the rate at which the system gains internal energy in the resistor. Therefore, the power P, representing the rate at which energy is delivered to the resistor, is

$$P = I \Delta V \qquad\qquad [17.8] \quad \blacktriangleleft \text{ Power}$$

Although this result was developed by considering a battery delivering energy to a resistor, Equation 17.8 can be used to determine the power transferred from a voltage source to *any* device carrying a current I and having a potential difference ΔV between its terminals.

Using Equation 17.8 and the fact that $\Delta V = IR$ for a resistor, we can express the power delivered to the resistor in the alternate forms

$$P = I^2 R = \frac{\Delta V^2}{R} \qquad\qquad [17.9] \quad \blacktriangleleft \begin{array}{l}\text{Power delivered to a}\\\text{resistor}\end{array}$$

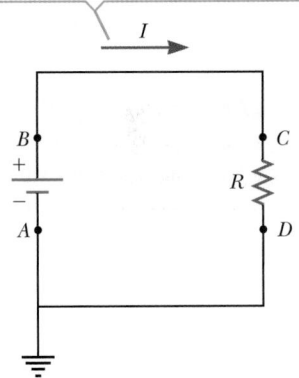

Positive current travels clockwise from the positive to the negative terminal of the battery.

Active Figure 17.9
A circuit consisting of a battery and a resistance R. Point A is grounded.

When I is in amperes, ΔV in volts, and R in ohms, the SI unit of power is the watt (introduced in Chapter 5). The power delivered to a conductor of resistance R is often referred to as an I^2R *loss*. Note that Equation 17.9 applies only to resistors and not to nonohmic devices such as lightbulbs and diodes.

Regardless of the ways in which you use electrical energy in your home, you ultimately must pay for it or risk having your power turned off. The unit of energy used by electric companies to calculate consumption, the **kilowatt-hour**, is defined in terms of the unit of power and the amount of time it's supplied. One kilowatt-hour (kWh) is the energy converted or consumed in 1 h at the constant rate of 1 kW. It has the numerical value

$$1 \text{ kWh} = (10^3 \text{ W})(3\,600 \text{ s}) = 3.60 \times 10^6 \text{ J} \qquad \text{[17.10]}$$

On an electric bill, the amount of electricity used in a given period is usually stated in multiples of kilowatt-hours.

■ APPLYING PHYSICS 17.2 | **Lightbulb Failures**

Why do lightbulbs fail so often immediately after they're turned on?

EXPLANATION Once the switch is closed, the line voltage is applied across the bulb. As the voltage is applied across the cold filament when the bulb is first turned on, the resistance of the filament is low, the current is high,

and a relatively large amount of power is delivered to the bulb. This current spike at the beginning of operation is the reason lightbulbs often fail immediately after they are turned on. As the filament warms, its resistance rises and the current decreases. As a result, the power delivered to the bulb decreases and the bulb is less likely to burn out. ■

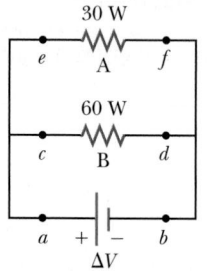

Figure 17.10 (Quick Quiz 17.8)

■ Quick Quiz

17.7 A voltage ΔV is applied across the ends of a Nichrome heater wire having a cross-sectional area A and length L. The same voltage is applied across the ends of a second Nichrome heater wire having a cross-sectional area A and length $2L$. Which wire gets hotter? (a) The shorter wire does. (b) The longer wire does. (c) More information is needed.

17.8 For the two resistors shown in Figure 17.10, rank the currents at points a through f from largest to smallest. (a) $I_a = I_b > I_e = I_f > I_c = I_d$ (b) $I_a = I_b > I_c = I_d > I_e = I_f$ (c) $I_e = I_f > I_c = I_d > I_a = I_b$

17.9 Two resistors, A and B, are connected in a series circuit with a battery. The resistance of A is twice that of B. Which resistor dissipates more power? (a) Resistor A does. (b) Resistor B does. (c) More information is needed.

17.10 The diameter of wire A is greater than the diameter of wire B, but their lengths and resistivities are identical. For a given voltage difference across the ends, what is the relationship between P_A and P_B, the dissipated power for wires A and B, respectively? (a) $P_A = P_B$ (b) $P_A < P_B$ (c) $P_A > P_B$

■ EXAMPLE 17.5 | **The Cost of Lighting Up Your Life**

GOAL Apply the electric power concept and calculate the cost of power usage using kilowatt-hours.

PROBLEM A circuit provides a maximum current of 20.0 A at an operating voltage of 1.20×10^2 V. **(a)** How many 75 W bulbs can operate with this voltage source? **(b)** At \$0.120 per kilowatt-hour, how much does it cost to operate these bulbs for 8.00 h?

STRATEGY Find the necessary power with $P = I\,\Delta V$ then divide by 75.0 W per bulb to get the total number of bulbs. To find the cost, convert power to kilowatts and multiply by the number of hours, then multiply by the cost per -kilowatt-hour.

SOLUTION

(a) Find the number of bulbs that can be lighted.

Substitute into Equation 17.8 to get the total power:

$$P_{total} = I\Delta V = (20.0\text{ A})(1.20 \times 10^2\text{ V}) = 2.40 \times 10^3\text{ W}$$

Divide the total power by the power per bulb to get the number of bulbs:

$$\text{Number of bulbs} = \frac{P_{total}}{P_{bulb}} = \frac{2.40 \times 10^3\text{ W}}{75.0\text{ W}} = \boxed{32.0}$$

(b) Calculate the cost of this electricity for an 8.00-h day.

Find the energy in kilowatt-hours:

$$\text{Energy} = Pt = (2.40 \times 10^3\text{ W})\left(\frac{1.00\text{ kW}}{1.00 \times 10^3\text{ W}}\right)(8.00\text{ h})$$
$$= 19.2\text{ kWh}$$

Multiply the energy by the cost per kilowatt-hour:

$$\text{Cost} = (19.2\text{ kWh})(\$0.12/\text{kWh}) = \boxed{\$2.30}$$

REMARKS This amount of energy might correspond to what a small office uses in a working day, taking into account all power requirements (not just lighting). In general, resistive devices can have variable power output, depending on how the circuit is wired. Here, power outputs were specified, so such considerations were unnecessary.

QUESTION 17.5 Considering how hot the parts of an incandescent light bulb get during operation, guess what fraction of the energy emitted by an incandescent lightbulb is in the form of visible light. (a) 10% (b) 50% (c) 80%

EXERCISE 17.5 (a) How many Christmas tree lights drawing 5.00 W of power each could be run on a circuit operating at 1.20×10^2 V and providing 15.0 A of current? (b) Find the cost to operate one such string 24.0 h per day for the Christmas season (two weeks), using the rate \$0.12/kWh.

ANSWERS (a) 3.60×10^2 bulbs (b) \$72.60

■ EXAMPLE 17.6 | The Power Converted by an Electric Heater

GOAL Calculate an electrical power output and link to its effect on the environment through the first law of thermodynamics.

PROBLEM An electric heater is operated by applying a potential difference of 50.0 V to a Nichrome wire of total resistance 8.00 Ω. **(a)** Find the current carried by the wire and the power rating of the heater. **(b)** Using this heater, how long would it take to heat 2.50×10^3 moles of diatomic gas (e.g., a mixture of oxygen and nitrogen, or air) from a chilly 10.0°C to 25.0°C? Take the molar specific heat at constant volume of air to be $\frac{5}{2}R$. **(c)** How many kilowatt-hours of electricity are used during the time calculated in part (b) and at what cost, at \$0.12 per kilowatt-hour?

STRATEGY For part (a), find the current with Ohm's law and substitute into the expression for power. Part (b) is an isovolumetric process, so the thermal energy provided by the heater all goes into the change in internal energy, ΔU. Calculate this quantity using the first law of thermodynamics and divide by the power to get the time. Finding the number of kilowatt-hours used requires a simple unit conversion technique. Multiplying by the cost per kilowatt yields the total cost of operating the heater for the given time.

SOLUTION

(a) Compute the current and power output.

Apply Ohm's law to get the current:

$$I = \frac{\Delta V}{R} = \frac{50.0\text{ V}}{8.00\text{ Ω}} = \boxed{6.25\text{ A}}$$

Substitute into Equation 17.9 to find the power:

$$P = I^2R = (6.25\text{ A})^2(8.00\text{ Ω}) = \boxed{313\text{ W}}$$

(b) How long does it take to heat the gas?

Calculate the thermal energy transfer from the first law. Note that $W = 0$ because the volume doesn't change.

$$Q = \Delta U = nC_v\Delta T$$
$$= (2.50 \times 10^3\text{ mol})(\tfrac{5}{2} \cdot 8.31\text{ J/mol}\cdot\text{K})(298\text{ K} - 283\text{ K})$$
$$= 7.79 \times 10^5\text{ J}$$

Divide the thermal energy by the power to get the time:

$$t = \frac{Q}{P} = \frac{7.79 \times 10^5\text{ J}}{313\text{ W}} = \boxed{2.49 \times 10^3\text{ s}}$$

(Continued)

(c) Calculate the kilowatt-hours of electricity used and the cost.

Convert the energy to kilowatt-hours, noting that $1 \text{ J} = 1 \text{ W} \cdot \text{s}$:

$$U = (7.79 \times 10^5 \text{ W} \cdot \text{s}) \left(\frac{1.00 \text{ kW}}{1.00 \times 10^3 \text{ W}} \right) \left(\frac{1.00 \text{ h}}{3.60 \times 10^3 \text{ s}} \right) = \boxed{0.216 \text{ kWh}}$$

Multiply by \$0.12/kWh to obtain the total cost of operation:

$$\text{Cost} = (0.216 \text{ kWh})(\$0.12/\text{kWh}) = \boxed{\$0.026}$$

REMARKS The number of moles of gas given here is approximately what would be found in a bedroom. Warming the air with this space heater requires only about 40 minutes. The calculation, however, doesn't take into account conduction losses. Recall that a 20-cm-thick concrete wall, as calculated in Chapter 11, permitted the loss of more than 2 megajoules an hour by conduction!

QUESTION 17.6 If the heater wire is replaced by a wire with lower resistance, is the time required to heat the gas (a) unchanged, (b) increased, or (c) decreased?

EXERCISE 17.6 A hot-water heater is rated at 4.50×10^3 W and operates at 2.40×10^2 V. (a) Find the resistance in the heating element and the current. (b) How long does it take to heat 125 L of water from 20.0°C to 50.0°C, neglecting conduction and other losses? (c) How much does it cost at \$0.12/kWh?

ANSWERS (a) 12.8 Ω, 18.8 A (b) 3.49×10^3 s (c) \$0.52

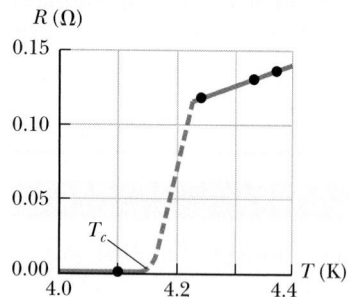

Figure 17.11 Resistance versus temperature for a sample of mercury (Hg). The graph follows that of a normal metal above the critical temperature T_c. The resistance drops to zero at the critical temperature, which is 4.2 K for mercury, and remains at zero for lower temperatures.

Table 17.2 Critical Temperatures for Various Superconductors

Material	T_c(K)
Zn	0.88
Al	1.19
Sn	3.72
Hg	4.15
Pb	7.18
Nb	9.46
Nb_3Sn	18.05
Nb_3Ge	23.2
$YBa_2Cu_3O_7$	92
Bi–Sr–Ca–Cu–O	105
Tl–Ba–Ca–Cu–O	125
$HgBa_2Ca_2Cu_3O_8$	134

17.7 Superconductors

There is a class of metals and compounds with resistances that fall virtually to *zero* below a certain temperature T_c called the *critical temperature*. These materials are known as **superconductors**. The resistance vs. temperature graph for a superconductor follows that of a normal metal at temperatures above T_c (Fig. 17.11). When the temperature is at or below T_c, however, the resistance suddenly drops to zero. This phenomenon was discovered in 1911 by Dutch physicist H. Kamerlingh Onnes as he and a graduate student worked with mercury, which is a superconductor below 4.1 K. Recent measurements have shown that the resistivities of superconductors below T_c are less than 4×10^{-25} Ω · m, around 10^{17} times smaller than the resistivity of copper and in practice considered to be zero.

Today thousands of superconductors are known, including such common metals as aluminum, tin, lead, zinc, and indium. Table 17.2 lists the critical temperatures of several superconductors. The value of T_c is sensitive to chemical composition, pressure, and crystalline structure. Interestingly, copper, silver, and gold, which are excellent conductors, don't exhibit superconductivity.

A truly remarkable feature of superconductors is that once a current is set up in them, it persists *without any applied voltage* (because $R = 0$). In fact, steady currents in superconducting loops have been observed to persist for years with no apparent decay!

An important development in physics that created much excitement in the scientific community was the discovery of high-temperature copper-oxide-based superconductors. The excitement began with a 1986 publication by J. Georg Bednorz and K. Alex Müller, scientists at the IBM Zurich Research Laboratory in Switzerland, in which they reported evidence for superconductivity at a temperature near 30 K in an oxide of barium, lanthanum, and copper. Bednorz and Müller were awarded the Nobel Prize in Physics in 1987 for their important discovery. The discovery was remarkable because the critical temperature was significantly higher than that of any previously known superconductor. Shortly thereafter a new family of compounds was investigated, and research activity in the field of superconductivity proceeded vigorously. In early 1987 groups at the University of Alabama at Huntsville and the University of Houston announced the discovery of superconductivity at about 92 K in an oxide of yttrium, barium, and copper ($YBa_2Cu_3O_7$).

Late in 1987, teams of scientists from Japan and the United States reported superconductivity at 105 K in an oxide of bismuth, strontium, calcium, and copper. More recently, scientists have reported superconductivity at temperatures as high as 150 K in an oxide containing mercury. The search for novel superconducting materials continues, with the hope of someday obtaining a room-temperature superconducting material. This research is important both for scientific reasons and for practical applications. A superconducting ceramic levitates a permanent magnet in Figure 17.12.

An important and useful application is the construction of superconducting magnets in which the magnetic field intensities are about ten times greater than those of the best normal electromagnets. Such magnets are being considered as a means of storing energy. The idea of using superconducting power lines to transmit power efficiently is also receiving serious consideration. Modern superconducting electronic devices consisting of two thin-film superconductors separated by a thin insulator have been constructed. Among these devices are magnetometers (magnetic-field measuring devices) and various microwave devices.

Figure 17.12 A small permanent magnet floats freely above a nitrogen-cooled ceramic superconductor. The superconductor has zero resistance and expels any magnetic field from inside the superconductor by creating a mirror image of the magnetic poles of the permanent magnet. This "Meissner effect" results in magnetic levitation of the permanent magnet.

17.8 Electrical Activity in the Heart BIO

Electrocardiograms

Every action involving the body's muscles is initiated by electrical activity. The voltages produced by muscular action in the heart are particularly important to physicians. Voltage pulses cause the heart to beat, and the waves of electrical excitation that sweep across the heart associated with the heartbeat are conducted through the body via the body fluids. These voltage pulses are large enough to be detected by suitable monitoring equipment attached to the skin. A sensitive voltmeter making good electrical contact with the skin by means of contacts attached with conducting paste can be used to measure heart pulses, which are typically of the order of 1 mV at the surface of the body. The voltage pulses can be recorded on an instrument called an **electrocardiograph**, and the pattern recorded by this instrument is called an **electrocardiogram** (EKG). To understand the information contained in an EKG pattern, it is necessary first to describe the underlying principles concerning electrical activity in the heart.

The right atrium of the heart contains a specialized set of muscle fibers called the SA (sinoatrial) node that initiates the heartbeat (Fig. 17.13). Electric impulses that originate in these fibers gradually spread from cell to cell throughout the right and left atrial muscles, causing them to contract. The pulse that passes through the muscle cells is often called a *depolarization wave* because of its effect on individual cells. If an individual muscle cell were examined in its resting state, a double-layer electric charge distribution would be found on its surface, as shown in Figure 17.14a. The impulse generated by the SA node momentarily and locally allows positive charge on the outside of the cell to flow in and neutralize the negative charge on the inside layer. This effect changes the cell's charge distribution

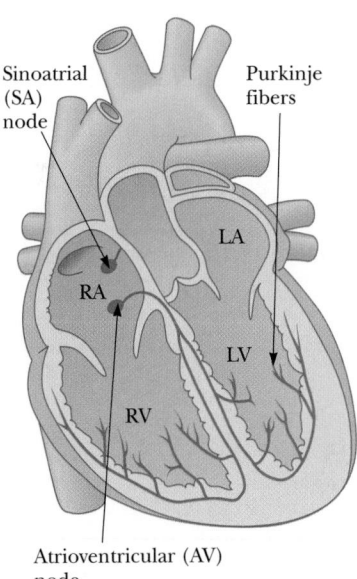

Figure 17.13 The electrical conduction system of the human heart. (RA: right atrium; LA: left atrium; RV: right ventricle; LV: left ventricle.)

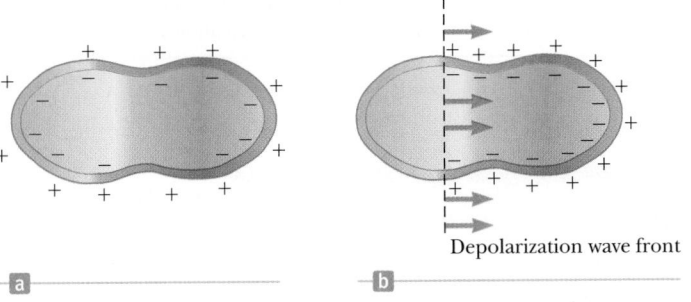

Depolarization wave front

a   b

Figure 17.14 (a) Charge distribution of a muscle cell in the atrium before a depolarization wave has passed through the cell. (b) Charge distribution as the wave passes.

Figure 17.15 An EKG response for a normal heart.

BIO APPLICATION

Cardiac Pacemakers

to that shown in Figure 17.14b. Once the depolarization wave has passed through an individual heart muscle cell, the cell recovers the resting-state charge distribution (positive out, negative in) shown in Figure 17.14a in about 250 ms. When the impulse reaches the atrioventricular (AV) node (Fig. 17.13), the muscles of the atria begin to relax, and the pulse is directed to the ventricular muscles by the AV node. The muscles of the ventricles contract as the depolarization wave spreads through the ventricles along a group of fibers called the *Purkinje fibers*. The ventricles then relax after the pulse has passed through. At this point, the SA node is again triggered and the cycle is repeated.

A sketch of the electrical activity registered on an EKG for one beat of a normal heart is shown in Figure 17.15. The pulse indicated by *P* occurs just before the atria begin to contract. The *QRS* pulse occurs in the ventricles just before they contract, and the *T* pulse occurs when the cells in the ventricles begin to recover. EKGs for an abnormal heart are shown in Figure 17.16. The *QRS* portion of the pattern shown in Figure 17.16a is wider than normal, indicating that the patient may have an enlarged heart. (Why?) Figure 17.16b indicates that there is no constant relationship between the *P* pulse and the *QRS* pulse. This suggests a blockage in the electrical conduction path between the SA and AV nodes that results in the atria and ventricles beating independently and inefficient heart pumping. Finally, Figure 17.16c shows a situation in which there is no *P* pulse and an irregular spacing between the *QRS* pulses. This is symptomatic of irregular atrial contraction, which is called *fibrillation*. In this condition, the atrial and ventricular contractions are irregular.

As noted previously, the sinoatrial node directs the heart to beat at the appropriate rate, usually about 72 beats per minute. Disease or the aging process, however, can damage the heart and slow its beating, and a medical assist may be necessary in the form of a *cardiac pacemaker* attached to the heart. This matchbox-sized electrical device implanted under the skin has a lead that is connected to the wall of the right ventricle. Pulses from this lead stimulate the heart to maintain its proper rhythm. In general, a pacemaker is designed to produce pulses at a rate of about 60 per minute, slightly slower than the normal number of beats per minute, but sufficient to maintain life. The circuitry consists of a capacitor charging up to

Figure 17.16 Abnormal EKGs.

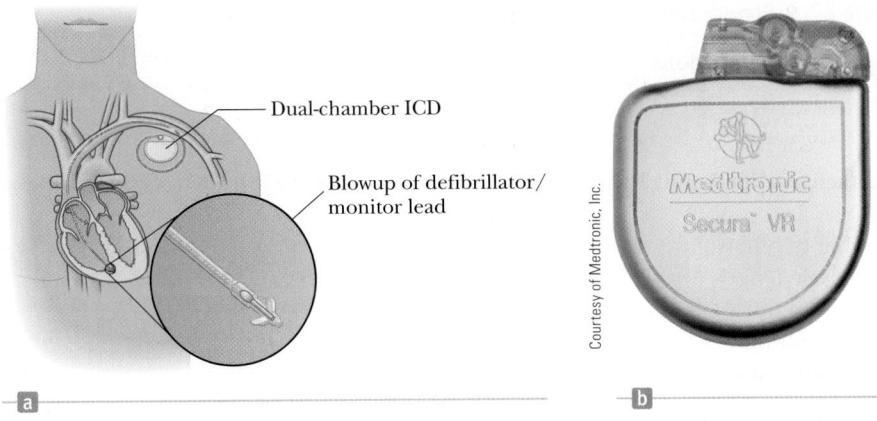

Figure 17.17 (a) A dual-chamber ICD with leads in the heart. One lead monitors and stimulates the right atrium, and the other monitors and stimulates the right ventricle. (b) Medtronic Dual Chamber ICD.

Courtesy of Medtronic, Inc.

a certain voltage from a lithium battery and then discharging. The design of the circuit is such that if the heart is beating normally, the capacitor is not allowed to charge completely and send pulses to the heart.

An Emergency Room in Your Chest

In June 2001 an operation on then–Vice President Dick Cheney focused attention on the progress in treating heart problems with tiny implanted electrical devices. Aptly called "an emergency room in your chest" by Cheney's attending physician, devices called *I*mplanted *C*ardioverter *D*efibrillators (**ICDs**) can monitor, record, and logically process heart signals and then supply different corrective signals to hearts beating too slowly, too rapidly, or irregularly. ICDs can even monitor and send signals to the atria and ventricles independently! Figure 17.17a shows a sketch of an ICD with conducting leads that are implanted in the heart. Figure 17.17b shows an actual titanium-encapsulated dual-chamber ICD.

The latest ICDs are sophisticated devices capable of a number of functions:

BIO APPLICATION

Implanted Cardioverter Defibrillators

1. monitoring both atrial and ventricular chambers to differentiate between atrial and potentially fatal ventricular arrhythmias, which require prompt regulation
2. storing about a half hour of heart signals that can easily be read out by a physician
3. being easily reprogrammed with an external magnetic wand
4. performing complicated signal analysis and comparison
5. supplying either 0.25- to 10-V repetitive pacing signals to speed up or slow down a malfunctioning heart, or a high-voltage pulse of about 800 V to halt the potentially fatal condition of ventricular fibrillation, in which the heart quivers rapidly rather than beats (people who have experienced such a high-voltage jolt say that it feels like a kick or a bomb going off in the chest)
6. automatically adjusting the number of pacing pulses per minute to match the patient's activity

ICDs are powered by lithium batteries and have implanted lifetimes of 4 to 6 years. Some basic properties of these adjustable ICDs are given in Table 17.3 (page 608). In the table *tachycardia* means "rapid heartbeat" and *bradycardia* means "slow heartbeat." A key factor in developing tiny electrical implants that serve as defibrillators is the development of capacitors with relatively large capacitance (125 μF) and small physical size.

Table 17.3 Properties of Implanted Cardioverter Defibrillators

Physical Specifications	
Mass (g)	85
Size (cm)	7.3 × 6.2 × 1.3 (about five stacked silver dollars)
Antitachycardia Pacing	ICD delivers a burst of critically timed low-energy pulses
Number of bursts	1–15
Burst cycle length (ms)	200–552
Number of pulses per burst	2–20
Pulse amplitude (V)	7.5 or 10
Pulse width (ms)	1.0 or 1.9
High-Voltage Defibrillation	
Pulse energy (J)	37 stored/33 delivered
Pulse amplitude (V)	801
Bradycardia Pacing	A dual-chamber ICD can steadily deliver repetitive pulses to both the atrium and the ventricle
Base frequency (beats/minute)	40–100
Pulse amplitude (V)	0.25–7.5
Pulse width (ms)	0.05, 0.1–1.5, 1.9

Note: For more information, go to **www.photonicd.com/specs.html.**

■ SUMMARY

17.1 Electric Current

The **average electric current** I in a conductor is defined as

$$I_{av} \equiv \frac{\Delta Q}{\Delta t} \qquad \text{[17.1a]}$$

	Current is the time rate of flow of charge through a surface.

where ΔQ is the charge that passes through a cross section of the conductor in time Δt. The SI unit of current is the **ampere** (A); 1 A = 1 C/s. By convention, the direction of current is the direction of flow of positive charge.

The **instantaneous current** I is the limit of the average current as the time interval goes to zero:

$$I = \lim_{\Delta t \to 0} I_{av} = \lim_{\Delta t \to 0} \frac{\Delta Q}{\Delta t} \qquad \text{[17.1b]}$$

17.2 A Microscopic View: Current and Drift Speed

The current in a conductor is related to the motion of the charge carriers by

$$I = nqv_d A \qquad \text{[17.2]}$$

where n is the number of mobile charge carriers per unit volume, q is the charge on each carrier, v_d is the drift speed of the charges, and A is the cross-sectional area of the conductor.

	The current I in a conductor is related to the number density n of charge carriers, the charge q per carrier, the drift speed $\vec{v}_d$, and the cross-sectional area of the conductor, A.

17.4 Resistance, Resistivity, and Ohm's Law

The **resistance** R of a conductor is defined as the ratio of the potential difference across the conductor to the current in it:

$$R \equiv \frac{\Delta V}{I} \qquad \text{[17.3]}$$

	The potential difference ΔV is proportional to the current, I.

The SI units of resistance are volts per ampere, or **ohms** (Ω); 1 Ω = 1 V/A.

Ohm's law describes many conductors for which the applied voltage is directly proportional to the current it causes. The proportionality constant is the resistance:

$$\Delta V = IR \qquad \text{[17.4]}$$

If a conductor has length ℓ and cross-sectional area A, its **resistance** is

$$R = \rho \frac{\ell}{A} \qquad \text{[17.5]}$$

where ρ is an intrinsic property of the conductor called the **electrical resistivity**. The SI unit of resistivity is the **ohm-meter** ($\Omega \cdot$ m).

17.5 Temperature Variation of Resistance

Over a limited temperature range, the resistivity of a conductor varies with temperature according to the expression

$$\rho = \rho_0[1 + \alpha(T - T_0)] \qquad \textbf{[17.6]}$$

where α is the **temperature coefficient of resistivity** and ρ_0 is the resistivity at some reference temperature T_0 (usually taken to be 20°C).

The resistance of a conductor varies with temperature according to the expression

$$R = R_0[1 + \alpha(T - T_0)] \qquad \textbf{[17.7]}$$

17.6 Electrical Energy and Power

If a potential difference ΔV is maintained across an electrical device, the **power,** or rate at which energy is supplied to the device, is

$$P = I\,\Delta V \qquad \textbf{[17.8]}$$

Because the potential difference across a resistor is $\Delta V = IR$, the **power delivered to a resistor** can be expressed as

$$P = I^2R = \frac{\Delta V^2}{R} \qquad \textbf{[17.9]}$$

A **kilowatt-hour** is the amount of energy converted or consumed in one hour by a device supplied with power at the rate of 1 kW. It is equivalent to

$$1 \text{ kWh} = 3.60 \times 10^6 \text{ J} \qquad \textbf{[17.10]}$$

■ MULTIPLE-CHOICE QUESTIONS

 WebAssign The multiple-choice questions in this chapter may be assigned online in Enhanced WebAssign.

1. A wire carries a current of 1.6 A. How many electrons per second pass a given point in the wire? Choose the best estimate. (a) 10^{17} (b) 10^{18} (c) 10^{19} (d) 10^{20} (e) 10^{21}

2. Wire A has the same length and twice the radius of wire B. Both wires are made of the same material and carry the same current. Which of the following equations is true concerning the drift velocities v_A and v_B of electrons in the wires? (a) $v_A = 2v_B$ (b) $v_A = v_B$ (c) $v_A = v_B/2$ (d) $v_A = 4v_B$ (e) $v_A = v_B/4$

3. A metal wire of resistance R is cut into three equal pieces that are then placed together side by side to form a new cable with a length equal to one-third the original length. What is the resistance of this new cable? (a) $\frac{1}{9}R$ (b) $\frac{1}{3}R$ (c) R (d) $3R$ (e) $9R$

4. Three wires are made of copper having circular cross sections. Wire 1 has a length L and radius r. Wire 2 has a length L and radius $2r$. Wire 3 has a length $2L$ and radius $3r$. Which wire has the smallest resistance? (a) wire 1 (b) wire 2 (c) wire 3 (d) All three wires have the same resistance. (e) Not enough information is given to answer the question.

5. Car batteries are often rated in ampere-hours. Does this information designate the amount of (a) current, (b) power, (c) energy, (d) charge, or (e) potential the battery can supply?

6. The current versus voltage behavior of a certain electrical device is shown in Figure MCQ17.6. When the potential difference across the device is 2 V, what is

the resistance? (a) 1 Ω (b) $\frac{3}{4}$Ω (c) $\frac{4}{3}$Ω (d) undefined (e) none of these

Figure MCQ17.6 Multiple-Choice Questions 6 and 9.

7. A color television set draws about 2.5 A when connected to a 120-V source. What is the cost (with electrical energy at 8 cents/kWh) of running the set for 8.0 hours? (a) 2.0 cents (b) 4.0 cents (c) 19 cents (d) 40 cents (e) 62 cents

8. A metal wire has a resistance of 10.00 Ω at a temperature of 20.0°C. If the same wire has a resistance of 10.55 Ω at 90.0°C, what is the resistance of this same wire when its temperature is −20.0°C? (a) 0.700 Ω (b) 9.69 Ω (c) 10.3 Ω (d) 13.8 Ω (e) 6.59 Ω

9. The current vs. voltage behavior of a certain electrical device is shown in Figure MCQ17.6. When the potential difference across the device is 3 V, what is the resistance? (a) 0.83 Ω (b) 1.2 Ω (c) 3.0 Ω (d) 1.33 Ω (e) 2.3 Ω

10. Three resistors, A, B, and C, are connected in parallel and attached to a battery, with the resistance of A being the smallest and the resistance of C the greatest. Which resistor carries the highest current? (a) A (b) B (c) C (d) All wires carry the same current. (e) More information is needed to answer the question.

11. A potential difference of 1.0 V is maintained across a 10.0-Ω resistor for a period of 20 s. What total charge passes through the wire in this time interval? (a) 200 C (b) 20 C (c) 2 C (d) 0.005 C (e) 0.05 C

12. Three resistors, A, B, and C, are connected in series in a closed loop with a battery, with the resistance of A being the smallest and the resistance of C the greatest. Across which resistor is the voltage drop the greatest?

(a) A (b) B (c) C (d) The voltage drops are the same for each. (e) More information is needed to answer the question.

13. Two conductors made of the same material are connected across the same potential difference. Conductor A has twice the diameter and twice the length of conductor B. What is the ratio of the power delivered to A to the power delivered to B? (a) 8 (b) 4 (c) 2 (d) 1 (e) $\frac{1}{2}$

14. Two wires A and B with circular cross sections are made of the same metal and have equal lengths, but the resistance of wire A is three times greater than that of wire B. What is the ratio of the cross-sectional area of A to that of B? (a) 3 (b) $\sqrt{3}$ (c) 1 (d) $1/\sqrt{3}$ (e) $\frac{1}{3}$

■ CONCEPTUAL QUESTIONS

WebAssign The conceptual questions in this chapter may be assigned online in Enhanced WebAssign.

1. We have seen that an electric field must exist inside a conductor that carries a current. How is that possible in view of the fact that in electrostatics we concluded that the electric field must be zero inside a conductor?

2. Use the atomic theory of matter to explain why the resistance of a material should increase as its temperature increases.

3. If charges flow very slowly through a metal, why does it not require several hours for a light to come on when you throw a switch?

4. In an analogy between traffic flow and electrical current, (a) what would correspond to the charge Q? (b) What would correspond to the current I?

5. When the voltage across a certain conductor is doubled, the current is observed to triple. What can you conclude about the conductor?

6. Two lightbulbs are each connected to a voltage of 120 V. One has a power of 25 W, the other 100 W. (a) Which

lightbulb has the higher resistance? (b) Which lightbulb carries more current?

7. Newspaper articles often have statements such as "10 000 volts of electricity surged *through* the victim's body." What is wrong with this statement?

8. There is an old admonition given to experimenters to "keep one hand in the pocket" when working around high voltages. Why is this warning a good idea?

9. What could happen to the drift velocity of the electrons in a wire and to the current in the wire if the electrons could move through it freely without resistance?

10. Some homes have light dimmers that are operated by rotating a knob. What is being changed in the electric circuit when the knob is rotated?

11. When is more power delivered to a lightbulb, immediately after it is turned on and the glow of the filament is increasing or after it has been on for a few seconds and the glow is steady?

■ PROBLEMS

WebAssign The problems in this chapter may be assigned online in Enhanced WebAssign. Selected problems also have Watch It video solutions.

1. denotes straightforward problem; 2. denotes intermediate problem;
3. denotes challenging problem
[1.] denotes full solution available in *Student Solutions Manual/ Study Guide*

1. denotes problems most often assigned in Enhanced WebAssign
BIO denotes biomedical problems
GP denotes guided problems
M denotes Master It tutorial available in Enhanced WebAssign
QC denotes asking for quantitative and conceptual reasoning
S denotes symbolic reasoning problem

17.1 Electric Current

17.2 A Microscopic View: Current and Drift Speed

1. If a current of 80.0 mA exists in a metal wire, (a) how many electrons flow past a given cross section of the

wire in 10.0 min? (b) In what direction do the electrons travel with respect to the current?

2. **QC** A copper wire has a circular cross section with a radius of 1.25 mm. (a) If the wire carries a current of

3.70 A, find the drift speed of the electrons in the wire. (See Example 17.2 for relevant data on copper.) (b) All other things being equal, what happens to the drift speed in wires made of metal having a larger number of conduction electrons per atom than copper? Explain.

3. In the Bohr model of the hydrogen atom, an electron in the lowest energy state moves at a speed equal to 2.19×10^6 m/s in a circular path having a radius of 5.29×10^{-11} m. What is the effective current associated with this orbiting electron?

4. The current supplied by a battery in a portable device is typically 0.15 A. Find the number of electrons passing through the device in one hour.

5. A certain laboratory experiment requires an aluminum wire of length of 32.0 m and a resistance of $2.50\ \Omega$ at $20.0°C$. What diameter wire must be used?

6. If 3.25×10^{-3} kg of gold is deposited on the negative electrode of an electrolytic cell in a period of 2.78 h, what is the current in the cell during that period? Assume the gold ions carry one elementary unit of positive charge.

7. **M** A 200-km-long high-voltage transmission line 2.0 cm in diameter carries a steady current of 1 000 A. If the conductor is copper with a free charge density of 8.5×10^{28} electrons per cubic meter, how many years does it take one electron to travel the full length of the cable?

8. An aluminum wire having a cross-sectional area of 4.00×10^{-6} m² carries a current of 5.00 A. The density of aluminum is 2.70 g/cm³. Assume each aluminum atom supplies one conduction electron per atom. Find the drift speed of the electrons in the wire.

9. **GP** An iron wire has a cross-sectional area of 5.00×10^{-6} m². Carry out steps (a) through (e) to compute the drift speed of the conduction electrons in the wire. (a) How many kilograms are there in 1 mole of iron? (b) Starting with the density of iron and the result of part (a), compute the molar density of iron (the number of moles of iron per cubic meter). (c) Calculate the number density of iron atoms using Avogadro's number. (d) Obtain the number density of conduction electrons given that there are two conduction electrons per iron atom. (e) If the wire carries a current of 30.0 A, calculate the drift speed of conduction electrons.

17.4 Resistance, Resistivity, and Ohm's Law

10. An electric heater carries a current of 13.5 A when operating at a voltage of 1.20×10^2 V. What is the resistance of the heater?

11. **BIO** A person notices a mild shock if the current along a path through the thumb and index finger exceeds 80 μA. Compare the maximum possible voltage without shock across the thumb and index finger with a dry-skin resistance of $4.0 \times 10^5\ \Omega$ and a wet-skin resistance of 2 000 Ω.

12. Suppose you wish to fabricate a uniform wire out of 1.00 g of copper. If the wire is to have a resistance $R = 0.500\ \Omega$, and if all the copper is to be used, what will be (a) the length and (b) the diameter of the wire?

13. Nichrome wire of cross-sectional radius 0.791 mm is to be used in winding a heating coil. If the coil must carry a current of 9.25 A when a voltage of 1.20×10^2 V is applied across its ends, find (a) the required resistance of the coil and (b) the length of wire you must use to wind the coil.

14. A wire of diameter 0.800 mm and length 25.0 m has a measured resistance of $1.60\ \Omega$. What is the resistivity of the wire?

15. A potential difference of 12 V is found to produce a current of 0.40 A in a 3.2-m length of wire with a uniform radius of 0.40 cm. What is (a) the resistance of the wire? (b) The resistivity of the wire?

16. **S** Aluminum and copper wires of equal length are found to have the same resistance. What is the ratio of their radii?

17. **M** A wire 50.0 m long and 2.00 mm in diameter is connected to a source with a potential difference of 9.11 V, and the current is found to be 36.0 A. Assume a temperature of 20°C and, using Table 17.1, identify the metal out of which the wire is made.

18. A rectangular block of copper has sides of length 10 cm, 20 cm, and 40 cm. If the block is connected to a 6.0-V source across two of its opposite faces, what are (a) the maximum current and (b) the minimum current the block can carry?

19. A wire of initial length L_0 and radius r_0 has a measured resistance of $1.0\ \Omega$. The wire is drawn under tensile stress to a new uniform radius of $r = 0.25r_0$. What is the new resistance of the wire?

20. **BIO** **Q|C** The human body can exhibit a wide range of resistances to current depending on the path of the current, contact area, and sweatiness of the skin. Suppose the resistance across the chest from the left hand to the right hand is $1.0 \times 10^6\ \Omega$. (a) How much voltage is required to cause possible heart fibrillation in a man, which corresponds to 500 mA of direct current? (b) Why should rubber-soled shoes and rubber gloves be worn when working around electricity?

21. **S** Starting from Ohm's law, show that $E = J\rho$, where E is the magnitude of the electric field (assumed constant) and $J = I/A$ is called the current density. The result is in fact true in general.

17.5 Temperature Variation of Resistance

22. If a certain silver wire has a resistance of 6.00 Ω at 20.0°C, what resistance will it have at 34.0°C?

23. While taking photographs in Death Valley on a day when the temperature is 58.0°C, Bill Hiker finds that a certain voltage applied to a copper wire produces a current of 1.000 A. Bill then travels to Antarctica and applies the same voltage to the same wire. What current does he register there if the temperature is −88.0°C? Assume no change occurs in the wire's shape and size.

24. **Q|C** A length of aluminum wire has a resistance of 30.0 Ω at 20.0°C. When the wire is warmed in an oven and reaches thermal equilibrium, the resistance of the wire increases to 46.2 Ω. (a) Neglecting thermal expansion, find the temperature of the oven. (b) Qualitatively, how would thermal expansion be expected to affect the answer?

25. Gold is the most ductile of all metals. For example, one gram of gold can be drawn into a wire 2.40 km long. The density of gold is 19.3×10^3 kg/m³, and its resistivity is 2.44×10^{-8} Ω · m. What is the resistance of such a wire at 20.0°C?

26. At what temperature will aluminum have a resistivity that is three times the resistivity of copper at room temperature?

27. At 20°C, the carbon resistor in an electric circuit connected to a 5.0-V battery has a resistance of 2.0×10^2 Ω. What is the current in the circuit when the temperature of the carbon rises to 80°C?

28. A wire 3.00 m long and 0.450 mm² in cross-sectional area has a resistance of 41.0 Ω at 20°C. If its resistance increases to 41.4 Ω at 29.0°C, what is the temperature coefficient of resistivity?

29. **M** (a) A 34.5-m length of copper wire at 20.0°C has a radius of 0.25 mm. If a potential difference of 9.0 V is applied across the length of the wire, determine the current in the wire. (b) If the wire is heated to 30.0°C while the 9.0-V potential difference is maintained, what is the resulting current in the wire?

30. An engineer needs a resistor with a zero overall temperature coefficient of resistance at 20.0°C. She designs a pair of circular cylinders, one of carbon and one of Nichrome as shown in Figure P17.30. The device must have an overall resistance of $R_1 + R_2 =$ 10.0 Ω independent of temperature and a uniform radius of $r = 1.50$ mm. Ignore thermal expansion of the cylinders and assume both are always at the same temperature. (a) Can she meet the design goal with this method? (b) If so, state what you can determine about the lengths L_1 and L_2 of each segment. If not, explain.

L_1　　　　　　L_2

Figure P17.30

31. **BIO** In one form of plethysmograph (a device for measuring volume), a rubber capillary tube with an inside diameter of 1.00 mm is filled with mercury at 20°C. The resistance of the mercury is measured with the aid of electrodes sealed into the ends of the tube. If 100.00 cm of the tube is wound in a spiral around a patient's upper arm, the blood flow during a heartbeat causes the arm to expand, stretching the tube to a length of 100.04 cm. From this observation, and assuming cylindrical symmetry, you can find the change in volume of the arm, which gives an indication of blood flow. (a) Calculate the resistance of the mercury. (b) Calculate the fractional change in resistance during the heartbeat. Take $\rho_{Hg} = 9.4 \times 10^{-7}$ Ω · m. *Hint:* Because the cylindrical volume is constant, $V = A_i L_i = A_f L_f$ and $A_f = A_i(L_i/L_f)$.

32. A platinum resistance thermometer has resistances of 200.0 Ω when placed in a 0°C ice bath and 253.8 Ω when immersed in a crucible containing melting potassium. What is the melting point of potassium? *Hint:* First determine the resistance of the platinum resistance thermometer at room temperature, 20°C.

17.6 Electrical Energy and Power

33. Suppose your waffle iron is rated at 1.00 kW when connected to a 1.20×10^2 V source. (a) What current does the waffle iron carry? (b) What is its resistance?

34. If electrical energy costs $0.12 per kilowatt-hour, how much does it cost to (a) burn a 100-W lightbulb for 24 h? (b) Operate an electric oven for 5.0 h if it carries a current of 20.0 A at 220 V?

35. **Q|C** Residential building codes typically require the use of 12-gauge copper wire (diameter 0.205 cm) for wiring receptacles. Such circuits carry currents as large as 20.0 A. If a wire of smaller diameter (with a higher gauge number) carried that much current, the wire could rise to a high temperature and cause a fire. (a) Calculate the rate at which internal energy is produced in 1.00 m of 12-gauge copper wire carrying 20.0 A. (b) Repeat the calculation for a 12-gauge aluminum wire. (c) Explain whether a 12-gauge aluminum wire would be as safe as a copper wire.

36. A high-voltage transmission line with a resistance of 0.31 Ω/km carries a current of 1 000 A. The line is at a potential of 700 kV at the power station and carries the current to a city located 160 km from the station. (a) What is the power loss due to resistance in the line? (b) What fraction of the transmitted power does this loss represent?

37. **M** The heating element of a coffeemaker operates at 120 V and carries a current of 2.00 A. Assuming the water absorbs all the energy converted by the resistor, calculate how long it takes to heat 0.500 kg of water from room temperature (23.0°C) to the boiling point.

38. The power supplied to a typical black-and-white television set is 90 W when the set is connected to 120 V. (a) How much electrical energy does this set consume in 1 hour? (b) A color television set draws about 2.5 A when connected to 120 V. How much time is required for it to consume the same energy as the black-and-white model consumes in 1 hour?

39. **Q|C** Lightbulb A is marked "25.0 W 120 V," and lightbulb B is marked "100 W 120 V." These labels mean that each lightbulb has its respective power delivered to it when it is connected to a constant 120-V source. (a) Find the resistance of each lightbulb. (b) During what time interval does 1.00 C pass into lightbulb A? (c) Is this charge different upon its exit versus its entry into the lightbulb? Explain. (d) In what time interval does 1.00 J pass into lightbulb A? (e) By what mechanisms does this energy enter and exit the lightbulb? Explain. (f) Find the cost of running lightbulb A continuously for 30.0 days, assuming the electric company sells its product at $0.110 per kWh.

40. A certain toaster has a heating element made of Nichrome resistance wire. When the toaster is first connected to a 120-V source of potential difference (and the wire is at a temperature of 20.0°C), the initial current is 1.80 A but the current begins to decrease as the resistive element warms up. When the toaster reaches its final operating temperature, the current has dropped to 1.53 A. (a) Find the power the toaster converts when it is at its operating temperature. (b) What is the final temperature of the heating element?

41. A copper cable is designed to carry a current of 300 A with a power loss of 2.00 W/m. What is the required radius of this cable?

42. Batteries are rated in terms of ampere-hours (A · h). For example, a battery that can deliver a current of 3.0 A for 5.0 h is rated at 15 A · h. (a) What is the total energy, in kilowatt-hours, stored in a 12-V battery rated at 55 A · h? (b) At $0.12 per kilowatt-hour, what is the value of the electricity that can be produced by this battery?

43. **BIO** The potential difference across a resting neuron in the human body is about 75.0 mV and carries a current of about 0.200 mA. How much power does the neuron release?

44. The cost of electricity varies widely throughout the United States; $0.120/kWh is a typical value. At this unit price, calculate the cost of (a) leaving a 40.0-W porch light on for 2 weeks while you are on vacation, (b) making a piece of dark toast in 3.00 min with a 970-W toaster, and (c) drying a load of clothes in 40.0 min in a 5 200-W dryer.

45. An electric utility company supplies a customer's house from the main power lines (120 V) with two copper wires, each of which is 50.0 m long and has a resistance of 0.108 Ω per 300 m. (a) Find the potential difference at the customer's house for a load current of 110 A. For this load current, find (b) the power delivered to the customer.

46. **Q|C** An office worker uses an immersion heater to warm 250 g of water in a light, covered, insulated cup from 20°C to 100°C in 4.00 minutes. The heater is a Nichrome resistance wire connected to a 120-V power supply. Assume the wire is at 100°C throughout the 4.00-min time interval. (a) Calculate the average power required to warm the water to 100°C in 4.00 min. (b) Calculate the required resistance in the heating element at 100°C. (c) Calculate the resistance of the heating element at 20.0°C. (d) Derive a relationship between the diameter of the wire, the resistivity at 20.0°C, ρ_0, the resistance at 20.0°C, R_0, and the length L. (e) If $L = 3.00$ m, what is the diameter of the wire?

47. **S** Two wires A and B made of the same material and having the same lengths are connected across the same voltage source. If the power supplied to wire A is three times the power supplied to wire B, what is the ratio of their diameters?

48. **Q|C** A tungsten wire in a vacuum has length 15.0 cm and radius 1.00 mm. A potential difference is applied across it. (a) What is the resistance of the wire at 293 K? (b) Suppose the wire reaches an equilibrium temperature such that it emits 75.0 W in the form of radiation. Neglecting absorption of any radiation from its environment, what is the temperature of the wire? (*Note:* $e = 0.320$ for tungsten.) (c) What is the resistance of the wire at the temperature found in part (b)? Assume the temperature changes linearly over this temperature range. (d) What voltage drop is required across the wire? (e) Why are tungsten lightbulbs energetically inefficient as light sources?

Additional Problems

49. If a battery is rated at 60.0 A · h, how much total charge can it deliver before it goes "dead"?

50. A car owner forgets to turn off the headlights of his car while it is parked in his garage. If the 12.0-V battery in his car is rated at 90.0 A · h and each headlight requires 36.0 W of power, how long will it take the battery to completely discharge?

51. Consider an aluminum wire of diameter 0.600 mm and length 15.0 m. The resistivity of aluminum at 20.0°C is

$2.82 \times 10^{-8} \, \Omega \cdot$ m. (a) Find the resistance of this wire at 20.0°C. (b) If a 9.00 V battery is connected across the ends of the wire, find the current in the wire.

52. A given copper wire has a resistance of 5.00 Ω at 20.0°C while a tungsten wire of the same diameter has a resistance of 4.75 Ω at 20.0°C. At what temperature will the two wires have the same resistance?

53. **M** A particular wire has a resistivity of $3.0 \times 10^{-8} \, \Omega \cdot$ m and a cross-sectional area of 4.0×10^{-6} m². A length of this wire is to be used as a resistor that will develop 48 W of power when connected across a 20-V battery. What length of wire is required?

54. Birds resting on high-voltage power lines are a common sight. The copper wire on which a bird stands is 2.2 cm in diameter and carries a current of 50 A. If the bird's feet are 4.0 cm apart, calculate the potential difference between its feet.

55. An experiment is conducted to measure the electrical resistivity of Nichrome in the form of wires with different lengths and cross-sectional areas. For one set of measurements, a student uses 30-gauge wire, which has a cross-sectional area of 7.30×10^{-8} m². The student measures the potential difference across the wire and the current in the wire with a voltmeter and an ammeter, respectively. For each of the measurements given in the following table taken on wires of three different lengths, calculate the resistance of the wires and the corresponding value of the resistivity.

L (m)	ΔV(V)	I(A)	R (Ω)	ρ (Ω · m)
0.540		5.22		0.500
1.028		5.82		0.276
1.543		5.94		0.187

What is the average value of the resistivity, and how does this value compare with the value given in Table 17.1?

56. A 50.0-g sample of a conducting material is all that is available. The resistivity of the material is measured to be $11 \times 10^{-8} \, \Omega \cdot$ m, and the density is 7.86 g/cm³. The material is to be shaped into a solid cylindrical wire that has a total resistance of 1.5 Ω. (a) What length of wire is required? (b) What must be the diameter of the wire?

57. You are cooking breakfast for yourself and a friend using a 1 200-W waffle iron and a 500-W coffeepot. Usually, you operate these appliances from a 110-V outlet for 0.500 h each day. (a) At 12 cents per kWh, how much do you spend to cook breakfast during a 30.0-day period? (b) You find yourself addicted to waffles and would like to upgrade to a 2 400-W waffle iron that will enable you to cook twice as many waffles dur-

ing a half-hour period, but you know that the circuit breaker in your kitchen is a 20-A breaker. Can you do the upgrade?

58. The current in a conductor varies in time as shown in Figure P17.58. (a) How many coulombs of charge pass through a cross section of the conductor in the interval from $t = 0$ to $t = 5.0$ s? (b) What constant current would transport the same total charge during the 5.0-s interval as does the actual current?

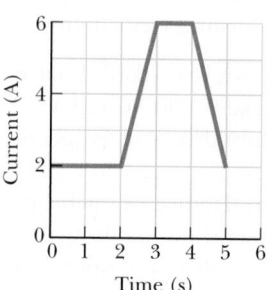

Figure P17.58

59. A 120-V motor has mechanical power output of 2.50 hp. It is 90.0% efficient in converting power that it takes in by electrical transmission into mechanical power. (a) Find the current in the motor. (b) Find the energy delivered to the motor by electrical transmission in 3.00 h of operation. (c) If the electric company charges $0.110/kWh, what does it cost to run the motor for 3.00 h?

60. **QC** A Nichrome heating element in an oven has a resistance of 8.0 Ω at 20°C. (a) What is its resistance at 350°C? (b) What assumption did you have to make to obtain your answer to part (a)?

61. A length of metal wire has a radius of 5.00×10^{-3} m and a resistance of 0.100 Ω. When the potential difference across the wire is 15.0 V, the electron drift speed is found to be 3.17×10^{-4} m/s. On the basis of these data, calculate the density of free electrons in the wire.

62. In a certain stereo system, each speaker has a resistance of 4.00 Ω. The system is rated at 60.0 W in each channel. Each speaker circuit includes a fuse rated at a maximum current of 4.00 A. Is this system adequately protected against overload?

63. A resistor is constructed by forming a material of resistivity $3.5 \times 10^5 \, \Omega \cdot$ m into the shape of a hollow cylinder of length 4.0 cm and inner and outer radii 0.50 cm and 1.2 cm, respectively. In use, a potential difference is applied between the ends of the cylinder, producing a current parallel to the length of the cylinder. Find the resistance of the cylinder.

64. **S** When a straight wire is heated, its resistance changes according to the equation

$$R = R_0[1 + \alpha(T - T_0)]$$

(Eq. 17.7), where α is the temperature coefficient of resistivity. (a) Show that a more precise result, which includes the length and area of a wire change when it is heated, is

$$R = \frac{R_0[1 + \alpha(T - T_0)][1 + \alpha'(T - T_0)]}{[1 + 2\alpha'(T - T_0)]}$$

where α' is the coefficient of linear expansion. (See Chapter 10.) (b) Compare the two results for a 2.00-m-long copper wire of radius 0.100 mm, starting at 20.0°C and heated to 100.0°C.

65. **BIO** An x-ray tube used for cancer therapy operates at 4.0 MV, with a beam current of 25 mA striking the metal target. Nearly all the power in the beam is transferred to a stream of water flowing through holes drilled in the target. What rate of flow, in kilograms per second, is needed if the rise in temperature (ΔT) of the water is not to exceed 50°C?

66. A man wishes to vacuum his car with a canister vacuum cleaner marked 535 W at 120 V. The car is parked far from the building, so he uses an extension cord 15.0 m long to plug the cleaner into a 120-V source. Assume the cleaner has constant resistance. (a) If the resistance of each of the two conductors of the extension cord is 0.900 Ω, what is the actual power delivered to the cleaner? (b) If, instead, the power is to be at least 525 W, what must be the diameter of each of two identical copper conductors in the cord the young man buys? (c) Repeat part (b) if the power is to be at least 532 W. *Suggestion:* A symbolic solution can simplify the calculations.

1. Which of the following wires would have the greatest resistivity?

   (A) Wire 1 = ρ, ℓ, A

   (B) Wire 2 = 2ρ, ℓ, $3A$

   (C) Wire 3 = $\rho/2$, ℓ, $A/4$

   (D) Wire 4 = 2ρ, 2ℓ, $4A$

   (E) Wire 5 = $\rho/2$, 3ℓ, $2A$

2. A 15 cm long wire with a diameter of 0.6 mm carries a current of 1.5 A when 4.5 V is applied to it. What is the resistivity of the wire?

   (A) 0.6 $\mu\Omega \cdot$ m

   (B) 0.6 $\mu\Omega \cdot$ m

   (C) 2.5 $\mu\Omega \cdot$ m

   (D) 5.6 $\mu\Omega \cdot$ m

   (E) 22.6 $\mu\Omega \cdot$ m

3. A copper wire in a circuit has more than double the necessary resistance. If the wire is replaced with another copper wire that will work in the circuit, what should happen to its dimensions compared to the original?

   (A) 2ℓ, $4A$

   (B) $\dfrac{\ell}{3}$, $6A$

   (C) ℓ, $\dfrac{A}{2}$

   (D) 4ℓ, $2A$

   (E) 3ℓ, $\dfrac{A}{3}$

4. If the resistance in a circuit remains constant while the power dissipated is increased ninefold, what happens to the potential difference across the resistor?

   (A) $9V$

   (B) $3V$

   (C) $V/3$

   (D) $V/9$

   (E) V

5. If the power dissipated in a circuit quadruples while the resistance doubles, what happens to the current?

   (A) $\sqrt{2}I$

   (B) $0.5I$

   (C) $2I$

   (D) $4I$

   (E) I

6. Two wires, A and B, are in circuits with identical currents running through them. If their lengths are the same, but $P_A < P_B$, what must be true about their areas and resistivities?

   (A) $\rho_A = \rho_B$, $A_A < A_B$

   (B) $\rho_A > \rho_B$, $A_A = A_B$

   (C) $\rho_A > \rho_B$, $A_A > A_B$

   (D) $\rho_A = \rho_B$, $A_A > A_B$

   (E) $\rho_A > \rho_B$, $A_A = A_B$

7. A wire with an area of 2 mm^3 and length of 20 cm is placed in a 100 V circuit. If the wire uses 20 kWh over the course of 20 hours, what is the resistivity of the wire?

   (A) 0.01 $\Omega \cdot$ m

   (B) 0.1 $\Omega \cdot$ m

   (C) 1.0 $\Omega \cdot$ m

   (D) 10 $\Omega \cdot$ m

   (E) 100 $\Omega \cdot$ m

8. A set of Christmas lights will run 10 hours a day for 10 weeks on a 100 V line. If the electric bill was $100.00 and the current electric rate is $0.20/kWh, what current do the lights draw?

   (A) 0.05A

   (B) 2 A

   (C) 5 A

   (D) 50 A

   (E) 500 A

9. Ten 100 W incandescent bulbs are run for 10 hours a day for 10 days. Ten similar compact fluorescent bulbs only use 20 W and run for the same period of time. If the electric company charges $0.20/kWh, what is the cost savings for the compact fluorescent bulbs?

   (A) $4.00

   (B) $16.00

   (C) $20.00

   (D) $24.00

   (E) $160.00

(A) *I*

(D) *I*

(B) *I*

(E) *I*

(C) *I*
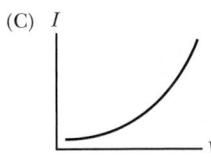

10. For a resistor that follows Ohm's Law, what does a graph of current vs. voltage look like?

11. The diagram above shows an ammeter in a circuit where $V = 15$ V, $R_1 = 10\ \Omega$, and $R_2 = 20\ \Omega$. What current will the ammeter read for R_2?

   (A) 0.5 A

   (B) 1.3 A

   (C) 1.5 A

   (D) 2.0 A

   (E) There will be no reading on the ammeter as it is not hooked into the circuit correctly.

12. The diagram shows a voltmeter in a circuit where $V = 16$ V, $R_1 = 2\ \Omega$, $R_3 = 2\ \Omega$, and $R_2 = 4\ \Omega$. What voltage will the voltmeter read for R_2?

   (A) 2 V

   (B) 4 V

   (C) 8 V

   (D) 16 V

   (E) There will be no reading on the voltmeter as it is not correctly hooked into the circuit.

This vision-impaired patient is wearing an artificial vision device. A camera on the lens sends video to a portable computer. The computer then converts the video to signals that stimulate implants in the patient's visual cortex, giving him enough sight to move around on his own.

© Najlah Feanny/Corbis

18 Direct-Current Circuits

Batteries, resistors, and capacitors can be used in various combinations to construct electric circuits, which direct and control the flow of electricity and the energy it conveys. Such circuits make possible all the modern conveniences in a home: electric lights, electric stove tops and ovens, washing machines, and a host of other appliances and tools. Electric circuits are also found in our cars, in tractors that increase farming productivity, and in all types of medical equipment that saves so many lives every day.

In this chapter we study and analyze a number of simple direct-current circuits. The analysis is simplified by the use of two rules known as Kirchhoff's rules, which follow from the principle of conservation of energy and the law of conservation of charge. Most of the circuits are assumed to be in *steady state,* which means that the currents are constant in magnitude and direction. We close the chapter with a discussion of circuits containing resistors and capacitors, in which current varies with time.

18.1 Sources of emf

A current is maintained in a closed circuit by a source of emf.[1] Among such sources are any devices (for example, batteries and generators) that increase the potential energy of the circulating charges. A source of emf can be thought of as a "charge pump" that forces electrons to move in a direction opposite the electrostatic field inside the source. The emf $\mathcal{E}$ of a source is the work done per unit charge; hence the SI unit of emf is the volt.

---

[1]The term was originally an abbreviation for *electromotive force,* but emf is not really a force, so the long form is discouraged.

Consider the circuit in Active Figure 18.1a consisting of a battery connected to a resistor. We assume the connecting wires have no resistance. If we neglect the internal resistance of the battery, the potential drop across the battery (the terminal voltage) equals the emf of the battery. Because a real battery always has some internal resistance r, however, the terminal voltage is not equal to the emf. The circuit of Active Figure 18.1a can be described schematically by the diagram in Active Figure 18.1b. The battery, represented by the dashed rectangle, consists of a source of emf $\mathcal{E}$ in series with an internal resistance r. Now imagine a positive charge moving through the battery from a to b in the figure. As the charge passes from the negative to the positive terminal of the battery, the potential of the charge increases by $\mathcal{E}$. As the charge moves through the resistance r, however, its potential decreases by the amount Ir, where I is the current in the circuit. The terminal voltage of the battery, $\Delta V = V_b - V_a$, is therefore given by

$$\Delta V = \mathcal{E} - Ir \qquad [18.1]$$

From this expression, we see that $\mathcal{E}$ **is equal to the terminal voltage when the current is zero**, called the **open-circuit voltage**. By inspecting Figure 18.1b, we find that the terminal voltage ΔV must also equal the potential difference across the external resistance R, often called the **load resistance**; that is, $\Delta V = IR$. Combining this relationship with Equation 18.1, we arrive at

$$\mathcal{E} = IR + Ir \qquad [18.2]$$

Solving for the current gives

$$I = \frac{\mathcal{E}}{R + r}$$

The preceding equation shows that the current in this simple circuit depends on both the resistance external to the battery and the internal resistance of the battery. If R is much greater than r, we can neglect r in our analysis (an option we usually select).

If we multiply Equation 18.2 by the current I, we get

$$I\mathcal{E} = I^2R + I^2r$$

This equation tells us that the total power output $I\mathcal{E}$ of the source of emf is converted at the rate I^2R at which energy is delivered to the load resistance, *plus* the rate I^2r at which energy is delivered to the internal resistance. Again, if $r \ll R$, most of the power delivered by the battery is transferred to the load resistance.

Unless otherwise stated, in our examples and end-of-chapter problems we will assume the internal resistance of a battery in a circuit is negligible.

■ Quick Quiz

18.1 True or False: While discharging, the terminal voltage of a battery can never be greater than the emf of the battery.

18.2 Why does a battery get warm while in use?

18.2 Resistors in Series

When two or more resistors are connected end to end as in Active Figure 18.2 (page 618), they are said to be in *series*. The resistors could be simple devices, such as lightbulbs or heating elements. When two resistors R_1 and R_2 are connected to a battery as in Active Figure 18.2, **the current is the same in the two resistors because any charge that flows through R_1 must also flow through R_2**. This is analogous to water flowing through a pipe with two constrictions, corresponding to R_1 and R_2. Whatever volume of water flows in one end in a given time interval must exit the opposite end.

a

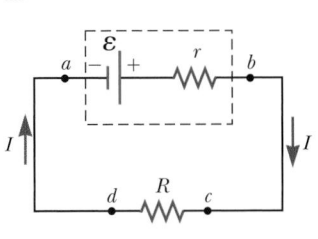
b

Active Figure 18.1
(a) A circuit consisting of a resistor connected to the terminals of a battery. (b) A circuit diagram of a source of emf $\mathcal{E}$ having internal resistance r connected to an external resistor R.

© Cengage Learning/George Semple

An assortment of batteries.

Tip 18.1 What's Constant in a Battery?

Equation 18.2 shows that the current in a circuit depends on the resistance of the battery, so a battery can't be considered a source of constant current. Even the terminal voltage of a battery given by Equation 18.1 can't be considered constant because the internal resistance can change (due to warming, for example, during the operation of the battery). A battery is, however, a source of constant emf.

Two resistors connected in series to a battery.

A circuit diagram for the two resistors and battery.

A circuit diagram of the equivalent resistance of the two resistors in series.

Active Figure 18.2

Two resistors, R_1 and R_2, in the form of incandescent light bulbs, in series with a battery. The currents in the resistors are the same, and the equivalent resistance of the combination is $R_{eq} = R_1 + R_2$.

Because the potential difference between a and b in Active Figure 18.2b equals IR_1 and the potential difference between b and c equals IR_2, the potential difference between a and c is

$$\Delta V = IR_1 + IR_2 = I(R_1 + R_2)$$

Regardless of how many resistors we have in series, the sum of the potential differences across the resistors is equal to the total potential difference across the combination. As we will show later, this result is a consequence of the conservation of energy. Active Figure 18.2c shows an equivalent resistor R_{eq} that can replace the two resistors of the original circuit. The equivalent resistor has the same effect on the circuit because it results in the same current in the circuit as the two resistors. Applying Ohm's law to this equivalent resistor, we have

$$\Delta V = IR_{eq}$$

Equating the preceding two expressions, we have

$$IR_{eq} = I(R_1 + R_2)$$

or

$$R_{eq} = R_1 + R_2 \quad \text{(series combination)} \qquad \text{[18.3]}$$

An extension of the preceding analysis shows that the equivalent resistance of three or more resistors connected in series is

◀ Equivalent resistance of a series combination of resistors

$$R_{eq} = R_1 + R_2 + R_3 + \cdots \qquad \text{[18.4]}$$

Therefore, **the equivalent resistance of a series combination of resistors is the algebraic sum of the individual resistances and is always greater than any individual resistance**.

Note that if the filament of one lightbulb in Active Figure 18.2 were to fail, the circuit would no longer be complete (an open-circuit condition would exist) and the second bulb would also go out.

■ APPLYING PHYSICS 18.1 | Christmas Lights in Series

A new design for Christmas lights allows them to be connected in series. A failed bulb in such a string would result in an open circuit, and all the bulbs would go out. How can the bulbs be redesigned to prevent that from happening?

EXPLANATION If the string of lights contained the usual kind of bulbs, a failed bulb would be hard to locate. Each bulb would have to be replaced with a good bulb, one by one, until the failed bulb was found. If there happened to be two or more failed bulbs in the string of lights, finding them would be a lengthy and annoying task.

Christmas lights use special bulbs that have an insulated loop of wire (a jumper) across the conducting supports to the bulb filaments (Fig. 18.3). If the filament breaks and the bulb fails, the bulb's resistance increases dramatically. As a result, most of the applied voltage appears across the loop of wire. This voltage causes the insulation around the loop of wire to burn, causing the metal wire to make electrical contact with the supports. This produces a conducting path through the bulb, so the other bulbs remain lit. ∎

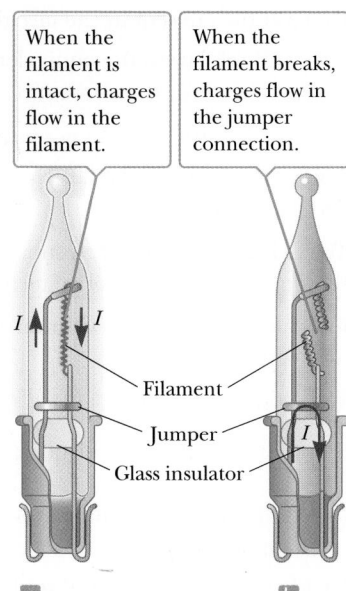

Figure 18.3 (Applying Physics 18.1) (a) Schematic diagram of a modern "miniature" holiday lightbulb, with a jumper connection to provide a current path if the filament breaks. (b) A holiday lightbulb with a broken filament.

▪ Quick Quiz

18.3 In Figure 18.4 the current is measured with the ammeter at the bottom of the circuit. When the switch is opened, does the reading on the ammeter (a) increase, (b) decrease, or (c) not change?

18.4 The circuit in Figure 18.4 consists of two resistors, a switch, an ammeter, and a battery. When the switch is closed, power P_c is delivered to resistor R_1. When the switch is opened, which of the following statements is true about the power P_o delivered to R_1? (a) $P_o < P_c$ (b) $P_o = P_c$ (c) $P_o > P_c$

Figure 18.4 (Quick Quizzes 18.3 and 18.4)

▪ EXAMPLE 18.1 | **Four Resistors in Series**

GOAL Analyze several resistors connected in series.

PROBLEM Four resistors are arranged as shown in Figure 18.5a. Find **(a)** the equivalent resistance of the circuit and **(b)** the current in the circuit if the closed-circuit terminal voltage of the battery is 6.0 V. **(c)** Calculate the electric potential at point A if the potential at the positive terminal is 6.0 V. **(d)** Suppose the open circuit voltage, or emf $\mathcal{E}$, is 6.2 V. Calculate the battery's internal resistance. **(e)** What fraction f of the battery's power is delivered to the load resistors?

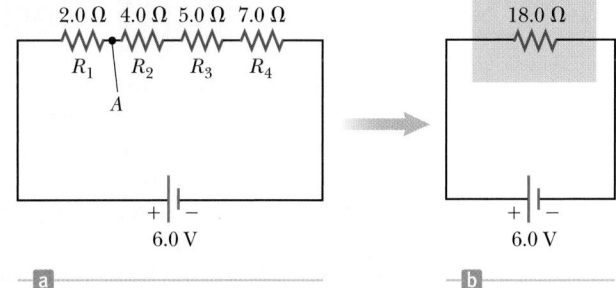

Figure 18.5 (Example 18.1) (a) Four resistors connected in series. (b) The equivalent resistance of the circuit in (a).

STRATEGY Because the resistors are connected in series, summing their resistances gives the equivalent resistance. Ohm's law can then be used to find the current. To find the electric potential at point A, calculate the voltage drop ΔV across the 2.0-Ω resistor and subtract the result from 6.0 V. In part (d) use Equation 18.1 to find the internal resistance of the battery. The fraction of the power delivered to the load resistance is just the power delivered to load, $I\Delta V$, divided by the total power, $I\mathcal{E}$.

∙ ∙

SOLUTION

(a) Find the equivalent resistance of the circuit.

Apply Equation 18.4, summing the resistances:

$$R_{eq} = R_1 + R_2 + R_3 + R_4 = 2.0\ \Omega + 4.0\ \Omega + 5.0\ \Omega + 7.0\ \Omega$$
$$= 18.0\ \Omega$$

(Continued)

(b) Find the current in the circuit.

Apply Ohm's law to the equivalent resistor in Figure 18.5b, solving for the current:

$$I = \frac{\Delta V}{R_{eq}} = \frac{6.0 \text{ V}}{18.0 \text{ }\Omega} = \boxed{0.33 \text{ A}}$$

(c) Calculate the electric potential at point A.

Apply Ohm's law to the 2.0-Ω resistor to find the voltage drop across it:

$$\Delta V = IR = (0.33 \text{ A})(2.0 \text{ }\Omega) = 0.66 \text{ V}$$

To find the potential at A, subtract the voltage drop from the potential at the positive terminal:

$$V_A = 6.0 \text{ V} - 0.66 \text{ V} = \boxed{5.3 \text{ V}}$$

(d) Calculate the battery's internal resistance if the battery's emf is 6.2 V.

Write Equation 18.1:

$$\Delta V = \mathcal{E} - Ir$$

Solve for the internal resistance r and substitute values:

$$r = \frac{\mathcal{E} - \Delta V}{I} = \frac{6.2 \text{ V} - 6.0 \text{ V}}{0.33 \text{ A}} = \boxed{0.6 \text{ }\Omega}$$

(e) What fraction f of the battery's power is delivered to the load resistors?

Divide the power delivered to the load by the total power output:

$$f = \frac{I\Delta V}{I\mathcal{E}} = \frac{\Delta V}{\mathcal{E}} = \frac{6.0 \text{ V}}{6.2 \text{ V}} = \boxed{0.97}$$

REMARKS A common misconception is that the current is "used up" and steadily declines as it progresses through a series of resistors. That would be a violation of the conservation of charge. What is actually used up is the electric potential energy of the charge carriers, some of which is delivered to each resistor.

QUESTION 18.1 Explain why the current in a real circuit very slowly decreases with time compared to its initial value.

EXERCISE 18.1 A circuit consists of a battery with a closed circuit, a terminal voltage of 12.0 V, and 3.0-Ω, 6.0-Ω, 8.0-Ω, and 9.0-Ω resistors connected in series, oriented as in Figure 18.5a, with the battery in the bottom of the loop, positive terminal on the left, and resistors in increasing order, left to right, in the top of the loop. Calculate (a) the equivalent resistance of the circuit, (b) the current, and (c) the total power dissipated by the load resistors. (d) What is the electric potential at a point between the 6.0-Ω and 8.0-Ω resistors, if the electric potential at the positive terminal is 12.0 V? (e) If the battery has an emf of 12.1 V, find the battery's internal resistance.

ANSWERS (a) 26.0 Ω (b) 0.462 A (c) 5.54 W (d) 7.84 V (e) 0.2 Ω

18.3 Resistors in Parallel

Now consider two resistors connected in parallel, as in Active Figure 18.6. In this case **the potential differences across the resistors are the same because each is connected directly across the battery terminals**. The currents are generally not the same. When charges reach point a (called a junction) in Active Figure 18.6b, the current splits into two parts: I_1, flowing through R_1; and I_2, flowing through R_2. If R_1 is greater than R_2, then I_1 is less than I_2. In general, more charge travels through the path with less resistance. **Because charge is conserved, the current I that enters point a must equal the total current $I_1 + I_2$ leaving that point.** Mathematically, this is written

$$I = I_1 + I_2$$

The potential drop must be the same for the two resistors and must also equal the potential drop across the battery. Ohm's law applied to each resistor yields

$$I_1 = \frac{\Delta V}{R_1} \qquad I_2 = \frac{\Delta V}{R_2}$$

Ohm's law applied to the equivalent resistor in Active Figure 18.6c gives

$$I = \frac{\Delta V}{R_{eq}}$$

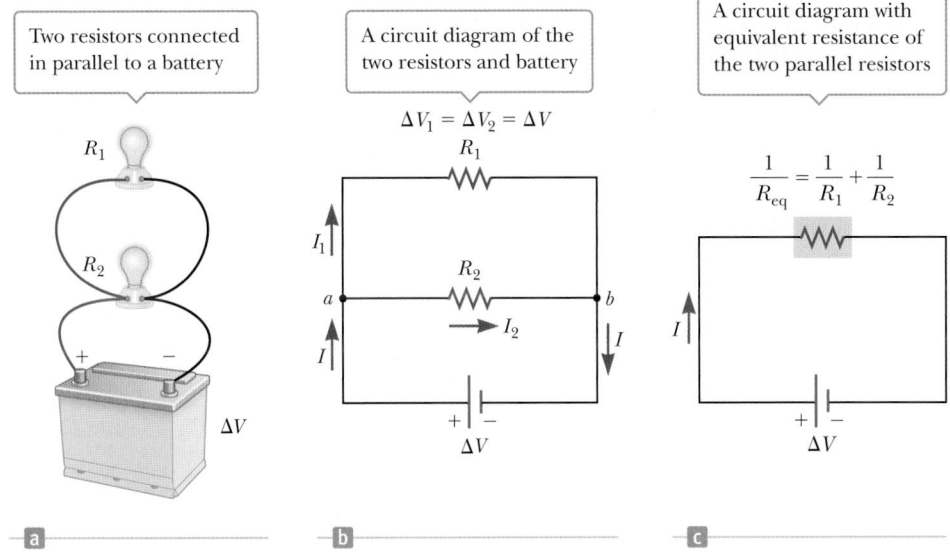

Two resistors connected in parallel to a battery

A circuit diagram of the two resistors and battery

$$\Delta V_1 = \Delta V_2 = \Delta V$$

A circuit diagram with equivalent resistance of the two parallel resistors

$$\frac{1}{R_{eq}} = \frac{1}{R_1} + \frac{1}{R_2}$$

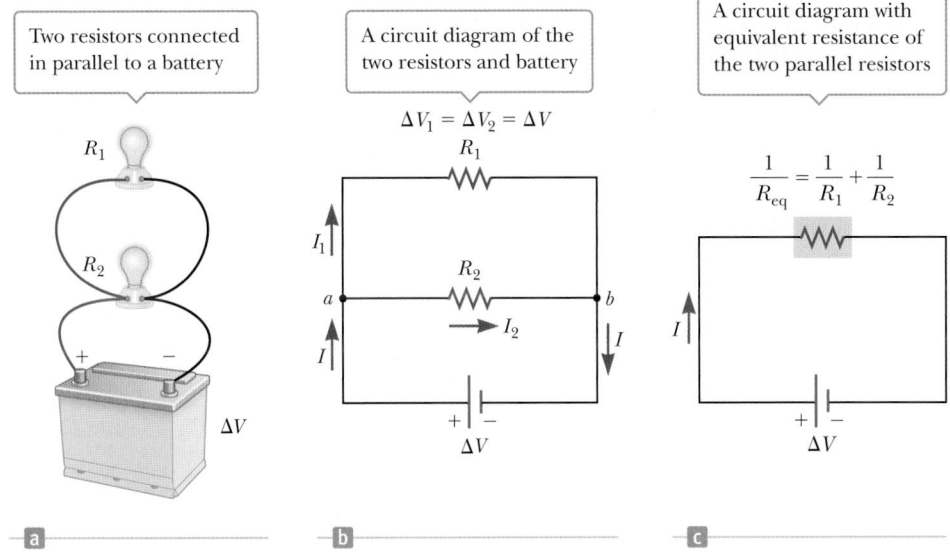

Active Figure 18.6
Two resistors, R_1 and R_2, in the form of incandescent light bulbs, in parallel with a battery. The potential differences across R_1 and R_2 are the same. Currents in the resistors are the same, and the equivalent resistance of the combination is $1/R_{eq} = 1/R_1 + 1/R_2$.

When these expressions for the currents are substituted into the equation $I = I_1 + I_2$ and the ΔV's are canceled, we obtain

$$\frac{1}{R_{eq}} = \frac{1}{R_1} + \frac{1}{R_2} \quad \text{(parallel combination)} \qquad [18.5]$$

An extension of this analysis to three or more resistors in parallel produces the following general expression for the equivalent resistance:

$$\frac{1}{R_{eq}} = \frac{1}{R_1} + \frac{1}{R_2} + \frac{1}{R_3} + \cdots \qquad [18.6]$$

◄ Equivalent resistance of a parallel combination of resistors

From this expression, we see that **the inverse of the equivalent resistance of two or more resistors connected in parallel is the sum of the inverses of the individual resistances and is always less than the smallest resistance in the group.**

■ *Quick Quiz*

18.5 In Figure 18.7 the current is measured with the ammeter on the right side of the circuit diagram. When the switch is closed, does the reading on the ammeter (a) increase, (b) decrease, or (c) remain the same?

18.6 When the switch is open in Figure 18.7, power P_o is delivered to the resistor R_1. When the switch is closed, which of the following is true about the power P_c delivered to R_1? (Neglect the internal resistance of the battery.) (a) $P_c < P_o$ (b) $P_c = P_o$ (c) $P_c > P_o$

Figure 18.7 (Quick Quizzes 18.5 and 18.6)

■ **EXAMPLE 18.2** | **Three Resistors in Parallel**

GOAL Analyze a circuit having resistors connected in parallel.

PROBLEM Three resistors are connected in parallel as in Figure 18.8. A potential difference of 18 V is maintained between points a and b. **(a)** Find the current in each resistor. **(b)** Calculate the power delivered to each resistor and the total power. **(c)** Find the equivalent resistance of the circuit. **(d)** Find the total power delivered to the equivalent resistance.

Figure 18.8 (Example 18.2) Three resistors connected in parallel. The voltage across each resistor is 18 V.

(Continued)

STRATEGY To get the current in each resistor we can use Ohm's law and the fact that the voltage drops across parallel resistors are all the same. The rest of the problem just requires substitution into the equation for power delivered to a resistor, $P = I^2R$, and the reciprocal-sum law for parallel resistors.

SOLUTION

(a) Find the current in each resistor.

Apply Ohm's law, solved for the current I delivered by the battery to find the current in each resistor:

$$I_1 = \frac{\Delta V}{R_1} = \frac{18\text{ V}}{3.0\ \Omega} = \boxed{6.0\text{ A}}$$

$$I_2 = \frac{\Delta V}{R_2} = \frac{18\text{ V}}{6.0\ \Omega} = \boxed{3.0\text{ A}}$$

$$I_3 = \frac{\Delta V}{R_3} = \frac{18\text{ V}}{9.0\ \Omega} = \boxed{2.0\text{ A}}$$

(b) Calculate the power delivered to each resistor and the total power.

Apply $P = I^2R$ to each resistor, substituting the results from part (a):

$3\ \Omega$: $P_1 = I_1^2R_1 = (6.0\text{ A})^2(3.0\ \Omega) = \boxed{110\text{ W}}$

$6\ \Omega$: $P_2 = I_2^2R_2 = (3.0\text{ A})^2(6.0\ \Omega) = \boxed{54\text{ W}}$

$9\ \Omega$: $P_3 = I_3^2R_3 = (2.0\text{ A})^2(9.0\ \Omega) = \boxed{36\text{ W}}$

Sum to get the total power:

$$P_{tot} = 110\text{ W} + 54\text{ W} + 36\text{ W} = \boxed{2.0 \times 10^2\text{ W}}$$

(c) Find the equivalent resistance of the circuit.

Apply the reciprocal-sum rule, Equation 18.6:

$$\frac{1}{R_{eq}} = \frac{1}{R_1} + \frac{1}{R_2} + \frac{1}{R_3}$$

$$\frac{1}{R_{eq}} = \frac{1}{3.0\ \Omega} + \frac{1}{6.0\ \Omega} + \frac{1}{9.0\ \Omega} = \frac{11}{18\ \Omega}$$

$$R_{eq} = \frac{18}{11}\ \Omega = \boxed{1.6\ \Omega}$$

(d) Compute the power dissipated by the equivalent resistance.

Use the alternate power equation:

$$P = \frac{(\Delta V)^2}{R_{eq}} = \frac{(18\text{ V})^2}{1.6\ \Omega} = \boxed{2.0 \times 10^2\text{ W}}$$

REMARKS There's something important to notice in part (a): the smallest 3.0 Ω resistor carries the largest current, whereas the other, larger resistors of 6.0 Ω and 9.0 Ω carry smaller currents. The largest current is always found in the path of least resistance. In part (b) the power could also be found with $P = (\Delta V)^2/R$. Note that $P_1 = 108$ W, but is rounded to 110 W because there are only two significant figures. Finally, notice that the total power dissipated in the equivalent resistor is the same as the sum of the power dissipated in the individual resistors, as it should be.

Tip 18.2 Don't Forget to Flip It!

The most common mistake in calculating the equivalent resistance for resistors in parallel is to forget to invert the answer after summing the reciprocals. Don't forget to flip it!

QUESTION 18.2 If a fourth resistor were added in parallel to the other three, how would the equivalent resistance change? (a) It would be larger. (b) It would be smaller. (c) More information is required to determine the effect.

EXERCISE 18.2 Suppose the resistances in the example are 1.0 Ω, 2.0 Ω, and 3.0 Ω, respectively, and a new voltage source is provided. If the current measured in the 3.0-Ω resistor is 2.0 A, find (a) the potential difference provided by the new battery and the currents in each of the remaining resistors, (b) the power delivered to each resistor and the total power, (c) the equivalent resistance, and (d) the total current and the power dissipated by the equivalent resistor.

ANSWERS (a) $\mathcal{E} = 6.0$ V, $I_1 = 6.0$ A, $I_2 = 3.0$ A (b) $P_1 = 36$ W, $P_2 = 18$ W, $P_3 = 12$ W, $P_{tot} = 66$ W (c) $\frac{6}{11}$ Ω (d) $I = 11$ A, $P_{eq} = 66$ W

■ *Quick Quiz*

18.7 Suppose you have three identical lightbulbs, some wire, and a battery. You connect one lightbulb to the battery and take note of its brightness. You add a second lightbulb, connecting it in parallel with the previous lightbulbs, and again take note of the brightness. Repeat the process with the third lightbulb, connecting it in parallel with the other two. As the lightbulbs are added, what happens to (a) the brightness of the lightbulbs? (b) The individual currents in the lightbulbs? (c) The power delivered by the battery? (d) The lifetime of the battery? (Neglect the battery's internal resistance.)

18.8 If the lightbulbs in Quick Quiz 18.7 are connected one by one in series instead of in parallel, what happens to (a) the brightness of the lightbulbs? (b) The individual currents in the lightbulbs? (c) The power delivered by the battery? (d) The lifetime of the battery? (Again, neglect the battery's internal resistance.)

Household circuits are always wired so that the electrical devices are connected in parallel, as in Active Figure 18.6a. In this way each device operates independently of the others so that if one is switched off, the others remain on. For example, if one of the lightbulbs in Active Figure 18.6 were removed from its socket, the other would continue to operate. Equally important is that each device operates at the same voltage. If the devices were connected in series, the voltage across any one device would depend on how many devices were in the combination and on their individual resistances.

In many household circuits, circuit breakers are used in series with other circuit elements for safety purposes. A circuit breaker is designed to switch off and open the circuit at some maximum value of the current (typically 15 A or 20 A) that depends on the nature of the circuit. If a circuit breaker were not used, excessive currents caused by operating several devices simultaneously could result in excessive wire temperatures, perhaps causing a fire. In older home construction, fuses were used in place of circuit breakers. When the current in a circuit exceeded some value, the conductor in a fuse melted and opened the circuit. The disadvantage of fuses is that they are destroyed in the process of opening the circuit, whereas circuit breakers can be reset.

APPLICATION
Circuit Breakers

■ APPLYING PHYSICS 18.2 | Lightbulb Combinations

Compare the brightness of the four identical lightbulbs shown in Figure 18.9. What happens if bulb A fails and so cannot conduct current? What if C fails? What if D fails?

EXPLANATION Bulbs A and B are connected in series across the emf of the battery, whereas bulb C is connected by itself across the battery. This means the voltage drop across C has the same magnitude as the battery emf, whereas this same emf is split between bulbs A and B. As a result, bulb C will glow more brightly than either of bulbs A and B, which will glow equally brightly. Bulb D has a wire connected across it—a short circuit—so the potential difference across bulb D is zero and it doesn't glow. If bulb A fails, B goes out, but C stays lit. If C fails, there is no effect on the other bulbs. If D fails, the event is undetectable because D was not glowing initially. ■

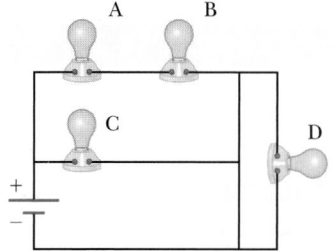

Figure 18.9 (Applying Physics 18.2)

■ APPLYING PHYSICS 18.3 | Three-Way Lightbulbs

Figure 18.10 (page 624) illustrates how a three-way lightbulb is constructed to provide three levels of light intensity. The socket of the lamp is equipped with a three-way switch for selecting different light intensities. The bulb contains two filaments. Why are the filaments connected in parallel? Explain how the two filaments are used to provide the three different light intensities.

EXPLANATION If the filaments were connected in series and one of them were to fail, there would be no current in the bulb and the bulb would not glow, regardless of the position of the switch. When the filaments are connected in parallel and one of them (say, the 75-W filament) fails, however, the bulb will still operate in one of the switch positions because there is current in the other (100-W) filament. The three light intensities are made possible by selecting one of three values of filament resistance, using a single value of 120 V for the applied voltage. The 75-W filament offers one value of resistance, the 100-W filament offers a second value, and the third resistance is obtained by combining the two filaments in parallel. When switch S_1 is closed and switch S_2 is opened, only the 75-W filament carries current. When switch S_1 is opened and switch S_2 is closed, only the 100-W filament carries current. When both switches are closed, both filaments carry current and a total illumination corresponding to 175 W is obtained. ∎

Figure 18.10 (Applying Physics 18.3)

▪ PROBLEM-SOLVING STRATEGY

Simplifying Circuits with Resistors

1. **Combine all resistors in series** by summing the individual resistances and draw the new, simplified circuit diagram.
   Useful facts: $R_{eq} = R_1 + R_2 + R_3 + \cdots$
   The current in each resistor is the same.

2. **Combine all resistors in parallel** by summing the reciprocals of the resistances and then taking the reciprocal of the result. Draw the new, simplified circuit diagram.
   Useful facts: $\dfrac{1}{R_{eq}} = \dfrac{1}{R_1} + \dfrac{1}{R_2} + \dfrac{1}{R_3} + \cdots$
   The potential difference across each resistor is the same.

3. **Repeat** the first two steps as necessary, until no further combinations can be made. If there is only a single battery in the circuit, the result will usually be a single equivalent resistor in series with the battery.

4. **Use Ohm's law,** $\Delta V = IR$, to determine the current in the equivalent resistor. Then work backwards through the diagrams, applying the useful facts listed in step 1 or step 2 to find the currents in the other resistors. (In more complex circuits, Kirchhoff's rules will be needed, as described in the next section).

▪ EXAMPLE 18.3 | Equivalent Resistance

GOAL Solve a problem involving both series and parallel resistors.

PROBLEM Four resistors are connected as shown in Figure 18.11a. **(a)** Find the equivalent resistance between points a and c. **(b)** What is the current in each resistor if a 42-V battery is connected between a and c?

STRATEGY Reduce the circuit in steps, as shown in Figures 18.11b and 18.11c, using the sum rule for resistors in series and the reciprocal-sum rule for resistors in parallel. Finding the currents is a matter of applying Ohm's law while working backwards through the diagrams.

Figure 18.11 (Example 18.3) The four resistors shown in (a) can be reduced in steps to an equivalent 14-Ω resistor.

SOLUTION

(a) Find the equivalent resistance of the circuit.

The 8.0-Ω and 4.0-Ω resistors are in series, so use the sum rule to find the equivalent resistance between a and b:

$$R_{eq} = R_1 + R_2 = 8.0\ \Omega + 4.0\ \Omega = 12.0\ \Omega$$

The 6.0-Ω and 3.0-Ω resistors are in parallel, so use the reciprocal-sum rule to find the equivalent resistance between b and c (don't forget to invert!):

$$\frac{1}{R_{eq}} = \frac{1}{R_1} + \frac{1}{R_2} = \frac{1}{6.0\ \Omega} + \frac{1}{3.0\ \Omega} = \frac{1}{2.0\ \Omega}$$

$$R_{eq} = 2.0\ \Omega$$

In the new diagram, 18.11b, there are now two resistors in series. Combine them with the sum rule to find the equivalent resistance of the circuit:

$$R_{eq} = R_1 + R_2 = 12.0\ \Omega + 2.0\ \Omega = \boxed{14.0\ \Omega}$$

(b) Find the current in each resistor if a 42-V battery is connected between points a and c.

Find the current in the equivalent resistor in Figure 18.11c, which is the total current. Resistors in series all carry the same current, so the value is the current in the 12-Ω resistor in Figure 18.11b and also in the 8.0-Ω and 4.0-Ω resistors in Figure 18.11a.

$$I = \frac{\Delta V_{ac}}{R_{eq}} = \frac{42\ \text{V}}{14\ \Omega} = \boxed{3.0\ \text{A}}$$

Calculate the voltage drop ΔV_{para} across the parallel circuit, which has an equivalent resistance of 2.0 Ω:

$$\Delta V_{para} = IR = (3.0\ \text{A})(2.0\ \Omega) = 6.0\ \text{V}$$

Apply Ohm's law again to find the currents in each resistor of the parallel circuit:

$$I_1 = \frac{\Delta V_{para}}{R_{6.0\ \Omega}} = \frac{6.0\ \text{V}}{6.0\ \Omega} = \boxed{1.0\ \text{A}}$$

$$I_2 = \frac{\Delta V_{para}}{R_{3.0\ \Omega}} = \frac{6.0\ \text{V}}{3.0\ \Omega} = \boxed{2.0\ \text{A}}$$

REMARKS As a final check, note that $\Delta V_{bc} = (6.0\ \Omega)I_1 = (3.0\ \Omega)I_2 = 6.0\ \text{V}$ and $\Delta V_{ab} = (12\ \Omega)I_1 = 36\ \text{V}$; therefore, $\Delta V_{ac} = \Delta V_{ab} + \Delta V_{bc} = 42\ \text{V}$, as expected.

QUESTION 18.3 Which of the original resistors dissipates energy at the greatest rate?

EXERCISE 18.3 Suppose the series resistors in Example 18.3 are now 6.00 Ω and 3.00 Ω while the parallel resistors are 8.00 Ω (top) and 4.00 Ω (bottom), and the battery provides an emf of 27.0 V. Find (a) the equivalent resistance and (b) the currents I, I_1, and I_2.

ANSWERS (a) 11.7 Ω (b) $I = 2.31\ \text{A}$, $I_1 = 0.770\ \text{A}$, $I_2 = 1.54\ \text{A}$

18.4 Kirchhoff's Rules and Complex DC Circuits

As demonstrated in the preceding section, we can analyze simple circuits using Ohm's law and the rules for series and parallel combinations of resistors. There are, however, many ways in which resistors can be connected so that the circuits formed can't be reduced to a single equivalent resistor. The procedure for analyzing more complex circuits can be facilitated by the use of two simple rules called **Kirchhoff's rules:**

1. The sum of the currents entering any junction must equal the sum of the currents leaving that junction. (This rule is often referred to as the **junction rule**.)
2. The sum of the potential differences across all the elements around any closed circuit loop must be zero. (This rule is usually called the **loop rule**.)

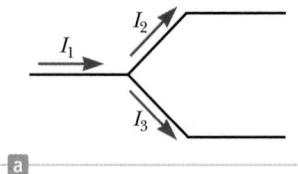

The current I_1 entering the junction must equal the sum of the currents I_2 and I_3 leaving the junction.

The net volume flow rate in must equal the net volume flow rate out.

Flow in

Flow out

Figure 18.12 (a) Kirchoff's junction rule. (b) A mechanical analog of the junction rule.

In each diagram, $\Delta V = V_b - V_a$ and the circuit element is traversed from a to b, left to right.

Figure 18.13 Rules for determining the potential differences across a resistor and a battery, assuming the battery has no internal resistance.

The junction rule is a statement of *conservation of charge*. Whatever current enters a given point in a circuit must leave that point because charge can't build up or disappear at a point. If we apply this rule to the junction in Figure 18.12a, we get

$$I_1 = I_2 + I_3$$

Figure 18.12b represents a mechanical analog of the circuit shown in Figure 18.12a. In this analog water flows through a branched pipe with no leaks. The flow rate into the pipe equals the total flow rate out of the two branches.

The loop rule is equivalent to the principle of *conservation of energy*. Any charge that moves around any closed loop in a circuit (starting and ending at the same point) must gain as much energy as it loses. It gains energy as it is pumped through a source of emf. Its energy may decrease in the form of a potential drop $-IR$ across a resistor or as a result of flowing backward through a source of emf, from the positive to the negative terminal inside the battery. In the latter case, electrical energy is converted to chemical energy as the battery is charged.

When applying Kirchhoff's rules, you must make two decisions at the beginning of the problem:

1. Assign symbols and directions to the currents in all branches of the circuit. Don't worry about guessing the direction of a current incorrectly; the resulting answer will be negative, but *its magnitude will be correct*. (Because the equations are *linear* in the currents, all currents are to the first power.)
2. When applying the loop rule, you must choose a direction for traversing the loop and be consistent in going either clockwise or counterclockwise. As you traverse the loop, record voltage drops and rises according to the following rules (summarized in Fig. 18.13, where it is assumed that movement is from point a toward point b):
   (a) If a resistor is traversed in the direction of the current, the change in electric potential across the resistor is $-IR$ (Fig. 18.13a).
   (b) If a resistor is traversed in the direction opposite the current, the change in electric potential across the resistor is $+IR$ (Fig. 18.13b).
   (c) If a source of emf is traversed in the direction of the emf (from $-$ to $+$ on the terminals), the change in electric potential is $+\mathcal{E}$ (Fig. 18.13c).
   (d) If a source of emf is traversed in the direction opposite the emf (from $+$ to $-$ on the terminals), the change in electric potential is $-\mathcal{E}$ (Fig. 18.13d).

There are limits to the number of times the junction rule and the loop rule can be used. You can use the junction rule as often as needed as long as, each time you write an equation, you include in it a current that has not been used in a previous junction-rule equation. (If this procedure isn't followed, the new equation will just be a combination of two other equations that you already have.) In general, the number of times the junction rule can be used is one fewer than the number of junction points in the circuit. The loop rule can also be used as often as needed, so long as a new circuit element (resistor or battery) or a new current appears in each new equation. **To solve a particular circuit problem, you need as many independent equations as you have unknowns.**

■ PROBLEM-SOLVING STRATEGY

Applying Kirchhoff's Rules to a Circuit

1. **Assign labels and symbols** to all the known and unknown quantities.
2. **Assign *directions* to the currents** in each part of the circuit. Although the assignment of current directions is arbitrary, you must stick with your original choices throughout the problem as you apply Kirchhoff's rules.

Gustav Kirchhoff
German Physicist (1824–1887)
Together with German chemist Robert Bunsen, Kirchhoff, a professor at Heidelberg, invented the spectroscopy that we study in Chapter 28. He also formulated another rule that states, "A cool substance will absorb light of the same wavelengths that it emits when hot."

3. **Apply the junction rule** to any junction in the circuit. The rule may be applied as many times as a new current (one not used in a previously found equation) appears in the resulting equation.
4. **Apply Kirchhoff's loop rule** to as many loops in the circuit as are needed to solve for the unknowns. To apply this rule, you must correctly identify the change in electric potential as you cross each element in traversing the closed loop. Watch out for signs!
5. **Solve the equations** simultaneously for the unknown quantities, using substitution or any other method familiar to the student.
6. **Check your answers** by substituting them into the original equations.

■ EXAMPLE 18.4 | Applying Kirchhoff's Rules

GOAL Use Kirchhoff's rules to find currents in a circuit with three currents and one battery.

PROBLEM Find the currents in the circuit shown in Figure 18.14 by using Kirchhoff's rules.

STRATEGY There are three unknown currents in this circuit, so we must obtain three independent equations, which then can be solved by substitution. We can find the equations with one application of the junction rule and two applications of the loop rule. We choose junction c. (Junction d gives the same equation.) For the loops, we choose the bottom loop and the top loop, both shown by blue arrows, which indicate the direction we are going to traverse the circuit mathematically (not necessarily the direction of the current). The third loop gives an equation that can be obtained by a linear combination of the other two, so it provides no additional information and isn't used.

Figure 18.14 (Example 18.4)

SOLUTION

Apply the junction rule to point c. I_1 is directed into the junction, I_2 and I_3 are directed out of the junction.

$$I_1 = I_2 + I_3$$

Select the bottom loop and traverse it clockwise starting at point a, generating an equation with the loop rule:

$$\sum \Delta V = \Delta V_{bat} + \Delta V_{4.0\ \Omega} + \Delta V_{9.0\ \Omega} = 0$$
$$6.0\ \text{V} - (4.0\ \Omega)I_1 - (9.0\ \Omega)I_3 = 0$$

Select the top loop and traverse it clockwise from point c. Notice the gain across the 9.0-Ω resistor because it is traversed *against* the direction of the current!

$$\sum \Delta V = \Delta V_{5.0\ \Omega} + \Delta V_{9.0\ \Omega} = 0$$
$$-(5.0\ \Omega)I_2 + (9.0\ \Omega)I_3 = 0$$

Rewrite the three equations, rearranging terms and dropping units for the moment, for convenience:

(1) $I_1 = I_2 + I_3$
(2) $4.0I_1 + 9.0I_3 = 6.0$
(3) $-5.0I_2 + 9.0I_3 = 0$

Solve Equation (3) for I_2 and substitute into Equation (1):

$$I_2 = 1.8I_3$$
$$I_1 = I_2 + I_3 = 1.8I_3 + I_3 = 2.8I_3$$

(Continued)

Substitute the latter expression into Equation (2) and solve for I_3:

$$4.0(2.8I_3) + 9.0I_3 = 6.0 \quad \rightarrow \quad I_3 = \boxed{0.30 \text{ A}}$$

Substitute I_3 back into Equation (3) to get I_2:

$$-5.0I_2 + 9.0(0.30 \text{ A}) = 0 \quad \rightarrow \quad I_2 = \boxed{0.54 \text{ A}}$$

Substitute I_3 into Equation (2) to get I_1:

$$4.0I_1 + 9.0(0.30 \text{ A}) = 6.0 \quad \rightarrow \quad I_1 = \boxed{0.83 \text{ A}}$$

REMARKS Substituting these values back into the original equations verifies that they are correct, with any small discrepancies due to rounding. The problem can also be solved by first combining resistors.

QUESTION 18.4 How would the answers change if the indicated directions of the currents in Figure 18.14 were all reversed?

EXERCISE 18.4 Suppose the 6.0-V battery is replaced by a battery of unknown emf and an ammeter measures $I_1 = 1.5$ A. Find the other two currents and the emf of the battery.

ANSWERS $I_2 = 0.96$ A, $I_3 = 0.54$ A, $\mathcal{E} = 11$ V

> **Tip 18.3 More Current Goes in the Path of Less Resistance**
>
> You may have heard the statement "Current takes the path of least resistance." For a parallel combination of resistors, this statement is inaccurate because current actually follows all paths. The most current, however, travels in the path of least resistance.

■ EXAMPLE 18.5 | Another Application of Kirchhoff's Rules

GOAL Find the currents in a circuit with three currents and two batteries when some current directions are chosen wrongly.

PROBLEM Find I_1, I_2, and I_3 in Figure 18.15a.

STRATEGY Use Kirchhoff's two rules, the junction rule once and the loop rule twice, to develop three equations for the three unknown currents. Solve the equations simultaneously.

Figure 18.15
(a) (Example 18.5)
(b) (Exercise 18.5)

SOLUTION

Apply Kirchhoff's junction rule to junction c. Because of the chosen current directions, I_1 and I_2 are directed into the junction and I_3 is directed out of the junction.

(1) $I_3 = I_1 + I_2$

Apply Kirchhoff's loop rule to the loops *abcda* and *befcb*. (Loop *aefda* gives no new information.) In loop *befcb*, a positive sign is obtained when the 6.0-Ω resistor is traversed because the direction of the path is opposite the direction of the current I_1.

(2) Loop *abcda*: $10 \text{ V} - (6.0 \ \Omega)I_1 - (2.0 \ \Omega)I_3 = 0$

(3) Loop *befcb*: $-(4.0 \ \Omega)I_2 - 14 \text{ V} + (6.0 \ \Omega)I_1 - 10 \text{ V} = 0$

Using Equation (1), eliminate I_3 from Equation (2) (ignore units for the moment):

$10 - 6.0I_1 - 2.0(I_1 + I_2) = 0$

(4) $10 = 8.0I_1 + 2.0I_2$

Divide each term in Equation (3) by 2 and rearrange the equation so that the currents are on the right side:

(5) $-12 = -3.0I_1 + 2.0I_2$

Subtracting Equation (5) from Equation (4) eliminates I_2 and gives I_1:

$22 = 11I_1 \quad \rightarrow \quad I_1 = \boxed{2.0 \text{ A}}$

Substituting this value of I_1 into Equation (5) gives I_2:

$2.0I_2 = 3.0I_1 - 12 = 3.0(2.0) - 12 = -6.0 \text{ A}$

$I_2 = \boxed{-3.0 \text{ A}}$

Finally, substitute the values found for I_1 and I_2 into Equation (1) to obtain I_3:

$$I_3 = I_1 + I_2 = 2.0\,\text{A} - 3.0\,\text{A} = \boxed{-1.0\,\text{A}}$$

. . . .

REMARKS The fact that I_2 and I_3 are both negative indicates that the wrong directions were chosen for these currents. Nonetheless, the magnitudes are correct. Choosing the right directions of the currents at the outset is unimportant because the equations are linear, and wrong choices result only in a minus sign in the answer.

QUESTION 18.5 Is it possible for the current in a battery to be directed from the positive terminal toward the negative terminal?

EXERCISE 18.5 Find the three currents in Figure 18.15b. (Note that the direction of one current was deliberately chosen wrongly!)

ANSWERS $I_1 = -1.0\,\text{A}$, $I_2 = 1.0\,\text{A}$, $I_3 = 2.0\,\text{A}$

18.5 RC Circuits

So far, we have been concerned with circuits with constant currents. We now consider direct-current circuits containing capacitors, in which the currents vary with time. Consider the series circuit in Active Figure 18.16. We assume the capacitor is initially uncharged with the switch opened. After the switch is closed, the battery begins to charge the plates of the capacitor and the charge passes through the resistor. As the capacitor is being charged, the circuit carries a changing current. The charging process continues until the capacitor is charged to its maximum equilibrium value, $Q = C\mathcal{E}$, where $\mathcal{E}$ is the maximum voltage across the capacitor. Once the capacitor is fully charged, the current in the circuit is zero. If we assume the capacitor is uncharged before the switch is closed, and if the switch is closed at $t = 0$, we find that the charge on the capacitor varies with time according to the equation

$$q = Q(1 - e^{-t/RC}) \qquad \text{[18.7]}$$

where $e = 2.718\ldots$ is Euler's constant, the base of the natural logarithms. Active Figure 18.16b is a graph of this equation. The charge is zero at $t = 0$ and approaches its maximum value, Q, as t approaches infinity. The voltage ΔV across the capacitor at any time is obtained by dividing the charge by the capacitance: $\Delta V = q/C$.

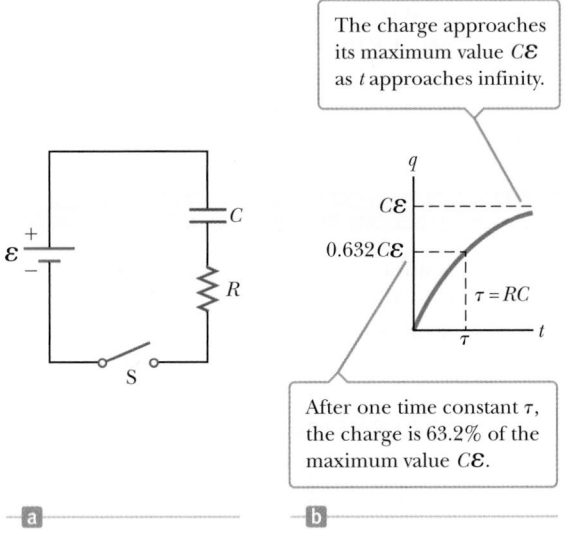

The charge approaches its maximum value $C\mathcal{E}$ as t approaches infinity.

After one time constant τ, the charge is 63.2% of the maximum value $C\mathcal{E}$.

Active Figure 18.16
(a) A capacitor in series with a resistor, a battery, and a switch. (b) A plot of the charge on the capacitor versus time after the switch on the circuit is closed.

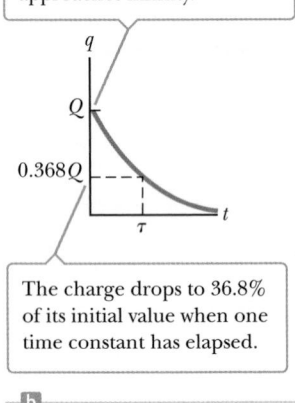

The charge has its maximum value Q at $t = 0$ and decays to zero exponentially as t approaches infinity.

The charge drops to 36.8% of its initial value when one time constant has elapsed.

Active Figure 18.17
(a) A charged capacitor connected to a resistor and a switch. (b) A graph of the charge on the capacitor versus time after the switch is closed.

As you can see from Equation 18.7, it would take an infinite amount of time, in this model, for the capacitor to become fully charged. The reason is mathematical: in obtaining that equation, charges are assumed to be infinitely small, whereas in reality the smallest charge is that of an electron, with a magnitude equal to 1.60×10^{-19} C. For all practical purposes, the capacitor is fully charged after a finite amount of time. The term RC that appears in Equation 18.7 is called the **time constant** τ (Greek letter tau), so

$$\tau = RC \qquad [18.8]$$

The time constant represents the time required for the charge to increase from zero to 63.2% of its maximum equilibrium value. This means that in a period of time equal to one time constant, the charge on the capacitor increases from zero to $0.632Q$. This can be seen by substituting $t = \tau = RC$ into Equation 18.7 and solving for q. (Note that $1 - e^{-1} = 0.632$.) It's important to note that a capacitor charges very slowly in a circuit with a long time constant, whereas it charges very rapidly in a circuit with a short time constant. After a time equal to ten time constants, the capacitor is more than 99.99% charged.

Now consider the circuit in Active Figure 18.17a, consisting of a capacitor with an initial charge Q, a resistor, and a switch. Before the switch is closed, the potential difference across the charged capacitor is Q/C. Once the switch is closed, the charge begins to flow through the resistor from one capacitor plate to the other until the capacitor is fully discharged. If the switch is closed at $t = 0$, it can be shown that the charge q on the capacitor varies with time according to the equation

$$q = Qe^{-t/RC} \qquad [18.9]$$

The charge decreases exponentially with time, as shown in Active Figure 18.17b. In the interval $t = \tau = RC$, the charge decreases from its initial value Q to $0.368Q$. In other words, in a time equal to one time constant, the capacitor loses 63.2% of its initial charge. Because $\Delta V = q/C$, the voltage across the capacitor also decreases exponentially with time according to the equation $\Delta V = \mathcal{E}e^{-t/RC}$, where $\mathcal{E}$ (which equals Q/C) is the initial voltage across the fully charged capacitor.

■ APPLYING PHYSICS 18.4 | Timed Windshield Wipers

Many automobiles are equipped with windshield wipers that can be used intermittently during a light rainfall. How does the operation of this feature depend on the charging and discharging of a capacitor?

EXPLANATION The wipers are part of an RC circuit with time constant that can be varied by selecting different values of R through a multiposition switch. The brief time that the wipers remain on and the time they are off are determined by the value of the time constant of the circuit. ■

■ APPLYING PHYSICS 18.5 | Bacterial Growth

In biological applications concerned with population growth, an equation is used that is similar to the exponential equations encountered in the analysis of RC circuits. Applied to a number of bacteria, this equation is

$$N_f = N_i 2^n$$

where N_f is the number of bacteria present after n doubling times, N_i is the number present initially, and n is the number of growth cycles or doubling times. Doubling times vary according to the organism. The doubling time for the bacteria responsible for leprosy is about 30 days, and that for the salmonella bacteria responsible for food poisoning

is about 20 minutes. Suppose only 10 salmonella bacteria find their way onto a turkey leg after your Thanksgiving meal. Four hours later you come back for a midnight snack. How many bacteria are present now?

EXPLANATION The number of doubling times is 240 min/20 min = 12. Thus,

$$N_f = N_i 2^n = (10 \text{ bacteria})(2^{12}) = 40\,960 \text{ bacteria}$$

So your system will have to deal with an invading host of about 41 000 bacteria, which are going to continue to double in a very promising environment. ■

■ **APPLYING PHYSICS 18.6** | **Roadway Flashers**

Many roadway construction sites have flashing yellow lights to warn motorists of possible dangers. What causes the lights to flash?

EXPLANATION A typical circuit for such a flasher is shown in Figure 18.18. The lamp L is a gas-filled lamp that acts as an open circuit until a large potential difference causes a discharge, which gives off a bright light. During this discharge, charge flows through the gas between the electrodes of the lamp. When the switch is closed, the battery charges the capacitor. At the beginning, the current is high and the charge on the capacitor is low, so most of the potential difference appears across the resistance *R*. As the capacitor charges, more potential difference appears across it, reflecting the lower current and lower potential difference across the resistor. Eventually, the potential difference across the capacitor reaches a value at which the lamp will conduct, causing a flash. This flash discharges the capacitor through the lamp, and the process of charging begins again. The period between flashes can be adjusted by changing the time constant of the *RC* circuit. ■

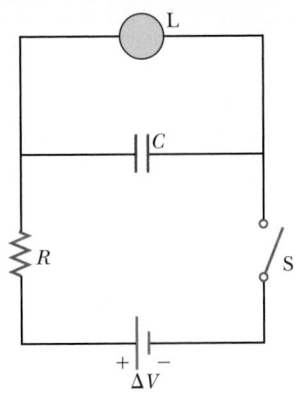

Figure 18.18 (Applying Physics 18.6)

■ *Quick Quiz*

18.9 The switch is closed in Figure 18.19. After a long time compared with the time constant of the circuit, what will the current be in the 2-Ω resistor? (a) 4 A (b) 3 A (c) 2 A (d) 1 A (e) More information is needed.

Figure 18.19 (Quick Quiz 18.9)

■ **EXAMPLE 18.6** | **Charging a Capacitor in an *RC* Circuit**

GOAL Calculate elementary properties of a simple *RC* circuit.

PROBLEM An uncharged capacitor and a resistor are connected in series to a battery, as in Active Figure 18.16a. If $\mathcal{E} = 12.0$ V, $C = 5.00$ μF, and $R = 8.00 \times 10^5$ Ω, find **(a)** the time constant of the circuit, **(b)** the maximum charge on the capacitor, **(c)** the charge on the capacitor after 6.00 s, **(d)** the potential difference across the resistor after 6.00 s, and **(e)** the current in the resistor at that time.

STRATEGY Finding the time constant in part (a) requires substitution into Equation 18.8. For part (b), the maximum charge occurs after a long time, when the current has dropped to zero. By Ohm's law, $\Delta V = IR$, the potential difference across the resistor is also zero at that time, and Kirchhoff's loop rule then gives the maximum charge. Finding the charge at some particular time, as in part (c), is a matter of substituting into Equation 18.7. Kirchhoff's loop rule and the capacitance equation can be used to indirectly find the potential drop across the resistor in part (d), and then Ohm's law yields the current.

. . . .

SOLUTION

(a) Find the time constant of the circuit.

Use the definition of the time constant, Equation 18.8:

$$\tau = RC = (8.00 \times 10^5 \text{ Ω})(5.00 \times 10^{-6} \text{ F}) = \boxed{4.00 \text{ s}}$$

(b) Calculate the maximum charge on the capacitor.

Apply Kirchhoff's loop rule to the *RC* circuit, going clockwise, which means that the voltage difference across the battery is positive and the differences across the capacitor and resistor are negative:

(1) $\Delta V_{\text{bat}} + \Delta V_C + \Delta V_R = 0$

From the definition of capacitance (Eq. 16.8) and Ohm's law, we have $\Delta V_C = -q/C$ and $\Delta V_R = -IR$. These are voltage drops, so they're negative. Also, $\Delta V_{\text{bat}} = +\mathcal{E}$.

(2) $\mathcal{E} - \dfrac{q}{C} - IR = 0$

(Continued)

When the maximum charge $q = Q$ is reached, $I = 0$. Solve Equation (2) for the maximum charge:

$$\mathcal{E} - \frac{Q}{C} = 0 \quad \rightarrow \quad Q = C\mathcal{E}$$

Substitute to find the maximum charge:

$$Q = (5.00 \times 10^{-6}\ \text{F})(12.0\ \text{V}) = \boxed{60.0\ \mu\text{C}}$$

(c) Find the charge on the capacitor after 6.00 s.

Substitute into Equation 18.7:

$$q = Q(1 - e^{-t/\tau}) = (60.0\ \mu\text{C})(1 - e^{-6.00\ \text{s}/4.00\ \text{s}})$$

$$= \boxed{46.6\ \mu\text{C}}$$

(d) Compute the potential difference across the resistor after 6.00 s.

Compute the voltage drop ΔV_C across the capacitor at that time:

$$\Delta V_C = -\frac{q}{C} = -\frac{46.6\ \mu\text{C}}{5.00\ \mu\text{F}} = -9.32\ \text{V}$$

Solve Equation (1) for ΔV_R and substitute:

$$\Delta V_R = -\Delta V_{\text{bat}} - \Delta V_C = -12.0\ \text{V} - (-9.32\ \text{V})$$

$$= \boxed{-2.68\ \text{V}}$$

(e) Find the current in the resistor after 6.00 s.

Apply Ohm's law, using the results of part (d) (remember that $\Delta V_R = -IR$ here):

$$I = \frac{-\Delta V_R}{R} = \frac{-(-2.68\ \text{V})}{(8.00 \times 10^5\ \Omega)}$$

$$= \boxed{3.35 \times 10^{-6}\ \text{A}}$$

REMARKS In solving this problem, we paid scrupulous attention to signs. These signs must always be chosen when applying Kirchhoff's loop rule and must remain consistent throughout the problem. Alternately, magnitudes can be used and the signs chosen by physical intuition. For example, the magnitude of the potential difference across the resistor must equal the magnitude of the potential difference across the battery minus the magnitude of the potential difference across the capacitor.

QUESTION 18.6 In an RC circuit as depicted in Figure 18.16a, what happens to the time required for the capacitor to be charged to half its maximum value if either the resistance or capacitance is increased? (a) It increases. (b) It decreases. (c) It remains the same.

EXERCISE 18.6 Find (a) the charge on the capacitor after 2.00 s have elapsed, (b) the magnitude of the potential difference across the capacitor after 2.00 s, and (c) the magnitude of the potential difference across the resistor at that same time.

ANSWERS (a) 23.6 μC (b) 4.72 V (c) 7.28 V

■ EXAMPLE 18.7 | **Discharging a Capacitor in an *RC* Circuit**

GOAL Calculate some elementary properties of a discharging capacitor in an RC circuit.

PROBLEM Consider a capacitor C being discharged through a resistor R as in Active Figure 18.17a (page 630). **(a)** How long does it take the charge on the capacitor to drop to one-fourth its initial value? Answer as a multiple of τ. **(b)** Compute the initial charge and time constant. **(c)** How long does it take to discharge all but the last quantum of charge, 1.60×10^{-19} C, if the initial potential difference across the capacitor is 12.0 V, the capacitance is equal to 3.50×10^{-6} F, and the resistance is 2.00 Ω? (Assume an exponential decrease during the entire discharge process.)

STRATEGY This problem requires substituting given values into various equations, as well as a few algebraic manipulations involving the natural logarithm. In part (a) set $q = \frac{1}{4}Q$ in Equation 18.9 for a discharging capacitor, where Q is the initial charge, and solve for time t. In part (b) substitute into Equations 16.8 and 18.8 to find the initial capacitor charge and time constant, respectively. In part (c) substitute the results of part (b) and the final charge $q = 1.60 \times 10^{-19}$ C into the discharging-capacitor equation, again solving for time.

SOLUTION

(a) How long does it take the charge on the capacitor to reduce to one-fourth its initial value?

Apply Equation 18.9:

$$q(t) = Qe^{-t/RC}$$

Substitute $q(t) = Q/4$ into the preceding equation and cancel Q:

$$\tfrac{1}{4}Q = Qe^{-t/RC} \quad \rightarrow \quad \tfrac{1}{4} = e^{-t/RC}$$

Take natural logarithms of both sides and solve for the time t:

$$\ln\left(\tfrac{1}{4}\right) = -t/RC$$

$$t = -RC\ln\left(\tfrac{1}{4}\right) = 1.39RC = \boxed{1.39\tau}$$

(b) Compute the initial charge and time constant from the given data.

Use the capacitance equation to find the initial charge:

$$C = \frac{Q}{\Delta V} \quad \rightarrow \quad Q = C\,\Delta V = (3.50 \times 10^{-6}\,\text{F})(12.0\,\text{V})$$

$$Q = \boxed{4.20 \times 10^{-5}\,\text{C}}$$

Now calculate the time constant:

$$\tau = RC = (2.00\,\Omega)(3.50 \times 10^{-6}\,\text{F}) = \boxed{7.00 \times 10^{-6}\,\text{s}}$$

(c) How long does it take to drain all but the last quantum of charge?

Apply Equation 18.9, divide by Q, and take natural logarithms of both sides:

$$q(t) = Qe^{-t/\tau} \quad \rightarrow \quad e^{-t/\tau} = \frac{q}{Q}$$

Take the natural logs of both sides:

$$-t/\tau = \ln\left(\frac{q}{Q}\right) \quad \rightarrow \quad t = -\tau\ln\left(\frac{q}{Q}\right)$$

Substitute $q = 1.60 \times 10^{-19}$ C and the values for Q and τ found in part (b):

$$t = -(7.00 \times 10^{-6}\,\text{s})\ln\left(\frac{1.60 \times 10^{-19}\,\text{C}}{4.20 \times 10^{-5}\,\text{C}}\right)$$

$$= \boxed{2.32 \times 10^{-4}\,\text{s}}$$

REMARKS Part (a) shows how useful information can often be obtained even when no details concerning capacitances, resistances, or voltages are known. Part (c) demonstrates that capacitors can be rapidly discharged (or conversely, charged), despite the mathematical form of Equations 18.7 and 18.9, which indicate an infinite time would be required.

QUESTION 18.7 Suppose the initial voltage used to charge the capacitor were doubled. Would the time required for discharging all but the last quantum of charge (a) increase, (b) decrease, (c) remain the same?

EXERCISE 18.7 Suppose the same type of series circuit has $R = 8.00 \times 10^4\,\Omega$, $C = 5.00\,\mu\text{F}$, and an initial voltage across the capacitor of 6.00 V. (a) How long does it take the capacitor to lose half its initial charge? (b) How long does it take to lose all but the last 10 electrons on the negative plate?

ANSWERS (a) 0.277 s (b) 12.2 s

18.6 Household Circuits

Household circuits are a practical application of some of the ideas presented in this chapter. In a typical installation the utility company distributes electric power to individual houses with a pair of wires, or power lines. Electrical devices in a house are then connected in parallel to these lines, as shown in Figure 18.20 (page 634). The potential difference between the two wires is about 120 V. (These currents and voltages are actually alternating currents and voltages, but for the present discussion we will assume they are direct currents and voltages.) One of the wires is connected to ground, and the other wire, sometimes called the "hot" wire, is at a potential of 120 V. A meter and a circuit breaker (or a fuse) are connected in series with the wire entering the house, as indicated in the figure.

In modern homes, circuit breakers are used in place of fuses. When the current in a circuit exceeds some value (typically 15 A or 20 A), the circuit breaker acts as a switch and opens the circuit. Figure 18.21 (page 634) shows one design for a circuit breaker. Current passes through a bimetallic strip, the top of which bends to the left when excessive current heats it. If the strip bends far enough to the left, it settles

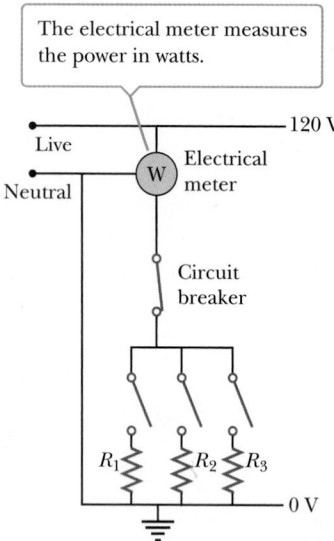

Figure 18.20 A wiring diagram for a household circuit. The resistances R_1, R_2, and R_3 represent appliances or other electrical devices that operate at an applied voltage of 120 V.

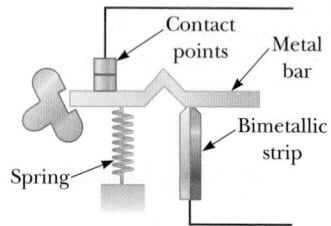

Figure 18.21 A circuit breaker that uses a bimetallic strip for its operation.

into a groove in the spring-loaded metal bar. When this settling occurs, the bar drops enough to open the circuit at the contact point. The bar also flips a switch that indicates that the circuit breaker is not operational. (After the overload is removed, the switch can be flipped back on.) Circuit breakers based on this design have the disadvantage that some time is required for the heating of the strip, so the circuit may not be opened rapidly enough when it is overloaded. Therefore, many circuit breakers are now designed to use electromagnets (discussed in Chapter 19).

The wire and circuit breaker are carefully selected to meet the current demands of a circuit. If the circuit is to carry currents as large as 30 A, a heavy-duty wire and an appropriate circuit breaker must be used. Household circuits that are normally used to power lamps and small appliances often require only 20 A. Each circuit has its own circuit breaker to accommodate its maximum safe load.

As an example, consider a circuit that powers a toaster, a microwave oven, and a heater (represented by R_1, R_2, and R_3 in Fig. 18.20). Using the equation $P = I\Delta V$, we can calculate the current carried by each appliance. The toaster, rated at 1 000 W, draws a current of 1 000/120 = 8.33 A. The microwave oven, rated at 800 W, draws a current of 6.67 A, and the heater, rated at 1 300 W, draws a current of 10.8 A. If the three appliances are operated simultaneously, they draw a total current of 25.8 A. Therefore, the breaker should be able to handle at least this much current, or else it will be tripped. As an alternative, the toaster and microwave oven could operate on one 20-A circuit and the heater on a separate 20-A circuit.

Many heavy-duty appliances, such as electric ranges and clothes dryers, require 240 V to operate. The power company supplies this voltage by providing, in addition to a live wire that is 120 V above ground potential, another wire, also considered live, that is 120 V below ground potential (Fig. 18.22). Therefore, the potential drop across the two live wires is 240 V. An appliance operating from a 240-V line requires half the current of one operating from a 120-V line; consequently, smaller wires can be used in the higher-voltage circuit without becoming overheated.

18.7 Electrical Safety

A person can be electrocuted by touching a live wire while in contact with ground. Such a hazard is often due to frayed insulation that exposes the conducting wire. The ground contact might be made by touching a water pipe (which is normally at ground potential) or by standing on the ground with wet feet because impure water is a good conductor. Obviously, such situations should be avoided at all costs.

Electric shock can result in fatal burns, or it can cause the muscles of vital organs, such as the heart, to malfunction. The degree of damage to the body depends on the magnitude of the current, the length of time it acts, and the part of the body through which it passes. Currents of 5 mA or less can cause a sensation of shock, but ordinarily do little or no damage. If the current is larger than about 10 mA, the hand muscles contract and the person may be unable to let go of the live wire. If a current of about 100 mA passes through the body for just a few seconds, it can be fatal. Such large currents paralyze the respiratory muscles. In some cases, currents of about 1 A through the body produce serious (and sometimes fatal) burns.

As an additional safety feature for consumers, electrical equipment manufacturers now use electrical cords that have a third wire, called a *case ground*. To understand how this works, consider the drill being used in Figure 18.23. A two-wire device that has one wire, called the "hot" wire, is connected to the high-potential (120-V) side of the input power line, and the second wire is connected to ground (0 V). If the high-voltage wire comes in contact with the case of the drill (Fig. 18.23a), a short circuit occurs. In this undesirable circumstance, the pathway for the current is from the high-voltage wire through the person holding the drill and to Earth, a pathway that can be fatal. Protection is provided by a third wire, connected to the case of the drill (Fig. 18.23b). In this case, if a short occurs, the path of least resistance for the current is from the high-voltage wire through the case and back to ground through the third wire. The resulting high current produced will blow a fuse or trip a circuit breaker before the consumer is injured.

Special power outlets called ground-fault interrupters (GFIs) are now being used in kitchens, bathrooms, basements, and other hazardous areas of new homes. They are designed to protect people from electrical shock by sensing small currents—approximately 5 mA and greater—leaking to ground. When current above this level is detected, the device shuts off (interrupts) the current in less than a millisecond. (Ground-fault interrupters will be discussed in Chapter 20.)

18.8 Conduction of Electrical Signals by Neurons[2] BIO

The most remarkable use of electrical phenomena in living organisms is found in the nervous system of animals. Specialized cells in the body called **neurons** form a complex network that receives, processes, and transmits information from one part of the body to another. The center of this network is located in the brain, which has the ability to store and analyze information. On the basis of this information, the nervous system controls parts of the body.

The nervous system is highly complex and consists of about 10^{10} interconnected neurons. Some aspects of the nervous system are well known. Over the past several decades the method of signal propagation through the nervous system has been established. The messages transmitted by neurons are voltage pulses called *action potentials*. When a neuron receives a strong enough stimulus, it produces identical voltage pulses that are actively propagated along its structure. The strength of the

Figure 18.22 (a) The connections for each of the openings in a 240-V outlet. (b) An outlet for connection to a 240-V supply.

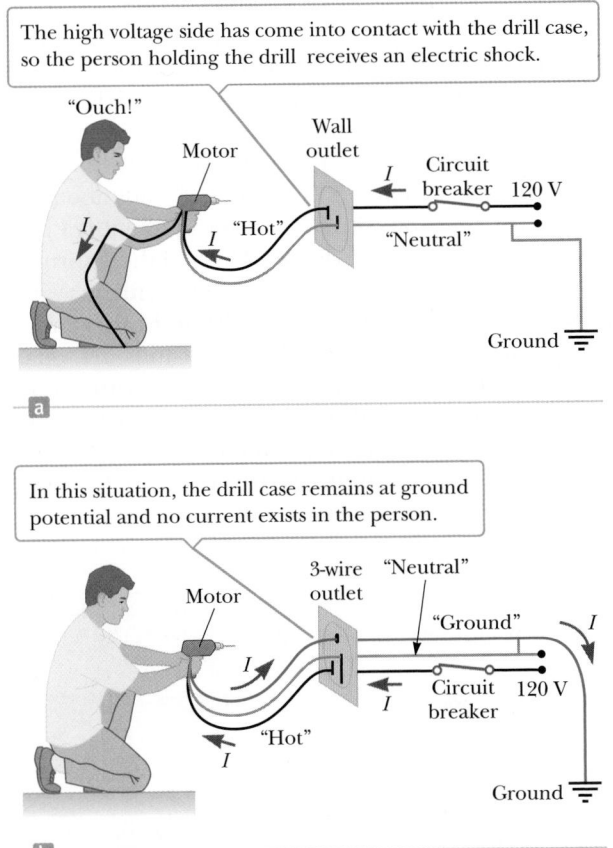

Figure 18.23 The "hot" (or "live") wire, at 120 V, always includes a circuit breaker for safety. (a) When the drill is operated with two wires, the normal current path is from the "hot" wire, through the motor connections, and back to ground through the "neutral" wire. (b) Shock can be prevented by a third wire running from the drill case to the ground. The wire colors represent electrical standards in the United States: the "hot" wire is black, the ground wire is green, and the neutral wire is white (shown as gray in the figure).

[2]This section is based on an essay by Paul Davidovits of Boston College.

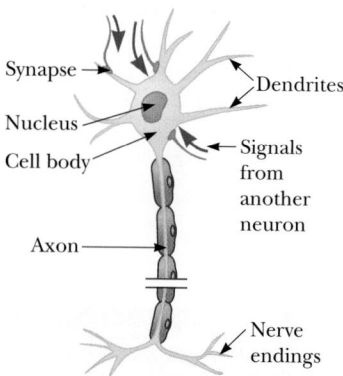

Figure 18.24 Diagram of a neuron.

Figure 18.25 A simple neural circuit.

Figure 18.26 Stellate neuron from human cortex.

Figure 18.27 An axon stimulated electrically. The left probe injects a short pulse of current, and the right probe measures the resulting action potential as a function of time.

stimulus is conveyed by the number of pulses produced. When the pulses reach the end of the neuron, they activate either muscle cells or other neurons. There is a "firing threshold" for neurons: action potentials propagate along a neuron only if the stimulus is sufficiently strong.

Neurons can be divided into three classes: sensory neurons, motor neurons, and interneurons. The sensory neurons receive stimuli from sensory organs that monitor the external and internal environment of the body. Depending on their specialized functions, the sensory neurons convey messages about factors such as light, temperature, pressure, muscle tension, and odor to higher centers in the nervous system. The motor neurons carry messages that control the muscle cells. The messages are based on the information provided by the sensory neurons and by the brain. The interneurons transmit information from one neuron to another.

Each neuron consists of a cell body to which are attached input ends called **dendrites** and a long tail called the **axon**, which transmits the signal away from the cell (Fig. 18.24). The far end of the axon branches into nerve endings that transmit the signal across small gaps to other neurons or to muscle cells. A simple sensorimotor neuron circuit is shown in Figure 18.25. A stimulus from a muscle produces nerve impulses that travel to the spine. Here the signal is transmitted to a motor neuron, which in turn sends impulses to control the muscle. Figure 18.26 shows an electron microscope image of neurons in the brain.

The axon, which is an extension of the neuron cell, conducts electric impulses away from the cell body. Some axons are extremely long. In humans, for example, the axons connecting the spine with the fingers and toes are more than 1 m long. The neuron can transmit messages because of the special active electrical characteristics of the axon. (The axon acts as an **active** source of energy like a battery, rather than like a **passive** stretch of resistive wire.) Much of the information about the electrical and chemical properties of the axon is obtained by inserting small needlelike probes into it. Figure 18.27 shows an experimental setup.

Note that the outside of the axon is grounded, so all measured voltages are with respect to a zero potential on the outside. With these probes it is possible to inject current into the axon, measure the resulting action potential as a function of time at a fixed point, and sample the cell's chemical composition. Such experiments are usually difficult to run because the diameter of most axons is very small. Even the largest axons in the human nervous system have a diameter of only about 20×10^{-4} cm. The giant squid, however, has an axon with a diameter of about 0.5 mm, which is large enough for the convenient insertion of probes. Much of the information about signal transmission in the nervous system has come from experiments with the squid axon.

In the aqueous environment of the body, salts and other molecules dissociate into positive and negative ions. As a result, body fluids are relatively good conductors of electricity. The inside of the axon is filled with an ionic fluid that is separated from the surrounding body fluid by a thin membrane that is only about 5 nm to 10 nm thick. The resistivities of the internal and external fluids are about the same, but their chemical compositions are substantially different. The exter-

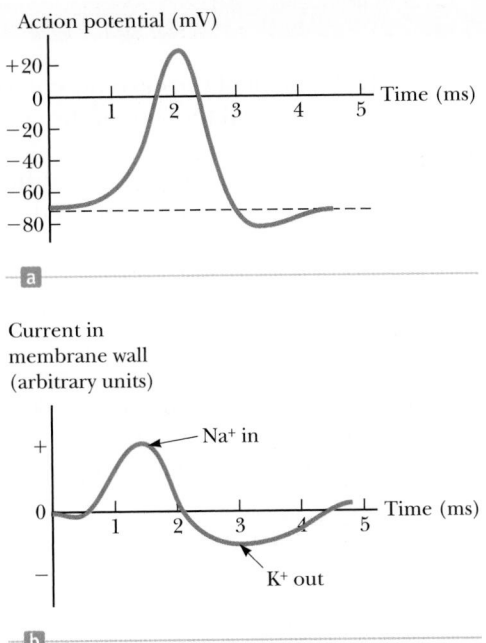

Figure 18.28 (a) Typical action potential as a function of time. (b) Current in the axon membrane wall as a function of time.

nal fluid is similar to seawater: its ionic solutes are mostly positive sodium ions and negative chloride ions. Inside the axon, the positive ions are mostly potassium ions and the negative ions are mostly large organic ions.

Ordinarily, the concentrations of sodium and potassium ions inside and outside the axon would be equalized by diffusion. The axon, however, is a living cell with an energy supply and can change the permeability of its membranes on a time scale of milliseconds.

When the axon is not conducting an electric pulse, the axon membrane is highly permeable to potassium ions, slightly permeable to sodium ions, and impermeable to large organic ions. Consequently, although sodium ions cannot easily enter the axon, potassium ions can leave it. As the potassium ions leave the axon, however, they leave behind large negative organic ions, which cannot follow them through the membrane. As a result, a negative potential builds up inside the axon with respect to the outside. The final negative potential reached, which has been measured at about -70 mV, holds back the outflow of potassium ions so that at equilibrium, the concentration of ions is as we have stated.

The mechanism for the production of an electric signal by the neuron is conceptually simple, but was experimentally difficult to sort out. When a neuron changes its resting potential because of an appropriate stimulus, the properties of its membrane change locally. As a result, there is a sudden flow of sodium ions into the cell that lasts for about 2 ms. This flow produces the $+30$ mV peak in the action potential shown in Figure 18.28a. Immediately after, there is an increase in potassium ion flow out of the cell that restores the resting action potential of -70 mV in an additional 3 ms. Both the Na^+ and K^+ ion flows have been measured by using radioactive Na and K tracers. The nerve signal has been measured to travel along the axon at speeds of 50 m/s to about 150 m/s. This flow of charged particles (or signal transmission) in a nerve axon is *unlike* signal transmission in a metal wire. In an axon charges move in a direction perpendicular to the direction of travel of the nerve signal, and the nerve signal moves much more slowly than a voltage pulse traveling along a metallic wire.

Although the axon is a highly complex structure and much of how Na^+ and K^+ ion channels open and close is not understood, standard electric circuit concepts of current and capacitance can be used to analyze axons. It is left as a problem (Problem 41) to show that the axon, having equal and opposite charges separated by a thin dielectric membrane, acts like a capacitor.

■ SUMMARY

18.1 Sources of emf

Any device, such as a battery or generator, that increases the electric potential energy of charges in an electric circuit is called a **source of emf**. Batteries convert chemical energy into electrical potential energy, and generators convert mechanical energy into electrical potential energy.

The terminal voltage ΔV of a battery is given by

$$\Delta V = \mathcal{E} - Ir \qquad [18.1]$$

where ε is the emf of the battery, I is the current, and r is the internal resistance of the battery. Generally, the internal resistance is small enough to be neglected.

18.2 Resistors in Series

The **equivalent resistance** of a set of resistors connected in **series** is

$$R_{eq} = R_1 + R_2 + R_3 + \cdots \qquad [18.4]$$

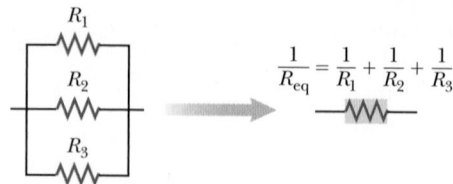

Several resistors in series can be replaced with a single equivalent resistor.

The current remains at a constant value as it passes through a series of resistors. The potential difference across any two resistors in series is different, unless the resistors have the same resistance.

18.3 Resistors in Parallel

The **equivalent resistance** of a set of resistors connected in **parallel** is

$$\frac{1}{R_{eq}} = \frac{1}{R_1} + \frac{1}{R_2} + \frac{1}{R_3} + \cdots \qquad [18.6]$$

Several resistors in parallel can be replaced with a single equivalent resistor.

The potential difference across any two parallel resistors is the same; the current in each resistor, however, will be different unless the two resistances are equal.

18.4 Kirchhoff's Rules and Complex DC Circuits

Complex circuits can be analyzed using **Kirchhoff's rules**:

1. The sum of the currents entering any junction must equal the sum of the currents leaving that junction.
2. The sum of the potential differences across all the elements around any closed circuit loop must be zero.

The first rule, called the junction rule, is a statement of **conservation of charge**. The second rule, called the loop rule, is a statement of **conservation of energy**. Solving problems involves using these rules to generate as many equations as there are unknown currents. The equations can then be solved simultaneously.

18.5 RC Circuits

In a simple RC circuit with a battery, a resistor, and a capacitor in series, the charge on the capacitor increases according to the equation

$$q = Q(1 - e^{-t/RC}) \qquad [18.7]$$

An RC circuit with a battery and a resistor charges a capacitor when the switch is closed.

The term RC in Equation 18.7 is called the **time constant** τ (Greek letter tau), so

$$\tau = RC \qquad [18.8]$$

The time constant represents the time required for the charge to increase from zero to 63.2% of its maximum equilibrium value.

A simple RC circuit consisting of a charged capacitor in series with a resistor discharges according to the expression

$$q = Qe^{-t/RC} \qquad [18.9]$$

An RC circuit with charged capacitor discharges across a resistor when the switch is closed.

Problems can be solved by substituting into these equations. The voltage ΔV across the capacitor at any time is obtained by dividing the charge by the capacitance: $\Delta V = q/C$. Using Kirchhoff's loop rule yields the potential difference across the resistor. Ohm's law applied to the resistor then gives the current.

■ MULTIPLE-CHOICE QUESTIONS

WebAssign The multiple-choice questions in this chapter may be assigned online in Enhanced WebAssign.

1. The terminals of a battery are connected across two different resistors in parallel. Which of the following statements are correct? (There may be more than one correct statement.) (a) The larger resistor carries more current than the smaller resistor. (b) The larger resistor carries less current than the smaller resistor. (c) The voltage difference across each resistor is the same. (d) The voltage difference across the larger resistor is greater than the voltage difference across the smaller resistor. (e) The voltage difference is greater across the resistor closer to the battery.

2. The terminals of a battery are connected across two different resistors in series. Which of the following statements are correct? (There may be more than one correct statement.) (a) The smaller resistor carries more current. (b) The larger resistor carries less current. (c) The current in each resistor is the same. (d) The voltage difference across each resistor is the same. (e) The voltage difference is greatest across the resistor closest to the positive terminal.

3. A $1.00\text{-}\Omega$ and a $2.00\text{-}\Omega$ resistor are in parallel. What is the equivalent single resistance? (a) $1.50\ \Omega$ (b) $3.00\ \Omega$ (c) $0.667\ \Omega$ (d) $0.333\ \Omega$ (e) $1.33\ \Omega$

4. Two lightbulbs are in series, one operating at 120 W and the other operating at 60.0 W. If the voltage drop across the series combination is 120 V, what is the current in the circuit? (a) 1.0 A (b) 1.5 A (c) 2.0 A (d) 2.5 A (e) 3.0 A

5. Which of the following equations is *not* a consequence of Kirchhoff's rules, when applied to Figure MCQ18.5? (a) $9 - I_1 - 2I_2 = 0$ (b) $I_1 + I_2 - I_3 = 0$ (c) $4 - 2I_2 - 3I_3 = 0$ (d) $5 - I_1 - 3I_3 = 0$ (e) All these equations are correct.

Figure MCQ18.5

6. What is the current in the $10\text{-}\Omega$ resistance in the circuit shown in Figure MCQ18.6? (a) 0.59 A (b) 1.0 A (c) 11 A (d) 16 A (e) 5.3 A

Figure MCQ18.6

7. When connected to a 120-V source, an electric heater is rated at 1 200 W and a toaster at 6.0×10^2 W. If both appliances are operating in parallel on a 120-V circuit, what total current is delivered by an external source? (a) 12 A (b) 24 A (c) 32 A (d) 8.0 A (e) 15 A

8. If the terminals of a battery are connected across two identical resistors in series, the total power delivered by the battery is 8.0 W. If the same battery is connected across the resistors in parallel, what is the total power delivered by the battery? (a) 16 W (b) 32 W (c) 2.0 W (d) 4.0 W (e) 8.0 W

9. What is the time constant of the circuit shown in Figure MCQ18.9? Each of the five resistors has resistance R, and each of the five capacitors has capacitance C. The internal resistance of the battery is negligible. (a) RC (b) $5RC$ (c) $10RC$ (d) $25RC$ (e) None of these answers is correct.

Figure MCQ18.9

10. The capacitor in Figure MCQ18.10 has a large capacitance and is initially uncharged. After the switch is closed, what happens to the lightbulb? (a) It never glows because the capacitor represents an open circuit. (b) It glows only after the capacitor is fully charged. (c) It glows for a very short time as the capacitor is being charged. (d) It glows continuously. (e) It glows intermittently.

Figure MCQ18.10

11. Several resistors are connected in parallel. Which of the following statements are true of the corresponding equivalent resistance? (There may be more than one correct statement.) (a) It is greater than the resistance of any of the individual resistors. (b) It is less than the resistance of any of the individual resistors. (c) It is dependent on the voltage applied across the group. (d) It is equal to the sum of the resistances of all the resistors in the group. (e) It is equal to the reciprocal of the sum of the inverses of the resistances of all the resistors.

12. When resistors with different resistances are connected in series, which of the following must be the same for each resistor? Choose all correct answers. (a) potential difference (b) current (c) power delivered (d) charge

entering each resistor in a given time interval (e) none of those answers

13. The capacitor in Figure MCQ18.13 is initially uncharged. When the switch is closed at $t = 0$ s, what is the voltage drop across the capacitor after one time constant has elapsed? (a) 2.05 V (b) 3.25 V (c) 6.63 V (d) 3.79 V (e) 4.43 V

6.00 V

2.00 F   5.00 Ω

Figure MCQ18.13

14. Is a circuit breaker wired (a) in series with the device it is protecting, (b) in parallel, or (c) neither in series or in parallel, or (d) is it impossible to tell?

15. Several resistors are connected in series. Which of the following statements are true of the corresponding equivalent resistance? (There may be more than one correct statement.) (a) It is greater than the resistance of any of the individual resistors. (b) It is less than the resistance of any of the individual resistors. (c) It is dependent on the voltage applied across the group. (d) It is equal to the sum of the resistances of all the individual resistors. (e) It is equal to the reciprocal of the sum of the inverses of the resistances of all the resistors.

■ CONCEPTUAL QUESTIONS

WebAssign The conceptual questions in this chapter may be assigned online in Enhanced WebAssign.

1. Is the direction of current in a battery always from the negative terminal to the positive one? Explain.

2. Given three lightbulbs and a battery, sketch as many different circuits as you can.

3. Suppose the energy transferred to a dead battery during charging is W. The recharged battery is then used until fully discharged again. Is the total energy transferred out of the battery during use also W?

4. A short circuit is a circuit containing a path of very low resistance in parallel with some other part of the circuit. Discuss the effect of a short circuit on the portion of the circuit it parallels. Use a lamp with a frayed line cord as an example.

5. Connecting batteries in series increases the emf applied to a circuit. What advantage might there be to connecting them in parallel?

6. If electrical power is transmitted over long distances, the resistance of the wires becomes significant. Why? Which mode of transmission would result in less energy loss, high current and low voltage or low current and high voltage? Discuss.

7. If you have your headlights on while you start your car, why do they dim while the car is starting?

8. Two sets of Christmas lights are available. For set A, when one bulb is removed, the remaining bulbs remain illuminated. For set B, when one bulb is removed, the remaining bulbs do not operate. Explain the difference in wiring for the two sets.

9. Why is it possible for a bird to sit on a high-voltage wire without being electrocuted? (See Fig. CQ18.9.)

Superstock

Figure CQ18.9

10. (a) Two resistors are connected in series across a battery. Is the power delivered to each resistor (i) the same or (ii) not necessarily the same? (b) Two resistors are connected in parallel across a battery. Is the power delivered to each resistor (i) the same or (ii) not necessarily the same?

11. Suppose a parachutist lands on a high-voltage wire and grabs the wire as she prepares to be rescued. Will she be electrocuted? If the wire then breaks, should she continue to hold onto the wire as she falls to the ground?

12. A ski resort consists of a few chairlifts and several interconnected downhill runs on the side of a mountain, with a lodge at the bottom. The lifts are analogous to batteries, and the runs are analogous to resistors. Describe how two runs can be in series. Describe how three runs can be in parallel. Sketch a junction of one lift and two runs. One of the skiers is carrying an altimeter. State Kirchhoff's junction rule and Kirchhoff's loop rule for ski resorts.

13. Embodied in Kirchhoff's rules are two conservation laws. What are they?

14. Why is it dangerous to turn on a light when you are in a bathtub?

■ PROBLEMS

18.1 Sources of emf

18.2 Resistors in Series

18.3 Resistors in Parallel

1. A battery having an emf of 9.00 V delivers 117 mA when connected to a 72.0-Ω load. Determine the internal resistance of the battery.

2. Three 9.0-Ω resistors are connected in series with a 12-V battery. Find (a) the equivalent resistance of the circuit and (b) the current in each resistor. (c) Repeat for the case in which all three resistors are connected in parallel across the battery.

3. A lightbulb marked "75 W [at] 120 V" is screwed into a socket at one end of a long extension cord in which each of the two conductors has a resistance of 0.800 Ω. The other end of the extension cord is plugged into a 120-V outlet. (a) Draw a circuit diagram, and (b) find the actual power of the bulb in the circuit described.

4. (a) Find the current in a 8.00-Ω resistor connected to a battery that has an internal resistance of 0.15 Ω if the voltage across the battery (the terminal voltage) is 9.00 V. (b) What is the emf of the battery?

5. M (a) Find the equivalent resistance between points *a* and *b* in Figure P18.5. (b) Calculate the current in each resistor if a potential difference of 34.0 V is applied between points *a* and *b*.

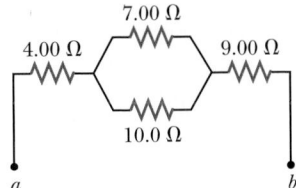

Figure P18.5

6. Consider the combination of resistors shown in Figure P18.6. (a) Find the equivalent resistance between point *a* and *b*. (b) If a voltage of 35.0 V is applied between points *a* and *b*, find the current in each resistor.

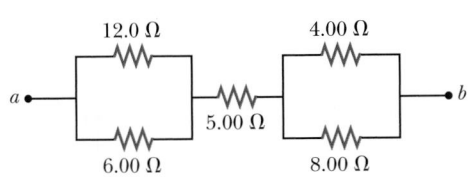

Figure P18.6

7. Two resistors connected in series have an equivalent resistance of 690 Ω. When they are connected in paral-

lel, their equivalent resistance is 150 Ω. Find the resistance of each resistor.

8. GP Consider the circuit shown in Figure P18.8. (a) Calculate the equivalent resistance of the 10.0-Ω and 5.00-Ω resistors connected in parallel. (b) Using the result of part (a), calculate the combined resistance of the 10.0-Ω, 5.00-Ω, and 4.00-Ω resistors. (c) Calculate the equivalent resistance of the combined resistance found in part (b) and the parallel 3.00-Ω resistor. (d) Combine the equivalent resistance found in part (c) with the 2.00-Ω resistor. (e) Calculate the total current in the circuit. (f) What is the voltage drop across the 2.00-Ω resistor? (g) Subtracting the result of part (f) from the battery voltage, find the voltage across the 3.00-Ω resistor. (h) Calculate the current in the 3.00-Ω resistor.

Figure P18.8

9. Consider the circuit shown in Figure P18.9. Find (a) the potential difference between points *a* and *b* and (b) the current in the 20.0-Ω resistor.

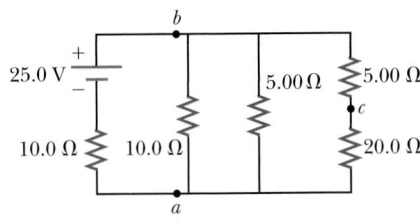

Figure P18.9

10. S Four resistors are connected to a battery as shown in Figure P18.10 (page 642). (a) Determine the

potential difference across each resistor in terms of $\mathcal{E}$. (b) Determine the current in each resistor in terms of I.

Figure P18.10

11. The resistance between terminals a and b in Figure P18.11 is 75 Ω. If the resistors labeled R have the same value, determine R.

Figure P18.11

12. A battery with $\mathcal{E}$ = 6.00 V and no internal resistance supplies current to the circuit shown in Figure P18.12. When the double-throw switch S is open as shown in the figure, the current in the battery is 1.00 mA. When the switch is closed in position a, the current in the battery is 1.20 mA. When the switch is closed in position b, the current in the battery is 2.00 mA. Find the resistances (a) R_1, (b) R_2, and (c) R_3.

Figure P18.12

13. Find the current in the 12-Ω resistor in Figure P18.13.

Figure P18.13

14. **QC** (a) Is it possible to reduce the circuit shown in Figure P18.14 to a single equivalent resistor connected across the battery? Explain. (b) Find the current in the 2.00-Ω resistor. (c) Calculate the power delivered by the battery to the circuit.

Figure P18.14

15. (a) You need a 45-Ω resistor, but the stockroom has only 20-Ω and 50-Ω resistors. How can the desired resistance be achieved under these circumstances? (b) What can you do if you need a 35-Ω resistor?

18.4 Kirchhoff's Rules and Complex DC Circuits

Note: For some circuits, the currents are not necessarily in the direction shown.

16. **S** (a) Find the current in each resistor of Figure P18.16 by using the rules for resistors in series and parallel. (b) Write three independent equations for the three currents using Kirchhoff's laws: one with the node rule; a second using the loop rule through the battery, the 6.0-Ω resistor, and the 24.0-Ω resistor; and the third using the loop rule through the 12.0-Ω and 24.0-Ω resistors. Solve to check the answers found in part (a).

Figure P18.16

17. The ammeter shown in Figure P18.17 reads 2.00 A. Find I_1, I_2, and $\mathcal{E}$.

Figure P18.17

18. For the circuit shown in Figure P18.18, calculate (a) the current in the 2.00-Ω resistor and (b) the potential difference between points a and b, $\Delta V = V_b - V_a$.

19. Taking $R = 1.00$ kΩ and $\mathcal{E} =$ 250 V in Figure P18.19, determine the direction and magnitude of the current in the horizontal wire between a and e.

Figure P18.18

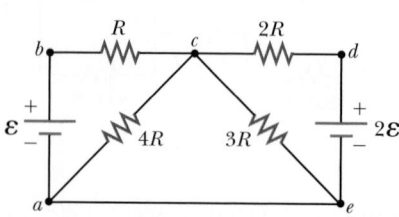

Figure P18.19

20. In the circuit of Figure P18.20, the current I_1 is 3.0 A and the values of $\mathcal{E}$ and R are unknown. What are the currents I_2 and I_3?

Figure P18.20

21. In the circuit of Figure P18.21, determine (a) the current in each resistor and (b) the potential difference across the 200-Ω resistor.

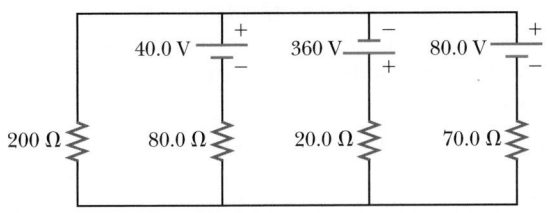

Figure P18.21

22. QC Four resistors are connected to a battery with a terminal voltage of 12 V, as shown in Figure P18.22. (a) How would you reduce the circuit to an equivalent single resistor connected to the battery? Use this procedure to find the equivalent resistance of the circuit. (b) Find the current delivered by the battery to this equivalent resistance. (c) Determine the power delivered by the battery. (d) Determine the power delivered to the 50.0-Ω resistor.

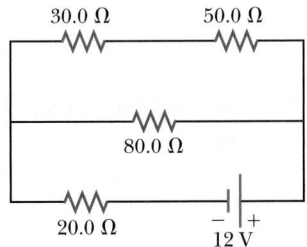

Figure P18.22

23. M Using Kirchhoff's rules, (a) find the current in each resistor shown in Figure P18.23 and (b) find the potential difference between points c and f.

Figure P18.23

24. Two 1.50-V batteries—with their positive terminals in the same direction—are inserted in series into the barrel of a flashlight. One battery has an internal resistance of 0.255 Ω, the other an internal resistance of 0.153 Ω. When the switch is closed, a current of 0.600 A passes through the lamp. (a) What is the lamp's resistance? (b) What fraction of the power dissipated is dissipated in the batteries?

25. QC (a) Can the circuit shown in Figure P18.25 be reduced to a single resistor connected to the batteries? Explain. (b) Calculate each of the unknown currents I_1, I_2, and I_3 for the circuit.

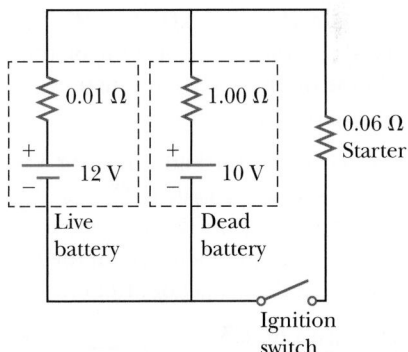

Figure P18.25

26. A dead battery is charged by connecting it to the live battery of another car with jumper cables (Fig. P18.26). Determine the current in (a) the starter and in (b) the dead battery.

Figure P18.26

27. QC (a) Can the circuit shown in Figure P18.27 be reduced to a single resistor connected to the batteries? Explain. (b) Find the magnitude of the current and its direction in each resistor.

Figure P18.27

28. GP S For the circuit shown in Figure P18.28, use Kirchhoff's rules to obtain equations for (a) the upper

Figure P18.28

loop, (b) the lower loop, and (c) the node on the left side. In each case suppress units for clarity and simplify, combining like terms. (d) Solve the node equation for I_{36}. (e) Using the equation found in (d), eliminate I_{36} from the equation found in part (b). (f) Solve the equations found in part (a) and part (e) simultaneously for the two unknowns for I_{18} and I_{12}, respectively. (g) Substitute the answers found in part (f) into the node equation found in part (d), solving for I_{36}. (h) What is the significance of the negative answer for I_{12}?

29. **M** Find the potential difference across each resistor in Figure P18.29.

Figure P18.29

18.5 *RC* Circuits

30. Show that $\tau = RC$ has units of time.

31. Consider the series *RC*-circuit shown in Active Figure 18.16 for which $R = 75.0$ kΩ, $C = 25.0$ μF, and $\mathcal{E} = 12.0$ V. Find (a) the time constant of the circuit and (b) the charge on the capacitor one time constant after the switch is closed.

32. An uncharged capacitor and a resistor are connected in series to a source of emf. If $\mathcal{E} = 9.00$ V, $C = 20.0$ μF, and $R = 100$ Ω, find (a) the time constant of the circuit, (b) the maximum charge on the capacitor, and (c) the charge on the capacitor after one time constant.

33. Consider a series *RC* circuit as in Figure P18.33 for which $R = 1.00$ MΩ, $C = 5.00$ μF, and $\mathcal{E} = 30.0$ V. Find (a) the time constant of the circuit and (b) the maximum charge on the capacitor after the switch is thrown closed. (c) Find the current in the resistor 10.0 s after the switch is closed.

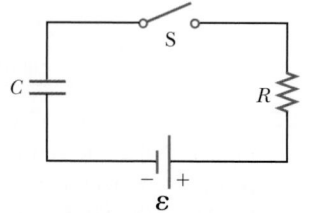

Figure P18.33
Problems 33 and 34.

34. Consider a series *RC* circuit for which $R = 1.0$ MΩ, $C = 5.0$ μF, and $\mathcal{E} = 30$ V as in Figure P18.33. Find the charge on the capacitor 10 s after the switch is closed.

35. A charged capacitor is connected to a resistor and a switch as in Figure P18.35. The circuit has a time constant of 1.50 s. Soon after the switch is closed, the charge on the capacitor is 75.0% of its initial charge. (a) Find the time interval required for the capacitor to reach this charge. (b) If $R = 250$ kΩ, what is the value of C?

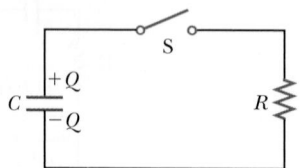

Figure P18.35

36. A 10.0-μF capacitor is charged by a 10.0-V battery through a resistance R. The capacitor reaches a potential difference of 4.00 V in a time interval of 3.00 s after charging begins. Find R.

18.6 Household Circuits

37. What minimum number of 75-W lightbulbs must be connected in parallel to a single 120-V household circuit to trip a 30.0-A circuit breaker?

38. A lamp ($R = 150$ Ω), an electric heater ($R = 25$ Ω), and a fan ($R = 50$ Ω) are connected in parallel across a 120-V line. (a) What total current is supplied to the circuit? (b) What is the voltage across the fan? (c) What is the current in the lamp? (d) What power is expended in the heater?

39. **M** A heating element in a stove is designed to dissipate 3 000 W when connected to 240 V. (a) Assuming the resistance is constant, calculate the current in the heating element if it is connected to 120 V. (b) Calculate the power it dissipates at that voltage.

40. **QIC** A coffee maker is rated at 1 200 W, a toaster at 1 100 W, and a waffle maker at 1 400 W. The three appliances are connected in parallel to a common 120-V household circuit. (a) What is the current in each appliance when operating independently? (b) What total current is delivered to the appliances when all are operating simultaneously? (c) Is a 15-A circuit breaker sufficient in this situation? Explain.

18.8 Conduction of Electrical Signals by Neurons

41. **BIO** Assume a length of axon membrane of about 0.10 m is excited by an action potential (length excited = nerve speed × pulse duration = 50.0 m/s × 2.0×10^{-3} s = 0.10 m). In the resting state, the outer surface of the axon wall is charged positively with K^+ ions and the inner wall has an equal and opposite charge of negative organic ions, as shown in Figure P18.41. Model the axon as a parallel-plate capacitor and take $C = \kappa \epsilon_0 A/d$ and $Q = C\Delta V$ to investigate the charge as follows. Use typical values for a cylindrical axon of cell wall thickness $d = 1.0 \times 10^{-8}$ m, axon radius $r = 1.0 \times 10^1$ μm, and cell-wall dielectric constant $\kappa = 3.0$. (a) Calculate the positive charge on the outside of a 0.10-m piece of axon when it is not conducting an electric pulse. How many K^+ ions are on the outside of the axon assuming an initial potential difference of 7.0×10^{-2} V? Is this a large charge per unit area? *Hint:* Calculate the charge per unit area in terms of electronic charge e per angstrom squared (Å²). An atom has a cross section of about 1 Å² (1 Å = 10^{-10} m). (b) How much positive charge must flow through the cell membrane to reach the excited state of $+3.0 \times 10^{-2}$ V from the resting state of -7.0×10^{-2} V? How many sodium ions (Na^+) is this? (c) If it takes 2.0 ms for the Na^+ ions to enter the axon, what is the average current in the axon wall in this process? (d) How much energy does it take to raise the potential

of the inner axon wall to $+3.0 \times 10^{-2}$ V, starting from the resting potential of -7.0×10^{-2} V?

Figure P18.41 Problems 41 and 42.

42. **BIO** Consider the model of the axon as a capacitor from Problem 41 and Figure P18.41. (a) How much energy does it take to restore the inner wall of the axon to -7.0×10^{-2} V, starting from $+3.0 \times 10^{-2}$ V? (b) Find the average current in the axon wall during this process.

43. **BIO** Using Figure 18.28b and the results of Problems 18.41d and 18.42a, find the power supplied by the axon per action potential.

Additional Problems

44. How many different resistance values can be constructed from a 2.0-Ω, a 4.0-Ω, and a 6.0-Ω resistor? Show how you would get each resistance value either individually or by combining them.

45. (a) Calculate the potential difference between points a and b in Figure P18.45 and (b) identify which point is at the higher potential.

Figure P18.45

46. **QC** For the circuit shown in Figure P18.46, the voltmeter reads 6.0 V and the ammeter reads 3.0 mA. Find (a) the value of R, (b) the emf of the battery, and (c) the voltage across the 3.0-kΩ resistor. (d) What

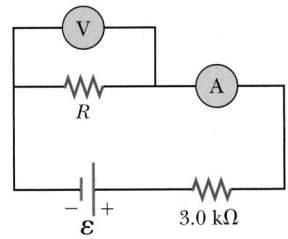

Figure P18.46

assumptions did you have to make to solve this problem?

47. Find (a) the equivalent resistance of the circuit in Figure P18.47, (b) each current in the circuit, (c) the potential difference across each resistor, and (d) the power dissipated by each resistor.

Figure P18.47

48. Three 60.0-W, 120-V lightbulbs are connected across a 120-V power source, as shown in Figure P18.48. Find (a) the total power delivered to the three bulbs and (b) the potential difference across each. Assume the resistance of each bulb is constant (even though, in reality, the resistance increases markedly with current).

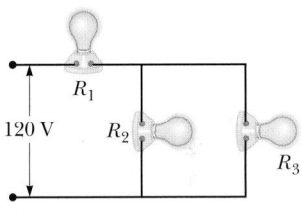

Figure P18.48

49. When two unknown resistors are connected in series with a battery, the battery delivers 225 W and carries a total current of 5.00 A. For the same total current, 50.0 W is delivered when the resistors are connected in parallel. Determine the value of each resistor.

50. **QC** The circuit in Figure P18.50a consists of three resistors and one battery with no internal resistance. (a) Find the current in the 5.00-Ω resistor. (b) Find the power delivered to the 5.00-Ω resistor. (c) In each of the circuits in Figures P18.50b, P18.50c, and P18.50d, an additional 15.0-V battery has been inserted into the circuit. Which diagram or diagrams represent a circuit

Figure P18.50

that requires the use of Kirchhoff's rules to find the currents? Explain why. (d) In which of these three new circuits is the smallest amount of power delivered to the 10.0-Ω resistor? (You need not calculate the power in each circuit if you explain your answer.)

51. **Q|C** **S** A circuit consists of three identical lamps, each of resistance R, connected to a battery as in Figure P18.51. (a) Calculate an expression for the equivalent resistance of the circuit when the switch is open. Repeat the calculation when the switch is closed. (b) Write an expression for the power supplied by the battery when the switch is open. Repeat the calculation when the switch is closed. (c) Using the results already obtained, explain what happens to the brightness of the lamps when the switch is closed.

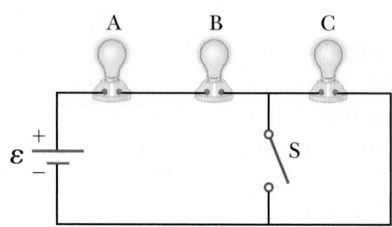

Figure P18.51

52. The resistance between points a and b in Figure P18.52 drops to one-half its original value when switch S is closed. Determine the value of R.

Figure P18.52

53. The circuit in Figure P18.53 has been connected for several seconds. Find the current (a) in the 4.00-V battery, (b) in the 3.00-Ω resistor, (c) in the 8.00-V battery, and (d) in the 3.00-V battery. (e) Find the charge on the capacitor.

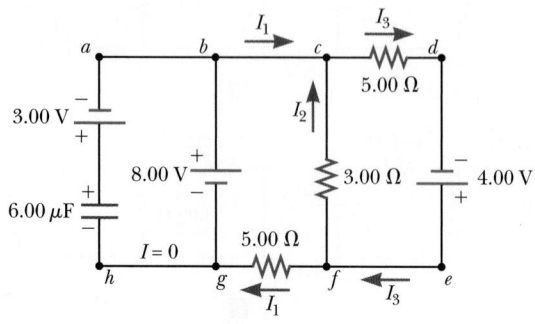

Figure P18.53

54. An emf of 10 V is connected to a series RC circuit consisting of a resistor of 2.0×10^6 Ω and an initially uncharged capacitor of 3.0 μF. Find the time required for the charge on the capacitor to reach 90% of its final value.

55. The student engineer of a campus radio station wishes to verify the effectiveness of the lightning rod on the antenna mast (Fig. P18.55). The unknown resistance R_x is between points C and E. Point E is a "true ground," but is inaccessible for direct measurement because the stratum in which it is located is several meters below Earth's surface. Two identical rods are driven into the ground at A and B, introducing an unknown resistance R_y. The procedure for finding the unknown resistance R_x is as follows. Measure resistance R_1 between points A and B. Then connect A and B with a heavy conducting wire and measure resistance R_2 between points A and C. (a) Derive a formula for R_x in terms of the observable resistances R_1 and R_2. (b) A satisfactory ground resistance would be $R_x < 2.0$ Ω. Is the grounding of the station adequate if measurements give $R_1 = 13$ Ω and $R_2 = 6.0$ Ω?

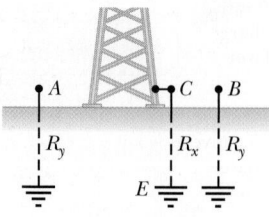

Figure P18.55

56. The resistor R in Figure P18.56 dissipates 20 W of power. Determine the value of R.

Figure P18.56

57. A voltage ΔV is applied to a series configuration of n resistors, each of resistance R. The circuit components are reconnected in a parallel configuration, and voltage ΔV is again applied. Show that the power consumed by the series configuration is $1/n^2$ times the power consumed by the parallel configuration.

58. For the network in Figure P18.58, show that the resistance between points a and b is $R_{ab} = \frac{27}{17}$ Ω. (*Hint:* Connect a battery with emf $\mathcal{E}$ across points a and b and determine $\mathcal{E}/I$, where I is the current in the battery.)

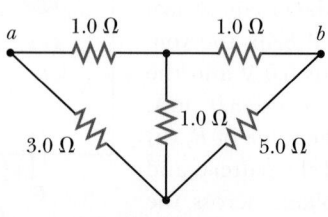

Figure P18.58

59. A battery with an internal resistance of 10.0 Ω produces an open circuit voltage of 12.0 V. A variable load resistance with a range from 0 to 30.0 Ω is connected across the battery. (*Note:* A battery has a resistance that depends on the condition of its chemicals and that increases as the battery ages. This internal resistance can be represented in a simple circuit diagram as a resistor in series with the battery.) (a) Graph the power dissipated in the load resistor as a function of the load resistance. (b) With your graph, demonstrate the following important theorem: *The power delivered to a load is a maximum if the load resistance equals the internal resistance of the source.*

60. The circuit in Figure P18.60 contains two resistors, $R_1 = 2.0$ kΩ and $R_2 = 3.0$ kΩ, and two capacitors, $C_1 = 2.0$ μF and $C_2 = 3.0$ μF, connected to a battery with emf $\mathcal{E} = 120$ V. If there are no charges on the capacitors before switch S is closed, determine the charges q_1 and q_2 on capacitors C_1 and C_2, respectively, as functions of time, after the switch is closed. *Hint:* First reconstruct the circuit so that it becomes a simple *RC* circuit containing a single resistor and single capacitor in series, connected to the battery, and then determine the total charge q stored in the circuit.

Figure P18.60

61. **BIO** An electric eel generates electric currents through its highly specialized Hunter's organ, in which thousands of disk-shaped cells called electrocytes are lined up in series, very much in the same way batteries are lined up inside a flashlight. When activated, each electrocyte can maintain a potential difference of about 150 mV at a current of 1 A for about 2.0 ms. Suppose a grown electric eel has 4.0×10^3 electrocytes and can deliver up to 300 shocks in rapid series over about 1 s. (a) What maximum electrical power can an electric eel generate? (b) Approximately how much energy does it release in one shock? (c) How high would a mass of 1 kg have to be lifted so that its gravitational potential energy equals the energy released in 300 such shocks?

62. In Figure P18.62, $R_1 = 0.100$ Ω, $R_2 = 1.00$ Ω, and $R_3 = 10.0$ Ω. Find the equivalent resistance of the circuit and the current in each resis-

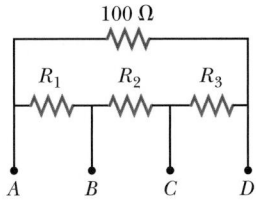

Figure P18.62

tor when a 5.00-V power supply is connected between (a) points A and B, (b) points A and C, and (c) points A and D.

63. **M** What are the expected readings of the ammeter and voltmeter for the circuit in Figure P18.63?

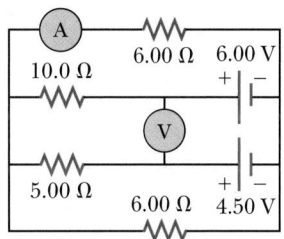

Figure P18.63

64. Consider the two arrangements of batteries and bulbs shown in Figure P18.64. The two bulbs are identical and have resistance R, and the two batteries are identical with output voltage ΔV. (a) In case 1, with the two bulbs in series, compare the brightness of each bulb, the current in each bulb, and the power delivered to each bulb. (b) In case 2, with the two bulbs in parallel, compare the brightness of each bulb, the current in each bulb, and the power supplied to each bulb. (c) Which bulbs are brighter, those in case 1 or those in case 2? (d) In each case, if one bulb fails, will the other go out as well? If the other bulb doesn't fail, will it get brighter or stay the same? (Problem 64 is courtesy of E. F. Redish. For other problems of this type, visit http://www.physics.umd.edu/perg/.)

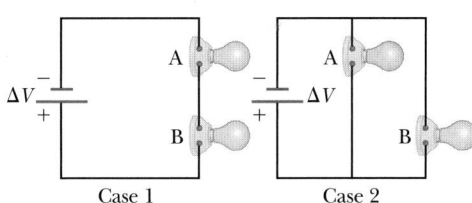

Figure P18.64

65. The given pair of capacitors in Figure P18.65 is fully charged by a 12.0-V battery. The battery is disconnected and the circuit closed. After 1.00 ms, how much charge remains on (a) the 3.00-μF capacitor? (b) The 2.00-μF capacitor? (c) What is the current in the resistor?

Figure P18.65

66. A 2.00-nF capacitor with an initial charge of 5.10 μC is discharged through a 1.30-kΩ resistor. (a) Calculate the magnitude of the current in the resistor 9.00 μs after the resistor is connected across the terminals of the capacitor. (b) What charge remains on the capacitor after 8.00 μs? (c) What is the maximum current in the resistor?

■ AP* REVIEW QUESTIONS

Questions 1–5 relate to the following circuit.

Use the above circuit diagram to answer questions 1 through 5. *A, B, C,* and *D* are identical bulbs. S_1 and S_2 are switches that are initially open.

1. What will happen to bulb *B* when S_1 is closed?

   (A) Gets brighter

   (B) Gets dimmer

   (C) Stays the same

   (D) Goes out

   (E) More information is needed

2. What will happen to bulb *C* when S_2 is now closed?

   (A) Gets brighter

   (B) Gets dimmer

   (C) Stays the same

   (D) Goes out

   (E) More information is needed

3. If S_1 remains closed and S_2 is reopened, what happens to bulb *D*?

   (A) Gets brighter

   (B) Gets dimmer

   (C) Stays the same

   (D) Goes out

   (E) More information is needed

4. If S_1 is closed but S_2 is open and each bulb has a resistance of 5 Ω, what is the total resistance in the circuit?

   (A) 4.4 mΩ

   (B) 0.6 Ω

   (C) 1.7 Ω

   (D) 15 Ω

   (E) 225 Ω

5. If both switches are closed and each bulb has a resistance of 5 Ω, what is the total resistance in the circuit?

   (A) 0.5 Ω

   (B) 1.25 Ω

   (C) 2 Ω

   (D) 12.5 Ω

   (E) 20 Ω

6. A 10 Ω resistor is connected to a battery with an internal resistance of 2 Ω. An ammeter connected in series with the battery and resistor measures 4 A. What is the emf ($\mathcal{E}$) in this circuit?

   (A) 8 V

   (B) 32 V

   (C) 40 V

   (D) 48 V

   (E) 52 V

Questions 7–9 relate to the following circuit.

7. What is the equivalent resistance (R_{eq}) for the entire circuit if $V = 12$ V, and each resistor has a resistance of 3 Ω?

(A) $\frac{1}{3}$ Ω

(B) 1 Ω

(C) 4 Ω

(D) $\frac{9}{2}$ Ω

(E) 12 Ω

8. What is the current and voltage in R_3?

(A) 3A, 12 V

(B) 3 A, 3 V

(C) 2 A, 3 V

(D) 1 A, 12 V

(E) 1 A, 3 V

9. If one additional resistor is added in series with R_3, what will happen to the current and resistance in R_3?

(A) Current increases, voltage increases

(B) Current decreases, voltage decreases

(C) Current increases, voltage decreases

(D) Current decreases, voltage increases

(E) Current and voltage will remain the same

Questions 10–12 relate to the following circuit.

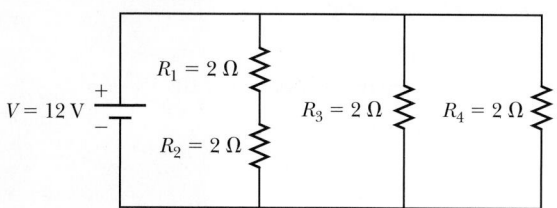

10. What is the equivalent resistance (R_{eq}) for the following circuit?

(A) $\frac{4}{5}$ Ω

(B) 1 Ω

(C) $\frac{5}{4}$ Ω

(D) 8 Ω

(E) 16 Ω

11. What is the current and voltage in R_1?

(A) 15 A, 12 V

(B) 6 A, 12 V

(C) 6 A, 6 V

(D) 3 A, 12 V

(E) 3 A, 6 V

12. If R_2 is removed from the circuit, what happens to the current and voltage in R_1?

(A) Current increases, voltage increases

(B) Current decreases, voltage decreases

(C) Current increases, voltage decreases

(D) Current decreases, voltage increases

(E) Current and voltage will remain the same

Constance McGuire/iStockPhoto

Aurora borealis, the northern lights. Displays such as this one are caused by cosmic ray particles trapped in the magnetic field of Earth. When the particles collide with atoms in the atmosphere, they cause the atoms to emit visible light.

19 Magnetism

In terms of applications, magnetism is one of the most important fields in physics. Large electromagnets are used to pick up heavy loads. Magnets are used in such devices as meters, motors, and loudspeakers. Magnetic tapes and disks are used routinely in sound- and video-recording equipment and to store computer data. Intense magnetic fields are used in magnetic resonance imaging (MRI) devices to explore the human body with better resolution and greater safety than x-rays can provide. Giant superconducting magnets are used in the cyclotrons that guide particles into targets at nearly the speed of light. Rail guns (Fig. 19.1) use magnetic forces to fire high-speed projectiles, and magnetic bottles hold antimatter, a possible key to future space propulsion systems.

Magnetism is closely linked with electricity. Magnetic fields affect moving charges, and moving charges produce magnetic fields. Changing magnetic fields can even create electric fields. These phenomena signify an underlying unity of electricity and magnetism, which James Clerk Maxwell first described in the 19th century. The ultimate source of any magnetic field is electric current.

19.1 Magnets

Most people have had experience with some form of magnet. You are most likely familiar with the common iron horseshoe magnet that can pick up iron-containing objects such as paper clips and nails. In the discussion that follows, we assume the magnet has the shape of a bar. Iron objects are most strongly attracted to either end of such a bar magnet, called its **poles**. One end is called the **north pole** and the other the **south pole.** The names come from the behavior of a magnet in the presence of Earth's magnetic field. If a bar magnet is suspended from its midpoint by a piece of string so that it can swing freely in a horizontal plane, it will rotate

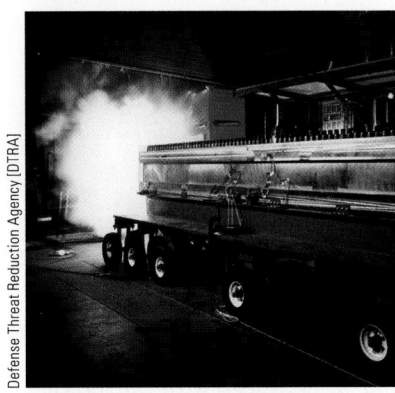

Defense Threat Reduction Agency [DTRA]

Figure 19.1 Rail guns launch projectiles at high speed using magnetic force. Larger versions could send payloads into space or be used as thrusters to move metal-rich asteroids from deep space to Earth orbit. In this photo a rail gun at Sandia National Laboratories in Albuquerque, New Mexico, fires a projectile at over three kilometers per second. (For more information on this, see Applying Physics 20.2 on pages 698–699.)

until its north pole points to the north and its south pole points to the south. The same idea is used to construct a simple compass. Magnetic poles also exert attractive or repulsive forces on each other similar to the electrical forces between charged objects. In fact, simple experiments with two bar magnets show that **like poles repel each other and unlike poles attract each other**.

Although the force between opposite magnetic poles is similar to the force between positive and negative electric charges, there is an important difference: positive and negative electric charges can exist in isolation of each other; north and south poles don't. No matter how many times a permanent magnet is cut, each piece always has a north pole and a south pole. There is some theoretical basis, however, for the speculation that magnetic monopoles (isolated north or south poles) exist in nature, and the attempt to detect them is currently an active experimental field of investigation.

An unmagnetized piece of iron can be magnetized by stroking it with a magnet. Magnetism can also be induced in iron (and other materials) by other means. For example, if a piece of unmagnetized iron is placed near a strong permanent magnet, the piece of iron eventually becomes magnetized. The process can be accelerated by heating and then cooling the iron.

Naturally occurring magnetic materials such as magnetite are magnetized in this way because they have been subjected to Earth's magnetic field for long periods of time. The extent to which a piece of material retains its magnetism depends on whether it is classified as magnetically hard or soft. **Soft** magnetic materials, such as iron, are easily magnetized but tend to lose their magnetization easily. These materials are used in the cores of transformers, generators, and motors. Iron is the most common choice because it's inexpensive. Other magnetically soft materials include nickel, nickel-iron alloys, and ferrites. Ferrites are combinations of a divalent metal oxide of nickel or magnesium with ferric oxide. Ferrites are used in high-frequency applications, such as radar.

Hard magnetic materials are used in permanent magnets. Such magnets provide magnetic fields without the use of electricity. Permanent magnets are used in many devices, including loudspeakers, permanent-magnet motors, and the read/write heads of computer hard drives. There are a large number of different materials used in permanent magnets. Alnico is a generic name for various alloys of iron, cobalt, and nickel, together with smaller amounts of aluminum, copper, or other elements. Rare earths such as samarium and neodymium are also used in conjunction with other elements to make strong permanent magnets.

In earlier chapters we described the interaction between charged objects in terms of electric fields. Recall that an electric field surrounds any stationary electric charge. The region of space surrounding a *moving* charge includes a magnetic field as well. A magnetic field also surrounds a properly magnetized magnetic material.

To describe any type of vector field, we must define its magnitude, or strength, and its direction. The direction of a magnetic field $\vec{\mathbf{B}}$ at any location is the direction

Active Figure 19.2
(a) Tracing the magnetic field of a bar magnet with compasses. (b) Several magnetic field lines of a bar magnet.

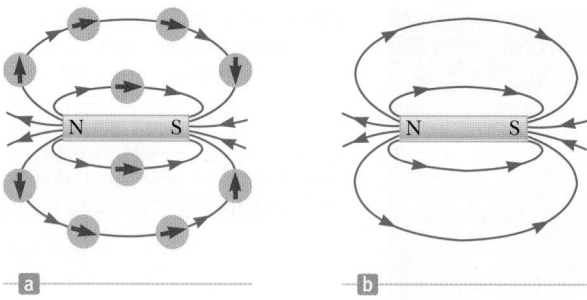

in which the north pole of a compass needle points at that location. Active Figure 19.2a shows how the magnetic field of a bar magnet can be traced with the aid of a compass, defining a **magnetic field line**. Several magnetic field lines of a bar magnet traced out in this way appear in the two-dimensional representation in Active Figure 19.2b. Magnetic field patterns can be displayed by placing small iron filings in the vicinity of a magnet, as in Figure 19.3.

Forensic scientists use a technique similar to that shown in Figure 19.3 to find fingerprints at a crime scene. One way to find latent, or invisible, prints is by sprinkling a powder of iron dust on a surface. The iron adheres to any perspiration or body oils that are present and can be spread around on the surface with a magnetic brush that never comes into contact with the powder or the surface.

APPLICATION
Dusting for Fingerprints

19.2 Earth's Magnetic Field

A small bar magnet is said to have north and south poles, but it's more accurate to say it has a "north-seeking" pole and a "south-seeking" pole. By these expressions, we mean that if such a magnet is used as a compass, one end will "seek," or point to, the geographic North Pole of Earth and the other end will "seek," or point to, the geographic South Pole of Earth. We conclude that **the geographic North Pole of Earth corresponds to a magnetic south pole, and the geographic South Pole of Earth corresponds to a magnetic north pole.** In fact, the configuration of Earth's magnetic field, pictured in Figure 19.4, very much resembles what would be observed if a huge bar magnet were buried deep in the Earth's interior.

If a compass needle is suspended in bearings that allow it to rotate in the vertical plane as well as in the horizontal plane, the needle is horizontal with respect to Earth's surface only near the equator. As the device is moved northward, the needle rotates so that it points more and more toward the surface of Earth. The angle between the direction of the magnetic field and the horizontal is called the **dip angle**. Finally, at a point just north of Hudson Bay in Canada, the north pole of the needle points directly downward, with a dip angle of 90°. That site, first found in 1832, is considered to be the location of the south magnetic pole of Earth. It

Tip 19.1 The Geographic North Pole Is the Magnetic South Pole

The north pole of a magnet in a compass points north because it's attracted to Earth's *magnetic* south pole, located near Earth's *geographic* north pole.

Figure 19.3 (a) The magnetic field pattern of a bar magnet, as displayed with iron filings on a sheet of paper. (b) The magnetic field pattern between *unlike* poles of two bar magnets, as displayed with iron filings. (c) The magnetic field pattern between two *like* poles.

  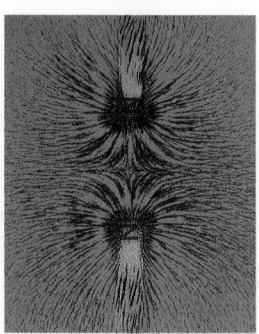

Henry Leap and Jim Lehman

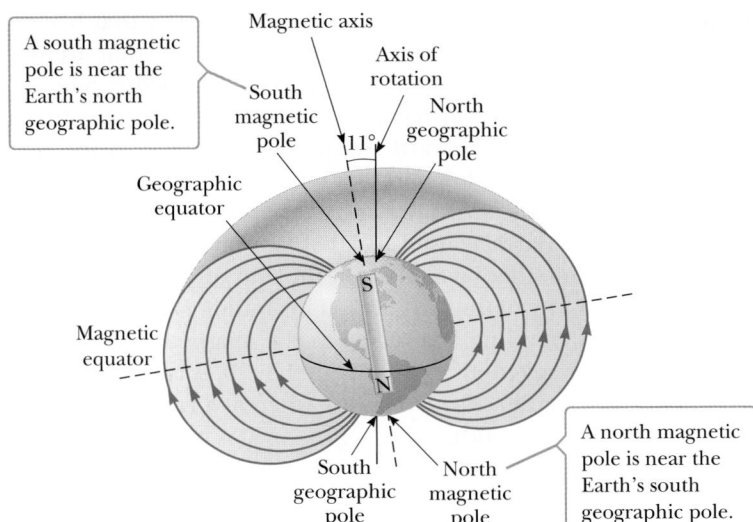

A south magnetic pole is near the Earth's north geographic pole.

Magnetic axis
Axis of rotation
South magnetic pole
North geographic pole
11°
Geographic equator
Magnetic equator
South geographic pole
North magnetic pole

A north magnetic pole is near the Earth's south geographic pole.

Figure 19.4 Earth's magnetic field lines. The lines leading away from the immediate vicinity of the north magnetic pole and entering the vicinity of the south magnetic pole have been left out for clarity.

is approximately 1 300 miles from Earth's geographic North Pole and varies with time. Similarly, Earth's magnetic north pole is about 1 200 miles from its geographic South Pole. This means that compass needles point only approximately north. The difference between true north, defined as the geographic North Pole, and north indicated by a compass varies from point to point on Earth, a difference referred to as *magnetic declination*. For example, along a line through South Carolina and the Great Lakes a compass indicates true north, whereas in Washington state it aligns 25° east of true north (Fig. 19.5).

Although the magnetic field pattern of Earth is similar to the pattern that would be set up by a bar magnet placed at its center, the source of Earth's field can't consist of large masses of permanently magnetized material. Earth does have large deposits of iron ore deep beneath its surface, but the high temperatures in the core prevent the iron from retaining any permanent magnetization. It's considered more likely that the true source of Earth's magnetic field is electric current in the liquid part of its core. This current, which is not well understood, may be driven by an interaction between the planet's rotation and convection in the hot liquid core. There is some evidence that the strength of a planet's magnetic field is related to the planet's rate of rotation. For example, Jupiter rotates faster than Earth, and recent space probes indicate that Jupiter's magnetic field is stronger than Earth's, even though Jupiter lacks an iron core. Venus, on the other hand, rotates more slowly than Earth, and its magnetic field is weaker. Investigation into the cause of Earth's magnetism continues.

An interesting fact concerning Earth's magnetic field is that its direction reverses every few million years. Evidence for this phenomenon is provided by basalt (an iron-containing rock) that is sometimes spewed forth by volcanic activity on the ocean floor. As the lava cools, it solidifies and retains a picture of the direction of Earth's magnetic field. When the basalt deposits are dated, they provide evidence for periodic reversals of the magnetic field. The cause of these field reversals is still not understood.

It has long been speculated that some animals, such as birds, use the magnetic field of Earth to guide their migrations. Studies have shown that a type of anaerobic bacterium that lives in swamps has a magnetized chain of magnetite as part of its internal structure. (The term *anaerobic* means that these bacteria live and grow without oxygen; in fact, oxygen is toxic to them.) The magnetized chain acts as a compass needle that enables the bacteria to align with Earth's magnetic field. When they find themselves out of the mud on the bottom of the swamp, they return to their oxygen-free environment by following the magnetic field lines of

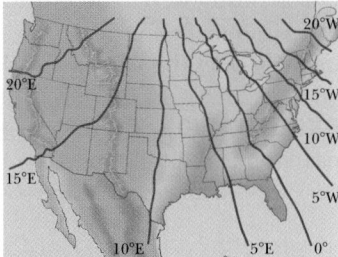

Figure 19.5 A map of the continental United States showing the declination of a compass from true north.

BIO APPLICATION
Magnetic Bacteria

Earth. Further evidence for their magnetic sensing ability is that bacteria found in the northern hemisphere have internal magnetite chains that are opposite in polarity to those of similar bacteria in the southern hemisphere. Similarly, in the northern hemisphere, Earth's field has a downward component, whereas in the southern hemisphere it has an upward component. Recently, a meteorite originating on Mars has been found to contain a chain of magnetite. NASA scientists believe it may be a fossil of ancient Martian bacterial life.

APPLICATION
Labeling Airport Runways

The magnetic field of Earth is used to label runways at airports according to their direction. A large number is painted on the end of the runway so that it can be read by the pilot of an incoming airplane. This number describes the direction in which the airplane is traveling, expressed as the magnetic heading, in degrees measured clockwise from magnetic north divided by 10. A runway marked 9 would be directed toward the east (90° divided by 10), whereas a runway marked 18 would be directed toward magnetic south.

■ **APPLYING PHYSICS 19.1** | **Compasses Down Under**

On a business trip to Australia, you take along your American-made compass that you may have used on a camping trip. Does this compass work correctly in Australia?

EXPLANATION There's no problem with using the compass in Australia. The north pole of the magnet in the compass will be attracted to the south magnetic pole near the geographic North Pole, just as it was in the United States. The only difference in the magnetic field lines is that they have an upward component in Australia, whereas they have a downward component in the United States. Held in a horizontal plane, your compass can't detect this difference, however; it only displays the direction of the horizontal component of the magnetic field. ■

19.3 Magnetic Fields

Experiments show that a stationary charged particle doesn't interact with a static magnetic field. **When a charged particle is *moving* through a magnetic field, however, a magnetic force acts on it**. This force has its maximum value when the charge moves in a direction perpendicular to the magnetic field lines, decreases in value at other angles, and becomes zero when the particle moves along the field lines. This is quite different from the electric force, which exerts a force on a charged particle whether it's moving or at rest. Further, the electric force is directed parallel to the electric field whereas the magnetic force on a moving charge is directed perpendicular to the magnetic field.

In our discussion of electricity, the electric field at some point in space was defined as the electric force per unit charge acting on some test charge placed at that point. In a similar way, we can describe the properties of the magnetic field $\vec{\mathbf{B}}$ at some point in terms of the magnetic force exerted on a test charge at that point. Our test object is a charge q moving with velocity $\vec{\mathbf{v}}$. It is found experimentally that the strength of the magnetic force on the particle is proportional to the magnitude of the charge q, the magnitude of the velocity $\vec{\mathbf{v}}$, the strength of the external magnetic field $\vec{\mathbf{B}}$, and the sine of the angle θ between the direction of $\vec{\mathbf{v}}$ and the direction of $\vec{\mathbf{B}}$. These observations can be summarized by writing the magnitude of the magnetic force as

$$F = qvB \sin \theta \qquad [19.1]$$

This expression is used to define the magnitude of the magnetic field as

$$B \equiv \frac{F}{qv \sin \theta} \qquad [19.2]$$

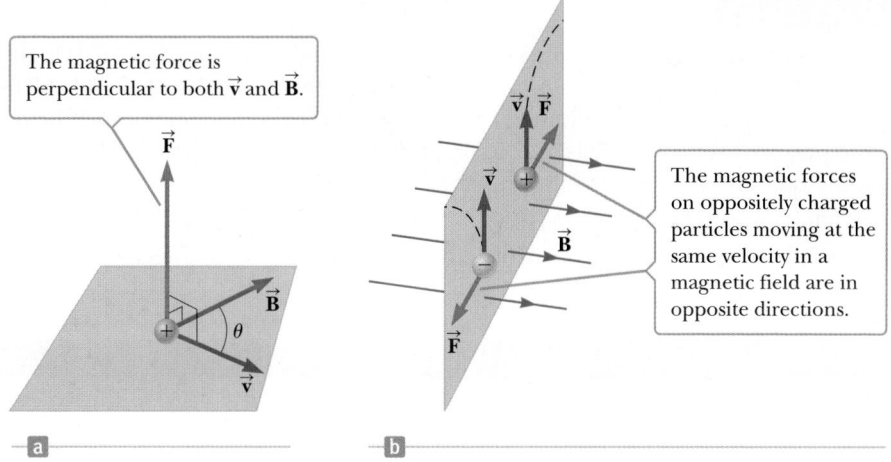

The magnetic force is perpendicular to both $\vec{v}$ and $\vec{B}$.

The magnetic forces on oppositely charged particles moving at the same velocity in a magnetic field are in opposite directions.

Figure 19.6 (a) The direction of the magnetic force $\vec{F}$ acting on a charged particle moving with a velocity $\vec{v}$ in the presence of a magnetic field $\vec{B}$. (b) Magnetic forces on positive and negative charges. The dashed lines show the paths of the particles, which are investigated in Section 19.6.

If F is in newtons, q in coulombs, and v in meters per second, the SI unit of magnetic field is the **tesla** (T), also called the **weber** (Wb) **per square meter** (1 T = 1 Wb/m^2). If a 1-C charge moves in a direction perpendicular to a magnetic field of magnitude 1 T with a speed of 1 m/s, the magnetic force exerted on the charge is 1 N. We can express the units of $\vec{B}$ as

$$[B] = T = \frac{Wb}{m^2} = \frac{N}{C \cdot m/s} = \frac{N}{A \cdot m} \qquad [19.3]$$

In practice, the cgs unit for magnetic field, the **gauss** (G), is often used. The gauss is related to the tesla through the conversion

$$1 \ T = 10^4 \ G$$

Conventional laboratory magnets can produce magnetic fields as large as about 25 000 G, or 2.5 T. Superconducting magnets that can generate magnetic fields as great as 3×10^5 G, or 30 T, have been constructed. These values can be compared with the small value of Earth's magnetic field near its surface, which is only about 0.5 G, or 0.5×10^{-4} T.

From Equation 19.1 we see that the force on a charged particle moving in a magnetic field has its maximum value when the particle's motion is *perpendicular* to the magnetic field, corresponding to $\theta = 90°$, so that $\sin \theta = 1$. The magnitude of this maximum force has the value

$$F_{max} = qvB \qquad [19.4]$$

Also from Equation 19.1, F is zero when $\vec{v}$ is parallel to $\vec{B}$ (corresponding to $\theta = 0°$ or $180°$), so no magnetic force is exerted on a charged particle when it moves in the direction of the magnetic field or opposite the field.

Experiments show that the direction of the magnetic force is always perpendicular to both $\vec{v}$ and $\vec{B}$, as shown in Figure 19.6 for a positively charged particle. To determine the direction of the force, we employ **right-hand rule number 1**:

1. Point the fingers of your right hand in the direction of the velocity $\vec{v}$.
2. Curl the fingers in the direction of the magnetic field $\vec{B}$, moving through the smallest angle (as in Fig. 19.7).
3. Your thumb is now pointing in the direction of the magnetic force $\vec{F}$ exerted on a positive charge.

If the charge is negative rather than positive, the force $\vec{F}$ is directed *opposite* that shown in Figures 19.6a and 19.7. So if q is negative, simply use the right-hand rule to find the direction for positive q and then reverse that direction for the negative charge. Figure 19.6b illustrates the effect of a magnetic field on charged particles with opposite signs.

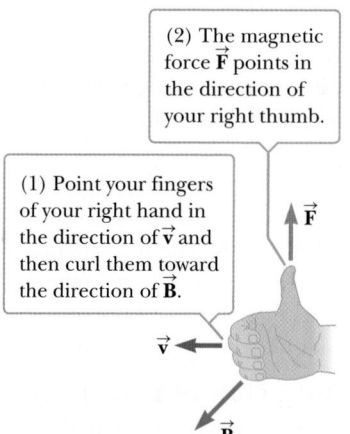

(2) The magnetic force $\vec{F}$ points in the direction of your right thumb.

(1) Point your fingers of your right hand in the direction of $\vec{v}$ and then curl them toward the direction of $\vec{B}$.

Figure 19.7 Right-hand rule number 1 for determining the direction of the magnetic force on a positive charge moving with a velocity $\vec{v}$ in a magnetic field $\vec{B}$.

19.1 A charged particle moves in a straight line through a region of space. Which of the following answers *must* be true? (Assume any other fields are negligible.) The magnetic field (a) has a magnitude of zero (b) has a zero component perpendicular to the particle's velocity (c) has a zero component parallel to the particle's velocity in that region.

19.2 The north-pole end of a bar magnet is held near a stationary positively charged piece of plastic. Is the plastic (a) attracted, (b) repelled, or (c) unaffected by the magnet?

■ EXAMPLE 19.1   A Proton Traveling in Earth's Magnetic Field

GOAL Calculate the magnitude and direction of a magnetic force.

PROBLEM A proton moves with a speed of 1.00×10^5 m/s through Earth's magnetic field, which has a value of 55.0 μT at a particular location. When the proton moves eastward, the magnetic force acting on it is directed straight upward, and when it moves northward, no magnetic force acts on it. **(a)** What is the direction of the magnetic field, and **(b)** what is the strength of the magnetic force when the proton moves eastward? **(c)** Calculate the gravitational force on the proton and compare it with the magnetic force. Compare it also with the electric force if

there were an electric field with a magnitude equal to $E = 1.50 \times 10^2$ N/C at that location, a common value at Earth's surface. Note that the mass of the proton is 1.67×10^{-27} kg.

STRATEGY The direction of the magnetic field can be found from an application of the right-hand rule, together with the fact that no force is exerted on the proton when it's traveling north. Substituting into Equation 19.1 yields the magnitude of the magnetic field.

SOLUTION

(a) Find the direction of the magnetic field.

No magnetic force acts on the proton when it's going north, so the angle such a proton makes with the magnetic field direction must be either 0° or 180°. Therefore, the magnetic field $\vec{B}$ must point either north or south. Now apply the right-hand rule. When the particle travels east,

the magnetic force is directed upward. Point your thumb in the direction of the force and your fingers in the direction of the velocity eastward. When you curl your fingers, they point north, which must therefore be the direction of the magnetic field.

(b) Find the magnitude of the magnetic force.

Substitute the given values and the charge of a proton into Equation 19.1. From part (a), the angle between the velocity $\vec{v}$ of the proton and the magnetic field $\vec{B}$ is 90.0°.

$$F = qvB \sin \theta$$
$$= (1.60 \times 10^{-19} \text{ C})(1.00 \times 10^5 \text{ m/s}) \times (55.0 \times 10^{-6} \text{ T}) \sin (90.0°)$$
$$= \boxed{8.80 \times 10^{-19} \text{ N}}$$

(c) Calculate the gravitational force on the proton and compare it with the magnetic force and also with the electric force if $E = 1.50 \times 10^2$ N/C.

$$F_{grav} = mg = (1.67 \times 10^{-27} \text{ kg})(9.80 \text{ m/s}^2)$$
$$= \boxed{1.64 \times 10^{-26} \text{ N}}$$
$$F_{elec} = qE = (1.60 \times 10^{-19} \text{ C})(1.50 \times 10^2 \text{ N/C})$$
$$= \boxed{2.40 \times 10^{-17} \text{ N}}$$

REMARKS The information regarding a proton moving north was necessary to fix the direction of the magnetic field. Otherwise, an upward magnetic force on an eastward-moving proton could be caused by a magnetic field pointing anywhere northeast or northwest. Notice in part (c) the relative strengths of the forces, with the electric force larger than the magnetic force and both much larger than the gravitational force, all for typical field values found in nature.

QUESTION 19.1 An electron and proton moving with the same velocity enter a uniform magnetic field. In what two ways does the magnetic field affect the electron differently from the proton?

EXERCISE 19.1 Suppose an electron is moving due west in the same magnetic field as in Example 19.1 at a speed of 2.50×10^5 m/s. Find the magnitude and direction of the magnetic force on the electron.

ANSWER 2.20×10^{-18} N, straight up. (Don't forget, the electron is negatively charged!)

■ EXAMPLE 19.2 | A Proton Moving in a Magnetic Field

GOAL Calculate the magnetic force and acceleration when a particle moves at an angle other than 90° to the field.

PROBLEM A proton moves at 8.00×10^6 m/s along the x-axis. It enters a region in which there is a magnetic field of magnitude 2.50 T, directed at an angle of 60.0° with the x-axis and lying in the xy-plane (Fig. 19.8). **(a)** Find the initial magnitude and direction of the magnetic force on the proton. **(b)** Calculate the proton's initial acceleration.

STRATEGY Finding the magnitude and direction of the magnetic force requires substituting values into the equation for magnetic force, Equation 19.1, and using the right-hand rule. Applying Newton's second law solves part (b).

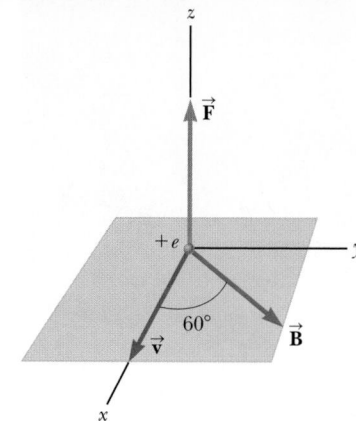

Figure 19.8 (Example 19.2) The magnetic force $\vec{\mathbf{F}}$ on a proton is in the positive z-direction when $\vec{\mathbf{v}}$ and $\vec{\mathbf{B}}$ lie in the xy-plane.

SOLUTION

(a) Find the magnitude and direction of the magnetic force on the proton.

Substitute $v = 8.00 \times 10^6$ m/s, the magnetic field strength $B = 2.50$ T, the angle, and the charge of a proton into Equation 19.1:

$$F = qvB \sin \theta$$
$$= (1.60 \times 10^{-19} \text{ C})(8.00 \times 10^6 \text{ m/s})(2.50 \text{ T})(\sin 60°)$$
$$F = \boxed{2.77 \times 10^{-12} \text{ N}}$$

Apply right-hand rule number 1 to find the initial direction of the magnetic force:

Point the fingers of the right hand in the x-direction (the direction of $\vec{\mathbf{v}}$) and then curl them toward $\vec{\mathbf{B}}$. The thumb points $\boxed{\text{upward, in the positive } z\text{-direction.}}$

(b) Calculate the proton's initial acceleration.

Substitute the force and the mass of a proton into Newton's second law:

$$ma = F \quad \rightarrow \quad (1.67 \times 10^{-27} \text{ kg})a = 2.77 \times 10^{-12} \text{ N}$$
$$a = \boxed{1.66 \times 10^{15} \text{ m/s}^2}$$

REMARKS The initial acceleration is also in the positive z-direction. Because the direction of $\vec{\mathbf{v}}$ changes, however, the subsequent direction of the magnetic force also changes. In applying right-hand rule number 1 to find the direction, it was important to take into consideration the charge. A negatively charged particle accelerates in the opposite direction.

QUESTION 19.2 Can a constant magnetic field change the speed of a charged particle? Explain.

EXERCISE 19.2 Calculate the acceleration of an electron that moves through the same magnetic field as in Example 19.2, at the same velocity as the proton. The mass of an electron is 9.11×10^{-31} kg.

ANSWER 3.04×10^{18} m/s² in the negative z-direction

19.4 Magnetic Force on a Current-Carrying Conductor

If a magnetic field exerts a force on a single charged particle when it moves through a magnetic field, it should be no surprise that magnetic forces are exerted on a current-carrying wire as well (see Fig. 19.9 on page 656). Because the current is a collection of many charged particles in motion, the resultant force on the wire is due to the sum of the individual forces on the charged particles. The force on

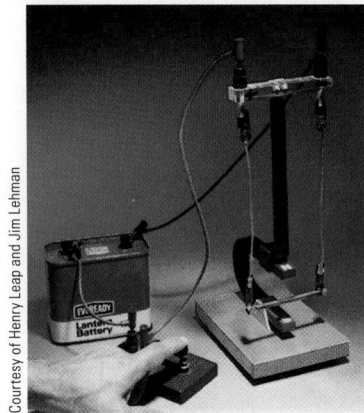

Figure 19.9 This apparatus demonstrates the force on a current-carrying conductor in an external magnetic field. Why does the bar swing *away* from the magnet after the switch is closed?

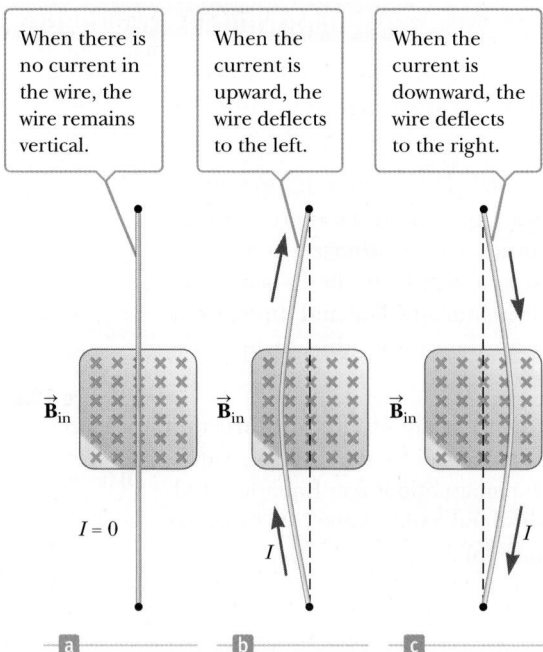

When there is no current in the wire, the wire remains vertical.

When the current is upward, the wire deflects to the left.

When the current is downward, the wire deflects to the right.

$\vec{\mathbf{B}}_{\text{in}}$ $\vec{\mathbf{B}}_{\text{in}}$ $\vec{\mathbf{B}}_{\text{in}}$

$I = 0$ I I

a   b   c

Figure 19.10 A segment of a flexible vertical wire partially stretched between the poles of a magnet, with the field (green crosses) directed into the page.

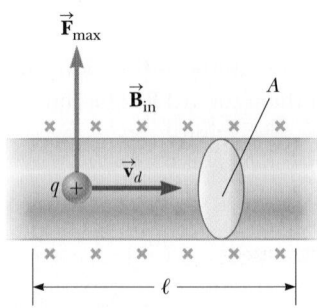

$\vec{\mathbf{F}}_{\text{max}}$ $\vec{\mathbf{B}}_{\text{in}}$ A $q\, +$ $\vec{\mathbf{v}}_d$ ℓ

Figure 19.11 A section of a wire containing moving charges in an external magnetic field $\vec{\mathbf{B}}$.

the particles is transmitted to the "bulk" of the wire through collisions with the atoms making up the wire.

Some explanation is in order concerning notation in many of the figures. To indicate the direction of $\vec{\mathbf{B}}$, we use the following conventions:

> If $\vec{\mathbf{B}}$ is directed into the page, as in Figure 19.10, we use a series of green crosses, representing the tails of arrows. If $\vec{\mathbf{B}}$ is directed out of the page, we use a series of green dots, representing the tips of arrows. If $\vec{\mathbf{B}}$ lies in the plane of the page, we use a series of green field lines with arrowheads.

The force on a current-carrying conductor can be demonstrated by hanging a wire between the poles of a magnet, as in Figure 19.10. In this figure, the magnetic field is directed into the page and covers the region within the shaded area. The wire deflects to the right or left when it carries a current.

We can quantify this discussion by considering a straight segment of wire of length ℓ and cross-sectional area A carrying current I in a uniform external magnetic field $\vec{\mathbf{B}}$, as in Figure 19.11. We assume that the magnetic field is perpendicular to the wire and is directed into the page. A force of magnitude $F_{\text{max}} = qv_dB$ is exerted on each charge carrier in the wire, where v_d is the drift velocity of the charge. To find the total force on the wire, we multiply the force on one charge carrier by the number of carriers in the segment. Because the volume of the segment is $A\ell$, the number of carriers is $nA\ell$, where n is the number of carriers per unit volume. Hence, the magnitude of the total magnetic force on the wire of length ℓ is as follows:

Total force = force on each charge carrier × total number of carriers

$$F_{\text{max}} = (qv_dB)(nA\ell)$$

From Chapter 17, however, we know that the current in the wire is given by the expression $I = nqv_dA$, so

$$F_{\text{max}} = BI\ell \qquad [19.5]$$

This equation can be used only when the current and the magnetic field are at right angles to each other.

Figure 19.12 A wire carrying a current I in the presence of an external magnetic field $\vec{\mathbf{B}}$ that makes an angle θ with the wire. The magnetic force vector comes out of the page.

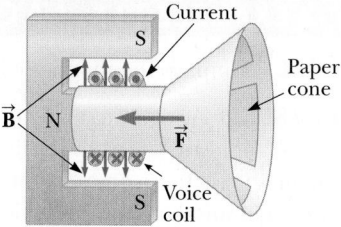

Figure 19.13 A diagram of a loudspeaker.

If the wire is not perpendicular to the field but is at some arbitrary angle, as in Figure 19.12, the magnitude of the magnetic force on the wire is

$$F = BI\ell \sin \theta \qquad \text{[19.6]}$$

where θ is the angle between $\vec{\mathbf{B}}$ and the direction of the current. The direction of this force can be obtained by the use of right-hand rule number 1. In this case, however, you must place your fingers in the direction of the positive current I, rather than in the direction of $\vec{\mathbf{v}}$, before curling them in the direction of $\vec{\mathbf{B}}$. The thumb then points in the direction of the force, as before. The current, naturally, is made up of charges moving at some velocity, so this really isn't a separate rule. In Figure 19.12 the direction of the magnetic force on the wire is out of the page.

Finally, when the current is either in the direction of the field or opposite the direction of the field, the magnetic force on the wire is zero.

A magnetic force acting on a current-carrying wire in a magnetic field is the operating principle of most speakers in sound systems. One speaker design, shown in Figure 19.13, consists of a coil of wire called the voice coil, a flexible paper cone that acts as the speaker, and a permanent magnet. The coil of wire surrounding the north pole of the magnet is shaped so that the magnetic field lines are directed radially outward from the coil's axis. When an electrical signal is sent to the coil, producing a current in the coil as in Figure 19.13, a magnetic force to the left acts on the coil. (This can be seen by applying right-hand rule number 1 to each turn of wire.) When the current reverses direction, as it would for a current that varied sinusoidally, the magnetic force on the coil also reverses direction, and the cone, which is attached to the coil, accelerates to the right. An alternating current through the coil causes an alternating force on the coil, which results in vibrations of the cone. The vibrating cone creates sound waves as it pushes and pulls on the air in front of it. In this way, a 1-kHz electrical signal is converted to a 1-kHz sound wave.

An application of the force on a current-carrying conductor is illustrated by the electromagnetic pump shown in Figure 19.14. Artificial hearts require a pump to keep the blood flowing, and kidney dialysis machines also require a pump to assist the heart in pumping blood that is to be cleansed. Ordinary mechanical pumps create problems because they damage the blood cells as they move through the pump. The mechanism shown in the figure has demonstrated some promise in such applications. A magnetic field is established across a segment of the tube containing the blood, flowing in the direction of the velocity $\vec{\mathbf{v}}$. An electric current passing through the fluid in the direction shown has a magnetic force acting on it in the direction of $\vec{\mathbf{v}}$, as applying the right-hand rule shows. This force helps to keep the blood in motion.

APPLICATION
Loudspeaker Operation

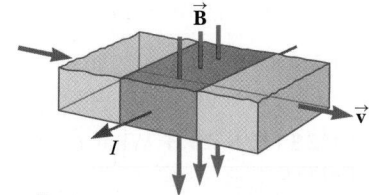

Figure 19.14 A simple electromagnetic pump has no moving parts that might damage a conducting fluid, such as blood passing through it. Application of right-hand rule number 1 (right fingers in the direction of the current I, curl them in the direction of $\vec{\mathbf{B}}$, thumb points in the direction of the force) shows that the force on the current-carrying segment of the fluid is in the direction of the velocity.

BIO APPLICATION
Electromagnetic Pumps for Artificial Hearts and Kidneys

■ APPLYING PHYSICS 19.2 | Lightning Strikes

In a lightning strike there is a rapid movement of negative charge from a cloud to the ground. In what direction is a lightning strike deflected by Earth's magnetic field?

EXPLANATION The downward flow of negative charge in a lightning stroke is equivalent to a current moving upward. Consequently, we have an upward-moving current in a northward-directed magnetic field. According to right-hand rule number 1, the lightning strike would be deflected toward the west. ■

■EXAMPLE 19.3   A Current-Carrying Wire in Earth's Magnetic Field

GOAL Compare the magnetic force on a current-carrying wire with the gravitational force exerted on the wire.

PROBLEM A wire carries a current of 22.0 A from west to east. Assume the magnetic field of Earth at this location is horizontal and directed from south to north and it has a magnitude of 0.500×10^{-4} T. **(a)** Find the magnitude and direction of the magnetic force on a 36.0-m length of wire. **(b)** Calculate the gravitational force on the same length of wire if it's made of copper and has a cross-sectional area of 2.50×10^{-6} m^2.

SOLUTION

(a) Calculate the magnetic force on the wire.

Substitute into Equation 19.6, using the fact that the magnetic field and the current are at right angles to each other:

$F = BI\ell \sin \theta = (0.500 \times 10^{-4} \text{ T})(22.0 \text{ A})(36.0 \text{ m}) \sin 90.0°$

$= \boxed{3.96 \times 10^{-2} \text{ N}}$

Apply right-hand rule number 1 to find the direction of the magnetic force:

With the fingers of your right hand pointing west to east in the direction of the current, curl them north in the direction of the magnetic field. Your thumb points upward.

(b) Calculate the gravitational force on the wire segment.

First, obtain the mass of the wire from the density of copper, the length, and cross-sectional area of the wire:

$m = \rho V = \rho(A\ell)$

$= (8.92 \times 10^3 \text{ kg/m}^3)(2.50 \times 10^{-6} \text{ m}^2 \cdot 36.0 \text{ m})$

$= 0.803 \text{ kg}$

To get the gravitational force, multiply the mass by the acceleration of gravity:

$F_{grav} = mg = \boxed{7.87 \text{ N}}$

REMARKS This calculation demonstrates that under normal circumstances, the gravitational force on a current-carrying conductor is much greater than the magnetic force due to Earth's magnetic field.

QUESTION 19.3 What magnetic force is exerted on a wire carrying current parallel to the direction of the magnetic field?

EXERCISE 19.3 What current would make the magnetic force in the example equal in magnitude to the gravitational force?

ANSWER 4.37×10^3 A, a large current that would very rapidly heat and melt the wire.

19.5 Torque on a Current Loop and Electric Motors

In the preceding section we showed how a magnetic force is exerted on a current-carrying conductor when the conductor is placed in an external magnetic field. With this starting point, we now show that a torque is exerted on a current loop placed in a magnetic field. The results of this analysis will be of great practical value when we discuss generators and motors in Chapter 20.

Consider a rectangular loop carrying current I in the presence of an external uniform magnetic field in the plane of the loop, as shown in Figure 19.15a. The forces on the sides of length a are zero because these wires are parallel to the field. The magnitudes of the magnetic forces on the sides of length b, however, are

$$F_1 = F_2 = BIb$$

The direction of $\vec{F}_1$, the force on the left side of the loop, is out of the page and that of $\vec{F}_2$, the force on the right side of the loop, is into the page. If we view the loop from the side, as in Figure 19.15b, the forces are directed as shown. If we

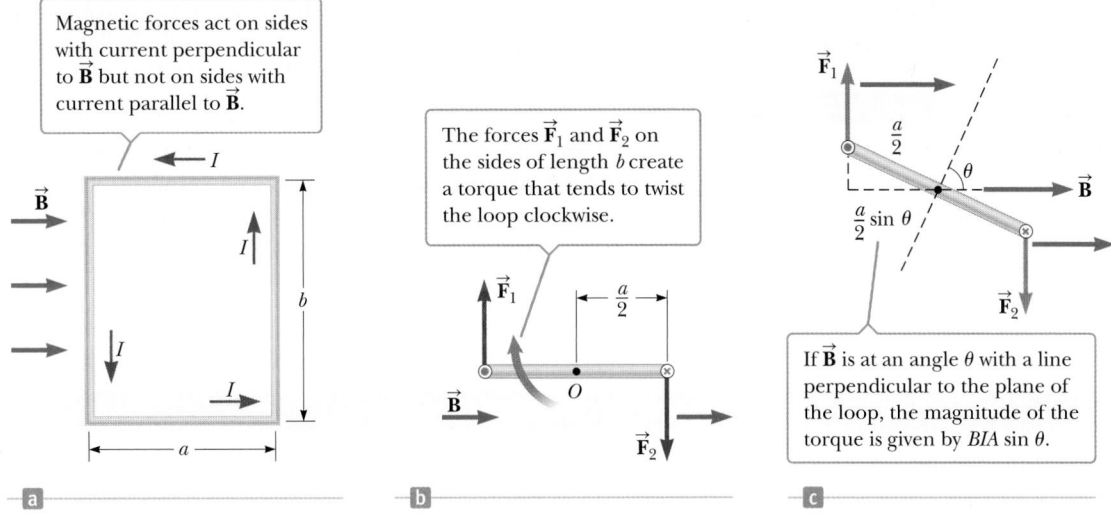

Figure 19.15 (a) Top view of a rectangular loop in a uniform magnetic field. (b) An edge view of the rectangular loop in part (a). (c) An edge view of the loop in part (a) with the normal to the loop at the angle θ with respect to the magnetic field.

assume the loop is pivoted so that it can rotate about point O, we see that these two forces produce a torque about O that rotates the loop clockwise. The magnitude of this torque, τ_{max}, is

$$\tau_{max} = F_1 \frac{a}{2} + F_2 \frac{a}{2} = (BIb)\frac{a}{2} + (BIb)\frac{a}{2} = BIab$$

where the moment arm about O is $a/2$ for both forces. Because the area of the loop is $A = ab$, the maximum torque can be expressed as

$$\tau_{max} = BIA \qquad\qquad \textbf{[19.7]}$$

This result is valid only when the magnetic field is *parallel* to the plane of the loop, as in Figure 19.15b. If the field makes an angle θ with a line perpendicular to the plane of the loop, as in Figure 19.15c, the moment arm for each force is given by $(a/2) \sin \theta$. An analysis similar to the previous one gives, for the magnitude of the torque,

$$\tau = BIA \sin \theta \qquad\qquad \textbf{[19.8]}$$

This result shows that the torque has the *maximum* value BIA when the field is parallel to the plane of the loop ($\theta = 90°$) and is *zero* when the field is perpendicular to the plane of the loop ($\theta = 0$). As seen in Figure 19.15c, the loop tends to rotate to smaller values of θ (so that the normal to the plane of the loop rotates toward the direction of the magnetic field).

Although the foregoing analysis was for a rectangular loop, a more general derivation shows that Equation 19.8 applies regardless of the shape of the loop. Further, the torque on a coil with N turns is

$$\tau = BIAN \sin \theta \qquad\qquad \textbf{[19.9a]}$$

The quantity $\mu = IAN$ is defined as the magnitude of a vector $\vec{\mu}$ called the *magnetic moment* of the coil. The vector $\vec{\mu}$ always points perpendicular to the plane of the loop(s) and is such that if the thumb of the right hand points in the direction of $\vec{\mu}$, the fingers of the right hand point in the direction of the current. The angle θ in Equations 19.8 and 19.9 lies between the directions of the magnetic moment $\vec{\mu}$ and the magnetic field $\vec{B}$. The magnetic torque can then be written

$$\tau = \mu B \sin \theta \qquad\qquad \textbf{[19.9b]}$$

Note that the torque $\vec{\tau}$ is always perpendicular to both the magnetic moment $\vec{\mu}$ and the magnetic field $\vec{B}$.

■ Quick Quiz

19.3 A square and a circular loop with the same area lie in the xy-plane, where there is a uniform magnetic field $\vec{B}$ pointing at some angle θ with respect to the positive z-direction. Each loop carries the same current, in the same direction. Which magnetic torque is larger? (a) the torque on the square loop (b) the torque on the circular loop (c) the torques are the same (d) more information is needed

■ EXAMPLE 19.4 | The Torque on a Circular Loop in a Magetic Field

GOAL Calculate a magnetic torque on a loop of current.

PROBLEM A circular wire loop of radius 1.00 m is placed in a magnetic field of magnitude 0.500 T. The normal to the plane of the loop makes an angle of 30.0° with the magnetic field (Fig. 19.16a). The current in the loop is 2.00 A in the direction shown. **(a)** Find the magnetic moment of the loop and the magnitude of the torque at this instant. **(b)** The same current is carried by the rectangular 2.00-m by 3.00-m coil with three loops shown in Figure 19.16b. Find the magnetic moment of the coil and the magnitude of the torque acting on the coil at that instant.

STRATEGY For each part, we just have to calculate the area, use it in the calculation of the magnetic moment, and multiply the result by $B \sin \theta$. Altogether, this process amounts to substituting values into Equation 19.9b.

Figure 19.16 (Example 19.4) (a) A circular current loop lying in the xy-plane in an external magnetic field $\vec{B}$. (b) A rectangular coil lying in the xy-plane in the same field. (c) (Exercise 19.4)

....

SOLUTION

(a) Find the magnetic moment of the circular loop and the magnetic torque exerted on it.

First, calculate the enclosed area of the circular loop:

$$A = \pi r^2 = \pi (1.00 \text{ m})^2 = 3.14 \text{ m}^2$$

Calculate the magnetic moment of the loop:

$$\mu = IAN = (2.00 \text{ A})(3.14 \text{ m}^2)(1) = \boxed{6.28 \text{ A} \cdot \text{m}^2}$$

Now substitute values for the magnetic moment, magnetic field, and θ into Equation 19.9b:

$$\tau = \mu B \sin \theta = (6.28 \text{ A} \cdot \text{m}^2)(0.500 \text{ T})(\sin 30.0°)$$
$$= \boxed{1.57 \text{ N} \cdot \text{m}}$$

(b) Find the magnetic moment of the rectangular coil and the magnetic torque exerted on it.

Calculate the area of the coil:

$$A = L \times H = (2.00 \text{ m})(3.00 \text{ m}) = 6.00 \text{ m}^2$$

Calculate the magnetic moment of the coil:

$$\mu = IAN = (2.00 \text{ A})(6.00 \text{ m}^2)(3) = \boxed{36.0 \text{ A} \cdot \text{m}^2}$$

Substitute values into Equation 19.9b:

$$\tau = \mu B \sin \theta = (0.500 \text{ T})(36.0 \text{ A} \cdot \text{m}^2)(\sin 30.0°)$$
$$= \boxed{9.00 \text{ N} \cdot \text{m}}$$

REMARKS In calculating a magnetic torque, it's not strictly necessary to calculate the magnetic moment. Instead, Equation 19.9a can be used directly.

QUESTION 19.4 What happens to the magnitude of the torque if the angle increases toward 90°? Goes beyond 90°?

EXERCISE 19.4 Suppose a right triangular coil with base of 2.00 m and height 3.00 m having two loops carries a current of 2.00 A as shown in Figure 19.16c. Find the magnetic moment and the torque on the coil. The magnetic field is again 0.500 T and makes an angle of 30.0° with respect to the normal direction.

ANSWERS $\mu = 12.0\,\text{A} \cdot \text{m}^2$, $\tau = 3.00\,\text{N} \cdot \text{m}$

Electric Motors

It's hard to imagine life in the 21st century without electric motors. Some appliances that contain motors include computer disk drives, CD players, DVD players, food processors and blenders, car starters, furnaces, and air conditioners. The motors convert electrical energy to kinetic energy of rotation and consist of a rigid current-carrying loop that rotates when placed in the field of a magnet.

As we have just seen (Fig. 19.15), the torque on such a loop rotates the loop to smaller values of θ until the torque becomes zero, when the magnetic field is perpendicular to the plane of the loop and $\theta = 0$. If the loop turns past this angle and the current remains in the direction shown in the figure, the torque reverses direction and turns the loop in the opposite direction, that is, counterclockwise. To overcome this difficulty and provide continuous rotation in one direction, the current in the loop must periodically reverse direction. In alternating-current (AC) motors, such a reversal occurs naturally 120 times each second. In direct-current (DC) motors, the reversal is accomplished mechanically with split-ring contacts (commutators) and brushes, as shown in Active Figure 19.17.

Although actual motors contain many current loops and commutators, for simplicity Active Figure 19.17 shows only a single loop and a single set of split-ring contacts rigidly attached to and rotating with the loop. Electrical stationary contacts called *brushes* are maintained in electrical contact with the rotating split ring. These brushes are usually made of graphite because it is a good electrical conductor as well as a good lubricant. Just as the loop becomes perpendicular to the magnetic field and the torque becomes zero, inertia carries the loop forward in the clockwise direction and the brushes cross the gaps in the ring, causing the loop current to reverse its direction. This reversal provides another pulse of torque in the clockwise direction for another 180°, the current reverses, and the process repeats itself. Figure 19.18 shows a modern motor used to power a hybrid gas–electric car.

APPLICATION
Electric Motors

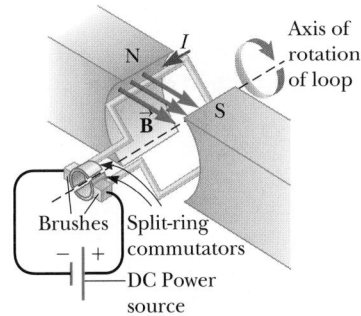

Active Figure 19.17
Simplified sketch of a DC electric motor.

19.6 Motion of a Charged Particle in a Magnetic Field

Consider the case of a positively charged particle moving in a uniform magnetic field so that the direction of the particle's velocity is *perpendicular to the field*, as in Active Figure 19.19 (page 662). The label $\vec{\mathbf{B}}_{\text{in}}$ and the crosses indicate that $\vec{\mathbf{B}}$ is directed into the page. Application of the right-hand rule to the particle at the bottom of the circle shows that the direction of the magnetic force $\vec{\mathbf{F}}$ at that location is upward. The force causes the particle to alter its direction of travel and to follow a curved path. Application of the right-hand rule to the particle at other points on the circle shows that **the magnetic force is always directed toward the center of the circular path**; therefore, the magnetic force causes a centripetal acceleration, which changes only the direction of $\vec{\mathbf{v}}$ and not its magnitude. Because $\vec{\mathbf{F}}$ produces the centripetal acceleration, we can equate its magnitude, qvB in this case, to the

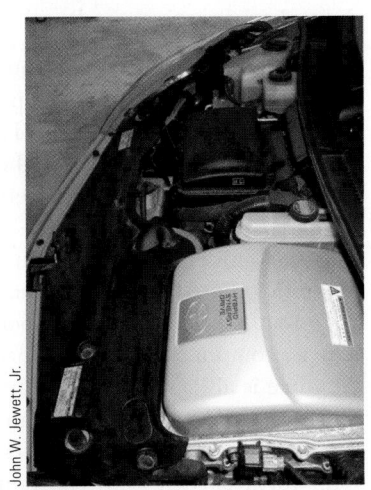

Figure 19.18 The engine compartment of the Toyota Prius, a hybrid vehicle.

John W. Jewett, Jr.

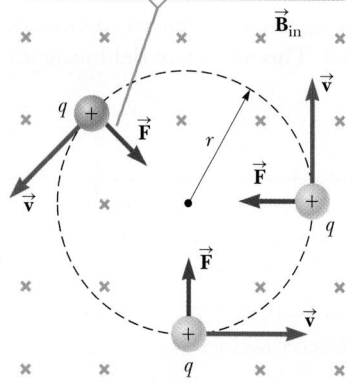

The magnetic force $\vec{\mathbf{F}}$ acting on the charge is always directed toward the center of the circle.

Active Figure 19.19
When the velocity of a charged particle is perpendicular to a uniform magnetic field, the particle moves in a circle in a plane perpendicular to $\vec{\mathbf{B}}$, which is directed into the page. (The crosses represent the tails of the magnetic field vectors.)

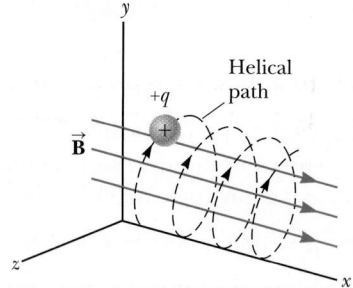

Active Figure 19.20
A charged particle having a velocity directed at an angle with a uniform magnetic field moves in a helical path.

mass of the particle multiplied by the centripetal acceleration v^2/r. From Newton's second law, we find that

$$F = qvB = \frac{mv^2}{r}$$

which gives

$$r = \frac{mv}{qB} \qquad [19.10]$$

This equation says that the radius of the path is proportional to the momentum mv of the particle and is inversely proportional to the charge and the magnetic field. Equation 19.10 is often called the *cyclotron equation* because it's used in the design of these instruments (popularly known as atom smashers).

If the initial direction of the velocity of the charged particle is not perpendicular to the magnetic field, as shown in Active Figure 19.20, the path followed by the particle is a spiral (called a helix) along the magnetic field lines.

■ APPLYING PHYSICS 19.3 | Trapping Charges

Storing charged particles is important for a variety of applications. Suppose a uniform magnetic field exists in a finite region of space. Can a charged particle be injected into this region from the outside and remain trapped in the region by magnetic force alone?

EXPLANATION It's best to consider separately the components of the particle velocity parallel and perpendicular to the field lines in the region. There is no magnetic force on the particle associated with the velocity component parallel to the field lines, so that velocity component remains unchanged.

Now consider the component of velocity perpendicular to the field lines. This component will result in a magnetic force that is perpendicular to both the field lines and the velocity component itself. The path of a particle for which the force is always perpendicular to the velocity is a circle. The particle therefore follows a circular arc and exits the field on the other side of the circle, as shown in Figure 19.21 for a particle with constant kinetic energy. On the other hand, a particle can become trapped if it loses some kinetic energy in a collision after entering the field, so that it turns in a smaller circle and stays within the field.

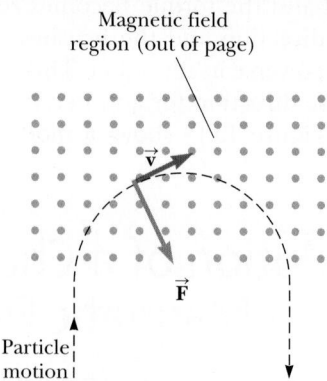

Figure 19.21 (Applying Physics 19.3)

Particles *can* be injected and contained if, in addition to the magnetic field, electrostatic fields are involved. These fields are used in the *Penning trap*. With these devices, it's possible to store charged particles for extended periods. Such traps are useful, for example, in the storage of antimatter, which disintegrates completely on contact with ordinary matter. ■

■ *Quick Quiz*

19.4 As a charged particle moves freely in a circular path in the presence of a constant magnetic field applied perpendicular to the particle's velocity, the particle's kinetic energy (a) remains constant, (b) increases, or (c) decreases.

■ EXAMPLE 19.5 | The Mass Spectrometer: Identifying Particles

GOAL Use the cyclotron equation to identify a particle.

PROBLEM A charged particle enters the magnetic field of a mass spectrometer at a speed of 1.79×10^6 m/s. It subsequently moves in a circular orbit with a radius of 16.0 cm in a uniform magnetic field of magnitude 0.350 T having a direction perpendicular to the particle's velocity. Find the particle's mass-to-charge ratio and identify it based on the table below.

STRATEGY After finding the mass-to-charge ratio with Equation 19.10, compare it with the values in the table, identifying the particle.

. . . .

SOLUTION

Write the cyclotron equation:

$$r = \frac{mv}{qB}$$

Solve this equation for the mass divided by the charge, m/q, and substitute values:

$$\frac{m}{q} = \frac{rB}{v} = \frac{(0.160 \text{ m})(0.350 \text{ T})}{1.79 \times 10^6 \text{ m/s}} = 3.13 \times 10^{-8} \frac{\text{kg}}{\text{C}}$$

Identify the particle from the table. All particles are completely ionized, bare nuclei.

Nucleus	m (kg)	q (C)	m/q (kg/C)
Hydrogen	1.67×10^{-27}	1.60×10^{-19}	1.04×10^{-8}
Deuterium	3.35×10^{-27}	1.60×10^{-19}	2.09×10^{-8}
Tritium	5.01×10^{-27}	1.60×10^{-19}	3.13×10^{-8}
Helium-3	5.01×10^{-27}	3.20×10^{-19}	1.57×10^{-8}

The particle is a tritium nucleus.

. . . .

REMARKS The mass spectrometer is an important tool in both chemistry and physics. Unknown chemicals can be heated and ionized, and the resulting particles passed through the mass spectrometer and subsequently identified.

QUESTION 19.5 What happens to the momentum of a charged particle in a uniform magnetic field?

EXERCISE 19.5 Suppose a second charged particle enters the mass spectrometer at the same speed as the particle in Example 19.5. If it travels in a circle with radius 10.7 cm, find the mass-to-charge ratio and identify the particle from the table above.

ANSWERS 2.09×10^{-8} kg/C; deuterium nucleus

■ EXAMPLE 19.6 | The Mass Spectrometer: Separating Isotopes

GOAL Apply the cyclotron equation to the process of separating isotopes.

PROBLEM Two singly ionized atoms move out of a slit at point S in Figure 19.22 and into a magnetic field of magnitude 0.100 T pointing into the page. Each has a speed of 1.00×10^6 m/s. The nucleus of the first atom contains one proton and has a mass of 1.67×10^{-27} kg, whereas the nucleus of the second atom contains a proton and a neutron and has a mass of 3.34×10^{-27} kg. Atoms with the same number of protons in the nucleus but different masses are called isotopes. The two isotopes here are hydrogen and deuterium. Find their distance of separation when they strike a photographic plate at P.

APPLICATION
Mass Spectrometers

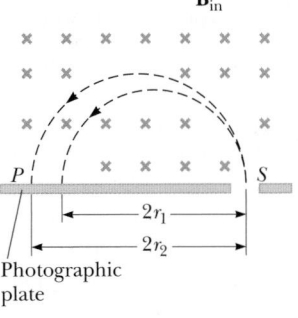

Figure 19.22 (Example 19.6) Two isotopes leave the slit at point S and travel in different circular paths before striking a photographic plate at P.

(Continued)

STRATEGY Apply the cyclotron equation to each atom, finding the radius of the path of each. Double the radii to find the path diameters and then find their difference.

SOLUTION

Use Equation 19.10 to find the radius of the circular path followed by the lighter isotope, hydrogen:

$$r_1 = \frac{m_1 v}{qB} = \frac{(1.67 \times 10^{-27} \text{ kg})(1.00 \times 10^6 \text{ m/s})}{(1.60 \times 10^{-19} \text{ C})(0.100 \text{ T})}$$

$$= 0.104 \text{ m}$$

Use the same equation to calculate the radius of the path of deuterium, the heavier isotope:

$$r_2 = \frac{m_2 v}{qB} = \frac{(3.34 \times 10^{-27} \text{ kg})(1.00 \times 10^6 \text{ m/s})}{(1.60 \times 10^{-19} \text{ C})(0.100 \text{ T})}$$

$$= 0.209 \text{ m}$$

Multiply the radii by 2 to find the diameters and take the difference, getting the separation x between the isotopes:

$$x = 2r_2 - 2r_1 = \boxed{0.210 \text{ m}}$$

REMARKS During World War II, mass spectrometers were used to separate the radioactive uranium isotope U-235 from its far more common isotope, U-238.

QUESTION 19.6 Estimate the radius of the circle traced out by a singly ionized lead atom moving at the same speed.

EXERCISE 19.6 Use the same mass spectrometer as in Example 19.6 to find the separation between two isotopes of helium: normal helium-4, which has a nucleus consisting of two protons and two neutrons, and helium-3, which has two protons and a single neutron. Assume both nuclei, doubly ionized (having a charge of $2e = 3.20 \times 10^{-19}$ C), enter the field at 1.00×10^6 m/s. The helium-4 nucleus has a mass of 6.64×10^{-27} kg, and the helium-3 nucleus has a mass equal to 5.01×10^{-27} kg.

ANSWER 0.102 m

19.7 Magnetic Field of a Long, Straight Wire and Ampère's Law

During a lecture demonstration in 1819, Danish scientist Hans Oersted (1777–1851) found that an electric current in a wire deflected a nearby compass needle. This momentous discovery, linking a magnetic field with an electric current for the first time, was the beginning of our understanding of the origin of magnetism.

A simple experiment first carried out by Oersted in 1820 clearly demonstrates that a current-carrying conductor produces a magnetic field. In this experiment, several compass needles are placed in a horizontal plane near a long vertical wire, as in Active Figure 19.23a. When there is no current in the wire, all needles point in the same direction (that of Earth's field), as one would expect. When the wire carries a strong, steady current, however, the needles all deflect in directions tan-

Active Figure 19.23
(a), (b) Compasses shown the effects of the current in a nearby wire.

When no current is present in the vertical wire, all compass needles point in the same direction (that of Earth's field).

$I = 0$

When the wire carries a strong current, the compass needles deflect in directions tangent to the circle, pointing in the direction of $\vec{B}$, due to the current.

I

$\vec{B}$

a

b

© Richard Megna, Fundamental Photographs

a   b

Figure 19.24 (a) Right-hand rule number 2 for determining the direction of the magnetic field due to a long, straight wire carrying a current. Note that the magnetic field lines form circles around the wire. (b) Circular magnetic field lines surrounding a current-carrying wire, displayed by iron filings.

gent to the circle, as in Active Figure 19.23b. These observations show that the direction of $\vec{B}$ is consistent with the following convenient rule, **right-hand rule number 2**:

> Point the thumb of your right hand along a wire in the direction of positive current, as in Figure 19.24a. Your fingers then naturally curl in the direction of the magnetic field $\vec{B}$.

When the current is reversed, the filings in Figure 19.24b also reverse.

Because the filings point in the direction of $\vec{B}$, we conclude that the lines of $\vec{B}$ form circles about the wire. By symmetry, the magnitude of $\vec{B}$ is the same everywhere on a circular path centered on the wire and lying in a plane perpendicular to the wire. By varying the current and distance from the wire, it can be experimentally determined that $\vec{B}$ is proportional to the current and inversely proportional to the distance from the wire. These observations lead to a mathematical expression for the strength of the magnetic field due to the current I in a long, straight wire:

$$B = \frac{\mu_0 I}{2\pi r}$$ [19.11]

The proportionality constant μ_0, called the **permeability of free space,** has the value

$$\mu_0 \equiv 4\pi \times 10^{-7}\,\text{T}\cdot\text{m/A}$$ [19.12]

Ampère's Law and a Long, Straight Wire

Equation 19.11 enables us to calculate the magnetic field due to a long, straight wire carrying a current. A general procedure for deriving such equations was proposed by French scientist André-Marie Ampère (1775–1836); it provides a relation between the current in an arbitrarily shaped wire and the magnetic field produced by the wire.

Consider an arbitrary closed path surrounding a current as in Figure 19.25 (page 666). The path consists of many short segments, each of length $\Delta \ell$. Multiply one of these lengths by the component of the magnetic field parallel to that segment, where the product is labeled $B_\parallel \Delta \ell$. According to Ampère, the sum of all such products over the closed path is equal to μ_0 times the net current I that passes through the surface bounded by the closed path. This statement, known as **Ampère's circuital law**, can be written

$$\sum B_\parallel \Delta \ell = \mu_0 I$$ [19.13]

◄ Magnetic field due to a long, straight wire

North Wind Picture Archives

HANS CHRISTIAN OERSTED.

Hans Christian Oersted
Danish Physicist and Chemist
(1777–1851)
Oersted is best known for observing that a compass needle deflects when placed near a wire carrying a current. This important discovery was the first evidence of the connection between electric and magnetic phenomena. Oersted was also the first to prepare pure aluminum.

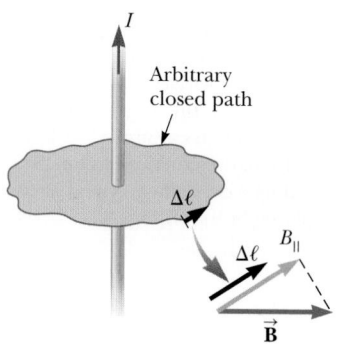

I

Arbitrary
closed path

$\Delta \ell$

$\Delta \ell$ $B_{\parallel}$

$\vec{\mathbf{B}}$

Figure 19.25 An arbitrary closed
path around a current is used to calculate the magnetic field of the current by the use of Ampère's rule.

Figure 19.26 A closed, circular path of
radius r around a long, straight, current-
carrying wire is used to calculate the magnetic field set up by the wire.

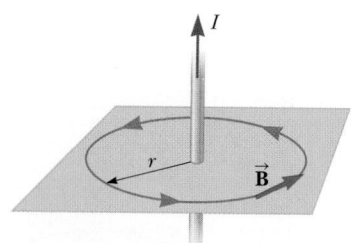

I

r $\vec{\mathbf{B}}$

where $B_{\parallel}$ is the component of $\vec{\mathbf{B}}$ parallel to the segment of length $\Delta \ell$ and $\Sigma B_{\parallel} \Delta \ell$ means that we take the sum over all the products $B_{\parallel} \Delta \ell$ around the closed path. Ampère's law is the fundamental law describing how electric currents create magnetic fields in the surrounding empty space.

We can use Ampère's circuital law to derive the magnetic field due to a long, straight wire carrying a current I. As discussed earlier, each of the magnetic field lines of this configuration forms a circle with the wire at its centers. The magnetic field is tangent to this circle at every point, and its magnitude has the same value B over the entire circumference of a circle of radius r, so $B_{\parallel} = B$, as shown in Figure 19.26. In calculating the sum $\sum B_{\parallel} \Delta \ell$ over the circular path, notice that $B_{\parallel}$ can be removed from the sum (because it has the same value B for each element on the circle). Equation 19.13 then gives

$$\sum B_{\parallel} \Delta \ell = B_{\parallel} \sum \Delta \ell = B(2\pi r) = \mu_0 I$$

Dividing both sides by the circumference $2\pi r$, we obtain

$$B = \frac{\mu_0 I}{2\pi r}$$

This result is identical to Equation 19.11, which is the magnetic field due to the current I in a long, straight wire.

Ampère's circuital law provides an elegant and simple method for calculating the magnetic fields of highly symmetric current configurations, but it can't easily be used to calculate magnetic fields for complex current configurations that lack symmetry. In addition, Ampère's circuital law in this form is valid only when the currents and fields don't change with time.

André-Marie Ampère
(1775–1836)
Ampère, a Frenchman, is credited with
the discovery of electromagnetism, the
relationship between electric currents
and magnetic fields.

■ EXAMPLE 19.7 | **The Magnetic Field of a Coaxial Cable**

GOAL Use Ampère's law to calculate the magnetic field for cylindrically symmetric currents.

PROBLEM A coaxial cable consists of an insulated wire carrying current $I_1 = 3.00$ A surrounded by a cylindrical conductor carrying current $I_2 = 1.00$ A in the opposite direction, as in Figure 19.27. **(a)** Calculate the magnetic field inside the cylindrical conductor at $r_{int} = 0.500$ cm. **(b)** Calculate the magnetic field outside the cylindrical conductor at $r_{ext} = 1.50$ cm.

STRATEGY Construct a circular path around the interior wire, as in Figure 19.27. Only the current inside that circle contributes to the magnetic field B_{int} at points on the circle. To compute the magnetic field B_{ext} exterior to the cylinder, construct a circular path outside the cylinder. Now both currents must be included in the calculation, but the current going down the page must be subtracted from the current in the wire.

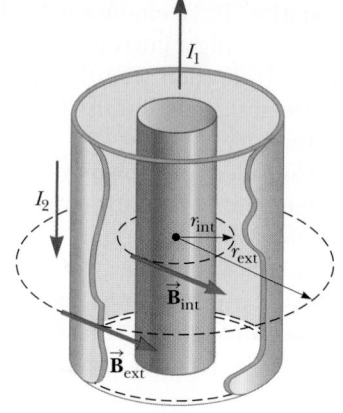

I_1

I_2

r_{int}
r_{ext}

$\vec{\mathbf{B}}_{int}$

$\vec{\mathbf{B}}_{ext}$

Figure 19.27 (Example 19.7)

SOLUTION

(a) Calculate the magnetic field B_{int} inside the cylindrical conductor at $r_{int} = 0.500$ cm.

Write Ampère's law:

$$\sum B_{\parallel} \Delta \ell = \mu_0 I$$

The magnetic field is constant on the given path and the total path length is $2\pi r_{int}$:

$$B_{int}(2\pi r_{int}) = \mu_0 I_1$$

Solve for B_{int} and substitute values:

$$B_{int} = \frac{\mu_0 I_1}{2\pi r_{int}} = \frac{(4\pi \times 10^{-7}\,\text{T} \cdot \text{m/A})(3.00\,\text{A})}{2\pi(0.005\,\text{m})}$$

$$= \boxed{1.20 \times 10^{-4}\,\text{T}}$$

(b) Calculate the magnetic field B_{ext} outside the cylindrical conductor at $r_{ext} = 1.50$ cm.

Write Ampère's law:

$$\sum B_{\parallel} \Delta \ell = \mu_0 I$$

The magnetic field is again constant on the given path and the total path length is $2\pi r_{ext}$:

$$B_{ext}(2\pi r_{ext}) = \mu_0(I_1 - I_2)$$

Solve for B_{ext} and substitute values:

$$B_{ext} = \frac{\mu_0(I_1 - I_2)}{2\pi r_{ext}} = \frac{(4\pi \times 10^{-7}\,\text{T} \cdot \text{m/A})(3.00\,\text{A} - 1.00\,\text{A})}{2\pi(0.015\,\text{m})}$$

$$= \boxed{2.67 \times 10^{-5}\,\text{T}}$$

REMARKS The direction of the field both inside and outside the cylinder is given by the right-hand rule, or counterclockwise in the perspective of Figure 19.27. Coaxial cables can be used to minimize the magnetic effects of current, provided that the currents inside the wire and the cylinder are equal in magnitude and opposite in direction.

QUESTION 19.7 What direction is the magnetic force on a proton traveling up the page (a) to the right of the cable? (b) On the left side?

EXERCISE 19.7 Suppose the current in the wire is 4.00 A downward and the current in the cylindrical conductor is 5.00 A upward. Find the magnitudes of the magnetic field (a) inside the cable at $r_{int} = 0.25$ cm and (b) outside the cable at $r_{ext} = 1.25$ cm.

ANSWERS (a) 3.20×10^{-4} T (b) 1.60×10^{-5} T

19.8 Magnetic Force Between Two Parallel Conductors

As we have seen, a magnetic force acts on a current-carrying conductor when the conductor is placed in an external magnetic field. Because a conductor carrying a current creates a magnetic field around itself, it is easy to understand that two current-carrying wires placed close together exert magnetic forces on each other. Consider two long, straight, parallel wires separated by the distance d and carrying currents I_1 and I_2 in the same direction, as shown in Active Figure 19.28. Wire 1 is directly above wire 2. What's the magnetic force on one wire due to a magnetic field set up by the other wire?

In this calculation we are finding the force on wire 1 due to the magnetic field of wire 2. The current I_2 sets up magnetic field $\vec{B}_2$ at wire 1. The direction of $\vec{B}_2$ is perpendicular to the wire, as shown in the figure. Using Equation 19.11, we find that the magnitude of this magnetic field is

$$B_2 = \frac{\mu_0 I_2}{2\pi d}$$

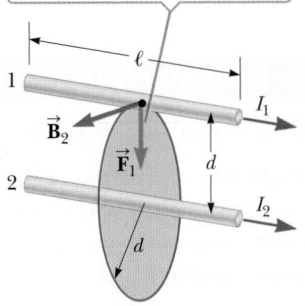

The field $\vec{B}_2$ at wire 1 due to wire 2 produces a force on wire 1 given by $F_1 = B_2 \ell I_1$.

Active Figure 19.28

Two parallel wires, oriented vertically, carry steady currents and exert forces on each other. The force is attractive if the currents have the same direction, as shown, and repulsive if the two currents have opposite directions.

According to Equation 19.5, the magnitude of the magnetic force on wire 1 in the presence of field $\vec{\mathbf{B}}_2$ due to I_2 is

$$F_1 = B_2 I_1 \ell = \left(\frac{\mu_0 I_2}{2\pi d}\right) I_1 \ell = \frac{\mu_0 I_1 I_2 \ell}{2\pi d}$$

We can rewrite this relationship in terms of the force per unit length:

$$\frac{F_1}{\ell} = \frac{\mu_0 I_1 I_2}{2\pi d} \qquad [19.14]$$

The direction of $\vec{\mathbf{F}}_1$ is downward, toward wire 2, as indicated by right-hand rule number 1. This calculation is completely symmetric, which means that the force $\vec{\mathbf{F}}_2$ on wire 2 is equal to and opposite $\vec{\mathbf{F}}_1$, as expected from Newton's third law of action–reaction.

We have shown that parallel conductors carrying currents in the same direction *attract* each other. You should use the approach indicated by Figure 19.28 and the steps leading to Equation 19.14 to show that parallel conductors carrying currents in opposite directions *repel* each other.

The force between two parallel wires carrying a current is used to define the SI unit of current, the **ampere** (A), as follows:

Definition of the ampere ▶ | If two long, parallel wires 1 m apart carry the same current and the magnetic force per unit length on each wire is 2×10^{-7} N/m, the current is defined to be 1 A.

The SI unit of charge, the **coulomb** (C), can now be defined in terms of the ampere as follows:

Definition of the coulomb ▶ | If a conductor carries a steady current of 1 A, the quantity of charge that flows through any cross section in 1 s is 1 C.

■ *Quick Quiz*

19.5 Which of the following actions would double the magnitude of the magnetic force per unit length between two parallel current-carrying wires? Choose all correct answers. (a) Double one of the currents. (b) Double the distance between them. (c) Reduce the distance between them by half. (d) Double both currents.

19.6 If, in Figure 19.28, $I_1 = 2$ A and $I_2 = 6$ A, which of the following is true? (a) $F_1 = 3F_2$ (b) $F_1 = F_2$ (c) $F_1 = F_2/3$

■ **EXAMPLE 19.8** | Levitating a Wire

GOAL Calculate the magnetic force of one current-carrying wire on a parallel current-carrying wire.

PROBLEM Two wires, each having a weight per unit length of 1.00×10^{-4} N/m, are parallel with one directly above the other. Assume the wires carry currents that are equal in magnitude and opposite in direction. The wires are 0.10 m apart, and the sum of the magnetic force and gravitational force on the upper wire is zero. Find the current in the wires. (Neglect Earth's magnetic field.)

STRATEGY The upper wire must be in equilibrium under the forces of magnetic repulsion and gravity. Set the sum of the forces equal to zero and solve for the unknown current, I.

SOLUTION

Set the sum of the forces equal to zero and substitute the appropriate expressions. Notice that the magnetic force between the wires is repulsive.

$$\vec{\mathbf{F}}_{grav} + \vec{\mathbf{F}}_{mag} = 0$$

$$-mg + \frac{\mu_0 I_1 I_2}{2\pi d}\ell = 0$$

The currents are equal, so $I_1 = I_2 = I$. Make these substitutions and solve for I^2:

$$\frac{\mu_0 I^2}{2\pi d}\ell = mg \quad \rightarrow \quad I^2 = \frac{(2\pi d)(mg/\ell)}{\mu_0}$$

Substitute given values, finding I^2, then take the square root. Notice that the weight per unit length, mg/ℓ, is given.

$$I^2 = \frac{(2\pi \cdot 0.100 \text{ m})(1.00 \times 10^{-4} \text{ N/m})}{(4\pi \times 10^{-7} \text{ T} \cdot \text{m})} = 50.0 \text{ A}^2$$

$$I = \boxed{7.07 \text{ A}}$$

REMARKS Exercise 19.3 showed that using Earth's magnetic field to levitate a wire required extremely large currents. Currents in wires can create much stronger magnetic fields than Earth's magnetic field in regions near the wire.

QUESTION 19.8 Why can't cars be constructed that can magnetically levitate in Earth's magnetic field?

EXERCISE 19.8 If the current in each wire is doubled, how far apart should the wires be placed if the magnitudes of the gravitational and magnetic forces on the upper wire are to be equal?

ANSWER 0.400 m

19.9 Magnetic Fields of Current Loops and Solenoids

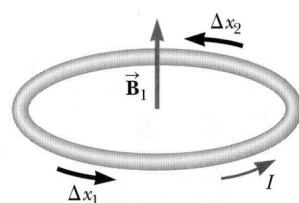

Figure 19.29 All segments of the current loop produce a magnetic field at the center of the loop, directed *upward*.

The strength of the magnetic field set up by a piece of wire carrying a current can be enhanced at a specific location if the wire is formed into a loop. You can understand this by considering the effect of several small segments of the current loop, as in Figure 19.29. The small segment at the bottom of the loop, labeled Δx_1, produces a magnetic field of magnitude B_1 at the loop's center, directed upward. The direction of $\vec{B}$ can be verified using right-hand rule number 2 for a long, straight wire. Imagine holding the wire with your right hand, with your thumb pointing in the direction of the current. Your fingers then curl around in the direction of $\vec{B}$.

A segment of length Δx_2 at the top of the loop also contributes to the field at the center, increasing its strength. The field produced at the center by the segment Δx_2 has the same magnitude as B_1 and is also directed upward. Similarly, all other such segments of the current loop contribute to the field. The net effect is a magnetic field for the current loop as pictured in Figure 19.30a.

Notice in Figure 19.30a that the magnetic field lines enter at the bottom of the current loop and exit at the top. Compare this figure with Figure 19.30b, illustrating the field of a bar magnet. The two fields are similar. One side of the loop acts as though it were the north pole of a magnet, and the other acts as a south pole. The similarity of these two fields will be used to discuss magnetism in matter in an upcoming section.

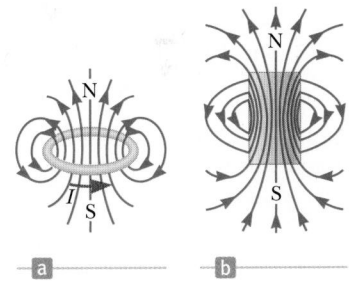

Figure 19.30 (a) Magnetic field lines for a current loop. Note that the lines resemble those of a bar magnet. (b) The magnetic field of a bar magnet is similar to that of a current loop.

■ APPLYING PHYSICS 19.4   Twisted Wires

In electrical circuits it is often the case that insulated wires carrying currents in opposite directions are twisted together. What is the advantage of doing this?

EXPLANATION If the wires are not twisted together, the combination of the two wires forms a current loop, which produces a relatively strong magnetic field. This magnetic field generated by the loop could be strong enough to affect adjacent circuits or components. When the wires are twisted together, their magnetic fields tend to cancel. ■

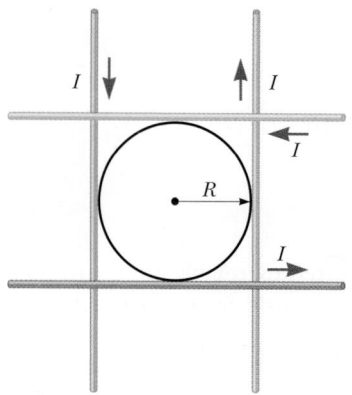

Figure 19.31 The field of a circular loop carrying current I can be approximated by the field due to four straight wires, each carrying current I.

The magnitude of the magnetic field at the center of a circular loop carrying current I is given by

$$B = \frac{\mu_0 I}{2R}$$

This equation must be derived with calculus. It can be shown, however, to be reasonable by calculating the field at the center of four long wires, each carrying current I and forming a square, as in Figure 19.31, with a circle of radius R inscribed within it. Intuitively, this arrangement should give a magnetic field at the center that is similar in magnitude to the field produced by the circular loop. The current in the circular wire is closer to the center, so that wire would have a magnetic field somewhat stronger than just the four legs of the rectangle, but the lengths of the straight wires beyond the rectangle compensate for it. Each wire contributes the same magnetic field at the exact center, so the total field is given by

$$B = 4 \times \frac{\mu_0 I}{2\pi R} = \frac{4}{\pi}\left(\frac{\mu_0 I}{2R}\right) = (1.27)\left(\frac{\mu_0 I}{2R}\right)$$

This result is *approximately* the same as the field produced by the circular loop of current.

When the coil has N loops, each carrying current I, the magnetic field at the center is given by

$$B = N\,\frac{\mu_0 I}{2R} \qquad\qquad\qquad \textbf{[19.15]}$$

Magnetic Field of a Solenoid

If a long, straight wire is bent into a coil of several closely spaced loops, the resulting device is a **solenoid**, often called an **electromagnet**. This device is important in many applications because it acts as a magnet only when it carries a current. The magnetic field inside a solenoid increases with the current and is proportional to the number of coils per unit length.

Figure 19.32 shows the magnetic field lines of a loosely wound solenoid of length ℓ and total number of turns N. Notice that the field lines inside the solenoid are nearly parallel, uniformly spaced, and close together. As a result, the field inside the solenoid is strong and approximately uniform. The exterior field at the sides of the solenoid is nonuniform, much weaker than the interior field, and *opposite in direction* to the field inside the solenoid.

If the turns are closely spaced, the field lines are as shown in Figure 19.33a, entering at one end of the solenoid and emerging at the other. One end of the

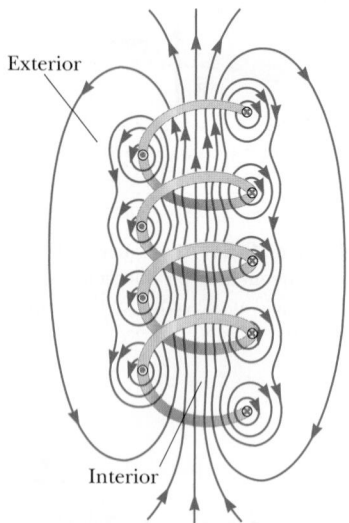

Figure 19.32 The magnetic field lines for a loosely wound solenoid.

Figure 19.33 (a) Magnetic field lines for a tightly wound solenoid of finite length carrying a steady current. The field inside the solenoid is nearly uniform and strong. (b) The magnetic field pattern of a bar magnet, displayed by small iron filings on a sheet of paper.

The magnetic field lines resemble those of a bar magnet, meaning that the solenoid effectively has north and south poles.

solenoid acts as a north pole and the other end acts as a south pole. If the length of the solenoid is much greater than its radius, the lines that leave the north end of the solenoid spread out over a wide region before returning to enter the south end. The more widely separated the field lines are, the weaker the field. This is in contrast to a much stronger field *inside* the solenoid, where the lines are close together. Also, the field inside the solenoid has a constant magnitude at all points far from its ends. As will be shown subsequently, these considerations allow the application of Ampère's law to the solenoid, giving a result of

$$B = \mu_0 nI \qquad \text{[19.16]}$$

for the field inside the solenoid, where $n = N/\ell$ is the number of turns per unit length of the solenoid.

Numerous devices create beams of charged particles for various purposes, and those particles are usually controlled and directed by electromagnetic fields. Old-style cathode ray TV sets use steering magnets that rapidly and accurately direct an electron beam across a screen of phosphors in a scanning motion, creating an illusion of a moving picture out of a series of bright dots. (See Fig. 19.34.) Electron microscopes (see Fig. 27.17b, page 924) use a similar gun and both electrostatic and electromagnetic lenses to focus the beam. Particle accelerators require very large electromagnets to turn particles moving at nearly the speed of light. Tokamaks, experimental devices used in fusion power research, use magnetic fields to contain hot plasmas. Figure 19.35 is a photograph of one such device.

◀ The magnetic field inside a solenoid

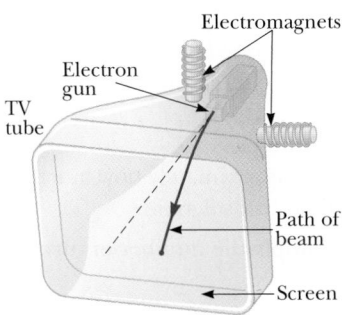

Figure 19.34 Electromagnets are used to deflect electrons to desired positions on the screen of a television tube.

Figure 19.35 Interior view of the closed Tokamak Fusion Test Reactor (TFTR) vacuum vessel at the Princeton Plasma Physics Laboratory.

■ EXAMPLE 19.9 | The Magnetic Field Inside a Solenoid

GOAL Calculate the magnetic field of a solenoid from given data and the momentum of a charged particle in this field.

PROBLEM A certain solenoid consists of 100 turns of wire and has a length of 10.0 cm. **(a)** Find the magnitude of the magnetic field inside the solenoid when it carries a current of 0.500 A. **(b)** What is the momentum of a proton orbiting inside the solenoid in a circle with a radius of 0.020 m? The axis of the solenoid is perpendicular to the plane of the orbit. **(c)** Approximately how much wire would be needed to build this solenoid? Assume the solenoid's radius is 5.00 cm.

STRATEGY In part (a) calculate the number of turns per meter and substitute that and given information into Equation 19.16, getting the magnitude of the magnetic field. Part (b) is an application of Newton's second law.

· ·

SOLUTION

(a) Find the magnitude of the magnetic field inside the solenoid when it carries a current of 0.500 A.

Calculate the number of turns per unit length:

$$n = \frac{N}{\ell} = \frac{100 \text{ turns}}{0.100 \text{ m}} = 1.00 \times 10^3 \text{ turns/m}$$

(Continued)

Substitute n and I into Equation 19.16 to find the magnitude of the magnetic field:

$$B = \mu_0 nI$$
$$= (4\pi \times 10^{-7}\,\text{T} \cdot \text{m/A})(1.00 \times 10^3\,\text{turns/m})(0.500\,\text{A})$$
$$= \boxed{6.28 \times 10^{-4}\,\text{T}}$$

(b) Find the momentum of a proton orbiting in a circle of radius 0.020 m near the center of the solenoid.

Write Newton's second law for the proton:

$$ma = F = qvB$$

Substitute the centripetal acceleration $a = v^2/r$:

$$m\frac{v^2}{r} = qvB$$

Cancel one factor of v on both sides and multiply by r, getting the momentum mv:

$$mv = rqB = (0.020\,\text{m})(1.60 \times 10^{-19}\,\text{C})(6.28 \times 10^{-4}\,\text{T})$$
$$p = mv = \boxed{2.01 \times 10^{-24}\,\text{kg} \cdot \text{m/s}}$$

(c) Approximately how much wire would be needed to build this solenoid?

Multiply the number of turns by the circumference of one loop:

$$\text{Length of wire} \approx (\text{number of turns})(2\pi r)$$
$$= (1.00 \times 10^2\,\text{turns})(2\pi \cdot 0.050\,0\,\text{m})$$
$$= \boxed{31.4\,\text{m}}$$

REMARKS An electron in part (b) would have the same momentum as the proton, but a much higher speed. It would also orbit in the opposite direction. The length of wire in part (c) is only an estimate because the wire has a certain thickness, slightly increasing the size of each loop. In addition, the wire loops aren't perfect circles because they wind slowly up along the solenoid.

QUESTION 19.9 What would happen to the orbiting proton if the solenoid were oriented vertically?

EXERCISE 19.9 Suppose you have a 32.0-m length of copper wire. If the wire is wrapped into a solenoid 0.240 m long and having a radius of 0.040 0 m, how strong is the resulting magnetic field in its center when the current is 12.0 A?

ANSWER $8.00 \times 10^{-3}\,\text{T}$

Ampère's Law Applied to a Solenoid

We can use Ampère's law to obtain the expression for the magnetic field inside a solenoid carrying a current I. A cross section taken along the length of part of our solenoid is shown in Figure 19.36. $\vec{B}$ inside the solenoid is uniform and parallel to the axis, and $\vec{B}$ outside is approximately zero. Consider a rectangular path of length L and width w, as shown in the figure. We can apply Ampère's law to this path by evaluating the sum of $B_{\parallel}\,\Delta\ell$ over each side of the rectangle. The contribution along side 3 is clearly zero because $\vec{B} = 0$ in this region. The contributions from sides 2 and 4 are both zero because $\vec{B}$ is perpendicular to $\Delta\vec{\ell}$ along these paths. Side 1 of length L gives a contribution BL to the sum because $\vec{B}$ is uniform along this path and parallel to $\Delta\vec{\ell}$. Therefore, the sum over the closed rectangular path has the value

$$\sum B_{\parallel}\,\Delta\ell = BL$$

The right side of Ampère's law involves the total current that passes through the area bounded by the path chosen. In this case, the total current through the rectangular path equals the current through each turn of the solenoid, multiplied by the number of turns. If N is the number of turns in the length L, then the total current through the rectangular path equals NI. Ampère's law applied to this path therefore gives

$$\sum B_{\parallel}\,\Delta\ell = BL = \mu_0 NI$$

or

$$B = \mu_0 \frac{N}{L} I = \mu_0 nI$$

where $n = N/L$ is the number of turns per unit length.

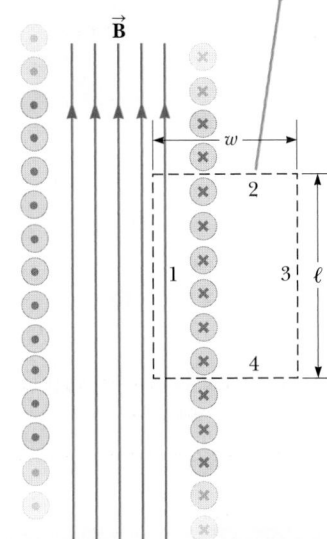

Ampère's law applied to the rectangular dashed path can be used to calculate the field inside the solenoid.

Figure 19.36 A cross-sectional view of a tightly wound solenoid. If the solenoid is long relative to its radius, we can assume the magnetic field inside is uniform and the field outside is zero.

19.10 Magnetic Domains

The magnetic field produced by a current in a coil of wire gives us a hint as to what might cause certain materials to exhibit strong magnetic properties. A single coil like that in Figure 19.30a has a north pole and a south pole, but if that is true for a coil of wire, it should also be true for any current confined to a circular path. In particular, *an individual atom should act as a magnet because of the motion of the electrons about the nucleus.* Each electron, with its charge of 1.6×10^{-19} C, circles the atom once in about 10^{-16} s. If we divide the electric charge by this time interval, we see that the orbiting electron is equivalent to a current of 1.6×10^{-3} A. Such a current produces a magnetic field on the order of 20 T at the center of the circular path. From this we see that a very strong magnetic field would be produced if several of these atomic magnets could be aligned inside a material. This doesn't occur, however, because the simple model we have described is not the complete story. A thorough analysis of atomic structure shows that the magnetic field produced by one electron in an atom is often canceled by an oppositely revolving electron in the same atom. The net result is that **the magnetic effect produced by the electrons orbiting the nucleus is either zero or very small for most materials**.

The magnetic properties of many materials can be explained by the fact that an electron not only circles in an orbit, but also spins on its axis like a top, with spin magnetic moment as shown (Fig. 19.37). (This classical description should not be taken too literally. The property of electron *spin* can be understood only in the context of quantum mechanics, which we will not discuss here.) The spinning electron represents a charge in motion that produces a magnetic field. The field due to the spinning is generally stronger than the field due to the orbital motion. In atoms containing many electrons, the electrons usually pair up with their spins opposite each other so that their fields cancel each other. That is why most substances are not magnets. In certain strongly magnetic materials, such as iron, cobalt, and nickel, however, the magnetic fields produced by the electron spins don't cancel completely. Such materials are said to be **ferromagnetic**. In ferromagnetic materials strong coupling occurs between neighboring atoms, forming large groups of atoms with spins that are aligned. Called **domains**, the sizes of these groups typically range from about 10^{-4} cm to 0.1 cm. In an unmagnetized substance the domains are randomly oriented, as shown in Figure 19.38a (on page 674). When an external field is applied, as in Figures 19.38b and 19.38c, the magnetic field of each domain tends to come nearer to alignment with the external field, resulting in magnetization.

In what are called hard magnetic materials, domains remain aligned even after the external field is removed; the result is a **permanent magnet**. In soft magnetic

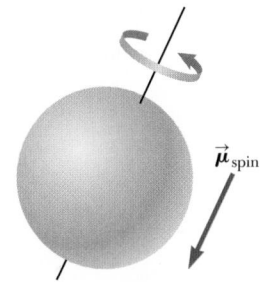

Figure 19.37 Classical model of a spinning electron.

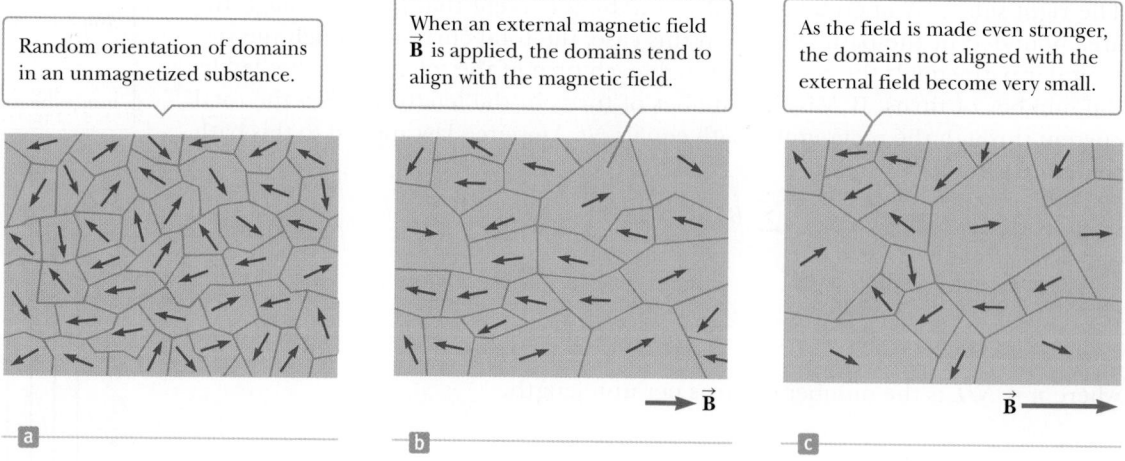

Figure 19.38 Orientation of magnetic dipoles before and after a magnetic field is applied to a ferromagnetic substance.

Figure 19.39 The permanent magnet (red) temporarily magnetizes some paper clips, which then cling to each other through magnetic forces.

materials, such as iron, once the external field is removed, thermal agitation produces motion of the domains and the material quickly returns to an unmagnetized state.

The alignment of domains explains why the strength of an electromagnet is increased dramatically by the insertion of an iron core into the magnet's center. The magnetic field produced by the current in the loops causes the domains to align, thus producing a large net external field. The use of iron as a core is also advantageous because it is a soft magnetic material that loses its magnetism almost instantaneously after the current in the coils is turned off.

The formation of domains in ferromagnetic substances also explains why such substances are attracted to permanent magnets. The magnetic field of a permanent magnet realigns domains in a ferromagnetic object so that the object becomes temporarily magnetized. The object's poles are then attracted to the corresponding opposite poles of the permanent magnet. The object can similarly attract other ferromagnetic objects, as illustrated in Figure 19.39.

Types of Magnetic Materials

Magnetic materials can be classified according to how they react to the application of a magnetic field. In **ferromagnetic** materials the atoms have permanent magnetic moments that align readily with an externally applied magnetic field. Examples of ferromagnetic materials are iron, cobalt, and nickel. Such substances can retain some of their magnetization even after the applied magnetic field is removed.

Paramagnetic materials also have magnetic moments that tend to align with an externally applied magnetic field, but the response is extremely weak compared with that of ferromagnetic materials. Examples of paramagnetic substances are aluminum, calcium, and platinum. A ferromagnetic material can become paramagnetic when warmed to a certain critical temperature, the Curie temperature, that depends on the material.

In **diamagnetic** materials, an externally applied magnetic field induces a very weak magnetization that is opposite the applied field. Ordinarily diamagnetism isn't observed because paramagnetic and ferromagnetic effects are far stronger. In Figure 19.40, however, a very high magnetic field exerts a levitating force on the diamagnetic water molecules in a frog.

Tip 19.4 The Electron Spins, but Doesn't!

Even though we use the word *spin*, the electron, unlike a child's top, isn't physically spinning in this sense. The electron has an intrinsic angular momentum that causes it to act *as if it were spinning*, but the concept of spin angular momentum is actually a relativistic quantum effect.

Figure 19.40 Diamagnetism. A frog is levitated in a 16-T magnetic field at the Nijmegen High Field Magnet Laboratory in the Netherlands. The levitation force is exerted on the diamagnetic water molecules in the frog's body. The frog suffered no ill effects from the levitation experience.

High Field Magnet Laboratory, University of Nijmegen, The Netherlands

■ SUMMARY

19.3 Magnetic Fields

The **magnetic force** that acts on a charge q moving with velocity $\vec{\mathbf{v}}$ in a magnetic field $\vec{\mathbf{B}}$ has magnitude

$$F = qvB \sin \theta \qquad [19.1]$$

where θ is the angle between $\vec{\mathbf{v}}$ and $\vec{\mathbf{B}}$.

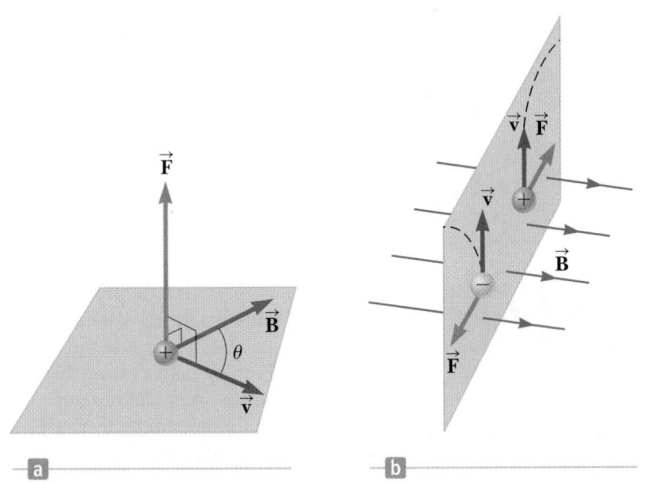

(a) The direction of the magnetic force $\vec{\mathbf{F}}$ acting on a charged particle moving with a velocity $\vec{\mathbf{v}}$ in the presence of a magnetic field $\vec{\mathbf{B}}$. The magnetic force is perpendicular to both $\vec{\mathbf{v}}$ and $\vec{\mathbf{B}}$. (b) Magnetic forces on positive and negative charges. The dashed lines show the paths of the particles, which are investigated in Section 19.6. The magnetic forces on oppositely charged particles moving at the same velocity in a magnetic field are in opposite directions.

To find the direction of this force, use **right-hand rule number 1**: point the fingers of your open right hand in the direction of $\vec{\mathbf{v}}$ and then curl them in the direction of $\vec{\mathbf{B}}$. Your thumb then points in the direction of the magnetic force $\vec{\mathbf{F}}$.

If the charge is *negative* rather than positive, the force is directed opposite the force given by the right-hand rule.

The SI unit of the magnetic field is the **tesla** (T), or weber per square meter (Wb/m²). An additional commonly used unit for the magnetic field is the **gauss** (G); $1 \text{ T} = 10^4 \text{ G}$.

19.4 Magnetic Force on a Current-Carrying Conductor

If a straight conductor of length ℓ carries current I, the magnetic force on that conductor when it is placed in a uniform external magnetic field $\vec{\mathbf{B}}$ is

$$F = BI\ell \sin \theta \qquad [19.6]$$

where θ is the angle between the direction of the current and the direction of the magnetic field.

The magnetic force on this current-carrying conductor is directed straight up out of the page.

Right-hand rule number 1 also gives the direction of the magnetic force on the conductor. In this case, however, you must point your fingers in the direction of the current rather than in the direction of $\vec{\mathbf{v}}$.

19.5 Torque on a Current Loop and Electric Motors

The torque τ on a current-carrying loop of wire in a magnetic field $\vec{\mathbf{B}}$ has magnitude

$$\tau = BIA \sin \theta \qquad [19.8]$$

where I is the current in the loop and A is its cross-sectional area. The magnitude of the magnetic moment of a current-carrying coil is defined by $\mu = IAN$, where N is the number of loops. The magnetic moment is considered a vector, $\vec{\boldsymbol{\mu}}$, that is perpendicular to the plane of the loop. The angle between $\vec{\mathbf{B}}$ and $\vec{\boldsymbol{\mu}}$ is θ.

19.6 Motion of a Charged Particle in a Magnetic Field

If a charged particle moves in a uniform magnetic field so that its initial velocity is perpendicular to the field, it will move in a circular path in a plane perpendicular to the magnetic field. The radius r of the circular path can be found from Newton's second law and centripetal acceleration, and is given by

$$r = \frac{mv}{qB} \qquad [19.10]$$

where m is the mass of the particle and q is its charge.

19.7 Magnetic Field of a Long, Straight Wire and Ampère's Law

The magnetic field at distance r from a **long, straight wire** carrying current I has the magnitude

$$B = \frac{\mu_0 I}{2\pi r} \qquad [19.11]$$

where $\mu_0 = 4\pi \times 10^{-7} \text{ T} \cdot \text{m/A}$ is the **permeability of free space**. The magnetic field lines around a long, straight wire are circles concentric with the wire.

Ampère's law can be used to find the magnetic field around certain simple current-carrying conductors. It can be written

$$\sum B_\parallel \, \Delta \ell = \mu_0 I \qquad [19.13]$$

where $B_\parallel$ is the component of $\vec{\mathbf{B}}$ tangent to a small current element of length $\Delta \ell$ that is part of a closed path and I is the total current that penetrates the closed path.

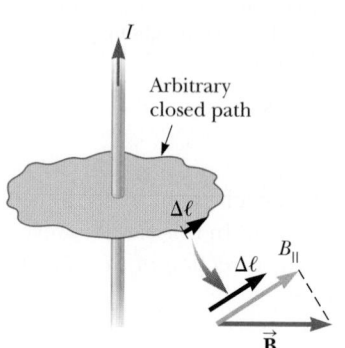

An arbitrary closed path around a current is used to calculate the magnetic field of the current by the use of Ampère's rule.

19.8 Magnetic Force Between Two Parallel Conductors

The force per unit length on each of two parallel wires separated by the distance d and carrying currents I_1 and I_2 has the magnitude

$$\frac{F}{\ell} = \frac{\mu_0 I_1 I_2}{2\pi d} \qquad [19.14]$$

The forces are attractive if the currents are in the same direction and repulsive if they are in opposite directions.

19.9 Magnetic Field of Current Loops and Solenoids

The magnetic field at the center of a coil of N circular loops of radius R, each carrying current I, is given by

$$B = N \frac{\mu_0 I}{2R} \qquad [19.15]$$

(a) Magnetic field lines for a current loop. Note that the lines resemble those of a bar magnet. (b) The magnetic field of a bar magnet is similar to that of a current loop.

The magnetic field inside a solenoid has the magnitude

$$B = \mu_0 n I \qquad [19.16]$$

where $n = N/\ell$ is the number of turns of wire per unit length.

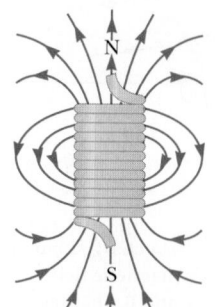

Magnetic field lines for a tightly wound solenoid of finite length carrying a steady current. The field inside the solenoid is nearly uniform and strong. Note that the field lines resemble those of a bar magnet, so the solenoid effectively has north and south poles.

■ MULTIPLE-CHOICE QUESTIONS

WebAssign The multiple-choice questions in this chapter may be assigned online in Enhanced WebAssign.

1. A wire of length 0.50 m carries a current of 0.10 A in the positive x-direction, parallel to the ground. If the wire has a weight of 1.0×10^{-2} N, what is the minimum magnitude magnetic field that exerts a magnetic force on the wire equal to the wire's weight? (a) 0.20 T (b) 0.30 T (c) 0.40 T (d) 0.50 T (e) 0.60 T

2. An electron moves across Earth's equator at a speed of 2.5×10^6 m/s and in a direction $35°$ N of E. At this point, Earth's magnetic field has a direction due north, is parallel to the surface, and has a magnitude of 0.10×10^{-4} T. What is the force acting on the electron due to its interaction with Earth's magnetic field? (a) 5.1×10^{-18} N due west (b) 4.0×10^{-18} N toward Earth's surface (c) 2.4×10^{-18} N away from Earth's surface (d) 3.3×10^{-18} N toward Earth's surface (e) 4.0×10^{-18} N away from Earth's surface

3. A rectangular coil of wire consisting of ten loops, each with length 0.20 m and width 0.30 m, lies in the xy-plane. If the coil carries a current of 2.0 A, what is the torque exerted by a magnetic field of magnitude 0.010 T directed at an angle of 30.0° with respect to the positive z-axis? (a) 1.2×10^{-2} N $\cdot$ m (b) 2.4×10^{-2} N $\cdot$ m (c) 6.0×10^{-3} N $\cdot$ m (d) 4.0×10^{-3} N $\cdot$ m (e) 3.0×10^{-3} N $\cdot$ m

4. A long wire carries a current of 1 A. Find the magnitude of the magnetic field 2 m away from the wire. (a) 1×10^{-3} T (b) 1×10^{-4} T (c) 1×10^{-6} T (d) 1×10^{-7} T (e) 1×10^{-10} T

5. A proton enters a constant magnetic field of magnitude 0.050 T and traverses a semicircle of radius 1.0 mm before leaving the field. What is the proton's speed? (a) 1.6×10^{3} m/s (b) 2.3×10^{3} m/s (c) 2.8×10^{4} m/s (d) 1.8×10^{2} m/s (e) 4.8×10^{3} m/s

6. Estimate the magnitude of the magnetic force per unit length between a pair of parallel wires separated by 2 m if they each carry a current of 3 A. (a) 1×10^{-1} N/m (b) 1×10^{-3} N/m (c) 1×10^{-4} N/m (d) 1×10^{-6} N/m (e) 1×10^{-8} N/m

7. What is the magnitude of the magnetic field at the core of a 120-turn solenoid of length 0.50 m carrying a current of 2.0 A? (a) 2.4×10^{-4} T (b) 4.8×10^{-5} T (c) 1.2×10^{-6} T (d) 3.6×10^{-5} T (e) 6.0×10^{-4} T

8. A charged particle is traveling through a uniform magnetic field. Which of the following statements are true of the magnetic field? (There may be more than one correct statement.) (a) It exerts a force on the particle that is parallel to the field. (b) It exerts a force on the particle along the direction of its motion. (c) It increases the kinetic energy of the particle. (d) It exerts a force that is perpendicular to the direction of motion. (e) It doesn't change the magnitude of the momentum of the particle.

9. A spatially uniform magnetic field cannot exert a magnetic force on a particle in which of the following circumstances? (There may be more than one correct statement.) (a) The particle is charged. (b) The particle moves perpendicular to the field. (c) The particle moves parallel to the field. (d) The magnitude of the magnetic field changes with time. (e) The particle is at rest.

10. A proton moving horizontally enters a region where a uniform magnetic field is directed perpendicular to the proton's velocity, as shown in Figure MCQ19.10.

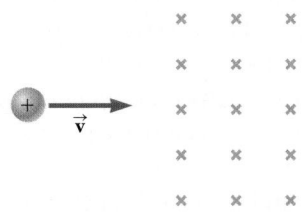

Figure MCQ19.10

After the proton enters the field, does it (a) deflect downward, with its speed remaining constant; (b) continue to move in the horizontal direction with constant velocity; (c) move in a circular orbit and become trapped by the field; (d) deflect upward, moving in a semicircular path with constant speed, and exit the field moving to the left; or (e) deflect out of the plane of the paper?

11. Two long, parallel wires each carry the same current I in the same direction (Fig. MCQ19.11). Is the total magnetic field at the point P midway between the wires (a) zero, (b) directed into the page, (c) directed out of the page, (d) directed to the left, or (e) directed to the right?

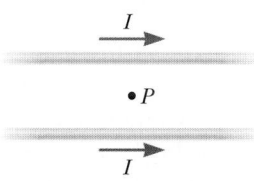

Figure MCQ19.11

12. Two long, straight wires cross each other at right angles, and each carries the same current as in Figure MCQ19.12. Which of the following statements are true regarding the total magnetic field at the various points due to the two wires? (There may be more than one correct statement.) (a) The field is strongest at points B and D. (b) The field is strongest at points A and C. (c) The field is out of the page at point B and into the page at point D. (d) The field is out of the page at point C and out of the page at point D. (e) The field has the same magnitude at all four points.

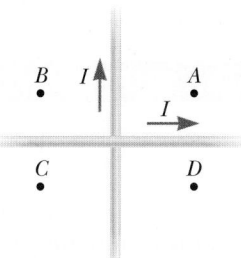

Figure MCQ19.12

13. A magnetic field exerts a torque on each of the current-carrying single loops of wire shown in Figure MCQ19.13. The loops lie in the xy-plane, each carrying the same magnitude current, and the uniform magnetic field points in the positive x-direction. Rank the

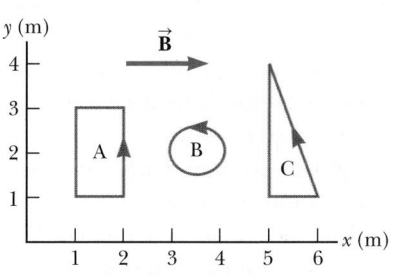

Figure MCQ19.13

coils by the magnitude of the torque exerted on them by the field, from largest to smallest. (a) A, B, C (b) A, C, B (c) B, A, C (d) B, C, A (e) C, A, B

14. Two long, parallel wires carry currents of 20 A and 10 A in opposite directions, as in Figure MCQ19.14. Which of the following statements must be true? (There may be more than one correct statement.) (a) In region I the magnetic field is into the page and is never zero. (b) In region II the field is into the page and can be zero. (c) In region III it is possible for the field to be zero. (d) In region I the magnetic field is out of the page and is never zero. (e) There are no points where the field is zero.

Figure MCQ19.14

15. A long, straight wire carries a current I as in Figure MCQ19.15. Which of the following statements are true regarding the magnetic field due to the wire? (There may be more than one correct state-

Figure MCQ19.15

ment.) (a) The field is proportional to I/r and is out of the page at P. (b) The field is proportional to I/r^2 and is out of the page at P. (c) The field is proportional to I/r and is into the page at P. (d) The field strength is proportional to I, but doesn't depend on r. (e) The field is proportional to I/r^2 and is into the page at P.

16. Solenoid A has length L and N turns, solenoid B has length $2L$ and N turns, and solenoid C has length $L/2$ and $2N$ turns. If each solenoid carries the same current, rank by the strength of the magnetic field in the center of each solenoid from largest to smallest. (a) A, B, C (b) A, C, B (c) B, C, A (d) C, A, B (e) C, B, A

17. At a certain instant, a proton is moving in the positive x-direction through a magnetic field in the negative z-direction. What is the direction of the magnetic force exerted on the proton? (a) positive z-direction (b) negative z-direction (c) positive y-direction (d) negative y-direction (e) The force is zero.

18. Answer each question yes or no. Assume the motions and currents mentioned are along the x-axis and fields are in the y-direction. (a) Does an electric field exert a force on a stationary charged object? (b) Does a magnetic field do so? (c) Does an electric field exert a force on a moving charged object? (d) Does a magnetic field do so? (e) Does an electric field exert a force on a straight current-carrying wire? (f) Does a magnetic field do so? (g) Does an electric field exert a force on a beam of moving electrons? (h) Does a magnetic field do so?

■ CONCEPTUAL QUESTIONS

WebAssign The conceptual questions in this chapter may be assigned online in Enhanced WebAssign.

1. In older television sets, a beam of electrons moves from the back of the picture tube to the screen, where it strikes a fluorescent dot that glows with a particular color when hit. Earth's magnetic field at the location of the television set is horizontal and toward the north. In which direction(s) should the set be oriented so that the beam undergoes the largest deflection?

2. Which way would a compass point if you were at Earth's north magnetic pole?

3. How can the motion of a charged particle be used to distinguish between a magnetic field and an electric field in a certain region? Give a specific example to justify your answer.

4. Can a constant magnetic field set a proton at rest into motion? Explain your answer.

5. Explain why two parallel wires carrying currents in opposite directions repel each other.

6. Will a nail be attracted to either pole of a magnet? Explain what is happening inside the nail when it is placed near the magnet.

7. A Hindu ruler once suggested that he be entombed in a magnetic coffin with the polarity arranged so that he could be forever suspended between heaven and Earth. Is such magnetic levitation possible? Discuss.

8. A magnet attracts a piece of iron. The iron can then attract another piece of iron. On the basis of domain alignment, explain what happens in each piece of iron.

9. Can you use a compass to detect the currents in wires in the walls near light switches in your home?

10. Is the magnetic field created by a current loop uniform? Explain.

11. Suppose you move along a wire at the same speed as the drift speed of the electrons in the wire. Do you now measure a magnetic field of zero?

12. Why do charged particles from outer space, called cosmic rays, strike Earth more frequently at the poles than at the equator?

13. A hanging Slinky® toy is attached to a powerful battery and a switch. When the switch is closed so that the

toy now carries current, does the Slinky compress or expand?

14. How can a current loop be used to determine the presence of a magnetic field in a given region of space?

15. Parallel wires exert magnetic forces on each other. What about perpendicular wires? Imagine two wires oriented perpendicular to each other and almost touching. Each wire carries a current. Is there a force between the wires?

16. Figure CQ19.16 shows four permanent magnets, each having a hole through its center. Notice that the blue and yellow magnets are levitated above the red ones.

(a) How does this levitation occur? (b) What purpose do the rods serve? (c) What can you say about the poles of the magnets from this observation? (d) If the upper magnet were inverted, what do you suppose would happen?

17. Two charged particles are projected in the same direction into a magnetic field perpendicular to their velocities. If the two particles are deflected in opposite directions, what can you say about them?

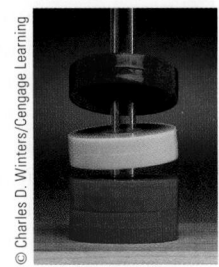

Figure CQ19.16

■ PROBLEMS

19.3 Magnetic Fields

1. Consider an electron near the Earth's equator. In which direction does it tend to deflect if its velocity is (a) directed downward? (b) Directed northward? (c) Directed westward? (d) Directed southeastward?

2. (a) Find the direction of the force on a proton (a positively charged particle) moving through the magnetic fields in Figure P19.2, as shown. (b) Repeat part (a), assuming the moving particle is an electron.

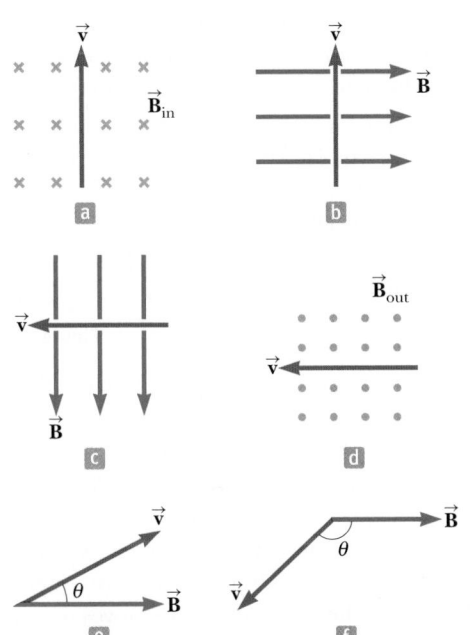

Figure P19.2 Problems 2 and 12.

3. Find the direction of the magnetic field acting on the positively charged particle moving in the various situations shown in Figure P19.3 if the direction of the magnetic force acting on it is as indicated.

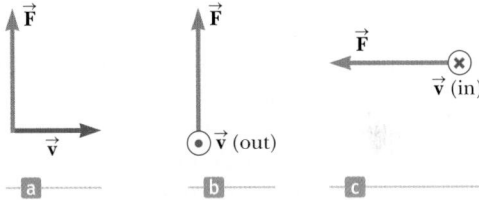

Figure P19.3 (Problems 3 and 15) For Problem 15, replace the velocity vector with a current in that direction.

4. Determine the initial direction of the deflection of charged particles as they enter the magnetic fields, as shown in Figure P19.4.

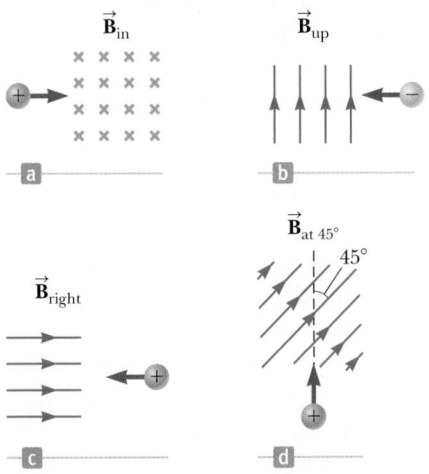

Figure P19.4

5. **Q|C** A laboratory electromagnet produces a magnetic field of magnitude 1.50 T. A proton moves through this field with a speed of 6.00×10^6 m/s. (a) Find the magnitude of the maximum magnetic force that could be exerted on the proton. (b) What is the magnitude of the maximum acceleration of the proton? (c) Would the field exert the same magnetic force on an electron moving through the field with the same speed? (d) Would the electron undergo the same acceleration? Explain.

6. **M** A proton moves perpendicular to a uniform magnetic field $\vec{B}$ at a speed of 1.00×10^7 m/s and experiences an acceleration of 2.00×10^{13} m/s² in the positive x-direction when its velocity is in the positive z-direction. Determine the magnitude and direction of the field.

7. What velocity would a proton need to circle Earth 1 000 km above the magnetic equator, where Earth's magnetic field is directed horizontally north and has a magnitude of 4.00×10^{-8} T?

8. An electron is accelerated through 2 400 V from rest and then enters a region where there is a uniform 1.70-T magnetic field. What are (a) the maximum and (b) the minimum magnitudes of the magnetic force acting on this electron?

9. **M** A proton moving at 4.00×10^6 m/s through a magnetic field of magnitude 1.70 T experiences a magnetic force of magnitude 8.20×10^{-13} N. What is the angle between the proton's velocity and the field?

10. **BIO** Sodium ions (Na^+) move at 0.851 m/s through a bloodstream in the arm of a person standing near a large magnet. The magnetic field has a strength of 0.254 T and makes an angle of 51.0° with the motion of the sodium ions. The arm contains 100 cm³ of blood with a concentration of 3.00×10^{20} Na^+ ions per cubic centimeter. If no other ions were present in the arm, what would be the magnetic force on the arm?

11. At the equator, near the surface of Earth, the magnetic field is approximately 50.0 μT northward, and the electric field is about 100 N/C downward in fair weather. Find the gravitational, electric, and magnetic forces on an electron with an instantaneous velocity of 6.00×10^6 m/s directed to the east in this environment.

19.4 Magnetic Force on a Current-Carrying Conductor

12. In Figure P19.2 assume in each case the velocity vector shown is replaced with a wire carrying a current in the direction of the velocity vector. For each case, find the direction of the magnetic force acting on the wire.

13. A current $I = 15$ A is directed along the positive x-axis and perpendicular to a magnetic field. A magnetic force per unit length of 0.12 N/m acts on the conductor in the negative y-direction. Calculate the magnitude and direction of the magnetic field in the region through which the current passes.

14. **Q|C** A straight wire carrying a 3.0-A current is placed in a uniform magnetic field of magnitude 0.28 T directed perpendicular to the wire. (a) Find the magnitude of the magnetic force on a section of the wire having a length of 14 cm. (b) Explain why you can't determine the direction of the magnetic force from the information given in the problem.

15. In Figure P19.3 assume in each case the velocity vector shown is replaced with a wire carrying a current in the direction of the velocity vector. For each case, find the direction of the magnetic field that will produce the magnetic force shown.

16. A wire having a mass per unit length of 0.500 g/cm carries a 2.00-A current horizontally to the south. What are the direction and magnitude of the minimum magnetic field needed to lift this wire vertically upward?

17. A wire carries a current of 10.0 A in a direction that makes an angle of 30.0° with the direction of a magnetic field of strength 0.300 T. Find the magnetic force on a 5.00-m length of the wire.

18. At a certain location, Earth has a magnetic field of 0.60×10^{-4} T, pointing 75° below the horizontal in a north–south plane. A 10.0-m-long straight wire carries a 15-A current. (a) If the current is directed horizontally toward the east, what are the magnitude and direction of the magnetic force on the wire? (b) What are the magnitude and direction of the force if the current is directed vertically upward?

19. A wire with a mass of 1.00 g/cm is placed on a horizontal surface with a coefficient of friction of 0.200. The wire carries a current of 1.50 A eastward and moves horizontally to the north. What are the magnitude and the direction of the *smallest* vertical magnetic field that enables the wire to move in this fashion?

20. A conductor suspended by two flexible wires as shown in Figure P19.20 has a mass per unit length of 0.040 0 kg/m. (a) What current must exist in the conductor for the tension in the supporting wires to be zero when the magnetic field is 3.60 T into the page? (b) What is the required direction for the current?

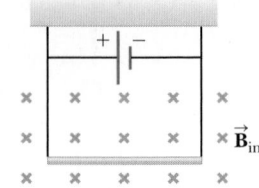

Figure P19.20

21. **Q|C** Consider the system pictured in Figure P19.21. A 15-cm length of conductor of mass 15 g, free to move vertically, is placed between two thin, vertical conductors, and a uniform magnetic field acts perpendicular to the page. When a 5.0-A current is directed as shown in the figure, the horizontal wire moves upward at constant velocity in the presence of gravity. (a) What forces act on the horizontal wire, and under what condition

is the wire able to move upward at constant velocity? (b) Find the magnitude and direction of the minimum magnetic field required to move the wire at constant speed. (c) What happens if the magnetic field exceeds this minimum value? (The wire slides without friction on the two vertical conductors.)

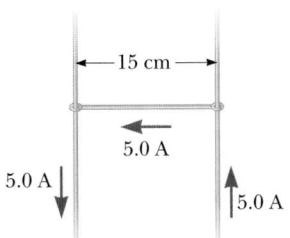

Figure P19.21

22. **S** A metal rod of mass m carrying a current I glides on two horizontal rails a distance d apart. If the coefficient of kinetic friction between the rod and rails is μ_k, what vertical magnetic field is required to keep the rod moving at a constant speed?

23. In Figure P19.23 the cube is 40.0 cm on each edge. Four straight segments of wire—ab, bc, cd, and da—form a closed loop that carries a current $I = 5.00$ A in the direction shown. A uniform magnetic field of magnitude $B = 0.020\ 0$ T is in the positive y-direction. Determine the magnitude and direction of the magnetic force on each segment.

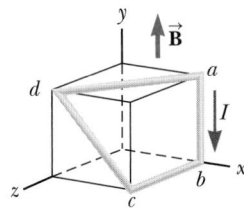

Figure P19.23

24. A horizontal power line of length 58 m carries a current of 2.2 kA as shown in Figure P19.24. Earth's magnetic field at this location has a magnitude equal to 5.0×10^{-5} T and makes an angle of 65° with the power line. Find the magnitude and direction of the magnetic force on the power line.

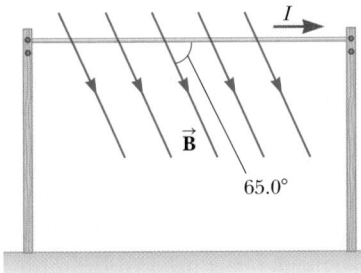

Figure P19.24

19.5 Torque on a Current Loop and Electric Motors

25. A wire is formed into a circle having a diameter of 10.0 cm and is placed in a uniform magnetic field of 3.00 mT. The wire carries a current of 5.00 A. Find the maximum torque on the wire.

26. A current of 17.0 mA is maintained in a single circular loop with a circumference of 2.00 m. A magnetic field of 0.800 T is directed parallel to the plane of the loop. What is the magnitude of the torque exerted by the magnetic field on the loop?

27. **M** An eight-turn coil encloses an elliptical area having a major axis of 40.0 cm and a minor axis of 30.0 cm (Fig. P19.27). The coil lies in the plane of the page and carries a clockwise current of 6.00 A. If the coil is in a uniform magnetic field of 2.00×10^{-4} T directed toward the left of the page, what is the magnitude of the torque on the coil? *Hint:* The area of an ellipse is $A = \pi ab$, where a and b are, respectively, the semimajor and semiminor axes of the ellipse.

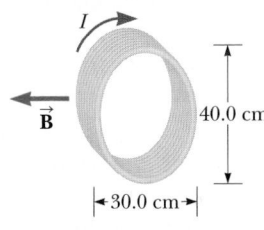

Figure P19.27

28. A rectangular loop consists of 100 closely wrapped turns and has dimensions 0.400 m by 0.300 m. The loop is hinged along the y-axis, and the plane of the coil makes an angle of 30.0° with the x-axis (Fig. P19.28). What is the magnitude of the torque exerted on the loop by a uniform magnetic field of 0.800 T directed along the x-axis when the current in the windings has a value of 1.20 A in the direction shown? What is the expected direction of rotation of the loop?

Figure P19.28

29. A 200-turn rectangular coil having dimensions of 3.0 cm by 5.0 cm is placed in a uniform magnetic field of magnitude 0.90 T. (a) Find the current in the coil if the maximum torque exerted on it by the magnetic field is 0.15 N · m. (b) Find the magnitude of the torque on the coil when the magnetic field makes an angle of 25° with the normal to the plane of the coil.

30. A copper wire is 8.00 m long and has a cross-sectional area of 1.00×10^{-4} m². The wire forms a one-turn loop in the shape of square and is then connected to a battery that applies a potential difference of 0.100 V. If the loop is placed in a uniform magnetic field of magnitude 0.400 T, what is the maximum torque that can act on it? The resistivity of copper is 1.70×10^{-8} Ω · m.

31. A long piece of wire with a mass of 0.100 kg and a total length of 4.00 m is used to make a square coil with a side of 0.100 m. The coil is hinged along a horizontal side, carries a 3.40-A current, and is placed in a vertical magnetic field with a magnitude of 0.010 0 T.

(a) Determine the angle that the plane of the coil makes with the vertical when the coil is in equilibrium. (b) Find the torque acting on the coil due to the magnetic force at equilibrium.

32. **GP** A rectangular loop has dimensions 0.500 m by 0.300 m. The loop is hinged along the x-axis and lies in the xy-plane (Fig. P19.32). A uniform magnetic field of 1.50 T is directed at an angle of 40.0° with respect to the positive y-axis and lies parallel everywhere to the yz-plane. The loop carries a current of 0.900 A in the direction shown. (Ignore gravitation.) (a) In what direction is magnetic force exerted on wire segment ab? What is the direction of the magnetic torque associated with this force, as computed with respect to the x-axis? (b) What is the direction of the magnetic force exerted on segment cd? What is the direction of the magnetic torque associated with this force, again computed with respect to the x-axis? (c) Can the forces examined in parts (a) and (b) combine to cause the loop to rotate around the x-axis? Can they affect the motion of the loop in any way? Explain. (d) What is the direction (in the yz-plane) of the magnetic force exerted on segment bc? Measuring torques with respect to the x-axis, what is the direction of the torque exerted by the force on segment bc? (e) Looking toward the origin along the positive x-axis, will the loop rotate clockwise or counterclockwise? (f) Compute the magnitude of the magnetic moment of the loop. (g) What is the angle between the magnetic moment vector and the magnetic field? (h) Compute the torque on the loop using the values found for the magnetic moment and magnetic field.

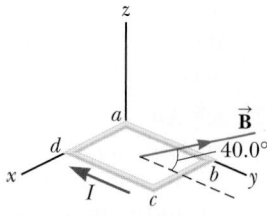

Figure P19.32

19.6 Motion of a Charged Particle in a Magnetic Field

33. An electron moves in a circular path perpendicular to a magnetic field of magnitude 0.235 T. If the kinetic energy of the electron is 3.30×10^{-19} J, find (a) the speed of the electron and (b) the radius of the circular path.

34. A proton travels with a speed of 5.02×10^6 m/s at an angle of 60° with the direction of a magnetic field of magnitude 0.180 T in the positive x-direction. What are (a) the magnitude of the magnetic force on the proton and (b) the proton's acceleration?

35. Figure P19.35a is a diagram of a device called a velocity selector, in which particles of a specific velocity pass through undeflected while those with greater or lesser velocities are deflected either upwards or downwards. An electric field is directed perpendicular to a magnetic field, producing an electric force and a magnetic

force on the charged particle that can be equal in magnitude and opposite in direction (Fig. P19.35b) and hence cancel. Show that particles with a speed of $v = E/B$ will pass through the velocity selector undeflected.

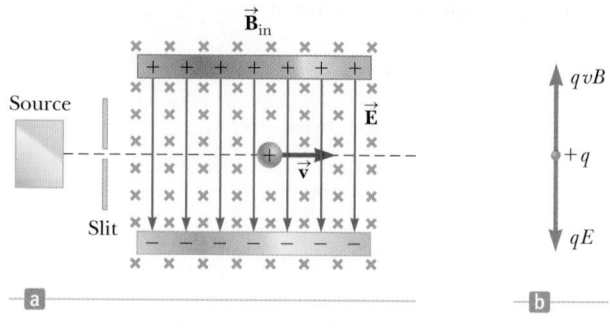

Figure P19.35

36. Consider the mass spectrometer shown schematically in Figure P19.36. The electric field between the plates of the velocity selector is 950 V/m, and the magnetic fields in both the velocity selector and the deflection chamber have magnitudes of 0.930 T. Calculate the radius of the path in the system for a singly charged ion with mass $m = 2.18 \times 10^{-26}$ kg. *Hint:* See Problem 35.

Figure P19.36 (Problems 36 and 41) A mass spectrometer. Charged particles are first sent through a velocity selector. They then enter a region where a magnetic field $\vec{B}_0$ (directed inward) causes positive ions to move in a semicircular path and strike a photographic film at P.

37. A singly charged positive ion has a mass of 2.50×10^{-26} kg. After being accelerated through a potential difference of 250 V, the ion enters a magnetic field of 0.500 T, in a direction perpendicular to the field. Calculate the radius of the path of the ion in the field.

38. A mass spectrometer is used to examine the isotopes of uranium. Ions in the beam emerge from the velocity selector at a speed of 3.00×10^5 m/s and enter a uniform magnetic field of 0.600 T directed perpendicularly to the velocity of the ions. What is the distance between the impact points formed on the photographic plate by singly charged ions of ^{235}U and ^{238}U?

39. A proton is at rest at the plane vertical boundary of a region containing a uniform vertical magnetic field B (Fig. P19.39). An alpha particle moving horizontally makes a head-on elastic collision with the proton. Immediately after the collision, both particles enter the magnetic field, moving perpendicular to the direction of the field. The radius of the proton's trajectory is R. The mass of the alpha particle is four times that of the proton, and its charge is twice that of the proton. Find the radius of the alpha particle's trajectory.

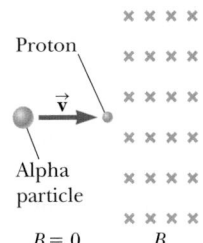

Figure P19.39

40. **S** A particle with charge q and kinetic energy KE travels in a uniform magnetic field of magnitude B. If the particle moves in a circular path of radius R, find expressions for (a) its speed and (b) its mass.

41. A particle passes through a mass spectrometer as illustrated in Figure P19.36. The electric field between the plates of the velocity selector has a magnitude of 8 250 V/m, and the magnetic fields in both the velocity selector and the deflection chamber have magnitudes of 0.093 1 T. In the deflection chamber the particle strikes a photographic plate 39.6 cm removed from its exit point after traveling in a semicircle. (a) What is the mass-to-charge ratio of the particle? (b) What is the mass of the particle if it is doubly ionized? (c) What is its identity, assuming it's an element?

42. **S** A proton (charge $+e$, mass m_p), a deuteron (charge $+e$, mass $2m_p$), and an alpha particle (charge $+2e$, mass $4m_p$) are accelerated from rest through a common potential difference ΔV. Each of the particles enters a uniform magnetic field $\vec{B}$, with its velocity in a direction perpendicular to $\vec{B}$. The proton moves in a circular path of radius r_p. In terms of r_p, determine (a) the radius r_d of the circular orbit for the deuteron and (b) the radius r_α for the alpha particle.

19.7 Magnetic Field of a Long, Straight Wire and Ampère's Law

43. A lightning bolt may carry a current of 1.00×10^4 A for a short time. What is the resulting magnetic field 100 m from the bolt? Suppose the bolt extends far above and below the point of observation.

44. In each of parts (a), (b), and (c) of Figure P19.44, find the direction of the current in the wire that would produce a magnetic field directed as shown.

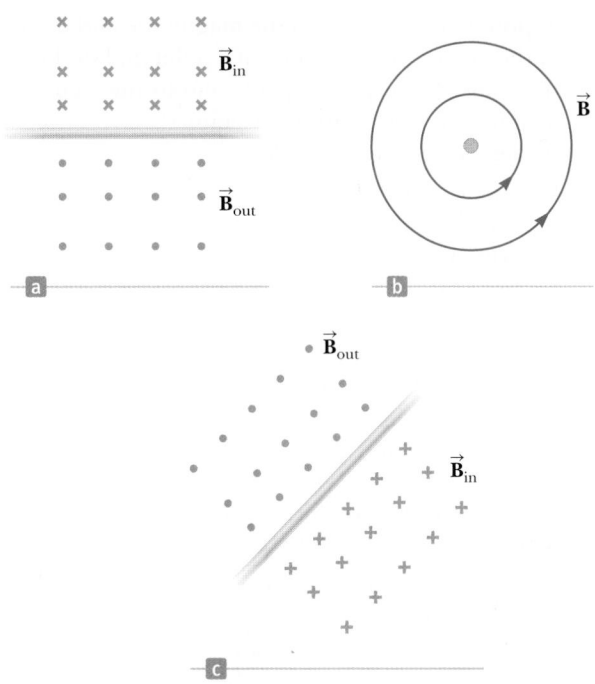

Figure P19.44

45. **BIO** Neurons in our bodies carry weak currents that produce detectable magnetic fields. A technique called *magnetoencephalography*, or MEG, is used to study electrical activity in the brain using this concept. This technique is capable of detecting magnetic fields as weak as 1.0×10^{-15} T. Model the neuron as a long wire carrying a current and find the current it must carry to produce a field of this magnitude at a distance of 4.0 cm from the neuron.

46. In 1962 measurements of the magnetic field of a large tornado were made at the Geophysical Observatory in Tulsa, Oklahoma. If the magnitude of the tornado's field was $B = 1.50 \times 10^{-8}$ T pointing north when the tornado was 9.00 km east of the observatory, what current was carried up or down the funnel of the tornado? Model the vortex as a long, straight wire carrying a current.

47. **BIO** A cardiac pacemaker can be affected by a static magnetic field as small as 1.7 mT. How close can a pacemaker wearer come to a long, straight wire carrying 20 A?

48. The two wires shown in Figure P19.48 are separated by $d = 10.0$ cm and carry currents of $I = 5.00$ A in

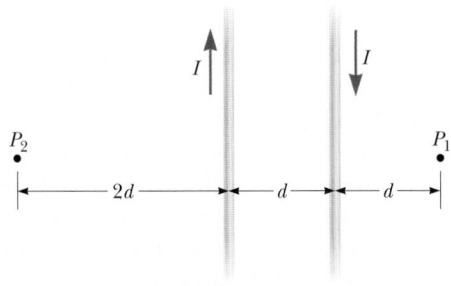

Figure P19.48

opposite directions. Find the magnitude and direction of the net magnetic field (a) at a point midway between the wires; (b) at point P_1, 10.0 cm to the right of the wire on the right; and (c) at point P_2, $2d = 20.0$ cm to the left of the wire on the left.

49. Four long, parallel conductors carry equal currents of $I = 5.00$ A. Figure P19.49 is an end view of the conductors. The direction of the current is into the page at points A and B (indicated by the crosses) and out of the page at C and D (indicated by the dots). Calculate the magnitude and direction of the magnetic field at point P, located at the center of the square with edge of length 0.200 m.

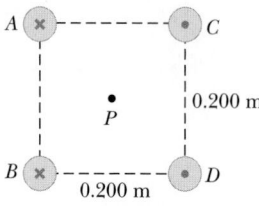

Figure P19.49

50. Two long, parallel wires carry currents of $I_1 = 3.00$ A and $I_2 = 5.00$ A in the direction indicated in Figure P19.50. (a) Find the magnitude and direction of the magnetic field at a point midway between the wires ($d = 20.0$ cm). (b) Find the magnitude and direction of the magnetic field at point P, located $d = 20.0$ cm above the wire carrying the 5.00-A current.

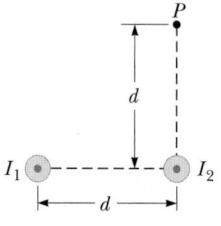

Figure P19.50

51. **M** A wire carries a 7.00-A current along the x-axis, and another wire carries a 6.00-A current along the y-axis, as shown in Figure P19.51. What is the magnetic field at point P, located at $x = 4.00$ m, $y = 3.00$ m?

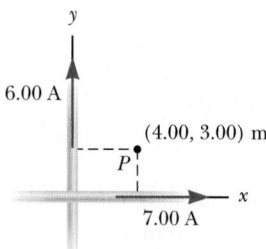

Figure P19.51

52. **GP** A long, straight wire lies on a horizontal table in the xy-plane and carries a current of 1.20 μA in the positive x-direction along the x-axis. A proton is traveling in the negative x-direction at speed 2.30×10^4 m/s a distance d above the wire (i.e., $z = d$). (a) What is the direction of the magnetic field of the wire at the position of the proton? (b) What is the direction of the magnetic force acting on the proton? (c) Explain why the direction of the proton's motion doesn't change. (d) Using Newton's second law, find a symbolic expression for d in terms of the acceleration of gravity g, the proton mass m, its speed v, charge q, and the current

I. (e) Find the numeric answer for the distance d using the results of part (d).

53. The magnetic field 40.0 cm away from a long, straight wire carrying current 2.00 A is 1.00 μT. (a) At what distance is it 0.100 μT? (b) At one instant, the two conductors in a long household extension cord carry equal 2.00-A currents in opposite directions. The two wires are 3.00 mm apart. Find the magnetic field 40.0 cm away from the middle of the straight cord, in the plane of the two wires. (c) At what distance is it one-tenth as large? (d) The center wire in a coaxial cable carries current 2.00 A in one direction, and the sheath around it carries current 2.00 A in the opposite direction. What magnetic field does the cable create at points outside?

54. **QC** **S** Two long, parallel wires separated by a distance $2d$ carry equal currents in the same direction. An end view of the two wires is shown in Figure P19.54, where the currents are out of the page. (a) What is the direction of the magnetic field at P on the x-axis set up by the two wires? (b) Find an expression for the magnitude of the field at P. (c) From your result to part (b), determine the field at a point midway between the two wires. Does your result meet with your expectation? Explain.

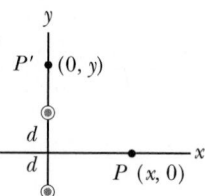

Figure P19.54

19.8 Magnetic Force Between Two Parallel Conductors

55. Two long, parallel wires separated by 2.50 cm carry currents in opposite directions. The current in one wire is 1.25 A, and the current in the other is 3.50 A. (a) Find the magnitude of the force per unit length that one wire exerts on the other. (b) Is the force attractive or repulsive?

56. **QC** Two parallel wires separated by 4.0 cm repel each other with a force per unit length of 2.0×10^{-4} N/m. The current in one wire is 5.0 A. (a) Find the current in the other wire. (b) Are the currents in the same direction or in opposite directions? (c) What would happen if the direction of one current were reversed and doubled?

57. A wire with a weight per unit length of 0.080 N/m is suspended directly above a second wire. The top wire carries a current of 30.0 A, and the bottom wire carries a current of 60.0 A. Find the distance of separation between the wires so that the top wire will be held in place by magnetic repulsion.

58. In Figure P19.58 the current in the long, straight wire is $I_1 = 5.00$ A, and the wire lies in the plane of the rectangular loop, which carries 10.0 A. The dimensions shown are $c = 0.100$ m, $a = 0.150$ m, and $\ell = 0.450$ m. Find the magnitude and direction of the net force

exerted by the magnetic field due to the straight wire on the loop.

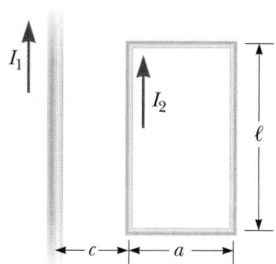

Figure P19.58

19.9 Magnetic Fields of Current Loops and Solenoids

59. **M** A long solenoid that has 1 000 turns uniformly distributed over a length of 0.400 m produces a magnetic field of magnitude 1.00×10^{-4} T at its center. What current is required in the windings for that to occur?

60. A certain superconducting magnet in the form of a solenoid of length 0.50 m can generate a magnetic field of 9.0 T in its core when its coils carry a current of 75 A. The windings, made of a niobium–titanium alloy, must be cooled to 4.2 K. Find the number of turns in the solenoid.

61. It is desired to construct a solenoid that will have a resistance of 5.00 Ω (at 20°C) and produce a magnetic field of 4.00×10^{-2} T at its center when it carries a current of 4.00 A. The solenoid is to be constructed from copper wire having a diameter of 0.500 mm. If the radius of the solenoid is to be 1.00 cm, determine (a) the number of turns of wire needed and (b) the length the solenoid should have.

62. A solenoid 10.0 cm in diameter and 75.0 cm long is made from copper wire of diameter 0.100 cm, with very thin insulation. The wire is wound onto a cardboard tube in a single layer, with adjacent turns touching each other. What power must be delivered to the solenoid if it is to produce a field of 8.00 mT at its center?

63. An electron is moving at a speed of 1.0×10^4 m/s in a circular path of radius 2.0 cm inside a solenoid. The magnetic field of the solenoid is perpendicular to the plane of the electron's path. Find (a) the strength of the magnetic field inside the solenoid and (b) the current in the solenoid if it has 25 turns per centimeter.

Additional Problems

64. **Q|C** Figure P19.64 is a setup that can be used to measure magnetic fields. A rectangular coil of wire contains N turns has a width w. The coil is attached to one arm of a balance and is suspended between the poles of a magnet. The field is uniform and perpendicular to the plane of the coil. The system is first balanced when the current in the coil is zero. When the switch is

closed and the coil carries a current I, a mass m must be added to the right side to balance the system. (a) Find an expression for the magnitude of the magnetic field and determine its direction. (b) Why is the result independent of the vertical dimension of the coil? (c) Suppose the coil has 50 turns and width of 5.0 cm. When the switch is closed, the coil carries a current of 0.30 A, and a mass of 20.0 g must be added to the right side to balance the system. What is the magnitude of the magnetic field?

Figure P19.64

65. Two coplanar and concentric circular loops of wire carry currents of $I_1 = 5.00$ A and $I_2 = 3.00$ A in opposite directions as in Figure P19.65. (a) If $r_1 = 12.0$ cm and $r_2 = 9.00$ cm, what are (a) the magnitude and (b) the direction of the net magnetic field at the center of the two loops? (c) Let r_1 remain fixed at 12.0 cm and let r_2 be a variable. Determine the value of r_2 such that the net field at the center of the loop is zero.

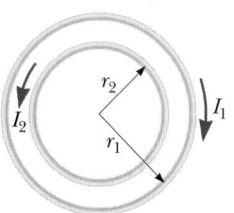

Figure P19.65

66. An electron moves in a circular path perpendicular to a constant magnetic field of magnitude 1.00 mT. The angular momentum of the electron about the center of the circle is 4.00×10^{-25} kg · m²/s. Determine (a) the radius of the circular path and (b) the speed of the electron.

67. Two long, straight wires cross each other at right angles, as shown in Figure P19.67. (a) Find the direc-

Figure P19.67

tion and magnitude of the magnetic field at point *P*, which is in the same plane as the two wires. (b) Find the magnetic field at a point 30.0 cm above the point of intersection (30.0 cm out of the page, toward you).

68. A 0.200-kg metal rod carrying a current of 10.0 A glides on two horizontal rails 0.500 m apart. What vertical magnetic field is required to keep the rod moving at a constant speed if the coefficient of kinetic friction between the rod and rails is 0.100?

69. **BIO** Using an electromagnetic flowmeter (Fig. P19.69), a heart surgeon monitors the flow rate of blood through an artery. Electrodes *A* and *B* make contact with the outer surface of the blood vessel, which has interior diameter 3.00 mm. (a) For a magnetic field magnitude of 0.040 0 T, a potential difference of 160 μV appears between the electrodes. Calculate the speed of the blood. (b) Verify that electrode *A* is positive, as shown. Does the sign of the emf depend on whether the mobile ions in the blood are predominantly positively or negatively charged? Explain.

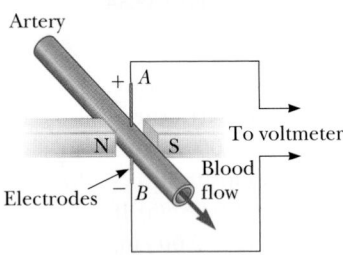

Figure P19.69

70. A uniform horizontal wire with a linear mass density of 0.50 g/m carries a 2.0-A current. It is placed in a constant magnetic field with a strength of 4.0×10^{-3} T. The field is horizontal and perpendicular to the wire. As the wire moves upward starting from rest, (a) what is its acceleration and (b) how long does it take to rise 50 cm? Neglect the magnetic field of Earth.

71. Three long, parallel conductors carry currents of *I* = 2.0 A. Figure P19.71 is an end view of the conductors, with each current coming out of the page. Given that *a* = 1.0 cm, determine the magnitude and direction of the magnetic field at points *A*, *B*, and *C*.

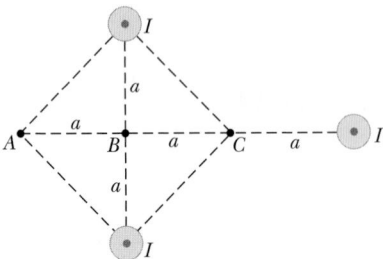

Figure P19.71

72. Two long, parallel wires, each with a mass per unit length of 40 g/m, are supported in a horizontal plane by 6.0-cm-long strings, as shown in Figure P19.72. Each wire carries the same current *I*, causing the wires to repel each other so that the angle θ between the supporting strings is 16°. (a) Are the currents in the same or opposite directions? (b) Determine the magnitude of each current.

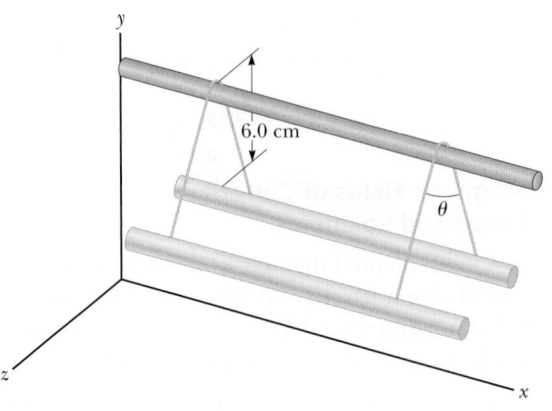

Figure P19.72

73. Protons having a kinetic energy of 5.00 MeV are moving in the positive *x*-direction and enter a magnetic field of 0.050 0 T in the *z*-direction, out of the plane of the page, and extending from *x* = 0 to *x* = 1.00 m as in Figure P19.73. (a) Calculate the *y*-component of the protons' momentum as they leave the magnetic field. (b) Find the angle α between the initial velocity vector of the proton beam and the velocity vector after the beam emerges from the field. *Hint:* Neglect relativistic effects and note that 1 eV = 1.60×10^{-19} J.

Figure P19.73

74. A straight wire of mass 10.0 g and length 5.0 cm is suspended from two identical springs that, in turn, form a closed circuit (Fig. P19.74). The springs stretch a distance of 0.50 cm under the weight of the wire. The circuit has a total resistance of 12 Ω. When a magnetic field directed out of the page (indicated by the dots in the figure) is turned on, the springs are observed to stretch an additional 0.30 cm. What is the strength of the magnetic field? (The upper portion of the circuit is fixed.)

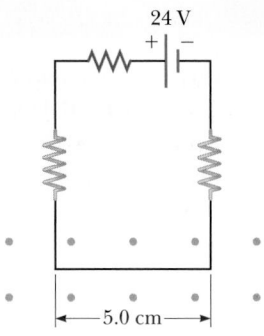

24 V

5.0 cm

Figure P19.74

75. A 1.00-kg ball having net charge $Q = 5.00\ \mu C$ is thrown out of a window horizontally at a speed $v = 20.0$ m/s. The window is at a height $h = 20.0$ m above the ground.

A uniform horizontal magnetic field of magnitude $B = 0.010\ 0$ T is perpendicular to the plane of the ball's trajectory. Find the magnitude of the magnetic force acting on the ball just before it hits the ground. *Hint:* Ignore magnetic forces in finding the ball's final velocity.

76. Two long, parallel conductors separated by 10.0 cm carry currents in the same direction. The first wire carries a current $I_1 = 5.00$ A, and the second carries $I_2 = 8.00$ A. (a) What is the magnitude of the magnetic field created by I_1 at the location of I_2? (b) What is the force per unit length exerted by I_1 on I_2? (c) What is the magnitude of the magnetic field created by I_2 at the location of I_1? (d) What is the force per length exerted by I_2 on I_1?

▪ AP* REVIEW QUESTIONS

1. A proton is moving at a velocity v at an angle of 90° in a magnetic field B. An electron is moving at $2v$ at an angle of 30° in a magnetic field of $B/2$. What is the ratio of magnetic force on the proton to the magnetic force on the electron?

   (A) 1:1

   (B) 2:1

   (C) 1:2

   (D) 4:1

   (E) 1:4

2. A proton travels at a speed of 3.0×10^6 m/s parallel to a magnetic field of 10 T. What is the magnetic force on the proton?

   (A) 0 N

   (B) 4.8×10^{-13} N

   (C) 4.8×10^{-10} N

   (D) 4.8×10^{28} N

   (E) More information is needed

3. An electron, moving north, moves through a magnetic field whose direction is east. What is the direction of the force on the electron?

   (A) Into the page

   (B) Out of the page

   (C) South

   (D) West

   (E) There is no force on the electron

4. An electron, moving into the page, is affected by a magnetic force directed south. What is the direction of the magnetic field?

   (A) West

   (B) East

   (C) North

   (D) Out of the page

   (E) South

5. Wire A, length ℓ, carrying a current I, sits in a magnetic field B at an angle of 60°. Wire B, length $\ell/3$, carrying a current $6I$, sits in a magnetic field $2B$ at an angle of 30°. What is the ratio of forces on wire A to wire B?

   (A) 2:1

   (B) $\sqrt{3/4}$:1

   (C) $4\sqrt{3}$:1

   (D) 4:1

   (E) 1:4

6. A current-carrying wire is aligned with a magnetic field B to give the maximum magnetic force. If the alignment does not change, how can the magnetic force be cut in half?

   (A) $I, \dfrac{\ell}{2}, 2B$

   (B) $2I, \ell, 3B$

   (C) $I, 3\ell, \dfrac{B}{6}$

   (D) $\dfrac{I}{2}, 3\ell, 6B$

   (E) $\dfrac{I}{4}, \dfrac{\ell}{3}, 4B$

7. A proton enters a magnetic field of 2 T with a velocity of 2×10^8 m/s. What is the approximate radius of its path?

   (A) 1×10^{-2} m

   (B) 4×10^{-2} m

   (C) 1 m

   (D) 4 m

   (E) 0 m. A proton continues in a straight line in a magnetic field.

Questions 8–9

8. A particle, moving at the speed of light, enters a 9 T magnetic field. If the radius of curve is approximately 1 m, what is the approximate mass to charge ratio?

   (A) 3×10^{-9} kg/C

   (B) 3×10^{-8} kg/C

   (C) 9×10^{-8} kg/C

   (D) 27×10^{-8} kg/C

   (E) More information is needed

9. Referring to question 8 above, is the particle most likely to be hydrogen (1 proton, 0 neutrons), deuterium (1 proton, 1 neutron), tritium (1 proton, 2 neutrons), or helium (2 protons, 2 neutrons)?

   (A) Hydrogen

   (B) Deuterium

   (C) Tritium

   (D) Helium

   (E) More information is needed

10. A long wire carries a current of 10 A. How far away should you be from the wire to have a magnetic field of 3.6 μT?

   (A) 0.18 μm

   (B) 0.55 μm

   (C) 0.18 m

   (D) 0.55 m

   (E) 1.8 m

11. Wire A creates a magnetic field of 10 μT 5 cm away. Wire B creates a magnetic field of 5 μT three times as far away. If the current in wire A is 6 A, what is the current in wire B?

   (A) 2/3 A

   (B) 3/2 A

   (C) 6 A

   (D) 9 A

   (E) More information is needed

12. Wire 1 carries current I_1 to the right while parallel wire 2 carries current I_2 to the left. If the wires are separated by a distance d, what is the force per unit length ℓ on wire 1 and is it attractive or repulsive?

   (A) $\dfrac{\mu_0 I_1 I_2}{2\pi d}$, attractive

   (B) $\dfrac{\mu_0 I_1 I_2}{2\pi d}$, repulsive

   (C) $\dfrac{\mu_0 I_1 I_2}{2\pi d\ell}$, attractive

   (D) $\dfrac{\mu_0 I_1 I_2}{2\pi d\ell}$, repulsive

   (E) More information is needed

A forest of fluorescent lights, not wired to any power source, are lighted by electromagnetic induction. Changing currents in the power wires overhead create time-dependent magnetic flux in the vicinity of the tubes, inducing a voltage across them.

South West News Service

20 Induced Voltages and Inductance

In 1819 Hans Christian Oersted discovered that an electric current exerted a force on a magnetic compass. Although there had long been speculation that such a relationship existed, Oersted's finding was the first evidence of a link between electricity and magnetism. Because nature is often symmetric, the discovery that electric currents produce magnetic fields led scientists to suspect that magnetic fields could produce electric currents. Indeed, experiments conducted by Michael Faraday in England and independently by Joseph Henry in the United States in 1831 showed that a changing magnetic field could induce an electric current in a circuit. The results of these experiments led to a basic and important law known as Faraday's law. In this chapter we discuss Faraday's law and several practical applications, one of which is the production of electrical energy in power generation plants throughout the world.

20.1 Induced emf and Magnetic Flux

An experiment first conducted by Faraday demonstrated that a current can be produced by a changing magnetic field. The apparatus shown in Figure 20.1 consists of a coil connected to a switch and a battery. We call this coil the *primary coil* and the corresponding circuit the primary circuit. The coil is wrapped around an iron ring to intensify the magnetic field produced by the current in the coil. A second coil, called the *secondary coil*, at the right, is wrapped around the iron ring and is connected to an ammeter. The corresponding circuit is called the secondary circuit. It's important to notice that **there is no battery in the secondary circuit**.

The emf in the secondary circuit is induced by the changing magnetic field through the coil in that circuit.

When the switch in the primary circuit is closed, the ammeter in the secondary circuit at the right measures a momentary current.

Figure 20.1 Faraday's experiment.

By kind permission of the President and Council of the Royal Society

At first glance, you might guess that no current would ever be detected in the secondary circuit. When the switch in the primary circuit in Figure 20.1 is suddenly closed, however, something amazing happens: the ammeter measures a current in the secondary circuit and then returns to zero! When the switch is opened again, the ammeter reads a current in the opposite direction and again returns to zero. Finally, whenever there is a steady current in the primary circuit, the ammeter reads zero.

From such observations, Faraday concluded that an electric current could be produced by a *changing* magnetic field. (A steady magnetic field doesn't produce a current unless the coil is moving, as explained below.) The current produced in the secondary circuit occurs for only an instant while the magnetic field through the secondary coil is changing. In effect, the secondary circuit behaves as though a source of emf were connected to it for a short time. It's customary to say that **an induced emf is produced in the secondary circuit by the changing magnetic field**.

Michael Faraday
British physicist and chemist
(1791–1867)
Faraday is often regarded as the greatest experimental scientist of the 1800s. His many contributions to the study of electricity include the inventions of the electric motor, electric generator, and transformer, as well as the discovery of electromagnetic induction and the laws of electrolysis. Greatly influenced by religion, he refused to work on military poison gas for the British government.

Magnetic Flux

To evaluate induced emfs quantitatively, we need to understand what factors affect the phenomenon. Although changing magnetic fields always induce electric fields, in other situations the magnetic field remains constant, yet an induced electric field is still produced. The best example of this is an electric generator: A loop of conductor rotating in a constant magnetic field creates an electric current.

The physical quantity associated with magnetism that creates an electric field is a **changing magnetic flux**. Magnetic flux is defined in the same way as electric flux (Section 15.9) and is proportional to both the strength of the magnetic field passing through the plane of a loop of wire and the area of the loop.

The **magnetic flux Φ_B** through a loop of wire with area A is defined by

$$\Phi_B \equiv B_\perp A = BA \cos \theta \qquad [20.1]$$

where $B_\perp$ is the component of a uniform magnetic field $\vec{B}$ perpendicular to the plane of the loop, as in Figure 20.2a (page 690), and θ is the angle between $\vec{B}$ and the normal (perpendicular) to the plane of the loop.

SI unit: weber (Wb)

◀ Magnetic flux

Note that there are always two directions normal to a given plane surface. In Figure 20.2, for example, that direction could be chosen to be to the right, resulting in positive flux. The normal direction could also be chosen to point to the

Figure 20.2 (a) A uniform magnetic field $\vec{B}$ making an angle θ with a direction normal to the plane of a wire loop of area A. (b) An edge view of the loop.

Loop of area A

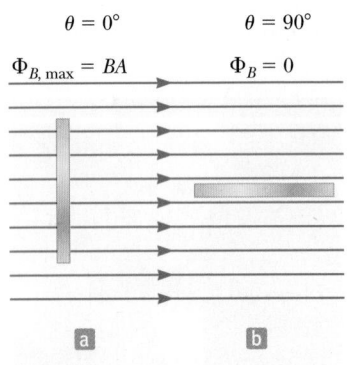

$\theta = 0°$ $\theta = 90°$

$\Phi_{B,\,max} = BA$ $\Phi_B = 0$

Figure 20.3 An edge view of a loop in a uniform magnetic field. (a) When the field lines are perpendicular to the plane of the loop, the magnetic flux through the loop is a maximum and equal to $\Phi_B = BA$. (b) When the field lines are parallel to the plane of the loop, the magnetic flux through the loop is zero.

left, which would result in a negative flux of the same magnitude. The choice of normal direction is called the orientation of the surface. Once chosen in a given problem, the normal direction remains fixed. A good default choice is to choose the normal direction so that the initial angle between the magnetic field and the normal direction is less than 90°.

From Equation 20.1, it follows that $B_\perp = B \cos \theta$. The magnetic flux, in other words, is the magnitude of the part of $\vec{B}$ that is perpendicular to the plane of the loop times the area of the loop. Figure 20.2b is an edge view of the loop and the penetrating magnetic field lines. When the field is perpendicular to the plane of the loop as in Figure 20.3a, $\theta = 0$ and Φ_B has a maximum value, $\Phi_{B,max} = BA$. When the plane of the loop is parallel to $\vec{B}$ as in Figure 20.3b, $\theta = 90°$ and $\Phi_B = 0$. The flux can also be negative. For example, when $\theta = 180°$, the flux is equal to $-BA$. Because the SI unit of B is the tesla, or weber per square meter, the unit of flux is $T \cdot m^2$, or weber (Wb).

We can emphasize the qualitative meaning of Equation 20.1 by first drawing magnetic field lines, as in Figure 20.3. The number of lines per unit area increases as the field strength increases. **The value of the magnetic flux is proportional to the total number of lines passing through the loop.** We see that the most lines pass through the loop when its plane is perpendicular to the field, as in Figure 20.3a, so the flux has its maximum value at that time. As Figure 20.3b shows, no lines pass through the loop when its plane is parallel to the field, so in that case $\Phi_B = 0$.

■ APPLYING PHYSICS 20.1 | **Flux Compared**

Argentina has more land area (2.8×10^6 km^2) than Greenland (2.2×10^6 km^2). Why is the magnetic flux of Earth's magnetic field larger through Greenland than through Argentina?

EXPLANATION Greenland (latitude 60° north to 80° north) is closer to a magnetic pole than Argentina (latitude 20° south to 50° south), so the magnetic field is stronger there. That in itself isn't sufficient to conclude that the magnetic flux is greater, but Greenland's proximity to a pole also means that the angle magnetic field lines make with the vertical is smaller than in Argentina. As a result, more field lines penetrate the surface in Greenland, despite Argentina's slightly larger area. ■

■ EXAMPLE 20.1 | **Magnetic Flux**

GOAL Calculate magnetic flux and a change in flux.

PROBLEM A conducting circular loop of radius 0.250 m is placed in the xy-plane in a uniform magnetic field of 0.360 T that points in the positive z-direction, the same direction as the normal to the plane. **(a)** Calculate the magnetic flux through the loop. **(b)** Suppose the loop is rotated clockwise around the x-axis, so the normal direction now points at a 45.0° angle with respect to the z-axis. Recalculate the magnetic flux through the loop. **(c)** What is the change in flux due to the rotation of the loop?

STRATEGY After finding the area, substitute values into the equation for magnetic flux for each part. Because the normal direction was chosen to be the same direction as the magnetic field, the angle between the magnetic field and the normal is initially 0°. After the rotation, that angle becomes 45°.

SOLUTION

(a) Calculate the initial magnetic flux through the loop.

First, calculate the area of the loop:

$$A = \pi r^2 = \pi(0.250 \text{ m})^2 = 0.196 \text{ m}^2$$

Substitute A, B, and $\theta = 0°$ into Equation 20.1 to find the initial magnetic flux:

$$\Phi_B = AB\cos\theta = (0.196 \text{ m}^2)(0.360 \text{ T})\cos(0°)$$
$$= 0.070\ 6 \text{ T} \cdot \text{m}^2 = \boxed{0.070\ 6 \text{ Wb}}$$

(b) Calculate the magnetic flux through the loop after it has rotated 45.0° around the x-axis.

Make the same substitutions as in part (a), except the angle between $\vec{\mathbf{B}}$ and the normal is now $\theta = 45.0°$:

$$\Phi_B = AB\cos\theta = (0.196 \text{ m}^2)(0.360 \text{ T})\cos(45.0°)$$
$$= 0.049\ 9 \text{ T} \cdot \text{m}^2 = \boxed{0.049\ 9 \text{ Wb}}$$

(c) Find the change in the magnetic flux due to the rotation of the loop.

Subtract the result of part (a) from the result of part (b):

$$\Delta\Phi_B = 0.049\ 9 \text{ Wb} - 0.070\ 6 \text{ Wb} = \boxed{-0.020\ 7 \text{ Wb}}$$

REMARKS Notice that the rotation of the loop, not any change in the magnetic field, is responsible for the change in flux. This changing magnetic flux is essential in the functioning of electric motors and generators.

QUESTION 20.1 True or False: If the loop is rotated in the opposite direction by the same amount, the change in magnetic flux has the same magnitude but opposite sign.

EXERCISE 20.1 The loop, having rotated by 45°, rotates clockwise another 30°, so the normal to the plane points at an angle of 75° with respect to the direction of the magnetic field. Find (a) the magnetic flux through the loop when $\theta = 75°$ and (b) the change in magnetic flux during the rotation from 45° to 75°.

ANSWERS (a) 0.018 3 Wb (b) −0.031 6 Wb

20.2 Faraday's Law of Induction and Lenz's Law

The usefulness of the concept of magnetic flux can be made obvious by another simple experiment that demonstrates the basic idea of electromagnetic induction. Consider a wire loop connected to an ammeter as in Active Figure 20.4 on page 692. If a magnet is moved toward the loop, the ammeter reads a current in one direction, as in Active Figure 20.4a. When the magnet is held stationary, as in Active Figure 20.4b, the ammeter reads zero current. If the magnet is moved away from the loop, the ammeter reads a current in the opposite direction, as in Active Figure 20.4c. If the magnet is held stationary and the loop is moved either toward or away from the magnet, the ammeter also reads a current. From these observations, it can be concluded that **a current is set up in the circuit as long as there is relative motion between the magnet and the loop**. The same experimental results are found whether the loop moves or the magnet moves. We call such a current an **induced current** because it is produced by an **induced emf**.

This experiment is similar to the Faraday experiment discussed in Section 20.1. In each case, an emf is induced in a circuit when the magnetic flux through the circuit changes with time. It turns out that the instantaneous emf induced in a circuit equals the negative of the rate of change of magnetic flux with respect to time through the circuit. This is **Faraday's law of magnetic induction**.

> **Tip 20.1 Induced Current Requires a Change in Magnetic Flux**
>
> The existence of magnetic flux through an area is not sufficient to create an induced emf. A *change* in the magnetic flux over some time interval Δt must occur for an emf to be induced.

Active Figure 20.4
A simple experiment showing that a current is induced in a loop when a magnet is moved toward or away from the loop.

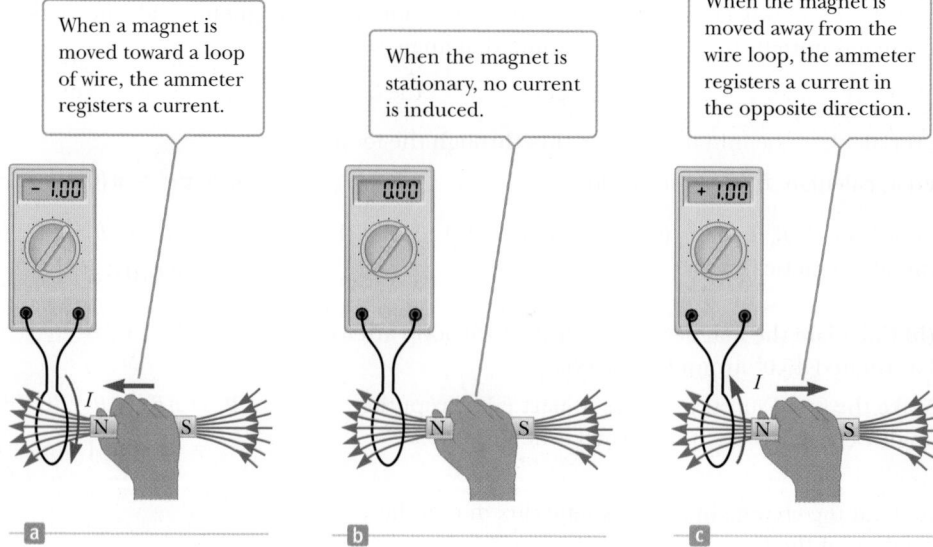

When a magnet is moved toward a loop of wire, the ammeter registers a current.

When the magnet is stationary, no current is induced.

When the magnet is moved away from the wire loop, the ammeter registers a current in the opposite direction.

Tip 20.2 There Are Two Magnetic Fields to Consider

When applying Lenz's law, there are *two* magnetic fields to consider. The first is the external changing magnetic field that induces the current in a conducting loop. The second is the magnetic field produced by the induced current in the loop.

Faraday's law ▶

If a circuit contains N tightly wound loops and the magnetic flux through each loop changes by the amount $\Delta\Phi_B$ during the interval Δt, the average emf induced in the circuit during time Δt is

$$\mathcal{E} = -N\frac{\Delta\Phi_B}{\Delta t} \qquad [20.2]$$

Because $\Phi_B = BA\cos\theta$, a change of any of the factors B, A, or θ with time produces an emf. We explore the effect of a change in each of these factors in the following sections. The minus sign in Equation 20.2 is included to indicate the polarity of the induced emf. This polarity determines which of two directions current will flow in a loop, a direction given by **Lenz's law**:

The current caused by the induced emf travels in the direction that creates a magnetic field with flux opposing the change in the original flux through the circuit.

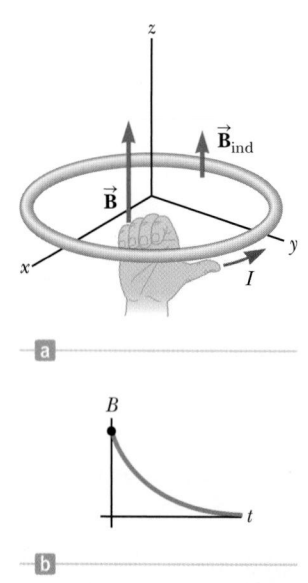

Figure 20.5 (a) The magnetic field $\vec{B}$ becomes smaller with time, reducing the flux, so current is induced in a direction that creates an induced magnetic field $\vec{B}_{ind}$ opposing the change in magnetic flux. (b) Graph of the magnitude of the magnetic field as a function of time.

Lenz's law says that if the magnetic flux through a loop is becoming more positive, say, then the induced emf creates a current and associated magnetic field that produces negative magnetic flux. Some mistakenly think this "counter magnetic field" created by the induced current, called $\vec{B}_{ind}$ ("ind" for induced), will always point in a direction opposite the applied magnetic field $\vec{B}$, but that is only true half the time! Figure 20.5a shows a field penetrating a loop. The graph in Figure 20.5b shows that the magnitude of the magnetic field $\vec{B}$ shrinks with time, which means that the flux of $\vec{B}$ is shrinking with time, so the induced field $\vec{B}_{ind}$ will actually be in the same direction as $\vec{B}$. In effect, $\vec{B}_{ind}$ "shores up" the field $\vec{B}$, slowing the loss of flux through the loop.

The direction of the current in Figure 20.5a can be determined by right-hand rule number 2: Point your right thumb in the direction that will cause the fingers on your right hand to curl in the direction of the induced field $\vec{B}_{ind}$. In this case, that direction is counterclockwise: with the right thumb pointed in the direction of the current, your fingers curl down outside the loop and around and ***up through the inside of the loop***. Remember, inside the loop is where it's important for the induced magnetic field to be pointing up.

■*Quick Quiz*

20.1 Figure 20.6 is a graph of the magnitude *B* versus time for a magnetic field that passes through a fixed loop and is oriented perpendicular to the plane of the loop. Rank the magnitudes of the emf generated in the loop at the three instants indicated from largest to smallest.

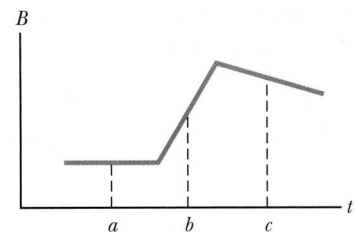

Figure 20.6 (Quick Quiz 20.1)

■ **EXAMPLE 20.2**   **Faraday and Lenz to the Rescue**

GOAL Calculate an induced emf and current with Faraday's law and apply Lenz's law when the magnetic field changes with time.

PROBLEM A coil with 25 turns of wire is wrapped on a frame with a square cross section 1.80 cm on a side. Each turn has the same area, equal to that of the frame, and the total resistance of the coil is 0.350 Ω. An applied uniform magnetic field is perpendicular to the plane of the coil, as in Figure 20.7. **(a)** If the field changes uniformly from 0.00 T to 0.500 T in 0.800 s, what is the induced emf in the coil while the field is changing? Find **(b)** the magnitude and **(c)** the direction of the induced current in the coil while the field is changing.

Figure 20.7 (Example 20.2)

STRATEGY Part (a) requires substituting into Faraday's law, Equation 20.2. The necessary information is given, except for $\Delta\Phi_B$, the change in the magnetic flux during the elapsed time. Using the normal direction to coincide with the positive z-axis, compute the initial and final magnetic fluxes with Equation 20.1, find the difference, and assemble all terms in Faraday's law. The current can then be found with Ohm's law, and its direction with Lenz's law.

· ·

SOLUTION

(a) Find the induced emf in the coil.

To compute the flux, the area of the coil is needed:

$$A = L^2 = (0.018\ 0\ \text{m})^2 = 3.24 \times 10^{-4}\ \text{m}^2$$

The magnetic flux $\Phi_{B,i}$ through the coil at $t = 0$ is zero because $B = 0$. Calculate the flux at $t = 0.800$ s:

$$\Phi_{B,f} = BA \cos\theta = (0.500\ \text{T})(3.24 \times 10^{-4}\ \text{m}^2)\cos(0°)$$
$$= 1.62 \times 10^{-4}\ \text{Wb}$$

Compute the change in the magnetic flux through the cross section of the coil over the 0.800-s interval:

$$\Delta\Phi_B = \Phi_{B,f} - \Phi_{B,i} = 1.62 \times 10^{-4}\ \text{Wb}$$

Substitute into Faraday's law of induction to find the induced emf in the coil:

$$\mathcal{E} = -N\frac{\Delta\Phi_B}{\Delta t} = -(25\ \text{turns})\left(\frac{1.62 \times 10^{-4}\ \text{Wb}}{0.800\ \text{s}}\right)$$
$$= \boxed{-5.06 \times 10^{-3}\ \text{V}}$$

(b) Find the magnitude of the induced current in the coil.

Substitute the voltage difference and the resistance into Ohm's law, where $\Delta V = \mathcal{E}$:

$$I = \frac{\Delta V}{R} = \frac{5.06 \times 10^{-3}\ \text{V}}{0.350\ \Omega} = \boxed{1.45 \times 10^{-2}\ \text{A}}$$

(c) Find the direction of the induced current in the coil.

The magnetic field is increasing up through the loop, in the same direction as the normal to the plane; hence, the flux is positive and is also increasing. A downward-pointing induced magnetic field will create negative flux, opposing the change. If you point your right thumb in the clockwise direction along the loop as viewed from above, your fingers curl down through the loop, which is the correct direction for the counter magnetic field. Hence the current must proceed in a clockwise direction as viewed from above the coil.

· ·

REMARKS Lenz's law can best be handled by first sketching a diagram.

QUESTION 20.2 What average emf is induced in the loop if, instead, the magnetic field changes uniformly from 0.500 T to 0? How would that affect the induced current?

(Continued)

EXERCISE 20.2 Suppose the magnetic field changes uniformly from 0.500 T to 0.200 T in the next 0.600 s. Compute (a) the induced emf in the coil and (b) the magnitude and direction of the induced current.

ANSWERS (a) 4.05×10^{-3} V (b) 1.16×10^{-2} A, counterclockwise

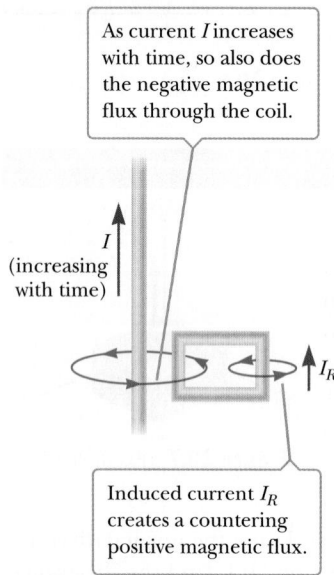

As current I increases with time, so also does the negative magnetic flux through the coil.

I (increasing with time)

I_R

Induced current I_R creates a countering positive magnetic flux.

Figure 20.8 (Lenz's Law Example 1) Current I increases in magnitude with time, strengthening the magnetic field that circulates around the wire.

Finding the Direction of the Induced Current

Finding the direction of the induced current can be tricky. The following three examples illustrate how the direction is found using Lenz's law.

Lenz's Law Example 1 The current in the wire of Figure 20.8 is steadily increasing in the direction indicated. Let's choose the normal direction to be out of the page so that magnetic field vectors coming out of the page will produce positive magnetic flux. The magnetic field created by the current I circulates around the wire, going into the page on the right side of the long wire in the region of the rectangular coil and coming out of the page on the left side of the long straight wire. Therefore, the magnetic flux through the rectangular coil due to the current I is negative. Because the current is increasing up the page, the magnetic field is becoming stronger, increasing the magnitude of the negative flux through the rectangular coil. By Lenz's law, the induced current in the coil must produce positive flux, countering the increasing negative flux. That requires an induced magnetic field pointing out of the page through the coil. Mentally curl the fingers of the right hand around the right branch of the rectangular coil, and note that the fingers come straight up out of the page through the coil, as required. The right thumb, meanwhile, points up the page, indicating the current direction in that part of the coil. Therefore the induced current in the coil is counterclockwise.

Lenz's Law Example 2 In Figure 20.9a, the north pole of the magnet moves toward the coil. If the normal direction is chosen to the right, then the magnetic flux through the coil due to the magnet is positive and increases with time. A negative flux to the left must therefore be created by the induced current in the coil, so the induced magnetic field must also point to the left as indicated in Figure 20.9b. Imagine curling the fingers of the right hand around the coil so they point through the coil to the left. The right thumb then points upward, indicating the induced current is counterclockwise as viewed from the left end of the loop.

Lenz's Law Example 3 Consider a coil of wire placed near a solenoid in Figure 20.10a. The wire is wrapped in such a way as to create a south magnetic pole at the right end when the switch is closed in Figure 20.10b. Choose the normal direction to the left. When the switch is closed, the current in the solenoid begins to increase, and the magnetic flux through the coil is positive and increasing with time. Therefore the induced current in the coil must create negative magnetic flux

Figure 20.9 (Lenz's Law Example 2) (a) The north pole of the magnet approaches the coil from the left, with the normal direction taken to the right. (b) A current is induced in the coil.

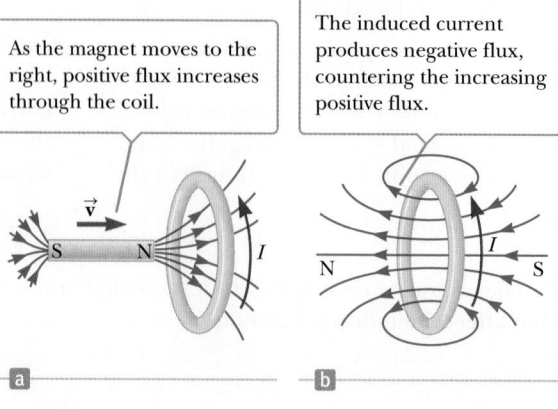

As the magnet moves to the right, positive flux increases through the coil.

The induced current produces negative flux, countering the increasing positive flux.

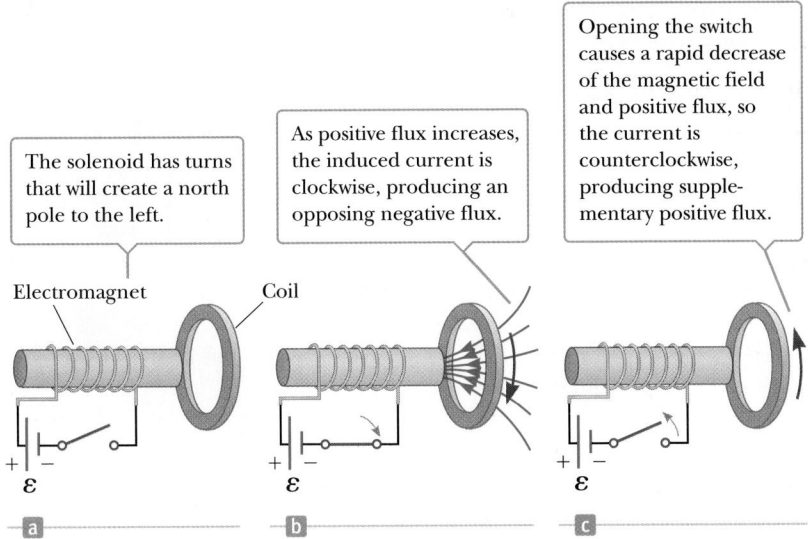

The solenoid has turns that will create a north pole to the left.

As positive flux increases, the induced current is clockwise, producing an opposing negative flux.

Opening the switch causes a rapid decrease of the magnetic field and positive flux, so the current is counterclockwise, producing supplementary positive flux.

Electromagnet   Coil

a   b   c

Figure 20.10 (Lenz's Law Example 3) (a) The turns of the solenoid create a magnetic field with north pole pointing left, which is also taken as the normal direction. (b) When the switch is closed, positive flux begins increasing through the coil as field lines converge on the solenoid's south pole. (c) Opening the switch causes the solenoid's field to rapidly decrease.

to counteract the increasing positive flux created by the current in the solenoid. That requires an induced magnetic field directed to the right through the coil. Turning the right hand so the thumb is pointed downward, the right fingers can curl through the coil and to the right. The induced current in the coil follows the direction of the right thumb, which is clockwise as viewed from the left end of the coil. When the switch is opened again in Figure 20.10c the current in the solenoid changes direction because the magnetic field and positive flux begin to decrease. Moving counterclockwise, the induced current creates positive flux through the coil, opposing the decrease in positive flux.

In all three of these examples, the critical idea is that a changing flux causes an induced current, and the associated induced magnetic field produces flux opposing the change in flux in accordance with Lenz's law. When the flux stops changing, the induced current stops. Although in each case the magnetic flux changed because of a changing magnetic field, induced currents can result even when the magnetic field is constant provided the flux through the loop changes. That fact will become clear when discussing motional emf in Section 20.3 and generators in Section 20.4.

■ Quick Quiz

20.2 A bar magnet is falling toward the center of a loop of wire, with the north pole oriented downward. Viewed from the same side of the loop as the magnet, as the north pole approaches the loop, what is the direction of the induced current? (a) clockwise (b) zero (c) counterclockwise (d) along the length of the magnet

20.3 Two circular loops are side by side and lie in the xy-plane. A switch is closed, starting a counterclockwise current in the left-hand loop, as viewed from a point on the positive z-axis passing through the center of the loop. Which of the following statements is true of the right-hand loop? (a) The current remains zero. (b) An induced current moves counterclockwise. (c) An induced current moves clockwise.

The ground fault interrupter (GFI) is an interesting safety device that protects people against electric shock when they touch appliances and power tools. Its operation makes use of Faraday's law. Figure 20.11 shows the essential parts of a ground fault interrupter. Wire 1 leads from the wall outlet to the appliance to be protected, and wire 2 leads from the appliance back to the wall outlet. An iron ring surrounds the two wires to confine the magnetic field set up by each wire. A sensing coil, which can activate a circuit breaker when changes in magnetic flux occur, is wrapped around part of the iron ring. Because the currents in the wires

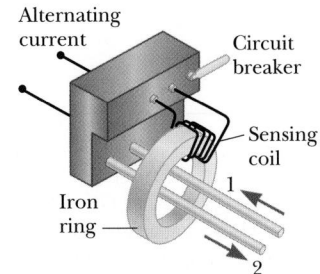

Alternating current

Circuit breaker

Sensing coil

Iron ring

1

2

Figure 20.11 Essential components of a ground fault interrupter (contents of the gray box in Fig. 20.12a, page 696). In newer homes such devices are built directly into wall outlets. The purpose of the sensing coil and circuit breaker is to cut off the current before damage is done.

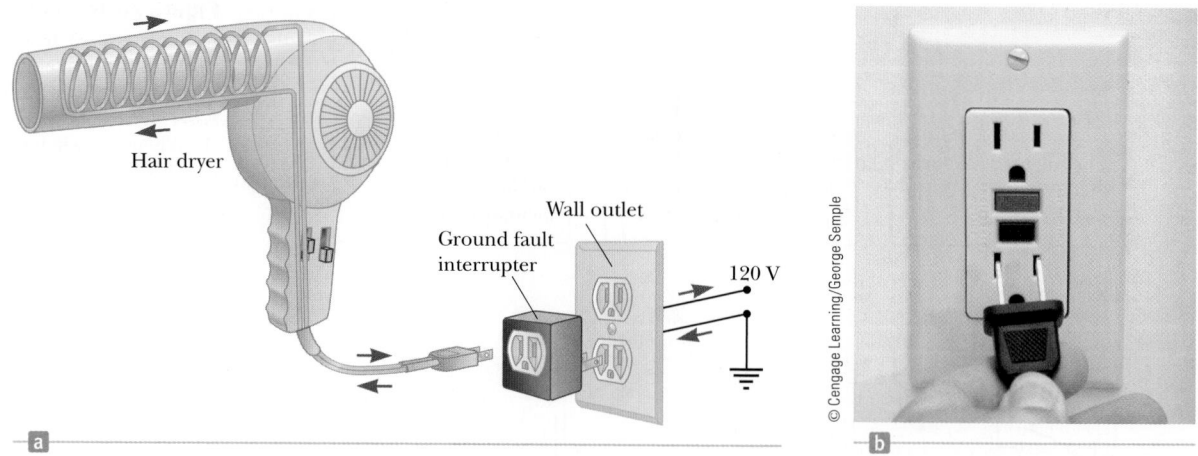

© Cengage Learning/George Semple

Figure 20.12 (a) This hair dryer has been plugged into a ground fault interrupter that is in turn plugged into an unprotected wall outlet. (b) You likely have seen this kind of ground fault interrupter in a hotel bathroom, where hair dryers and electric shavers are often used by people just out of the shower or who might touch a water pipe, providing a ready path to ground in the event of a short circuit.

APPLICATION
Ground fault interrupters

are in opposite directions, the net magnetic field through the sensing coil due to the currents is zero. If a short circuit occurs in the appliance so that there is no returning current, however, the net magnetic field through the sensing coil is no longer zero. A short circuit can happen if, for example, one of the wires loses its insulation, providing a path through you to ground if you happen to be touching the appliance and are grounded as in Figure 18.23a. Because the current is alternating, the magnetic flux through the sensing coil changes with time, producing an induced voltage in the coil. This induced voltage is used to trigger a circuit breaker, stopping the current quickly (in about 1 ms) before it reaches a level that might be harmful to the person using the appliance. A ground fault interrupter provides faster and more complete protection than even the case-ground-and-circuit-breaker combination shown in Figure 18.23b. For this reason, ground fault interrupters are commonly found in bathrooms, where electricity poses a hazard to people. (See Fig. 20.12.)

APPLICATION
Electric guitar pickups

Another interesting application of Faraday's law is the production of sound in an electric guitar. A vibrating string induces an emf in a coil (Fig. 20.13). The pickup coil is placed near the vibrating guitar string, which is made of a metal that can be magnetized. The permanent magnet inside the coil magnetizes the portion of the string nearest the coil. When the guitar string vibrates at some frequency, its magnetized segment produces a changing magnetic flux through the pickup coil. The changing flux induces a voltage in the coil; the voltage is fed to an amplifier. The output of the amplifier is sent to the loudspeakers, producing the sound waves that we hear.

Figure 20.13 (a) In an electric guitar a vibrating string induces a voltage in the pickup coil. (b) Several pickups allow the vibration to be detected from different portions of the string.

© Charles D. Winters/Cengage Learning

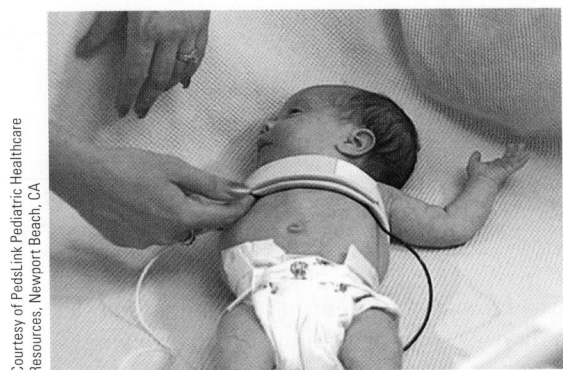

Courtesy of PedsLink Pediatric Healthcare Resources, Newport Beach, CA

Figure 20.14 This infant is wearing a monitor designed to alert caregivers if breathing stops. Notice the two wires attached to opposite sides of the chest.

Sudden infant death syndrome, or SIDS, is a devastating affliction in which a baby suddenly stops breathing during sleep without an apparent cause. One type of monitoring device, called an apnea monitor, is sometimes used to alert caregivers of the cessation of breathing. The device uses induced currents, as shown in Figure 20.14. A coil of wire attached to one side of the chest carries an alternating current. The varying magnetic flux produced by this current passes through a pickup coil attached to the opposite side of the chest. Expansion and contraction of the chest caused by breathing or movement change the strength of the voltage induced in the pickup coil. If breathing stops, however, the pattern of the induced voltage stabilizes, and external circuits monitoring the voltage sound an alarm to the caregivers after a momentary pause to ensure that a problem actually does exist.

BIO APPLICATION
Apnea monitors

20.3 Motional emf

In Section 20.2 we considered emfs induced in a circuit when the magnetic field changes with time. In this section we describe a particular application of Faraday's law in which a so-called **motional emf** is produced. It is the emf induced in a conductor moving through a magnetic field.

First consider a straight conductor of length ℓ moving with constant velocity through a uniform magnetic field directed into the paper, as in Figure 20.15. For simplicity, we assume the conductor moves in a direction perpendicular to the field. A magnetic force of magnitude $F_m = qvB$, directed downward, acts on the electrons in the conductor. Because of this magnetic force, the free electrons move to the lower end of the conductor and accumulate there, leaving a net positive charge at the upper end. As a result of this charge separation, an electric field is produced in the conductor. The charge at the ends builds up until the downward magnetic force qvB is balanced by the upward electric force qE. At this point, charge stops flowing and the condition for equilibrium requires that

$$qE = qvB \qquad \text{or} \qquad E = vB$$

Because the electric field is uniform, the field produced in the conductor is related to the potential difference across the ends by $\Delta V = E\ell$, giving

$$\Delta V = E\ell = B\ell v \qquad \text{[20.3]}$$

Because there is an excess of positive charge at the upper end of the conductor and an excess of negative charge at the lower end, the upper end is at a higher potential than the lower end. There is a potential difference across a conductor as long as it moves through a field. If the motion is reversed, the polarity of the potential difference is also reversed.

A more interesting situation occurs if the moving conductor is part of a closed conducting path. This situation is particularly useful for illustrating how

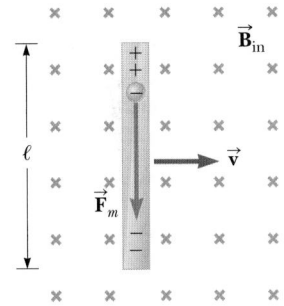

Figure 20.15 A straight conductor of length ℓ moving with velocity $\vec{v}$ through a uniform magnetic field $\vec{B}$ directed perpendicular to $\vec{v}$. The vector $\vec{F}_m$ is the magnetic force on an electron in the conductor. An emf of $B\ell v$ is induced between the ends of the bar.

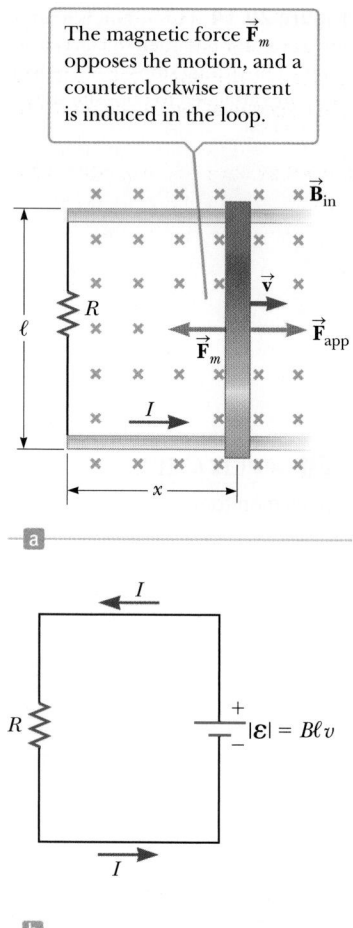

The magnetic force $\vec{\mathbf{F}}_m$ opposes the motion, and a counterclockwise current is induced in the loop.

a

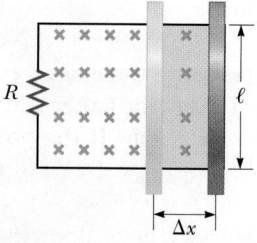

Figure 20.17 As the bar moves to the right, the area of the loop increases by the amount $\ell\Delta x$ and the magnetic flux through the loop increases by $B\ell\Delta x$.

b

Active Figure 20.16

(a) A conducting bar sliding with velocity $\vec{\mathbf{v}}$ along two conducting rails under the action of an applied force $\vec{\mathbf{F}}_{app}$. (b) The equivalent circuit of that in (a).

a changing loop area induces a current in a closed circuit described by Faraday's law. Consider a circuit consisting of a conducting bar of length ℓ, sliding along two fixed, parallel conducting rails, as in Active Figure 20.16a. For simplicity, assume the moving bar has zero resistance and the stationary part of the circuit has constant resistance R. Take the normal direction to coincide with the z-axis, out of the page. A uniform and constant magnetic field $\vec{\mathbf{B}}$ is applied perpendicular to the plane of the circuit. As the bar is pulled to the right in the positive x-direction with velocity $\vec{\mathbf{v}}$ under the influence of an applied force $\vec{\mathbf{F}}_{app}$, a magnetic force along the length of the bar acts on the free charges in the bar. This force in turn sets up an induced current because the charges are free to move in a closed conducting path. In this case, the changing magnetic flux through the loop and the corresponding induced emf across the moving bar arise from the *change in area of the loop* as the bar moves through the magnetic field. Because the flux into the page increases, by Lenz's law the induced current circulates counterclockwise, producing flux out of the page that opposes the change.

Assume the bar moves a distance Δx in time Δt, as shown in Figure 20.17. The increase in flux $\Delta\Phi_B$ through the loop in that time is the amount of flux that now passes through the portion of the circuit that has area $\ell\,\Delta x$:

$$\Delta\Phi_B = BA = B\ell\,\Delta x$$

Using Faraday's law and noting that there is one loop ($N = 1$), we find that the magnitude of the induced emf is

$$|\mathbf{\mathcal{E}}| = \frac{\Delta\Phi_B}{\Delta t} = B\ell\,\frac{\Delta x}{\Delta t} = B\ell v \qquad [20.4]$$

This induced emf is often called a **motional emf** because it arises from the motion of a conductor through a magnetic field.

Further, if the resistance of the circuit is R, the magnitude of the induced current in the circuit is

$$I = \frac{|\mathbf{\mathcal{E}}|}{R} = \frac{B\ell v}{R} \qquad [20.5]$$

Active Figure 20.16b shows the equivalent circuit diagram for this example.

■ APPLYING PHYSICS 20.2 | Space Catapult

Applying a force on the bar will result in an induced emf in the circuit shown in Active Figure 20.16. Suppose we remove the external magnetic field in the diagram and replace the resistor with a high-voltage source and a switch, as in Figure 20.18. What will happen when the switch is closed? Will the bar move, and does it matter which way we connect the high-voltage source?

EXPLANATION Suppose the source is capable of establishing high current. Then the two horizontal conducting rods will create a strong magnetic field in the area between them, directed into the page. (The movable bar also cre-

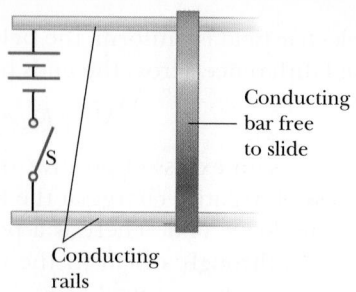

Conducting bar free to slide

Conducting rails

Figure 20.18 (Applying Physics 20.2)

ates a magnetic field, but this field can't exert force on the bar itself.) Because the moving bar carries a downward current, a magnetic force is exerted on the bar, directed to the right. Hence, the bar accelerates along the rails away from the power supply. If the polarity of the power were reversed, the magnetic field would be out of the page, the current in the bar would be upward, and the force on the bar would still be directed to the right. The $BI\ell$ force exerted by a magnetic field according to Equation 19.6 causes the bar to accelerate away from the voltage source. Studies have shown that it's possible to launch payloads into space with this technology. (This is the working princi-

ple of a rail gun.) Very large accelerations can be obtained with currently available technology, with payloads being accelerated to a speed of several kilometers per second in a fraction of a second. This acceleration is larger than humans can tolerate.

Rail guns have been proposed as propulsion systems for moving asteroids into more useful orbits. The material of the asteroid could be mined and launched off the surface by a rail gun, which would act like a rocket engine, modifying the velocity and hence the orbit of the asteroid. Some asteroids contain trillions of dollars worth of valuable metals. ■

■ **Quick Quiz**

20.4 A horizontal metal bar oriented east-west drops straight down in a location where Earth's magnetic field is due north. As a result, an emf develops between the ends. Which end is positively charged? (a) the east end (b) the west end (c) neither end carries a charge

20.5 You intend to move a rectangular loop of wire into a region of uniform magnetic field at a given speed so as to induce an emf in the loop. The plane of the loop must remain perpendicular to the magnetic field lines. In which orientation should you hold the loop while you move it into the region with the magnetic field to generate the largest emf? (a) with the long dimension of the loop parallel to the velocity vector (b) with the short dimension of the loop parallel to the velocity vector (c) either way because the emf is the same regardless of orientation

---

■ **EXAMPLE 20.3**   A Potential Difference Induced Across Airplane Wings

GOAL Find the emf induced by motion through a magnetic field.

PROBLEM An airplane with a wingspan of 30.0 m flies due north at a location where the downward component of Earth's magnetic field is 0.600×10^{-4} T. There is also a component pointing due north that has a magnitude of 0.470×10^{-4} T. **(a)** Find the difference in potential between the wingtips when the speed of the plane is 2.50×10^2 m/s. **(b)** Which wingtip is positive?

STRATEGY Because the plane is flying north, the northern component of magnetic field won't have any effect on the induced emf. The induced emf across the wing is caused solely by the downward component of the Earth's magnetic field. Substitute the given quantities into Equation 20.4. Use right-hand rule number 1 to find the direction positive charges would be propelled by the magnetic force.

SOLUTION

(a) Calculate the difference in potential across the wingtips.

Write the motional emf equation and substitute the given quantities:

$$\mathcal{E} = B\ell v = (0.600 \times 10^{-4} \text{ T})(30.0 \text{ m})(2.50 \times 10^2 \text{ m/s})$$
$$= \boxed{0.450 \text{ V}}$$

(b) Which wingtip is positive?

Apply right-hand rule number 1:

Point the fingers of your right hand north, in the direction of the velocity, and curl them down, in the direction of the magnetic field. Your thumb points west. Therefore the west wingtip is positive.

REMARKS An induced emf such as this one can cause problems on an aircraft.

QUESTION 20.3 In what directions are magnetic forces exerted on electrons in the metal aircraft if it is flying due west? (a) north (b) south (c) east (d) west (e) up (f) down

(Continued)

EXERCISE 20.3 Suppose the magnetic field in a given region of space is parallel to Earth's surface, points north, and has magnitude 1.80×10^{-4} T. A metal cable attached to a space station stretches radially outwards 2.50 km. (a) Estimate the potential difference that develops between the ends of the cable if it's traveling eastward around Earth at a speed of 7.70×10^3 m/s. (b) Which end of the cable is positive, the lower end or the upper end?

ANSWERS (a) 3.47×10^3 V (b) The upper end is positive.

■ EXAMPLE 20.4 | Where Is the Energy Source?

GOAL Use motional emf to find an induced emf and a current.

PROBLEM (a) The sliding bar in Figure 20.16a has a length of 0.500 m and moves at 2.00 m/s in a magnetic field of magnitude 0.250 T. Using the concept of motional emf, find the induced voltage in the moving rod. (b) If the resistance in the circuit is 0.500 Ω, find the current in the circuit and the power delivered to the resistor. (*Note:* The current in this case goes counterclockwise around the loop.) (c) Calculate the magnetic force on the bar. (d) Use the concepts of work and power to calculate the applied force.

STRATEGY For part (a), substitute into Equation 20.4 for the motional emf. Once the emf is found, substitution into Ohm's law gives the current. In part (c), use Equation 19.6 for the magnetic force on a current-carrying conductor. In part (d), use the fact that the power dissipated by the resistor multiplied by the elapsed time must equal the work done by the applied force.

SOLUTION

(a) Find the induced emf with the concept of motional emf.

Substitute into Equation 20.4 to find the induced emf:

$$\mathcal{E} = B\ell v = (0.250 \text{ T})(0.500 \text{ m})(2.00 \text{ m/s}) = \boxed{0.250 \text{ V}}$$

(b) Find the induced current in the circuit and the power dissipated by the resistor.

Substitute the emf and the resistance into Ohm's law to find the induced current:

$$I = \frac{\mathcal{E}}{R} = \frac{0.250 \text{ V}}{0.500 \text{ Ω}} = \boxed{0.500 \text{ A}}$$

Substitute $I = 0.500$ A and $\mathcal{E} = 0.250$ V into Equation 17.8 to find the power dissipated by the 0.500-Ω resistor:

$$P = I\,\Delta V = (0.500 \text{ A})(0.250 \text{ V}) = \boxed{0.125 \text{ W}}$$

(c) Calculate the magnitude and direction of the magnetic force on the bar.

Substitute values for I, B, and ℓ into Equation 19.6, with $\sin \theta = \sin (90°) = 1$, to find the magnitude of the force:

$$F_m = IB\ell = (0.500 \text{ A})(0.250 \text{ T})(0.500 \text{ m}) = \boxed{6.25 \times 10^{-2} \text{ N}}$$

Apply right-hand rule number 2 to find the direction of the force:

Point the fingers of your right hand in the direction of the positive current, then curl them in the direction of the magnetic field. Your thumb points in the $\boxed{\text{negative}}$ x-direction.

(d) Find the value of F_{app}, the applied force.

Set the work done by the applied force equal to the dissipated power times the elapsed time:

$$W_{app} = F_{app}d = P\Delta t$$

Solve for F_{app} and substitute $d = v\,\Delta t$:

$$F_{app} = \frac{P\Delta t}{d} = \frac{P\Delta t}{v\Delta t} = \frac{P}{v} = \frac{0.125 \text{ W}}{2.00 \text{ m/s}} = \boxed{6.25 \times 10^{-2} \text{ N}}$$

REMARKS Part (d) could be solved by using Newton's second law for an object in equilibrium: Two forces act horizontally on the bar and the acceleration of the bar is zero, so the forces must be equal in magnitude and opposite in direction. Notice the agreement between the answers for F_m and F_{app}, despite the very different concepts used.

QUESTION 20.4 Suppose the applied force and magnetic field in Figure 20.16a are removed, but a battery creates a current in the same direction as indicated. What happens to the bar?

EXERCISE 20.4 Suppose the current suddenly increases to 1.25 A in the same direction as before due to an increase in speed of the bar. Find (a) the emf induced in the rod and (b) the new speed of the rod.

ANSWERS (a) 0.625 V (b) 5.00 m/s

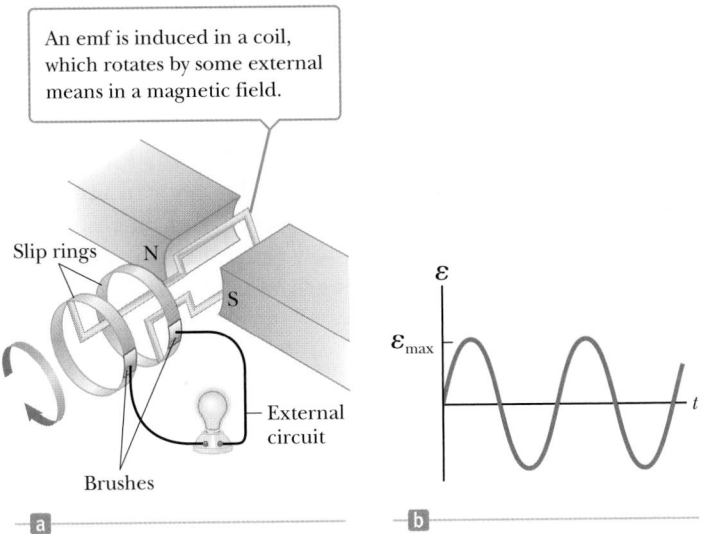

Active Figure 20.19
(a) A schematic diagram of an AC generator. An emf is induced in a coil, which rotates by some external means in a magnetic field. (b) A plot of the alternating emf induced in the loop versus time.

An emf is induced in a coil, which rotates by some external means in a magnetic field.

Slip rings

N

S

External circuit

Brushes

20.4 Generators

Generators and motors are important practical devices that operate on the principle of electromagnetic induction. First, consider the **alternating-current** (AC) **generator**, a device that converts mechanical energy to electrical energy. In its simplest form, the AC generator consists of a wire loop rotated in a magnetic field by some external means (Active Fig. 20.19a). In commercial power plants, the energy required to rotate the loop can be derived from a variety of sources. In a hydroelectric plant, for example, falling water directed against the blades of a turbine produces the rotary motion; in a coal-fired plant, heat produced by burning coal is used to convert water to steam, and this steam is directed against the turbine blades. As the loop rotates, the magnetic flux through it changes with time, inducing an emf and a current in an external circuit. The ends of the loop are connected to slip rings that rotate with the loop. Connections to the external circuit are made by stationary brushes in contact with the slip rings.

We can derive an expression for the emf generated in the rotating loop by making use of the equation for motional emf, $\mathcal{E} = B\ell v$. Figure 20.20a shows a loop of wire rotating clockwise in a uniform magnetic field directed to the right. The magnetic force (qvB) on the charges in wires AB and CD is not along the lengths of

APPLICATION
Alternating-current generators

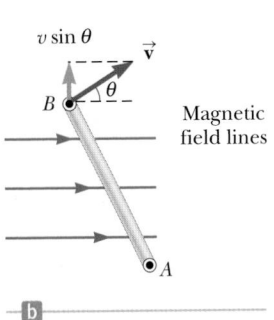

Figure 20.20 (a) A loop rotating at a constant angular velocity in an external magnetic field. The emf induced in the loop varies sinusoidally with time. (b) An edge view of the rotating loop.

Luis Castaneda, Inc.

Turbines turn electric generators at a hydroelectric power plant.

the wires. (The force on the electrons in these wires is perpendicular to the wires.) Hence, an emf is generated only in wires BC and AD. At any instant, wire BC has velocity $\vec{v}$ at an angle θ with the magnetic field, as shown in Figure 20.20b. (Note that the component of velocity parallel to the field has no effect on the charges in the wire, whereas the component of velocity perpendicular to the field produces a magnetic force on the charges that moves electrons from C to B.) The emf generated in wire BC equals $B\ell v_\perp$, where ℓ is the length of the wire and $v_\perp$ is the component of velocity perpendicular to the field. An emf of $B\ell v_\perp$ is also generated in wire DA, and the sense of this emf is the same as that in wire BC. Because $v_\perp = v \sin\theta$, the total induced emf is

$$\mathcal{E} = 2B\ell v_\perp = 2B\ell v \sin\theta \qquad [20.6]$$

If the loop rotates with a constant angular speed ω, we can use the relation $\theta = \omega t$ in Equation 20.6. Furthermore, because every point on the wires BC and DA rotates in a circle about the axis of rotation with the same angular speed ω, we have $v = r\omega = (a/2)\omega$, where a is the length of sides AB and CD. Equation 20.6 therefore reduces to

$$\mathcal{E} = 2B\ell \left(\frac{a}{2}\right)\omega \sin\omega t = B\ell a\omega \sin\omega t$$

If a coil has N turns, the emf is N times as large because each loop has the same emf induced in it. Further, because the area of the loop is $A = \ell a$, the total emf is

$$\mathcal{E} = NBA\omega \sin\omega t \qquad [20.7]$$

This result shows that the emf varies sinusoidally with time, as plotted in Active Figure 20.19b. Note that the maximum emf has the value

$$\mathcal{E}_{max} = NBA\omega \qquad [20.8]$$

which occurs when $\omega t = 90°$ or $270°$. In other words, $\mathcal{E} = \mathcal{E}_{max}$ when the plane of the loop is parallel to the magnetic field. Further, the emf is zero when $\omega t = 0$ or $180°$, which happens whenever the magnetic field is perpendicular to the plane of the loop. In the United States and Canada the frequency of rotation for commercial generators is 60 Hz, whereas in some European countries 50 Hz is used. (Recall that $\omega = 2\pi f$, where f is the frequency in hertz.)

APPLICATION

Direct-current generators

The **direct-current** (DC) **generator** is illustrated in Active Figure 20.21a. The components are essentially the same as those of the AC generator except that the contacts to the rotating loop are made by a split ring, or commutator. In this design the output voltage always has the same polarity and the current is a pulsating direct current, as in Active Figure 20.21b. Note that the contacts to the split ring reverse their roles every half cycle. At the same time, the polarity of the induced emf reverses. Hence, the polarity of the split ring remains the same.

Active Figure 20.21

(a) A schematic diagram of a DC generator. (b) The emf fluctuates in magnitude, but always has the same polarity.

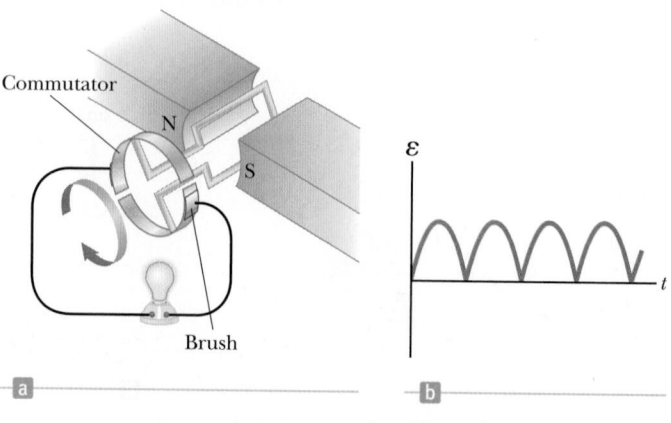

Commutator

Brush

A pulsating DC current is not suitable for most applications. To produce a steady DC current, commercial DC generators use many loops and commutators distributed around the axis of rotation so that the sinusoidal pulses from the loops overlap in phase. When these pulses are superimposed, the DC output is almost free of fluctuations.

▪ EXAMPLE 20.5 | emf Induced in an AC Generator

GOAL Understand physical aspects of an AC generator.

PROBLEM An AC generator consists of eight turns of wire, each having area $A = 0.090\ 0\ \text{m}^2$, with a total resistance of $12.0\ \Omega$. The coil rotates in a magnetic field of 0.500 T at a constant frequency of 60.0 Hz, with axis of rotation perpendicular to the direction of the magnetic field. **(a)** Find the maximum induced emf. **(b)** What is the maximum induced current? **(c)** Determine the induced emf and current as functions of time. **(d)** What maximum torque must be applied to keep the coil turning?

STRATEGY From the given frequency, calculate the angular frequency ω and substitute it, together with given quantities, into Equation 20.8. As functions of time, the emf and current have the form $A \sin \omega t$, where A is the maximum emf or current, respectively. For part (d), calculate the magnetic torque on the coil when the current is at a maximum. (See Chapter 19.) The applied torque must do work against this magnetic torque to keep the coil turning.

SOLUTION

(a) Find the maximum induced emf.

First, calculate the angular frequency of the rotational motion:

$$\omega = 2\pi f = 2\pi(60.0\ \text{Hz}) = 377\ \text{rad/s}$$

Substitute the values for N, A, B, and ω into Equation 20.8, obtaining the maximum induced emf:

$$\mathcal{E}_{max} = NAB\omega = 8(0.090\ 0\ \text{m}^2)(0.500\ \text{T})(377\ \text{rad/s})$$
$$= \boxed{136\ \text{V}}$$

(b) What is the maximum induced current?

Substitute the maximum induced emf $\mathcal{E}_{max}$ and the resistance R into Ohm's law to find the maximum induced current:

$$I_{max} = \frac{\mathcal{E}_{max}}{R} = \frac{136\ \text{V}}{12.0\ \Omega} = \boxed{11.3\ \text{A}}$$

(c) Determine the induced emf and the current as functions of time.

Substitute $\mathcal{E}_{max}$ and ω into Equation 20.7 to obtain the variation of $\mathcal{E}$ with time t in seconds:

$$\mathcal{E} = \mathcal{E}_{max} \sin \omega t = \boxed{(136\ \text{V}) \sin 377t}$$

The time variation of the current looks just like this expression, except with the maximum current out in front:

$$I = \boxed{(11.3\ \text{A}) \sin 377t}$$

(d) Calculate the maximum applied torque necessary to keep the coil turning.

Write the equation for magnetic torque:

$$\tau = \mu B \sin \theta$$

Calculate the maximum magnetic moment of the coil, μ:

$$\mu = I_{max}AN = (11.3\ \text{A})(0.090\ \text{m}^2)(8) = 8.14\ \text{A} \cdot \text{m}^2$$

Substitute into the magnetic torque equation, with $\theta = 90°$ to find the maximum applied torque:

$$\tau_{max} = (8.14\ \text{A} \cdot \text{m}^2)(0.500\ \text{T}) \sin 90° = \boxed{4.07\ \text{N} \cdot \text{m}}$$

REMARKS The number of loops, N, can't be arbitrary because there must be a force strong enough to turn the coil.

QUESTION 20.5 What effect does doubling the frequency have on the maximum induced emf?

(Continued)

EXERCISE 20.5 An AC generator is to have a maximum output of 301 V. Each circular turn of wire has an area of 0.100 m² and a resistance of 0.80 Ω. The coil rotates in a magnetic field of 0.600 T with a frequency of 40.0 Hz, with the axis of rotation perpendicular to the direction of the magnetic field. (a) How many turns of wire should the coil have to produce the desired emf? (b) Find the maximum current induced in the coil. (c) Determine the induced emf as a function of time.

ANSWERS (a) 20 turns (b) 18.8 A (c) $\mathcal{E} = (301 \text{ V}) \sin 251t$

Motors and Back emf

APPLICATION

Motors

Motors are devices that convert electrical energy to mechanical energy. Essentially, **a motor is a generator run in reverse**: instead of a current being generated by a rotating loop, a current is supplied to the loop by a source of emf, and the magnetic torque on the current-carrying loop causes it to rotate.

A motor can perform useful mechanical work when a shaft connected to its rotating coil is attached to some external device. As the coil in the motor rotates, however, the changing magnetic flux through it induces an emf that acts to reduce the current in the coil. If it *increased* the current, Lenz's law would be violated. The phrase **back emf** is used for an emf that tends to reduce the applied current. The back emf increases in magnitude as the rotational speed of the coil increases. We can picture this state of affairs as the equivalent circuit in Figure 20.22. For illustrative purposes, assume the external power source supplying current in the coil of the motor has a voltage of 120 V, the coil has a resistance of 10 Ω, and the back emf induced in the coil at this instant is 70 V. The voltage available to supply current equals the difference between the applied voltage and the back emf, or 50 V in this case. The current is always reduced by the back emf.

Figure 20.22 A motor can be represented as a resistance plus a back emf.

When a motor is turned on, there is no back emf initially and the current is very large because it's limited only by the resistance of the coil. As the coil begins to rotate, the induced back emf opposes the applied voltage and the current in the coil is reduced. If the mechanical load increases, the motor slows down, which decreases the back emf. This reduction in the back emf increases the current in the coil and therefore also increases the power needed from the external voltage source. As a result, the power requirements for starting a motor and for running it under heavy loads are greater than those for running the motor under average loads. If the motor is allowed to run under no mechanical load, the back emf reduces the current to a value just large enough to balance energy losses by heat and friction.

■ EXAMPLE 20.6 | Induced Current in a Motor

GOAL Apply the concept of a back emf in calculating the induced current in a motor.

PROBLEM A motor has coils with a resistance of 10.0 Ω and is supplied by a voltage of $\Delta V = 1.20 \times 10^2$ V. When the motor is running at its maximum speed, the back emf is 70.0 V. Find the current in the coils (a) when the motor is first turned on and (b) when the motor has reached its maximum rotation rate.

STRATEGY For each part, find the net voltage, which is the applied voltage minus the induced emf. Divide the net voltage by the resistance to get the current.

· ·

SOLUTION

(a) Find the initial current, when the motor is first turned on.

If the coil isn't rotating, the back emf is zero and the current has its maximum value. Calculate the difference between the emf and the initial back emf and divide by the resistance R, obtaining the initial current:

$$I = \frac{\mathcal{E} - \mathcal{E}_{back}}{R} = \frac{1.20 \times 10^2 \text{ V} - 0}{10.0 \ \Omega} = \boxed{12.0 \text{ A}}$$

(b) Find the current when the motor is rotating at its maximum rate.

Repeat the calculation, using the maximum value of the back emf:

$$I = \frac{\mathcal{E} - \mathcal{E}_{back}}{R} = \frac{1.20 \times 10^2\,\text{V} - 70.0\,\text{V}}{10.0\,\Omega} = \frac{50.0\,\text{V}}{10.0\,\Omega}$$

$$= \boxed{5.00\,\text{A}}$$

REMARKS The phenomenon of back emf is one way in which the rotation rate of electric motors is limited.

QUESTION 20.6 As a motor speeds up, what happens to the magnitude of the magnetic torque? (a) It increases. (b) It decreases. (c) It remains constant.

EXERCISE 20.6 If the current in the motor is 8.00 A at some instant, what is the back emf at that time?

ANSWER 40.0 V

20.5 Self-Inductance

Consider a circuit consisting of a switch, a resistor, and a source of emf, as in Figure 20.23. When the switch is closed, the current doesn't immediately change from zero to its maximum value, $\mathcal{E}/R$. The law of electromagnetic induction, Faraday's law, prevents this change. What happens instead is the following: as the current increases with time, the magnetic flux through the loop due to this current also increases. The increasing flux induces an emf in the circuit that opposes the change in magnetic flux. By Lenz's law, the induced emf is in the direction indicated by the dashed battery in the figure. The net potential difference across the resistor is the emf of the battery minus the opposing induced emf. As the magnitude of the current increases, the *rate* of increase lessens and hence the induced emf decreases. This opposing emf results in a gradual increase in the current. For the same reason, when the switch is opened, the current doesn't immediately fall to zero. This effect is called **self-induction** because the changing flux through the circuit arises from the circuit itself. The emf that is set up in the circuit is called a **self-induced emf**.

As a second example of self-inductance, consider Figure 20.24, which shows a coil wound on a cylindrical iron core. (A practical device would have several hundred turns.) Assume the current changes with time. When the current is in the direction shown, a magnetic field is set up inside the coil, directed from right to left. As a result, some lines of magnetic flux pass through the cross-sectional area of the coil. As the current changes with time, the flux through the coil changes and induces an emf in the coil. Lenz's law shows that this induced emf has a direction that opposes the change in the current. If the current is increasing, the induced emf is as pictured in Figure 20.24b, and if the current is decreasing, the induced emf is as shown in Figure 20.24c.

As the current increases toward its maximum value it creates changing magnetic flux, inducing an opposing emf in the loop.

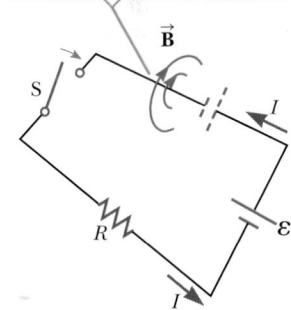

Figure 20.23 After the switch in the circuit is closed, the current produces its own magnetic flux through the loop. An opposing emf is therefore induced, meaning the current relatively slowly increases toward its maximum value rather than jumping to that value right away. The battery with the dashed lines is a symbol for the self-induced emf.

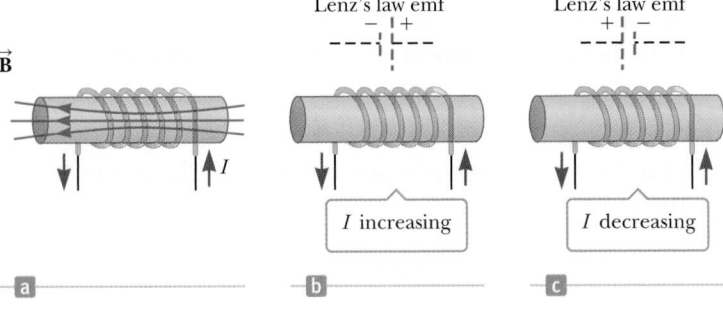

Lenz's law emf
I increasing

Lenz's law emf
I decreasing

Figure 20.24 (a) A current in the coil produces a magnetic field directed to the left. (b) If the current increases, the coil acts as a source of emf directed as shown by the dashed battery. (c) The induced emf in the coil changes its polarity if the current decreases. The battery symbols drawn with dashed lines represent the included emf in the coil.

Joseph Henry
American physicist (1797–1878)
Henry became the first director of the Smithsonian Institution and first president of the Academy of Natural Science. He was the first to produce an electric current with a magnetic field, but he failed to publish his results as early as Faraday because of his heavy teaching duties at the Albany Academy in New York State. He improved the design of the electromagnet and constructed one of the first motors. He also discovered the phenomenon of self-induction. The unit of inductance, the henry, is named in his honor.

To evaluate self-inductance quantitatively, first note that, according to Faraday's law, the induced emf is given by Equation 20.2:

$$\mathcal{E} = -N\frac{\Delta \Phi_B}{\Delta t}$$

The magnetic flux is proportional to the magnetic field, which is proportional to the current in the coil. Therefore, **the self-induced emf must be proportional to the rate of change of the current with time,** or

$$\mathcal{E} \equiv -L\frac{\Delta I}{\Delta t} \qquad [20.9]$$

where L is a proportionality constant called the **inductance** of the device. The negative sign indicates that a changing current induces an emf in opposition to the change. In other words, if the current is increasing (ΔI positive), the induced emf is negative, indicating opposition to the increase in current. Likewise, if the current is decreasing (ΔI negative), the sign of the induced emf is positive, indicating that the emf is acting to oppose the decrease.

The inductance of a coil depends on the cross-sectional area of the coil and other quantities, which can all be grouped under the general heading of geometric factors. The SI unit of inductance is the **henry** (H), which, from Equation 20.9, is equal to 1 volt-second per ampere:

$$1 \text{ H} = 1 \text{ V} \cdot \text{s/A}$$

In the process of calculating self-inductance, it is often convenient to equate Equations 20.2 and 20.9 to find an expression for L:

$$N\frac{\Delta \Phi_B}{\Delta t} = L\frac{\Delta I}{\Delta t}$$

Inductance ▶

$$L = N\frac{\Delta \Phi_B}{\Delta I} = \frac{N\Phi_B}{I} \qquad [20.10]$$

■ APPLYING PHYSICS 20.3 | **Making Sparks Fly**

In some circuits a spark occurs between the poles of a switch when the switch is opened. Why isn't there a spark when the switch for this circuit is closed?

EXPLANATION According to Lenz's law, the direction of induced emfs is such that the induced magnetic field opposes change in the original magnetic flux. When the switch is opened, the sudden drop in the magnetic field in the circuit induces an emf in a direction that opposes change in the original current. This induced emf can cause a spark as the current bridges the air gap between the poles of the switch. The spark doesn't occur when the switch is closed, because the original current is zero and the induced emf opposes any change in that current. ■

In general, determining the inductance of a given current element can be challenging. Finding an expression for the inductance of a common solenoid, however, is straightforward. Let the solenoid have N turns and length ℓ. Assume ℓ is large compared with the radius and the core of the solenoid is air. We take the interior magnetic field to be uniform and given by Equation 19.16,

$$B = \mu_0 nI = \mu_0 \frac{N}{\ell} I$$

where $n = N/\ell$ is the number of turns per unit length. The magnetic flux through each turn is therefore

$$\Phi_B = BA = \mu_0 \frac{N}{\ell} AI$$

where A is the cross-sectional area of the solenoid. From this expression and Equation 20.10, we find that

$$L = \frac{N\Phi_B}{I} = \frac{\mu_0 N^2 A}{\ell}$$ [20.11a]

This equation shows that L depends on the geometric factors ℓ and A and on μ_0 and is proportional to the square of the number of turns. Because $N = n\ell$, we can also express the result in the form

$$L = \mu_0 \frac{(n\ell)^2}{\ell} A = \mu_0 n^2 A\ell = \mu_0 n^2 V$$ [20.11b]

where $V = A\ell$ is the volume of the solenoid.

▪ EXAMPLE 20.7 | Inductance, Self-Induced emf, and Solenoids

GOAL Calculate the inductance and self-induced emf of a solenoid.

PROBLEM (a) Calculate the inductance of a solenoid containing 300 turns if the length of the solenoid is 25.0 cm and its cross-sectional area is 4.00×10^{-4} m². (b) Calculate the self-induced emf in the solenoid described in part (a) if the current in the solenoid decreases at the rate of 50.0 A/s.

STRATEGY Substituting given quantities into Equation 20.11a gives the inductance L. For part (b), substitute the result of part (a) and $\Delta I/\Delta t = -50.0$ A/s into Equation 20.9 to get the self-induced emf.

. . . .

SOLUTION

(a) Calculate the inductance of the solenoid.

Substitute the number N of turns, the area A, and the length ℓ into Equation 20.11a to find the inductance:

$$L = \frac{\mu_0 N^2 A}{\ell}$$

$$= (4\pi \times 10^{-7}\,\text{T} \cdot \text{m/A}) \frac{(300)^2(4.00 \times 10^{-4}\,\text{m}^2)}{25.0 \times 10^{-2}\,\text{m}}$$

$$= 1.81 \times 10^{-4}\,\text{T} \cdot \text{m}^2/\text{A} = \boxed{0.181\,\text{mH}}$$

(b) Calculate the self-induced emf in the solenoid.

Substitute L and $\Delta I/\Delta t = -50.0$ A/s into Equation 20.9, finding the self-induced emf:

$$\mathcal{E} = -L\frac{\Delta I}{\Delta t} = -(1.81 \times 10^{-4}\,\text{H})(-50.0\,\text{A/s})$$

$$= \boxed{9.05\,\text{mV}}$$

. . . .

REMARKS Notice that $\Delta I/\Delta t$ is negative because the current is decreasing with time. The expression for the inductance in part (a) relies on the assumption that the radius of the solenoid is small compared to its length.

QUESTION 20.7 If the solenoid were wrapped into a circle so as to become a toroidal solenoid, what would be true of its self-inductance? (a) It would be the same. (b) It would be larger. (c) It would be smaller.

EXERCISE 20.7 A solenoid is to have an inductance of 0.285 mH, a cross-sectional area of 6.00×10^{-4} m², and a length of 36.0 cm. (a) How many turns per unit length should it have? (b) If the self-induced emf is -12.5 mV at a given time, at what rate is the current changing at that instant?

ANSWERS (a) 1.02×10^3 turns/m (b) 43.9 A/s

20.6 *RL* Circuits

A circuit element that has a large inductance, such as a closely wrapped coil of many turns, is called an **inductor**. The circuit symbol for an inductor is —⟋⟋⟋⟋—. We will always assume the self-inductance of the remainder of the circuit is negligible compared with that of the inductor in the circuit.

To gain some insight into the effect of an inductor in a circuit, consider the two circuits in Figure 20.25 (page 708). Figure 20.25a shows a resistor connected

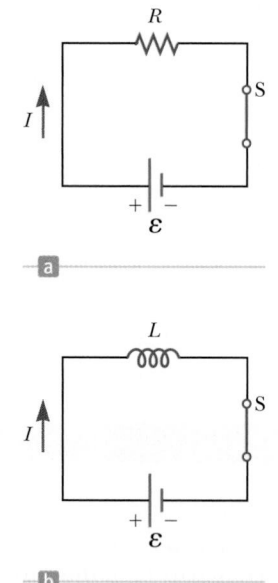

Figure 20.25 A comparison of the effect of a resistor with that of an inductor in a simple circuit.

to the terminals of a battery. For this circuit, Kirchhoff's loop rule is $\mathcal{E} - IR = 0$. The voltage drop across the resistor is

$$\Delta V_R = -IR \qquad \text{[20.12]}$$

In this case, **we interpret resistance as a measure of opposition to the current.** Now consider the circuit in Figure 20.25b, consisting of an inductor connected to the terminals of a battery. At the instant the switch in this circuit is closed, because $IR = 0$, the emf of the battery equals the back emf generated in the coil. Hence, we have

$$\mathcal{E}_L = -L \frac{\Delta I}{\Delta t} \qquad \text{[20.13]}$$

From this expression, **we can interpret L as a measure of opposition to the rate of change of current.**

Active Figure 20.26 shows a circuit consisting of a resistor, an inductor, and a battery. Suppose the switch is closed at $t = 0$. The current begins to increase, but the inductor produces an emf that opposes the increasing current. As a result, the current can't change from zero to its maximum value of $\mathcal{E}/R$ instantaneously. Equation 20.13 shows that the induced emf is a maximum when the current is changing most rapidly, which occurs when the switch is first closed. As the current approaches its steady-state value, the back emf of the coil falls off because the current is changing more slowly. Finally, when the current reaches its steady-state value, the rate of change is zero and the back emf is also zero. Active Figure 20.27 plots current in the circuit as a function of time. This plot is similar to that of the charge on a capacitor as a function of time, discussed in Chapter 18, section 5, in connection with RC circuits. In that case, we found it convenient to introduce a quantity called the *time constant of the circuit*, which told us something about the time required for the capacitor to approach its steady-state charge. In the same way, time constants are defined for circuits containing resistors and inductors. The **time constant τ** for an *RL* circuit is the time required for the current in the circuit to reach 63.2% of its final value $\mathcal{E}/R$; the time constant of an *RL* circuit is given by

Time constant for an ▶
RL circuit

$$\tau = \frac{L}{R} \qquad \text{[20.14]}$$

Using methods of calculus, it can be shown that the current in such a circuit is given by

$$I = \frac{\mathcal{E}}{R}\left(1 - e^{-t/\tau}\right) \qquad \text{[20.15]}$$

This equation is consistent with our intuition: when the switch is closed at $t = 0$, the current is initially zero, rising with time to some maximum value. Notice the mathematical similarity between Equation 20.15 and Equation 18.7, which features

Active Figure 20.26
A series *RL* circuit. As the current increases toward its maximum value, the inductor produces an emf that opposes the increasing current.

Active Figure 20.27
A plot of current versus time for the *RL* circuit shown in Figure 20.26. The switch is closed at $t = 0$, and the current increases toward its maximum value $\mathcal{E}/R$. The time constant τ is the time it takes the current to reach 63.2% of its maximum value.

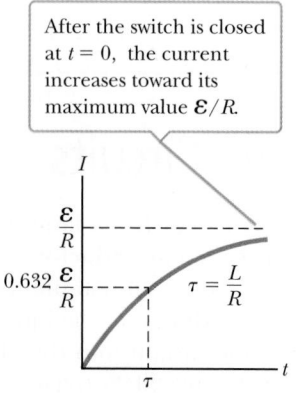

After the switch is closed at $t = 0$, the current increases toward its maximum value $\mathcal{E}/R$.

a capacitor instead of an inductor. As in the case of a capacitor, the equation's form suggests an infinite amount of time is required for the current in the inductor to reach its maximum value. That is an artifact of assuming current is composed of moving charges that are infinitesimal, as will be demonstrated in Example 20.9.

■ **Quick Quiz**

20.6 The switch in the circuit shown in Figure 20.28 is closed, and the lightbulb glows steadily. The inductor is a simple air-core solenoid. An iron rod is inserted into the interior of the solenoid, increasing the magnitude of the magnetic field in the solenoid. As the rod is inserted, the brightness of the lightbulb (a) increases, (b) decreases, or (c) remains the same.

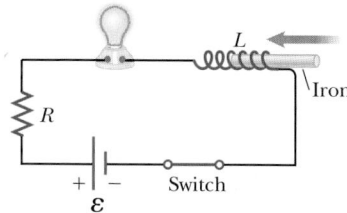

Figure 20.28 (Quick Quiz 20.6)

■ **EXAMPLE 20.8** | An *RL* Circuit

GOAL Calculate a time constant and relate it to current in an *RL* circuit.

PROBLEM A 12.6-V battery is in a circuit with a 30.0-mH inductor and a 0.150-Ω resistor, as in Active Figure 20.26. The switch is closed at $t = 0$. **(a)** Find the time constant of the circuit. **(b)** Find the current after one time constant has elapsed. **(c)** Find the voltage drops across the resistor when $t = 0$ and $t =$ one time constant. **(d)** What's the rate of change of the current after one time constant?

STRATEGY Part (a) requires only substitution into the definition of time constant. With this value and Ohm's law, the current after one time constant can be found, and multiplying this current by the resistance yields the voltage drop across the resistor after one time constant. With the voltage drop and Kirchhoff's loop law, the voltage across the inductor can be found. This value can be substituted into Equation 20.13 to obtain the rate of change of the current.

SOLUTION

(a) What's the time constant of the circuit?

Substitute the inductance *L* and resistance *R* into Equation 20.14, finding the time constant:

$$\tau = \frac{L}{R} = \frac{30.0 \times 10^{-3}\,\text{H}}{0.150\,\Omega} = \boxed{0.200\ \text{s}}$$

(b) Find the current after one time constant has elapsed.

First, use Ohm's law to compute the final value of the current after many time constants have elapsed:

$$I_{max} = \frac{\mathcal{E}}{R} = \frac{12.6\,\text{V}}{0.150\,\Omega} = 84.0\ \text{A}$$

After one time constant, the current rises to 63.2% of its final value:

$$I_{1\tau} = (0.632)I_{max} = (0.632)(84.0\ \text{A}) = \boxed{53.1\ \text{A}}$$

(c) Find the voltage drops across the resistance when $t = 0$ and $t =$ one time constant.

Initially, the current in the circuit is zero, so, from Ohm's law, the voltage across the resistor is zero:

$$\Delta V_R = IR$$
$$\Delta V_R\ (t = 0\ \text{s}) = (0\ \text{A})(0.150\ \Omega) = \boxed{0}$$

Next, using Ohm's law, find the magnitude of the voltage drop across the resistor after one time constant:

$$\Delta V_R\ (t = 0.200\ \text{s}) = (53.1\ \text{A})(0.150\ \Omega) = \boxed{7.97\ \text{V}}$$

(d) What's the rate of change of the current after one time constant?

Using Kirchhoff's voltage rule, calculate the voltage drop across the inductor at that time:

$$\mathcal{E} + \Delta V_R + \Delta V_L = 0$$

Solve for ΔV_L:

$$\Delta V_L = -\mathcal{E} - \Delta V_R = -12.6\ \text{V} - (-7.97\ \text{V}) = -4.6\ \text{V}$$

(Continued)

Now solve Equation 20.13 for $\Delta I/\Delta t$ and substitute:

$$\Delta V_L = -L\frac{\Delta I}{\Delta t}$$

$$\frac{\Delta I}{\Delta t} = -\frac{\Delta V_L}{L} = -\frac{-4.6\ \text{V}}{30.0 \times 10^{-3}\ \text{H}} = \boxed{150\ \text{A/s}}$$

REMARKS The values used in this problem were taken from actual components salvaged from the starter system of a car. Because the current in such an *RL* circuit is initially zero, inductors are sometimes referred to as "chokes" because they temporarily choke off the current. In solving part (d), we traversed the circuit in the direction of positive current, so the voltage difference across the battery was positive and the differences across the resistor and inductor were negative.

QUESTION 20.8 Find the current in the circuit after two time constants.

EXERCISE 20.8 A 12.6-V battery is in series with a resistance of 0.350 Ω and an inductor. (a) After a long time, what is the current in the circuit? (b) What is the current after one time constant? (c) What's the voltage drop across the inductor at this time? (d) Find the inductance if the time constant is 0.130 s.

ANSWERS (a) 36.0 A (b) 22.8 A (c) 4.62 V (d) 4.55×10^{-2} H

■ EXAMPLE 20.9 | **Formation of a Magnetic Field**

GOAL Understand the role of time in setting up an inductor's magnetic field.

PROBLEM Given the *RL* circuit of Example 20.8, find the time required for the current to reach 99.9% of its maximum value after the switch is closed.

STRATEGY The solution requires solving Equation 20.15 for time followed by substitution. Notice that the maximum current is $I_{max} = \mathcal{E}/R$.

SOLUTION

Write Equation 20.15, with I_f substituted for the current:

$$I_f = \frac{\mathcal{E}}{R}(1 - e^{-t/\tau}) = I_{max}(1 - e^{-t/\tau})$$

Divide both sides by I_{max}:

$$\frac{I_f}{I_{max}} = 1 - e^{-t/\tau}$$

Subtract 1 from both sides and then multiply both sides by -1:

$$1 - \frac{I_f}{I_{max}} = e^{-t/\tau}$$

Take the natural log of both sides:

$$\ln\left(1 - \frac{I_f}{I_{max}}\right) = \ln\left(e^{-t/\tau}\right) = -t/\tau$$

Solve for *t* and substitute the expression for τ from Equation 20.14:

$$t = -\frac{L}{R}\ln\left(1 - \frac{I_f}{I_{max}}\right)$$

Substitute values, obtaining the desired time:

$$t = -\frac{30.0 \times 10^{-3}\ \text{H}}{0.150\ \Omega}\ln(1 - 0.999) = \boxed{1.38\ \text{s}}$$

REMARKS From this calculation, it's found that forming the magnetic field in an inductor and approaching the maximum current occurs relatively rapidly. Contrary to what might be expected from the mathematical form of Equation 20.15, an infinite amount of time is not actually required.

QUESTION 20.9 If the inductance were doubled, by what factor would the length of time found be changed? (a) 1 (i.e., no change) (b) 2 (c) $\frac{1}{2}$

EXERCISE 20.9 Suppose a series *RL* circuit is composed of a 2.00-Ω resistor, a 15.0 H inductor, and a 6.00 V battery. (a) What is the time constant for this circuit? (b) Once the switch is closed, how long does it take the current to reach half its maximum value?

ANSWERS (a) 7.50 s (b) 5.20 s

20.7 Energy Stored in a Magnetic Field

The emf induced by an inductor prevents a battery from establishing an instantaneous current in a circuit. The battery has to do work to produce a current. We can think of this needed work as energy stored in the inductor in its magnetic field. In a manner similar to that used in Section 16.9 to find the energy stored in a capacitor, we find that the energy stored by an inductor is

$$PE_L = \tfrac{1}{2}LI^2$$ [20.16]   ◀ Energy stored in an inductor

Notice that the result is similar in form to the expression for the energy stored in a charged capacitor (Eq. 16.18):

$$PE_C = \tfrac{1}{2}C(\Delta V)^2$$ ◀ Energy stored in a capacitor

■ EXAMPLE 20.10 | Magnetic Energy

GOAL Relate the storage of magnetic energy to currents in an RL circuit.

PROBLEM A 12.0-V battery is connected in series to a 25.0-Ω resistor and a 5.00-H inductor. **(a)** Find the maximum current in the circuit. **(b)** Find the energy stored in the inductor at this time. **(c)** How much energy is stored in the inductor when the current is changing at a rate of 1.50 A/s?

STRATEGY In part (a) Ohm's law and Kirchhoff's voltage rule yield the maximum current because the voltage across the inductor is zero when the current is maximal. Substituting the current into Equation 20.16 gives the energy stored in the inductor. In part (c) the given rate of change of the current can be used to calculate the voltage drop across the inductor at the specified time. Kirchhoff's voltage rule and Ohm's law then give the current I at that time, which can be used to find the energy stored in the inductor.

SOLUTION

(a) Find the maximum current in the circuit.

Apply Kirchhoff's voltage rule to the circuit:

$$\Delta V_{batt} + \Delta V_R + \Delta V_L = 0$$

$$\mathcal{E} - IR - L\frac{\Delta I}{\Delta t} = 0$$

When the maximum current is reached, $\Delta I/\Delta t$ is zero, so the voltage drop across the inductor is zero. Solve for the maximum current I_{max}:

$$I_{max} = \frac{\mathcal{E}}{R} = \frac{12.0\text{ V}}{25.0\text{ Ω}} = \boxed{0.480\text{ A}}$$

(b) Find the energy stored in the inductor at this time.

Substitute known values into Equation 20.16:

$$PE_L = \tfrac{1}{2}LI^2_{max} = \tfrac{1}{2}(5.00\text{ H})(0.480\text{ A})^2 = \boxed{0.576\text{ J}}$$

(c) Find the energy in the inductor when the current changes at a rate of 1.50 A/s.

Apply Kirchhoff's voltage rule to the circuit once again:

$$\mathcal{E} - IR - L\frac{\Delta I}{\Delta t} = 0$$

Solve this equation for the current I and substitute:

$$I = \frac{1}{R}\left(\mathcal{E} - L\frac{\Delta I}{\Delta t}\right)$$

$$= \frac{1}{25.0\text{ Ω}}[12.0\text{ V} - (5.00\text{ H})(1.50\text{ A/s})] = 0.180\text{ A}$$

Finally, substitute the value for the current into Equation 20.15, finding the energy stored in the inductor:

$$PE_L = \tfrac{1}{2}LI^2 = \tfrac{1}{2}(5.00\text{ H})(0.180\text{ A})^2 = \boxed{0.081\,0\text{ J}}$$

(Continued)

REMARKS Notice how important it is to combine concepts from previous chapters. Here, Ohm's law and Kirchhoff's loop rule were essential to the solution of the problem.

QUESTION 20.10 True or False: The larger the value of the inductance in such an *RL* circuit, the larger the maximum current.

EXERCISE 20.10 For the same circuit, find the energy stored in the inductor when the rate of change of the current is 1.00 A/s.

ANSWER 0.196 J

■ SUMMARY

20.1 Induced emf and Magnetic Flux

The magnetic flux Φ_B through a closed loop is defined as

$$\Phi_B \equiv BA \cos \theta \qquad [20.1]$$

where B is the strength of the uniform magnetic field, A is the cross-sectional area of the loop, and θ is the angle between $\vec{B}$ and a direction perpendicular to the plane of the loop.

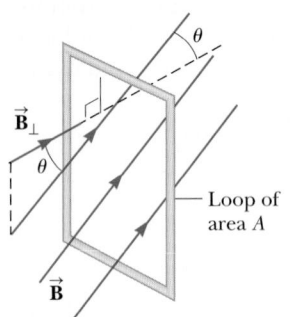

In this view of a loop of area A, the component of the magnetic field $\vec{B}$ perpendicular to surface multiplied by the area gives the magnetic flux through the surface.

Loop of area A

20.2 Faraday's Law of Induction and Lenz's Law

Faraday's law of induction states that the instantaneous emf induced in a circuit equals the negative of the rate of change of magnetic flux through the circuit,

$$\mathcal{E} = -N\frac{\Delta\Phi_B}{\Delta t} \qquad [20.2]$$

where N is the number of loops in the circuit. The magnetic flux Φ_B can change with time whenever the magnetic field $\vec{B}$, the area A, or the angle θ changes with time.

Lenz's law states that the current from the induced emf creates a magnetic field with flux opposing the *change* in magnetic flux through a circuit.

20.3 Motional emf

If a conducting bar of length ℓ moves through a magnetic field with a speed v so that $\vec{B}$ is perpendicular to the bar, the emf induced in the bar, often called a **motional emf**, is

$$|\mathcal{E}| = B\ell v \qquad [20.4]$$

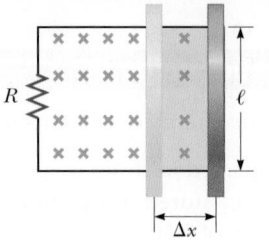

As the bar moves to the right, the area of the loop increases by the amount $\ell\Delta x$ and the magnetic flux through the loop increases by $B\ell\Delta x$.

20.4 Generators

When a coil of wire with N turns, each of area A, rotates with constant angular speed ω in a uniform magnetic field $\vec{B}$, the emf induced in the coil is

$$\mathcal{E} = NBA\omega \sin \omega t \qquad [20.7]$$

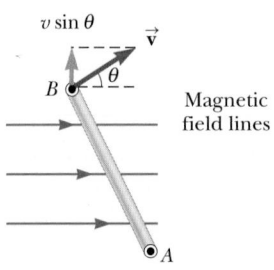

In this edge view of a rotating loop, the magnetic flux changes continuously, generating an alternating current in the loop.

Such generators naturally produce alternating current (AC), which changes direction with frequency $\omega/2\pi$. The AC current can be transformed to direct current.

20.5 Self-Inductance

20.6 *RL* Circuits

When the current in a coil changes with time, an emf is induced in the coil according to Faraday's law. This **self-induced emf** is defined by the expression

$$\mathcal{E} \equiv -L\frac{\Delta I}{\Delta t} \qquad [20.9]$$

where L is the inductance of the coil. The SI unit for inductance is the henry (H); $1\ \text{H} = 1\ \text{V} \cdot \text{s/A}$.

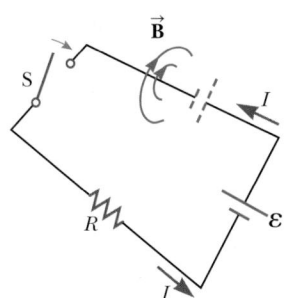

When the switch is closed, a magnetic field begins to develop as shown. The changing magnetic flux creates a self-induced emf in the opposite direction, represented by the dashed lines.

The **inductance** of a coil can be found from the expression

$$L = \frac{N\Phi_B}{I} \qquad [20.10]$$

where N is the number of turns on the coil, I is the current in the coil, and Φ_B is the magnetic flux through the coil produced by that current. For a solenoid, the inductance is given by

$$L = \frac{\mu_0 N^2 A}{\ell} \qquad [20.11a]$$

If a resistor and inductor are connected in series to a battery and a switch is closed at $t = 0$, the current in the circuit doesn't rise instantly to its maximum value. After one

time constant $\tau = L/R$, the current in the circuit is 63.2% of its final value $\mathcal{E}/R$. As the current approaches its final, maximum value, the voltage drop across the inductor approaches zero. The current I in such a circuit any time t after the circuit is completed is

$$I = \frac{\mathcal{E}}{R}\left(1 - e^{-t/\tau}\right) \qquad [20.15]$$

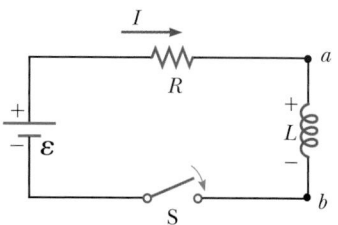

A series RL circuit. As the current increases toward its maximum value, the inductor produces an emf that opposes the increasing current.

20.7 Energy Stored in a Magnetic Field

The **energy stored** in the magnetic field of an inductor carrying current I is

$$PE_L = \tfrac{1}{2}LI^2 \qquad [20.16]$$

As the current in an RL circuit approaches its maximum value, the stored energy also approaches a maximum value.

■ MULTIPLE-CHOICE QUESTIONS

WebAssign The multiple-choice questions in this chapter may be assigned online in Enhanced WebAssign.

1. A flat coil of wire is placed in a uniform magnetic field that is in the y-direction. The magnetic flux through the coil is a maximum if the plane of the coil is where? (a) in the xy-plane (b) in the yz-plane (c) in the xz-plane (d) in any orientation, because it is a constant

2. A 10-turn square coil 0.50 m on a side lies in the xy-plane. A uniform magnetic field with magnitude 1.0 T in the negative z-direction changes steadily to 3.0 T in the positive z-direction, a process that takes 2.0 s. What is the magnitude of the induced emf in the coil? (a) 2.0 V (b) 5.0 V (c) 3.0 V (d) 4.0 V (e) 6.0 V

3. The current in a 5.00-H inductor decreases uniformly at a rate of 2.00 A/s. What is the voltage drop across the inductor? (a) 2.50 V (b) 5.00 V (c) 0.400 V (d) 10.0 V (e) 7.50 V

4. A generator contains a 100-turn coil that rotates 10.0 times per second. If each turn has an area of 0.100 m² and the magnetic field through the coils is 0.050 0 T, what is the maximum emf induced in the coil? (a) 31.4 V (b) 62.8 V (c) 0.314 V (d) 6.28 V (e) 3.14 V

5. A small airplane with a wingspan of 12 m flies horizontally and due north at a speed of 60.0 m/s in a region where the magnetic field of Earth is 60.0 μT

directed 60.0° below the horizontal. What is the magnitude of the induced emf between the tips of the airplane's wings? (a) 51 mV (b) 31 mV (c) 37 mV (d) 44 mV (e) 22 mV

6. The bar in Figure MCQ20.6 moves on rails to the right with a velocity $\vec{v}$, and a uniform, constant magnetic field is directed out of the page. Which of the following statements are correct? (More than one statement may be correct.) (a) The induced current in the loop is zero. (b) The induced current in the loop is clockwise. (c) The induced current in the loop is counterclockwise. (d) An external force is required to keep the bar moving at constant speed. (e) No force is required to keep the bar moving at constant speed.

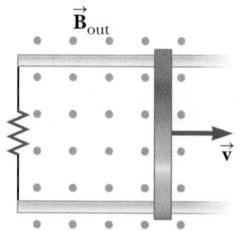

Figure MCQ20.6

7. What happens to the amplitude of the induced emf when the rate of rotation of a generator coil is doubled? (a) It becomes four times larger. (b) It becomes two times larger. (c) It is unchanged. (d) It becomes one-half as large. (e) It becomes one-fourth as large.

8. When a coil is placed in a constant external magnetic field directed perpendicular to the plane of the coil, which of the following actions does *not* induce an emf in the coil? (a) Collapsing the coil. (b) Changing the strength of the magnetic field. (c) Moving the coil through the field without changing its orientation with respect to the field. (d) Rotating the coil. (e) Removing the coil from the field.

9. A rectangular loop is placed near a long wire carrying a current *I* as shown in Figure MCQ20.9. If *I* decreases in time, what can be said of the current induced in the loop? (a) The direction of the current depends on the size of the loop. (b) The current is clockwise. (c) The current is counterclockwise. (d) The current is zero. (e) Nothing can be said about the current in the loop without more information.

Figure MCQ20.9

10. Two rectangular loops of wire lie in the same plane, as shown in Figure MCQ20.10. If the current *I* in the outer loop is counterclockwise and increases with time, what is true of the current induced in the inner loop? (a) It is zero. (b) It is clockwise. (c) It is counterclock-

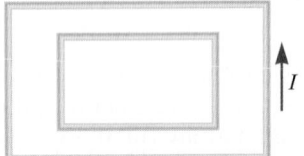

Figure MCQ20.10

wise. (d) Its magnitude depends on the dimensions of the loops. (e) Its direction depends on the dimensions of the loops.

11. A bar magnet is held above the center of a wire loop lying in the horizontal plane, as shown in Figure MCQ20.11. The south end of the magnet is toward the loop. After the magnet is dropped, what is the direction of the induced current in the loop as viewed from above? (a) It is clockwise as the magnet falls toward the loop. (b) It is counterclockwise as the magnet falls toward the loop. (c) It is clockwise after the magnet has moved through the loop and moves away from it. (d) It is always clockwise. (e) It is first counterclockwise as the magnet approaches the loop and then clockwise after it has passed through the loop.

Figure MCQ20.11

12. A circuit consists of a conducting movable bar and a lightbulb connected to two conducting rails, as shown in Figure MCQ20.12. An external magnetic field is directed perpendicular to the plane of the circuit. Which of the following actions will make the bulb light up? More than one statement may be correct. (a) The bar is moved to the left. (b) The bar is moved to the right. (c) The magnitude of the magnetic field is increased. (d) The magnitude of the magnetic field is decreased. (e) The bar is lifted off the rails.

Figure MCQ20.12

■ CONCEPTUAL QUESTIONS

WebAssign The conceptual questions in this chapter may be assigned online in Enhanced WebAssign.

1. A spacecraft orbiting Earth has a coil of wire in it. An astronaut measures a small current in the coil, although there is no battery connected to it and there are no magnets in the spacecraft. What is causing the current?

2. Does dropping a magnet down a copper tube produce a current in the tube? Explain.

3. A circular loop is located in a uniform and constant magnetic field. Describe how an emf can be induced in the loop in this situation.

4. A loop of wire is placed in a uniform magnetic field. (a) For what orientation of the loop is the magnetic

flux a maximum? (b) For what orientation is the flux zero?

5. As the conducting bar in Figure CQ20.5 moves to the right, an electric field directed downward is set up. If the bar were moving to the left, explain why the electric field would be upward.

6. How is electrical energy produced in dams? (That is, how

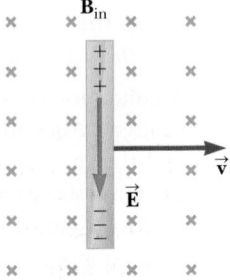

Figure CQ20.5 Conceptual Questions 5 and 8.

is the energy of motion of the water converted to AC electricity?)

7. Wearing a metal bracelet in a region of strong magnetic field could be hazardous. Discuss this statement.

8. As the bar in Figure CQ20.5 moves perpendicular to the field, is an external force required to keep it moving with constant speed?

9. Eddy currents are induced currents set up in a piece of metal when it moves through a nonuniform magnetic field. For example, consider the flat metal plate swinging at the end of a bar as a pendulum, as shown in Figure CQ20.9. (a) At position 1, the pendulum is moving from a region where there is no magnetic field into a region where the field $\vec{\mathbf{B}}_{\text{in}}$ is directed into the paper. Show that at position 1 the direction of the eddy current is counterclockwise. (b) At position 2, the pendulum is moving out of the field into a region of zero field. Show that the direction of the eddy current is clockwise in this case. (c) Use right-hand rule number 2 to show that these eddy currents lead to a magnetic force on the plate directed as shown in the figure. Because the induced eddy current always produces a retarding force when the plate enters or leaves the field, the swinging plate quickly comes to rest.

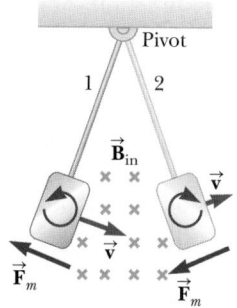

Figure CQ20.9

10. A bar magnet is dropped toward a conducting ring lying on the floor. As the magnet falls toward the ring, does it move as a freely falling object? Explain.

11. A piece of aluminum is dropped vertically downward between the poles of an electromagnet. Does the magnetic field affect the velocity of the aluminum? *Hint:* See Conceptual Question 9.

12. When the switch in Figure CQ20.12a is closed, a current is set up in the coil and the metal ring springs upward (Fig. CQ20.12b). Explain this behavior.

Figure CQ20.12 Conceptual Questions 12 and 13.

13. Assume the battery in Figure CQ20.12a is replaced by an AC source and the switch is held closed. If held down, the metal ring on top of the solenoid becomes hot. Why?

14. A magneto is used to cause the spark in a spark plug in many lawn mowers today. A magneto consists of a permanent magnet mounted on a flywheel so that it spins past a fixed coil. Explain how this arrangement generates a large enough potential difference to cause the spark.

■ PROBLEMS

20.1 Induced EMF and Magnetic Flux

1. A uniform magnetic field of magnitude 0.50 T is directed perpendicular to the plane of a rectangular loop having dimensions 8.0 cm by 12 cm. Find the magnetic flux through the loop.

2. Find the flux of Earth's magnetic field of magnitude 5.00×10^{-5} T through a square loop of area 20.0 cm² (a) when the field is perpendicular to the plane of the loop, (b) when the field makes a 30.0° angle with the normal to the plane of the loop, and (c) when the field makes a 90.0° angle with the normal to the plane.

3. A circular loop of radius 12.0 cm is placed in a uniform magnetic field. (a) If the field is directed perpendicular to the plane of the loop and the magnetic flux through the loop is 8.00×10^{-3} T · m², what is the strength of the magnetic field? (b) If the magnetic field is directed parallel to the plane of the loop, what is the magnetic flux through the loop?

4. A long, straight wire carrying a current of 2.00 A is placed along the axis of a cylinder of radius 0.500 m and a length of 3.00 m. Determine the total magnetic flux through the cylinder.

5. A long, straight wire lies in the plane of a circular coil with a radius of 0.010 m. The wire carries a current of 2.0 A and is placed along a diameter of the coil. (a) What is the net flux through the coil? (b) If the wire passes through the center of the coil and is perpendicular to the plane of the coil, what is the net flux through the coil?

6. A 400-turn solenoid of length 36.0 cm and radius 3.00 cm carries a current of 5.00 A. Find (a) the magnetic field strength inside the coil at its midpoint and (b) the magnetic flux through a circular cross-sectional area of the solenoid at its midpoint.

7. ☒ A cube of edge length ℓ = 2.5 cm is positioned as shown in Figure P20.7. There is a uniform magnetic field throughout the region with components B_x = +5.0 T, B_y = +4.0 T, and B_z = +3.0 T. (a) Calculate the flux through the shaded face of the cube. (b) What is the total flux emerging from the volume enclosed by the cube (i.e., the total flux through all six faces)?

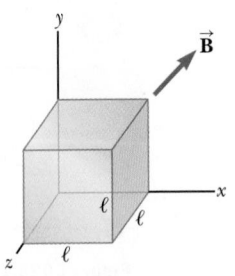

Figure P20.7

20.2 Faraday's Law of Induction and Lenz's Law

8. BIO Transcranial magnetic stimulation (TMS) is a noninvasive technique used to stimulate regions of the human brain. A small coil is placed on the scalp, and a brief burst of current in the coil produces a rapidly changing magnetic field inside the brain. The induced emf can be sufficient to stimulate neuronal activity. One such device generates a magnetic field within the brain that rises from zero to 1.5 T in 120 ms. Determine the induced emf within a circle of tissue of radius 1.6 mm and that is perpendicular to the direction of the field.

9. Three loops of wire move near a long straight wire carrying a current as in Figure P20.9. What is the direction of the induced current, if any, in (a) loop A, (b) loop B, and (c) loop C.

Figure P20.9

10. The flexible loop in Figure P20.10 has a radius of 12 cm and is in a magnetic field of strength 0.15 T. The loop is grasped at points A and B and stretched until its area is nearly zero. If it takes 0.20 s to close the loop,

what is the magnitude of the average induced emf in it during this time?

11. A wire loop of radius 0.30 m lies so that an external magnetic field of magnitude 0.30 T is perpendicular to the loop. The field reverses its direction, and its magnitude changes to 0.20 T in 1.5 s. Find the magnitude of the average induced emf in the loop during this time.

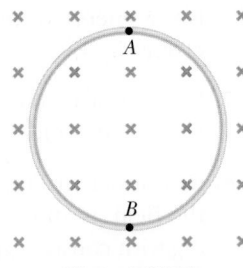

Figure P20.10
Problems 10, 12, and 22.

12. A circular loop of wire of radius 12.0 cm is placed in a magnetic field directed perpendicular to the plane of the loop, as shown in Figure P20.10. If the field decreases at the rate of 0.050 0 T/s in some time interval, what is the magnitude of the emf induced in the loop during this interval?

13. A technician wearing a circular metal band on his wrist moves his hand into a uniform magnetic field of magnitude 2.5 T in a time of 0.18 s. If the diameter of the band is 6.5 cm and the field is at an angle of 45° with the plane of the metal band while the hand is in the field, find the magnitude of the average emf induced in the band.

14. In Figure P20.14 what is the direction of the current induced in the resistor at the instant the switch is closed?

Figure P20.14

15. A bar magnet is positioned near a coil of wire, as shown in Figure P20.15. What is the direction of the current in the resistor when the magnet is moved (a) to the left and (b) to the right?

Figure P20.15

16. Find the direction of the current in the resistor shown in Figure P20.16 (a) at the instant the switch is closed, (b) after the switch has been closed for several minutes, and (c) at the instant the switch is opened.

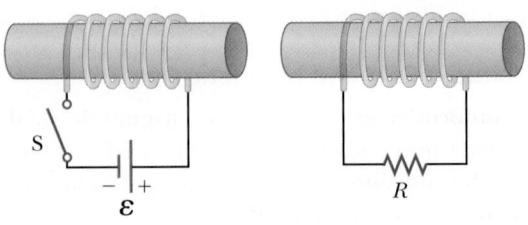

Figure P20.16

17. A circular loop of wire lies below a long wire carrying a current that is increasing as in Figure P20.17a. (a) What is the direction of the induced current in the loop, if any? (b) Now suppose the loop is next to the same wire as in P20.17b. What is the direction of the induced current in the loop, if any? Explain your answers.

Figure P20.17

18. A square, single-turn wire loop $\ell = 1.00$ cm on a side is placed inside a solenoid that has a circular cross section of radius $r = 3.00$ cm, as shown in the end view of Figure P20.18. The solenoid is 20.0 cm long and wound with 100 turns of wire. (a) If the current in the solenoid is 3.00 A, what is the flux through the square loop? (b) If the current in the solenoid is reduced to zero in 3.00 s, what is the magnitude of the average induced emf in the square loop?

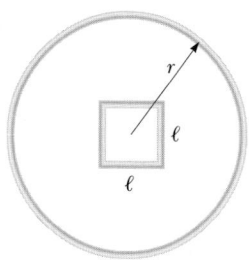

Figure P20.18

19. **GP** A 300-turn solenoid with a length of 20.0 cm and a radius of 1.50 cm carries a current of 2.00 A. A second coil of four turns is wrapped tightly around this solenoid, so it can be considered to have the same radius as the solenoid. The current in the 300-turn solenoid increases steadily to 5.00 A in 0.900 s. (a) Use Ampere's law to calculate the initial magnetic field in the middle of the 300-turn solenoid. (b) Calculate the magnetic field of the 300-turn solenoid after 0.900 s. (c) Calculate the area of the 4-turn coil. (d) Calculate the change in the magnetic flux through the 4-turn coil during the same period. (e) Calculate the average induced emf in the 4-turn coil. Is it equal to the instantaneous induced emf? Explain. (f) Why could contributions to the magnetic field by the current in the 4-turn coil be neglected in this calculation?

20. **M** A circular coil enclosing an area of 100 cm^2 is made of 200 turns of copper wire. The wire making up the coil has resistance of 5.0 Ω, and the ends of the wire are connected to form a closed circuit. Initially, a 1.1-T uniform magnetic field points perpendicularly upward through the plane of the coil. The direction of the field then reverses so that the final magnetic field has a magnitude of 1.1 T and points downward through the coil. If the time required for the field to reverse directions is 0.10 s, what is the average current in the coil during that time?

21. **BIO** To monitor the breathing of a hospital patient, a thin belt is girded around the patient's chest as in Figure P20.21. The belt is a 200-turn coil. When the patient inhales, the area encircled by the coil increases by 39.0 cm^2. The magnitude of Earth's magnetic field is 50.0 μT and makes an angle of 28.0° with the plane of the coil. Assuming a patient takes 1.80 s to inhale, find the magnitude of the average induced emf in the coil during that time.

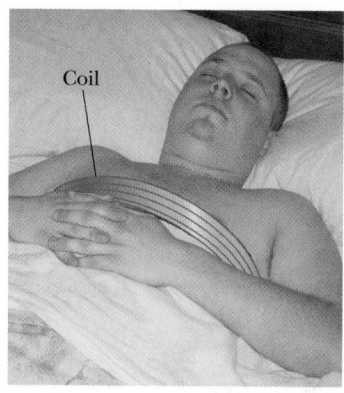

Coil

Figure P20.21

22. **Q|C** **S** An N-turn circular wire coil of radius r lies in the xy-plane (the plane of the page), as in Figure P20.10. A uniform magnetic field is turned on, increasing steadily from 0 to B_0 in the positive z-direction in t seconds. (a) Find a symbolic expression for the emf, $\mathcal{E}$, induced in the coil in terms of the variables given. (b) Looking down on at the xy-plane from the positive z-axis, is the direction of the induced current clockwise or counterclockwise? (c) If each loop has resistance R, find an expression for the magnitude of the induced current, I.

20.3 Motional emf

23. A truck is carrying a steel beam of length 15.0 m on a freeway. An accident causes the beam to be dumped off the truck and slide horizontally along the ground at a speed of 25.0 m/s. The velocity of the center of mass of the beam is northward while the length of the beam maintains an east–west orientation. The vertical component of the Earth's magnetic field at this location has a magnitude of 35.0 μT. What is the magnitude of the induced emf between the ends of the beam?

24. A 2.00-m length of wire is held in an east–west direction and moves horizontally to the north with a speed of 15.0 m/s. The vertical component of Earth's magnetic field in this region is 40.0 μT directed downward. Calculate the induced emf between the ends of the wire and determine which end is positive.

25. A pickup truck has a width of 79.8 in. If it is traveling north at 37 m/s through a magnetic field with vertical component of 35 μT, what magnitude emf is induced between the driver and passenger sides of the truck?

26. QC A bar magnet is held stationary while a circular loop of wire is moved toward the magnet at constant velocity at position A as in Figure P20.26. The loop passes over the magnet at position B and moves away from the magnet at position C. Find the direction of the induced current in the loop using Lenz's law (a) at position A and (b) at position C. (c) What is the induced current in the loop at position B? Explain.

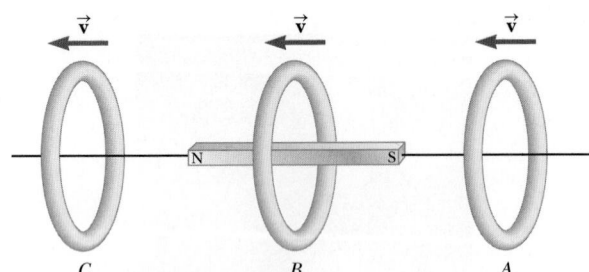

Figure P20.26 Problems 26 and 43.

27. M An automobile has a vertical radio antenna 1.20 m long. The automobile travels at 65.0 km/h on a horizontal road where Earth's magnetic field is 50.0 μT, directed toward the north and downward at an angle of 65.0° below the horizontal. (a) Specify the direction the automobile should move so as to generate the maximum motional emf in the antenna, with the top of the antenna positive relative to the bottom. (b) Calculate the magnitude of this induced emf.

28. QC An astronaut is connected to her spacecraft by a 25-m-long tether cord as she and the spacecraft orbit Earth in a circular path at a speed of 3.0×10^3 m/s. At one instant, the voltage measured between the ends of a wire embedded in the cord is measured to be 0.45 V. Assume the long dimension of the cord is perpendicular to the vertical component of Earth's magnetic field at that instant. (a) What is the magnitude of the vertical component of Earth's field at this location? (b) Does the measured voltage change as the system moves from one location to another? Explain.

29. Figure P20.29 shows a bar of mass $m = 0.200$ kg that can slide without friction on a pair of rails separated

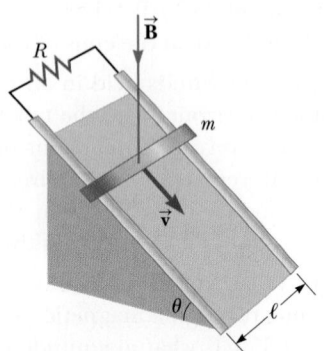

Figure P20.29

by a distance $\ell = 1.20$ m and located on an inclined plane that makes an angle $\theta = 25.0°$ with respect to the ground. The resistance of the resistor is $R = 1.00$ Ω, and a uniform magnetic field of magnitude $B = 0.500$ T is directed downward, perpendicular to the ground, over the entire region through which the bar moves. With what constant speed v does the bar slide along the rails?

30. Consider the arrangement shown in Figure P20.30. Assume $R = 6.00$ Ω, $\ell = 1.20$ m, and a uniform 2.50-T magnetic field is directed *into* the page. At what speed should the bar be moved to produce a current of 0.500 A in the resistor?

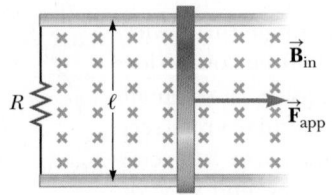

Figure P20.30 Problems 30, 56, and 59.

20.4 Generators

31. A square coil of wire of side 2.80 cm is placed in a uniform magnetic field of magnitude 1.25 T directed into the page as in Figure P20.31. The coil has 28.0 turns and a resistance of 0.780 Ω. If the coil is rotated through an angle of 90.0° about the horizontal axis shown in 0.335 s, find (a) the magnitude of the average emf induced in the coil during this rotation and (b) the average current induced in the coil during this rotation.

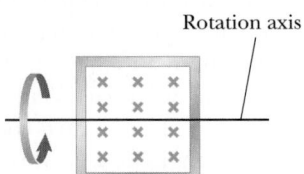

Figure P20.31

32. A 100-turn square wire coil of area 0.040 m² rotates about a vertical axis at 1 500 rev/min, as indicated in Figure P20.32. The horizontal component of Earth's magnetic field at the location of the loop is 2.0×10^{-5} T. Calculate the maximum emf induced in the coil by Earth's field.

Figure P20.32

33. BIO Considerable scientific work is currently under way to determine whether weak oscillating magnetic fields such as those found near outdoor electric power lines can affect human health. One study indicated that a magnetic field of magnitude 1.0×10^{-3} T, oscillating at 60 Hz, might stimulate red blood cells to become cancerous. If the diameter of a red blood cell is 8.0 μm, determine the maximum emf that can be generated around the perimeter of the cell.

34. A flat coil enclosing an area of 0.10 m^2 is rotating at 60 rev/s, with its axis of rotation perpendicular to a 0.20-T magnetic field. (a) If there are 1 000 turns on the coil, what is the maximum voltage induced in the coil? (b) When the maximum induced voltage occurs, what is the orientation of the coil with respect to the magnetic field?

35. In a model AC generator, a 500-turn rectangular coil 8.0 cm by 20 cm rotates at 120 rev/min in a uniform magnetic field of 0.60 T. (a) What is the maximum emf induced in the coil? (b) What is the instantaneous value of the emf in the coil at $t = (\pi/32)$ s? Assume the emf is zero at $t = 0$. (c) What is the smallest value of t for which the emf will have its maximum value?

36. A motor has coils with a resistance of 30 Ω and operates from a voltage of 240 V. When the motor is operating at its maximum speed, the back emf is 145 V. Find the current in the coils (a) when the motor is first turned on and (b) when the motor has reached maximum speed. (c) If the current in the motor is 6.0 A at some instant, what is the back emf at that time?

37. A coil of 10.0 turns is in the shape of an ellipse having a major axis of 10.0 cm and a minor axis of 4.00 cm. The coil rotates at 100 rpm in a region in which the magnitude of Earth's magnetic field is 55 μT. What is the maximum voltage induced in the coil if the axis of rotation of the coil is along its major axis and is aligned (a) perpendicular to Earth's magnetic field and (b) parallel to Earth's magnetic field? *Note:* The area of an ellipse is given by $A = \pi ab$, where a is the length of the *semi*major axis and b is the length of the *semi*minor axis.

20.5 Self-Inductance

38. A technician wraps wire around a tube of length 36 cm having a diameter of 8.0 cm. When the windings are evenly spread over the full length of the tube, the result is a solenoid containing 580 turns of wire. (a) Find the self-inductance of this solenoid. (b) If the current in this solenoid increases at the rate of 4.0 A/s, what is the self-induced emf in the solenoid?

39. The current in a coil drops from 3.5 A to 2.0 A in 0.50 s. If the average emf induced in the coil is 12 mV, what is the self-inductance of the coil?

40. **S** Show that the two expressions for inductance given by

$$L = \frac{N\Phi_B}{I} \quad \text{and} \quad L = \frac{-\mathcal{E}}{\Delta I/\Delta t}$$

have the same units.

41. **M** A solenoid of radius 2.5 cm has 400 turns and a length of 20 cm. Find (a) its inductance and (b) the rate at which current must change through it to produce an emf of 75 mV.

42. An emf of 24.0 mV is induced in a 500-turn coil when the current is changing at a rate of 10.0 A/s. What is the magnetic flux through each turn of the coil at an instant when the current is 4.00 A?

20.6 RL Circuits

43. An electromagnet can be modeled as an inductor in series with a resistor. Consider a large electromagnet of inductance $L = 12.0$ H and resistance $R = 4.50\ \Omega$ connected to a 24.0 V battery and switch as in Figure P20.43. After the switch is closed, find (a) the maximum current carried by the electromagnet, (b) the time constant of the circuit, and (c) the time it takes the current to reach 95.0% of its maximum value.

Figure P20.43
Problems 43, 45, 46, and 48

44. An RL circuit with $L = 3.00$ H and an RC circuit with $C = 3.00\ \mu$F have the same time constant. If the two circuits have the same resistance R, (a) what is the value of R and (b) what is this common time constant?

45. A battery is connected in series with a 0.30-Ω resistor and an inductor, as in Figure P20.43. The switch is closed at $t = 0$. The time constant of the circuit is 0.25 s, and the maximum current in the circuit is 8.0 A. Find (a) the emf of the battery, (b) the inductance of the circuit, (c) the current in the circuit after one time constant has elapsed, (d) the voltage across the resistor after one time constant has elapsed, and (e) the voltage across the inductor after one time constant has elapsed.

46. A 25-mH inductor, an 8.0-Ω resistor, and a 6.0-V battery are connected in series as in Figure P20.43. The switch is closed at $t = 0$. Find the voltage drop across the resistor (a) at $t = 0$ and (b) after one time constant has passed. Also, find the voltage drop across the inductor (c) at $t = 0$ and (d) after one time constant has elapsed.

47. Calculate the resistance in an RL circuit in which $L = 2.50$ H and the current increases to 90.0% of its final value in 3.00 s.

48. Consider the circuit shown in Figure P20.43. Take $\mathcal{E} = 6.00$ V, $L = 8.00$ mH, and $R = 4.00\ \Omega$. (a) What is the inductive time constant of the circuit? (b) Calculate the current in the circuit 250 μs after the switch is closed. (c) What is the value of the final steady-state current? (d) How long does it take the current to reach 80.0% of its maximum value?

20.7 Energy Stored in a Magnetic Field

49. (a) If an inductor carrying a 1.70-A current stores an energy of 0.300 mJ, what is its inductance? (b) How much energy does the same inductor store if it carries a 3.0-A current?

50. A 300-turn solenoid has a radius of 5.00 cm and a length of 20.0 cm. Find (a) the inductance of the solenoid and (b) the energy stored in the solenoid when the current in its windings is 0.500 A.

51. **M** A 24-V battery is connected in series with a resistor and an inductor, with $R = 8.0\ \Omega$ and $L = 4.0$ H, respectively. Find the energy stored in the inductor (a) when the current reaches its maximum value and (b) one time constant after the switch is closed.

52. **GP** A 60.0-m length of insulated copper wire is wound to form a solenoid of radius 2.0 cm. The copper wire has a radius of 0.50 mm. (a) What is the resistance of the wire? (b) Treating each turn of the solenoid as a circle, how many turns can be made with the wire? (c) How long is the resulting solenoid? (d) What is the self-inductance of the solenoid? (e) If the solenoid is attached to a battery with an emf of 6.0 V and internal resistance of 350 mΩ, compute the time constant of the circuit. (f) What is the maximum current attained? (g) How long would it take to reach 99.9% of its maximum current? (h) What maximum energy is stored in the inductor?

Additional Problems

53. Two circular loops of wire surround an insulating rod as in Figure P20.53. Loop 1 carries a current I in the clockwise direction when viewed from the left end. If loop 1 moves toward loop 2, which remains stationary, what is the direction of the induced current in loop 2 when viewed from the left end?

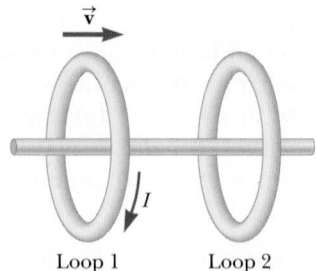

Loop 1   Loop 2

Figure P20.53

54. A circular loop of wire of resistance $R = 0.500\ \Omega$ and radius $r = 8.00$ cm is in a uniform magnetic field directed out of the page as in Figure P20.54. If a clockwise current of $I = 2.50$ mA is induced in the loop, (a) is the magnetic field increasing or decreasing in time? (b) Find the rate at which the field is changing with time.

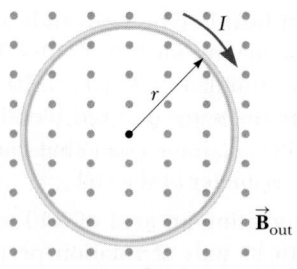

Figure P20.54

55. A rectangular coil with resistance R has N turns, each of length ℓ and width w, as shown in Figure P20.55. The coil moves into a uniform magnetic field $\vec{\mathbf{B}}_{\text{in}}$ with constant velocity $\vec{\mathbf{v}}$. What are the magnitude and direction of the total magnetic force on the coil (a) as it enters the magnetic field, (b) as it moves within the field, and (c) as it leaves the field?

Figure P20.55

56. **QC** A conducting bar of length ℓ moves to the right on two frictionless rails, as shown in Figure P20.30. A uniform magnetic field directed into the page has a magnitude of 0.30 T. Assume $\ell = 35$ cm and $R = 9.0\ \Omega$. (a) At what constant speed should the bar move to produce an 8.5-mA current in the resistor? What is the direction of this induced current? (b) At what rate is energy delivered to the resistor? (c) Explain the origin of the energy being delivered to the resistor.

57. An 820-turn wire coil of resistance 24.0 Ω is placed on top of a 12 500-turn, 7.00-cm-long solenoid, as in Figure P20.57. Both coil and solenoid have cross-sectional areas of 1.00×10^{-4} m². (a) How long does it take the solenoid current to reach 0.632 times its maximum value? (b) Determine the average back emf caused by the self-inductance of the solenoid during this interval. The magnetic field produced by the solenoid at the location of the coil is one-half as strong as the field at the center of the solenoid. (c) Determine the average rate of change in magnetic flux through each turn of

Figure P20.57

the coil during the stated interval. (d) Find the magnitude of the average induced current in the coil.

58. **Q|C** A spacecraft is in a circular orbit of radius equal to 3.0×10^4 km around a 2.0×10^{30} kg pulsar. The magnetic field of the pulsar at that radial distance is 1.0×10^2 T directed perpendicular to the velocity of the spacecraft. The spacecraft is 0.20 km long with a radius of 0.040 km and moves counterclockwise in the xy-plane around the pulsar. (a) What is the speed of the spacecraft? (b) If the magnetic field points in the positive z-direction, is the emf induced from the back to the front of the spacecraft or from side to side? (c) Compute the induced emf. (d) Describe the hazards for astronauts inside any spacecraft moving in the vicinity of a pulsar.

59. **Q|C** A conducting rod of length ℓ moves on two horizontal frictionless rails, as in Figure P20.30. A constant force of magnitude 1.00 N moves the bar at a uniform speed of 2.00 m/s through a magnetic field $\vec{B}$ that is directed into the page. (a) What is the current in an 8.00-Ω resistor R? (b) What is the rate of energy dissipation in the resistor? (c) What is the mechanical power delivered by the constant force?

60. A long solenoid of radius $r = 2.00$ cm is wound with 3.50×10^3 turns/m and carries a current that changes at the rate of 28.5 A/s as in Figure P20.60. What is the magnitude of the emf induced in the square conducting loop surrounding the center of the solenoid?

Figure P20.60

61. The bolt of lightning depicted in Figure P20.61 passes 200 m from a 100-turn coil oriented as shown. If the current in the lightning bolt falls from 6.02×10^6 A to zero in 10.5 μs, what is the average voltage induced in the coil? Assume the distance to the center of the coil determines the average magnetic field at the coil's position. Treat the lightning bolt as a long, vertical wire.

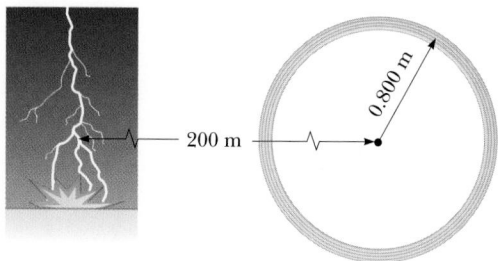

Figure P20.61

62. The square loop in Figure P20.62 is made of wires with a total series resistance of 10.0 Ω. It is placed in a uniform 0.100-T magnetic field directed perpendicular into the plane of the paper. The loop, which is hinged at each corner, is pulled as shown until the separation between points A and B is 3.00 m. If this process takes 0.100 s, what is the average current generated in the loop? What is the direction of the current?

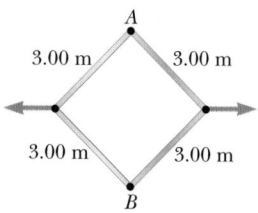

Figure P20.62

63. The magnetic field shown in Figure P20.63 has a uniform magnitude of 25.0 mT directed into the paper. The initial diameter of the kink is 2.00 cm. (a) The wire is quickly pulled taut, and the kink shrinks to a diameter of zero in 50.0 ms. Determine the average voltage induced between endpoints A and B. Include the polarity. (b) Suppose the kink is undisturbed, but the magnetic field increases to 100 mT in 4.00×10^{-3} s. Determine the average voltage across terminals A and B, including polarity, during this period.

Figure P20.63

64. An aluminum ring of radius 5.00 cm and resistance 3.00×10^{-4} Ω is placed around the top of a long air-core solenoid with 1 000 turns per meter and a smaller radius of 3.00 cm, as in Figure P20.64. If the current in the solenoid is increasing at a constant rate of 270 A/s, what is the induced current in the ring? Assume the magnetic field produced by the solenoid over the area at the end of the solenoid is one-half as strong as the field at the center of the solenoid. Assume also the solenoid produces a negligible field outside its cross-sectional area.

Figure P20.64

65. In Figure P20.65 (page 722) the rolling axle of length 1.50 m is pushed along horizontal rails at a constant speed $v = 3.00$ m/s. A resistor $R = 0.400$ Ω is connected

to the rails at points *a* and *b*, directly opposite each other. (The wheels make good electrical contact with the rails, so the axle, rails, and *R* form a closed-loop circuit. The only significant resistance in the circuit is *R*.) A uniform magnetic field $B = 0.800$ T is directed vertically downward. (a) Find the induced current *I* in the resistor. (b) What horizontal force $\vec{F}$ is required to keep the axle rolling at constant speed? (c) Which end of the resistor, *a* or *b*, is at the higher electric potential? (d) After the axle rolls past the resistor, does the current in *R* reverse direction? Explain your answer.

Figure P20.65

66. Q C S An *N*-turn square coil with side ℓ and resistance *R* is pulled to the right at constant speed *v* in the positive *x*-direction in the presence of a uniform magnetic field *B* acting perpendicular to the coil, as shown in Figure P20.66. At $t = 0$, the right side of the coil is at the edge of the field. After a time *t* has elapsed, the entire coil is in the region where $B = 0$. In terms of the quantities *N*, *B*, ℓ, *v*, and *R*, find symbolic expressions for (a) the magnitude of the induced emf in the loop

during the time interval *t*, (b) the magnitude of the induced current in the coil, (c) the power delivered to the coil, and (d) the force required to remove the coil from the field. (e) What is the direction of the induced current in the loop? (f) What is the direction of the magnetic force on the loop while it is being pulled out of the field?

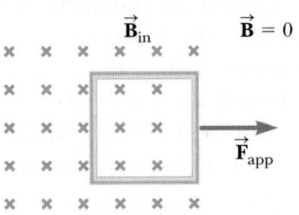

Figure P20.66

67. S A conducting rectangular loop of mass *M*, resistance *R*, and dimensions *w* by ℓ falls from rest into a magnetic field $\vec{B}$, as shown in Figure P20.67. During the time interval before the top edge of the loop reaches the field, the loop approaches a terminal speed v_T. (a) Show that

$$v_T = \frac{MgR}{B^2 w^2}$$

Figure P20.67

(b) Why is v_T proportional to *R*? (c) Why is it inversely proportional to B^2?

▪ AP* REVIEW QUESTIONS

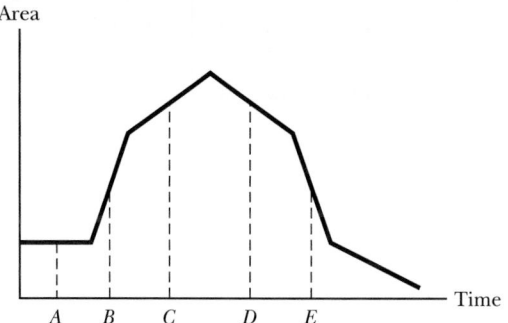

1. A coil of wire is oriented at 45° to a magnetic field. As the coil is rotated toward 90°, which of the following does NOT happen?

(A) Magnetic field increases

(B) Magnetic field lines through area of coil increase

(C) Effective area increases

(D) Magnetic flux increases

(E) Cosine θ approaches a maximum

2. A coil of wire is oriented so that its plane is perpendicular to a magnetic field. Which of the following will NOT induce an emf ($\mathcal{E}$) in the coil?

(A) Spin coil around tangent line drawn anywhere on coil

(B) Spin coil around an axis perpendicular to coil

(C) Spin coil around an axis in plane of coil

(D) Change the magnetic field

(E) Change the size of the coil

3. A coil with a diameter of 40 cm and 100 turns of wire is sitting in a magnetic field of 0.5 T. If the coil is oriented perpendicular to the magnetic field, what is the approximate magnetic flux through the coil?

(A) 0.314 T·m^2

(B) 3.14 T·m^2

(C) 31.4 T·m^2

(D) 314 T·m^2

(E) Zero. There is no magnetic flux through the coil.

4. A circular loop sitting on a lab table has a radius of 10 cm and 50 turns of wire. The perpendicular magnetic field drops from 10 T to 4 T in 3 s. What is the induced emf ($\mathcal{E}$) in the coil?

(A) 0.02πV

(B) πV

(C) 200πV

(D) 1 × 10^4 πV

(E) Zero. There is no induced emf in the coil.

5. A coil is oriented perpendicular to a constant magnetic field. The graph above shows how the area of the coil is changing with time. Which location on the graph will have the greatest induced emf (ε) while decreasing the flux?

(A) A

(B) B

(C) C

(D) D

(E) E

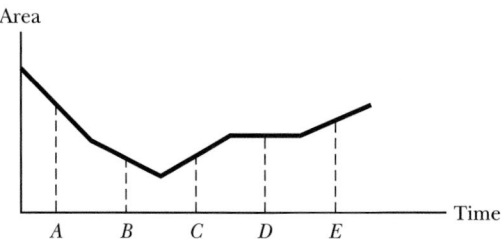

6. A coil is oriented perpendicular to a magnetic field. The graphs above show how the magnetic field and area of the coil change with time. Which location on the graphs will have the greatest induced emf ($\mathcal{E}$)?

(A) A

(B) B

(C) C

(D) D

(E) E

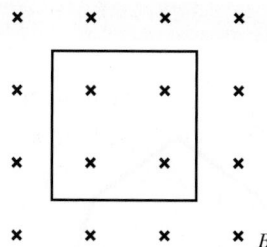

7. A coil sits perpendicular to a magnetic field that is directed into the page and is changing at a rate of −2 T/s. What is happening to the flux and what is the direction of the induced current?

(A) Increasing, clockwise

(B) Decreasing, clockwise

(C) Increasing, counterclockwise

(D) Decreasing, counterclockwise

(E) Remains constant, no induced current

8. A coil sits perpendicular to a constant magnetic field that is directed out of the page. The loop is expanding at a rate of 2 cm²/s. What is happening to the magnetic flux and what is the direction of the induced current?

(A) Increasing, clockwise

(B) Decreasing, clockwise

(C) Increasing, counterclockwise

(D) Decreasing, counterclockwise

(E) Remains constant, no induced current

9. A square coil of wire, 10 cm on a side with 40 turns, has a resistance of 8 Ω. A magnetic field directed into the page is applied perpendicular to the coil and is increasing from 0.1 T to 0.9 T in 3.2 s. What is the magnitude and direction of the induced current in the wire?

(A) 0.13 A, clockwise

(B) 0.13 A, counterclockwise

(C) 3.1 mA, clockwise

(D) 3.1 mA, counterclockwise

(E) Zero. There is no induced current in the coil.

10. In the figure above, a 10 cm long metal bar moves to the left at a velocity of 8 cm/s in a constant magnetic

field of 2 T. If the induced current is 15 mA, what is the resistance in the circuit?

(A) 0.09 Ω

(B) 0.94 Ω

(C) 1.1 Ω

(D) 10.7 Ω

(E) 107 Ω

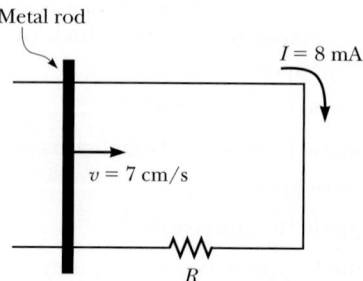

11. In the figure above, a 5 cm long metal bar moves to the right at a velocity of 7 cm/s in a constant magnetic field. If the resistance of the circuit is 3 Ω and the induced current is 8 mA clockwise, what is the magnitude and direction of the magnetic field?

(A) 0.69 T, into the page

(B) 0.69 T, out of the page

(C) 6.9 T, into the page

(D) 6.9 T, out of the page

(E) More information is needed

12. A 7 cm long metal bar moves to the left at a velocity of 6 cm/s in a constant magnetic field of 3 T directed out of the page. If the resistance in the circuit is 4 Ω, what is the magnitude and direction of the induced current?

(A) 3.2 mA, clockwise

(B) 3.2 mA, counterclockwise

(C) 31.5 A, clockwise

(D) 31.5 A, counterclockwise

(E) More information is needed

© Bettmann/Corbis

Arecibo, a large radio telescope in Puerto Rico, gathers electromagnetic radiation in the form of radio waves. These long wavelengths pass through obscuring dust clouds, allowing astronomers to create images of the core region of the Milky Way galaxy, which can't be observed in the visible spectrum.

Alternating-Current Circuits and Electromagnetic Waves

21

Every time we turn on a television set, a stereo system, or any other electric appliances, we call on alternating currents (AC) to provide the power to operate them. We begin our study of AC circuits by examining the characteristics of a circuit containing a source of emf and one other circuit element: a resistor, a capacitor, or an inductor. Then we examine what happens when these elements are connected in combination with each other. Our discussion is limited to simple series configurations of the three kinds of elements.

We conclude this chapter with a discussion of **electromagnetic waves**, which are composed of fluctuating electric and magnetic fields. Electromagnetic waves in the form of visible light enable us to view the world around us; infrared waves warm our environment; radio-frequency waves carry our television and radio programs, as well as information about processes in the core of our galaxy; and X-rays allow us to perceive structures hidden inside our bodies and study properties of distant, collapsed stars. Light is key to our understanding of the universe.

21.1 Resistors in an AC Circuit

An AC circuit consists of combinations of circuit elements and an AC generator or an AC source, which provides the alternating current. We have seen that the output of an AC generator is sinusoidal and varies with time according to

$$\Delta v = \Delta V_{\max} \sin 2\pi f t \qquad [21.1]$$

Active Figure 21.1

A series circuit consisting of a resistor R connected to an AC generator,

designated by the symbol —$\sim$—

where Δv is the instantaneous voltage, ΔV_{max} is the maximum voltage of the AC generator, and f is the frequency at which the voltage changes, measured in hertz (Hz). (Compare Equations 20.7 and 20.8 with Equation 21.1, and recall that $\omega = 2\pi f$.) We first consider a simple circuit consisting of a resistor and an AC source (designated by the symbol —$\sim$—), as in Active Figure 21.1. The current and the voltage versus time across the resistor are shown in Active Figure 21.2.

To explain the concept of alternating current, we begin by discussing the current versus time curve in Active Figure 21.2. At point a on the curve, the current has a maximum value in one direction, arbitrarily called the positive direction. Between points a and b, the current is decreasing in magnitude but is still in the positive direction. At point b, the current is momentarily zero; it then begins to increase in the opposite (negative) direction between points b and c. At point c, the current has reached its maximum value in the negative direction.

The current and voltage are in step with each other because they vary identically with time. **Because the current and the voltage reach their maximum values at the same time, they are said to be in phase.** Notice that **the average value of the current over one cycle is zero** because the current is maintained in one direction (the positive direction) for the same amount of time and at the same magnitude as it is in the opposite direction (the negative direction). The direction of the current, however, has no effect on the behavior of the resistor in the circuit: the collisions between electrons and the fixed atoms of the resistor result in an increase in the resistor's temperature regardless of the direction of the current.

We can quantify this discussion by recalling that the rate at which electrical energy is dissipated in a resistor, the power P, is

$$P = i^2 R$$

where i is the *instantaneous* current in the resistor. Because the heating effect of a current is proportional to the *square* of the current, it makes no difference whether the sign associated with the current is positive or negative. The heating effect produced by an alternating current with a maximum value of I_{max} *is not the same* as that produced by a direct current of the same value, however. The reason is that the alternating current has this maximum value for only an instant of time during a cycle. The important quantity in an AC circuit is a special kind of average value of current, called the **rms current**: the direct current that dissipates the same amount of energy in a resistor that is dissipated by the actual alternating current. Finding the average of the alternating current i, depicted in Figure 21.3a, would not be useful because that average is zero, whereas the rms current is always positive. To find the rms current, we first square the current, then find its average value, and finally take the square root of this average value. Hence, the rms current is the square *root* of the average (*mean*) of the *square* of the current. Because i^2 varies as

Active Figure 21.2

A plot of current and voltage across a resistor versus time.

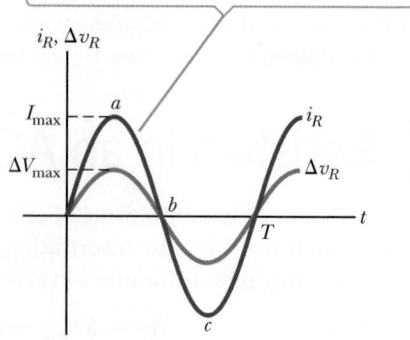

The current and the voltage are in phase: they simultaneously reach their maximum values, their minimum values, and their zero values.

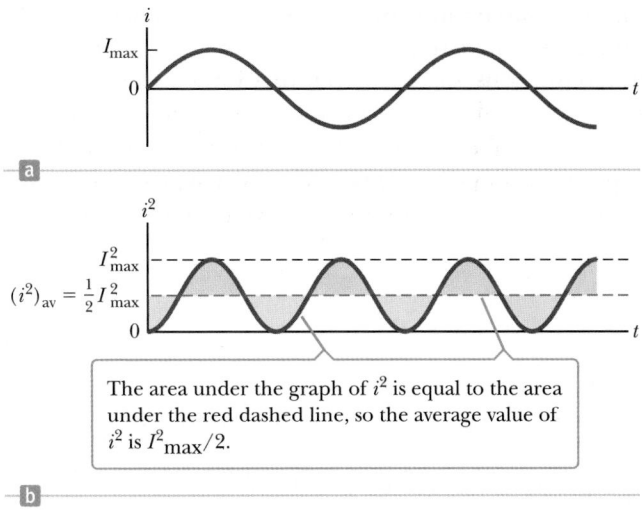

Figure 21.3 (a) Plot of the current in a resistor as a function of time. (b) Plot of the square of the current in a resistor as a function of time. The area under the red-dashed line omits the tan-shaded regions, but that is made up by the inclusion of the gray-shaded regions with the same area. That shows the area under the curve of i^2 is the same as the area under the red dashed line, so $(i^2)_{av} = I^2_{max}/2$.

The area under the graph of i^2 is equal to the area under the red dashed line, so the average value of i^2 is $I^2_{max}/2$.

$\sin^2 2\pi ft$, the average value of i^2 is $\frac{1}{2}I^2_{max}$ (Fig. 21.3b).[1] Therefore, the rms current I_{rms} is related to the maximum value of the alternating current I_{max} by

$$I_{rms} = \frac{I_{max}}{\sqrt{2}} = 0.707 I_{max} \qquad [21.2]$$

This equation says that an alternating current with a maximum value of 3 A produces the same heating effect in a resistor as a direct current of $(3/\sqrt{2})$ A. We can therefore say that the average power dissipated in a resistor that carries alternating current I is

$$P_{av} = I^2_{rms}R$$

Alternating voltages are also best discussed in terms of rms voltages, with a relationship identical to the preceding one,

$$\Delta V_{rms} = \frac{\Delta V_{max}}{\sqrt{2}} = 0.707 \Delta V_{max} \qquad [21.3]$$

◄ rms voltage

where ΔV_{rms} is the rms voltage and ΔV_{max} is the maximum value of the alternating voltage.

When we speak of measuring an AC voltage of 120 V from an electric outlet, we actually mean an rms voltage of 120 V. A quick calculation using Equation 21.3 shows that such an AC voltage actually has a peak value of about 170 V. In this chapter we use rms values when discussing alternating currents and voltages. One reason is that AC ammeters and voltmeters are designed to read rms values. Further, if we use rms values, many of the equations for alternating current will have the same form as those used in the study of direct-current (DC) circuits. Table 21.1 (page 726) summarizes the notations used throughout this chapter.

[1]We can show that $(i^2)_{av} = I^2_{max}/2$ as follows: The current in the circuit varies with time according to the expression $i = I_{max} \sin 2\pi ft$, so $i^2 = I^2_{max} \sin^2 2\pi ft$. Therefore, we can find the average value of i^2 by calculating the average value of $\sin^2 2\pi ft$. Note that a graph of $\cos^2 2\pi ft$ versus time is identical to a graph of $\sin^2 2\pi ft$ versus time, except that the points are shifted on the time axis. Thus, the time average of $\sin^2 2\pi ft$ is equal to the time average of $\cos^2 2\pi ft$, taken over one or more cycles. That is,

$$(\sin^2 2\pi ft)_{av} = (\cos^2 2\pi ft)_{av}$$

With this fact and the trigonometric identity $\sin^2 \theta + \cos^2 \theta = 1$, we get

$$(\sin^2 2\pi ft)_{av} + (\cos^2 2\pi ft)_{av} = 2(\sin^2 2\pi ft)_{av} = 1$$

$$(\sin^2 2\pi ft)_{av} = \tfrac{1}{2}$$

When this result is substituted into the expression $i^2 = I^2_{max} \sin^2 2\pi ft$, we get $(i^2)_{av} = I^2_{rms} = I^2_{max}/2$, or $I_{rms} = I_{max}/\sqrt{2}$, where I_{rms} is the rms current.

Table 21.1 Notation Used in This Chapter

	Voltage	Current
Instantaneous value	Δv	i
Maximum value	ΔV_{max}	I_{max}
rms value	ΔV_{rms}	I_{rms}

Consider the series circuit in Figure 21.1 (page 724), consisting of a resistor connected to an AC generator. A resistor impedes the current in an AC circuit, just as it does in a DC circuit. Ohm's law is therefore valid for an AC circuit, and we have

$$\Delta V_{R,rms} = I_{rms}R \qquad \text{[21.4a]}$$

The rms voltage across a resistor is equal to the rms current in the circuit times the resistance. This equation is also true if maximum values of current and voltage are used:

$$\Delta V_{R,max} = I_{max}R \qquad \text{[21.4b]}$$

■ Quick Quiz

21.1 Which of the following statements can be true for a resistor connected in a simple series circuit to an operating AC generator? (a) $P_{av} = 0$ and $i_{av} = 0$ (b) $P_{av} = 0$ and $i_{av} > 0$ (c) $P_{av} > 0$ and $i_{av} = 0$ (d) $P_{av} > 0$ and $i_{av} > 0$

■ EXAMPLE 21.1 | **What Is the rms Current?**

GOAL Perform basic AC circuit calculations for a purely resistive circuit.

PROBLEM An AC voltage source has an output of $\Delta v = (2.00 \times 10^2 \text{ V}) \sin 2\pi ft$. This source is connected to a $1.00 \times 10^2 \Omega$ resistor as in Figure 21.1. Find the rms voltage and rms current in the resistor.

STRATEGY Compare the expression for the voltage output just given with the general form, $\Delta v = \Delta V_{max} \sin 2\pi ft$, finding the maximum voltage. Substitute this result into the expression for the rms voltage.

SOLUTION

Obtain the maximum voltage by comparison of the given expression for the output with the general expression:

$\Delta v = (2.00 \times 10^2 \text{ V}) \sin 2\pi ft \qquad \Delta v = \Delta V_{max} \sin 2\pi ft$

$\rightarrow \quad \Delta V_{max} = 2.00 \times 10^2 \text{ V}$

Next, substitute into Equation 21.3 to find the rms voltage of the source:

$\Delta V_{rms} = \dfrac{\Delta V_{max}}{\sqrt{2}} = \dfrac{2.00 \times 10^2 \text{ V}}{\sqrt{2}} = \boxed{141 \text{ V}}$

Substitute this result into Ohm's law to find the rms current:

$I_{rms} = \dfrac{\Delta V_{rms}}{R} = \dfrac{141 \text{ V}}{1.00 \times 10^2 \Omega} = \boxed{1.41 \text{ A}}$

REMARKS Notice how the concept of rms values allows the handling of an AC circuit quantitatively in much the same way as a DC circuit.

QUESTION 21.1 True or False: The rms current in an AC circuit oscillates sinusoidally with time.

EXERCISE 21.1 Find the maximum current in the circuit and the average power delivered to the circuit.

ANSWER 2.00 A; 2.00×10^2 W

■ APPLYING PHYSICS 21.1 | **Electric Fields and Cancer Treatment** BIO

Cancer cells multiply far more frequently than most normal cells, spreading throughout the body, using its resources and interfering with normal functioning. Most therapies damage both cancerous and healthy cells, so finding methods that target cancer cells is important in developing better treatments for the disease.

Because cancer cells multiply so rapidly, it's natural to consider treatments that prevent or disrupt cell division. Treatments such as chemotherapy interfere with the cell division cycle, but can also damage healthy cells. It has recently been found that alternating electric fields produced by alternating currents in the range of 100 kHz can disrupt the cell division cycle, either by slowing the division or by causing a dividing cell to disintegrate. Healthy cells that divide at only a very slow rate are less vulnerable than the rapidly dividing cancer cells, so such therapy holds out promise for certain types of cancer.

The alternating electric fields are thought to affect the process of mitosis, which is the dividing of the cell nucleus into two sets of identical chromosomes. Near the end of the first phase of mitosis, called the prophase, the mitotic spindle forms, a structure of fine filaments that guides the

two replicated sets of chromosomes into separate daughter cells. The mitotic spindle is made up of a polymerization of dimers of tubulin, a protein with a large electric dipole moment. The alternating electric field exerts forces on these dipoles, disrupting their proper functioning.

Electric field therapy is especially promising for the treatment of brain tumors because healthy brain cells don't divide and therefore would be unharmed by the alternating electric fields. Research on such therapies is ongoing. ■

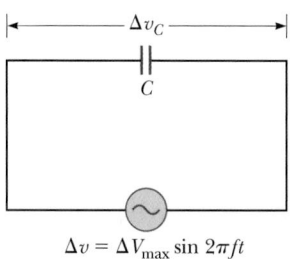

$$\Delta v = \Delta V_{max} \sin 2\pi f t$$

Active Figure 21.4
A series circuit consisting of a capacitor C connected to an AC generator.

21.2 Capacitors in an AC Circuit

To understand the effect of a capacitor on the behavior of a circuit containing an AC voltage source, we first review what happens when a capacitor is placed in a circuit containing a DC source, such as a battery. When the switch is closed in a series circuit containing a battery, a resistor, and a capacitor, the initial charge on the plates of the capacitor is zero. The motion of charge through the circuit is therefore relatively free, and there is a large current in the circuit. As more charge accumulates on the capacitor, the voltage across it increases, opposing the current. After some time interval, which depends on the time constant RC, the current approaches zero. Consequently, a capacitor in a DC circuit limits or impedes current so that it approaches zero after a brief time.

Now consider the simple series circuit in Figure 21.4, consisting of a capacitor connected to an AC generator. We sketch curves of current versus time and voltage versus time, and then attempt to make the graphs seem reasonable. The curves are shown in Figure 21.5. First, notice that the segment of the current curve from a to b indicates that the current starts out at a rather large value. This large value can be understood by recognizing that there is no charge on the capacitor at $t = 0$; as a consequence, there is nothing in the circuit except the resistance of the wires to hinder the flow of charge at this instant. The current decreases, however, as the voltage across the capacitor increases from c to d on the voltage curve. When the voltage is at point d, the current reverses and begins to increase in the opposite direction (from b to e on the current curve). During this time, the voltage across the capacitor decreases from d to f because the plates are now losing the charge they accumulated earlier. The remainder of the cycle for both voltage and current is a repeat of what happened during the first half of the cycle. The current reaches a maximum value in the opposite direction at point e on the current curve and then decreases as the voltage across the capacitor builds up.

In a purely resistive circuit, the current and voltage are always in step with each other. That isn't the case when a capacitor is in the circuit. In Figure 21.5, when an alternating voltage is applied across a capacitor, the voltage reaches its maximum value one-quarter of a cycle after the current reaches its maximum value. We say that **the voltage across a capacitor always lags the current by 90°.**

The impeding effect of a capacitor on the current in an AC circuit is expressed in terms of a factor called the **capacitive reactance** X_C, defined as

$$X_C \equiv \frac{1}{2\pi f C} \qquad [21.5]$$

When C is in farads and f is in hertz, the unit of X_C is the ohm. Notice that $2\pi f = \omega$, the angular frequency.

From Equation 21.5, as the frequency f of the voltage source increases, the capacitive reactance X_C (the impeding effect of the capacitor) decreases, so the current increases. At high frequency, there is less time available to charge the capacitor, so less charge and voltage accumulate on the capacitor, which

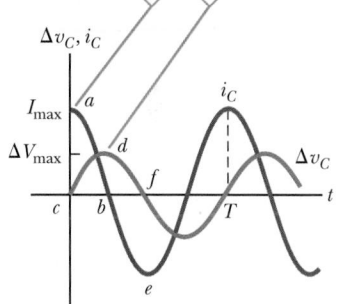

The voltage reaches its maximum value 90° after the current reaches its maximum value, so the voltage "lags" the current.

Active Figure 21.5
Plots of current and voltage across a capacitor versus time in an AC circuit.

◀ The voltage across a capacitor lags the current by 90°

◀ Capacitive reactance

translates into less opposition to the flow of charge and, consequently, a higher current. The analogy between capacitive reactance and resistance means that we can write an equation of the same form as Ohm's law to describe AC circuits containing capacitors. This equation relates the rms voltage and rms current in the circuit to the capacitive reactance:

$$\Delta V_{C,\text{rms}} = I_{\text{rms}} X_C \qquad [21.6]$$

■ EXAMPLE 21.2 | A Purely Capacitive AC Circuit

GOAL Perform basic AC circuit calculations for a capacitive circuit.

PROBLEM An 8.00-μF capacitor is connected to the terminals of an AC generator with an rms voltage of 1.50×10^2 V and a frequency of 60.0 Hz. Find the capacitive reactance and the rms current in the circuit.

STRATEGY Substitute values into Equations 21.5 and 21.6.

....

SOLUTION

Substitute the values of f and C into Equation 21.5:

$$X_C = \frac{1}{2\pi f C} = \frac{1}{2\pi(60.0 \text{ Hz})(8.00 \times 10^{-6} \text{ F})} = \boxed{332 \; \Omega}$$

Solve Equation 21.6 for the current and substitute the values for X_C and the rms voltage to find the rms current:

$$I_{\text{rms}} = \frac{\Delta V_{C,\text{rms}}}{X_C} = \frac{1.50 \times 10^2 \text{ V}}{332 \; \Omega} = \boxed{0.452 \text{ A}}$$

....

REMARKS Again, notice how similar the technique is to that of analyzing a DC circuit with a resistor.

QUESTION 21.2 True or False: The larger the capacitance of a capacitor, the larger the capacitive reactance.

EXERCISE 21.2 If the frequency is doubled, what happens to the capacitive reactance and the rms current?

ANSWER X_C is halved, and I_{rms} is doubled.

21.3 Inductors in an AC Circuit

Now consider an AC circuit consisting only of an inductor connected to the terminals of an AC source, as in Active Figure 21.6. (In any real circuit there is some resistance in the wire forming the inductive coil, but we ignore this consideration for now.) The changing current output of the generator produces a back emf that impedes the current in the circuit. The magnitude of this back emf is

$$\Delta v_L = L \frac{\Delta I}{\Delta t} \qquad [21.7]$$

The effective resistance of the coil in an AC circuit is measured by a quantity called the **inductive reactance**, X_L:

$$\boxed{X_L \equiv 2\pi f L} \qquad [21.8]$$

When f is in hertz and L is in henries, the unit of X_L is the ohm. The inductive reactance *increases* with increasing frequency and increasing inductance. Contrast these facts with capacitors, where increasing frequency or capacitance *decreases* the capacitive reactance.

To understand the meaning of inductive reactance, compare Equation 21.8 with Equation 21.7. First, note from Equation 21.8 that the inductive reactance depends on the inductance L, which is reasonable because the back emf (Eq. 21.7) is large for large values of L. Second, note that the inductive reactance depends on the

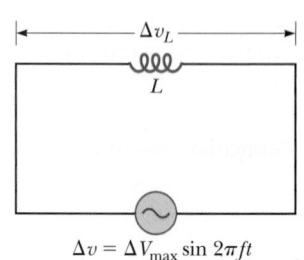

$$\Delta v = \Delta V_{\text{max}} \sin 2\pi f t$$

Active Figure 21.6

A series circuit consisting of an inductor L connected to an AC generator.

frequency f. This dependence, too, is reasonable because the back emf depends on $\Delta I/\Delta t$, a quantity that is large when the current changes rapidly, as it would for high frequencies.

With inductive reactance defined in this way, we can write an equation of the same form as Ohm's law for the voltage across the coil or inductor:

$$\Delta V_{L,\text{rms}} = I_{\text{rms}} X_L \qquad\qquad \text{[21.9]}$$

where $\Delta V_{L,\text{rms}}$ is the rms voltage across the coil and I_{rms} is the rms current in the coil.

Active Figure 21.7 shows the instantaneous voltage and instantaneous current across the coil as functions of time. When a sinusoidal voltage is applied across an inductor, the voltage reaches its maximum value one-quarter of an oscillation period before the current reaches its maximum value. In this situation we say that **the voltage across an inductor always leads the current by 90°.**

To see why there is a phase relationship between voltage and current, we examine a few points on the curves of Active Figure 21.7. At point a on the current curve, the current is beginning to increase in the positive direction. At this instant the rate of change of current, $\Delta I/\Delta t$ (the slope of the current curve), is at a maximum, and we see from Equation 21.7 that the voltage across the inductor is consequently also at a maximum. As the current rises between points a and b on the curve, $\Delta I/\Delta t$ gradually decreases until it reaches zero at point b. As a result, the voltage across the inductor is decreasing during this same time interval, as the segment between c and d on the voltage curve indicates. Immediately after point b, the current begins to decrease, although it still has the same direction it had during the previous quarter cycle. As the current decreases to zero (from b to e on the curve), a voltage is again induced in the coil (from d to f), but the polarity of this voltage is opposite the polarity of the voltage induced between c and d. This occurs because back emfs always oppose the change in the current.

We could continue to examine other segments of the curves, but no new information would be gained because the current and voltage variations are repetitive.

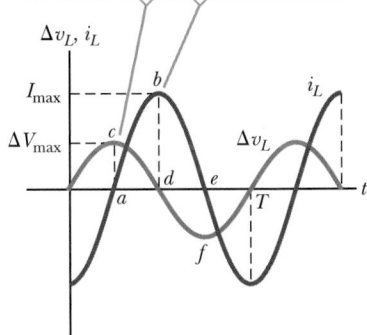

The voltage reaches its maximum value 90° before the current reaches its maximum value, so the voltage "leads" the current.

Active Figure 21.7
Plots of current and voltage across an inductor versus time in an AC circuit.

■ **EXAMPLE 21.3** | **A Purely Inductive AC Circuit**

GOAL Perform basic AC circuit calculations for an inductive circuit.

PROBLEM In a purely inductive AC circuit (see Active Fig. 21.6), $L = 25.0$ mH and the rms voltage is 1.50×10^2 V. Find the inductive reactance and rms current in the circuit if the frequency is 60.0 Hz.

SOLUTION

Substitute L and f into Equation 21.8 to get the inductive reactance:

$$X_L = 2\pi f L = 2\pi(60.0\ \text{s}^{-1})(25.0 \times 10^{-3}\ \text{H}) = \boxed{9.42\ \Omega}$$

Solve Equation 21.9 for the rms current and substitute:

$$I_{\text{rms}} = \frac{\Delta V_{L,\text{rms}}}{X_L} = \frac{1.50 \times 10^2\ \text{V}}{9.42\ \Omega} = \boxed{15.9\ \text{A}}$$

REMARKS The analogy with DC circuits is even closer than in the capacitive case because in the inductive equivalent of Ohm's law, the voltage across an inductor is *proportional* to the inductance L, just as the voltage across a resistor is proportional to R in Ohm's law.

QUESTION 21.3 True or False: A larger inductance or frequency results in a larger inductive reactance.

EXERCISE 21.3 Calculate the inductive reactance and rms current in a similar circuit if the frequency is again 60.0 Hz, but the rms voltage is 85.0 V and the inductance is 47.0 mH.

ANSWER $X_L = 17.7\ \Omega$, $I = 4.80$ A

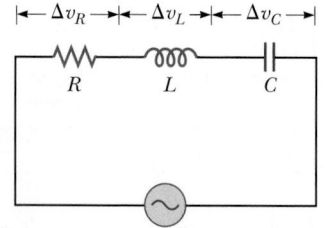

Active Figure 21.8

A series circuit consisting of a resistor, an inductor, and a capacitor connected to an AC generator.

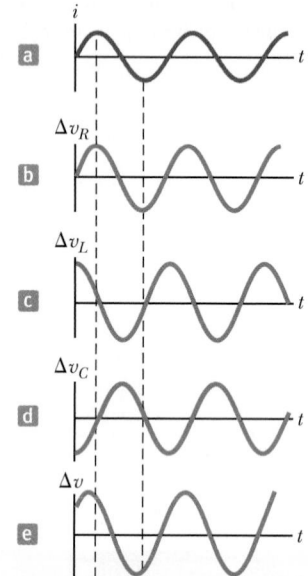

Active Figure 21.9

Phase relations in the series *RLC* circuit shown in Active Figure 21.8.

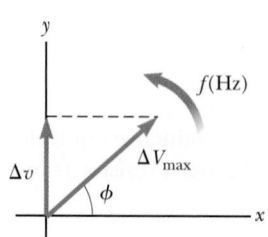

Figure 21.10 A phasor diagram for the voltage in an AC circuit, where ϕ is the phase angle between the voltage and the current and Δv is the instantaneous voltage.

21.4 The *RLC* Series Circuit

In the foregoing sections we examined the effects of an inductor, a capacitor, and a resistor when they are connected separately across an AC voltage source. We now consider what happens when these elements are combined.

Active Figure 21.8 shows a circuit containing a resistor, an inductor, and a capacitor connected in series across an AC source that supplies a total voltage Δv at some instant. The current in the circuit is the same at all points in the circuit at any instant and varies sinusoidally with time, as indicated in Active Figure 21.9a. This fact can be expressed mathematically as

$$i = I_{max} \sin 2\pi ft$$

Earlier, we learned that the voltage across each element may or may not be in phase with the current. The instantaneous voltages across the three elements, shown in Active Figure 21.9, have the following phase relations to the instantaneous current:

1. The instantaneous voltage Δv_R across the resistor is *in phase* with the instantaneous current. (See Active Fig. 21.9b.)
2. The instantaneous voltage Δv_L across the inductor *leads* the current by 90°. (See Active Fig. 21.9c.)
3. The instantaneous voltage Δv_C across the capacitor *lags* the current by 90°. (See Active Fig. 21.9d.)

The net instantaneous voltage Δv supplied by the AC source equals the sum of the instantaneous voltages across the separate elements: $\Delta v = \Delta v_R + \Delta v_C + \Delta v_L$. This doesn't mean, however, that the voltages measured with an AC voltmeter across R, C, and L sum to the measured source voltage! In fact, the measured voltages *don't* sum to the measured source voltage because the voltages across R, C, and L all have different phases.

To account for the different phases of the voltage drops, we use a technique involving vectors. We represent the voltage across each element with a rotating vector, as in Figure 21.10. The rotating vectors are referred to as **phasors**, and the diagram is called a **phasor diagram**. This particular diagram represents the circuit voltage given by the expression $\Delta v = \Delta V_{max} \sin(2\pi ft + \phi)$, where ΔV_{max} is the maximum voltage (the magnitude or length of the rotating vector or phasor) and ϕ is the angle between the phasor and the positive *x*-axis when $t = 0$. The phasor can be viewed as a vector of magnitude ΔV_{max} rotating at a constant frequency f so that its projection along the *y*-axis is the instantaneous voltage in the circuit. Because ϕ is the phase angle between the voltage and current in the circuit, the phasor for the current (not shown in Fig. 21.10) lies along the positive *x*-axis when $t = 0$ and is expressed by the relation $i = I_{max} \sin(2\pi ft)$.

The phasor diagrams in Figure 21.11 are useful for analyzing the *series RLC* circuit. Voltages in phase with the current are represented by vectors along the positive *x*-axis, and voltages out of phase with the current lie along other directions. ΔV_R is horizontal and to the right because it's in phase with the current. Likewise, ΔV_L is represented by a phasor along the positive *y*-axis because it leads the current by 90°. Finally, ΔV_C is along the negative *y*-axis because it lags the current[2] by 90°. If the phasors are added as vector quantities so as to account for the different phases of the voltages across R, L, and C, Figure 21.11a shows that the only *x*-component for the voltages is ΔV_R and the net *y*-component is $\Delta V_L - \Delta V_C$. We now add the pha-

---

[2]A mnemonic to help you remember the phase relationships in *RLC* circuits is "*ELI* the *ICE* man." *E* represents the voltage $\mathcal{E}$, *I* the current, *L* the inductance, and *C* the capacitance. Thus, the name *ELI* means that in an inductive circuit, the voltage $\mathcal{E}$ leads the current *I*. In a capacitive circuit *ICE* means that the current leads the voltage.

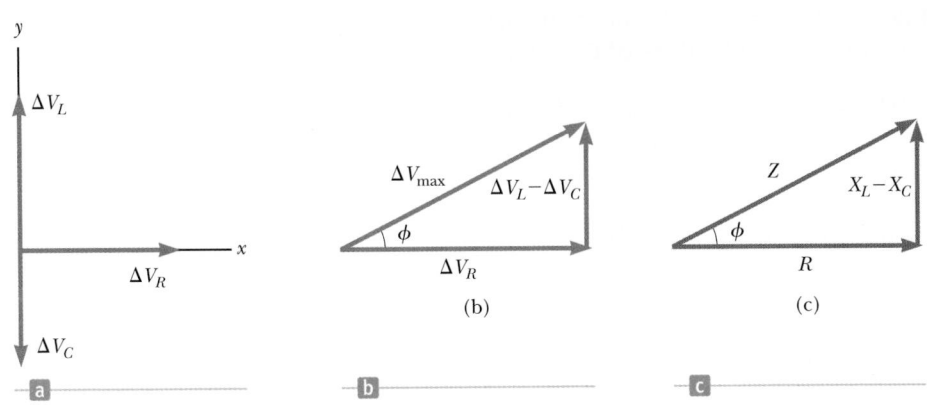

Figure 21.11 (a) A phasor diagram for the *RLC* circuit. (b) Addition of the phasors as vectors gives $\Delta V_{max} = \sqrt{\Delta V_R{}^2 + (\Delta V_L - \Delta V_C)^2}$. (c) The reactance triangle that gives the impedance relation $Z = \sqrt{R^2 + (X_L - X_C)^2}$.

sors vectorially to find the phasor ΔV_{max} (Fig. 21.11b), which represents the maximum voltage. The right triangle in Figure 21.11b gives the following equations for the maximum voltage and the phase angle ϕ between the maximum voltage and the current:

$$\Delta V_{max} = \sqrt{\Delta V_R{}^2 + (\Delta V_L - \Delta V_C)^2} \qquad \text{[21.10]}$$

$$\tan \phi = \frac{\Delta V_L - \Delta V_C}{\Delta V_R} \qquad \text{[21.11]}$$

In these equations, all voltages are maximum values. Although we choose to use maximum voltages in our analysis, the preceding equations apply equally well to rms voltages because the two quantities are related to each other by the same factor for all circuit elements. The result for the maximum voltage ΔV_{max} given by Equation 21.10 reinforces the fact that **the voltages across the resistor, capacitor, and inductor are not in phase, so one cannot simply add them to get the voltage across the combination of element or to get the source voltage.**

■ *Quick Quiz*

21.2 For the circuit of Figure 21.8, is the instantaneous voltage of the source equal to (a) the sum of the maximum voltages across the elements, (b) the sum of the instantaneous voltages across the elements, or (c) the sum of the rms voltages across the elements?

We can write Equation 21.10 in the form of Ohm's law, using the relations $\Delta V_R = I_{max}R$, $\Delta V_L = I_{max}X_L$, and $\Delta V_C = I_{max}X_C$, where I_{max} is the maximum current in the circuit:

$$\Delta V_{max} = I_{max}\sqrt{R^2 + (X_L - X_C)^2} \qquad \text{[21.12]}$$

It's convenient to define a parameter called the **impedance** Z of the circuit as

$$Z \equiv \sqrt{R^2 + (X_L - X_C)^2} \qquad \text{[21.13]} \qquad \blacktriangleleft \text{ Impedance}$$

so that Equation 21.12 becomes

$$\Delta V_{max} = I_{max}Z \qquad \text{[21.14]}$$

Equation 21.14 is in the form of Ohm's law, $\Delta V = IR$, with R replaced by the impedance in ohms. Indeed, Equation 21.14 can be regarded as a generalized form of Ohm's law applied to a series AC circuit. Both the impedance and therefore the current in an AC circuit depend on the resistance, the inductance, the capacitance, *and* the frequency (because the reactances are frequency dependent).

Bettmann/Corbis

Nikola Tesla
(1856–1943)
Tesla was born in Croatia, but spent most of his professional life as an inventor in the United States. He was a key figure in the development of alternating-current electricity, high-voltage transformers, and the transport of electrical power via AC transmission lines. Tesla's viewpoint was at odds with the ideas of Edison, who committed himself to the use of direct current in power transmission. Tesla's AC approach won out.

Table 21.2 Impedance Values and Phase Angles for Various Combinations of Circuit Elements

Circuit Elements	Impedance Z	Phase Angle ϕ
R	R	$0°$
C	X_C	$-90°$
L	X_L	$+90°$
R C	$\sqrt{R^2 + X_C^2}$	Negative, between $-90°$ and $0°$
R L	$\sqrt{R^2 + X_L^2}$	Positive, between $0°$ and $90°$
R L C	$\sqrt{R^2 + (X_L - X_C)^2}$	Negative if $X_C > X_L$ Positive if $X_C < X_L$

Note: In each case an AC voltage (not shown) is applied across the combination of elements (that is, across the dots).

It's useful to represent the impedance Z with a vector diagram such as the one depicted in Figure 21.11c. A right triangle is constructed with right side $X_L - X_C$, base R, and hypotenuse Z. Applying the Pythagorean theorem to this triangle, we see that

$$Z = \sqrt{R^2 + (X_L - X_C)^2}$$

which is Equation 21.13. Furthermore, we see from the vector diagram in Figure 21.11c that the phase angle ϕ between the current and the voltage obeys the relationship

◀ Phase angle ϕ

$$\tan \phi = \frac{X_L - X_C}{R} \qquad [21.15]$$

The physical significance of the phase angle will become apparent in Section 21.5.

Table 21.2 provides impedance values and phase angles for some series circuits containing different combinations of circuit elements.

Parallel alternating current circuits are also useful in everyday applications. We won't discuss them here, however, because their analysis is beyond the scope of this book.

Figure 21.12 (Quick Quizzes 21.3–21.6)

■ *Quick Quiz*

21.3 If switch A is closed in Figure 21.12, what happens to the impedance of the circuit? (a) It increases. (b) It decreases. (c) It doesn't change.

21.4 Suppose $X_L > X_C$ in Figure 21.12. If switch A is closed, what happens to the phase angle? (a) It increases. (b) It decreases. (c) It doesn't change.

21.5 Suppose $X_L > X_C$ in Figure 21.12. If switch A is left open and switch B is closed, what happens to the phase angle? (a) It increases. (b) It decreases. (c) It doesn't change.

21.6 Suppose $X_L > X_C$ in Figure 21.12 and, with both switches open, a piece of iron is slipped into the inductor. During this process, what happens to the brightness of the bulb? (a) It increases. (b) It decreases. (c) It doesn't change.

■ PROBLEM-SOLVING STRATEGY

RLC Circuits

The following procedure is recommended for solving series RLC circuit problems:

1. Calculate the inductive and capacitive reactances, X_L and X_C.
2. Use X_L and X_C together with the resistance R to calculate the impedance Z of the circuit.
3. Find the maximum current or maximum voltage drop with the equivalent of Ohm's law, $\Delta V_{max} = I_{max}Z$.
4. Calculate the voltage drops across the individual elements with the appropriate variations of Ohm's law: $\Delta V_{R,max} = I_{max}R$, $\Delta V_{L,max} = I_{max}X_L$, and $\Delta V_{C,max} = I_{max}X_C$.
5. Obtain the phase angle using $\tan \phi = (X_L - X_C)/R$.

■ EXAMPLE 21.4 │ An *RLC* Circuit

GOAL Analyze a series *RLC* AC circuit and find the phase angle.

PROBLEM A series *RLC* AC circuit has resistance $R = 2.50 \times 10^2 \ \Omega$, inductance $L = 0.600$ H, capacitance $C = 3.50 \ \mu$F, frequency $f = 60.0$ Hz, and maximum voltage $\Delta V_{max} = 1.50 \times 10^2$ V. Find **(a)** the impedance of the circuit, **(b)** the maximum current in the circuit, **(c)** the phase angle, and **(d)** the maximum voltages across the elements.

STRATEGY Calculate the inductive and capacitive reactances, which can be used with the resistance to calculate the impedance and phase angle. The impedance and Ohm's law yield the maximum current.

. . . .

SOLUTION

(a) Find the impedance of the circuit.

First, calculate the inductive and capacitive reactances:

$$X_L = 2\pi fL = 226 \ \Omega \qquad X_C = 1/2\pi fC = 758 \ \Omega$$

Substitute these results and the resistance R into Equation 21.13 to obtain the impedance of the circuit:

$$Z = \sqrt{R^2 + (X_L - X_C)^2}$$
$$= \sqrt{(2.50 \times 10^2 \ \Omega)^2 + (226 \ \Omega - 758 \ \Omega)^2} = \boxed{588 \ \Omega}$$

(b) Find the maximum current in the circuit.

Use Equation 21.12, the equivalent of Ohm's law, to find the maximum current:

$$I_{max} = \frac{\Delta V_{max}}{Z} = \frac{1.50 \times 10^2 \ \text{V}}{588 \ \Omega} = \boxed{0.255 \ \text{A}}$$

(c) Find the phase angle.

Calculate the phase angle between the current and the voltage with Equation 21.15:

$$\phi = \tan^{-1} \frac{X_L - X_C}{R} = \tan^{-1}\left(\frac{226 \ \Omega - 758 \ \Omega}{2.50 \times 10^2 \ \Omega}\right) = \boxed{-64.8°}$$

(d) Find the maximum voltages across the elements.

Substitute into the "Ohm's law" expressions for each individual type of current element:

$$\Delta V_{R,max} = I_{max}R = (0.255 \ \text{A})(2.50 \times 10^2 \ \Omega) = \boxed{63.8 \ \text{V}}$$
$$\Delta V_{L,max} = I_{max}X_L = (0.255 \ \text{A})(2.26 \times 10^2 \ \Omega) = \boxed{57.6 \ \text{V}}$$
$$\Delta V_{C,max} = I_{max}X_C = (0.255 \ \text{A})(7.58 \times 10^2 \ \Omega) = \boxed{193 \ \text{V}}$$

. . . .

REMARKS Because the circuit is more capacitive than inductive ($X_C > X_L$), ϕ is negative. A negative phase angle means that the current leads the applied voltage. Notice also that the sum of the maximum voltages across the elements is $\Delta V_R + \Delta V_L + \Delta V_C = 314$ V, which is much greater than the maximum voltage of the generator, 150 V. As we saw in Quick Quiz 21.2, the sum of the maximum voltages is a meaningless quantity because when alternating voltages are added, *both their amplitudes and their phases* must be taken into account. We know that the maximum voltages across the various elements occur at different times, so it doesn't make sense to add all the maximum values. The correct way to "add" the voltages is through Equation 21.10.

(Continued)

QUESTION 21.4 True or False: In an *RLC* circuit, the impedance must always be greater than or equal to the resistance.

EXERCISE 21.4 Analyze a series *RLC* AC circuit for which $R = 175\ \Omega$, $L = 0.500$ H, $C = 22.5\ \mu$F, $f = 60.0$ Hz, and $\Delta V_{max} = 325$ V. Find (a) the impedance, (b) the maximum current, (c) the phase angle, and (d) the maximum voltages across the elements.

ANSWERS (a) 189 Ω (b) 1.72 A (c) 22.0° (d) $\Delta V_{R,max} = 301$ V, $\Delta V_{L,max} = 324$ V, $\Delta V_{C,max} = 203$ V

21.5 Power in an AC Circuit

No power losses are associated with pure capacitors and pure inductors in an AC circuit. A pure capacitor, by definition, has no resistance or inductance, whereas a pure inductor has no resistance or capacitance. (These definitions are idealizations: in a real capacitor, for example, inductive effects could become important at high frequencies.) We begin by analyzing the power dissipated in an AC circuit that contains only a generator and a capacitor.

When the current increases in one direction in an AC circuit, charge accumulates on the capacitor and a voltage drop appears across it. When the voltage reaches its maximum value, the energy stored in the capacitor is

$$PE_C = \tfrac{1}{2}C(\Delta V_{max})^2$$

This energy storage is only momentary, however: When the current reverses direction, the charge leaves the capacitor plates and returns to the voltage source. During one-half of each cycle the capacitor is being charged, and during the other half the charge is being returned to the voltage source. Therefore, the average power supplied by the source is zero. In other words, **no power losses occur in a capacitor in an AC circuit**.

Similarly, the source must do work against the back emf of an inductor that is carrying a current. When the current reaches its maximum value, the energy stored in the inductor is a maximum and is given by

$$PE_L = \tfrac{1}{2}LI_{max}^2$$

When the current begins to decrease in the circuit, this stored energy is returned to the source as the inductor attempts to maintain the current in the circuit. The average power delivered to a resistor in an *RLC* circuit is

$$\boxed{P_{av} = I_{rms}^2 R} \qquad \text{[21.16]}$$

The average power delivered by the generator is converted to internal energy in the resistor. No power loss occurs in an ideal capacitor or inductor.

An alternate equation for the average power loss in an AC circuit can be found by substituting (from Ohm's law) $R = \Delta V_{R,rms}/I_{rms}$ into Equation 21.16:

$$P_{av} = I_{rms}\Delta V_{R,rms}$$

It's convenient to refer to a voltage triangle that shows the relationship among ΔV_{rms}, $\Delta V_{R,rms}$, and $\Delta V_{L,rms} - \Delta V_{C,rms}$, such as Figure 21.11b. (Remember that Fig. 21.11 applies to *both* maximum and rms voltages.) From this figure, we see that the voltage drop across a resistor can be written in terms of the voltage of the source, ΔV_{rms}:

$$\Delta V_{R,rms} = \Delta V_{rms} \cos \phi$$

Hence, the average power delivered by a generator in an AC circuit is

Average power ▶ $$\boxed{P_{av} = I_{rms}\Delta V_{rms} \cos \phi} \qquad \text{[21.17]}$$

where the quantity $\cos \phi$ is called the **power factor**.

Equation 21.17 shows that the power delivered by an AC source to any circuit depends on the phase difference between the source voltage and the resulting current. This fact has many interesting applications. For example, factories often use devices such as large motors in machines, generators, and transformers that have a large inductive load due to all the windings. To deliver greater power to such devices without using excessively high voltages, factory technicians introduce capacitance in the circuits to shift the phase.

■ EXAMPLE 21.5 | Average Power in an *RLC* Series Circuit

GOAL Understand power in *RLC* series circuits.

PROBLEM Calculate the average power delivered to the series *RLC* circuit described in Example 21.4.

STRATEGY After finding the rms current and rms voltage with Equations 21.2 and 21.3, substitute into Equation 21.17, using the phase angle found in Example 21.4.

SOLUTION

First, use Equations 21.2 and 21.3 to calculate the rms current and rms voltage:

$$I_{rms} = \frac{I_{max}}{\sqrt{2}} = \frac{0.255 \text{ A}}{\sqrt{2}} = 0.180 \text{ A}$$

$$\Delta V_{rms} = \frac{\Delta V_{max}}{\sqrt{2}} = \frac{1.50 \times 10^2 \text{ V}}{\sqrt{2}} = 106 \text{ V}$$

Substitute these results and the phase angle $\phi = -64.8°$ into Equation 21.17 to find the average power:

$$P_{av} = I_{rms} \, \Delta V_{rms} \cos \phi = (0.180 \text{ A})(106 \text{ V}) \cos (-64.8°)$$

$$= \boxed{8.12 \text{ W}}$$

REMARKS The same result can be obtained from Equation 21.16, $P_{av} = I_{rms}^2 R$.

QUESTION 21.5 Under what circumstance can the average power of an *RLC* circuit be zero?

EXERCISE 21.5 Repeat this problem, using the system described in Exercise 21.4.

ANSWER 259 W

21.6 Resonance in a Series *RLC* Circuit

In general, the rms current in a series *RLC* circuit can be written

$$I_{rms} = \frac{\Delta V_{rms}}{Z} = \frac{\Delta V_{rms}}{\sqrt{R^2 + (X_L - X_C)^2}} \qquad \text{[21.18]}$$

From this equation, we see that if the frequency is varied, the current has its *maximum* value when the impedance has its *minimum* value, which occurs when $X_L = X_C$. In such a circumstance, the impedance of the circuit reduces to $Z = R$. The frequency f_0 at which this happens is called the **resonance frequency** of the circuit. To find f_0, we set $X_L = X_C$, which gives, from Equations 21.5 and 21.8,

$$2\pi f_0 L = \frac{1}{2\pi f_0 C}$$

$$f_0 = \frac{1}{2\pi \sqrt{LC}} \qquad \text{[21.19]}$$

Figure 21.13 is a plot of current as a function of frequency for a circuit containing a fixed value for both the capacitance and the inductance. From Equation 21.18, it must be concluded that the current would become infinite at resonance when $R = 0$. Although Equation 21.18 predicts this result, real circuits always have some resistance, which limits the value of the current.

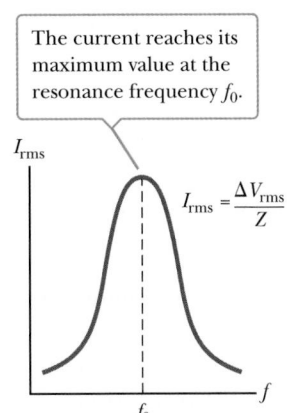

Active Figure 21.13
A plot of current amplitude in a series *RLC* circuit versus frequency of the generator voltage.

The tuning circuit of a radio is an important application of a series resonance circuit. The radio is tuned to a particular station (which transmits a specific radio-frequency signal) by varying a capacitor, which changes the resonance frequency of the tuning circuit. When this resonance frequency matches that of the incoming radio wave, the current in the tuning circuit increases.

■ APPLYING PHYSICS 21.2 | Metal Detectors at the Courthouse

When you walk through the doorway of a courthouse metal detector, as the person in Figure 21.14 is doing, you are really walking through a coil of many turns. How might the metal detector work?

EXPLANATION The metal detector is essentially a resonant circuit. The portal you step through is an inductor (a large loop of conducting wire) that is part of the circuit. The frequency of the circuit is tuned to the resonant frequency of the circuit when there is no metal in the inductor. When you walk through with metal in your pocket, you change the effective inductance of the resonance circuit, resulting in a change in the current in the circuit. This change in current is detected, and an electronic circuit causes a sound to be emitted as an alarm. ■

Figure 21.14 (Applying Physics 21.2) A courthouse metal detector.

■ EXAMPLE 21.6 | A Circuit in Resonance

GOAL Understand resonance frequency and its relation to inductance, capacitance, and the rms current.

PROBLEM Consider a series RLC circuit for which $R = 1.50 \times 10^2\ \Omega$, $L = 20.0$ mH, $\Delta V_{rms} = 20.0$ V, and $f = 796\ \text{s}^{-1}$. **(a)** Determine the value of the capacitance for which the rms current is a maximum. **(b)** Find the maximum rms current in the circuit.

STRATEGY The current is a maximum at the resonance frequency f_0, which should be set equal to the driving frequency, $796\ \text{s}^{-1}$. The resulting equation can be solved for C. For part (b), substitute into Equation 21.18 to get the maximum rms current.

···

SOLUTION

(a) Find the capacitance giving the maximum current in the circuit (the resonance condition).

Solve the resonance frequency for the capacitance:

$$f_0 = \frac{1}{2\pi\sqrt{LC}} \quad \rightarrow \quad \sqrt{LC} = \frac{1}{2\pi f_0} \quad \rightarrow \quad LC = \frac{1}{4\pi^2 f_0{}^2}$$

$$C = \frac{1}{4\pi^2 f_0{}^2 L}$$

Insert the given values, substituting the source frequency for the resonance frequency, f_0:

$$C = \frac{1}{4\pi^2 (796\ \text{Hz})^2 (20.0 \times 10^{-3}\ \text{H})} = \boxed{2.00 \times 10^{-6}\ \text{F}}$$

(b) Find the maximum rms current in the circuit.

The capacitive and inductive reactances are equal, so $Z = R = 1.50 \times 10^2\ \Omega$. Substitute into Equation 21.18 to find the rms current:

$$I_{rms} = \frac{\Delta V_{rms}}{Z} = \frac{20.0\ \text{V}}{1.50 \times 10^2\ \Omega} = \boxed{0.133\ \text{A}}$$

···

REMARKS Because the impedance Z is in the denominator of Equation 21.18, the maximum current will always occur when $X_L = X_C$ because that yields the minimum value of Z.

QUESTION 21.6 True or False: The magnitude of the current in an RLC circuit is never larger than the rms current.

EXERCISE 21.6 Consider a series *RLC* circuit for which $R = 1.20 \times 10^2\ \Omega$, $C = 3.10 \times 10^{-5}$ F, $\Delta V_{rms} = 35.0$ V, and $f = 60.0\ \text{s}^{-1}$. (a) Determine the value of the inductance for which the rms current is a maximum. (b) Find the maximum rms current in the circuit.

ANSWERS (a) 0.227 H (b) 0.292 A

21.7 The Transformer

It's often necessary to change a small AC voltage to a larger one or vice versa. Such changes are effected with a device called a transformer.

In its simplest form the **AC transformer** consists of two coils of wire wound around a core of soft iron, as shown in Figure 21.15. The coil on the left, which is connected to the input AC voltage source and has N_1 turns, is called the primary winding, or the *primary*. The coil on the right, which is connected to a resistor R and consists of N_2 turns, is the *secondary*. The purposes of the common iron core are to increase the magnetic flux and to provide a medium in which nearly all the flux through one coil passes through the other.

When an input AC voltage ΔV_1 is applied to the primary, the induced voltage across it is given by

$$\Delta V_1 = -N_1 \frac{\Delta \Phi_B}{\Delta t} \qquad [21.20]$$

where Φ_B is the magnetic flux through each turn. If we assume that no flux leaks from the iron core, then the flux through each turn of the primary equals the flux through each turn of the secondary. Hence, the voltage across the secondary coil is

$$\Delta V_2 = -N_2 \frac{\Delta \Phi_B}{\Delta t} \qquad [21.21]$$

The term $\Delta \Phi_B / \Delta t$ is common to Equations 21.20 and 21.21 and can be algebraically eliminated, giving

$$\Delta V_2 = \frac{N_2}{N_1} \Delta V_1 \qquad [21.22]$$

When N_2 is greater than N_1, ΔV_2 exceeds ΔV_1 and the transformer is referred to as a *step-up transformer*. When N_2 is less than N_1, making ΔV_2 less than ΔV_1, we have a *step-down transformer*.

By Faraday's law, a voltage is generated across the secondary only when there is a *change* in the number of flux lines passing through the secondary. The input current in the primary must therefore change with time, which is what happens when an alternating current is used. When the input at the primary is a direct current, however, a voltage output occurs at the secondary only at the instant a switch in the primary circuit is opened or closed. Once the current in the primary reaches a steady value, the output voltage at the secondary is zero.

It may seem that a transformer is a device in which it is possible to get something for nothing. For example, a step-up transformer can change an input voltage from, say, 10 V to 100 V. This means that each coulomb of charge leaving the secondary has 100 J of energy, whereas each coulomb of charge entering the primary has only 10 J of energy. That is not the case, however, because **the power input to the primary equals the power output at the secondary**:

$$I_1 \Delta V_1 = I_2 \Delta V_2 \qquad [21.23]$$

Although the *voltage* at the secondary may be, say, ten times greater than the voltage at the primary, the *current* in the secondary will be smaller than the primary's current by a factor of ten. Equation 21.23 assumes an **ideal transformer** in which there are no power losses between the primary and the secondary. Real

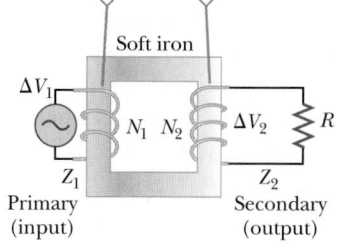

An AC voltage ΔV_1 is applied to the primary coil, and the output voltage ΔV_2 is observed across the load resistance R.

Figure 21.15 An ideal transformer consists of two coils wound on the same soft iron core. An AC voltage ΔV_1 is applied to the primary coil, and the output voltage ΔV_2 is observed across the load resistance R after the switch is closed.

◀ In an ideal transformer, the input power equals the output power transformers typically have power efficiencies ranging from 90% to 99%. Power losses occur because of such factors as eddy currents induced in the iron core of the transformer, which dissipate energy in the form of I^2R losses.

When electric power is transmitted over large distances, it's economical to use a high voltage and a low current because the power lost via resistive heating in the transmission lines varies as I^2R. If a utility company can reduce the current by a factor of ten, for example, the power loss is reduced by a factor of one hundred. In practice, the voltage is stepped up to around 230 000 V at the generating station, then stepped down to around 20 000 V at a distribution station, and finally stepped down to 120 V at the customer's utility pole.

■ EXAMPLE 21.7 | Distributing Power to a City

GOAL Understand transformers and their role in reducing power loss.

PROBLEM A generator at a utility company produces 1.00×10^2 A of current at 4.00×10^3 V. The voltage is stepped up to 2.40×10^5 V by a transformer before being sent on a high-voltage transmission line across a rural area to a city. Assume the effective resistance of the power line is 30.0 Ω and that the transformers are ideal. **(a)** Determine the percentage of power lost in the transmission line. **(b)** What percentage of the original power would be lost in the transmission line if the voltage were not stepped up?

STRATEGY Solving this problem is just a matter of substitution into the equation for transformers and the equation for power loss. To obtain the fraction of power lost, it's also necessary to compute the power output of the generator: the current times the potential difference created by the generator.

SOLUTION

(a) Determine the percentage of power lost in the line.

Substitute into Equation 21.23 to find the current in the transmission line:

$$I_2 = \frac{I_1 \Delta V_1}{\Delta V_2} = \frac{(1.00 \times 10^2 \text{ A})(4.00 \times 10^3 \text{ V})}{2.40 \times 10^5 \text{ V}} = 1.67 \text{ A}$$

Now use Equation 21.16 to find the power lost in the transmission line:

$$\textbf{(1)} \ P_{\text{lost}} = I_2^2 R = (1.67 \text{ A})^2 (30.0 \text{ Ω}) = 83.7 \text{ W}$$

Calculate the power output of the generator:

$$P = I_1 \Delta V_1 = (1.00 \times 10^2 \text{ A})(4.00 \times 10^3 \text{ V}) = 4.00 \times 10^5 \text{ W}$$

Finally, divide P_{lost} by the power output and multiply by 100 to find the percentage of power lost:

$$\% \text{ power lost} = \left(\frac{83.7 \text{ W}}{4.00 \times 10^5 \text{ W}} \right) \times 100 = \boxed{0.020 \ 9\%}$$

(b) What percentage of the original power would be lost in the transmission line if the voltage were not stepped up?

Replace the stepped-up current in Equation (1) by the original current of 1.00×10^2 A:

$$P_{\text{lost}} = I^2 R = (1.00 \times 10^2 \text{ A})^2 (30.0 \text{ Ω}) = 3.00 \times 10^5 \text{ W}$$

Calculate the percentage loss, as before:

$$\% \text{ power lost} = \left(\frac{3.00 \times 10^5 \text{ W}}{4.00 \times 10^5 \text{ W}} \right) \times 100 = \boxed{75\%}$$

REMARKS This example illustrates the advantage of high-voltage transmission lines. At the city, a transformer at a substation steps the voltage back down to about 4 000 V, and this voltage is maintained across utility lines throughout the city. When the power is to be used at a home or business, a transformer on a utility pole near the establishment reduces the voltage to 240 V or 120 V.

QUESTION 21.7 If the voltage is stepped up to double the amount in this problem, by what factor is the power loss changed? (a) 2 (b) no change (c) $\frac{1}{2}$ (d) $\frac{1}{4}$

This cylindrical step-down transformer drops the voltage from 4 000 V to 220 V for delivery to a group of residences.

© George Semple/Cengage Learning

EXERCISE 21.7 Suppose the same generator has the voltage stepped up to only 7.50×10^4 V and the resistance of the line is 85.0 Ω. Find the percentage of power lost in this case.

ANSWER 0.604%

21.8 Maxwell's Predictions

During the early stages of their study and development, electric and magnetic phenomena were thought to be unrelated. In 1865, however, James Clerk Maxwell (1831–1879) provided a mathematical theory that showed a close relationship between all electric and magnetic phenomena. In addition to unifying the formerly separate fields of electricity and magnetism, his brilliant theory predicted that electric and magnetic fields can move through space as waves. The theory he developed is based on the following four pieces of information:

1. Electric field lines originate on positive charges and terminate on negative charges.
2. Magnetic field lines always form closed loops; they don't begin or end anywhere.
3. A varying magnetic field induces an emf and hence an electric field. This fact is a statement of Faraday's law (Chapter 20).
4. Magnetic fields are generated by moving charges (or currents), as summarized in Ampère's law (Chapter 19).

The first statement is a consequence of the nature of the electrostatic force between charged particles, given by Coulomb's law. It embodies the fact that **free charges (electric monopoles) exist in nature**.

The second statement—that magnetic fields form continuous loops—is exemplified by the magnetic field lines around a long, straight wire, which are closed circles, and the magnetic field lines of a bar magnet, which form closed loops. It says, in contrast to the first statement, that **free magnetic charges (magnetic monopoles) don't exist in nature**.

The third statement is equivalent to Faraday's law of induction, and the fourth is equivalent to Ampère's law.

In one of the greatest theoretical developments of the 19th century, Maxwell used these four statements within a corresponding mathematical framework to prove that electric and magnetic fields play symmetric roles in nature. It was already known from experiments that a changing magnetic field produced an electric field according to Faraday's law. Maxwell believed that nature was symmetric, and he therefore hypothesized that a changing electric field should produce a magnetic field. This hypothesis could not be proven experimentally at the time it was developed because the magnetic fields generated by changing electric fields are generally very weak and therefore difficult to detect.

To justify his hypothesis, Maxwell searched for other phenomena that might be explained by it. He turned his attention to the motion of rapidly oscillating (accelerating) charges, such as those in a conducting rod connected to an alternating voltage. Such charges are accelerated and, according to Maxwell's predictions, generate changing electric and magnetic fields. The changing fields cause electromagnetic disturbances that travel through space as waves, similar to the spreading water waves created by a pebble thrown into a pool. The waves sent out by the oscillating charges are fluctuating electric and magnetic fields, so they are called *electromagnetic waves*. From Faraday's law and from Maxwell's own generalization of Ampère's law, Maxwell calculated the speed of the waves to be equal to the speed of light, $c = 3 \times 10^8$ m/s. He concluded that visible light and other electromagnetic waves consist of fluctuating electric and magnetic fields traveling through empty

North Wind Photo Archives

James Clerk Maxwell
Scottish Theoretical Physicist
(1831–1879)
Maxwell developed the electromagnetic theory of light and the kinetic theory of gases, and he explained the nature of Saturn's rings and color vision. Maxwell's successful interpretation of the electromagnetic field resulted in the equations that bear his name. Formidable mathematical ability combined with great insight enabled him to lead the way in the study of electromagnetism and kinetic theory.

space, with each varying field inducing the other! His was truly one of the greatest discoveries of science, on a par with Newton's discovery of the laws of motion. Like Newton's laws, it had a profound influence on later scientific developments.

21.9 Hertz's Confirmation of Maxwell's Predictions

In 1887, after Maxwell's death, Heinrich Hertz (1857–1894) was the first to generate and detect electromagnetic waves in a laboratory setting, using LC circuits. In such a circuit a charged capacitor is connected to an inductor, as in Figure 21.16. When the switch is closed, oscillations occur in the current in the circuit and in the charge on the capacitor. If the resistance of the circuit is neglected, no energy is dissipated and the oscillations continue.

In the following analysis, we neglect the resistance in the circuit. We assume the capacitor has an initial charge of Q_{max} and the switch is closed at $t = 0$. When the capacitor is fully charged, the total energy in the circuit is stored in the electric field of the capacitor and is equal to $Q_{max}^2/2C$. At this time, the current is zero, so no energy is stored in the inductor. As the capacitor begins to discharge, the energy stored in its electric field decreases. At the same time, the current increases and energy equal to $LI^2/2$ is now stored in the magnetic field of the inductor. Thus, energy is transferred from the electric field of the capacitor to the magnetic field of the inductor. When the capacitor is fully discharged, it stores no energy. At this time, the current reaches its maximum value and all the energy is stored in the inductor. The process then repeats in the reverse direction. The energy continues to transfer between the inductor and the capacitor, corresponding to oscillations in the current and charge.

As we saw in Section 21.6, the frequency of oscillation of an LC circuit is called the *resonance frequency* of the circuit and is given by

$$f_0 = \frac{1}{2\pi\sqrt{LC}}$$

The circuit Hertz used in his investigations of electromagnetic waves is similar to that just discussed and is shown schematically in Figure 21.17. An induction coil (a large coil of wire) is connected to two metal spheres with a narrow gap between them to form a capacitor. Oscillations are initiated in the circuit by short voltage pulses sent via the coil to the spheres, charging one positive, the other negative. Because L and C are quite small in this circuit, the frequency of oscillation is quite high, $f \approx 100$ MHz. This circuit is called a transmitter because it produces electromagnetic waves.

Several meters from the transmitter circuit, Hertz placed a second circuit, the receiver, which consisted of a single loop of wire connected to two spheres. It had its own effective inductance, capacitance, and natural frequency of oscillation. Hertz found that energy was being sent from the transmitter to the receiver when the resonance frequency of the receiver was adjusted to match that of the transmitter. The energy transfer was detected when the voltage across the spheres in the receiver circuit became high enough to produce ionization in the air, which caused sparks to appear in the air gap separating the spheres. Hertz's experiment is analogous to the mechanical phenomenon in which a tuning fork picks up the vibrations from another, identical tuning fork.

Hertz hypothesized that the energy transferred from the transmitter to the receiver is carried in the form of waves, now recognized as electromagnetic waves. In a series of experiments, he also showed that the radiation generated by the transmitter exhibits wave properties: interference, diffraction, reflection, refraction, and polarization. As you will see shortly, all these properties are exhibited by light. It became evident that Hertz's electromagnetic waves had the same known

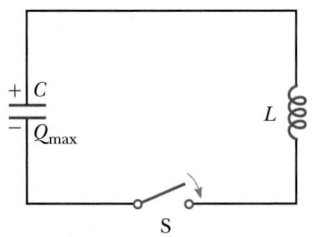

Figure 21.16 A simple LC circuit. The capacitor has an initial charge of Q_{max}, and the switch is closed at $t = 0$.

The transmitter consists of two spherical electrodes connected to an induction coil, which provides short voltage surges to the spheres, setting up oscillations in the discharge.

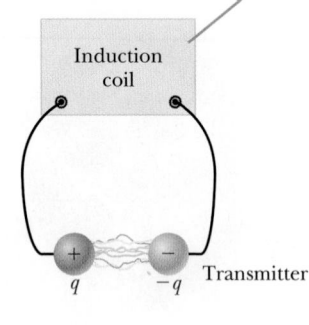

The receiver is a nearby loop of wire containing a second spark gap.

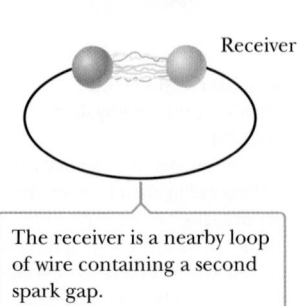

Figure 21.17 A schematic diagram of Hertz's apparatus for generating and detecting electromagnetic waves.

properties of light waves and differed only in frequency and wavelength. Hertz effectively confirmed Maxwell's theory by showing that Maxwell's mysterious electromagnetic waves existed and had all the properties of light waves.

Perhaps the most convincing experiment Hertz performed was the measurement of the speed of waves from the transmitter, accomplished as follows: waves of known frequency from the transmitter were reflected from a metal sheet so that an interference pattern was set up, much like the standing-wave pattern on a stretched string. As we learned in our discussion of standing waves, the distance between nodes is $\lambda/2$, so Hertz was able to determine the wavelength λ. Using the relationship $v = \lambda f$, he found that v was close to 3×10^8 m/s, the known speed of visible light. Hertz's experiments thus provided the first evidence in support of Maxwell's theory.

Heinrich Rudolf Hertz
German Physicist (1857–1894)
Hertz made his most important discovery of radio waves in 1887. After finding that the speed of a radio wave was the same as that of light, Hertz showed that radio waves, like light waves, could be reflected, refracted, and diffracted. Hertz died of blood poisoning at the age of 36. During his short life, he made many contributions to science. The hertz, equal to one complete vibration or cycle per second, is named after him.

APPLICATION

Radio-Wave Transmission

21.10 Production of Electromagnetic Waves by an Antenna

In the previous section we found that the energy stored in an LC circuit is continually transferred between the electric field of the capacitor and the magnetic field of the inductor. This energy transfer, however, continues for prolonged periods of time only when the changes occur slowly. If the current alternates rapidly, the circuit loses some of its energy in the form of electromagnetic waves. In fact, electromagnetic waves are radiated by *any* circuit carrying an alternating current. The fundamental mechanism responsible for this radiation is the acceleration of a charged particle. **Whenever a charged particle accelerates, it radiates energy.**

An alternating voltage applied to the wires of an antenna forces electric charges in the antenna to oscillate. This common technique for accelerating charged particles is the source of the radio waves emitted by the broadcast antenna of a radio station.

Figure 21.18 illustrates the production of an electromagnetic wave by oscillating electric charges in an antenna. Two metal rods are connected to an AC source, which causes charges to oscillate between the rods. The output voltage of the generator is sinusoidal. At $t = 0$, the upper rod is given a maximum positive charge and the bottom rod an equal negative charge, as in Figure 21.18a. The electric field near the antenna at this instant is also shown in the figure. As the charges oscillate, the rods become less charged, the field near the rods decreases in strength, and the downward-directed maximum electric field produced at $t = 0$ moves away from the rod. When the charges are neutralized, as in Figure 21.18b, the electric field has dropped to zero, after an interval equal to one-quarter of the period of oscillation. Continuing in this fashion, the upper rod soon obtains a maximum negative charge and the lower rod becomes positive, as in Figure 21.18c, resulting in an electric field directed upward. This occurs after an interval equal to one-half the period of oscillation. The oscillations continue as indicated in Figure 21.18d.

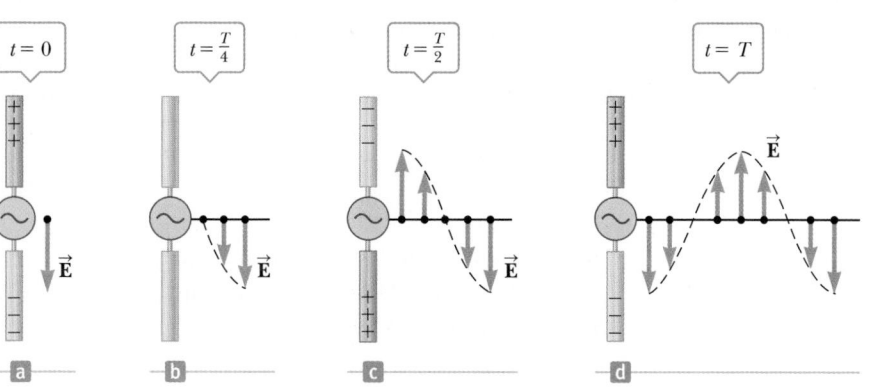

Figure 21.18 An electric field set up by oscillating charges in an antenna. The field moves away from the antenna at the speed of light.

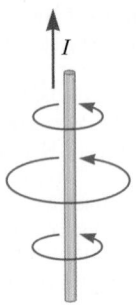

Figure 21.19 Magnetic field lines around an antenna carrying a changing current.

Note that the electric field near the antenna oscillates in phase with the charge distribution: the field points down when the upper rod is positive and up when the upper rod is negative. Further, the magnitude of the field at any instant depends on the amount of charge on the rods at that instant.

As the charges continue to oscillate (and accelerate) between the rods, the electric field set up by the charges moves away from the antenna in all directions at the speed of light. Figure 21.18 shows the electric field pattern on one side of the antenna at certain times during the oscillation cycle. As you can see, one cycle of charge oscillation produces one full wavelength in the electric field pattern.

Because the oscillating charges create a current in the rods, a magnetic field is also generated when the current in the rods is upward, as shown in Figure 21.19. The magnetic field lines circle the antenna (recall right-hand rule number 2) and are perpendicular to the electric field at all points. As the current changes with time, the magnetic field lines spread out from the antenna. At great distances from the antenna, the strengths of the electric and magnetic fields become very weak. At these distances, however, it is necessary to take into account the facts that (1) a changing magnetic field produces an electric field and (2) a changing electric field produces a magnetic field, as predicted by Maxwell. These induced electric and magnetic fields are in phase: at any point, the two fields reach their maximum values at the same instant. This synchrony is illustrated at one instant of time in Active Figure 21.20. Note that (1) the $\vec{E}$ and $\vec{B}$ fields are perpendicular to each other and (2) both fields are perpendicular to the direction of motion of the wave. This second property is characteristic of transverse waves. Hence, we see that **an electromagnetic wave is a transverse wave**.

21.11 Properties of Electromagnetic Waves

We have seen that Maxwell's detailed analysis predicted the existence and properties of electromagnetic waves. In this section we summarize what we know about electromagnetic waves thus far and consider some additional properties. In our discussion here and in future sections, we will often make reference to a type of wave called a **plane wave**. A plane electromagnetic wave is a wave traveling from a very distant source. Active Figure 21.20 pictures such a wave at a given instant of time. In this case the oscillations of the electric and magnetic fields take place in planes perpendicular to the x-axis and are therefore perpendicular to the direction of travel of the wave. Because of the latter property, electromagnetic waves are transverse waves. In the figure the electric field $\vec{E}$ is in the y-direction and the magnetic field $\vec{B}$ is in the z-direction. Light propagates in a direction perpendicular to these two fields. That direction is determined by yet another right-hand rule: (1) point the fingers of your right hand in the direction of $\vec{E}$, (2) curl them in the direction of $\vec{B}$, and (3) the right thumb then points in the direction of propagation of the wave.

Electromagnetic waves travel with the speed of light. In fact, it can be shown that the speed of an electromagnetic wave is related to the permeability and permittivity of the medium through which it travels. Maxwell found this relationship for free space to be

Speed of light ▶

$$c = \frac{1}{\sqrt{\mu_0 \epsilon_0}}$$

[21.24]

where c is the speed of light, $\mu_0 = 4\pi \times 10^{-7}$ N·s²/C² is the permeability constant of vacuum, and $\epsilon_0 = 8.854\ 19 \times 10^{-12}$ C²/N·m² is the permittivity of free space. Substituting these values into Equation 21.24, we find that

$$c = 2.997\ 92 \times 10^8 \text{ m/s}$$

[21.25]

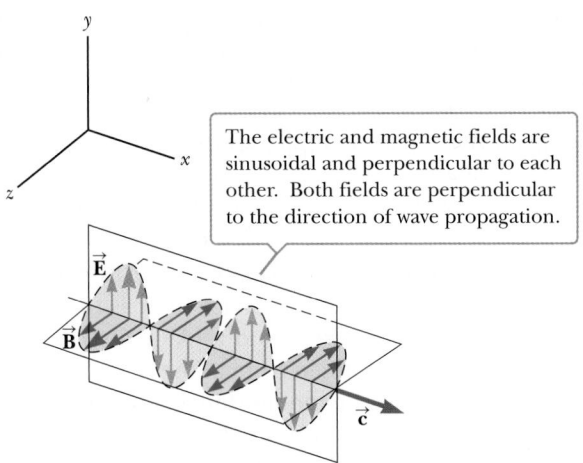

The electric and magnetic fields are sinusoidal and perpendicular to each other. Both fields are perpendicular to the direction of wave propagation.

Active Figure 21.20
An electromagnetic wave sent out by oscillating charges in an antenna, represented at one instant of time and far from the antenna, moving in the positive x-direction with speed c.

Because electromagnetic waves travel at the same speed as light in vacuum, scientists concluded (correctly) that **light is an electromagnetic wave**.

Maxwell also proved the following relationship for electromagnetic waves:

$$\frac{E}{B} = c \qquad \text{[21.26]}$$

which states that the ratio of the magnitude of the electric field to the magnitude of the magnetic field equals the speed of light.

Electromagnetic waves carry energy as they travel through space, and this energy can be transferred to objects placed in their paths. The average rate at which energy passes through an area perpendicular to the direction of travel of a wave, or the average power per unit area, is called the **intensity I** of the wave and is given by

$$I = \frac{E_{\text{max}}B_{\text{max}}}{2\mu_0} \qquad \text{[21.27]}$$

where E_{max} and B_{max} are the *maximum* values of E and B. The quantity I is analogous to the intensity of sound waves introduced in Chapter 14. From Equation 21.26, we see that $E_{\text{max}} = cB_{\text{max}} = B_{\text{max}}/\sqrt{\mu_0\epsilon_0}$. Equation 21.27 can therefore also be expressed as

$$I = \frac{E_{\text{max}}^2}{2\mu_0 c} = \frac{c}{2\mu_0}B_{\text{max}}^2 \qquad \text{[21.28]}$$

Note that in these expressions we use the *average* power per unit area. A detailed analysis would show that the energy carried by an electromagnetic wave is shared equally by the electric and magnetic fields.

Electromagnetic waves have an average intensity given by Equation 21.28. When the waves strike an area A of an object's surface for a given time Δt, energy $U = IA\Delta t$ is transferred to the surface. Momentum is transferred, as well. Hence, pressure is exerted on a surface when an electromagnetic wave impinges on it. In what follows, we assume the electromagnetic wave transports a total energy U to a surface in a time Δt. If the surface absorbs all the incident energy U in this time, Maxwell showed that the total momentum $\vec{\mathbf{p}}$ delivered to this surface has a magnitude

$$p = \frac{U}{c} \qquad \text{(complete absorption)} \qquad \text{[21.29]}$$

If the surface is a perfect reflector, then the momentum transferred in a time Δt for normal incidence is twice that given by Equation 21.29. This is analogous to a

Tip 21.2 *E* Stronger than *B*?
The relationship $E = Bc$ makes it appear that the electric fields associated with light are much larger than the magnetic fields. That is not the case: The units are different, so the quantities can't be directly compared. The two fields contribute equally to the energy of a light wave.

◀ Light is an electromagnetic wave and transports energy and momentum

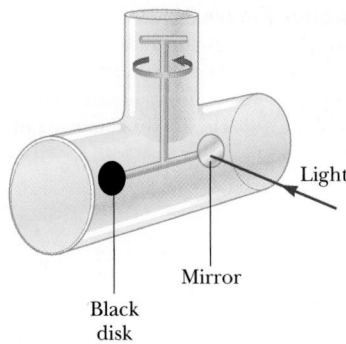

Figure 21.21 An apparatus for measuring the radiation pressure of light. In practice, the system is contained in a high vacuum.

molecule of gas bouncing off the wall of a container in a perfectly elastic collision. If the molecule is initially traveling in the positive x-direction at velocity v and after the collision is traveling in the negative x-direction at velocity $-v$, its change in momentum is given by $\Delta p = mv - (-mv) = 2mv$. Light bouncing off a perfect reflector is a similar process, so for complete reflection,

$$p = \frac{2U}{c} \qquad \text{(complete reflection)} \qquad \text{[21.30]}$$

Although radiation pressures are very small (about 5×10^{-6} N/m² for direct sunlight), they have been measured with a device such as the one shown in Figure 21.21. Light is allowed to strike a mirror and a black disk that are connected to each other by a horizontal bar suspended from a fine fiber. Light striking the black disk is completely absorbed, so *all* the momentum of the light is transferred to the disk. Light striking the mirror head-on is totally reflected; hence, the momentum transfer to the mirror is twice that transmitted to the disk. As a result, the horizontal bar supporting the disks twists counterclockwise as seen from above. The bar comes to equilibrium at some angle under the action of the torques caused by radiation pressure and the twisting of the fiber. The radiation pressure can be determined by measuring the angle at which equilibrium occurs. The apparatus must be placed in a high vacuum to eliminate the effects of air currents. It's interesting that similar experiments demonstrate that electromagnetic waves carry angular momentum, as well.

In summary, electromagnetic waves traveling through free space have the following properties:

Some properties of ▶
electromagnetic waves

1. Electromagnetic waves travel at the speed of light.
2. Electromagnetic waves are transverse waves because the electric and magnetic fields are perpendicular to the direction of propagation of the wave and to each other.
3. The ratio of the electric field to the magnetic field in an electromagnetic wave equals the speed of light.
4. Electromagnetic waves carry both energy and momentum, which can be delivered to a surface.

■ APPLYING PHYSICS 21.3 | Solar System Dust

In the interplanetary space in the solar system, there is a large amount of dust. Although interplanetary dust can in theory have a variety of sizes—from molecular size upward—why are there very few dust particles smaller than about 0.2 μm in the solar system? *Hint:* The solar system originally contained dust particles of all sizes.

EXPLANATION Dust particles in the solar system are subject to two forces: the gravitational force toward the Sun and the force from radiation pressure, which is directed away from the Sun. The gravitational force is propor-

tional to the cube of the radius of a spherical dust particle because it is proportional to the mass (ρV) of the particle. The radiation pressure is proportional to the square of the radius because it depends on the cross-sectional area of the particle. For large particles, the gravitational force is larger than the force of radiation pressure, and the weak attraction to the Sun causes such particles to move slowly toward it. For small particles, less than about 0.2 μm, the larger force from radiation pressure sweeps them out of the solar system. ■

■ *Quick Quiz*

21.7 In an apparatus such as that in Figure 21.21, suppose the black disk is replaced by one with half the radius. Which of the following are different after the disk is replaced? (a) radiation pressure on the disk (b) radiation force on the disk (c) radiation momentum delivered to the disk in a given time interval

■ EXAMPLE 21.8 | A Hot Tin Roof (Solar-Powered Homes)

GOAL Calculate some basic properties of light and relate them to thermal radiation.

PROBLEM Assume the Sun delivers an average power per unit area of about 1.00×10^3 W/m^2 to Earth's surface. **(a)** Calculate the total power incident on a flat tin roof 8.00 m by 20.0 m. Assume the radiation is incident *normal* (perpendicular) to the roof. **(b)** The tin roof reflects some light, and convection, conduction, and radiation transport the rest of the thermal energy away until some equilibrium temperature is established. If the roof is a perfect blackbody and rids itself of one-half of the incident radiation through thermal radiation, what's its equilibrium temperature? Assume the ambient temperature is 298 K.

(Example 21.8) A solar home.

SOLUTION

(a) Calculate the power delivered to the roof.

Multiply the intensity by the area to get the power:

$$P = IA = (1.00 \times 10^3 \text{ W/m}^2)(8.00 \text{ m} \times 20.0 \text{ m})$$
$$= \boxed{1.60 \times 10^5 \text{ W}}$$

(b) Find the equilibrium temperature of the roof.

Substitute into Stefan's law. Only one-half the incident power should be substituted, and twice the area of the roof (both the top and the underside of the roof count).

$$P = \sigma e A (T^4 - T_0{}^4)$$
$$T^4 = T_0{}^4 + \frac{P}{\sigma e A}$$
$$= (298 \text{ K})^4 + \frac{(0.500)(1.60 \times 10^5 \text{ W/m}^2)}{(5.67 \times 10^{-8} \text{ W/m}^2 \cdot \text{K}^4)(1)(3.20 \times 10^2 \text{ m}^2)}$$
$$T = 333 \text{ K} = \boxed{6.0 \times 10^1 \,°\text{C}}$$

REMARKS If the incident power could *all* be converted to electric power, it would be more than enough for the average home. Unfortunately, solar energy isn't easily harnessed, and the prospects for large-scale conversion are not as bright as they may appear from this simple calculation. For example, the conversion efficiency from solar to electrical energy is far less than 100%; 10–20% is typical for photovoltaic cells. Roof systems for using solar energy to raise the temperature of water with efficiencies of around 50% have been built. Other practical problems must be considered, however, such as overcast days, geographic location, and energy storage.

QUESTION 21.8 Does the angle the roof makes with respect to the horizontal affect the amount of power absorbed by the roof? Explain.

EXERCISE 21.8 A spherical satellite orbiting Earth is lighted on one side by the Sun, with intensity 1 340 W/m^2. If the radius of the satellite is 1.00 m, what power is incident upon it? *Note:* The satellite effectively intercepts radiation only over a cross section, an area equal to that of a disk, πr^2.

ANSWERS 4.21×10^3 W

■ EXAMPLE 21.9 | Clipper Ships of Space

GOAL Relate the intensity of light to its mechanical effect on matter.

PROBLEM Aluminized Mylar film is a highly reflective, lightweight material that could be used to make sails for spacecraft driven by the light of the Sun. Suppose a sail with area 1.00 km^2 is orbiting the Sun at a distance of 1.50×10^{11} m. The sail has a mass of 5.00×10^3 kg and is tethered to a payload of mass 2.00×10^4 kg. **(a)** If the intensity of sunlight is 1.34×10^3 W and the sail is oriented perpendicular to the incident light, what radial force is exerted on the sail? **(b)** About how long would it take to change the radial speed of the sail by 1.00 km/s? Assume the sail is perfectly reflecting. **(c)** Suppose the light were supplied by a large, powerful laser beam instead of the Sun. (Such systems have been proposed.) Calculate the peak electric and magnetic fields of the laser light.

(Continued)

STRATEGY Equation 21.30 gives the momentum imparted when light strikes an object and is totally reflected. The change in this momentum with time is a force. For part (b), use Newton's second law to obtain the acceleration. The velocity kinematics equation then yields the necessary time to achieve the desired change in speed. Part (c) follows from Equation 21.27 and $E = Bc$.

SOLUTION

(a) Find the force exerted on the sail.

Write Equation 21.30 and substitute $U = P\Delta t = IA\,\Delta t$ for the energy delivered to the sail:

$$\Delta p = \frac{2U}{c} = \frac{2P\Delta t}{c} = \frac{2IA\Delta t}{c}$$

Divide both sides by Δt, obtaining the force $\Delta p/\Delta t$ exerted by the light on the sail:

$$F = \frac{\Delta p}{\Delta t} = \frac{2IA}{c} = \frac{2(1\,340\ \text{W/m}^2)(1.00 \times 10^6\ \text{m}^2)}{3.00 \times 10^8\ \text{m/s}}$$

$$= \boxed{8.93\ \text{N}}$$

(b) Find the time it takes to change the radial speed by 1.00 km/s.

Substitute the force into Newton's second law and solve for the acceleration of the sail:

$$a = \frac{F}{m} = \frac{8.93\ \text{N}}{2.50 \times 10^4\ \text{kg}} = 3.57 \times 10^{-4}\ \text{m/s}^2$$

Apply the kinematics velocity equation:

$$v = at + v_0$$

Solve for t:

$$t = \frac{v - v_0}{a} = \frac{1.00 \times 10^3\ \text{m/s}}{3.57 \times 10^{-4}\ \text{m/s}^2} = \boxed{2.80 \times 10^6\ \text{s}}$$

(c) Calculate the peak electric and magnetic fields if the light is supplied by a laser.

Solve Equation 21.28 for E_{max}:

$$I = \frac{E_{max}^2}{2\mu_0 c} \quad \rightarrow \quad E_{max} = \sqrt{2\mu_0 cI}$$

$$E_{max} = \sqrt{2(4\pi \times 10^{-7}\ \text{N} \cdot \text{s}^2/\text{C}^2)(3.00 \times 10^8\ \text{m/s})(1.34 \times 10^3\ \text{W/m}^2)}$$

$$= \boxed{1.01 \times 10^3\ \text{N/C}}$$

Obtain B_{max} using $E_{max} = B_{max}c$:

$$B_{max} = \frac{E_{max}}{c} = \frac{1.01 \times 10^3\ \text{N/C}}{3.00 \times 10^8\ \text{m/s}} = \boxed{3.37 \times 10^{-6}\ \text{T}}$$

REMARKS The answer to part (b) is a little over a month. While the acceleration is very low, there are no fuel costs, and within a few months the velocity can change sufficiently to allow the spacecraft to reach any planet in the solar system. Such spacecraft may be useful for certain purposes and are highly economical, but require a considerable amount of patience.

QUESTION 21.9 By what factor will the force exerted by the Sun's light be changed when the spacecraft is twice as far from the Sun? (a) no change (b) $\frac{1}{2}$ (c) $\frac{1}{4}$ (d) $\frac{1}{8}$

EXERCISE 21.9 A laser has a power of 22.0 W and a beam radius of 0.500 mm. (a) Find the intensity of the laser. (b) Suppose you were floating in space and pointed the laser beam away from you. What would your acceleration be? Assume your total mass, including equipment, is 72.0 kg and the force is directed through your center of mass. *Hint:* The change in momentum is the same as in the nonreflective case. (c) Calculate your acceleration if it were due to the gravity of a space station with mass 1.00×10^6 kg and center of mass 100.0 m away. (d) Calculate the peak electric and magnetic fields of the laser.

ANSWERS (a) 2.80×10^7 W/m^2 (b) 1.02×10^{-9} m/s^2 (c) 6.67×10^{-9} m/s^2 (d) 1.45×10^5 N/C, 4.84×10^{-4} T. If you were planning to use your laser welding torch as a thruster to get you back to the station, don't bother, because the force of gravity is stronger. Better yet, get somebody to toss you a line.

21.12 The Spectrum of Electromagnetic Waves

All electromagnetic waves travel in a vacuum with the speed of light, c. These waves transport energy and momentum from some source to a receiver. In 1887 Hertz successfully generated and detected the radio-frequency electromagnetic waves predicted by Maxwell. Maxwell himself had recognized as electromagnetic waves both visible light and the infrared radiation discovered in 1800 by William Herschel. It is now known that other forms of electromagnetic waves exist that are distinguished by their frequencies and wavelengths.

Because all electromagnetic waves travel through free space with a speed c, their frequency f and wavelength λ are related by the important expression

$$c = f\lambda \qquad [21.31]$$

The various types of electromagnetic waves are presented in Figure 21.22. Notice the wide and overlapping range of frequencies and wavelengths. For instance, an AM radio wave with a frequency of 1.50 MHz (a typical value) has a wavelength of

$$\lambda = \frac{c}{f} = \frac{3.00 \times 10^8 \text{ m/s}}{1.50 \times 10^6 \text{ s}^{-1}} = 2.00 \times 10^2 \text{ m}$$

The following abbreviations are often used to designate short wavelengths and distances:

$$1 \text{ micrometer } (\mu\text{m}) = 10^{-6} \text{ m}$$
$$1 \text{ nanometer } (\text{nm}) = 10^{-9} \text{ m}$$
$$1 \text{ angstrom } (\text{Å}) = 10^{-10} \text{ m}$$

The wavelengths of visible light, for example, range from 0.4 μm to 0.7 μm, or 400 nm to 700 nm, or 4 000 Å to 7 000 Å.

Wearing sunglasses lacking ultraviolet (UV) protection is worse for your eyes than wearing no sunglasses at all. Sunglasses without protection absorb some visible light, causing the pupils to dilate. This allows more UV light to enter the eye, increasing the damage to the lens of the eye over time. Without the sunglasses, the pupils constrict, reducing both visible and dangerous UV radiation. Be cool: wear sunglasses with UV protection.

■ Quick Quiz

21.8 Which of the following statements are true about light waves? (a) The higher the frequency, the longer the wavelength. (b) The lower the frequency, the longer the wavelength. (c) Higher-frequency light travels faster than lower-frequency light. (d) The shorter the wavelength, the higher the frequency. (e) The lower the frequency, the shorter the wavelength.

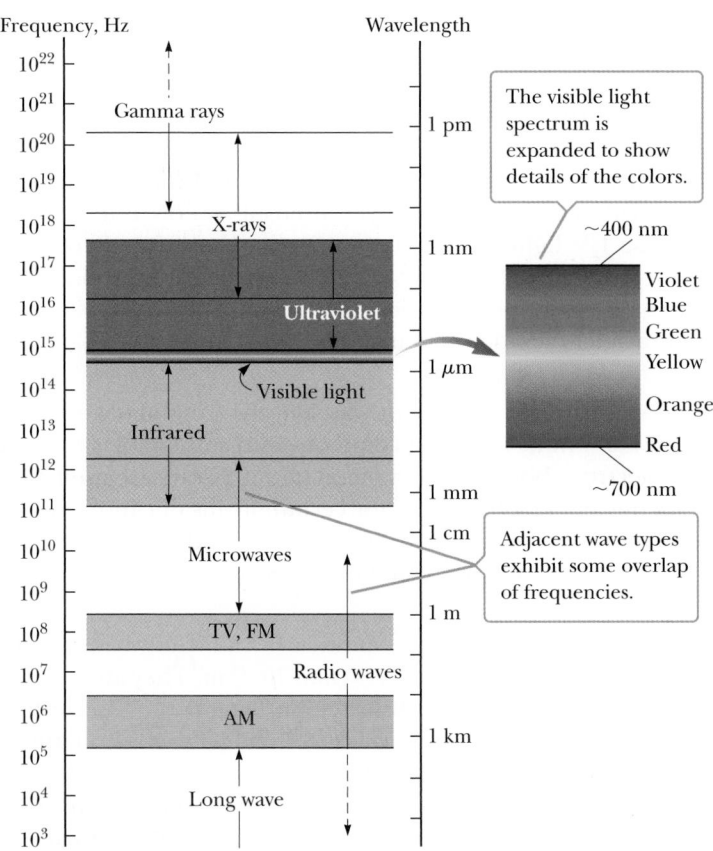

Figure 21.22 The electromagnetic spectrum.

Brief descriptions of the wave types follow, in order of decreasing wavelength. There is no sharp division between one kind of electromagnetic wave and the next. All forms of electromagnetic radiation are produced by accelerating charges.

Radio waves, which were discussed in Section 21.10, are the result of charges accelerating through conducting wires. They are, of course, used in radio and television communication systems.

Microwaves (short-wavelength radio waves) have wavelengths ranging between about 1 mm and 30 cm and are generated by electronic devices. Their short wavelengths make them well suited for the radar systems used in aircraft navigation and for the study of atomic and molecular properties of matter. Microwave ovens are an interesting domestic application of these waves. It has been suggested that solar energy might be harnessed by beaming microwaves to Earth from a solar collector in space.

Infrared waves (sometimes incorrectly called "heat waves"), produced by hot objects and molecules, have wavelengths ranging from about 1 mm to the longest wavelength of visible light, 7×10^{-7} m. They are readily absorbed by most materials. The infrared energy absorbed by a substance causes it to get warmer because the energy agitates the atoms of the object, increasing their vibrational or translational motion. The result is a rise in temperature. Infrared radiation has many practical and scientific applications, including physical therapy, infrared photography, and the study of the vibrations of atoms.

Visible light, the most familiar form of electromagnetic waves, may be defined as the part of the spectrum that is detected by the human eye. Light is produced by the rearrangement of electrons in atoms and molecules. The wavelengths of visible light are classified as colors ranging from violet ($\lambda \approx 4 \times 10^{-7}$ m) to red ($\lambda \approx 7 \times 10^{-7}$ m). The eye's sensitivity is a function of wavelength and is greatest at a wavelength of about 5.6×10^{-7} m (yellow green).

Ultraviolet (UV) light covers wavelengths ranging from about 4×10^{-7} m (400 nm) down to 6×10^{-10} m (0.6 nm). The Sun is an important source of ultraviolet light (which is the main cause of suntans). Most of the ultraviolet light from the Sun is absorbed by atoms in the upper atmosphere, or stratosphere, which is fortunate, because UV light in large quantities has harmful effects on humans. One important constituent of the stratosphere is ozone (O_3), produced from reactions of oxygen with ultraviolet radiation. The resulting ozone shield causes lethal high-energy ultraviolet radiation to warm the stratosphere.

X-rays are electromagnetic waves with wavelengths from about 10^{-8} m (10 nm) down to 10^{-13} m (10^{-4} nm). The most common source of x-rays is the acceleration of high-energy electrons bombarding a metal target. X-rays are used as a diagnostic tool in medicine and as a treatment for certain forms of cancer. Because x-rays easily penetrate and damage or destroy living tissues and organisms, care must be taken to avoid unnecessary exposure and overexposure.

Gamma rays—electromagnetic waves emitted by radioactive nuclei—have wavelengths ranging from about 10^{-10} m to less than 10^{-14} m. They are highly penetrating and cause serious damage when absorbed by living tissues. Accordingly, those working near such radiation must be protected by garments containing heavily absorbing materials, such as layers of lead.

When astronomers observe the same celestial object using detectors sensitive to different regions of the electromagnetic spectrum, striking variations in the

NASA/CXC/SAO   Palomar Observatory   WM Keck Observatory   VLA/NRAO

a   b   c   d

Figure 21.23 Observations in different parts of the electromagnetic spectrum show different features of the Crab Nebula. (a) X-ray image. (b) Optical image. (c) Polarized visible light. (d) Radio image.

object's features can be seen. Figure 21.23 shows images of the Crab Nebula made in three different wavelength ranges. The Crab Nebula is the remnant of a supernova explosion that was seen on Earth in 1054 A.D. (Compare with Fig. 8.31.)

■ APPLYING PHYSICS 21.4 | Light and Wound Treatment BIO

An important issue in human health is wound management. Chronic wounds affect five million to seven million people in the United States at an annual cost of more than twenty billion dollars. Low-level laser therapy has been shown to facilitate the healing and closure of wounds.

Infrared light increases the generation of adenosine triphosphate (ATP) in mitochondria and may stimulate the activation of genes and enzymes associated with cellular respiration. (ATP molecules provide energy for a variety of important cell functions.) Infrared light may also increase the concentration of reactive oxygen molecules, which could increase communication between the nucleus, cytosol, and the mitochondria. This mechanism may enhance and accelerate the healing process.

Green laser light can also be used to stimulate the body's repair mechanisms via a different mechanism. A pink dye, called "rose bengal," is applied to the tissue, which is then exposed to the laser light for a few minutes. When the dye absorbs the light, it causes cross-linkages between collagen molecules in the tissue. The cross-linked molecules promote the closing of the tissue while reducing

Wellman Center for Photomedicine, Massachusetts General Hospital

Figure 21.24 After bringing the sides of this wound together with deep sutures, closure on the left side was achieved with light-activated technology, whereas on the right side closure was carried out with sutures. This photo, taken at the end of two weeks, shows that healing was enhanced with light activation.

or eliminating the formation of scar tissue. Figure 21.24 shows the contrast between tissue receiving the normal treatment and tissue irradiated by lasers. The technique is also being studied for application to damaged peripheral nerves, blood vessels, and other tissues, such as incisions made in the cornea during eye surgery. ■

■ APPLYING PHYSICS 21.5 | The Sun and the Evolution of the Eye BIO

The center of sensitivity of our eyes coincides with the center of the wavelength distribution of the Sun. Is this an amazing coincidence?

EXPLANATION This fact is not a coincidence; rather, it's the result of biological evolution. Humans have evolved

with vision most sensitive to wavelengths that are strongest from the Sun. If aliens from another planet ever arrived at Earth, their eyes would have the center of sensitivity at wavelengths different from ours. If their sun were a red dwarf, for example, the alien's eyes would be most sensitive to red light. ■

21.13 The Doppler Effect for Electromagnetic Waves

As we saw in Section 14.6, sound waves exhibit the Doppler effect when the observer, the source, or both are moving relative to the medium of propagation. Recall that in the Doppler effect, the observed frequency of the wave is larger or smaller than the frequency emitted by the source of the wave.

A Doppler effect also occurs for electromagnetic waves, but it differs from the Doppler effect for sound waves in two ways. First, in the Doppler effect for sound waves, motion relative to the medium is most important because sound waves require a medium in which to propagate. In contrast, the medium of propagation plays no role in the Doppler effect for electromagnetic waves because the waves require no medium in which to propagate. Second, the speed of sound that appears in the equation for the Doppler effect for sound depends on the reference frame in which it is measured. In contrast, as we see in Chapter 26, the speed of electromagnetic waves has the same value in all coordinate systems that are either at rest or moving at constant velocity with respect to one another.

The single equation that describes the Doppler effect for electromagnetic waves is given by the approximate expression

$$f_O \approx f_S \left(1 \pm \frac{u}{c} \right) \qquad \text{if } u < c \qquad \text{[21.32]}$$

where f_O is the observed frequency, f_S is the frequency emitted by the source, u is the *relative* speed of the observer and source, and c is the speed of light in a vacuum. Note that Equation 21.32 is valid only if u is much smaller than c. Further, it can also be used for sound as long as the relative velocity of the source and observer is much less than the velocity of sound. The positive sign in the equation must be used when the source and observer are moving toward each other, whereas the negative sign must be used when they are moving away from each other. Thus, we anticipate an increase in the observed frequency if the source and observer are approaching each other and a decrease if the source and observer recede from each other.

Astronomers have made important discoveries using Doppler observations on light reaching Earth from distant galaxies. Such measurements have shown that the more distant a galaxy is from Earth, the more its light is shifted toward the red end of the spectrum. This *cosmological red shift* is evidence that the Universe is expanding. The stretching and expanding of space, like a rubber sheet being pulled in all directions, is consistent with Einstein's theory of general relativity. A given star or galaxy, however, can have a peculiar motion toward or away from Earth. For example, Doppler effect measurements made with the Hubble Space Telescope have shown that a galaxy labeled M87 is rotating, with one edge moving toward us and the other moving away. Its measured speed of rotation was used to identify a supermassive black hole located at its center.

■ SUMMARY

21.1 Resistors in an AC Circuit

If an AC circuit consists of a generator and a resistor, the current in the circuit is in phase with the voltage, which means that the current and voltage reach their maximum values at the same time.

In discussions of voltages and currents in AC circuits, **rms values** of voltages are usually used. One reason is that

AC ammeters and voltmeters are designed to read rms values. The rms values of currents and voltage (I_{rms} and ΔV_{rms}) are related to the maximum values of these quantities (I_{max} and ΔV_{max}) as follows:

$$I_{rms} = \frac{I_{max}}{\sqrt{2}} \quad \text{and} \quad \Delta V_{rms} = \frac{\Delta V_{max}}{\sqrt{2}} \qquad \text{[21.2, 21.3]}$$

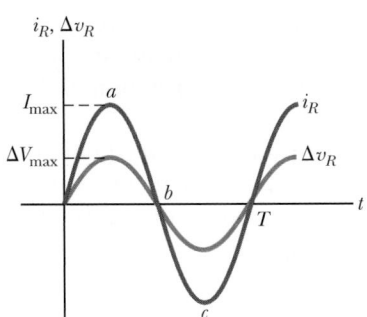

The voltage across a resistor and the current are in phase: they simultaneously reach their maximum values, their minimum values, and their zero values.

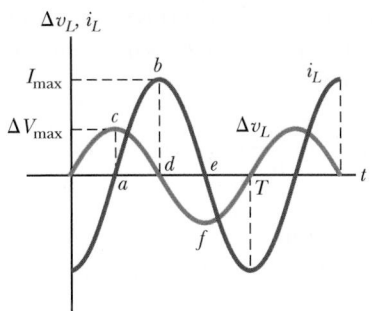

The voltage across an inductor reaches its maximum value 90° before the current reaches its maximum value, so the voltage "leads" the current.

The rms voltage across a resistor is related to the rms current in the resistor by **Ohm's law**:

$$\Delta V_{R,\text{rms}} = I_{\text{rms}}R \qquad \text{[21.4a]}$$

The rms voltage across a coil is related to the rms current in the coil by

$$\Delta V_{L,\text{rms}} = I_{\text{rms}}X_L \qquad \text{[21.9]}$$

21.2 Capacitors in an AC Circuit

If an AC circuit consists of a generator and a capacitor, the voltage lags behind the current by 90°. This means that the voltage reaches its maximum value one-quarter of a period after the current reaches its maximum value.

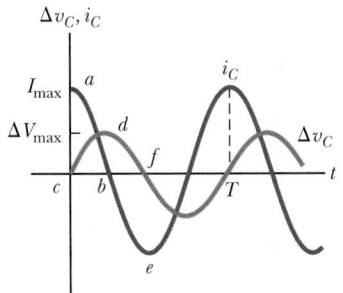

The voltage across a capacitor reaches its maximum value 90° after the current reaches its maximum value, so the voltage "lags" the current.

The impeding effect of a capacitor on current in an AC circuit is given by the **capacitive reactance** X_C, defined as

$$X_C \equiv \frac{1}{2\pi f C} \qquad \text{[21.5]}$$

where f is the frequency of the AC voltage source.

The rms voltage across and the rms current in a capacitor are related by

$$\Delta V_{C,\text{rms}} = I_{\text{rms}}X_C \qquad \text{[21.6]}$$

21.3 Inductors in an AC Circuit

If an AC circuit consists of a generator and an inductor, the voltage leads the current by 90°. This means the voltage reaches its maximum value one-quarter of a period before the current reaches its maximum value.

The effective impedance of a coil in an AC circuit is measured by a quantity called the **inductive reactance** X_L, defined as

$$X_L \equiv 2\pi f L \qquad \text{[21.8]}$$

21.4 The *RLC* Series Circuit

In an *RLC* series AC circuit, the maximum applied voltage ΔV is related to the maximum voltages across the resistor (ΔV_R), capacitor (ΔV_C), and inductor (ΔV_L) by

$$\Delta V_{\text{max}} = \sqrt{\Delta V_R^{\,2} + (\Delta V_L - \Delta V_C)^2} \qquad \text{[21.10]}$$

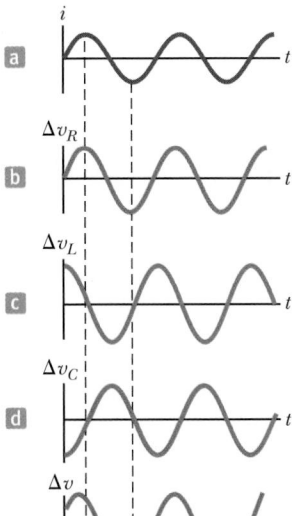

The time dependence of voltage differences of different circuit elements of an *RLC* series circuit are shown in these graphs. Notice that Δv_R is in phase with the current, Δv_L leads the current, and Δv_C lags the current.

If an AC circuit contains a resistor, an inductor, and a capacitor connected in series, the limit they place on the current is given by the **impedance Z** of the circuit, defined as

$$Z \equiv \sqrt{R^2 + (X_L - X_C)^2} \qquad \text{[21.13]}$$

The relationship between the maximum voltage supplied to an *RLC* series AC circuit and the maximum current in the circuit, which is the same in every element, is

$$\Delta V_{\text{max}} = I_{\text{max}}Z \qquad \text{[21.14]}$$

In an *RLC* series AC circuit, the applied rms voltage and current are out of phase. The **phase angle** ϕ between the current and voltage is given by

$$\tan \phi = \frac{X_L - X_C}{R} \qquad \text{[21.15]}$$

21.5 Power in an AC Circuit

The **average power** delivered by the voltage source in an *RLC* series AC circuit is

$$P_{av} = I_{rms} \Delta V_{rms} \cos \phi \qquad \text{[21.17]}$$

where the constant $\cos \phi$ is called the **power factor**.

21.6 Resonance in a Series *RLC* Circuit

In general, the rms current in a series *RLC* circuit can be written

$$I_{rms} = \frac{\Delta V_{rms}}{Z} = \frac{\Delta V_{rms}}{\sqrt{R^2 + (X_L - X_C)^2}} \qquad \text{[21.18]}$$

The current has its *maximum* value when the impedance has its *minimum* value, corresponding to $X_L = X_C$ and $Z = R$. The frequency f_0 at which this happens is called the **resonance frequency** of the circuit, given by

$$f_0 = \frac{1}{2\pi \sqrt{LC}} \qquad \text{[21.19]}$$

21.7 The Transformer

If the primary winding of a transformer has N_1 turns and the secondary winding consists of N_2 turns and then an input AC voltage ΔV_1 is applied to the primary, the induced voltage in the secondary winding is given by

$$\Delta V_2 = \frac{N_2}{N_1} \Delta V_1 \qquad \text{[21.22]}$$

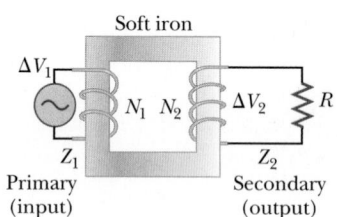

Soft iron

ΔV_1 N_1 N_2 ΔV_2 R

Z_1 Z_2

Primary   Secondary
(input)   (output)

An AC voltage ΔV_1 is applied to the primary coil, and the output voltage ΔV_2 is observed across the load resistance R.

When N_2 is greater than N_1, ΔV_2 exceeds ΔV_1 and the transformer is referred to as a *step-up transformer*. When N_2 is less than N_1, making ΔV_2 less than ΔV_1, we have a *step-down transformer*. In an ideal transformer, the power output equals the power input.

21.8–21.13 Electromagnetic Waves and Their Properties

Electromagnetic waves were predicted by James Clerk Maxwell and experimentally confirmed by Heinrich Hertz. These waves are created by accelerating electric charges and have the following properties:

1. Electromagnetic waves are transverse waves because the electric and magnetic fields are perpendicular to the direction of propagation of the waves.
2. Electromagnetic waves travel at the speed of light.
3. The ratio of the electric field to the magnetic field at a given point in an electromagnetic wave equals the speed of light:

$$\frac{E}{B} = c \qquad \text{[21.26]}$$

4. Electromagnetic waves carry energy as they travel through space. The average power per unit area is the intensity I, given by

$$I = \frac{E_{max} B_{max}}{2\mu_0} = \frac{E_{max}^2}{2\mu_0 c} = \frac{c}{2\mu_0} B_{max}^2 \qquad \text{[21.27, 21.28]}$$

where E_{max} and B_{max} are the maximum values of the electric and magnetic fields.

5. Electromagnetic waves transport linear and angular momentum as well as energy. The momentum p delivered in time Δt at normal incidence to an object that completely absorbs light energy U is given by

$$p = \frac{U}{c} \quad \text{(complete absorption)} \qquad \text{[21.29]}$$

If the surface is a perfect reflector, the momentum delivered in time Δt at normal incidence is twice that given by Equation 21.29:

$$p = \frac{2U}{c} \quad \text{(complete reflection)} \qquad \text{[21.30]}$$

6. The speed c, frequency f, and wavelength λ of an electromagnetic wave are related by

$$c = f\lambda \qquad \text{[21.31]}$$

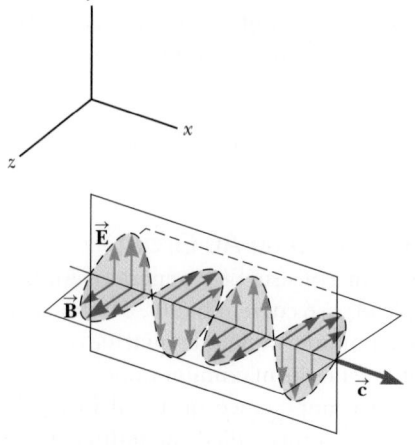

An electromagnetic wave sent out by oscillating charges in an antenna, represented at one instant of time and far from the antenna, moving in the positive *x*-direction with speed c.

The **electromagnetic spectrum** includes waves covering a broad range of frequencies and wavelengths. These waves have a variety of applications and characteristics, depending on their frequencies or wavelengths. The frequency of a given wave can be shifted by the relative velocity of observer and source, with the observed frequency f_O given by

$$f_O \approx f_S\left(1 \pm \frac{u}{c}\right) \quad \text{if } u < c \quad \text{[21.32]}$$

where f_S is the frequency of the source, u is the *relative* speed of the observer and source, and c is the speed of light in a vacuum. The positive sign is used when the source and observer approach each other, the negative sign when they recede from each other.

■ MULTIPLE-CHOICE QUESTIONS

WebAssign The multiple-choice questions in this chapter may be assigned online in Enhanced WebAssign.

1. Consider an electromagnetic wave traveling in the positive y-direction. The magnetic field associated with the wave at some location and at some instant points in the negative x-direction are shown in Figure MCQ21.1. What is the direction of the electric field at this position and at this instant? (a) the positive x-direction (b) the positive y-direction (c) the positive z-direction (d) the negative z-direction (e) the negative y-direction

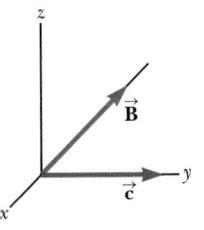

Figure MCQ21.1

2. When a particular inductor is connected to a source of sinusoidally varying voltage with constant amplitude and a frequency of 60.0 Hz, the rms current is 3.0 A. What is the rms current if the source frequency is doubled? (a) 12 A (b) 6.0 A (c) 4.2 A (d) 3.0 A (e) 1.5 A

3. A series RLC circuit contains a resistor of 20 Ω, a capacitor of 0.75 μF, and an inductor of 120 mH. If a sinusoidally varying rms voltage of 120 V is applied across this combination of elements, what is the rms current in the circuit when operating at its resonance frequency? (a) 2.4 A (b) 6.0 A (c) 10 A (d) 17 A (e) 8.2 A

4. Find the voltage across a $(1.0/2\pi)$-H inductor when it carries 2.0 A of rms current at 60.0 Hz. (a) 160 V (b) 140 V (c) 120 V (d) 95 V (e) 85 V

5. What is the rms voltage across a capacitor with capacitance $(1.00/2\pi)$ μF carrying 1.00-mA rms AC current at 60.0 Hz? (a) 16.7 V (b) 13.2 V (c) 32.2 V (d) 0.560 V (e) 4.43 V

6. A 6.0-V battery is connected across the primary coil of a transformer having 50 turns. If the secondary coil of the transformer has 100 turns, what voltage appears across the secondary? (a) 24 V (b) 12 V (c) 6.0 V (d) 3.0 V (e) none of these

7. A typical microwave oven operates at a frequency of 2.45 GHz. What is the wavelength associated with the electromagnetic waves in the oven? (a) 8.20 m (b) 12.2 cm (c) 1.20×10^8 m (d) 8.20×10^{-9} m (e) none of those answers

8. An inductor and a resistor are connected in series across an AC generator, as shown in Figure MCQ21.8. Immediately after the switch is closed, which of the following statements is true? (a) The current is $\Delta V/R$. (b) The voltage across the inductor is zero. (c) The current in the circuit is zero. (d) The voltage across the resistor is ΔV. (e) The voltage across the inductor is half its maximum value.

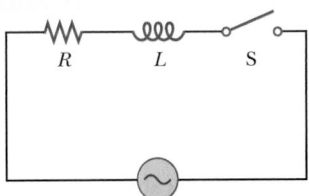

Figure MCQ21.8

9. A capacitor and a resistor are connected in series across an AC generator, as shown in Figure MCQ21.9. After the switch is closed, which of the following statements is true? (a) The voltage across the capacitor lags the current by 90°. (b) The voltage across the resistor is out of phase with the current. (c) The voltage across the capacitor leads the current by 90°. (d) The current decreases as the frequency of the generator is increased, but its peak voltage remains the same. (e) none of these

Figure MCQ21.9

10. A resistor, capacitor, and inductor are connected in series across an AC generator. Which of the following statements is true? (a) All the power is lost in the inductor. (b) All the power is lost in the capacitor. (c) All the power is lost in the resistor. (d) Power is lost in all

three elements. (e) The power delivered by the generator does not depend on the phase difference between the generator voltage and current.

11. A resistor, capacitor, and inductor are connected in series across an AC generator. Which of the following statements is false? (a) The instantaneous voltage across the capacitor lags the current by 90°. (b) The instantaneous voltage across the inductor leads the current by 90°. (c) The instantaneous voltage across the resistor is in phase with the current. (d) The voltages across the resistor, capacitor, and inductor are not in phase. (e) The rms voltage across the combination of the three elements equals the algebraic sum of the rms voltages across each element separately.

12. If the voltage across a circuit element has its maximum value when the current in the circuit is zero, which of the following statements *must* be true? (a) The circuit element is a resistor. (b) The circuit element is a capacitor. (c) The circuit element is an inductor. (d) The current and voltage are 90° out of phase. (e) The current and voltage are 180° out of phase.

13. What is the impedance of a series RLC circuit at resonance? (a) X_L (b) X_C (c) R (d) $X_L - X_C$ (e) 0

14. A series RLC circuit contains a 20.0-Ω resistor, a 0.75-μF capacitor, and a 120-mH inductor. If a sinusoidally varying rms voltage of 120 V at $f = 5.0 \times 10^2$ Hz is applied across this combination of elements, what is the rms current in the circuit? (a) 2.3 A (b) 6.0 A (c) 10 A (d) 17 A (e) 4.8 A

15. Which of the following statements are true regarding electromagnetic waves traveling through a vacuum? More than one statement may be correct. (a) All waves have the same wavelength. (b) All waves have the same frequency. (c) All waves travel at 3.00×10^8 m/s. (d) The electric and magnetic fields associated with the waves are perpendicular to each other and to the direction of wave propagation. (e) The speed of the waves depends on their frequency.

■ CONCEPTUAL QUESTIONS

1. Despite the advent of digital television, some viewers still use "rabbit ears" atop their sets (Fig. CQ21.1) instead of purchasing cable television service or satellite dishes. Certain orientations of the receiving antenna on a television set give better reception than others. Furthermore, the best orientation varies from station to station. Explain.

© iStockPhoto.com/kdow

Figure CQ21.1

2. (a) Does the phase angle in an RLC series circuit depend on frequency? (b) What is the phase angle for the circuit when the inductive reactance equals the capacitive reactance?

3. If the fundamental source of a sound wave is a vibrating object, what is the fundamental source of an electromagnetic wave?

4. Receiving radio antennas can be in the form of conducting lines or loops. What should the orientation of

each of these antennas be relative to a broadcasting antenna that is vertical?

5. In radio transmission a radio wave serves as a carrier wave, and the sound signal is superimposed on the carrier wave. In amplitude modulation (AM) radio, the amplitude of the carrier wave varies according to the sound wave. The U.S. Navy sometimes uses flashing lights to send Morse code between neighboring ships, a process that has similarities to radio broadcasting. (a) Is this process AM or FM? (b) What is the carrier frequency? (c) What is the signal frequency? (d) What is the broadcasting antenna? (e) What is the receiving antenna?

6. When light (or other electromagnetic radiation) travels across a given region, (a) what is it that oscillates? (b) What is it that is transported?

7. In space sailing, which is a proposed alternative for transport to the planets, a spacecraft carries a very large sail. Sunlight striking the sail exerts a force, accelerating the spacecraft. Should the sail be absorptive or reflective to be most effective?

8. What does a radio wave do to the charges in the receiving antenna to provide a signal for your car radio?

9. Does a wire connected to a battery emit an electromagnetic wave?

10. Suppose a creature from another planet had eyes that were sensitive to infrared radiation. Describe what it would see if it looked around the room that you are

now in. That is, what would be bright and what would be dim?

11. Why should an infrared photograph of a person look different from a photograph taken using visible light?

12. If a high-frequency current is passed through a solenoid containing a metallic core, the core becomes warm due to induction. Explain why the temperature of the material rises in this situation.

13. What is the advantage of transmitting power at high voltages?

14. Why is the sum of the maximum voltages across each of the elements in a series *RLC* circuit usually greater than the maximum applied voltage? Doesn't this violate Kirchhoff's loop rule?

15. If the resistance in an *RLC* circuit remains the same, but the capacitance and inductance are each doubled, how will the resonance frequency change?

■ PROBLEMS

WebAssign The problems in this chapter may be assigned online in Enhanced WebAssign. Selected problems also have Watch It video solutions.

1. denotes straightforward problem; 2. denotes intermediate problem;
3. denotes challenging problem
1. denotes full solution available in *Student Solutions Manual/ Study Guide*

1.	denotes problems most often assigned in Enhanced WebAssign
BIO	denotes biomedical problems
GP	denotes guided problems
M	denotes Master It tutorial available in Enhanced WebAssign
QC	denotes asking for quantitative and conceptual reasoning
S	denotes symbolic reasoning problem

21.1 Resistors in an AC Circuit

1. (a) What is the resistance of a lightbulb that uses an average power of 75.0 W when connected to a 60.0-Hz power source having a maximum voltage of 170 V? (b) What is the resistance of a 100-W lightbulb?

2. QC A certain lightbulb is rated at 60.0 W when operating at an rms voltage of 120 V. (a) What is the peak voltage applied across the bulb? (b) What is the resistance of the bulb? (c) Does a 100-W bulb have greater or less resistance than a 60.0-W bulb? Explain.

3. The current in the circuit shown in Figure P21.3 equals 60.0% of the peak current at $t = 7.00$ ms. What is the lowest source frequency that gives this current?

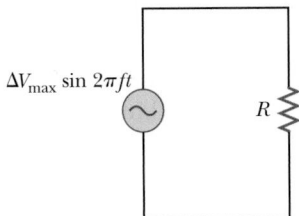

Figure P21.3

4. Figure P21.4 shows three lamps connected to a 120-V AC (rms) household supply voltage. Lamps 1 and 2 have 150-W bulbs; lamp 3 has a 100-W bulb. For each bulb, find (a) the rms current and (b) the resistance.

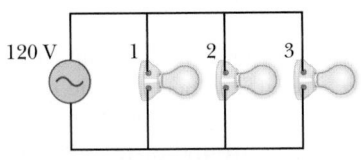

Figure P21.4

5. An audio amplifier, represented by the AC source and the resistor *R* in Figure P21.5, delivers alternating voltages at audio frequencies to the speaker. If the source puts out an alternating voltage of 15.0 V (rms), the resistance *R* is 8.20 Ω, and the speaker is equivalent to a resistance of 10.4 Ω, what is the time-averaged power delivered to the speaker?

Figure P21.5

6. GP The output voltage of an AC generator is given by $\Delta v = (170\text{ V}) \sin(60\pi t)$. The generator is connected across a 20.0-Ω resistor. By inspection, what are the (a) maximum voltage and (b) frequency? Find the (c) rms voltage across the resistor, (d) rms current in the resistor, (e) maximum current in the resistor, (f) power delivered to the resistor, and (g) current when $t = 0.005\ 0$ s. (h) Should the argument of the sine function be in degrees or radians?

21.2 Capacitors in an AC Circuit

7. (a) For what frequencies does a 22.0-μF capacitor have a reactance below 175 Ω? (b) What is the reactance of a 44.0-μF capacitor over this same frequency range?

8. What is the maximum current delivered to a circuit containing a 2.20-μF capacitor when it is connected across (a) a North American outlet having $\Delta V_{rms} = 120$ V and $f = 60.0$ Hz and (b) a European outlet having $\Delta V_{rms} = 240$ V and $f = 50.0$ Hz?

9. When a 4.0-μF capacitor is connected to a generator whose rms output is 30 V, the current in the circuit is observed to be 0.30 A. What is the frequency of the source?

10. [Q|C] An AC generator with an output rms voltage of 36.0 V at a frequency of 60.0 Hz is connected across a 12.0-μF capacitor. Find the (a) capacitive reactance, (b) rms current, and (c) maximum current in the circuit. (d) Does the capacitor have its maximum charge when the current takes its maximum value? Explain.

11. [M] What maximum current is delivered by an AC source with ΔV_{max} = 48.0 V and f = 90.0 Hz when connected across a 3.70-μF capacitor?

12. A generator delivers an AC voltage of the form Δv = (98.0 V) sin (80πt) to a capacitor. The maximum current in the circuit is 0.500 A. Find the (a) rms voltage of the generator, (b) frequency of the generator, (c) rms current, (d) reactance, and (e) value of the capacitance.

21.3 Inductors in an AC Circuit

13. An inductor has a 54.0-Ω reactance when connected to a 60.0-Hz source. The inductor is removed and then connected to a 50.0-Hz source that produces a 100-V rms voltage. What is the maximum current in the inductor?

14. An AC generator has an output rms voltage of 78.0 V at a frequency of 80.0 Hz. If the generator is connected across a 25.0-mH inductor, find the (a) inductive reactance, (b) rms current, and (c) maximum current in the circuit.

15. [M] In a purely inductive AC circuit as shown in Figure P21.15, ΔV_{max} = 100 V. (a) The maximum current is 7.50 A at 50.0 Hz. Calculate the inductance L. (b) At what angular frequency ω is the maximum current 2.50 A?

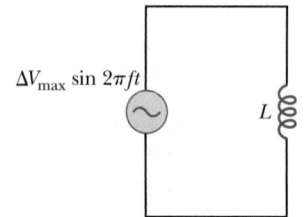

ΔV_{max} sin 2$\pi f t$ L

Figure P21.15

16. [GP] The output voltage of an AC generator is given by Δv = (1.20 × 10^2 V) sin (30πt). The generator is connected across a 0.500-H inductor. Find the (a) frequency of the generator, (b) rms voltage across the inductor, (c) inductive reactance, (d) rms current in the inductor, (e) maximum current in the inductor, and (f) average power delivered to the inductor. (g) Find an expression for the instantaneous current. (h) At what time after t = 0 does the instantaneous current first reach 1.00 A? (Use the inverse sine function.)

17. Determine the maximum magnetic flux through an inductor connected to a standard outlet (ΔV_{rms} = 120 V, f = 60.0 Hz).

21.4 The *RLC* Series Circuit

18. A sinusoidal voltage Δv = (80.0 V) sin (150t) is applied to a series *RLC* circuit with L = 80.0 mH, C = 125.0 μF,

and R = 40.0 Ω. (a) What is the impedance of the circuit? (b) What is the maximum current in the circuit?

19. A 40.0-μF capacitor is connected to a 50.0-Ω resistor and a generator whose rms output is 30.0 V at 60.0 Hz. Find (a) the rms current in the circuit, (b) the rms voltage drop across the resistor, (c) the rms voltage drop across the capacitor, and (d) the phase angle for the circuit.

20. [M] An inductor (L = 400 mH), a capacitor (C = 4.43 μF), and a resistor (R = 500 Ω) are connected in series. A 50.0-Hz AC generator connected in series to these elements produces a maximum current of 250 mA in the circuit. (a) Calculate the required maximum voltage ΔV_{max}. (b) Determine the phase angle by which the current leads or lags the applied voltage.

21. A resistor (R = 9.00 × 10^2 Ω), a capacitor (C = 0.250 μF), and an inductor (L = 2.50 H) are connected in series across a 2.40 × 10^2-Hz AC source for which ΔV_{max} = 1.40 × 10^2 V. Calculate (a) the impedance of the circuit, (b) the maximum current delivered by the source, and (c) the phase angle between the current and voltage. (d) Is the current leading or lagging the voltage?

22. A 50.0-Ω resistor, a 0.100-H inductor, and a 10.0-μF capacitor are connected in series to a 60.0-Hz source. The rms current in the circuit is 2.75 A. Find the rms voltages across (a) the resistor, (b) the inductor, (c) the capacitor, and (d) the *RLC* combination. (e) Sketch the phasor diagram for this circuit.

23. An *RLC* circuit consists of a 150-Ω resistor, a 21.0-μF capacitor, and a 460-mH inductor connected in series with a 120-V, 60.0-Hz power supply. (a) What is the phase angle between the current and the applied voltage? (b) Which reaches its maximum earlier, the current or the voltage?

24. An AC source operating at 60 Hz with a maximum voltage of 170 V is connected in series with a resistor (R = 1.2 kΩ) and an inductor (L = 2.8 H). (a) What is the maximum value of the current in the circuit? (b) What are the maximum values of the potential difference across the resistor and the inductor? (c) When the current is at a maximum, what are the magnitudes of the potential differences across the resistor, the inductor, and the AC source? (d) When the current is zero, what are the magnitudes of the potential difference across the resistor, the inductor, and the AC source?

25. A person is working near the secondary of a transformer, as shown in Figure P21.25. The primary voltage is 120 V (rms) at 60.0 Hz. The capacitance C_s, which is the stray capacitance between the hand and the secondary winding, is 20.0 pF. Assuming the person has a body resistance to ground of R_b = 50.0 kΩ, determine the rms voltage across the body. *Hint:* Redraw the cir-

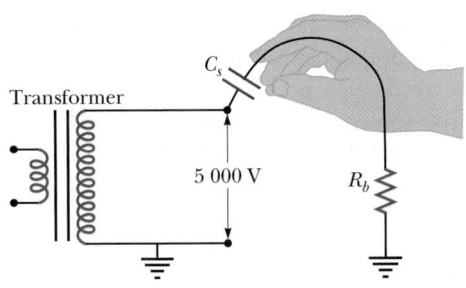

Transformer

5 000 V R_b

Figure P21.25

cuit with the secondary of the transformer as a simple AC source.

26. **Q|C** A 60.0-Ω resistor is connected in series with a 30.0-μF capacitor and a generator having a maximum voltage of 1.20×10^2 V and operating at 60.0 Hz. Find the (a) capacitive reactance of the circuit, (b) impedance of the circuit, and (c) maximum current in the circuit. (d) Does the voltage lead or lag the current? (e) How will putting an inductor in series with the existing capacitor and resistor affect the current? Explain.

27. **GP** A series AC circuit contains a resistor, an inductor of 150 mH, a capacitor of 5.00 μF, and a generator with ΔV_{max} = 240 V operating at 50.0 Hz. The maximum current in the circuit is 100 mA. Calculate (a) the inductive reactance, (b) the capacitive reactance, (c) the impedance, (d) the resistance in the circuit, and (e) the phase angle between the current and the generator voltage.

28. At what frequency does the inductive reactance of a 57.0-μH inductor equal the capacitive reactance of a 57.0-μF capacitor?

29. An AC source with a maximum voltage of 150 V and f = 50.0 Hz is connected between points a and d in Figure P21.29. Calculate the rms voltages between points (a) a and b, (b) b and c, (c) c and d, and (d) b and d.

a b c d

40.0 Ω   185 mH   65.0 μF

Figure P21.29

21.5 Power in an AC Circuit

30. An AC source operating at 60 Hz with a maximum voltage of 170 V is connected in series with a resistor (R = 1.2 kΩ) and a capacitor (C = 2.5 μF). (a) What is the maximum value of the current in the circuit? (b) What are the maximum values of the potential difference across the resistor and the capacitor? (c) When the current is zero, what are the magnitudes of the potential difference across the resistor, the capacitor, and the AC source? How much charge is on the capacitor at this instant? (d) When the current is at a maximum, what are the magnitudes of the potential differences across

the resistor, the capacitor, and the AC source? How much charge is on the capacitor at this instant?

31. A multimeter in an RL circuit records an rms current of 0.500 A and a 60.0-Hz rms generator voltage of 104 V. A wattmeter shows that the average power delivered to the resistor is 10.0 W. Determine (a) the impedance in the circuit, (b) the resistance R, and (c) the inductance L.

32. An AC voltage of the form Δv = (90.0 V) sin (350t) is applied to a series RLC circuit. If R = 50.0 Ω, C = 25.0 μF, and L = 0.200 H, find the (a) impedance of the circuit, (b) rms current in the circuit, and (c) average power delivered to the circuit.

33. An AC voltage of the form Δv = 100 sin (1 000t), where Δv is in volts and t is in seconds, is applied to a series RLC circuit. Assume the resistance is 400 Ω, the capacitance is 5.00 μF, and the inductance is 0.500 H. Find the average power delivered to the circuit.

34. A series RLC circuit has a resistance of 22.0 Ω and an impedance of 80.0 Ω. If the rms voltage applied to the circuit is 160 V, what average power is delivered to the circuit?

35. An inductor and a resistor are connected in series. When connected to a 60-Hz, 90-V (rms) source, the voltage drop across the resistor is found to be 50 V (rms) and the power delivered to the circuit is 14 W. Find (a) the value of the resistance and (b) the value of the inductance.

36. **Q|C** Consider a series RLC circuit with R = 25 Ω, L = 6.0 mH, and C = 25 μF. The circuit is connected to a 10-V (rms), 600-Hz AC source. (a) Is the sum of the voltage drops across R, L, and C equal to 10 V (rms)? (b) Which is greatest, the power delivered to the resistor, to the capacitor, or to the inductor? (c) Find the average power delivered to the circuit.

21.6 Resonance in a Series *RLC* Circuit

37. **M** An RLC circuit is used in a radio to tune into an FM station broadcasting at f = 99.7 MHz. The resistance in the circuit is R = 12.0 Ω, and the inductance is L = 1.40 μH. What capacitance should be used?

38. The resonant frequency of a certain series RLC circuit is 2.84 kHz, and the value of its capacitance is 6.50 μF. What is the value of the resonant frequency when the capacitance of the circuit is 9.80 μF?

39. The AM band extends from approximately 500 kHz to 1 600 kHz. If a 2.0-μH inductor is used in a tuning circuit for a radio, what are the extremes that a capacitor must reach to cover the complete band of frequencies?

40. Consider a series RLC circuit with R = 15 Ω, L = 200 mH, C = 75 μF, and a maximum voltage of 150 V. (a) What is the impedance of the circuit at resonance? (b) What is the resonance frequency of the circuit? (c) When will the current be greatest: at resonance, at 10% below the resonant frequency, or at 10% above the

resonant frequency? (d) What is the rms current in the circuit at a frequency of 60 Hz?

41. Two electrical oscillators are used in a heterodyne metal detector to detect buried metal objects (see Fig. P21.41). The detector uses two identical electrical oscillators in the form of LC circuits having resonant frequencies of 725 kHz. When the signals from the two oscillating circuits are combined, the beat frequency is zero because each has the same resonant frequency. However, when the coil of one circuit encounters a buried metal object, the inductance of this circuit increases by 1.000%, while that of the second is unchanged. Determine the beat frequency that would be detected in this situation.

Figure P21.41

42. A series circuit contains a 3.00-H inductor, a 3.00-μF capacitor, and a 30.0-Ω resistor connected to a 120-V (rms) source of variable frequency. Find the power delivered to the circuit when the frequency of the source is (a) the resonance frequency, (b) one-half the resonance frequency, (c) one-fourth the resonance frequency, (d) two times the resonance frequency, and (e) four times the resonance frequency. From your calculations, can you draw a conclusion about the frequency at which the maximum power is delivered to the circuit?

21.7 The Transformer

43. The primary coil of a transformer has $N_1 = 250$ turns, and its secondary coil has $N_2 = 1\,500$ turns. If the input voltage across the primary coil is $\Delta v = (170\text{ V})\sin \omega t$, what rms voltage is developed across the secondary coil?

44. A step-down transformer is used for recharging the batteries of portable devices. The turns ratio N_2/N_1 for a particular transformer used in a CD player is 1:13. When used with 120-V (rms) household service, the transformer draws an rms current of 250 mA. Find the (a) rms output voltage of the transformer and (b) power delivered to the CD player.

45. An AC power generator produces 50 A (rms) at 3 600 V. The voltage is stepped up to 100 000 V by an ideal transformer, and the energy is transmitted through a long-distance power line that has a resistance of 100 Ω. What percentage of the power delivered by the generator is dissipated as heat in the power line?

46. A transformer is to be used to provide power for a computer disk drive that needs 6.0 V (rms) instead of the 120 V (rms) from the wall outlet. The number of turns in the primary is 400, and it delivers 500 mA (the sec-

ondary current) at an output voltage of 6.0 V (rms). (a) Should the transformer have more turns in the secondary compared with the primary, or fewer turns? (b) Find the current in the primary. (c) Find the number of turns in the secondary.

47. A transformer on a pole near a factory steps the voltage down from 3 600 V (rms) to 120 V (rms). The transformer is to deliver 1 000 kW to the factory at 90% efficiency. Find (a) the power delivered to the primary, (b) the current in the primary, and (c) the current in the secondary.

48. A transmission line that has a resistance per unit length of 4.50×10^{-4} Ω/m is to be used to transmit 5.00 MW over 400 miles (6.44×10^5 m). The output voltage of the generator is 4.50 kV (rms). (a) What is the line loss if a transformer is used to step up the voltage to 500 kV (rms)? (b) What fraction of the input power is lost to the line under these circumstances? (c) What difficulties would be encountered on attempting to transmit the 5.00 MW at the generator voltage of 4.50 kV (rms)?

21.10 Production of Electromagnetic Waves by an Antenna

21.11 Properties of Electromagnetic Waves

49. The U.S. Navy has long proposed the construction of extremely low frequency (ELF waves) communications systems; such waves could penetrate the oceans to reach distant submarines. Calculate the length of a quarter-wavelength antenna for a transmitter generating ELF waves of frequency 75 Hz. How practical is this antenna?

50. (a) The distance to Polaris, the North Star, is approximately 6.44×10^{18} m. If Polaris were to burn out today, how many years would it take to see it disappear? (b) How long does it take sunlight to reach Earth? (c) How long does it take a microwave signal to travel from Earth to the Moon and back? (The distance from Earth to the Moon is 3.84×10^5 km.)

51. Q|C The Earth reflects approximately 38.0% of the incident sunlight from its clouds and surface. (a) Given that the intensity of solar radiation at the top of the atmosphere is 1 370 W/m^2, find the radiation pressure on the Earth, in pascals, at the location where the Sun is straight overhead. (b) State how this quantity compares with normal atmospheric pressure at the Earth's surface, which is 101 kPa.

52. Experimenters at the National Institute of Standards and Technology have made precise measurements of the speed of light using the fact that, in vacuum, the speed of electromagnetic waves is $c = 1/\sqrt{\mu_0\epsilon_0}$, where the constants $\mu_0 = 4\pi \times 10^{-7}$ N · s^2/C^2 and $\epsilon_0 = 8.854 \times 10^{-12}$ C^2/N · m^2. What value (to four significant figures) does this formula give for the speed of light in vacuum?

53. **BIO** Oxygenated hemoglobin absorbs weakly in the red (hence its red color) and strongly in the near infrared, whereas deoxygenated hemoglobin has the opposite absorption. This fact is used in a "pulse oximeter" to measure oxygen saturation in arterial blood. The device clips onto the end of a person's finger and has two light-emitting diodes—a red (660 nm) and an infrared (940 nm)—and a photocell that detects the amount of light transmitted through the finger at each wavelength. (a) Determine the frequency of each of these light sources. (b) If 67% of the energy of the red source is absorbed in the blood, by what factor does the amplitude of the electromagnetic wave change? *Hint:* The intensity of the wave is equal to the average power per unit area as given by Equation 21.28.

54. **BIO** **Operation of the pulse oximeter (see previous problem).** The transmission of light energy as it passes through a solution of light-absorbing molecules is described by the Beer–Lambert law

$$I = I_0 10^{-\epsilon CL} \quad \text{or} \quad \log_{10}\left(\frac{I}{I_0}\right) = -\epsilon CL$$

which gives the decrease in intensity I in terms of the distance L the light has traveled through a fluid with a concentration C of the light-absorbing molecule. The quantity ϵ is called the extinction coefficient, and its value depends on the frequency of the light. (It has units of m^2/mol.) Assume the extinction coefficient for 660-nm light passing through a solution of oxygenated hemoglobin is identical to the coefficient for 940-nm light passing through deoxygenated hemoglobin. Also assume 940-nm light has zero absorption ($\epsilon = 0$) in oxygenated hemoglobin and 660-nm light has zero absorption in deoxygenated hemoglobin. If 33% of the energy of the red source and 76% of the infrared energy is transmitted through the blood, what is the fraction of hemoglobin that is oxygenated?

55. The Sun delivers an average power of 1 370 W/m^2 to the top of Earth's atmosphere. Find the magnitudes of $\vec{E}_{max}$ and $\vec{B}_{max}$ for the electromagnetic waves at the top of the atmosphere.

56. **QC** A laser beam is used to levitate a metal disk against the force of Earth's gravity. (a) Derive an equation giving the required intensity of light, I, in terms of the mass m of the disk, the gravitational acceleration g, the speed of light c, and the cross-sectional area of the disk A. Assume the disk is perfectly reflecting and the beam is directed perpendicular to the disk. (b) If the disk has mass 5.00 g and radius 4.00 cm, find the necessary light intensity. (c) Give two reasons why using light pressure as propulsion near Earth's surface is impractical.

57. A microwave oven is powered by an electron tube called a magnetron that generates electromagnetic waves of frequency 2.45 GHz. The microwaves enter the oven and are reflected by the walls. The standing-wave pat-

tern produced in the oven can cook food unevenly, with hot spots in the food at antinodes and cool spots at nodes, so a turntable is often used to rotate the food and distribute the energy. If a microwave oven is used with a cooking dish in a fixed position, the antinodes can appear as burn marks on foods such as carrot strips or cheese. The separation distance between the burns is measured to be 6.00 cm. Calculate the speed of the microwaves from these data.

58. Consider a bright star in our night sky. Assume its distance from the Earth is 20.0 light-years (ly) and its power output is 4.00×10^{28} W, about 100 times that of the Sun. (a) Find the intensity of the starlight at the Earth. (b) Find the power of the starlight the Earth intercepts. One light-year is the distance traveled by light through a vacuum in one year.

21.12 The Spectrum of Electromagnetic Waves

59. What are the wavelengths of electromagnetic waves in free space that have frequencies of (a) 5.00×10^{19} Hz and (b) 4.00×10^9 Hz?

60. **BIO** A diathermy machine, used in physiotherapy, generates electromagnetic radiation that gives the effect of "deep heat" when absorbed in tissue. One assigned frequency for diathermy is 27.33 MHz. What is the wavelength of this radiation?

61. What are the wavelength ranges in (a) the AM radio band (540–1 600 kHz) and (b) the FM radio band (88–108 MHz)?

62. An important news announcement is transmitted by radio waves to people who are 100 km away, sitting next to their radios, and by sound waves to people sitting across the newsroom, 3.0 m from the newscaster. Who receives the news first? Explain. Take the speed of sound in air to be 343 m/s.

63. Infrared spectra are used by chemists to help identify an unknown substance. Atoms in a molecule that are bound together by a particular bond vibrate at a predictable frequency, and light at that frequency is absorbed strongly by the atom. In the case of the $C{=}O$ double bond, for example, the oxygen atom is bound to the carbon by a bond that has an effective spring constant of 2 800 N/m. If we assume the carbon atom remains stationary (it is attached to other atoms in the molecule), determine the resonant frequency of this bond and the wavelength of light that matches that frequency. Verify that this wavelength lies in the infrared region of the spectrum. (The mass of an oxygen atom is 2.66×10^{-26} kg.)

21.13 The Doppler Effect for Electromagnetic Waves

64. A spaceship is approaching a space station at a speed of 1.8×10^5 m/s. The space station has a beacon that emits green light with a frequency of 6.0×10^{14} Hz. (a) What is the frequency of the beacon observed on

the spaceship? (b) What is the change in frequency? (Carry five digits in these calculations.)

65. While driving at a constant speed of 80 km/h, you are passed by a car traveling at 120 km/h. If the frequency of light emitted by the taillights of the car that passes you is 4.3×10^{14} Hz, what frequency will you observe? What is the change in frequency?

66. A speeder tries to explain to the police that the yellow warning lights she was approaching on the side of the road looked green to her because of the Doppler shift. How fast would she have been traveling if yellow light of wavelength 580 nm had been shifted to green with a wavelength of 560 nm? *Note:* For speeds less than $0.03c$, Equation 21.32 will lead to a value for the observed frequency accurate to approximately two significant digits.

Additional Problems

67. A 25.0-mW laser beam of diameter 2.00 mm is reflected at normal incidence by a perfectly reflecting mirror. Calculate the radiation pressure on the mirror.

68. The intensity of solar radiation at the top of Earth's atmosphere is 1 370 W/m³. Assuming 60% of the incoming solar energy reaches Earth's surface and assuming you absorb 50% of the incident energy, make an order-of-magnitude estimate of the amount of solar energy you absorb in a 60-minute sunbath.

69. A 200-Ω resistor is connected in series with a 5.0-μF capacitor and a 60-Hz, 120-V rms line. If electrical energy costs $0.080/kWh, how much does it cost to leave this circuit connected for 24 h?

70. **S** In an *RLC* series circuit that includes a source of alternating current operating at fixed frequency and voltage, the resistance R is equal to the inductive reactance. If the plate separation of the parallel-plate capacitor is reduced to one-half its original value, the current in the circuit doubles. Find the initial capacitive reactance in terms of R.

71. As a way of determining the inductance of a coil used in a research project, a student first connects the coil to a 12.0-V battery and measures a current of 0.630 A. The student then connects the coil to a 24.0-V (rms), 60.0-Hz generator and measures an rms current of 0.570 A. What is the inductance?

72. (a) What capacitance will resonate with a one-turn loop of inductance 400 pH to give a radar wave of wavelength 3.0 cm? (b) If the capacitor has square parallel plates separated by 1.0 mm of air, what should the edge length of the plates be? (c) What is the common reactance of the loop and capacitor at resonance?

73. **M** A dish antenna with a diameter of 20.0 m receives (at normal incidence) a radio signal from a distant source, as shown in Figure P21.73. The radio signal is a continuous sinusoidal wave with amplitude E_{max} = 0.20 μV/m. Assume the antenna absorbs all the radiation that falls on the dish. (a) What is the amplitude of the magnetic field in this wave? (b) What is the intensity of the radiation received by the antenna? (c) What is the power received by the antenna?

Figure P21.73

74. A particular inductor has appreciable resistance. When the inductor is connected to a 12-V battery, the current in the inductor is 3.0 A. When it is connected to an AC source with an rms output of 12 V and a frequency of 60 Hz, the current drops to 2.0 A. What are (a) the impedance at 60 Hz and (b) the inductance of the inductor?

75. One possible means of achieving space flight is to place a perfectly reflecting aluminized sheet into Earth's orbit and to use the light from the Sun to push this solar sail. Suppose such a sail, of area 6.00×10^4 m² and mass 6 000 kg, is placed in orbit facing the Sun. (a) What force is exerted on the sail? (b) What is the sail's acceleration? (c) How long does it take this sail to reach the Moon, 3.84×10^8 m away? Ignore all gravitational effects and assume a solar intensity of 1 340 W/m². *Hint:* The radiation pressure by a reflected wave is given by 2 (average power per unit area)/c.

76. **BIO** **QC** The U.S. Food and Drug Administration limits the radiation leakage of microwave ovens to no more than 5.0 mW/cm² at a distance of 2.0 in. A typical cell phone, which also transmits microwaves, has a peak output power of about 2.0 W. (a) Approximating the cell phone as a point source, calculate the radiation intensity of a cell phone at a distance of 2.0 in. How does the answer compare with the maximum allowable microwave oven leakage? (b) The distance from your ear to your brain is about 2 in. What would the radiation intensity in your brain be if you used a Bluetooth headset, keeping the phone in your pocket, 1.0 m away from your brain? Most headsets are so-called Class 2 devices with a maximum output power of 2.5 mW.

■ AP* REVIEW QUESTIONS

1. Which of the following shows the selected electromagnetic waves in order from the smallest to largest wavelengths?

   (A) Gamma rays, infrared, radio waves, x-rays

   (B) X-rays, gamma rays, infrared, radio waves

   (C) Infrared, gamma rays, x-rays, radio waves

   (D) Radio waves, infrared, x-rays, gamma rays

   (E) Gamma rays, x-rays, infrared, radio waves

2. Which of the following radio stations has the longest wavelength?

   (A) 1200 AM

   (B) 1410 AM

   (C) 88.9 FM

   (D) 101.3 FM

   (E) 107.6 FM

3. Which of the following shows the selected electromagnetic waves in order from lowest to highest frequency?

   (A) Microwaves, ultraviolet waves, AM radio waves, FM radio waves

   (B) AM radio waves, FM radio waves, microwaves, ultraviolet waves

   (C) Ultraviolet waves, microwaves, AM radio waves, FM radio waves

   (D) Ultraviolet waves, microwaves, FM radio waves, AM radio waves

   (E) FM radio waves, AM radio waves, microwaves, ultraviolet waves

4. Which of the following shows the selected visible colors of light in order from highest to lowest frequency?

   (A) Red, yellow, green, blue

   (B) Yellow, red, blue, green

   (C) Blue, green, yellow, red

   (D) Green, blue, red, yellow

   (E) Blue, yellow, green, red

5. Which of the following shows the selected visible colors in order from largest to smallest wavelength?

   (A) Violet, blue, yellow-green, orange

   (B) Blue, violet, yellow-green, orange

   (C) Yellow-green, orange, violet, blue

   (D) Orange, yellow-green, blue, violet

   (E) Orange, yellow-green, violet, blue

6. Which of the following radio stations is least likely to be lost as you drive through a tunnel?

   (A) 1200 AM

   (B) 1410 AM

   (C) 88.9 FM

   (D) 101.3 FM

   (E) 107.6 FM

7. What is the approximate wavelength of AM radio station 1400 if its frequency is 1400 kHz?

   (A) 4.7×10^{-3} m

   (B) 214.3 m

   (C) 2.14×10^5 m

   (D) 4.2×10^{14} m

   (E) More information is needed

8. What is the approximate frequency of red light that has a wavelength of 700 nm?

   (A) 2.3×10^{-15} Hz

   (B) 210 Hz

   (C) 2.1×10^{11} Hz

   (D) 4.3×10^{14} Hz

   (E) More information is needed

9. Which of the following electromagnetic waves have been shown to cause serious tissue damage in humans and why?

    (A) Infrared waves, small wavelength

    (B) Infrared waves, high frequency

    (C) Gamma rays, large wavelength

    (D) Gamma rays, high frequency

    (E) X-rays, large wavelength

10. Which of the following electromagnetic waves is useful for finding people in the dark?

    (A) X-rays

    (B) Ultraviolet waves

    (C) Infrared waves

    (D) Microwaves

    (E) Long wave radio waves

11. Which electromagnetic wave, with a wavelength of about 40 nm, comes mainly from the Sun and is partially blocked by the Earth's ozone layer?

    (A) X-rays

    (B) Ultraviolet waves

    (C) Infrared waves

    (D) Microwaves

    (E) Long wave radio waves

12. Which of the following statements about electromagnetic (EM) waves is NOT correct?

    (A) All EM waves travel at the speed of light.

    (B) As wavelength increases, frequency decreases.

    (C) All forms of EM radiation are produced by accelerating charges.

    (D) As wavelength decreases, frequency increases.

    (E) Visible light is the only section of EM waves that travels at the speed of light.

Dianne Kowing

Light is bent (refracted) as it passes through water, with different wavelengths bending by different amounts, a phenomenon called dispersion. Together with reflection, these physical phenomena lead to the creation of a rainbow when light passes through small, suspended droplets of water.

Reflection and Refraction of Light

22

Light has a dual nature. In some experiments it acts like a particle, while in others it acts like a wave. In this and the next two chapters, we concentrate on the aspects of light that are best understood through the wave model. First we discuss the reflection of light at the boundary between two media and the refraction (bending) of light as it travels from one medium into another. We use these ideas to study the refraction of light as it passes through lenses and the reflection of light from mirrored surfaces. Finally, we describe how lenses and mirrors can be used to view objects with telescopes and microscopes and how lenses are used in photography. The ability to manipulate light has greatly enhanced our capacity to investigate and understand the nature of the Universe.

22.1 The Nature of Light

Until the beginning of the 19th century, light was modeled as a stream of particles emitted by a source that stimulated the sense of sight on entering the eye. The chief architect of the particle theory of light was Newton. With this theory, he provided simple explanations of some known experimental facts concerning the nature of light, namely, the laws of reflection and refraction.

Most scientists accepted Newton's particle theory of light. During Newton's lifetime, however, another theory was proposed. In 1678 Dutch physicist and astronomer Christian Huygens (1629–1695) showed that a wave theory of light could also explain the laws of reflection and refraction.

The wave theory didn't receive immediate acceptance, for several reasons. First, all the waves known at the time (sound, water, and so on) traveled through some

761

Christian Huygens
(1629–1695), Dutch Physicist and
Astronomer
Huygens is best known for his contributions to the fields of optics and dynamics. To Huygens, light was a vibratory motion in the ether, spreading out and producing the sensation of light when impinging on the eye. On the basis of this theory, he deduced the laws of reflection and refraction and explained the phenomenon of double refraction.

sort of medium, but light from the Sun could travel to Earth through empty space. Further, it was argued that if light were some form of wave, it would bend around obstacles; hence, we should be able to see around corners. It is now known that light does indeed bend around the edges of objects. This phenomenon, known as *diffraction*, is difficult to observe because light waves have such short wavelengths. Even though experimental evidence for the diffraction of light was discovered by Francesco Grimaldi (1618–1663) around 1660, for more than a century most scientists rejected the wave theory and adhered to Newton's particle theory, probably due to Newton's great reputation as a scientist.

The first clear demonstration of the wave nature of light was provided in 1801 by Thomas Young (1773–1829), who showed that under appropriate conditions, light exhibits interference behavior. Light waves emitted by a single source and traveling along two different paths can arrive at some point and combine and cancel each other by destructive interference. Such behavior couldn't be explained at that time by a particle model because scientists couldn't imagine how two or more particles could come together and cancel one another.

The most important development in the theory of light was the work of Maxwell, who predicted in 1865 that light was a form of high-frequency electromagnetic wave (Chapter 21). His theory also predicted that these waves should have a speed of 3×10^8 m/s, in agreement with the measured value.

Although the classical theory of electricity and magnetism explained most known properties of light, some subsequent experiments couldn't be explained by the assumption that light was a wave. The most striking experiment was the *photoelectric effect* (which we examine more closely in Chapter 27), discovered by Hertz. Hertz found that clean metal surfaces emit charges when exposed to ultraviolet light.

In 1905, Einstein published a paper that formulated the theory of light quanta ("particles") and explained the photoelectric effect. He reached the conclusion that light was composed of corpuscles, or discontinuous quanta of energy. These corpuscles or quanta are now called *photons* to emphasize their particle-like nature. According to Einstein's theory, the energy of a photon is proportional to the frequency of the electromagnetic wave associated with it, or

Energy of a photon ▶

$$E = hf \qquad \text{[22.1]}$$

where $h = 6.63 \times 10^{-34}$ J · s is *Planck's constant*. This theory retains some features of both the wave and particle theories of light. As we discuss later, the photoelectric effect is the result of energy transfer from a single photon to an electron in the metal. This means the electron interacts with one photon of light as if the electron had been struck by a particle. Yet the photon has wave-like characteristics, as implied by the fact that a frequency is used in its definition.

In view of these developments, light must be regarded as having a *dual nature*: **In some experiments light acts as a wave and in others it acts as a particle.** Classical electromagnetic wave theory provides adequate explanations of light propagation and of the effects of interference, whereas the photoelectric effect and other experiments involving the interaction of light with matter are best explained by assuming light is a particle.

So in the final analysis, is light a wave or a particle? The answer is neither and both: light has a number of physical properties, some associated with waves and others with particles.

22.2 Reflection and Refraction

When light traveling in one medium encounters a boundary leading into a second medium, the processes of reflection and refraction can occur. In **reflection** part of the light encountering the second medium bounces off that medium. In

refraction the light passing into the second medium bends through an angle with respect to the normal to the boundary. Often, both processes occur at the same time, with part of the light being reflected and part refracted. To study reflection and refraction we need a way of thinking about beams of light, and this is given by the ray approximation.

The Ray Approximation in Geometric Optics

An important property of light that can be understood based on common experience is the following: **light travels in a straight-line path in a homogeneous medium, until it encounters a boundary between two different materials.** When light strikes a boundary, it is reflected from that boundary, passes into the material on the other side of the boundary, or partially does both.

The preceding observation leads us to use what is called the **ray approximation** to represent beams of light. As shown in Figure 22.1, a ray of light is an imaginary line drawn along the direction of travel of the light beam. For example, a beam of sunlight passing through a darkened room traces out the path of a light ray. We also make use of the concept of wave fronts of light. A **wave front** is a surface passing through the points of a wave that have the same phase and amplitude. For instance, the wave fronts in Figure 22.1 could be surfaces passing through the crests of waves. The rays, corresponding to the direction of wave motion, are straight lines perpendicular to the wave fronts. When light rays travel in parallel paths, the wave fronts are planes perpendicular to the rays.

Reflection of Light

When a light ray traveling in a transparent medium encounters a boundary leading into a second medium, part of the incident ray is reflected back into the first medium. Figure 22.2a shows several rays of a beam of light incident on a smooth, mirror-like reflecting surface. The reflected rays are parallel to one another, as indicated in the figure. The reflection of light from such a smooth surface is called **specular reflection**. On the other hand, if the reflecting surface is rough, as in Figure 22.2b, the surface reflects the rays in a variety of directions. Reflection from any rough surface is known as **diffuse reflection**. A surface behaves as a smooth surface as long as its variations are small compared with the wavelength of the incident light. Figures 22.2c and 22.2d are photographs of specular and diffuse reflection of laser light, respectively.

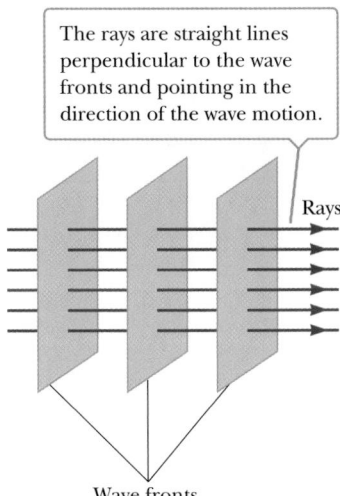

The rays are straight lines perpendicular to the wave fronts and pointing in the direction of the wave motion.

Figure 22.1 A plane wave traveling to the right.

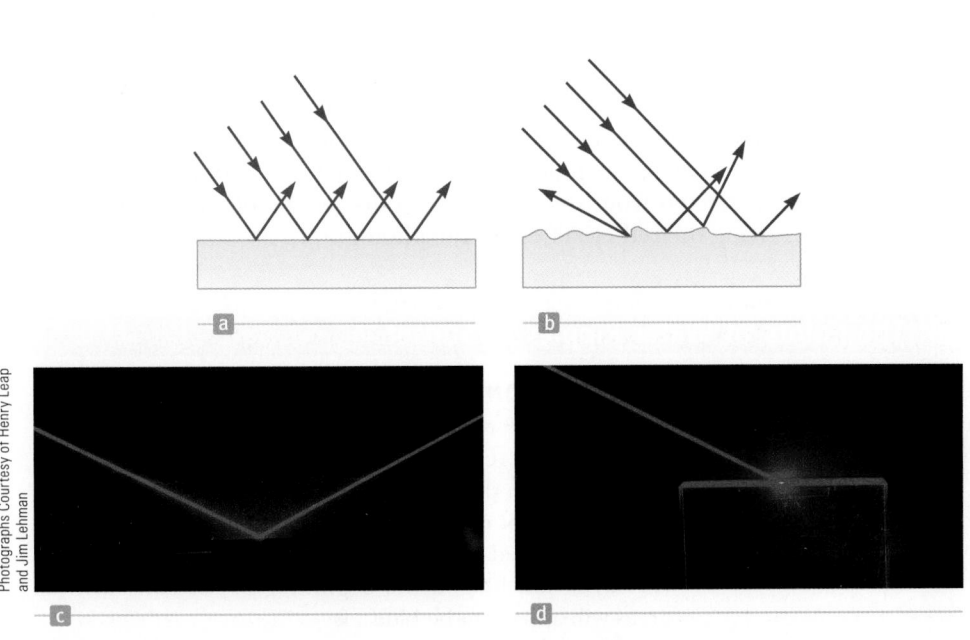

Figure 22.2 A schematic representation of (a) specular reflection, where the reflected rays are all parallel to one another, and (b) diffuse reflection, where the reflected rays travel in random directions. (c, d) Photographs of specular and diffuse reflection, made with laser light.

Photographs Courtesy of Henry Leap and Jim Lehman

As an example, consider the two types of reflection from a road surface that a driver might observe while driving at night. When the road is dry, light from oncoming vehicles is scattered off the road in different directions (diffuse reflection) and the road is clearly visible. On a rainy night when the road is wet, the road's irregularities are filled with water. Because the wet surface is smooth, the light undergoes specular reflection. This means that the light is reflected straight ahead, and the driver of a car sees only what is directly in front of him. Light from the side never reaches the driver's eye. In this book we concern ourselves only with specular reflection, and we use the term *reflection* to mean specular reflection.

APPLICATION
Seeing the Road on a Rainy Night

■ *Quick Quiz*

22.1 Which part of Figure 22.3, (a) or (b), better shows specular reflection of light from the roadway?

Figure 22.3 (Quick Quiz 22.1)

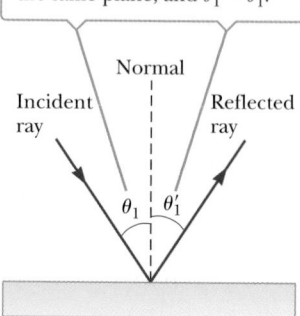

The incident ray, the reflected ray, and the normal all lie in the same plane, and $\theta_1 = \theta_1'$.

Active Figure 22.4
The wave under reflection model.

BIO APPLICATION
Red Eyes in Flash Photographs

Consider a light ray traveling in air and incident at some angle on a flat, smooth surface, as in Active Figure 22.4. The incident and reflected rays make angles θ_1 and θ_1', respectively, **with a line perpendicular to the surface** at the point where the incident ray strikes the surface. We call this line the *normal* to the surface. Experiments show that **the angle of reflection equals the angle of incidence**:

$$\theta_1' = \theta_1 \qquad [22.2]$$

You may have noticed a common occurrence in photographs of individuals: their eyes appear to be glowing red. "Red-eye" occurs when a photographic flash device is used and the flash unit is close to the camera lens. Light from the flash unit enters the eye and is reflected back along its original path from the retina. This type of reflection back along the original direction is called *retroreflection*. If the flash unit and lens are close together, retroreflected light can enter the lens. Most of the light reflected from the retina is red due to the blood vessels at the back of the eye, giving the red-eye effect in the photograph.

■ APPLYING PHYSICS 22.1 | The Colors of Water Ripples at Sunset

An observer on the west-facing beach of a large lake is watching the beginning of a sunset. The water is very smooth except for some areas with small ripples. The observer notices that some areas of the water are blue and some are pink. Why does the water appear to be different colors in different areas?

EXPLANATION The different colors arise from specular and diffuse reflection. The smooth areas of the water will specularly reflect the light from the west, which is the pink light from the sunset. The areas with small ripples will reflect the light diffusely, so light from all parts of the sky will be reflected into the observer's eyes. Because most of the sky is still blue at the beginning of the sunset, these areas will appear to be blue. ■

■ APPLYING PHYSICS 22.2 | Double Images

When standing outside in the Sun close to a single-pane window looking to the darker interior of a building, why can you often see two images of yourself, one superposed on the other?

EXPLANATION Reflection occurs whenever there is an interface between two different media. For the glass in the

window, there are two such surfaces, the window surface facing outdoors and the window surface facing indoors. Each of these interfaces results in an image. You will notice that one image is slightly smaller than the other, because the reflecting surface is farther away. ■

■ EXAMPLE 22.1 | The Double-Reflecting Light Ray

GOAL Calculate a resultant angle from two reflections.

PROBLEM Two mirrors make an angle of 120° with each other, as in Figure 22.5. A ray is incident on mirror M_1 at an angle of 65° to the normal. Find the angle the ray makes with the normal to M_2 after it is reflected from both mirrors.

STRATEGY Apply the law of reflection twice. Given the incident ray at angle θ_{inc}, find the final resultant angle, β_{ref}.

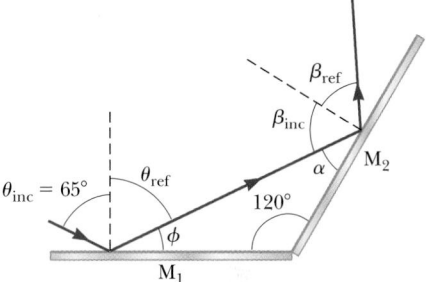

Figure 22.5 (Example 22.1) Mirrors M_1 and M_2 make an angle of 120° with each other.

. . . .

SOLUTION

Apply the law of reflection to M_1 to find the angle of reflection, θ_{ref}:

$$\theta_{ref} = \theta_{inc} = 65°$$

Find the angle ϕ that is the complement of the angle θ_{ref}:

$$\phi = 90° - \theta_{ref} = 90° - 65° = 25°$$

Find the unknown angle α in the triangle of M_1, M_2, and the ray traveling from M_1 to M_2, using the fact that the three angles sum to 180°:

$$180° = 25° + 120° + \alpha \quad \rightarrow \quad \alpha = 35°$$

The angle α is complementary to the angle of incidence, β_{inc}, for M_2:

$$\alpha + \beta_{inc} = 90° \quad \rightarrow \quad \beta_{inc} = 90° - 35° = 55°$$

Apply the law of reflection a second time, obtaining β_{ref}:

$$\beta_{ref} = \beta_{inc} = \boxed{55°}$$

. . . .

REMARKS Notice the heavy reliance on elementary geometry and trigonometry in these reflection problems.

QUESTION 22.1 In general, what is the relationship between the incident angle θ_{inc} and the final reflected angle β_{ref} when the angle between the mirrors is 90.0°? (a) $\theta_{inc} + \beta_{ref} = 90.0°$ (b) $\theta_{inc} - \beta_{ref} = 90.0°$ (c) $\theta_{inc} + \beta_{ref} = 180°$

EXERCISE 22.1 Repeat the problem if the angle of incidence is 55° and the second mirror makes an angle of 100° with the first mirror.

ANSWER 45°

Refraction of Light

When a ray of light traveling through a transparent medium encounters a boundary leading into another transparent medium, as in Active Figure 22.6a (page 766), part of the ray is reflected and part enters the second medium. The ray that enters the second medium is bent at the boundary and is said to be *refracted*. The incident ray, the reflected ray, the refracted ray, and the normal at the point of incidence all lie in the same plane. The **angle of refraction**, θ_2, in Active Figure 22.6a depends

Active Figure 22.6
(a) The wave under refraction model. (b) Light incident on the Lucite block refracts both when it enters the block and when it leaves the block.

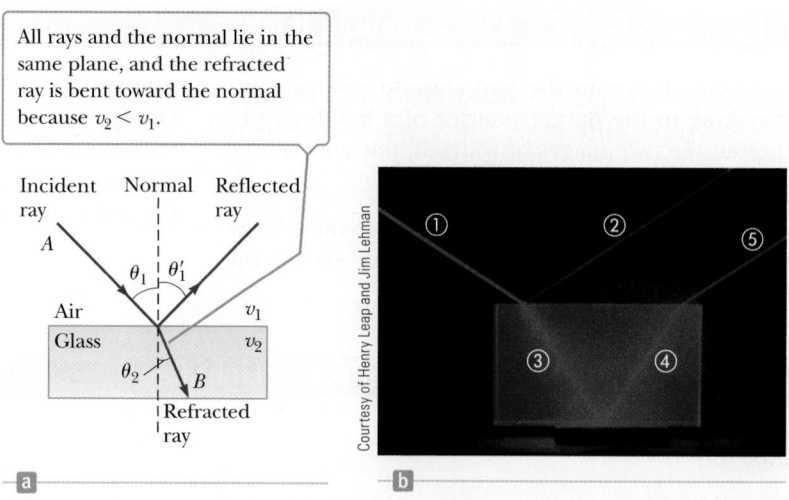

All rays and the normal lie in the same plane, and the refracted ray is bent toward the normal because $v_2 < v_1$.

on the properties of the two media and on the angle of incidence, through the relationship

$$\frac{\sin \theta_2}{\sin \theta_1} = \frac{v_2}{v_1} = \text{constant} \qquad [22.3]$$

where v_1 is the speed of light in medium 1 and v_2 is the speed of light in medium 2. Note that the angle of refraction is also measured with respect to the normal. In Section 22.7 we derive the laws of reflection and refraction using Huygens' principle.

Experiment shows that **the path of a light ray through a refracting surface is reversible**. For example, the ray in Active Figure 22.6a travels from point A to point B. If the ray originated at B, it would follow the same path to reach point A, but the reflected ray would be in the glass.

■ *Quick Quiz*

22.2 If beam 1 is the incoming beam in Active Figure 22.6b, which of the other four beams are due to reflection? Which are due to refraction?

When light moves from a material in which its speed is high to a material in which its speed is lower, the angle of refraction θ_2 is less than the angle of incidence. The refracted ray therefore bends toward the normal, as shown in Active Figure 22.7a. If the ray moves from a material in which it travels slowly to a material in which it travels more rapidly, θ_2 is greater than θ_1, so the ray bends away from the normal, as shown in Active Figure 22.7b.

Active Figure 22.7
The refraction of light as it (a) moves from air into glass and (b) moves from glass into air.

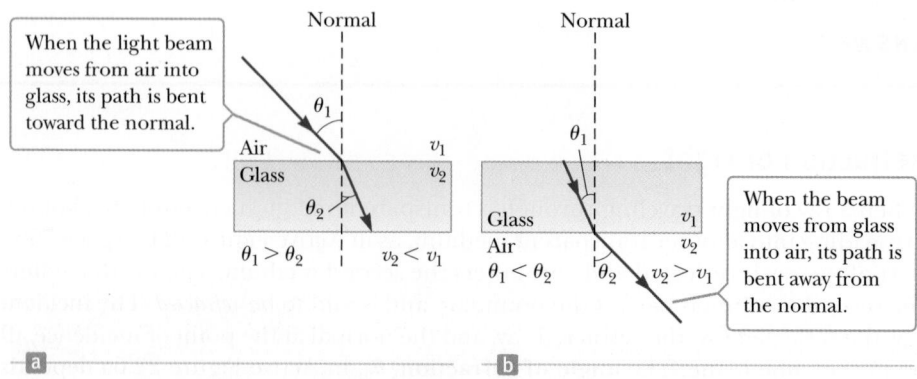

When the light beam moves from air into glass, its path is bent toward the normal.

When the beam moves from glass into air, its path is bent away from the normal.

22.3 The Law of Refraction

When light passes from one transparent medium to another, it's refracted because the speed of light is different in the two media.[1] The **index of refraction**, n, of a medium is defined as the ratio c/v;

$$n \equiv \frac{\text{speed of light in vacuum}}{\text{speed of light in a medium}} = \frac{c}{v} \qquad [22.4]$$

From this definition, we see that the index of refraction is a dimensionless number that is greater than or equal to 1 because v is always less than c. Further, n is equal to one for vacuum. Table 22.1 lists the indices of refraction for various substances.

As light travels from one medium to another, its frequency doesn't change. To see why, consider Figure 22.8. Wave fronts pass an observer at point A in medium 1 with a certain frequency and are incident on the boundary between medium 1 and medium 2. The frequency at which the wave fronts pass an observer at point B in medium 2 must equal the frequency at which they arrive at point A. If not, the wave fronts would either pile up at the boundary or be destroyed or created at the boundary. Because neither of these events occurs, the frequency must remain the same as a light ray passes from one medium into another.

Therefore, because the relation $v = f\lambda$ must be valid in both media and because $f_1 = f_2 = f$, we see that

$$v_1 = f\lambda_1 \text{ and } v_2 = f\lambda_2$$

Because $v_1 \neq v_2$, it follows that $\lambda_1 \neq \lambda_2$. A relationship between the index of refraction and the wavelength can be obtained by dividing these two equations and making use of the definition of the index of refraction given by Equation 22.4:

$$\frac{\lambda_1}{\lambda_2} = \frac{v_1}{v_2} = \frac{c/n_1}{c/n_2} = \frac{n_2}{n_1} \qquad [22.5]$$

which gives

$$\lambda_1 n_1 = \lambda_2 n_2 \qquad [22.6]$$

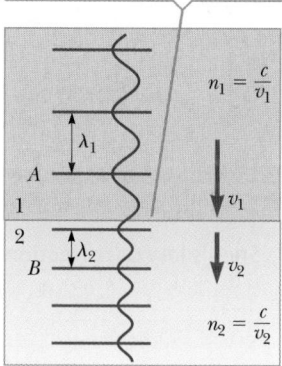

> As a wave moves from medium 1 to medium 2, its wavelength changes but its frequency remains constant.

$$n_1 = \frac{c}{v_1}$$

$$n_2 = \frac{c}{v_2}$$

Figure 22.8 A wave travels from medium 1 to medium 2, in which it moves with lower speed.

Tip 22.1 An Inverse Relationship

The index of refraction is *inversely* proportional to the wave speed. Therefore, as the wave speed v decreases, the index of refraction, n, *increases*.

Tip 22.2 The Frequency Remains the Same

The *frequency* of a wave does *not* change as the wave passes from one medium to another. Both the wave speed and the wavelength *do* change, but the frequency remains the same.

Table 22.1 Indices of Refraction for Various Substances, Measured with Light of Vacuum Wavelength $\lambda_0 = 589$ mn

Substance	Index of Refraction	Substance	Index of Refraction
Solids at 20°C		**Liquids at 20°C**	
Diamond (C)	2.419	Benzene	1.501
Fluorite (CaF_2)	1.434	Carbon disulfide	1.628
Fused quartz (SiO_2)	1.458	Carbon tetrachloride	1.461
Glass, crown	1.52	Ethyl alcohol	1.361
Glass, flint	1.66	Glycerine	1.473
Ice (H_2O) (at 0°C)	1.309	Water	1.333
Polystyrene	1.49		
Sodium chloride (NaCl)	1.544	**Gases at 0°C, 1 atm**	
Zircon	1.923	Air	1.000 293
		Carbon dioxide	1.000 45

---

[1]The speed of light varies between media because the time lags caused by the absorption and reemission of light as it travels from atom to atom depend on the particular electronic structure of the atoms constituting each material.

Let medium 1 be the vacuum so that $n_1 = 1$. It follows from Equation 22.6 that the index of refraction of any medium can be expressed as the ratio

$$n = \frac{\lambda_0}{\lambda_n} \qquad [22.7]$$

where λ_0 is the wavelength of light in vacuum and λ_n is the wavelength in the medium having index of refraction n. Figure 22.9 is a schematic representation of this reduction in wavelength when light passes from a vacuum into a transparent medium.

We are now in a position to express Equation 22.3 in an alternate form. If we substitute Equation 22.5 into Equation 22.3, we get

Snell's law of refraction ▶

$$n_1 \sin \theta_1 = n_2 \sin \theta_2 \qquad [22.8]$$

The experimental discovery of this relationship is usually credited to Willebrørd Snell (1591–1626) and is therefore known as **Snell's law of refraction**.

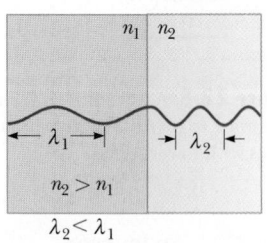

Figure 22.9 A schematic diagram of the *reduction* in wavelength when light travels from a medium with a low index of refraction to one with a higher index of refraction.

■ *Quick Quiz*

22.3 A material has an index of refraction that increases continuously from top to bottom. Of the three paths shown in Figure 22.10, which path will a light ray follow as it passes through the material?

22.4 As light travels from a vacuum ($n = 1$) to a medium such as glass ($n > 1$), which of the following properties remains the same, the (a) wavelength, (b) wave speed, or (c) frequency?

Figure 22.10 (Quick Quiz 22.3)

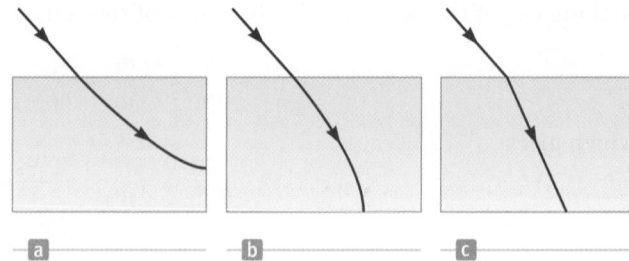

■ EXAMPLE 22.2 | **Angle of Refraction for Glass**

GOAL Apply Snell's law.

PROBLEM A light ray of wavelength 589 nm (produced by a sodium lamp) traveling through air is incident on a smooth, flat slab of crown glass at an angle θ_1 of 30.0° to the normal, as sketched in Figure 22.11. **(a)** Find the angle of refraction, θ_2. **(b)** At what angle θ_3 does the ray leave the glass as it re-enters the air? **(c)** How does the answer for θ_3 change if the ray enters water below the slab instead of the air?

STRATEGY Substitute quantities into Snell's law and solve for the unknown angles of refraction.

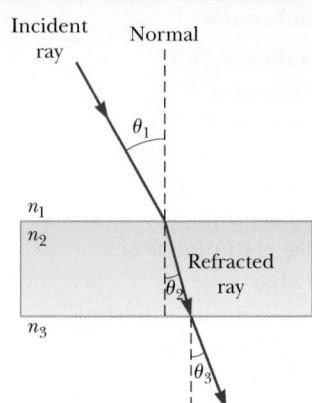

Figure 22.11 (Example 22.2) Refraction of light by glass.

SOLUTION

(a) Find the angle of refraction, θ_2.

Solve Snell's law (Eq. 22.8) for $\sin \theta_2$:

$$(1) \quad \sin \theta_2 = \frac{n_1}{n_2} \sin \theta_1$$

From Table 22.1, find $n_1 = 1.00$ for air and $n_2 = 1.52$ for crown glass. Substitute these values into Equation (1) and take the inverse sine of both sides:

$$\sin \theta_2 = \left(\frac{1.00}{1.52}\right)(\sin 30.0°) = 0.329$$

$$\theta_2 = \sin^{-1}(0.329) = \boxed{19.2°}$$

(b) At what angle θ_3 does the ray leave the glass as it re-enters the air?

Write Equation (1), replacing θ_3 with θ_2 and θ_1 with θ_2:

$$(2) \quad \sin \theta_3 = \frac{n_2}{n_3} \sin \theta_2 = \frac{1.52}{1.00} \sin(19.2°) = 0.500$$

Take the inverse sine of both sides to find θ_3:

$$\theta_3 = \sin^{-1}(0.500) = \boxed{30.0°}$$

(c) How does the answer for θ_3 change if the ray enters water below the slab instead of air?

Write Equation (2) and substitute a different value for n_3:

$$\sin \theta_3 = \frac{n_2}{n_3} \sin \theta_2 = \frac{1.52}{1.33} \sin(19.2°) = 0.376$$

$$\theta_3 = \sin^{-1}(0.376) = \boxed{22.1°}$$

REMARKS Notice that the light ray bends toward the normal when it enters a material of a higher index of refraction, and away from the normal when entering a material with a lower index of refraction. In passing through a slab of material with parallel surfaces, for example from air to glass and back to air, the final direction of the ray is parallel to the direction of the incident ray. The only effect in that case is a lateral displacement of the light ray.

QUESTION 22.2 If the glass is replaced by a transparent material with smaller index of refraction, will the refraction angle θ_2 be (a) smaller, (b) larger, or (c) unchanged?

EXERCISE 22.2 Suppose a light ray in air ($n = 1.00$) enters a cube of material ($n = 2.50$) at a 45.0° angle with respect to the normal and then exits the bottom of the cube into water ($n = 1.33$). At what angle to the normal does the ray leave the slab?

ANSWER 32.1°

■ EXAMPLE 22.3 | Light in Fused Quartz

GOAL Use the index of refraction to determine the effect of a medium on light's speed and wavelength.

PROBLEM Light of wavelength 589 nm in vacuum passes through a piece of fused quartz of index of refraction $n = 1.458$. **(a)** Find the speed of light in fused quartz. **(b)** What is the wavelength of this light in fused quartz? **(c)** What is the frequency of the light in fused quartz?

STRATEGY Substitute values into Equations 22.4 and 22.7.

SOLUTION

(a) Find the speed of light in fused quartz.

Obtain the speed from Equation 22.4:

$$v = \frac{c}{n} = \frac{3.00 \times 10^8 \text{ m/s}}{1.458} = \boxed{2.06 \times 10^8 \text{ m/s}}$$

(b) What is the wavelength of this light in fused quartz?

Use Equation 22.7 to calculate the wavelength:

$$\lambda_n = \frac{\lambda_0}{n} = \frac{589 \text{ nm}}{1.458} = \boxed{404 \text{ nm}}$$

(c) What is the frequency of the light in fused quartz?

The frequency in quartz is the same as in vacuum. Solve $c = f\lambda$ for the frequency:

$$f = \frac{c}{\lambda} = \frac{3.00 \times 10^8 \text{ m/s}}{589 \times 10^{-9} \text{ m}} = \boxed{5.09 \times 10^{14} \text{ Hz}}$$

REMARKS It's interesting to note that the speed of light in vacuum, 3.00×10^8 m/s, is an upper limit for the speed of material objects. In our treatment of relativity in Chapter 26, we will find that this upper limit is consistent with experimental observations. However, it's possible for a particle moving in a medium to have a speed that exceeds the speed of light in

(Continued)

that medium. For example, it's theoretically possible for a particle to travel through fused quartz at a speed greater than 2.06×10^8 m/s, but it must still have a speed less than 3.00×10^8 m/s.

QUESTION 22.3 True or False: If light with wavelength λ in glass passes into water with index n_w, the new wavelength of the light is λ/n_w.

EXERCISE 22.3 Light with wavelength 589 nm passes through crystalline sodium chloride. In this medium, find (a) the speed of light, (b) the wavelength, and (c) the frequency of the light.

ANSWER (a) 1.94×10^8 m/s (b) 381 nm (c) 5.09×10^{14} Hz

■ EXAMPLE 22.4 | Refraction of Laser Light in a Digital Videodisc (DVD)

GOAL Apply Snell's law together with geometric constraints.

PROBLEM A DVD is a video recording consisting of a spiral track about 1.0 μm wide with digital information. (See Fig. 22.12a.) The digital information consists of a series of pits that are "read" by a laser beam sharply focused on a track in the information layer. If the width a of the beam at the information layer must equal 1.0 μm to distinguish individual tracks and the width w of the beam as it enters the plastic is 0.700 0 mm, find the angle θ_1 at which the conical beam should enter the plastic. (See Fig. 22.12b.) Assume the plastic has a thickness $t = 1.20$ mm and an index of refraction $n = 1.55$. Note that this system is relatively immune to small dust particles degrading the video quality because particles would have to be as large as 0.700 mm to obscure the beam at the point where it enters the plastic.

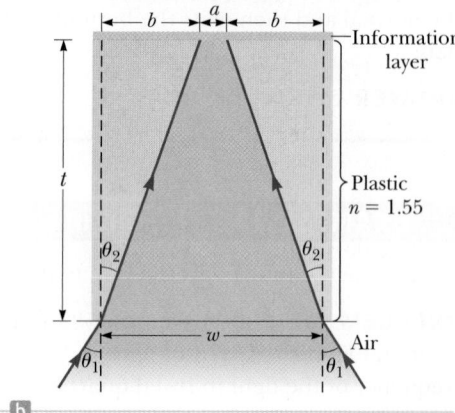

Figure 22.12 (Example 22.4) A micrograph of a DVD surface showing tracks and pits along each track. (b) Cross section of a cone-shaped laser beam used to read a DVD.

STRATEGY Use right-triangle trigonometry to determine the angle θ_2 and then apply Snell's law to obtain the angle θ_1.

· ·

SOLUTION

From the top and bottom of Figure 22.12b, obtain an equation relating w, b, and a:

$$w = 2b + a$$

Solve this equation for b and substitute given values:

$$b = \frac{w - a}{2} = \frac{700.0 \times 10^{-6}\,\text{m} - 1.0 \times 10^{-6}\,\text{m}}{2} = 349.5\ \mu\text{m}$$

Now use the tangent function to find θ_2:

$$\tan \theta_2 = \frac{b}{t} = \frac{349.5\ \mu\text{m}}{1.20 \times 10^3\ \mu\text{m}} \quad \rightarrow \quad \theta_2 = 16.2°$$

Finally, use Snell's law to find θ_1:

$$n_1 \sin \theta_1 = n_2 \sin \theta_2$$

$$\sin \theta_1 = \frac{n_2 \sin \theta_2}{n_1} = \frac{1.55 \sin 16.2°}{1.00} = 0.432$$

$$\theta_1 = \sin^{-1}(0.433) = \boxed{25.6°}$$

· ·

REMARKS Despite its apparent complexity, the problem isn't that different from Example 22.2.

QUESTION 22.4 Suppose the plastic were replaced by a material with a higher index of refraction. How would the width of the beam at the information layer be affected? (a) It would remain the same. (b) It would decrease. (c) It would increase.

EXERCISE 22.4 Suppose you wish to redesign the system to decrease the initial width of the beam from 0.700 0 mm to 0.600 0 mm but leave the incident angle θ_1 and all other parameters the same as before, except the index of refraction for the plastic material (n_2) and the angle θ_2. What index of refraction should the plastic have?

ANSWER 1.79

22.4 Dispersion and Prisms

In Table 22.1 we presented values for the index of refraction of various materials. If we make careful measurements, however, we find that the index of refraction in anything but vacuum depends on the wavelength of light. The dependence of the index of refraction on wavelength is called **dispersion**. Figure 22.13 is a graphical representation of this variation in the index of refraction with wavelength. Because n is a function of wavelength, Snell's law indicates that **the angle of refraction made when light enters a material depends on the wavelength of the light**. As seen in the figure, the index of refraction for a material usually decreases with increasing wavelength. This means that violet light ($\lambda \cong 400$ nm) refracts more than red light ($\lambda \cong 650$ nm) when passing from air into a material.

To understand the effects of dispersion on light, consider what happens when light strikes a prism, as in Figure 22.14a. A ray of light of a single wavelength that is incident on the prism from the left emerges bent away from its original direction of travel by an angle δ, called the **angle of deviation**. Now suppose a beam of white light (a combination of all visible wavelengths) is incident on a prism. Because of dispersion, the different colors refract through different angles of deviation, as illustrated in Figure 22.14b, and the rays that emerge from the second face of the prism spread out in a series of colors known as a visible **spectrum**, as shown in Figure 22.15 on page 772. These colors, in order of decreasing wavelength, are red, orange, yellow, green, blue, and violet. Violet light deviates the most, red light the least, and the remaining colors in the visible spectrum fall between these extremes.

Figure 22.13 Variations of index of refraction in the visible spectrum with respect to vacuum wavelength for three materials.

Tip 22.3 Dispersion

Light of shorter wavelength, such as violet light, refracts more than light of longer wavelengths, such as red light.

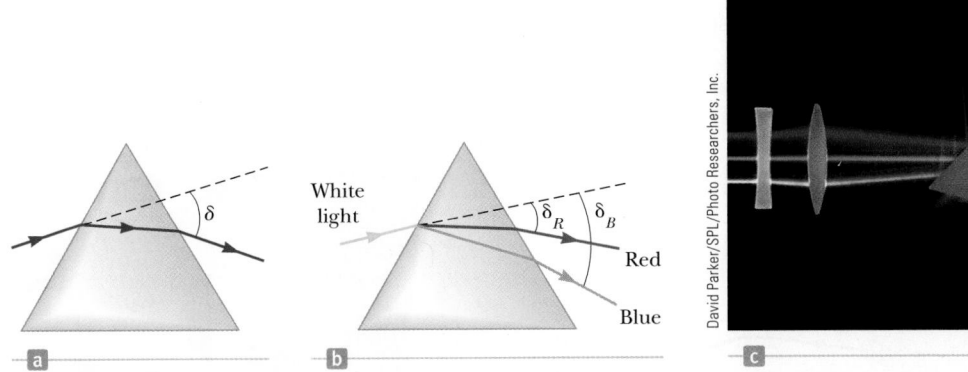

David Parker/SPL/Photo Researchers, Inc.

Figure 22.14 (a) A prism refracts a light ray and deviates the light through the angle δ. (b) When light is incident on a prism, the blue light is bent more than the red light. (c) Light of different colors passes through a prism and two lenses. Note that as the light passes through the prism, different wavelengths are refracted at different angles.

Figure 22.15 (a) Dispersion of white light by a prism. (b) White light enters a glass prism at the upper left.

Because *n* varies with wavelength, the prism disperses the white light into its various spectral components.

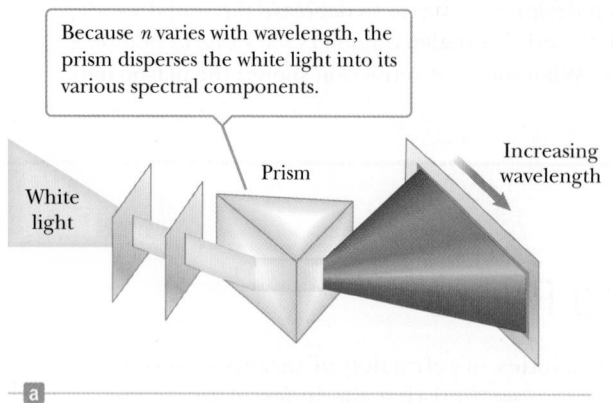

White light

Prism

Increasing wavelength

Different colors of light that pass through a prism are refracted at different angles because the index of refraction of the glass depends on wavelength. Violet light bends the most, red light the least.

David Parker/Science Photo Library/ Photo Researchers, Inc.

a

b

Prisms are often used in an instrument known as a **prism spectrometer**, the essential elements of which are shown in Figure 22.16a. This instrument is commonly used to study the wavelengths emitted by a light source, such as a sodium vapor lamp. Light from the source is sent through a narrow, adjustable slit and lens to produce a parallel, or collimated, beam. The light then passes through the prism and is dispersed into a spectrum. The refracted light is observed through a telescope. The experimenter sees different colored images of the slit through the eyepiece of the telescope. The telescope can be moved or the prism can be rotated to view the various wavelengths, which have different angles of deviation. Figure 22.16b shows one type of prism spectrometer used in undergraduate laboratories.

All hot, low-pressure gases emit their own characteristic spectra, so one use of a prism spectrometer is to identify gases. For example, sodium emits only two wavelengths in the visible spectrum: two closely spaced yellow lines. (The bright line-like images of the slit seen in a spectroscope are called *spectral lines*.) A gas emitting these, and only these, colors can be identified as sodium. Likewise, mercury vapor has its own characteristic spectrum, consisting of four prominent wavelengths— orange, green, blue, and violet lines—along with some wavelengths of lower intensity. The particular wavelengths emitted by a gas serve as "fingerprints" of that gas. Spectral analysis, which is the measurement of the wavelengths emitted or absorbed by a substance, is a powerful general tool in many scientific areas. As examples, chemists and biologists use infrared spectroscopy to identify molecules, astronomers use visible-light spectroscopy to identify elements on distant stars, and geologists use spectral analysis to identify minerals.

APPLICATION

Identifying Gases with a Spectrometer

Figure 22.16 (a) A diagram of a prism spectrometer. The colors in the spectrum are viewed through a telescope. (b) A prism spectrometer with interchangeable components.

Slit

Source

Telescope

Courtesy of PASCO Scientific

a

b

■ APPLYING PHYSICS 22.3 | Dispersion

When a beam of light enters a glass prism, which has non-parallel sides, the rainbow of color exiting the prism is a testimonial to the dispersion occurring in the glass. Suppose a beam of light enters a slab of material with parallel sides. When the beam exits the other side, traveling in the same direction as the original beam, is there any evidence of dispersion?

EXPLANATION Due to dispersion, light at the violet end of the spectrum exhibits a larger angle of refraction on entering the glass than light at the red end. All colors of light return to their original direction of propagation as they refract back out into the air. As a result, the outgoing beam is white. The net shift in the position of the violet light along the edge of the slab is larger than the shift of the red light, however, so one edge of the outgoing beam has a bluish tinge to it (it appears blue rather than violet because the eye is not very sensitive to violet light), whereas the other edge has a reddish tinge. This effect is indicated in Figure 22.17. The colored edges of the outgoing beam of white light are evidence of dispersion. ■

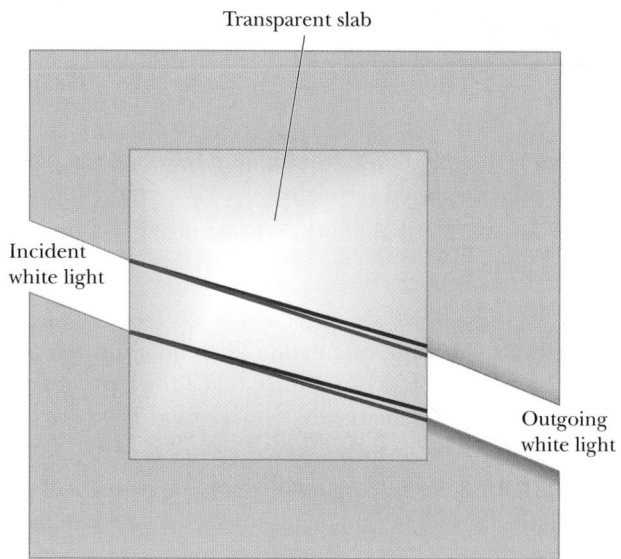

Figure 22.17 (Applying Physics 22.3)

■ EXAMPLE 22.5 | Light Through a Prism

GOAL Calculate the consequences of dispersion.

PROBLEM A beam of light is incident on a prism of a certain glass at an angle of $\theta_1 = 30.0°$, as shown in Figure 22.18. If the index of refraction of the glass for violet light is 1.80, find **(a)** θ_2, the angle of refraction at the air–glass interface, **(b)** ϕ_2, the angle of incidence at the glass–air interface, and **(c)** ϕ_1, the angle of refraction when the violet light exits the prism. **(d)** What is the value of Δy, the amount by which the violet light is displaced vertically?

STRATEGY This problem requires Snell's law to find the refraction angles and some elementary geometry and trigonometry based on Figure 22.18.

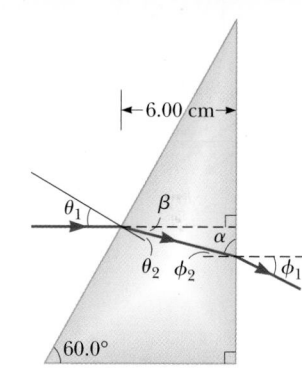

Figure 22.18
(Example 22.5)

. . . .

SOLUTION

(a) Find θ_2, the angle of refraction at the air–glass interface.

Use Snell's law to find the first angle of refraction:

$$n_1 \sin \theta_1 = \sin \theta_2 \quad \rightarrow \quad (1.00) \sin 30.0 = (1.80) \sin \theta_2$$

$$\theta_2 = \sin^{-1}\left(\frac{0.500}{1.80}\right) = \boxed{16.1°}$$

(b) Find ϕ_2, the angle of incidence at the glass–air interface.

Compute the angle β:

$$\beta = 30.0° - \theta_2 = 30.0° - 16.1° = 13.9°$$

Compute the angle α using the fact that the sum of the interior angles of a triangle equals 180°:

$$180° = 13.9° + 90° + \alpha \quad \rightarrow \quad \alpha = 76.1°$$

The incident angle ϕ_2 at the glass–air interface is complementary to α:

$$\phi_2 = 90° - \alpha = 90° - 76.1° = \boxed{13.9°}$$

(Continued)

(c) Find ϕ_1, the angle of refraction when the violet light exits the prism.

Apply Snell's law:

$$\phi_1 = \left(\frac{1}{n_1}\right) \sin^{-1}(n_2 \sin \phi_2)$$

$$= \left(\frac{1}{1.00}\right) \sin^{-1}[(1.80) \sin 13.9°] = \boxed{25.6°}$$

(d) What is the value of Δy, the amount by which the violet light is displaced vertically?

Use the tangent function to find the vertical displacement:

$$\tan \beta = \frac{\Delta y}{\Delta x} \rightarrow \Delta y = \Delta x \tan \beta$$

$$\Delta y = (6.00 \text{ cm}) \tan(13.9°) = \boxed{1.48 \text{ cm}}$$

REMARKS The same calculation for red light is left as an exercise. The violet light is bent more and displaced farther down the face of the prism. Notice that a theorem in geometry about parallel lines and the angles created by a transverse line give $\phi_2 = \beta$ immediately, which would have saved some calculation. In general, however, this tactic might not be available.

QUESTION 22.5 On passing through the prism, will yellow light bend through a larger angle or smaller angle than the violet light? (a) Yellow light bends through a larger angle. (b) Yellow light bends through a smaller angle. (c) The angles are the same.

EXERCISE 22.5 Repeat parts (a) through (d) of the example for red light passing through the prism, given that the index of refraction for red light is 1.72.

ANSWERS (a) 16.9° (b) 13.1° (c) 22.9° (d) 1.40 cm

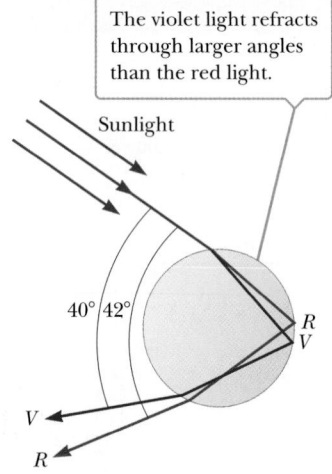

The violet light refracts through larger angles than the red light.

Sunlight

40° 42°

R
V

V

R

Active Figure 22.19
Refraction of sunlight by a spherical raindrop.

Figure 22.20 The formation of a rainbow seen by an observer standing with the Sun behind his back. (b) This photograph of a rainbow shows a distinct secondary rainbow with the colors reversed.

22.5 The Rainbow

The dispersion of light into a spectrum is demonstrated most vividly in nature through the formation of a rainbow, often seen by an observer positioned between the Sun and a rain shower. To understand how a rainbow is formed, consider Active Figure 22.19. A ray of light passing overhead strikes a drop of water in the atmosphere and is refracted and reflected as follows: It is first refracted at the front surface of the drop, with the violet light deviating the most and the red light the least. At the back surface of the drop, the light is reflected and returns to the front surface, where it again undergoes refraction as it moves from water into air. The rays leave the drop so that the angle between the incident white light and the returning violet ray is 40° and the angle between the white light and the returning red ray is 42°. This small angular difference between the returning rays causes us to see the bow as explained in the next paragraph.

Now consider an observer viewing a rainbow, as in Figure 22.20a. If a raindrop high in the sky is being observed, the red light returning from the drop can reach the observer because it is deviated the most, but the violet light passes over the

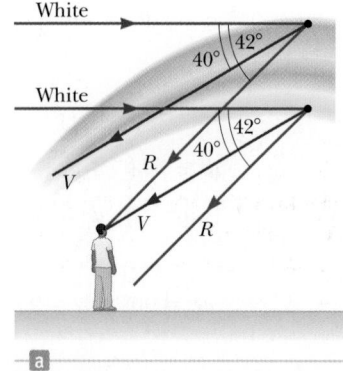

White

42°
40° 42°

White

42°
40°

R

V

V R

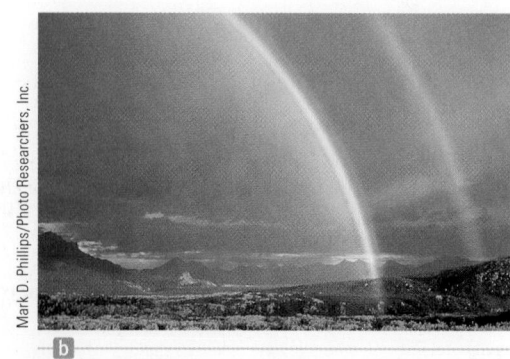

Mark D. Phillips/Photo Researchers, Inc.

a

b

observer because it is deviated the least. Hence, the observer sees this drop as being red. Similarly, a drop lower in the sky would direct violet light toward the observer and appear to be violet. (The red light from this drop would strike the ground and not be seen.) The remaining colors of the spectrum would reach the observer from raindrops lying between these two extreme positions. Figure 22.20b shows a beautiful rainbow and a secondary rainbow with its colors reversed.

22.6 Huygens' Principle

The laws of reflection and refraction can be deduced using a geometric method proposed by Huygens in 1678. Huygens assumed light is a form of wave motion rather than a stream of particles. He had no knowledge of the nature of light or of its electromagnetic character. Nevertheless, his simplified wave model is adequate for understanding many practical aspects of the propagation of light.

Huygens' principle is a geometric construction for determining at some instant the position of a new wave front from knowledge of the wave front that preceded it. (A wave front is a surface passing through those points of a wave which have the same phase and amplitude. For instance, a wave front could be a surface passing through the crests of waves.) In Huygens' construction, **all points on a given wave front are taken as point sources for the production of spherical secondary waves, called wavelets, that propagate in the forward direction with speeds characteristic of waves in that medium. After some time has elapsed, the new position of the wave front is the surface tangent to the wavelets.**

◀ Huygens' principle

Figure 22.21 illustrates two simple examples of Huygens' construction. First, consider a plane wave moving through free space, as in Figure 22.21a. At $t = 0$, the wave front is indicated by the plane labeled AA'. In Huygens' construction, each point on this wave front is considered a point source. For clarity, only a few points on AA' are shown. With these points as sources for the wavelets, we draw circles of radius $c \Delta t$, where c is the speed of light in vacuum and Δt is the period of propagation from one wave front to the next. The surface drawn tangent to these wavelets is the plane BB', which is parallel to AA'. In a similar manner, Figure 22.21b shows Huygens' construction for an outgoing spherical wave.

Huygens' Principle Applied to Reflection and Refraction

The laws of reflection and refraction were stated earlier in the chapter without proof. We now derive these laws using Huygens' principle. Figure 22.22a (page 776) illustrates the law of reflection. The line AA' represents a wave front of the incident light. As ray 3 travels from A' to C, ray 1 reflects from A and produces a spherical wavelet of radius AD. (Recall that the radius of a Huygens wavelet is $v \Delta t$.)

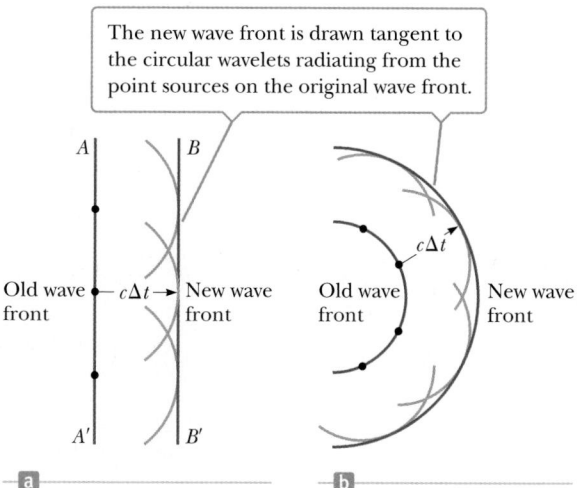

The new wave front is drawn tangent to the circular wavelets radiating from the point sources on the original wave front.

Figure 22.21 Huygens' constructions for (a) a plane wave propagating to the right and (b) a spherical wave.

Figure 22.22 (a) Huygens' construction for proving the law of reflection. (b) Triangle ADC is congruent to triangle $AA'C$.

Because the two wavelets having radii $A'C$ and AD are in the same medium, they have the same speed v, so $AD = A'C$. Meanwhile, the spherical wavelet centered at B has spread only half as far as the one centered at A because ray 2 strikes the surface later than ray 1.

From Huygens' principle, we find that the reflected wave front is CD, a line tangent to all the outgoing spherical wavelets. The remainder of our analysis depends on geometry, as summarized in Figure 22.22b. Note that the right triangles ADC and $AA'C$ are congruent because they have the same hypotenuse, AC, and because $AD = A'C$. From the figure, we have

$$\sin \theta_1 = \frac{A'C}{AC} \qquad \text{and} \qquad \sin \theta_1' = \frac{AD}{AC}$$

The right-hand sides are equal, so $\sin \theta = \sin \theta_1'$, and it follows that $\theta_1 = \theta_1'$, which is the law of reflection.

Huygens' principle and Figure 22.23a can be used to derive Snell's law of refraction. In the time interval Δt, ray 1 moves from A to B and ray 2 moves from A' to C. The radius of the outgoing spherical wavelet centered at A is equal to $v_2 \Delta t$. The distance $A'C$ is equal to $v_1 \Delta t$. Geometric considerations show that angle $A'AC$ equals θ_1 and angle ACB equals θ_2. From triangles $AA'C$ and ACB, we find that

$$\sin \theta_1 = \frac{v_1 \Delta t}{AC} \qquad \text{and} \qquad \sin \theta_2 = \frac{v_2 \Delta t}{AC}$$

If we divide the first equation by the second, we get

$$\frac{\sin \theta_1}{\sin \theta_2} = \frac{v_1}{v_2}$$

From Equation 22.4, though, we know that $v_1 = c/n_1$ and $v_2 = c/n_2$. Therefore,

$$\frac{\sin \theta_1}{\sin \theta_2} = \frac{c/n_1}{c/n_2} = \frac{n_2}{n_1}$$

and it follows that

$$n_1 \sin \theta_1 = n_2 \sin \theta_2$$

which is the law of refraction.

Figure 22.23 (a) Huygens' construction for proving the law of refraction. (b) Overhead view of a barrel rolling from concrete onto grass.

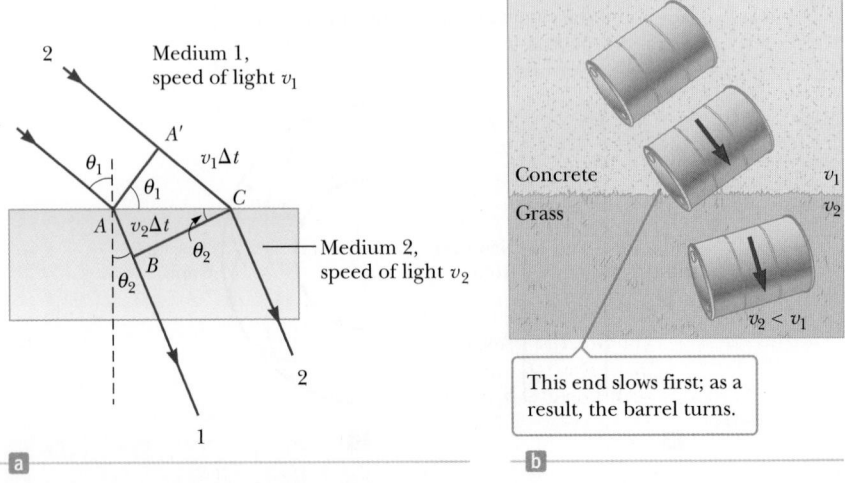

A mechanical analog of refraction is shown in Figure 22.23b. When the left end of the rolling barrel reaches the grass, it slows down, while the right end remains on the concrete and moves at its original speed. This difference in speeds causes the barrel to pivot, changing the direction of its motion.

22.7 Total Internal Reflection

An interesting effect called *total internal reflection* can occur when light encounters the boundary between a medium with a *higher* index of refraction and one with a *lower* index of refraction. Consider a light beam traveling in medium 1 and meeting the boundary between medium 1 and medium 2, where n_1 is greater than n_2 (Active Fig. 22.24). Possible directions of the beam are indicated by rays 1 through 5. Note that the refracted rays are bent away from the normal because n_1 is greater than n_2. At some particular angle of incidence θ_c, called the **critical angle**, the refracted light ray moves parallel to the boundary so that $\theta_2 = 90°$ (Active Fig. 22.24b). *For angles of incidence greater than θ_c, the beam is entirely reflected at the boundary, as is ray 5 in Active Figure 22.24a. This ray is reflected as though it had struck a perfectly reflecting surface. It and all rays like it obey the law of reflection: the angle of incidence equals the angle of reflection.

We can use Snell's law to find the critical angle. When $\theta_1 = \theta_c$ and $\theta_2 = 90°$, Snell's law (Eq. 22.8) gives

$$n_1 \sin \theta_c = n_2 \sin 90° = n_2$$

$$\boxed{\sin \theta_c = \frac{n_2}{n_1}} \qquad \text{for } n_1 > n_2 \qquad [22.9]$$

Equation 22.9 can be used only when n_1 is greater than n_2 because **total internal reflection occurs only when light is incident on the boundary of a medium having a lower index of refraction than the medium in which it's traveling.** If n_1 were less than n_2, Equation 22.9 would give $\sin \theta_c > 1$, which is an absurd result because the sine of an angle can never be greater than 1.

When medium 2 is air, the critical angle is small for substances with large indices of refraction, such as diamond, where $n = 2.42$ and $\theta_c = 24.0°$. By comparison,

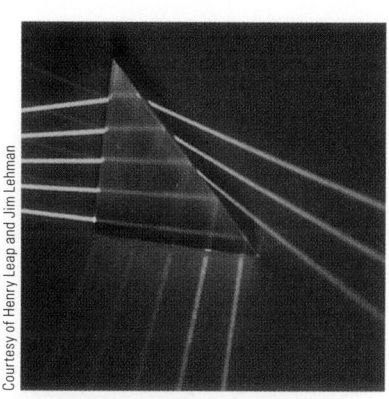

This photograph shows nonparallel light rays entering a glass prism. The bottom two rays undergo total internal reflection at the longest side of the prism. The top three rays are refracted at the longest side as they leave the prism.

Courtesy of Henry Leap and Jim Lehman

Active Figure 22.24
(a) Rays from a medium with index of refraction n_1 travel to a medium with index of refraction n_2, where $n_1 > n_2$. (b) Ray 4 is singled out.

As the angle of incidence θ_1 increases, the angle of refraction θ_2 increases until θ_2 is 90° (ray 4). The dashed line indicates that no energy actually propagates in this direction.

The angle of incidence producing an angle of refraction equal to 90° is the *critical angle θ_c*. At this angle of incidence, all the energy of the incident light is reflected.

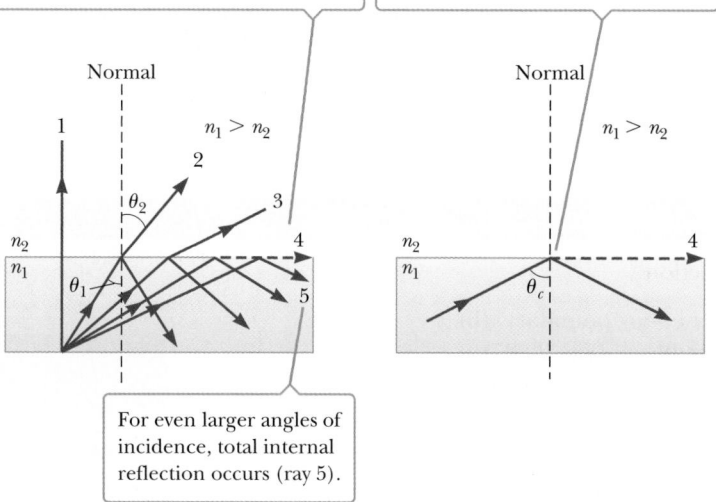

For even larger angles of incidence, total internal reflection occurs (ray 5).

a   b

Figure 22.25 Internal reflection in a prism. (a) The ray is deviated by 90°. (b) The direction of the ray is reversed. (c) Two prisms used as a periscope.

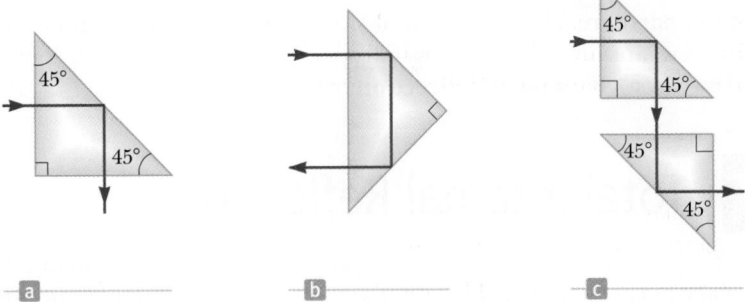

a

b

c

for crown glass, $n = 1.52$ and $\theta_c = 41.0°$. This property, combined with proper faceting, causes a diamond to sparkle brilliantly.

APPLICATION

Submarine Periscopes

A prism and the phenomenon of total internal reflection can alter the direction of travel of a light beam. Figure 22.25 illustrates two such possibilities. In one case the light beam is deflected by 90° (Fig. 22.25a), and in the second case the path of the beam is reversed (Fig. 22.25b). A common application of total internal reflection is a submarine periscope. In this device two prisms are arranged as in Figure 22.25c so that an incident beam of light follows the path shown and the user can "see around corners."

■ **APPLYING PHYSICS 22.4**   **Total Internal Reflection and Dispersion**

A beam of white light is incident on the curved edge of a semicircular piece of glass, as shown in Figure 22.26. The light enters the curved surface along the normal, so it shows no refraction. It encounters the straight side of the glass at the center of curvature of the curved side and refracts into the air. The incoming beam is moved clockwise (so that the angle θ increases) such that the beam always enters along the normal to the curved side and encounters the straight side at the center of curvature of the curved side. Why does the refracted beam become redder as it approaches a direction parallel to the straight side?

EXPLANATION When the outgoing beam approaches the direction parallel to the straight side, the incident angle is approaching the critical angle for total internal reflection. Dispersion occurs as the light passes out of the glass. The index of refraction for light at the violet end of the visible spectrum is larger than at the red end. As a result, as the outgoing beam approaches the straight side, the violet light undergoes total internal reflection, followed by the other colors. The red light is the last to undergo total internal reflection, so just before the outgoing light disappears, it's composed of light from the red end of the visible spectrum. ■

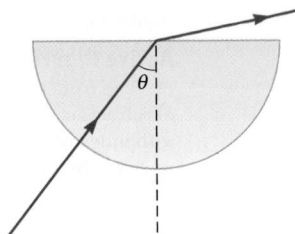

Figure 22.26 (Applying Physics 22.4)

■ **EXAMPLE 22.6**   **A View from the Fish's Eye**

GOAL Apply the concept of total internal reflection.

PROBLEM (a) Find the critical angle for a water–air boundary. (b) Use the result of part (a) to predict what a fish will see (Fig. 22.27) if it looks up toward the water surface at angles of 40.0°, 48.6°, and 60.0°.

STRATEGY After finding the critical angle by substitution, use that the path of a light ray is reversible: at a given angle, wherever a light beam can go is also where a light beam can come from, along the same path.

Figure 22.27 (Example 22.6) A fish looks upward toward the water's surface.

SOLUTION

(a) Find the critical angle for a water–air boundary.

Substitute into Equation 22.9 to find the critical angle:

$$\sin \theta_c = \frac{n_2}{n_1} = \frac{1.00}{1.333} = 0.750$$

$$\theta_c = \sin^{-1}(0.750) = \boxed{48.6°}$$

(b) Predict what a fish will see if it looks up toward the water surface at angles of 40.0°, 48.6°, and 60.0°.

At an angle of 40.0°, a beam of light from underwater will be refracted at the surface and enter the air above. Because the path of a light ray is reversible (Snell's law works both going and coming), light from above can follow the same path and be perceived by the fish. At an angle of 48.6°, the critical angle for water, light from underwater is bent so that it travels along the surface. So light following the same path in reverse can reach the fish only by skimming along the water surface before being refracted toward the fish's eye. At angles greater than the critical angle of 48.6°, a beam of light shot toward the surface will be completely reflected down toward the bottom of the pool. Reversing the path, the fish sees a reflection of some object on the bottom.

QUESTION 22.6 If the water is replaced by a transparent fluid with a higher index of refraction, is the critical angle of the fluid–air boundary (a) larger, (b) smaller, or (c) the same as for water?

EXERCISE 22.6 Suppose a layer of oil with $n = 1.50$ coats the surface of the water. What is the critical angle for total internal reflection for light traveling in the oil layer and encountering the oil–water boundary?

ANSWER 62.7°

Fiber Optics

Another interesting application of total internal reflection is the use of solid glass or transparent plastic rods to "pipe" light from one place to another. As indicated in Figure 22.28, light is confined to traveling within the rods, even around gentle curves, as a result of successive internal reflections. Such a light pipe can be quite flexible if thin fibers are used rather than thick rods. If a bundle of parallel fibers is used to construct an optical transmission line, images can be transferred from one point to another.

Very little light intensity is lost in these fibers as a result of reflections on the sides. Any loss of intensity is due essentially to reflections from the two ends and absorption by the fiber material. Fiber-optic devices are particularly useful for viewing images produced at inaccessible locations. Physicians often use fiber-optic cables to aid in the diagnosis and correction of certain medical problems without the intrusion of major surgery. For example, a fiber-optic cable can be threaded through the esophagus and into the stomach to look for ulcers. In this application the cable consists of two fiber-optic lines: one to transmit a beam of light into the stomach for illumination and the other to allow the light to be transmitted out of the stomach. The resulting image can, in some cases, be viewed directly by the physician, but more often is displayed on a television monitor or saved in digital form. In a similar way, fiber-optic cables can be used to examine the colon or to help physicians perform surgery without the need for large incisions.

The field of fiber optics has revolutionized the entire communications industry. Billions of kilometers of optical fiber have been installed in the United States to carry high-speed Internet traffic, radio and television signals, and telephone calls. The fibers can carry much higher volumes of telephone calls and other forms of communication than electrical wires because of the higher frequency of the infrared light used to carry the information on optical fibers. Optical fibers are also preferable to copper wires because they are insulators and don't pick up stray electric and magnetic fields or electronic "noise."

Figure 22.28 Light travels in a curved transparent rod by multiple internal reflections.

BIO APPLICATION

Fiber Optics in Medical Diagnosis and Surgery

APPLICATION

Fiber Optics in Telecommunications

(*Left*) Strands of glass optical fibers are used to carry voice, video, and data signals in telecommunication networks. (*Right*) A bundle of optical fibers is illuminated by a laser.

■ APPLYING PHYSICS 22.5 | Design of an Optical Fiber

An optical fiber consists of a transparent core surrounded by cladding, which is a material with a lower index of refraction than the core (Fig. 22.29). A cone of angles, called the acceptance cone, is at the entrance to the fiber. Incoming light at angles within this cone will be transmitted through

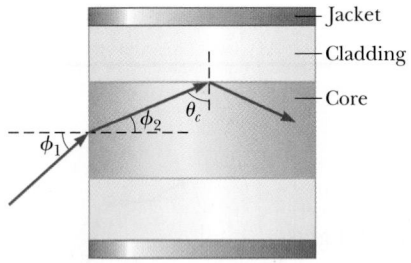

Figure 22.29 (Applying Physics 22.5)

the fiber, whereas light entering the core from angles outside the cone will not be transmitted. The figure shows a light ray entering the fiber just within the acceptance cone and undergoing total internal reflection at the interface between the core and the cladding. If it is technologically difficult to produce light so that it enters the fiber from a small range of angles, how could you adjust the indices of refraction of the core and cladding to increase the size of the acceptance cone? Would you design the indices to be farther apart or closer together?

EXPLANATION The acceptance cone would become larger if the critical angle (θ_c in the figure) could be made smaller. This adjustment can be done by making the index of refraction of the cladding material smaller so that the indices of refraction of the core and cladding material would be farther apart. ■

■ SUMMARY

22.1 The Nature of Light

Light has a dual nature. In some experiments it acts like a wave, in others like a particle, called a photon by Einstein. The energy of a photon is proportional to its frequency,

$$E = hf \qquad [22.1]$$

where $h = 6.63 \times 10^{-34}$ J · s is *Planck's constant*.

22.2 Reflection and Refraction

In the reflection of light off a flat, smooth surface, the angle of incidence, θ_1, with respect to a line perpendicular to the surface is equal to the angle of reflection, θ_1':

$$\theta_1' = \theta_1 \qquad [22.2]$$

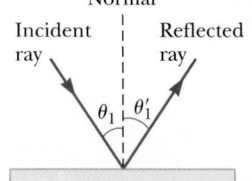

The wave under reflection model.

Light that passes into a transparent medium is bent at the boundary and is said to be *refracted*. The angle of refraction is the angle the ray makes with respect to a line perpendicular to the surface after it has entered the new medium.

22.3 The Law of Refraction

The **index of refraction** of a material, n, is defined as

$$n = \frac{c}{v} \qquad [22.4]$$

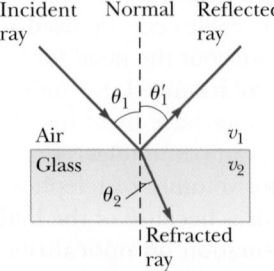

The wave under refraction model.

where c is the speed of light in a vacuum and v is the speed of light in the material. The index of refraction of a material is also

$$n = \frac{\lambda_0}{\lambda_n} \qquad [22.7]$$

where λ_0 is the wavelength of the light in vacuum and λ_n is its wavelength in the material.

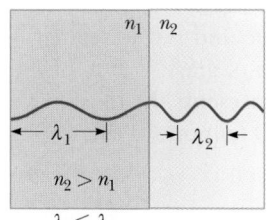

When entering a material with higher index of refraction, the wavelength of light is reduced.

The **law of refraction**, or **Snell's law**, states that

$$n_1 \sin \theta_1 = n_2 \sin \theta_2 \qquad [22.8]$$

where n_1 and n_2 are the indices of refraction in the two media. The incident ray, the reflected ray, the refracted ray, and the normal to the surface all lie in the same plane.

22.4 Dispersion and Prisms

22.5 The Rainbow

The index of refraction of a material depends on the wavelength of the incident light, an effect called *dispersion*. Light at the violet end of the spectrum exhibits a larger angle of refraction on entering glass than light at the red end. Rainbows are a consequence of dispersion.

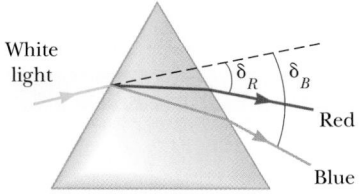

Due to dispersion, blue light is bent more than red light.

22.6 Huygens' Principle

Huygens' principle states that all points on a wave front are point sources for the production of spherical secondary waves called wavelets. These wavelets propagate forward at a speed characteristic of waves in a particular medium. After some time has elapsed, the new position of the wave front is the surface tangent to the wavelets. This principle can be used to deduce the laws of reflection and refraction.

22.7 Total Internal Reflection

When light propagating in a medium with index of refraction n_1 is incident on the boundary of a region with index of refraction n_2, and $n_1 > n_2$, then total internal reflection can occur if the angle of incidence equals or exceeds a **critical angle** θ_c given by

$$\sin \theta_c = \frac{n_2}{n_1} \qquad (n_1 > n_2) \qquad [22.9]$$

Total internal reflection is used in the optical fibers that carry data at high speed around the world.

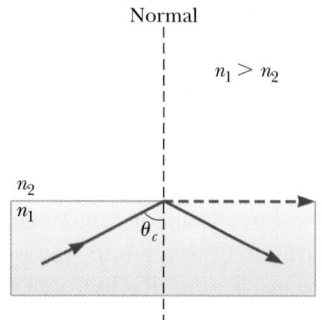

A ray undergoes total internal reflection at angles equal to or greater than the critical angle.

■ MULTIPLE-CHOICE QUESTIONS

WebAssign The multiple-choice questions in this chapter may be assigned online in Enhanced WebAssign.

1. A source emits monochromatic light of wavelength 495 nm in air. When the light passes through a liquid, its wavelength reduces to 434 nm. What is the liquid's index of refraction? (a) 1.26 (b) 1.49 (c) 1.14 (d) 1.33 (e) 2.03

2. Carbon disulfide ($n = 1.63$) is poured into a container made of crown glass ($n = 1.52$). What is the critical angle for total internal reflection of a light ray in the liquid when it is incident on the liquid-to-glass surface? (a) 89.2° (b) 68.8° (c) 21.2° (d) 1.07° (e) 43.0°

3. How many 800-nm photons does it take to have the same total energy as four 200-nm photons? (a) 1 (b) 2 (c) 4 (d) 8 (e) 16

4. A light ray travels through two parallel slabs having different indices of refraction as in Figure MCQ22.4.

Figure MCQ22.4

The rays shown are only the refracted rays. Which of the following choices is true regarding the relative size of the indices of refraction? (a) $n_1 \geq n_2$ (b) $n_1 \leq n_2$ (c) $n_1 = n_2$ (d) $n_1 > n_2$ (e) $n_1 < n_2$

5. Light traveling in a medium of index of refraction n_1 is incident on another medium having an index of refraction n_2. Under which of the following conditions can total internal reflection occur at the interface of the two media? (a) The indices of refraction have the relation $n_2 > n_1$. (b) The indices of refraction have the relation $n_1 > n_2$. (c) Light travels slower in the second medium than in the first. (d) The angle of incidence is less than the critical angle. (e) The angle of incidence must equal the refraction angle.

6. Light can travel from air into water. Some possible paths for the light ray in the water are shown in Figure MCQ22.6. Which path will the light most likely follow? (a) A (b) B (c) C (d) D (e) E

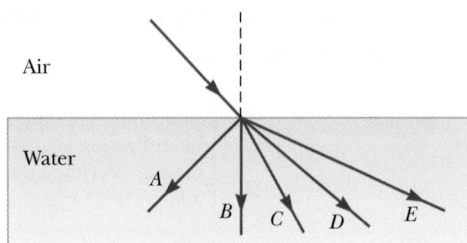

Figure MCQ22.6

7. The index of refraction for water is about 4/3. What happens to light when it travels from air into water? (a) Its speed increases to $4c/3$, and its frequency decreases. (b) Its speed decreases to $3c/4$, and its

wavelength decreases by a factor of 3/4. (c) Its speed decreases to $3c/4$, and its wavelength increases by a factor of 4/3. (d) Its speed and frequency remain the same. (e) Its speed decreases to $3c/4$, and its frequency increases.

8. Which color light is bent the most when entering crown glass from air at some incident angle θ with respect to the normal? (a) violet (b) blue (c) green (d) yellow (e) red

9. A light ray containing both blue and red wavelengths is incident at an angle on a slab of glass. Which of the sketches in Figure MCQ22.9 represents the most likely outcome? (a) A (b) B (c) C (d) D (e) none of these

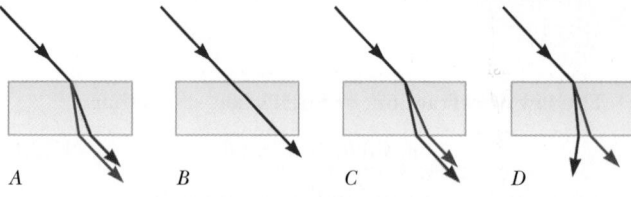

Figure MCQ22.9

10. A light ray travels from vacuum into a slab of material with index of refraction n_1 with incident angle θ. It subsequently passes into a second slab of material with index of refraction n_2 before passing back into vacuum again. The surfaces of the different materials are all parallel to one another. As the light exits the second slab, what can be said of the final angle ϕ that the light makes with the normal? (a) $\phi > \theta$ (b) $\phi < \theta$ (c) $\phi = \theta$ (d) The angle depends on the magnitudes of n_1 and n_2. (e) The angle depends on the wavelengths of the light.

■ CONCEPTUAL QUESTIONS

WebAssign The conceptual questions in this chapter may be assigned online in Enhanced WebAssign.

1. Why does the arc of a rainbow appear with red on top and violet on the bottom?

2. A ray of light is moving from a material having a high index of refraction into a material with a lower index of refraction. (a) Is the ray bent toward the normal or away from it? (b) If the wavelength is 600 nm in the material with the high index of refraction, is it greater, smaller, or the same in the material with the lower index of refraction? (c) How does the frequency change as the light moves between the two materials? Does it increase, decrease, or remain the same?

3. A light ray travels through three parallel slabs having different indices of refraction as in Figure CQ22.3. The rays shown are only the refracted rays. Rank the materials according to the size of their indices of refraction, from largest to smallest.

Figure CQ22.3

4. Under what conditions is a mirage formed? On a hot day, what are we seeing when we observe a mirage of a water puddle on the road?

5. Explain why a diamond loses most of its sparkle when submerged in carbon disulfide.

6. A type of mirage called a *pingo* is often observed in Alaska. Pingos occur when the light from a small hill passes to an observer by a path that takes the light over a body of water warmer than the air. What is seen is the

hill and an inverted image directly below it. Explain how these mirages are formed.

7. In dispersive materials, the angle of refraction for a light ray depends on the wavelength of the light. Does the angle of reflection from the surface of the material depend on the wavelength? Why or why not?

8. The level of water in a clear, colorless glass can easily be observed with the naked eye. The level of liquid helium in a clear glass vessel is extremely difficult to see with the naked eye. Explain. *Hint:* The index of refraction of liquid helium is close to that of air.

9. Suppose you are told that only two colors of light (X and Y) are sent through a glass prism and that X is bent more than Y. Which color travels more slowly in the prism?

10. Is it possible to have total internal reflection for light incident from air on water? Explain.

11. Figure CQ22.11 shows a pencil partially immersed in a cup of water. Why does the pencil appear to be bent?

Figure CQ22.11

12. Try this simple experiment on your own. Take two opaque cups, place a coin at the bottom of each cup near the edge, and fill one cup with water. Next, view the cups at some angle from the side so that the coin in water is just visible as shown on the left in Figure CQ22.12. Notice that the coin in air is not visible as shown on the right in Figure CQ22.12. Explain this observation.

Figure CQ22.12

13. Why do astronomers looking at distant galaxies talk about looking backward in time?

■ PROBLEMS

WebAssign The problems in this chapter may be assigned online in Enhanced WebAssign. Selected problems also have Watch It video solutions.

1. denotes straightforward problem; 2. denotes intermediate problem;

3. denotes challenging problem

1. denotes full solution available in *Student Solutions Manual/Study Guide*

1. denotes problems most often assigned in Enhanced WebAssign

BIO denotes biomedical problems

GP denotes guided problems

M denotes Master It tutorial available in Enhanced WebAssign

Q|C denotes asking for quantitative and conceptual reasoning

S denotes symbolic reasoning problem

22.1 The Nature of Light

1. During the Apollo XI Moon landing, a retroreflecting panel was erected on the Moon's surface. The speed of light can be found by measuring the time it takes a laser beam to travel from Earth, reflect from the panel, and return to Earth. If this interval is found to be 2.51 s, what is the measured speed of light? Take the center-to-center distance from Earth to the Moon to be 3.84×10^8 m. Assume the Moon is directly overhead and do not neglect the sizes of Earth and the Moon.

2. **Q|C** (a) What is the energy in joules of an x-ray photon with wavelength 1.00×10^{-10} m? (b) Convert the energy to electron volts. (c) If more penetrating x-rays are desired, should the wavelength be increased or decreased? (d) Should the frequency be increased or decreased?

3. [M] Find the energy of (a) a photon having a frequency of 5.00×10^{17} Hz and (b) a photon having a wavelength of 3.00×10^2 nm. Express your answers in units of electron volts, noting that 1 eV $= 1.60 \times 10^{-19}$ J.

4. [QC] (a) Calculate the wavelength of light in vacuum that has a frequency of 5.45×10^{14} Hz. (b) What is its wavelength in benzene? (c) Calculate the energy of one photon of such light in vacuum. Express the answer in electron volts. (d) Does the energy of the photon change when it enters the benzene? Explain.

5. Find the speed of light in (a) water, (b) crown glass, and (c) diamond.

6. [S] (a) Find a symbolic expression for the wavelength λ of a photon in terms of its energy E, Planck's constant h, and the speed of light c. (b) What does the equation say about the wavelengths of higher-energy photons?

7. A ray of light travels from air into another medium, making an angle of $\theta_1 = 45.0°$ with the normal as in Figure P22.7. Find the angle of refraction θ_2 if the second medium is (a) fused quartz, (b) carbon disulfide, and (c) water.

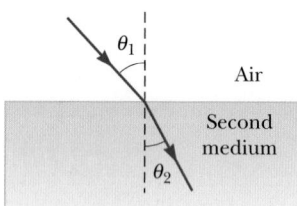

Figure P22.7

22.2 Reflection and Refraction

22.3 The Law of Refraction

8. The two mirrors in Figure P22.8 meet at a right angle. The beam of light in the vertical plane P strikes mirror 1 as shown. (a) Determine the distance the reflected light beam travels before striking mirror 2. (b) In what direction does the light beam travel after being reflected from mirror 2?

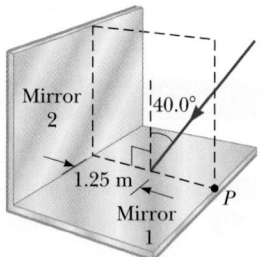

Figure P22.8

9. An underwater scuba diver sees the Sun at an apparent angle of $45.0°$ from the vertical. What is the actual direction of the Sun?

10. Two plane mirrors are at right angles to each other as shown by the side view in Figure P22.10. A light ray is incident on mirror 1 at an angle θ with the vertical. Using the law of reflection and geometry, show that after the ray is reflected off of both mirrors, the outgoing reflected ray is parallel to the incident ray.

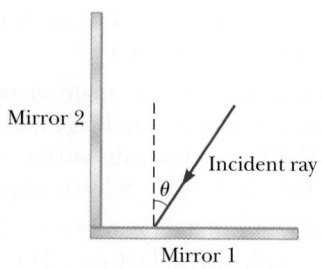

Figure P22.10

11. A laser beam is incident at an angle of $30.0°$ to the vertical onto a solution of corn syrup in water. If the beam is refracted to $19.24°$ to the vertical, (a) what is the index of refraction of the syrup solution? Suppose the light is red, with wavelength 632.8 nm in a vacuum. Find its (b) wavelength, (c) frequency, and (d) speed in the solution.

12. Light containing wavelengths of 400 nm, 500 nm, and 650 nm is incident from air on a block of crown glass at an angle of $25.0°$. (a) Are all colors refracted alike, or is one color bent more than the others? (b) Calculate the angle of refraction in each case to verify your answer.

13. A ray of light is incident on the surface of a block of clear ice at an angle of $40.0°$ with the normal. Part of the light is reflected, and part is refracted. Find the angle between the reflected and refracted light.

14. Two plane mirrors are at an angle of $\theta_1 = 50.0°$ with each other as in the side view shown in Figure P22.14. If a horizontal ray is incident on mirror 1, at what angle θ_2 does the outgoing reflected ray make with the surface of mirror 2?

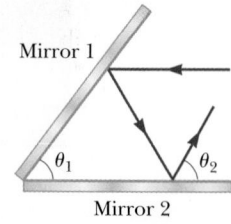

Figure P22.14

15. The light emitted by a helium–neon laser has a wavelength of 632.8 nm in air. As the light travels from air into zircon, find its (a) speed, (b) wavelength, and (c) frequency, all in the zircon.

16. Figure P22.16 shows a light ray traveling in a slab of crown glass surrounded by air. The ray is incident on the right surface at an angle of $55°$ with the normal and then reflects from points A, B, and C. (a) At which of these points does part of the ray enter the air? (b) If the glass slab is surrounded by carbon disulfide, at which point does part of the ray enter the carbon disulfide?

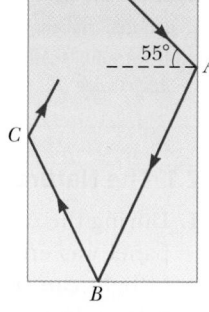

Figure P22.16

17. How many times will the incident beam shown in Figure P22.17 be reflected by each of the parallel mirrors?

Figure P22.17

18. QC A ray of light strikes a flat, 2.00-cm-thick block of glass ($n = 1.50$) at an angle of 30.0° with respect to the normal (Fig. P22.18). (a) Find the angle of refraction at the top surface. (b) Find the angle of incidence at the bottom surface and the refracted angle. (c) Find the lateral distance d by which the light beam is shifted. (d) Calculate the speed of light in the glass and (e) the time required for the light to pass through the glass block. (f) Is the travel time through the block affected by the angle of incidence? Explain.

Figure P22.18

19. M The light beam shown in Figure P22.19 makes an angle of 20.0° with the normal line NN' in the linseed oil. Determine the angles θ and θ'. (The refractive index for linseed oil is 1.48.)

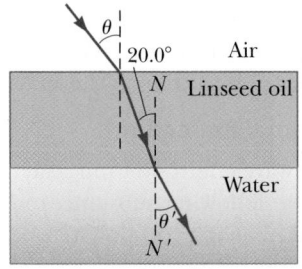

Figure P22.19

20. A laser beam is incident on a 45°–45°–90° prism perpendicular to one of its faces, as shown in Figure P22.20. The transmitted beam that exits the hypotenuse of the prism makes an angle of $\theta = 15.0°$ with the direction of the incident beam. Find the index of refraction of the prism.

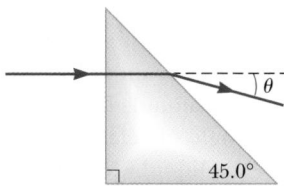

Figure P22.20

21. A block of crown glass is immersed in water as in Figure P22.21. A light ray is incident on the top face at an angle of $\theta_1 = 42.0°$ with the normal and exits the block at point P. (a) Find the vertical distance y from the top

of the block to P. (b) Find the angle of refraction θ_2 of the light ray leaving the block at P.

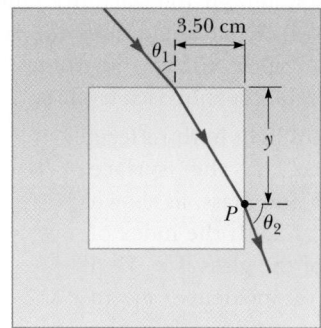

Figure P22.21

22. BIO A narrow beam of ultrasonic waves reflects off the liver tumor in Figure P22.22. If the speed of the wave is 10.0% less in the liver than in the surrounding medium, determine the depth of the tumor.

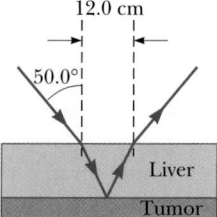

Figure P22.22

23. S A person looking into an empty container is able to see the far edge of the container's bottom, as shown in Figure P22.23a. The height of the container is h, and its width is d. When the container is completely filled with a fluid of index of refraction n and viewed from the same angle, the person can see the center of a coin at the middle of the container's bottom, as shown in Figure P22.23b. (a) Show that the ratio h/d is given by

$$\frac{h}{d} = \sqrt{\frac{n^2 - 1}{4 - n^2}}$$

(b) Assuming the container has a width of 8.00 cm and is filled with water, use the expression above to find the height of the container.

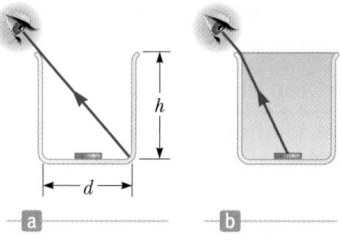

Figure P22.23

24. GP A submarine is 3.00×10^2 m horizontally from shore and 1.00×10^2 m beneath the surface of the water. A laser beam is sent from the submarine so that the beam strikes the surface of the water 2.10×10^2 m from the shore. A building stands on the shore, and the laser beam hits a target at the top of the building. The goal is to find the height of the target above sea level. (a) Draw a diagram of the situation, identifying the two triangles that are important to finding the solution. (b) Find the angle of incidence of the beam striking the water–air interface. (c) Find the angle of refraction. (d) What angle does the refracted beam make with respect to the horizontal? (e) Find the height of the target above sea level.

25. **S** A beam of light both reflects and refracts at the surface between air and glass, as shown in Figure P22.25. If the index of refraction of the glass is n_g, find the angle of incidence, θ_1, in the air that would result in the reflected ray and the refracted ray being perpendicular to each other. *Hint:* Remember the identity $\sin(90° - \theta) = \cos\theta$.

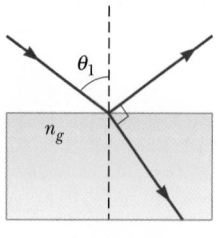

Figure P22.25

26. Figure P22.26 shows a light ray incident on a series of slabs having different refractive indices, where $n_1 < n_2 < n_3 < n_4$. Notice that the path of the ray steadily bends toward the normal. If the variation in n were continuous, the path would form a smooth curve. Use this idea and a ray diagram to explain why you can see the Sun at sunset after it has fallen below the horizon.

Figure P22.26

27. **M** An opaque cylindrical tank with an open top has a diameter of 3.00 m and is completely filled with water. When the afternoon Sun reaches an angle of 28.0° above the horizon, sunlight ceases to illuminate the bottom of the tank. How deep is the tank?

22.4 Dispersion and Prisms

28. A certain kind of glass has an index of refraction of 1.650 for blue light of wavelength 430 nm and an index of 1.615 for red light of wavelength 680 nm. If a beam containing these two colors is incident at an angle of 30.00° on a piece of this glass, what is the angle between the two beams inside the glass?

29. The index of refraction for red light in water is 1.331 and that for blue light is 1.340. If a ray of white light enters the water at an angle of incidence of 83.00°, what are the underwater angles of refraction for the (a) blue and (b) red components of the light?

30. The index of refraction for crown glass is 1.512 at a wavelength of 660 nm (red), whereas its index of refraction is 1.530 at a wavelength of 410 nm (violet). If both wavelengths are incident on a slab of crown glass at the same angle of incidence, 60.0°, what is the angle of refraction for each wavelength?

31. A light beam containing red and violet wavelengths is incident on a slab of quartz at an angle of incidence of 50.00°. The index of refraction of quartz is 1.455 at 660 nm (red light), and its index of refraction is 1.468 at 410 nm (violet light). Find the dispersion of the slab, which is defined as the difference in the angles of refraction for the two wavelengths.

32. The index of refraction for violet light in silica flint glass is 1.66 and that for red light is 1.62. What is the angular dispersion of visible light passing through an equilateral prism of apex angle 60.0° if the angle of incidence is 50.0°? (See Fig. P22.32.)

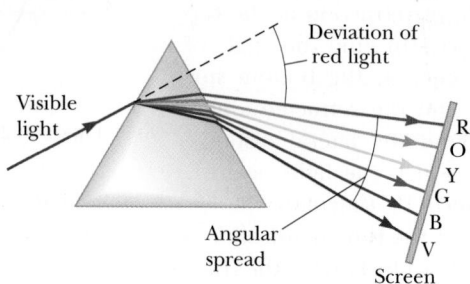

Figure P22.32

33. **M** A ray of light strikes the midpoint of one face of an equiangular (60°–60°–60°) glass prism ($n = 1.5$) at an angle of incidence of 30°. (a) Trace the path of the light ray through the glass and find the angles of incidence and refraction at each surface. (b) If a small fraction of light is also reflected at each surface, what are the angles of reflection at the surfaces?

22.7 Total Internal Reflection

34. For light of wavelength 589 nm, calculate the critical angles for the following substances when surrounded by air: (a) fused quartz, (b) polystyrene, and (c) sodium chloride.

35. Repeat Problem 34, but this time assume the quartz, polystyrene, and sodium chloride are surrounded by water.

36. **M** A beam of light is incident from air on the surface of a liquid. If the angle of incidence is 30.0° and the angle of refraction is 22.0°, find the critical angle for the liquid when surrounded by air.

37. A plastic light pipe has an index of refraction of 1.53. For total internal reflection, what is the minimum angle of incidence if the pipe is in (a) air and (b) water?

38. Determine the maximum angle θ for which the light rays incident on the end of the light pipe in Figure P22.38 are

Figure P22.38

subject to total internal reflection along the walls of the pipe. Assume the light pipe has an index of refraction of 1.36 and the outside medium is air.

39. A light ray is incident normally to the long face (the hypotenuse) of a 45°–45°–90° prism surrounded by air, as shown in Figure 22.26b. Calculate the minimum index of refraction of the prism for which the ray will totally internally reflect at each of the two sides making the right angle.

40. **Q|C** A beam of laser light with wavelength 612 nm is directed through a slab of glass having index of refraction 1.78. (a) For what minimum incident angle would a ray of light undergo total internal reflection? (b) If a layer of water is placed over the glass, what is the minimum angle of incidence on the glass–water interface that will result in total internal reflection at the water–air interface? (c) Does the thickness of the water layer or glass affect the result? (d) Does the index of refraction of the intervening layer affect the result?

41. A room contains air in which the speed of sound is 343 m/s. The walls of the room are made of concrete, in which the speed of sound is 1 850 m/s. (a) Find the critical angle for total internal reflection of sound at the concrete–air boundary. (b) In which medium must the sound be traveling in order to undergo total internal reflection? (c) "A bare concrete wall is a highly efficient mirror for sound." Give evidence for or against this statement.

42. **GP** **Q|C** Consider a light ray traveling between air and a diamond cut in the shape shown in Figure P22.42. (a) Find the critical angle for total internal reflection for light in the diamond incident on the interface

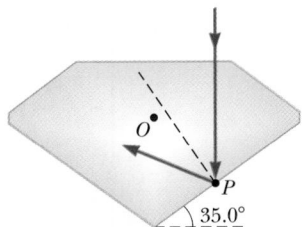
Figure P22.42

between the diamond and the outside air. (b) Consider the light ray incident normally on the top surface of the diamond as shown in Figure P22.42. Show that the light traveling toward point P in the diamond is totally reflected. (c) If the diamond is immersed in water, find the critical angle at the diamond–water interface? (d) When the diamond is immersed in water, does the light ray entering the top surface in Figure P22.42 undergo total internal reflection at P? Explain. (e) If the light ray entering the diamond remains vertical as shown in Figure P22.42, which way should the diamond in the water be rotated about an axis perpendicular to the page through O so that light will exit the diamond at P? (f) At what angle of rotation in part (e) will light first exit the diamond at point P?

43. The light beam in Figure P22.43 strikes surface 2 at the critical angle. Determine the angle of incidence, θ_1.

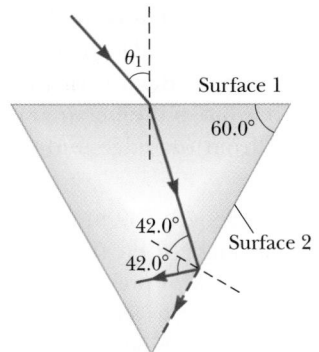
Figure P22.43

44. A jewel thief hides a diamond by placing it on the bottom of a public swimming pool. He places a circular raft on the surface of the water directly above and centered over the diamond, as shown in Figure P22.44. If the surface of the water is calm and the pool is 2.00 m deep, find the minimum diameter of the raft that would prevent the diamond from being seen.

Figure P22.44

Additional Problems

45. A layer of ice having parallel sides floats on water. If light is incident on the upper surface of the ice at an angle of incidence of 30.0°, what is the angle of refraction in the water?

46. **Q|C** A ray of light is incident at an angle 30.0° on a plane slab of flint glass surrounded by water. (a) Find the refraction angle. (b) Suppose the index of refraction of the surrounding medium can be adjusted, but the incident angle of the light remains the same. As the index of refraction of the medium approaches that of the glass, what happens to the refraction angle? (c) What happens to the refraction angle when the medium's index of refraction exceeds that of the glass?

47. When a man stands near the edge of an empty drainage ditch of depth 2.80 m, he can barely see the boundary between the opposite wall and bottom of the ditch as in Figure P22.47a. The distance from his eyes to the

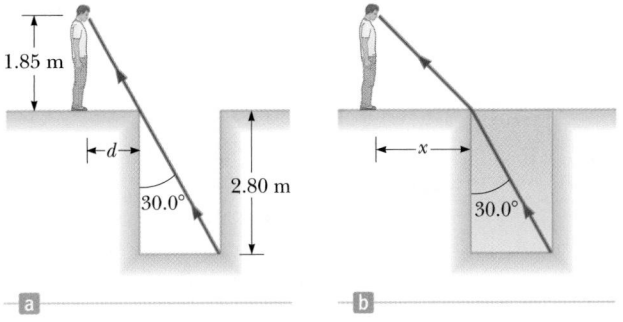
Figure P22.47

ground is 1.85 m. (a) What is the horizontal distance *d* from the man to the edge of the drainage ditch? (b) After the drainage ditch is filled with water as in Figure P22.47b, what is the maximum distance *x* the man can stand from the edge and still see the same boundary?

48. A light ray of wavelength 589 nm is incident at an angle θ on the top surface of a block of polystyrene surrounded by air, as shown in Figure P22.48. (a) Find the maximum value of θ for which the refracted ray will undergo total internal reflection at the left vertical face of the block.

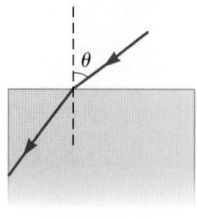

Figure P22.48

(b) Repeat the calculation for the case in which the polystyrene block is immersed in water. (c) What happens if the block is immersed in carbon disulfide?

49. As shown in Figure P22.49, a light ray is incident normal to one face of a 30°–60°–90° block of flint glass (a prism) that is immersed in water. (a) Determine the exit angle θ_3 of the ray. (b) A substance is dissolved in the water to increase the index of refraction n_2. At what value of n_2 does total internal reflection cease at point *P*?

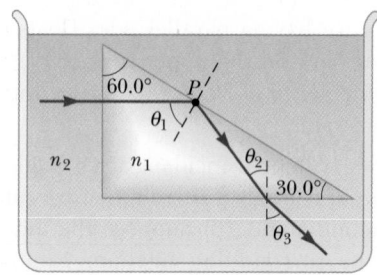

Figure P22.49

50. A narrow beam of light is incident from air onto a glass surface with index of refraction 1.56. Find the angle of incidence for which the corresponding angle of refraction is one-half the angle of incidence. *Hint:* You might want to use the trigonometric identity $\sin 2\theta = 2 \sin \theta \cos \theta$.

51. One technique for measuring the angle of a prism is shown in Figure P22.51. A parallel beam of light is

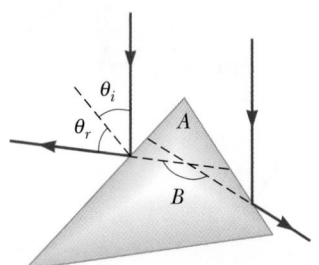

Figure P22.51

directed onto the apex of the prism so that the beam reflects from opposite faces of the prism. Show that the angular separation of the two reflected beams is given by $B = 2A$.

52. An optical fiber with index of refraction *n* and diameter *d* is surrounded by air. Light is sent into the fiber along its axis, as shown in Figure P22.52. (a) Find the smallest outside radius *R* permitted for a bend in the fiber if no light is to escape. (b) Does the result for part

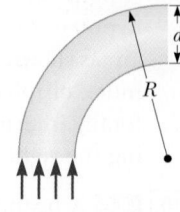

Figure P22.52

(a) predict reasonable behavior as *d* approaches zero? As *n* increases? As *n* approaches unity? (c) Evaluate *R*, assuming the diameter of the fiber is 100 μm and its index of refraction is 1.40.

53. A piece of wire is bent through an angle θ. The bent wire is partially submerged in benzene (index of refraction = 1.50) so that, to a person looking along the dry part, the wire appears to be straight and makes an angle of 30.0° with the horizontal. Determine the value of θ.

54. A light ray traveling in air is incident on one face of a right-angle prism with index of refraction *n* = 1.50, as shown in Figure P22.54, and the ray follows the path shown in the figure. Assuming θ = 60.0° and the base of the prism is mirrored, determine the angle ϕ made by the outgoing ray with the normal to the right face of the prism.

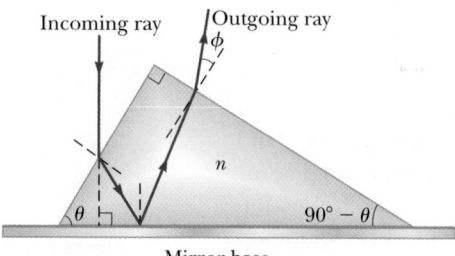

Figure P22.54

55. A transparent cylinder of radius *R* = 2.00 m has a mirrored surface on its right half, as shown in Figure P22.55. A light ray traveling in air is incident on the left side of the cylinder. The incident light ray and the exiting light ray are parallel, and *d* = 2.00 m. Determine the index of refraction of the material.

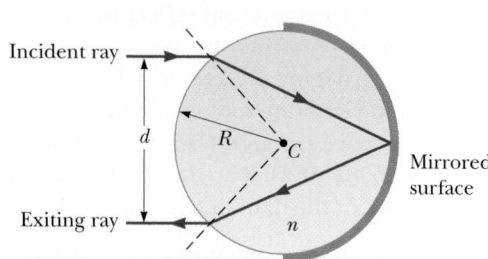

Figure P22.55

56. A laser beam strikes one end of a slab of material, as in Figure P22.56. The index of refraction of the slab is 1.48. Determine the number of internal reflections of the beam before it emerges from the opposite end of the slab.

Figure P22.56

57. A light ray enters a rectangular block of plastic at an angle $\theta_1 = 45.0°$ and emerges at an angle $\theta_2 = 76.0°$, as shown in Figure P22.57. (a) Determine the index of refraction of the plastic. (b) If the light ray enters the plastic at a point $L = 50.0$ cm from the bottom edge, how long does it take the light ray to travel through the plastic?

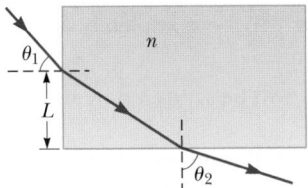

Figure P22.57

58. Students allow a narrow beam of laser light to strike a water surface. They arrange to measure the angle of refraction for selected angles of incidence and record the data shown in the following table:

Angle of Incidence (degrees)	Angle of Refraction (degrees)
10.0	7.5
20.0	15.1
30.0	22.3
40.0	28.7
50.0	35.2
60.0	40.3
70.0	45.3
80.0	47.7

Use the data to verify Snell's law of refraction by plotting the sine of the angle of incidence versus the sine of the angle of refraction. From the resulting plot, deduce the index of refraction of water.

59. Figure P22.59 shows the path of a beam of light through several layers with different indices of refraction. (a) If $\theta_1 = 30.0°$, what is the angle θ_2 of the emerging beam? (b) What must the incident angle θ_1 be to have total internal reflection at the surface between the medium with $n = 1.20$ and the medium with $n = 1.00$?

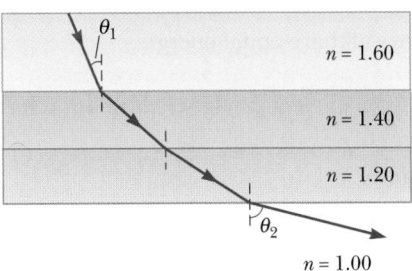

Figure P22.59

60. Three sheets of plastic have unknown indices of refraction. Sheet 1 is placed on top of sheet 2, and a laser beam is directed onto the sheets from above so that it strikes the interface at an angle of 26.5° with the normal. The refracted beam in sheet 2 makes an angle of 31.7° with the normal. The experiment is repeated with sheet 3 on top of sheet 2, and with the same angle of incidence, the refracted beam makes an angle of 36.7° with the normal. If the experiment is repeated again with sheet 1 on top of sheet 3, what is the expected angle of refraction in sheet 3? Assume the same angle of incidence.

61. A thick piece of Lucite ($n = 1.50$) is has the shape of a quarter circle of radius $R = 12.0$ cm as shown in the side view of Figure P22.61. A light ray traveling in air parallel to the base of the Lucite is incident at a distance $h = 6.00$ cm above the base and emerges out of the Lucite at an angle θ with the horizontal. Determine the value of θ.

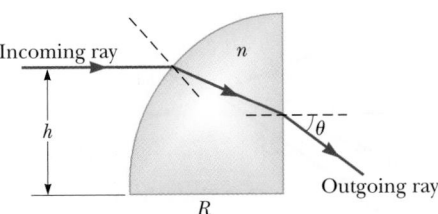

Figure P22.61

■ AP* REVIEW QUESTIONS

1. Which type of electromagnetic radiation provides the greatest energy?

(A) Gamma

(B) X-ray

(C) Infrared

(D) Radio

(E) They all have equal energies

2. Which type of electromagnetic radiation has the greatest speed in a vacuum?

(A) Radio

(B) Infrared

(C) X-ray

(D) Gamma

(E) They all have equal speeds in a vacuum

3. Which type of visible light has the greatest speed in a glass?

(A) Red

(B) Yellow

(C) Green

(D) Violet

(E) They all have equal speeds in a glass

4. Which of the following electromagnetic radiations has the smallest period?

(A) Red light

(B) Yellow light

(C) Green light

(D) Violet light

(E) They all have equal periods

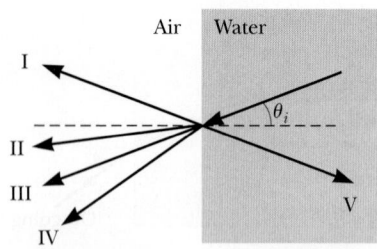

5. A ray of light passes from water into air with a very small angle of incidence, as seen in the figure above. Which path is the ray most likely to follow?

(A) I   (D) IV

(B) II   (E) V

(C) III

6. A monochromatic ray of light travels from a medium with a low index of refraction toward a medium with a higher index of refraction. The corresponding refracted ray is shown in the figure above. If the angle of incidence is increased, which of the following statements is true?

(A) The refracted ray will bend less and be closer to the normal.

(B) The refracted ray will reflect back into the incident medium.

(C) The frequency of the refracted ray will change.

(D) The ray will be completely absorbed by the new medium.

(E) The ray will be scattered in all angles.

7. Which of the following graphs best represents the relationship between the energy of a photon and the frequency of light?

(A)   (D)

(B)   (E)

(C)

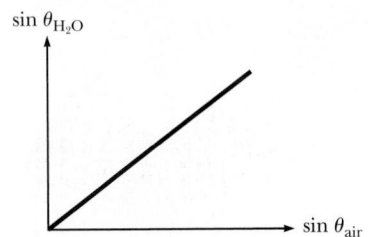

8. In an experiment, a laser is directed from air into a tank of water. The angle of the incident ray and transmitted ray is recorded. A plot of $\sin \theta_{H_2O}$ versus $\sin \theta_{air}$ produces the relationship seen above. Which statement is true?

(A) The slope is the wavelength of the laser light.

(B) The slope is the frequency of the laser light.

(C) The slope is the index of refraction of the air.

(D) The slope is the index of refraction of the water.

(E) The slope is the reciprocal of the index of refraction of the water.

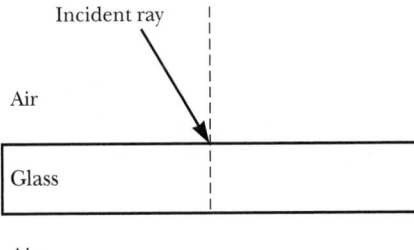

9. A thin slab of glass is surrounded on all sides by air. An incident ray of monochromatic light is directed at the top surface of the glass, as shown above. Which of the following statements is true?

(A) The ray will bounce off the bottom surface of the glass perpendicular to the incident ray.

(B) The ray will exit the bottom surface of the glass into the air at an angle parallel to the original incident ray.

(C) The ray will exit the bottom surface of the glass a different color from the original ray.

(D) The ray will exit the bottom surface of the glass a different frequency from the original ray.

(E) The ray must exhibit total internal reflection and remain inside the slab of glass.

10. A wave front with wavelength λ_0 passes between mediums. The original medium has an index of refraction

n_1 and the transmitted medium has an index of refraction n_2. The wavelength in the second medium will be:

(A) $\dfrac{\sin \theta_1}{\sin \theta_2}\lambda_0$

(B) $\dfrac{\lambda_0}{c}$

(C) $\dfrac{n_1}{n_2}\lambda_0$

(D) $\dfrac{n_2}{n_1}\lambda_0$

(E) $(\sin \theta_1)(\sin \theta_2)\lambda_0$

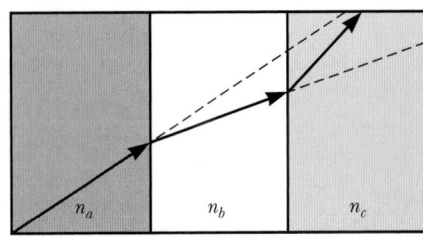

11. Light travels through three different media with index of refractions n_a, n_b, and n_c. Which statements must be true?

     I. $n_a > n_b$

     II. $n_b > n_c$

     III. $n_c > n_a$

     IV. $n_c < n_a$

(A) I only

(B) II only

(C) I and III

(D) II and III

(E) II and IV

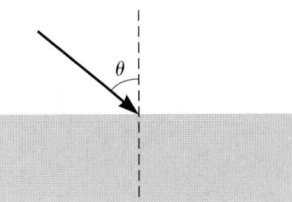

12. A monochromatic ray of light passes from one medium into another medium with a larger index of refraction, as seen in the figure above. Which of the following statements is NOT correct?

(A) The wavelength of the ray changes.

(B) The velocity of the ray changes.

(C) The angle of the ray changes.

(D) The frequency of the ray changes.

(E) All statements above are true.

Funhouse mirrors distort images because the curved surfaces essentially change the angle of incidence of incoming rays, change that differs depending on the mirror's shape in a given location. In every case, however, the angle of reflection equals the angle of incidence.

Gail Mooney/Masterfile Corporation

23 Mirrors and Lenses

The development of the technology of mirrors and lenses led to a revolution in the progress of science. These devices, relatively simple to construct from cheap materials, led to microscopes and telescopes, extending human sight and opening up new pathways to knowledge, from microbes to distant planets.

This chapter covers the formation of images when plane and spherical light waves fall on plane and spherical surfaces. Images can be formed by reflection from mirrors or by refraction through lenses. In our study of mirrors and lenses, we continue to assume light travels in straight lines (the ray approximation), ignoring diffraction.

23.1 Flat Mirrors

We begin by examining the flat mirror. Consider a point source of light placed at O in Figure 23.1, a distance p in front of a flat mirror. The distance p is called the **object distance**. Light rays leave the source and are reflected from the mirror. After reflection, the rays diverge (spread apart), but they appear to the viewer to come from a point I behind the mirror. Point I is called the **image** of the object at O. Regardless of the system under study, **images are formed at the point where rays of light actually intersect or where they appear to originate**. Because the rays in the figure appear to originate at I, which is a distance q behind the mirror, that is the location of the image. The distance q is called the **image distance**.

Images are classified as real or virtual. In the formation of a *real image*, light actually passes through the image point. For a *virtual image*, light doesn't pass through the image point, but appears to come (diverge) from there. The image formed by the flat mirror in Figure 23.1 is a virtual image. In fact, the images seen in flat mirrors are always virtual (for real objects). Real images can be displayed on a screen (as at a movie), but virtual images cannot.

We examine some of the properties of the images formed by flat mirrors by using the simple geometric techniques. To find out where an image is formed, it's necessary to follow at least two rays of light as they reflect from the mirror as in Active Figure 23.2. One of those rays starts at P, follows the horizontal path PQ to the mirror, and reflects back on itself. The second ray follows the oblique path PR and reflects as shown. An observer to the left of the mirror would trace the two reflected rays back to the point from which they appear to have originated: point P'. A continuation of this process for points other than P on the object would result in a virtual image (drawn as a yellow arrow) to the right of the mirror. Because triangles PQR and $P'QR$ are identical, $PQ = P'Q$. Hence, we conclude that **the image formed by an object placed in front of a flat mirror is as far behind the mirror as the object is in front of the mirror**. Geometry also shows that the object height h equals the image height h'. The **lateral magnification** M is defined as

$$M \equiv \frac{\text{image height}}{\text{object height}} = \frac{h'}{h} \qquad [23.1]$$

Equation 23.1 is a general definition of the lateral magnification of any type of mirror. For a flat mirror, $M = 1$ because $h' = h$.

In summary, the image formed by a flat mirror has the following properties:

1. The image is as far behind the mirror as the object is in front.
2. The image is unmagnified, virtual, and upright. (By *upright*, we mean that if the object arrow points upward, as in Active Figure 23.2, so does the image arrow. The opposite of an upright image is an inverted image.)

Finally, note that a flat mirror produces an image having an *apparent* left–right reversal. You can see this reversal standing in front of a mirror and raising your right hand. Your image in the mirror raises the left hand. Likewise, your hair appears to be parted on the opposite side, and a mole on your right cheek appears to be on your image's left cheek.

■ Quick Quiz

23.1 In the overhead view of Figure 23.3, the image of the stone seen by observer 1 is at C. Where does observer 2 see the image: at A, at B, at C, at D, at E, or not at all?

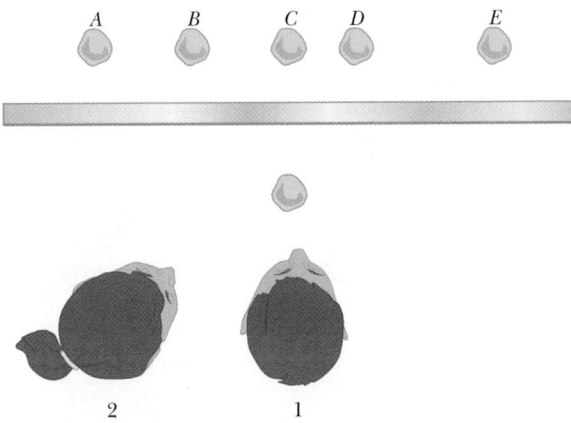

Figure 23.3 (Quick Quiz 23.1)

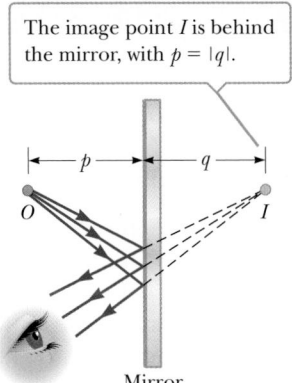

Figure 23.1 An image formed by reflection from a flat mirror. The image at point I is virtual. In Section 23.3, it will be shown that q must be taken as negative for virtual images: the object distance p, therefore, equals the absolute value of the image distance q.

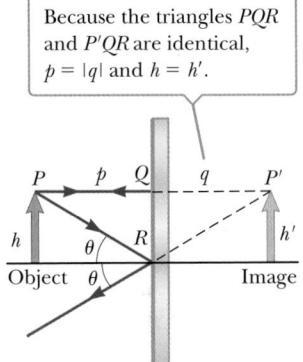

Active Figure 23.2
A geometric construction to locate the image of an object placed in front of a flat mirror.

Tip 23.1 Magnification ≠ Enlargement

Note that the word *magnification*, as used in optics, doesn't always mean *enlargement* because the image could be smaller than the object.

■ EXAMPLE 23.1 | "Mirror, Mirror, on the Wall"

GOAL Apply the properties of a flat mirror.

PROBLEM A man 1.80 m tall stands in front of a mirror and sees his full height, no more and no less. If his eyes are 0.14 m from the top of his head, what is the minimum height of the mirror?

STRATEGY Figure 23.4 shows two rays of light, one from the man's feet and the other from the top of his head, reflecting off the mirror and entering his eye. The ray from his feet just strikes the bottom of the mirror, so if the mirror were longer, it would be too long, and if shorter, the ray would not be reflected. The angle of incidence and the angle of reflection are equal, labeled θ. This means the two triangles, *ABD* and *DBC*, are identical because they are right triangles with a common side (*DB*) and two identical angles θ. Use this key fact and the small isosceles triangle *FEC* to solve the problem.

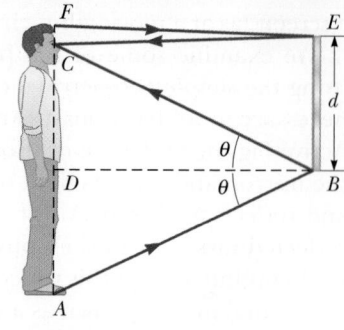

Figure 23.4 (Example 23.1)

SOLUTION

We need to find *BE*, which equals *d*. Relate this length to lengths on the man's body:

(1) $BE = DC + \frac{1}{2}CF$

We need the lengths *DC* and *CF*. Set the sum of sides opposite the identical angles θ equal to *AC*:

(2) $AD + DC = AC = (1.80 - 0.14) = 1.66$ m

$AD = DC$, so substitute into Equation (2) and solve for *DC*:

$AD + DC = 2DC = 1.66$ m $\rightarrow$ $DC = 0.83$ m

CF is given as 0.14 m. Substitute this value and *DC* into Equation (1):

$BE = d = DC + \frac{1}{2}CF = 0.83$ m $+ \frac{1}{2}(0.14$ m$) = $ 0.90 m

REMARKS The mirror must be exactly equal to half the height of the man for him to see only his full height and nothing more or less. Notice that the answer doesn't depend on his distance from the mirror.

QUESTION 23.1 Would a taller man be able to see his full height in the same mirror?

EXERCISE 23.1 How large should the mirror be if he wants to see only the upper third of his body?

ANSWER 0.30 m

APPLICATION

Day and Night Settings for Rearview Mirrors

Most rearview mirrors in cars have a day setting and a night setting. The night setting greatly diminishes the intensity of the image so that lights from trailing cars will not blind the driver. To understand how such a mirror works, consider Figure 23.5. The mirror is a wedge of glass with a reflecting metallic coating on the back side. When the mirror is in the day setting, as in Figure 23.5a, light from an object behind the car strikes the mirror at point 1. Most of the light enters the wedge, is refracted, and reflects from the back of the mirror to return to the front

Figure 23.5 Cross-sectional views of a rearview mirror. (a) With the day setting, the silvered back surface of the mirror reflects a bright ray *B* into the driver's eyes. (b) With the night setting, the glass of the unsilvered front surface of the mirror reflects a dim ray *D* into the driver's eyes.

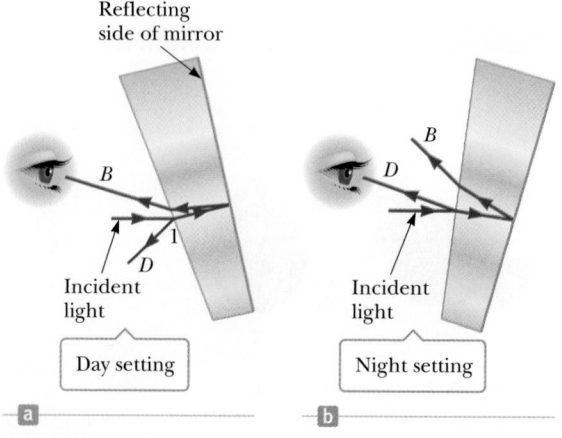

surface, where it is refracted again as it reenters the air as ray *B* (for *bright*). In addition, a small portion of the light is reflected at the front surface, as indicated by ray *D* (for *dim*). This dim reflected light is responsible for the image observed when the mirror is in the night setting, as in Figure 23.5b. Now the wedge is rotated so that the path followed by the bright light (ray *B*) doesn't lead to the eye. Instead, the dim light reflected from the front surface travels to the eye, and the brightness of trailing headlights doesn't become a hazard.

■ APPLYING PHYSICS 23.1 | Illusionist's Trick

The professor in the box shown in Figure 23.6 appears to be balancing himself on a few fingers with both of his feet elevated from the floor. He can maintain this position for a long time, and appears to defy gravity. How do you suppose this illusion was created?

EXPLANATION This trick is an example of an optical illusion, used by magicians, that makes use of a mirror. The box the professor is standing in is a cubical open frame that contains a flat, vertical mirror through a diagonal plane. The professor straddles the mirror so that one leg is in front of the mirror and the other leg is behind it, out of view. When he raises his front leg, that leg's reflection rises also, making it appear both his feet are off the ground, creating the illusion that he's floating in the air. In fact, he supports himself with the leg behind the mirror, which remains in contact with the ground. ■

Courtesy of Henry Leap and Jim Lehman

Figure 23.6 (Applying Physics 23.1)

23.2 Images Formed by Concave Mirrors

A **spherical mirror**, as its name implies, has the shape of a segment of a sphere. Figure 23.7 shows a spherical mirror with a silvered inner, concave surface; this type of mirror is called a **concave mirror**. The mirror has radius of curvature *R*, and its center of curvature is at point *C*. Point *V* is the center of the spherical segment, and a line drawn from *C* to *V* is called the **principal axis** of the mirror.

Now consider a point source of light placed at point *O* in Figure 23.7b, on the principal axis and outside point *C*. Several diverging rays originating at *O* are shown. After reflecting from the mirror, these rays converge to meet at *I*, called the **image point**. The rays then continue and diverge from *I* as if there were an object there. As a result, a real image is formed. **Whenever reflected light actually passes through a point, the image formed there is real.**

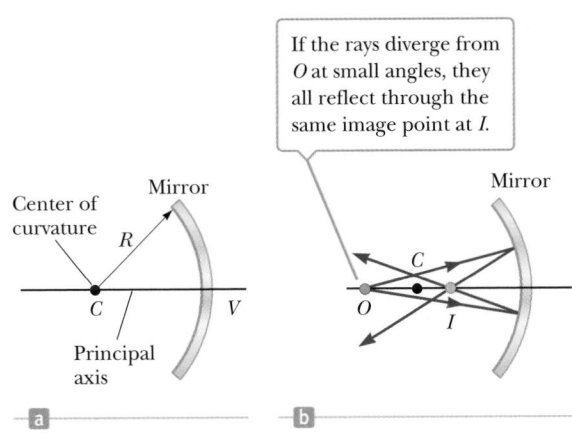

If the rays diverge from *O* at small angles, they all reflect through the same image point at *I*.

Center of curvature

Mirror

R

C

V

Principal axis

Mirror

C

O

I

a

b

Figure 23.7 (a) A concave mirror of radius *R*. The center of curvature, *C*, is located on the principal axis. (b) A point object placed at *O* in front of a concave spherical mirror of radius *R*, where *O* is any point on the principal axis farther than *R* from the surface of the mirror, forms a real image at *I*.

The reflected rays intersect at different points on the principal axis.

Figure 23.8 A spherical concave mirror inhibits *spherical aberration* when light rays make large angles with the principal axis.

We often assume all rays that diverge from the object make small angles with the principal axis. All such rays reflect through the image point, as in Figure 23.7b. Rays that make a large angle with the principal axis, as in Figure 23.8, converge to other points on the principal axis, producing a blurred image. This effect, called **spherical aberration**, is present to some extent with any spherical mirror and will be discussed in Section 23.7.

We can use the geometry shown in Figure 23.9 to calculate the image distance q from the object distance p and radius of curvature R. By convention, these distances are measured from point V. The figure shows two rays of light leaving the tip of the object. One ray passes through the center of curvature, C, of the mirror, hitting the mirror head-on (perpendicular to the mirror surface) and reflecting back on itself. The second ray strikes the mirror at point V and reflects as shown, obeying the law of reflection. The image of the tip of the arrow is at the point where the two rays intersect. From the largest triangle in Figure 23.9, we see that $\tan \theta = h/p$; the light-blue triangle gives $\tan \theta = -h'/q$. The negative sign has been introduced to satisfy our convention that h' is negative when the image is inverted with respect to the object, as it is here. From Equation 23.1 and these results, we find that the magnification of the mirror is

$$M = \frac{h'}{h} = -\frac{q}{p} \qquad [23.2]$$

From two other triangles in the figure, we get

$$\tan \alpha = \frac{h}{p - R} \qquad \text{and} \qquad \tan \alpha = -\frac{h'}{R - q}$$

from which we find that

$$\frac{h'}{h} = -\frac{R - q}{p - R} \qquad [23.3]$$

If we compare Equation 23.2 with Equation 23.3, we see that

$$\frac{R - q}{p - R} = \frac{q}{p}$$

Simple algebra reduces this equation to

Mirror equation ▶

$$\frac{1}{p} + \frac{1}{q} = \frac{2}{R} \qquad [23.4]$$

This expression is called the **mirror equation**.

If the object is very far from the mirror—if the object distance p is great enough compared with R that p can be said to approach infinity—then $1/p \approx 0$, and we see from Equation 23.4 that $q \approx R/2$. In other words, when the object is very far from

Figure 23.9 The image formed by a spherical concave mirror, where the object at O lies outside the center of curvature, C.

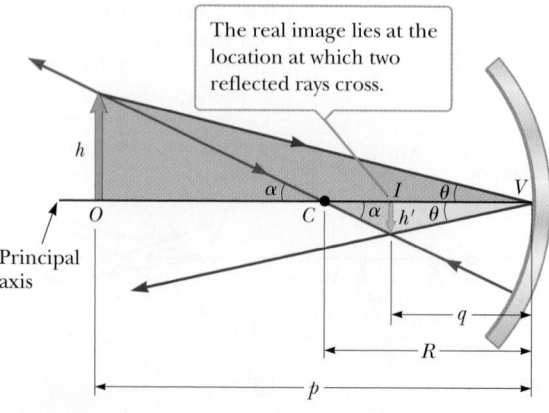

The real image lies at the location at which two reflected rays cross.

For p approaching infinity, q approaches $R/2 = f$, the focal length of the mirror.

Henry Leap and Jim Lehman

Figure 23.10 (a) Light rays from a distant object ($p = \infty$) reflect from a concave mirror through the focal point F. (b) A photograph of the reflection of parallel rays from a concave mirror.

the mirror, **the image point is halfway between the center of curvature and the center of the mirror**, as in Figure 23.10a. The incoming rays are essentially parallel in that figure because the source is assumed to be very far from the mirror. In this special case we call the image point the **focal point** F and the image distance the **focal length** f, where

$$f = \frac{R}{2} \qquad [23.5]$$

◄ Focal length

The mirror equation can therefore be expressed in terms of the focal length:

$$\frac{1}{p} + \frac{1}{q} = \frac{1}{f} \qquad [23.6]$$

Note that rays from objects at infinity are always focused at the focal point.

Tip 23.2 Focal Point ≠ Focus Point

The focal point is *not* the point at which light rays focus to form an image. The focal point of a mirror is determined *solely* by its curvature; it doesn't depend on the location of any object.

23.3 Convex Mirrors and Sign Conventions

Figure 23.11 shows the formation of an image by a **convex mirror**, which is silvered so that light is reflected from the outer, convex surface. It is sometimes called a **diverging mirror** because the rays from any point on the object diverge after reflection, as though they were coming from some point behind the mirror. The image in Figure 23.11 is virtual rather than real because it lies behind the mirror at the point the reflected rays appear to originate. In general, the image formed by a convex mirror is upright, virtual, and smaller than the object.

We won't derive any equations for convex spherical mirrors. If we did, we would find that the equations developed for concave mirrors can be used with convex mirrors if particular sign conventions are used. We call the region in which light

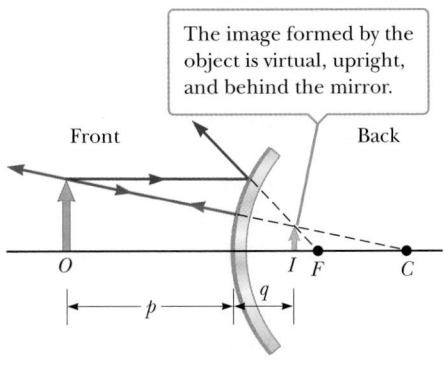

The image formed by the object is virtual, upright, and behind the mirror.

Figure 23.11 Formation of an image by a spherical, convex mirror.

Table 23.1 Sign Conventions for Mirrors

Quantity	Symbol	In Front	In Back	Upright Image	Inverted Image
Object location	p	+	−		
Image location	q	+	−		
Focal length	f	+	−		
Image height	h'			+	−
Magnification	M			+	−

rays move the *front side* of the mirror, and the other side, where virtual images are formed, the *back side*. For example, in Figures 23.9 and 23.11, the side to the left of the mirror is the front side and the side to the right is the back side. Figure 23.12 is helpful for understanding the rules for object and image distances, and Table 23.1 summarizes the sign conventions for all the necessary quantities. Notice that when the quantities p, q, and f (and R) are located where the light is—in front of the mirror—they are positive, whereas when they are located behind the mirror (where the light isn't), they are negative.

Ray Diagrams for Mirrors

We can conveniently determine the positions and sizes of images formed by mirrors by constructing *ray diagrams* similar to the ones we have been using. This kind of graphical construction tells us the overall nature of the image and can be used to check parameters calculated from the mirror and magnification equations. Making a ray diagram requires knowing the position of the object and the location of the center of curvature. To locate the image, three rays are constructed (rather than only the two we have been constructing so far), as shown by the examples in Active Figure 23.13. All three rays start from the same object point; for these examples, the tip of the arrow was chosen. For the concave mirrors in Active Figures 23.13a and 23.13b, the rays are drawn as follows:

1. Ray 1 is drawn parallel to the principal axis and is reflected back through the focal point F.
2. Ray 2 is drawn through the focal point and is reflected parallel to the principal axis.
3. Ray 3 is drawn through the center of curvature, C, and is reflected back on itself.

Note that rays actually go in all directions from the object; we choose to follow those moving in a direction that simplifies our drawing.

The intersection of any *two* of these rays at a point locates the image. The third ray serves as a check of our construction. The image point obtained in this fashion must always agree with the value of q calculated from the mirror formula.

In the case of a concave mirror, note what happens as the object is moved closer to the mirror. The real, inverted image in Active Figure 23.13a moves to the left as the object approaches the focal point. When the object is at the focal point, the image is infinitely far to the left. When the object lies between the focal point and the mirror surface, as in Active Figure 23.13b, however, the image is virtual and upright.

With the convex mirror shown in Active Figure 23.13c, the image of a real object is always virtual and upright. As the object distance increases, the virtual image shrinks and approaches the focal point as p approaches infinity. You should construct a ray diagram to verify these statements.

The image-forming characteristics of curved mirrors obviously determine their uses. For example, suppose you want to design a mirror that will help people shave

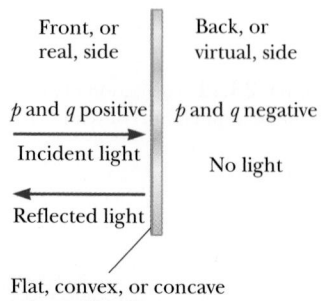

Figure 23.12 A diagram describing the signs of p and q for convex and concave mirrors.

Active Figure 23.13
Ray diagrams for spherical mirrors and corresponding photographs of the images of candles.

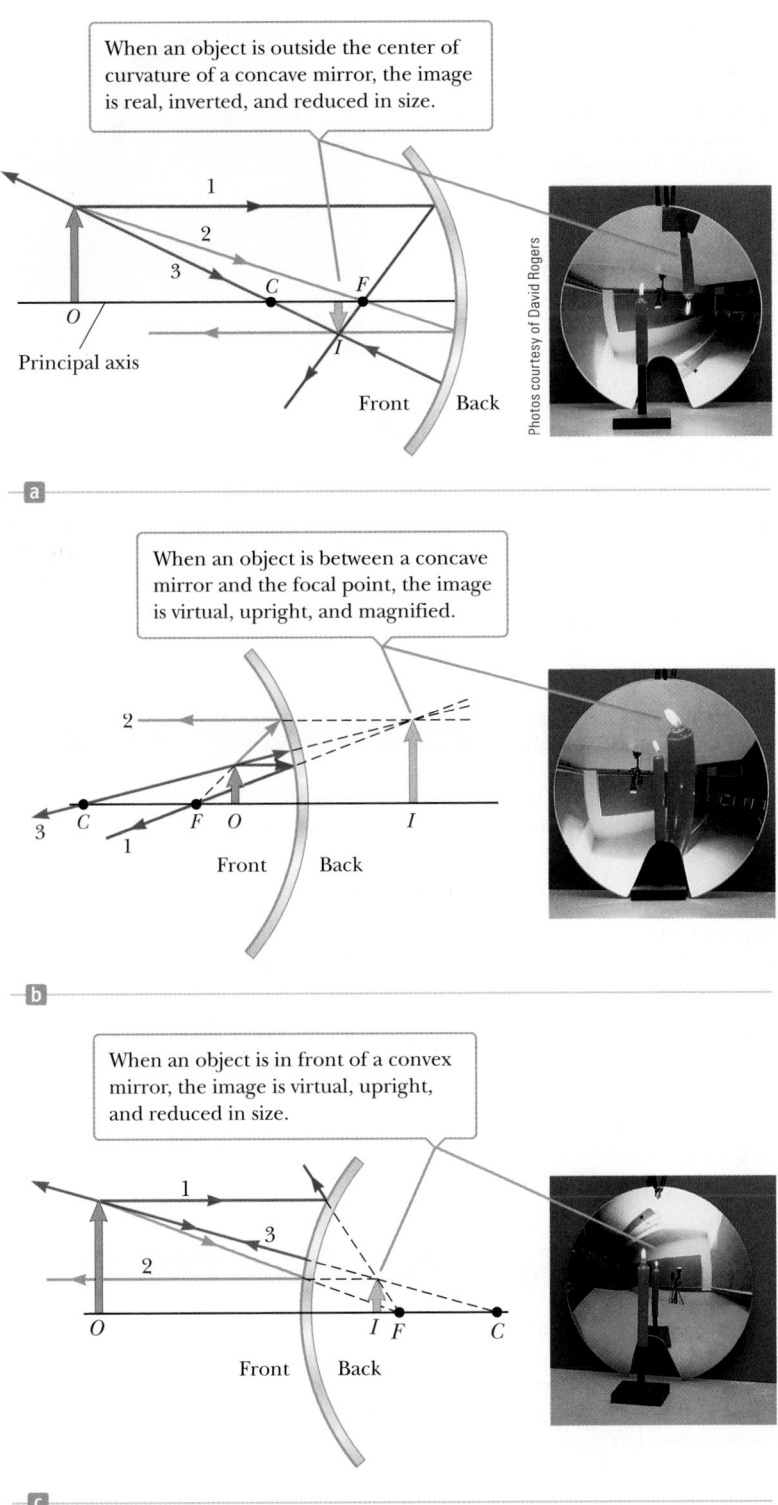

When an object is outside the center of curvature of a concave mirror, the image is real, inverted, and reduced in size.

Principal axis

Front   Back

Photos courtesy of David Rogers

a

When an object is between a concave mirror and the focal point, the image is virtual, upright, and magnified.

Front   Back

b

When an object is in front of a convex mirror, the image is virtual, upright, and reduced in size.

Front   Back

c

or apply cosmetics. For this, you need a concave mirror that puts the user inside the focal point, such as the mirror in Active Figure 23.13b. With that mirror, the image is upright and greatly enlarged. In contrast, suppose the primary purpose of a mirror is to observe a large field of view. In that case you need a convex mirror such as the one in Active Figure 23.13c. The diminished size of the image means that a fairly large field of view is seen in the mirror. Mirrors like this one are often placed in stores to help employees watch for shoplifters. A second use of such a

Figure 23.14 A convex side-view mirror on a vehicle produces an upright image that is smaller than the object. The smaller image means that the object is closer than its apparent distance as observed in the mirror.

© Junebug Clark 1988/Photo Researchers, Inc.

mirror is as a side-view mirror on a car (Fig. 23.14). This kind of mirror is usually placed on the passenger side of the car and carries the warning "Objects are closer than they appear." Without such warning, a driver might think she is looking into a flat mirror, which doesn't alter the size of the image. She could be fooled into believing that a truck is far away because it looks small, when it's actually a large semi very close behind her, but diminished in size because of the image formation characteristics of the convex mirror.

■ **APPLYING PHYSICS 23.2** | **Concave Versus Convex**

A virtual image can be anywhere behind a concave mirror. Why is there a maximum distance at which the image can exist behind a *convex* mirror?

EXPLANATION Consider the concave mirror first and imagine two different light rays leaving a tiny object and striking the mirror. If the object is at the focal point, the light rays reflecting from the mirror will be parallel to the mirror axis. They can be interpreted as forming a virtual image infinitely far away behind the mirror. As the object is brought closer to the mirror, the reflected rays will diverge through larger and larger angles, resulting in their extensions converging closer and closer to the back of the mir-

ror. When the object is brought right up to the mirror, the image is right behind the mirror. When the object is much closer to the mirror than the focal length, the mirrors acts like a flat mirror and the image is just as far behind the mirror as the object is in front of it. The image can therefore be anywhere from infinitely far away to right at the surface of the mirror. For the convex mirror, an object at infinity produces a virtual image at the focal point. As the object is brought closer, the reflected rays diverge more sharply and the image moves closer to the mirror. As a result, the virtual image is restricted to the region between the mirror and the focal point. ■

■ **APPLYING PHYSICS 23.3** | **Reversible Waves**

Large trucks often have a sign on the back saying, "If you can't see my mirror, I can't see you." Explain this sign.

EXPLANATION The trucking companies are making use of the principle of the reversibility of light rays. For

an image of you to be formed in the driver's mirror, there must be a pathway for rays of light to reach the mirror, allowing the driver to see your image. If you can't see the mirror, this pathway doesn't exist. ■

■ **EXAMPLE 23.2** | **Images Formed by a Concave Mirror**

GOAL Calculate properties of a concave mirror.

PROBLEM Assume a certain concave, spherical mirror has a focal length of 10.0 cm. **(a)** Locate the image and find the magnification for an object distance of 25.0 cm. Determine whether the image is real or virtual, inverted or upright, and larger or smaller. Do the same for object distances of **(b)** 10.0 cm and **(c)** 5.00 cm.

STRATEGY For each part, substitute into the mirror and magnification equations. Part (b) involves a limiting process because the answers are infinite.

SOLUTION

(a) Find the image position for an object distance of 25.0 cm. Calculate the magnification and describe the image.

Use the mirror equation to find the image distance:

$$\frac{1}{p} + \frac{1}{q} = \frac{1}{f}$$

Substitute and solve for q. According to Table 23.1, p and f are positive.

$$\frac{1}{25.0 \text{ cm}} + \frac{1}{q} = \frac{1}{10.0 \text{ cm}}$$

$$q = \boxed{16.7 \text{ cm}}$$

Because q is positive, the image is in front of the mirror and is real. The magnification is given by substituting into Equation 23.2:

$$M = -\frac{q}{p} = -\frac{16.7 \text{ cm}}{25.0 \text{ cm}} = \boxed{-0.668}$$

The image is smaller than the object because $|M| < 1$, and it is inverted because M is negative. (See Fig. 23.13a.)

(b) Locate the image distance when the object distance is 10.0 cm. Calculate the magnification and describe the image.

The object is at the focal point. Substitute $p = 10.0$ cm and $f = 10.0$ cm into the mirror equation:

$$\frac{1}{10.0 \text{ cm}} + \frac{1}{q} = \frac{1}{10.0 \text{ cm}}$$

$$\frac{1}{q} = 0 \quad \rightarrow \quad \boxed{q = \infty}$$

Because $M = -q/p$, the magnification is also infinite.

(c) Locate the image distance when the object distance is 5.00 cm. Calculate the magnification and describe the image.

Once again, substitute into the mirror equation:

$$\frac{1}{5.00 \text{ cm}} + \frac{1}{q} = \frac{1}{10.0 \text{ cm}}$$

$$\frac{1}{q} = \frac{1}{10.0 \text{ cm}} - \frac{1}{5.00 \text{ cm}} = -\frac{1}{10.0 \text{ cm}}$$

$$q = \boxed{-10.0 \text{ cm}}$$

The image is virtual (behind the mirror) because q is negative. Use Equation 23.2 to calculate the magnification:

$$M = -\frac{q}{p} = -\left(\frac{-10.0 \text{ cm}}{5.00 \text{ cm}}\right) = \boxed{2.00}$$

The image is larger (magnified by a factor of 2) because $|M| > 1$, and upright because M is positive. (See Fig. 23.13b.)

REMARKS Note the characteristics of an image formed by a concave, spherical mirror. When the object is outside the focal point, the image is inverted and real; at the focal point, the image is formed at infinity; inside the focal point, the image is upright and virtual.

QUESTION 23.2 What location does the image approach as the object gets arbitrarily far away from the mirror? (a) infinity (b) the focal point (c) the radius of curvature of the mirror (d) the mirror itself

EXERCISE 23.2 If the object distance is 20.0 cm, find the image distance and the magnification of the mirror.

ANSWER $q = 20.0$ cm, $M = -1.00$

▪ EXAMPLE 23.3 │ Images Formed by a Convex Mirror

GOAL Calculate properties of a convex mirror.

PROBLEM An object 3.00 cm high is placed 20.0 cm from a convex mirror with a focal length of magnitude 8.00 cm. Find (a) the position of the image, (b) the magnification of the mirror, and (c) the height of the image.

STRATEGY This problem again requires only substitution into the mirror and magnification equations. Multiplying the object height by the magnification gives the image height.

SOLUTION

(a) Find the position of the image.

Because the mirror is convex, its focal length is negative. Substitute into the mirror equation:

$$\frac{1}{p} + \frac{1}{q} = \frac{1}{f}$$

$$\frac{1}{20.0 \text{ cm}} + \frac{1}{q} = \frac{1}{-8.00 \text{ cm}}$$

Solve for q:

$$q = \boxed{-5.71 \text{ cm}}$$

(b) Find the magnification of the mirror.

Substitute into Equation 23.2:

$$M = -\frac{q}{p} = -\left(\frac{-5.71 \text{ cm}}{20.0 \text{ cm}}\right) = \boxed{0.286}$$

(c) Find the height of the image.

Multiply the object height by the magnification:

$$h' = hM = (3.00 \text{ cm})(0.286) = \boxed{0.858 \text{ cm}}$$

REMARKS The negative value of q indicates the image is virtual, or behind the mirror, as in Figure 23.13c. The image is upright because M is positive.

QUESTION 23.3 True or False: A convex mirror can produce only virtual images.

EXERCISE 23.3 Suppose the object is moved so that it is 4.00 cm from the same mirror. Repeat parts (a) through (c).

ANSWERS (a) −2.67 cm (b) 0.668 (c) 2.00 cm; the image is upright and virtual.

▪ EXAMPLE 23.4 │ The Face in the Mirror

GOAL Find a focal length from a magnification and an object distance.

PROBLEM When a woman stands with her face 40.0 cm from a cosmetic mirror, the upright image is twice as tall as her face. What is the focal length of the mirror?

STRATEGY To find f in this example, we must first find q, the image distance. Because the problem states that the image is upright, the magnification must be positive (in this case, $M = +2$), and because $M = -q/p$, we can determine q.

SOLUTION

Obtain q from the magnification equation:

$$M = -\frac{q}{p} = 2$$

$$q = -2p = -2(40.0 \text{ cm}) = -80.0 \text{ cm}$$

Because q is negative, the image is on the opposite side of the mirror and hence is virtual. Substitute q and p into the mirror equation and solve for f:

$$\frac{1}{40.0 \text{ cm}} - \frac{1}{80.0 \text{ cm}} = \frac{1}{f}$$

$$f = \boxed{80.0 \text{ cm}}$$

REMARKS The positive sign for the focal length tells us that the mirror is concave, a fact we already knew because the mirror magnified the object. (A convex mirror would have produced a smaller image.)

QUESTION 23.4 If she moves the mirror closer to her face, what happens to the image? (a) It becomes inverted and smaller. (b) It remains upright and becomes smaller. (c) It becomes inverted and larger. (d) It remains upright and becomes larger.

EXERCISE 23.4 Suppose a fun-house spherical mirror makes you appear to be one-third your normal height. If you are 1.20 m away from the mirror, find its focal length. Is the mirror concave or convex?

ANSWERS −0.600 m, convex

23.4 Images Formed by Refraction

In this section we describe how images are formed by refraction at a spherical surface. Consider two transparent media with indices of refraction n_1 and n_2, where the boundary between the two media is a spherical surface of radius R (Fig. 23.15). We assume the medium to the right has a higher index of refraction than the one to the left: $n_2 > n_1$. That would be the case for light entering a curved piece of glass from air or for light entering the water in a fishbowl from air. The rays originating at the object location O are refracted at the spherical surface and then converge to the image point I. We can begin with Snell's law of refraction and use simple geometric techniques to show that the object distance, image distance, and radius of curvature are related by the equation

$$\frac{n_1}{p} + \frac{n_2}{q} = \frac{n_2 - n_1}{R}$$ [23.7]

Further, the magnification of a refracting surface is

$$M = \frac{h'}{h} = -\frac{n_1 q}{n_2 p}$$ [23.8]

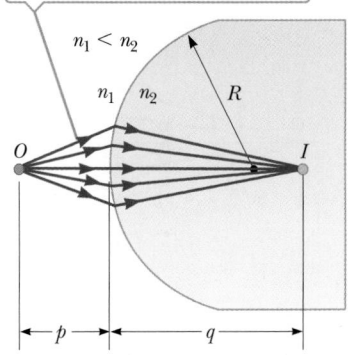

Rays making small angles with the principal axis diverge from a point object at O and pass through the image point I.

Figure 23.15 An image formed by refraction at a spherical surface.

As with mirrors, certain sign conventions hold, depending on circumstances. First note that real images are formed by refraction on the side of the surface *opposite* the side from which the light comes, in contrast to mirrors, where real images are formed on the *same* side of the reflecting surface. This makes sense because light reflects off mirrors, so any real images must form on the same side the light comes from. With a transparent medium, the rays pass through and naturally form real images on the opposite side. We define the side of the surface where light rays originate as the front side. The other side is called the back side. Because of the difference in location of real images, the refraction sign conventions for q and R are the opposite of those for reflection. For example, p, q, and R are all positive in Figure 23.15. The sign conventions for spherical refracting surfaces are summarized in Table 23.2.

Table 23.2 Sign Conventions for Refracting Surfaces

Quantity	Symbol	In Front	In Back	Upright Image	Inverted Image
Object location	p	+	−		
Image location	q	−	+		
Radius	R	−	+		
Image height	h'			+	−

Why does a person with normal vision see a blurry image if the eyes are opened underwater with no goggles or diving mask in use?

EXPLANATION The eye presents a spherical refraction surface. The eye normally functions so that light entering from the air is refracted to form an image in the retina located at the back of the eyeball. The difference in the index of refraction between water and the eye is smaller than the difference in the index of refraction between air and the eye. Consequently, light entering the eye from the water doesn't undergo as much refraction as does light entering from the air, and the image is formed behind the retina. A diving mask or swimming goggles have no optical action of their own; they are simply flat pieces of glass or plastic in a rubber mount. They do, however, provide a region of air adjacent to the eyes so that the correct refraction relationship is established and images will be in focus. ■

Flat Refracting Surfaces

If the refracting surface is flat, then R approaches infinity and Equation 23.7 reduces to

$$\frac{n_1}{p} = -\frac{n_2}{q}$$

$$q = -\frac{n_2}{n_1} p \qquad [23.9]$$

From Equation 23.9, we see that the sign of q is opposite that of p. Consequently, **the image formed by a flat refracting surface is on the same side of the surface as the object.** This statement is illustrated in Active Figure 23.16 for the situation in which n_1 is greater than n_2, where a virtual image is formed between the object and the surface. Note that the refracted ray bends *away* from the normal in this case because $n_1 > n_2$.

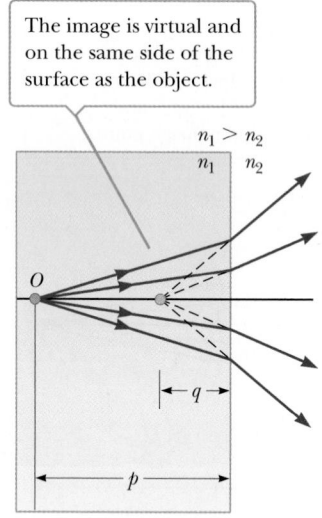

The image is virtual and on the same side of the surface as the object.

Active Figure 23.16
The image formed by a flat refracting surface.

■ *Quick Quiz*

23.2 A person spearfishing from a boat sees a fish located 3 m from the boat at an apparent depth of 1 m. To spear the fish, should the person aim (a) at, (b) above, or (c) below the image of the fish?

23.3 True or False: (a) The image of an object placed in front of a concave mirror is always upright. (b) The height of the image of an object placed in front of a concave mirror must be smaller than or equal to the height of the object. (c) The image of an object placed in front of a convex mirror is always upright and smaller than the object.

■ **EXAMPLE 23.5** | **Gaze into the Crystal Ball**

GOAL Calculate the properties of an image created by a spherical lens.

PROBLEM A coin 2.00 cm in diameter is embedded in a solid glass ball of radius 30.0 cm (Fig. 23.17). The index of refraction of the ball is 1.50, and the coin is 20.0 cm from the surface. Find the position of the image of the coin and the height of the coin's image.

STRATEGY Because the rays are moving from a medium of high index of refraction (the glass ball) to a medium of lower index of refraction (air), the rays originating at the coin are refracted away from the normal at the surface and diverge outward. The image is formed in the glass and is virtual. Substitute into Equations 23.7 and 23.8 for the image position and magnification, respectively.

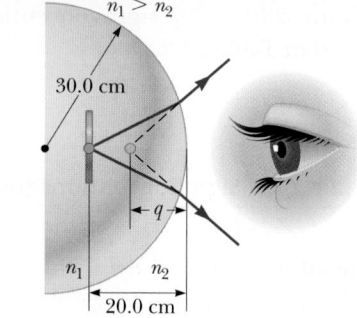

Figure 23.17 (Example 23.5) A coin embedded in a glass ball forms a virtual image between the coin and the surface of the glass.

SOLUTION

Apply Equation 23.7 and take $n_1 = 1.50$, $n_2 = 1.00$, $p = 20.0$ cm, and $R = -30.0$ cm:

$$\frac{n_1}{p} + \frac{n_2}{q} = \frac{n_2 - n_1}{R}$$

$$\frac{1.50}{20.0 \text{ cm}} + \frac{1.00}{q} = \frac{1.00 - 1.50}{-30.0 \text{ cm}}$$

Solve for q:

$$q = \boxed{-17.1 \text{ cm}}$$

To find the image height, use Equation 23.8 for the magnification:

$$M = -\frac{n_1 q}{n_2 p} = -\frac{1.50(-17.1 \text{ cm})}{1.00(20.0 \text{ cm})} = \frac{h'}{h}$$

$$h' = 1.28h = (1.28)(2.00 \text{ cm}) = \boxed{2.56 \text{ cm}}$$

REMARKS The negative sign on q indicates that the image is in the same medium as the object (the side of incident light), in agreement with our ray diagram, and therefore must be virtual. The positive value for M means that the image is upright.

QUESTION 23.5 How would the final answer be affected if the ball and observer were immersed in water? (a) It would be smaller. (b) It would be larger. (c) There would be no change.

EXERCISE 23.5 A coin is embedded 20.0 cm from the surface of a similar ball of transparent substance having radius 30.0 cm and unknown composition. If the coin's image is virtual and located 15.0 cm from the surface, find the (a) index of refraction of the substance and (b) magnification.

ANSWERS (a) 2.00 (b) 1.50

■ EXAMPLE 23.6 | The One That Got Away

GOAL Calculate the properties of an image created by a flat refractive surface.

PROBLEM A small fish is swimming at a depth d below the surface of a pond (Fig. 23.18). **(a)** What is the *apparent depth* of the fish as viewed from directly overhead? **(b)** If the fish is 12 cm long, how long is its image?

STRATEGY In this example the refracting surface is flat, so R is infinite. Hence, we can use Equation 23.9 to determine the location of the image, which is the apparent location of the fish.

Figure 23.18 (Example 23.6) The apparent depth q of the fish is less than the true depth d.

$n_2 = 1.00$
$n_1 = 1.33$

SOLUTION

(a) Find the apparent depth of the fish.

Substitute $n_1 = 1.33$ for water and $p = d$ into Equation 23.9:

$$q = -\frac{n_2}{n_1}p = -\frac{1}{1.33}d = \boxed{-0.752d}$$

(b) What is the size of the fish's image?

Use Equation 23.9 to eliminate q from the Equation 23.8, the magnification equation:

$$M = \frac{h'}{h} = -\frac{n_1 q}{n_2 p} = -\frac{n_1\left(-\dfrac{n_2}{n_1}p\right)}{n_2 p} = 1$$

$$h' = h = \boxed{12 \text{ cm}}$$

REMARKS Again, because q is negative, the image is virtual, as indicated in Figure 23.18. The apparent depth is approximately three-fourths the actual depth. For instance, if $d = 4.0$ m, then $q = -3.0$ m.

QUESTION 23.6 Suppose a similar experiment is carried out with an object immersed in oil ($n = 1.5$) the same distance below the surface. How does the apparent depth of the object compare with its apparent depth when immersed in water? (a) The apparent depth is unchanged. (b) The apparent depth is larger. (c) The apparent depth is smaller.

(Continued)

EXERCISE 23.6 A spear fisherman estimates that a trout is 1.5 m below the water's surface. What is the actual depth of the fish?

ANSWER 2.0 m

23.5 Atmospheric Refraction

Images formed by refraction in our atmosphere lead to some interesting phenomena. One such phenomenon that occurs daily is the visibility of the Sun at dusk even though it has passed below the horizon. Figure 23.19 shows why it occurs. Rays of light from the Sun strike Earth's atmosphere (represented by the shaded area around the planet) and are bent as they pass into a medium that has an index of refraction different from that of the almost empty space in which they have been traveling. The bending in this situation differs somewhat from the bending we have considered previously in that it is gradual and continuous as the light moves through the atmosphere toward an observer at point O. This is because the light moves through layers of air that have a continuously changing index of refraction. When the rays reach the observer, the eye follows them back along the direction from which they appear to have come (indicated by the dashed path in the figure). The end result is that the Sun appears to be above the horizon even after it has fallen below it.

The **mirage** is another phenomenon of nature produced by refraction in the atmosphere. A mirage can be observed when the ground is so hot that the air directly above it is warmer than the air at higher elevations. The desert is a region in which such circumstances prevail, but mirages are also seen on heated roadways during the summer. The layers of air at different heights above Earth have different densities and different refractive indices. The effect these differences can have is pictured in Figure 23.20a. The observer sees the sky and a tree in two different ways. One group of light rays reaches the observer by the straight-line path A, and the eye traces these rays back to see the tree in the normal fashion. In addition, a second group of rays travels along the curved path B. These rays are directed toward the ground and are then bent as a result of refraction. As a consequence, the observer also sees an inverted image of the tree and the background of the sky as he traces the rays back to the point at which they appear to have originated.

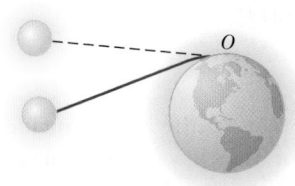

Figure 23.19 Because light is refracted by Earth's atmosphere, an observer at O sees the Sun even though it has fallen below the horizon.

John M. Dunay IV, Fundamental Photographs, NYC

Figure 23.20 (a) A mirage is produced by the bending of light rays in the atmosphere when there are large temperature differences between the ground and the air. (b) Notice the reflection of the cars in this photograph of a mirage. The road looks like it's flooded with water, but it is actually dry.

Because an upright image and an inverted image are seen when the image of a tree is observed in a reflecting pool of water, the observer unconsciously calls on this past experience and concludes that the sky is reflected by a pool of water in front of the tree.

23.6 Thin Lenses

A typical **thin lens** consists of a piece of glass or plastic, ground so that each of its two refracting surfaces is a segment of either a sphere or a plane. Lenses are commonly used to form images by refraction in optical instruments, such as cameras, telescopes, and microscopes. The equation that relates object and image distances for a lens is virtually identical to the mirror equation derived earlier, and the method used to derive it is also similar.

Figure 23.21 shows some representative shapes of lenses. Notice that we have placed these lenses in two groups. Those in Figure 23.21a are thicker at the center than at the rim, and those in Figure 23.21b are thinner at the center than at the rim. The lenses in the first group are examples of **converging lenses**, and those in the second group are **diverging lenses**. The reason for these names will become apparent shortly.

As we did for mirrors, it is convenient to define a point called the **focal point** for a lens. For example, in Figure 23.22a, a group of rays parallel to the axis passes through the focal point *F* after being converged by the lens. The distance from the focal point to the lens is called the **focal length *f*. The focal length is the image distance that corresponds to an infinite object distance.** Recall that we are considering the lens to be very thin. As a result, it makes no difference whether we take the focal length to be the distance from the focal point to the surface of the lens or the distance from the focal point to the center of the lens because the difference between these two lengths is negligible. A thin lens has *two* focal points, as illustrated in Figure 23.22, one on each side of the lens. One focal point corresponds to parallel rays traveling from the left and the other corresponds to parallel rays traveling from the right.

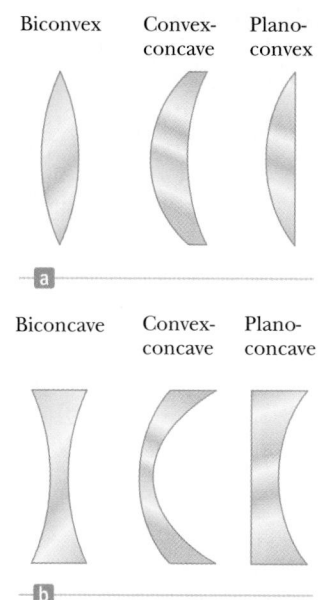

Figure 23.21 Various lens shapes. (a) Converging lenses have positive focal lengths and are thickest at the middle. (b) Diverging lenses have negative focal lengths and are thickest at the edges.

Figure 23.22 (*Left*) Photographs of the effects of converging and diverging lenses on parallel rays. (*Right*) The focal points of the (a) biconvex lens and (b) biconcave lens.

Figure 23.23 A geometric construction for developing the thin-lens equation.

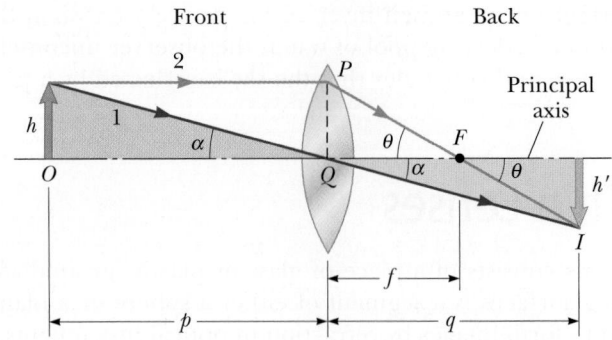

Rays parallel to the axis diverge after passing through a lens of biconcave shape, shown in Figure 23.22b. In this case the focal point is defined to be the point where the diverged rays appear to originate, labeled F in the figure. Figures 23.22a and 23.22b indicate why the names *converging* and *diverging* are applied to these lenses.

Now consider a ray of light passing through the center of a lens. Such a ray is labeled ray 1 in Figure 23.23. For a thin lens, a ray passing through the center is undeflected. Ray 2 in the same figure is parallel to the principal axis of the lens (the horizontal axis passing through O), and as a result it passes through the focal point F after refraction. Rays 1 and 2 intersect at the point that is the tip of the image arrow.

We first note that the tangent of the angle α can be found by using the blue and gold shaded triangles in Figure 23.23:

$$\tan \alpha = \frac{h}{p} \quad \text{or} \quad \tan \alpha = -\frac{h'}{q}$$

From this result, we find that

$$M = \frac{h'}{h} = -\frac{q}{p} \qquad \text{[23.10]}$$

The equation for magnification by a lens is the same as the equation for magnification by a mirror. We also note from Figure 23.23 that

$$\tan \theta = \frac{PQ}{f} \quad \text{or} \quad \tan \theta = -\frac{h'}{q-f}$$

The height PQ used in the first of these equations, however, is the same as h, the height of the object. Therefore,

$$\frac{h}{f} = -\frac{h'}{q-f}$$

$$\frac{h'}{h} = -\frac{q-f}{f}$$

Using the latter equation in combination with Equation 23.10 gives

$$\frac{q}{p} = \frac{q-f}{f}$$

which reduces to

Thin-lens equation ▶

$$\frac{1}{p} + \frac{1}{q} = \frac{1}{f} \qquad \text{[23.11]}$$

This equation, called the **thin-lens equation**, can be used with both converging and diverging lenses if we adhere to a set of sign conventions. Figure 23.24 is useful

Table 23.3 Sign Conventions for Thin Lenses

Quantity	Symbol	In Front	In Back	Convergent	Divergent
Object location	p	+	−		
Image location	q	−	+		
Lens radii	R_1, R_2	−	+		
Focal length	f			+	−

Front, or virtual, side Back, or real, side

p positive
q negative

p negative
q positive

Incident light   Refracted light

Converging or diverging lens

Figure 23.24 A diagram for obtaining the signs of p and q for a thin lens or a refracting surface.

for obtaining the signs of p and q, and Table 23.3 gives the complete sign conventions for lenses. Note that **a converging lens has a positive focal length** under this convention and **a diverging lens has a negative focal length**. Hence, the names *positive* and *negative* are often given to these lenses.

The focal length for a lens in air is related to the curvatures of its front and back surfaces and to the index of refraction n of the lens material by

$$\frac{1}{f} = (n-1)\left(\frac{1}{R_1} - \frac{1}{R_2}\right) \qquad [23.12]$$

◀ Lens-maker's equation

where R_1 is the radius of curvature of the front surface of the lens and R_2 is the radius of curvature of the back surface. (As with mirrors, we arbitrarily call the side from which the light approaches the *front* of the lens.) Table 23.3 gives the sign conventions for R_1 and R_2. Equation 23.12, called the **lens-maker's equation**, enables us to calculate the focal length from the known properties of the lens.

Ray Diagrams for Thin Lenses

Ray diagrams are essential for understanding the overall image formation by a thin lens or a system of lenses. They should also help clarify the sign conventions already discussed. Active Figure 23.25 illustrates this method for three single-lens situations. To locate the image formed by a converging lens (Active Figs. 23.25a and 23.25b), the following three rays are drawn from the top of the object:

1. The first ray is drawn parallel to the principal axis. After being refracted by the lens, this ray passes through (or appears to come from) one of the focal points.
2. The second ray is drawn through the center of the lens. This ray continues in a straight line.
3. The third ray is drawn through the other focal point and emerges from the lens parallel to the principal axis.

Tip 23.4 Positive Is Again Where the Light Is

For lenses, p and q are positive where the light is, where the object or image is real. For real objects, the light originates with the object in front of the lens, so p is positive there as indicated in Figure 23.24. If the image forms in back of the lens, q is positive there, as well.

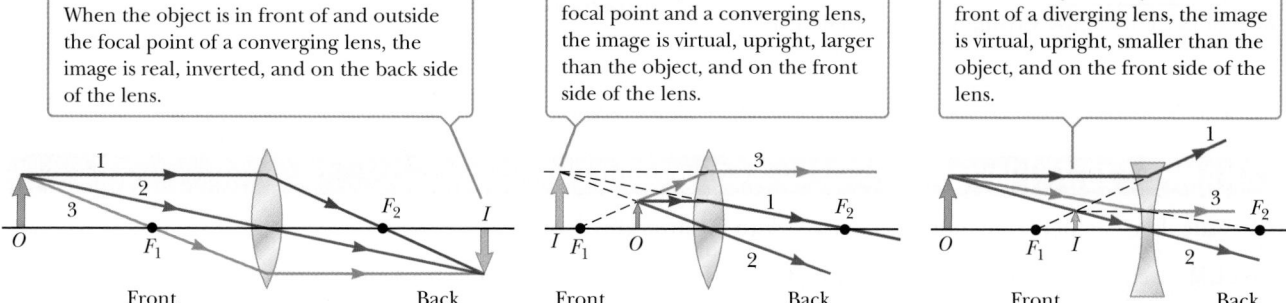

When the object is in front of and outside the focal point of a converging lens, the image is real, inverted, and on the back side of the lens.

When the object is between the focal point and a converging lens, the image is virtual, upright, larger than the object, and on the front side of the lens.

When an object is anywhere in front of a diverging lens, the image is virtual, upright, smaller than the object, and on the front side of the lens.

a   b   c

Active Figure 23.25
Ray diagrams for locating the image formed by a thin lens.

A similar construction is used to locate the image formed by a diverging lens, as shown in Active Figure 23.25c. The point of intersection of *any two* of the rays in these diagrams can be used to locate the image. The third ray serves as a check on construction.

For the converging lens in Active Figure 23.25a, where the object is *outside* the front focal point ($p > f$), the ray diagram shows that the image is real and inverted. When the real object is *inside* the front focal point ($p < f$), as in Active Figure 23.25b, the image is virtual and upright. For the diverging lens of Active Figure 23.25c, the image is virtual and upright.

■ Quick Quiz

23.4 A clear plastic sandwich bag filled with water can act as a crude converging lens in air. If the bag is filled with air and placed under water, is the effective lens (a) converging or (b) diverging?

23.5 In Active Figure 23.25a the blue object arrow is replaced by one that is much taller than the lens. How many rays from the object will strike the lens?

23.6 An object is placed to the left of a converging lens. Which of the following statements are true, and which are false? (a) The image is always to the right of the lens. (b) The image can be upright or inverted. (c) The image is always smaller or the same size as the object.

Your success in working lens or mirror problems will be determined largely by whether you make sign errors when substituting into the lens or mirror equations. The only way to ensure you don't make sign errors is to become adept at using the sign conventions. The best ways to do so are to work a multitude of problems on your own and to construct confirming ray diagrams. Watching an instructor or reading the example problems is no substitute for practice.

■ APPLYING PHYSICS 23.5 | Vision and Diving Masks BIO

Diving masks often have a lens built into the glass faceplate for divers who don't have perfect vision. This lens allows the individual to dive without the necessity of glasses because the faceplate performs the necessary refraction to produce clear vision. Normal glasses have lenses that are curved on both the front and rear surfaces. The lenses in a diving-mask faceplate often have curved surfaces only on the inside of the glass. Why is this design desirable?

SOLUTION The main reason for curving only the inner surface of the lens in the diving-mask faceplate is to enable the diver to see clearly while underwater and in the air. If there were curved surfaces on both the front and the back of the diving lens, there would be two refractions. The lens could be designed so that these two refractions would give clear vision while the diver is in air. When the diver went underwater, however, the refraction between the water and the glass at the first interface would differ because the index of refraction of water is different from that of air. Consequently, the diver's vision wouldn't be clear underwater. ■

■ EXAMPLE 23.7 | Images Formed by a Converging Lens

GOAL Calculate geometric quantities associated with a converging lens.

PROBLEM A converging lens of focal length 10.0 cm forms images of an object situated at various distances. **(a)** If the object is placed 30.0 cm from the lens, locate the image, state whether it's real or virtual, and find its magnification. **(b)** Repeat the problem when the object is at 10.0 cm and **(c)** again when the object is 5.00 cm from the lens.

STRATEGY All three problems require only substitution into the thin-lens equation and the associated magnification equation, Equations 23.10 and 23.11, respectively. The conventions of Table 23.3 must be followed.

Figure 23.26 (Example 23.7)

···

SOLUTION

(a) Find the image distance and describe the image when the object is placed at 30.0 cm.

The ray diagram is shown in Figure 23.26a. Substitute values into the thin-lens equation to locate the image:

$$\frac{1}{p} + \frac{1}{q} = \frac{1}{f}$$

$$\frac{1}{30.0 \text{ cm}} + \frac{1}{q} = \frac{1}{10.0 \text{ cm}}$$

Solve for q, the image distance. It's positive, so the image is real and on the far side of the lens:

$$q = \boxed{+15.0 \text{ cm}}$$

The magnification of the lens is obtained from Equation 23.10. M is negative and less than 1 in absolute value, so the image is inverted and smaller than the object:

$$M = -\frac{q}{p} = -\frac{15.0 \text{ cm}}{30.0 \text{ cm}} = \boxed{-0.500}$$

(b) Repeat the problem, when the object is placed at 10.0 cm.

Locate the image by substituting into the thin-lens equation:

$$\frac{1}{10.0 \text{ cm}} + \frac{1}{q} = \frac{1}{10.0 \text{ cm}} \quad \rightarrow \quad \frac{1}{q} = 0$$

This equation is satisfied only in the limit as q becomes infinite. Similarly, M becomes infinite, as well.

$$q \rightarrow \boxed{\infty}$$

(c) Repeat the problem when the object is placed 5.00 cm from the lens.

See the ray diagram shown in Figure 23.26b. Substitute into the thin-lens equation to locate the image:

$$\frac{1}{5.00 \text{ cm}} + \frac{1}{q} = \frac{1}{10.0 \text{ cm}}$$

Solve for q, which is negative, meaning the image is on the same side as the object and is virtual:

$$q = \boxed{-10.0 \text{ cm}}$$

Substitute the values of p and q into the magnification equation. M is positive and larger than 1, so the image is upright and double the object size:

$$M = -\frac{q}{p} = -\left(\frac{-10.0 \text{ cm}}{5.00 \text{ cm}}\right) = \boxed{+2.00}$$

···

REMARKS The ability of a lens to magnify objects led to the inventions of reading glasses, microscopes, and telescopes.

QUESTION 23.7 If the lens is used to form an image of the Sun on a screen, how far from the lens should the screen be located?

EXERCISE 23.7 Suppose the image of an object is upright and magnified 1.75 times when the object is placed 15.0 cm from a lens. Find (a) the location of the image and (b) the focal length of the lens.

ANSWERS (a) −26.3 cm (virtual, on the same side as the object)   (b) 34.9 cm

■ EXAMPLE 23.8 | The Case of a Diverging Lens

GOAL Calculate geometric quantities associated with a diverging lens.

PROBLEM Repeat the problem of Example 23.7 for a *diverging* lens of focal length 10.0 cm.

STRATEGY Once again, substitution into the thin-lens equation and the associated magnification equation, together with the conventions in Table 23.3, solve the various parts. The only difference is the negative focal length.

. . . .

SOLUTION

(a) Locate the image and its magnification if the object is at 30.0 cm.

The ray diagram is given in Figure 23.27a. Apply the thin-lens equation with $p = 30.0$ cm to locate the image:

$$\frac{1}{p} + \frac{1}{q} = \frac{1}{f}$$

$$\frac{1}{30.0 \text{ cm}} + \frac{1}{q} = -\frac{1}{10.0 \text{ cm}}$$

Solve for q, which is negative and hence virtual:

$$q = \boxed{-7.50 \text{ cm}}$$

Substitute into Equation 23.10 to get the magnification. Because M is positive and has absolute value less than 1, the image is upright and smaller than the object:

$$M = -\frac{q}{p} = -\left(\frac{-7.50 \text{ cm}}{30.0 \text{ cm}}\right) = \boxed{+0.250}$$

(b) Locate the image and find its magnification if the object is 10.0 cm from the lens.

Apply the thin-lens equation, taking $p = 10.0$ cm:

$$\frac{1}{10.0 \text{ cm}} + \frac{1}{q} = -\frac{1}{10.0 \text{ cm}}$$

Solve for q (once again, the result is negative, so the image is virtual):

$$q = \boxed{-5.00 \text{ cm}}$$

Calculate the magnification. Because M is positive and has absolute value less than 1, the image is upright and smaller than the object:

$$M = -\frac{q}{p} = -\left(\frac{-5.00 \text{ cm}}{10.0 \text{ cm}}\right) = \boxed{+0.500}$$

(c) Locate the image and find its magnification when the object is at 5.00 cm.

The ray diagram is given in Figure 23.27b. Substitute $p = 5.00$ cm into the thin-lens equation to locate the image:

$$\frac{1}{5.00 \text{ cm}} + \frac{1}{q} = -\frac{1}{10.0 \text{ cm}}$$

Solve for q. The answer is negative, so once again the image is virtual:

$$q = \boxed{-3.33 \text{ cm}}$$

Figure 23.27 (Example 23.8)

Calculate the magnification. Because M is positive and less than 1, the image is upright and smaller than the object:

$$M = -\left(\frac{-3.33 \text{ cm}}{5.00 \text{ cm}}\right) = \boxed{+ 0.666}$$

REMARKS Notice that in every case the image is virtual, hence on the same side of the lens as the object. Further, the image is smaller than the object. For a diverging lens and a real object, this is *always* the case, as can be proven mathematically.

QUESTION 23.8 Can a diverging lens be used as a magnifying glass? Explain.

EXERCISE 23.8 Repeat the calculation, finding the position of the image and the magnification if the object is 20.0 cm from the lens.

ANSWERS $q = -6.67$ cm, $M = 0.334$

Combinations of Thin Lenses

Many useful optical devices require two lenses. Handling problems involving two lenses is not much different from dealing with a single-lens problem twice. First, the image produced by the first lens is calculated as though the second lens were not present. The light then approaches the second lens *as if* it had come from the image formed by the first lens. Hence, **the image formed by the first lens is treated as the object for the second lens**. The image formed by the second lens is the final image of the system. If the image formed by the first lens lies on the back side of the second lens, the image is treated as a virtual object for the second lens, so p is negative. The same procedure can be extended to a system of three or more lenses. The overall magnification of a system of thin lenses is the *product* of the magnifications of the separate lenses. It's also possible to combine thin lenses and mirrors as shown in Example 23.10.

■ EXAMPLE 23.9 | Two Lenses in a Row

GOAL Calculate geometric quantities for a sequential pair of lenses.

PROBLEM Two converging lenses are placed 20.0 cm apart, as shown in Figure 23.28a (page 812), with an object 30.0 cm in front of lens 1 on the left. **(a)** If lens 1 has a focal length of 10.0 cm, locate the image formed by this lens and determine its magnification. **(b)** If lens 2 on the right has a focal length of 20.0 cm, locate the final image formed and find the total magnification of the system.

STRATEGY We apply the thin-lens equation to each lens. The image formed by lens 1 is treated as the object for lens 2. Also, we use the fact that the total magnification of the system is the product of the magnifications produced by the separate lenses.

SOLUTION

(a) Locate the image and determine the magnification of lens 1.

See the ray diagram, Figure 23.28b. Apply the thin-lens equation to lens 1:

$$\frac{1}{30.0 \text{ cm}} + \frac{1}{q} = \frac{1}{10.0 \text{ cm}}$$

Solve for q, which is positive and hence to the right of the first lens:

$$q = \boxed{+ 15.0 \text{ cm}}$$

Compute the magnification of lens 1:

$$M_1 = -\frac{q}{p} = -\frac{15.0 \text{ cm}}{30.0 \text{ cm}} = \boxed{-0.500}$$

(b) Locate the final image and find the total magnification.

The image formed by lens 1 becomes the object for lens 2. Compute the object distance for lens 2:

$$p = 20.0 \text{ cm} - 15.0 \text{ cm} = 5.00 \text{ cm}$$

(Continued)

Figure 23.28 (Example 23.9)

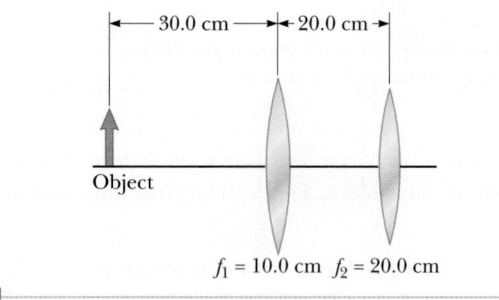

$f_1 = 10.0$ cm $f_2 = 20.0$ cm

a

b

Once again apply the thin-lens equation to lens 2 to locate the final image:

$$\frac{1}{5.00 \text{ cm}} + \frac{1}{q} = \frac{1}{20.0 \text{ cm}}$$

$$q = \boxed{-6.67 \text{ cm}}$$

Calculate the magnification of lens 2:

$$M_2 = -\frac{q}{p} = -\frac{(-6.67 \text{ cm})}{5.00 \text{ cm}} = +1.33$$

Multiply the two magnifications to get the overall magnification of the system:

$$M = M_1 M_2 = (-0.500)(1.33) = \boxed{-0.665}$$

REMARKS The negative sign for M indicates that the final image is inverted and smaller than the object because the absolute value of M is less than 1. Because q is negative, the final image is virtual.

QUESTION 23.9 If lens 2 is moved so it is 40 cm away from lens 1, would the final image be upright or inverted?

EXERCISE 23.9 If the two lenses in Figure 23.28 are separated by 10.0 cm, locate the final image and find the magnification of the system. *Hint:* The object for the second lens is virtual!

ANSWERS 4.00 cm behind the second lens, $M = -0.400$

■ **EXAMPLE 23.10** | **Thin Lens and a Concave Mirror**

GOAL Solve a problem involving both a lens and a mirror.

PROBLEM An object is placed 20.0 cm to the right of a concave mirror with focal length 12.0 cm and 30.0 cm to the left of a converging lens with focal length 10.0 cm, as in Figure 23.29. Locate **(a)** the image formed by the lens alone, **(b)** the image created by the mirror alone, and **(c)** the image created by both the mirror and lens. **(d)** The mirror is moved so that it is 6.00 cm away from the object. Locate the image formed by the mirror and lens.

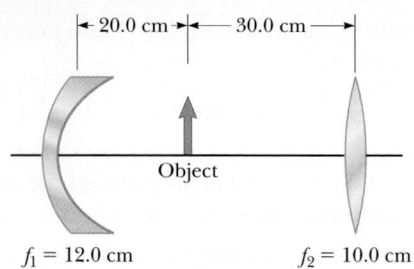

$f_1 = 12.0$ cm $f_2 = 10.0$ cm

Figure 23.29 (Example 23.10)

STRATEGY Part (a) is a simple application of the thin-lens equation, Equation 23.11. Part (b) can be calculated from Equation 23.6. Using the image formed by the mirror as the object for the lens, find the image location asked for in part (c), for light that first reflects off the mirror before passing through the lens.

. . . .

SOLUTION

(a) Locate the image formed by the lens alone.

Apply Equation 23.11:

$$\frac{1}{p_2} + \frac{1}{q_2} = \frac{1}{f_2}$$

Substitute values and solve for the image position, q_2:

$$\frac{1}{q_2} = \frac{1}{f_2} - \frac{1}{p_2} = \frac{1}{10.0 \text{ cm}} - \frac{1}{30.0 \text{ cm}} = \frac{1}{15.0 \text{ cm}}$$

$$q_2 = \boxed{15.0 \text{ cm}}$$

(b) Locate the image created by the mirror alone.

Apply Equation 23.6:

$$\frac{1}{p_1} + \frac{1}{q_1} = \frac{1}{f_1}$$

Substitute values for f_1 and p_1, which are both positive, and solve for q_1:

$$\frac{1}{q_1} = \frac{1}{f_1} - \frac{1}{p_1} = \frac{1}{12.0 \text{ cm}} - \frac{1}{20.0 \text{ cm}} = \frac{1}{30.0 \text{ cm}}$$

$$q_1 = \boxed{30.0 \text{ cm}}$$

(c) Locate the image created by both the mirror and lens.

Apply Equation 23.11 to the image found in part (b), which becomes a real object for the lens, noticing that the image formed by the mirror is 20.0 cm from the lens:

$$\frac{1}{q_{2f}} = \frac{1}{f_2} - \frac{1}{p_{2f}} = \frac{1}{10.0 \text{ cm}} - \frac{1}{20.0 \text{ cm}} = \frac{1}{20.0 \text{ cm}}$$

$$q_{2f} = \boxed{20.0 \text{ cm}}$$

(d) The mirror is moved so that it is 6.00 cm to the left of the object. Locate the image formed by the mirror and lens.

The object is now much closer to the mirror. Find the new location of the image created by the mirror:

$$\frac{1}{q_1} = \frac{1}{f_1} - \frac{1}{p_1} = \frac{1}{12.0 \text{ cm}} - \frac{1}{6.0 \text{ cm}} = -\frac{1}{12.0 \text{ cm}}$$

$$q_1 = -12.0 \text{ cm}$$

The image created by the mirror is virtual and therefore behind the mirror. However, it acts like a real object for the lens. Apply Equation 23.11 with $p_2 = 30.0 \text{ cm} + 18.0 \text{ cm} = 48.0 \text{ cm}$:

$$\frac{1}{q_2} = \frac{1}{f_2} - \frac{1}{p_2} = \frac{1}{10.0 \text{ cm}} - \frac{1}{48.0 \text{ cm}} = \frac{19}{2.40 \times 10^2 \text{ cm}}$$

$$q_2 = \boxed{12.6 \text{ cm}}$$

. . . .

REMARKS There are two final images created to the right of the lens, as expected. As the mirror is moved closer to the object, the final image due to both the mirror and lens moves closer to the lens. The image of part (a) is inverted; however, the image of part (c) goes through two inversions, hence is upright. The virtual mirror image of part (d) is upright, so its lens image is inverted.

QUESTION 23.10 Is it possible to have a virtual object for a mirror? Explain, giving an example.

EXERCISE 23.10 The same mirror and lens are repositioned so that the mirror is 24.0 cm to the left of the lens and the object is 20.0 cm to the right of the lens. Locate the image of (a) the lens alone, (b) the first image formed by the mirror, and (c) the final, second image formed by the lens.

ANSWERS (a) 20.0 cm to the left of the lens (b) 6.00 cm behind the mirror (c) 15.0 cm to the right of the lens

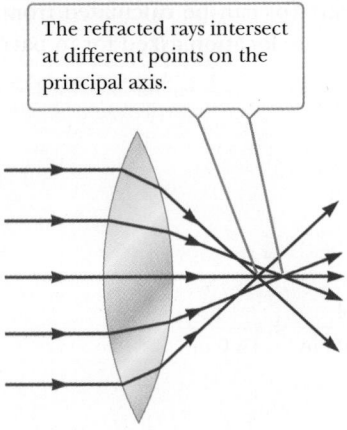

The refracted rays intersect at different points on the principal axis.

Figure 23.30 Spherical aberration used by a converging lens. Does a diverging lens use spherical aberration?

23.7 Lens and Mirror Aberrations

One of the basic problems of systems containing mirrors and lenses is the imperfect quality of the images, which is largely the result of defects in shape and form. The simple theory of mirrors and lenses assumes rays make small angles with the principal axis and all rays reaching the lens or mirror from a point source are focused at a single point, producing a sharp image. This is not always true in the real world. Where the approximations used in this theory do not hold, imperfect images are formed.

If one wishes to analyze image formation precisely, it is necessary to trace each ray, using Snell's law, at each refracting surface. This procedure shows that there is no single point image; instead, the image is blurred. The departures of real (imperfect) images from the ideal predicted by the simple theory are called **aberrations.** Two common types of aberrations are spherical aberration and chromatic aberration.

Spherical Aberration

Spherical aberration results from the fact that the focal points of light rays passing far from the principal axis of a spherical lens (or mirror) are different from the focal points of rays with the same wavelength passing near the axis. Figure 23.30 illustrates spherical aberration for parallel rays passing through a converging lens. Rays near the middle of the lens are imaged farther from the lens than rays at the edges. Hence, there is no single focal length for a spherical lens.

Most cameras are equipped with an adjustable aperture to control the light intensity and, when possible, reduce spherical aberration. (An aperture is an opening that controls the amount of light transmitted through the lens.) As the aperture size is reduced, sharper images are produced because only the central portion of the lens is exposed to the incident light when the aperture is very small. At the same time, however, progressively less light is imaged. To compensate for this loss, a longer exposure time is used. An example of the results obtained with small apertures is the sharp image produced by a pinhole camera, with an aperture size of approximately 0.1 mm.

In the case of mirrors used for very distant objects, one can eliminate, or at least minimize, spherical aberration by employing a parabolic rather than spherical surface. Parabolic surfaces are not used in many applications, however, because they are very expensive to make with high-quality optics. Parallel light rays incident on such a surface focus at a common point. Parabolic reflecting surfaces are used in many astronomical telescopes to enhance the image quality. They are also used in flashlights, in which a nearly parallel light beam is produced from a small lamp placed at the focus of the reflecting surface.

Rays of different wavelengths focus at different points.

Violet
Red
F_R
F_V
Red
Violet
Red

Figure 23.31 Chromatic aberration produced by a converging lens.

Chromatic Aberration

Different wavelengths of light refracted by a lens focus at different points, which gives rise to chromatic aberration. In Chapter 22 we described how the index of refraction of a material varies with wavelength. When white light passes through a lens, for example, violet light rays are refracted more than red light rays (see Fig. 23.31), so the focal length for red light is greater than for violet light. Other wavelengths (not shown in the figure) would have intermediate focal points. Chromatic aberration for a diverging lens is opposite that for a converging lens. Chromatic aberration can be greatly reduced by a combination of converging and diverging lenses.

■ SUMMARY

23.1 Flat Mirrors

Images are formed where rays of light intersect or where they appear to originate. A **real image** is formed when light intersects, or passes through, an image point. In a **virtual image** the light doesn't pass through the image point, but appears to diverge from it.

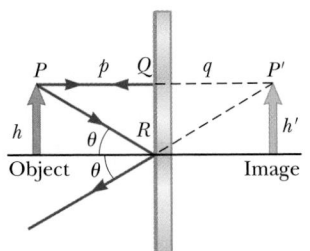

A geometric construction to locate the image of an object placed in front of a flat mirror. Because the triangles PQR and $P'QR$ are identical, $p = |q|$ and $h = h'$.

The image formed by a flat mirror has the following properties: **1.** The image is as far behind the mirror as the object is in front of it. **2.** The image is unmagnified, virtual, and upright.

23.2 Images Formed by Concave Mirrors

23.3 Convex Mirrors and Sign Conventions

The **magnification** M of a spherical mirror is defined as the ratio of the **image height** h' to the **object height** h, which is the negative of the ratio of the image distance q to the object distance p:

$$M = \frac{h'}{h} = -\frac{q}{p} \qquad [23.2]$$

The **object distance** and **image distance** for a spherical mirror of radius R are related by the **mirror equation**:

$$\frac{1}{p} + \frac{1}{q} = \frac{1}{f} \qquad [23.6]$$

where $f = R/2$ is the **focal length** of the mirror.

Equations 23.2 and 23.6 hold for both concave and convex mirrors, subject to the sign conventions given in Table 23.1.

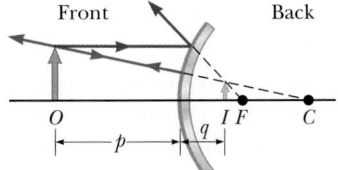

The image of a convex mirror is virtual, upright, and behind the mirror.

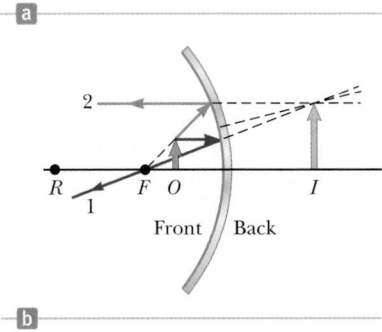

(a) The image of a concave mirror is real and inverted when the object is outside the focal point, i.e. $p > f$. The image is larger than the object when $f < p < R$, and smaller than the object when $p > R$. (b) The image of a concave mirror is virtual, upright, and larger than the object when $p < f$.

23.4 Images Formed by Refraction

An image can be formed by refraction at a spherical surface of radius R. The object and image distances for refraction from such a surface are related by

$$\frac{n_1}{p} + \frac{n_2}{q} = \frac{n_2 - n_1}{R} \qquad [23.7]$$

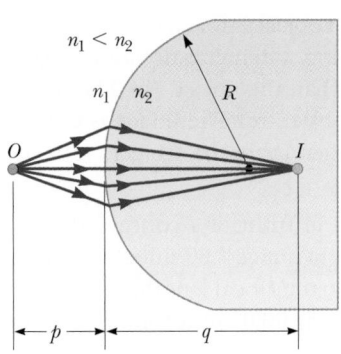

An image formed by refraction at a spherical surface. Rays making small angles with the principal axis diverge from a point object at O and pass through the image point I.

The **magnification of a refracting surface** is

$$M = \frac{h'}{h} = -\frac{n_1 q}{n_2 p} \qquad [23.8]$$

where the object is located in the medium with index of refraction n_1 and the image is formed in the medium with index of refraction n_2. Equations 23.7 and 23.8 are subject to the sign conventions of Table 23.2.

23.6 Thin Lenses

The **magnification of a thin lens** is

$$M = \frac{h'}{h} = -\frac{q}{p} \qquad [23.10]$$

The object and image distances of a thin lens are related by the **thin-lens equation**:

$$\frac{1}{p} + \frac{1}{q} = \frac{1}{f} \qquad [23.11]$$

Equations 23.10 and 23.11 are subject to the sign conventions of Table 23.3.

23.7 Lens and Mirror Aberrations

Aberrations are responsible for the formation of imperfect images by lenses and mirrors. **Spherical aberration** results from the focal points of light rays far from the principal axis of a spherical lens or mirror being different from those of rays passing through the center. **Chromatic aberration** arises because light rays of different wavelengths focus at different points when refracted by a lens.

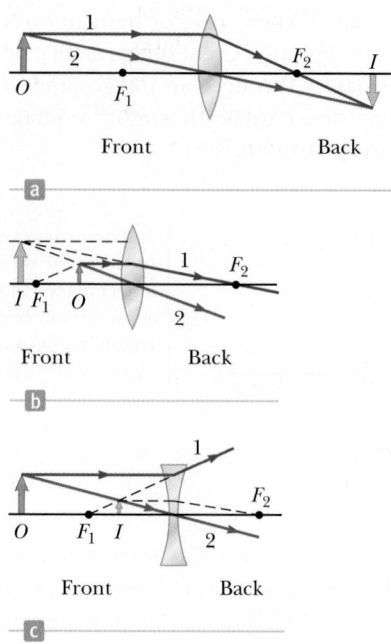

Ray diagrams for locating the image of an object. (a) The object is outside the focal point of a converging lens. (b) The object is inside the focal point of a converging lens. (c) The object is outside the focal point of a diverging lens.

■ MULTIPLE-CHOICE QUESTIONS

1. When an image of a real object is formed by a flat mirror, which of the following statements are always true? (a) The image is larger than the object. (b) The image is the same size as the object. (c) The image is virtual. (d) The image is smaller than the object. (e) The image is upright.

2. If Josh's face is 30.0 cm in front of a concave shaving mirror creating an upright image 1.50 times as large as the object, what is the mirror's focal length? (a) 12.0 cm (b) 20.0 cm (c) 70.0 cm (d) 90.0 cm (e) none of those answers

3. A thin, convergent lens has a focal length of 8.00 cm. If a real, inverted image is located 12.0 cm to the right of the lens, where is the object located? (a) 12.0 cm to the left of the lens (b) 24.0 cm to the right of the lens (c) 24.0 cm to the left of the lens (d) 18.0 cm to the right of the lens (e) 18.0 cm to the left of the lens

4. A converging lens has a virtual object located a finite distance away. Which of the following must be true? (a) The image is virtual. (b) The image is real. (c) $p < 0$ (d) $p > 0$ (e) $f > q$

5. An object is placed 16.0 cm away from a convex mirror with a focal length of magnitude 6.00 cm. What is the location of the image? (a) 9.60 cm in front of the mirror (b) 4.36 cm in front of the mirror (c) 9.60 cm behind the mirror (d) 4.36 cm behind the mirror (e) 10.0 cm in front of the mirror

6. A real object is 10.0 cm to the left of a thin, diverging lens having a focal length of magnitude 16.0 cm. What is the location of the image? (a) 6.15 cm to the right of the lens (b) 6.15 cm to the left of the lens (c) 26.7 cm to the right of the lens (d) 26.7 cm to the left of the lens (e) 6.00 cm to the right of the lens

7. When the image of a real object is formed by a concave mirror, which of the following statements are true? (a) The image is always real. (b) The image is always virtual. (c) If the object distance is less than the focal length, the image is real. (d) If the object distance is greater than the focal length, the image is real. (e) If $q < 0$, the image is virtual.

8. An object is located 50 cm from a converging lens having a focal length of 15 cm. Which of the following is

true regarding the image formed by the lens? (a) It is virtual, upright, and larger than the object. (b) It is virtual, inverted, and smaller than the object. (c) It is real, inverted, and smaller than the object. (d) It is real, inverted, and larger than the object. (e) It is real, upright, and larger than the object.

9. A convex mirror forms an image of a real object. Which of the following statements is always true? (a) The image is real and upright. (b) The image is virtual and larger than the object. (c) The image is virtual and upright. (d) The image is larger than the object. (e) The image is virtual and inverted.

10. For a real object, is the image formed by a diverging lens always (a) virtual and inverted, (b) virtual and upright, (c) real and upright, (d) real and inverted, or (e) real and magnified?

11. A person spearfishing from a boat sees a stationary fish a few meters away in a direction about 30° below the horizontal. To spear the fish, and assuming the spear does not change direction when it enters the water, should the person (a) aim above where he sees the fish, (b) aim below the fish, or (c) aim precisely at the fish?

12. An object, represented by a gray arrow, is placed in front of a plane mirror. Which of the diagrams in Figure MCQ23.12 best describes the image, represented by the pink arrow?

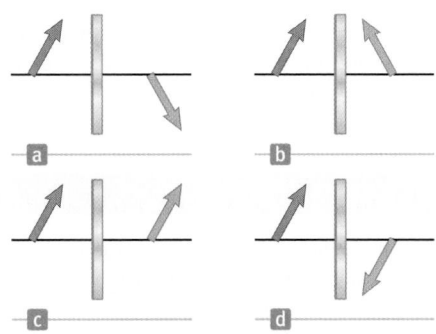

Figure MCQ23.12

■ CONCEPTUAL QUESTIONS

WebAssign The conceptual questions in this chapter may be assigned online in Enhanced WebAssign.

1. Tape a picture of yourself on a bathroom mirror. Stand several centimeters away from the mirror. Can you focus your eyes on *both* the picture taped to the mirror *and* your image in the mirror *at the same time*? So where is the image of yourself?

2. Why does a clear stream always appear to be shallower than it actually is?

3. A flat mirror creates a virtual image of your face. Suppose the flat mirror is combined with another optical element. Can the mirror form a real image in such a combination?

4. Explain why a mirror cannot give rise to chromatic aberration.

5. A common mirage is formed when the air gets gradually cooler as the height above the ground increases. What might happen if the air grows gradually warmer as the height increases? This often happens over bodies of water or snow-covered ground; the effect is called *looming*.

6. A virtual image is often described as an image through which light rays don't actually travel, as they do for a real image. Can a virtual image be photographed?

7. Suppose you want to use a converging lens to project the image of two trees onto a screen. One tree is a distance x from the lens; the other is at $2x$, as in Figure CQ23.7. You adjust the screen so that the near tree is in focus. If you now want the far tree to be in focus, do you move the screen toward or away from the lens?

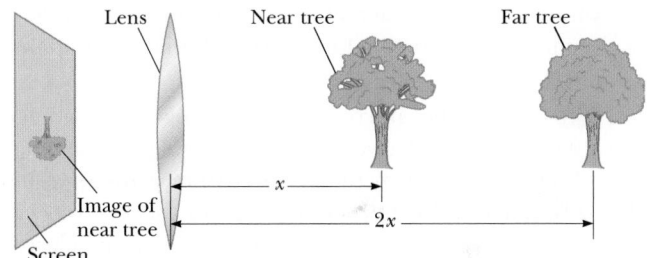

Figure CQ23.7

8. Lenses used in eyeglasses, whether converging or diverging, are always designed such that the middle of the lens curves away from the eye. Why?

9. In a Jules Verne novel, a piece of ice is shaped into a magnifying lens to focus sunlight to start a fire. Is that possible?

10. If a cylinder of solid glass or clear plastic is placed above the words LEAD OXIDE and viewed from the side, as shown in Figure CQ23.10, the word LEAD appears inverted, but the word OXIDE does not. Explain.

Figure CQ23.10

11. Can a converging lens be made to diverge light if placed in a liquid? How about a converging mirror?

12. Light from an object passes through a lens and forms a visible image on a screen. If the screen is removed, would you be able to see the image (a) if you remained in your present position and (b) if you could look at the lens along its axis, beyond the original position of the screen?

13. Why does the focal length of a mirror not depend on the mirror material when the focal length of a lens does depend on the lens material?

14. An inverted image of an object is viewed on a screen from the side facing a converging lens. An opaque card is then introduced covering only the upper half of the lens. What happens to the image on the screen? (a) Half the image would disappear. (b) The entire image would appear and remain unchanged. (c) Half the image would disappear and be dimmer. (d) The entire image would appear, but would be dimmer.

15. Why do some emergency vehicles have the symbol AMBULANCE written on the front?

■ PROBLEMS

WebAssign The problems in this chapter may be assigned online in Enhanced WebAssign. Selected problems also have Watch It video solutions.

1. denotes straightforward problem; 2. denotes intermediate problem;

3. denotes challenging problem

1. denotes full solution available in *Student Solutions Manual/ Study Guide*

1. denotes problems most often assigned in Enhanced WebAssign

BIO denotes biomedical problems

GP denotes guided problems

M denotes Master It tutorial available in Enhanced WebAssign

Q|C denotes asking for quantitative and conceptual reasoning

S denotes symbolic reasoning problem

23.1 Flat Mirrors

1. (a) Does your bathroom mirror show you older or younger than your actual age? (b) Compute an order-of-magnitude estimate for the age difference, based on data you specify.

2. **Q|C** Two plane mirrors stand facing each other, 3.00 m apart, and a woman stands between them. The woman faces one of the mirrors from a distance of 1.00 m and holds her left arm out to the side of her body with the palm of her left hand facing the closer mirror. (a) What is the apparent position of the closest image of her left hand, measured perpendicularly from the surface of the mirror in front of her? (b) Does it show the palm of her hand or the back of her hand? (c) What is the position of the next image? (d) Does it show the palm of her hand or the back of her hand? (e) What is the position of the third closest image? (f) Does it show the palm of her hand or the back of her hand? (g) Which of the images are real and which are virtual?

3. A person walks into a room that has, on opposite walls, two plane mirrors producing multiple images. Find the distances from the person to the first three images seen in the left-hand mirror when the person is 5.00 ft from the mirror on the left wall and 10.0 ft from the mirror on the right wall.

4. In a church choir loft, two parallel walls are 5.30 m apart. The singers stand against the north wall. The organist faces the south wall, sitting 0.800 m away from it. So that she can see the choir, a flat mirror 0.600 m wide is mounted on the south wall, straight in front of the organist. What width of the north wall can she see? *Hint:* Draw a top-view diagram to justify your answer.

5. A periscope (Fig. P23.5) is useful for viewing objects that cannot be seen directly. It can be used in submarines and when watching golf matches or parades from behind a crowd of people. Suppose the object is a distance p_1 from the upper mirror and the centers of the two flat mirrors are separated by a distance h. (a) What is the distance of the final image from the lower mirror? (b) Is the final image real or virtual? (c) Is it upright or inverted? (d) What is its magnification? (e) Does it appear to be left–right reversed?

Figure P23.5

23.2 Images Formed by Concave Mirrors

23.3 Convex Mirrors and Sign Conventions

In the following problems, algebraic signs are not given. We leave it to you to determine the correct sign to use with each quantity, based on an analysis of the problem and the sign conventions in Table 23.1.

6. A dentist uses a mirror to examine a tooth that is 1.00 cm in front of the mirror. The image of the tooth is formed 10.0 cm behind the mirror. Determine

(a) the mirror's radius of curvature and (b) the magnification of the image.

7. A convex spherical mirror, whose focal length has a magnitude of 15.0 cm, is to form an image 10.0 cm behind the mirror. (a) Where should the object be placed? (b) What is the magnification of the mirror?

8. **BIO** To fit a contact lens to a patient's eye, a *keratometer* can be used to measure the curvature of the cornea—the front surface of the eye. This instrument places an illuminated object of known size at a known distance p from the cornea, which then reflects some light from the object, forming an image of it. The magnification M of the image is measured by using a small viewing telescope that allows a comparison of the image formed by the cornea with a second calibrated image projected into the field of view by a prism arrangement. Determine the radius of curvature of the cornea when $p = 30.0$ cm and $M = 0.013\ 0$.

9. A virtual image is formed 20.0 cm from a concave mirror having a radius of curvature of 40.0 cm. (a) Find the position of the object. (b) What is the magnification of the mirror?

10. **QC** While looking at her image in a cosmetic mirror, Dina notes that her face is highly magnified when she is close to the mirror, but as she backs away from the mirror, her image first becomes blurry, then disappears when she is about 30 cm from the mirror, and then inverts when she is beyond 30 cm. Based on these observations, what can she conclude about the properties of the mirror?

11. A 2.00-cm-high object is placed 3.00 cm in front of a concave mirror. If the image is 5.00 cm high and virtual, what is the focal length of the mirror?

12. A dedicated sports car enthusiast polishes the inside and outside surfaces of a hubcap that is a section of a sphere. When he looks into one side of the hubcap, he sees an image of his face 30.0 cm in back of it. He then turns the hubcap over, keeping it the same distance from his face. He now sees an image of his face 10.0 cm in back of the hubcap. (a) How far is his face from the hubcap? (b) What is the magnitude of the radius of curvature of the hubcap?

13. A concave makeup mirror is designed so that a person 25 cm in front of it sees an upright image magnified by a factor of two. What is the radius of curvature of the mirror?

14. A concave mirror has a focal length of 30.0 cm. (a) What is its radius of curvature? Locate and describe the properties of the image when the object distance is (b) 100 cm and (c) 10.0 cm.

15. **M** A man standing 1.52 m in front of a shaving mirror produces an inverted image 18.0 cm in front of it. How close to the mirror should he stand if he wants to form an upright image of his chin that is twice the chin's actual size?

16. A convex mirror has a focal length of magnitude 8.0 cm. (a) If the image is virtual, what is the object location for which the magnitude of the image distance is one third the magnitude of the object distance? (b) Find the magnification of the image and state whether it is upright or inverted.

17. **M** At an intersection of hospital hallways, a convex spherical mirror is mounted high on a wall to help people avoid collisions. The magnitude of the mirror's radius of curvature is 0.550 m. (a) Locate the image of a patient located 10.0 m from the mirror. (b) Indicate whether the image is upright or inverted. (c) Determine the magnification of the image.

18. **QC** A concave mirror has a radius of curvature of 24.0 cm. (a) Determine the object position for which the resulting image is upright and larger than the object by a factor of 3.00. (b) Draw a ray diagram to determine the position of the image. (c) Is the image real or virtual?

19. **QC** A spherical mirror is to be used to form an image, five times as tall as an object, on a screen positioned 5.0 m from the mirror. (a) Describe the type of mirror required. (b) Where should the mirror be positioned relative to the object?

20. **QC** A ball is dropped from rest 3.00 m directly above the vertex of a concave mirror having a radius of 1.00 m and lying in a horizontal plane. (a) Describe the motion of the ball's image in the mirror. (b) At what time do the ball and its image coincide?

23.4 Images Formed by Refraction

21. A cubical block of ice 50.0 cm on an edge is placed on a level floor over a speck of dust. Locate the image of the speck, when viewed from directly above, if the index of refraction of ice is 1.309.

22. A goldfish is swimming inside a spherical bowl of water having an index of refraction $n = 1.333$. Suppose the goldfish is $p = 10.0$ cm from the wall of a bowl of *radius* $|R| = 15.0$ cm, as in Figure P23.22. Neglecting the refraction of light caused by the wall of the bowl, determine the apparent distance of the goldfish from the wall according to an observer outside the bowl.

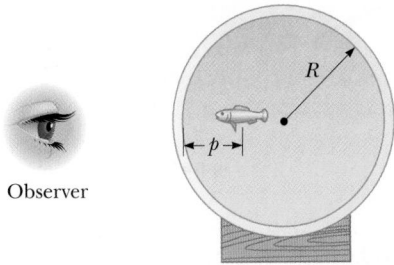

Observer

Figure P23.22

23. A paperweight is made of a solid glass hemisphere with index of refraction 1.50. The radius of the circular cross section is 4.0 cm. The hemisphere is placed on its flat surface, with the center directly over a 2.5-mm-long line drawn on a sheet of paper. What length of line is seen by someone looking vertically down on the hemisphere?

24. The top of a swimming pool is at ground level. If the pool is 2.00 m deep, how far below ground level does the bottom of the pool appear to be located when (a) the pool is completely filled with water? (b) When it is filled halfway with water?

25. A transparent sphere of unknown composition is observed to form an image of the Sun on its surface opposite the Sun. What is the refractive index of the sphere material?

26. A flint glass plate ($n = 1.66$) rests on the bottom of an aquarium tank. The plate is 8.00 cm thick (vertical dimension) and covered with water ($n = 1.33$) to a depth of 12.0 cm. Calculate the apparent thickness of the plate as viewed from above the water. (Assume nearly normal incidence of light rays.)

27. **Q|C** A jellyfish is floating in a water-filled aquarium 1.00 m behind a flat pane of glass 6.00 cm thick and having an index of refraction of 1.50. (a) Where is the image of the jellyfish located? (b) Repeat the problem when the glass is so thin that its thickness can be neglected. (c) How does the thickness of the glass affect the answer to part (a)?

28. **S** Figure P23.28 shows a curved surface separating a material with index of refraction n_1 from a material with index n_2. The surface forms an image I of object O. The ray shown in red passes through the surface along a radial line. Its angles of incidence and refraction are both zero, so its direction does not change at the surface. For the ray shown in blue, the direction changes according to $n_1 \sin \theta_1 = n_2 \sin \theta_2$. For paraxial rays, we assume θ_1 and θ_2 are small, so we may write $n_1 \tan \theta_1 = n_2 \tan \theta_2$. The magnification is defined as $M = h'/h$. Prove that the magnification is given by $M = -n_1 q / n_2 p$.

30. An object is placed 50.0 cm from a screen. (a) Where should a converging lens of focal length 10.0 cm be placed to form an image on the screen? (b) Find the magnification of the lens.

31. A converging lens has a focal length of 10.0 cm. Locate the images for object distances of (a) 20.0 cm, (b) 10.0 cm, and (c) 5.00 cm, if they exist. For each case, state whether the image is real or virtual, upright or inverted, and find the magnification.

32. An object is placed 20.0 cm from a concave spherical mirror having a focal length of magnitude 40.0 cm. (a) Use graph paper to construct an accurate ray diagram for this situation. (b) From your ray diagram, determine the location of the image. (c) What is the magnification of the image? (d) Check your answers to parts (b) and (c) using the mirror equation.

33. A diverging lens has a focal length of magnitude 20.0 cm. (a) Locate the images for object distances of (i) 40.0 cm, (ii) 20.0 cm, and (iii) 10.0 cm. For each case, state whether the image is (b) real or virtual and (c) upright or inverted. (d) For each case, find the magnification.

34. **Q|C** A diverging lens has a focal length of 20.0 cm. Use graph paper to construct accurate ray diagrams for object distances of (a) 40.0 cm and (b) 10.0 cm. In each case determine the location of the image from the diagram and the image magnification, and state whether the image is upright or inverted. (c) Estimate the magnitude of uncertainty in locating the points in the graph. Are your answers and the uncertainty consistent with the algebraic answers found in Problem 33?

35. A transparent photographic slide is placed in front of a converging lens with a focal length of 2.44 cm. An image of the slide is formed 12.9 cm from the slide. How far is the lens from the slide if the image is (a) real? (b) Virtual?

36. The nickel's image in Figure P23.36 has twice the diameter of the nickel when the lens is 2.84 cm from the nickel. Determine the focal length of the lens.

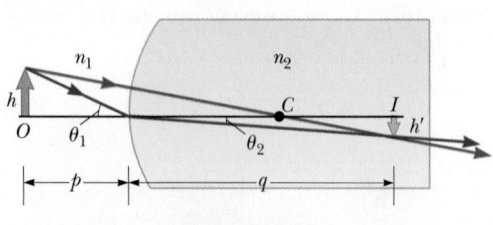

Figure P23.28

23.6 Thin Lenses

29. **BIO** A contact lens is made of plastic with an index of refraction of 1.50. The lens has an outer radius of curvature of +2.00 cm and an inner radius of curvature of +2.50 cm. What is the focal length of the lens?

Figure P23.36

37. The projection lens in a certain slide projector is a single thin lens. A slide 24.0 mm high is to be projected so that its image fills a screen 1.80 m high. The slide-

to-screen distance is 3.00 m. (a) Determine the focal length of the projection lens. (b) How far from the slide should the lens of the projector be placed to form the image on the screen?

38. **M** An object is located 20.0 cm to the left of a diverging lens having a focal length $f = -32.0$ cm. Determine (a) the location and (b) the magnification of the image. (c) Construct a ray diagram for this arrangement.

39. A converging lens is placed 30.0 cm to the right of a diverging lens of focal length 10.0 cm. A beam of parallel light enters the diverging lens from the left, and the beam is again parallel when it emerges from the converging lens. Calculate the focal length of the converging lens.

40. **QC** **S** (a) Use the thin-lens equation to derive an expression for q in terms of f and p. (b) Prove that for a real object and a diverging lens, the image must always be virtual. *Hint:* Set $f = -|f|$ and show that q must be less than zero under the given conditions. (c) For a real object and converging lens, what inequality involving p and f must hold if the image is to be real?

41. Two converging lenses, each of focal length 15.0 cm, are placed 40.0 cm apart, and an object is placed 30.0 cm in front of the first lens. Where is the final image formed, and what is the magnification of the system?

42. Object O_1 is 15.0 cm to the left of a converging lens with a 10.0-cm focal length. A second lens is positioned 10.0 cm to the right of the first lens and is observed to form a virtual image at the position of the original object O_1. (a) What is the focal length of the second lens? (b) What is the overall magnification of this system? (c) What is the nature (i.e., real or virtual, upright or inverted) of the final image?

43. **M** A 1.00-cm-high object is placed 4.00 cm to the left of a converging lens of focal length 8.00 cm. A diverging lens of focal length -16.00 cm is 6.00 cm to the right of the converging lens. Find the position and height of the final image. Is the image inverted or upright? Real or virtual?

44. Two converging lenses having focal lengths of $f_1 = 10.0$ cm and $f_2 = 20.0$ cm are placed $d = 50.0$ cm apart, as shown in Figure P23.44. The final image is to be located between the lenses, at the position $x = 31.0$ cm

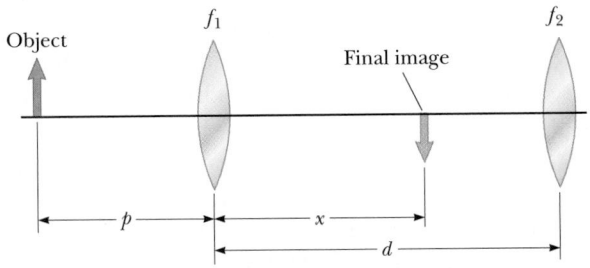

Figure P23.44

indicated. (a) How far to the left of the first lens should the object be positioned? (b) What is the overall magnification of the system? (c) Is the final image upright or inverted?

45. Lens L_1 in Figure P23.45 has a focal length of 15.0 cm and is located a fixed distance in front of the film plane of a camera. Lens L_2 has a focal length of 13.0 cm, and its distance d from the film plane can be varied from 5.00 cm to 10.0 cm. Determine the range of distances for which objects can be focused on the film.

Figure P23.45

46. **GP** An object is placed 15.0 cm from a first converging lens of focal length 10.0 cm. A second converging lens with focal length 5.00 cm is placed 10.0 cm to the right of the first converging lens. (a) Find the position q_1 of the image formed by the first converging lens. (b) How far from the second lens is the image of the first lens? (c) What is the value of p_2, the object position for the second lens? (d) Find the position q_2 of the image formed by the second lens. (e) Calculate the magnification of the first lens. (f) Calculate the magnification of the second lens. (g) What is the total magnification for the system? (h) Is the final image real or virtual? Is it upright or inverted (compared to the original object for the lens system)?

Additional Problems

47. An object placed 10.0 cm from a concave spherical mirror produces a real image 8.00 cm from the mirror. If the object is moved to a new position 20.0 cm from the mirror, what is the position of the image? Is the final image real or virtual?

48. **S** A real object's distance from a converging lens is five times the focal length. (a) Determine the location of the image q in terms of the focal length f. (b) Find the magnification of the image. (c) Is the image real or virtual? Is it upright or inverted? Is the image on the same side of the lens as the object or on the opposite side?

49. The magnitudes of the radii of curvature are 32.5 cm and 42.5 cm for the two faces of a biconcave lens. The glass has index of refraction 1.53 for violet light and 1.51 for red light. For a very distant object, locate (a) the image formed by violet light and (b) the image formed by red light.

50. A diverging lens ($n = 1.50$) is shaped like that in Active Figure 23.25c. The radius of the first surface is 15.0 cm, and that of the second surface is 10.0 cm. (a) Find the focal length of the lens. Determine the positions of

the images for object distances of (b) infinity, (c) $3|f|$, (d) $|f|$, and (e) $|f|/2$.

51. The lens and the mirror in Figure P23.51 are separated by 1.00 m and have focal lengths of +80.0 cm and −50.0 cm, respectively. If an object is placed 1.00 m to the left of the lens, where will the final image be located? State whether the image is upright or inverted, and determine the overall magnification.

Figure P23.51

52. The object in Figure P23.52 is midway between the lens and the mirror, which are separated by a distance $d = 25.0$ cm. The magnitude of the mirror's radius of curvature is 20.0 cm, and the lens has a focal length of −16.7 cm. (a) Considering only the light that leaves the object and travels first toward the mirror, locate the final image formed by this system. (b) Is the image real or virtual? (c) Is it upright or inverted? (d) What is the overall magnification of the image?

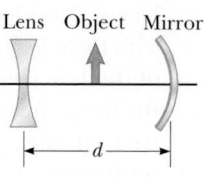

Figure P23.52

53. A parallel beam of light enters a glass hemisphere perpendicular to the flat face, as shown in Figure P23.53. The radius of the hemisphere is $R = 6.00$ cm, and the index of refraction is $n = 1.56$. Determine the point at which the beam is focused. (Assume paraxial rays; i.e., assume all rays are located close to the principal axis.)

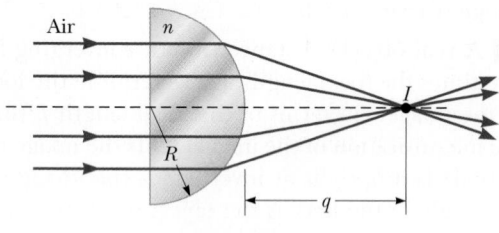

Figure P23.53

54. Two rays traveling parallel to the principal axis strike a large plano-convex lens having a refractive index of 1.60 (Fig. P23.54). If the convex face is spherical, a ray near the edge does not pass through the focal point (spherical aberration occurs). Assume this face has a radius of curvature of $R = 20.0$ cm and the two rays are at distances $h_1 = 0.500$ cm and $h_2 = 12.0$ cm from the principal axis. Find the difference Δx in the positions where each crosses the principal axis.

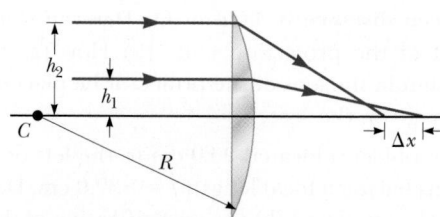

Figure P23.54

55. To work this problem, use the fact that the image formed by the first surface becomes the object for the second surface. Figure P23.55 shows a piece of glass with index of refraction $n = 1.50$ surrounded by air. The

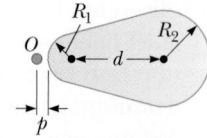

Figure P23.55

ends are hemispheres with radii $R_1 = 2.00$ cm and $R_2 = 4.00$ cm, and the centers of the hemispherical ends are separated by a distance of $d = 8.00$ cm. A point object is in air, a distance $p = 1.00$ cm from the left end of the glass. (a) Locate the image of the object due to refraction at the two spherical surfaces. (b) Is the image real or virtual?

56. **S** Consider two thin lenses, one of focal length f_1 and the other of focal length f_2, placed in contact with each other, as shown in Figure P23.56. Apply the thin-lens equation to each of these lenses and combine the results to show that this combination of lenses behaves like a thin lens having a focal length f given by $1/f = 1/f_1 + 1/f_2$. Assume the thicknesses of the lenses can be ignored in comparison to the other distances involved.

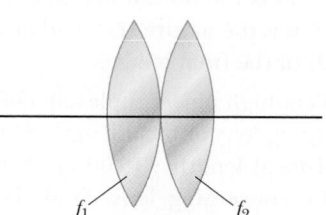

Figure P23.56

57. An object 2.00 cm high is placed 40.0 cm to the left of a converging lens having a focal length of 30.0 cm. A diverging lens having a focal length of −20.0 cm is placed 110 cm to the right of the converging lens. (a) Determine the final position and magnification of the final image. (b) Is the image upright or inverted? (c) Repeat parts (a) and (b) for the case in which the second lens is a converging lens having a focal length of +20.0 cm.

58. A "floating strawberry" illusion can be produced by two parabolic mirrors, each with a focal length of 7.5 cm, facing each other so that their centers are 7.5 cm apart (Fig. P23.58). If a strawberry is placed on the bottom mirror, an image of the strawberry forms

at the small opening at the center of the top mirror. Show that the final image forms at that location and describe its characteristics. *Note:* A flashlight beam shone on these *images* has a very startling effect: Even at a glancing angle, the incoming light beam is seemingly reflected off the *images* of the strawberry! Do you understand why?

Figure P23.58

59. Figure P23.59 shows a converging lens with radii $R_1 = 9.00$ cm and $R_2 = -11.00$ cm, in front of a concave spherical mirror of radius $R = 8.00$ cm. The focal points (F_1 and F_2) for the thin lens and the center of curvature (C) of the mirror are also shown. (a) If the focal points F_1 and F_2 are 5.00 cm from the vertex of the thin lens, what is the index of refraction of the lens? (b) If the lens and mirror are 20.0 cm apart and an object is placed 8.00 cm to the left of the lens, what is the position of the final image and its magnification as seen by the eye in the figure? (c) Is the final image inverted or upright? Explain.

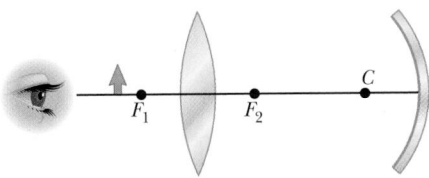

Figure P23.59

60. **S** Find the object distances (in terms of f) for a thin converging lens of focal length f if (a) the image is real and the image distance is four times the focal length and (b) the image is virtual and the absolute value of the image distance is three times the focal length. (c) Calculate the magnification of the lens for cases (a) and (b).

61. The lens-maker's equation for a lens with index n_1 immersed in a medium with index n_2 takes the form

$$\frac{1}{f} = \left(\frac{n_1}{n_2} - 1\right)\left(\frac{1}{R_1} - \frac{1}{R_2}\right)$$

A thin diverging glass (index = 1.50) lens with $R_1 = -3.00$ m and $R_2 = -6.00$ m is surrounded by air. An arrow is placed 10.0 m to the left of the lens. (a) Determine the position of the image. Repeat part (a) with the arrow and lens immersed in (b) water (index = 1.33) (c) a medium with an index of refraction of 2.00. (d) How can a lens that is diverging in air be changed into a converging lens?

62. An observer to the right of the mirror–lens combination shown in Figure P23.62 sees two real images that are the same size and in the same location. One image is upright, and the other is inverted. Both images are 1.50 times larger than the object. The lens has a focal length of 10.0 cm. The lens and mirror are separated by 40.0 cm. Determine the focal length of the mirror. (Don't assume the figure is drawn to scale.)

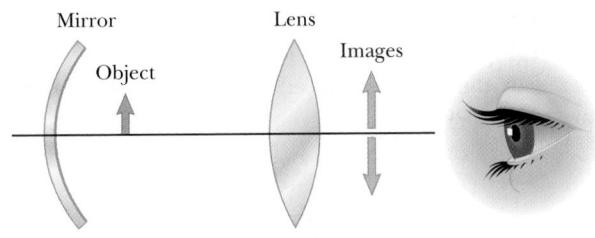

Figure P23.62

63. The lens-maker's equation applies to a lens immersed in a liquid if n in the equation is replaced by n_1/n_2. Here n_1 refers to the refractive index of the lens material and n_2 is that of the medium surrounding the lens. (a) A certain lens has focal length of 79.0 cm in air and a refractive index of 1.55. Find its focal length in water. (b) A certain mirror has focal length of 79.0 cm in air. Find its focal length in water.

64. A certain Christmas tree ornament is a silver sphere having a diameter of 8.50 cm. (a) If the size of an image created by reflection in the ornament is three-fourth's the reflected object's actual size, determine the object's location. (b) Use a principal-ray diagram to determine whether the image is upright or inverted.

65. **M** A glass sphere ($n = 1.50$) with a radius of 15.0 cm has a tiny air bubble 5.00 cm above its center. The sphere is viewed looking down along the extended radius containing the bubble. What is the apparent depth of the bubble below the surface of the sphere?

66. An object 10.0 cm tall is placed at the zero mark of a meterstick. A spherical mirror located at some point on the meterstick creates an image of the object that is upright, 4.00 cm tall, and located at the 42.0-cm mark of the meterstick. (a) Is the mirror convex or concave? (b) Where is the mirror? (c) What is the mirror's focal length?

■ AP* REVIEW QUESTIONS

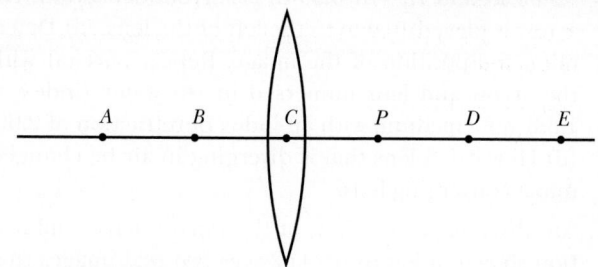

1. A biconvex lens is placed at point *C*. The first focal point is determined to be at point *P*. Which point is nearest the second focal point?

(A) *A*   (D) *D*

(B) *B*   (E) *E*

(C) *C*

Questions 2–3

A converging lens has a focal length of *x*. An object, represented by the arrow, is placed at point *A*, as seen in the figure below.

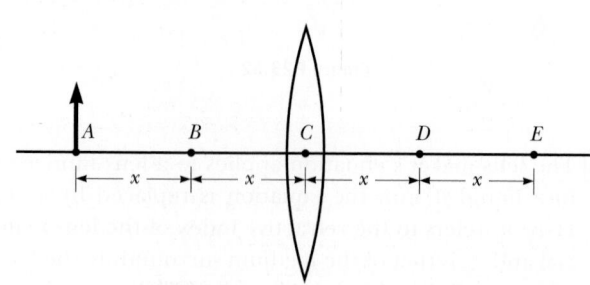

2. The image of the object is most near which point?

(A) *A*   (D) *D*

(B) *B*   (E) *E*

(C) *C*

3. Which of the following statements is true regarding the image produced?

I.   The image is real.

II. The image is virtual.

III. The image is inverted.

IV. The lens causes parallel rays and no image is formed.

(A) I only

(B) II only

(C) I and III

(D) II and III

(E) IV only

Questions 4–5

A diverging lens has a focal length of *x*. An object, represented by an arrow, is placed at point *A*, as seen in the figure below.

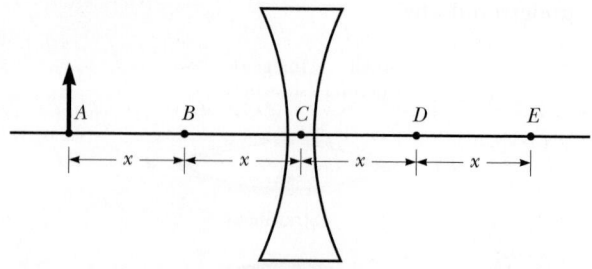

4. Where is the image seen?

(A) At point *A*

(B) Between points *B* and *C*

(C) Between points *C* and *D*

(D) Between points *D* and *E*

(E) At point *E*

5. Which of the following statements is true regarding the image produced?

I.   The image is real.

II. The image is virtual.

III. The image is inverted.

IV. The lens causes parallel rays and no image is formed.

(A) I only   (D) II and III

(B) II only   (E) IV only

(C) I and III

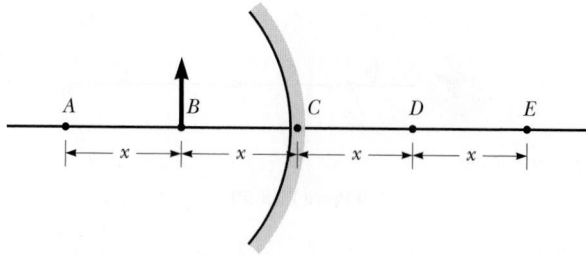

6. A converging mirror has a focal length of *x*. An object, represented by an arrow, is placed at point *B*, as seen in the figure above. The image location is best described as:

(A) Left of point *A*

(B) Between points *A* and *B*

(C) At point *B*

(D) Between points *D* and *E*

(E) The mirror causes parallel rays and no image is formed

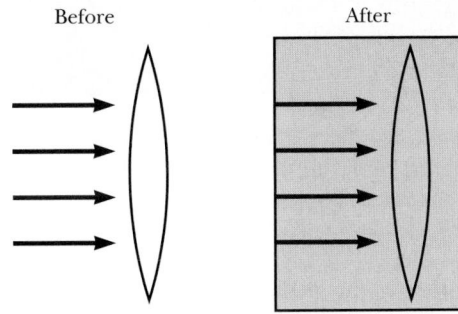

7. An object placed in which region of the graph seen above would produce a virtual image?

(A) I

(B) II

(C) III

(D) IV

(E) V

Before   **After**

8. The biconvex plastic lens seen above has a positive focal length when in air. The lens is immersed in a fluid with an index of refraction greater than that of the plastic. Which of the following statements is correct?

(A) The focal length of the lens will remain unchanged.

(B) The focal length of the lens will decrease but remain positive.

(C) The focal length of the lens will increase but remain positive.

(D) The focal length of the lens will become a negative value.

(E) The plastic will no longer function as a lens.

9. Light passes through a two-lens combination. The first lens creates a magnification M_1 and the second lens creates a magnification M_2. The total magnification of the system is:

(A) $M_1 + M_2$

(B) $M_1 - M_2$

(C) $(M_1)(M_2)$

(D) $\dfrac{M_1}{M_2}$

(E) $(M_1{}^2 + M_2{}^2)^{1/2}$

10. What are the image properties when you look at an object in a flat mirror?

	Image type	Orientation	Magnification
(A)	Real	Inverted	Less than 1
(B)	Real	Erect	Equal to 1
(C)	Virtual	Inverted	Less than 1
(D)	Virtual	Erect	Equal to 1
(E)	Virtual	Inverted	Greater than 1

11. A fish in a pool is observed from directly overhead in the air. The properties of the fish seen by the observer are:

	Depth	Magnification
(A)	Same depth	Less than 1
(B)	Same depth	Equal to 1
(C)	Closer to surface	Equal to 1
(D)	Closer to surface	Less than 1
(E)	Deeper	Greater than 1

12. In practical applications, a lens exhibits a tendency to not create sharp images because the outer radius rays focus to a point nearer to the lens than the inner radius rays. This problem is called:

(A) Chromatic aberration

(B) Spherical aberration

(C) Resolving power

(D) Parallax error

(E) Elastic deformation

The colors in many of a hummingbird's feathers are not due to pigment. The *iridescence* that makes the brilliant colors that often appear on the bird's throat and belly is due to an interference effect caused by structures in the feathers. The colors vary with the viewing angle.

RO-MA/Index Stock Imagery

24 Wave Optics

Colors swirl on a soap bubble as it drifts through the air on a summer day, and vivid rainbows reflect from the filth of oil films in the puddles of a dirty city street. Beachgoers, covered with thin layers of oil, wear their coated sunglasses that absorb half the incoming light. In laboratories scientists determine the precise composition of materials by analyzing the light they give off when hot, and in observatories around the world, telescopes gather light from distant galaxies, filtering out individual wavelengths in bands and thereby determining the speed of expansion of the Universe.

Understanding how these rainbows are made and how certain scientific instruments can determine wavelengths is the domain of *wave optics*. Light can be viewed as either a particle or a wave. Geometric optics, the subject of the previous chapter, depends on the particle nature of light. Wave optics depends on the wave nature of light. The three primary topics we examine in this chapter are interference, diffraction, and polarization. These phenomena can't be adequately explained with ray optics, but can be understood if light is viewed as a wave.

24.1 Conditions for Interference

In our discussion of interference of mechanical waves in Chapter 13, we found that two waves could add together either constructively or destructively. In constructive interference the amplitude of the resultant wave is greater than that of either of the individual waves, whereas in destructive interference, the resultant amplitude is less than that of either individual wave. Light waves also interfere with one another. Fundamentally, all interference associated with light waves arises when the electromagnetic fields that constitute the individual waves combine.

Interference effects in light waves aren't easy to observe because of the short wavelengths involved (about 4×10^{-7} m to about 7×10^{-7} m). The following two conditions, however, facilitate the observation of interference between two sources of light:

1. The sources are **coherent**, which means that the waves they emit must maintain a constant phase with respect to one another.
2. The waves have identical wavelengths.

◀ Conditions for interference

Two sources (producing two traveling waves) are needed to create interference. To produce a stable interference pattern, the individual waves must maintain a constant phase with one another. When this situation prevails, the sources are said to be coherent. The sound waves emitted by two side-by-side loudspeakers driven by a single amplifier can produce interference because the two speakers respond to the amplifier in the same way at the same time: they are in phase.

If two light sources are placed side by side, however, no interference effects are observed because the light waves from one source are emitted independently of the waves from the other source; hence, the emissions from the two sources don't maintain a constant phase relationship with each other during the time of observation. An ordinary light source undergoes random changes about once every 10^{-8} s. Therefore, the conditions for constructive interference, destructive interference, and intermediate states have durations on the order of 10^{-8} s. The result is that no interference effects are observed because the eye can't follow such short-term changes. Ordinary light sources are said to be **incoherent**.

An older method for producing two coherent light sources is to pass light from a single wavelength (monochromatic) source through a narrow slit and then allow the light to fall on a screen containing two other narrow slits. The first slit is needed to create a single wave front that illuminates both slits coherently. The light emerging from the two slits is coherent because a single source produces the original light beam and the slits serve only to separate the original beam into two parts. Any random change in the light emitted by the source will occur in the two separate beams at the same time, and interference effects can be observed.

Currently it's much more common to use a laser as a coherent source to demonstrate interference. A laser produces an intense, coherent, monochromatic beam over a width of several millimeters. The laser may therefore be used to illuminate multiple slits directly, and interference effects can be easily observed in a fully lighted room. The principles of operation of a laser are explained in Chapter 28.

24.2 Young's Double-Slit Experiment

Thomas Young first demonstrated interference in light waves from two sources in 1801. Active Figure 24.1a (page 826) is a schematic diagram of the apparatus used in this experiment. (Young used pinholes rather than slits in his original experiments.) Light is incident on a screen containing a narrow slit S_0. The light waves emerging from this slit arrive at a second screen that contains two narrow, parallel slits S_1 and S_2. These slits serve as a pair of coherent light sources because waves emerging from them originate from the same wave front and therefore are always in phase. The light from the two slits produces a visible pattern on screen C consisting of a series of bright and dark parallel bands called **fringes** (Active Fig. 24.1b). When the light from slits S_1 and S_2 arrives at a point on the screen so that constructive interference occurs at that location, a bright fringe appears. When the light from the two slits combines destructively at any location on the screen,

Active Figure 24.1

(a) A diagram of Young's double-slit experiment. The narrow slits act as sources of waves. Slits S_1 and S_2 behave as coherent sources that produce an interference pattern on screen C. (The drawing is not to scale.) (b) The fringe pattern formed on screen C could look like this.

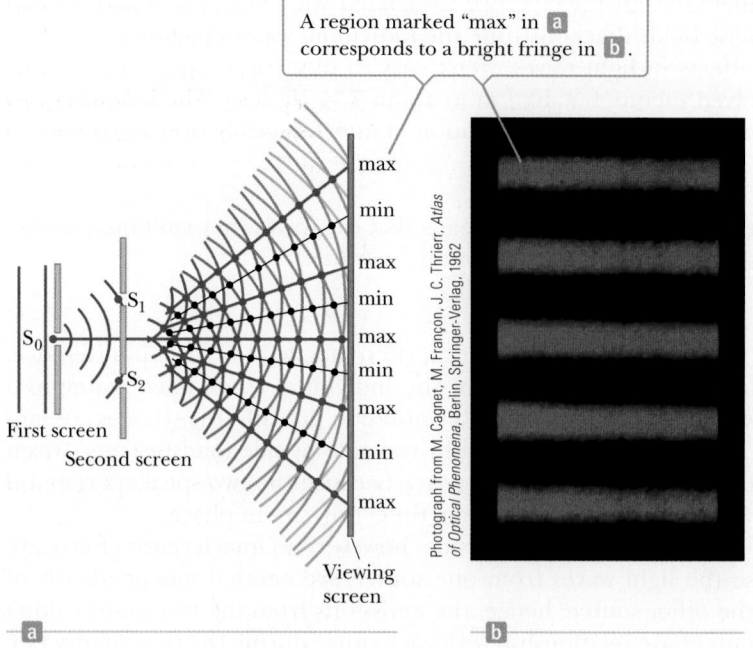

A region marked "max" in **a** corresponds to a bright fringe in **b**.

Photograph from M. Cagnet, M. Françon, J. C. Thierr, *Atlas of Optical Phenomena*, Berlin, Springer-Verlag, 1962

Figure 24.2 An interference pattern involving water waves is produced by two vibrating sources at the water's surface. The pattern is analogous to that observed in Young's double-slit experiment. Note the regions of constructive and destructive interference.

Richard Megna, Fundamental Photographs, NYC

a dark fringe results. Figure 24.2 is a photograph of an interference pattern produced by two coherent vibrating sources in a water tank.

Figure 24.3 is a schematic diagram of some of the ways in which the two waves can combine at screen C of Figure 24.1. In Figure 24.3a two waves, which leave the two slits in phase, strike the screen at the central point P. Because these waves travel equal distances, they arrive in phase at P, and as a result, constructive interference occurs there and a bright fringe is observed. In Figure 24.3b the two light waves again start in phase, but the upper wave has to travel one wavelength farther to reach point Q on the screen. Because the upper wave falls behind the lower one by exactly one wavelength, the two waves still arrive in phase at Q, so a second bright fringe appears at that location. Now consider point R, midway between P and Q, in Figure 24.3c. At R, the upper wave has fallen half a wavelength behind the lower wave. This means that the trough of the bottom wave overlaps the crest of the upper wave, giving rise to destructive interference. As a result, a dark fringe can be observed at R.

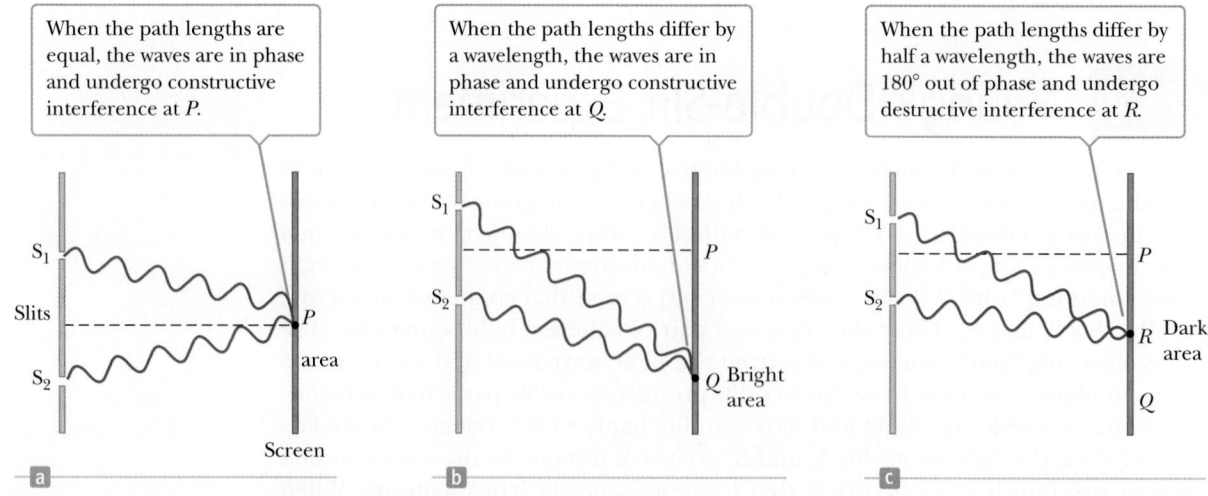

Figure 24.3 Waves leave the slits and combine at various points on the viewing screen. (All figures not to scale.)

We can describe Young's experiment quantitatively with the help of Figure 24.4. Consider point P on the viewing screen; the screen is positioned a perpendicular distance L from the screen containing slits S_1 and S_2, which are separated by distance d, and r_1 and r_2 are the distances the secondary waves travel from slit to screen. We assume the waves emerging from S_1 and S_2 have the same constant frequency, have the same amplitude, and start out in phase. The light intensity on the screen at P is the result of light from both slits. A wave from the lower slit, however, travels farther than a wave from the upper slit by the amount $d \sin \theta$. This distance is called the **path difference** δ (lowercase Greek delta), where

$$\delta = r_2 - r_1 = d \sin \theta \qquad \text{[24.1]}$$

◀ Path difference

Equation 24.1 assumes the two waves travel in parallel lines, which is approximately true because L is much greater than d. As noted earlier, the value of this path difference determines whether the two waves are in phase when they arrive at P. If the path difference is either zero or some integral multiple of the wavelength, the two waves are in phase at P and constructive interference results. Therefore, the condition for bright fringes, or **constructive interference**, at P is

$$\delta = d \sin \theta_{\text{bright}} = m\lambda \qquad m = 0, \pm 1, \pm 2, \ldots \qquad \text{[24.2]}$$

◀ Condition for constructive interference (two slits)

The number m is called the **order number**. The central bright fringe that appears at $\theta_{\text{bright}} = 0$ ($m = 0$) is called the *zeroth-order maximum*. The first maximum on either side, where $m = \pm 1$, is called the *first-order maximum*, and so forth.

When δ is an odd multiple of $\lambda/2$, the two waves arriving at P are 180° out of phase and give rise to destructive interference. Therefore, the condition for dark fringes, or **destructive interference**, at P is

$$\delta = d \sin \theta_{\text{dark}} = \left(m + \tfrac{1}{2}\right)\lambda \qquad m = 0, \pm 1, \pm 2, \ldots \qquad \text{[24.3]}$$

◀ Condition for destructive interference (two slits)

If $m = 0$ in this equation, the path difference is $\delta = \lambda/2$, which is the condition for the location of the first dark fringe on either side of the central (bright) maximum. Likewise, if $m = 1$, the path difference is $\delta = 3\lambda/2$, which is the condition for the second dark fringe on each side, and so forth.

It's useful to obtain expressions for the positions of the bright and dark fringes measured vertically from O to P. In addition to our assumption that $L \gg d$, we assume $d \gg \lambda$. These assumptions can be valid because, in practice, L is often on the order of 1 m, d is a fraction of a millimeter, and λ is a fraction of a micrometer for visible light. Under these conditions θ is small, so we can use the approximation $\sin \theta \cong \tan \theta$. Then, from triangle OPQ in Figure 24.4, we see that

$$y = L \tan \theta \approx L \sin \theta \qquad \text{[24.4]}$$

Tip 24.1 Small-Angle Approximation: Size Matters!

The small-angle approximation $\sin \theta \cong \tan \theta$ is true to three-digit precision only for angles less than about 4°.

Figure 24.4 A geometric construction that describes Young's double-slit experiment. (This figure is not drawn to scale.)

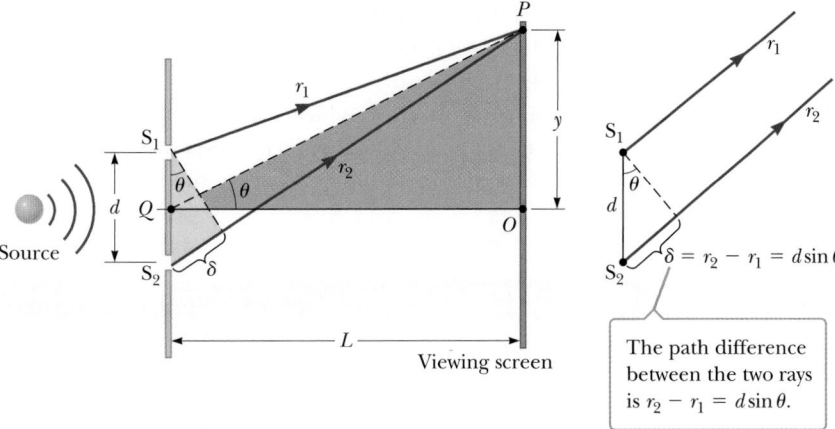

The path difference between the two rays is $r_2 - r_1 = d \sin \theta$.

John S. Shelton

Reflection, interference, and diffraction can be seen in this aerial photograph of waves in the sea.

Solving Equation 24.2 for $\sin\theta$ and substituting the result into Equation 24.4, we find that the positions of the *bright fringes*, measured from O, are

$$y_{\text{bright}} = \frac{\lambda L}{d}m \qquad m = 0, \pm 1, \pm 2, \ldots \qquad \text{[24.5]}$$

Using Equations 24.3 and 24.4, we find that the *dark fringes* are located at

$$y_{\text{dark}} = \frac{\lambda L}{d}\left(m + \tfrac{1}{2}\right) \qquad m = 0, \pm 1, \pm 2, \ldots \qquad \text{[24.6]}$$

As we will show in Example 24.1, Young's double-slit experiment provides a method for measuring the wavelength of light. In fact, Young used this technique to do just that. In addition, his experiment gave the wave model of light a great deal of credibility. It was inconceivable that particles of light coming through the slits could cancel each other in a way that would explain the dark fringes.

■ APPLYING PHYSICS 24.1 | A Smoky Young's Experiment

Consider a double-slit experiment in which a laser beam is passed through a pair of very closely spaced slits and a clear interference pattern is displayed on a distant screen. Now suppose you place smoke particles between the double slit and the screen. With the presence of the smoke particles, will you see the effects of interference in the space between the slits and the screen, or will you see only the effects on the screen?

EXPLANATION You will see the interference pattern both on the screen and in the area filled with smoke between the slits and the screen. There will be bright lines directed toward the bright areas on the screen and dark lines directed toward the dark areas on the screen. This is because Equations 24.5 and 24.6 depend on the distance to the screen, L, which can take any value. ■

■ APPLYING PHYSICS 24.2 | Television Signal Interference

Suppose you are watching television by means of an antenna rather than a cable system. If an airplane flies near your location, you may notice wavering ghost images in the television picture. What might cause this phenomenon?

EXPLANATION Your television antenna receives two signals: the direct signal from the transmitting antenna

and a signal reflected from the surface of the airplane. As the airplane changes position, there are some times when these two signals are in phase and other times when they are out of phase. As a result, the intensity of the combined signal received at your antenna will vary. The wavering of the ghost images of the picture is evidence of this variation. ■

■ Quick Quiz

24.1 In a two-slit interference pattern projected on a screen, are the fringes equally spaced on the screen (a) everywhere, (b) only for large angles, or (c) only for small angles?

24.2 If the distance between the slits is doubled in Young's experiment, what happens to the width of the central maximum? (a) The width is doubled. (b) The width is unchanged. (c) The width is halved.

24.3 A Young's double-slit experiment is performed with three different colors of light: red, green, and blue. Rank the colors by the distance between adjacent bright fringes, from smallest to largest. (a) red, green, blue (b) green, blue, red (c) blue, green, red

■ EXAMPLE 24.1 | Measuring the Wavelength of a Light Source

GOAL Show how Young's experiment can be used to measure the wavelength of coherent light.

PROBLEM A screen is separated from a double-slit source by 1.20 m. The distance between the two slits is 0.030 0 mm. The second-order bright fringe ($m = 2$) is measured to be 4.50 cm from the centerline. Determine **(a)** the wavelength of the light and **(b)** the distance between adjacent bright fringes.

STRATEGY Equation 24.5 relates the positions of the bright fringes to the other variables, including the wavelength of the light. Substitute into this equation and solve for λ. Taking the difference between y_{m+1} and y_m results in a general expression for the distance between bright fringes.

· ·

SOLUTION

(a) Determine the wavelength of the light.

Solve Equation 24.5 for the wavelength and substitute the values $m = 2$, $y_2 = 4.50 \times 10^{-2}$ m, $L = 1.20$ m, and $d = 3.00 \times 10^{-5}$ m:

$$\lambda = \frac{y_2 d}{mL} = \frac{(4.50 \times 10^{-2}\,\text{m})(3.00 \times 10^{-5}\,\text{m})}{2(1.20\,\text{m})}$$

$$= 5.63 \times 10^{-7}\,\text{m} = \boxed{563\,\text{nm}}$$

(b) Determine the distance between adjacent bright fringes.

Use Equation 24.5 to find the distance between *any* adjacent bright fringes (here, those characterized by m and $m + 1$):

$$\Delta y = y_{m+1} - y_m = \frac{\lambda L}{d}(m + 1) - \frac{\lambda L}{d}m = \frac{\lambda L}{d}$$

$$= \frac{(5.63 \times 10^{-7}\,\text{m})(1.20\,\text{m})}{3.00 \times 10^{-5}\,\text{m}} = \boxed{2.25\,\text{cm}}$$

· ·

REMARKS This calculation depends on the angle θ being small because the small-angle approximation was implicitly used. The measurement of the position of the bright fringes yields the wavelength of light, which in turn is a signature of atomic processes, as is discussed in the chapters on modern physics. This kind of measurement therefore helped open the world of the atom.

QUESTION 24.1 True or False: A larger slit creates a larger separation between interference fringes.

EXERCISE 24.1 Suppose the same experiment is run with a different light source. If the first-order maximum is found at 1.85 cm from the centerline, what is the wavelength of the light?

ANSWER 463 nm

24.3 Change of Phase Due to Reflection

Young's method of producing two coherent light sources involves illuminating a pair of slits with a single source. Another simple, yet ingenious, arrangement for producing an interference pattern with a single light source is known as *Lloyd's mirror*. A point source of light is placed at point *S*, close to a mirror, as illustrated in Figure 24.5. Light waves can reach the viewing point *P* either by the direct path *SP* or by the path involving reflection from the mirror. The reflected ray can be treated as a ray originating at the source *S'* behind the mirror. Source *S'*, which is the image of *S*, can be considered a virtual source.

At points far from the source, an interference pattern due to waves from *S* and *S'* is observed, just as for two real coherent sources. The positions of the dark and bright fringes, however, are *reversed* relative to the pattern obtained from two real coherent sources (Young's experiment). This is because the coherent sources *S* and *S'* differ in phase by 180°, a phase change produced by reflection.

To illustrate the point further, consider *P'*, the point where the mirror intersects the screen. This point is equidistant from *S* and *S'*. If path difference alone were responsible for the phase difference, a bright fringe would be observed at *P'* (because the path difference is zero for this point), corresponding to the central fringe of the two-slit interference pattern. Instead, we observe a *dark* fringe at *P*, from which we conclude that a 180° phase change must be produced by reflection from the mirror. In general, **an electromagnetic wave undergoes a phase change of 180° upon reflection from a medium that has an index of refraction higher than the one in which the wave was traveling**.

An analogy can be drawn between reflected light waves and the reflections of a transverse wave on a stretched string when the wave meets a boundary, as in Figure 24.6 (page 830). The reflected pulse on a string undergoes a phase change of 180°

An interference pattern is produced on a screen at *P* as a result of the combination of the direct ray (red) and the reflected ray (blue). The reflected ray undergoes a phase change of 180°.

Figure 24.5 Lloyd's mirror.

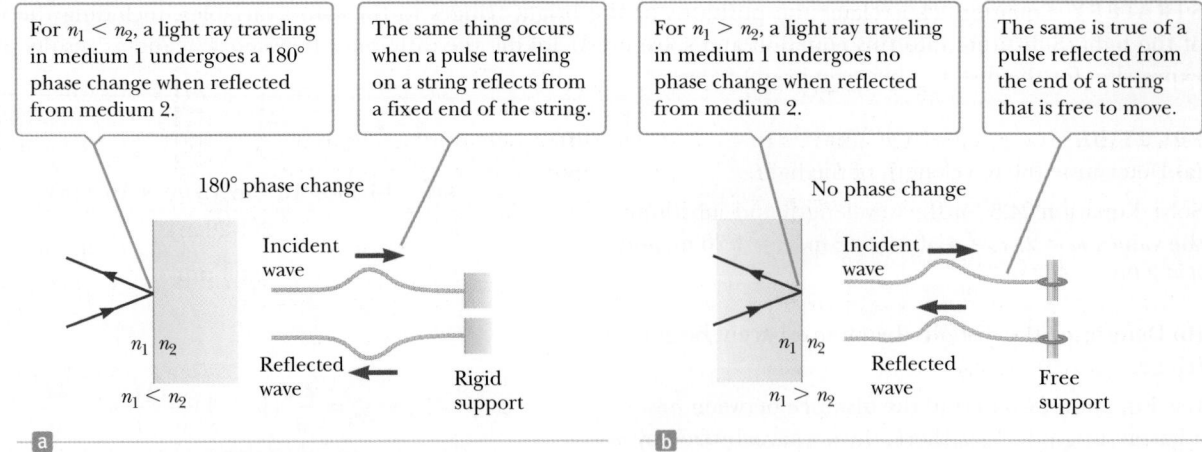

For $n_1 < n_2$, a light ray traveling in medium 1 undergoes a 180° phase change when reflected from medium 2.

The same thing occurs when a pulse traveling on a string reflects from a fixed end of the string.

For $n_1 > n_2$, a light ray traveling in medium 1 undergoes no phase change when reflected from medium 2.

The same is true of a pulse reflected from the end of a string that is free to move.

Figure 24.6 Comparisons of reflections of light waves and waves on strings.

Interference in light reflected from a thin film is due to a combination of rays 1 and 2 reflected from the upper and lower surfaces of the film.

Figure 24.7 Light passes through a thin film.

Dr. Jeremy Burgess/Science Photo Library/ Photo Researchers, Inc.

The colors observed in soap bubbles are due to interference between light rays reflected from the front and back of the thin film of soap making up the bubble. The color depends on the thickness of the film, ranging from black where the film is at its thinnest to magenta where it is thickest.

when it is reflected from the boundary of a denser string or from a rigid barrier and undergoes no phase change when it is reflected from the boundary of a less dense string. Similarly, an electromagnetic wave undergoes a 180° phase change when reflected from the boundary of a medium with index of refraction higher than the one in which it has been traveling. There is no phase change when the wave is reflected from a boundary leading to a medium of lower index of refraction. The transmitted wave that crosses the boundary also undergoes no phase change.

24.4 Interference in Thin Films

Interference effects are commonly observed in thin films, such as the thin surface of a soap bubble or thin layers of oil on water. The varied colors observed when incoherent white light is incident on such films result from the interference of waves reflected from the two surfaces of the film.

Consider a film of uniform thickness t and index of refraction n, as in Figure 24.7. Assume the light rays traveling in air are nearly normal to the two surfaces of the film. To determine whether the reflected rays interfere constructively or destructively, we first note the following facts:

1. An electromagnetic wave traveling from a medium of index of refraction n_1 toward a medium of index of refraction n_2 undergoes a 180° phase change on reflection when $n_2 > n_1$. There is no phase change in the reflected wave if $n_2 < n_1$.
2. The wavelength of light λ_n in a medium with index of refraction n is

$$\lambda_n = \frac{\lambda}{n} \qquad [24.7]$$

where λ is the wavelength of light in vacuum.

We apply these rules to the film of Figure 24.7. According to the first rule, ray 1, which is reflected from the upper surface A, undergoes a phase change of 180° with respect to the incident wave. Ray 2, which is reflected from the lower surface B, undergoes no phase change with respect to the incident wave. Therefore, ray 1 is 180° out of phase with respect to ray 2, which is equivalent to a path difference of $\lambda_n/2$. We must also consider, though, that ray 2 travels an extra distance of $2t$ before the waves recombine in the air above the surface. For example, if $2t = \lambda_n/2$, rays 1 and 2 recombine in phase and constructive interference results. In general, the condition for *constructive interference* in thin films is

$$2t = \left(m + \tfrac{1}{2}\right)\lambda_n \qquad m = 0, 1, 2, \ldots \qquad \text{[24.8]}$$

This condition takes into account two factors: (1) the difference in path length for the two rays (the term $m\lambda_n$) and (2) the 180° phase change upon reflection (the term $\lambda_n/2$). Because $\lambda_n = \lambda/n$, we can write Equation 24.8 in the form

$$2nt = \left(m + \tfrac{1}{2}\right)\lambda \qquad m = 0, 1, 2, \ldots \qquad \text{[24.9]}$$

If the extra distance $2t$ traveled by ray 2 is a multiple of λ_n, the two waves combine out of phase and the result is destructive interference. The general equation for *destructive interference* in thin films is

$$2nt = m\lambda \qquad m = 0, 1, 2, \ldots \qquad \text{[24.10]}$$

Equations 24.9 and 24.10 for constructive and destructive interference are valid when there is only one phase reversal. This will occur when the media above and below the thin film both have indices of refraction greater than the film or when both have indices of refraction less than the film. Figure 24.7 is a case in point: the air ($n = 1$) that is both above and below the film has an index of refraction less than that of the film. As a result, there is a phase reversal on reflection off the top layer of the film but not the bottom, and Equations 24.9 and 24.10 apply. **If the film is placed between two different media, one of lower refractive index than the film and one of higher refractive index, Equations 24.9 and 24.10 are reversed: Equation 24.9 is used for destructive interference and Equation 24.10 for constructive interference.** In this case either there is a phase change of 180° for both ray 1 reflecting from surface A and ray 2 reflecting from surface B, as in Figure 24.9 of Example 24.3, or there is no phase change for either ray, which would be the case if the incident ray came from underneath the film. Hence, the net change in relative phase due to the reflections is *zero*.

A thin film of oil on water displays interference, evidenced by the pattern of colors when white light is incident on the film. Variations in the film's thickness produce the intersecting color pattern. The razor blade gives you an idea of the size of the colored bands.

■ *Quick Quiz*

24.4 Suppose Young's experiment is carried out in air, and then, in a second experiment, the apparatus is immersed in water. In what way does the distance between bright fringes change? (a) They move farther apart. (b) They move closer together. (c) There is no change.

Newton's Rings

Another method for observing interference in light waves is to place a plano-convex lens on top of a flat glass surface, as in Figure 24.8a. With this arrangement, the air film between the glass surfaces varies in thickness from zero at the

Tip 24.2 The Two Tricks of Thin Films

Be sure to include *both* effects—path length and phase change—when you analyze an interference pattern from a thin film.

Figure 24.8 (a) The combination of rays reflected from the glass plate and the curved surface of the lens gives rise to an interference pattern known as Newton's rings. (b) A photograph of Newton's rings.

point of contact to some value t at P. If the radius of curvature R of the lens is much greater than the distance r and the system is viewed from above using light of wavelength λ, a pattern of light and dark rings is observed (Fig. 24.8b). These circular fringes, discovered by Newton, are called **Newton's rings**. The interference is due to the combination of ray 1, reflected from the plate, with ray 2, reflected from the lower surface of the lens. Ray 1 undergoes a phase change of 180° on reflection because it is reflected from a boundary leading into a medium of higher refractive index, whereas ray 2 undergoes no phase change because it is reflected from a medium of lower refractive index. Hence, the conditions for constructive and destructive interference are given by Equations 24.9 and 24.10, respectively, with $n = 1$ because the "film" is air. The contact point at O is dark, as seen in Figure 24.8b, because there is no path difference and the total phase change is due only to the 180° phase change upon reflection. Using the geometry shown in Figure 24.8a, we can obtain expressions for the radii of the bright and dark bands in terms of the radius of curvature R and vacuum wavelength λ. For example, the dark rings have radii of $r \approx \sqrt{m\lambda R / n}$.

APPLICATION

Checking for Imperfections in Optical Lenses

One important use of Newton's rings is in the testing of optical lenses. A circular pattern like that in Figure 24.8b is achieved only when the lens is ground to a perfectly spherical curvature. Variations from such symmetry produce distorted patterns that also give an indication of how the lens must be reground and repolished to remove imperfections.

■ PROBLEM-SOLVING STRATEGY

Thin-Film Interference

The following steps are recommended in addressing thin-film interference problems:

1. Identify the thin film causing the interference, and the indices of refraction in the film and in the media on either side of it.
2. Determine the number of phase reversals: zero, one, or two.
3. Consult the following table, which contains Equations 24.9 and 24.10, and select the correct column for the problem in question:

Equation ($m = 0, 1, \ldots$)	1 Phase Reversal	0 or 2 Phase Reversals
$2nt = \left(m + \frac{1}{2}\right)\lambda$ **[24.9]**	Constructive	Destructive
$2nt = m\lambda$ **[24.10]**	Destructive	Constructive

4. Substitute values in the appropriate equations, as selected in the previous step.

■ EXAMPLE 24.2 | Interference in a Soap Film

GOAL Study constructive interference effects in a thin film.

PROBLEM (a) Calculate the minimum thickness of a soap-bubble film ($n = 1.33$) that will result in constructive interference in the reflected light if the film is illuminated by light with wavelength 602 nm in free space. (b) Recalculate the minimum thickness for constructive interference when the soap-bubble film is on top of a glass slide with $n = 1.50$.

STRATEGY In part (a) there is only one inversion, so the condition for constructive interference is $2nt = \left(m + \frac{1}{2}\right)\lambda$. The minimum film thickness for constructive interference corresponds to $m = 0$ in this equation. Part (b) involves two inversions, so $2nt = m\lambda$ is required.

....

SOLUTION

(a) Calculate the minimum thickness of the soap-bubble film that will result in constructive interference.

Solve $2nt = \lambda/2$ for the thickness t and substitute:

$$t = \frac{\lambda}{4n} = \frac{602 \text{ nm}}{4(1.33)} = \boxed{113 \text{ nm}}$$

(b) Find the minimum soap-film thickness when the film is on top of a glass slide with $n = 1.50$.

Write the condition for constructive interference, when two inversions take place:

$$2nt = m\lambda$$

Solve for t and substitute:

$$t = \frac{m\lambda}{2n} = \frac{1 \cdot (602 \text{ nm})}{2(1.33)} = \boxed{226 \text{ nm}}$$

REMARKS The swirling colors in a soap bubble result from the thickness of the soap layer varying from one place to another.

QUESTION 24.2 A soap film looks red in one area and violet in a nearby area. In which area is the soap film thicker?

EXERCISE 24.2 What other film thicknesses in part (a) will produce constructive interference?

ANSWERS 339 nm, 566 nm, 792 nm, and so on

■ EXAMPLE 24.3 | Nonreflective Coatings for Solar Cells and Optical Lenses

GOAL Study destructive interference effects in a thin film when there are two inversions.

PROBLEM Semiconductors such as silicon are used to fabricate solar cells, devices that generate electric energy when exposed to sunlight. Solar cells are often coated with a transparent thin film, such as silicon monoxide (SiO; $n = 1.45$), to minimize reflective losses (Fig. 24.9). A silicon solar cell ($n = 3.50$) is coated with a thin film of silicon monoxide for this purpose. Assuming normal incidence, determine the minimum thickness of the film that will produce the least reflection at a wavelength of 552 nm.

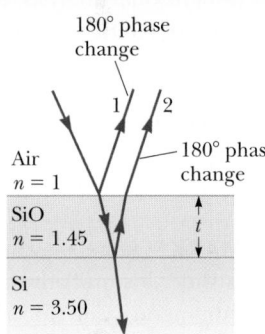

Figure 24.9 (Example 24.3) Reflective losses from a silicon solar cell are minimized by coating it with a thin film of silicon monoxide (SiO).

STRATEGY Reflection is least when rays 1 and 2 in Figure 24.9 meet the condition for destructive interference. Note that *both* rays undergo 180° phase changes on reflection. The condition for a reflection *minimum* is therefore $2nt = \lambda/2$.

SOLUTION
Solve $2nt = \lambda/2$ for t, the required thickness:

$$t = \frac{\lambda}{4n} = \frac{552 \text{ nm}}{4(1.45)} = \boxed{95.2 \text{ nm}}$$

REMARKS Typically, such coatings reduce the reflective loss from 30% (with no coating) to 10% (with a coating), thereby increasing the cell's efficiency because more light is available to create charge carriers in the cell. In reality the coating is never perfectly nonreflecting because the required thickness is wavelength dependent and the incident light covers a wide range of wavelengths.

QUESTION 24.3 To minimize reflection of a smaller wavelength, should the thickness of the coating be thicker or thinner?

EXERCISE 24.3 Glass lenses used in cameras and other optical instruments are usually coated with one or more transparent thin films, such as magnesium fluoride (MgF_2), to reduce or eliminate unwanted reflection. Carl Zeiss developed this method; his first coating was 1.00×10^2 nm thick, on glass. Using $n = 1.38$ for MgF_2, what visible wavelength would be eliminated by destructive interference in the reflected light?

ANSWER 552 nm

EXAMPLE 24.4 | Interference in a Wedge-Shaped Film

GOAL Calculate interference effects when the film has variable thickness.

PROBLEM A pair of glass slides 10.0 cm long and with $n = 1.52$ are separated on one end by a hair, forming a triangular wedge of air, as illustrated in Figure 24.10. When coherent light from a helium–neon laser with wavelength 633 nm is incident on the film from above, 15.0 dark fringes per centimeter are observed. How thick is the hair?

STRATEGY The interference pattern is created by the thin film of air having variable thickness. The pattern is a series of alternating bright and dark parallel bands. A dark band corresponds to destructive interference, and there is one phase reversal, so $2nt = m\lambda$ should be used. We can also use the similar triangles in Figure 24.10 to obtain the relation $t/x = D/L$. We can find the thickness for any m, and if the position x can also be found, this last equation gives the diameter of the hair, D.

Figure 24.10 (Example 24.4) Interference bands in reflected light can be observed by illuminating a wedge-shaped film with monochromatic light. The dark areas in the interference pattern correspond to positions of destructive interference.

SOLUTION

Solve the destructive-interference equation for the thickness of the film, t, with $n = 1$ for air:

$$t = \frac{m\lambda}{2}$$

If d is the distance from one dark band to the next, then the x-coordinate of the mth band is a multiple of d:

$$x = md$$

By dimensional analysis, d is just the inverse of the number of bands per centimeter.

$$d = \left(15.0 \,\frac{\text{bands}}{\text{cm}}\right)^{-1} = 6.67 \times 10^{-2} \,\frac{\text{cm}}{\text{band}}$$

Now use similar triangles and substitute all the information:

$$\frac{t}{x} = \frac{m\lambda/2}{md} = \frac{\lambda}{2d} = \frac{D}{L}$$

Solve for D and substitute given values:

$$D = \frac{\lambda L}{2d} = \frac{(633 \times 10^{-9}\,\text{m})(0.100\,\text{m})}{2(6.67 \times 10^{-4}\,\text{m})} = \boxed{4.75 \times 10^{-5}\,\text{m}}$$

REMARKS Some may be concerned about interference caused by light bouncing off the top and bottom of, say, the upper glass slide. It's unlikely, however, that the thickness of the slide will be half an integer multiple of the wavelength of the helium–neon laser (for some very large value of m). In addition, in contrast to the air wedge, the thickness of the glass doesn't vary.

QUESTION 24.4 If the air wedge is filled with water, how is the distance between dark bands affected? Explain.

EXERCISE 24.4 The air wedge is replaced with water, with $n = 1.33$. Find the distance between dark bands when the helium–neon laser light hits the glass slides.

ANSWER $5.02 \times 10^{-4}\,\text{m}$

APPLYING PHYSICS 24.3 | Perfect Mirrors

When light hits a metallic mirror, electrons in the metal move in response to the electromagnetic fields, absorbing some of the light's energy. For many applications, such as directing high-intensity laser light, that reduction in intensity is undesirable. A dielectric mirror, on the other hand, is made of glass or plastic and doesn't conduct electricity. To improve reflectance, thin layers of different dielectric materials are stacked on the glass surface. If the thicknesses and dielectric constants are chosen properly, light reflected off one layer combines constructively with light reflected from the layer underneath, increasing the mirror's reflectance. Nearly perfect mirrors can be constructed using several thin dielectric layers. The mirrors can be designed to reflect a particular wavelength or a range of wavelengths.

Dielectric mirrors, first developed at MIT in 1998, have an enormous number of applications. One of the most important is the OmniGuide fiber, a hollow tube the size of a spaghetti noodle that can guide light without any significant loss of intensity. (Ordinary optical fibers tend to heat up.) Such fibers have up to forty concentric layers of plastic and glass and are highly flexible. Using an OmniGuide fiber, an intense laser light can be safely guided into the human body during surgery to remove tumors and other diseased tissues without harming the healthy surrounding tissue. ■

24.5 Using Interference to Read CDs and DVDs

Compact discs (CDs) and digital videodiscs (DVDs) have revolutionized the computer and entertainment industries by providing fast access; high-density storage of text, graphics, and movies; and high-quality sound recordings. The data on these videodiscs are stored digitally as a series of zeros and ones, and these zeros and ones are read by laser light reflected from the disc. Strong reflections (constructive interference) from the disc are chosen to represent zeros, and weak reflections (destructive interference) represent ones.

To see in more detail how thin-film interference plays a crucial role in reading CDs and DVDs, consider Figure 24.11. This figure shows a photomicrograph of several DVD tracks, which consist of a sequence of pits (when viewed from the top or label side of the disc) of varying length formed in a reflecting-metal information layer. A cross-sectional view of a CD as shown in Figure 24.12 reveals that the pits appear as bumps to the laser beam, which shines on the metallic layer through a clear plastic coating from below.

As the disk rotates, the laser beam reflects off the sequence of bumps and lower areas into a photodetector, which converts the fluctuating reflected light intensity into an electrical string of zeros and ones. To make the light fluctuations more pronounced and easier to detect, the pit depth t is made equal to one-quarter of a wavelength of the laser light in the plastic. When the beam hits a rising or falling bump edge, part of the beam reflects from the top of the bump and part from the lower adjacent area, ensuring destructive interference and very low intensity when the reflected beams combine at the detector. Bump edges are read as ones, and flat bump tops and intervening flat plains are read as zeros.

In Example 24.5 the pit depth for a standard CD, using an infrared laser of wavelength 780 nm, is calculated. DVDs use shorter wavelength lasers of 635 nm, and the track separation, pit depth, and minimum pit length are all smaller. These differences allow a DVD to store about 30 times more information than a CD.

Andrew Syred/Photo Researchers, Inc.

Figure 24.11 A photomicrograph of adjacent tracks on a digital video disc (DVD). The information encoded in these pits and smooth areas is read by a laser beam.

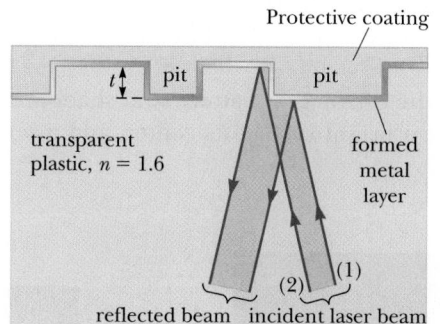

Figure 24.12 Cross section of a CD showing metallic pits of depth t and a laser beam detecting the edge of a pit.

■ EXAMPLE 24.5 | Pit Depth in a CD

GOAL Apply interference principles to a CD.

PROBLEM Find the pit depth in a CD that has a plastic transparent layer with index of refraction of 1.60 and is designed for use in a CD player using a laser with a wavelength of 7.80×10^2 nm in air.

STRATEGY (See Fig. 24.12.) Rays 1 and 2 both reflect from the metal layer, which acts like a mirror, so there is no phase difference due to reflection between those rays. There is, however, the usual phase difference caused by the extra distance $2t$ traveled by ray 2. The wavelength is λ/n, where n is the index of refraction in the substance.

(Continued)

SOLUTION

Use the appropriate condition for destructive interference in a thin film:

$$2t = \frac{\lambda}{2n}$$

Solve for the thickness t and substitute:

$$t = \frac{\lambda}{4n} = \frac{7.80 \times 10^2 \text{ nm}}{(4)(1.60)} = \boxed{1.22 \times 10^2 \text{ nm}}$$

REMARKS Different CD systems have different tolerances for scratches. Anything that changes the reflective properties of the disk can affect the readability of the disk.

QUESTION 24.5 True or False: Given two plastics with different indices of refraction, the material with the larger index of refraction will have a larger pit depth.

EXERCISE 24.5 Repeat the example for a laser with wavelength 635 nm.

ANSWER 99.2 nm

24.6 Diffraction

Suppose a light beam is incident on two slits, as in Young's double-slit experiment. If the light truly traveled in straight-line paths after passing through the slits, as in Figure 24.13a, the waves wouldn't overlap and no interference pattern would be seen. Instead, Huygens' principle requires that the waves spread out from the slits, as shown in Figure 24.13b. In other words, the light bends from a straight-line path and enters the region that would otherwise be shadowed. This spreading out of light from its initial line of travel is called **diffraction**.

In general, diffraction occurs when waves pass through small openings, around obstacles, or by sharp edges. For example, when a single narrow slit is placed between a distant light source (or a laser beam) and a screen, the light produces a diffraction pattern like that in Figure 24.14. The pattern consists of a broad, intense central band flanked by a series of narrower, less intense secondary bands (called **secondary maxima**) and a series of dark bands, or **minima**. This phenomenon can't be explained within the framework of geometric optics, which says that light rays traveling in straight lines should cast a sharp image of the slit on the screen.

Figure 24.15 shows the diffraction pattern and shadow of a penny. The pattern consists of the shadow, a bright spot at its center, and a series of bright and dark

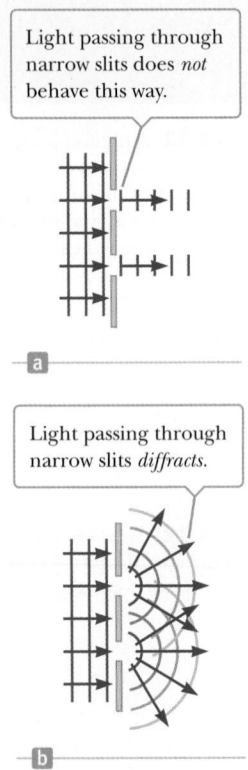

Figure 24.13 (a) If light did not spread out after passing through the slits, no interference would occur. (b) The light from the two slits overlaps as it spreads out, filling the expected shadowed regions with light and producing interference fringes.

Light passing through narrow slits does not behave this way.

Light passing through narrow slits diffracts.

Douglas C. Johnson/California State Polytechnic University, Pomona

Figure 24.14 The diffraction pattern that appears on a screen when light passes through a narrow vertical slit. The pattern consists of a broad central band and a series of less intense and narrower side bands.

Courtesy of P. M. Rinard, from *Am. J. Phys.* 44:70, 1976

Figure 24.15 The diffraction pattern of a penny placed midway between the screen and the source. Notice the bright spot at the center.

circular bands of light near the edge of the shadow. The bright spot at the center (called the *Fresnel bright spot*) is explained by Augustin Fresnel's wave theory of light, which predicts constructive interference at this point for certain locations of the penny. From the viewpoint of geometric optics, there shouldn't be any bright spot: the center of the pattern would be completely screened by the penny.

One type of diffraction, called **Fraunhofer diffraction,** occurs when the rays leave the diffracting object in parallel directions. Fraunhofer diffraction can be achieved experimentally either by placing the observing screen far from the slit or by using a converging lens to focus the parallel rays on a nearby screen, as in Active Figure 24.16a. A bright fringe is observed along the axis at $\theta = 0$, with alternating dark and bright fringes on each side of the central bright fringe. Active Figure 24.16b is a photograph of a single-slit Fraunhofer diffraction pattern.

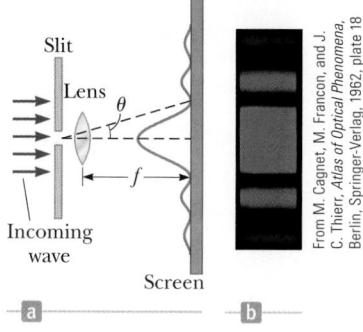

Active Figure 24.16
(a) The Fraunhofer diffraction pattern of a single slit. The parallel rays are brought into focus on the screen with a converging lens. The pattern consists of a central bright region flanked by much weaker maxima. (This drawing is not to scale.) (b) A photograph of a single-slit Fraunhofer diffraction pattern.

From M. Cagnet, M. Francon, and J. C. Thierr, Atlas of Optical Phenomena, Berlin, Springer-Verlag, 1962, plate 18

24.7 Single-Slit Diffraction

Until now we have assumed slits have negligible width, acting as line sources of light. In this section we determine how their nonzero widths are the basis for understanding the nature of the Fraunhofer diffraction pattern produced by a single slit.

We can deduce some important features of this problem by examining waves coming from various portions of the slit, as shown in Figure 24.17. According to Huygens' principle, **each portion of the slit acts as a source of waves. Hence, light from one portion of the slit can interfere with light from another portion,** and the resultant intensity on the screen depends on the direction θ.

To analyze the diffraction pattern, it's convenient to divide the slit into halves, as in Figure 24.17. All the waves that originate at the slit are in phase. Consider waves 1 and 3, which originate at the bottom and center of the slit, respectively. Wave 1 travels farther than wave 3 by an amount equal to the path difference $(a/2) \sin \theta$, where a is the width of the slit. Similarly, the path difference between waves 3 and 5 is $(a/2) \sin \theta$. If this path difference is exactly half of a wavelength (corresponding to a phase difference of 180°), the two waves cancel each other, and destructive interference results. This is true, in fact, for any two waves that originate at points separated by half the slit width because the phase difference between two such points is 180°. Therefore, waves from the upper half of the slit interfere *destructively* with waves from the lower half of the slit when

$$\frac{a}{2} \sin \theta = \frac{\lambda}{2}$$

or when

$$\sin \theta = \frac{\lambda}{a}$$

If we divide the slit into four parts rather than two and use similar reasoning, we find that the screen is also dark when

$$\sin \theta = \frac{2\lambda}{a}$$

Continuing in this way, we can divide the slit into six parts and show that darkness occurs on the screen when

$$\sin \theta = \frac{3\lambda}{a}$$

Each portion of the slit acts as a point source of light waves.

The path difference between rays 1 and 3, rays 2 and 4, or rays 3 and 5 is $(a/2) \sin \theta$.

Figure 24.17 Diffraction of light by a narrow slit of width a. (This drawing is not to scale, and the waves are assumed to converge at a distant point.)

Figure 24.18 Positions of the minima for the Fraunhofer diffraction pattern of a single slit of width a. (This drawing is not to scale.)

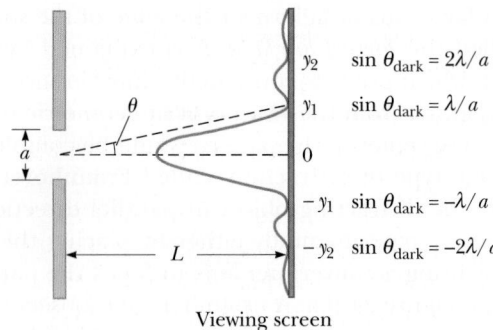

Viewing screen

Therefore, the general condition for **destructive interference** for a single slit of width a is

$$\sin \theta_{dark} = m\frac{\lambda}{a} \qquad m = \pm 1, \pm 2, \pm 3, \dots \qquad \text{[24.11]}$$

Equation 24.11 gives the values of θ for which the diffraction pattern has zero intensity, where a dark fringe forms. The equation tells us nothing about the variation in intensity along the screen, however. The general features of the intensity distribution along the screen are shown in Figure 24.18. A broad central bright fringe is flanked by much weaker bright fringes alternating with dark fringes. The various dark fringes (points of zero intensity) occur at the values of θ that satisfy Equation 24.11. The points of constructive interference lie approximately halfway between the dark fringes. Note that the central bright fringe is twice as wide as the weaker maxima having $m > 1$.

Tip 24.3 The Same, but Different

Although Equations 24.2 and 24.11 have the same form, they have different meanings. Equation 24.2 describes the *bright* regions in a two-slit interference pattern, whereas Equation 24.11 describes the *dark* regions in a single-slit interference pattern.

■ *Quick Quiz*

24.5 In a single-slit diffraction experiment, as the width of the slit is made smaller, does the width of the central maximum of the diffraction pattern (a) becomes smaller, (b) become larger, or (c) remain the same?

■ **APPLYING PHYSICS 24.4** | **Diffraction of Sound Waves**

If a classroom door is open even a small amount, you can hear sounds coming from the hallway, yet you can't see what is going on in the hallway. How can this difference be explained?

EXPLANATION The space between the slightly open door and the wall is acting as a single slit for waves. Sound waves have wavelengths larger than the width of the slit, so sound is effectively diffracted by the opening and the central maximum spreads throughout the room. Light wavelengths are much smaller than the slit width, so there is virtually no diffraction for the light. You must have a direct line of sight to detect the light waves. ■

■ **EXAMPLE 24.6** | **A Single-Slit Experiment**

GOAL Find the positions of the dark fringes in single-slit diffraction.

PROBLEM Light of wavelength 5.80×10^2 nm is incident on a slit of width 0.300 mm. The observing screen is placed 2.00 m from the slit. Find the positions of the first dark fringes and the width of the central bright fringe.

STRATEGY This problem requires substitution into Equation 24.11 to find the sines of the angles of the first dark fringes. The positions can then be found with the tangent function because for small angles $\sin \theta \approx \tan \theta$. The extent of the central maximum is defined by these two dark fringes.

. . . .

SOLUTION

The first dark fringes that flank the central bright fringe correspond to $m = \pm 1$ in Equation 24.11:

$$\sin \theta = \pm\frac{\lambda}{a} = \pm\frac{5.80 \times 10^{-7}\,\text{m}}{0.300 \times 10^{-3}\,\text{m}} = \pm 1.93 \times 10^{-3}$$

Use the triangle in Figure 24.18 to relate the position of the fringe to the tangent function:

$$\tan \theta = \frac{y_1}{L}$$

Because θ is very small, we can use the approximation $\sin \theta \approx \tan \theta$ and then solve for y_1:

$$\sin \theta \approx \tan \theta \approx \frac{y_1}{L}$$

$$y_1 \approx L \sin \theta = (2.00 \text{ m})(\pm 1.93 \times 10^{-3}) = \boxed{\pm 3.86 \times 10^{-3} \text{ m}}$$

Compute the distance between the positive and negative first-order maxima, which is the width w of the central maximum:

$$w = +3.86 \times 10^{-3} \text{ m} - (-3.86 \times 10^{-3} \text{ m}) = \boxed{7.72 \times 10^{-3} \text{ m}}$$

REMARKS Note that this value of w is much greater than the width of the slit. As the width of the slit is *increased*, however, the diffraction pattern *narrows*, corresponding to smaller values of θ. In fact, for large values of a, the maxima and minima are so closely spaced that the only observable pattern is a large central bright area resembling the geometric image of the slit. Because the width of the geometric image increases as the slit width increases, the narrowest image occurs when the geometric and diffraction widths are equal.

QUESTION 24.6 Suppose the entire apparatus is immersed in water. If the same wavelength of light (in air) is incident on the slit immersed in water, is the resulting central maximum larger or smaller? Explain.

EXERCISE 24.6 Determine the width of the first-order bright fringe in the example, when the apparatus is in air.

ANSWER 3.86 mm

24.8 The Diffraction Grating

The diffraction grating, a useful device for analyzing light sources, consists of a large number of equally spaced parallel slits. A grating can be made by scratching parallel lines on a glass plate with a precision machining technique. The clear panes between scratches act like slits. A typical grating contains several thousand lines per centimeter. For example, a grating ruled with 5 000 lines/cm has a slit spacing d equal to the reciprocal of that number; hence, $d = (1/5\ 000)$ cm $= 2 \times 10^{-4}$ cm.

Active Figure 24.19 is a schematic diagram of a section of a plane diffraction grating. A plane wave is incident from the left, normal to the plane of the grating.

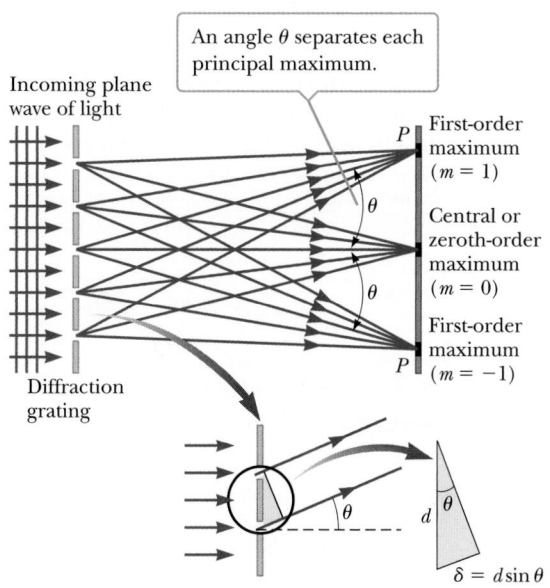

An angle θ separates each principal maximum.

Incoming plane wave of light

Diffraction grating

First-order maximum ($m = 1$)

Central or zeroth-order maximum ($m = 0$)

First-order maximum ($m = -1$)

$\delta = d \sin \theta$

Active Figure 24.19
A side view of a diffraction grating. The slit separation is d, and the path difference between adjacent slits is $d \sin \theta$.

The intensity of the pattern on the screen is the result of the combined effects of interference and diffraction. Each slit causes diffraction, and the diffracted beams in turn interfere with one another to produce the pattern. Moreover, each slit acts as a source of waves, and all waves start in phase at the slits. For some arbitrary direction θ measured from the horizontal, however, the waves must travel *different* path lengths before reaching a particular point P on the screen. In Figure 24.19, note that the path difference between waves from any two adjacent slits is $d \sin \theta$. If this path difference equals one wavelength or some integral multiple of a wavelength, waves from all slits will be in phase at P and a bright line will be observed at that point. Therefore, the condition for **maxima** in the interference pattern at the angle θ is

Condition for maxima in ▶
the interference pattern
of a diffraction grating

$$d \sin \theta_{\text{bright}} = m\lambda \qquad m = 0, \pm 1, \pm 2, \ldots \qquad \text{[24.12]}$$

Light emerging from a slit at an angle other than that for a maximum interferes nearly completely destructively with light from some other slit on the grating. All such pairs will result in little or no transmission in that direction, as illustrated in Active Figure 24.20.

Equation 24.12 can be used to calculate the wavelength from the grating spacing and the angle of deviation, θ. The integer m is the **order number** of the diffraction pattern. If the incident radiation contains several wavelengths, each wavelength deviates through a specific angle, which can be found from Equation 24.12. All wavelengths are focused at $\theta = 0$, corresponding to $m = 0$. This point is called the *zeroth-order maximum*. The *first-order maximum*, corresponding to $m = 1$, is observed at an angle that satisfies the relationship $\sin \theta = \lambda/d$; the *second-order maximum*, corresponding to $m = 2$, is observed at a larger angle θ, and so on. Active Figure 24.20 is a sketch of the intensity distribution for some of the orders produced by a diffraction grating. Note the sharpness of the principal maxima and the broad range of the dark areas, a pattern in direct contrast to the broad bright fringes characteristic of the two-slit interference pattern.

A simple arrangement that can be used to measure the angles in a diffraction pattern is shown in Active Figure 24.21. This setup is a form of a diffraction-grating spectrometer. The light to be analyzed passes through a slit and is formed into a parallel beam by a lens. The light then strikes the grating at a 90° angle. The diffracted light leaves the grating at angles that satisfy Equation 24.12. A telescope is used to view the image of the slit. The wavelength can be determined by measuring the angles at which the images of the slit appear for the various orders.

Active Figure 24.20
Intensity versus $\sin \theta$ for the diffraction grating. The zeroth-, first-, and second-order principal maxima are shown.

■ Quick Quiz

24.6 If laser light is reflected from a phonograph record or a compact disc, a diffraction pattern appears. The pattern arises because both devices contain parallel tracks of information that act as a reflection diffraction grating. Which device, record or compact disc, results in diffraction maxima that are farther apart?

Active Figure 24.21
A diagram of a diffraction grating spectrometer. The collimated beam incident on the grating is diffracted into the various orders at the angles θ that satisfy the equation $d \sin \theta = m\lambda$, where $m = 0, \pm 1, \pm 2, \ldots$

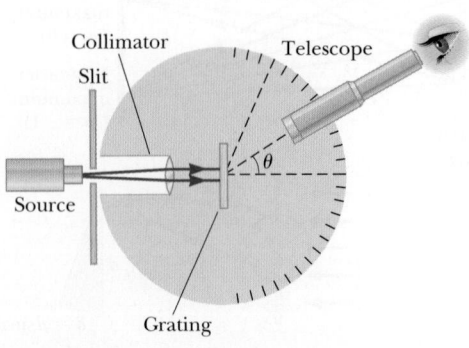

■ APPLYING PHYSICS 24.5 | Prism vs. Grating

When white light enters through an opening in an opaque box and exits through an opening on the other side of the box, a spectrum of colors appears on the wall. From this observation, how would you be able to determine whether the box contains a prism or a diffraction grating?

EXPLANATION The determination could be made by noticing the order of the colors in the spectrum relative to the direction of the original beam of white light. For a prism, in which the separation of light is a result of disper-

sion, the violet light will be refracted more than the red light. Hence, the order of the spectrum from a prism will be from red, closest to the original direction, to violet. For a diffraction grating, the angle of diffraction increases with wavelength, so the spectrum from the diffraction grating will have colors in the order from violet, closest to the original direction, to red. Further, the diffraction grating will produce *two* first-order spectra on either side of the grating, whereas the prism will produce only a single spectrum. ■

■ APPLYING PHYSICS 24.6 | Rainbows from a Compact Disc

White light reflected from the surface of a CD has a multi-colored appearance, as shown in Figure 24.22. The observation depends on the orientation of the disc relative to

the eye and the position of the light source. Explain how all this works.

EXPLANATION The surface of a CD has a spiral-shaped track (with a spacing of approximately 1 μm) that acts as a reflection grating. The light scattered by these closely spaced parallel tracks interferes constructively in certain directions that depend on both the wavelength and the direction of the incident light. Any one section of the disc serves as a diffraction grating for white light, sending beams of constructive interference for different colors in different directions. The different colors you see when viewing one section of the disc change as the light source, the disc, or you move to change the angles of incidence or diffraction. ■

© Kristen Brochmann/Fundamental Photographs

Figure 24.22 (Applying Physics 24.5) Compact discs act as diffraction gratings when observed under white light.

Use of a Diffraction Grating in CD Tracking

If a CD player is to reproduce sound faithfully, the laser beam must follow the spiral track of information perfectly. Sometimes the laser beam can drift off track, however, and without a feedback procedure to let the player know that is happening, the fidelity of the music can be greatly reduced.

Figure 24.23 shows how a diffraction grating is used in a three-beam method to keep the beam on track. The central maximum of the diffraction pattern reads the information on the CD track, and the two first-order maxima steer the beam. The grating is designed so that the first-order maxima fall on the smooth surfaces on either side of the information track. Both of these reflected beams have their

APPLICATION
Tracking Information on a CD

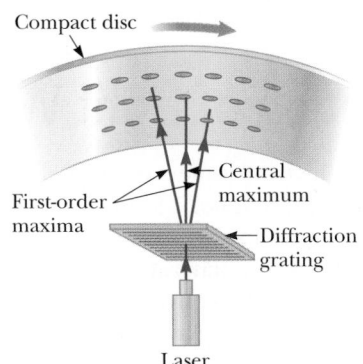

Compact disc

First-order maxima

Central maximum

Diffraction grating

Laser

Figure 24.23 The laser beam in a CD player is able to follow the spiral track by using three beams produced with a diffraction grating.

own detectors, and because both beams are reflected from smooth surfaces, they should have the same strong intensity when they are detected. If the central beam wanders off the track, however, one of the steering beams will begin to strike bumps on the information track and the amount of light reflected will decrease. This information is then used by electronic circuits to drive the main beam back to its desired location.

■ EXAMPLE 24.7 | **A Diffraction Grating**

GOAL Calculate different-order principal maxima for a diffraction grating.

PROBLEM Monochromatic light from a helium–neon laser ($\lambda = 632.8$ nm) is incident normally on a diffraction grating containing 6.00×10^3 lines/cm. Find the angles at which one would observe the first-order maximum, the second-order maximum, and so forth.

STRATEGY Find the slit separation by inverting the number of lines per centimeter, then substitute values into Equation 24.12.

. . . .

SOLUTION

Invert the number of lines per centimeter to obtain the slit separation:

$$d = \frac{1}{6.00 \times 10^3 \, \text{cm}^{-1}} = 1.67 \times 10^{-4} \, \text{cm} = 1.67 \times 10^3 \, \text{nm}$$

Substitute $m = 1$ into Equation 24.12 to find the sine of the angle corresponding to the first-order maximum:

$$\sin \theta_1 = \frac{\lambda}{d} = \frac{632.8 \, \text{nm}}{1.67 \times 10^3 \, \text{nm}} = 0.379$$

Take the inverse sine of the preceding result to find θ_1:

$$\theta_1 = \sin^{-1} 0.379 = \boxed{22.3°}$$

Repeat the calculation for $m = 2$:

$$\sin \theta_2 = \frac{2\lambda}{d} = \frac{2(632.8 \, \text{nm})}{1.67 \times 10^3 \, \text{nm}} = 0.758$$

$$\theta_2 = \boxed{49.3°}$$

Repeat the calculation for $m = 3$:

$$\sin \theta_3 = \frac{3\lambda}{d} = \frac{3(632.8 \, \text{nm})}{1.67 \times 10^3 \, \text{nm}} = 1.14$$

Because $\sin \theta$ can't exceed 1, there is no solution for θ_3.

. . . .

REMARKS The foregoing calculation shows that there can only be a finite number of principal maxima. In this case only zeroth-, first-, and second-order maxima would be observed.

QUESTION 24.7 Does a diffraction grating with more lines have a smaller or larger separation between adjacent principal maxima?

EXERCISE 24.7 Suppose light with wavelength 7.80×10^2 nm is used instead and the diffraction grating has 3.30×10^3 lines per centimeter. Find the angles of all the principal maxima.

ANSWERS 0°, 14.9°, 31.0°, 50.6°

24.9 Polarization of Light Waves

In Chapter 21 we described the transverse nature of electromagnetic waves. Figure 24.24 shows that the electric and magnetic field vectors associated with an electromagnetic wave are at right angles to each other and also to the direction of wave propagation. The phenomenon of polarization, described in this section, is firm evidence of the transverse nature of electromagnetic waves.

An ordinary beam of light consists of a large number of electromagnetic waves emitted by the atoms or molecules of the light source. The vibrating charges associated with the atoms act as tiny antennas. Each atom produces a wave with its own orientation of $\vec{E}$, as in Figure 24.24, corresponding to the direction of atomic vibration. Because all directions of vibration are possible, however, the resultant electromagnetic wave is a superposition of waves produced by the individual atomic sources. The result is an **unpolarized** light wave, represented schematically in Figure 24.25a. The direction of wave propagation shown in the figure is perpendicular to the page. Note that *all* directions of the electric field vector are equally probable and lie in a plane (such as the plane of this page) perpendicular to the direction of propagation.

A wave is said to be **linearly polarized** if the resultant electric field $\vec{E}$ vibrates in the same direction *at all times* at a particular point, as in Figure 24.25b. (Sometimes such a wave is described as *plane polarized* or simply *polarized*.) The wave in Figure 24.24 is an example of a wave that is linearly polarized in the *y*-direction. As the wave propagates in the *x*-direction, $\vec{E}$ is always in the *y*-direction. The plane formed by $\vec{E}$ and the direction of propagation is called the *plane of polarization* of the wave. In Figure 24.24 the plane of polarization is the *xy*-plane.

It's possible to obtain a linearly polarized beam from an unpolarized beam by removing all waves from the beam except those with electric field vectors that oscillate in a single plane. We now discuss three processes for doing this: (1) selective absorption, (2) reflection, and (3) scattering.

Polarization by Selective Absorption

The most common technique for polarizing light is to use a material that transmits waves having electric field vectors that vibrate in a plane parallel to a certain direction and absorbs those waves with electric field vectors vibrating in directions perpendicular to that direction.

In 1932 E. H. Land discovered a material, which he called **Polaroid**, that polarizes light through selective absorption by oriented molecules. This material is fabricated in thin sheets of long-chain hydrocarbons, which are stretched during manufacture so that the molecules align. After a sheet is dipped into a solution containing iodine, the molecules become good electrical conductors. Conduction takes place primarily along the hydrocarbon chains, however, because the valence electrons of the molecules can move easily only along those chains. (Recall that valence electrons are "free" electrons that can move easily through the conductor.) As a result, the molecules readily *absorb* light having an electric field vector parallel to their lengths and *transmit* light with an electric field vector perpendicular to their lengths. It's common to refer to the direction perpendicular to the molecular chains as the **transmission axis**. In an ideal polarizer all light with $\vec{E}$ parallel to the transmission axis is transmitted and all light with $\vec{E}$ perpendicular to the transmission axis is absorbed.

Polarizing material reduces the intensity of light passing through it. In Active Figure 24.26 an unpolarized light beam is incident on the first polarizing sheet,

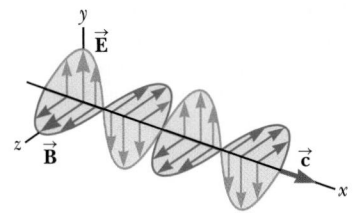

Figure 24.24 A schematic diagram of a polarized electromagnetic wave propagating in the *x*-direction. The electric field vector $\vec{E}$ vibrates in the *xy*-plane, whereas the magnetic field vector $\vec{B}$ vibrates in the *xz*-plane.

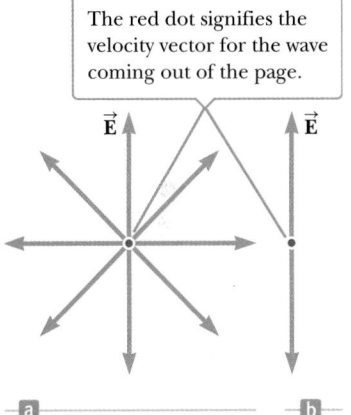

The red dot signifies the velocity vector for the wave coming out of the page.

Figure 24.25 (a) An unpolarized light beam viewed along the direction of propagation. The transverse electric field vector can vibrate in any direction with equal probability. (b) A linearly polarized light beam with the electric field vector vibrating in the vertical direction.

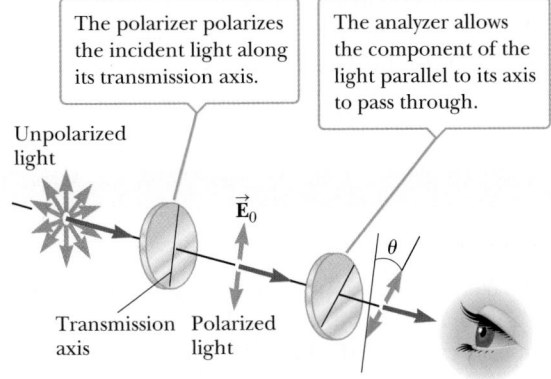

The polarizer polarizes the incident light along its transmission axis.

The analyzer allows the component of the light parallel to its axis to pass through.

Active Figure 24.26
Two polarizing sheets whose transmission axes make an angle θ with each other. Only a fraction of the polarized light incident on the analyzer is transmitted.

Figure 24.27 The intensity of light transmitted through two polarizers depends on the relative orientations of their transmission axes.

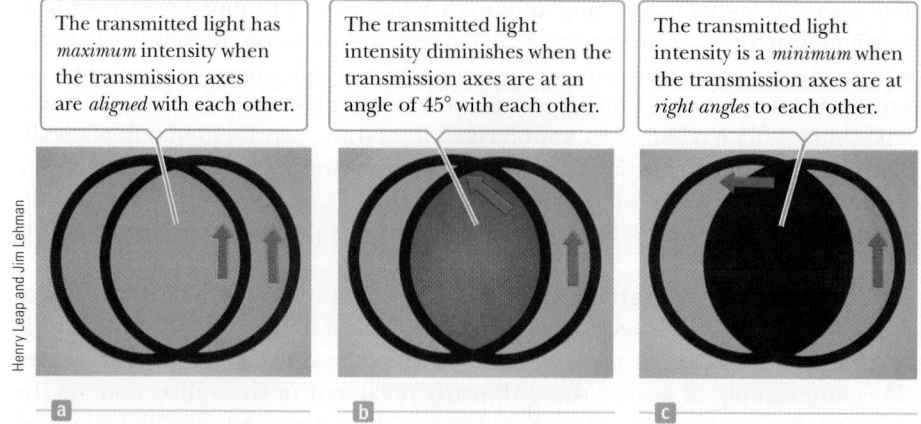

The transmitted light has *maximum* intensity when the transmission axes are *aligned* with each other.

The transmitted light intensity diminishes when the transmission axes are at an angle of 45° with each other.

The transmitted light intensity is a *minimum* when the transmission axes are at *right angles* to each other.

a   b   c

Henry Leap and Jim Lehman

called the **polarizer**; the transmission axis is as indicated. The light that passes through this sheet is polarized vertically, and the transmitted electric field vector is $\vec{E}_0$. A second polarizing sheet, called the **analyzer**, intercepts this beam with its transmission axis at an angle of θ to the axis of the polarizer. The component of $\vec{E}_0$ that is perpendicular to the axis of the analyzer is completely absorbed. The component of $\vec{E}_0$ that is parallel to the analyzer axis, $E_0 \cos \theta$, is allowed to pass through the analyzer. Because the intensity of the transmitted beam varies as the *square* of its amplitude E, we conclude that the intensity of the (polarized) beam transmitted through the analyzer varies as

Malus's law ▶

$$I = I_0 \cos^2 \theta \qquad [24.13]$$

where I_0 is the intensity of the polarized wave incident on the analyzer. This expression, known as **Malus's law**, applies to any two polarizing materials having transmission axes at an angle of θ to each other. Note from Equation 24.13 that the transmitted intensity is a maximum when the transmission axes are parallel ($\theta = 0$ or $180°$) and is a minimum (complete absorption by the analyzer) when the transmission axes are perpendicular to each other. This variation in transmitted intensity through a pair of polarizing sheets is illustrated in Figure 24.27.

When unpolarized light of intensity I_0 is sent through a single ideal polarizer, the transmitted linearly polarized light has intensity $I_0/2$. This fact follows from Malus's law because the average value of $\cos^2 \theta$ is one-half.

■ **APPLYING PHYSICS 24.7**   **Polarizing Microwaves**

A polarizer for microwaves can be made as a grid of parallel metal wires about 1 cm apart. Is the electric field vector for microwaves transmitted through this polarizer parallel or perpendicular to the metal wires?

EXPLANATION Electric field vectors parallel to the metal wires cause electrons in the metal to oscillate parallel to the wires. Thus, the energy from the waves with these

electric field vectors is transferred to the metal by accelerating the electrons and is eventually transformed to internal energy through the resistance of the metal. Waves with electric field vectors perpendicular to the metal wires are not able to accelerate electrons and pass through the wires. Consequently, the electric field polarization is perpendicular to the metal wires. ■

■ **EXAMPLE 24.8**   **Polarizer**

GOAL Understand how polarizing materials affect light intensity.

PROBLEM Unpolarized light is incident upon three polarizers. The first polarizer has a vertical transmission axis, the second has a transmission axis rotated 30.0° with respect to the first, and the third has a transmission axis rotated 75.0° relative to the first. If the initial light intensity of the beam is I_b, calculate the light intensity after the beam passes through **(a)** the second polarizer and **(b)** the third polarizer.

STRATEGY After the beam passes through the first polarizer, it is polarized and its intensity is cut in half. Malus's law can then be applied to the second and third polarizers. The angle used in Malus's law must be relative to the immediately preceding transmission axis.

SOLUTION

(a) Calculate the intensity of the beam after it passes through the second polarizer.

The incident intensity is $I_b/2$. Apply Malus's law to the second polarizer:

$$I_2 = I_0 \cos^2 \theta = \frac{I_b}{2} \cos^2 (30.0°) = \frac{I_b}{2} \left(\frac{\sqrt{3}}{2} \right)^2 = \boxed{\frac{3}{8} I_b}$$

(b) Calculate the intensity of the beam after it passes through the third polarizer.

The incident intensity is now $3I_b/8$. Apply Malus's law to the third polarizer.

$$I_3 = I_2 \cos^2 \theta = \frac{3}{8} I_b \cos^2 (45.0°) = \frac{3}{8} I_b \left(\frac{\sqrt{2}}{2} \right)^2 = \boxed{\frac{3}{16} I_b}$$

REMARKS Notice that the angle used in part (b) was not 75.0°, but 75.0° − 30.0° = 45.0°. The angle is always with respect to the previous polarizer's transmission axis because the polarizing material physically determines what direction the transmitted electric fields can have.

QUESTION 24.8 At what angle relative to the previous polarizer must an additional polarizer be placed so as to completely block the light?

EXERCISE 24.8 The polarizers are rotated so that the second polarizer has a transmission axis of 40.0° with respect to the first polarizer, and the third polarizer has an angle of 90.0° with respect to the first. If I_b is the intensity of the original unpolarized light, what is the intensity of the beam after it passes through (a) the second polarizer and (b) the third polarizer? (c) What is the final transmitted intensity if the second polarizer is removed?

ANSWERS (a) $0.293I_b$ (b) $0.121I_b$ (c) 0

Polarization by Reflection

When an unpolarized light beam is reflected from a surface, the reflected light is completely polarized, partially polarized, or unpolarized, depending on the angle of incidence. If the angle of incidence is either 0° or 90° (a normal or grazing angle), the reflected beam is unpolarized. For angles of incidence between 0° and 90°, however, the reflected light is polarized to some extent. For one particular angle of incidence the reflected beam is completely polarized.

Suppose an unpolarized light beam is incident on a surface, as in Figure 24.28a on page 846. The beam can be described by two electric field components, one parallel to the surface (represented by dots) and the other perpendicular to the first component and to the direction of propagation (represented by orange arrows). It is found that the parallel component reflects more strongly than the other components, and the result is a partially polarized beam. In addition, the refracted beam is also partially polarized.

Now suppose the angle of incidence, θ_1, is varied until the angle between the reflected and refracted beams is 90° (Fig. 24.28b). At this particular angle of incidence, called the **polarizing angle** θ_p, the reflected beam is completely polarized, with its electric field vector parallel to the surface, while the refracted beam is partially polarized.

An expression relating the polarizing angle to the index of refraction of the reflecting surface can be obtained by the use of Figure 24.28b. From this figure, we see that at the polarizing angle, $\theta_p + 90° + \theta_2 = 180°$, so $\theta_2 = 90° - \theta_p$. Using Snell's law and taking $n_1 = n_{air} = 1.00$ and $n_2 = n$ yields

$$n = \frac{\sin \theta_1}{\sin \theta_2} = \frac{\sin \theta_p}{\sin \theta_2}$$

Figure 24.28 (a) When unpolarized light is incident on a reflecting surface, the reflected and refracted beams are partially polarized. (b) The reflected beam is completely polarized when the angle of incidence equals the polarizing angle θ_p, satisfying the equation $n = \tan \theta_p$.

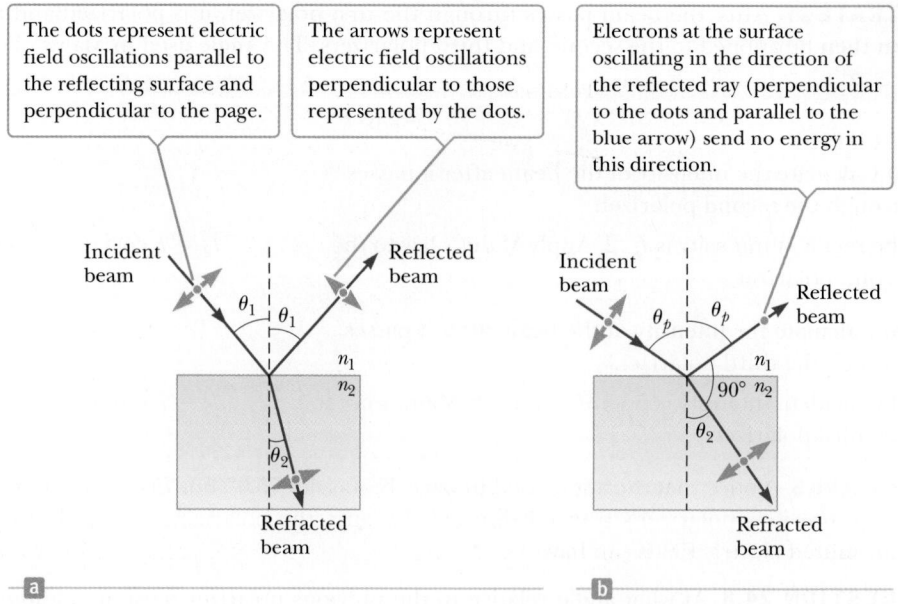

The dots represent electric field oscillations parallel to the reflecting surface and perpendicular to the page.

The arrows represent electric field oscillations perpendicular to those represented by the dots.

Electrons at the surface oscillating in the direction of the reflected ray (perpendicular to the dots and parallel to the blue arrow) send no energy in this direction.

Because $\sin \theta_2 = \sin (90° - \theta_p) = \cos \theta_p$, the expression for n can be written

Brewster's law ▶

$$n = \frac{\sin \theta_p}{\cos \theta_p} = \tan \theta_p \qquad [24.14]$$

Equation 24.14 is called **Brewster's law**, and the polarizing angle θ_p is sometimes called **Brewster's angle** after its discoverer, Sir David Brewster (1781–1868). For example, Brewster's angle for crown glass (where $n = 1.52$) has the value $\theta_p = \tan^{-1}(1.52) = 56.7°$. Because n varies with wavelength for a given substance, Brewster's angle is also a function of wavelength.

APPLICATION
Polaroid Sunglasses

Polarization by reflection is a common phenomenon. Sunlight reflected from water, glass, or snow is partially polarized. If the surface is horizontal, the electric field vector of the reflected light has a strong horizontal component. Sunglasses made of polarizing material reduce the glare, which *is* the reflected light. The transmission axes of the lenses are oriented vertically to absorb the strong horizontal component of the reflected light. Because the reflected light is mostly polarized, most of the glare can be eliminated without removing most of the normal light.

Polarization by Scattering

When light is incident on a system of particles, such as a gas, the electrons in the medium can absorb and reradiate part of the light. The absorption and reradiation of light by the medium, called **scattering**, is what causes sunlight reaching an observer on Earth from straight overhead to be polarized. You can observe this effect by looking directly up through a pair of sunglasses made of polarizing glass. Less light passes through at certain orientations of the lenses than at others.

Figure 24.29 illustrates how the sunlight becomes polarized. The left side of the figure shows an incident unpolarized beam of sunlight on the verge of striking an air molecule. When the beam strikes the air molecule, it sets the electrons of the molecule into vibration. These vibrating charges act like those in an antenna except that they vibrate in a complicated pattern. The horizontal part of the electric field vector in the incident wave causes the charges to vibrate horizontally, and the vertical part of the vector simultaneously causes them to vibrate vertically. A horizontally polarized wave is emitted by the electrons as a result of their horizontal motion, and a vertically polarized wave is emitted parallel to Earth as a result of their vertical motion.

The scattered light traveling perpendicular to the incident light is plane-polarized because the vertical vibrations of the charges in the air molecule send no light in this direction.

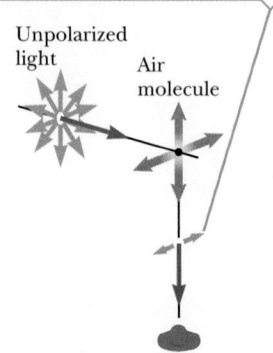

Unpolarized light   Air molecule

Figure 24.29 The scattering of unpolarized sunlight by air molecules.

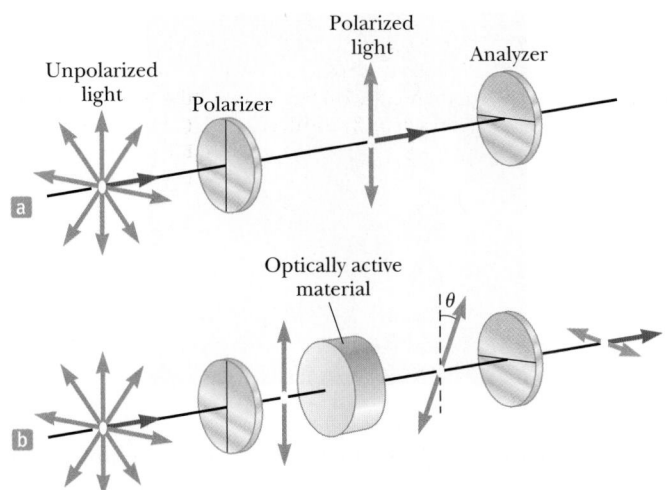

Figure 24.30 (a) When crossed polarizers are used, none of the polarized light can pass through the analyzer. (b) An optically active material rotates the direction of polarization through the angle θ, enabling some of the polarized light to pass through the analyzer.

Scientists have found that bees and homing pigeons use the polarization of sunlight as a navigational aid.

Optical Activity

Many important practical applications of polarized light involve the use of certain materials that display the property of **optical activity**. A substance is said to be optically active if it rotates the plane of polarization of transmitted light. Suppose unpolarized light is incident on a polarizer from the left, as in Figure 24.30a. The transmitted light is polarized vertically, as shown. If this light is then incident on an analyzer with its axis perpendicular to that of the polarizer, no light emerges from it. If an optically active material is placed between the polarizer and analyzer, as in Figure 24.30b, the material causes the direction of the polarized beam to rotate through the angle θ. As a result, some light is able to pass through the analyzer. The angle through which the light is rotated by the material can be found by rotating the polarizer until the light is again extinguished. It is found that the angle of rotation depends on the length of the sample and, if the substance is in solution, on the concentration. One optically active material is a solution of common sugar, dextrose. A standard method for determining the concentration of a sugar solution is to measure the rotation produced by a fixed length of the solution.

Optical activity occurs in a material because of an asymmetry in the shape of its constituent molecules. For example, some proteins are optically active because of their spiral shapes. Other materials, such as glass and plastic, become optically active when placed under stress. If polarized light is passed through an unstressed piece of plastic and then through an analyzer with an axis perpendicular to that of the polarizer, none of the polarized light is transmitted. If the plastic is placed under stress, however, the regions of greatest stress produce the largest angles of rotation of polarized light, and a series of light and dark bands are observed in the transmitted light. Engineers often use this property in the design of structures ranging from bridges to small tools. A plastic model is built and analyzed under different load conditions to determine positions of potential weakness and failure under stress. If the design is poor, patterns of light and dark bands will indicate the points of greatest weakness, and the design can be corrected at an early stage. Figure 24.31 (page 848) shows examples of stress patterns in plastic.

APPLICATION

Finding the Concentrations of Solutions by Means of Their Optical Activity

Liquid Crystals

An effect similar to rotation of the plane of polarization is used to create the familiar displays on pocket calculators, wristwatches, notebook computers, and so forth. The properties of a unique substance called a liquid crystal make these displays

APPLICATION

Liquid Crystal Displays (LCDs)

Figure 24.31 A plastic model of an arch structure under load conditions observed between perpendicular polarizers. Such patterns are useful in the optimum design of architectural components.

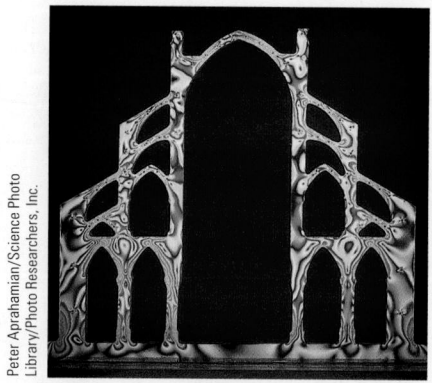

Peter Aprahamian/Science Photo Library/Photo Researchers, Inc.

(called LCDs, for *liquid crystal displays*) possible. As its name implies, a **liquid crystal** is a substance with properties intermediate between those of a crystalline solid and those of a liquid; that is, the molecules of the substance are more orderly than those in a liquid, but less orderly than those in a pure crystalline solid. The forces that hold the molecules together in such a state are just barely strong enough to enable the substance to maintain a definite shape, so it is reasonable to call it a solid. Small inputs of mechanical or electrical energy, however, can disrupt these weak bonds and make the substance flow, rotate, or twist.

To see how liquid crystals can be used to create a display, consider Figure 24.32a. The liquid crystal is placed between two glass plates in the pattern shown, and electrical contacts, indicated by the thin lines, are made. When a voltage is applied across any segment in the display, that segment turns dark. In this fashion any number between 0 and 9 can be formed by the pattern, depending on the voltages applied to the seven segments.

To see why a segment can be changed from dark to light by the application of a voltage, consider Figure 24.32b, which shows the basic construction of a por-

Figure 24.32 (a) The light-segment pattern of a liquid crystal display. (b) Rotation of a polarized light beam by a liquid crystal when the applied voltage is zero. (c) Molecules of the liquid crystal align with the electric field when a voltage is applied.

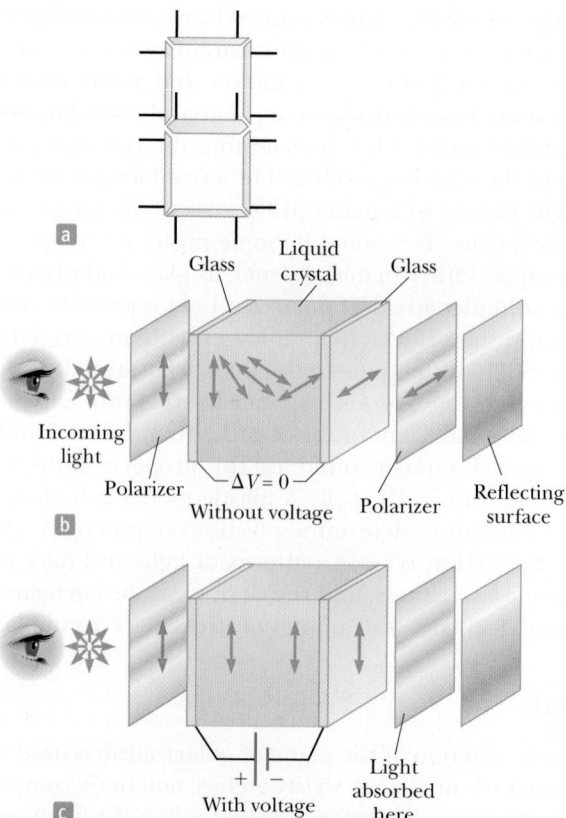

tion of the display. The liquid crystal is placed between two glass substrates that are packaged between two pieces of Polaroid material with their transmission axes perpendicular. A reflecting surface is placed behind one of the pieces of Polaroid. First consider what happens when light falls on this package and no voltages are applied to the liquid crystal, as shown in Figure 24.32b. Incoming light is polarized by the polarizer on the left and then falls on the liquid crystal. As the light passes through the crystal, its plane of polarization is rotated by 90°, allowing it to pass through the polarizer on the right. It reflects from the reflecting surface and retraces its path through the crystal. Thus, an observer to the left of the crystal sees the segment as being bright. When a voltage is applied as in Figure 24.32c, the molecules of the liquid crystal don't rotate the plane of polarization of the light. In this case the light is absorbed by the polarizer on the right, and none is reflected back to the observer to the left of the crystal. As a result, the observer sees this segment as black. Changing the applied voltage to the crystal in a precise pattern at precise times can make the pattern tick off the seconds on a watch, display a letter on a computer display, and so forth.

■ SUMMARY

24.1 Conditions for Interference

Interference occurs when two or more light waves overlap at a given point. A sustained interference pattern is observed if (1) the sources are coherent (that is, they maintain a constant phase relationship with one another), (2) the sources have identical wavelengths, and (3) the superposition principle is applicable.

24.2 Young's Double-Slit Experiment

In **Young's double-slit experiment** two slits separated by distance d are illuminated by a single-wavelength light source. An interference pattern consisting of bright and dark fringes is observed on a screen a distance L from the slits. The condition for **bright fringes** (constructive interference) is

$$d \sin \theta_{\text{bright}} = m\lambda \qquad m = 0, \pm 1, \pm 2, \ldots \qquad [24.2]$$

The number m is called the **order number** of the fringe.

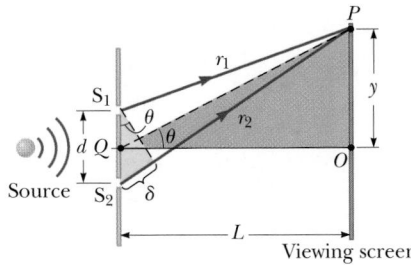

A geometric construction that describes Young's double-slit experiment. (This figure is not drawn to scale.)

The condition for **dark fringes** (destructive interference) is

$$d \sin \theta_{\text{dark}} = \left(m + \tfrac{1}{2} \right)\lambda \qquad m = 0, \pm 1, \pm 2, \ldots \qquad [24.3]$$

The position y_m of the bright fringes on the screen can be determined by using the relation $\sin \theta \approx \tan \theta = y_m/L$, which is true for small angles. This relation can be substituted into Equations 24.2 and 24.3, yielding the location of the bright fringes:

$$y_{\text{bright}} = \frac{\lambda L}{d} m \qquad m = 0, \pm 1, \pm 2, \ldots \qquad [24.5]$$

A similar expression can be derived for the dark fringes. This equation can be used either to locate the maxima or to determine the wavelength of light by measuring y_m.

24.3 Change of Phase Due to Reflection

24.4 Interference in Thin Films

An electromagnetic wave undergoes a phase change of 180° on reflection from a medium with an index of refraction higher than that of the medium in which the wave is traveling. There is no change when the wave, traveling in a medium with higher index of refraction, reflects from a medium with a lower index of refraction.

Interference in light reflected from a thin film is due to a combination of rays 1 and 2 reflected from the upper and lower surfaces of the film.

The wavelength λ_n of light in a medium with index of refraction n is

$$\lambda_n = \frac{\lambda}{n} \qquad [24.7]$$

where λ is the wavelength of the light in free space. Light encountering a thin film of thickness t will reflect off the top and bottom of the film, each ray undergoing a possible phase change as described above. The two rays recombine, and bright and dark fringes will be observed, with the conditions of interference given by the following table:

Equation ($m = 0, 1, \ldots$)		1 Phase Reversal	0 or 2 Phase Reversals
$2nt = \left(m + \frac{1}{2}\right)\lambda$	**[24.9]**	Constructive	Destructive
$2nt = m\lambda$	**[24.10]**	Destructive	Constructive

24.6 Diffraction

24.7 Single-Slit Diffraction

Diffraction occurs when waves pass through small openings, around obstacles, or by sharp edges. The **diffraction pattern** produced by a single slit on a distant screen consists of a central bright maximum flanked by less bright fringes alternating with dark regions. The angles θ at which the diffraction pattern has zero intensity (regions of destructive interference) are described by

$$\sin \theta_{\text{dark}} = m\frac{\lambda}{a} \qquad m = \pm 1, \pm 2, \pm 3, \ldots \qquad \textbf{[24.11]}$$

where λ is the wavelength of the light incident on the slit and a is the width of the slit.

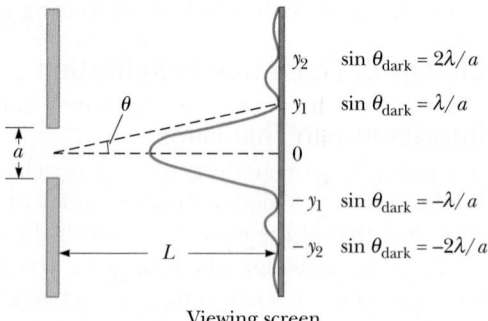

Positions of the minima for the Fraunhofer diffraction pattern of a single slit of width a. (This drawing is not to scale.)

24.8 The Diffraction Grating

A **diffraction grating** consists of many equally spaced, identical slits. The condition for **maximum intensity** in the interference pattern of a diffraction grating is

$$d \sin \theta_{\text{bright}} = m\lambda \qquad m = 0, \pm 1, \pm 2, \ldots \qquad \textbf{[24.12]}$$

where d is the spacing between adjacent slits and m is the order number of the diffraction pattern. A diffraction grating can be made by putting a large number of evenly spaced scratches on a glass slide. The number of such lines per centimeter is the inverse of the spacing d.

24.9 Polarization of Light Waves

Unpolarized light can be polarized by selective absorption, reflection, or scattering. A material can polarize light if it transmits waves having electric field vectors that vibrate in a plane parallel to a certain direction and absorbs waves with electric field vectors vibrating in directions perpendicular to that direction. When unpolarized light passes through a polarizing sheet, its intensity is reduced by half and the light becomes polarized. When this light passes through a second polarizing sheet with transmission axis at an angle of θ with respect to the transmission axis of the first sheet, the transmitted intensity is given by

$$I = I_0 \cos^2 \theta \qquad \textbf{[24.13]}$$

where I_0 is the intensity of the light after passing through the first polarizing sheet.

In general, light reflected from an amorphous material, such as glass, is partially polarized. Reflected light is completely polarized, with its electric field parallel to the surface, when the angle of incidence produces a 90° angle between the reflected and refracted beams. This angle of incidence, called the **polarizing angle** θ_p, satisfies **Brewster's law,** given by

$$n = \tan \theta_p \qquad \textbf{[24.14]}$$

where n is the index of refraction of the reflecting medium.

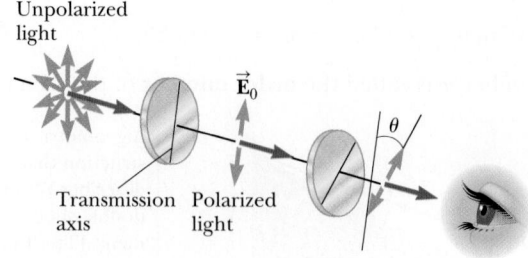

Two polarizing sheets, with transmission axes at angle θ, transmit only a fraction of the incident light.

■ MULTIPLE-CHOICE QUESTIONS

WebAssign The multiple-choice questions in this chapter may be assigned online in Enhanced WebAssign.

1. A thin layer of oil ($n = 1.25$) is floating on water ($n = 1.33$). What is the minimum nonzero thickness of the oil in the region that strongly reflects green light ($\lambda = 530$ nm)? (a) 500 nm (b) 313 nm (c) 404 nm (d) 212 nm (e) 285 nm

2. A monochromatic light beam having a wavelength of 5.0×10^2 nm illuminates a double slit having a slit separation of 2.0×10^{-5} m. What is the angle of the second-order bright fringe? (a) 0.050 rad (b) 0.025 rad (c) 0.10 rad (d) 0.25 rad (e) 0.010 rad

3. A Fraunhofer diffraction pattern is produced on a screen located 1.00 m from a single slit. If a light source of wavelength 5.00×10^{-7} m is used and the distance from the center of the central bright fringe to the first dark fringe is 5.00×10^{-3} m, what is the slit width? (a) 0.010 0 mm (b) 0.100 mm (c) 0.200 mm (d) 1.00 mm (e) 0.005 00 mm

4. If plane-polarized light is sent through two polarizers, the first polarizer at 45° to the original plane of polarization and the second polarizer at 90° to the original plane of polarization, what fraction of the original polarized intensity gets through the last polarizer? (a) 0 (b) 0.25 (c) 0.50 (d) 0.125 (e) 0.10

5. A plane monochromatic light wave is incident on a double-slit as illustrated in Figure 24.4. As the slit separation decreases, what happens to the separation between the interference fringes on the screen? (a) It decreases. (b) It increases. (c) It remains the same. (d) It may increase or decrease, depending on the wavelength of the light. (e) More information is required.

6. A plane monochromatic light wave is incident on a double-slit as illustrated in Figure 24.4. If the viewing screen is moved away from the double slit, what happens to the separation between the interference fringes on the screen? (a) It increases. (b) It decreases. (c) It remains the same. (d) It may increase or decrease, depending on the wavelength of the light. (e) More information is required.

7. In one experiment light of wavelength λ_1 passes through a single slit and forms an interference pattern on a screen. In a second experiment light of wavelength λ_2 passes through the same slit and forms another interference pattern on the screen. If $\lambda_2 > \lambda_1$, what is the separation between bright lines in the two experiments? (a) It's the same for both experiments.

(b) It's greater in the first experiment. (c) It's greater in the second experiment. (d) It's dependent on the intensity of the light. (e) More information is required.

8. What happens to light when it is reflected off a shiny surface on a sunny day? (a) It undergoes refraction. (b) It is totally polarized. (c) It is unpolarized. (d) It tends to be partially polarized. (e) More information is required.

9. What causes the brightly colored patterns sometimes seen on wet streets covered with a layer of oil? Choose the best answer. (a) diffraction and polarization (b) interference and deflection (c) polarization and reflection (d) refraction and diffraction (e) reflection and interference

10. Consider a wave passing through a single slit. What happens to the width of the central maximum of its diffraction pattern as the slit is made half as wide? (a) It becomes one-fourth as wide. (b) It becomes one-half as wide. (c) Its width does not change. (d) It becomes twice as wide. (e) It becomes four times wider.

11. A film of oil on a puddle in a parking lot shows a variety of bright colors in swirled patches. What can you say about the thickness of the oil film? (a) It is much less than the wavelength of visible light. (b) It is of the same order of magnitude as the wavelength of visible light. (c) It is much greater than the wavelength of visible light. (d) It might have any relationship to the wavelength of visible light.

12. When you receive a chest x-ray at a hospital, the x-rays pass through a set of parallel ribs in your chest. Do your ribs act as a diffraction grating for x-rays? (a) Yes. They produce diffracted beams that can be observed separately. (b) Not to a measurable extent. The ribs are too far apart. (c) Essentially not. The ribs are too close together. (d) Essentially not. The ribs are too few in number. (e) Absolutely not. X-rays cannot diffract.

■ CONCEPTUAL QUESTIONS

WebAssign The conceptual questions in this chapter may be assigned online in Enhanced WebAssign.

1. Your automobile has two headlights. What sort of interference pattern do you expect to see from them? Why?

2. Holding your hand at arm's length, you can readily block direct sunlight from your eyes. Why can you not block sound from your ears this way?

3. Consider a dark fringe in an interference pattern at which almost no light energy is arriving. Light from both slits is arriving at this point, but the waves cancel. Where does the energy go?

4. If Young's double-slit experiment were performed under water, how would the observed interference pattern be affected?

5. In a laboratory accident, you spill two liquids onto water, neither of which mixes with the water. They both form thin films on the water surface. As the films spread and become very thin, you notice that one film becomes bright and the other black in reflected light. Why might that be?

6. If white light is used in Young's double-slit experiment rather than monochromatic light, how does the interference pattern change?

7. A lens with outer radius of curvature R and index of refraction n rests on a flat glass plate, and the combination is illuminated from white light from above. Is

there a dark spot or a light spot at the center of the lens? What does it mean if the observed rings are noncircular?

8. Fingerprints left on a piece of glass such as a windowpane can show colored spectra like that from a diffraction grating. Why?

9. In everyday experience, why are radio waves polarized, whereas light is not?

10. Suppose reflected white light is used to observe a thin, transparent coating on glass as the coating material is gradually deposited by evaporation in a vacuum. Describe some color changes that might occur during the process of building up the thickness of the coating.

11. Would it be possible to place a nonreflective coating on an airplane to cancel radar waves of wavelength 3 cm?

12. Certain sunglasses use a polarizing material to reduce the intensity of light reflected from shiny surfaces, such as water or the hood of a car. What orientation

of the transmission axis should the material have to be most effective?

13. Why is it so much easier to perform interference experiments with a laser than with an ordinary light source?

14. A soap film is held vertically in air and is viewed in reflected light as in Figure CQ24.14. Explain why the film appears to be dark at the top.

Figure CQ24.14

PROBLEMS

WebAssign The problems in this chapter may be assigned online in Enhanced WebAssign. Selected problems also have Watch It video solutions.

1. denotes straightforward problem; 2. denotes intermediate problem; 3. denotes challenging problem

1. denotes full solution available in *Student Solutions Manual/Study Guide*

1. denotes problems most often assigned in Enhanced WebAssign
BIO denotes biomedical problems
GP denotes guided problems
M denotes Master It tutorial available in Enhanced WebAssign
Q|C denotes asking for quantitative and conceptual reasoning
S denotes symbolic reasoning problem

24.2 Young's Double-Slit Experiment

1. A laser beam is incident on two slits with a separation of 0.200 mm, and a screen is placed 5.00 m from the slits. If the bright interference fringes on the screen are separated by 1.58 cm, what is the wavelength of the laser light?

2. In a Young's double-slit experiment, a set of parallel slits with a separation of 0.100 mm is illuminated by light having a wavelength of 589 nm, and the interference pattern is observed on a screen 4.00 m from the slits. (a) What is the difference in path lengths from each of the slits to the location of a third-order bright fringe on the screen? (b) What is the difference in path lengths from the two slits to the location of the third dark fringe on the screen, away from the center of the pattern?

3. A pair of narrow, parallel slits separated by 0.250 mm is illuminated by the green component from a mercury vapor lamp (λ = 546.1 nm). The interference pattern is observed on a screen 1.20 m from the plane of the parallel slits. Calculate the distance (a) from the central maximum to the first bright region on either side

of the central maximum and (b) between the first and second dark bands in the interference pattern.

4. Light of wavelength 620 nm falls on a double slit, and the first bright fringe of the interference pattern is seen at an angle of 15.0° from the central maximum. Find the separation between the slits.

5. In a location where the speed of sound is 354 m/s, a 2 000-Hz sound wave impinges on two slits 30.0 cm apart. (a) At what angle is the first maximum located? (b) If the sound wave is replaced by 3.00-cm microwaves, what slit separation gives the same angle for the first maximum? (c) If the slit separation is 1.00 μm, what frequency of light gives the same first maximum angle?

6. A double slit separated by 0.058 0 mm is placed 1.50 m from a screen. (a) If yellow light of wavelength 588 nm strikes the double slit, what is the separation between the zeroth-order and first-order maxima on the screen? (b) If blue light of wavelength 412 nm strikes the double slit, what is the separation between the second-order and fourth-order maxima?

7. [M] Two radio antennas separated by $d = 300$ m, as shown in Figure P24.7, simultaneously broadcast identical signals at the same wavelength. A car travels due north along a straight line at position $x = 1\,000$ m from the center point between the antennas, and its radio receives the signals. (a) If the car is at the position of the second maximum after that at point O when it has traveled a distance of $y = 400$ m northward, what is the wavelength of the signals? (b) How much farther must the car travel from this position to encounter the next minimum in reception? *Hint:* Do not use the small-angle approximation in this problem.

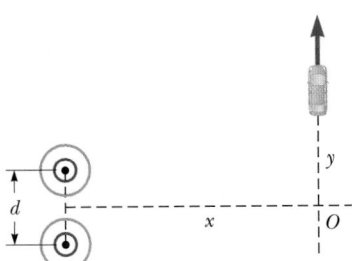

Figure P24.7

8. Light of wavelength 6.0×10^2 nm falls on a double slit, and the first bright fringe of the interference pattern is observed to make an angle of $12°$ with the horizontal. Find the separation between the slits.

9. Monochromatic light falls on a screen 1.75 m from two slits separated by 2.10 mm. The first- and second-order bright fringes are separated by 0.552 mm. What is the wavelength of the light?

10. A pair of slits, separated by 0.150 mm, is illuminated by light having a wavelength of $\lambda = 643$ nm. An interference pattern is observed on a screen 140 cm from the slits. Consider a point on the screen located at $y = 1.80$ cm from the central maximum of this pattern. (a) What is the path difference δ for the two slits at the location y? (b) Express this path difference in terms of the wavelength. (c) Will the interference correspond to a maximum, a minimum, or an intermediate condition?

11. A riverside warehouse has two open doors, as in Figure P24.11. Its interior is lined with a sound-absorbing

Figure P24.11

material. A boat on the river sounds its horn. To person A, the sound is loud and clear. To person B, the sound is barely audible. The principal wavelength of the sound waves is 3.00 m. Assuming person B is at the position of the first minimum, determine the distance between the doors, center to center.

12. [Q|C] A student sets up a double-slit experiment using monochromatic light of wavelength λ. The distance between the slits is equal to 25λ. (a) Find the angles at which the $m = 1$, 2, and 3 maxima occur on the viewing screen. (b) At what angles do the first three dark fringes occur? (c) Why are the answers so evenly spaced? Is the spacing even for all orders? Explain.

13. Radio waves from a star, of wavelength 250 m, reach a radio telescope by two separate paths, as shown in Figure P24.13. One is a direct path to the receiver, which is situated on the edge of a cliff by the ocean. The second is by reflection off the water. The first minimum of destructive interference occurs when the star is $\theta = 25.0°$ above the horizon. Find the height of the cliff. (Assume no phase change on reflection.)

Figure P24.13

14. [GP] Monochromatic light of wavelength λ is incident on a pair of slits separated by 2.40×10^{-4} m, and forms an interference pattern on a screen placed 1.80 m away from the slits. The first-order bright fringe is 4.52 mm from the center of the central maximum. (a) Draw a picture, labeling the angle θ and the legs of the right triangle associated with the first-order bright fringe. (b) Compute the tangent of the angle θ associated with the first-order bright fringe. (c) Find the angle corresponding to the first-order bright fringe and compute the sine of that angle. Are the sine and tangent of the angle comparable in value? Does your answer always hold true? (d) Calculate the wavelength of the light. (e) Compute the angle of the fifth-order bright fringe. (f) Find its position on the screen.

15. Waves from a radio station have a wavelength of 300 m. They travel by two paths to a home receiver 20.0 km from the transmitter. One path is a direct path, and the second is by reflection from a mountain directly behind the home receiver. What is the minimum distance from the mountain to the receiver that produces destructive interference at the receiver? (Assume that no phase change occurs on reflection from the mountain.)

24.3 Change of Phase Due to Reflection

24.4 Interference in Thin Films

16. **Q|C** A soap bubble ($n = 1.33$) having a wall thickness of 120 nm is floating in air. (a) What is the wavelength of the visible light that is most strongly reflected? (b) Explain how a bubble of different thickness could also strongly reflect light of this same wavelength. (c) Find the two smallest film thicknesses larger than the one given that can produce strongly reflected light of this same wavelength.

17. A thin layer of liquid methylene iodide ($n = 1.756$) is sandwiched between two flat, parallel plates of glass ($n = 1.50$). What is the minimum thickness of the liquid layer if normally incident light with $\lambda = 6.00 \times 10^2$ nm in air is to be strongly reflected?

18. **S** A thin film of oil ($n = 1.25$) is located on smooth, wet pavement. When viewed from a direction perpendicular to the pavement, the film reflects most strongly red light at 640 nm and reflects no green light at 512 nm. (a) What is the minimum thickness of the oil film? (b) Let m_1 correspond to the order of the constructive interference and m_2 to the order of the destructive interference. Obtain a relationship between m_1 and m_2 that is consistent with the given data.

19. A thin film of glass ($n = 1.52$) of thickness 0.420 μm is viewed under white light at near normal incidence. What wavelength of *visible* light is most strongly reflected by the film when surrounded by air?

20. A transparent oil with index of refraction 1.29 spills on the surface of water (index of refraction 1.33), producing a maximum of reflection with normally incident orange light (wavelength 600 nm in air). Assuming the maximum occurs in the first order, determine the thickness of the oil slick.

21. **M** A possible means for making an airplane invisible to radar is to coat the plane with an antireflective polymer. If radar waves have a wavelength of 3.00 cm and the index of refraction of the polymer is $n = 1.50$, how thick would you make the coating?

22. **Q|C** An oil film ($n = 1.45$) floating on water is illuminated by white light at normal incidence. The film is 2.80×10^2 nm thick. Find (a) the wavelength and color of the light in the visible spectrum most strongly reflected and (b) the wavelength and color of the light in the visible spectrum most strongly transmitted. Explain your reasoning.

23. **Q|C** Astronomers observe the chromosphere of the Sun with a filter that passes the red hydrogen spectral line of wavelength 656.3 nm, called the H_α line. The filter consists of a transparent dielectric of thickness d held between two partially aluminized glass plates. The filter is kept at a constant temperature. (a) Find

the minimum value of d that will produce maximum transmission of perpendicular H_α light if the dielectric has an index of refraction of 1.378. (b) If the temperature of the filter increases above the normal value increasing its thickness, what happens to the transmitted wavelength? (c) The dielectric will also pass what near-visible wavelength? One of the glass plates is colored red to absorb this light.

24. Two rectangular optically flat plates ($n = 1.52$) are in contact along one end and are separated along the other end by a 2.00-μm-thick spacer (Fig. P24.24). The top plate is illuminated by monochromatic light of wavelength 546.1 nm. Calculate the number of dark parallel bands crossing the top plate (including the dark band at zero thickness along the edge of contact between the plates).

Figure P24.24
Problems 24 and 25.

25. An investigator finds a fiber at a crime scene that he wishes to use as evidence against a suspect. He gives the fiber to a technician to test the properties of the fiber. To measure the diameter of the fiber, the technician places it between two flat glass plates at their ends as in Figure P24.24. When the plates, of length 14.0 cm, are illuminated from above with light of wavelength 650 nm, she observes bright interference bands separated by 0.580 mm. What is the diameter of the fiber?

26. A plano-convex lens with radius of curvature $R = 3.0$ m is in contact with a flat plate of glass. A light source and the observer's eye are both close to the normal, as shown in Figure 24.8a. The radius of the 50th bright Newton's ring is found to be 9.8 mm. What is the wavelength of the light produced by the source?

27. A plano-convex lens rests with its curved side on a flat glass surface and is illuminated from above by light of wavelength 500 nm. (See Fig. 24.8.) A dark spot is observed at the center, surrounded by 19 concentric dark rings (with bright rings in between). How much thicker is the air wedge at the position of the 19th dark ring than at the center?

28. Nonreflective coatings on camera lenses reduce the loss of light at the surfaces of multilens systems and prevent internal reflections that might mar the image. Find the minimum thickness of a layer of magnesium fluoride ($n = 1.38$) on flint glass ($n = 1.66$) that will cause destructive interference of reflected light of wavelength 550 nm near the middle of the visible spectrum.

29. A thin film of glycerin ($n = 1.473$) of thickness 524 nm with air on both sides is illuminated with white light at near normal incidence. What wavelengths will be strongly reflected in the range 300 nm to 700 nm?

30. **Q|C** A lens made of glass (n_g = 1.52) is coated with a thin film of MgF_2 (n_s = 1.38) of thickness t. Visible light is incident normally on the coated lens as in Figure P24.30. (a) For what minimum value of t will the reflected light of wavelength 540 nm (in air) be missing? (b) Are there other values of t that will minimize the reflected light at this wavelength? Explain.

Figure P24.30

24.7 Single-Slit Diffraction

31. Light of wavelength 5.40×10^2 nm passes through a slit of width 0.200 mm. (a) Find the width of the central maximum on a screen located 1.50 m from the slit. (b) Determine the width of the first-order bright fringe.

32. Light of wavelength 600 nm falls on a 0.40-mm-wide slit and forms a diffraction pattern on a screen 1.5 m away. (a) Find the position of the first dark band on each side of the central maximum. (b) Find the width of the central maximum.

33. **M** Light of wavelength 587.5 nm illuminates a slit of width 0.75 mm. (a) At what distance from the slit should a screen be placed if the first minimum in the diffraction pattern is to be 0.85 mm from the central maximum? (b) Calculate the width of the central maximum.

34. Microwaves of wavelength 5.00 cm enter a long, narrow window in a building that is otherwise essentially opaque to the incoming waves. If the window is 36.0 cm wide, what is the distance from the central maximum to the first-order minimum along a wall 6.50 m from the window?

35. A beam of monochromatic light is diffracted by a slit of width 0.600 mm. The diffraction pattern forms on a wall 1.30 m beyond the slit. The width of the central maximum is 2.00 mm. Calculate the wavelength of the light.

36. A screen is placed 50.0 cm from a single slit that is illuminated with light of wavelength 680 nm. If the distance between the first and third minima in the diffraction pattern is 3.00 mm, what is the width of the slit?

37. A slit of width 0.50 mm is illuminated with light of wavelength 500 nm, and a screen is placed 120 cm in front of the slit. Find the widths of the first and second maxima on each side of the central maximum.

38. The second-order dark fringe in a single-slit diffraction pattern is 1.40 mm from the center of the central maximum. Assuming the screen is 85.0 cm from a slit of width 0.800 mm and assuming monochromatic incident light, calculate the wavelength of the incident light.

24.8 The Diffraction Grating

39. Three discrete spectral lines occur at angles of 10.1°, 13.7°, and 14.8°, respectively, in the first-order spectrum of a diffraction-grating spectrometer. (a) If the grating has 3 660 slits/cm, what are the wavelengths of the light? (b) At what angles are these lines found in the second-order spectra?

40. Intense white light is incident on a diffraction grating that has 600 lines/mm. (a) What is the highest order in which the complete visible spectrum can be seen with this grating? (b) What is the angular separation between the violet edge (400 nm) and the red edge (700 nm) of the first-order spectrum produced by the grating?

41. **M** The hydrogen spectrum has a red line at 656 nm and a violet line at 434 nm. What angular separation between these two spectral lines is obtained with a diffraction grating that has 4 500 lines/cm?

42. Consider an array of parallel wires with uniform spacing of 1.30 cm between centers. In air at 20.0°C, ultrasound with a frequency of 37.2 kHz from a distant source is incident perpendicular to the array. (Take the speed of sound to be 343 m/s.) (a) Find the number of directions on the other side of the array in which there is a maximum of intensity. (b) Find the angle for each of these directions relative to the direction of the incident beam.

43. A helium–neon laser (λ = 632.8 nm) is used to calibrate a diffraction grating. If the first-order maximum occurs at 20.5°, what is the spacing between adjacent grooves in the grating?

44. White light is spread out into its spectral components by a diffraction grating. If the grating has 2 000 lines per centimeter, at what angle does red light of wavelength 640 nm appear in the first-order spectrum?

45. Light from an argon laser strikes a diffraction grating that has 5 310 grooves per centimeter. The central and first-order principal maxima are separated by 0.488 m on a wall 1.72 m from the grating. Determine the wavelength of the laser light.

46. **S** Take red light at 700 nm and violet at 400 nm as the ends of the visible spectrum and consider the continuous spectrum of white light formed by a diffraction grating with a spacing of d meters between adjacent lines. Show that the interval $\theta_{v2} \leq \theta \leq \theta_{r2}$ of the continuous spectrum in second order must overlap the interval $\theta_{v3} \leq \theta \leq \theta_{r3}$ of the third-order spectrum. *Note:* θ_{v2} is the angle of the violet light in second order, and θ_{r2} is the angle made by red light in second order.

47. Sunlight is incident on a diffraction grating that has 2 750 lines/cm. The second-order spectrum over the visible range (400–700 nm) is to be limited to 1.75 cm along a screen that is a distance L from the grating. What is the required value of L?

48. **GP** A diffraction grating has 4.200×10^3 rulings per centimeter. The screen is 2.000 m from the grating. In parts (a) through (e), round each result to four digits, using the rounded values for subsequent calculations. (a) Compute the value of d, the distance between adjacent rulings. Express the answer in meters. (b) Calculate the angle of the second-order maximum made by the 589.0-nm wavelength of sodium. (c) Find the position of this second-order maximum on the screen. (d) Repeat parts (b) and (c) for the second-order maximum of the 589.6-nm wavelength of sodium, finding the angle and position on the screen. (e) What is the distance between the two second-order maxima on the screen? (f) Now find the distance between the two second-order maxima without rounding, carrying all digits in calculator memory. How many significant digits are in agreement? What can you conclude about rounding and the use of intermediate answers in this case?

49. Light of wavelength 500 nm is incident normally on a diffraction grating. If the third-order maximum of the diffraction pattern is observed at 32.0°, (a) what is the number of rulings per centimeter for the grating? (b) Determine the total number of primary maxima that can be observed in this situation.

50. Light containing two different wavelengths passes through a diffraction grating with 1 200 slits/cm. On a screen 15.0 cm from the grating, the third-order maximum of the shorter wavelength falls midway between the central maximum and the first side maximum for the longer wavelength. If the neighboring maxima of the longer wavelength are 8.44 mm apart on the screen, what are the wavelengths in the light? *Hint:* Use the small-angle approximation.

24.9 Polarization of Light Waves

51. The angle of incidence of a light beam in air onto a reflecting surface is continuously variable. The reflected ray is found to be completely polarized when the angle of incidence is 48.0°. (a) What is the index of refraction of the reflecting material? (b) If some of the incident light (at an angle of 48.0°) passes into the material below the surface, what is the angle of refraction?

52. Unpolarized light passes through two Polaroid sheets. The transmission axis of the analyzer makes an angle of 35.0° with the axis of the polarizer. (a) What fraction of the original unpolarized light is transmitted through the analyzer? (b) What fraction of the original light is absorbed by the analyzer?

53. The index of refraction of a glass plate is 1.52. What is the Brewster's angle when the plate is (a) in air and (b) in water? (See Problem 57.)

54. At what angle above the horizon is the Sun if light from it is completely polarized upon reflection from water?

55. A light beam is incident on a piece of fused quartz ($n = 1.458$) at the Brewster's angle. Find (a) the value of Brewster's angle and (b) the angle of refraction for the transmitted ray.

56. The critical angle for total internal reflection for sapphire surrounded by air is 34.4°. Calculate the Brewster's angle for sapphire if the light is incident from the air.

57. Equation 24.14 assumes the incident light is in air. If the light is incident from a medium of index n_1 onto a medium of index n_2, follow the procedure used to derive Equation 24.14 to show that $\tan \theta_p = n_2/n_1$.

58. Plane-polarized light is incident on a single polarizing disk, with the direction of E_0 parallel to the direction of the transmission axis. Through what angle should the disk be rotated so that the intensity in the transmitted beam is reduced by a factor of (a) 2.00, (b) 4.00, and (c) 6.00?

59. **M** Three polarizing plates whose planes are parallel are centered on a common axis. The directions of the transmission axes relative to the common vertical direction are shown in Figure P24.59. A linearly polarized beam of light with plane of polarization parallel to the vertical reference direction is incident from the left onto the first disk with intensity $I_i = 10.0$ units (arbitrary). Calculate the transmitted intensity I_f when $\theta_1 = 20.0°$, $\theta_2 = 40.0°$, and $\theta_3 = 60.0°$. *Hint:* Make repeated use of Malus's law.

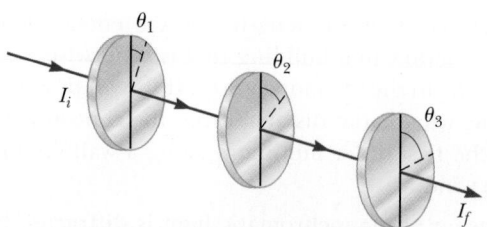

Figure P24.59 Problems 59 and 70.

60. Light of intensity I_0 and polarized parallel to the transmission axis of a polarizer is incident on an analyzer. (a) If the transmission axis of the analyzer makes an angle of 45° with the axis of the polarizer, what is the intensity of the transmitted light? (b) What should the angle between the transmission axes be to make $I/I_0 = 1/3$?

61. **BIO** Light with a wavelength in vacuum of 546.1 nm falls perpendicularly on a biological specimen that is 1.000 μm thick. The light splits into two beams polarized at right angles, for which the indices of refraction are 1.320 and 1.333, respectively. (a) Calculate the wavelength of each component of the light while it is traversing the specimen. (b) Calculate the phase

difference between the two beams when they emerge from the specimen.

Additional Problems

62. Light from a helium–neon laser ($\lambda = 632.8$ nm) is incident on a single slit. What is the maximum width of the slit for which no diffraction minima are observed?

63. **Q|C** Laser light with a wavelength of 632.8 nm is directed through one slit or two slits and allowed to fall on a screen 2.60 m beyond. Figure P24.63 shows the pattern on the screen, with a centimeter ruler below it. Did the light pass through one slit or two slits? Explain how you can tell. If the answer is one slit, find its width. If the answer is two slits, find the distance between their centers.

Figure P24.63

64. **S** In a Young's interference experiment, the two slits are separated by 0.150 mm and the incident light includes two wavelengths: $\lambda_1 = 540$ nm (green) and $\lambda_2 = 450$ nm (blue). The overlapping interference patterns are observed on a screen 1.40 m from the slits. (a) Find a relationship between the orders m_1 and m_2 that determines where a bright fringe of the green light coincides with a bright fringe of the blue light. (The order m_1 is associated with λ_1, and m_2 is associated with λ_2.) (b) Find the minimum values of m_1 and m_2 such that the overlapping of the bright fringes will occur and find the position of the overlap on the screen.

65. Light of wavelength 546 nm (the intense green line from a mercury source) produces a Young's interference pattern in which the second minimum from the central maximum is along a direction that makes an angle of 18.0 min of arc with the axis through the central maximum. What is the distance between the parallel slits?

66. The two speakers are placed 35.0 cm apart. A single oscillator makes the speakers vibrate in phase at a frequency of 2.00 kHz. At what angles, measured from the perpendicular bisector of the line joining the speakers, would a distant observer hear maximum sound intensity? Minimum sound intensity? (Take the speed of sound to be 340 m/s.)

67. Interference effects are produced at point P on a screen as a result of direct rays from a 500-nm source and reflected rays off a mirror, as shown in Figure P24.67.

If the source is $L = 100$ m to the left of the screen and $h = 1.00$ cm above the mirror, find the distance y (in millimeters) to the first dark band above the mirror.

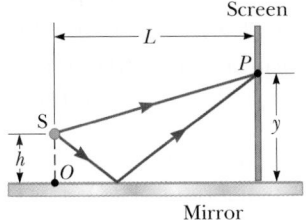

Figure P24.67

68. **BIO** Many cells are transparent and colorless. Structures of great interest in biology and medicine can be practically invisible to ordinary microscopy. An *interference microscope* reveals a difference in refractive index as a shift in interference fringes to indicate the size and shape of cell structures. The idea is exemplified in the following problem: An air wedge is formed between two glass plates in contact along one edge and slightly separated at the opposite edge. When the plates are illuminated with monochromatic light from above, the reflected light has 85 dark fringes. Calculate the number of dark fringes that appear if water ($n = 1.33$) replaces the air between the plates.

69. Figure P24.69 shows a radio-wave transmitter and a receiver, both $h = 50.0$ m above the ground and $d = 600$ m apart. The receiver can receive signals directly from the transmitter and indirectly from signals that bounce off the ground. If the ground is level between the transmitter and receiver and a $\lambda/2$ phase shift occurs upon reflection, determine the longest wavelengths that interfere (a) constructively and (b) destructively.

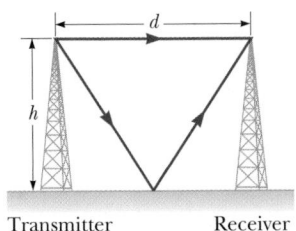

Figure P24.69

70. Three polarizers, centered on a common axis and with their planes parallel to one another, have transmission axes oriented at angles of θ_1, θ_2, and θ_3 from the vertical, as shown in Figure P24.59. Light of intensity I_i, polarized with its plane of polarization oriented vertically, is incident from the left onto the first polarizer. What is the ratio I_f/I_i of the final transmitted intensity to the incident intensity if (a) $\theta_1 = 45°$, $\theta_2 = 90°$, and $\theta_3 = 0°$? (b) $\theta_1 = 0°$, $\theta_2 = 45°$, and $\theta_3 = 90°$?

71. The transmitting antenna on a submarine is 5.00 m above the water when the ship surfaces. The captain wishes to transmit a message to a receiver on a 90.0-m-tall cliff at the ocean shore. If the signal is to be completely polarized by reflection off the ocean surface, how far must the ship be from the shore?

72. **S** A plano-convex lens (flat on one side, convex on the other) with index of refraction n rests with its curved side (radius of curvature R) on a flat glass surface of the same index of refraction with a film of index n_{film} between them. The lens is illuminated from above by light of wavelength λ. Show that the dark Newton rings that appear have radii of

$$r \approx \sqrt{m\lambda R / n_{film}}$$

where m is an integer.

73. A diffraction pattern is produced on a screen 140 cm from a single slit, using monochromatic light of wavelength 500 nm. The distance from the center of the central maximum to the first-order maximum is 3.00 mm. Calculate the slit width. *Hint:* Assume that the first-order maximum is halfway between the first- and second-order minima.

74. A flat piece of glass is supported horizontally above the flat end of a 10.0-cm-long metal rod that has its lower end rigidly fixed. The thin film of air between the rod and the glass is observed to be bright when illuminated by light of wavelength 500 nm. As the temperature is slowly increased by 25.0°C, the film changes from bright to dark and back to bright 200 times. What is the coefficient of linear expansion of the metal?

■ AP* REVIEW QUESTIONS

1. The following patterns are created by the interference of monochromatic light. The shaded regions are dark bands while the clear regions are bright. Which pattern is caused by single-slit interference?

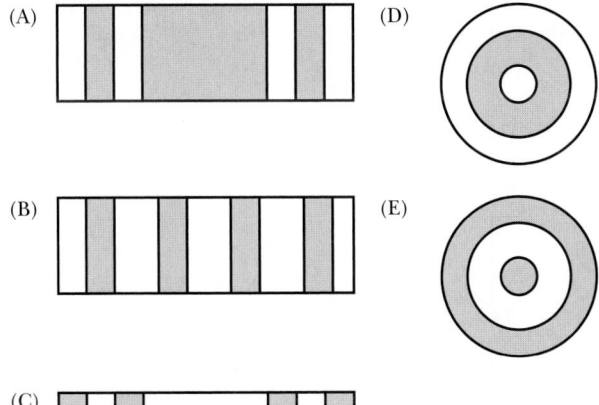

(A)

(B)

(C)

(D)

(E)

2. The following patterns are created by the interference of monochromatic light. The shaded regions are dark bands while the clear regions are bright. Which pattern is caused by double-slit interference?

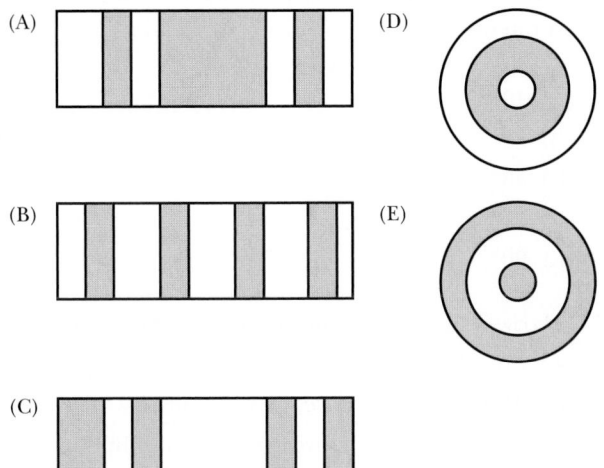

(A)

(B)

(C)

(D)

(E)

3. In Young's double-slit experiment, the first dark band is formed when:

(A) The wavelengths are the same and the phase is shifted by $1/4\lambda$

(B) The wavelengths are different and the phase is shifted by $1/4\lambda$

(C) The wavelengths are the same and the phase is shifted by $1/2\lambda$

(D) The wavelengths are different and the phase is shifted by $1/2\lambda$

(E) The wavelengths are the same and the phase is shifted by λ

4. In Young's double-slit experiment, what would you be observing when the second wave travels an extra $3/2\lambda$?

(A) The central maximum

(B) The first dark band

(C) The first bright band

(D) The second dark band

(E) The second light band

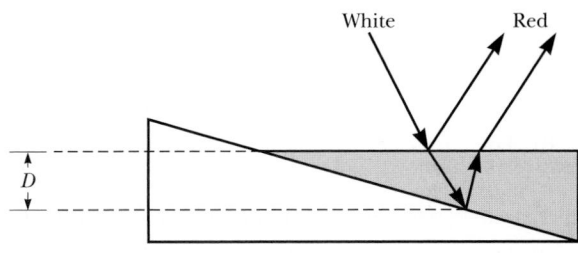

5. A thin film of oil rests on an inclined plane, as seen in the figure above. White light is incident on the oil from above and an observer sees colored bands of red light (600 nm) on the oil. The distance D is:

(A) Exactly 300 nm   (D) A multiple of 200 nm

(B) Exactly 200 nm   (E) A multiple of 150 nm

(C) Exactly 150 nm

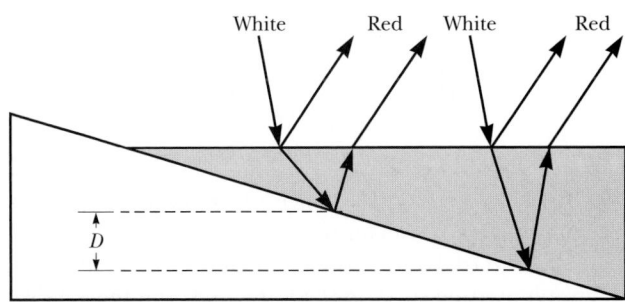

6. A thin film of oil rests on an inclined plane, as seen in the figure above. White light is incident on the oil from above and an observer sees two adjacent colored bands of red light (600 nm) on the oil. The distance D is:

(A) Exactly 600 nm

(B) Exactly 300 nm

(C) Exactly 200 nm

(D) An integer multiple of 300 nm

(E) An integer multiple of 200 nm

7. White light is incident from above on two glass plates that are separated by a small air-filled gap on the right side, as seen above. An observer sees three adjacent bands of color. Starting from left to right, the colors could be:

(A) Yellow, green, blue

(B) Green, yellow, blue

(C) Yellow, blue, green

(D) Blue, yellow, green

(E) Blue, green, yellow

8. Two light rays will only create total destructive interference at a node if:

(A) The two waves have the same frequency

(B) The two waves have the same magnitude wavelength

(C) The two waves are out of phase by 1/2 wavelength

(D) The two waves have the same amplitude

(E) All of these must be true

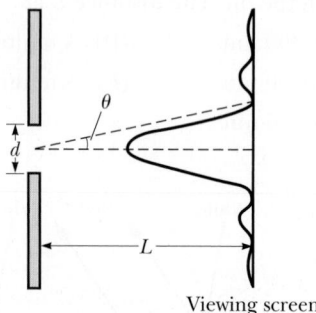

Viewing screen

9. A single-slit diffraction experiment is conducted where the slit size (d) and distance to the wall (L) are kept constant. The observer records the angle created (θ) to the first dark band as the wavelength (λ) is adjusted. A graph plotting $\sin \theta$ on the y-axis and λ on the x-axis is created. The plot would determine:

(A) The slope of the line to be L

(B) The slope of the line to be d

(C) The slope of the line to be $1/L$

(D) The slope of the line to be $1/d$

(E) The slope of the line to be the frequency f

10. Light is directed from air toward a medium with a greater index of refraction. Relative to the initial wave, the reflected light would have a phase shift of:

(A) 0°

(B) 45°

(C) 90°

(D) 180°

(E) 360°

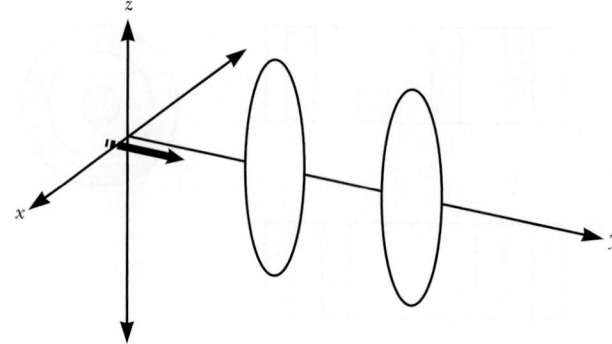

11. Unpolarized light is directed along the positive y-axis and passes through two circular polarizing sheets. An observer looks along the y-axis toward the sheets in the direction of the light and cannot see any light passing through the second polarized sheet. To see the greatest intensity of light, the observer could rotate the second sheet by an angle of:

(A) 10°

(B) 30°

(C) 45°

(D) 60°

(E) 90°

12. Polarized sunglasses diminish the intensity of light by:

(A) Absorbing light waves below a cutoff frequency

(B) Absorbing light waves below a cutoff wavelength

(C) Absorbing light waves below a minimum amplitude electric field strength

(D) Absorbing light waves whose electric field vector is not aligned with the polarizer

(E) Absorbing light waves below a minimum speed

Joe McNally/Getty Images

The twin Keck telescopes atop the summit of Hawaii's Mauna Kea volcano are the world's largest optical and infrared telescopes. Each telescope has a primary mirror 10 m in diameter comprised of 36 hexagonal segments that function together as a single piece of reflective glass. Far from city lights, high on a dormant volcano in dry, unpolluted air, the telescopes are ideally placed to probe the mysteries of the Universe.

Optical Instruments

We use devices made from lenses, mirrors, and other optical components every time we put on a pair of eyeglasses or contact lenses, take a photograph, look at the sky through a telescope, and so on. In this chapter we examine how optical instruments work. For the most part, our analyses involve the laws of reflection and refraction and the procedures of geometric optics. To explain certain phenomena, however, we must use the wave nature of light.

25.1 The Camera

The single-lens photographic camera is a simple optical instrument having the features shown in Figure 25.1 on page 860. It consists of an opaque box, a converging lens that produces a real image, and a photographic film behind the lens to receive the image. Digital cameras differ in that the image is formed on a charge-coupled device (CCD) or a complementary metal-oxide semiconductor (CMOS) sensor instead of on film. Both the CCD and the CMOS image sensors convert the image into digital form, which can then be stored in the camera's memory.

Focusing of a camera is accomplished by varying the distance between the lens and film, with an adjustable bellows in antique cameras and other mechanisms in contemporary models. For proper focusing, which leads to sharp images, the lens-to-film distance depends on the object distance as well as on the focal length of the lens. The shutter, located behind the lens, is a mechanical device that is opened for selected time intervals. With this arrangement, moving objects can be photographed by using short exposure times and dark scenes (with low light levels) by using long exposure times. If this adjustment were not available, it would be

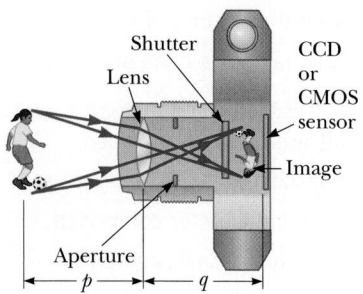

Figure 25.1 Cross-sectional view of a simple digital camera. The CCD or CMOS image sensor is the light-sensitive component of the camera. In a nondigital camera the light from the lens falls onto photographic film. In reality $p \gg q$.

impossible to take stop-action photographs. A rapidly moving vehicle, for example, could move far enough while the shutter was open to produce a blurred image. Another major cause of blurred images is movement of the *camera* while the shutter is open. To prevent such movement, you should mount the camera on a tripod or use short exposure times. Typical shutter speeds (that is, exposure times) are 1/30 s, 1/60 s, 1/125 s, and 1/250 s. Stationary objects are often shot with a shutter speed of 1/60 s.

Most cameras also have an aperture of adjustable diameter to further control the intensity of the light reaching the film. When an aperture of small diameter is used, only light from the central portion of the lens reaches the film, so spherical aberration is reduced.

The intensity I of the light reaching the film is proportional to the area of the lens. Because this area in turn is proportional to the square of the lens diameter D, the intensity is also proportional to D^2. Light intensity is a measure of the rate at which energy is received by the film per unit area of the image. Because the area of the image is proportional to q^2 in Figure 25.1 and $q \approx f$ (when $p \gg f$, so that p can be approximated as infinite), we conclude that the intensity is also proportional to $1/f^2$. Therefore, $I \propto D^2/f^2$. The brightness of the image formed on the film depends on the light intensity, so we see that it ultimately depends on both the focal length f and diameter D of the lens. The ratio f/D is called the **f-number** (or focal ratio) of a lens:

$$f\text{-number} \equiv \frac{f}{D} \qquad [25.1]$$

The *f*-number is often given as a description of the lens "speed." A lens with a low *f*-number is a "fast" lens. Extremely fast lenses, which have an *f*-number as low as approximately 1.2, are expensive because of the difficulty of keeping aberrations acceptably small with light rays passing through a large area of the lens. Camera lenses are often marked with a range of *f*-numbers, such as 1.4, 2, 2.8, 4, 5.6, 8, and 11. Any one of these settings can be selected by adjusting the aperture, which changes the value of D. Increasing the setting from one *f*-number to the next-higher value (for example, from 2.8 to 4) decreases the area of the aperture by a factor of 2. The lowest *f*-number setting on a camera corresponds to a wide open aperture and the use of the maximum possible lens area.

Simple cameras usually have a fixed focal length and fixed aperture size, with an *f*-number of about 11. This high value for the *f*-number allows for a large **depth of field** and means that objects at a wide range of distances from the lens form reasonably sharp images on the film. In other words, the camera doesn't have to be focused. Most cameras with variable *f*-numbers adjust them automatically.

25.2 The Eye BIO

Like a camera, a normal eye focuses light and produces a sharp image. The mechanisms by which the eye controls the amount of light admitted and adjusts to produce correctly focused images, however, are far more complex, intricate, and effective than those in even the most sophisticated camera. In all respects the eye is a physiological wonder.

Figure 25.2a shows the essential parts of the eye. Light entering the eye passes through a transparent structure called the *cornea*, behind which are a clear liquid (the *aqueous humor*), a variable aperture (the *pupil*, which is an opening in the *iris*), and the *crystalline lens*. Most of the refraction occurs at the outer surface of the eye, where the cornea is covered with a film of tears. Relatively little refraction occurs in the crystalline lens because the aqueous humor in contact with the lens has an average index of refraction close to that of the lens. The iris, which is the colored portion of the eye, is a muscular diaphragm that controls pupil size. The iris regu-

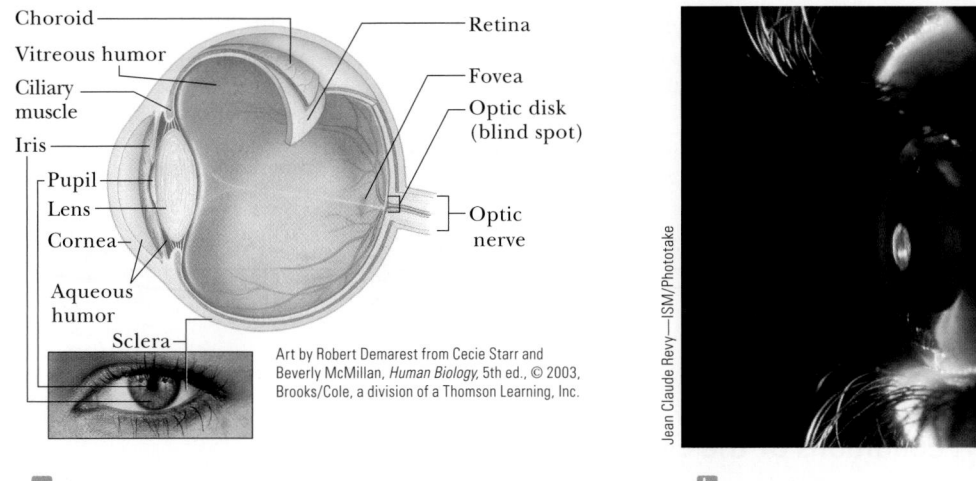

Choroid
Vitreous humor
Ciliary muscle
Iris
Pupil
Lens
Cornea
Aqueous humor
Sclera
Retina
Fovea
Optic disk (blind spot)
Optic nerve

Art by Robert Demarest from Cecie Starr and Beverly McMillan, *Human Biology*, 5th ed., © 2003, Brooks/Cole, a division of a Thomson Learning, Inc.

Jean Claude Revy—ISM/Phototake

a

b

Figure 25.2 (a) Essential parts of the eye. Can you correlate the essential parts of the eye with those of the simple camera in Figure 25.1? (b) Close-up photograph of the human cornea.

lates the amount of light entering the eye by dilating the pupil in low-light conditions and contracting the pupil under conditions of bright light. The *f*-number range of the eye is from about 2.8 to 16.

The cornea–lens system focuses light onto the back surface of the eye—the *retina*—which consists of millions of sensitive receptors called *rods* and *cones*. When stimulated by light, these structures send impulses to the brain via the optic nerve, converting them into our conscious view of the world. The process by which the brain performs this conversion is not well understood and is the subject of much speculation and research. Unlike film in a camera, the rods and cones chemically adjust their sensitivity according to the prevailing light conditions. This adjustment, which takes about 15 minutes, is responsible for the experience of "getting used to the dark" in such places as movie theaters. Iris aperture control, which takes less than 1 second, helps protect the retina from overload in the adjustment process.

The eye focuses on an object by varying the shape of the pliable crystalline lens through an amazing process called **accommodation**. An important component in accommodation is the *ciliary muscle*, which is situated in a circle around the rim of the lens. Thin filaments, called *zonules*, run from this muscle to the edge of the lens. When the eye is focused on a distant object, the ciliary muscle is relaxed, tightening the zonules that attach the ciliary muscle to the edge of the lens. The force of the zonules causes the lens to flatten, increasing its focal length. For an object distance of infinity, the focal length of the eye is equal to the fixed distance between lens and retina, about 1.7 cm. The eye focuses on nearby objects by tensing the ciliary muscle, which relaxes the zonules. This action allows the lens to bulge a bit and its focal length decreases, resulting in the image being focused on the retina. All these lens adjustments take place so swiftly that we are not even aware of the change. In this respect even the finest electronic camera is a toy compared with the eye.

There is a limit to accommodation because objects that are very close to the eye produce blurred images. The **near point** is the closest distance for which the lens can accommodate to focus light on the retina. This distance usually increases with age and has an average value of 25 cm. Typically, at age 10 the near point of the eye is about 18 cm. This increases to about 25 cm at age 20, 50 cm at age 40, and 500 cm or greater at age 60. The **far point** of the eye represents the farthest distance for which the lens of the relaxed eye can focus light on the retina. A person with normal vision is able to see very distant objects, such as the Moon, and so has a far point at infinity.

Figure 25.3 (a) An uncorrected farsighted eye. (b) A farsighted eye corrected with a converging lens. (The object is assumed to be very small in these figures.)

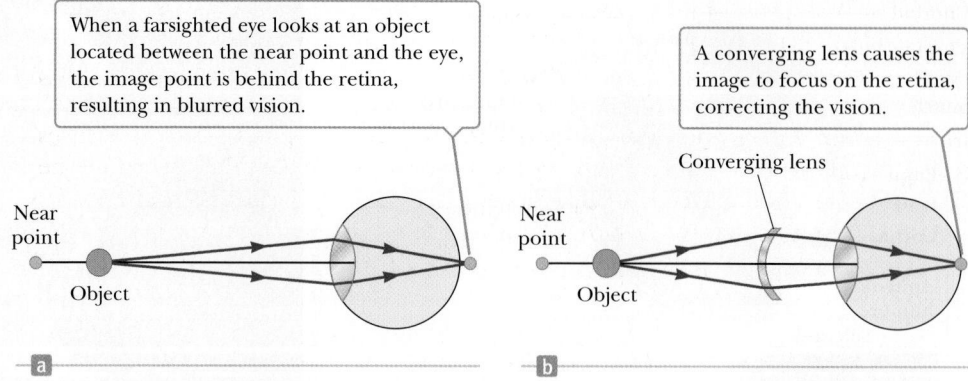

Conditions of the Eye

When the eye suffers a mismatch between the focusing power of the lens–cornea system and the length of the eye so that light rays reach the retina before they converge to form an image, as in Figure 25.3a, the condition is known as **farsightedness** (or *hyperopia*). A farsighted person can usually see faraway objects clearly but not nearby objects. Although the near point of a normal eye is approximately 25 cm, the near point of a farsighted person is much farther than that. The eye of a farsighted person tries to focus by accommodation, by shortening its focal length. Accommodation works for distant objects, but because the focal length of the farsighted eye is longer than normal, the light from nearby objects can't be brought to a sharp focus before it reaches the retina, causing a blurred image. The condition can be corrected by placing a converging lens in front of the eye, as in Figure 25.3b. The lens refracts the incoming rays more toward the principal axis before entering the eye, allowing them to converge and focus on the retina.

Nearsightedness (or *myopia*) is another mismatch condition in which a person is able to focus on nearby objects, but not faraway objects. In the case of *axial myopia*, nearsightedness is caused by the lens being too far from the retina. It is also possible to have *refractive myopia*, in which the lens–cornea system is too powerful for the normal length of the eye. The far point of the nearsighted eye is not at infinity and may be less than 1 meter. The maximum focal length of the nearsighted eye is insufficient to produce a sharp image on the retina, and rays from a distant object converge to a focus in front of the retina. They then continue past that point, diverging before they finally reach the retina and produce a blurred image (Fig. 25.4a).

Nearsightedness can be corrected with a diverging lens, as shown in Figure 25.4b. The lens refracts the rays away from the principal axis before they enter the eye, allowing them to focus on the retina.

Beginning with middle age, most people lose some of their accommodation ability as the ciliary muscle weakens and the lens hardens. Unlike farsightedness, which is a mismatch of focusing power and eye length, **presbyopia** (literally, "old-

BIO APPLICATION
Using Optical Lenses to Correct for Defects

Figure 25.4 (a) An uncorrected nearsighted eye. (b) A nearsighted eye corrected with a diverging lens. (The object is assumed to be very small in these figures.)

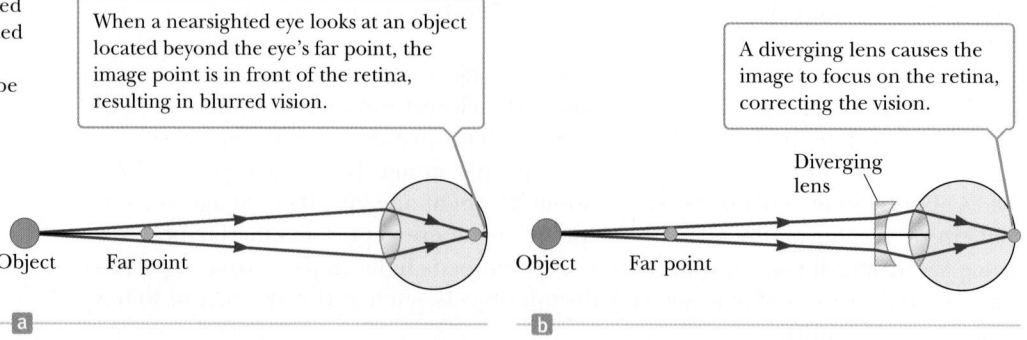

age vision") is due to a reduction in accommodation ability. The cornea and lens aren't able to bring nearby objects into focus on the retina. The symptoms are the same as with farsightedness, and the condition can be corrected with converging lenses.

In the eye defect known as **astigmatism**, light from a point source produces a line image on the retina. This condition arises when either the cornea or the lens (or both) is not perfectly symmetric. Astigmatism can be corrected with lenses having different curvatures in two mutually perpendicular directions.

Optometrists and ophthalmologists usually prescribe lenses measured in **diopters**:

> The **power** P of a lens in diopters equals the inverse of the focal length in meters: $P = 1/f$.

For example, a converging lens with a focal length of $+20$ cm has a power of $+5.0$ diopters, and a diverging lens with a focal length of -40 cm has a power of -2.5 diopters. (Although the symbol P is the same as for mechanical power, there is no relationship between the two concepts.)

The position of the lens relative to the eye causes differences in power, but they usually amount to less than one-quarter diopter, which isn't noticeable to most patients. As a result, practicing optometrists deal in increments of one-quarter diopter. Neglecting the eye–lens distance is equivalent to doing the calculation for a contact lens, which rests directly on the eye.

■ EXAMPLE 25.1 | Prescribing a Corrective Lens for a Farsighted Patient   BIO

GOAL Apply geometric optics to correct farsightedness.

PROBLEM The near point of a patient's eye is 50.0 cm. **(a)** What focal length must a corrective lens have to enable the eye to see clearly an object 25.0 cm away? Neglect the eye–lens distance. **(b)** What is the power of this lens? **(c)** Repeat the problem, taking into account that, for typical eyeglasses, the corrective lens is 2.00 cm in front of the eye.

STRATEGY This problem requires substitution into the thin-lens equation (Eq. 23.11) and then using the definition of lens power in terms of diopters. The object is at 25.0 cm, but the lens must form an image at the patient's near point, 50.0 cm, the closest point at which the patient's eye can see clearly. In part (c) 2.00 cm must be subtracted from both the object distance and the image distance to account for the position of the lens.

....

SOLUTION

(a) Find the focal length of the corrective lens, neglecting its distance from the eye.

Apply the thin-lens equation:

$$\frac{1}{p} + \frac{1}{q} = \frac{1}{f}$$

Substitute $p = 25.0$ cm and $q = -50.0$ cm (the latter is negative because the image must be virtual) on the same side of the lens as the object:

$$\frac{1}{25.0 \text{ cm}} + \frac{1}{-50.0 \text{ cm}} = \frac{1}{f}$$

Solve for f. The focal length is positive, corresponding to a converging lens.

$$f = \boxed{50.0 \text{ cm}}$$

(b) What is the power of this lens?

The power is the reciprocal of the focal length in meters:

$$P = \frac{1}{f} = \frac{1}{0.500 \text{ m}} = \boxed{+\ 2.00 \text{ diopters}}$$

(c) Repeat the problem, noting that the corrective lens is actually 2.00 cm in front of the eye.

Substitute the corrected values of p and q into the thin-lens equation:

$$\frac{1}{p} + \frac{1}{q} = \frac{1}{23.0 \text{ cm}} + \frac{1}{(-48.0 \text{ cm})} = \frac{1}{f}$$

$$f = 44.2 \text{ cm}$$

(Continued)

Compute the power:

$$P = \frac{1}{f} = \frac{1}{0.442 \text{ m}} = \boxed{+ 2.26 \text{ diopters}}$$

REMARKS Notice that the calculation in part (c), which doesn't neglect the eye–lens distance, results in a difference of 0.26 diopter.

QUESTION 25.1 True or False: The larger the distance to a near point, the larger the power of the required corrective lens.

EXERCISE 25.1 Suppose a lens is placed in a device that determines its power as 2.75 diopters. Find (a) the focal length of the lens and (b) the minimum distance at which a patient will be able to focus on an object if the patient's near point is 60.0 cm. Neglect the eye–lens distance.

ANSWERS (a) 36.4 cm (b) 22.7 cm

■ EXAMPLE 25.2 | **A Corrective Lens for Nearsightedness**

GOAL Apply geometric optics to correct nearsightedness.

PROBLEM A particular nearsighted patient can't see objects clearly when they are beyond 25 cm (the far point of the eye). **(a)** What focal length should the prescribed contact lens have to correct this problem? **(b)** Find the power of the lens, in diopters. Neglect the distance between the eye and the corrective lens.

STRATEGY The purpose of the lens in this instance is to take objects at infinity and create an image of them at the patient's far point. Apply the thin-lens equation.

SOLUTION

(a) Find the focal length of the corrective lens.

Apply the thin-lens equation for an object at infinity and image at 25.0 cm:

$$\frac{1}{p} + \frac{1}{q} = \frac{1}{\infty} + \frac{1}{(-25.0 \text{ cm})} = \frac{1}{f}$$

$$f = \boxed{-25.0 \text{ cm}}$$

(b) Find the power of the lens in diopters.

$$P = \frac{1}{f} = \frac{1}{-0.250 \text{ m}} = -4.00 \text{ diopters}$$

REMARKS The focal length is negative, consistent with a diverging lens. Notice that the power is also negative and has the same numeric value as the sum on the left side of the thin-lens equation.

QUESTION 25.2 True or False: The shorter the distance to a patient's far point, the more negative the power of the required corrective lens.

EXERCISE 25.2 (a) What power lens would you prescribe for a patient with a far point of 35.0 cm? Neglect the eye–lens distance. (b) Repeat, assuming an eye-corrective lens distance of 2.00 cm.

ANSWERS (a) −2.86 diopters (b) −3.03 diopters

■ APPLYING PHYSICS 25.1 | **Vision of the Invisible Man**

A classic science fiction story, *The Invisible Man* by H. G. Wells, tells of a man who becomes invisible by changing the index of refraction of his body to that of air. Students who know how the eye works have criticized this story; they claim that the invisible man would be unable to see. On the basis of your knowledge of the eye, would he be able to see?

EXPLANATION He wouldn't be able to see. For the eye to see an object, incoming light must be refracted at the cornea and lens to form an image on the retina. If the cornea and lens have the same index of refraction as air, refraction can't occur and an image wouldn't be formed. ■

25.1 Two campers wish to start a fire during the day. One camper is nearsighted and one is farsighted. Whose glasses should be used to focus the Sun's rays onto some paper to start the fire? (a) either camper's (b) the nearsighted camper's (c) the farsighted camper's

25.3 The Simple Magnifier

The **simple magnifier** is one of the most basic of all optical instruments because it consists only of a single converging lens. As the name implies, this device is used to increase the apparent size of an object. Suppose an object is viewed at some distance p from the eye, as in Figure 25.5. Clearly, the size of the image formed at the retina depends on the angle θ subtended by the object at the eye. As the object moves closer to the eye, θ increases and a larger image is observed. A normal eye, however, can't focus on an object closer than about 25 cm, the near point (Fig. 25.6a). (Try it!) Therefore, θ is a maximum at the near point.

To further increase the apparent angular size of an object, a converging lens can be placed in front of the eye with the object positioned at point O, just inside the focal point of the lens, as in Figure 25.6b. At this location, the lens forms a virtual, upright, and enlarged image, as shown. The lens allows the object to be viewed closer to the eye than is possible without the lens. We define the **angular magnification** m as the ratio of the angle subtended by a small object when the lens is in use (angle θ in Fig. 25.6b) to the angle subtended by the object placed at the near point with no lens in use (angle θ_0 in Fig. 25.6a):

$$m \equiv \frac{\theta}{\theta_0} \qquad [25.2]$$

◀ Angular magnification with the object at the near point

For the case in which the lens is held close to the eye, the angular magnification is a maximum when the image formed by the lens is at the near point of the eye, which corresponds to $q = -25$ cm (see Fig. 25.6b). The object distance corresponding to this image distance can be calculated from the thin-lens equation:

$$\frac{1}{p} + \frac{1}{-25 \text{ cm}} = \frac{1}{f} \qquad [25.3]$$

$$p = \frac{25f}{25 + f}$$

Here, f is the focal length of the magnifier in centimeters. From Figures 25.6a and 25.6b, the small-angle approximation gives

$$\tan \theta_0 \approx \theta_0 \approx \frac{h}{25} \quad \text{and} \quad \tan \theta \approx \theta \approx \frac{h}{p} \qquad [25.4]$$

Equation 25.2 therefore becomes

$$m_{\text{max}} = \frac{\theta}{\theta_0} = \frac{h/p}{h/25} = \frac{25}{p} = \frac{25}{25f/(25 + f)}$$

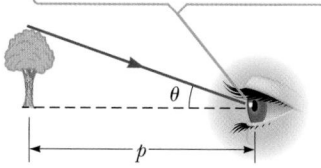

The size of the image formed on the retina depends on the angle θ subtended at the eye.

Figure 25.5 An observer looks at an object at distance p.

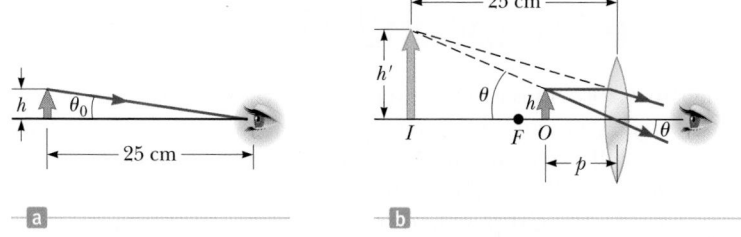

Figure 25.6 (a) An object placed at the near point ($p = 25$ cm) subtends an angle of $\theta_0 \approx h/25$ at the eye. (b) An object placed near the focal point of a converging lens produces a magnified image, which subtends an angle of $\theta \approx h'/25$ at the eye. Note that in this situation $q = -25$ cm.

so that

$$m_{max} = 1 + \frac{25 \text{ cm}}{f} \qquad [25.5]$$

The maximum angular magnification given by Equation 25.5 is the ratio of the angular size seen with the lens to the angular size seen without the lens, with the object at the near point of the eye. Although the normal eye can focus on an image formed anywhere between the near point and infinity, it's most relaxed when the image is at infinity (Sec. 25.2). For the image formed by the magnifying lens to appear at infinity, the object must be placed at the focal point of the lens so that $p = f$. In this case Equation 25.4 becomes

$$\theta_0 \approx \frac{h}{25} \quad \text{and} \quad \theta \approx \frac{h}{f}$$

and the angular magnification is

$$m = \frac{\theta}{\theta_0} = \frac{25 \text{ cm}}{f} \qquad [25.6]$$

With a single lens, it's possible to achieve angular magnifications up to about 4 without serious aberrations. Magnifications up to about 20 can be achieved by using one or two additional lenses to correct for aberrations.

■ EXAMPLE 25.3 | **Magnification of a Lens**

GOAL Compute magnifications of a lens when the image is at the near point and when it's at infinity.

PROBLEM (a) What is the maximum angular magnification of a lens with a focal length of 10.0 cm? (b) What is the angular magnification of this lens when the eye is relaxed? Assume an eye–lens distance of zero.

STRATEGY The maximum angular magnification occurs when the image formed by the lens is at the near point of the eye. Under these circumstances, Equation 25.5 gives us the maximum angular magnification. In part (b) the eye is relaxed only if the image is at infinity, so Equation 25.6 applies.

. . . .

SOLUTION

(a) Find the maximum angular magnification of the lens.

Substitute into Equation 25.5:

$$m_{max} = 1 + \frac{25 \text{ cm}}{f} = 1 + \frac{25 \text{ cm}}{10.0 \text{ cm}} = \boxed{3.5}$$

(b) Find the magnification of the lens when the eye is relaxed.

When the eye is relaxed, the image is at infinity, so substitute into Equation 25.6:

$$m = \frac{25 \text{ cm}}{f} = \frac{25 \text{ cm}}{10.0 \text{ cm}} = \boxed{2.5}$$

. . . .

QUESTION 25.3 For greater magnification, should a lens with a larger or smaller focal length be selected?

EXERCISE 25.3 What focal length would be necessary if the lens were to have a maximum angular magnification of 4.0?

ANSWER 8.3 cm

25.4 The Compound Microscope

A simple magnifier provides only limited assistance with inspection of the minute details of an object. Greater magnification can be achieved by combining two lenses in a device called a compound microscope, a schematic diagram of which is shown in Active Figure 25.7a. The instrument consists of two lenses: an objective with a very short focal length f_o (where $f_o < 1$ cm) and an ocular lens, or eyepiece,

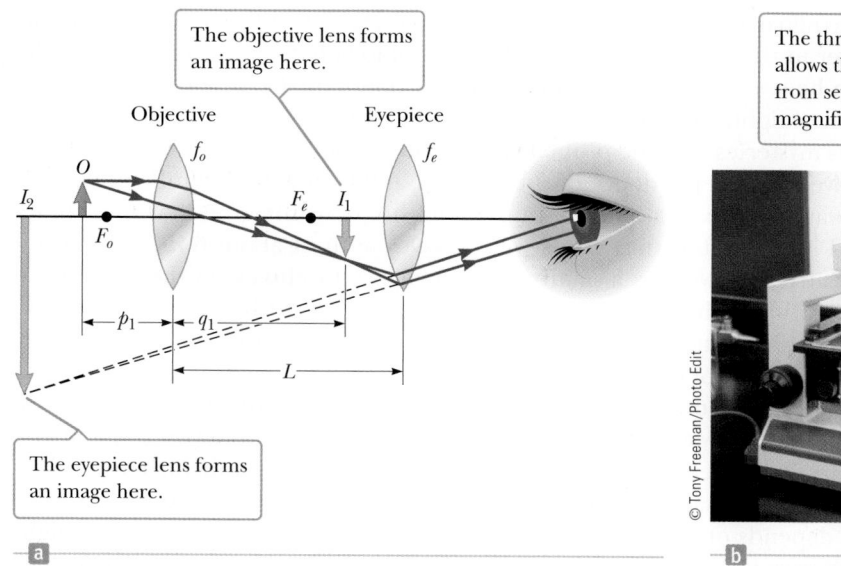

The objective lens forms an image here.

The three-objective turret allows the user to choose from several powers of magnification.

The eyepiece lens forms an image here.

© Tony Freeman/Photo Edit

a

b

Active Figure 25.7

(a) A diagram of a compound microscope, which consists of an objective and an eyepiece, or ocular lens. (b) A compound microscope. Combinations of eyepieces with different focal lengths and different objectives can produce a wide range of magnifications.

with a focal length f_e of a few centimeters. The two lenses are separated by distance L that is much greater than either f_o or f_e.

The basic approach used to analyze the image formation properties of a microscope is that of two lenses in a row: the image formed by the first becomes the object for the second. The object O placed just outside the focal length of the objective forms a real, inverted image at I_1 that is at or just inside the focal point of the eyepiece. This image is much enlarged. (For clarity, the enlargement of I_1 is not shown in Active Fig. 25.7a.) The eyepiece, which serves as a simple magnifier, uses the image at I_1 as its object and produces an image at I_2. The image seen by the eye at I_2 is virtual, inverted, and very much enlarged.

The lateral magnification M_1 of the first image is $-q_1/p_1$. Note that q_1 is approximately equal to L because the object is placed close to the focal point of the objective lens, which ensures that the image formed will be far from the objective lens. Further, because the object is very close to the focal point of the objective lens, $p_1 \approx f_o$. Therefore, the lateral magnification of the objective is

$$M_1 = -\frac{q_1}{p_1} \approx -\frac{L}{f_o}$$

From Equation 25.6, the angular magnification of the eyepiece for an object (corresponding to the image at I_1) placed at the focal point is found to be

$$m_e = \frac{25\ \text{cm}}{f_e}$$

The overall magnification of the compound microscope is defined as the product of the lateral and angular magnifications:

$$m = M_1 m_e = -\frac{L}{f_o}\left(\frac{25\ \text{cm}}{f_e}\right) \qquad \text{[25.7]} \qquad \blacktriangleleft \text{Magnification of a microscope}$$

The negative sign indicates that the image is inverted with respect to the object.

The microscope has extended our vision into the previously unknown realm of incredibly small objects, and the capabilities of this instrument have increased steadily with improved techniques in precision grinding of lenses. A natural question is whether there is any limit to how powerful a microscope could be. For example, could a microscope be made powerful enough to allow us to see an atom? The answer to this question is no, as long as visible light is used to illuminate the object. To be seen, the object under a microscope must be at least as large as a wavelength of light. An atom is many times smaller than the wavelength of visible light, so its mysteries must be probed via other techniques.

The wavelength dependence of the "seeing" ability of a wave can be illustrated by water waves set up in a bathtub in the following way. Imagine that you vibrate your hand in the water until waves with a wavelength of about 6 in. are moving along the surface. If you fix a small object, such as a toothpick, in the path of the waves, you will find that the waves are not appreciably disturbed by the toothpick, but continue along their path. Now suppose you fix a larger object, such as a toy sailboat, in the path of the waves. In this case the waves are considerably disturbed by the object. The toothpick was much smaller than the wavelength of the waves, and as a result the waves didn't "see" it. The toy sailboat, however, is about the same size as the wavelength of the waves and hence creates a disturbance. Light waves behave in this same general way. The ability of an optical microscope to view an object depends on the size of the object relative to the wavelength of the light used to observe it. Hence, it will never be possible to observe atoms or molecules with such a microscope because their dimensions are so small (≈ 0.1 nm) relative to the wavelength of the light (≈ 500 nm).

▪ EXAMPLE 25.4 | **Microscope Magnifications**

GOAL Understand the critical factors involved in determining the magnifying power of a microscope.

PROBLEM A certain microscope has two interchangeable objectives. One has a focal length of 2.0 cm, and the other has a focal length of 0.20 cm. Also available are two eyepieces of focal lengths 2.5 cm and 5.0 cm. If the length of the microscope is 18 cm, compute the magnifications for the following combinations: the 2.0-cm objective and 5.0-cm eyepiece, the 2.0-cm objective and 2.5-cm eyepiece, and the 0.20-cm objective and 5.0-cm eyepiece.

STRATEGY The solution consists of substituting into Equation 25.7 for three different combinations of lenses.

SOLUTION

Apply Equation 25.7 and combine the 2.0-cm objective with the 5.0-cm eyepiece:

$$m = -\frac{L}{f_o}\left(\frac{25 \text{ cm}}{f_e}\right) = -\frac{18 \text{ cm}}{2.0 \text{ cm}}\left(\frac{25 \text{ cm}}{5.0 \text{ cm}}\right) = \boxed{-45}$$

Combine the 2.0-cm objective with the 2.5-cm eyepiece:

$$m = -\frac{18 \text{ cm}}{2.0 \text{ cm}}\left(\frac{25 \text{ cm}}{2.5 \text{ cm}}\right) = \boxed{-9.0 \times 10^1}$$

Combine the 0.20-cm objective with the 5.0-cm eyepiece:

$$m = -\frac{18 \text{ cm}}{0.20 \text{ cm}}\left(\frac{25 \text{ cm}}{5.0 \text{ cm}}\right) = \boxed{-450}$$

REMARKS much higher magnifications can be achieved, but the resolution starts to fall, resulting in fuzzy images that don't convey any details. (See Section 25.6 for further discussion of this point.)

QUESTION 25.4 True or False: A shorter focal length for either the eyepiece or objective lens will result in greater magnification.

EXERCISE 25.4 Combine the 0.20-cm objective with the 2.5-cm eyepiece and find the magnification.

ANSWER -9.0×10^2

25.5 The Telescope

There are two fundamentally different types of telescope, both designed to help us view distant objects such as the planets in our solar system: (1) the **refracting telescope**, which uses a combination of lenses to form an image, and (2) the **reflecting**

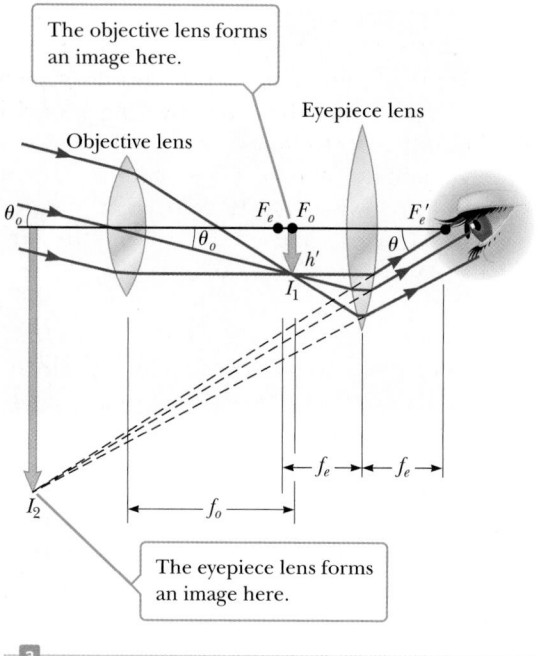

The objective lens forms an image here.

Objective lens

Eyepiece lens

I_1

h'

f_e f_e

f_o

I_2

The eyepiece lens forms an image here.

a

© Tony Freeman/Photo Edit

b

Active Figure 25.8
(a) A diagram of a refracting telescope, with the object at infinity.
(b) A refracting telescope.

telescope, which uses a curved mirror and a lens to form an image. Once again, we can analyze the telescope by considering it to be a system of two optical elements in a row. As before, the basic technique followed is that the image formed by the first element becomes the object for the second.

In the refracting telescope two lenses are arranged so that the objective forms a real, inverted image of the distant object very near the focal point of the eyepiece (Active Fig. 25.8a). Further, the image at I_1 is formed at the focal point of the objective because the object is essentially at infinity. Hence, the two lenses are separated by the distance $f_o + f_e$, which corresponds to the length of the telescope's tube. Finally, at I_2, the eyepiece forms an enlarged image of the image at I_1.

The angular magnification of the telescope is given by θ/θ_o, where θ_o is the angle subtended by the object at the objective and θ is the angle subtended by the final image. From the triangles in Active Figure 25.8a, and for small angles, we have

$$\theta \approx \frac{h'}{f_e} \quad \text{and} \quad \theta_o \approx \frac{h'}{f_o}$$

Therefore, the angular magnification of the telescope can be expressed as

$$m = \frac{\theta}{\theta_o} = \frac{h'/f_e}{h'/f_o} = \frac{f_o}{f_e} \qquad [25.8]$$

This equation says that the angular magnification of the telescope equals the ratio of the objective focal length to the eyepiece focal length. Here again, the angular magnification is the ratio of the angular size seen with the telescope to the angular size seen with the unaided eye.

In some applications—for instance, the observation of relatively nearby objects such as the Sun, the Moon, or planets—angular magnification is important. Stars, however, are so far away that they always appear as small points of light regardless of how much angular magnification is used. The large research telescopes used to study very distant objects must have great diameters to gather as much light as possible. It's difficult and expensive to manufacture such large lenses for refracting telescopes. In addition, the heaviness of large lenses leads to sagging, which is another source of aberration.

NASA

The Hubble Space Telescope enables us to see both further into space and further back in time than ever before.

◀ Angular magnification of a telescope

A

M

Eyepiece

Parabolic mirror

Figure 25.9 A reflecting telescope with a Newtonian focus.

Figure 25.10 The Hale telescope at Mount Palomar Observatory. Just before taking the elevator up to the prime-focus cage, a first-time observer is always told, "Good viewing! And, if you should fall, try to miss the mirror."

Courtesy of Palomar Observatory/ California Institute of Technology

These problems can be partially overcome by replacing the objective lens with a reflecting, concave mirror, usually having a parabolic shape so as to avoid spherical aberration. Figure 25.9 shows the design of a typical reflecting telescope. Incoming light rays pass down the barrel of the telescope and are reflected by a parabolic mirror at the base. These rays converge toward point *A* in the figure, where an image would be formed on a photographic plate or another detector. Before this image is formed, however, a small, flat mirror at *M* reflects the light toward an opening in the side of the tube that passes into an eyepiece. This design is said to have a *Newtonian focus*, after its developer. Note that in the reflecting telescope the light never passes through glass (except for the small eyepiece). As a result, problems associated with chromatic aberration are virtually eliminated.

The largest optical telescopes in the world are the two 10-m-diameter Keck reflectors on Mauna Kea in Hawaii. The largest single-mirrored reflecting telescope in the United States is the 5-m-diameter instrument on Mount Palomar in California. (See Fig. 25.10.) In contrast, the largest refracting telescope in the world, at the Yerkes Observatory in Williams Bay, Wisconsin, has a diameter of only 1 m.

■ **EXAMPLE 25.5** | **Hubble Power**

GOAL Understand magnification in telescopes.

PROBLEM The Hubble Space Telescope is 13.2 m long, but has a secondary mirror that increases its effective focal length to 57.8 m. (See Fig. 25.11.) The telescope doesn't have an eyepiece because various instruments, not a human eye, record the collected light. It can, however, produce images several thousand times larger than they would appear with the unaided human eye. What focal-length eyepiece used with the Hubble mirror system would produce a magnification of 8.00×10^3?

STRATEGY Equation 25.8 for telescope magnification can be solved for the eyepiece focal length. The equation for finding the angular magnification of a reflector is the same as that for a refractor.

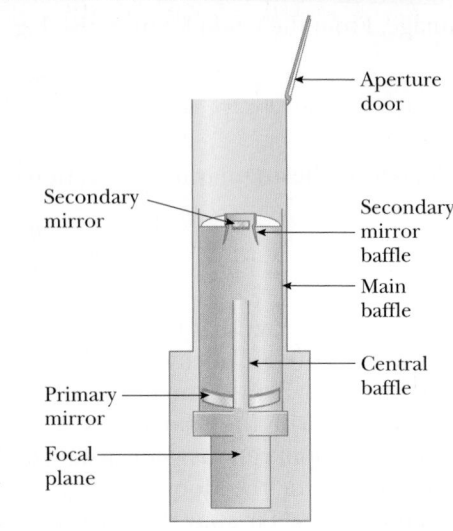

Figure 25.11 A schematic of the Hubble Space Telescope.

Aperture door

Secondary mirror

Secondary mirror baffle

Main baffle

Central baffle

Primary mirror

Focal plane

SOLUTION

Solve for f_e in Equation 25.8 and substitute values:

$$m = \frac{f_o}{f_e} \quad \rightarrow \quad f_e = \frac{f_o}{m} = \frac{57.8 \text{ m}}{8.00 \times 10^3} = \boxed{7.23 \times 10^{-3} \text{ m}}$$

REMARKS The light-gathering power of a telescope and the length of the baseline over which light is gathered are in fact more important than a telescope's magnification, because these two factors contribute to the resolution of the image. A high resolution image can always be magnified so its details can be examined. A low resolution image, however, is often fuzzy when magnified. (See Section 25.6.)

QUESTION 25.5 Can greater magnification of a telescope be achieved by increasing the focal length of the mirror? What effect will increasing the focal length of the eyepiece have on the magnification?

EXERCISE 25.5 The Hale telescope on Mount Palomar has a focal length of 16.8 m. Find the magnification of the telescope in conjunction with an eyepiece having a focal length of 5.00 mm.

ANSWER 3.36×10^3

25.6 Resolution of Single-Slit and Circular Apertures

The ability of an optical system such as the eye, a microscope, or a telescope to distinguish between closely spaced objects is limited because of the wave nature of light. To understand this difficulty, consider Figure 25.12, which shows two light sources far from a narrow slit of width a. The sources can be taken as two point sources S_1 and S_2 that are *not* coherent. For example, they could be two distant stars. If no diffraction occurred, two distinct bright spots (or images) would be observed on the screen at the right in the figure. Because of diffraction, however, each source is imaged as a bright central region flanked by weaker bright and dark rings. What is observed on the screen is the sum of two diffraction patterns, one from S_1 and the other from S_2.

If the two sources are separated so that their central maxima don't overlap, as in Figure 25.12a, their images can be distinguished and are said to be *resolved*. If the sources are close together, however, as in Figure 25.12b, the two central maxima may overlap and the images are *not resolved*. To decide whether two images are resolved, the following condition is often applied to their diffraction patterns:

> When the central maximum of one image falls on the first minimum of another image, the images are said to be just resolved. This limiting condition of resolution is known as **Rayleigh's criterion**.

◀ Rayleigh's criterion

Figure 25.13 (page 872) shows diffraction patterns in three situations. The images are just resolved when their angular separation satisfies Rayleigh's criterion (Fig. 25.13a). As the objects are brought closer together, their images are

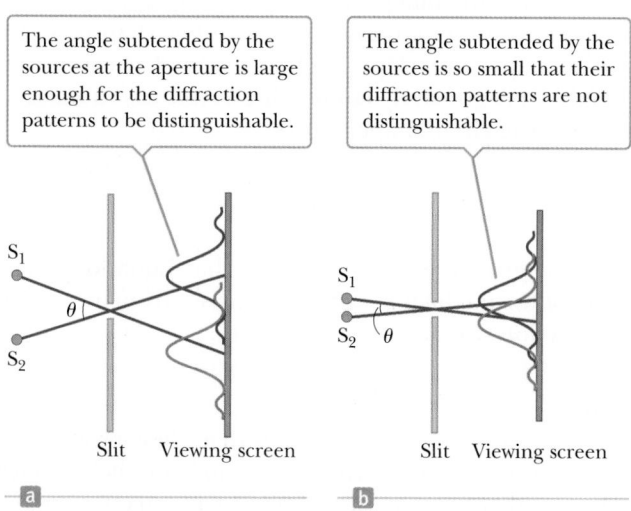

The angle subtended by the sources at the aperture is large enough for the diffraction patterns to be distinguishable.

The angle subtended by the sources is so small that their diffraction patterns are not distinguishable.

S_1
θ
S_2

Slit   Viewing screen

a

S_1
S_2 θ

Slit   Viewing screen

b

Figure 25.12 Two point sources far from a narrow slit each produce a diffraction pattern. (a) The sources are separated by a large angle. (b) The sources are separated by a small angle. (Notice that the angles are greatly exaggerated. The drawing is not to scale.)

The sources are closer together, and the patterns are barely resolved.

The sources are far apart, and the patterns are just resolved.

The sources are so close together that their patterns are not resolved.

From M. Cagnet, M. Francon, and J. C. Thierr, *Atlas of Optical Phenomena*, Berlin, Springer-Verlag, 1962, plate 16

a b c

Figure 25.13 The diffraction patterns of two point sources (solid curves) and the resultant pattern (dashed curve) for three angular separations of the sources.

barely resolved (Fig. 25.13b). Finally, when the sources are very close to each other, their images are not resolved (Fig. 25.13c).

From Rayleigh's criterion, we can determine the minimum angular separation θ_{min} subtended by the source at the slit so that the images will be just resolved. In Chapter 24 we found that the first minimum in a single-slit diffraction pattern occurs at the angle that satisfies the relationship

$$\sin\theta = \frac{\lambda}{a}$$

where a is the width of the slit. According to Rayleigh's criterion, this expression gives the smallest angular separation for which the two images can be resolved. Because $\lambda << a$ in most situations, $\sin\theta$ is small and we can use the approximation $\sin\theta \approx \theta$. Therefore, the limiting angle of resolution for a slit of width a is

Limiting angle for a slit ▶

$$\theta_{min} \approx \frac{\lambda}{a} \qquad [25.9]$$

where θ_{min} is in radians. Hence, the angle subtended by the two sources at the slit must be *greater* than λ/a if the images are to be resolved.

Many optical systems use circular apertures rather than slits. The diffraction pattern of a circular aperture (Fig. 25.14) consists of a central circular bright region surrounded by progressively fainter rings. Analysis shows that the limiting angle of resolution of the circular aperture is

$$\theta_{min} = 1.22\frac{\lambda}{D} \qquad [25.10]$$

where D is the diameter of the aperture. Note that Equation 25.10 is similar to Equation 25.9 except for the factor 1.22, which arises from a complex mathematical analysis of diffraction from a circular aperture.

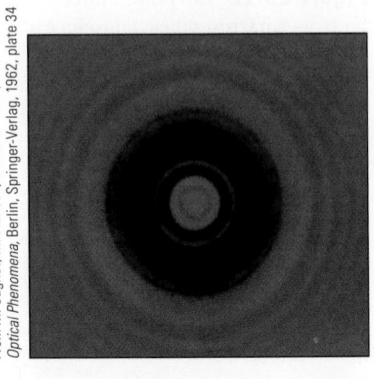

From M. Cagnet, M. Francon, and J. C. Thierr, *Atlas of Optical Phenomena*, Berlin, Springer-Verlag, 1962, plate 34

Figure 25.14 The diffraction pattern of a circular aperture consists of a central bright disk surrounded by concentric bright and dark rings.

■ *Quick Quiz*

25.2 Suppose you are observing a binary star with a telescope and are having difficulty resolving the two stars. Which color filter will better help resolve the stars? (a) blue (b) red (c) neither because colored filters have no effect on resolution

■ APPLYING PHYSICS 25.2 | Cat's Eyes BIO

Cats' eyes have vertical pupils in dim light. Which would cats be most successful at resolving at night, headlights on a distant car or vertically separated running lights on a distant boat's mast having the same separation as the car's headlights?

EXPLANATION The effective slit width in the vertical direction of the cat's eye is larger than that in the horizontal direction. Thus, it has more resolving power for lights separated in the vertical direction and would be more effective at resolving the mast lights on the boat. ■

■ EXAMPLE 25.6 | Resolution of a Microscope

GOAL Study limitations on the resolution of a microscope.

PROBLEM Sodium light of wavelength 589 nm is used to view an object under a microscope. The aperture of the objective has a diameter of 0.90 cm. **(a)** Find the limiting angle of resolution for this microscope. **(b)** Using visible light of any wavelength you desire, find the maximum limit of resolution for this microscope. **(c)** Water of index of refraction 1.33 now fills the space between the object and the objective. What effect would this water have on the resolving power of the microscope, using 589-nm light?

STRATEGY Parts (a) and (b) require substitution into Equation 25.10. Because the wavelength appears in the numerator, violet light, with the shortest visible wavelength, gives the maximum resolution. In part (c) the only difference is that the wavelength changes to λ/n, where n is the index of refraction of water.

SOLUTION

(a) Find the limiting angle of resolution for this microscope.

Substitute into Equation 25.10 to obtain the limiting angle of resolution:

$$\theta_{min} = 1.22 \frac{\lambda}{D} = 1.22 \left(\frac{589 \times 10^{-9} \text{ m}}{0.90 \times 10^{-2} \text{ m}} \right)$$

$$= \boxed{8.0 \times 10^{-5} \text{ rad}}$$

(b) Calculate the microscope's maximum limit of resolution.

To obtain the maximum resolution, substitute the shortest visible wavelength available, which is violet light, of wavelength 4.0×10^2 nm:

$$\theta_{min} = 1.22 \frac{\lambda}{D} = 1.22 \left(\frac{4.0 \times 10^{-7} \text{ m}}{0.90 \times 10^{-2} \text{ m}} \right)$$

$$= \boxed{5.4 \times 10^{-5} \text{ rad}}$$

(c) What effect does water between the object and the objective lens have on the resolution, with 589-nm light?

Calculate the wavelength of the sodium light in the water:

$$\lambda_w = \frac{\lambda_a}{n} = \frac{589 \text{ nm}}{1.33} = 443 \text{ nm}$$

Substitute this wavelength into Equation 25.10 to get the resolution:

$$\theta_{min} = 1.22 \left(\frac{443 \times 10^{-9} \text{ m}}{0.90 \times 10^{-2} \text{ m}} \right) = \boxed{6.0 \times 10^{-5} \text{ rad}}$$

REMARKS In each case any two points on the object subtending an angle of less than the limiting angle θ_{min} at the objective cannot be distinguished in the image. Consequently, it may be possible to see a cell but then be unable to clearly see smaller structures within the cell. Obtaining an increase in resolution is the motivation behind placing a drop of oil on the slide for certain objective lenses.

QUESTION 25.6 Does having two eyes instead of one improve the human ability to resolve distant objects? In general, would more widely spaced eyes increase visual resolving power? Explain.

EXERCISE 25.6 Suppose oil with $n = 1.50$ fills the space between the object and the objective for this microscope. Calculate the limiting angle θ_{min} for sodium light of wavelength 589 nm in air.

ANSWER 5.3×10^{-5} rad

■ EXAMPLE 25.7 Resolving Craters on the Moon

GOAL Calculate the resolution of a telescope.

PROBLEM The Hubble Space Telescope has an aperture of diameter 2.40 m. **(a)** What is its limiting angle of resolution at a wavelength of 6.00×10^2 nm? **(b)** What's the smallest crater it could resolve on the Moon? (The Moon's distance from Earth is 3.84×10^8 m.)

STRATEGY After substituting into Equation 25.10 to find the limiting angle, use $s = r\theta$ to compute the minimum size of crater that can be resolved.

SOLUTION

(a) What is the limiting angle of resolution at a wavelength of 6.00×10^2 nm?

Substitute $D = 2.40$ m and $\lambda = 6.00 \times 10^{-7}$ m into Equation 25.10:

$$\theta_{min} = 1.22 \frac{\lambda}{D} = 1.22 \left(\frac{6.00 \times 10^{-7} \text{ m}}{2.40 \text{ m}} \right)$$

$$= 3.05 \times 10^{-7} \text{ rad}$$

(b) What's the smallest lunar crater the Hubble Space Telescope can resolve?

The two opposite sides of the crater must subtend the minimum angle. Use the arc length formula:

$$s = r\theta = (3.84 \times 10^8 \text{ m})(3.05 \times 10^{-7} \text{ rad}) = 117 \text{ m}$$

REMARKS The distance is so great and the angle so small that using the arc length of a circle is justified because the circular arc is very nearly a straight line. The Hubble Space Telescope has produced several gigabytes of data every day since it first began operation.

QUESTION 25.7 Is the resolution of a telescope better at the red end of the visible spectrum or the violet end?

EXERCISE 25.7 The Hale telescope on Mount Palomar has a diameter of 5.08 m (200 in.). (a) Find the limiting angle of resolution for a wavelength of 6.00×10^2 nm. (b) Calculate the smallest crater diameter the telescope can resolve on the Moon. (c) The answers appear better than what the Hubble can achieve. Why are the answers misleading?

ANSWERS (a) 1.44×10^{-7} rad (b) 55.3 m (c) Although the numbers are better than Hubble's, the Hale telescope must contend with the effects of atmospheric turbulence, so the smaller space-based telescope actually obtains far better results.

It's interesting to compare the resolution of the Hale telescope with that of a large radio telescope, such as the system at Arecibo, Puerto Rico, which has a diameter of 1 000 ft (305 m). This telescope detects radio waves at a wavelength of 0.75 m. The corresponding minimum angle of resolution can be calculated as 3.0×10^{-3} rad (10 min 19 s of arc), which is more than 10 000 times larger than the calculated minimum angle for the Hale telescope.

With such relatively poor resolution, why is Arecibo considered a valuable astronomical instrument? Unlike its optical counterparts, Arecibo can see through clouds of dust. The center of our Milky Way galaxy is obscured by such dust clouds, which absorb and scatter visible light. Radio waves easily penetrate the clouds, so radio telescopes allow direct observations of the galactic core.

Resolving Power of the Diffraction Grating

The diffraction grating studied in Chapter 24 is most useful for making accurate wavelength measurements. Like the prism, it can be used to disperse a spectrum into its components. Of the two devices, the grating is better suited to distinguishing between two closely spaced wavelengths. We say that the grating spectrometer has a higher *resolution* than the prism spectrometer. If λ_1 and λ_2 are two nearly equal wavelengths between which the spectrometer can just barely distinguish, the **resolving power** of the grating is defined as

$$R \equiv \frac{\lambda}{\lambda_2 - \lambda_1} = \frac{\lambda}{\Delta\lambda} \qquad [25.11]$$

where $\lambda \approx \lambda_1 \approx \lambda_2$ and $\Delta\lambda = \lambda_2 - \lambda_1$. From this equation, it's clear that a grating with a high resolving power can distinguish small differences in wavelength. Further, if N lines of the grating are illuminated, it can be shown that the resolving power in the mth-order diffraction is given by

$$R = Nm \qquad [25.12]$$

◄ Resolving power of a grating

So, the resolving power R increases with the order number m and is large for a grating with a great number of illuminated slits. Note that for $m = 0$, $R = 0$, which signifies that *all wavelengths are indistinguishable* for the zeroth-order maximum. (All wavelengths fall at the same point on the screen.) Consider, however, the second-order diffraction pattern of a grating that has 5 000 rulings illuminated by the light source. The resolving power of such a grating in second order is $R = 5\,000 \times 2 = 10\,000$. Therefore, the *minimum* wavelength separation between two spectral lines that can be just resolved, assuming a mean wavelength of 600 nm, is calculated from Equation 25.12 to be $\Delta\lambda = \lambda/R = 6 \times 10^{-2}$ nm. For the third-order principal maximum, $R = 15\,000$ and $\Delta\lambda = 4 \times 10^{-2}$ nm, and so on.

▪ EXAMPLE 25.8 | Light from Sodium Atoms

GOAL Find the necessary resolving power to distinguish spectral lines.

PROBLEM Two bright lines in the spectrum of sodium have wavelengths of 589.00 nm and 589.59 nm, respectively. **(a)** What must the resolving power of a grating be so as to distinguish these wavelengths? **(b)** To resolve these lines in the second-order spectrum, how many lines of the grating must be illuminated?

STRATEGY This problem requires little more than substituting into Equations 25.11 and 25.12.

. . . .

SOLUTION

(a) What must the resolving power of a grating be in order to distinguish the given wavelengths?

Substitute into Equation 25.11 to find R:

$$R = \frac{\lambda}{\Delta\lambda} = \frac{589.00 \text{ nm}}{589.59 \text{ nm} - 589.00 \text{ nm}} = \frac{589 \text{ nm}}{0.59 \text{ nm}}$$

$$= \boxed{1.0 \times 10^3}$$

(b) To resolve these lines in the second-order spectrum, how many lines of the grating must be illuminated?

Solve Equation 25.12 for N and substitute:

$$N = \frac{R}{m} = \frac{1.0 \times 10^3}{2} = \boxed{5.0 \times 10^2 \text{ lines}}$$

. . . .

REMARKS The ability to resolve spectral lines is particularly important in experimental atomic physics.

QUESTION 25.8 True or False: If two diffraction gratings differ only by the number of lines, the grating with the larger number of lines has the greater resolving power.

EXERCISE 25.8 Due to a phenomenon called electron spin, when the lines of a spectrum are examined at high resolution, each line is actually found to be two closely spaced lines called a doublet. An example is the doublet in the hydrogen spectrum having wavelengths of 656.272 nm and 656.285 nm. (a) What must be the resolving power of a grating so as to distinguish these wavelengths? (b) How many lines of the grating must be illuminated to resolve these lines in the third-order spectrum?

ANSWERS (a) 5.0×10^4 (b) 1.7×10^4 lines

25.7 The Michelson Interferometer

The Michelson interferometer is an optical instrument having great scientific importance. Invented by American physicist A. A. Michelson (1852–1931), it is an ingenious device that splits a light beam into two parts and then recombines them to form an interference pattern. The interferometer is used to make accurate length measurements.

Active Figure 25.15 is a schematic diagram of an interferometer. A beam of light provided by a monochromatic source is split into two rays by a partially silvered mirror M inclined at an angle of 45° relative to the incident light beam. One ray is reflected vertically upward to mirror M_1, and the other ray is transmitted horizontally through mirror M to mirror M_2. Hence, the two rays travel separate paths, L_1 and L_2. After reflecting from mirrors M_1 and M_2, the two rays eventually recombine to produce an interference pattern, which can be viewed through a telescope. The glass plate P, equal in thickness to mirror M, is placed in the path of the horizontal ray to ensure that the two rays travel the same distance through glass.

The interference pattern for the two rays is determined by the difference in their path lengths. When the two rays are viewed as shown, the image of M_2 is at M_2', parallel to M_1. Hence, the space between M_2' and M_1 forms the equivalent of a parallel air film. The effective thickness of the air film is varied by using a finely threaded screw to move mirror M_1 in the direction indicated by the arrows in Active Figure 25.15. If one of the mirrors is tipped slightly with respect to the other, the thin film between the two is wedge shaped and an interference pattern consisting of parallel fringes is set up, as described in Example 24.4. Now suppose we focus on one of the dark lines with the crosshairs of a telescope. As mirror M_1 is moved to lengthen the path L_1, the thickness of the wedge increases. When the thickness increases by $\lambda/4$, the destructive interference that initially produced the dark fringe has changed to constructive interference, and we now observe a bright fringe at the location of the crosshairs. The term *fringe shift* is used to describe the change in a fringe from dark to light or from light to dark. Successive light and dark fringes are formed each time M_1 is moved a distance of $\lambda/4$. The wavelength

Active Figure 25.15

A diagram of the Michelson interferometer.

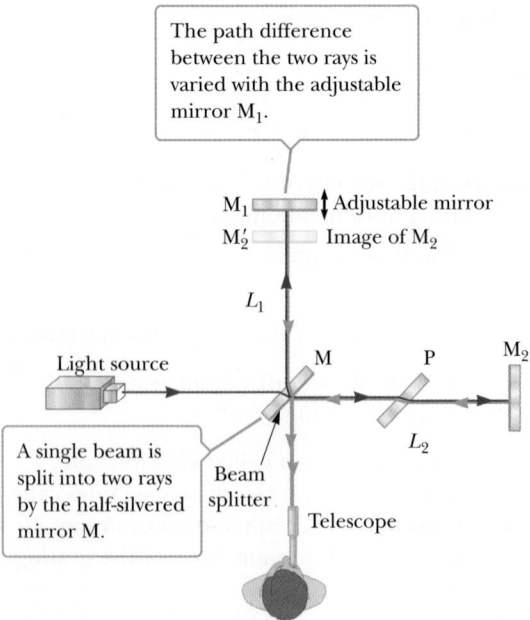

of light can be measured by counting the number of fringe shifts for a measured displacement of M$_1$. Conversely, if the wavelength is accurately known (as with a laser beam), the mirror displacement can be determined to within a fraction of the wavelength. Because the interferometer can measure displacements precisely, it is often used to make highly accurate measurements of the dimensions of mechanical components.

If the mirrors are perfectly aligned rather than tipped with respect to each other, the path difference differs slightly for different angles of view. This arrangement results in an interference pattern that resembles Newton's rings. The pattern can be used in a fashion similar to that for tipped mirrors. An observer pays attention to the center spot in the interference pattern. For example, suppose the spot is initially dark, indicating that destructive interference is occurring. If M$_1$ is now moved a distance of $\lambda/4$, this central spot changes to a light region, corresponding to a fringe shift.

■ SUMMARY

25.1 The Camera
The light-concentrating power of a lens of focal length f and diameter D is determined by the *f*-number, defined as

$$f\text{-number} \equiv \frac{f}{D} \qquad [25.1]$$

The smaller the *f*-number of a lens, the brighter the image formed.

25.2 The Eye
Hyperopia (farsightedness) is a defect of the eye that occurs either when the eyeball is too short or when the ciliary muscle cannot change the shape of the lens enough to form a properly focused image. **Myopia** (nearsightedness) occurs either when the eye is longer than normal or when the maximum focal length of the lens is insufficient to produce a clearly focused image on the retina.

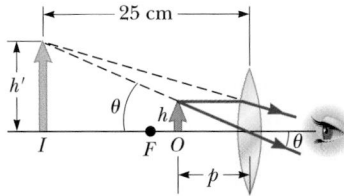

An object placed near the focal point of a converging lens produces a magnified image, which subtends an angle of $\theta \approx h'/25$ at the eye. Note that in this situation $q = -25$ cm.

The **power** of a lens in **diopters** is the inverse of the focal length in meters.

25.3 The Simple Magnifier
The **angular magnification of a lens** is defined as

$$m \equiv \frac{\theta}{\theta_0} \qquad [25.2]$$

where θ is the angle subtended by an object at the eye with a lens in use and θ_0 is the angle subtended by the object when it is placed at the near point of the eye and no lens is used. The **maximum angular magnification of a lens** is

$$m_{max} = 1 + \frac{25\text{ cm}}{f} \qquad [25.5]$$

When the eye is relaxed, the angular magnification is

$$m = \frac{25\text{ cm}}{f} \qquad [25.6]$$

25.4 The Compound Microscope
The overall **magnification of a compound microscope** of length L is the product of the magnification produced by the objective, of focal length f_o, and the magnification produced by the eyepiece, of focal length f_e:

$$m = -\frac{L}{f_o}\left(\frac{25\text{ cm}}{f_e}\right) \qquad [25.7]$$

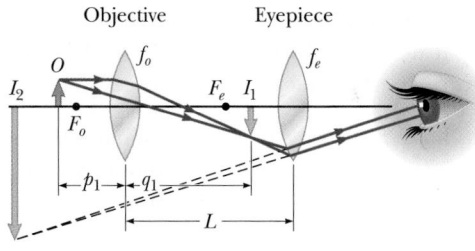

A ray diagram for a compound microscope, which consists of an objective and an eyepiece, or ocular lens.

25.5 The Telescope

The **angular magnification of a telescope** is

$$m = \frac{f_o}{f_e}. \qquad [25.8]$$

where f_o is the focal length of the objective and f_e is the focal length of the eyepiece.

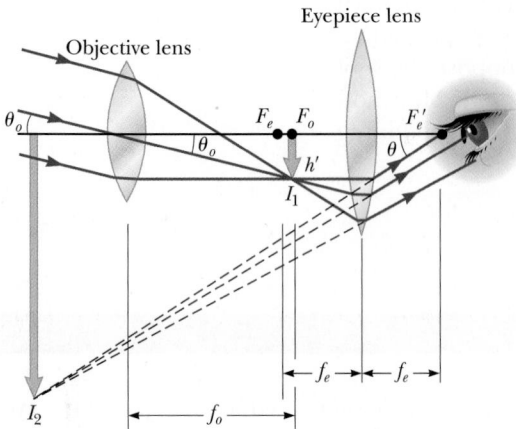

A ray diagram for a refracting telescope, with the object at infinity.

25.6 Resolution of Single-Slit and Circular Apertures

Two images are said to be **just resolved** when the central maximum of the diffraction pattern for one image falls on the first minimum of the other image. This limiting condition of resolution is known as **Rayleigh's criterion**. The limiting angle of resolution for a **slit** of width a is

$$\theta_{min} \approx \frac{\lambda}{a} \qquad [25.9]$$

Two point sources far from a narrow slit each produce a diffraction pattern. (a) The sources are separated by a large angle. (b) The sources are separated by a small angle.

The limiting angle of resolution of a **circular aperture** is

$$\theta_{min} = 1.22 \frac{\lambda}{D} \qquad [25.10]$$

where D is the diameter of the aperture.

If λ_1 and λ_2 are two nearly equal wavelengths between which a grating spectrometer can just barely distinguish, the **resolving power** R of the grating is defined as

$$R \equiv \frac{\lambda}{\lambda_2 - \lambda_1} = \frac{\lambda}{\Delta\lambda} \qquad [25.11]$$

where $\lambda \approx \lambda_1 \approx \lambda_2$ and $\Delta\lambda = \lambda_2 - \lambda_1$. The **resolving power** of a diffraction grating in the mth order is

$$R = Nm \qquad [25.12]$$

where N is the number of illuminated rulings on the grating.

■ MULTIPLE-CHOICE QUESTIONS

WebAssign The multiple-choice questions in this chapter may be assigned onaline in Enhanced WebAssign.

1. If you increase the aperture diameter of a camera by a factor of 3, how is the intensity of the light striking the film affected? (a) It increases by a factor of 3. (b) It decreases by a factor of 3. (c) It increases by a factor of 9. (d) It decreases by a factor of 9. (e) Increasing the aperture doesn't affect the intensity.

2. A lens has a focal length of 25 cm. What is the power of the lens? (a) 2.0 diopters (b) 4.0 diopters (c) 6.0 diopters (d) 8.0 diopters (e) none of these

3. Why is it advantageous to use a large-diameter objective lens in a telescope? (a) It diffracts the light more effectively than smaller-diameter objective lenses. (b) It increases its magnification. (c) It increases its resolution. (d) It enables you to see more objects in the field of view. (e) It reflects unwanted wavelengths.

4. BIO If a woman's eyes are longer than normal, how is her vision affected and how can her vision be corrected? (a) The woman is farsighted (hyperopia), and her vision can be corrected with a diverging lens. (b) The woman is nearsighted (myopia), and her vision can be corrected with a diverging lens. (c) The woman is farsighted, and her vision can be corrected with a converging lens. (d) The woman is nearsighted, and her vision can be corrected with a converging lens. (e) The woman's vision is not correctible.

5. BIO If a man has eyes that are shorter than normal, how is his vision affected and how can it be corrected? (a) The man is farsighted (hyperopia), and his vision can be corrected with a diverging lens. (b) The man is nearsighted (myopia), and his vision can be corrected with a diverging lens. (c) The man is farsighted, and

his vision can be corrected with a converging lens. (d) The man is nearsighted, and his vision can be corrected with a converging lens. (e) The man's vision is not correctible.

6. **BIO** The near point of a given individual's eye is 55 cm. What focal length corrective lens should be prescribed so that an object can be clearly seen when placed 25 cm in front of the eye? (a) -25 cm (b) 17 cm (c) 46 cm (d) 32 cm (e) 54 cm

7. A telescope can be used as a camera if the film is placed at the image position of the objective lens (or mirror); so the objective lens becomes the lens of the camera. If a 2.00-m focal length objective lens of a telescope is used to photograph the image of two stars that are 20.0 mm apart on the film, what is the angular separation of the two stars? (a) $0.010°$ (b) $0.10°$ (c) $0.286°$ (d) $0.573°$ (e) $0.353°$

8. A compound microscope has objective and eyepiece lenses of focal lengths 0.80 cm and 4.0 cm, respectively. If the microscope length is 15 cm, what is the approximate magnification of the microscope? (a) 3.2 (b) 6.3 (c) 48 (d) 120 (e) 160

9. A diffraction grating must distinguish two wavelengths that are 0.1 nm apart in the visible band. What minimum resolving power must the grating have? (a) 3 000 (b) 4 000 (c) 5 000 (d) 6 000 (e) 7 000

10. Estimate the size aperture required of a telescope to resolve two stars that are 200 ly from Earth and orbiting within 10^{-5} ly of each other. (a) 10 cm (b) 1 m (c) 10 m (d) 50 m (e) 100 m

11. Off in the distance, you see the headlights of a car, but they are indistinguishable from the single headlight of a motorcycle. Assume the car's headlights are now switched from low beam to high beam so that the light intensity you receive becomes three times greater. Also, neglect any change in the pupils of your eyes. What then happens to your ability to resolve the two light sources? (a) It increases by a factor of 9. (b) It increases by a factor of 3. (c) It remains the same. (d) It becomes one-third as good. (e) It becomes one-ninth as good.

■ CONCEPTUAL QUESTIONS

WebAssign The conceptual questions in this chapter may be assigned online in Enhanced WebAssign.

1. A lens is used to examine an object across a room. Is the lens probably being used as a simple magnifier? Explain in terms of focal length, the image, and magnification.

2. A laser beam is incident at a shallow angle on a horizontal machinist's ruler that has a finely calibrated scale. The engraved rulings on the scale give rise to a diffraction pattern on a vertical screen. Discuss how you can use this technique to obtain a measure of the wavelength of the laser light.

3. **BIO** The optic nerve and the brain invert the image formed on the retina. Why don't we see everything upside down?

4. Suppose you are observing the interference pattern formed by a Michelson interferometer in a laboratory and a joking colleague holds a lit match in the light path of one arm of the interferometer. Will this match have an effect on the interference pattern?

5. If you want to examine the fine detail of an object with a magnifying glass with a power of +20.0 diopters, where should the object be placed so as to observe a magnified image of the object?

6. **BIO** Compare and contrast the eye and a camera. What parts of the camera correspond to the iris, the retina, and the cornea of the eye?

7. If you want to use a converging lens to set fire to a piece of paper, why should the light source be farther from the lens than its focal point?

8. Large telescopes are usually reflecting rather than refracting. List some reasons for this choice.

9. Explain why it is theoretically impossible to see an object as small as an atom regardless of the quality of the light microscope being used.

10. Which is most important in the use of a camera photoflash unit, the intensity of the light (the energy per unit area per unit time) or the product of the intensity and the time of the flash, assuming the time is less than the shutter speed?

11. **BIO** A patient has a near point of 1.25 m. Is she nearsighted or farsighted? Should the corrective lens be converging or diverging?

12. A lens with a certain power is used as a simple magnifier. If the power of the lens is doubled, does the angular magnification increase or decrease?

13. A laser produces a beam a few millimeters wide, with uniform intensity across its width. A hair is stretched vertically across the front of the laser to cross the beam. (a) How is the diffraction pattern it produces on a distant screen related to that of a vertical slit equal in width to the hair? (b) How could you determine the width of the hair from measurements of its diffraction pattern?

14. **BIO** During LASIK eye surgery (laser-assisted *in situ* keratomileusis), the shape of the cornea is modified by vaporizing some of its material. If the surgery is performed to correct for nearsightedness, how does the cornea need to be reshaped?

■ PROBLEMS

25.1 The Camera

1. A lens has a focal length of 28 cm and a diameter of 4.0 cm. What is the *f*-number of the lens?

2. A certain camera has *f*-numbers that range from 1.2 to 22. If the focal length of the lens is 55 mm, what is the range of aperture diameters for the camera?

3. A photographic image of a building is 0.092 0 m high. The image was made with a lens with a focal length of 52.0 mm. If the lens was 100 m from the building when the photograph was made, determine the height of the building.

4. The image area of a typical 35 mm slide is 23.5 mm by 35.0 mm. If a camera's lens has a focal length of 55.0 mm and forms an image of the constellation Orion, which is 20° across, will the full image fit on a 35-mm slide?

5. A camera is being used with a correct exposure at *f*/4 and a shutter speed of $\frac{1}{15}$ s. In addition to the *f*-numbers listed in Section 25.1, this camera has *f*-numbers *f*/1, *f*/1.4, and *f*/2. To photograph a rapidly moving subject, the shutter speed is changed to $\frac{1}{125}$ s. Find the new *f*-number setting needed on this camera to maintain satisfactory exposure.

6. (a) Use conceptual arguments to show that the intensity of light (energy per unit area per unit time) reaching the film in a camera is proportional to the square of the reciprocal of the *f*-number as

$$I \propto \frac{1}{(f/D)^2}$$

(b) The correct exposure time for a camera set to *f*/1.8 is (1/500) s. Calculate the correct exposure time if the *f*-number is changed to *f*/4 under the same lighting conditions. *Note:* "*f*/4," on a camera, means "an *f*-number of 4."

7. A certain type of film requires an exposure time of 0.010 s with an *f*/11 lens setting. Another type of film requires twice the light energy to produce the same level of exposure. What *f*-number does the second type of film need with the 0.010-s exposure time?

8. A certain camera lens has a focal length of 175 mm. Its position can be adjusted to produce images when the lens is between 180 mm and 210 mm from the plane of the film. Over what range of object distances is the lens useful?

25.2 The Eye

9. **BIO** The near point of a person's eye is 60.0 cm. To see objects clearly at a distance of 25.0 cm, what should be the (a) focal length and (b) power of the appropriate corrective lens? (Neglect the distance from the lens to the eye.)

10. **BIO** **GP** A patient can't see objects closer than 40.0 cm and wishes to clearly see objects that are 20.0 cm from his eye. (a) Is the patient nearsighted or farsighted? (b) If the eye–lens distance is 2.00 cm, what is the minimum object distance *p* from the lens? (c) What image position with respect to the lens will allow the patient to see the object? (d) Is the image real or virtual? Is the image distance *q* positive or negative? (e) Calculate the required focal length. (f) Find the power of the lens in diopters. (g) If a contact lens is to be prescribed instead, find *p*, *q*, and *f*, and the power of the lens.

11. **BIO** **M** The accommodation limits for Nearsighted Nick's eyes are 18.0 cm and 80.0 cm. When he wears his glasses, he is able to see faraway objects clearly. At what minimum distance is he able to see objects clearly?

12. **BIO** A certain child's near point is 10.0 cm; her far point (with eyes relaxed) is 125 cm. Each eye lens is 2.00 cm from the retina. (a) Between what limits, measured in diopters, does the power of this lens–cornea combination vary? (b) Calculate the power of the eyeglass lens the child should use for relaxed distance vision. Is the lens converging or diverging?

13. **BIO** An individual is nearsighted; his near point is 13.0 cm and his far point is 50.0 cm. (a) What lens power is needed to correct his nearsightedness? (b) When the lenses are in use, what is this person's near point?

14. **BIO** **Q|C** A patient has a near point of 45.0 cm and far point of 85.0 cm. (a) Can a single lens correct the patient's vision? Explain the patient's options. (b) Calculate the power lens needed to correct the near point so that the patient can see objects 25.0 cm away. Neglect the eye–lens distance. (c) Calculate the power lens needed to correct the patient's far point, again neglecting the eye–lens distance.

15. **BIO** An artificial lens is implanted in a person's eye to replace a diseased lens. The distance between the artificial lens and the retina is 2.80 cm. In the absence of the lens, an image of a distant object (formed by refraction at the cornea) falls 5.33 cm behind the implanted lens. The lens is designed to put the image of the distant object on the retina. What is the power of the implanted lens? *Hint:* Consider the image formed by the cornea to be a virtual object.

16. **BIO** A person is to be fitted with bifocals. She can see clearly when the object is between 30 cm and 1.5 m from the eye. (a) The upper portions of the bifocals (Fig. P25.16) should be designed to enable her to see distant objects clearly. What power should they have? (b) The lower portions of the bifocals should enable her to see objects located 25 cm in front of the eye. What power should they have?

Far vision

Near vision

Figure P25.16

17. **BIO** A nearsighted woman can't see objects clearly beyond 40.0 cm (her far point). If she has no astigmatism and contact lenses are prescribed, what power and type of lens are required to correct her vision?

18. **BIO** **QC** A person sees clearly wearing eyeglasses that have a power of −4.00 diopters when the lenses are 2.00 cm in front of the eyes. (a) What is the focal length of the lens? (b) Is the person nearsighted or farsighted? (c) If the person wants to switch to contact lenses placed directly on the eyes, what lens power should be prescribed?

25.3 The Simple Magnifier

19. A stamp collector uses a lens with 7.5-cm focal length as a simple magnifier. The virtual image is produced at the normal near point (25 cm). (a) How far from the lens should the stamp be placed? (b) What is the expected angular magnification?

20. A lens that has a focal length of 5.00 cm is used as a magnifying glass. (a) To obtain maximum magnification and an image that can be seen clearly by a normal eye, where should the object be placed? (b) What is the angular magnification?

21. A biology student uses a simple magnifier to examine the structural features of an insect's wing. The wing is held 3.50 cm in front of the lens, and the image is formed 25.0 cm from the eye. (a) What is the focal length of the lens? (b) What angular magnification is achieved?

22. A jeweler's lens of focal length 5.0 cm is used as a magnifier. With the lens held near the eye, determine

(a) the angular magnification when the object is at the focal point of the lens and (b) the angular magnification when the image formed by the lens is at the near point of the eye (25 cm). (c) What is the object distance giving the maximum magnification?

23. A leaf of length h is positioned 71.0 cm in front of a converging lens with a focal length of 39.0 cm. An observer views the image of the leaf from a position 1.26 m behind the lens, as shown in Figure P25.23. (a) What is the magnitude of the lateral magnification (the ratio of the image size to the object size) produced by the lens? (b) What angular magnification is achieved by viewing the image of the leaf rather than viewing the leaf directly?

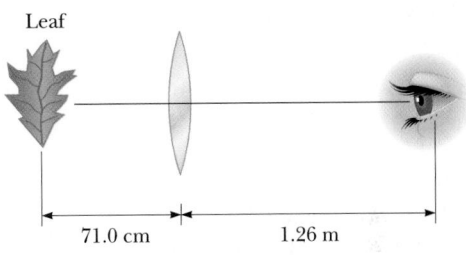

Leaf

71.0 cm   1.26 m

Figure P25.23

24. (a) What is the maximum angular magnification of an eyeglass lens having a focal length of 18.0 cm when used as a simple magnifier? (b) What is the magnification of this lens when the eye is relaxed?

25.4 The Compound Microscope

25.5 The Telescope

25. The desired overall magnification of a compound microscope is 140×. The objective alone produces a lateral magnification of 12×. Determine the required focal length of the eyepiece.

26. The distance between the eyepiece and the objective lens in a certain compound microscope is 20.0 cm. The focal length of the objective is 0.500 cm, and that of the eyepiece is 1.70 cm. Find the overall magnification of the microscope.

27. Find the magnification of a telescope that uses a 2.75-diopter objective lens and a 35.0-diopter eyepiece.

28. **BIO** A microscope has an objective lens with a focal length of 16.22 mm and an eyepiece with a focal length of 9.50 mm. With the length of the barrel set at 29.0 cm, the diameter of a red blood cell's image subtends an angle of 1.43 mrad with the eye. If the final image distance is 29.0 cm from the eyepiece, what is the actual diameter of the red blood cell? *Hint:* To solve this question, go back to basics and use the thin-lens equation.

29. A certain telescope has an objective mirror with an aperture diameter of 200 mm and a focal length of 2 000 mm. It captures the image of a nebula on

photographic film at its prime focus with an exposure time of 1.50 min. To produce the same light energy per unit area on the film, what is the required exposure time to photograph the same nebula with a smaller telescope that has an objective with a 60.0-mm diameter and a 900-mm focal length?

30. **S** (a) Find an equation for the length L of a refracting telescope in terms of the focal length of the objective f_o and the magnification m. (b) A knob adjusts the eyepiece forward and backward. Suppose the telescope is in focus with an eyepiece giving a magnification of 50.0. By what distance must the eyepiece be adjusted when the eyepiece is replaced, with a resulting magnification of 1.00×10^2? Must the eyepiece be adjusted backward or forward? Assume the objective lens has a focal length of 2.00 m.

31. Suppose an astronomical telescope is being designed to have an angular magnification of 34.0. If the focal length of the objective lens being used is 86.0 cm, find (a) the required focal length of the eyepiece and (b) the distance between the two lenses for a relaxed eye. *Hint:* For a relaxed eye, the image formed by the objective lens is at the focal point of the eyepiece.

32. A certain telescope has an objective of focal length 1 500 cm. If the Moon is used as an object, a 1.0-cm-long image formed by the objective corresponds to what distance, in miles, on the Moon? Assume 3.8×10^8 m for the Earth–Moon distance.

33. **S** Astronomers often take photographs with the objective lens or mirror of a telescope alone, without an eyepiece. (a) Show that the image size h' for a telescope used in this manner is given by $h' = fh/(f - p)$, where h is the object size, f is the objective focal length, and p is the object distance. (b) Simplify the expression in part (a) if the object distance is much greater than the objective focal length. (c) The "wingspan" of the International Space Station is 108.6 m, the overall width of its solar panel configuration. When it is orbiting at an altitude of 407 km, find the width of the image formed by a telescope objective of focal length 4.00 m.

34. **BIO** An elderly sailor is shipwrecked on a desert island, but manages to save his eyeglasses. The lens for one eye has a power of +1.20 diopters, and the other lens has a power of +9.00 diopters. (a) What is the magnifying power of the telescope he can construct with these lenses? (b) How far apart are the lenses when the telescope is adjusted for minimum eyestrain?

35. **M** A person decides to use an old pair of eyeglasses to make some optical instruments. He knows that the near point in his left eye is 50.0 cm and the near point in his right eye is 100 cm. (a) What is the maximum angular magnification he can produce in a telescope? (b) If he places the lenses 10.0 cm apart, what is the maximum overall magnification he can produce in a

microscope? *Hint:* Go back to basics and use the thin-lens equation to solve part (b).

36. **Q|C** Galileo devised a simple terrestrial telescope that produces an upright image. It consists of a converging objective lens and a diverging eyepiece at opposite ends of the telescope tube. For distant objects, the tube length is the objective focal length less the absolute value of the eyepiece focal length. (a) Does the user of the telescope see a real or virtual image? (b) Where is the final image? (c) If a telescope is to be constructed with a tube of length 10.0 cm and a magnification of 3.00, what are the focal lengths of the objective and eyepiece?

25.6 Resolution of Single-Slit and Circular Apertures

37. A converging lens with a diameter of 30.0 cm forms an image of a satellite passing overhead. The satellite has two green lights (wavelength 500 nm) spaced 1.00 m apart. If the lights can just be resolved according to the Rayleigh criterion, what is the altitude of the satellite?

38. While flying at an altitude of 9.50 km, you look out the window at various objects on the ground. If your ability to distinguish two objects is limited only by diffraction, find the smallest separation between two objects on the ground that are distinguishable. Assume your pupil has a diameter of 4.0 mm and take $\lambda = 575$ nm.

39. **M** To increase the resolving power of a microscope, the object and the objective are immersed in oil ($n = 1.5$). If the limiting angle of resolution without the oil is 0.60 μrad, what is the limiting angle of resolution with the oil? *Hint:* The oil changes the wavelength of the light.

40. **BIO** (a) Calculate the limiting angle of resolution for the eye, assuming a pupil diameter of 2.00 mm, a wavelength of 500 nm *in air*, and an index of refraction for the eye of 1.33. (b) What is the maximum distance from the eye at which two points separated by 1.00 cm could be resolved?

41. A vehicle with headlights separated by 2.00 m approaches an observer holding an infrared detector sensitive to radiation of wavelength 885 nm. What aperture diameter is required in the detector if the two headlights are to be resolved at a distance of 10.0 km?

42. Two stars located 23 light-years from Earth are barely resolved using a reflecting telescope having a mirror of diameter 68 cm. Assuming $\lambda = 575$ nm and assuming that the resolution is limited only by diffraction, find the separation between the stars.

43. Suppose a 5.00-m-diameter telescope were constructed on the Moon, where the absence of atmospheric distortion would permit excellent viewing. If observations were made using 500-nm light, what minimum separation between two objects could just be resolved on Mars at closest approach (when Mars is 8.0×10^7 km from the Moon)?

44. A spy satellite circles Earth at an altitude of 200 km and carries out surveillance with a special high-resolution telescopic camera having a lens diameter of 35 cm. If the angular resolution of this camera is limited by diffraction, estimate the separation of two small objects on Earth's surface that are just resolved in yellow-green light ($\lambda = 550$ nm).

45. A 15.0-cm-long grating has 6 000 slits per centimeter. Can two lines of wavelengths 600.000 nm and 600.003 nm be separated with this grating? Explain.

46. The H_α line in hydrogen has a wavelength of 656.20 nm. This line differs in wavelength from the corresponding spectral line in deuterium (the heavy stable isotope of hydrogen) by 0.18 nm. (a) Determine the minimum number of lines a grating must have to resolve these two wavelengths in the first order. (b) Repeat part (a) for the second order.

25.7 The Michelson Interferometer

47. Light of wavelength 550 nm is used to calibrate a Michelson interferometer. With the use of a micrometer screw, the platform on which one mirror is mounted is moved 0.180 mm. How many fringe shifts are counted?

48. **QC** Monochromatic light is beamed into a Michelson interferometer. The movable mirror is displaced 0.382 mm, causing the central spot in the interferometer pattern to change from bright to dark and back to bright $N = 1\ 700$ times. (a) Determine the wavelength of the light. What color is it? (b) If monochromatic red light is used instead and the mirror is moved the same distance, would N be larger or smaller? Explain.

49. **BIO** An interferometer is used to measure the length of a bacterium. The wavelength of the light used is 650 nm. As one arm of the interferometer is moved from one end of the cell to the other, 310 fringe shifts are counted. How long is the bacterium?

50. Mirror M_1 in Active Figure 25.15 is displaced a distance ΔL. During this displacement, 250 fringe shifts are counted. The light being used has a wavelength of 632.8 nm. Calculate the displacement ΔL.

51. A thin sheet of transparent material has an index of refraction of 1.40 and is 15.0 μm thick. When it is inserted in the light path along one arm of an interferometer, how many fringe shifts occur in the pattern? Assume the wavelength (in a vacuum) of the light used is 600 nm. *Hint:* The wavelength will change within the material.

52. **M** The Michelson interferometer can be used to measure the index of refraction of a gas by placing an evacuated transparent tube in the light path along one arm of the device. Fringe shifts occur as the gas is slowly added to the tube. Assume 600-nm light is used, the tube is 5.00 cm long, and 160 fringe shifts occur as the pressure of the gas in the tube increases to atmo-

spheric pressure. What is the index of refraction of the gas? *Hint:* The fringe shifts occur because the wavelength of the light changes inside the gas-filled tube.

Additional Problems

53. The Yerkes refracting telescope has a 1.00-m-diameter objective lens of focal length 20.0 m. Assume it is used with an eyepiece of focal length 2.50 cm. (a) Determine the magnification of the planet Mars as seen through the telescope. (b) Are the observed Martian polar caps right side up or upside down?

54. Estimate the minimum angle subtended at the eye of a hawk flying at an altitude of 50 m necessary to recognize a mouse on the ground.

55. An American standard analog television picture (non-HDTV), also known as NTSC, is composed of approximately 485 visible horizontal lines of varying light intensity. Assume your ability to resolve the lines is limited only by the Rayleigh criterion, the pupils of your eyes are 5.00 mm in diameter, and the average wavelength of the light coming from the screen is 550 nm. Calculate the ratio of the minimum viewing distance to the vertical dimension of the picture such that you will not be able to resolve the lines.

56. **BIO** A person with a nearsighted eye has near and far points of 16 cm and 25 cm, respectively. (a) Assuming a lens is placed 2.0 cm from the eye, what power must the lens have to correct this condition? (b) Suppose contact lenses placed directly on the cornea are used to correct the person's eyesight. What is the power of the lens required in this case, and what is the new near point? *Hint:* The contact lens and the eyeglass lens require slightly different powers because they are at different distances from the eye.

57. **BIO** The near point of an eye is 75.0 cm. (a) What should be the power of a corrective lens prescribed to enable the eye to see an object clearly at 25.0 cm? (b) If, using the corrective lens, the person can see an object clearly at 26.0 cm but not at 25.0 cm, by how many diopters did the lens grinder miss the prescription?

58. **BIO** If a typical eyeball is 2.00 cm long and has a pupil opening that can range from about 2.00 mm to 6.00 mm, what are (a) the focal length of the eye when it is focused on objects 1.00 m away, (b) the smallest f-number of the eye when it is focused on objects 1.00 m away, and (c) the largest f-number of the eye when it is focused on objects 1.00 m away?

59. **BIO** **M** A cataract-impaired lens in an eye may be surgically removed and replaced by a manufactured lens. The focal length required for the new lens is determined by the lens-to-retina distance, which is measured by a sonarlike device, and by the requirement that the implant provide for correct distance vision. (a) If the distance from lens to retina is 22.4 mm, calculate the power of the implanted lens in diopters.

(b) Since there is no accommodation and the implant allows for correct distance vision, a corrective lens for close work or reading must be used. Assume a reading distance of 33.0 cm, and calculate the power of the lens in the reading glasses.

60. **BIO** If the aqueous humor of the eye has an index of refraction of 1.34 and the distance from the vertex of the cornea to the retina is 2.00 cm, what is the radius of curvature of the cornea for which distant objects will be focused on the retina? (For simplicity, assume all refraction occurs in the aqueous humor.)

61. A Boy Scout starts a fire by using a lens from his eyeglasses to focus sunlight on kindling 5.0 cm from the lens. The Boy Scout has a near point of 15 cm. When the lens is used as a simple magnifier, (a) what is the maximum magnification that can be achieved and (b) what is the magnification when the eye is relaxed? *Caution:* The equations derived in the text for a simple magnifier assume a "normal" eye.

62. A laboratory (astronomical) telescope is used to view a scale that is 300 cm from the objective, which has a focal length of 20.0 cm; the eyepiece has a focal length of 2.00 cm. Calculate the angular magnification when the telescope is adjusted for minimum eyestrain. *Note:* The object is not at infinity, so the simple expression $m = f_o/f_e$ is not sufficiently accurate for this problem. Also, assume small angles, so that $\tan \theta \approx \theta$.

■ AP* REVIEW QUESTIONS

1. A person of height L stands in front of a flat mirror hung on the wall. The minimum length of the flat mirror needed so that the person can view his entire body is:

(A) $2L$

(B) L

(C) $\frac{2}{3}L$

(D) $\frac{1}{2}L$

(E) $\frac{1}{4}L$

2. A candle is placed in front of a convex mirror of focal length f to try and create a beam of parallel light. To create the parallel rays, the candle should be placed in front of the mirror at a distance:

(A) $4f$

(B) $2f$

(C) f

(D) $\frac{1}{2}f$

(E) No location will work

Questions 3–4
The following image is used in questions 3 and 4.

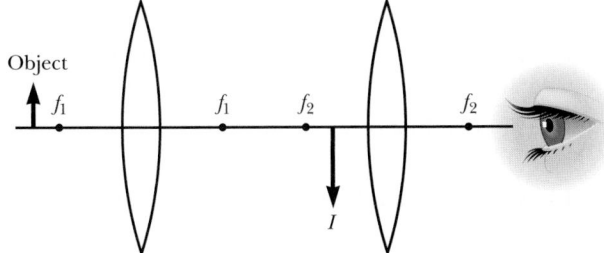

3. In the compound lens system seen above, an object is placed in front of an objective lens, which creates the primary image seen. Compared to the object, the image seen by the observer through the eyepiece lens would be:

   I. inverted

   II. real

   III. smaller

(A) I only

(B) II only

(C) III only

(D) I and II

(E) II and III

4. In the compound lens system seen above, an object is placed in front of an objective lens, which creates the primary image seen. Compared to the object, the image seen by the observer through the eyepiece lens would be:

   I. same orientation

   II. virtual

   III. bigger

(A) I only

(B) II only

(C) III only

(D) I and II

(E) II and III

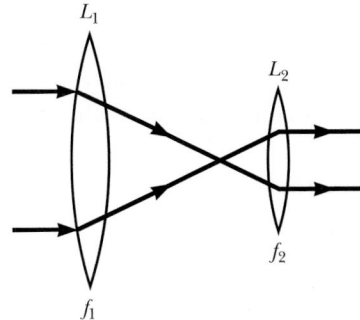

5. In a refracting telescope, the objective lens gathers light from distant stars and produces a primary image between the objective lens (L_1) and the eyepiece (L_2). The distance from the primary image to the eyepiece should be closest to which value?

(A) $2f_1$

(B) f_1

(C) $2f_2$

(D) f_2

(E) $\frac{1}{2}f_2$

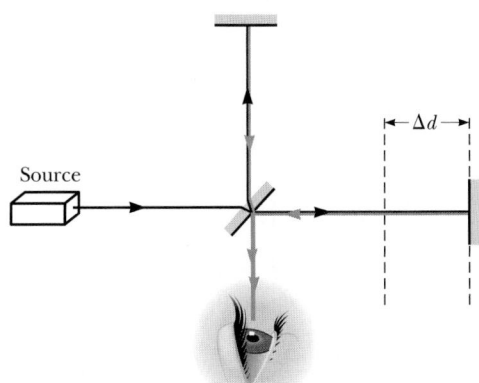

6. In the Michelson–Morley experiment, a source beam of wavelength λ is split into two different paths. One mirror can be adjusted through a distance Δd, as seen in the figure above. For the observer to view a dark band turn bright and dark again, the distance Δd must be changed by:

(A) $\lambda/4$

(B) $\lambda/2$

(C) λ

(D) 2λ

(E) 4λ

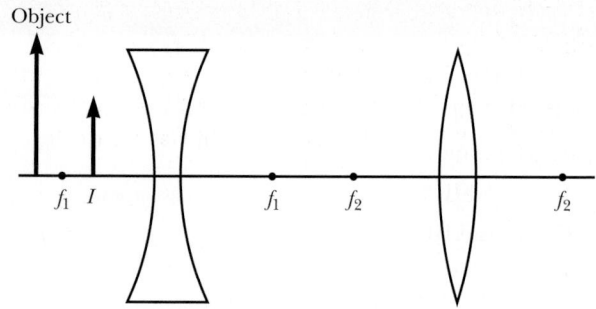

7. In the compound lens system seen above, an object is placed in front of an objective lens, which creates the primary image (*I*) on the diagram. Compared to the object, the image seen by the observer through the eyepiece lens would be:

> I. inverted
>
> II. real
>
> III. smaller

(A) I only

(B) II only

(C) I and II only

(D) II and III only

(E) I, II, and III

8. A converging lens can be used as a simple magnifier if the object is located:

(A) At a distance greater than $2f$

(B) At $2f$

(C) At a distance less than $2f$ but greater than f

(D) At a distance less than f

(E) At all of these positions

Questions 9–10

The following image is used in questions 9 and 10.

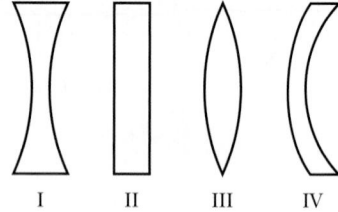

9. In air, which of the four glass lenses seen above cause parallel rays to converge?

(A) I only

(B) II only

(C) III only

(D) I and III only

(E) II and III only

10. Four glass lenses are seen at the bottom of the previous column. Which of their focal lengths will change when immersed in water?

(A) I

(B) I and IV

(C) I, III, and IV

(D) All of them

(E) None of them

11. To create the largest field of view from a mirror of fixed diameter, you would:

(A) Use a concave mirror

(B) Use a convex mirror

(C) Use a flat mirror

(D) Use a concave mirror and place your eye at a location closer than the focal length of the mirror

(E) Field of view is independent of the type of mirror

12. On a long, straight highway on warm day, a driver often sees an inverted image of an oncoming car directly below the car. The phenomenon is best described by:

(A) The reflection due to water on the road

(B) The reflection due to the cement road

(C) The bending of light as it passes through the glass window of the car

(D) The bending of light through air due to the heat and gradual variations of the density of air

(E) A thin film on the window causing an interference pattern

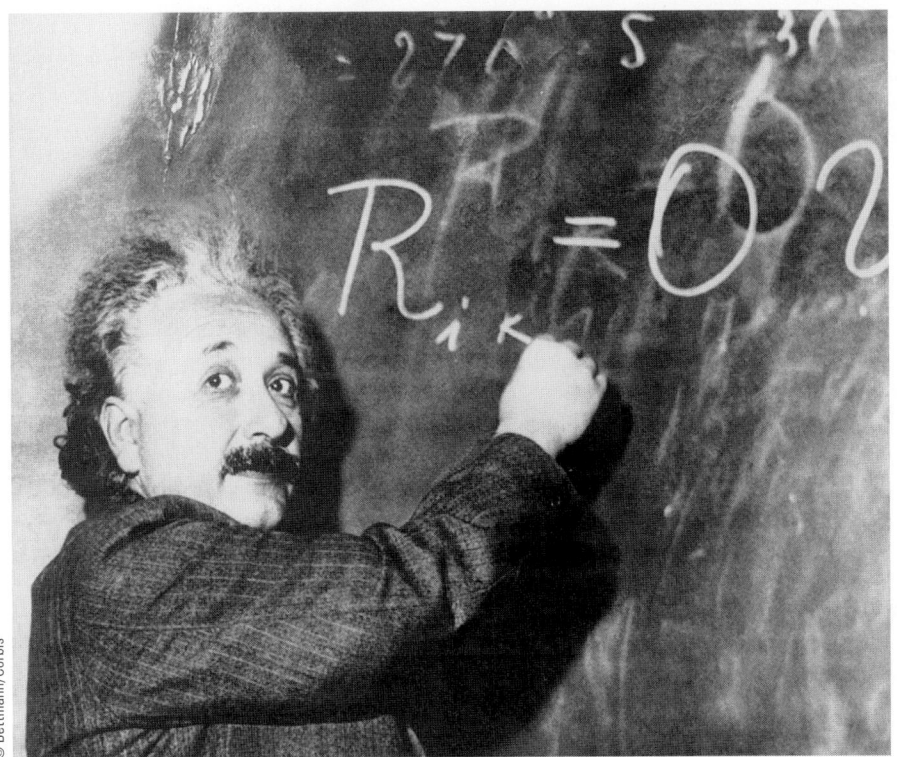

© Bettmann/Corbis

Albert Einstein revolutionized modern physics. He explained the random motion of pollen grains, which proved the existence of atoms, and the photoelectric effect, which showed that light was a particle as well as a wave. With Satyendra Nath Bose he predicted a new form of matter, the Bose-Einstein condensate, which was only recently discovered in the laboratory. His theory of special relativity made clear the foundations of space and time, and established a key relationship between mass and energy. His theory of gravitation, general relativity, led to a deeper understanding of planetary motion, the structure and evolution of stars, and the expanding universe. The equation in this photo, loosely translated, says that the average curvature of spacetime is zero in empty space.

Relativity 26

Most of our everyday experiences and observations have to do with objects that move at speeds much less than the speed of light. Newtonian mechanics was formulated to describe the motion of such objects, and its formalism is quite successful in describing a wide range of phenomena that occur at low speeds. It fails, however, when applied to particles having speeds approaching that of light.

Experimentally, for example, it's possible to accelerate an electron to a speed of $0.99c$ (where c is the speed of light) by using a potential difference of several million volts. According to Newtonian mechanics, if the potential difference is increased by a factor of 4, the electron's kinetic energy is four times greater and its speed should double to $1.98c$. Experiments, however, show that the speed of the electron—as well as the speed of any other particle that has mass—always remains *less* than the speed of light, regardless of the size of the accelerating voltage.

The existence of a universal speed limit has far-reaching consequences. It means that the usual concepts of force, momentum, and energy no longer apply for rapidly moving objects. A less obvious consequence is that observers moving at different speeds will measure different time intervals and displacements between the same two events. Relating the measurements made by different observers is the subject of relativity.

26.1 Galilean Relativity

To describe a physical event, it's necessary to choose a *frame of reference*. When you perform an experiment in a laboratory, for example, you select a coordinate system, or frame of reference, that is at rest with respect to the laboratory. Sup-

Figure 26.1 Two observers watch the path of a thrown ball and obtain different results.

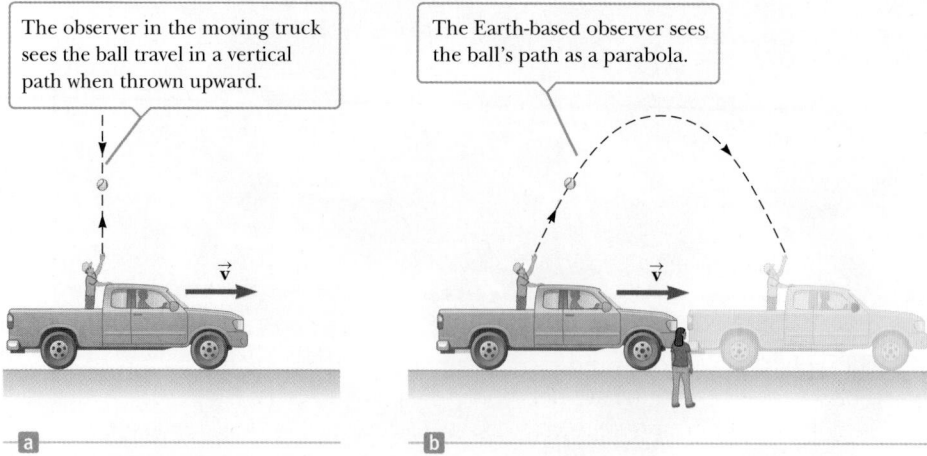

The observer in the moving truck sees the ball travel in a vertical path when thrown upward.

The Earth-based observer sees the ball's path as a parabola.

pose, instead, you choose to do an experiment in the back of a truck moving at a constant velocity $\vec{\mathbf{v}}$. You can then select a moving frame of reference that's at rest with respect to the truck. If you found Newton's first law to be valid in that frame, would an observer at rest with respect to the Earth agree with you?

According to the principle of Galilean relativity, **the laws of mechanics must be the same in all inertial frames of reference**. Inertial frames of reference are those reference frames in which Newton's laws are valid. In these frames, objects move in straight lines at constant speed unless acted on by a nonzero net force, thus the name "inertial frame" because objects observed from these frames obey Newton's first law, the law of inertia. For the situation described in the previous paragraph, the laboratory coordinate system and the coordinate system of the moving car are both inertial frames of reference. Consequently, if the laws of mechanics are found to be true in the laboratory, then the person in the car must also observe the same laws.

Consider a truck in motion, moving with a constant velocity, as in Figure 26.1a. If a passenger in the truck throws a ball straight up in the air, the passenger observes that the ball moves in a vertical path. The motion of the ball is precisely the same as it would be if the ball were thrown while at rest on Earth. The law of gravity and the equations of motion under constant acceleration are obeyed whether the truck is at rest or in uniform motion.

Now consider the same experiment when viewed by another observer at rest on Earth. This stationary observer views the path of the ball in the truck to be a parabola, as in Figure 26.1b. Further, according to this observer, the ball has a velocity to the right equal to the velocity of the truck. Although the two observers disagree on the shape of the ball's path, both agree that the motion of the ball obeys the law of gravity and Newton's laws of motion, and they even agree on how long the ball is in the air. We draw the following important conclusion: **There is no preferred frame of reference for describing the laws of mechanics.**

26.2 The Speed of Light

It's natural to ask whether the concept of Galilean relativity in mechanics also applies to experiments in electricity, magnetism, optics, and other areas. Experiments indicate that the answer is no. Further, if we assume the laws of electricity and magnetism are the same in all inertial frames, a paradox concerning the speed of light immediately arises. According to electromagnetic theory, the speed of light always has the fixed value of $2.997\,924\,58 \times 10^8$ m/s in free space. According to Galilean relativity, however, the speed of the pulse relative to the stationary observer S outside the boxcar in Figure 26.2 should be $c + v$. Hence, Galilean relativity is inconsistent with Maxwell's well-tested theory of electromagnetism.

Figure 26.2 A pulse of light is sent out by a person in a moving boxcar. According to Galilean relativity, the speed of the pulse should be $\vec{c} + \vec{v}$ relative to a stationary observer.

Electromagnetic theory predicts that light waves must propagate through free space with a speed equal to the speed of light. The theory doesn't require the presence of a medium for wave propagation, however. This is in contrast to other types of waves, such as water or sound waves, that do require a medium to support the disturbances. In the 19th century physicists thought that electromagnetic waves also required a medium to propagate. They proposed that such a medium existed and gave it the name **luminiferous ether**. The ether was assumed to be present everywhere, even in empty space, and light waves were viewed as ether oscillations. Further, the ether would have to be a massless but rigid medium with no effect on the motion of planets or other objects. These concepts are indeed strange. In addition, it was found that the troublesome laws of electricity and magnetism would take on their simplest forms in a special frame of reference at *rest* with respect to the ether. This frame was called the *absolute frame*. The laws of electricity and magnetism would be valid in this absolute frame, but they would have to be modified in any reference frame moving with respect to the absolute frame.

As a result of the importance attached to the ether and the absolute frame, it became of considerable interest in physics to prove by experiment that they existed. Because it was considered likely that Earth was in motion through the ether, from the view of an experimenter on Earth, there was an "ether wind" blowing through the laboratory. A direct method for detecting the ether wind would use an apparatus fixed to Earth to measure the wind's influence on the speed of light. If v is the speed of the ether relative to Earth, then the speed of light should have its maximum value, $c + v$, when propagating downwind, as shown in Figure 26.3a. Likewise, the speed of light should have its minimum value, $c - v$, when propagating upwind, as in Figure 26.3b, and an intermediate value, $(c^2 - v^2)^{1/2}$, in the direction perpendicular to the ether wind, as in Figure 26.3c. If the Sun were assumed to be at rest in the ether, then the velocity of the ether wind would be equal to the orbital velocity of Earth around the Sun, which has a magnitude of approximately 3×10^4 m/s. Because $c = 3 \times 10^8$ m/s, it should be possible to detect a change in speed of about 1 part in 10^4 for measurements in the upwind or downwind direction.

The Michelson–Morley Experiment

The most famous experiment designed to detect these small changes in the speed of light was first performed in 1881 by Albert A. Michelson (1852–1931) and later repeated under various conditions by Michelson and Edward W. Morley (1838–1923). The experiment was designed to determine the velocity of Earth relative to the hypothetical ether. The experimental tool used was the Michelson interferometer, shown in Active Figure 26.4 (page 888). Arm 2 is aligned along the direction of Earth's motion through space. Earth's moving through the ether at speed v is equivalent to the ether flowing past Earth in the opposite direction with speed v. This ether wind blowing in the direction opposite the direction of Earth's motion should cause the speed of light measured in the Earth frame to be $c - v$ as the light approaches mirror M_2 and $c + v$ after reflection, where c is the speed of light in the ether frame.

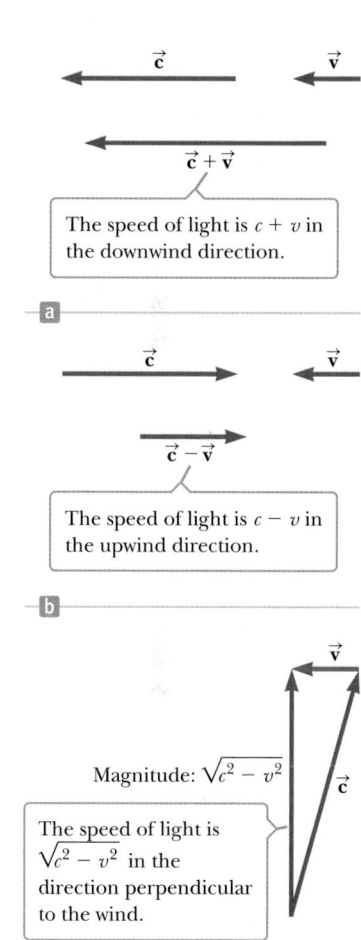

Figure 26.3 If the speed of the ether wind relative to Earth is v and c is the speed of light relative to the ether, the speed of light relative to Earth is (a) $c + v$ in the down-wind direction, (b) $c - v$ in the upwind direction, and (c) $\sqrt{c^2 - v^2}$ in the direction perpendicular to the wind. The Michelson–Morley experiment, however, disproved the ether wind hypothesis, leading to Einstein's postulate that the speed of light in vacuum has the same value regardless of the motion of an inertial observer.

Albert Einstein
German–American Physicist
(1879–1955)

One of the greatest physicists of all time, Einstein was born in Ulm, Germany. In 1905 at the age of 26 he published four scientific papers that revolutionized physics. Two of these papers introduced the special theory of relativity, considered by many to be his most important work. In 1916, in an exciting race with mathematician David Hilbert, Einstein published his theory of gravity, called the general theory of relativity. The most dramatic prediction of this theory is the degree to which light is deflected by a gravitational field. Measurements made by astronomers on bright stars in the vicinity of the eclipsed Sun in 1919 confirmed Einstein's prediction, and as a result Einstein became a world celebrity. Einstein was deeply disturbed by the development of quantum mechanics in the 1920s despite his own role as a scientific revolutionary. In particular, he could never accept the probabilistic view of events in nature that is a central feature of quantum theory. The last few decades of his life were devoted to an unsuccessful search for a unified theory that would combine gravitation and electromagnetism.

Active Figure 26.4
According to the ether wind theory, the speed of light should be $c - v$ as the beam approaches mirror M_2 and $c + v$ after reflection.

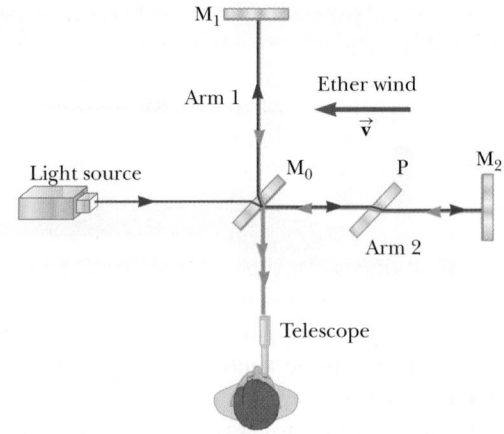

The two beams reflected from M_1 and M_2 recombine, and an interference pattern consisting of alternating dark and bright fringes is formed. The interference pattern was observed while the interferometer was rotated through an angle of 90°. This rotation supposedly would change the speed of the ether wind along the direction of arm 1. The effect of such rotation should have been to cause the fringe pattern to shift slightly but measurably, but measurements failed to show any change in the interference pattern! Even though the Michelson–Morley experiment was repeated at different times of the year when the ether wind was expected to change direction, the results were always the same: **no fringe shift of the magnitude required was ever observed**.

The negative results of the Michelson–Morley experiment not only contradicted the ether hypothesis, but also showed that it was impossible to measure the absolute velocity of Earth with respect to the ether frame. As we will see in the next section, however, Einstein suggested a postulate in the special theory of relativity that places quite a different interpretation on these negative results. In later years, when more was known about the nature of light, the idea of an ether that permeates all space was discarded. **Light is now understood to be an electromagnetic wave that requires no medium for its propagation.**

26.3 Einstein's Principle of Relativity

In 1905 Albert Einstein proposed a theory that explained the result of the Michelson–Morley experiment and completely altered our notions of space and time. He based his special theory of relativity on two postulates:

◀ Postulates of relativity

1. **The principle of relativity:** All the laws of physics are the same in all inertial frames.
2. **The constancy of the speed of light:** The speed of light in a vacuum has the same value, $c = 2.997\ 924\ 58 \times 10^8$ m/s, in all inertial reference frames, regardless of the velocity of the observer or the velocity of the source emitting the light.

The first postulate asserts that *all* the laws of physics are the same in all reference frames moving with constant velocity relative to each other. This postulate is a sweeping generalization of the principle of Galilean relativity, which refers only to the laws of mechanics. From an experimental point of view, Einstein's principle of relativity means that *any* kind of experiment—mechanical, thermal, optical, or electrical—performed in a laboratory at rest must give the same result when performed in a laboratory moving at a constant speed past the first one. Hence, no preferred inertial reference frame exists, and it is impossible to detect absolute motion.

Although postulate 2 was a brilliant theoretical insight on Einstein's part in 1905, it has since been confirmed experimentally in many ways. Perhaps the most direct demonstration involves measuring the speed of photons emitted by particles traveling at 99.99% of the speed of light. The measured photon speed in this case agrees to five significant figures with the speed of light in empty space.

The null result of the Michelson–Morley experiment can be readily understood within the framework of Einstein's theory. According to his principle of relativity, the premises of the Michelson–Morley experiment were incorrect. In the process of trying to explain the expected results, we stated that when light traveled against the ether wind its speed was $c - v$. If, however, the state of motion of the observer or of the source has no influence on the value found for the speed of light, the measured value must always be c. Likewise, the light makes the return trip after reflection from the mirror at a speed of c, not at a speed of $c + v$. Thus, the motion of Earth does not influence the fringe pattern observed in the Michelson–Morley experiment, and a null result should be expected.

If we accept Einstein's theory of relativity, we must conclude that uniform relative motion is unimportant when measuring the speed of light. At the same time, we have to adjust our commonsense notions of space and time and be prepared for some rather bizarre consequences.

■ Quick Quiz

26.1 True or False: If you were traveling in a spaceship at a speed of $c/2$ relative to Earth and you fired a laser beam in the direction of the spaceship's motion, the light from the laser would travel at a speed of $3c/2$ relative to Earth.

26.4 Consequences of Special Relativity

Almost everyone who has dabbled even superficially in science is aware of some of the startling predictions that arise because of Einstein's approach to relative motion. As we examine some of the consequences of relativity in this section, we'll find that they conflict with some of our basic notions of space and time. We restrict our discussion to the concepts of length, time, and simultaneity, which are quite different in relativistic mechanics from what they are in Newtonian mechanics. For example, in relativistic mechanics the distance between two points and the time interval between two events depend on the frame of reference in which they are measured. **In relativistic mechanics there is no such thing as absolute length or absolute time.** Further, **events at different locations that are observed to occur simultaneously in one frame are not observed to be simultaneous in another frame moving uniformly past the first.**

◀ Length and time measurements depend on the frame of reference

Simultaneity and the Relativity of Time

A basic premise of Newtonian mechanics is that a universal time scale exists that is the same for all observers. Newton and his followers simply took simultaneity for granted. In his special theory of relativity, Einstein abandoned that assumption.

Einstein devised the following thought experiment to illustrate this point. A boxcar moves with uniform velocity, and two lightning bolts strike its ends, as in Figure 26.5a (page 890), leaving marks on the boxcar and the ground. The marks on the boxcar are labeled A' and B', and those on the ground are labeled A and B. An observer at O' moving with the boxcar is midway between A' and B', and an observer on the ground at O is midway between A and B. The events recorded by the observers are the striking of the boxcar by the two lightning bolts.

The light signals recording the instant when the two bolts struck reach observer O at the same time, as indicated in Figure 26.5b. This observer realizes that the signals have traveled at the same speed over equal distances and so rightly concludes

Figure 26.5 (a) Two lightning bolts strike the ends of a moving boxcar. (b) The leftward-traveling light signal has already passed O', but the rightward-traveling signal has not yet reached O'.

To observer O, the two bolts strike simultaneously.

To observer O', a bolt strikes the front of the car first, followed by a second bolt striking the rear.

that the events at A and B occurred simultaneously. Now consider the same events as viewed by observer O'. By the time the signals have reached observer O, observer O' has moved as indicated in Figure 26.5b. Thus, the signal from B' has already swept past O', but the signal from A' has not yet reached O'. In other words, O' sees the signal from B' before seeing the signal from A'. According to Einstein, *the two observers must find that light travels at the same speed.* Therefore, observer O' concludes that the lightning struck the front of the boxcar before it struck the back.

This thought experiment clearly demonstrates that the two events that appear to be simultaneous to observer O do not appear to be simultaneous to observer O'. In other words,

> Two events that are simultaneous in one reference frame are in general not simultaneous in a second frame moving relative to the first. Simultaneity depends on the state of motion of the observer and is therefore not an absolute concept.

At this point, you might wonder which observer is right concerning the two events. The answer is that *both* are correct because the principle of relativity states that **there is no preferred inertial frame of reference**. Although the two observers reach different conclusions, both are correct in their own reference frames because the concept of simultaneity is not absolute. In fact, this is the central point of relativity: Any inertial frame of reference can be used to describe events and do physics.

Time Dilation

We can illustrate that observers in different inertial frames may measure different time intervals between a pair of events by considering a vehicle moving to the right with a speed v as in Active Figure 26.6a. A mirror is fixed to the ceiling of the vehicle, and an observer O' at rest in this system holds a laser a distance d below the mirror. At some instant, the laser emits a pulse of light directed toward the mirror (event 1), and at some later time after reflecting from the mirror, the pulse arrives back at the laser (event 2). Observer O' carries a clock and uses it to measure the time interval Δt_p between these two events, which she views as occurring at the same place. (The subscript p stands for *proper*, as we'll see in a moment.) Because the light pulse has a speed c, the time it takes it to travel from point A to the mirror and back to point A is

$$\Delta t_p = \frac{\text{distance traveled}}{\text{speed}} = \frac{2d}{c} \qquad [26.1]$$

The time interval Δt_p measured by O' requires only a single clock located at the same place as the laser in this frame.

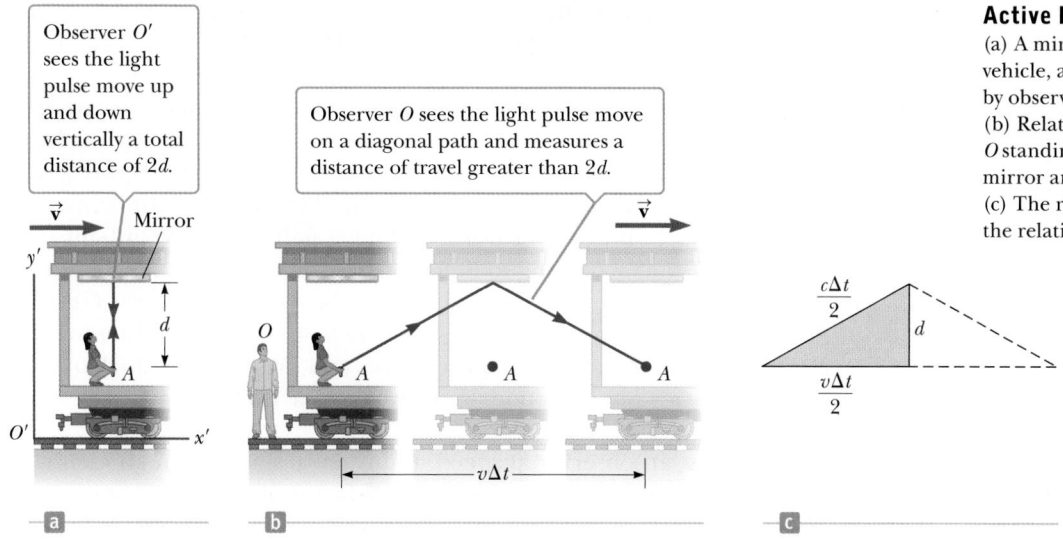

Active Figure 26.6
(a) A mirror is fixed to a moving vehicle, and a light pulse is sent out by observer O' at rest in the vehicle. (b) Relative to a stationary observer O standing alongside the vehicle, the mirror and O' move with a speed v. (c) The right triangle for calculating the relationship between Δt and Δt_p.

Now consider the same set of events as viewed by O in a second frame, as shown in Active Figure 26.6b. According to this observer, the mirror and laser are moving to the right with a speed v, and, as a result, the sequence of events appears different. By the time the light from the laser reaches the mirror, the mirror has moved to the right a distance $v\Delta t/2$, where Δt is the time it takes the light pulse to travel from point A to the mirror and back to point A as measured by O. In other words, O concludes that because of the motion of the vehicle, if the light is to hit the mirror, it must leave the laser at an angle with respect to the vertical direction. Comparing Active Figures 26.6a and 26.6b, we see that the light must travel farther in (b) than in (a). (Note that neither observer "knows" that he or she is moving. Each is at rest in his or her own inertial frame.)

According to the second postulate of the special theory of relativity, both observers must measure c for the speed of light. Because the light travels farther in the frame of O, it follows that the time interval Δt measured by O is longer than the time interval Δt_p measured by O'. To obtain a relationship between these two time intervals, it is convenient to examine the right triangle shown in Active Figure 26.6c. The Pythagorean theorem gives

$$\left(\frac{c\Delta t}{2}\right)^2 = \left(\frac{v\Delta t}{2}\right)^2 + d^2$$

Solving for Δt yields

$$\Delta t = \frac{2d}{\sqrt{c^2 - v^2}} = \frac{2d}{c\sqrt{1 - v^2/c^2}}$$

Because $\Delta t_p = 2d/c$, we can express this result as

$$\Delta t = \frac{\Delta t_p}{\sqrt{1 - v^2/c^2}} = \gamma \Delta t_p \qquad \text{[26.2]} \qquad \blacktriangleleft \text{ Time dilation}$$

where

$$\gamma = \frac{1}{\sqrt{1 - v^2/c^2}} \qquad \text{[26.3]}$$

Because γ is always greater than 1, Equation 26.2 says that **the time interval Δt between two events measured by an observer moving with respect to a clock[1] is longer than the time interval Δt_p between the same two events measured by an**

[1]Actually, Figure 26.6 shows the clock moving and not the observer, but that is equivalent to observer O moving to the left with velocity $\vec{v}$ with respect to the clock.

observer at rest with respect to the clock. Consequently, $\Delta t > \Delta t_p$, and the proper time interval is expanded or dilated by the factor γ. Hence, this effect is known as **time dilation**.

For example, suppose the observer at rest with respect to the clock measures the time required for the light flash to leave the laser and return. We assume the measured time interval in this frame of reference, Δt_p, is 1 s. (This would require a very tall vehicle.) Now we find the time interval as measured by observer O moving with respect to the same clock. If observer O is traveling at half the speed of light ($v = 0.500c$), then $\gamma = 1.15$ and, according to Equation 26.2, $\Delta t = \gamma \, \Delta t_p = 1.15(1.00 \text{ s}) = 1.15$ s. Therefore, when observer O' claims that 1.00 s has passed, observer O claims that 1.15 s has passed. Observer O considers the clock of O' to be reading too low a value for the elapsed time between the two events and says that the clock of O' is "running slow." From this phenomenon, we may conclude the following:

◀ A clock in motion runs more slowly than an identical stationary clock

| A clock moving past an observer at speed v runs more slowly than an identical clock at rest with respect to the observer by a factor of γ^{-1}. |

The time interval Δt_p in Equations 26.1 and 26.2 is called the **proper time**. In general, **proper time is the time interval between two events as measured by an observer who sees the events occur at the same position**.

Although you may have realized it by now, it's important to spell out that relativity is a scientific democracy: the view of O' that O is actually the one moving with speed v to the left and that the clock of O is running more slowly is just as valid as the view of O. The principle of relativity requires that the views of two observers in uniform relative motion be equally valid and capable of being checked experimentally.

Tip 26.2 Proper Time Interval

You must be able to correctly identify the observer who measures the proper time interval. The proper time interval between two events is the time interval measured by an observer for whom the two events take place at the same position.

We have seen that moving clocks run slow by a factor of γ^{-1}. This is true for ordinary mechanical clocks as well as for the light clock just described. In fact we can generalize these results by stating that all physical processes, including chemical and biological ones, slow down relative to a clock when those processes occur in a frame moving with respect to the clock. For example, the heartbeat of an astronaut moving through space would keep time with a clock inside the spaceship. Both the astronaut's clock and heartbeat would be slowed down relative to a clock back on Earth (although the astronaut would have no sensation of life slowing down in the spaceship).

Time dilation is a very real phenomenon that has been verified by various experiments involving the ticking of natural clocks. An interesting example of time dilation involves the observation of *muons*, unstable elementary particles that are very similar to electrons, having the same charge, but 207 times the mass. Muons can be produced by the collision of cosmic radiation with atoms high in the atmosphere. These particles have a lifetime of 2.2 μs when measured in a reference frame at rest with respect to them. If we take 2.2 μs as the average lifetime of a muon and assume that their speed is close to the speed of light, we find that these particles can travel only about 600 m before they decay (Fig. 26.7a). Hence, they could never reach Earth from the upper atmosphere where they are produced. Experiments, however, show that a large number of muons *do* reach Earth, and the phenomenon of time dilation explains how. Relative to an observer on Earth, the muons have a lifetime equal to $\gamma \tau_p$, where $\tau_p = 2.2$ μs is the lifetime in a frame of reference traveling with the muons. For example, for $v = 0.99c$, $\gamma \approx 7.1$, and $\gamma \tau_p \approx 16$ μs. Hence, the average distance muons travel as measured by an observer on Earth is $\gamma v \tau_p \approx 4\,800$ m, as indicated in Figure 26.7b. Consequently, muons can reach Earth's surface.

In 1976 experiments with muons were conducted at the laboratory of the European Council for Nuclear Research (CERN) in Geneva. Muons were injected into a large storage ring, reaching speeds of about 0.999 4c. Electrons produced by the decaying muons were detected by counters around the ring, enabling scientists to measure the decay rate and hence the lifetime of the muons. The lifetime of

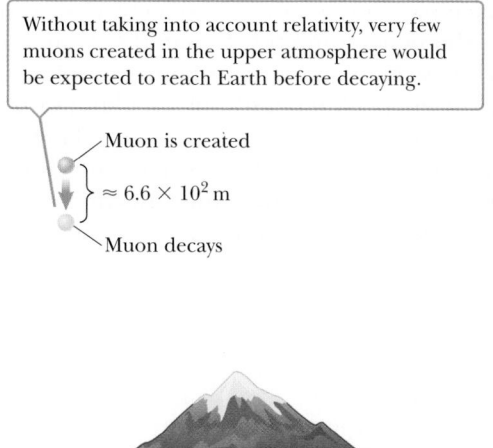

Without taking into account relativity, very few muons created in the upper atmosphere would be expected to reach Earth before decaying.

Muon is created

$\approx 6.6 \times 10^2$ m

Muon decays

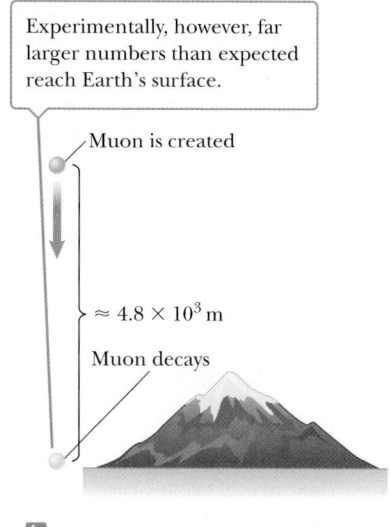

Experimentally, however, far larger numbers than expected reach Earth's surface.

Muon is created

$\approx 4.8 \times 10^3$ m

Muon decays

a

b

Figure 26.7 (a) A muon created in the upper atmosphere and moving at $0.99c$ relative Earth would ordinarily travel only 660 m, on the average, before decaying after 2.2×10^{-6} s. (b) Because of time dilation, an Earth observer measures a longer muon lifetime, so the muons travel an average of 4.8×10^3 m before decaying. Consequently, far more muons are observed reaching Earth's surface than expected. From the muons' point of view, by contrast, their lifetime is only 2.2×10^{-6} s on the average, but the distance between them and the Earth is contracted, again making it possible for more of them to reach the surface before decaying.

the moving muons was measured to be about 30 times as long as that of stationary muons to within two parts in a thousand, in agreement with the prediction of relativity.

■ Quick Quiz

26.2 Suppose you're an astronaut being paid according to the time you spend traveling in space. You take a long voyage traveling at a speed near that of light. Upon your return to Earth, you're asked how you'd like to be paid: according to the time elapsed on a clock on Earth or according to your ship's clock. To maximize your paycheck, which should you choose? (a) the Earth clock (b) the ship's clock (c) either clock because it doesn't make a difference

■ EXAMPLE 26.1 | Pendulum Periods

GOAL Apply the concept of time dilation.

PROBLEM The period of a pendulum is measured to be 3.00 s in the inertial frame of the pendulum at Earth's surface. What is the period as measured by an observer moving at a speed of $0.950c$ with respect to the pendulum?

STRATEGY Here, we're given the period of the clock as measured by an observer in the rest frame of the clock, so that's a proper time interval Δt_p. We want to know how much time passes as measured by an observer in a frame moving relative to the clock, which is Δt. Substitution into Equation 26.2 then solves the problem.

SOLUTION

Substitute the proper time and relative speed into Equation 26.2:

$$\Delta t = \frac{\Delta t_p}{\sqrt{1 - v^2/c^2}} = \frac{3.00 \text{ s}}{\sqrt{1 - \frac{(0.950c)^2}{c^2}}} = \boxed{9.61 \text{ s}}$$

REMARKS The moving observer considers the *pendulum* to be moving, and moving clocks are observed to run more slowly: while the pendulum oscillates once in 3 s for an observer in the rest frame of the clock, it takes nearly 10 s to oscillate once according the moving observer.

QUESTION 26.1 Suppose a mass-spring system with the same period as the pendulum is placed in the observer's spaceship. When the spaceship is traveling at a speed of $0.95c$ relative to an observer on Earth, what is the period of the pendulum as measured by the Earth observer?

EXERCISE 26.1 What is the period of the pendulum as measured by a third observer moving at $0.900c$?

ANSWER 6.88 s

Confusion arises in problems like Example 26.1 because movement is relative: from the point of view of someone in the pendulum's rest frame, the pendulum is standing still (except, of course, for the swinging motion), whereas to someone in a frame that is moving with respect to the pendulum, it's the pendulum that's doing the moving. To keep it straight, always focus on the observer making the measurement and ask yourself whether the clock being used to measure time is moving with respect to that observer. If the answer is no, then the observer is in the rest frame of the clock and measures the clock's proper time. If the answer is yes, then the time measured by the observer will be dilated, or larger than the clock's proper time. This confusion of perspectives led to the famous "twin paradox."

The Twin Paradox

An intriguing consequence of time dilation is the so-called twin paradox (Fig. 26.8). Consider an experiment involving a set of twins named Speedo and Goslo. When they are 20 years old, Speedo, the more adventuresome of the two, sets out on an epic journey to Planet X, located 20 light-years from Earth. Further, his spaceship is capable of reaching a speed of $0.95c$ relative to the inertial frame of his twin brother back home. After reaching Planet X, Speedo becomes homesick and immediately returns to Earth at the same speed of $0.95c$. Upon his return, Speedo is shocked to discover that Goslo has aged $2D/v = 2(20 \text{ ly})/(0.95 \text{ ly/yr}) = 42$ years and is now 62 years old. Speedo, on the other hand, has aged only 13 years.

Some wrongly consider *this* the paradox; that twins could age at different rates and end up after a period of time having very different ages. Although contrary to our common sense, that isn't the paradox at all. The paradox is that, from Speedo's point of view, *he* was at rest while Goslo (on Earth) sped away from *him* at $0.95c$ and returned later. So Goslo's clock was moving relative to Speedo and hence running slow compared with Speedo's clock. The conclusion: Speedo, not Goslo, should be the older of the twins!

To resolve this apparent paradox, consider a third observer moving at a constant speed of $0.5c$ relative to Goslo. To the third observer, Goslo never changes inertial frames: his speed relative to the third observer is always the same. The third observer notes, however, that Speedo accelerates during his journey, *changing reference frames in the process*. From the third observer's perspective, it's clear that there is something very different about the motion of Goslo when compared with that of Speedo. The roles played by Goslo and Speedo are not symmetric, so it isn't surprising that time flows differently for each. Further, because Speedo accelerates, he is in a noninertial frame of reference and is technically outside the bounds of special relativity (although there are methods for dealing with acceler-

Figure 26.8 The twin paradox. Speedo takes a journey to Planet X 20 light-years away and returns to the Earth.

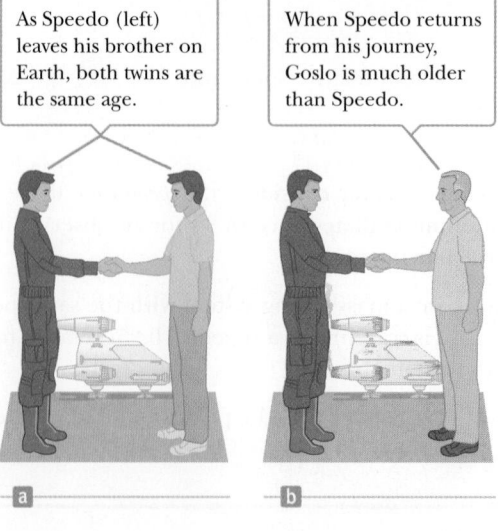

ated motion in relativity). Only Goslo, who is in a single inertial frame, can apply the simple time-dilation formula to Speedo's trip. Goslo finds that instead of aging 42 years, Speedo ages only $(1 - v^2/c^2)^{1/2}(42 \text{ years}) = 13 \text{ years}$. Of these 13 years, Speedo spends 6.5 years traveling to Planet X and 6.5 years returning, for a total travel time of 13 years, in agreement with our earlier statement.

Quick Quiz

26.3 True or False: People traveling near the speed of light relative to Earth would measure their lifespans and find them, on the average, longer than the average human lifespan as measured on Earth.

Length Contraction

The measured distance between two points depends on the frame of reference of the observer. The **proper length** L_p of an object is **the length of the object as measured by an observer at rest relative to the object**. The length of an object measured in a reference frame that is moving with respect to the object is always less than the proper length. This effect is known as **length contraction**.

To understand length contraction quantitatively, consider a spaceship traveling with a speed v from one star to another as seen by two observers, one on Earth and the other in the spaceship. The observer at rest on Earth (and also assumed to be at rest with respect to the two stars) measures the distance between the stars to be L_p. According to this observer, the time it takes the spaceship to complete the voyage is $\Delta t = L_p/v$. Because of time dilation, the space traveler, using his spaceship clock, measures a smaller time of travel: $\Delta t_p = \Delta t/\gamma$. The space traveler claims to be at rest and sees the destination star moving toward the spaceship with speed v. Because the space traveler reaches the star in time Δt_p, he concludes that the distance L between the stars is shorter than L_p. The distance measured by the space traveler is

$$L = v\,\Delta t_p = v\,\frac{\Delta t}{\gamma}$$

Because $L_p = v\,\Delta t$, it follows that

$$L = \frac{L_p}{\gamma} = L_p\sqrt{1 - v^2/c^2} \qquad \text{[26.4]}$$

According to this result, illustrated in Active Figure 26.9, if an observer at rest with respect to an object measures its length to be L_p, an observer moving at a speed v relative to the object will find it to be shorter than its proper length by the factor $\sqrt{1 - v^2/c^2}$. Note that **length contraction takes place only along the direction of motion**.

Time-dilation and length contraction effects have interesting applications for future space travel to distant stars. For the star to be reached in a fraction of a human lifetime, the trip must be taken at very high speeds. According to an Earth-bound observer, the time for a spacecraft to reach the destination star will be dilated compared with the time interval measured by travelers. As discussed in the treatment of the twin paradox, the travelers will be younger than their twins when they return to Earth. Therefore, by the time the travelers reach the star, they will have aged by some number of years, while their partners back on Earth will have aged a larger number of years, the exact ratio depending on the speed of the spacecraft. At a spacecraft speed of $0.94c$, this ratio is about 3:1.

Quick Quiz

26.4 You are packing for a trip to another star, and on your journey you will be traveling at a speed of $0.99c$. Can you sleep in a smaller cabin than usual, because you will be shorter when you lie down? Explain your answer.

Tip 26.3 The Proper Length
You must be able to correctly identify the observer who measures the proper length. The proper length between two points in space is the length measured by an observer at rest with respect to the length. Very often, the proper time interval and the proper length are not measured by the same observer.

Observer O', at rest with respect to the meterstick, measures a length of one meter.

To observer O the meterstick is moving and is shorter than a meter by a factor of $\sqrt{1-v^2/c^2}$.

Active Figure 26.9
The length of a meterstick is measured by two observers.

26.5 You observe a rocket moving away from you. **(i)** Compared with its length when it was at rest on the ground, will you measure its length to be (a) shorter, (b) longer, or (c) the same? Compared to the passage of time measured by the watch on your wrist, is the passage of time on the rocket's clock (d) faster, (e) slower, or (f) the same? **(ii)** Answer the same questions from part (i) if the rocket turns around and comes toward you.

■**EXAMPLE 26.2** | **Speedy Plunge**

GOAL Apply the concept of length contraction to a distance.

PROBLEM **(a)** An observer on Earth sees a spaceship at an altitude of 4 350 km moving downward toward Earth with a speed of 0.970c. What is the distance from the spaceship to Earth as measured by the spaceship's captain? **(b)** After firing his engines, the captain measures her ship's altitude as 267 km, whereas the observer on Earth measures it to be 625 km. What is the speed of the spaceship at this instant?

STRATEGY To the captain, Earth is rushing toward her ship at 0.970c; hence, the distance between her ship and Earth is contracted. Substitution into Equation 26.9 yields the answer. In part (b) use the same equation, substituting the distances and solving for the speed.

SOLUTION

(a) Find the distance from the ship to Earth as measured by the captain.

Substitute into Equation 26.4, getting the altitude as measured by the captain in the ship:

$$L = L_p\sqrt{1 - v^2/c^2} = (4\,350 \text{ km})\sqrt{1 - (0.970c)^2/c^2}$$
$$= \boxed{1.06 \times 10^3 \text{ km}}$$

(b) What is the subsequent speed of the spaceship if the Earth observer measures the distance from the ship to Earth as 625 km and the captain measures it as 267 km?

Apply the length-contraction equation:

$$L = L_p\sqrt{1 - v^2/c^2}$$

Square both sides of this equation and solve for v:

$$L^2 = L_p^2(1 - v^2/c^2) \quad \rightarrow \quad 1 - v^2/c^2 = \left(\frac{L}{L_p}\right)^2$$
$$v = c\sqrt{1 - (L/L_p)^2} = c\sqrt{1 - (267 \text{ km}/625 \text{ km})^2}$$
$$v = \boxed{0.904c}$$

REMARKS The proper length is always the length measured by an observer at rest with respect to that length.

QUESTION 26.2 As a spaceship approaches an observer at nearly the speed of light, the captain directs a beam of yellow light at the observer. What would the observer report upon seeing the light? (a) Its wavelength would be shifted toward the red end of the spectrum. (b) Its wavelength would correspond to yellow light. (c) Its wavelength would be shifted toward the blue end of the spectrum.

EXERCISE 26.2 Suppose the observer on the ship measures the distance from Earth as 50.0 km, whereas the observer on Earth measures the distance as 125 km. At what speed is the spacecraft approaching Earth?

ANSWER 0.917c

Length contraction occurs only in the direction of the observer's motion. No contraction occurs perpendicular to that direction. For example, a spaceship at rest relative to an observer may have the shape of an equilateral triangle, but if it passes the observer at relativistic speed in a direction parallel to its base, the base will shorten while the height remains the same. Hence the observer will report that the craft has the form of an isosceles triangle. An observer traveling with the ship will still observe it to be equilateral.

26.5 Relativistic Momentum

Properly describing the motion of particles within the framework of special relativity requires generalizing Newton's laws of motion and the definitions of momentum and energy. These generalized definitions reduce to the classical (nonrelativistic) definitions when v is much less than c.

First, recall that conservation of momentum states that when two objects collide, the total momentum of the system remains constant, assuming the objects are isolated, reacting only with each other. When analyzing such collisions from rapidly moving inertial frames, however, it is found that momentum is not conserved if the classical definition of momentum, $p = mv$, is used. To have momentum conservation in all inertial frames—even those moving at an appreciable fraction of c—the definition of momentum must be modified to read

$$p \equiv \frac{mv}{\sqrt{1 - v^2/c^2}} = \gamma mv \qquad\qquad [26.5]$$

◀ Relativistic momentum

where v is the speed of the particle and m is its mass as measured by an observer at rest with respect to the particle. Note that when v is much less than c, the denominator of Equation 26.5 approaches 1, so that p approaches mv. Therefore, the relativistic equation for momentum reduces to the classical expression when v is small compared with c.

■ EXAMPLE 26.3 | The Relativistic Momentum of an Electron

GOAL Contrast the classical and relativistic definitions of momentum.

PROBLEM An electron, which has a mass of 9.11×10^{-31} kg, moves with a speed of $0.750c$. Find the classical (nonrelativistic) momentum and compare it with its relativistic counterpart p_{rel}.

STRATEGY Substitute into the classical definition to get the classical momentum, then multiply by the gamma factor to obtain the relativistic version.

. . . .

SOLUTION

First, compute the classical (nonrelativistic) momentum with $v = 0.750c$:

$p = mv = (9.11 \times 10^{-31}$ kg$)(0.750 \times 3.00 \times 10^8$ m/s$)$

$= 2.05 \times 10^{-22}$ kg · m/s

Multiply this result by γ to obtain the relativistic momentum:

$p_{rel} = \dfrac{mv}{\sqrt{1 - v^2/c^2}} = \dfrac{2.05 \times 10^{-22}\,\text{kg} \cdot \text{m/s}}{\sqrt{1 - (0.750c/c)^2}}$

$= 3.10 \times 10^{-22}$ kg · m/s

. . . .

REMARKS The (correct) relativistic result is 50% greater than the classical result. In subsequent calculations no notational distinction will be made between classical and relativistic momentum. For problems involving relative speeds of $0.2c$, the answer using the classical expression is about 2% below the correct answer.

QUESTION 26.3 A particle with initial momentum p_i doubles its speed. How does its final momentum p_f compare with its initial momentum? (a) $p_f > 2p_i$ (b) $p_f = 2p_i$ (c) $p_f < 2p_i$

EXERCISE 26.3 Repeat the calculation for a proton traveling at $0.600c$.

ANSWERS $p = 3.01 \times 10^{-19}$ kg · m/s, $p_{rel} = 3.76 \times 10^{-19}$ kg · m/s

26.6 Relative Velocity in Special Relativity

In Galilean relativity, if a man in a spaceship traveling at velocity v shines a laser straight ahead, the light beam would be expected to travel at velocity $c + v$ relative to an observer on Earth. The null result of the Michelson–Morley experiment, however, indicates the laser light will still travel at speed c relative to that same observer, although the light's frequency increases. (When light's frequency increases, the light is said to be "blue-shifted." When the frequency decreases, the light is said to be "red-shifted.") Evidently, some new formula must be derived to allow the comparison of velocities by observers moving at high relative speeds.

The procedure is very similar to that used in Chapter 3 for nonrelativistic relative velocity. Here, an observer in a spaceship will be labeled B and the Earth observer E, with B moving in the positive x-direction at speed v_{BE} with respect to the Earth observer E. The goal is to find the relationship between their independent measurements of an object A. Given v_{AE}, the velocity of A according to observer E, what is v_{AB}, the velocity of A relative to observer B? According to Galilean relativity, the answer derived in Chapter 3 is

Relative velocity in ▶ Galilean relativity

$$v_{AB} = v_{AE} - v_{BE}$$ [26.6]

For velocities that are about 10% of the speed of light and greater, the correct expression relating the relative velocities is[2]

Relative velocity in ▶ special relativity

$$v_{AB} = \frac{v_{AE} - v_{BE}}{1 - \dfrac{v_{AE}v_{BE}}{c^2}}$$ [26.7]

Notice that when either v_{AE} or v_{BE} is much smaller than c, this expression agrees with the Galilean (nonrelativistic) relationship, as it should. Equation 26.7 is useful for determining velocities measured by B in the moving frame of reference when the velocity measured by observer E in the rest frame is known. On the other hand, when the velocity in question is measured by observer B and the task is to find the velocity measured by observer E, Equation 26.7 must be algebraically solved for v_{AE}. The resulting expression is

Relativistic addition of ▶ velocities

$$v_{AE} = \frac{v_{AB} + v_{BE}}{1 + \dfrac{v_{AB}v_{BE}}{c^2}}$$ [26.8]

Ignoring the expression in the denominator, Equation 26.8 has the expected form: if observer B is moving with respect to observer E at velocity v_{BE} and fires a projectile at velocity v_{AB} relative to himself, then adding v_{AB} and v_{BE} should give the velocity of the projectile v_{AE} as measured by the Earth observer. Special relativity contributes the denominator of Equation 26.8, an equation often called the relativistic addition of velocities.

Using Equation 26.8, the speed of an object projected forward from a moving vehicle as measured by an observer on Earth can be calculated. Suppose, for example, that observer B is moving at v_{BE} with respect to the Earth observer and directs the beam of a laser in front of his rapidly moving spacecraft. Here v_{AB} is the velocity of light relative to observer B on the spacecraft. The speed of the light v_{AE} as measured by the Earth observer is, therefore,

---

[2] The derivation of Equation 26.7 requires the use of Lorentz transformations and will not be presented in this textbook.

$$v_{AE} = \frac{v_{AB} + v_{BE}}{1 + \dfrac{v_{AB}v_{BE}}{c^2}} = \frac{c + v_{BE}}{1 + \dfrac{cv_{BE}}{c^2}} = \frac{c\left(1 + \dfrac{v_{BE}}{c}\right)}{1 + \dfrac{v_{BE}}{c}} = c$$

This calculation shows that the derived velocity transformation is consistent with the experimental result proving the speed of light is the same for all observers.

■ EXAMPLE 26.4 | Urgent Course Correction Required!

GOAL Apply the concept of relative velocity in relativity.

PROBLEM Suppose that Alice's spacecraft is traveling at $0.600c$ in the positive x-direction, as measured by a nearby Earth-based observer at rest, while Bob is traveling in his own vehicle directly toward Alice in the negative x-direction at velocity $-0.800c$ relative the same Earth observer. What's the velocity of Alice according to Bob?

STRATEGY Alice's spacecraft is the object of interest that both the Earth observer and Bob are tracking. We're given the Earth observer's velocity measurements and wish to find Bob's measurement. Use the relative velocity equation for relativity, Equation 26.7, with v_{AB} corresponding to the measurement of Alice's velocity made by Bob and v_{AE} is the measurement of Alice's velocity according to the Earth observer. Notice that the velocity of Bob's frame is in the negative x-direction, so $v_{BE} < 0$.

....

SOLUTION

Write Equation 26.7:

$$v_{AB} = \frac{v_{AE} - v_{BE}}{1 - \dfrac{v_{AE}v_{BE}}{c^2}}$$

Substitute values:

$$v_{AB} = \frac{0.600c - (-0.800c)}{1 - \dfrac{(0.600c)(-0.800c)}{c^2}} = \frac{1.400c}{1 - (-0.480)} = \boxed{0.946c}$$

....

REMARKS Notice that care was taken to use the correct signs. Common sense might lead us to believe that Bob would measure Alice's velocity as $1.40c$, but as the calculation shows, Bob measures Alice's velocity as less than that of light.

QUESTION 26.4 What is Bob's velocity according to Alice?

EXERCISE 26.4 Suppose yet another observer, Ray, reports that Alice's velocity is only $0.400c$. What is Ray's velocity according to the Earth observer?

ANSWER $0.263c$

26.7 Relativistic Energy and the Equivalence of Mass and Energy

We have seen that the definition of momentum required generalization to make it compatible with the principle of relativity. Likewise, the definition of kinetic energy requires modification in relativistic mechanics. Einstein found that the correct expression for the **kinetic energy** of an object is

$$KE = \gamma mc^2 - mc^2 \qquad \text{[26.9]} \qquad \blacktriangleleft \text{ Kinetic energy}$$

The constant term mc^2 in Equation 26.9, which is independent of the speed of the object, is called the **rest energy** of the object, E_R:

$$E_R = mc^2 \qquad \text{[26.10]} \qquad \blacktriangleleft \text{ Rest energy}$$

The term γmc^2 in Equation 26.9 depends on the object's speed and is the sum of the kinetic and rest energies. We define γmc^2 to be the **total energy** E, so

Total energy = kinetic energy + rest energy

or, using Equation 26.9,

$$E = KE + mc^2 = \gamma mc^2 \qquad \text{[26.11]}$$

Because $\gamma = (1 - v^2/c^2)^{-1/2}$, we can also express the total energy E as

Total energy ▶

$$E = \frac{mc^2}{\sqrt{1 - v^2/c^2}} \qquad \text{[26.12]}$$

This is Einstein's famous mass-energy equivalence equation.[3]

The relation $E = \gamma mc^2 = KE + mc^2$ shows the amazing result that **a stationary particle with zero kinetic energy has an energy proportional to its mass**. Further, a small mass corresponds to an enormous amount of energy because the proportionality constant between mass and energy is large: $c^2 = 9 \times 10^{16} \text{ m}^2/\text{s}^2$. The equation $E_R = mc^2$, as Einstein first suggested, indirectly implies that the mass of a particle may be completely convertible to energy and that pure energy—for example, electromagnetic energy—may be converted to particles having mass. That is indeed the case, as has been shown in the laboratory many times in interactions involving matter and antimatter.

On a larger scale, nuclear power plants produce energy by the fission of uranium, which involves the conversion of a small amount of the mass of the uranium into energy. The Sun, too, converts mass into energy and continually loses mass in pouring out a tremendous amount of electromagnetic energy in all directions.

It's extremely interesting that although we have been talking about the interconversion of mass and energy for particles, the expression $E = mc^2$ is universal and applies to all objects, processes, and systems: a hot object has slightly more mass and is slightly more difficult to accelerate than an identical cold object because it has more thermal energy, and a stretched spring has more elastic potential energy and more mass than an identical unstretched spring. A key point, however, is that these changes in mass are often far too small to measure. Our best bet for measuring mass changes is in nuclear transformations, where a measurable fraction of the mass is converted into energy.

■ Quick Quiz

26.6 True or False: Because the speed of a particle cannot exceed the speed of light, there is an upper limit to its momentum and kinetic energy.

Energy and Relativistic Momentum

Often the momentum or energy of a particle rather than its speed is measured, so it's useful to find an expression relating the total energy E to the relativistic momentum p. We can do so by using the expressions $E = \gamma mc^2$ and $p = \gamma mv$. By squaring these equations and subtracting, we can eliminate v. The result, after some algebra, is

$$E^2 = p^2 c^2 + (mc^2)^2 \qquad \text{[26.13]}$$

When the particle is at rest, $p = 0$, so $E = E_R = mc^2$. In this special case the total energy equals the rest energy. For the case of particles that have zero mass, such as photons (massless, chargeless particles of light), we set $m = 0$ in Equation 26.13 and find that

$$E = pc \qquad \text{[26.14]}$$

This equation is an exact expression relating energy and momentum for photons, which always travel at the speed of light.

---

[3]Although this expression doesn't look exactly like the famous equation $E = mc^2$, it used to be common to write $m = \gamma m_0$ (Einstein himself wrote it that way), where m is the effective mass of an object moving at speed v and m_0 is the mass of that object as measured by an observer at rest with respect to the object. Then our $E = \gamma mc^2$ becomes the familiar $E = mc^2$. It is currently unfashionable to use $m = \gamma m_0$.

In dealing with subatomic particles, it's convenient to express their energy in electron volts (eV) because the particles are given energy when accelerated through an electrostatic potential difference. The conversion factor is

$$1 \text{ eV} = 1.60 \times 10^{-19} \text{ J}$$

For example, the mass of an electron is 9.11×10^{-31} kg. Hence, the rest energy of the electron is

$$m_e c^2 = (9.11 \times 10^{-31} \text{ kg})(3.00 \times 10^8 \text{ m/s})^2 = 8.20 \times 10^{-14} \text{ J}$$

Converting to eV, we have

$$m_e c^2 = (8.20 \times 10^{-14} \text{ J})(1 \text{ eV}/1.60 \times 10^{-19} \text{ J}) = 0.511 \text{ MeV}$$

where 1 MeV $= 10^6$ eV. Because we frequently use the expression $E = \gamma m c^2$ in nuclear physics and because m is usually in atomic mass units, u, it is useful to have the conversion factor 1 u $= 931.494$ MeV/c^2. Using this factor makes it easy, for example, to find the rest energy in MeV of the nucleus of a uranium atom with a mass of 235.043 924 u:

$$E_R = mc^2 = (235.043\ 924 \text{ u})(931.494 \text{ MeV/u} \cdot c^2)(c^2) = 2.189\ 42 \times 10^5 \text{ MeV}$$

Quick Quiz

26.7 A photon is reflected from a mirror. True or False: (a) Because a photon has zero mass, it does not exert a force on the mirror. (b) Although the photon has energy, it can't transfer any energy to the surface because it has zero mass. (c) The photon carries momentum, and when it reflects off the mirror, it undergoes a change in momentum and exerts a force on the mirror. (d) Although the photon carries momentum, its change in momentum is zero when it reflects from the mirror, so it can't exert a force on the mirror.

EXAMPLE 26.5 | A Speedy Electron

GOAL Compute a total energy and a relativistic kinetic energy.

PROBLEM An electron moves with a speed $v = 0.850c$. Find its total energy and kinetic energy in mega electron volts (MeV) and compare the latter to the classical kinetic energy (10^6 eV = 1 MeV).

STRATEGY Substitute into Equation 26.12 to get the total energy and subtract the rest mass energy to obtain the kinetic energy.

. . . .

SOLUTION

Substitute values into Equation 26.12 to obtain the total energy:

$$E = \frac{m_e c^2}{\sqrt{1 - v^2/c^2}} = \frac{(9.11 \times 10^{-31} \text{ kg})(3.00 \times 10^8 \text{ m/s})^2}{\sqrt{1 - (0.850c/c)^2}}$$

$$= 1.56 \times 10^{-13} \text{ J} = (1.56 \times 10^{-13} \text{ J})\left(\frac{1.00 \text{ eV}}{1.60 \times 10^{-19} \text{ J}}\right)$$

$$= \boxed{0.975 \text{ MeV}}$$

The kinetic energy is obtained by subtracting the rest energy from the total energy:

$$KE = E - m_e c^2 = 0.975 \text{ MeV} - 0.511 \text{ MeV} = \boxed{0.464 \text{ MeV}}$$

Calculate the classical kinetic energy:

$$KE_{\text{classical}} = \tfrac{1}{2} m_e v^2$$

$$= \tfrac{1}{2}(9.11 \times 10^{-31} \text{ kg})(0.850 \times 3.00 \times 10^8 \text{ m/s})^2$$

$$= 2.96 \times 10^{-14} \text{ J} = 0.185 \text{ MeV}$$

. . . .

REMARKS Notice the large discrepancy between the relativistic kinetic energy and the classical kinetic energy.

(Continued)

QUESTION 26.5 According to an observer, the speed v of a particle with kinetic energy KE_i increases to $2v$. How does the final kinetic energy KE_f compare with the initial kinetic energy? (a) $KE_f > 4KE_i$ (b) $KE_f = 4KE_i$ (c) $KE_f < 4KE_i$

EXERCISE 26.5 Calculate the total energy and the kinetic energy in MeV of a proton traveling at $0.600c$. (The rest energy of a proton is approximately 938 MeV.)

ANSWERS $E = 1.17 \times 10^3$ MeV, $KE = 2.3 \times 10^2$ MeV

▪ EXAMPLE 26.6 │ The Conversion of Mass to Kinetic Energy in Uranium Fission

GOAL Understand the production of energy from nuclear sources.

PROBLEM The fission, or splitting, of uranium was discovered in 1938 by Lise Meitner, who successfully interpreted some curious experimental results found by Otto Hahn as due to fission. (Hahn received the Nobel Prize.) The fission of $^{235}_{92}U$ begins with the absorption of a slow-moving neutron that produces an unstable nucleus of ^{236}U. The ^{236}U nucleus then quickly decays into two heavy fragments moving at high speed, as well as several neutrons. Most of the kinetic energy released in such a fission is carried off by the two large fragments. (a) For the typical fission process,

$$^{1}_{0}n + {}^{235}_{92}U \rightarrow {}^{141}_{56}Ba + {}^{92}_{36}Kr + 3{}^{1}_{0}n$$

calculate the kinetic energy in MeV carried off by the fission fragments, neglecting the kinetic energy of the reactants. (b) What percentage of the initial energy is converted into kinetic energy? The atomic masses involved, given in atomic mass units, are

$$^{1}_{0}n = 1.008\ 665\ u \qquad {}^{235}_{92}U = 235.043\ 923\ u$$
$$^{141}_{56}Ba = 140.903\ 496\ u \qquad {}^{92}_{36}Kr = 91.907\ 936\ u$$

STRATEGY This problem is an application of the conservation of relativistic energy. Write the conservation law as a sum of kinetic energy and rest energy, and solve for the final kinetic energy.

SOLUTION

(a) Calculate the final kinetic energy for the given process.

Apply the conservation of relativistic energy equation, assuming $KE_{initial} = 0$:

$$(KE + mc^2)_{initial} = (KE + mc^2)_{final}$$
$$0 + m_n c^2 + m_U c^2 = m_{Ba} c^2 + m_{Kr} c^2 + 3m_n c^2 + KE_{final}$$

Solve for KE_{final} and substitute, converting to MeV in the last step:

$$KE_{final} = [(m_n + m_U) - (m_{Ba} + m_{Kr} + 3m_n)]c^2$$
$$KE_{final} = (1.008\ 665\ u + 235.043\ 923\ u)c^2$$
$$\qquad\qquad - [140.903\ 496\ u + 91.907\ 936\ u + 3(1.008\ 665\ u)]c^2$$
$$= (0.215\ 161\ u)(931.494\ \text{MeV/u} \cdot c^2)(c^2)$$
$$= \boxed{200.421\ \text{MeV}}$$

(b) What percentage of the initial energy is converted into kinetic energy?

Compute the total energy, which is the initial energy:

$$E_{initial} = 0 + m_n c^2 + m_U c^2$$
$$= (1.008\ 665\ u + 235.043\ 923\ u)c^2$$
$$= (236.052\ 59\ u)(931.494\ \text{MeV/u} \cdot c^2)(c^2)$$
$$= 2.198\ 82 \times 10^5\ \text{MeV}$$

Divide the kinetic energy by the total energy and multiply by 100%:

$$\frac{200.421\ \text{MeV}}{2.198\ 82 \times 10^5\ \text{MeV}} \times 100\% = \boxed{9.115 \times 10^{-2}\%}$$

REMARKS This calculation shows that nuclear reactions liberate only about one-tenth of 1% of the rest energy of the constituent particles. Some fusion reactions result in a percent yield several times as large.

QUESTION 26.6 Why is so little of the mass converted to other forms of energy?

EXERCISE 26.6 In a fusion reaction light elements combine to form a heavier element. Deuterium, which is also called heavy hydrogen, has an extra neutron in its nucleus. Two such particles can fuse into a heavier form of hydrogen, called tritium, plus an ordinary hydrogen atom. The reaction is

$$^{2}_{1}D + {}^{2}_{1}D \rightarrow {}^{3}_{1}T + {}^{1}_{1}H$$

(a) Calculate the energy released in the form of kinetic energy, assuming for simplicity the initial kinetic energy is zero.
(b) What percentage of the rest mass is converted to energy? The atomic masses involved are

$$^2_1D = 2.014\ 102\ u \qquad ^3_1T = 3.016\ 049\ u \qquad ^1_1H = 1.007\ 825\ u$$

ANSWERS (a) 4.033 37 MeV   (b) 0.107 5%

26.8 General Relativity

Special relativity relates observations of inertial observers. Einstein sought a more general theory that would address accelerating systems. His search was motivated in part by the following curious fact: mass determines the inertia of an object and also the strength of the gravitational field. The mass involved in inertia is called inertial mass, m_i, whereas the mass responsible for the gravitational field is called the gravitational mass, m_g. These masses appear in Newton's law of gravitation and in the second law of motion:

$$\text{Gravitational property} \qquad F_g = G\frac{m_g m'_g}{r^2}$$

$$\text{Inertial property} \qquad F_i = m_i a$$

The value for the gravitational constant G was chosen to make the magnitudes of m_g and m_i numerically equal. Regardless of how G is chosen, however, the strict proportionality of m_g and m_i has been established experimentally to an extremely high degree: a few parts in 10^{12}. It appears that gravitational mass and inertial mass may indeed be exactly equal: $m_i = m_g$.

In Einstein's view the remarkable coincidence that m_g and m_i were exactly equal was evidence for an intimate connection between the two concepts. He pointed out that no mechanical experiment (such as releasing a mass) could distinguish between the two situations illustrated in Figures 26.10a and 26.10b. In each case a mass released by the observer undergoes a downward acceleration of g relative to the floor.

Einstein carried this idea further and proposed that *no* experiment, mechanical or otherwise, could distinguish between the two cases. This extension to include all phenomena (not just mechanical ones) has interesting consequences. For

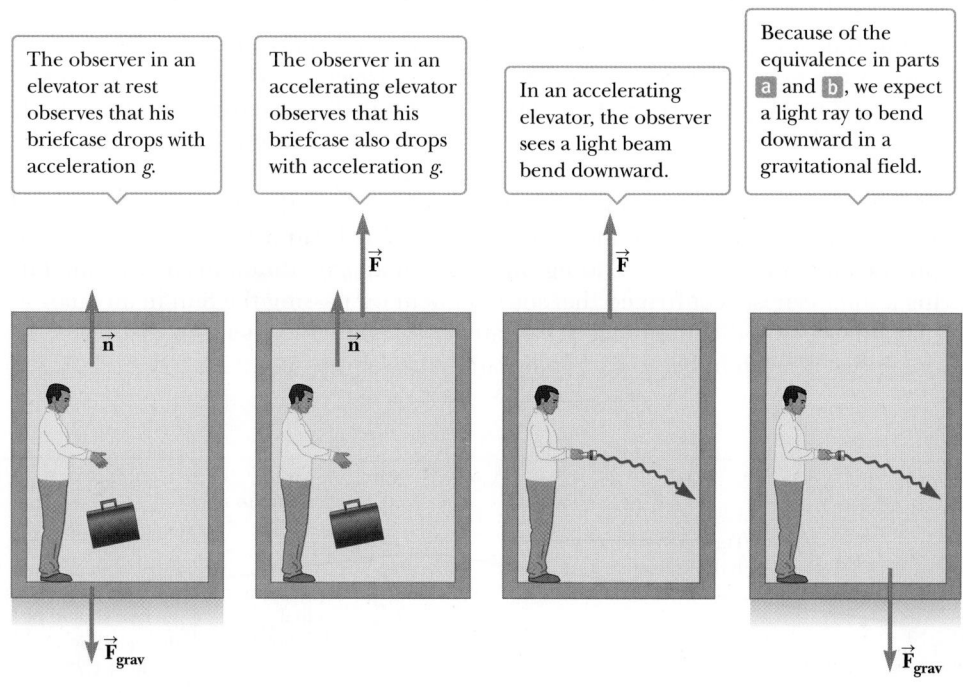

The observer in an elevator at rest observes that his briefcase drops with acceleration g.

The observer in an accelerating elevator observes that his briefcase also drops with acceleration g.

In an accelerating elevator, the observer sees a light beam bend downward.

Because of the equivalence in parts a and b, we expect a light ray to bend downward in a gravitational field.

Figure 26.10 (a) The observer in the cubicle is at rest in a uniform gravitational field $\vec{g}$. He experiences a normal force $\vec{n}$. (b) Now the observer is in a region where gravity is negligible, but an external force $\vec{F}$ acts on the frame of reference, producing an acceleration with magnitude g. Again, the man experiences a normal force $\vec{n}$ that accelerates him along with the cubicle. According to Einstein, the frames of reference in (a) and (b) are equivalent in every way. No local experiment could distinguish between them. (c) The observer turns on his pocket flashlight. Because of the acceleration of the cubicle, the beam would appear to bend toward the floor, just as a tossed ball would. (d) Given the equivalence of the frames, the same phenomenon should be observed in the presence of a gravity field.

example, suppose a light pulse is sent horizontally across the box, as in Figure 26.10c. The trajectory of the light pulse bends downward as the box accelerates upward to meet it. Einstein proposed that a beam of light should also be bent downward by a gravitational field (Fig. 26.10d).

The two postulates of Einstein's **general relativity** are as follows:

1. All the laws of nature have the same form for observers in any frame of reference, accelerated or not.
2. In the vicinity of any given point, a gravitational field is equivalent to an accelerated frame of reference without a gravitational field. (This is the *principle of equivalence.*)

The second postulate implies that gravitational mass and inertial mass are completely equivalent, not just proportional. What were thought to be two different types of mass are actually identical.

One interesting effect predicted by general relativity is that time scales are altered by gravity. A clock in the presence of gravity runs more slowly than one in which gravity is negligible. As a consequence, light emitted from atoms in a strong gravity field, such as the Sun's, is observed to have a lower frequency than the same light emitted by atoms in the laboratory. This gravitational shift has been detected in spectral lines emitted by atoms in massive stars. It has also been verified on Earth by comparing the frequencies of gamma rays emitted from nuclei separated vertically by about 20 m.

The second postulate suggests a gravitational field may be "transformed away" at any point if we choose an appropriate accelerated frame of reference: a freely falling one. Einstein developed an ingenious method of describing the acceleration necessary to make the gravitational field "disappear." He specified a certain quantity, the *curvature of spacetime*, that describes the gravitational effect at every point. In fact, the curvature of spacetime completely replaces Newton's gravitational theory. According to Einstein, there is no such thing as a gravitational force. Rather, the presence of a mass causes a curvature of spacetime in the vicinity of the mass. Planets going around the Sun follow the natural contours of the spacetime, much as marbles roll around inside a bowl. The fundamental equation of general relativity can be roughly stated as a proportion as follows:

$$\text{Average curvature of spacetime} \propto \text{energy density}$$

Einstein pursued a new theory of gravity in large part because of a discrepancy in the orbit of Mercury as calculated from Newton's second law. The closest approach of Mercury to the Sun, called the perihelion, changes position slowly over time. Newton's theory accounted for all but 43 arc seconds per century; Einstein's general relativity explained the discrepancy.

The most dramatic test of general relativity came shortly after the end of World War I. Einstein's theory predicts that a star would bend a light ray by a certain precise amount. Sir Arthur Eddington mounted an expedition to Africa and, during a solar eclipse, confirmed that starlight bent on passing the Sun in an amount matching the prediction of general relativity (Fig. 26.11). When this discovery was announced, Einstein became an international celebrity.

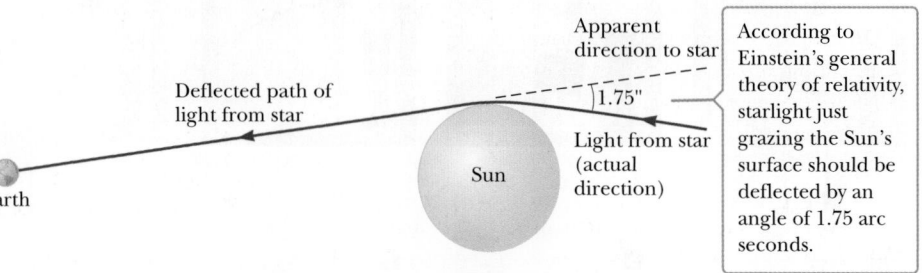

Figure 26.11 Deflection of starlight passing near the Sun. Because of this effect, the Sun and other remote objects can act as a *gravitational lens.*

Apparent direction to star

Deflected path of light from star

1.75"

Light from star (actual direction)

Sun

Earth

According to Einstein's general theory of relativity, starlight just grazing the Sun's surface should be deflected by an angle of 1.75 arc seconds.

General relativity also predicts that a large star can exhaust its nuclear fuel and collapse to a very small volume, turning into a **black hole**. Here the curvature of spacetime is so extreme that all matter and light within a certain radius becomes trapped. This radius, called the *Schwarzschild radius* or *event horizon*, is about 3 km for a black hole with the mass of our Sun. At the black hole's center may lurk a *singularity*, a point of infinite density and curvature where spacetime comes to an end.

There is strong evidence for the existence of a black hole having a mass of millions of Suns at the center of our galaxy.

■ **APPLYING PHYSICS 26.1** | **Faster Clocks in a "Mile-High City"**

Atomic clocks are extremely accurate; in fact, an error of 1 s in 3 million years is typical. This error can be described as about one part in 10^{14}. On the other hand, the atomic clock in Boulder, Colorado, is often 15 ns faster than the atomic clock in Washington, D.C., after only one day. This error is about one part in 6×10^{12}, which is about 17 times larger than the typical error. If atomic clocks are so accurate, why does a clock in Boulder not remain synchronous with one in Washington, D.C.?

EXPLANATION According to the general theory of relativity, the passage of time depends on gravity: clocks run more slowly in strong gravitational fields. Washington, D.C., is at an elevation very close to sea level, whereas Boulder is about a mile higher in altitude, so the gravitational field at Boulder is weaker than at Washington, D.C. As a result, an atomic clock runs more rapidly in Boulder than in Washington, D.C. (This effect has been verified by experiment.) ■

■ **SUMMARY**

26.3 Einstein's Principle of Relativity

The two basic postulates of the **special theory of relativity** are as follows:

1. The laws of physics are the same in all inertial frames of reference.
2. The speed of light is the same for all inertial observers, independently of their motion or of the motion of the source of light.

26.4 Consequences of Special Relativity

Some of the consequences of the special theory of relativity are as follows:

1. Clocks in motion relative to an observer slow down, a phenomenon known as **time dilation**. The relationship between time intervals in the moving and at-rest systems is

$$\Delta t = \gamma \, \Delta t_p \qquad [26.2]$$

where Δt is the time interval measured in the system in relative motion with respect to the clock,

$$\gamma = \frac{1}{\sqrt{1 - v^2/c^2}} \qquad [26.3]$$

and Δt_p is the proper time interval measured in the system moving with the clock.

2. The length of an object in motion is *contracted* in the direction of motion. The equation for **length contraction** is

$$L = L_p\sqrt{1 - v^2/c^2} \qquad [26.4]$$

where L is the length measured by an observer in motion relative to the object and L_p is the proper length measured by an observer for whom the object is at rest.

3. Events that are simultaneous for one observer are not simultaneous for another observer in motion relative to the first.

26.5 Relativistic Momentum

The relativistic expression for the **momentum** of a particle moving with velocity v is

$$p \equiv \frac{mv}{\sqrt{1 - v^2/c^2}} = \gamma mv \qquad [26.5]$$

26.6 Relative Velocity in Special Relativity

When observers E and B are in relative motion, they will measure different velocities for some third object. Those measurements are related by

$$v_{AB} = \frac{v_{AE} - v_{BE}}{1 - \dfrac{v_{AE}v_{BE}}{c^2}} \qquad [26.7]$$

At low relative velocities compared to that of light, this expression agrees with the Galilean form, Equation 26.6. Equation 26.7 can be inverted to give the equation of relativistic velocity addition:

$$v_{AE} = \frac{v_{AB} + v_{BE}}{1 + \dfrac{v_{AB}v_{BE}}{c^2}} \qquad [26.8]$$

Equation 26.8 gives the intuitive answer agreeing with everyday experience when $v \ll c$ (i.e., $v_{AE} = v_{AB} + v_{BE}$).

26.7 Relativistic Energy and the Equivalence of Mass and Energy

The relativistic expression for the **kinetic energy** of an object is

$$KE = \gamma mc^2 - mc^2 \qquad [26.9]$$

where mc^2 is the **rest energy** of the object, E_R.

The **total energy** of a particle is

$$E = \frac{mc^2}{\sqrt{1 - v^2/c^2}} \qquad [26.12]$$

Einstein's famous mass-energy equivalence equation results when $v = 0$.

The relativistic momentum is related to the total energy through the equation

$$E^2 = p^2c^2 + (mc^2)^2 \qquad [26.13]$$

■ MULTIPLE-CHOICE QUESTIONS

WebAssign The multiple-choice questions in this chapter may be assigned online in Enhanced WebAssign.

1. Which of the following statements are fundamental postulates of the special theory of relativity? (a) Light moves through a substance called the ether. (b) The speed of light depends on the inertial reference frame in which it is measured. (c) The laws of physics depend on the inertial reference frame in which they are used. (d) The laws of physics are the same in all inertial reference frames. (e) The speed of light is independent of the inertial reference frame in which it is measured.

2. A spaceship moves at one-quarter the speed of light relative to Earth in a direction perpendicular to the line of sight of an observer at rest with respect to Earth. If the spaceship has a length L when at rest, which statement is true concerning the moving ship's length L' as measured by the observer? (a) $L' > L$ (b) $L' < L$ (c) $L' = L$ (d) $L' << L$ (e) $L' >> L$

3. A car's headlights come on, and an observer on the ground measures the speed of the light beam to be $c = 3.00 \times 10^8$ m/s. As the driver heads down the highway traveling at a speed v away from the ground observer, which of the following statements are true about the measured speed of the light beam? (a) The ground observer measures the light speed to be $c + v$. (b) The driver measures the light speed to be c. (c) The ground observer measures the light speed to be c. (d) The driver measures the light's speed to be slightly less than c. (e) The ground observer measures the light's speed to be slightly less than c.

4. An astronaut is traveling in a rocket in outer space in a straight line at a constant speed of $0.5c$. Which of the following effects would she experience? (a) She would feel heavier. (b) She would find it harder to breathe. (c) Her heart rate would change. (d) Some of her dimensions would be shorter. (e) None of these effects would occur.

5. A pendulum in a spaceship traveling through space at a speed of $0.9c$ relative to Earth has a period P as measured by an astronaut in the spaceship. What is true about the period T as measured by an observer on Earth? (a) $P > T$ (b) $P = T$ (c) $P < T$ (d) $P < T$ or $P >$

T, depending on the direction of motion of the spacecraft (e) None of these

6. A cube measured at rest has volume V. An observer then passes the cube parallel to one of its sides at $0.98c$, so $\gamma \approx 5$. What is the volume of the cube as measured by the moving observer? (a) $V/125$ (b) $V/25$ (c) $V/5$ (d) V (e) $5V$

7. Suppose a photon, proton, and electron all have the same total energy E. Rank their momenta from smallest to greatest. (a) photon, electron, proton (b) proton, photon, electron (c) electron, photon, proton (d) electron, proton, photon (e) proton, electron, photon

8. Two identical clocks are set side by side and synchronized. One remains on the Earth. The other is put into orbit around the Earth moving rapidly toward the east. As measured by an observer on the Earth, does the orbiting clock (a) run faster than the Earth-based clock, (b) run at the same rate, or (c) run slower?

9. A mass–spring system moving with simple harmonic motion has a period T when measured by a ground observer. If the same system is then placed in an inertial frame of reference that moves past the ground observer at a speed of $0.50c$, by what factor should T be multiplied to give the system's period as measured by the ground observer? (a) 0.50 (b) 0.87 (c) 1.00 (d) 1.15 (e) 1.35

10. A spacecraft zooms past the Earth with a constant velocity. An observer on the Earth measures that an undamaged clock on the spacecraft is ticking at one-third the rate of an identical clock on the Earth. What does an observer on the spacecraft measure about the Earth-based clock's ticking rate? (a) It runs more than three times faster than his own clock. (b) It runs three times faster than his own. (c) It runs at the same rate as his own. (d) It runs at one-third the rate of his own. (e) It runs at less than one-third the rate of his own.

11. A distant astronomical object (a quasar) is moving away from us at half the speed of light. What is the speed of the light we receive from this quasar? (a) greater than c (b) c (c) between $c/2$ and c (d) $c/2$ (e) between 0 and $c/2$

CONCEPTUAL QUESTIONS

WebAssign The conceptual questions in this chapter may be assigned online in Enhanced WebAssign.

1. A spacecraft with the shape of a sphere of diameter D moves past an observer on Earth with a speed of $0.5c$. What shape does the observer measure for the spacecraft as it moves past?

2. What two speed measurements will two observers in relative motion always agree upon?

3. The speed of light in water is 2.30×10^8 m/s. Suppose an electron is moving through water at 2.50×10^8 m/s. Does this particle speed violate the principle of relativity?

4. With regard to reference frames, how does general relativity differ from special relativity?

5. Give a physical argument that shows it is impossible to accelerate an object of mass m to the speed of light, even with a continuous force acting on it.

6. It is said that Einstein, in his teenage years, asked the question, "What would I see in a mirror if I carried it in my hands and ran at a speed near that of light?" How would you answer this question?

7. List some ways our day-to-day lives would change if the speed of light were only 50 m/s.

8. Two identically constructed clocks are synchronized. One is put into orbit around Earth, and the other remains on Earth. (a) Which clock runs more slowly? (b) When the moving clock returns to Earth, will the two clocks still be synchronized? Discuss from the standpoints of both special and general relativity.

9. Photons of light have zero mass. How is it possible that they have momentum?

10. Imagine an astronaut on a trip to Sirius, which lies 8 light-years from Earth. Upon arrival at Sirius, the astronaut finds that the trip lasted 6 years. If the trip was made at a constant speed of $0.8c$, how can the 8-light-year distance be reconciled with the 6-year duration?

11. Explain why, when defining the length of a rod, it is necessary to specify that the positions of the ends of the rod are to be measured simultaneously.

PROBLEMS

WebAssign The problems in this chapter may be assigned online in Enhanced WebAssign. Selected problems also have Watch It video solutions.

1. denotes straightforward problem; 2. denotes intermediate problem;
3. denotes challenging problem
1. denotes full solution available in *Student Solutions Manual/ Study Guide*

1. denotes problems most often assigned in Enhanced WebAssign
BIO denotes biomedical problems
GP denotes guided problems
M denotes Master It tutorial available in Enhanced WebAssign
Q|C denotes asking for quantitative and conceptual reasoning
S denotes symbolic reasoning problem

26.4 Consequences of Special Relativity

1. If astronauts could travel at $v = 0.950c$, we on Earth would say it takes $(4.20/0.950) = 4.42$ years to reach Alpha Centauri, 4.20 light-years away. The astronauts disagree. (a) How much time passes on the astronauts' clocks? (b) What is the distance to Alpha Centauri as measured by the astronauts?

2. Q|C A meterstick moving at $0.900c$ relative to the Earth's surface approaches an observer at rest with respect to the Earth's surface. (a) What is the meterstick's length as measured by the observer? (b) Qualitatively, how would the answer to part (a) change if the observer started running toward the meterstick?

3. The length of a moving spaceship is 28.0 m according to an astronaut on the spaceship. If the spaceship is contracted by 15.0 cm according an Earth observer, what is the speed of the spaceship?

4. BIO An astronaut at rest on Earth has a heart rate of 70 beats/min. When the astronaut is traveling in a spaceship at $0.90c$, what will this rate be as measured by

(a) an observer also in the ship and (b) an observer at rest on Earth?

5. M The average lifetime of a pi meson in its own frame of reference (i.e., the proper lifetime) is 2.6×10^{-8} s. If the meson moves with a speed of $0.98c$, what is (a) its mean lifetime as measured by an observer on Earth, and (b) the average distance it travels before decaying, as measured by an observer on Earth? (c) What distance would it travel if time dilation did not occur?

6. BIO An astronaut is traveling in a space vehicle that has a speed of $0.500c$ relative to Earth. The astronaut measures his pulse rate at 75.0 per minute. Signals generated by the astronaut's pulse are radioed to Earth when the vehicle is moving perpendicular to a line that connects the vehicle with an Earth observer. (a) What pulse rate does the Earth observer measure? (b) What would be the pulse rate if the speed of the space vehicle were increased to $0.990c$?

7. GP A muon formed high in Earth's atmosphere travels toward Earth at a speed $v = 0.990c$ for a distance

of 4.60 km as measured by an observer at rest with respect to Earth. It then decays into an electron, a neutrino, and an antineutrino. (a) How long does the muon survive according to an observer at rest on Earth? (b) Compute the gamma factor associated with the muon. (c) How much time passes according to an observer traveling with the muon? (d) What distance does the muon travel according to an observer traveling with the muon? (e) A third observer traveling toward the muon at $c/2$ measures the lifetime of the particle. According to this observer, is the muon's lifetime shorter or longer than the lifetime measured by the observer at rest with respect to Earth? Explain.

8. A deep-space probe moves away from Earth with a speed of $0.80c$. An antenna on the probe requires 3.0 s, in probe time, to rotate through 1.0 rev. How much time is required for 1.0 rev according to an observer on Earth?

9. The proper length of one spaceship is three times that of another. The two spaceships are traveling in the same direction and, while both are passing overhead, an Earth observer measures the two spaceships to have the same length. If the slower spaceship has a speed of $0.350c$ with respect to Earth, determine the speed of the faster spaceship.

10. A car traveling at 35.0 m/s takes 26.0 minutes to travel a certain distance according to the driver's clock in the car. How long does the trip take according to an observer at rest on Earth? *Hint:* The following approximation is helpful: $[1 - x]^{-\frac{1}{2}} \approx 1 + \frac{1}{2}x$ for $x \ll 1$.

11. A supertrain of proper length 100 m travels at a speed of $0.95c$ as it passes through a tunnel having proper length 50 m. As seen by a trackside observer, is the train ever completely within the tunnel? If so, by how much?

12. A box is cubical with sides of proper lengths $L_1 = L_2 = L_3$, as shown in Figure P26.12, when viewed in its own rest frame. If this block moves parallel to one of its edges with a speed of $0.80c$ past an observer, (a) what shape does it appear to have to this observer? (b) What is the length of each side as measured by the observer?

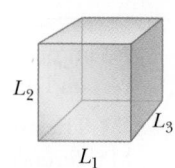

Figure P26.12

26.5 Relativistic Momentum

13. **QC** An electron has a momentum with magnitude three times the magnitude of its classical momentum. (a) Find the speed of the electron. (b) How would your result change if the particle were a proton?

14. **QC** Calculate the classical momentum of a proton traveling at $0.990c$, neglecting relativistic effects. (b) Repeat the calculation while including relativistic effects. (c) Does it make sense to neglect relativity at such speeds?

15. An unstable particle at rest breaks up into two fragments of *unequal mass*. The mass of the lighter frag-

ment is equal to 2.50×10^{-28} kg and that of the heavier fragment is 1.67×10^{-27} kg. If the lighter fragment has a speed of $0.893c$ after the breakup, what is the speed of the heavier fragment?

26.6 Relative Velocity in Special Relativity

16. Spaceship R is moving to the right at a speed of $0.70c$ with respect to Earth. A second spaceship, L, moves to the left at the same speed with respect to Earth. What is the speed of L with respect to R?

17. An electron moves to the right with a speed of $0.90c$ relative to the laboratory frame. A proton moves to the left with a speed of $0.70c$ relative to the electron. Find the speed of the proton relative to the laboratory frame.

18. A spaceship travels at $0.750c$ relative to Earth. If the spaceship fires a small rocket in the forward direction, how fast (relative to the ship) must it be fired for it to travel at $0.950c$ relative to Earth?

19. Spaceship A moves away from Earth at a speed of $0.800c$ (Fig. P26.19). Spaceship B pursues at a speed of $0.900c$ relative to Earth. Observers on Earth see B overtaking A at a relative speed of $0.100c$. With what speed is B overtaking A as seen by the crew of spaceship B?

Figure P26.19

20. A pulsar is a stellar object that emits light in short bursts. Suppose a pulsar with a speed of $0.950c$ approaches Earth, and a rocket with a speed of $0.995c$ heads toward the pulsar. (Both speeds are measured in Earth's frame of reference.) If the pulsar emits 10.0 pulses per second in its own frame of reference, at what rate are the pulses emitted in the rocket's frame of reference?

21. **M** A rocket moves with a velocity of $0.92c$ to the right with respect to a stationary observer A. An observer B moving relative to observer A finds that the rocket is moving with a velocity of $0.95c$ to the left. What is the velocity of observer B relative to observer A? (*Hint:* Consider observer B's velocity in the frame of reference of the rocket.)

26.7 Relativistic Energy and the Equivalence of Mass and Energy

22. A proton moves with a speed of $0.950c$. Calculate (a) its rest energy, (b) its total energy, and (c) its kinetic energy.

23. Protons in an accelerator at the Fermi National Laboratory near Chicago are accelerated to a total energy that is 400 times their rest energy. (a) What is the speed of these protons in terms of c? (b) What is their kinetic energy in MeV?

24. **S** A proton in a large accelerator has a kinetic energy of 175 GeV. (a) Compare this kinetic energy to the rest energy of the proton, and find an approximate expression for the proton's kinetic energy. (b) Find the speed of the proton.

25. What speed must a particle attain before its kinetic energy is double the value predicted by the nonrelativistic expression $KE = \frac{1}{2}mv^2$?

26. Determine the energy required to accelerate an electron from (a) $0.500c$ to $0.900c$ and (b) $0.900c$ to $0.990c$.

27. A spaceship of mass 2.40×10^6 kg is to be accelerated to a speed of $0.700c$. (a) What minimum amount of energy does this acceleration require from the spaceship's fuel, assuming perfect efficiency? (b) How much fuel would it take to provide this much energy if all the rest energy of the fuel could be transformed to kinetic energy of the spaceship?

28. An unstable particle with a mass equal to 3.34×10^{-27} kg is initially at rest. The particle decays into two fragments that fly off with velocities of $0.987c$ and $-0.868c$, respectively. Find the masses of the fragments. *Hint:* Conserve both mass–energy and momentum.

29. **Q|C** Starting with the definitions of relativistic energy and momentum, show that $E^2 = p^2c^2 + m^2c^4$ (Eq. 26.13).

30. **GP** Consider the reaction $^{235}_{92}\text{U} + ^1_0\text{n} \rightarrow ^{148}_{57}\text{La} + ^{87}_{35}\text{Br} + ^1_0\text{n}$. (a) Write the conservation of relativistic energy equation symbolically in terms of the rest energy and the kinetic energy, setting the initial total energy to the final total energy. (b) Using values from Appendix B, find the total mass of the initial particles. (c) Using the values given below, find the total mass of the particles after the reaction takes place. (d) Subtract the final particle mass from the initial particle mass. (e) Convert the answer to part (d) to MeV, obtaining the kinetic energy of the daughter particles, neglecting the kinetic energy of the reactants. *Note:* Lanthanum-148 has atomic mass 147.932 236 u; bromine-87 has atomic mass 86.920 711 19 u.

Additional Problems

31. Consider electrons accelerated to a total energy of 20.0 GeV in the 3.00-km-long Stanford Linear Accelerator. (a) What is the γ factor for the electrons? (b) How long does the accelerator appear to the electrons? Electron mass energy: 0.511 MeV.

32. An electron has a speed of $0.750c$. (a) Find the speed of a proton that has the same kinetic energy as the electron. (b) Find the speed of a proton that has the same momentum as the electron.

33. The rest energy of an electron is 0.511 MeV. The rest energy of a proton is 938 MeV. Assume both particles have kinetic energies of 2.00 MeV. Find the speed of (a) the electron and (b) the proton. (c) By how much does the speed of the electron exceed that of the proton? *Note:* Perform the calculations in MeV; don't convert the energies to joules. The answer is sensitive to rounding.

34. **Q|C** A spring of force constant k is compressed by a distance x from its equilibrium length. (a) Does the mass of the spring change when the spring is compressed? Explain. (b) Find an expression for the change in mass of the spring in terms of k, x, and c. (c) What is the change in mass if the force constant is 2.0×10^2 N/m and $x = 15$ cm?

35. A star is 5.00 ly from the Earth. At what speed must a spacecraft travel on its journey to the star such that the Earth–star distance measured in the frame of the spacecraft is 2.00 ly?

36. An electron has a total energy equal to five times its rest energy. (a) What is its momentum? (b) Repeat for a proton.

37. **M** An astronaut wishes to visit the Andromeda galaxy, making a one-way trip that will take 30.0 years in the spaceship's frame of reference. Assume the galaxy is 2.00 million light-years away and his speed is constant. (a) How fast must he travel relative to Earth? (b) What will be the kinetic energy of his spaceship, which has mass of 1.00×10^6 kg? (c) What is the cost of this energy if it is purchased at a typical consumer price for electric energy, 13.0 cents per kWh? The following approximation will prove useful:

$$\frac{1}{\sqrt{1 + x}} \approx 1 - \frac{x}{2} \quad \text{for } x \ll 1$$

38. An alarm clock is set to sound in 10 h. At $t = 0$, the clock is placed in a spaceship moving with a speed of $0.75c$ (relative to Earth). What distance, as determined by an Earth observer, does the spaceship travel before the alarm clock sounds?

39. Owen and Dina are at rest in frame S′, which is moving with a speed of $0.600c$ with respect to frame S. They play a game of catch while Ed, at rest in frame S, watches the action (Fig. P26.39). Owen throws the ball to Dina with a speed of $0.800c$ (according to Owen) and their separation (measured in S′) is equal to 1.80×10^{12} m. (a) According to Dina, how fast is the ball moving? (b) According to Dina, what time interval is required for the ball to reach her? According to Ed, (c) how far apart are Owen and Dina, and (d) how fast is the ball moving?

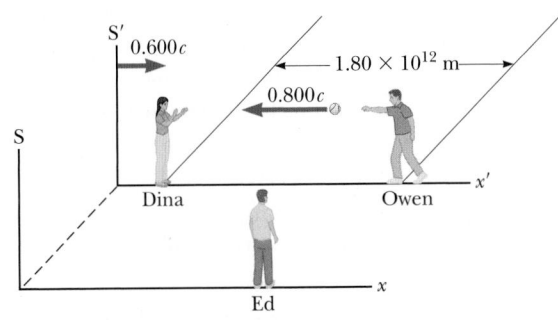

Figure P26.39

40. An observer in a coasting spacecraft moves toward a mirror at speed v relative to the reference frame labeled by S in Figure P26.40. The mirror is stationary with respect to S. A light pulse emitted by the spacecraft travels toward the mirror and is reflected back to the spacecraft. The spacecraft is a distance d from the mirror (as measured by observers in S) at the moment the light pulse leaves the spacecraft. What is the total travel time of the pulse as measured by observers in (a) the S frame and (b) the spacecraft?

Figure P26.40

41. A spaceship of proper length 300 m takes 0.75 μs to pass an Earth observer. Determine the speed of this spaceship as measured by the Earth observer.

42. The cosmic rays of highest energy are protons that have kinetic energy on the order of 10^{13} MeV. (a) From the point of view of the proton, how many kilometers across is the galaxy? (b) How long would it take a proton of this energy to travel across the Milky Way galaxy, having a diameter $\sim 10^5$ light-years, as measured in the proton's frame?

43. **M** The nonrelativistic expression for the momentum of a particle, $p = mv$, can be used if $v \ll c$. For what speed does the use of this formula give an error in the momentum of (a) 1.00% and (b) 10.0%?

44. (a) Show that a potential difference of 1.02×10^6 V would be sufficient to give an electron a speed equal to twice the speed of light if Newtonian mechanics remained valid at high speeds. (b) What speed would an electron actually acquire in falling through a potential difference equal to 1.02×10^6 V?

45. The muon is an unstable particle that spontaneously decays into an electron and two neutrinos. In a reference frame in which the muons are stationary, if the number of muons at $t = 0$ is N_0, the number at time t is given by $N = N_0 e^{-t/\tau}$, where τ is the mean lifetime, equal to 2.2 μs. Suppose the muons move at a speed of $0.95c$ and there are 5.0×10^4 muons at $t = 0$. (a) What is the observed lifetime of the muons? (b) How many muons remain after traveling a distance of 3.0 km?

46. Imagine that the entire Sun collapses to a sphere of radius R_g such that the work required to remove a small mass m from the surface would be equal to its rest energy mc^2. This radius is called the *gravitational radius* for the Sun. Find R_g. (It is believed that the ultimate fate of very massive stars is to collapse beyond their gravitational radii into black holes.)

47. The identical twins Speedo and Goslo join a migration from Earth to Planet X, which is 20.0 light-years away in a reference frame in which both planets are at rest. The twins, of the same age, depart at the same time on different spacecraft. Speedo's craft travels steadily at $0.950c$, Goslo's at $0.750c$. Calculate the age difference between the twins after Goslo's spacecraft lands on Planet X. Which twin is the older?

48. **M** An interstellar space probe is launched from Earth. After a brief period of acceleration, it moves with a constant velocity, 70.0% of the speed of light. Its nuclear-powered batteries supply the energy to keep its data transmitter active continuously. The batteries have a lifetime of 15.0 years as measured in a rest frame. (a) How long do the batteries on the space probe last as measured by mission control on Earth? (b) How far is the probe from Earth when its batteries fail as measured by mission control? (c) How far is the probe from Earth as measured by its built-in trip odometer when its batteries fail? (d) For what total time after launch are data received from the probe by mission control? Note that radio waves travel at the speed of light and fill the space between the probe and Earth at the time the battery fails.

49. An observer moving at a speed of $0.995c$ relative to a rod (Fig. P26.49) measures its length to be 2.00 m and sees its length to be oriented at 30.0° with respect to its direction of motion. (a) What is the proper length of the rod? (b) What is the orientation angle in a reference frame moving with the rod?

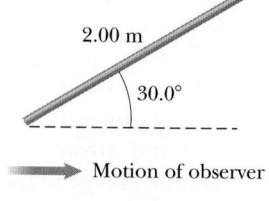

Figure P26.49

50. An alien spaceship traveling $0.600c$ toward Earth launches a landing craft with an advance guard of purchasing agents. The lander travels in the same direction with a velocity $0.800c$ relative to the spaceship. As observed on Earth, the spaceship is 0.200 light-years from Earth when the lander is launched. (a) With what velocity is the lander observed to be approaching by observers on Earth? (b) What is the distance to Earth at the time of lander launch, as observed by the aliens on the mother ship? (c) How long does it take the lander to reach Earth as observed by the aliens on the mother ship? (d) If the lander has a mass of 4.00×10^5 kg, what is its kinetic energy as observed in Earth's reference frame?

■ AP* REVIEW QUESTIONS

1. Which of the following statements is/are true?

    I. Photons have energy

    II. Photons have mass

    III. Photons have momentum

(A) I only

(B) I and II

(C) II and III

(D) I and III

(E) I, II, and III

2. A photon has an energy E and a momentum p. Another photon with an energy $2E$ would have a momentum of

(A) p

(B) $2p$

(C) $\dfrac{p}{2}$

(D) $4p$

(E) $\dfrac{p}{4}$

3. Two different-colored photons—one red and one violet—are observed in the laboratory. Which photon has more momentum?

(A) The red photon

(B) The violet photon

(C) Both have the same momentum since they are both going light speed

(D) Neither; photons have no mass, therefore no momentum

(E) Impossible to tell without knowing how fast the photons are traveling

4. Which of the following equations is a statement of mass-energy equivalence?

(A) $K = \dfrac{1}{2}mv^2$

(B) $U = mgy$

(C) $E = hf$

(D) $U = \dfrac{kqq'}{r}$

(E) $E = mc^2$

5. Photon A has a frequency f. Photon B has a frequency of $2f$. How do the momenta of the photons compare?

(A) Both photons have the same momentum.

(B) Photon A has twice the momentum of photon B.

(C) Photon B has twice the momentum of photon C.

(D) Photon A has four times the momentum of photon B.

(E) Photon B has four times the momentum of photon C.

6. Photon A has a wavelength λ. Photon B has a wavelength of 2λ. How do the momenta of the photons compare?

(A) Both photons have the same momentum.

(B) Photon A has twice the momentum of photon B.

(C) Photon B has twice the momentum of photon C.

(D) Photon A has four times the momentum of photon B.

(E) Photon B has four times the momentum of photon C.

7. Particle A has a rest-mass of m while particle B has a rest-mass of $2m$. Which of the following statements in true?

(A) Particle A has twice the rest-mass energy of particle B.

(B) Particle B has twice the rest-mass energy of particle A.

(C) Particle A has four times the rest-mass energy of particle B.

(D) Particle B has four times the rest-mass energy of particle A.

(E) Particle A and particle B have the same rest-mass energy.

8. The fission of Uranium-235 involves bombarding a $^{235}_{92}U$ nucleus with a slow moving electron, resulting in two large, fast-moving nuclei and some extra electrons, as shown in the equation below.

$$^{1}_{0}n + {}^{235}_{92}U \rightarrow {}^{141}_{56}Ba + {}^{92}_{36}Kr + 3{}^{1}_{0}n$$

Which statement is true about the reactants and products in this nuclear reaction?

(A) The total rest-mass of the reactants is equal to the total rest-mass of the products

(B) The total rest-mass of the reactants is greater than the total rest-mass of the products

(C) The total rest-mass of the reactants is less than the total rest-mass of the products

(D) The total rest-mass of the uranium nucleus is equal to the total rest-mass of the barium and krypton nuclei

(E) The total rest-mass of the uranium nucleus is less than the total rest-mass of the barium and krypton nuclei

9. In the fission of $^{238}_{92}U$, about 200 MeV of energy is released per reaction. Approximately what percentage of the initial rest-mass is converted into energy as a result of the reaction?

(A) 0.01%

(B) 0.1%

(C) 1%

(D) 10%

(E) 100%

Questions 10–12

Use the graphs below to answer questions 10–12.

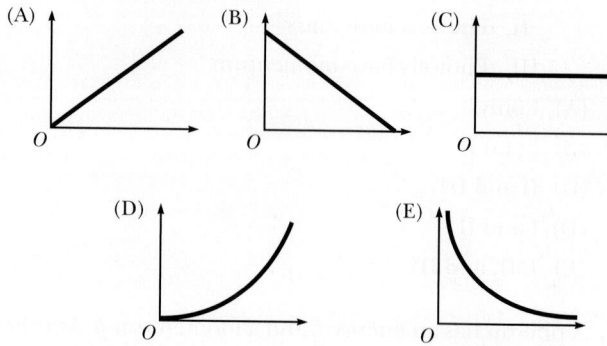

10. Which graph represents the momentum of a photon as a function of its energy?

11. Which graph represents the momentum of a photon as a function of its wavelength?

12. Which graph represents the total relativistic energy of a particle as a function of its mass?

© Eye of Science/Science Source/Photo Researchers, Inc.

Color-enhanced scanning electron micrograph of the storage mite *Lepidoglyphus destructor*. These common mites grow to 0.75 mm and feed on molds, flour, and rice. They thrive at 25°C and high humidity and can trigger allergies.

Quantum Physics 27

Although many problems were resolved by the theory of relativity in the early part of the 20th century, many others remained unsolved. Attempts to explain the behavior of matter on the atomic level with the laws of classical physics were consistently unsuccessful. Various phenomena, such as the electromagnetic radiation emitted by a heated object (blackbody radiation), the emission of electrons by illuminated metals (the photoelectric effect), and the emission of sharp spectral lines by gas atoms in an electric discharge tube, couldn't be understood within the framework of classical physics. Between 1900 and 1930, however, a modern version of mechanics called *quantum mechanics* or *wave mechanics* was highly successful in explaining the behavior of atoms, molecules, and nuclei.

The earliest ideas of quantum theory were introduced by Planck, and most of the subsequent mathematical developments, interpretations, and improvements were made by a number of distinguished physicists, including Einstein, Bohr, Schrödinger, de Broglie, Heisenberg, Born, and Dirac. In this chapter we introduce the underlying ideas of quantum theory and the wave-particle nature of matter, and discuss some simple applications of quantum theory, including the photoelectric effect, the Compton effect, and x-rays.

27.1 Blackbody Radiation and Planck's Hypothesis

An object at any temperature emits electromagnetic radiation, called **thermal radiation**. Stefan's law, discussed in Section 11.5, describes the total power radiated. The spectrum of the radiation depends on the temperature and properties of the object. At low temperatures, the wavelengths of the thermal radiation are

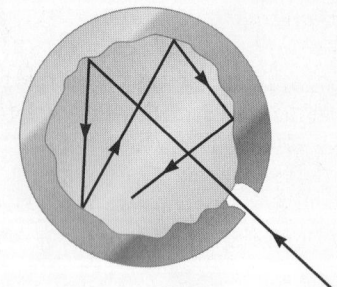

Figure 27.1 An opening in the cavity of a body is a good approximation of a blackbody. As light enters the cavity through the small opening, part is reflected and part is absorbed on each reflection from the interior walls. After many reflections, essentially all the incident energy is absorbed.

Tip 27.1 Expect the Unexpected

Our life experiences take place in the macroscopic world, where quantum effects are not evident. Quantum effects can be even more bizarre than relativistic effects. As Nobel Prize–winning physicist Richard Feynman once said, "Nobody understands quantum mechanics."

Max Planck
German Physicist (1858–1947)
Planck introduced the concept of a "quantum of action" (Planck's constant h) in an attempt to explain the spectral distribution of blackbody radiation, which formed the foundations for quantum theory. In 1918 he was awarded the Nobel Prize in Physics for this discovery of the quantized nature of energy.

mainly in the infrared region and hence not observable by the eye. As the temperature of an object increases, the object eventually begins to glow red. At sufficiently high temperatures, it appears to be white, as in the glow of the hot tungsten filament of a lightbulb. A careful study of thermal radiation shows that it consists of a continuous distribution of wavelengths from the infrared, visible, and ultraviolet portions of the spectrum.

From a classical viewpoint, thermal radiation originates from accelerated charged particles near the surface of an object; such charges emit radiation, much as small antennas do. The thermally agitated charges can have a distribution of frequencies, which accounts for the continuous spectrum of radiation emitted by the object. By the end of the 19th century, it had become apparent that the classical theory of thermal radiation was inadequate. The basic problem was in understanding the observed distribution energy as a function of wavelength in the radiation emitted by a blackbody. By definition, a **blackbody** is an ideal system that absorbs *all* radiation incident on it. A good approximation of a blackbody is a small hole leading to the inside of a hollow object, as shown in Figure 27.1. The nature of the radiation emitted through the small hole leading to the cavity depends *only on the temperature* of the cavity walls and not at all on the material composition of the object, its shape, or other factors.

Experimental data for the distribution of energy in blackbody radiation at three temperatures are shown in Active Figure 27.2. The radiated energy varies with wavelength and temperature. As the temperature of the blackbody increases, the total amount of energy (area under the curve) it emits increases. Also, with increasing temperature, the peak of the distribution shifts to shorter wavelengths. This shift obeys the following relationship, called **Wien's displacement law**,

$$\lambda_{max} T = 0.289\,8 \times 10^{-2}\ \text{m} \cdot \text{K} \qquad \text{[27.1]}$$

where λ_{max} is the wavelength at which the curve peaks and T is the absolute temperature of the object emitting the radiation.

■ APPLYING PHYSICS 27.1 | Star Colors

If you look carefully at stars in the night sky, you can distinguish three main colors: red, white, and blue. What causes these particular colors?

EXPLANATION These colors result from the different surface temperatures of stars. A relatively cool star, with a surface temperature of 3 000 K, has a radiation curve similar to the middle curve in Active Figure 27.2. The peak in this curve is above the visible wavelengths, 0.4 μm to 0.7 μm, beyond the wavelength of red light, so significantly more radiation is emitted within the visible range at the red end than the blue end of the spectrum. Consequently, the star appears reddish in color, similar to the red glow from the burner of an electric range. ■

A hotter star has a radiation curve more like the upper curve in Active Figure 27.2. In this case the star emits significant radiation throughout the visible range, and the combination of all colors causes the star to look white. Such is the case with our own Sun, with a surface temperature of 5 800 K. For much hotter stars, the peak can be shifted so far below the visible range that significantly more blue radiation is emitted than red, so the star appears bluish in color. Stars cooler than the Sun tend to have orange or red colors. The surface temperature of a star can be obtained by first finding the wavelength corresponding to the maximum in the intensity versus wavelength curve, then substituting that wavelength into Wien's law. For example, if the wavelength were 2.30×10^{-7} m, the surface temperature would be given by

$$T = \frac{0.289\,8 \times 10^{-2} \text{ m} \cdot \text{K}}{\lambda_{\max}} = \frac{0.289\,8 \times 10^{-2} \text{ m} \cdot \text{K}}{2.30 \times 10^{-7} \text{ m}} = 1.26 \times 10^4 \text{ K}$$

Attempts to use classical ideas to explain the shapes of the curves shown in Active Figure 27.2 failed. Active Figure 27.3 shows an experimental plot of the blackbody radiation spectrum (blue curve), together with the theoretical picture of what this curve should look like based on classical theories (rust-colored curve). At long wavelengths, classical theory is in good agreement with the experimental data. At short wavelengths, however, major disagreement exists between classical theory and experiment. As λ approaches zero, classical theory erroneously predicts that the intensity should go to infinity, when the experimental data show it should approach zero.

In 1900 Planck developed a formula for blackbody radiation that was in complete agreement with experiments at all wavelengths, leading to a curve shown by the red line in Active Figure 27.3. Planck hypothesized that blackbody radiation was produced by submicroscopic charged oscillators, which he called *resonators*. He assumed the walls of a glowing cavity were composed of billions of these resonators, although their exact nature was unknown. The resonators were allowed to have only certain discrete energies E_n, given by

$$E_n = nhf \qquad \text{[27.2]}$$

where n is a positive integer called a **quantum number**, f is the frequency of vibration of the resonator, and h is a constant known as **Planck's constant**, which has the value

$$h = 6.626 \times 10^{-34} \text{ J} \cdot \text{s} \qquad \text{[27.3]}$$

Because the energy of each resonator can have only discrete values given by Equation 27.2, we say the energy is *quantized*. Each discrete energy value represents a different *quantum state*, with each value of n representing a specific quantum state. (When the resonator is in the $n = 1$ quantum state, its energy is hf; when it is in the $n = 2$ quantum state, its energy is $2hf$; and so on.)

The key point in Planck's theory is the assumption of quantized energy states. This radical departure from classical physics is the "quantum leap" that led to a totally new understanding of nature. It's shocking: it's like saying a pitched baseball can have only a fixed number of different speeds, and no speeds in between those fixed values. The fact that energy can assume only certain, discrete values instead of any one of a continuum of values is the single most important difference between quantum theory and the classical theories of Newton and Maxwell.

27.2 The Photoelectric Effect and the Particle Theory of Light

In the latter part of the 19th century, experiments showed that light incident on certain metallic surfaces caused the emission of electrons from the surfaces. This phenomenon is known as the **photoelectric effect**, and the emitted electrons are called **photoelectrons**. The first discovery of this phenomenon was made by Hertz, who was also the first to produce the electromagnetic waves predicted by Maxwell.

Active Figure 27.4 (page 914) is a schematic diagram of a photoelectric effect apparatus. An evacuated glass tube known as a photocell contains a metal plate

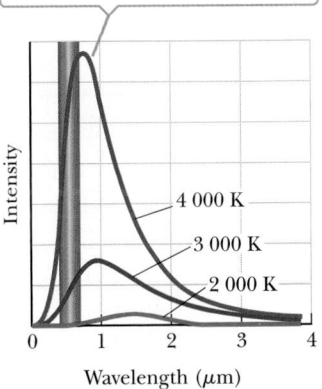

The total radiation emitted (the area under a curve) increases with increasing temperature.

Active Figure 27.2
Intensity of blackbody radiation versus wavelength at three temperatures. The visible range of wavelengths is between 0.4 μm and 0.7 μm. At approximately 6 000 K, the peak is in the center of the visible wavelengths, and the object appears white.

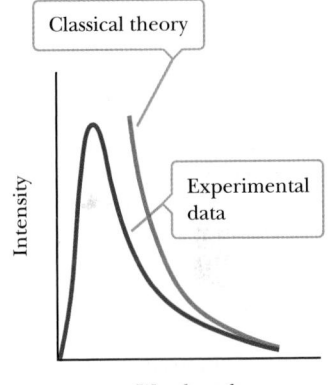

Active Figure 27.3
Comparison of experimental data with the classical theory of blackbody radiation. Planck's theory matches the experimental data perfectly.

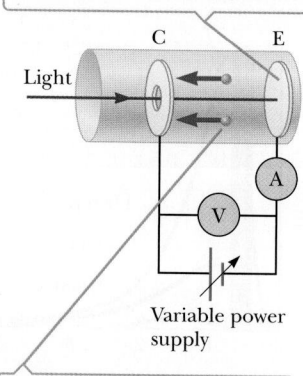

When light strikes plate E (the emitter), photoelectrons are ejected from the plate.

Electrons moving from plate E to plate C (the collector) create a current in the circuit, registered at the ammeter, A.

Active Figure 27.4
A circuit diagram for studying the photoelectric effect.

E (the emitter) connected to the negative terminal of a variable power supply. Another metal plate, C (the collector), is maintained at a positive potential by the power supply. When the tube is kept in the dark, the ammeter reads zero, indicating that there is no current in the circuit. When plate E is illuminated by light having a wavelength shorter than some particular wavelength that depends on the material used to make plate E, however, a current is detected by the ammeter, indicating a flow of charges across the gap between E and C. This current arises from photoelectrons emitted from the negative plate E and collected at the positive plate C.

Figure 27.5 is a plot of the photoelectric current versus the potential difference ΔV between E and C for two light intensities. At large values of ΔV, the current reaches a maximum value. In addition, the current increases as the incident light intensity increases, as you might expect. Finally, when ΔV is negative—that is, when the power supply in the circuit is reversed to make E positive and C negative—the current drops to a low value because most of the emitted photoelectrons are repelled by the now negative plate C. In this situation only those electrons having a kinetic energy greater than the magnitude of $e\,\Delta V$ reach C, where e is the charge on the electron.

When ΔV is equal to or more negative than $-\Delta V_s$, the **stopping potential**, no electrons reach C, and the current is zero. The stopping potential is *independent* of the radiation intensity. The maximum kinetic energy of the photoelectrons is related to the stopping potential through the relationship

$$KE_{max} = e\Delta V_s \qquad \text{[27.4]}$$

Several features of the photoelectric effect can't be explained with classical physics or with the wave theory of light:

- No electrons are emitted if the incident light frequency falls below some **cut-off frequency** f_c, also called the threshold frequency, which is characteristic of the material being illuminated. This fact is inconsistent with the wave theory, which predicts that the photoelectric effect should occur at *any* frequency, provided the light intensity is sufficiently high.
- The maximum kinetic energy of the photoelectrons is independent of light intensity. According to wave theory, light of higher intensity should carry more energy into the metal per unit time and therefore eject photoelectrons having higher kinetic energies.
- The maximum kinetic energy of the photoelectrons increases with increasing light frequency. The wave theory predicts no relationship between photoelectron energy and incident light frequency.
- Electrons are emitted from the surface almost instantaneously (less than 10^{-9} s after the surface is illuminated), even at low light intensities.

The current increases with intensity but reaches a saturation level for large values of ΔV.

At voltages equal to or more negative than $-\Delta V_s$, the current is zero.

Figure 27.5 Photoelectric current versus applied potential difference for two light intensities.

$-\Delta V_s$ is the stopping potential.

Classically, we expect the photoelectrons to require some time to absorb the incident radiation before they acquire enough kinetic energy to escape from the metal.

A successful explanation of the photoelectric effect was given by Einstein in 1905, the same year he published his special theory of relativity. As part of a general paper on electromagnetic radiation, for which he received the Nobel Prize in Physics in 1921, Einstein extended Planck's concept of quantization to electromagnetic waves. He suggested that a tiny packet of light energy or **photon** would be emitted when a quantized oscillator made a jump from an energy state $E_n = nhf$ to the next lower state $E_{n-1} = (n - 1)hf$. Conservation of energy would require the decrease in oscillator energy, hf, to be equal to the photon's energy E, so that

$$E = hf \qquad [27.5]$$

◀ Energy of a photon

where h is Planck's constant and f is the frequency of the light, which is equal to the frequency of Planck's oscillator.

The key point here is that the light energy lost by the emitter, hf, stays sharply localized in a tiny packet or particle called a photon. In Einstein's model a photon is so localized that it can give *all* its energy hf to a single electron in the metal. According to Einstein, the maximum kinetic energy for these liberated photoelectrons is

$$KE_{max} = hf - \phi \qquad [27.6]$$

◀ Photoelectric effect equation

where ϕ is called the **work function** of the metal. The work function, which represents the minimum energy with which an electron is bound in the metal, is on the order of a few electron volts. Table 27.1 lists work functions for various metals.

With the photon theory of light, we can explain the previously mentioned features of the photoelectric effect that cannot be understood using concepts of classical physics:

- Photoelectrons are created by absorption of a single photon, so the energy of that photon must be greater than or equal to the work function, else no photoelectrons will be produced. This explains the cutoff frequency.
- From Equation 27.6, KE_{max} depends only on the frequency of the light and the value of the work function. Light intensity is immaterial because absorption of a single photon is responsible for the electron's change in kinetic energy.
- Equation 27.6 is linear in the frequency, so KE_{max} increases with increasing frequency.
- Electrons are emitted almost instantaneously, regardless of intensity, because the light energy is concentrated in packets rather than spread out in waves. If the frequency is high enough, no time is needed for the electron to gradually acquire sufficient energy to escape the metal.

Experimentally, a linear relationship is observed between f and KE_{max}, as sketched in Figure 27.6. The intercept on the horizontal axis, corresponding to $KE_{max} = 0$, gives the cutoff frequency below which no photoelectrons are emitted, regardless of light intensity. The cutoff *wavelength* λ_c can be derived from Equation 27.6:

$$KE_{max} = hf_c - \phi = 0 \quad \rightarrow \quad h\frac{c}{\lambda_c} - \phi = 0$$

$$\lambda_c = \frac{hc}{\phi} \qquad [27.7]$$

where c is the speed of light. Wavelengths *greater* than λ_c incident on a material with work function ϕ don't result in the emission of photoelectrons.

Table 27.1 Work Functions of Selected Metals

Metal	ϕ (eV)
Ag	4.73
Al	4.08
Cu	4.70
Fe	4.50
Na	2.46
Pb	4.14
Pt	6.35
Zn	4.31

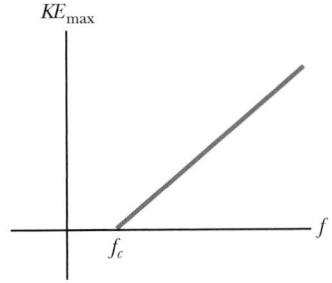

Figure 27.6 A sketch of KE_{max} versus the frequency of incident light for photoelectrons in a typical photoelectric effect experiment. Photons with frequency less than f_c don't have sufficient energy to eject an electron from the metal.

EXAMPLE 27.1 | Photoelectrons from Sodium

GOAL Understand the quantization of light and its role in the photoelectric effect.

PROBLEM A sodium surface is illuminated with light of wavelength 0.300 μm. The work function for sodium is 2.46 eV. Calculate (a) the energy of each photon in electron volts, (b) the maximum kinetic energy of the ejected photoelectrons, and (c) the cutoff wavelength for sodium.

STRATEGY Parts (a), (b), and (c) require substitution of values into Equations 27.5, 27.6, and 27.7, respectively.

SOLUTION

(a) Calculate the energy of each photon.

Obtain the frequency from the wavelength:

$$c = f\lambda \quad \rightarrow \quad f = \frac{c}{\lambda} = \frac{3.00 \times 10^8 \text{ m/s}}{0.300 \times 10^{-6} \text{ m}}$$

$$f = 1.00 \times 10^{15} \text{ Hz}$$

Use Equation 27.5 to calculate the photon's energy:

$$E = hf = (6.63 \times 10^{-34} \text{ J·s})(1.00 \times 10^{15} \text{ Hz})$$

$$= 6.63 \times 10^{-19} \text{ J}$$

$$= (6.63 \times 10^{-19} \text{ J})\left(\frac{1.00 \text{ eV}}{1.60 \times 10^{-19} \text{ J}}\right) = \boxed{4.14 \text{ eV}}$$

(b) Find the maximum kinetic energy of the photoelectrons.

Substitute into Equation 27.6:

$$KE_{\text{max}} = hf - \phi = 4.14 \text{ eV} - 2.46 \text{ eV} = \boxed{1.68 \text{ eV}}$$

(c) Compute the cutoff wavelength.

Convert ϕ from electron volts to joules:

$$\phi = 2.46 \text{ eV} = (2.46 \text{ eV})(1.60 \times 10^{-19} \text{ J/eV})$$

$$= 3.94 \times 10^{-19} \text{ J}$$

Find the cutoff wavelength using Equation 27.7.

$$\lambda_c = \frac{hc}{\phi} = \frac{(6.63 \times 10^{-34} \text{ J·s})(3.00 \times 10^8 \text{ m/s})}{3.94 \times 10^{-19} \text{ J}}$$

$$= 5.05 \times 10^{-7} \text{ m} = \boxed{505 \text{ nm}}$$

REMARKS The cutoff wavelength is in the yellow-green region of the visible spectrum.

QUESTION 27.1 True or False: Suppose in a given photoelectric experiment the frequency of light is larger than the cutoff frequency. The magnitude of the stopping potential, then, is larger than the energy of the incident photons.

EXERCISE 27.1 (a) What minimum-frequency light will eject photoelectrons from a copper surface? (b) If this frequency is tripled, find the maximum kinetic energy (in eV) of the resulting photoelectrons.

ANSWERS (a) 1.13×10^{15} Hz   (b) 9.40 eV

Photocells

APPLICATION
Photocells

The photoelectric effect has many interesting applications using a device called the *photocell*. The photocell shown in Active Figure 27.4 produces a current in the circuit when light of sufficiently high frequency falls on the cell, but it doesn't allow a current in the dark. This device is used in streetlights: a photoelectric control unit in the base of the light activates a switch that turns off the streetlight when ambient light strikes it. Many garage-door systems and elevators use a light beam and a photocell as a safety feature in their design. When the light beam strikes the photocell, the electric current generated is sufficiently large to maintain a closed circuit. When an object or a person blocks the light beam, the current is interrupted, which signals the door to open.

27.3 X-Rays

X-rays were discovered in 1895 by Wilhelm Röntgen and much later identified as electromagnetic waves, following a suggestion by Max von Laue in 1912. X-rays have higher frequencies than ultraviolet radiation and can penetrate most materials with relative ease. Typical x-ray wavelengths are about 0.1 nm, which is on the

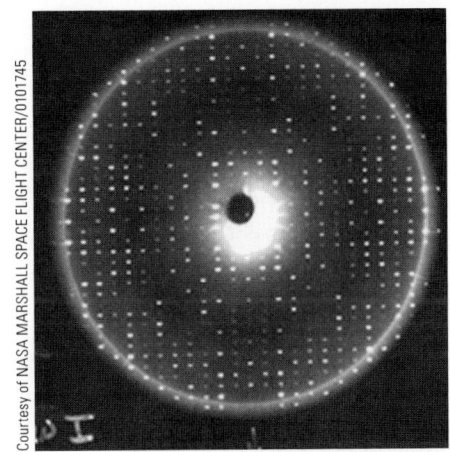

Figure 27.7 An x-ray diffraction pattern of a well-ordered protein crystal can be analyzed mathematically with powerful computers, leading to a determination of the structure of the protein. Once the structure is known, molecules can be designed that fit the active site of the protein. Such molecules can be used in developing therapeutic drugs that deactivate a given protein without affecting other biological systems.

Figure 27.8 (a) Diagram of an x-ray tube. (b) Photograph of an x-ray tube.

order of the atomic spacing in a solid. As a result, they can be diffracted by the regular atomic spacings in a crystal lattice, which act as a diffraction grating. The x-ray diffraction pattern of a well-ordered protein crystal is shown in Figure 27.7.

X-rays are produced when high-speed electrons are suddenly slowed down, such as when a metal target is struck by electrons that have been accelerated through a potential difference of several thousand volts. Figure 27.8a shows a schematic diagram of an x-ray tube. A current in the filament causes electrons to be emitted, and these freed electrons are accelerated toward a dense metal target, such as tungsten, which is held at a higher potential than the filament.

Figure 27.9 represents a plot of x-ray intensity versus wavelength for the spectrum of radiation emitted by an x-ray tube. Note that the spectrum has two distinct components. One component is a continuous broad spectrum that depends on the voltage applied to the tube. Superimposed on this component is a series of sharp, intense lines that depend on the nature of the target material. To observe these sharp lines, which represent radiation emitted by the target atoms as their electrons undergo rearrangements, the accelerating voltage must exceed a certain value, called the **threshold voltage**. We discuss threshold voltage further in Chapter 28. The continuous radiation is sometimes called **bremsstrahlung**, a German word meaning "braking radiation," because electrons emit radiation when they undergo an acceleration inside the target.

Figure 27.10 illustrates how x-rays are produced when an electron passes near a charged target nucleus. As the electron passes close to a positively charged nucleus contained in the target material, it is deflected from its path because of its electrical attraction to the nucleus; hence, it undergoes an acceleration. An analysis from classical physics shows that any charged particle will emit electromagnetic radiation when it is accelerated. (An example of this phenomenon is the production of electromagnetic waves by accelerated charges in a radio antenna, as described in Chapter 21.) According to quantum theory, this radiation must appear in the form of photons. Because the radiated photon shown in Figure 27.10 carries energy, the electron must lose kinetic energy because of its encounter with the target nucleus. An extreme example consists of the electron losing all of its energy in a single collision. In this case the initial energy of the electron ($e \Delta V$) is transformed completely into the energy of the photon (hf_{max}). In equation form,

$$e \Delta V = hf_{max} = \frac{hc}{\lambda_{min}}$$ [27.8]

Figure 27.9 The x-ray spectrum of a metal target consists of a broad continuous spectrum plus a number of sharp lines, which are due to *characteristic x-rays*. The data shown were obtained when 35-keV electrons bombarded a molybdenum target. Note that 1 pm $= 10^{-12}$ m $= 10^{-3}$ nm.

Figure 27.10 An electron passing near a charged target atom experiences an acceleration, and a photon is emitted in the process.

where $e \Delta V$ is the energy of the electron after it has been accelerated through a potential difference of ΔV volts and e is the charge on the electron. This equation says that the shortest wavelength radiation that can be produced is

$$\lambda_{min} = \frac{hc}{e \Delta V} \qquad [27.9]$$

Not all the radiation produced has this particular wavelength because many of the electrons aren't stopped in a single collision. The result is the production of the continuous spectrum of wavelengths.

Interesting insights into the process of painting and revising a masterpiece are being revealed by x-rays. Long-wavelength x-rays are absorbed in varying degrees by some paints, such as those having lead, cadmium, chromium, or cobalt as a base. The x-ray interactions with the paints give contrast because the different elements in the paints have different electron densities. Also, thicker layers will absorb more than thin layers. To examine a painting by an old master, a film is placed behind it while it is x-rayed from the front. Ghost outlines of earlier paintings and earlier forms of the final masterpiece are sometimes revealed when the film is developed.

APPLICATION
Using X-Rays to Study the Work of Master Painters

27.4 Diffraction of X-Rays by Crystals

In Chapter 24 we described how a diffraction grating could be used to measure the wavelength of light. In principle the wavelength of *any* electromagnetic wave can be measured if a grating having a suitable line spacing can be found. The spacing between lines must be approximately equal to the wavelength of the radiation to be measured. X-rays are electromagnetic waves with wavelengths on the order of 0.1 nm. It would be impossible to construct a grating with such a small spacing. As noted in the previous section, however, the regular array of atoms in a crystal could act as a three-dimensional grating for observing the diffraction of x-rays.

One experimental arrangement for observing x-ray diffraction is shown in Figure 27.11. A narrow beam of x-rays with a continuous wavelength range is incident on a crystal such as sodium chloride. The diffracted radiation is very intense in certain directions, corresponding to constructive interference from waves reflected from layers of atoms in the crystal. The diffracted radiation is detected by a photographic film and forms an array of spots known as a *Laue pattern*. The crystal structure is determined by analyzing the positions and intensities of the various spots in the pattern.

The arrangement of atoms in a crystal of NaCl is shown in Figure 27.12. The smaller red spheres represent Na$^+$ ions, and the larger blue spheres represent Cl$^-$ ions. The spacing between successive Na$^+$ (or Cl$^-$) ions in this cubic structure, denoted by the symbol a in Figure 27.12, is approximately 0.563 nm.

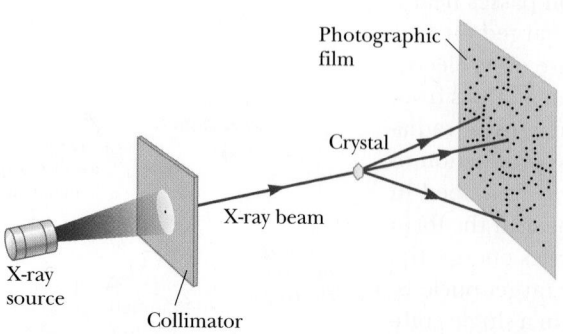

Figure 27.11 Schematic diagram of the technique used to observe the diffraction of x-rays by a single crystal. The array of spots formed on the film by the diffracted beams is called a Laue pattern. (See Fig. 27.7.)

The blue spheres represent Cl$^-$ ions, the red spheres Na$^+$ ions.

Figure 27.12 A model of the cubic crystalline structure of sodium chloride. The length of the cube edge is $a = 0.563$ nm.

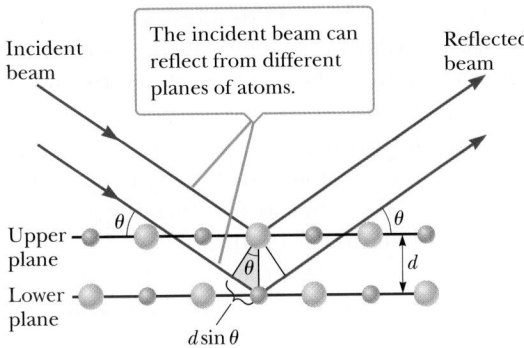

Incident beam

The incident beam can reflect from different planes of atoms.

Reflected beam

Upper plane

Lower plane

θ θ θ d

$d \sin \theta$

Figure 27.13 A two-dimensional depiction of the reflection of an x-ray beam from two parallel crystalline planes separated by a distance d. The beam reflected from the lower plane travels farther than the one reflected from the upper plane by an amount equal to $2d \sin \theta$.

A careful examination of the NaCl structure shows that the ions lie in various planes. The shaded areas in Figure 27.12 represent one example, in which the atoms lie in equally spaced planes. Now suppose an x-ray beam is incident at grazing angle θ on one of the planes, as in Figure 27.13. The beam can be reflected from both the upper and lower plane of atoms. The geometric construction in Figure 27.13, however, shows that the beam reflected from the lower surface travels farther than the beam reflected from the upper surface by a distance of $2d \sin \theta$. The two portions of the reflected beam will combine to produce constructive interference when this path difference equals some integral multiple of the wavelength λ. The condition for constructive interference is given by

$$2d \sin \theta = m\lambda \qquad m = 1, 2, 3, \ldots \qquad \text{[27.10]}$$ ◀ Bragg's law

This condition is known as **Bragg's law**, after W. L. Bragg (1890–1971), who first derived the relationship. If the wavelength and diffraction angle are measured, Equation 27.10 can be used to calculate the spacing between atomic planes.

The technique of x-ray diffraction has been used to determine the atomic arrangement of complex organic molecules such as proteins. Proteins are large molecules containing thousands of atoms that help regulate and speed up chemical life processes in cells. Some proteins are amazing catalysts, speeding up the slow room-temperature reactions in cells by 17 orders of magnitude. To understand this incredible biochemical reactivity, it is important to determine the structure of these intricate molecules.

The main technique used to determine the molecular structure of proteins, DNA, and RNA is x-ray diffraction using x-rays of wavelength of about 1 Å (1 Å = 0.1 nm = 1×10^{-10} m). This technique allows the experimenter to "see" individual atoms that are separated by about this distance in molecules. Because the biochemical x-ray diffraction sample is prepared in crystal form, the *geometry* (position of the bright spots in space) of the diffraction pattern is determined by the regular three-dimensional crystal lattice arrangement of molecules in the sample. The *intensities* of the bright diffraction spots are determined by the atoms and their electronic distributions in the fundamental building block of the crystal: the unit cell. Using complicated computational techniques, investigators can essentially deduce the molecular structure by matching the observed intensities of diffracted beams with a series of assumed atomic positions that determine the atomic structure and electron density of the molecule.

Crystallizing a large molecule such as DNA and obtaining its x-ray diffraction pattern is highly challenging. In the case of DNA, obtaining sufficiently pure crystals is especially difficult because there exist two crystalline forms, A and B, which arise in mixed form during preparation. These two forms result in diffraction patterns that can't be easily deciphered. In 1951 Rosalind Franklin, a researcher at King's College in London, developed an ingenious method of separating the two forms and managed to obtain excellent x-ray diffraction images of pure crystalline DNA in B-form. With these images she determined that the helical shape of DNA consisted of two interwoven strands, with the sugar-phosphate backbone on the outside of the molecule, refuting prior models that had the backbone on the inside. One of her images is shown in Figure 27.14.

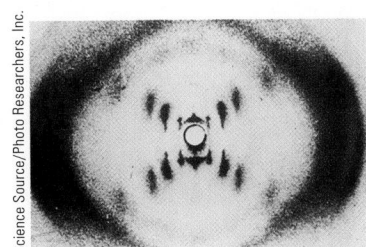

Figure 27.14 An x-ray diffraction photograph of DNA taken by Rosalind Franklin. The cross pattern of spots was a clue that DNA has a helical structure.

James Watson and Francis Crick used Franklin's work to uncover further details of the molecule and its function in heredity, particularly in regards to the internal structure. Attached to each sugar-phosphate unit of each strand is one of four base molecules: adenine, cytosine, guanine, or thymine. The bases are arranged sequentially along the strand, with patterns in the sequence of bases acting as codes for proteins that carry out various functions for a given organism. The bases in one strand bind to those in the other strand, forming a double helix. A model of the double helix is shown in Figure 27.15. In 1962 Watson, Crick, and a colleague of Franklin's, Maurice Wilkins, received the Nobel Prize for Physiology and Medicine for their work on understanding the structure and function of DNA. Franklin would have shared the prize, but died in 1958 of cancer at the age of thirty-eight. (The prize is not awarded posthumously.)

|←— 2 nm —→|

Figure 27.15 The double-helix structure of DNA.

■ EXAMPLE 27.2 | X-Ray Diffraction from Calcite

GOAL Understand Bragg's law and apply it to a crystal.

PROBLEM If the spacing between certain planes in a crystal of calcite ($CaCO_3$) is 0.314 nm, find the grazing angles at which first- and third-order interference will occur for x-rays of wavelength 0.070 0 nm.

STRATEGY Solve Bragg's law for $\sin \theta$ and substitute, using the inverse-sine function to obtain the angle.

SOLUTION

Find the grazing angle corresponding to $m = 1$, for first-order interference:

$$\sin \theta = \frac{m\lambda}{2d} = \frac{(0.070\ 0\ \text{nm})}{2(0.314\ \text{nm})} = 0.111$$

$$\theta = \sin^{-1}(0.111) = \boxed{6.37°}$$

Repeat the calculation for third-order interference ($m = 3$):

$$\sin \theta = \frac{m\lambda}{2d} = \frac{3(0.070\ 0\ \text{nm})}{2(0.314\ \text{nm})} = 0.334$$

$$\theta = \sin^{-1}(0.334) = \boxed{19.5°}$$

REMARKS Notice there is little difference between this kind of problem and a Young's slit experiment.

QUESTION 27.2 True or False: A smaller grazing angle implies a smaller distance between planes in the crystal lattice.

EXERCISE 27.2 X-rays of wavelength 0.060 0 nm are scattered from a crystal with a grazing angle of 11.7°. Assume $m = 1$ for this process. Calculate the spacing between the crystal planes.

ANSWER 0.148 nm

27.5 The Compton Effect

Further justification for the photon nature of light came from an experiment conducted by Arthur H. Compton in 1923. In his experiment Compton directed an x-ray beam of wavelength λ_0 toward a block of graphite. He found that the scattered x-rays had a slightly longer wavelength λ than the incident x-rays and hence the energies of the scattered rays were lower. The amount of energy reduction depended on the angle at which the x-rays were scattered. The change in wavelength $\Delta\lambda$ between a scattered x-ray and an incident x-ray is called the **Compton shift**.

To explain this effect, Compton assumed if a photon behaves like a particle, its collision with other particles is similar to a collision between two billiard balls. Hence, the x-ray photon carries both measurable *energy* and *momentum*, and these two quantities must be conserved in a collision. If the incident photon collides

Arthur Holly Compton
American Physicist (1892–1962)
Compton attended Wooster College and Princeton University. He became director of the laboratory at the University of Chicago, where experimental work concerned with sustained chain reactions was conducted. This work was of central importance to the construction of the first atomic bomb. Because of his discovery of the Compton effect and his work with cosmic rays, he shared the 1927 Nobel Prize in Physics with Charles Wilson.

The scattered photon, having lost energy, has a longer wavelength (and lower frequency) than the incident photon.

f', λ'

θ

f_0, λ_0

ϕ

The electron recoils just as if struck by a classical particle.

Figure 27.16 Diagram representing Compton scattering of a photon by an electron.

with an electron initially at rest, as in Figure 27.16, the photon transfers some of its energy and momentum to the electron. As a consequence, the energy and frequency of the scattered photon are lowered and its wavelength increases. Applying relativistic energy and momentum conservation to the collision described in Figure 27.16, the shift in wavelength of the scattered photon is given by

$$\Delta\lambda = \lambda - \lambda_0 = \frac{h}{m_e c}(1 - \cos\theta)$$ [27.11]

◀ The Compton shift formula

where m_e is the mass of the electron and θ is the angle between the directions of the scattered and incident photons. The quantity $h/m_e c$ is called the **Compton wavelength** and has a value of 0.002 43 nm. The Compton wavelength is very small relative to the wavelengths of visible light, so the shift in wavelength would be difficult to detect if visible light were used. Further, note that the Compton shift depends on the scattering angle θ and not on the wavelength. Experimental results for x-rays scattered from various targets obey Equation 27.11 and strongly support the photon concept.

■ Quick Quiz

27.1 True or False: When a photon scatters off an electron, the photon loses energy.

27.2 An x-ray photon is scattered by an electron. Does the frequency of the scattered photon relative to that of the incident photon (a) increase, (b) decrease, or (c) remain the same?

27.3 A photon of energy E_0 strikes a free electron, with the scattered photon of energy E moving in the direction opposite that of the incident photon. In this Compton effect interaction, what is the resulting kinetic energy of the electron? (a) E_0 (b) E (c) $E_0 - E$ (d) $E_0 + E$

■ EXAMPLE 27.3 | Scattering X-Rays

GOAL Understand Compton scattering and its effect on the photon's energy.

PROBLEM X-rays of wavelength $\lambda_i = 0.200\,000$ nm are scattered from a block of material. The scattered x-rays are observed at an angle of 45.0° to the incident beam. **(a)** Calculate the wavelength of the x-rays scattered at this angle. **(b)** Compute the fractional change in the energy of a photon in the collision.

STRATEGY To find the wavelength of the scattered x-ray photons, substitute into Equation 27.11 to obtain the wavelength shift, then add the result to the initial wavelength, λ_i. In part (b), calculating the fractional change in energy involves calculating the energy of the x-ray photon before and after, using $E = hf = hc/\lambda$. Taking the difference and dividing by the initial energy yields the desired fractional change in energy. Here, however, a symbolic expression is derived that relates energy terms and wavelengths.

(Continued)

SOLUTION

(a) Calculate the wavelength of the x-rays.

Substitute into Equation 27.11 to obtain the wavelength shift:

$$\Delta\lambda = \frac{h}{m_e c}(1 - \cos\theta)$$

$$= \frac{6.63 \times 10^{-34}\,\text{J}\cdot\text{s}}{(9.11 \times 10^{-31}\,\text{kg})(3.00 \times 10^8\,\text{m/s})}(1 - \cos 45.0°)$$

$$= 7.11 \times 10^{-13}\,\text{m} = 0.000\,711\,\text{nm}$$

Add this shift to the original wavelength to obtain the wavelength of the scattered photon:

$$\lambda_f = \Delta\lambda + \lambda_i = \boxed{0.200\,711\,\text{nm}}$$

(b) Find the fraction of energy lost by the photon in the collision.

Rewrite the energy E in terms of wavelength, using $c = f\lambda$:

$$E = hf = h\frac{c}{\lambda}$$

Compute $\Delta E/E$ using this expression:

$$\frac{\Delta E}{E} = \frac{E_f - E_i}{E_i} = \frac{hc/\lambda_f - hc/\lambda_i}{hc/\lambda_i}$$

Cancel hc and rearrange terms:

$$\frac{\Delta E}{E} = \frac{1/\lambda_f - 1/\lambda_i}{1/\lambda_i} = \frac{\lambda_i}{\lambda_f} - 1 = \frac{\lambda_i - \lambda_f}{\lambda_f} = -\frac{\Delta\lambda}{\lambda_f}$$

Substitute values from part (a):

$$\frac{\Delta E}{E} = -\frac{0.000\,711\,\text{nm}}{0.200\,711\,\text{nm}} = \boxed{-3.54 \times 10^{-3}}$$

REMARKS It is also possible to find this answer by substituting into the energy expression at an earlier stage, but the algebraic derivation is more elegant and instructive because it shows how changes in energy are related to changes in wavelength.

QUESTION 27.3 The incident photon loses energy. Where does it go?

EXERCISE 27.3 Repeat the example for a photon with wavelength 3.00×10^{-2} nm that scatters at an angle of 60.0°.

ANSWERS (a) 3.12×10^{-2} nm (b) $\Delta E/E = -3.88 \times 10^{-2}$

27.6 The Dual Nature of Light and Matter

Phenomena such as the photoelectric effect and the Compton effect offer evidence that when light (or other forms of electromagnetic radiation) and matter interact, the light behaves as if it were composed of particles having energy hf and momentum h/λ. In other contexts, however, light acts like a wave, exhibiting interference and diffraction effects. This apparent duality can be partly explained by considering the energies of photons in different contexts. For example, photons with frequencies in the radio wavelengths carry very little energy, and it may take 10^{10} such photons to create a signal in an antenna. These photons therefore act together like a wave to create the effect. Gamma rays, on the other hand, are so energetic that a single gamma ray photon can be detected.

In his doctoral dissertation in 1924, Louis de Broglie postulated that **because photons have wave and particle characteristics, perhaps all forms of matter have both properties**. This highly revolutionary idea had no experimental confirmation at that time. According to de Broglie, electrons, just like light, have a dual particle–wave nature.

◄ De Broglie's hypothesis

In Chapter 26 we found that the relationship between energy and momentum for a photon, which has a rest energy of zero, is $p = E/c$. We also know from Equation 27.5 that the energy of a photon is

$$E = hf = \frac{hc}{\lambda} \qquad\qquad [27.12]$$

Consequently, the momentum of a photon can be expressed as

$$p = \frac{E}{c} = \frac{hc}{c\lambda} = \frac{h}{\lambda}$$

[27.13] ◀ Momentum of a photon

From this equation, we see that the photon wavelength can be specified by its momentum, or $\lambda = h/p$. De Broglie suggested that *all* material particles with momentum p should have a characteristic wavelength $\lambda = h/p$. Because the momentum of a particle of mass m and speed v is $mv = p$, the **de Broglie wavelength** of a particle is

$$\lambda = \frac{h}{p} = \frac{h}{mv}$$

[27.14] ◀ De Broglie wavelength

Further, de Broglie postulated that the frequencies of matter waves (waves associated with particles having nonzero rest energy) obey the Einstein relationship for photons, $E = hf$, so that

$$f = \frac{E}{h}$$

[27.15] ◀ Frequency of matter waves

The dual nature of matter is quite apparent in Equations 27.14 and 27.15 because each contains both particle concepts (mv and E) and wave concepts (λ and f). The fact that these relationships had been established experimentally for photons made the de Broglie hypothesis that much easier to accept. The Davisson–Germer experiment in 1927 confirmed de Broglie's hypothesis by showing that electrons scattering off crystals form a diffraction pattern. The regularly spaced planes of atoms in crystalline regions of a nickel target act as a diffraction grating for electron matter waves.

Louis de Broglie
French Physicist (1892–1987)
De Broglie attended the Sorbonne in Paris, where he changed his major from history to theoretical physics. He was awarded the Nobel Prize in Physics in 1929 for his discovery of the wave nature of electrons.

■ *Quick Quiz*

27.4 True or False: As the momentum of a particle of mass m increases, its wavelength increases.

27.5 A nonrelativistic electron and a nonrelativistic proton are moving and have the same de Broglie wavelength. Which of the following are also the same for the two particles? (a) speed (b) kinetic energy (c) momentum (d) frequency

■ **EXAMPLE 27.4**   **The Electron Versus the Baseball**

GOAL Apply the de Broglie hypothesis to a quantum and a classical object.

PROBLEM (a) Compare the de Broglie wavelength for an electron ($m_e = 9.11 \times 10^{-31}$ kg) moving at a speed equal to 1.00×10^7 m/s with that of a baseball of mass 0.145 kg pitched at 45.0 m/s. (b) Compare these wavelengths with that of an electron traveling at $0.999c$.

STRATEGY This problem is a matter of substitution into Equation 27.14 for the de Broglie wavelength. In part (b) the relativistic momentum must be used.

SOLUTION

(a) Compare the de Broglie wavelengths of the electron and the baseball.

Substitute data for the electron into Equation 27.14:

$$\lambda_e = \frac{h}{m_e v} = \frac{6.63 \times 10^{-34}\,\text{J}\cdot\text{s}}{(9.11 \times 10^{-31}\,\text{kg})(1.00 \times 10^7\,\text{m/s})}$$

$$= 7.28 \times 10^{-11}\,\text{m}$$

Repeat the calculation with the baseball data:

$$\lambda_b = \frac{h}{m_b v} = \frac{6.63 \times 10^{-34}\,\text{J}\cdot\text{s}}{(0.145\,\text{kg})(45.0\,\text{m/s})} = 1.02 \times 10^{-34}\,\text{m}$$

(Continued)

(b) Find the wavelength for an electron traveling at 0.999c.

Replace the momentum in Equation 27.14 with the relativistic momentum:

$$\lambda_e = \frac{h}{m_e v / \sqrt{1 - v^2/c^2}} = \frac{h\sqrt{1 - v^2/c^2}}{m_e v}$$

Substitute:

$$\lambda_e = \frac{(6.63 \times 10^{-34}\,\text{J}\cdot\text{s})\sqrt{1 - (0.999c)^2/c^2}}{(9.11 \times 10^{-31}\,\text{kg})(0.999 \cdot 3.00 \times 10^8\,\text{m/s})}$$

$$= \boxed{1.09 \times 10^{-13}\,\text{m}}$$

REMARKS The electron wavelength corresponds to that of x-rays in the electromagnetic spectrum. The baseball, by contrast, has a wavelength much smaller than any aperture through which the baseball could possibly pass, so we couldn't observe any of its diffraction effects. It is generally true that the wave properties of large-scale objects can't be observed. Notice that even at extreme relativistic speeds, the electron wavelength is still far larger than the baseball's.

QUESTION 27.4 How does doubling the speed of a particle affect its wavelength? Is your answer always true? Explain.

EXERCISE 27.4 Find the de Broglie wavelength of a proton ($m_p = 1.67 \times 10^{-27}$ kg) moving at 1.00×10^7 m/s.

ANSWER 3.97×10^{-14} m

Application: The Electron Microscope

BIO APPLICATION
Electron Microscopes

A practical device that relies on the wave characteristics of electrons is the **electron microscope**. A *transmission* electron microscope, used for viewing flat, thin samples, is shown in Figure 27.17. In many respects it is similar to an optical micro-

Electron gun
Cathode
Anode
Electromagnetic lens
Electromagnetic condenser lens
Screen
Visual transmission

Vacuum
Core
Coil
Electron beam
Specimen holder
Specimen chamber door
Projector lens
Photo chamber

Steven Allen/Brand X Pictures/Jupiter Images

a

b

Figure 27.17 (a) Diagram of a transmission electron microscope for viewing a thin, sectioned sample. The "lenses" that control the electron beam are magnetic deflection coils. (b) An electron microscope.

scope, but the electron microscope has a much greater resolving power because it can accelerate electrons to very high kinetic energies, giving them very short wavelengths. No microscope can resolve details that are significantly smaller than the wavelength of the radiation used to illuminate the object. Typically, the wavelengths of electrons in an electron microscope are smaller than the visible wavelengths by a factor of about 10^{-5}.

The electron beam in an electron microscope is controlled by electrostatic or magnetic deflection, which acts on the electrons to focus the beam to an image. Due to limitations in the electromagnetic lenses used, however, the improvement in resolution over light microscopes is only about a factor of 1 000, two orders of magnitude smaller than that implied by the electron wavelength. Rather than examining the image through an eyepiece as in an optical microscope, the viewer looks at an image formed on a fluorescent screen. (The viewing screen must be fluorescent because otherwise the image produced wouldn't be visible.)

■ **APPLYING PHYSICS 27.2** | **X-Ray Microscopes?**

Electron microscopes (Fig. 27.17) take advantage of the wave nature of particles. Electrons are accelerated to high speeds, giving them a short de Broglie wavelength. Imagine an electron microscope using electrons with a de Broglie wavelength of 0.2 nm. Why don't we design a microscope using 0.2-nm *photons* to do the same thing?

EXPLANATION Because electrons are charged particles, they interact electrically with the sample in the microscope and scatter according to the shape and density of various portions of the sample, providing a means of viewing the sample. Photons of wavelength 0.2 nm are uncharged and in the x-ray region of the spectrum. They tend to simply pass through the thin sample without interacting. ■

27.7 The Wave Function

De Broglie's revolutionary idea that particles should have a wave nature soon moved out of the realm of skepticism to the point where it was viewed as a necessary concept in understanding the subatomic world. In 1926 Austrian–German physicist Erwin Schrödinger proposed a wave equation that described how matter waves change in space and time. The Schrödinger wave equation represents a key element in the theory of quantum mechanics. It's as important in quantum mechanics as Newton's laws in classical mechanics. Schrödinger's equation has been successfully applied to the hydrogen atom and to many other microscopic systems.

Solving Schrödinger's equation (beyond the level of this course) determines a quantity Ψ called the **wave function**. Each particle is represented by a wave function Ψ that depends both on position and on time. Once Ψ is found, Ψ^2 gives us information on the **probability** (per unit volume) of finding the particle in any given region. To understand this, we return to Young's experiment involving coherent light passing through a double slit.

First, recall from Chapter 21 that the intensity of a light beam is proportional to the square of the electric field strength E associated with the beam: $I \propto E^2$. According to the wave model of light, there are certain points on the viewing screen where the net electric field is zero as a result of destructive interference of waves from the two slits. Because E is zero at these points, the intensity is also zero and the screen is dark there. Likewise, at points on the screen at which constructive interference occurs, E is large, as is the intensity; hence, these locations are bright.

Now consider the same experiment when light is viewed as having a particle nature. The number of photons reaching a point on the screen per second increases as the intensity (brightness) increases. Consequently, the number of photons that strike a unit area on the screen each second is proportional to the square of the electric field, or $N \propto E^2$. From a probabilistic point of view, a photon has a high probability of striking the screen at a point where the intensity (and E^2) is high and a low probability of striking the screen where the intensity is low.

AIP Emilio Segre Visual Archives

Erwin Schrödinger
Austrian Theoretical Physicist
(1887–1961)
Schrödinger is best known as the creator of wave mechanics, a less cumbersome theory than the equivalent matrix mechanics developed by Werner Heisenberg. In 1933 Schrödinger left Germany and eventually settled at the Dublin Institute of Advanced Study, where he spent 17 happy, creative years working on problems in general relativity, cosmology, and the application of quantum physics to biology. In 1956 he returned home to Austria and his beloved Tyrolean mountains, where he died in 1961.

When describing particles rather than photons, Ψ rather than E plays the role of the amplitude. Using an analogy with the description of light, we make the following interpretation of Ψ for particles: If Ψ is a wave function used to describe a single particle, the value of Ψ^2 at some location at a given time is proportional to the probability per unit volume of finding the particle at that location at that time. Adding all the values of Ψ^2 in a given region gives the probability of finding the particle in that region.

27.8 The Uncertainty Principle

If you were to measure the position and speed of a particle at any instant, you would always be faced with experimental uncertainties in your measurements. According to classical mechanics, no fundamental barrier to an ultimate refinement of the apparatus or experimental procedures exists. In other words, it's possible, in principle, to make such measurements with arbitrarily small uncertainty. Quantum theory predicts, however, that such a barrier does exist. In 1927 Werner Heisenberg (1901–1976) introduced this notion, which is now known as the **uncertainty principle**:

> If a measurement of the position of a particle is made with precision Δx and a simultaneous measurement of linear momentum is made with precision Δp_x, the product of the two uncertainties can never be smaller than $h/4\pi$:
>
> $$\Delta x\, \Delta p_x \geq \frac{h}{4\pi} \qquad \text{[27.16]}$$

In other words, **it is physically impossible to measure simultaneously the exact position and exact linear momentum of a particle**. If Δx is very small, then Δp_x is large, and vice versa.

To understand the physical origin of the uncertainty principle, consider the following thought experiment introduced by Heisenberg. Suppose you wish to measure the position and linear momentum of an electron as accurately as possible. You might be able to do so by viewing the electron with a powerful light microscope. For you to see the electron and determine its location, at least one photon of light must bounce off the electron, as shown in Figure 27.18a, and pass through the microscope into your eye, as shown in Figure 27.18b. When it strikes the electron, however, the photon transfers some unknown amount of its momentum to the electron. Thus, in the process of locating the electron very accurately (that is, by making Δx very small), the light that enables you to succeed in your measure-

Werner Heisenberg
German Theoretical Physicist
(1901–1976)
Heisenberg obtained his Ph.D. in 1923 at the University of Munich, where he studied under Arnold Sommerfeld. While physicists such as de Broglie and Schrödinger tried to develop physical models of the atom, Heisenberg developed an abstract mathematical model called *matrix mechanics* to explain the wavelengths of spectral lines. Heisenberg made many other significant contributions to physics, including his famous uncertainty principle, for which he received the Nobel Prize in Physics in 1932; the prediction of two forms of molecular hydrogen; and theoretical models of the nucleus of an atom.

Figure 27.18 A thought experiment for viewing an electron with a powerful microscope. (a) The electron is viewed before colliding with the photon. (b) The electron recoils (is disturbed) as the result of the collision with the photon.

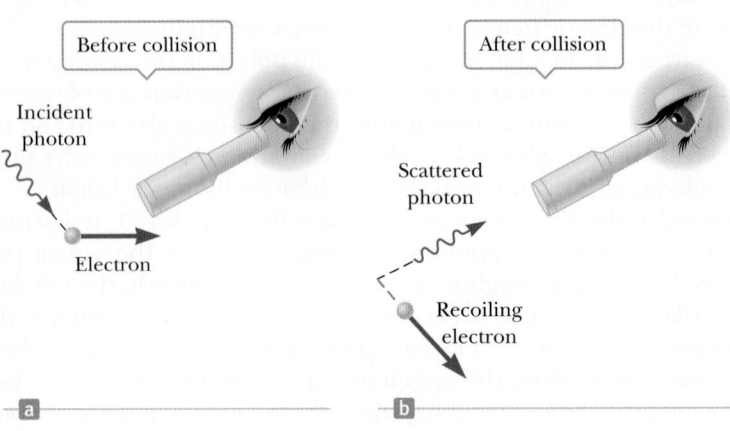

ment changes the electron's momentum to some undeterminable extent (making Δp_x very large).

   The incoming photon has momentum h/λ. As a result of the collision, the photon transfers part or all of its momentum along the x-axis to the electron. Therefore, the *uncertainty* in the electron's momentum after the collision is as great as the momentum of the incoming photon: $\Delta p_x = h/\lambda$. Further, because the photon also has wave properties, we expect to be able to determine the electron's position to within one wavelength of the light being used to view it, so $\Delta x = \lambda$. Multiplying these two uncertainties gives

$$\Delta x\, \Delta p_x = \lambda\left(\frac{h}{\lambda}\right) = h$$

The value h represents the minimum in the product of the uncertainties. Because the uncertainty can always be greater than this minimum, we have

$$\Delta x\, \Delta p_x \geq h$$

Apart from the numerical factor $1/4\pi$ introduced by Heisenberg's more precise analysis, this inequality agrees with Equation 27.16.

   Another form of the uncertainty relationship sets a limit on the accuracy with which the energy E of a system can be measured in a finite time interval Δt:

$$\Delta E\, \Delta t \geq \frac{h}{4\pi} \qquad\qquad \textbf{[27.17]}$$

It can be inferred from this relationship that the energy of a particle cannot be measured with complete precision in a very short interval of time. Thus, when an electron is viewed as a particle, the uncertainty principle tells us that (a) its position and velocity cannot both be known precisely at the same time and (b) its energy can be uncertain for a period given by $\Delta t = h/(4\pi\, \Delta E)$.

■ EXAMPLE 27.5 | Locating an Electron

GOAL Apply Heisenberg's position–momentum uncertainty principle.

PROBLEM The speed of an electron is measured to be 5.00×10^3 m/s to an accuracy of 0.003 00%. Find the minimum uncertainty in determining the position of this electron.

STRATEGY After computing the momentum and its uncertainty, substitute into Heisenberg's uncertainty principle, Equation 27.16.

....

SOLUTION

Calculate the momentum of the electron:

$$p_x = m_e v = (9.11 \times 10^{-31}\,\text{kg})(5.00 \times 10^3\,\text{m/s})$$
$$= 4.56 \times 10^{-27}\,\text{kg} \cdot \text{m/s}$$

The uncertainty in p_x is 0.003 00% of this value:

$$\Delta p_x = 0.000\,030\,0 p_x = (0.000\,030\,0)(4.56 \times 10^{-27}\,\text{kg} \cdot \text{m/s})$$
$$= 1.37 \times 10^{-31}\,\text{kg} \cdot \text{m/s}$$

Now calculate the uncertainty in position using this value of Δp_x and Equation 27.17:

$$\Delta x\, \Delta p_x \geq \frac{h}{4\pi} \quad \rightarrow \quad \Delta x \geq \frac{h}{4\pi\, \Delta p_x}$$

$$\Delta x \geq \frac{6.626 \times 10^{-34}\,\text{J} \cdot \text{s}}{4\pi(1.37 \times 10^{-31}\,\text{kg} \cdot \text{m/s})} = 0.385 \times 10^{-3}\,\text{m}$$

$$= \boxed{0.385\,\text{mm}}$$

....

REMARKS Notice that this isn't an exact calculation: the uncertainty in position can take any value as long as it's greater than or equal to the value given by the uncertainty principle.

(Continued)

QUESTION 27.5 True or False: The uncertainty in the position of a proton in the helium nucleus is, on average, less than the uncertainty of a proton in a uranium atom.

EXERCISE 27.5 Suppose an electron is found somewhere in an atom of diameter 1.25×10^{-10} m. Estimate the uncertainty in the electron's momentum (in one dimension).

ANSWER $\Delta p \geq 4.22 \times 10^{-25}$ kg $\cdot$ m/s

■ SUMMARY

27.1 Blackbody Radiation and Planck's Hypothesis

The characteristics of **blackbody radiation** can't be explained with classical concepts. The peak of a blackbody radiation curve is given by **Wien's displacement law,**

$$\lambda_{max} T = 0.289\,8 \times 10^{-2} \text{ m} \cdot \text{K} \qquad [27.1]$$

where λ_{max} is the wavelength at which the curve peaks and T is the absolute temperature of the object emitting the radiation.

Planck first introduced the quantum concept when he assumed the subatomic oscillators responsible for blackbody radiation could have only discrete amounts of energy given by

$$E_n = nhf \qquad [27.2]$$

where n is a positive integer called a **quantum number** and f is the frequency of vibration of the resonator.

27.2 The Photoelectric Effect and the Particle Theory of Light

The **photoelectric effect** is a process whereby electrons are ejected from a metal surface when light is incident on that surface. Einstein provided a successful explanation of this effect by extending Planck's quantum hypothesis to electromagnetic waves. In this model, light is viewed as a stream of particles called photons, each with energy $E = hf$, where f is the light frequency and h is **Planck's constant**. The maximum kinetic energy of the ejected photoelectrons is

$$KE_{max} = hf - \phi \qquad [27.6]$$

where ϕ is the **work function** of the metal.

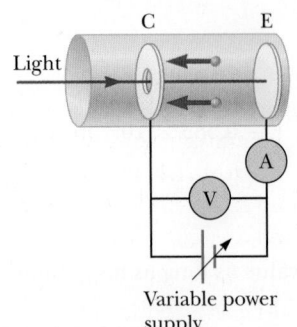

A circuit diagram for studying the photoelectric effect.

27.3 X-Rays

27.4 Diffraction of X-Rays by Crystals

X-rays are produced when high-speed electrons are suddenly decelerated. When electrons have been accelerated through a voltage V, the shortest-wavelength radiation that can be produced is

$$\lambda_{min} = \frac{hc}{e\,\Delta V} \qquad [27.9]$$

An electron passing near a charged target atom experiences an acceleration, and a photon is emitted in the process.

The regular array of atoms in a crystal can act as a diffraction grating for x-rays and for electrons. The condition for constructive interference of the diffracted rays is given by **Bragg's law:**

$$2d \sin \theta = m\lambda \qquad m = 1, 2, 3, \ldots \qquad [27.10]$$

Bragg's law bears a similarity to the equation for the diffraction pattern of a double slit.

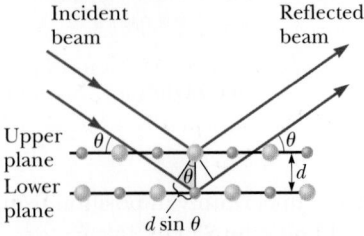

A two-dimensional depiction of the reflection of an x-ray beam from two parallel crystalline planes separated by a distance d. The beam reflected from the lower plane travels farther than the one reflected from the upper plane by an amount equal to $2d \sin \theta$.

27.5 The Compton Effect

X-rays from an incident beam are scattered at various angles by electrons in a target such as carbon. In such a scattering event, a shift in wavelength is observed for the scattered x-rays. This phenomenon is known as the **Compton shift**. Conservation of momentum and energy applied to a photon–electron collision yields the following expression for the shift in wavelength of the scattered x-rays:

$$\Delta\lambda = \lambda - \lambda_0 = \frac{h}{m_e c}(1 - \cos\theta) \qquad [27.11]$$

Here, m_e is the mass of the electron, c is the speed of light, and θ is the scattering angle.

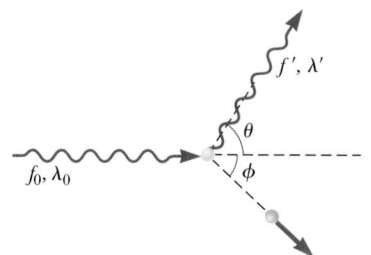

Diagram representing Compton scattering of a photon by an electron.

27.6 The Dual Nature of Light and Matter
Light exhibits both a particle and a wave nature. De Broglie proposed that *all* matter has both a particle and a wave nature. The **de Broglie wavelength** of any particle of mass m and speed v is

$$\lambda = \frac{h}{p} = \frac{h}{mv} \qquad [27.14]$$

De Broglie also proposed that the frequencies of the waves associated with particles obey the Einstein relationship $E = hf$.

27.7 The Wave Function
In the theory of **quantum mechanics,** each particle is described by a quantity Ψ called the **wave function**. The probability per unit volume of finding the particle at a particular point at some instant is proportional to Ψ^2. Quantum mechanics has been highly successful in describing the behavior of atomic and molecular systems.

27.8 The Uncertainty Principle
According to Heisenberg's **uncertainty principle**, it is impossible to measure simultaneously the exact position and exact momentum of a particle. If Δx is the uncertainty in the measured position and Δp_x the uncertainty in the momentum, the product $\Delta x \, \Delta p_x$ is given by

$$\Delta x \, \Delta p_x \geq \frac{h}{4\pi} \qquad [27.16]$$

Also,

$$\Delta E \, \Delta t \geq \frac{h}{4\pi} \qquad [27.17]$$

where ΔE is the uncertainty in the energy of the particle and Δt is the uncertainty in the time it takes to measure the energy.

■ MULTIPLE-CHOICE QUESTIONS

WebAssign The multiple-choice questions in this chapter may be assigned online in Enhanced WebAssign.

---

1. In a photoelectric experiment, a metal is irradiated with light of energy 3.56 eV. If a stopping potential of 1.10 V is required, what is the work function of the metal? (a) 1.83 eV (b) 2.46 eV (c) 3.20 eV (d) 4.66 eV (e) 0.644 eV

2. What is the surface temperature of a distant star having a peak wavelength of 475 nm? (a) 6 100 K (b) 5 630 K (c) 5 510 K (d) 6 350 K (e) 6 560 K

3. What is the de Broglie wavelength of an electron accelerated from rest through a potential difference of 50.0 V? (a) 0.100 nm (b) 0.174 nm (c) 0.139 nm (d) 0.834 nm (e) 0.435 nm

4. An electron is accelerated through a potential difference of 3.00 V before colliding with a metal target. What minimum-wavelength light can such an electron emit? (a) 204 nm (b) 352 nm (c) 414 nm (d) 536 nm (e) 612 nm

5. Which of the following statements are true according to the uncertainty principle? (a) It is impossible to simultaneously determine both the position and the momentum of a particle with arbitrary accuracy. (b) It is impossible to simultaneously determine both the energy and the momentum of a particle with arbitrary accuracy. (c) It is impossible to determine a particle's energy with arbitrary accuracy in a finite amount of time. (d) It is impossible to measure the position of a particle with arbitrary accuracy in a finite amount of time. (e) It is impossible to simultaneously measure both the energy and position of a particle with arbitrary accuracy.

6. A photon scatters off an electron at an angle of $1.80 \times 10^2°$ with respect to its initial motion. What is the change in the photon's wavelength? (a) 0.002 43 nm (b) 0.243 nm (c) 0.001 72 nm (d) 0.004 85 nm (e) 0.121 nm

7. A proton, electron, and a helium nucleus all move at speed v. Rank their de Broglie wavelengths from longest to shortest. (a) proton, helium nucleus, electron (b) helium nucleus, proton, electron (c) proton, electron, helium nucleus (d) helium nucleus, electron, proton (e) electron, proton, helium nucleus

8. The first order x-ray scattering angle of crystal A is greater than the corresponding scattering angle of crystal B for x-rays of a given energy. What can be said

of the separation distance d_A of crystalline planes in crystal A as compared with the separation distance d_B in B? (a) $d_A = d_B$ (b) $d_A > d_B$ (c) $d_A < d_B$ (d) The answer depends on the energy of the x-rays. (e) The answer depends on the intensity of the x-rays.

9. Which one of the following phenomena most clearly demonstrates the particle nature of light? (a) diffraction (b) the photoelectric effect (c) polarization (d) interference (e) refraction

10. Which one of the following phenomena most clearly demonstrates the wave nature of electrons? (a) the photoelectric effect (b) Wien's law (c) blackbody radiation (d) the Compton effect (e) diffraction of electrons by crystals

11. An x-ray photon is scattered by an originally stationary electron. Relative to the frequency of the incident photon, is the frequency of the scattered photon (a) lower, (b) higher, or (c) unchanged?

12. An electron and a proton, moving in opposite directions, are accelerated from rest through the same potential difference. Which particle has the longer wavelength? (a) The electron does. (b) The proton does. (c) Both are the same. (d) Neither has a wavelength.

CONCEPTUAL QUESTIONS

WebAssign The conceptual questions in this chapter may be assigned online in Enhanced WebAssign.

1. If you observe objects inside a very hot kiln, why is it difficult to discern the shapes of the objects?

2. Why is an electron microscope more suitable than an optical microscope for "seeing" objects of atomic size?

3. Are blackbodies black?

4. Why is it impossible to simultaneously measure the position and velocity of a particle with infinite accuracy?

5. All objects radiate energy. Why, then, are we not able to see all the objects in a dark room?

6. Is light a wave or a particle? Support your answer by citing specific experimental evidence.

7. In the photoelectric effect, explain why the stopping potential depends on the frequency of the light but not on the intensity.

8. Which has more energy, a photon of ultraviolet radiation or a photon of yellow light?

9. Why does the existence of a cutoff frequency in the photoelectric effect favor a particle theory of light rather than a wave theory?

10. What effect, if any, would you expect the temperature of a material to have on the ease with which electrons can be ejected from it via the photoelectric effect?

11. The cutoff frequency of a material is f_0. Are electrons emitted from the material when (a) light of frequency greater than f_0 is incident on the material? (b) Less than f_0?

12. The brightest star in the constellation Lyra is the bluish star Vega, whereas the brightest star in Boötes is the reddish star Arcturus. How do you account for the difference in color of the two stars?

13. If the photoelectric effect is observed in one metal, can you conclude that the effect will also be observed in another metal under the same conditions? Explain.

14. The atoms in a crystal lie in planes separated by a few tenths of a nanometer. Can a crystal be used to produce a diffraction pattern with visible light as it does for x-rays? Explain your answer with reference to Bragg's law.

15. Is an electron a wave or a particle? Support your answer by citing some experimental results.

16. If matter has a wave nature, why is this wave-like characteristic not observable in our daily experiences?

PROBLEMS

WebAssign The problems in this chapter may be assigned online in Enhanced WebAssign. Selected problems also have Watch It video solutions.

1. denotes straightforward problem; 2. denotes intermediate problem;

3. denotes challenging problem

1. denotes full solution available in *Student Solutions Manual/ Study Guide*

1.	denotes problems most often assigned in Enhanced WebAssign
BIO	denotes biomedical problems
GP	denotes guided problems
M	denotes Master It tutorial available in Enhanced WebAssign
Q|C	denotes asking for quantitative and conceptual reasoning
S	denotes symbolic reasoning problem

27.1 Blackbody Radiation and Planck's Hypothesis

1. (a) What is the surface temperature of Betelgeuse, a red giant star in the constellation of Orion, which radiates with a peak wavelength of about 970 nm?

(b) Rigel, a bluish-white star in Orion, radiates with a peak wavelength of 145 nm. Find the temperature of Rigel's surface.

2. (a) Lightning produces a maximum air temperature on the order of 10^4 K, whereas (b) a nuclear explosion produces a temperature on the order of 10^7 K. Use Wien's displacement law to find the order of magnitude of the wavelength of the thermally produced photons radiated with greatest intensity by each of these sources. Name the part of the electromagnetic spectrum where you would expect each to radiate most strongly.

3. **BIO** The temperature of a student's skin is 33.0°C. At what wavelength does the radiation emitted from the skin reach its peak?

4. The radius of our Sun is 6.96×10^8 m, and its total power output is 3.85×10^{26} W. (a) Assuming the Sun's surface emits as a black body, calculate its surface temperature. (b) Using the result of part (a), find λ_{max} for the Sun.

5. Calculate the energy in electron volts of a photon having a wavelength (a) in the microwave range, 5.00 cm, (b) in the visible light range, 500 nm, and (c) in the x-ray range, 5.00 nm.

6. Suppose a star with radius 8.50×10^8 m has a peak wavelength of 685 nm in the spectrum of its emitted radiation. (a) Find the energy of a photon with this wavelength. (b) What is surface temperature of the star? (c) At what rate is energy emitted from the star in the form of radiation? Assume the star is a blackbody ($e = 1$). (d) Using the answer to part (a), estimate the rate at which photons leave the surface of the star.

7. **M** Calculate the energy, in electron volts, of a photon whose frequency is (a) 620 THz, (b) 3.10 GHz, and (c) 46.0 MHz.

8. **BIO** The threshold of dark-adapted (scotopic) vision is 4.0×10^{-11} W/m^2 at a central wavelength of 500 nm. If light with this intensity and wavelength enters the eye when the pupil is open to its maximum diameter of 8.5 mm, how many photons per second enter the eye?

27.2 The Photoelectric Effect and the Particle Theory of Light

9. When light of wavelength 350 nm falls on a potassium surface, electrons having a maximum kinetic energy of 1.31 eV are emitted. Find (a) the work function of potassium, (b) the cutoff wavelength, and (c) the frequency corresponding to the cutoff wavelength.

10. The work function for zinc is 4.31 eV. (a) Find the cutoff wavelength for zinc. (b) What is the lowest frequency of light incident on zinc that releases photoelectrons from its surface? (c) If photons of energy 5.50 eV are incident on zinc, what is the maximum kinetic energy of the ejected photoelectrons?

11. **GP** The work function for platinum is 6.35 eV. (a) Convert the value of the work function from electron volts to joules. (b) Find the cutoff frequency for platinum. (c) What maximum wavelength of light

incident on platinum releases photoelectrons from the platinum's surface? (d) If light of energy 8.50 eV is incident on zinc, what is the maximum kinetic energy of the ejected photoelectrons? Give the answer in electron volts. (e) For photons of energy 8.50 eV, what stopping potential would be required to arrest the current of photoelectrons?

12. **Q|C** Lithium, beryllium, and mercury have work functions of 2.30 eV, 3.90 eV, and 4.50 eV, respectively. Light with a wavelength of 4.00×10^2 nm is incident on each of these metals. (a) Which of these metals emit photoelectrons in response to the light? Why? (b) Find the maximum kinetic energy for the photoelectrons in each case.

13. When light of wavelength 254 nm falls on cesium, the required stopping potential is 3.00 V. If light of wavelength 436 nm is used, the stopping potential is 0.900 V. Use this information to plot a graph like that shown in Figure 27.6, and from the graph determine the cutoff frequency for cesium and its work function.

14. Two light sources are used in a photoelectric experiment to determine the work function for a particular metal surface. When green light from a mercury lamp ($\lambda = 546.1$ nm) is used, a stopping potential of 0.376 V reduces the photocurrent to zero. (a) Based on this measurement, what is the work function for this metal? (b) What stopping potential would be observed when using the yellow light from a helium discharge tube ($\lambda = 587.5$ nm)?

27.3 X-Rays

15. The extremes of the x-ray portion of the electromagnetic spectrum range from approximately 1.0×10^{-8} m to 1.0×10^{-13} m. Find the minimum accelerating voltages required to produce wavelengths at these two extremes.

16. **Q|C** Calculate the minimum-wavelength x-ray that can be produced when a target is struck by an electron that has been accelerated through a potential difference of (a) 15.0 kV and (b) 1.00×10^2 kV. (c) What happens to the minimum wavelength as the potential difference increases?

17. What minimum accelerating voltage is required to produce an x-ray with a wavelength of 70.0 pm?

27.4 Diffraction of X-Rays by Crystals

18. When x-rays of wavelength of 0.129 nm are incident on the surface of a crystal having a structure similar to that of NaCl, a first-order maximum is observed at 8.15°. Calculate the interplanar spacing of the crystal based on this information.

19. **M** Potassium iodide has an interplanar spacing of $d = 0.296$ nm. A monochromatic x-ray beam shows a first-order diffraction maximum when the grazing angle is 7.6°. Calculate the x-ray wavelength.

20. QC The first-order diffraction maximum is observed at 12.6° for a crystal having an interplanar spacing of 0.240 nm. How many other orders can be observed in the diffraction pattern, and at what angles do they appear? Why is there an upper limit to the number of observed orders?

21. X-rays of wavelength 0.140 nm are reflected from a certain crystal, and the first-order maximum occurs at an angle of 14.4°. What value does this give for the interplanar spacing of the crystal?

27.5 The Compton Effect

22. X-rays are scattered from a target at an angle of 55.0° with the direction of the incident beam. Find the wavelength shift of the scattered x-rays.

23. M A 0.001 60-nm photon scatters from a free electron. For what (photon) scattering angle does the recoiling electron have kinetic energy equal to the energy of the scattered photon?

24. S A photon having wavelength λ scatters off a free electron at A (Fig. P27.24), producing a second photon having wavelength λ'. This photon then scatters off another free electron at B, producing a third photon having wavelength λ'' and moving in a direction directly opposite the original photon as shown in the figure. Determine the value of $\Delta\lambda = \lambda'' - \lambda$.

Figure P27.24

25. A 0.110-nm photon collides with a stationary electron. After the collision, the electron moves forward and the photon recoils backwards. Find (a) the momentum and (b) the kinetic energy of the electron.

26. In a Compton scattering experiment, an x-ray photon scatters through an angle of 17.4° from a free electron that is initially at rest. The electron recoils with a speed of 2 180 km/s. Calculate (a) the wavelength of the incident photon and (b) the angle through which the electron scatters.

27.6 The Dual Nature of Light and Matter

27. (a) If the wavelength of an electron is 5.00×10^{-7} m, how fast is it moving? (b) If the electron has a speed equal to 1.00×10^7 m/s, what is its wavelength?

28. Calculate the de Broglie wavelength of a proton moving at (a) 2.00×10^4 m/s and (b) 2.00×10^7 m/s.

29. De Broglie postulated that the relationship $\lambda = h/p$ is valid for relativistic particles. What is the de Broglie wavelength for a (relativistic) electron having a kinetic energy of 3.00 MeV?

30. (a) An electron has a kinetic energy of 3.00 eV. Find its wavelength. (b) A photon has energy 3.00 eV. Find its wavelength.

31. The resolving power of a microscope is proportional to the wavelength used. A resolution of 1.0×10^{-11} m (0.010 nm) would be required in order to "see" an atom. (a) If electrons were used (electron microscope), what minimum kinetic energy would be required of the electrons? (b) If photons were used, what minimum photon energy would be needed to obtain 1.0×10^{-11} m resolution?

32. QC A nonrelativistic particle of mass m and charge q is accelerated from rest through a potential difference ΔV. (a) Use conservation of energy to find a symbolic expression for the momentum of the particle in terms of m, q, and ΔV. (b) Write a symbolic expression for the de Broglie wavelength using the result of part (a). (c) If an electron and proton go through the same potential difference but in opposite directions, which particle will have the shorter wavelength?

27.7 The Wave Function

27.8 The Uncertainty Principle

33. In the ground state of hydrogen, the uncertainty in the position of the electron is roughly 0.10 nm. If the speed of the electron is approximately the same as the uncertainty in its speed, about how fast is it moving?

34. An electron is located on a pinpoint having a diameter of 2.5 μm. What is the minimum uncertainty in the speed of the electron?

35. M An electron and a 0.020 0-kg bullet each have a velocity of magnitude 500 m/s, accurate to within 0.010 0%. Within what lower limit could we determine the position of each object along the direction of the velocity?

36. Suppose Fuzzy, a quantum mechanical duck, lives in a world in which $h = 2\pi$ J · s. Fuzzy has a mass of 2.00 kg and is initially known to be within a pond 1.00 m wide. (a) What is the minimum uncertainty in the duck's speed? (b) Assuming this uncertainty in speed to prevail for 5.00 s, determine the uncertainty in Fuzzy's position after this time.

37. The average lifetime of a muon is about 2 μs. Estimate the minimum uncertainty in the energy of a muon.

38. QC (a) Show that the kinetic energy of a nonrelativistic particle can be written in terms of its momentum as $KE = p^2/2m$. (b) Use the results of part (a) to find the minimum kinetic energy of a proton confined within a nucleus having a diameter of 1.0×10^{-15} m.

Additional Problems

39. A microwave photon in the x-band region has a wavelength of 3.00 cm. Find (a) the momentum, (b) the frequency, and (c) the energy of the photon in electron volts.

40. Find the speed of an electron having a de Broglie wavelength equal to its Compton wavelength. *Hint:* This electron is relativistic.

41. A 2.0-kg object falls from a height of 5.0 m to the ground. If all the gravitational potential energy of this mass could be converted to visible light of wavelength 5.0×10^{-7} m, how many photons would be produced?

42. An x-ray tube is operated at 50 000 V. (a) Find the minimum wavelength of the radiation emitted by this tube. (b) If the radiation is directed at a crystal, the first-order maximum in the reflected radiation occurs when the grazing angle is 2.5°. What is the spacing between reflecting planes in the crystal?

43. **Q|C** Figure P27.43 shows the spectrum of light emitted by a firefly. (a) Determine the temperature of a blackbody that would emit radiation peaked at the same frequency. (b) Based on your result, explain whether firefly radiation is blackbody radiation.

Figure P27.43

44. Johnny Jumper's favorite trick is to step out of his 16th-story window and fall 50.0 m into a pool. A news reporter takes a picture of 75.0-kg Johnny just before he makes a splash, using an exposure time of 5.00 ms. Find (a) Johnny's de Broglie wavelength at this moment, (b) the uncertainty of his kinetic energy measurement during such a period of time, and (c) the percent error caused by such an uncertainty.

45. **M** Photons of wavelength 450 nm are incident on a metal. The most energetic electrons ejected from the metal are bent into a circular arc of radius 20.0 cm by a magnetic field with a magnitude of 2.00×10^{-5} T. What is the work function of the metal?

46. An electron initially at rest recoils after a head-on collision with a 6.20-keV photon. Determine the kinetic energy acquired by the electron.

47. A light source of wavelength λ illuminates a metal and ejects photoelectrons with a maximum kinetic energy of 1.00 eV. A second light source of wavelength $\lambda/2$ ejects photoelectrons with a maximum kinetic energy of 4.00 eV. What is the work function of the metal?

48. Red light of wavelength 670 nm produces photoelectrons from a certain photoemissive material. Green light of wavelength 520 nm produces photoelectrons from the same material with 1.50 times the maximum kinetic energy. What is the material's work function?

49. How fast must an electron be moving if all its kinetic energy is lost to a single x-ray photon (a) at the high end of the x-ray electromagnetic spectrum with a wavelength of 1.00×10^{-8} m and (b) at the low end of the x-ray electromagnetic spectrum with a wavelength of 1.00×10^{-13} m?

50. **Q|C** From the scattering of sunlight, J. J. Thomson calculated the classical radius of the electron as having the value 2.82×10^{-15} m. Sunlight with an intensity of 500 W/m² falls on a disk with this radius. Assume light is a classical wave and the light striking the disk is completely absorbed. (a) Calculate the time interval required to accumulate 1.00 eV of energy. (b) Explain how your result for part (a) compares with the observation that photoelectrons are emitted promptly (within 10^{-9} s).

■ AP* REVIEW QUESTIONS

1. A 7 MW transmitter emits radio waves with a wavelength of 3 m. What is the approximate rate of photon emission?

   (A) 10^8 photons/s

   (B) 10^{22} photons/s

   (C) 10^{26} photons/s

   (D) 10^{32} photons/s

   (E) 10^{48} photons/s

2. The range of wavelengths of visible light is approximately 400 nm–700 nm. What is this range in terms of photon energy?

   (A) 3.1 keV − 1.8 keV

   (B) 3.1 eV − 1.8 eV

   (C) 3.1 MeV − 1.8 MeV

   (D) 3.1 GeV − 1.8 GeV

   (E) 3.1 μeV − 1.8 μeV

3. When a beam of 4 eV photons strike a metallic surface, the maximum kinetic energy of the photoelectrons emitted is observed to be 3 eV. What is the minimum amount of energy required just to liberate the electrons from the surface?

   (A) 1 eV

   (B) 2 eV

   (C) 3 eV

   (D) 4 eV

   (E) 7 eV

4. To produce x-rays, electrons are accelerated through a potential difference of 24,800 V toward a metallic surface. What is the minimum wavelength of the emitted x-ray photons?

   (A) 25 nm

   (B) 0.25 nm

   (C) 0.5 nm

   (D) 0.05 nm

   (E) 0.005 nm

5. The maximum kinetic energy of photoelectrons emitted from a metallic surface depends on which of the following?

       I. the physical properties of the metal

       II. the frequency of the incident radiation

       III. the intensity of the incident radiation

   (A) II only

   (B) I and II only

   (C) I and III only

   (D) II and III only

   (E) I, II, and III

6. The Compton effect is a shift in wavelength as a result of an interaction between a photon and an electron. Which of the following is the best description of the interaction?

	Type of collision	Photon wavelength after collision
(A)	elastic	longer
(B)	elastic	shorter
(C)	inelastic	longer
(D)	inelastic	shorter
(E)	completely inelastic	longer

7. The shift in wavelength $\Delta\lambda$ as a result of the Compton effect is dependent on which of the following?

       I. the wavelength of the incident photon

       II. the angle through which the photon is scattered

       III. the energy of the incident photon

   (A) I only

   (B) I and II only

   (C) I and III only

   (D) II only

   (E) I, II, and III

8. To support de Broglie's hypothesis of matter waves, the Davisson–Germer experiment yielded which of the following observations?

(A) A diffraction pattern after firing electrons at a metallic surface

(B) An interference pattern after passing coherent light through two parallel slits

(C) The dispersion of white light into its component colors after passing through a prism

(D) The production of radiation after firing electrons at a metallic surface

(E) The production of an electric current after irradiating a metallic surface

9. Which of the following graphs represent the de Broglie wavelength of a particle as a function of its speed?

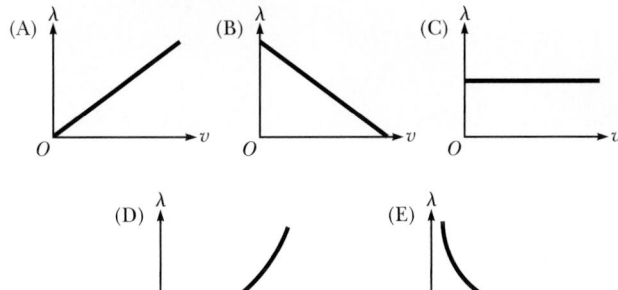

10. Which of the following demonstrates the particle properties of light?

    I. the photoelectric effect

    II. Davisson–Germer electron-diffraction

    III. Compton scattering

(A) I only

(B) I and II only

(C) I and III only

(D) II and III only

(E) I, II, and III

11. The Compton shift is given by $\Delta\lambda = \dfrac{h}{m_e c}(1 - \cos\theta)$. What is the maximum value of $\Delta\lambda$?

(A) $\dfrac{h}{m_e c}$

(B) $\dfrac{\sqrt{2}h}{2m_e c}$

(C) $\dfrac{\sqrt{2}h}{m_e c}$

(D) $\dfrac{2h}{m_e c}$

(E) There is no upper limit

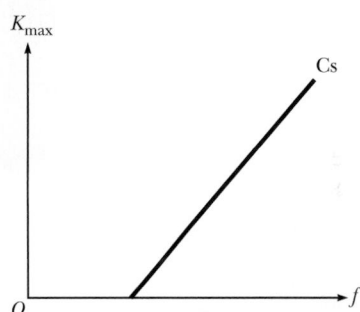

12. The photoelectric effect graph of maximum kinetic energy of photoelectrons as a function of incident radiation frequency for cesium (Cs) is shown above. Beryllium (Be) has a greater work function than cesium. Which of the graphs below best represents beryllium compared to cesium?

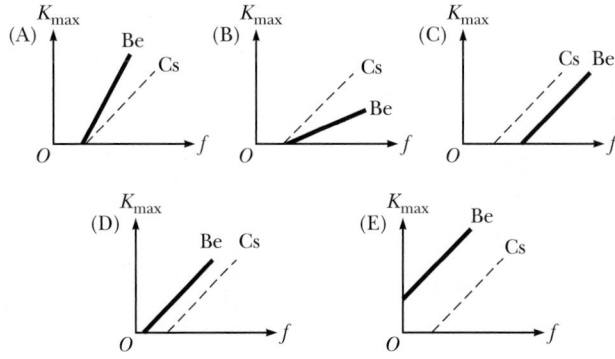

Burning gunpowder transfers energy to the atoms of color-producing chemicals, exciting their electrons to higher energy states. In returning to the ground state, the electrons emit light of specific colors, resulting in spectacular fireworks displays. Strontium produces red, and sodium produces yellow/orange.

© Sunnybeach/istockphoto.com

28 Atomic Physics

A hot gas emits light of certain characteristic wavelengths that can be used to identify it, much as a fingerprint can identify a person. For a given atom, these characteristic emitted wavelengths can be understood using physical quantities called quantum numbers. The simplest atom is hydrogen, and understanding it can lead to understanding the structure of other atoms and their combinations. The fact that no two electrons in an atom can have the same set of quantum numbers—the Pauli exclusion principle—is extremely important in understanding the properties of complex atoms and the arrangement of elements in the periodic table. Knowledge of atomic structure can be used to describe the mechanisms involved in the production of x-rays and the operation of a laser, among many other applications.

28.1 Early Models of the Atom

The model of the atom in the days of Newton was a tiny, hard, indestructible sphere. Although this model was a good basis for the kinetic theory of gases, new models had to be devised when later experiments revealed the electronic nature of atoms. J. J. Thomson (1856–1940) suggested a model of the atom as a volume of positive charge with electrons embedded throughout the volume, much like the seeds in a watermelon (Fig. 28.1).

In 1911 Ernest Rutherford (1871–1937) and his students Hans Geiger and Ernest Marsden performed a critical experiment showing that Thomson's model couldn't be correct. In this experiment a beam of positively charged **alpha particles** was projected against a thin metal foil, as in Figure 28.2a. Most of the alpha particles passed through the foil as if it were empty space, but a few particles were scattered through large angles, some even traveling backward.

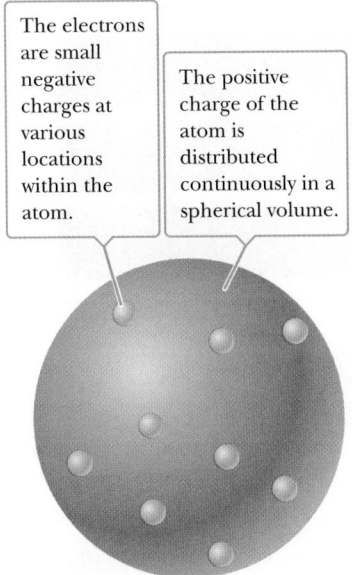

The electrons are small negative charges at various locations within the atom.

The positive charge of the atom is distributed continuously in a spherical volume.

Figure 28.1 Thomson's model of the atom.

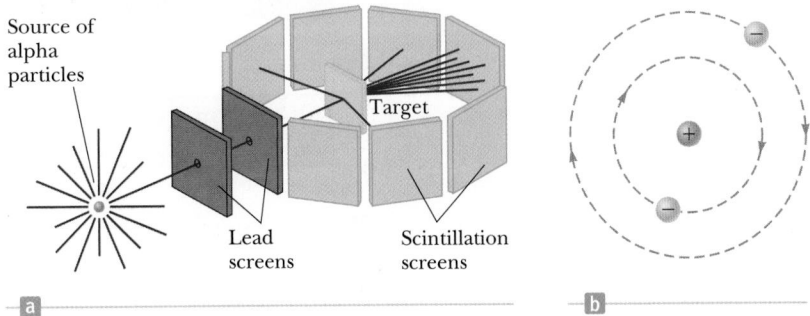

Figure 28.2 (a) Geiger and Marsden's technique for observing the scattering of alpha particles from a thin foil target. The source is a naturally occurring radioactive substance, such as radium. (b) Rutherford's planetary model of the atom.

Such large deflections weren't expected. In Thomson's model a positively charged alpha particle would never come close enough to a large positive charge to cause any large-angle deflections. Rutherford explained these results by assuming the positive charge in an atom was concentrated in a region called the **nucleus** that was small relative to the size of the atom. Any electrons belonging to the atom were visualized as orbiting the nucleus, much as planets orbit the Sun, as shown in Figure 28.2b. The alpha particles used in Rutherford's experiments were later identified as the nuclei of helium atoms.

There were two basic difficulties with Rutherford's planetary model. First, an atom emits certain discrete characteristic frequencies of electromagnetic radiation and no others; the Rutherford model was unable to explain this phenomenon. Second, the electrons in Rutherford's model undergo a centripetal acceleration. According to Maxwell's theory of electromagnetism, centripetally accelerated charges revolving with frequency f should radiate electromagnetic waves of the same frequency. As the electron radiates energy, the radius of its orbit steadily decreases and its frequency of revolution increases. This process leads to an ever-increasing frequency of emitted radiation and a rapid collapse of the atom as the electron spirals into the nucleus.

Rutherford's model of the atom gave way to that of Niels Bohr, which explained the characteristic radiation emitted from atoms. Bohr's theory, in turn, was supplanted by quantum mechanics. Both the latter theories are based on studies of atomic spectra: the special pattern in the wavelengths of emitted light that is unique for every different element.

28.2 Atomic Spectra

Suppose an evacuated glass tube is filled with hydrogen (or some other gas) at low pressure. If a voltage applied between metal electrodes in the tube is great enough to produce an electric current in the gas, the tube emits light having a color that depends on the gas inside. (That's how a neon sign works.) When the emitted light is analyzed with a spectrometer, discrete bright lines are observed, each having a different wavelength, or color. Such a series of spectral lines is called an **emission spectrum**. The wavelengths contained in such a spectrum are characteristic of the element emitting the light. Because no two elements emit the same line spectrum,

Stock Montage, Inc.

Sir Joseph John Thomson
English Physicist (1856–1940)
Thomson, usually considered the discoverer of the electron, opened up the field of subatomic particle physics with his extensive work on the deflection of cathode rays (electrons) in an electric field. He received the 1906 Nobel Prize in Physics for his discovery of the electron.

Figure 28.3 Visible spectra.
(a) Line spectra produced by emission in the visible range for the elements hydrogen, mercury, and neon.
(b) The absorption spectrum for hydrogen. The dark absorption lines occur at the same wavelengths as the emission lines for hydrogen shown in (a).

K. W. Whitten, R. E. Davis, M. L. Peck, and G. G. Stanley, *General Chemistry*, 7th ed., Belmont, CA, Brooks/Cole, 2004.

this phenomenon represents a reliable technique for identifying elements in a gaseous substance. Several emission spectra are shown in Figure 28.3a.

The emission spectrum of hydrogen shown in Figure 28.4 includes four prominent lines that occur at wavelengths of 656.3 nm, 486.1 nm, 434.1 nm, and 410.2 nm. In 1885 Johann Balmer (1825–1898) found that the wavelengths of these and less prominent lines can be described by the simple empirical equation

Balmer series ▶

$$\frac{1}{\lambda} = R_H\left(\frac{1}{2^2} - \frac{1}{n^2}\right) \qquad [28.1]$$

where n may have integral values of 3, 4, 5, . . . , and R_H is a constant, called the **Rydberg constant**. If the wavelength is in meters, then R_H has the value

Rydberg constant ▶

$$R_H = 1.097\ 373\ 2 \times 10^7\ \text{m}^{-1} \qquad [28.2]$$

The first line in the Balmer series, at 656.3 nm, corresponds to $n = 3$ in Equation 28.1, the line at 486.1 nm corresponds to $n = 4$, and so on. In addition to the Balmer series of spectral lines, the Lyman series was subsequently discovered in the far ultraviolet, with the radiated wavelengths described by a similar equation, with 2^2 in Equation 28.1 replaced by 1^2 and the integer n greater than 1. The Paschen series corresponded to longer wavelengths than the Balmer series, with the 2^2 in Equation 28.1 replaced by 3^2 and $n > 3$. These models, together with many other observations, can be combined to yield the Rydberg equation,

Rydberg equation ▶

$$\frac{1}{\lambda} = R_H\left(\frac{1}{m^2} - \frac{1}{n^2}\right) \qquad [28.3]$$

where m and n are positive integers and $n > m$.

In addition to emitting light at specific wavelengths, an element can absorb light at specific wavelengths. The spectral lines corresponding to this process form what is known as an **absorption spectrum**. An absorption spectrum can be obtained by passing a continuous radiation spectrum (one containing all wavelengths) through a vapor of the element being analyzed. The absorption spectrum consists of a series of dark lines superimposed on the otherwise bright, continuous spectrum. Each line in the absorption spectrum of a given element coincides with a line in the emission spectrum of the element. If hydrogen is the absorbing vapor, for example, dark lines will appear at the visible wavelengths 656.3 nm, 486.1 nm, 434.1 nm, and 410.2 nm, as shown in Figures 28.3b and 28.4.

The absorption spectrum of an element has many practical applications. For example, the continuous spectrum of radiation emitted by the Sun must pass through the cooler gases of the solar atmosphere before reaching Earth. The various absorption lines observed in the solar spectrum have been used to identify elements in the solar atmosphere, including helium, which was previously unknown.

Figure 28.4 The Balmer series of spectral lines for atomic hydrogen, with several lines marked with the wavelength in nanometers. The line labeled 364.6 is the shortest-wavelength line and is in the ultraviolet region of the electromagnetic spectrum. The other labeled lines are in the visible region.

■ APPLYING PHYSICS 28.1 | Thermal or Spectral

On observing a yellow candle flame, your laboratory partner claims that the light from the flame originates from excited sodium atoms in the flame. You disagree, stating that because the candle flame is hot, the radiation must be thermal in origin. Before the disagreement becomes more intense, how could you determine who is correct?

EXPLANATION A simple determination could be made by observing the light from the candle flame through a spectrometer, which is a slit and diffraction grating combination discussed in Chapter 25. If the spectrum of the light is continuous, it's probably thermal in origin. If the spectrum shows discrete lines, it's atomic in origin. The results of the experiment show that the light is indeed thermal in origin and originates from random molecular motion in the candle flame. ■

■ APPLYING PHYSICS 28.2 | Auroras

At extreme northern latitudes, the aurora borealis provides a beautiful and colorful display in the night sky. A similar display, called the aurora australis, occurs near the southern polar region. What is the origin of the various colors seen in the auroras?

EXPLANATION The aurora results from high-speed particles interacting with Earth's magnetic field and entering the atmosphere. When these particles collide with molecules in the atmosphere, they excite the molecules just as does the voltage in the spectrum tubes discussed earlier in this section. In response the molecules emit colors of light according to the characteristic spectra of their atomic constituents. For our atmosphere, the primary constituents are nitrogen and oxygen, which provide the red, blue, and green colors of the aurora. ■

28.3 The Bohr Model

At the beginning of the 20th century, it wasn't understood why atoms of a given element emitted and absorbed only certain wavelengths. In 1913 Bohr provided an explanation of the spectra of hydrogen that includes some features of the currently accepted theory. His model of the hydrogen atom included the following basic assumptions:

1. The electron moves in circular orbits about the proton under the influence of the Coulomb force of attraction, as in Figure 28.5. The Coulomb force produces the electron's centripetal acceleration.
2. Only certain electron orbits are stable and allowed. In these orbits no energy in the form of electromagnetic radiation is emitted, so the total energy of the atom remains constant.
3. Radiation is emitted by the hydrogen atom when the electron "jumps" from a more energetic initial state to a less energetic state. The "jump" can't be visualized or treated classically. The frequency f of the radiation emitted in the jump is related to the change in the atom's energy, given by

$$E_i - E_f = hf \qquad \text{[28.4]}$$

where E_i is the energy of the initial state, E_f is the energy of the final state, h is Planck's constant, and $E_i > E_f$. The frequency of the radiation is *independent of the frequency of the electron's orbital motion*.
4. The circumference of an electron's orbit must contain an integral number of de Broglie wavelengths,

$$2\pi r = n\lambda \qquad n = 1, 2, 3, \ldots$$

(See Fig. 28.6.) Because the de Broglie wavelength of an electron is given by $\lambda = h/m_e v$, we can write the preceding equation as

$$m_e v r = n\hbar \qquad n = 1, 2, 3, \ldots \qquad \text{[28.5]}$$

where $\hbar = h/2\pi$.

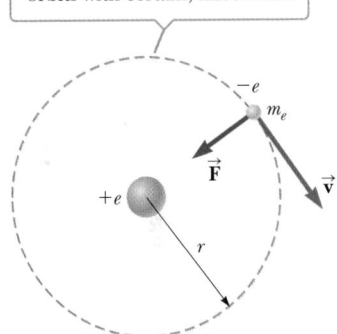

The electron occupies only orbits with certain, fixed radii.

Figure 28.5 Diagram representing Bohr's model of the hydrogen atom.

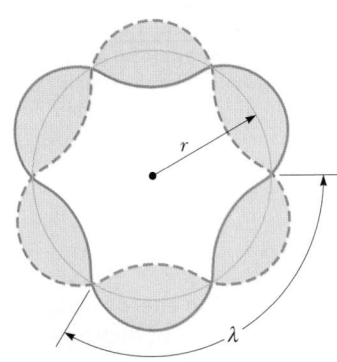

Figure 28.6 Standing-wave pattern for an electron wave in a stable orbit of hydrogen. There are three full wavelengths in this orbit.

Niels Bohr
Danish Physicist (1885–1962)
Bohr was an active participant in the early development of quantum mechanics and provided much of its philosophical framework. During the 1920s and 1930s he headed the Institute for Advanced Studies in Copenhagen, where many of the world's best physicists came to exchange ideas. Bohr was awarded the 1922 Nobel Prize in Physics for his investigation of the structure of atoms and of the radiation emanating from them.

With these four assumptions, we can calculate the allowed energies and emission wavelengths of the hydrogen atom using the model pictured in Figure 28.5, in which the electron travels in a circular orbit of radius r with an orbital speed v. The electrical potential energy of the atom is

$$PE = k_e \frac{q_1 q_2}{r} = k_e \frac{(-e)(e)}{r} = -k_e \frac{e^2}{r}$$

where k_e is the Coulomb constant. Assuming the nucleus is at rest, the total energy E of the atom is the sum of the kinetic and potential energy:

$$E = KE + PE = \tfrac{1}{2}m_e v^2 - k_e \frac{e^2}{r} \qquad [28.6]$$

By Newton's second law, the electric force of attraction on the electron, $k_e e^2/r^2$, must equal $m_e a_r$, where $a_r = v^2/r$ is the centripetal acceleration of the electron, so

$$m_e \frac{v^2}{r} = k_e \frac{e^2}{r^2} \qquad [28.7]$$

Multiply both sides of this equation by $r/2$ to get an expression for the kinetic energy:

$$\tfrac{1}{2}m_e v^2 = \frac{k_e e^2}{2r} \qquad [28.8]$$

Combining this result with Equation 28.6 gives an expression for the energy of the atom,

$$E = -\frac{k_e e^2}{2r} \qquad [28.9]$$

where the negative value of the energy indicates that the electron is bound to the proton.

An expression for r can be obtained by solving Equations 28.5 and 28.7 for v^2 and equating the results:

$$v^2 = \frac{n^2 \hbar}{m_e^2 r^2} = \frac{k_e e^2}{m_e r}$$

$$r_n = \frac{n^2 \hbar^2}{m_e k_e e^2} \qquad n = 1, 2, 3, \ldots \qquad [28.10]$$

This equation is based on the assumption that the **electron can exist only in certain allowed orbits determined by the integer n**.

The orbit with the smallest radius, called the **Bohr radius**, a_0, corresponds to $n = 1$ and has the value

$$a_0 = \frac{\hbar^2}{m k_e e^2} = 0.052\ 9 \text{ nm} \qquad [28.11]$$

A general expression for the radius of any orbit in the hydrogen atom is obtained by substituting Equation 28.11 into Equation 28.10:

$$r_n = n^2 a_0 = n^2 (0.052\ 9 \text{ nm}) \qquad [28.12]$$

The first three Bohr orbits for hydrogen are shown in Active Figure 28.7.

Equation 28.10 can then be substituted into Equation 28.9 to give the following expression for the energies of the quantum states:

$$E_n = -\frac{m_e k_e^2 e^4}{2\hbar^2}\left(\frac{1}{n^2}\right) \qquad n = 1, 2, 3, \ldots \qquad [28.13]$$

If we substitute numerical values into Equation 28.13, we obtain

$$E_n = -\frac{13.6}{n^2} \text{ eV} \qquad [28.14]$$

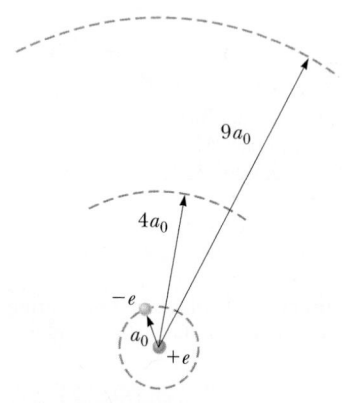

Active Figure 28.7
The first three circular orbits predicted by the Bohr model of the hydrogen atom. The electron is shown in the ground state orbit.

► The energy levels of hydrogen

The lowest-energy state, or **ground state**, corresponds to $n = 1$ and has an energy $E_1 = -m_e k_e^2 e^4 / 2\hbar^2 = -13.6$ eV. The next state, corresponding to $n = 2$, has an energy $E_2 = E_1/4 = -3.40$ eV, and so on. An energy level diagram showing the energies of these stationary states and the corresponding quantum numbers is given in Active Figure 28.8. The uppermost level shown, corresponding to $E = 0$ and $n \to \infty$, represents the state for which the electron is completely removed from the atom. In this state the electron's *KE* and *PE* are both zero, which means that the electron is at rest infinitely far away from the proton. The minimum energy required to ionize the atom—that is, to completely remove the electron—is called the **ionization energy**. The ionization energy for hydrogen is 13.6 eV.

Equations 28.4 and 28.13 and the third Bohr postulate show that if the electron jumps from one orbit with quantum number n_i to a second orbit with quantum number n_f, it emits a photon of frequency f given by

$$f = \frac{E_i - E_f}{\hbar} = \frac{m_e k_e^2 e^4}{4\pi \hbar^3}\left(\frac{1}{n_f^2} - \frac{1}{n_i^2}\right) \quad [28.15]$$

where $n_f < n_i$.

To convert this equation into one analogous to the Rydberg equation, substitute $f = c/\lambda$ and divide both sides by c, obtaining

$$\frac{1}{\lambda} = R_H\left(\frac{1}{n_f^2} - \frac{1}{n_i^2}\right) \quad [28.16]$$

where

$$R_H = \frac{m_e k_e^2 e^4}{4\pi c \hbar^3} \quad [28.17]$$

Substituting the known values of m_e, k_e, e, c, and $\hbar$ verifies that this theoretical value for the Rydberg constant is in excellent agreement with the experimentally derived value in Equations 12.1 through 12.3. When Bohr demonstrated this agreement, it was recognized as a major accomplishment of his theory.

We can use Equation 28.16 to evaluate the wavelengths for the various series in the hydrogen spectrum. For example, in the Balmer series, $n_f = 2$ and $n_i = 3, 4, 5, \ldots$ (Eq. 28.1). The energy level diagram for hydrogen shown in Active Figure 28.8 indicates the origin of the spectral lines. The transitions between levels are represented by vertical arrows. Note that whenever a transition occurs between a state designated by n_i to one designated by n_f (where $n_i > n_f$), a photon with a frequency $(E_i - E_f)/h$ is emitted. This process can be interpreted as follows: the lines in the visible part of the hydrogen spectrum arise when the electron jumps from the third, fourth, or even higher orbit to the second orbit. The Bohr theory successfully predicts the wavelengths of all the observed spectral lines of hydrogen.

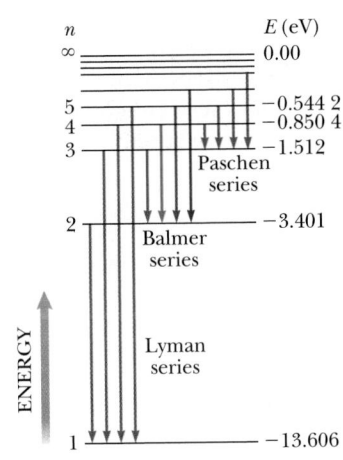

Active Figure 28.8

An energy level diagram for hydrogen. Quantum numbers are given on the left, and energies (in electron volts) are given on the right. Vertical arrows represent the four lowest-energy transitions for each of the spectral series shown. The colored arrows for the Balmer series indicate that this series results in visible light.

Tip 28.1 Energy Depends on *n* Only for Hydrogen

Because all other quantities in Equation 28.13 are constant, the energy levels of a hydrogen atom depend only on the quantum number *n*. For more complicated atoms, the energy levels depend on other quantum numbers as well.

■ **EXAMPLE 28.1**   **The Balmer Series for Hydrogen**

GOAL Calculate the wavelength, frequency, and energy of a photon emitted during an electron transition in an atom.

PROBLEM The Balmer series for the hydrogen atom corresponds to electronic transitions that terminate in the state with quantum number $n = 2$, as shown in Figure 28.9. **(a)** Find the longest-wavelength photon emitted in the Balmer series and determine its frequency and energy. **(b)** Find the shortest-wavelength photon emitted in the same series.

STRATEGY This problem is a matter of substituting values into Equation 28.16. The frequency can then be obtained from $c = f\lambda$ and the energy from $E = hf$. The longest-wavelength photon corresponds to the one that is emitted when the electron jumps from the $n_i = 3$ state to the $n_f = 2$ state. The shortest-wavelength photon corresponds to the one that is emitted when the electron jumps from $n_i = \infty$ to the $n_f = 2$ state.

(Continued)

Figure 28.9 (Example 28.1) Transitions responsible for the Balmer series for the hydrogen atom. All transitions terminate at the $n = 2$ level.

SOLUTION

(a) Find the longest-wavelength photon emitted in the Balmer series and determine its frequency and energy.

Substitute into Equation 28.16, with $n_i = 3$ and $n_f = 2$:

$$\frac{1}{\lambda} = R_H \left(\frac{1}{n_f^2} - \frac{1}{n_i^2} \right) = R_H \left(\frac{1}{2^2} - \frac{1}{3^2} \right) = \frac{5R_H}{36}$$

Take the reciprocal and substitute, finding the wavelength:

$$\lambda = \frac{36}{5R_H} = \frac{36}{5(1.097 \times 10^7 \text{ m}^{-1})} = 6.563 \times 10^{-7} \text{ m}$$

$$= \boxed{656.3 \text{ nm}}$$

Now use $c = f\lambda$ to obtain the frequency:

$$f = \frac{c}{\lambda} = \frac{2.998 \times 10^8 \text{ m/s}}{6.563 \times 10^{-7} \text{ m}} = \boxed{4.568 \times 10^{14} \text{ Hz}}$$

Calculate the photon's energy by substituting into Equation 27.5:

$$E = hf = (6.626 \times 10^{-34} \text{ J} \cdot \text{s})(4.568 \times 10^{14} \text{ Hz}) = 3.027 \times 10^{-19} \text{ J}$$

$$= 3.027 \times 10^{-19} \text{ J} \left(\frac{1 \text{ eV}}{1.602 \times 10^{-19} \text{ J}} \right) = \boxed{1.892 \text{ eV}}$$

(b) Find the shortest-wavelength photon emitted in the Balmer series.

Substitute into Equation 28.16, with $1/n_i \to 0$ as $n_i \to \infty$ and $n_f = 2$:

$$\frac{1}{\lambda} = R_H \left(\frac{1}{n_f^2} - \frac{1}{n_i^2} \right) = R_H \left(\frac{1}{2^2} - 0 \right) = \frac{R_H}{4}$$

Take the reciprocal and substitute, finding the wavelength:

$$\lambda = \frac{4}{R_H} = \frac{4}{(1.097 \times 10^7 \text{ m}^{-1})} = 3.646 \times 10^{-7} \text{ m}$$

$$= \boxed{364.6 \text{ nm}}$$

REMARKS The first wavelength is in the red region of the visible spectrum. We could also obtain the energy of the photon by using Equation 28.4 in the form $hf = E_3 - E_2$, where E_2 and E_3 are the energy levels of the hydrogen atom, calculated from Equation 28.14. Note that this photon is the lowest-energy photon in the Balmer series because it involves the smallest energy change. The second photon, the most energetic, is in the ultraviolet region.

QUESTION 28.1 What is the upper-limit energy of a photon that can be emitted from hydrogen due to the transition of an electron between energy levels? Explain.

EXERCISE 28.1 (a) Calculate the energy of the shortest-wavelength photon emitted in the Balmer series for hydrogen. (b) Calculate the wavelength of the photon emitted when an electron transits from $n = 4$ to $n = 2$.

ANSWERS (a) 3.40 eV   (b) 486 nm

Bohr's Correspondence Principle

In our study of relativity in Chapter 26, we found that Newtonian mechanics can't be used to describe phenomena that occur at speeds approaching the speed of light. Newtonian mechanics is a special case of relativistic mechanics and applies only when v is much smaller than c. Similarly, **quantum mechanics is in agreement with classical physics when the energy differences between quantized levels are very small**. This principle, first set forth by Bohr, is called the **correspondence principle**.

Hydrogen-like Atoms

The analysis used in the Bohr theory is also successful when applied to *hydrogen-like* atoms. An atom is said to be hydrogen-like when it contains only one electron. Examples are singly ionized helium, doubly ionized lithium, and triply ionized beryllium. The results of the Bohr theory for hydrogen can be extended to hydrogen-like atoms by substituting Ze^2 for e^2 in the hydrogen equations, where

Z is the atomic number of the element. For example, Equations 28.13 and 28.16 through 28.17 become

$$E_n = -\frac{m_e k_e^2 Z^2 e^4}{2\hbar^2}\left(\frac{1}{n^2}\right) \qquad n = 1, 2, 3, \dots \qquad \text{[28.18]}$$

and

$$\frac{1}{\lambda} = \frac{m_e k_e^2 Z^2 e^4}{4\pi c\hbar^3}\left(\frac{1}{n_f^2} - \frac{1}{n_i^2}\right) \qquad \text{[28.19]}$$

Although many attempts were made to extend the Bohr theory to more complex, multi-electron atoms, the results were unsuccessful. Even today, only approximate methods are available for treating multi-electron atoms.

■ Quick Quiz

28.1 Consider a hydrogen atom and a singly ionized helium atom. Which atom has the lower ground state energy? (a) Hydrogen (b) Helium (c) The ground state energy is the same for both.

■ EXAMPLE 28.2 │ Singly Ionized Helium

GOAL Apply the modified Bohr theory to a hydrogen-like atom.

PROBLEM Singly ionized helium, He$^+$, a hydrogen-like system, has one electron in the orbit corresponding to $n = 1$ when the atom is in its ground state. Find **(a)** the energy of the system in the ground state in electron volts and **(b)** the radius of the ground-state orbit.

STRATEGY Part (a) requires substitution into the modified Bohr model, Equation 28.18. In part (b) modify Equation 28.10 for the radius of the Bohr orbits by replacing e^2 by Ze^2, where Z is the number of protons in the nucleus.

SOLUTION

(a) Find the energy of the system in the ground state.

Write Equation 28.18 for the energies of a hydrogen-like system:

$$E_n = -\frac{m_e k_e^2 Z^2 e^4}{2\hbar^2}\left(\frac{1}{n^2}\right)$$

Substitute the constants and convert to electron volts:

$$E_n = -\frac{Z^2(13.6\text{ eV})}{n^2}$$

Substitute $Z = 2$ (the atomic number of helium) and $n = 1$ to obtain the ground state energy:

$$E_1 = -4(13.6\text{ eV}) = \boxed{-54.4\text{ eV}}$$

(b) Find the radius of the ground state.

Generalize Equation 28.10 to a hydrogen-like atom by substituting Ze^2 for e^2:

$$r_n = \frac{n^2\hbar^2}{m_e k_e Ze^2} = \frac{n^2}{Z}(a_0) = \frac{n^2}{Z}(0.052\,9\text{ nm})$$

For our case, $n = 1$ and $Z = 2$:

$$r_1 = \boxed{0.026\,5\text{ nm}}$$

REMARKS Notice that for higher Z, the energy of a hydrogen-like atom is lower (more negative), which means that the electron is more tightly bound than in hydrogen. The result is a smaller atom, as seen in part (b).

QUESTION 28.2 When an electron undergoes a transition from a higher to lower state in singly ionized helium, how will the energy of the emitted photon compare with the analogous transition in hydrogen? Explain.

EXERCISE 28.2 Repeat the problem for the first excited state of doubly ionized lithium ($Z = 3$, $n = 2$).

ANSWERS (a) $E_2 = -30.6$ eV   (b) $r_2 = 0.070\,5$ nm

Bohr's theory was extended in an ad hoc manner so as to include further details of atomic spectra. All these modifications were replaced with the theory of quantum mechanics, developed independently by Werner Heisenberg and Erwin Schrödinger.

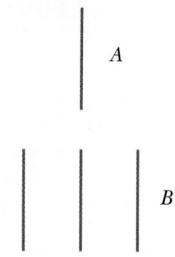

Figure 28.10 A single line (*A*) can split into three separate lines (*B*) in a magnetic field.

28.4 Quantum Mechanics and the Hydrogen Atom

One of the first great achievements of quantum mechanics was the solution of the wave equation for the hydrogen atom. Although the details of the solution are beyond the level of this book, the solution and its implications for atomic structure can be described.

According to quantum mechanics, the energies of the allowed states are in exact agreement with the values obtained by the Bohr theory (Eq. 28.13) when the allowed energies depend only on the principal quantum number n.

In addition to the principal quantum number, two other quantum numbers emerged from the solution of the Schrödinger wave equation: the **orbital quantum number,** ℓ, and the **orbital magnetic quantum number**, m_ℓ.

The effect of the magnetic quantum number m_ℓ can be observed in spectra when magnetic fields are present, which results in a splitting of individual spectral lines into several lines. This splitting is called the *Zeeman effect*. Figure 28.10 shows a single spectral line being split into three closely spaced lines. This indicates that the energy of an electron is slightly modified when the atom is immersed in a magnetic field.

The allowed ranges of the values of these quantum numbers are as follows:

- The value of n can range from 1 to ∞ in integer steps.
- The value of ℓ can range from 0 to $n - 1$ in integer steps.
- The value of m_ℓ can range from $-\ell$ to ℓ in integer steps.

From these rules, it can be seen that for a given value of n, there are n possible values of ℓ, whereas for a given value of ℓ, there are $2\ell + 1$ possible values of m_ℓ. For example, if $n = 1$, there is only 1 value of ℓ, which is $\ell = 0$. Because $2\ell + 1 = 2 \cdot 0 + 1 = 1$, there is only one value of m_ℓ, which is $m_\ell = 0$. If $n = 2$, the value of ℓ may be 0 or 1; if $\ell = 0$, then $m_\ell = 0$; but if $\ell = 1$, then m_ℓ may be 1, 0, or -1. Table 28.1 summarizes the rules for determining the allowed values of ℓ and m_ℓ for a given value of n.

For historical reasons, **all states with the same principal quantum number n are said to form a shell**. Shells are identified by the letters K, L, M, . . . , which designate the states for which $n = 1, 2, 3$, and so forth. **The states with given values of n and are said to form a subshell**. The letters $s, p, d, f, g, \ldots$ are used to designate the states for which $\ell = 0, 1, 2, 3, 4, \ldots$. These notations are summarized in Table 28.2.

States that violate the rules given in Table 28.1 can't exist. One state that cannot exist, for example, is the $2d$ state, which would have $n = 2$ and $\ell = 2$. This state is not allowed because the highest allowed value of ℓ is $n - 1$, or 1 in this case. So for $n = 2$, $2s$ and $2p$ are allowed states, but $2d$, $2f, \ldots$ are not. For $n = 3$, the allowed states are $3s$, $3p$, and $3d$.

In general, for a given value of n, there are n^2 states with distinct pairs of values of ℓ and m_ℓ.

Table 28.1 Three Quantum Numbers for the Hydrogen Atom

Quantum Number	Name	Allowed Values	Number of Allowed States
n	Principal quantum number	1, 2, 3, . . .	Any number
ℓ	Orbital quantum number	0, 1, 2, . . . , $n - 1$	n
m_ℓ	Orbital magnetic quantum number	$-\ell, -\ell + 1, \ldots,$ 0, . . . , $\ell - 1, \ell$	$2\ell + 1$

Table 28.2 Shell and Subshell Notation

n	Shell Symbol	ℓ	Subshell Symbol
1	K	0	s
2	L	1	p
3	M	2	d
4	N	3	f
5	O	4	g
6	P	5	h
. . .		. . .	

28.2 When the principal quantum number is $n = 5$, how many different values of (a) ℓ and (b) m_ℓ are possible? (c) How many states have distinct pairs of values of ℓ and m_ℓ?

Spin

In high-resolution spectrometers, close examination of one of the prominent lines of sodium vapor shows that it is, in fact, two very closely spaced lines. The wavelengths of these lines occur in the yellow region of the spectrum, at 589.0 nm and 589.6 nm. This kind of splitting is referred to as **fine structure**. In 1925, when this doublet was first noticed, atomic theory couldn't explain it, so Samuel Goudsmit and George Uhlenbeck, following a suggestion by Austrian physicist Wolfgang Pauli, proposed the introduction of a fourth quantum number to describe atomic energy levels, m_s, called the **spin magnetic quantum number**. Spin isn't found in the solutions of Schrödinger's equations; rather, it naturally arises in the Dirac equation, derived in 1927 by Paul Dirac. This equation is important in relativistic quantum theory.

In describing the spin quantum number, it's convenient (but technically incorrect) to think of the electron as spinning on its axis as it orbits the nucleus, just as Earth spins on its axis as it orbits the Sun. Unlike the spin of a world, however, there are only two ways in which the electron can spin as it orbits the nucleus, as shown in Figure 28.11. If the direction of spin is as shown in Figure 28.11a, the electron is said to have "spin up." If the direction of spin is reversed as in Figure 28.11b, the electron is said to have "spin down." The energy of the electron is slightly different for the two spin directions, and this energy difference accounts for the sodium doublet. The quantum numbers associated with electron spin are $m_s = \frac{1}{2}$ for the spin-up state and $m_s = -\frac{1}{2}$ for the spin-down state. As we see in Example 28.3, this new quantum number doubles the number of allowed states specified by the quantum numbers n, ℓ, and m_ℓ.

For each electron, there are two spin states. A subshell corresponding to a given factor of ℓ can contain no more than $2(2\ell + 1)$ electrons. This number is used because electrons in a subshell must have unique pairs of the quantum numbers (m_ℓ, m_s). There are $2\ell + 1$ different magnetic quantum numbers m_ℓ and two different spin quantum numbers m_s, making $2(2\ell + 1)$ unique pairs (m_ℓ, m_s). For example, the p subshell ($\ell = 1$) is filled when it contains $2(2 \cdot 1 + 1) = 6$ electrons. This fact can be extended to include all four quantum numbers, as will be important to us later when we discuss the *Pauli exclusion principle*.

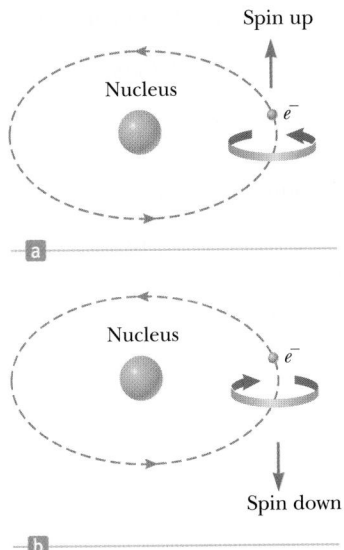

Figure 28.11 As an electron moves in its orbit about the nucleus, its spin can be either (a) up or (b) down.

Tip 28.2 The Electron Isn't Actually Spinning

The electron is *not* physically spinning. Electron spin is a purely quantum effect that gives the electron an angular momentum *as if* it were physically spinning.

■ EXAMPLE 28.3 | The $n = 2$ Level of Hydrogen

GOAL Count and tabulate distinct quantum states and determine their energy based on atomic energy level.

PROBLEM (a) Determine the number of states with a unique set of values for ℓ, m_ℓ, and m_s in the hydrogen atom for $n = 2$. (b) Tabulate the distinct possible quantum states, including spin. (c) Calculate the energies of these states in the absence of a magnetic field, disregarding small differences caused by spin.

STRATEGY This problem is a matter of counting, following the quantum rules for n, ℓ, m_ℓ, and m_s. "Unique" means that no other quantum state has the same set of numbers. The energies—disregarding spin or Zeeman splitting in magnetic fields—are all the same because all states have the same principal quantum number, $n = 2$.

· ·

SOLUTION

(a) Determine the number of states with a unique set of values for ℓ and m_ℓ in the hydrogen atom for $n = 2$.

Determine the different possible values of ℓ for $n = 2$:

$0 \le \ell \le n - 1$, so for $n = 2$, $0 \le \ell \le 1$ and $\ell = 0$ or 1

Find the different possible values of m_ℓ for $\ell = 0$:

$-\ell \le m_\ell \le \ell$, so $-0 \le m_\ell \le 0$ implies that $m_\ell = 0$

(Continued)

	List the distinct pairs of (ℓ, m_ℓ) for $\ell = 0$:	There is only one: $(\ell, m_\ell) = (0, 0)$.

List the distinct pairs of (ℓ, m_ℓ) for $\ell = 0$:   There is only one: $(\ell, m_\ell) = (0, 0)$.

Find the different possible values of m_ℓ for $\ell = 1$: $-\ell \le m_\ell \le \ell$, so $-1 \le m_\ell \le 1$ implies that $m_\ell = -1, 0,$ or 1

List the distinct pairs of (ℓ, m_ℓ) for $\ell = 1$:   There are three: $(\ell, m_\ell) = (1, -1), (1, 0),$ and $(1, 1)$.

Sum the results for $\ell = 0$ and $\ell = 1$ and multiply by 2 to account for the two possible spins of each state: Number of states = $2(1 + 3) = \boxed{8}$

(b) Tabulate the different possible sets of quantum numbers.

Use the results of part (a) and recall that the spin quantum number is always $+\frac{1}{2}$ or $-\frac{1}{2}$.

n	ℓ	m_ℓ	m_s
2	1	−1	$-\frac{1}{2}$
2	1	−1	$\frac{1}{2}$
2	1	0	$-\frac{1}{2}$
2	1	0	$\frac{1}{2}$
2	1	1	$-\frac{1}{2}$
2	1	1	$\frac{1}{2}$
2	0	0	$-\frac{1}{2}$
2	0	0	$\frac{1}{2}$

(c) Calculate the energies of these states.

The common energy of all the states, disregarding Zeeman splitting and spin, can be found with Equation 28.14:

$$E_n = -\frac{13.6 \text{ eV}}{n^2} \quad \rightarrow \quad E_2 = -\frac{13.6 \text{ eV}}{2^2} = \boxed{-3.40 \text{ eV}}$$

REMARKS Although these states normally have the same energy, the application of a magnetic field causes them to take slightly different energies centered around the energy corresponding to $n = 2$. In addition, the slight difference in energy due to spin state was neglected.

QUESTION 28.3 Which of the four quantum numbers are never negative?

EXERCISE 28.3 (a) Determine the number of states with a unique pair of values for ℓ, m_ℓ, and m_s in the $n = 3$ level of hydrogen. (b) Determine the energies of those states, disregarding any splitting effects.

ANSWERS (a) 18   (b) $E_3 = -1.51$ eV

Electron Clouds

The solution of the wave equation, as discussed in Section 27.7, yields a wave function Ψ that depends on the quantum numbers n, ℓ, and m_ℓ. Recall that if p is a point and V_p a very small volume containing that point, then $\Psi^2 V_p$ is approximately the probability of finding the electron inside the volume V_p. Figure 28.12 gives the probability per unit length of finding the electron at various distances from the nucleus in the 1s state of hydrogen ($n = 1$, $\ell = 0$, and $m_\ell = 0$). Note that the curve peaks at a value of $r = 0.052\,9$ nm, the Bohr radius for the first ($n = 1$) electron orbit in hydrogen. This peak means that there is a maximum probability of finding the electron in a small interval of a given, fixed length centered at that distance from the nucleus. As the curve indicates, however, there is also a probability of finding the electron in such a small interval centered at any other distance from the nucleus. In quantum mechanics the electron is not confined to a particular orbital distance from the nucleus, as assumed in the Bohr model. The electron may be found at various distances from the nucleus, but finding it in a small interval centered on the Bohr radius has the greatest probability. Quantum mechanics also predicts that the wave function for the hydrogen atom in the ground state is spherically symmetric; hence, the electron can be found in a spherical region surrounding the nucleus. This is in contrast to the Bohr theory, which confines the position of the electron to points in a plane. The quantum mechanical result is often interpreted by viewing the electron as a cloud surrounding the nucleus. An attempt at picturing this cloud-like behavior is shown in Figure 28.13. The densest regions of the cloud represent those locations where the electron is most likely to be found.

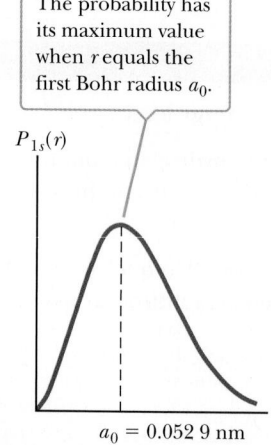

The probability has its maximum value when r equals the first Bohr radius a_0.

$P_{1s}(r)$

$a_0 = 0.052\,9$ nm

Figure 28.12 The probability per unit length of finding the electron versus distance from the nucleus for the hydrogen atom in the 1s (ground) state.

If a similar analysis is carried out for the $n = 2$, $\ell = 0$ state of hydrogen, a peak of the probability curve is found at $4a_0$, whereas for the $n = 3$, $\ell = 0$ state, the curve peaks at $9a_0$. In general, quantum mechanics predicts a most probable electron distance to the nucleus that is in agreement with the location predicted by the Bohr theory.

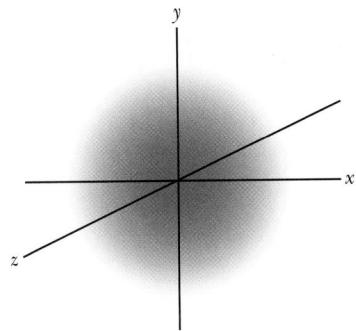

Figure 28.13 The spherical electron cloud for the hydrogen atom in its 1s state.

28.5 The Exclusion Principle and the Periodic Table

The state of an electron in a hydrogen atom is specified by four quantum numbers: n, ℓ, m_ℓ, and m_s. As it turns out, the state of any electron in any other atom can also be specified by this same set of quantum numbers.

How many electrons in an atom can have a particular set of quantum numbers? This important question was answered by Pauli in 1925 in a powerful statement known as the **Pauli exclusion principle**:

> No two electrons in an atom can ever have the same set of values for the set of quantum numbers n, ℓ, m_ℓ, and m_s.

◄ The Pauli exclusion principle

The Pauli exclusion principle explains the electronic structure of complex atoms as a succession of filled levels with different quantum numbers increasing in energy, where the outermost electrons are primarily responsible for the chemical properties of the element. If this principle weren't valid, every electron would end up in the lowest energy state of the atom and the chemical behavior of the elements would be grossly different. Nature as we know it would not exist, and *we* would not exist to wonder about it!

As a general rule, the order that electrons fill an atom's subshell is as follows. Once one subshell is filled, the next electron goes into the vacant subshell that is lowest in energy. If the atom were not in the lowest energy state available to it, it would radiate energy until it reached that state. A subshell is filled when it contains $2(2\ell + 1)$ electrons. This rule is based on the analysis of quantum numbers to be described later. Following the rule, shells and subshells can contain numbers of electrons according to the pattern given in Table 28.3.

The exclusion principle can be illustrated by examining the electronic arrangement in a few of the lighter atoms. *Hydrogen* has only one electron, which, in its ground state, can be described by either of two sets of quantum numbers: 1, 0, 0, $\frac{1}{2}$ or 1, 0, 0, $-\frac{1}{2}$. The electronic configuration of this atom is often designated as $1s^1$. The notation $1s$ refers to a state for which $n = 1$ and $\ell = 0$, and the superscript indicates that one electron is present in this level.

Tip 28.3 The Exclusion Principle Is More General

The exclusion principle stated here is a limited form of the more general exclusion principle, which states that no two *fermions* (particles with spin $\frac{1}{2}$, $\frac{3}{2}$...) can be in the same quantum state.

Wolfgang Pauli
Austrian Theoretical Physicist (1900–1958)
The extremely talented Pauli first gained public recognition at the age of 21 with a masterful review article on relativity. In 1945 he received the Nobel Prize in Physics for his discovery of the exclusion principle. Among his other major contributions were the explanation of the connection between particle spin and statistics, the theory of relativistic quantum electrodynamics, the neutrino hypothesis, and the hypothesis of nuclear spin.

Table 28.3 Number of Electrons in Filled Subshells and Shells

Shell	Subshell	Number of Electrons in Filled Subshell	Number of Electrons in Filled Shell
K ($n=1$)	$s(\ell=0)$	2	2
L ($n=2$)	$s(\ell=0)$	2	8
	$p(\ell=1)$	6	
M ($n=3$)	$s(\ell=0)$	2	18
	$p(\ell=1)$	6	
	$d(\ell=2)$	10	
N ($n=4$)	$s(\ell=0)$	2	32
	$p(\ell=1)$	6	
	$d(\ell=2)$	10	
	$f(\ell=3)$	14	

Neutral *helium* has two electrons. In the ground state, the quantum numbers for these two electrons are 1, 0, 0, $\frac{1}{2}$ and 1, 0, 0, $-\frac{1}{2}$. No other possible combinations of quantum numbers exist for this level, and we say that the K shell is filled. The helium electronic configuration is designated as $1s^2$.

Neutral *lithium* has three electrons. In the ground state, two of them are in the $1s$ subshell and the third is in the $2s$ subshell because the latter subshell is lower in energy than the $2p$ subshell. Hence, the electronic configuration for lithium is $1s^2 2s^1$.

A list of electronic ground-state configurations for a number of atoms is provided in Table 28.4. In 1871 Dmitry Mendeleyev (1834–1907), a Russian chemist, arranged the elements known at that time into a table according to their atomic masses and chemical similarities. The first table Mendeleyev proposed contained many blank spaces, and he boldly stated that the gaps were there only because those elements had not yet been discovered. By noting the column in which these missing elements should be located, he was able to make rough predictions about their chemical properties. Within 20 years of this announcement, those elements were indeed discovered.

The elements in our current version of the periodic table are still arranged so that all those in a vertical column have similar chemical properties. For example, consider the elements in the last column: He (helium), Ne (neon), Ar (argon), Kr (krypton), Xe (xenon), and Rn (radon). The outstanding characteristic of these elements is that they don't normally take part in chemical reactions, joining with other atoms to form molecules, and are therefore classified as inert. They are called the *noble gases*. We can partially understand their behavior by looking at the electronic configurations shown in Table 28.4. The element helium has the electronic configuration $1s^2$. In other words, one shell is filled. The electrons in this filled shell are considerably separated in energy from the next available level, the $2s$ level.

The electronic configuration for neon is $1s^2 2s^2 2p^6$. Again, the outer shell is filled and there is a large difference in energy between the $2p$ level and the $3s$ level.

Table 28.4 Electronic Configurations of Some Elements

Z	Symbol	Ground-State Configuration	Ionization Energy (eV)	Z	Symbol	Ground-State Configuration	Ionization Energy (eV)
1	H	$1s^1$	13.595	19	K	[Ar] $4s^1$	4.339
2	He	$1s^2$	24.581	20	Ca	$4s^2$	6.111
				21	Sc	$3d 4s^2$	6.54
3	Li	[He] $2s^1$	5.390	22	Ti	$3d^2 4s^2$	6.83
4	Be	$2s^2$	9.320	23	V	$3d^3 4s^2$	6.74
5	B	$2s^2 2p^1$	8.296	24	Cr	$3d^5 4s^1$	6.76
6	C	$2s^2 2p^2$	11.256	25	Mn	$3d^5 4s^2$	7.432
7	N	$2s^2 2p^3$	14.545	26	Fe	$3d^6 4s^2$	7.87
8	O	$2s^2 2p^4$	13.614	27	Co	$3d^7 4s^2$	7.86
9	F	$2s^2 2p^5$	17.418	28	Ni	$3d^8 4s^2$	7.633
10	Ne	$2s^2 2p^6$	21.559	29	Cu	$3d^{10} 4s^1$	7.724
				30	Zn	$3d^{10} 4s^2$	9.391
11	Na	[Ne] $3s^1$	5.138	31	Ga	$3d^{10} 4s^2 4p^1$	6.00
12	Mg	$3s^2$	7.644	32	Ge	$3d^{10} 4s^2 4p^2$	7.88
13	Al	$3s^2 3p^1$	5.984	33	As	$3d^{10} 4s^2 4p^3$	9.81
14	Si	$3s^2 3p^2$	8.149	34	Se	$3d^{10} 4s^2 4p^4$	9.75
15	P	$3s^2 3p^3$	10.484	35	Br	$3d^{10} 4s^2 4p^5$	11.84
16	S	$3s^2 3p^4$	10.357	36	Kr	$3d^{10} 4s^2 4p^6$	13.996
17	Cl	$3s^2 3p^5$	13.01				
18	Ar	$3s^2 3p^6$	15.755				

Note: The bracket notation is used as a shorthand method to avoid repetition in indicating inner-shell electrons. Thus, [He] represents $1s^2$, [Ne] represents $1s^2 2s^2 2p^6$, [Ar] represents $1s^2 2s^2 2p^6 3s^2 3p^6$, and so on.

Argon has the configuration $1s^2 2s^2 2p^6 3s^2 3p^6$. Here, the $3p$ subshell is filled and there is a wide gap in energy between the $3p$ subshell and the $3d$ subshell. Through all the noble gases, the pattern remains the same: a noble gas is formed when either a shell or a subshell is filled, and there is a large gap in energy before the next possible level is encountered.

The elements in the first column of the periodic table are called the *alkali metals* and are highly active chemically. Referring to Table 28.4, we can understand why these elements interact so strongly with other elements. These alkali metals all have a single outer electron in an s subshell. This electron is shielded from the nucleus by all the electrons in the inner shells. Consequently, it's only loosely bound to the atom and can readily be accepted by other atoms that bind it more tightly to form molecules.

The elements in the seventh column of the periodic table are called the *halogens* and are also highly active chemically. All these elements are lacking one electron in a subshell, so they readily accept electrons from other atoms to form molecules.

■ Quick Quiz

28.3 Krypton (atomic number 36) has how many electrons in its next-to-outer shell ($n = 3$)? (a) 2 (b) 4 (c) 8 (d) 18

28.6 Characteristic X-Rays

X-rays are emitted when a metal target is bombarded with high-energy electrons. The x-ray spectrum typically consists of a broad continuous band and a series of intense sharp lines that are dependent on the type of metal used for the target, as shown in Figure 28.14. These discrete lines, called **characteristic x-rays**, were discovered in 1908, but their origin remained unexplained until the details of atomic structure were developed.

The first step in the production of characteristic x-rays occurs when a bombarding electron collides with an electron in an inner shell of a target atom with sufficient energy to remove the electron from the atom. The vacancy created in the shell is filled when an electron in a higher level drops down into the lower-energy level containing the vacancy. The time it takes for that to happen is very short, less than 10^{-9} s. The transition is accompanied by the emission of a photon with energy equaling the difference in energy between the two levels. Typically, the energy of such transitions is greater than 1 000 eV, and the emitted x-ray photons have wavelengths in the range of 0.01 nm to 1 nm.

We assume the incoming electron has dislodged an atomic electron from the innermost shell, the K shell. If the vacancy is filled by an electron dropping from the next-higher shell, the L shell, the photon emitted in the process is referred to as the K_α line on the curve of Figure 28.14. If the vacancy is filled by an electron dropping from the M shell, the line produced is called the K_β line.

Other characteristic x-ray lines are formed when electrons drop from upper levels to vacancies other than those in the K shell. For example, L lines are produced when vacancies in the L shell are filled by electrons dropping from higher shells. An L_α line is produced as an electron drops from the M shell to the L shell, and an L_β line is produced by a transition from the N shell to the L shell.

We can estimate the energy of the emitted x-rays as follows. Consider two electrons in the K shell of an atom whose atomic number is Z. Each electron partially shields the other from the charge of the nucleus, Ze, so each is subject to an effective nuclear charge $Z_{eff} = (Z - 1)e$. We can now use a modified form of Equation 28.18 to estimate the energy of either electron in the K shell (with $n = 1$). We have

$$E_K = -m_e Z_{eff}^2 \frac{k_e^2 e^4}{2\hbar^2} = -Z_{eff}^2 E_0$$

The peaks represent *characteristic x-rays*. Their appearance depends on the target material.

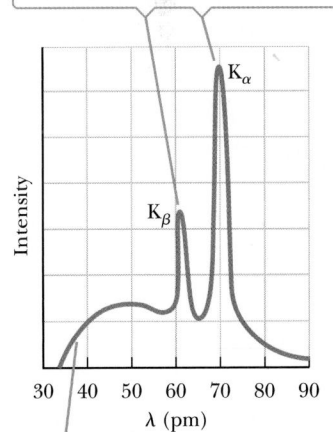

The continuous curve represents *bremsstrahlung*. The shortest wavelength depends on the accelerating voltage.

Figure 28.14 The x-ray spectrum of a metal target. The data shown were obtained when 35-keV electrons bombarded a molybdenum target. Note that 1 pm = 10^{-12} m = 0.001 nm.

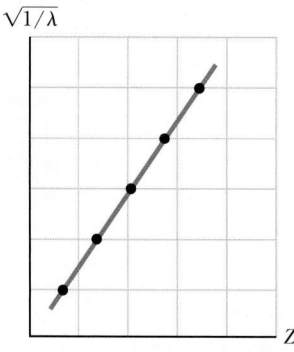

Figure 28.15 A Moseley plot of $\sqrt{1/\lambda}$ versus Z, where λ is the wavelength of the K_α x-ray line of the element of atomic number Z.

where E_0 is the ground-state energy. Substituting $Z_{eff} = Z - 1$ gives

$$E_K = -(Z - 1)^2(13.6 \text{ eV}) \qquad \text{[28.20]}$$

As Example 28.4 shows, we can estimate the energy of an electron in an L or an M shell in a similar fashion. Taking the energy difference between these two levels, we can then calculate the energy and wavelength of the emitted photon.

In 1914 Henry G. J. Moseley plotted the Z values for a number of elements against $\sqrt{1/\lambda}$, where λ is the wavelength of the K_α line for each element. He found that such a plot produced a straight line, as in Figure 28.15, which is consistent with our rough calculations of the energy levels based on Equation 28.20. From his plot, Moseley was able to determine the Z values of other elements, providing a periodic chart in excellent agreement with the known chemical properties of the elements.

■ EXAMPLE 28.4 | **Characteristic X-Rays**

GOAL Calculate the energy and wavelength of characteristic x-rays.

PROBLEM Estimate the energy and wavelength of the characteristic x-ray emitted from a tungsten target when an electron drops from an M shell ($n = 3$ state) to a vacancy in the K shell ($n = 1$ state).

STRATEGY Develop two estimates, one for the electron in the K shell ($n = 1$) and one for the electron in the M shell ($n = 3$). For the K-shell estimate, we can use Equation 28.20. For the M-shell estimate, we need a new equation. There is 1 electron in the K shell (because one is missing) and there are 8 in the L shell, making 9 electrons shielding the nuclear charge. Therefore $Z_{eff} = 74 - 9$ and $E_M = -Z_{eff}^2 E_3$, where E_3 is the energy of the $n = 3$ level in hydrogen. The difference $E_M - E_K$ is the energy of the photon.

SOLUTION

Use Equation 28.20 to estimate the energy of an electron in the K shell of tungsten, atomic number $Z = 74$:

$$E_K = -(74 - 1)^2(13.6 \text{ eV}) = -72\,500 \text{ eV}$$

Estimate the energy of an electron in the M shell in the same way:

$$E_M = -Z_{eff}^2 E_3 = -(Z - 9)^2 \frac{E_0}{3^2} = -(74 - 9)^2 \frac{(13.6 \text{ eV})}{9}$$
$$= -6\,380 \text{ eV}$$

Calculate the difference in energy between the M and K shells:

$$E_M - E_K = -6\,380 \text{ eV} - (-72\,500 \text{ eV}) = \boxed{66\,100 \text{ eV}}$$

Find the wavelength of the emitted x-ray:

$$\Delta E = hf = h\frac{c}{\lambda} \quad \rightarrow \quad \lambda = \frac{hc}{\Delta E}$$

$$\lambda = \frac{(6.63 \times 10^{-34} \text{ J} \cdot \text{s})(3.00 \times 10^8 \text{ m/s})}{(6.61 \times 10^4 \text{ eV})(1.60 \times 10^{-19} \text{ J/eV})}$$

$$= 1.88 \times 10^{-11} \text{ m} = \boxed{0.018\,8 \text{ nm}}$$

REMARKS These estimates depend on the amount of shielding of the nuclear charge, which can be difficult to determine.

QUESTION 28.4 Could a transition from the L shell to the K shell ever result in a more energetic photon than a transition from the M to the K shell? Discuss.

EXERCISE 28.4 Repeat the problem for a $2p$ electron transiting from the L shell to the K shell. (For technical reasons, the L shell electron must have $\ell = 1$, so a single $1s$ electron and two $2s$ electrons shield the nucleus.)

ANSWERS (a) 5.54×10^4 eV (b) 0.022 4 nm

28.7 Atomic Transitions and Lasers

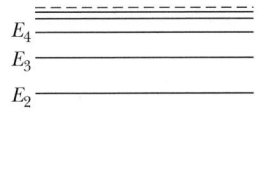

We have seen that an atom will emit radiation only at certain frequencies that correspond to the energy separation between the various allowed states. Consider an atom with many allowed energy states, labeled E_1, E_2, E_3, ..., as in Figure 28.16. When light is incident on the atom, only those photons with energy hf matching the energy separation ΔE between two levels can be absorbed by the atom. A schematic diagram representing this **stimulated absorption process** is shown in Active Figure 28.17. At ordinary temperatures, most of the atoms in a sample are in the ground state. If a vessel containing many atoms of a gas is illuminated with a light beam containing all possible photon frequencies (that is, a continuous spectrum), only those photons of energies $E_2 - E_1$, $E_3 - E_1$, $E_4 - E_1$, and so on can be absorbed. As a result of this absorption, some atoms are raised to various allowed higher-energy levels, called **excited states**.

Once an atom is in an excited state, there is a constant probability that it will jump back to a lower level by emitting a photon, as shown in Figure 28.18. This process is known as **spontaneous emission**. Typically, an atom will remain in an excited state for only about 10^{-8} s.

A third process that is important in lasers, **stimulated emission**, was predicted by Einstein in 1917. Suppose an atom is in the excited state E_2, as in Figure 28.19 (page 950), and a photon with energy $hf = E_2 - E_1$ is incident on it. The incoming photon increases the probability that the excited atom will return to the ground state and thereby emit a second photon having the same energy hf. Note that two identical photons result from stimulated emission: the incident photon and the emitted photon. *The emitted photon is exactly in phase with the incident photon.* These photons can stimulate other atoms to emit photons in a chain of similar processes.

The intense, coherent (in-phase) light in a laser (*l*ight *a*mplification by *s*timulated *e*mission of *r*adiation) is a result of stimulated emission. In a laser, voltages can be used to put more electrons in excited states than in the ground state. This process is called **population inversion**. The excited state of the system must be a *metastable state*, which means that its lifetime must be relatively long. When that is the case, stimulated emission will occur before spontaneous emission. Finally, the photons produced must be retained in the system for a while so that they can stimulate the production of still more photons. This step can be done with mirrors, one of which is partly transparent.

Figure 28.16 Energy level diagram of an atom with various allowed states. The lowest-energy state, E_1, is the ground state. All others are excited states.

Scientist checking the performance of an experimental laser-cutting device mounted on a robot arm. The laser is being used to cut through a metal plate.

The electron is transferred from the ground state to the excited state when the atom absorbs a photon of energy $hf = E_2 - E_1$.

Active Figure 28.17
Diagram representing the process of *stimulated absorption* of a photon by an atom.

When the atom falls from the excited state to the ground state, it emits a photon of energy $hf = E_2 - E_1$.

Figure 28.18 Diagram representing the process of *spontaneous emission* of a photon by an atom that is initially in the excited state E_2.

The incoming photon stimulates the atom to emit a second photon of energy $hf = E_2 - E_1$.

Before (atom in excited state)

After (atom in ground state)

Figure 28.19 Diagram representing the process of *stimulated emission* of a photon by an incoming photon of energy hf. Initially, the atom is in the excited state.

The source of coherent light in the laser is the stimulated emission of 632.8-nm photons in the transition $E_3^* \rightarrow E_2$.

Metastable state

$\lambda = 632.8$ nm

Output energy

Input energy

Figure 28.20 Energy level diagram for the neon atom in a helium–neon laser.

Figure 28.20 is an energy level diagram for the neon atom in a helium–neon gas laser. The mixture of helium and neon is confined to a glass tube sealed at the ends by mirrors. A high voltage applied to the tube causes electrons to sweep through it, colliding with the atoms of the gas and raising them into excited states. Neon atoms are excited to state E_3^* through this process and also as a result of collisions with excited helium atoms. When a neon atom makes a transition to state E_2, it stimulates emission by neighboring excited atoms. The result is the production of coherent light at a wavelength of 632.8 nm. Figure 28.21 summarizes the steps in the production of a laser beam.

APPLICATION

Laser Technology

Lasers that cover wavelengths in the infrared, visible, and ultraviolet regions of the spectrum are now available. Applications include the surgical "welding" of detached retinas, "lasik" surgery, precision surveying and length measurement, a potential source for inducing nuclear fusion reactions, precision cutting of metals and other materials, and telephone communication along optical fibers.

The tube contains the atoms that are the active medium.

Due to spontaneous emission, some photons leave the side of the tube.

The parallel end mirrors provide the feedback of the stimulating wave.

Laser output

Mirror 1

Mirror 2

The stimulating wave moves parallel to the axis of the tube.

Energy input

An external source of energy (optical, electrical, etc.) is needed to "pump" the atoms to excited energy states.

Courtesy of HRL Laboratories LLC, Malibu, CA

Figure 28.21 (a) Steps in the production of a laser beam. (b) Photograph of the first ruby laser, showing the flash lamp surrounding the ruby rod.

■ SUMMARY

28.3 The Bohr Model

The **Bohr model** of the atom is successful in describing the spectra of atomic hydrogen and hydrogen-like ions. One basic assumption of the model is that the electron can exist only in certain orbits such that its angular momentum mvr is an integral multiple of $\hbar$, where $\hbar$ is Planck's constant divided by 2π. Assuming circular orbits and a Coulomb force of attraction between electron and proton, the energies of the quantum states for hydrogen are

$$E_n = -\frac{m_e k_e^2 e^4}{2\hbar^2}\left(\frac{1}{n^2}\right) \qquad n = 1, 2, 3, \ldots \qquad [28.13]$$

where k_e is the Coulomb constant, e is the charge on the electron, and n is an integer called a **quantum number**.

If the electron in the hydrogen atom jumps from an orbit having quantum number n_i to an orbit having quantum number n_f, it emits a photon of frequency f, given by

$$f = \frac{E_i - E_f}{h} = \frac{m_e k_e^2 e^4}{4\pi\hbar^3}\left(\frac{1}{n_f^2} - \frac{1}{n_i^2}\right) \qquad [28.15]$$

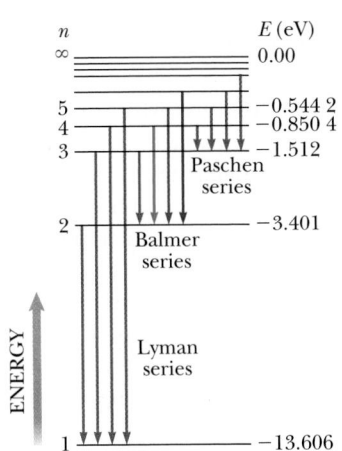

Energy level diagram for hydrogen. Vertical arrows represent the lowest-energy transitions for each of the spectral series shown.

Bohr's **correspondence principle** states that quantum mechanics is in agreement with classical physics when the quantum numbers for a system are very large.

The Bohr theory can be generalized to hydrogen-like atoms, such as singly ionized helium or doubly ionized lithium. This modification consists of replacing e^2 by Ze^2 wherever it occurs.

28.4 Quantum Mechanics and the Hydrogen Atom

One of the many successes of quantum mechanics is that the quantum numbers n, ℓ, and m_ℓ associated with atomic structure arise directly from the mathematics of the theory. The quantum number n is called the **principal quantum number**, ℓ is the **orbital quantum number**, and m_ℓ is the **orbital magnetic quantum number.** These quantum numbers can take only certain values: $1 \leq n < \infty$ in integer steps, $0 \leq \ell \leq n - 1$, and $-\ell \leq m_\ell \leq \ell$. In addition, a fourth quantum number, called the **spin magnetic quantum number** m_s, is needed to explain a fine doubling of lines in atomic spectra, with $m_s = \pm\frac{1}{2}$.

28.5 The Exclusion Principle and the Periodic Table

An understanding of the periodic table of the elements became possible when Pauli formulated the **exclusion principle**, which states that no two electrons in the same atom can have the same values for the set of quantum numbers n, ℓ, m_ℓ, and m_s. A particular set of these quantum numbers is called a quantum state. The exclusion principle explains how different energy levels in atoms are populated. Once one subshell is filled, the next electron goes into the vacant subshell that is lowest in energy. Atoms with similar configurations in their outermost shell have similar chemical properties and are found in the same column of the periodic table.

28.6 Characteristic X-Rays

Characteristic x-rays are produced when a bombarding electron collides with an electron in an inner shell of an atom with sufficient energy to remove the electron from the atom. The vacancy is filled when an electron from a higher level drops down into the level containing the vacancy, emitting a photon in the x-ray part of the spectrum in the process.

28.7 Atomic Transitions and Lasers

When an atom is irradiated by light of all different wavelengths, it will only absorb wavelengths equal to the difference in energy of two of its energy levels. This phenomenon, called **stimulated absorption**, places an atom's electrons into **excited states**. Atoms in an excited state have a probability of returning to a lower level of excitation by **spontaneous emission**. The wavelengths that can be emitted are the same as the wavelengths that can be absorbed. If an atom is in an excited state and a photon with energy $hf = E_2 - E_1$ is incident on it, the probability of emission of a second photon of this energy is greatly enhanced. The emitted photon is exactly in phase with the incident photon. This process is called **stimulated emission**. The emitted and original photon can then stimulate more emission, creating an amplifying effect.

Lasers are monochromatic, coherent light sources that work on the principle of **stimulated emission** of radiation from a system of atoms.

■ MULTIPLE-CHOICE QUESTIONS

ENHANCED
WebAssign The multiple-choice questions in this chapter may be assigned online in Enhanced WebAssign.

1. A beryllium atom is stripped of all but one of its electrons. What is the energy of the ground state? (a) -13.6 eV (b) -218 eV (c) -122 eV (d) -40.8 eV (e) 0

2. An electron in the $n = 5$ energy level of hydrogen undergoes a transition to the $n = 3$ energy level. What wavelength photon does the atom emit in this process? (a) 1.28×10^{-6} m (b) 2.37×10^{-6} m (c) 4.22×10^{-7} m (d) 3.04×10^{-6} m (e) 5.92×10^{-5} m

3. Consider an atom having four distinct energy levels. If an electron is able to make transitions between any two levels, how many different wavelengths of radiation could the atom emit? (a) 2 (b) 3 (c) 4 (d) 5 (e) 6

4. Consider the $n = 3$ energy level in a hydrogen atom. How many electrons can be placed in this level? (a) 1 (b) 2 (c) 8 (d) 9 (e) 18

5. The periodic table is based mainly on which of the following principles? (a) It is based on the uncertainty principle. (b) All electrons in an atom must have the same set of quantum numbers. (c) No two electrons in an atom can have the same set of quantum numbers. (d) All electrons in an atom are in orbitals having the same energy. (e) Energy is conserved in all interactions.

6. Which of the following electronic configurations are *not* allowed for an atom? Choose all correct answers. (a) $2s^2 2p^6$ (b) $3s^2 3p^7$ (c) $3d^7 4s^2$ (d) $3d^{10} 4s^2 4p^6$ (e) $1s^2 2s^2 2d^1$

7. If an electron in an atom has the quantum numbers $n = 3$, $\ell = 2$, $m_\ell = 1$, and $m_s = \frac{1}{2}$, what state is it in? (a) $3s$ (b) $3p$ (c) $3d$ (d) $4d$ (e) $3f$

8. If an electron had a spin of $\frac{3}{2}$, its spin quantum number could have the following four values: $m_s = +\frac{3}{2}, +\frac{1}{2}, -\frac{1}{2}$, and $-\frac{3}{2}$. If that were true, which one of the following elements with a filled shell would become the first of the noble gases? (a) He with 2 electrons (b) Li with 3 electrons (c) Be with 4 electrons (d) B with 5 electrons (e) C with 6 electrons

9. What can be concluded about a hydrogen atom with an electron in the d state? (a) The atom is ionized. (b) The orbital angular momentum of the atom is zero. (c) The orbital angular momentum of the atom is not zero. (d) The atom is in its ground state. (e) The principal quantum number is $n = 2$.

10. In relating Bohr's theory to the de Broglie wavelength of electrons, why does the circumference of an electron's orbit become nine times greater when the electron moves from the $n = 1$ level to the $n = 3$ level? (a) There are nine times as many wavelengths in the new orbit. (b) The wavelength of the electron becomes nine times as long. (c) There are three times as many wavelengths, and each wavelength is three times as long. (d) The electron is moving nine times faster. (e) The atom is partly ionized.

11. When an electron collides with an atom, it can transfer all or some of its energy to the atom. A hydrogen atom is in its ground state. Incident on the atom are several electrons, each having a kinetic energy of 10.5 eV. What is the result? (a) The atom can be excited to a higher allowed state. (b) The atom is ionized. (c) The electrons pass by the atom without interaction.

12. Which of the following is *not* one of the basic assumptions of the Bohr model of hydrogen? (a) Only certain electron orbits are stable and allowed. (b) The electron moves in circular orbits about the proton under the influence of the Coulomb force. (c) The charge on the electron is quantized. (d) Radiation is emitted by the atom when the electron moves from a higher energy state to a lower energy state. (e) The angular momentum associated with the electron's orbital motion is quantized.

13. When an atom emits a photon, what happens? (a) One of its electrons leaves the atom. (b) The atom moves to a state of higher energy. (c) The atom moves to a state of lower energy. (d) One of its electrons collides with another particle. (e) None of those events occur.

■ CONCEPTUAL QUESTIONS

ENHANCED
WebAssign The conceptual questions in this chapter may be assigned online in Enhanced WebAssign.

1. In the hydrogen atom, the quantum number n can increase without limit. Because of this fact, does the frequency of possible spectral lines from hydrogen also increase without limit?

2. Does the light emitted by a neon sign constitute a continuous spectrum or only a few colors? Defend your answer.

3. In an x-ray tube, if the energy with which the electrons strike the metal target is increased, the wavelengths of the characteristic x-rays do not change. Why not?

4. An energy of about 21 eV is required to excite an electron in a helium atom from the $1s$ state to the $2s$ state. The same transition for the He$^+$ ion requires approximately twice as much energy. Explain.

5. Is it possible for a spectrum from an x-ray tube to show the continuous spectrum of x-rays without the presence of the characteristic x-rays?

6. Suppose the electron in the hydrogen atom obeyed classical mechanics rather than quantum mechanics. Why should such a hypothetical atom emit a continuous spectrum rather than the observed line spectrum?

7. When a hologram is produced, the system (including light source, object, beam splitter, and so on) must be held motionless within a quarter of the light's wavelength. Why?

8. Why are three quantum numbers needed to describe the state of a one-electron atom (ignoring spin)?

9. Describe how the structure of atoms would differ if the Pauli exclusion principle were not valid. What consequences would follow, both at the atomic level and in the world at large?

10. Can the electron in the ground state of hydrogen absorb a photon of energy less than 13.6 eV? Can it absorb a photon of energy greater than 13.6 eV? Explain.

11. Why do lithium, potassium, and sodium exhibit similar chemical properties?

12. List some ways in which quantum mechanics altered our view of the atom pictured by the Bohr theory.

13. It is easy to understand how two electrons (one with spin up, one with spin down) can fill the $1s$ shell for a helium atom. How is it possible that eight more electrons can fit into the $2s$, $2p$ level to complete the $1s^2 2s^2 2p^6$ shell for a neon atom?

14. The ionization energies for Li, Na, K, Rb, and Cs are 5.390, 5.138, 4.339, 4.176, and 3.893 eV, respectively. Explain why these values are to be expected in terms of the atomic structures.

15. Why is stimulated emission so important in the operation of a laser?

▪ PROBLEMS

28.1 Early Models of the Atom

28.2 Atomic Spectra

1. **Q|C** The wavelengths of the Lyman series for hydrogen are given by

$$\frac{1}{\lambda} = R_H\left(1 - \frac{1}{n^2}\right) \qquad n = 2, 3, 4, \ldots$$

(a) Calculate the wavelengths of the first three lines in this series. (b) Identify the region of the electromagnetic spectrum in which these lines appear.

2. **Q|C** The wavelengths of the Paschen series for hydrogen are given by

$$\frac{1}{\lambda} = R_H\left(\frac{1}{3^2} - \frac{1}{n^2}\right) \qquad n = 4, 5, 6, \ldots$$

(a) Calculate the wavelengths of the first three lines in this series. (b) Identify the region of the electromagnetic spectrum in which these lines appear.

3. The "size" of the *atom* in Rutherford's model is about 1.0×10^{-10} m. (a) Determine the attractive electrostatic force between an electron and a proton separated by this distance. (b) Determine (in eV) the electrostatic potential energy of the atom.

4. An isolated atom of a certain element emits light of wavelength 520 nm when the atom falls from its fifth excited state into its second excited state. The atom emits a photon of wavelength 410 nm when it drops from its sixth excited state into its second excited state. Find the wavelength of the light radiated when the atom makes a transition from its sixth to its fifth excited state.

5. **Q|C** The "size" of the atom in Rutherford's model is about 1.0×10^{-10} m. (a) Determine the speed of an electron moving about the proton using the attractive electrostatic force between an electron and a proton separated by this distance. (b) Does this speed suggest that Einsteinian relativity must be considered in studying the atom? (c) Compute the de Broglie wavelength of the electron as it moves about the proton. (d) Does this wavelength suggest that wave effects, such as diffraction and interference, must be considered in studying the atom?

6. In a Rutherford scattering experiment, an α-particle (charge = $+2e$) heads directly toward a gold nucleus (charge = $+79e$). The α-particle had a kinetic energy of 5.0 MeV when very far ($r \to \infty$) from the nucleus. Assuming the gold nucleus to be fixed in space, determine the distance of closest approach. *Hint:* Use conservation of energy with $PE = k_e q_1 q_2 / r$.

28.3 The Bohr Model

7. **M** A hydrogen atom is in its first excited state ($n = 2$). Using the Bohr theory of the atom, calculate (a) the radius of the orbit, (b) the linear momentum of the electron, (c) the angular momentum of the electron, (d) the kinetic energy, (e) the potential energy, and (f) the total energy.

8. For a hydrogen atom in its ground state, use the Bohr model to compute (a) the orbital speed of the electron, (b) the kinetic energy of the electron, and (c) the electrical potential energy of the atom.

9. **S** Show that the speed of the electron in the nth Bohr orbit in hydrogen is given by

$$v_n = \frac{k_e e^2}{n\hbar}$$

10. A photon is emitted when a hydrogen atom undergoes a transition from the $n = 5$ state to the $n = 3$ state. Calculate (a) the wavelength, (b) the frequency, and (c) the energy (in electron volts) of the emitted photon.

11. A hydrogen atom emits a photon of wavelength 656 nm. From what energy orbit to what lower-energy orbit did the electron jump?

12. Following are four possible transitions for a hydrogen atom

   I. $n_i = 2$; $n_f = 5$ II. $n_i = 5$; $n_f = 3$
   III. $n_i = 7$; $n_f = 4$ IV. $n_i = 4$; $n_f = 7$

   (a) Which transition will emit the shortest-wavelength photon? (b) For which transition will the atom gain the most energy? (c) For which transition(s) does the atom lose energy?

13. **M** What is the energy of a photon that, when absorbed by a hydrogen atom, could cause an electronic transition from (a) the $n = 2$ state to the $n = 5$ state and (b) the $n = 4$ state to the $n = 6$ state?

14. A hydrogen atom initially in its ground state ($n = 1$) absorbs a photon and ends up in the state for which $n = 3$. (a) What is the energy of the absorbed photon? (b) If the atom eventually returns to the ground state, what photon energies could the atom emit?

15. The Balmer series for the hydrogen atom corresponds to electronic transitions that terminate in the state with quantum number $n = 2$ as shown in Figure P28.15. Consider the photon of longest wavelength corresponding to a transition shown in the figure. Determine (a) its energy and (b) its wavelength. Consider the spectral line of shortest wavelength corresponding

to a transition shown in the figure. Find (c) its photon energy and (d) its wavelength. (e) What is the shortest possible wavelength in the Balmer series?

Figure P28.15

16. **S** A particle of charge q and mass m, moving with a constant speed v, perpendicular to a constant magnetic field B, follows a circular path. If in this case the angular momentum about the center of this circle is quantized so that $mvr = 2n\hbar$, show that the allowed radii for the particle are

$$r_n = \sqrt{\frac{2n\hbar}{qB}}$$

where $n = 1, 2, 3, \ldots$.

17. **M** (a) If an electron makes a transition from the $n = 4$ Bohr orbit to the $n = 2$ orbit, determine the wavelength of the photon created in the process. (b) Assuming that the atom was initially at rest, determine the recoil speed of the hydrogen atom when this photon is emitted.

18. Consider a large number of hydrogen atoms, with electrons all initially in the $n = 4$ state. (a) How many different wavelengths would be observed in the emission spectrum of these atoms? (b) What is the longest wavelength that could be observed? (c) To which series does the wavelength found in (b) belong?

19. A photon with energy 2.28 eV is absorbed by a hydrogen atom. Find (a) the minimum n for a hydrogen atom that can be ionized by such a photon and (b) the speed of the electron released from the state in part (a) when it is far from the nucleus.

20. (a) Calculate the angular momentum of the Moon due to its orbital motion about Earth. In your calculation use 3.84×10^8 m as the average Earth–Moon distance and 2.36×10^6 s as the period of the Moon in its orbit. (b) If the angular momentum of the Moon obeys Bohr's quantization rule ($L = n\hbar$), determine the value of the quantum number n. (c) By what fraction would the Earth–Moon radius have to be increased to increase the quantum number by 1?

21. An electron is in the second excited orbit of hydrogen, corresponding to $n = 3$. Find (a) the radius of the orbit and (b) the wavelength of the electron in this orbit.

22. **S** (a) Write an expression relating the kinetic energy KE of the electron and the potential energy PE in the

Bohr model of the hydrogen atom. (b) Suppose a hydrogen atom absorbs a photon of energy E, resulting in the transfer of the electron to a higher-energy level. Express the resulting change in the potential energy of the system in terms of E. (c) What is the change in the electron's kinetic energy during this process?

23. The orbital radii of a hydrogen-like atom is given by the equation

$$r_n = \frac{n^2 \hbar^2}{Z m_e k_e e^2}$$

What is the radius of the first Bohr orbit in (a) He$^+$, (b) Li^{2+}, and (c) Be^{3+}?

24. **GP** Consider a Bohr model of doubly ionized lithium. (a) Write an expression similar to Equation 28.14 for the energy levels of the sole remaining electron. (b) Find the energy corresponding to $n = 4$. (c) Find the energy corresponding to $n = 2$. (d) Calculate the energy of the photon emitted when the electron transits from the fourth energy level to the second energy level. Express the answer both in electron volts and in joules. (e) Find the frequency and wavelength of the emitted photon. (f) In what part of the spectrum is the emitted light?

25. A general expression for the energy levels of one-electron atoms and ions is

$$E_n = -\frac{\mu k_e^2 q_1^2 q_2^2}{2\hbar^2 n^2}$$

Here μ is the reduced mass of the atom, given by $\mu = m_1 m_2/(m_1 + m_2)$, where m_1 is the mass of the electron and m_2 is the mass of the nucleus; k_e is the Coulomb constant; and q_1 and q_2 are the charges of the electron and the nucleus, respectively. The wavelength for the $n = 3$ to $n = 2$ transition of the hydrogen atom is 656.3 nm (visible red light). What are the wavelengths for this same transition in (a) positronium, which consists of an electron and a positron, and (b) singly ionized helium? *Note:* A positron is a positively charged electron.

26. **S** Using the concept of standing waves, de Broglie was able to derive Bohr's stationary orbit postulate. He assumed a confined electron could exist only in states where its de Broglie waves form standing-wave patterns, as in Figure 28.6. Consider a particle confined in a box of length L to be equivalent to a string of length L and fixed at both ends. Apply de Broglie's concept to show that (a) the linear momentum of this particle is quantized with $p = mv = nh/2L$ and (b) the allowed states correspond to particle energies of $E_n = n^2 E_0$, where $E_0 = h^2/(8mL^2)$.

28.4 Quantum Mechanics and the Hydrogen Atom

27. List the possible sets of quantum numbers for electrons in the $3d$ subshell.

28. When the principal quantum number is $n = 4$, how many different values of (a) ℓ and (b) m_ℓ are possible?

29. The ρ-meson has a charge of $-e$, a spin quantum number of 1, and a mass 1 507 times that of the electron. If the electrons in atoms were replaced by ρ-mesons, list the possible sets of quantum numbers for ρ-mesons in the $3d$ subshell.

28.5 The Exclusion Principle and the Periodic Table

30. (a) Write out the electronic configuration of the ground state for nitrogen ($Z = 7$). (b) Write out the values for the possible set of quantum numbers n, ℓ, m_ℓ, and m_s for the electrons in nitrogen.

31. A certain element has its outermost electron in a $3p$ subshell. It has valence +3 because it has three more electrons than a certain noble gas. What element is it?

32. Two electrons in the same atom have $n = 3$ and $\ell = 1$. (a) List the quantum numbers for the possible states of the atom. (b) How many states would be possible if the exclusion principle did not apply to the atom?

33. Zirconium ($Z = 40$) has two electrons in an incomplete d subshell. (a) What are the values of n and ℓ for each electron? (b) What are all possible values of m_ℓ and m_s? (c) What is the electron configuration in the ground state of zirconium?

28.6 Characteristic X-Rays

34. A tungsten target is struck by electrons that have been accelerated from rest through a 40.0-kV potential difference. Find the shortest wavelength of the radiation emitted.

35. A bismuth target is struck by electrons, and x-rays are emitted. Estimate (a) the M- to L-shell transitional energy for bismuth and (b) the wavelength of the x-ray emitted when an electron falls from the M shell to the L shell.

36. When an electron drops from the M shell ($n = 3$) to a vacancy in the K shell ($n = 1$), the measured wavelength of the emitted x-ray is found to be 0.101 nm. Identify the element.

37. **M** The K series of the discrete spectrum of tungsten contains wavelengths of 0.018 5 nm, 0.020 9 nm, and 0.021 5 nm. The K-shell ionization energy is 69.5 keV. Determine the ionization energies of the L, M, and N shells.

Additional Problems

38. In a hydrogen atom, what is the principal quantum number of the electron orbit with a radius closest to 1.0 μm?

39. (a) How much energy is required to cause an electron in hydrogen to move from the $n = 1$ state to the $n = 2$ state? (b) If the electrons gain this energy by collision between hydrogen atoms in a high-temperature gas,

find the minimum temperature of the heated hydrogen gas. The thermal energy of the heated atoms is given by $3k_B T/2$, where k_B is the Boltzmann constant.

40. A pulsed ruby laser emits light at 694.3 nm. For a 14.0-ps pulse containing 3.00 J of energy, find (a) the physical length of the pulse as it travels through space and (b) the number of photons in it. (c) If the beam has a circular cross section 0.600 cm in diameter, what is the number of photons per cubic millimeter?

41. An electron in chromium moves from the $n = 2$ state to the $n = 1$ state without emitting a photon. Instead, the excess energy is transferred to an outer electron (one in the $n = 4$ state), which is then ejected by the atom. In this Auger (pronounced "ohjay") process, the ejected electron is referred to as an Auger electron. (a) Find the change in energy associated with the transition from $n = 2$ into the vacant $n = 1$ state using Bohr theory. Assume only one electron in the K shell is shielding part of the nuclear charge. (b) Find the energy needed to ionize an $n = 4$ electron, assuming 22 electrons shield the nucleus. (c) Find the kinetic energy of the ejected (Auger) electron. (All answers should be in electron volts.)

42. QC S As the Earth moves around the Sun, its orbits are quantized. (a) Follow the steps of Bohr's analysis of the hydrogen atom to show that the allowed radii of the Earth's orbit are given by

$$r_n = \frac{n^2 \hbar^2}{G M_S M_E^2}$$

where n is an integer quantum number, M_S is the mass of the Sun, and M_E is the mass of the Earth. (b) Calculate the numerical value of n for the Sun–Earth system. (c) Find the distance between the orbit for quantum number n and the next orbit out from the Sun corresponding to the quantum number $n + 1$. (d) Discuss the significance of your results from parts (b) and (c).

43. BIO M A laser used in eye surgery emits a 3.00-mJ pulse in 1.00 ns, focused to a spot 30.0 μm in diameter on the retina. (a) Find (in SI units) the power per unit area at the retina. (This quantity is called the *irradiance*.) (b) What energy is delivered per pulse to an area of molecular size (say, a circular area 0.600 nm in diameter)?

44. An electron has a de Broglie wavelength equal to the diameter of a hydrogen atom in its ground state. (a) What is the kinetic energy of the electron? (b) How does this energy compare with the magnitude of the ground-state energy of the hydrogen atom?

45. S Use Bohr's model of the hydrogen atom to show that when the atom makes a transition from the state n to the state $n - 1$, the frequency of the emitted light is given by

$$f = \frac{2\pi^2 m k_e^2 e^4}{h^3} \left[\frac{2n - 1}{(n-1)^2 n^2} \right]$$

46. Suppose the ionization energy of an atom is 4.100 eV. In this same atom, we observe emission lines that have wavelengths of 310.0 nm, 400.0 nm, and 1 378 nm. Use this information to construct the energy level diagram with the least number of levels. Assume that the higher energy levels are closer together.

■ AP* REVIEW QUESTIONS

1. Which color of light would be associated with the least change in energy of an atom?

   (A) Red

   (B) Green

   (C) Blue

   (D) Yellow

   (E) Violet

Questions 2–5

Use the hypothetical energy-level diagram below to answer questions 2–5.

Note: Energy levels not drawn to scale.

2. How much energy does an electron have in the ground state?

   (A) −14 eV

   (B) −6 eV

   (C) 0 eV

   (D) 6 eV

   (E) 14 eV

3. How much energy is required to completely ionize the atom?

   (A) 0 eV

   (B) 6 eV

   (C) 7 eV

   (D) 12 eV

   (E) 14 eV

4. Which of the following transitions will produce photons with the shortest wavelength?

   (A) $n = 2$ to $n = 1$

   (B) $n = 3$ to $n = 2$

   (C) $n = 4$ to $n = 3$

   (D) $n = 3$ to $n = 1$

   (E) $n = 4$ to $n = 1$

5. The atom is irradiated with continuous radiation from 5 eV to 10 eV. Which of the following transitions will be included in the absorption spectrum?

   I. $n = 1$ to $n = 2$

   II. $n = 1$ to $n = 3$

   III. $n = 1$ to $n = 4$

   (A) I only

   (B) I and II only

   (C) II and III only

   (D) III only

   (E) I, II, and III

6. The ground state of a hypothetical atom is −10 eV. An electron interacts with an incident 16 eV photon. What happens?

(A) Electron remains in ground state.

(B) The electron moves up to an energy level of −6 eV.

(C) The electron moves up to an energy level of +6 eV.

(D) The electron moves down to an energy level of −16 eV.

(E) The electron is freed with a kinetic energy of 6 eV.

Questions 7–9

Use the hypothetical energy-level diagram below to answer questions 7–9.

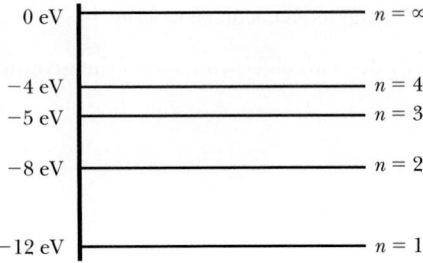

Note: Energy levels not drawn to scale.

7. If the atom is continuously irradiated with 7 eV photons, which of the following would NOT be present in the emission spectrum as the electrons return to the ground state?

(A) 1 eV

(B) 3 eV

(C) 4 eV

(D) 7 eV

(E) None of these—all are present in the emission spectrum

8. If the absorption spectrum is from the ground state only, which of the following photon energies will be absorbed?

    I. 4 eV

    II. 5 eV

    III. 8 eV

(A) I only

(B) I and II only

(C) I and III only

(D) II only

(E) I, II, and III

9. If the atom is continuously radiated from 1 eV to 10 eV, how many spectral lines will be visible in the emission spectrum?

(A) 2

(B) 3

(C) 4

(D) 6

(E) 8

Questions 10–11

Use the hypothetical energy-level diagram below to answer questions 10–11.

Note: Energy levels not drawn to scale.

10. Assuming the ionization energy of the atom is +10 eV, what is the energy of the ground state?

(A) 0 eV

(B) +10 eV

(C) −10 eV

(D) +14 eV

(E) −14 eV

11. For a different hypothetical atom with a similar energy-level diagram, the ground state is −15 eV. The absorption spectrum from the ground state includes photon energies of 5 eV, 10 eV, and 12 eV. If no energies outside of this range are observed, which of the following are possible values for excited energy levels?

    I. −5 eV

    II. −10 eV

    III. −12 eV

(A) I only

(B) I and II only

(C) II and III only

(D) III only

(E) I, II, and III

12. Which of the following characteristics of line spectra is accurate?

	Absorption spectra	Emission spectra
(A)	bright lines	bright lines
(B)	bright lines	dark lines
(C)	dark lines	dark lines
(D)	dark lines	bright lines
(E)	bright or dark lines	bright or dark lines

Peter Ginter/Science Faction/Getty Images

Technicians prepare the vacuum chamber of the ASDEX Upgrade Fusion Reactor (Axially Symmetric Divertor Experiment), where plasma is heated to over sixty million degrees, leading to the fusion of deuterium and tritium and the release of energy. Such experimental tokamaks may lead to working fusion reactors.

Nuclear Physics

In this chapter we discuss the properties and structure of the atomic nucleus. We start by describing the basic properties of nuclei and follow with a discussion of the phenomenon of radioactivity. Finally, we explore nuclear reactions and the various processes by which nuclei decay.

29.1 Some Properties of Nuclei

All nuclei are composed of two types of particles: protons and neutrons. The only exception is the ordinary hydrogen nucleus, which is a single proton. In describing some of the properties of nuclei, such as their charge, mass, and radius, we make use of the following quantities:

- the **atomic number** Z, which equals the number of protons in the nucleus
- the **neutron number** N, which equals the number of neutrons in the nucleus
- the **mass number** A, which equals the number of nucleons in the nucleus (*nucleon* is a generic term used to refer to either a proton or a neutron)

The symbol we use to represent nuclei is $_Z^A X$, where X represents the chemical symbol for the element. For example, $_{13}^{27} Al$ has the mass number 27 and the atomic number 13; therefore, it contains 13 protons and 14 neutrons. When no confusion is likely to arise, we often omit the subscript Z because the chemical symbol can always be used to determine Z.

Ernest Rutherford
New Zealand Physicist (1871–1937)
Rutherford was awarded the 1908 Nobel Prize in Chemistry for studying radioactivity and for discovering that atoms can be broken apart by alpha rays. "On consideration, I realized that this scattering backward must be the result of a single collision, and when I made calculations I saw that it was impossible to get anything of that order of magnitude unless you took a system in which the greater part of the mass of the atom was concentrated in a minute nucleus. It was then that I had the idea of an atom with a minute massive center carrying a charge."

Definition of the unified ▶ mass unit, u

Table 29.1 Masses of the Proton, Neutron, and Electron in Various Units

Particle	Mass		
	kg	**u**	**MeV/c^2**
Proton	$1.672\ 6 \times 10^{-27}$	1.007 276	938.28
Neutron	$1.675\ 0 \times 10^{-27}$	1.008 665	939.57
Electron	9.109×10^{-31}	5.486×10^{-4}	0.511

The nuclei of all atoms of a particular element must contain the same number of protons, but they may contain different numbers of neutrons. Nuclei that are related in this way are called **isotopes**. **The isotopes of an element have the same Z value, but different N and A values.** The natural abundances of isotopes can differ substantially. For example, $^{11}_{6}C$, $^{12}_{6}C$, $^{13}_{6}C$, and $^{14}_{6}C$ are four isotopes of carbon. The natural abundance of the $^{12}_{6}C$ isotope is about 98.9%, whereas that of the $^{13}_{6}C$ isotope is only about 1.1%. Some isotopes don't occur naturally, but can be produced in the laboratory through nuclear reactions. Even the simplest element, hydrogen, has isotopes: $^{1}_{1}H$, hydrogen; $^{2}_{1}H$, deuterium; and $^{3}_{1}H$, tritium.

Charge and Mass

The proton carries a single positive charge $+e = 1.602\ 177\ 33 \times 10^{-19}$ C, the electron carries a single negative charge $-e$, and the neutron is electrically neutral. Because the neutron has no charge, it's difficult to detect. The proton is about 1 836 times as massive as the electron, and the masses of the proton and the neutron are almost equal (Table 29.1).

For atomic masses, it is convenient to define the **unified mass unit, u**, in such a way that the mass of one atom of the isotope ^{12}C is exactly 12 u, where 1 u = $1.660\ 559 \times 10^{-27}$ kg. The proton and neutron each have a mass of about 1 u, and the electron has a mass that is only a small fraction of an atomic mass unit.

Because the rest energy of a particle is given by $E_R = mc^2$, it is often convenient to express the particle's mass in terms of its energy equivalent. For one atomic mass unit, we have an energy equivalent of

$$E_R = mc^2 = (1.660\ 559 \times 10^{-27}\ \text{kg})(2.997\ 92 \times 10^8\ \text{m/s})^2$$

$$= 1.492\ 431 \times 10^{-10}\ \text{J} = 931.494\ \text{MeV}$$

In calculations nuclear physicists often express *mass* in terms of the unit MeV/c^2, where

$$1\ \text{u} = 931.494\ \text{MeV}/c^2$$

The Size of Nuclei

The size and structure of nuclei were first investigated in the scattering experiments of Rutherford, discussed in Section 28.1. Using the principle of conservation of energy, Rutherford found an expression for how close an alpha particle moving directly toward the nucleus can come to the nucleus before being turned around by Coulomb repulsion.

In such a head-on collision, the kinetic energy of the incoming alpha particle must be converted completely to electrical potential energy when the particle stops at the point of closest approach and turns around (Active Fig. 29.1). If we equate the initial kinetic energy of the alpha particle to the maximum electrical potential energy of the system (alpha particle plus target nucleus), we have

$$\tfrac{1}{2}mv^2 = k_e \frac{q_1 q_2}{r} = k_e \frac{(2e)(Ze)}{d}$$

An alpha particle approaches a nucleus no closer than distance d because of the repulsive electric force between them.

Active Figure 29.1
An alpha particle on a head-on collision course with a nucleus of charge Ze.

where d is the distance of closest approach. Solving for d, we get

$$d = \frac{4k_e Z e^2}{m v^2}$$

From this expression, Rutherford found that alpha particles approached to within 3.2×10^{-14} m of a nucleus when the foil was made of gold, implying that the radius of the gold nucleus must be less than this value. For silver atoms, the distance of closest approach was 2×10^{-14} m. From these results, Rutherford concluded that the positive charge in an atom is concentrated in a small sphere, which he called the nucleus, with radius no greater than about 10^{-14} m. Because such small lengths are common in nuclear physics, a convenient unit of length is the *femtometer* (fm), sometimes called the **fermi** and defined as

$$1 \text{ fm} \equiv 10^{-15}$$

Since the time of Rutherford's scattering experiments, a multitude of other experiments have shown that most nuclei are approximately spherical and have an average radius given by

$$r = r_0 A^{1/3} \qquad [29.1]$$

where r_0 is a constant equal to 1.2×10^{-15} m and A is the total number of nucleons. Because the volume of a sphere is proportional to the cube of its radius, it follows from Equation 29.1 that the volume of a nucleus (assumed to be spherical) is directly proportional to A, the total number of nucleons. This relationship then suggests **all nuclei have nearly the same density**. Nucleons combine to form a nucleus *as though* they were tightly packed spheres (Fig. 29.2).

Figure 29.2 A nucleus can be visualized as a cluster of tightly packed spheres, each of which is a nucleon.

Tip 29.1 Mass Number Is Not the Atomic Mass

Don't confuse the mass number A with the atomic mass. Mass number is an integer that specifies an isotope and has no units; it's simply equal to the number of nucleons. Atomic mass is an average of the masses of the isotopes of a given element and has units of u.

Nuclear Stability

Given that the nucleus consists of a closely packed collection of protons and neutrons, you might be surprised that it can even exist. The very large repulsive electrostatic forces between protons should cause the nucleus to fly apart. Nuclei, however, are stable because of the presence of another, short-range (about 2-fm) force: the **nuclear force**, an attractive force that acts between all nuclear particles. The protons attract each other via the nuclear force, and at the same time they repel each other through the Coulomb force. The attractive nuclear force also acts between pairs of neutrons and between neutrons and protons.

The nuclear attractive force is stronger than the Coulomb repulsive force within the nucleus (at short ranges). If it were not, stable nuclei would not exist. Moreover, the strong nuclear force is nearly independent of charge. In other words, the nuclear forces associated with proton–proton, proton–neutron, and neutron–neutron interactions are approximately the same, apart from the additional repulsive Coulomb force for the proton–proton interaction.

There are about 260 stable nuclei; hundreds of others have been observed, but are unstable. A plot of N versus Z for a number of stable nuclei is given in Figure 29.3 (page 960). Note that light nuclei are most stable if they contain equal numbers of protons and neutrons so that $N = Z$, but heavy nuclei are more stable if $N > Z$. This difference can be partially understood by recognizing that as the number of protons increases, the strength of the Coulomb force increases, which tends to break the nucleus apart. As a result, more neutrons are needed to keep the nucleus stable because neutrons are affected only by the attractive nuclear forces. In effect, the additional neutrons "dilute" the nuclear charge density. Eventually, when $Z = 83$, the repulsive forces between protons cannot be compensated for by the addition of neutrons. Elements that contain more than 83 protons don't have stable nuclei, but, rather, decay or disintegrate into other particles in various amounts of time. The masses and some other properties of selected isotopes are provided in Appendix B.

Courtesy of Louise Barker/API Niels Bohr Library

Maria Goeppert-Mayer
German Physicist (1906–1972)
Goeppert-Mayer is best known for her development of the shell model of the nucleus, published in 1950. A similar model was simultaneously developed by Hans Jensen, a German scientist. Maria Goeppert-Mayer and Hans Jensen were awarded the Nobel Prize in Physics in 1963 for their extraordinary work in understanding the structure of the nucleus.

Figure 29.3 A plot of the neutron number N versus the proton number Z for the stable nuclei (black dots).

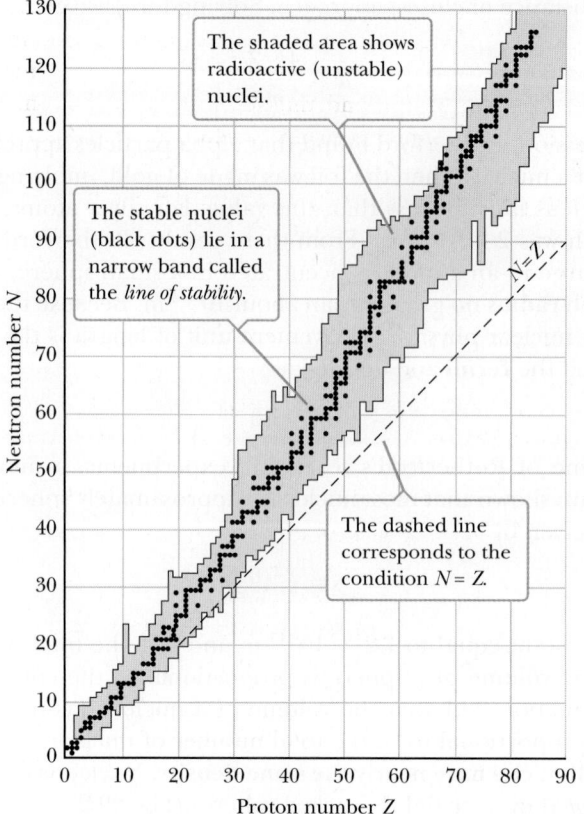

The shaded area shows radioactive (unstable) nuclei.

The stable nuclei (black dots) lie in a narrow band called the *line of stability*.

The dashed line corresponds to the condition $N = Z$.

29.2 Binding Energy

The total mass of a nucleus is always less than the sum of the masses of its nucleons. Also, because mass is another manifestation of energy, **the total energy of the bound system (the nucleus) is less than the combined energy of the separated nucleons**. This difference in energy is called the **binding energy** of the nucleus and can be thought of as the energy that must be added to a nucleus to break it apart into its separated neutrons and protons.

■ EXAMPLE 29.1 | **The Binding Energy of the Deuteron**

GOAL Calculate the binding energy of a nucleus.

PROBLEM The nucleus of the deuterium atom, called the deuteron, consists of a proton and a neutron. Calculate the deuteron's binding energy in MeV, given that its atomic mass, *the mass of a deuterium nucleus plus an electron*, is 2.014 102 u.

STRATEGY Calculate the sum of the masses of the individual particles and subtract the mass of the combined particle. The masses of the neutral atoms can be used instead of the nuclei because the electron masses cancel. Use the values from Appendix B. The mass of an atom given in Appendix B includes the mass of Z electrons, where Z is the atom's atomic number.

....

SOLUTION

To find the binding energy, first sum the masses of the hydrogen atom and neutron and subtract the mass of the deuteron:

$$\Delta m = (m_p + m_n) - m_d$$
$$= (1.007\,825\text{ u} + 1.008\,665\text{ u}) - 2.014\,102\text{ u}$$
$$= 0.002\,388\text{ u}$$

Convert this mass difference to its equivalent in MeV:

$$E_b = (0.002\,388\text{ u})\,\frac{931.5\text{ MeV}}{1\text{ u}} = \boxed{2.224\text{ MeV}}$$

....

REMARKS This result tells us that to separate a deuteron into a proton and a neutron, it's necessary to add 2.224 MeV of energy to the deuteron to overcome the attractive nuclear force between the proton and the neutron. One way to supply the deuteron with this energy is bombard it with energetic particles.

If the binding energy of a nucleus were zero, the nucleus would separate into its constituent protons and neutrons without the addition of any energy; that is, it would spontaneously break apart.

QUESTION 29.1 Tritium and helium-3 have the same number of nucleons, but tritium has one proton and two neutrons whereas helium-3 has two protons and one neutron. Without doing a calculation, which nucleus has a greater binding energy? Explain.

EXERCISE 29.1 Calculate the binding energy of $^3_2$He.

ANSWER 7.718 MeV

It's interesting to examine a plot of binding energy per nucleon, E_b/A, as a function of mass number for various stable nuclei (Fig. 29.4). Except for the lighter nuclei, the average binding energy per nucleon is about 8 MeV. Note that the curve peaks in the vicinity of $A = 60$, which means that nuclei with mass numbers greater or less than 60 are not as strongly bound as those near the middle of the periodic table. As we'll see later, this fact allows energy to be released in fission and fusion reactions. The curve is slowly varying for $A > 40$, which suggests the nuclear force saturates. In other words, a particular nucleon can interact with only a limited number of other nucleons, which can be viewed as the "nearest neighbors" in the close-packed structure illustrated in Figure 29.2.

■ APPLYING PHYSICS 29.1 | Binding Nucleons and Electrons

Figure 29.4 shows a graph of the amount of energy required to remove a nucleon from the nucleus. The figure indicates that an approximately constant amount of energy is necessary to remove a nucleon above $A = 40$, whereas we saw in Chapter 28 that widely varying amounts of energy are required to remove an electron from the atom. What accounts for this difference?

EXPLANATION In the case of Figure 29.4, the approximately constant value of the nuclear binding energy is a

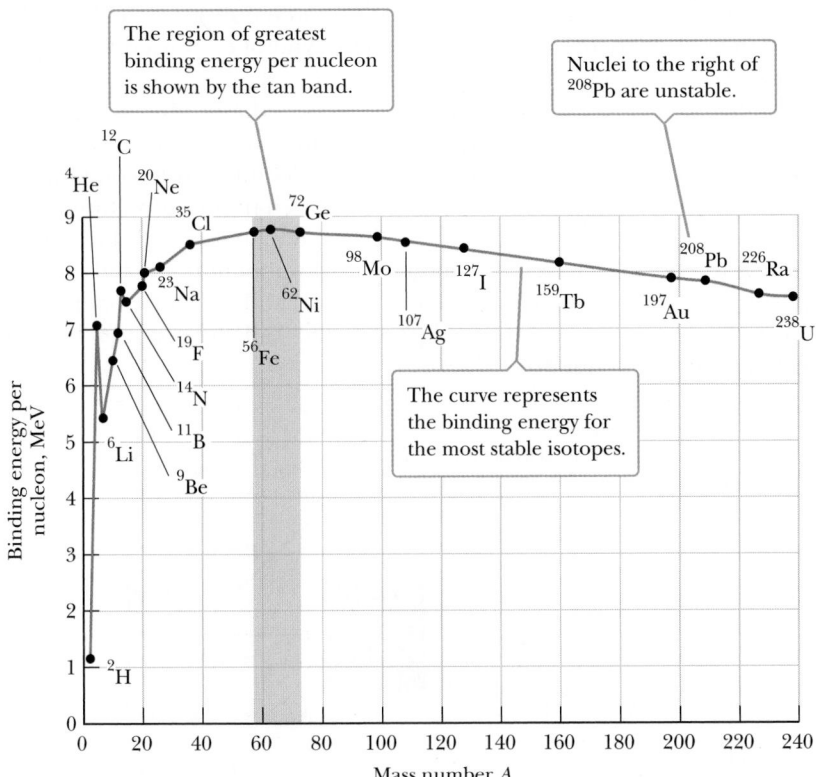

Figure 29.4 Binding energy per nucleon versus the mass number A for nuclei that are along the line of stability shown in Figure 29.3. Some representative nuclei appear as black dots with labels.

result of the short-range nature of the nuclear force. A given nucleon interacts only with its few nearest neighbors rather than with all the nucleons in the nucleus. Consequently, no matter how many nucleons are present in the nucleus, removing any nucleon involves separating it only from its nearest neighbors. The energy to do so is therefore approximately independent of how many nucleons are present. For the clearest comparison with the electron, think of averaging the energies required to remove all the electrons

from an atom, from the outermost valence electron to the innermost K-shell electron. This average increases with increasing atomic number. The electrical force binding the electrons to the nucleus in an atom is a long-range force. An electron in an atom interacts with all the protons in the nucleus. When the nuclear charge increases, there is a stronger attraction between the nucleus and the electrons. Therefore, as the nuclear charge increases, more energy is necessary to remove an average electron. ∎

Marie Curie
Polish Scientist (1867–1934)
In 1903 Marie Curie shared the Nobel Prize in Physics with her husband, Pierre, and with Antoine Henri Becquerel for their studies of radioactive substances. In 1911 she was awarded a second Nobel Prize, this time in chemistry, for the discovery of radium and polonium. Marie Curie died of leukemia caused by years of exposure to radioactive substances. "I persist in believing that the ideas that then guided us are the only ones which can lead to the true social progress. We cannot hope to build a better world without improving the individual. Toward this end, each of us must work toward his own highest development, accepting at the same time his share of responsibility in the general life of humanity."

29.3 Radioactivity

In 1896 Becquerel accidentally discovered that uranium salt crystals emit an invisible radiation that can darken a photographic plate even if the plate is covered to exclude light. After several such observations under controlled conditions, he concluded that the radiation emitted by the crystals was of a new type, one requiring no external stimulation. This spontaneous emission of radiation was soon called **radioactivity**. Subsequent experiments by other scientists showed that other substances were also radioactive.

The most significant investigations of this type were conducted by Marie and Pierre Curie. After several years of careful and laborious chemical separation processes on tons of pitchblende, a radioactive ore, the Curies reported the discovery of two previously unknown elements, both of which were radioactive. These elements were named polonium and radium. Subsequent experiments, including Rutherford's famous work on alpha-particle scattering, suggested that radioactivity was the result of the decay, or disintegration, of unstable nuclei.

Three types of radiation can be emitted by a radioactive substance: alpha (α) particles, in which the emitted particles are $^4_2$He nuclei; beta (β) particles, in which the emitted particles are either electrons or positrons; and gamma (γ) rays, in which the emitted "rays" are high-energy photons. A **positron** is a particle similar to the electron in all respects except that it has a charge of $+e$. (The positron is said to be the **antiparticle** of the electron.) The symbol e^- is used to designate an electron, and e^+ designates a positron.

It's possible to distinguish these three forms of radiation by using the scheme described in Figure 29.5. The radiation from a radioactive sample is directed into a region with a magnetic field, and the beam splits into three components, two bending in opposite directions and the third not changing direction. From this simple observation, it can be concluded that the radiation of the undeflected beam (the gamma ray) carries no charge, the component deflected upward contains positively charged particles (alpha particles), and the component deflected downward contains negatively charged particles (e^-). If the beam includes a positron (e^+), it is deflected upward.

Figure 29.5 The radiation from radioactive sources can be separated into three components by using a magnetic field to deflect the charged particles. The detector array at the right records the events.

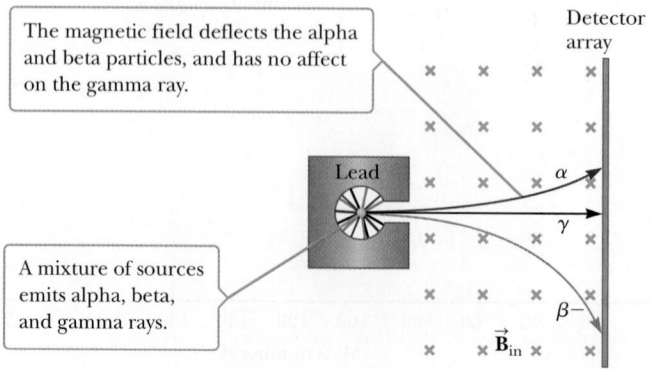

The magnetic field deflects the alpha and beta particles, and has no affect on the gamma ray.

A mixture of sources emits alpha, beta, and gamma rays.

Detector array

$\vec{B}_{in}$

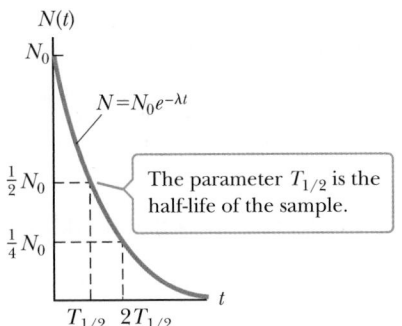

Active Figure 29.6
Plot of the exponential decay law for radioactive nuclei. The vertical axis represents the number of radioactive nuclei present at any time t, and the horizontal axis is time.

The three types of radiation have quite different penetrating powers. Alpha particles barely penetrate a sheet of paper, beta particles can penetrate a few millimeters of aluminum, and gamma rays can penetrate several centimeters of lead.

The Decay Constant and Half-Life

Observation has shown that if a radioactive sample contains N radioactive nuclei at some instant, the number of nuclei, ΔN, that decay in a small time interval Δt is proportional to N; mathematically,

$$\frac{\Delta N}{\Delta t} \propto N$$

or

$$\Delta N = -\lambda N \Delta t \qquad \text{[29.2]}$$

where λ is a constant called the **decay constant**. The negative sign signifies that N decreases with time; that is, ΔN is negative. The value of λ for any isotope determines the rate at which that isotope will decay. **The decay rate, or activity R, of a sample is defined as the number of decays per second.** From Equation 29.2, we see that the decay rate is

$$R = \left|\frac{\Delta N}{\Delta t}\right| = \lambda N \qquad \text{[29.3]}$$ ◄ Decay rate

Isotopes with a large λ value decay rapidly; those with small λ decay slowly.

A general decay curve for a radioactive sample is shown in Active Figure 29.6. It can be shown from Equation 29.2 (using calculus) that the number of nuclei present varies with time according to the equation

$$N = N_0 e^{-\lambda t} \qquad \text{[29.4a]}$$

where N is the number of radioactive nuclei present at time t, N_0 is the number present at time $t = 0$, and $e = 2.718\ldots$ is Euler's constant. Processes that obey Equation 29.4a are sometimes said to undergo **exponential decay**.[1]

Another parameter that is useful for characterizing radioactive decay is the **half-life $T_{1/2}$. The half-life of a radioactive substance is the time it takes for half of a given number of radioactive nuclei to decay.** Using the concept of half-life, it can be shown that Equation 29.4a can also be written as

$$N = N_0\left(\frac{1}{2}\right)^n \qquad \text{[29.4b]}$$

where n is the number of half-lives. The number n can take any nonnegative value and need not be an integer. From the definition, it follows that n is related to time t and the half-life $T_{1/2}$ by

---

[1]Other examples of exponential decay were discussed in Chapter 18 in connection with RC circuits and in Chapter 20 in connection with RL circuits.

$$n = \frac{t}{T_{1/2}}$$ [29.4c]

Setting $N = N_0/2$ and $t = T_{1/2}$ in Equation 29.4a gives

$$\frac{N_0}{2} = N_0 e^{-\lambda T_{1/2}}$$

Writing this expression in the form $e^{\lambda T_{1/2}} = 2$ and taking the natural logarithm of both sides, we get

$$T_{1/2} = \frac{\ln 2}{\lambda} = \frac{0.693}{\lambda}$$ [29.5]

Equation 29.5 is a convenient expression relating the half-life to the decay constant. Note that after an elapsed time of one half-life, $N_0/2$ radioactive nuclei remain (by definition); after two half-lives, half of those will have decayed and $N_0/4$ radioactive nuclei will be left; after three half-lives, $N_0/8$ will be left; and so on.

The unit of activity R is the **curie** (Ci), defined as

$$1 \text{ Ci} \equiv 3.7 \times 10^{10} \text{ decays/s}$$ [29.6]

This unit was selected as the original activity unit because it is the approximate activity of 1 g of radium. The SI unit of activity is the **becquerel** (Bq):

$$1 \text{ Bq} = 1 \text{ decay/s}$$ [29.7]

Therefore, 1 Ci = 3.7×10^{10} Bq. The most commonly used units of activity are the millicurie (10^{-3} Ci) and the microcurie (10^{-6} Ci).

> **Tip 29.2 Two Half-Lives Don't Make a Whole Life**
>
> A half-life is the time it takes for half of a given number of nuclei to decay. During a second half-life, half the remaining nuclei decay, so in two half-lives, three-quarters of the original material has decayed, not all of it.

■ *Quick Quiz*

29.1 True or False: A radioactive atom always decays after two half-lives have elapsed.

29.2 What fraction of a radioactive sample has decayed after three half-lives have elapsed? (a) 1/8   (b) 3/4   (c) 7/8   (d) none of these

29.3 Suppose the decay constant of radioactive substance A is twice the decay constant of radioactive substance B. If substance B has a half-life of 4 h, what's the half-life of substance A? (a) 8 h   (b) 4 h   (c) 2 h

---

■ **EXAMPLE 29.2** | **The Activity of Radium**

GOAL Calculate the activity of a radioactive substance at different times.

PROBLEM The half-life of the radioactive nucleus $^{226}_{88}$Ra is 1.6×10^3 yr. If a sample initially contains 3.00×10^{16} such nuclei, determine **(a)** the initial activity in curies, **(b)** the number of radium nuclei remaining after 4.8×10^3 yr, and **(c)** the activity at this later time.

STRATEGY For parts (a) and (c), find the decay constant and multiply it by the number of nuclei. Part (b) requires multiplying the initial number of nuclei by one-half for every elapsed half-life. (Essentially, this is an application of Eq. 29.4b.)

SOLUTION

(a) Determine the initial activity in curies.

Convert the half-life to seconds:

$$T_{1/2} = (1.6 \times 10^3 \text{ yr})(3.156 \times 10^7 \text{ s/yr}) = 5.0 \times 10^{10} \text{ s}$$

Substitute this value into Equation 29.5 to get the decay constant:

$$\lambda = \frac{0.693}{T_{1/2}} = \frac{0.693}{5.0 \times 10^{10} \text{ s}} = 1.4 \times 10^{-11} \text{ s}^{-1}$$

Calculate the activity of the sample at $t = 0$, using $R_0 = \lambda N_0$, where R_0 is the decay rate at $t = 0$ and N_0 is the number of radioactive nuclei present at $t = 0$:

$$R_0 = \lambda N_0 = (1.4 \times 10^{-11} \text{ s}^{-1})(3.0 \times 10^{16} \text{ nuclei})$$
$$= 4.2 \times 10^5 \text{ decays/s}$$

Convert to curies to obtain the activity at $t = 0$, using $1 \text{ Ci} = 3.7 \times 10^{10}$ decays/s:

$$R_0 = (4.2 \times 10^5 \text{ decays/s})\left(\frac{1 \text{ Ci}}{3.7 \times 10^{10} \text{ decays/s}}\right)$$

$$= 1.1 \times 10^{-5} \text{ Ci} = \boxed{11 \ \mu\text{Ci}}$$

(b) How many radium nuclei remain after 4.8×10^3 yr?

Calculate the number of half-lives, n:

$$n = \frac{4.8 \times 10^3 \text{ yr}}{1.6 \times 10^3 \text{ yr/half-life}} = 3.0 \text{ half-lives}$$

Multiply the initial number of nuclei by the number of factors of one-half:

$$\textbf{(1)} \quad N = N_0\left(\frac{1}{2}\right)^n$$

Substitute $N_0 = 3.0 \times 10^{16}$ and $n = 3.0$:

$$N = (3.0 \times 10^{16} \text{ nuclei})\left(\frac{1}{2}\right)^{3.0} = \boxed{3.8 \times 10^{15} \text{ nuclei}}$$

(c) Calculate the activity after 4.8×10^3 yr.

Multiply the number of remaining nuclei by the decay constant to find the activity R:

$$R = \lambda N = (1.4 \times 10^{-11} \text{ s}^{-1})(3.8 \times 10^{15} \text{ nuclei})$$

$$= 5.3 \times 10^4 \text{ decays/s}$$

$$= \boxed{1.4 \ \mu\text{Ci}}$$

REMARKS The activity is reduced by half every half-life, which is naturally the case because activity is proportional to the number of remaining nuclei. The precise number of nuclei at any time is never truly exact because particles decay according to a probability. The larger the sample, however, the more accurate the predictions from Equation 29.4.

QUESTION 29.2 How would doubling the initial mass of radioactive material affect the initial activity? How would it affect the half-life?

EXERCISE 29.2 Find (a) the number of remaining radium nuclei after 3.2×10^3 yr and (b) the activity at this time.

ANSWERS (a) 7.5×10^{15} nuclei (b) $2.8 \ \mu\text{Ci}$

29.4 The Decay Processes

As stated in the previous section, radioactive nuclei decay spontaneously via alpha, beta, and gamma decay. As we'll see in this section, these processes are very different from one another.

Alpha Decay

If a nucleus emits an alpha particle (^4_2He), it loses two protons and two neutrons. Therefore, the neutron number N of a single nucleus decreases by 2, Z decreases by 2, and A decreases by 4. The decay can be written symbolically as

$$^A_Z\text{X} \quad \rightarrow \quad ^{A-4}_{Z-2}\text{Y} + ^4_2\text{He} \qquad \textbf{[29.8]}$$

where X is called the **parent nucleus** and Y is known as the **daughter nucleus**. As examples, ^{238}U and ^{226}Ra are both alpha emitters and decay according to the schemes

$$^{238}_{92}\text{U} \quad \rightarrow \quad ^{234}_{90}\text{Th} + ^4_2\text{He} \qquad \textbf{[29.9]}$$

and

$$^{226}_{88}\text{Ra} \quad \rightarrow \quad ^{222}_{86}\text{Rn} + ^4_2\text{He} \qquad \textbf{[29.10]}$$

The half-life for ^{238}U decay is 4.47×10^9 years, and the half-life for ^{226}Ra decay is 1.60×10^3 years. In both cases, note that the mass number A of the daughter nucleus is four less than that of the parent nucleus, and the atomic number Z is

$KE_{Ra} = 0$
$\vec{p}_{Ra} = 0$

Before decay

KE_{Rn} KE_α

$\overset{\longleftarrow}{\vec{p}_{Rn}}$ $\overset{\longrightarrow}{\vec{p}_\alpha}$

After decay

Active Figure 29.7

The alpha decay of radium-226. The radium nucleus is initially at rest. After the decay, the radon nucleus has kinetic energy KE_{Rn} and momentum $\vec{p}_{Rn}$, and the alpha particle has kinetic energy KE_α and momentum $\vec{p}_\alpha$.

reduced by two. The differences are accounted for in the emitted alpha particle (the ^{4}He nucleus).

The decay of ^{226}Ra is shown in Active Figure 29.7. When one element changes into another, as happens in alpha decay, the process is called **spontaneous decay** or transmutation. As a general rule, (1) the sum of the mass numbers A must be the same on both sides of the equation, and (2) the sum of the atomic numbers Z must be the same on both sides of the equation.

For alpha emission to occur, the mass of the parent must be greater than the combined mass of the daughter and the alpha particle. In the decay process, this excess mass is converted into energy of other forms and appears in the form of kinetic energy in the daughter nucleus and the alpha particle. Most of the kinetic energy is carried away by the alpha particle because it is much less massive than the daughter nucleus. This can be understood by first noting that a particle's kinetic energy and momentum p are related as follows:

$$KE = \frac{p^2}{2m}$$

Because momentum is conserved, the two particles emitted in the decay of a nucleus at rest must have equal, but oppositely directed, momenta. As a result, the lighter particle, with the smaller mass in the denominator, has more kinetic energy than the more massive particle.

■ APPLYING PHYSICS 29.2 | Energy and Half-Life

In comparing alpha decay energies from a number of radioactive nuclides, why is it found that the half-life of the decay goes down as the energy of the decay goes up?

EXPLANATION It should seem reasonable that the higher the energy of the alpha particle, the more likely it

is to escape the confines of the nucleus. The higher probability of escape translates to a faster rate of decay, which appears as a shorter half-life. ■

■ EXAMPLE 29.3 | Decaying Radium

GOAL Calculate the energy released during an alpha decay.

PROBLEM We showed that the $^{226}_{88}$Ra nucleus undergoes alpha decay to $^{222}_{86}$Rn (Eq. 29.10). Calculate the amount of energy liberated in this decay. Take the mass of $^{226}_{88}$Ra to be 226.025 402 u, that of $^{222}_{86}$Rn to be 222.017 571 u, and that of $^4_2$He to be 4.002 602 u, as found in Appendix B.

STRATEGY The solution is a matter of subtracting the neutral masses of the daughter particles from the original mass of the radon atom.

SOLUTION

Compute the sum of the mass of the daughter particle, m_d, and the mass of the alpha particle, m_α:

$m_d + m_\alpha = 222.017\ 571\ \text{u} + 4.002\ 602\ \text{u} = 226.020\ 173\ \text{u}$

Compute the loss of mass, Δm, during the decay by subtracting the previous result from M_p, the mass of the original particle:

$\Delta m = M_p - (m_d + m_\alpha) = 226.025\ 402\ \text{u} - 226.020\ 173\ \text{u}$
$= 0.005\ 229\ \text{u}$

Convert the loss of mass Δm to its equivalent energy in MeV:

$E = (0.005\ 229\ \text{u})(931.494\ \text{MeV/u}) = \boxed{4.871\ \text{MeV}}$

REMARKS The potential barrier is typically higher than this value of the energy, but quantum tunneling permits the event to occur anyway.

QUESTION 29.3 Convert the final answer to joules and estimate the energy produced by an Avogadro's number of such decays.

EXERCISE 29.3 Calculate the energy released when $^8_4$Be splits into two alpha particles. Beryllium-8 has an atomic mass of 8.005 305 u.

ANSWER 0.094 1 MeV

Beta Decay

When a radioactive nucleus undergoes beta decay, the daughter nucleus has the same number of nucleons as the parent nucleus, but the atomic number is changed by 1:

$$^A_Z X \quad \rightarrow \quad _{z+1}^A Y + e^- \qquad \qquad \text{[29.11]}$$

$$^A_Z X \quad \rightarrow \quad _{z-1}^A Y + e^+ \qquad \qquad \text{[29.12]}$$

Again, note that the nucleon number and total charge are both conserved in these decays. As we will see shortly, however, these processes are not described completely by these expressions. A typical beta decay event is

$$^{14}_6 C \quad \rightarrow \quad ^{14}_7 N + e^- \qquad \qquad \text{[29.13]}$$

The emission of electrons from a *nucleus* is surprising because, in all our previous discussions, we stated that the nucleus is composed of protons and neutrons only. This apparent discrepancy can be explained by noting that the emitted electron is created in the nucleus by a process in which a neutron is transformed into a proton. This process can be represented by

$$^1_0 n \quad \rightarrow \quad ^1_1 p + e^- \qquad \qquad \text{[29.14]}$$

Consider the energy of the system of Equation 29.13 before and after decay. As with alpha decay, energy must be conserved in beta decay. The next example illustrates how to calculate the amount of energy released in the beta decay of $^{14}_6$C.

■ EXAMPLE 29.4 | **The Beta Decay of Carbon-14**

GOAL Calculate the energy released in a beta decay.

PROBLEM Find the energy liberated in the beta decay of $^{14}_6$C to $^{14}_7$N, as represented by Equation 29.13. That equation refers to nuclei, whereas Appendix B gives the masses of neutral atoms. Adding six electrons to both sides of Equation 29.13 yields

$$^{14}_6 C \text{ atom} \quad \rightarrow \quad ^{14}_7 N \text{ atom}$$

STRATEGY As in preceding problems, finding the released energy involves computing the difference in mass between the resultant particle(s) and the initial particle(s) and converting to MeV.

. . . .

SOLUTION

Obtain the masses of $^{14}_6$C and $^{14}_7$N from Appendix B and compute the difference between them:

$\Delta m = m_C - m_N = 14.003\ 242 \text{ u} - 14.003\ 074 \text{ u} = 0.000\ 168 \text{ u}$

Convert the mass difference to MeV:

$E = (0.000\ 168 \text{ u})(931.494 \text{ MeV/u}) = \boxed{0.156 \text{ MeV}}$

. . . .

REMARKS The calculated energy is generally more than the energy observed in this process. The discrepancy led to a crisis in physics because it appeared that energy wasn't conserved. As discussed below, this crisis was resolved by the discovery that another particle was also produced in the reaction.

QUESTION 29.4 Is the binding energy per nucleon of the nitrogen-14 nucleus greater or less than the binding energy per nucleon for the carbon-14 nucleus? Justify your answer.

EXERCISE 29.4 Calculate the maximum energy liberated in the beta decay of radioactive potassium to calcium: $^{40}_{19}K \rightarrow ^{40}_{20}Ca + e^-$.

ANSWER 1.31 MeV

The observed energies of beta particles are continuous, having all values up to a maximum value.

Number of β-particles

KE_{max}

Kinetic energy

a

The observed energies of alpha particles are discrete, having only a few values.

Number of α-particles

Kinetic energy

b

Figure 29.8 (a) Distribution of beta-particle energies in a typical beta decay. (b) Distribution of alpha-particle energies in a typical alpha decay.

Tip 29.3   Mass Number of the Electron

Another notation that is sometimes used for an electron is $_{-1}^{0}$e. This notation does not imply that the electron has zero rest energy. The mass of the electron is much smaller than that of the lightest nucleon, so we can approximate it as zero when we study nuclear decays and reactions.

From Example 29.4, we see that the energy released in the beta decay of ^{14}C is approximately 0.16 MeV. As with alpha decay, we expect the electron to carry away virtually all this energy as kinetic energy because, apparently, it is the lightest particle produced in the decay. As Figure 29.8 shows, however, only a small number of electrons have this maximum kinetic energy, represented as KE_{max} on the graph; most of the electrons emitted have kinetic energies lower than that predicted value. If the daughter nucleus and the electron aren't carrying away this liberated energy, where has the energy gone? As an additional complication, further analysis of beta decay shows that the principles of conservation of both angular momentum and linear momentum appear to have been violated!

In 1930 Pauli proposed that a third particle must be present to carry away the "missing" energy and to conserve momentum. Later, Enrico Fermi developed a complete theory of beta decay and named this particle the **neutrino** ("little neutral one") because it had to be electrically neutral and have little or no mass. Although it eluded detection for many years, the neutrino (ν) was finally detected experimentally in 1956. The neutrino has the following properties:

- Zero electric charge
- A mass much smaller than that of the electron, but probably not zero. (Recent experiments suggest that the neutrino definitely has mass, but the value is uncertain, perhaps less than 1 eV/c^2.)
- A spin of $\frac{1}{2}$
- Very weak interaction with matter, making it difficult to detect

With the introduction of the neutrino, we can now represent the beta decay process of Equation 29.13 in its correct form:

$$^{14}_{6}\text{C} \rightarrow {}^{14}_{7}\text{N} + \text{e}^- + \bar{\nu} \qquad [29.15]$$

The bar in the symbol $\bar{\nu}$ indicates an **antineutrino**. To explain what an antineutrino is, we first consider the following decay:

$$^{12}_{7}\text{N} \rightarrow {}^{12}_{6}\text{C} + \text{e}^+ + \nu \qquad [29.16]$$

Here, we see that when ^{12}N decays into ^{12}C, a particle is produced that is identical to the electron except that it has a positive charge of $+e$. This particle is called a **positron**. Because it is like the electron in all respects except charge, the positron is said to be the **antiparticle** of the electron. We discuss antiparticles further in Chapter 30; for now, it suffices to say that, **in beta decay, an electron and an antineutrino are emitted or a positron and a neutrino are emitted**.

Unlike beta decay, which results in a daughter particle with a variety of possible kinetic energies, alpha decays come in discrete amounts, as seen in Figure 29.8b. This is because the two daughter particles have momenta with equal magnitude and opposite direction and are each composed of a fixed number of nucleons.

Gamma Decay

Very often a nucleus that undergoes radioactive decay is left in an excited energy state. The nucleus can then undergo a second decay to a lower energy state—perhaps even to the ground state—by emitting one or more high-energy photons. The process is similar to the emission of light by an atom. An atom emits radiation to release some extra energy when an electron "jumps" from a state of high energy to a state of lower energy. Likewise, the nucleus uses essentially the same method to release any extra energy it may have following a decay or some other nuclear event. In nuclear de-excitation, the "jumps" that release energy are made by protons or neutrons in the nucleus as they move from a higher energy level to a lower level. The photons emitted in the process are called **gamma rays**, which have very high energy relative to the energy of visible light.

A nucleus may reach an excited state as the result of a violent collision with another particle. It's more common, however, for a nucleus to be in an excited state as a result of alpha or beta decay. The following sequence of events typifies the gamma decay processes:

$$^{12}_{5}\text{B} \rightarrow {}^{12}_{6}\text{C*} + \text{e}^- + \bar{\nu} \qquad \text{[29.17]}$$

$$^{12}_{6}\text{C*} \rightarrow {}^{12}_{6}\text{C} + \gamma \qquad \text{[29.18]}$$

Equation 29.17 represents a beta decay in which ^{12}B decays to $^{12}\text{C*}$, where the asterisk indicates that the carbon nucleus is left in an excited state following the decay. The excited carbon nucleus then decays to the ground state by emitting a gamma ray, as indicated by Equation 29.18. Note that gamma emission doesn't result in any change in either Z or A.

Practical Uses of Radioactivity

Carbon Dating The beta decay of ^{14}C given by Equation 29.15 is commonly used to date organic samples. Cosmic rays (high-energy particles from outer space) in the upper atmosphere cause nuclear reactions that create ^{14}C from ^{14}N. In fact, the ratio of ^{14}C to ^{12}C (by numbers of nuclei) in the carbon dioxide molecules of our atmosphere has a constant value of about 1.3×10^{-12}, as determined by measuring carbon ratios in tree rings. All living organisms have the same ratio of ^{14}C to ^{12}C because they continuously exchange carbon dioxide with their surroundings. When an organism dies, however, it no longer absorbs ^{14}C from the atmosphere, so the ratio of ^{14}C to ^{12}C decreases as the result of the beta decay of ^{14}C. It's therefore possible to determine the age of a material by measuring its activity per unit mass as a result of the decay of ^{14}C. Through carbon dating, samples of wood, charcoal, bone, and shell have been identified as having lived from 1 000 to 25 000 years ago. This knowledge has helped researchers reconstruct the history of living organisms—including humans—during that time span.

Smoke Detectors Smoke detectors are frequently used in homes and industry for fire protection. Most of the common ones are the ionization-type that use radioactive materials. (See Fig. 29.9.) A smoke detector consists of an ionization chamber, a sensitive current detector, and an alarm. A weak radioactive source ionizes the air in the chamber of the detector, which creates charged particles. A voltage is maintained between the plates inside the chamber, setting up a small but detectable current in the external circuit. As long as the current is maintained, the alarm is deactivated. If smoke drifts into the chamber, though, the ions become attached to the smoke particles. These heavier particles do not drift as readily as do the lighter ions and cause a decrease in the detector current. The external circuit senses this decrease in current and sets off the alarm.

Radon Detection Radioactivity can also affect our daily lives in harmful ways. Soon after the discovery of radium by the Curies, it was found that the air in contact with radium compounds becomes radioactive. It was then shown that this radioactivity came from the radium itself, and the product was therefore called "radium emanation." Rutherford and Frederick Soddy succeeded in condensing this "emanation," confirming that it was a real substance: the inert, gaseous element now called **radon** (Rn). Later, it was discovered that the air in uranium mines is radioactive because of the presence of radon gas. The mines must therefore be well ventilated to help protect the miners. Finally, the fear of radon pollution has moved from uranium mines into our own homes. Because certain types of rock, soil, brick, and concrete contain small quantities of radium, some of the resulting radon gas finds its way into our homes and other buildings. The most serious problems arise from leakage of radon from the ground into the structure. One

© Bettmann/Corbis

Enrico Fermi
Italian Physicist (1901–1954)
Fermi was awarded the Nobel Prize in Physics in 1938 for producing the transuranic elements by neutron irradiation and for his discovery of nuclear reactions brought about by slow neutrons. He made many other outstanding contributions to physics, including his theory of beta decay, the free-electron theory of metals, and the development of the world's first fission reactor in 1942. Fermi was truly a gifted theoretical and experimental physicist. He was also well known for his ability to present physics in a clear and exciting manner. "Whatever Nature has in store for mankind, unpleasant as it may be, men must accept, for ignorance is never better than knowledge."

APPLICATION
Smoke Detectors

Figure 29.9 An ionization-type smoke detector. Smoke entering the chamber reduces the detected current, causing the alarm to sound.

APPLICATION

Radon Pollution

practical remedy is to exhaust the air through a pipe just above the underlying soil or gravel directly to the outdoors by means of a small fan or blower.

To use radioactive dating techniques, we need to recast some of the equations already introduced. We start by multiplying both sides of Equation 29.4 by λ:

$$\lambda N = \lambda N_0 e^{-\lambda t}$$

From Equation 29.3, we have $\lambda N = R$ and $\lambda N_0 = R_0$. Substitute these expressions into the above equation and divide through by R_0:

$$\frac{R}{R_0} = e^{-\lambda t}$$

where R is the present activity and R_0 was the activity when the object in question was part of a living organism. We can solve for time by taking the natural logarithm of both sides of the foregoing equation:

$$\ln\left(\frac{R}{R_0}\right) = \ln\left(e^{-\lambda t}\right) = -\lambda t$$

$$t = -\frac{\ln\left(\dfrac{R}{R_0}\right)}{\lambda} \qquad\qquad [29.19]$$

■ EXAMPLE 29.5 | Should We Report This Skeleton to Homicide?

GOAL Apply the technique of carbon-14 dating.

PROBLEM A 50.0-g sample of carbon taken from the pelvic bone of a skeleton is found to have a carbon-14 decay rate of 200.0 decays/min. It is known that carbon from a living organism has a decay rate of 15.0 decays/min · g and that ^{14}C has a half-life of 5 730 yr $= 3.01 \times 10^9$ min. Find the age of the skeleton.

STRATEGY Calculate the original activity and the decay constant and then substitute those numbers and the current activity into Equation 29.19.

. . . .

SOLUTION

Calculate the original activity R_0 from the decay rate and the mass of the sample:

$$R_0 = \left(15.0\,\frac{\text{decays}}{\text{min} \cdot \text{g}}\right)(50.0\,\text{g}) = 7.50 \times 10^2\,\frac{\text{decays}}{\text{min}}$$

Find the decay constant from Equation 29.5:

$$\lambda = \frac{0.693}{T_{1/2}} = \frac{0.693}{3.01 \times 10^9\,\text{min}} = 2.30 \times 10^{-10}\,\text{min}^{-1}$$

R is given, so now we substitute all values into Equation 29.19 to find the age of the skeleton:

$$t = -\frac{\ln\left(\dfrac{R}{R_0}\right)}{\lambda} = -\frac{\ln\left(\dfrac{200.0\,\text{decays/min}}{7.50 \times 10^2\,\text{decays/min}}\right)}{2.30 \times 10^{-10}\,\text{min}^{-1}}$$

$$= \frac{1.32}{2.30 \times 10^{-10}\,\text{min}^{-1}}$$

$$= 5.74 \times 10^9\,\text{min} = \boxed{1.09 \times 10^4\,\text{yr}}$$

. . . .

REMARKS For much longer periods, other radioactive substances with longer half-lives must be used to develop estimates.

QUESTION 29.5 Do the results of carbon dating depend on the mass of the original sample?

EXERCISE 29.5 A sample of carbon of mass 7.60 g taken from an animal jawbone has an activity of 4.00 decays/min. How old is the jawbone?

ANSWER 2.77×10^4 yr

Table 29.2 The Four Radioactive Series

Series	Starting Isotope	Half-life (years)	Stable End Product
Uranium	$^{238}_{92}U$	4.47×10^9	$^{206}_{82}Pb$
Actinium	$^{235}_{92}U$	7.04×10^8	$^{207}_{82}Pb$
Thorium	$^{232}_{90}Th$	1.41×10^{10}	$^{208}_{82}Pb$
Neptunium	$^{237}_{93}Np$	2.14×10^6	$^{209}_{82}Pb$

Decays with violet arrows toward the lower left are alpha decays, in which A changes by 4.

Decays with blue arrows toward the lower right are beta decays, in which A does not change.

Figure 29.10 Decay series beginning with ^{232}Th.

29.5 Natural Radioactivity

Radioactive nuclei are generally classified into two groups: (1) unstable nuclei found in nature, which give rise to what is called **natural radioactivity**, and (2) nuclei produced in the laboratory through nuclear reactions, which exhibit **artificial radioactivity**.

Three series of naturally occurring radioactive nuclei exist (Table 29.2). Each starts with a specific long-lived radioactive isotope with half-life exceeding that of any of its descendants. The fourth series in Table 29.2 begins with ^{237}Np, a transuranic element (an element having an atomic number greater than that of uranium) not found in nature. This element has a half-life of "only" 2.14×10^6 yr.

The two uranium series are somewhat more complex than the ^{232}Th series (Fig. 29.10). Also, there are several other naturally occurring radioactive isotopes, such as ^{14}C and ^{40}K, that are not part of either decay series.

Natural radioactivity constantly supplies our environment with radioactive elements that would otherwise have disappeared long ago. For example, because the solar system is about 5×10^9 years old, the supply of ^{226}Ra (with a half-life of only 1 600 yr) would have been depleted by radioactive decay long ago were it not for the decay series that starts with ^{238}U, with a half-life of 4.47×10^9 yr.

29.6 Nuclear Reactions

It is possible to change the structure of nuclei by bombarding them with energetic particles. Such changes are called **nuclear reactions**. Rutherford was the first to observe nuclear reactions, using naturally occurring radioactive sources for the bombarding particles. He found that protons were released when alpha particles were allowed to collide with nitrogen atoms. The process can be represented symbolically as

$$^4_2He + ^{14}_7N \rightarrow X + ^1_1H \qquad [29.20]$$

This equation says that an alpha particle ($^4_2$He) strikes a nitrogen nucleus and produces an unknown product nucleus (X) and a proton ($^1_1$H). Balancing atomic numbers and mass numbers, as we did for radioactive decay, enables us to conclude that the unknown is characterized as $^{17}_8$X. Because the element with atomic number 8 is oxygen, we see that the reaction is

$$^4_2He + ^{14}_7N \rightarrow ^{17}_8O + ^1_1H \qquad [29.21]$$

This nuclear reaction starts with two stable isotopes, helium and nitrogen, and produces two different stable isotopes, hydrogen and oxygen.

Since the time of Rutherford, thousands of nuclear reactions have been observed, particularly following the development of charged-particle accelerators in the 1930s. With today's advanced technology in particle accelerators and particle detectors, it is possible to achieve particle energies of at least 1 000 GeV = 1 TeV. These high-energy particles are used to create new particles whose properties are helping solve the mysteries of the nucleus (and indeed, of the Universe itself).

■*Quick Quiz*

29.4 Which of the following are possible reactions?

(a) $^{1}_{0}n + ^{235}_{92}U \rightarrow ^{140}_{54}Xe + ^{94}_{38}Sr + 2(^{1}_{0}n)$

(b) $^{1}_{0}n + ^{235}_{92}U \rightarrow ^{132}_{50}Sn + ^{101}_{42}Mo + 3(^{1}_{0}n)$

(c) $^{1}_{0}n + ^{239}_{94}Pu \rightarrow ^{127}_{53}I + ^{93}_{41}Nb + 3(^{1}_{0}n)$

■**EXAMPLE 29.6** | **The Discovery of the Neutron**

GOAL Balance a nuclear reaction to determine an unknown decay product.

PROBLEM A nuclear reaction of significant note occurred in 1932 when Robert Chadwick, in England, bombarded a beryllium target with alpha particles. Analysis of the experiment indicated that the following reaction occurred:

$$^{4}_{2}He + ^{9}_{4}Be \rightarrow ^{12}_{6}C + ^{A}_{Z}X$$

What is $^{A}_{Z}X$ in this reaction?

STRATEGY Balancing mass numbers and atomic numbers yields the answer.

. . . .

SOLUTION

Write an equation relating the atomic masses on either side:

$$4 + 9 = 12 + A \rightarrow A = 1$$

Write an equation relating the atomic numbers:

$$2 + 4 = 6 + Z \rightarrow Z = 0$$

Identify the particle:

$$^{A}_{Z}X = \boxed{^{1}_{0}n \text{ (a neutron)}}$$

. . . .

REMARKS This was the first experiment to provide positive proof of the existence of neutrons.

QUESTION 29.6 Where in nature is the reaction between helium and beryllium commonly found?

EXERCISE 29.6 Identify the unknown particle in the reaction

$$^{4}_{2}He + ^{14}_{7}N \rightarrow ^{17}_{8}O + ^{A}_{Z}X$$

ANSWER $^{A}_{Z}X = ^{1}_{1}H$ (a neutral hydrogen atom)

Q Values

We have just examined some nuclear reactions for which mass numbers and atomic numbers must be balanced in the equations. We will now consider the energy involved in these reactions because energy is another important quantity that must be conserved.

We illustrate this procedure by analyzing the nuclear reaction

$$^{2}_{1}H + ^{14}_{7}N \rightarrow ^{12}_{6}C + ^{4}_{2}He \qquad [29.22]$$

The total mass on the left side of the equation is the sum of the mass of $^{2}_{1}H$ (2.014 102 u) and the mass of $^{14}_{7}N$ (14.003 074 u), which equals 16.017 176 u. Similarly, the mass on the right side of the equation is the sum of the mass of $^{12}_{6}C$ (12.000 000 u) plus the mass of $^{4}_{2}He$ (4.002 602 u), for a total of 16.002 602 u. Thus, the total mass before the reaction is greater than the total mass after the reaction. The mass difference in the reaction is 16.017 176 u − 16.002 602 u = 0.014 574 u. This "lost" mass is converted to the kinetic energy of the nuclei present after the reaction. In energy units, 0.014 574 u is equivalent to 13.576 MeV of kinetic energy carried away by the carbon and helium nuclei.

The energy required to balance the equation is called the Q value of the reaction. In Equation 29.22, the Q value is 13.576 MeV. Nuclear reactions in which there is a release of energy—that is, positive Q values—are said to be **exothermic reactions**.

The energy balance sheet isn't complete, however, because we must also consider the kinetic energy of the incident particle before the collision. As an example, assume the deuteron in Equation 29.22 has a kinetic energy of 5 MeV. Adding this value to our Q value, we find that the carbon and helium nuclei have a total kinetic energy of 18.576 MeV following the reaction.

Now consider the reaction

$$\ce{^4_2He + ^{14}_7N} \rightarrow \ce{^{17}_8O + ^1_1H} \qquad [29.23]$$

Before the reaction, the total mass is the sum of the masses of the alpha particle and the nitrogen nucleus: 4.002 602 u + 14.003 074 u = 18.005 676 u. After the reaction, the total mass is the sum of the masses of the oxygen nucleus and the proton: 16.999 133 u + 1.007 825 u = 18.006 958 u. In this case the total mass after the reaction is *greater* than the total mass before the reaction. The mass deficit is 0.001 282 u, equivalent to an energy deficit of 1.194 MeV. This deficit is expressed by the negative Q value of the reaction, −1.194 MeV. Reactions with negative Q values are called **endothermic reactions**. Such reactions won't take place unless the incoming particle has at least enough kinetic energy to overcome the energy deficit.

At first it might appear that the reaction in Equation 29.23 can take place if the incoming alpha particle has a kinetic energy of 1.194 MeV. In practice, however, the alpha particle must have more energy than that. If it has an energy of only 1.194 MeV, energy is conserved; careful analysis, though, shows that momentum isn't, which can be understood by recognizing that the incoming alpha particle has some momentum before the reaction. If its kinetic energy is only 1.194 MeV, however, the products (oxygen and a proton) would be created with zero kinetic energy and thus zero momentum. It can be shown that to conserve both energy and momentum, the incoming particle must have a minimum kinetic energy given by

$$KE_{\min} = \left(1 + \frac{m}{M}\right)|Q| \qquad [29.24]$$

where m is the mass of the incident particle, M is the mass of the target, and the absolute value of the Q value is used. For the reaction given by Equation 29.23, we find that

$$KE_{\min} = \left(1 + \frac{4.002\ 602}{14.003\ 074}\right)|-1.194\text{ MeV}| = 1.535\text{ MeV}$$

This minimum value of the kinetic energy of the incoming particle is called the **threshold energy**. The nuclear reaction shown in Equation 29.23 won't occur if the incoming alpha particle has a kinetic energy of less than 1.535 MeV, but can occur if its kinetic energy is equal to or greater than 1.535 MeV.

■ *Quick Quiz*

29.5 If the Q value of an endothermic reaction is −2.17 MeV, the minimum kinetic energy needed in the reactant nuclei for the reaction to occur must be (a) equal to 2.17 MeV, (b) greater than 2.17 MeV, (c) less than 2.17 MeV, or (d) exactly half of 2.17 MeV.

29.7 Medical Applications of Radiation BIO

Radiation Damage in Matter

Radiation absorbed by matter can cause severe damage. The degree and kind of damage depend on several factors, including the type and energy of the radiation and the properties of the absorbing material. Radiation damage in biological organisms is due primarily to ionization effects in cells. The normal function of a cell may be disrupted when highly reactive ions or radicals are formed as the result of ionizing radiation. For example, hydrogen and hydroxyl radicals produced from water molecules can induce chemical reactions that may break bonds in proteins and other vital molecules. Large acute doses of radiation are especially dangerous because damage to a great number of molecules in a cell may cause the cell to die. Also, cells that do survive the radiation may become defective, which can lead to cancer.

In biological systems it is common to separate radiation damage into two categories: somatic damage and genetic damage. **Somatic damage** is radiation damage to any cells except the reproductive cells. Such damage can lead to cancer at high radiation levels or seriously alter the characteristics of specific organisms. **Genetic damage** affects only reproductive cells. Damage to the genes in reproductive cells can lead to defective offspring. Clearly, we must be concerned about the effect of diagnostic treatments, such as x-rays and other forms of exposure to radiation.

Several units are used to quantify radiation exposure and dose. The **roentgen** (R) is defined as **the amount of ionizing radiation that will produce 2.08×10^9 ion pairs in 1 cm^3 of air under standard conditions**. Equivalently, the roentgen is **the amount of radiation that deposits 8.76×10^{-3} J of energy into 1 kg of air**.

For most applications, the roentgen has been replaced by the **rad** (an acronym for *r*adiation *a*bsorbed *d*ose), defined as follows: **One rad is the amount of radiation that deposits 10^{-2} J of energy into 1 kg of absorbing material.**

Although the rad is a perfectly good physical unit, it's not the best unit for measuring the degree of biological damage produced by radiation because the degree of damage depends not only on the dose, but also on the *type* of radiation. For example, a given dose of alpha particles causes about ten times more biological damage than an equal dose of x-rays. The **RBE** (*r*elative *b*iological *e*ffectiveness) factor is defined as **the number of rads of x-radiation or gamma radiation that produces the same biological damage as 1 rad of the radiation being used**. The RBE factors for different types of radiation are given in Table 29.3. Note that the values are only approximate because they vary with particle energy and the form of damage.

Finally, the **rem** (*r*oentgen *e*quivalent in *m*an) is defined as the product of the dose in rads and the RBE factor:

$$\text{Dose in rem} = \text{dose in rads} \times \text{RBE}$$

According to this definition, 1 rem of any two kinds of radiation will produce the same amount of biological damage. From Table 29.3, we see that a dose of 1 rad of fast neutrons represents an effective dose of 10 rem and that 1 rad of x-radiation is equivalent to a dose of 1 rem.

Low-level radiation from natural sources, such as cosmic rays and radioactive rocks and soil, delivers a dose of about 0.13 rem/year per person. The upper limit of radiation dose recommended by the U.S. government (apart from background radiation and exposure related to medical procedures) is 0.5 rem/year. Many occupations involve higher levels of radiation exposure, and for individuals in these occupations, an upper limit of 5 rem/year has been set for whole-body

BIO APPLICATION
Occupational Radiation
Exposure Limits

Table 29.3 RBE Factors for Several Types of Radiation

Radiation	RBE Factor
X-rays and gamma rays	1.0
Beta particles	1.0–1.7
Alpha particles	10–20
Slow neutrons	4–5
Fast neutrons and protons	10
Heavy ions	20

exposure. Higher upper limits are permissible for certain parts of the body, such as the hands and forearms. An acute whole-body dose of 400 to 500 rem results in a mortality rate of about 50%. The most dangerous form of exposure is ingestion or inhalation of radioactive isotopes, especially those elements the body retains and concentrates, such as ^{90}Sr. In some cases a dose of 1 000 rem can result from ingesting 1 mCi of radioactive material.

Sterilizing objects by exposing them to radiation has been going on for years, but in recent years the methods used have become safer to use and more economical. Most bacteria, worms, and insects are easily destroyed by exposure to gamma radiation from radioactive cobalt. There is no intake of radioactive nuclei by an organism in such sterilizing processes as there is in the use of radioactive tracers. The process is highly effective in destroying *Trichinella* worms in pork, salmonella bacteria in chickens, insect eggs in wheat, and surface bacteria on fruits and vegetables that can lead to rapid spoilage. Recently, the procedure has been expanded to include the sterilization of medical equipment while in its protective covering. Surgical gloves, sponges, sutures, and so forth are irradiated while packaged. Also, bone, cartilage, and skin used for grafting are often irradiated to reduce the chance of infection.

BIO APPLICATION
Irradiation of Food and Medical Equipment

Tracing

Radioactive particles can be used to trace chemicals participating in various reactions. One of the most valuable uses of radioactive tracers is in medicine. For example, ^{131}I is an artificially produced isotope of iodine. (The natural, nonradioactive isotope is ^{127}I.) Iodine, a necessary nutrient for our bodies, is obtained largely through the intake of seafood and iodized salt. The thyroid gland plays a major role in the distribution of iodine throughout the body. To evaluate the performance of the thyroid, the patient drinks a small amount of radioactive sodium iodide. Two hours later, the amount of iodine in the thyroid gland is determined by measuring the radiation intensity in the neck area.

BIO APPLICATION
Radioactive Tracers in Medicine

A medical application of the use of radioactive tracers occurring in emergency situations is that of locating a hemorrhage inside the body. Often the location of the site cannot easily be determined, but radioactive chromium can identify the location with a high degree of precision. Chromium is taken up by red blood cells and carried uniformly throughout the body. The blood, however, will be dumped at a hemorrhage site, and the radioactivity of that region will increase markedly.

Tracing techniques are as wide ranging as human ingenuity can devise. Current applications range from checking the absorption of fluorine by teeth to checking contamination of food-processing equipment by cleansers to monitoring deterioration inside an automobile engine. In the last case a radioactive material is used in the manufacture of the pistons, and the oil is checked for radioactivity to determine the amount of wear on the pistons.

Magnetic Resonance Imaging (MRI)

The heart of magnetic resonance imaging (MRI) is that when a nucleus having a magnetic moment is placed in an external magnetic field, its moment precesses about the magnetic field with a frequency that is proportional to the field. For example, a proton, with a spin of $\frac{1}{2}$, can occupy one of two energy states when placed in an external magnetic field. The lower-energy state corresponds to the case in which the spin is aligned with the field, whereas the higher-energy state corresponds to the case in which the spin is opposite the field. Transitions between these two states can be observed with a technique known as **nuclear magnetic resonance**. A DC magnetic field is applied to align the magnetic moments, and a second, weak oscillating magnetic field is applied perpendicular to the DC field. When the frequency of the oscillating field is adjusted to match the precessional frequency of the magnetic moments, the nuclei will "flip" between the two spin

Figure 29.11 Computer-enhanced MRI images of (a) a normal human brain and (b) a human brain with a glioma tumor.

states. These transitions result in a net absorption of energy by the spin system, which can be detected electronically.

In MRI, image reconstruction is obtained using spatially varying magnetic fields and a procedure for encoding each point in the sample being imaged. Two MRI images taken on a human head are shown in Figure 29.11. In practice, a computer-controlled pulse-sequencing technique is used to produce signals that are captured by a suitable processing device. The signals are then subjected to appropriate mathematical manipulations to provide data for the final image. The main advantage of MRI over other imaging techniques in medical diagnostics is that it causes minimal damage to cellular structures. Photons associated with the radio frequency signals used in MRI have energies of only about 10^{-7} eV. Because molecular bond strengths are much larger (on the order of 1 eV), the rf photons cause little cellular damage. In comparison, x-rays or γ-rays have energies ranging from 10^4 to 10^6 eV and can cause considerable cellular damage.

SUMMARY

29.1 Some Properties of Nuclei

29.2 Binding Energy

Nuclei are represented symbolically as $_{Z}^{A}X$, where X represents the chemical symbol for the element. The quantity A is the **mass number**, which equals the total number of nucleons (neutrons plus protons) in the nucleus. The quantity Z is the **atomic number**, which equals the number of protons in the nucleus. Nuclei that contain the same number of protons but different numbers of neutrons are called **isotopes**. In other words, isotopes have the same Z values but different A values.

Most nuclei are approximately spherical, with an average radius given by

$$r = r_0 A^{1/3} \qquad \text{[29.1]}$$

where r_0 is a constant equal to 1.2×10^{-15} m and A is the mass number.

The total mass of a nucleus is always less than the sum of the masses of its individual nucleons. This mass difference Δm, multiplied by c^2, gives the **binding energy** of the nucleus.

29.3 Radioactivity

The spontaneous emission of radiation by certain nuclei is called **radioactivity**. There are three processes by which a

radioactive substance can decay: alpha (α) decay, in which the emitted particles are $_{2}^{4}$He nuclei; beta (β) decay, in which the emitted particles are electrons or positrons; and gamma (γ) decay, in which the emitted particles are high-energy photons.

The **decay rate**, or **activity**, R, of a sample is given by

$$R = \left| \frac{\Delta N}{\Delta t} \right| = \lambda N \qquad \text{[29.3]}$$

where N is the number of radioactive nuclei at some instant and λ is a constant for a given substance called the **decay constant**.

Nuclei in a radioactive substance decay in such a way that the number of nuclei present varies with time according to the expression

$$N = N_0 e^{-\lambda t} \qquad \text{[29.4a]}$$

where N is the number of radioactive nuclei present at time t, N_0 is the number at time $t = 0$, and $e = 2.718\ldots$ is the base of the natural logarithms.

The **half-life** $T_{1/2}$ of a radioactive substance is the time required for half of a given number of radioactive nuclei to decay. The half-life is related to the decay constant by

$$T_{1/2} = \frac{0.693}{\lambda} \qquad \text{[29.5]}$$

29.4 The Decay Processes

If a nucleus decays by alpha emission, it loses two protons and two neutrons. A typical alpha decay is

$$\ _{92}^{238}\text{U} \quad \rightarrow \quad \ _{90}^{234}\text{Th} + \ _{2}^{4}\text{He} \qquad [29.9]$$

Note that in this decay, as in all radioactive decay processes, the sum of the Z values on the left equals the sum of the Z values on the right; the same is true for the A values.

A typical beta decay is

$$\ _{6}^{14}\text{C} \quad \rightarrow \quad \ _{7}^{14}\text{N} + e^{-} + \bar{\nu} \qquad [29.15]$$

When a nucleus undergoes beta decay, an **antineutrino** is emitted along with an electron, or a **neutrino** along with a positron. A neutrino has zero electric charge and a small mass (which may be zero) and interacts weakly with matter.

Nuclei are often in an excited state following radioactive decay, and they release their extra energy by emitting a high-energy photon called a **gamma ray** (γ). A typical gamma-ray emission is

$$\ _{6}^{12}\text{C*} \quad \rightarrow \quad \ _{6}^{12}\text{C} + \gamma \qquad [29.18]$$

where the asterisk indicates that the carbon nucleus was in an excited state before gamma emission.

29.6 Nuclear Reactions

Nuclear reactions can occur when a bombarding particle strikes another nucleus. A typical nuclear reaction is

$$\ _{2}^{4}\text{He} + \ _{7}^{14}\text{N} \quad \rightarrow \quad \ _{8}^{17}\text{O} + \ _{1}^{1}\text{H} \qquad [29.21]$$

In this reaction, an alpha particle strikes a nitrogen nucleus, producing an oxygen nucleus and a proton. As in radioactive decay, atomic numbers and mass numbers balance on the two sides of the arrow.

Nuclear reactions in which energy is released are said to be **exothermic reactions** and are characterized by positive Q values. Reactions with negative Q values, called **endothermic reactions**, cannot occur unless the incoming particle has at least enough kinetic energy to overcome the energy deficit. To conserve both energy and momentum, the incoming particle must have a minimum kinetic energy, called the **threshold energy**, given by

$$KE_{min} = \left(1 + \frac{m}{M}\right)|Q| \qquad [29.24]$$

where m is the mass of the incident particle and M is the mass of the target atom.

■ MULTIPLE-CHOICE QUESTIONS

WebAssign The multiple-choice questions in this chapter may be assigned online in Enhanced WebAssign.

---

1. Estimate the ratio of the volume of a neon nucleus to that of a helium nucleus. (a) 1 (b) 2 (c) 4 (d) 5 (e) 7

2. Convert the atomic mass of an oxygen atom to units of MeV/c^2. (a) 1.88×10^4 MeV/c^2 (b) 2.47×10^4 MeV/c^2 (c) 7.37×10^3 MeV/c^2 (d) 9.21×10^5 MeV/c^2 (e) 1.49×10^4 MeV/c^2

3. The atomic mass of oxygen is 15.999 u. Convert this mass to kilograms. (a) 1.28×10^{-26} kg (b) 3.37×10^{-26} kg (c) 1.67×10^{-27} kg (d) 4.72×10^{-26} kg (e) 2.66×10^{-26} kg

4. Rank chlorine, nickel, and gold by binding energy per nucleon, from smallest to largest. (a) gold, chlorine, nickel (b) chlorine, gold, nickel (c) nickel, gold, chlorine (d) gold, nickel, chlorine (e) chlorine, nickel, gold

5. Does a neutral atom designated as $_{18}^{40}$X contain (a) 20 neutrons and 20 protons, (b) 22 protons and 18 neutrons, (c) 18 protons and 22 neutrons, (d) 18 protons and 40 neutrons, or (e) 40 protons and 18 neutrons?

6. The half-life of radium-224 is about 3.6 days. What approximate fraction of a sample remains undecayed after two weeks? (a) $\frac{1}{2}$ (b) $\frac{1}{4}$ (c) $\frac{1}{8}$ (d) $\frac{1}{16}$ (e) $\frac{1}{32}$

7. Substance A has a decay constant λ that is three times that of B. Find the ratio of the half-life of substance A to the half-life of substance B. (a) $\frac{1}{3}$ (b) 1 (c) 3 (d) 2 (e) $\frac{1}{2}$

8. When the $_{36}^{95}$Kr nucleus undergoes beta decay, does the daughter nucleus (Rb) contain (a) 58 neutrons and 37 protons, (b) 58 protons and 37 neutrons, (c) 54 neutrons and 41 protons, (d) 59 neutrons and 36 protons, or (e) 55 neutrons and 40 protons?

9. When $_{15}^{32}$P decays to $_{16}^{32}$S, which of the following particles are emitted? (a) a proton (b) an alpha particle (c) an electron (d) a gamma ray (e) an antineutrino

10. In the decay $_{90}^{234}$Th $\rightarrow$ $_{Z}^{A}$Ra $+$ $_{2}^{4}$He, identify the mass number and the atomic number of the Ra nucleus. (a) $A = 230$, $Z = 92$ (b) $A = 238$, $Z = 88$ (c) $A = 230$, $Z = 88$ (d) $A = 234$, $Z = 88$ (e) $A = 238$, $Z = 86$

11. Which of the following statements is true regarding a radioactive isotope $_{Z}^{A}$X that decays by emitting a gamma ray? (a) The resulting isotope has a different Z value. (b) The resulting isotope has the same A value and the same Z value. (c) The resulting isotope has a different A value. (d) Both A and Z are different. (e) The atom jumps to a state of higher energy.

12. What is the Q value for the reaction ^{9}Be $+ \alpha \rightarrow$ ^{12}C $+$ n? (a) 8.4 MeV (b) 7.3 MeV (c) 6.2 MeV (d) 5.7 MeV (e) 4.2 MeV

■ CONCEPTUAL QUESTIONS

WebAssign The conceptual questions in this chapter may be assigned online in Enhanced WebAssign.

1. A student claims that a heavy form of hydrogen decays by alpha emission. How do you respond?

2. If a heavy nucleus that is initially at rest undergoes alpha decay, which has more kinetic energy after the decay, the alpha particle or the daughter nucleus?

3. Why do isotopes of a given element have different physical properties, such as mass, but the same chemical properties?

4. Why do nearly all the naturally occurring isotopes lie above the $N = Z$ line in Figure 29.3?

5. Consider two heavy nuclei X and Y having similar mass numbers. If X has the higher binding energy, which nucleus tends to be more unstable? Explain your answer.

6. Explain the main differences between alpha, beta, and gamma rays.

7. In beta decay, the energy of the electron or positron emitted from the nucleus lies somewhere in a relatively large range of possibilities. In alpha decay however, the alpha particle energy can only have discrete values. Why is there this difference?

8. What fraction of a radioactive sample has decayed after two half-lives have elapsed?

9. Pick any beta-decay process and show that the neutrino must have zero charge.

10. If film is kept in a box, alpha particles from a radioactive source outside the box cannot expose the film, but beta particles can. Explain.

11. In positron decay a proton in the nucleus becomes a neutron, and the positive charge is carried away by the positron. A neutron, though, has a larger rest energy than a proton. How is that possible?

12. An alpha particle has twice the charge of a beta particle. Why does the former deflect less than the latter when passing between electrically charged plates, assuming they both have the same speed?

13. Can carbon-14 dating be used to measure the age of a rock? Explain.

■ PROBLEMS

WebAssign The problems in this chapter may be assigned online in Enhanced WebAssign. Selected problems also have Watch It video solutions.

1. denotes straightforward problem; **2.** denotes intermediate problem;

3. denotes challenging problem

1. denotes full solution available in *Student Solutions Manual/ Study Guide*

1. denotes problems most often assigned in Enhanced WebAssign

BIO denotes biomedical problems

GP denotes guided problems

M denotes Master It tutorial available in Enhanced WebAssign

Q|C denotes asking for quantitative and conceptual reasoning

S denotes symbolic reasoning problem

A list of atomic masses is given in Appendix B.

29.1 Some Properties of Nuclei

1. Find the nuclear radii of the following nuclides: (a) $^{2}_{1}H$ (b) $^{60}_{27}Co$ (c) $^{197}_{79}Au$ (d) $^{239}_{94}Pu$.

2. Find the radius of a nucleus of (a) $^{4}_{2}He$ and (b) $^{238}_{92}U$.

3. Using 2.3×10^{17} kg/m³ as the density of nuclear matter, find the radius of a sphere of such matter that would have a mass equal to that of Earth. Earth has a mass equal to 5.98×10^{24} kg and average radius of 6.37×10^{6} m.

4. Consider the $^{65}_{29}Cu$ nucleus. Find approximate values for its (a) radius, (b) volume, and (c) density.

5. **M** An alpha particle ($Z = 2$, mass $= 6.64 \times 10^{-27}$ kg) approaches to within 1.00×10^{-14} m of a carbon nucleus ($Z = 6$). What are (a) the maximum Coulomb force on the alpha particle, (b) the acceleration of the alpha particle at this time, and (c) the potential energy of the alpha particle at the same time?

6. **Q|C** Singly ionized carbon atoms are accelerated through 1 000 V and passed into a mass spectrometer to determine the isotopes present. (See Chapter 19.) The magnetic field strength in the spectrometer is 0.200 T. (a) Determine the orbital radii for the ^{12}C and the ^{13}C isotopes as they pass through the field. (b) Show that the ratio of the radii may be written in the form

$$\frac{r_1}{r_2} = \sqrt{\frac{m_1}{m_2}}$$

and verify that your radii in part (a) satisfy this formula.

7. (a) Find the speed an alpha particle requires to come within 3.2×10^{-14} m of a gold nucleus. (b) Find the energy of the alpha particle in MeV.

8. At the end of its life, a star with a mass of two times the Sun's mass is expected to collapse, combining its protons and electrons to form a neutron star. Such a star could be thought of as a gigantic atomic nucleus. If a star of mass $2 \times 1.99 \times 10^{30}$ kg collapsed into neutrons ($m_n = 1.67 \times 10^{-27}$ kg), what would its radius be? Assume $r = r_0 A^{1/3}$.

29.2 Binding Energy

9. Find the average binding energy per nucleon of (a) $^{24}_{12}\text{Mg}$ and (b) $^{85}_{37}\text{Rb}$.

10. Calculate the binding energy per nucleon for (a) ^2H, (b) ^4He, (c) ^{56}Fe, and (d) ^{238}U.

11. A pair of nuclei for which $Z_1 = N_2$ and $Z_2 = N_1$ are called *mirror isobars*. (The atomic and neutron numbers are interchangeable.) Binding-energy measurements on such pairs can be used to obtain evidence of the charge independence of nuclear forces. Charge independence means that the proton–proton, proton–neutron, and neutron–neutron forces are approximately equal. Calculate the difference in binding energy for the two mirror nuclei $^{15}_{8}\text{O}$ and $^{15}_{7}\text{N}$.

12. The peak of the stability curve occurs at ^{56}Fe, which is why iron is prominent in the spectrum of the Sun and stars. Show that ^{56}Fe has a higher binding energy per nucleon than its neighbors ^{55}Mn and ^{59}Co. Compare your results with Figure 29.4.

13. QC Two nuclei having the same mass number are known as *isobars*. (a) Calculate the difference in binding energy per nucleon for the isobars $^{23}_{11}\text{Na}$ and $^{23}_{12}\text{Mg}$. (b) How do you account for this difference? (The mass of $^{23}_{12}\text{Mg} = 22.994\ 127$ u.)

14. Calculate the binding energy of the last neutron in the $^{43}_{20}\text{Ca}$ nucleus. *Hint:* You should compare the mass of $^{43}_{20}\text{Ca}$ with the mass of $^{42}_{20}\text{Ca}$ plus the mass of a neutron. The mass of $^{42}_{20}\text{Ca} = 41.958\ 622$ u, whereas the mass of $^{43}_{20}\text{Ca} = 42.958\ 770$ u.

29.3 Radioactivity

15. Radon gas has a half-life of 3.83 days. If 3.00 g of radon gas is present at time $t = 0$, what mass of radon will remain after 1.50 days have passed?

16. BIO A drug tagged with $^{99}_{43}\text{Tc}$ (half-life = 6.05 h) is prepared for a patient. If the original activity of the sample was 1.1×10^4 Bq, what is its activity after it has been on the shelf for 2.0 h?

17. GP The half-life of ^{131}I is 8.04 days. (a) Convert the half-life to seconds. (b) Calculate the decay constant for this isotope. (c) Convert 0.500 μCi to the SI unit the becquerel. (d) Find the number of ^{131}I nuclei necessary to produce a sample with an activity of 0.500 μCi. (e) Suppose the activity of a certain ^{131}I sample is 6.40 mCi at a given time. Find the number of half-lives the sample goes through in 40.2 d and the activity at the end of that period.

18. QC Tritium has a half-life of 12.33 years. What fraction of the nuclei in a tritium sample will remain (a) after 5.00 yr? (b) After 10.0 yr? (c) After 123.3 yr? (d) According to Equation 29.4a, an infinite amount of time is required for the entire sample to decay. Discuss whether that is realistic.

19. After 2.00 days, the activity of a sample of an unknown type radioactive material has decreased to 84.2% of the initial activity. What is the half-life of this material?

20. BIO After a plant or animal dies, its ^{14}C content decreases with a half-life of 5 730 yr. If an archaeologist finds an ancient firepit containing partially consumed firewood and the ^{14}C content of the wood is only 12.5% that of an equal carbon sample from a present-day tree, what is the age of the ancient site?

21. M A freshly prepared sample of a certain radioactive isotope has an activity of 10.0 mCi. After 4.00 h, the activity is 8.00 mCi. (a) Find the decay constant and half-life of the isotope. (b) How many atoms of the isotope were contained in the freshly prepared sample? (c) What is the sample's activity 30 h after it is prepared?

22. A building has become accidentally contaminated with radioactivity. The longest-lived material in the building is strontium-90. (The atomic mass of $^{90}_{38}\text{Sr}$ is 89.907 7 u.) If the building initially contained 5.0 kg of this substance and the safe level is less than 10.0 counts/min, how long will the building be unsafe?

29.4 The Decay Processes

23. Identify the missing nuclides in the following decays:
    (a) $^{212}_{83}\text{Bi} \rightarrow ? + ^4_2\text{He}$
    (b) $^{95}_{36}\text{Kr} \rightarrow ? + e^- + \bar{\nu}$
    (c) $? \rightarrow ^4_2\text{He} + ^{140}_{58}\text{Ce}$

24. Complete the following radioactive decay formulas:
    (a) $^{12}_{5}\text{B} \rightarrow ? + e^- + \bar{\nu}$
    (b) $^{234}_{90}\text{Th} \rightarrow ^{230}_{88}\text{Ra} + ?$
    (c) $? \rightarrow ^{14}_{7}\text{N} + e^- + \bar{\nu}$

25. The mass of ^{56}Fe is 55.934 9 u, and the mass of ^{56}Co is 55.939 9 u. Which isotope decays into the other and by what process?

26. Find the energy released in the alpha decay of $^{238}_{92}\text{U}$. The following mass value will be useful: $^{234}_{90}\text{Th}$ has a mass of 234.043 583 u.

27. Determine which of the following suggested decays can occur spontaneously:
    (a) $^{40}_{20}\text{Ca} \rightarrow e^+ + ^{40}_{19}\text{K}$ (b) $^{144}_{60}\text{Nd} \rightarrow ^4_2\text{He} + ^{140}_{58}\text{Ce}$

28. $^{66}_{28}\text{Ni}$ (mass = 65.929 1 u) undergoes beta decay to $^{66}_{29}\text{Cu}$ (mass = 65.928 9 u). (a) Write the complete decay formula for this process. (b) Find the maximum kinetic energy of the emerging electrons.

29. A ^3H (tritium) nucleus beta decays into ^3He by creating an electron and an antineutrino according to the reaction

$$^3_1\text{H} \rightarrow ^3_2\text{He} + e^- + \bar{\nu}$$

Use Appendix B to determine the total energy released in this reaction.

30. A piece of charcoal used for cooking is found at the remains of an ancient campsite. A 1.00-kg sample

of carbon from the wood has an activity equal to 5.00×10^2 decays per minute. Find the age of the charcoal. *Hint:* Living material has an activity equal to 15.0 decays/minute per gram of carbon present.

31. **M** A wooden artifact is found in an ancient tomb. Its carbon-14 ($^{14}_{6}$C) activity is measured to be 60.0% of that in a fresh sample of wood from the same region. Assuming the same amount of ^{14}C was initially present in the artifact as is now contained in the fresh sample, determine the age of the artifact.

29.6 Nuclear Reactions

32. A beam of 6.61-MeV protons is incident on a target of $^{27}_{13}$Al. Those protons that collide with the target produce the reaction

$$\text{p} + ^{27}_{13}\text{Al} \rightarrow ^{27}_{14}\text{Si} + \text{n}$$

($^{27}_{14}$Si has a mass of 26.986 721 u.) Neglecting any recoil of the product nucleus, determine the kinetic energy of the emerging neutrons.

33. Identify the unknown particles X and X′ in the following nuclear reactions:
    (a) $X + ^{4}_{2}\text{He} \rightarrow ^{24}_{12}\text{Mg} + ^{1}_{0}\text{n}$
    (b) $^{235}_{92}\text{U} + ^{1}_{0}\text{n} \rightarrow ^{90}_{38}\text{Sr} + X + 2^{1}_{0}\text{n}$
    (c) $2^{1}_{1}\text{H} \rightarrow 2^{2}_{1}\text{H} + X + X′$

34. **GP** One method of producing neutrons for experimental use is to bombard $^{7}_{3}$Li with protons. The neutrons are emitted according to the reaction

$$^{1}_{1}\text{H} + ^{7}_{3}\text{Li} \rightarrow ^{7}_{4}\text{Be} + ^{1}_{0}\text{n}$$

(a) Calculate the mass in atomic mass units of the particles on the left side of the equation. (b) Calculate the mass (in atomic mass units) of the particles on the right side of the equation. (c) Subtract the answer for part (b) from that for part (a) and convert the result to mega electron volts, obtaining the Q value for this reaction. (d) Assuming lithium is initially at rest, the proton is moving at velocity v, and the resulting beryllium and neutron are both moving at velocity V after the collision, write an expression describing conservation of momentum for this reaction in terms of the masses m_p, m_{Be}, m_n, and the velocities. (e) Write an expression relating the kinetic energies of particles before and after together with Q. (f) What minimum kinetic energy must the incident proton have if this reaction is to occur?

35. (a) Suppose $^{10}_{5}$B is struck by an alpha particle, releasing a proton and a product nucleus in the reaction. What is the product nucleus? (b) An alpha particle and a product nucleus are produced when $^{13}_{6}$C is struck by a proton. What is the product nucleus?

36. **Q|C** Consider two reactions:
    $$(1) \quad \text{n} + ^{2}_{1}\text{H} \rightarrow ^{3}_{1}\text{H}$$
    $$(2) \quad ^{1}_{1}\text{H} + ^{2}_{1}\text{H} \rightarrow ^{3}_{2}\text{He}$$

(a) Compute the Q values for these reactions. Identify whether each reaction is exothermic or endothermic. (b) Which reaction results in more released energy? Why? (c) Assuming the difference is primarily due to the work done by the electric force, calculate the distance between the two protons in helium-3.

37. Natural gold has only one isotope, $^{197}_{79}$Au. If gold is bombarded with slow neutrons, e$^-$ particles are emitted. (a) Write the appropriate reaction equation. (b) Calculate the maximum energy of the emitted beta particles. The mass of $^{198}_{80}$Hg is 197.966 75 u.

38. Complete the following nuclear reactions:
    (a) ? $+ ^{14}_{7}\text{N} \rightarrow ^{1}_{1}\text{H} + ^{17}_{8}\text{O}$ (b) $^{7}_{3}\text{Li} + ^{1}_{1}\text{H} \rightarrow ^{4}_{2}\text{He} + $?

39. (a) Determine the product of the reaction $^{7}_{3}\text{Li} + ^{4}_{2}\text{He} \rightarrow$? $+$ n (b) What is the Q value of the reaction?

29.7 Medical Applications of Radiation

40. **BIO** In terms of biological damage, how many rad of heavy ions are equivalent to 100 rad of x-rays?

41. **BIO** **M** A person whose mass is 75.0 kg is exposed to a whole-body dose of 25.0 rad. How many joules of energy are deposited in the person's body?

42. **BIO** A 200-rad dose of radiation is administered to a patient in an effort to combat a cancerous growth. Assuming all the energy deposited is absorbed by the growth, (a) calculate the amount of energy delivered per unit mass. (b) Assuming the growth has a mass of 0.25 kg and a specific heat equal to that of water, calculate its temperature rise.

43. A "clever" technician decides to heat some water for his coffee with an x-ray machine. If the machine produces 10 rad/s, how long will it take to raise the temperature of a cup of water by 50°C? Ignore heat losses during this time.

44. **BIO** An x-ray technician works 5 days per week, 50 weeks per year. Assume the technician takes an average of eight x-rays per day and receives a dose of 5.0 rem/yr as a result. (a) Estimate the dose in rem per x-ray taken. (b) How does this result compare with the amount of low-level background radiation the technician is exposed to?

45. **BIO** A patient swallows a radiopharmaceutical tagged with phosphorus-32 ($^{32}_{15}$P), a β^- emitter with a half-life of 14.3 days. The average kinetic energy of the emitted electrons is 700 keV. If the initial activity of the sample is 1.31 MBq, determine (a) the number of electrons emitted in a 10-day period, (b) the total energy deposited in the body during the 10 days, and (c) the absorbed dose if the electrons are completely absorbed in 100 g of tissue.

46. **BIO** A particular radioactive source produces 100 mrad of 2-MeV gamma rays per hour at a distance of 1.0 m. (a) How long could a person stand at this distance before accumulating an intolerable dose of

1 rem? (b) Assuming the gamma radiation is emitted uniformly in all directions, at what distance would a person receive a dose of 10 mrad/h from this source?

Additional Problems

47. A radioactive sample contains 3.50 μg of pure ^{11}C, which has a half-life of 20.4 min. (a) How many moles of ^{11}C are present initially? (b) Determine the number of nuclei present initially. What is the activity of the sample (c) initially and (d) after 8.00 h?

48. Find the threshold energy that the incident neutron must have to produce the reaction: $^1_0n + ^4_2He \rightarrow ^2_1H + ^3_1H$.

49. M A 200.0-mCi sample of a radioactive isotope is purchased by a medical supply house. If the sample has a half-life of 14.0 days, how long will it keep before its activity is reduced to 20.0 mCi?

50. The ^{14}C isotope undergoes beta decay according to the process given by Equation 29.15. Find the Q value for this process.

51. QC In a piece of rock from the Moon, the ^{87}Rb content is assayed to be 1.82×10^{10} atoms per gram of material and the ^{87}Sr content is found to be 1.07×10^9 atoms per gram. (The relevant decay is ^{87}Rb $\rightarrow$ ^{87}Sr + e^-. The half-life of the decay is 4.8×10^{10} yr.) (a) Determine the age of the rock. (b) Could the material in the rock actually be much older? (c) What assumption is implicit in using the radioactive-dating method?

52. Many radioisotopes have important industrial, medical, and research applications. One of these is ^{60}Co, which has a half-life of 5.2 years and decays by the emission of a beta particle (energy 0.31 MeV) and two gamma photons (energies 1.17 MeV and 1.33 MeV). A scientist wishes to prepare a ^{60}Co sealed source that will have an activity of at least 10 Ci after 30 months of use. What is the minimum initial mass of ^{60}Co required?

53. BIO A medical laboratory stock solution is prepared with an initial activity due to ^{24}Na of 2.5 mCi/mL, and 10.0 mL of the stock solution is diluted at $t_0 = 0$ to a working solution whose total volume is 250 mL. After 48 h, a 5.0-mL sample of the working solution is monitored with a counter. What is the measured activity? *Note:* 1 mL = 1 milliliter.

54. After the sudden release of radioactivity from the Chernobyl nuclear reactor accident in 1986, the radioactivity of milk in Poland rose to 2 000 Bq/L due to iodine-131, with a half-life of 8.04 days. Radioactive iodine is particularly hazardous because the thyroid gland concentrates iodine. The Chernobyl accident caused a measurable increase in thyroid cancers among children in Belarus. (a) For comparison, find the activity of milk due to potassium. Assume 1 liter of milk contains 2.00 g of potassium, of which 0.011 7% is the isotope ^{40}K, which has a half-life of 1.28×10^9 yr. (b) After what length of time would the activity due to iodine fall below that due to potassium?

55. The theory of nuclear astrophysics is that all the heavy elements like uranium are formed in the interior of massive stars. These stars eventually explode, releasing the elements into space. If we assume that at the time of explosion there were equal amounts of ^{235}U and ^{238}U, how long ago were the elements that formed our Earth released, given that the present ^{235}U/^{238}U ratio is 0.007? (The half-lives of ^{235}U and ^{238}U are 0.70×10^9 yr and 4.47×10^9 yr, respectively.)

56. A by-product of some fission reactors is the isotope $^{239}_{94}$Pu, which is an alpha emitter with a half-life of 24 000 years:

$$^{239}_{94}\text{Pu} \rightarrow ^{235}_{92}\text{U} + ^4_2\text{He}$$

Consider a sample of 1.0 kg of pure $^{239}_{94}$Pu at $t = 0$. Calculate (a) the number of $^{239}_{94}$Pu nuclei present at $t = 0$ and (b) the initial activity of the sample. (c) How long does the sample have to be stored if a "safe" activity level is 0.10 Bq?

■ AP* REVIEW QUESTIONS

1. A single atom of $^{14}_{6}C$ contains how many protons and how many neutrons?

	Protons	Neutrons
(A)	6	14
(B)	14	6
(C)	8	6
(D)	6	8
(E)	7	7

2. A single atom of uranium has 92 protons and 146 neutrons. Which of the following is a correct notation for this isotope?

(A) ^{54}U

(B) ^{92}U

(C) ^{146}U

(D) ^{235}U

(E) ^{238}U

3. What do all isotopes of carbon have in common?

    I. the same number of protons

    II. the same number of neutrons

    III. the same atomic mass

(A) I only

(B) I and II only

(C) I and III only

(D) II and III only

(E) I, II, and III

4. Generally, for the first 20 elements on the periodic table the number of neutrons and the number of protons are about the same for stable nuclei. After the first 20 elements, what general trend can be observed regarding the number of neutrons (N) compared to the number of protons (Z) for stable nuclei?

(A) N becomes increasingly greater than Z

(B) N becomes increasingly less than Z

(C) N and Z stay approximately the same

(D) There is no general trend

(E) There are no stable nuclei above the first 20 elements

5. A single atom of ^{12}C has 6 protons, 6 neutrons, and 6 electrons. The respective atomic masses of a proton, neutron, and electron are 1.007276 u, 1.008665 u, and 0.000549 u. Although the masses of a proton and neutron are each greater than 1 u, the mass of a single atom of ^{12}C is equal to exactly 12.0000 u. Which of the following concepts best explains this?

(A) Nuclear fission

(B) Nuclear fusion

(C) Electromagnetism

(D) The photoelectric effect

(E) Nuclear binding energy

6. Which of the following modes of radioactive decay involve the emission of particles with mass?

    I. alpha (α)

    II. beta (β)

    III. gamma (γ)

(A) I only

(B) I and II only

(C) II and III only

(D) III only

(E) I, II, and III

7. $^{234}_{90}Th$ undergoes radioactive decay by emitting an electron. Which of the following best describes the atomic number and the mass number of the resultant nuclide?

	Atomic number	Mass number
(A)	90	235
(B)	91	235
(C)	91	234
(D)	89	234
(E)	89	235

8. $^{222}_{86}Rn$ undergoes alpha decay, resulting in which of the following nuclides?

(A) $^{218}_{84}Po$

(B) $^{222}_{84}Po$

(C) $^{222}_{87}Fr$

(D) $^{218}_{87}Fr$

(E) $^{226}_{88}Ra$

---

9. When alpha particles collide with nitrogen nuclei ($^{14}_{7}N$), protons are released along with what other nuclide?

(A) $^{15}_{8}O$

(B) $^{16}_{8}O$

(C) $^{17}_{8}O$

(D) $^{14}_{6}C$

(E) $^{13}_{6}C$

10. Which of the following best describes the charges for α, β, and γ decay?

	Alpha (α)	Beta (β)	Gamma (γ)
(A)	positive	neutral	negative
(B)	negative	neutral	positive
(C)	positive	negative	neutral
(D)	negative	positive	neutral
(E)	neutral	negative	positive

11. Which of the following nuclear equations describes the positron decay of $^{11}_{6}C$?

(A) $^{11}_{6}C \rightarrow ^{0}_{-1}e + ^{11}_{5}B$

(B) $^{11}_{6}C \rightarrow ^{1}_{0}e + ^{10}_{6}C$

(C) $^{11}_{6}C \rightarrow ^{0}_{-1}e + ^{11}_{7}N$

(D) $^{11}_{6}C \rightarrow ^{0}_{1}e + ^{11}_{5}B$

(E) $^{11}_{6}C \rightarrow ^{0}_{1}e + ^{11}_{7}N$

Radioactive source

12. The diagram above shows the paths of three radioactive decay particles in an electric field directed toward the bottom of the page. Which of the following accurately labels the particles?

	Particle I	Particle II	Particle III
(A)	Alpha (α)	Beta (β)	Gamma (γ)
(B)	Gamma (γ)	Alpha (α)	Beta (β)
(C)	Alpha (α)	Gamma (γ)	Beta (β)
(D)	Beta (β)	Gamma (γ)	Alpha (α)
(E)	Gamma (γ)	Beta (β)	Alpha (α)

High-intensity light from twenty-four lasers, focused on a fuel pellet made of deuterium and tritium, explodes the outer layers of the pellet. A powerful reaction force then implodes the inner part of the pellet, compressing and heating it. Shock waves develop and meet at the center, igniting fusion reactions and liberating energy. A recent successful test at the National Ignition Facility (NIF) fired a million joules of energy into a target in a few billionths of a second.

Roger Ressmeyer/CORBIS

30 Nuclear Energy and Elementary Particles

In this concluding chapter we discuss the two means by which energy can be derived from nuclear reactions: fission, in which a nucleus of large mass number splits into two smaller nuclei, and fusion, in which two light nuclei fuse to form a heavier nucleus. In either case, there is a release of large amounts of energy that can be used destructively through bombs or constructively through the production of electric power. We end our study of physics by examining the known subatomic particles and the fundamental interactions that govern their behavior. We also discuss the current theory of elementary particles, which states that all matter in nature is constructed from only two families of particles: quarks and leptons. Finally, we describe how such models help us understand the evolution of the Universe.

30.1 Nuclear Fission

Nuclear fission occurs when a heavy nucleus, such as ^{235}U, splits, or fissions, into two smaller nuclei. In such a reaction **the total mass of the products is less than the original mass of the heavy nucleus**.

The fission of ^{235}U by slow (low-energy) neutrons can be represented by the sequence of events

$$\,^{1}_{0}n + \,^{235}_{92}U \quad \rightarrow \quad \,^{236}_{92}U^{*} \rightarrow X + Y + \text{neutrons} \qquad [30.1]$$

where ^{236}U* is an intermediate state that lasts only for about 10^{-12} s before splitting into nuclei X and Y, called **fission fragments**. Many combinations of X and Y satisfy the requirements of conservation of energy and charge. In the fission of uranium, about 90 different daughter nuclei can be formed. The process also results

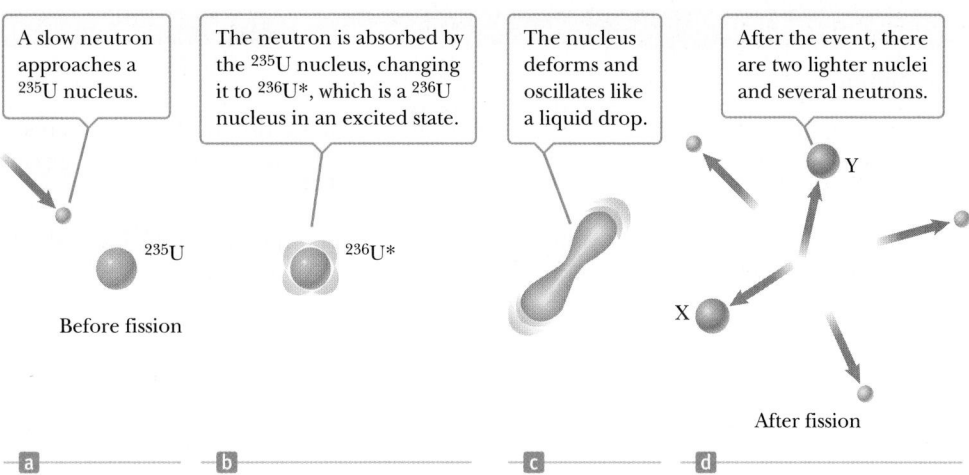

A slow neutron approaches a ^{235}U nucleus.

The neutron is absorbed by the ^{235}U nucleus, changing it to ^{236}U*, which is a ^{236}U nucleus in an excited state.

The nucleus deforms and oscillates like a liquid drop.

After the event, there are two lighter nuclei and several neutrons.

^{235}U

^{236}U*

Before fission

After fission

Figure 30.1 A nuclear fission event as described by the liquid-drop model of the nucleus.

in the production of several (typically two or three) neutrons per fission event. On the average, 2.47 neutrons are released per event.

A typical reaction of this type is

$$^{1}_{0}\text{n} + \,^{235}_{92}\text{U} \;\rightarrow\; \,^{141}_{56}\text{Ba} + \,^{92}_{36}\text{Kr} + 3^{1}_{0}\text{n} \qquad [30.2]$$

The fission fragments, barium and krypton, and the released neutrons have a great deal of kinetic energy following the fission event. Notice that the sum of the mass numbers, or number of nucleons, on the left ($1 + 235 = 236$) is the same as the total number of nucleons on the right ($141 + 92 + 3 = 236$). The total number of protons (92) is also the same on both sides. The energy Q released through the disintegration in Equation 30.2 can be easily calculated using the data in Appendix B. The details of this calculation can be found in Chapter 26 (Example 26.5), with an answer of $Q = 200.422$ MeV.

The breakup of the uranium nucleus can be compared to what happens to a drop of water when excess energy is added to it. All the atoms in the drop have energy, but not enough to break up the drop. If enough energy is added to set the drop vibrating, however, it will undergo elongation and compression until the amplitude of vibration becomes large enough to cause the drop to break apart. In the uranium nucleus a similar process occurs (Fig. 30.1). The sequence of events is as follows:

1. The ^{235}U nucleus captures a thermal (slow-moving) neutron.
2. The capture results in the formation of ^{236}U*, and the excess energy of this nucleus causes it to undergo violent oscillations.
3. The ^{236}U* nucleus becomes highly elongated, and the force of repulsion between protons in the two halves of the dumbbell-shaped nucleus tends to increase the distortion.
4. The nucleus splits into two fragments, emitting several neutrons in the process.

◀ Sequence of events in a nuclear fission process

Typically, the amount of energy released by the fission of a single heavy radioactive atom is about one hundred million times the energy released in the combustion of one molecule of the octane used in gasoline engines.

▪ APPLYING PHYSICS 30.1 | Unstable Products

If a heavy nucleus were to fission into only two product nuclei, they would be very unstable. Why?

EXPLANATION According to Figure 29.3, the ratio of the number of neutrons to the number of protons increases with Z. As a result, when a heavy nucleus splits in a fission reaction to two lighter nuclei, the lighter nuclei tend to have too many neutrons. The result is instability because the nuclei return to the curve in Figure 29.3 by decay processes that reduce the number of neutrons. ▪

■ EXAMPLE 30.1 │ A Fission-Powered World

GOAL Relate raw material to energy output.

PROBLEM (a) Calculate the total energy released if 1.00 kg of ^{235}U undergoes fission, taking the disintegration energy per event to be $Q = 208$ MeV. (b) How many kilograms of ^{235}U would be needed to satisfy the world's annual energy consumption (about 4×10^{20} J)?

STRATEGY In part (a), use the concept of a mole and Avogadro's number to obtain the total number of nuclei. Multiplying by the energy per reaction then gives the total energy released. Part (b) requires some light algebra.

. . . .

SOLUTION

(a) Calculate the total energy released from 1.00 kg of ^{235}U.

Find the total number of nuclei in 1.00 kg of uranium:

$$N = \left(\frac{6.02 \times 10^{23} \text{ nuclei/mol}}{235 \text{ g/mol}} \right) (1.00 \times 10^3 \text{ g})$$

$$= 2.56 \times 10^{24} \text{ nuclei}$$

Multiply N by the energy yield per nucleus, obtaining the total disintegration energy:

$$E = NQ = (2.56 \times 10^{24} \text{ nuclei}) \left(208 \frac{\text{MeV}}{\text{nucleus}} \right)$$

$$= 5.32 \times 10^{26} \text{ MeV}$$

(b) How many kilograms would provide for the world's annual energy needs?

Set the energy per kilogram, E_{kg}, times the number of kilograms, N_{kg}, equal to the total annual energy consumption. Solve for N_{kg}:

$$E_{kg} N_{kg} = E_{tot}$$

$$N_{kg} = \frac{E_{tot}}{E_{kg}} = \frac{4 \times 10^{20} \text{ J}}{(5.32 \times 10^{32} \text{ eV/kg})(1.60 \times 10^{-19} \text{ J/eV})}$$

$$= 5 \times 10^6 \text{ kg}$$

. . . .

REMARKS The calculation implicitly assumes perfect conversion to usable power, which is never the case in real systems. There are sufficient easily recoverable reserves of uranium to supply the entire world's energy needs for about seven years at current levels of usage. Breeder reactor technology can greatly extend those reserves.

QUESTION 30.1 Estimate the average mass of ^{235}U needed to provide power for one family for one year.

EXERCISE 30.1 How long can 1 kg of uranium-235 keep a 100-watt lightbulb burning if all its released energy is converted to electrical energy?

ANSWER $\sim 30\,000$ yr

Nuclear Reactors

The neutrons emitted when ^{235}U undergoes fission can in turn trigger other nuclei to undergo fission, with the possibility of a chain reaction (Active Fig. 30.2 on page 986). Calculations show that if the chain reaction isn't controlled, it will proceed too rapidly and possibly result in the sudden release of an enormous amount of energy (an explosion), even from only 1 g of ^{235}U. If the energy in 1 kg of ^{235}U were released, it would equal that released by the detonation of about 20 000 tons of TNT! An uncontrolled fission reaction, of course, is the principle behind the first nuclear bomb.

A nuclear reactor is a system designed to maintain what is called a **self-sustained chain reaction**, first achieved in 1942 by a team led by Enrico Fermi. Most reactors in operation today also use uranium as fuel. Natural uranium contains only about 0.7% of the ^{235}U isotope, with the remaining 99.3% being the ^{238}U isotope. This fact is important to the operation of a reactor because ^{238}U almost never undergoes fission. Instead, it tends to absorb neutrons, producing neptunium and plutonium. For this reason, reactor fuels must be artificially enriched so that they contain several percent of the ^{235}U isotope.

Active Figure 30.2
A nuclear chain reaction initiated by the capture of a neutron.

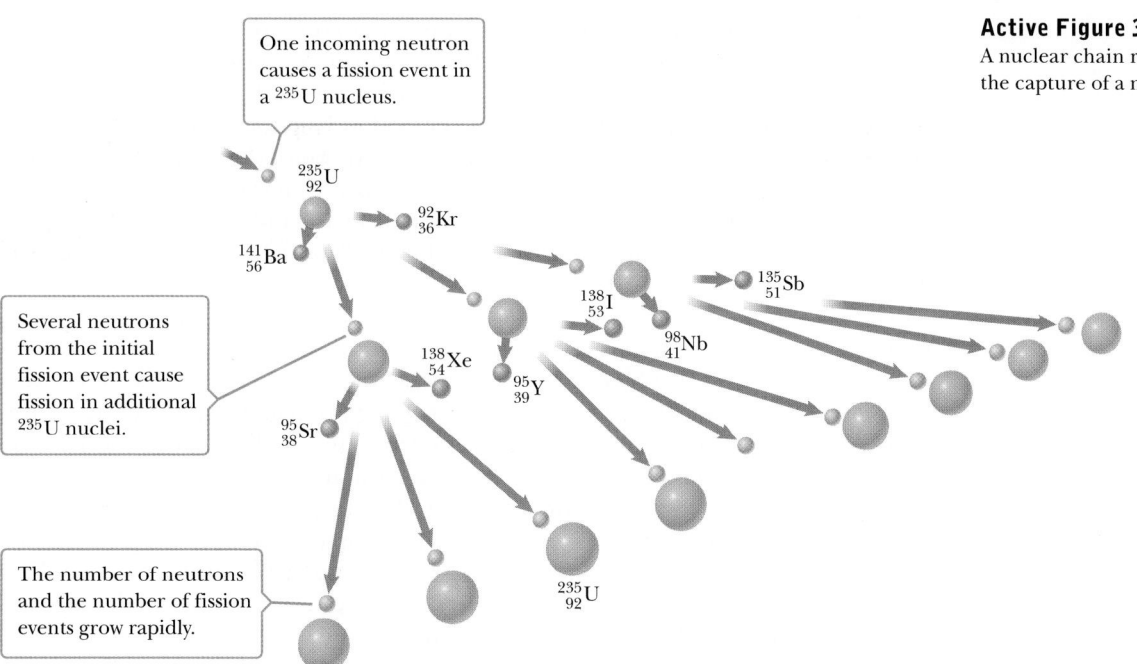

One incoming neutron causes a fission event in a $^{235}_{92}$U nucleus.

$^{235}_{92}$U

$^{92}_{36}$Kr

$^{141}_{56}$Ba

Several neutrons from the initial fission event cause fission in additional ^{235}U nuclei.

$^{138}_{54}$Xe

$^{138}_{53}$I

$^{135}_{51}$Sb

$^{98}_{41}$Nb

$^{95}_{39}$Y

$^{95}_{38}$Sr

$^{235}_{92}$U

The number of neutrons and the number of fission events grow rapidly.

On average, about 2.5 neutrons are emitted in each fission event of ^{235}U. To achieve a self-sustained chain reaction, one of these neutrons must be captured by another ^{235}U nucleus and cause it to undergo fission. A useful parameter for describing the level of reactor operation is the **reproduction constant K, defined as the average number of neutrons from each fission event that will cause another event**.

A self-sustained chain reaction is achieved when $K = 1$. Under this condition, the reactor is said to be **critical**. When K is less than 1, the reactor is subcritical and the reaction dies out. When K is greater than 1, the reactor is said to be supercritical and a runaway reaction occurs. In a nuclear reactor used to furnish power to a utility company, it is necessary to maintain a K value close to 1.

The basic design of a nuclear reactor is shown in Figure 30.3. The fuel elements consist of enriched uranium. The size of the reactor is important in reducing neutron leakage: a large reactor has a smaller surface-to-volume ratio and smaller leakage than a smaller reactor.

It's also important to regulate the neutron energies because slow neutrons are far more likely to cause fissions than fast neutrons in ^{235}U. Further, ^{238}U doesn't absorb slow neutrons. For the chain reaction to continue, the neutrons must, therefore, be slowed down. This slowing is accomplished by surrounding the fuel with a substance called a **moderator**, such as graphite (carbon) or heavy water (D_2O). Most modern reactors use heavy water. Collisions in the moderator slow the neutrons and enhance the fissioning of ^{235}U.

The power output of a fission reactor is controlled by the control rods depicted in Figure 30.3. These rods are made of materials like cadmium that readily absorb neutrons.

Fissions in a nuclear reactor heat molten sodium (or water, depending on the system), which is pumped through a heat exchanger. There, the thermal energy is transferred to water in a secondary system. The water is converted to steam, which drives a turbine-generator to create electric power.

Fission reactors are extremely safe. According to the *Oak Ridge National Laboratory Review*, "The health risk of living within 8 km (5 miles) of a nuclear reactor for 50 years is no greater than the risk of smoking 1.4 cigarettes, drinking 0.5 L of wine, traveling 240 km by car, flying 9 600 km by jet, or having one chest x-ray in a hospital. Each activity, by itself, is estimated to increase a person's chance of dying in any given year by one in a million."

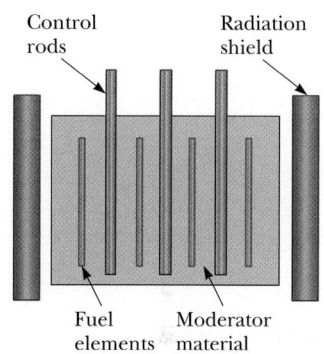

Control rods   Radiation shield

Fuel elements   Moderator material

Figure 30.3 Cross section of a reactor core showing the control rods, fuel elements containing enriched fuel, and moderating material, all surrounded by a radiation shield.

APPLICATION

Nuclear Reactor Design

Cost is an important factor; the cost per kilowatt-hour for nuclear power is slightly less than that of coal, and much less than oil or gas. Over time, nuclear power's lower cost per kilowatt-hour and lower impact on the environment more than compensate for higher start up costs. The safety issues associated with nuclear power reactors are complex and often emotional. All sources of energy have associated risks. Coal, for example, exposes workers to health hazards (including radioactive radon) and produces atmospheric pollution (including greenhouse gases and highly radioactive ash). In each case the risks must be weighed against the benefits and the availability of the energy source.

The known sources of uranium ore are sufficient to supply all humanity's power requirements for several years at the current rate of usage if burned in conventional reactors. (See Problem 8.) Breeder reactors, on the other hand, convert nuclear waste into nuclear fuel and can also change thorium to an isotope of uranium suitable for a reactor. Using that technology, current reserves would likely be sufficient for well over a thousand years, even without the discovery and exploitation of new sources of uranium or thorium. The largest untapped source is the 4.5 billion metric tons of uranium dissolved in Earth's oceans. Several methods of extracting this uranium economically are currently under study. The dissolved uranium is steadily replenished by Earth's rivers and could potentially provide reactor fuel almost indefinitely. (See Problem 10.)

30.2 Nuclear Fusion

When two light nuclei combine to form a heavier nucleus, the process is called nuclear fusion. Because the mass of the final nucleus is less than the sum of the masses of the original nuclei, there is a loss of mass, accompanied by a release of energy. Although fusion power plants have not yet been developed, a worldwide effort is under way to harness the energy from fusion reactions in the laboratory.

Fusion in the Sun

All stars generate their energy through fusion processes. About 90% of stars, including the Sun, fuse hydrogen, whereas some older stars fuse helium or other heavier elements. The energy produced by fusion increases the pressure inside the star and prevents its collapse due to gravity.

Two conditions must be met before fusion reactions in the star can sustain its energy needs. First, the temperature must be high enough (about 10^7 K for hydrogen) to allow the kinetic energy of the positively charged hydrogen nuclei to overcome their mutual Coulomb repulsion as they collide. Second, the density of nuclei must be high enough to ensure a high rate of collision.

It's interesting to note that a quantum effect is key in making sunshine. Temperatures inside stars like the Sun are not high enough to allow colliding protons to overcome the Coulomb repulsion. In a certain percentage of collisions, however, the nuclei pass through the barrier anyway an example of *quantum tunneling*.

The **proton–proton cycle** is a series of three nuclear reactions that are believed to be the stages in the liberation of energy in the Sun and other stars rich in hydrogen. An overall view of the proton–proton cycle is that four protons combine to form an alpha particle and two positrons, with the release of 25 MeV of energy in the process.

The specific steps in the proton–proton cycle are

$$_1^1\text{H} + {}_1^1\text{H} \;\rightarrow\; {}_1^2\text{D} + \text{e}^+ + \nu$$

and

$$_1^1\text{H} + {}_1^2\text{D} \;\rightarrow\; {}_2^3\text{He} + \gamma \qquad\qquad \textbf{[30.3]}$$

where D stands for deuterium, the isotope of hydrogen having one proton and one neutron in the nucleus. (It can also be written as $^2_1$H.) The second reaction is followed by either hydrogen-helium fusion or helium-helium fusion:

$$^1_1\text{H} + {}^3_2\text{He} \rightarrow {}^4_2\text{He} + e^+ + \nu$$

or

$$^3_2\text{He} + {}^3_2\text{He} \rightarrow {}^4_2\text{He} + 2({}^1_1\text{H})$$

The energy liberated is carried primarily by gamma rays, positrons, and neutrinos, as can be seen from the reactions. The gamma rays are soon absorbed by the dense gas, raising its temperature. The positrons combine with electrons to produce gamma rays, which in turn are also absorbed by the gas within a few centimeters. The neutrinos, however, almost never interact with matter; hence, they escape from the star, carrying about 2% of the energy generated with them. These energy-liberating fusion reactions are called **thermonuclear fusion reactions**. The hydrogen (fusion) bomb, first exploded in 1952, is an example of an uncontrolled thermonuclear fusion reaction.

Fusion Reactors

A great deal of effort is under way to develop a sustained and controllable fusion power reactor. Controlled fusion is often called the ultimate energy source because of the availability of water, its fuel source. For example, if deuterium, the isotope of hydrogen consisting of a proton and a neutron, were used as the fuel, 0.06 g of it could be extracted from 1 gal of water at a cost of about four cents. Hence, the fuel costs of even an inefficient reactor would be almost insignificant. An additional advantage of fusion reactors is that comparatively few radioactive by-products are formed. As noted in Equation 30.3, the end product of the fusion of hydrogen nuclei is safe, nonradioactive helium. Unfortunately, a thermonuclear reactor that can deliver a net power output over a reasonable time interval is not yet a reality, and many problems must be solved before a successful device is constructed.

The fusion reactions that appear most promising in the construction of a fusion power reactor involve deuterium (D) and tritium (T), which are isotopes of hydrogen. These reactions are

$$^2_1\text{D} + {}^2_1\text{D} \rightarrow {}^3_2\text{He} + {}^1_0\text{n} \qquad Q = 3.27 \text{ MeV}$$

$$^2_1\text{D} + {}^2_1\text{D} \rightarrow {}^3_1\text{T} + {}^1_1\text{H} \qquad Q = 4.03 \text{ MeV} \qquad \textbf{[30.4]}$$

and

$$^2_1\text{D} + {}^3_1\text{T} \rightarrow {}^4_2\text{He} + {}^1_0\text{n} \qquad Q = 17.59 \text{ MeV}$$

where the Q values refer to the amount of energy released per reaction. As noted earlier, deuterium is available in almost unlimited quantities from our lakes and oceans and is very inexpensive to extract. Tritium, however, is radioactive ($T_{1/2}$ = 12.3 yr) and undergoes beta decay to ^{3}He. For this reason, tritium doesn't occur naturally to any great extent and must be artificially produced.

The fundamental challenge of nuclear fusion power is to give the nuclei enough kinetic energy to overcome the repulsive Coulomb force between them at close proximity. This step can be accomplished by heating the fuel to extremely high temperatures (about 10^8 K, far greater than the interior temperature of the Sun). Such high temperatures are not easy to obtain in a laboratory or a power plant. At these high temperatures, the atoms are ionized and the system then consists of a collection of electrons and nuclei, commonly referred to as a *plasma*.

In addition to the high temperature requirements, two other critical factors determine whether or not a thermonuclear reactor will function: the **plasma ion density** n and the **plasma confinement time** τ, the time the interacting ions are maintained at a temperature equal to or greater than that required for the reaction to proceed. The density and confinement time must both be large enough to ensure that more fusion energy will be released than is required to heat the plasma.

APPLICATION
Fusion Reactors

Lawson's criterion ▶   **Lawson's criterion** states that a net power output in a fusion reactor is possible under the following conditions:

$$n\tau \geq 10^{14} \text{ s/cm}^3 \qquad \text{Deuterium–tritium interaction} \qquad [30.5]$$

$$n\tau \geq 10^{16} \text{ s/cm}^3 \qquad \text{Deuterium–deuterium interaction}$$

The problem of plasma confinement time has yet to be solved. How can a plasma be confined at a temperature of 10^8 K for times on the order of 1 s? Most fusion experiments use magnetic field confinement to contain a plasma. One device, called a **tokamak**, has a doughnut-shaped geometry (a toroid), as shown in Figure 30.4. This device uses a combination of two magnetic fields to confine the plasma inside the doughnut. A strong magnetic field is produced by the current in the windings, and a weaker magnetic field is produced by the current in the toroid. The resulting magnetic field lines are helical, as shown in the figure. In this configuration the field lines spiral around the plasma and prevent it from touching the walls of the vacuum chamber.

In inertial confinement fusion, the fuel, typically deuterium and tritium, is put in the form of a small pellet. Directly or indirectly, powerful lasers deliver energy rapidly to the pellet, exploding off the outer layers and imploding the rest of the pellet, heating and compressing it. Shock waves form and meet at the center, greatly increasing the density and pressure and causing fusion reactions. The released energy then causes further fusion reactions. Fusion can also take place in a device the size of a TV set and in fact was invented by Philo Farnsworth, one of the pioneers of electronic television. In this method, called inertial electrostatic confinement, positively charged particles are rapidly attracted toward a negatively charged grid. Some of the positive particles then collide and fuse.

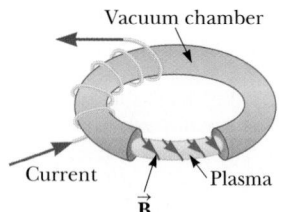

Figure 30.4 Diagram of a tokamak used in the magnetic confinement scheme. The plasma is trapped within the spiraling magnetic field lines as shown.

■ EXAMPLE 30.2 | Astrofuel on the Moon

GOAL Calculate the energy released in a fusion reaction.

PROBLEM Find the energy released in the reaction of helium-3 with deuterium:

$$^3_2\text{He} + {}^2_1\text{D} \rightarrow {}^4_2\text{He} + {}^1_1\text{H}$$

STRATEGY The energy released is the difference between the mass energy of the reactants and the products.

SOLUTION

Add the masses on the left-hand side and subtract the masses on the right, obtaining Δm in atomic mass units:

$$\Delta m = m_{\text{He-3}} + m_{\text{D}} - m_{\text{He-4}} - m_{\text{H}}$$
$$= 3.016\,029 \text{ u} + 2.014\,102 \text{ u} - 4.002\,603 \text{ u} - 1.007\,825 \text{ u}$$
$$= 0.019\,703 \text{ u}$$

Convert the mass difference to an equivalent amount of energy in MeV:

$$E = (0.019\,703 \text{ u})\left(\frac{931.5 \text{ MeV}}{1 \text{ u}}\right) = \boxed{18.35 \text{ MeV}}$$

REMARKS The result is a large amount of energy per reaction. Helium-3 is rare on Earth but plentiful on the Moon, where it has become trapped in the fine dust of the lunar soil. Helium-3 has the advantage of producing more protons than neutrons (some neutrons are still produced by side reactions, such as D–D), but has the disadvantage of a higher ignition temperature. If fusion power plants using helium-3 became a reality, studies indicate that it would be economically advantageous to mine helium-3 robotically and return it to Earth. The energy return per dollar would be far greater than for mining coal or drilling for oil!

QUESTION 30.2 How much energy, in joules, could be obtained from an Avogadro's number of helium-3–deuterium fusion reactions?

EXERCISE 30.2 Find the energy yield in the fusion of two helium-3 nuclei:

$$^3_2\text{He} + {}^3_2\text{He} \rightarrow {}^4_2\text{He} + 2({}^1_1\text{H})$$

ANSWER 12.9 MeV

30.3 Elementary Particles and the Fundamental Forces

Besides the constituents of atoms—protons, electrons, and neutrons—numerous other particles can be found in high-energy experiments or observed in nature, subsequent to collisions involving cosmic rays. Unlike the highly stable protons and electrons, these particles decay rapidly, with half-lives ranging from 10^{-23} s to 10^{-6} s. There is very strong indirect evidence that most of these particles, including neutrons and protons, are combinations of more elementary particles called quarks. Quarks, leptons (the electron is an example), and the particles that convey forces (the photon is an example) are now thought to be the truly fundamental particles. The key to understanding the properties of elementary particles is the description of the forces of nature in which they participate.

All particles in nature are subject to four fundamental forces: the strong, electromagnetic, weak, and gravitational forces. The **strong force** is responsible for the tight binding of quarks to form neutrons and protons and for the nuclear force, a sort of residual strong force, binding neutrons and protons into nuclei. This force represents the "glue" that holds the nucleons together and is the strongest of all the fundamental forces. It is a very short-range force and is negligible for separations greater than about 10^{-15} m (the approximate size of the nucleus). The **electromagnetic force**, which is about 10^{-2} times the strength of the strong force, is responsible for the binding of atoms and molecules. It's a long-range force that decreases in strength as the inverse square of the separation between interacting particles. The **weak force** is a short-range nuclear force that is exhibited in the instability of certain nuclei. It's involved in the mechanism of beta decay, and its strength is only about 10^{-6} times that of the strong force. Finally, the **gravitational force** is a long-range force with a strength only about 10^{-43} times that of the strong force. Although this familiar interaction is the force that holds the planets, stars, and galaxies together, its effect on elementary particles is negligible. The gravitational force is by far the weakest of all the fundamental forces.

Modern physics often describes the forces between particles in terms of the actions of field particles or quanta. In the case of the familiar electromagnetic interaction, the field particles are photons. In the language of modern physics, the electromagnetic force is *mediated* (carried) by photons, which are the quanta of the electromagnetic field. The strong force is mediated by field particles called *gluons*, the weak force is mediated by particles called the W and Z *bosons*, and the gravitational force is thought to be mediated by quanta of the gravitational field called *gravitons*. Forces between two particles are conveyed by an exchange of field quanta. This process is analogous to the covalent bond between two atoms created by an exchange or sharing of electrons. The electromagnetic interaction, for example, involves an exchange of photons.

The force between two particles can be understood in general with a simple illustration called a *Feynman diagram*, developed by Richard P. Feynman (1918–1988). Figure 30.5 is a Feynman diagram for the electromagnetic interaction between two electrons. In this simple case, a photon is the field particle that mediates the electromagnetic force between the electrons. The photon transfers energy and momentum from one electron to the other in the interaction. Such a photon, called a *virtual photon*, can never be detected directly because it is absorbed by the second electron very shortly after being emitted by the first electron. The existence of a virtual photon might be expected to violate the law of conservation of energy, but doesn't because of the time–energy uncertainty principle. Recall that the uncertainty principle says that the energy is uncertain or not conserved by an amount ΔE for a time Δt such that $\Delta E \, \Delta t \approx \hbar$. If the exchange of the virtual photon happens quickly enough, the brief discrepancy in energy conservation is less than the minimum uncertainty in energy and the exchange is physically an acceptable process.

© Shelly Gazin/CORBIS

Richard Feynman
American Physicist (1918–1988)
Feynman, together with Julian S. Schwinger and Shinichiro Tomonaga, won the 1965 Nobel Prize in Physics for fundamental work in the principles of quantum electrodynamics. His many important contributions to physics include work on the first atomic bomb in the Manhattan project, the invention of simple diagrams to represent particle interactions graphically, the theory of the weak interaction of subatomic particles, a reformulation of quantum mechanics, and the theory of superfluid helium. Later he served on the commission investigating the *Challenger* tragedy, demonstrating the problem with the space shuttle's O-rings by dipping a scale-model O-ring in his glass of ice water and then shattering it with a hammer. He also contributed to physics education through the magnificent three-volume text *The Feynman Lectures on Physics*.

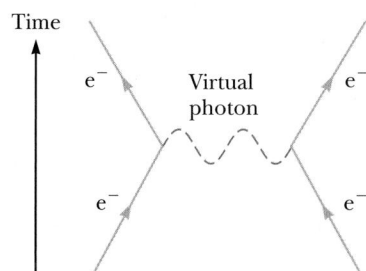

Figure 30.5 Feynman diagram representing a photon mediating the electromagnetic force between two electrons.

Table 30.1 Particle Interactions

Interaction (Force)	Relative Strength[a]	Range of Force	Mediating Field Particle
Strong	1	Short (≈ 1 fm)	Gluon
Electromagnetic	10^{-2}	Long ($\propto 1/r^2$)	Photon
Weak	10^{-6}	Short ($\approx 10^{-3}$ fm)	$W^{\pm}$ and Z bosons
Gravitational	10^{-43}	Long ($\propto 1/r^2$)	Graviton

[a]For two quarks separated by 3×10^{-17} m.

All the field quanta have been detected except for the graviton, which may never be found directly because of the weakness of the gravitational field. These interactions, their ranges, and their relative strengths are summarized in Table 30.1.

30.4 Positrons and Other Antiparticles

In the 1920s theoretical physicist Paul Dirac (1902–1984) developed a version of quantum mechanics that incorporated special relativity. Dirac's theory accounted for the electron's spin and its magnetic moment, but had an apparent flaw in that it predicted negative energy states. The theory was rescued by positing the existence of an anti-electron having the same mass as an electron but the opposite charge, called a *positron*. The general and profound implication of Dirac's theory is that **for every particle, there is an antiparticle with the same mass as the particle, but the opposite charge**. An antiparticle is usually designated by a bar over the symbol for the particle. For example, $\bar{p}$ denotes the antiproton and $\bar{\nu}$ the antineutrino. In this book the notation e^+ is preferred for the positron. Practically every known elementary particle has a distinct antiparticle. Among the exceptions are the photon and the neutral pion (π^0), which are their own antiparticles.

In 1932 the positron was discovered by Carl Anderson in a cloud chamber experiment. To discriminate between positive and negative charges, he placed the cloud chamber in a magnetic field, causing moving charges to follow curved paths. He noticed that some of the electron-like tracks deflected in a direction corresponding to a positively charged particle: positrons.

When a particle meets its antiparticle, both particles are annihilated, resulting in high-energy photons. The process of electron–positron annihilation is used in the medical diagnostic technique of positron-emission tomography (PET). The patient is injected with a glucose solution containing a radioactive substance that decays by positron emission. Examples of such substances are oxygen-15, nitrogen-13, carbon-11, and fluorine-18. The radioactive material is carried to the brain. When a decay occurs, the emitted positron annihilates with an electron in the brain tissue, resulting in two gamma ray photons. With the assistance of a computer, an image can be created of the sites in the brain where the glucose accumulates.

The images from a PET scan can point to a wide variety of disorders in the brain, including Alzheimer's disease. In addition, because glucose metabolizes more rapidly in active areas of the brain than in other parts of the body, a PET scan can indicate which areas of the brain are involved in various processes such as language, music, and vision.

Tip 30.1 Antiparticles

An antiparticle is not identified solely on the basis of opposite charge. Even neutral particles have antiparticles.

BIO APPLICATION

Positron-Emission Tomography (PET) Scanning

30.5 Classification of Particles

All particles other than those that transmit forces can be classified into two broad categories, hadrons and leptons, according to their interactions. The hadrons are composites of quarks, whereas the leptons are thought to be truly elementary, although there have been suggestions that they might also have internal structure.

Hadrons

Particles that interact through the strong force are called *hadrons*. The two classes of hadrons, known as *mesons* and *baryons*, are distinguished by their masses and spins.

All mesons are known to decay finally into electrons, positrons, neutrinos, and photons. A good example of a meson is the pion (π), the lightest of the known mesons, with a mass of about 140 MeV/c^2 and a spin of 0. As seen in Table 30.2, the pion comes in three varieties, corresponding to three charge states: π^+, π^-, and π^0. Pions are highly unstable particles. For example, the π^-, which has a lifetime of about 2.6×10^{-8} s, decays into a muon and an antineutrino. The μ^- muon, essentially a heavy electron with a lifetime of 2.2 μs, then decays into an electron, a neutrino, and an antineutrino. The sequence of decays is

$$\pi^- \rightarrow \mu^- + \bar{\nu} \qquad\qquad [30.6]$$

$$\mu^- \rightarrow e^- + \nu + \bar{\nu}$$

Baryons have masses equal to or greater than the proton mass (the name *baryon* means "heavy" in Greek), and their spin is always a noninteger value ($\frac{1}{2}$ or $\frac{3}{2}$). Protons and neutrons are baryons, as are many other particles. With the exception of the proton, all baryons decay in such a way that the end products include a proton. For example, the baryon called the Ξ hyperon first decays to a Λ^0 in about 10^{-10} s. The Λ^0 then decays to a proton and a π^- in about 3×10^{-10} s.

Today it is believed that hadrons are composed of quarks. Some of the important properties of hadrons are listed in Table 30.2.

Courtesy AIP Emilio Segre Visual Archives

Paul Adrien Maurice Dirac
British physicist (1902–1984)
Dirac was instrumental in the understanding of antimatter and in the unification of quantum mechanics and relativity. He made numerous contributions to the development of quantum physics and cosmology. In 1933 he won the Nobel Prize in Physics.

Table 30.2 Some Particles and Their Properties

Category	Particle Name	Symbol	Anti-particle	Mass (MeV/c^2)	B	L_e	L_μ	L_τ	S	Lifetime(s)	Principal Decay Modes[a]
Leptons	Electron	e^-	e^+	0.511	0	+1	0	0	0	Stable	
	Electron–neutrino	ν_e	$\bar{\nu}_e$	$< 7\text{eV}/c^2$	0	+1	0	0	0	Stable	
	Muon	μ^-	μ^+	105.7	0	0	+1	0	0	2.20×10^{-6}	$e^- \bar{\nu}_e \nu_\mu$
	Muon–neutrino	ν_μ	$\bar{\nu}_\mu$	< 0.3	0	0	+1	0	0	Stable	
	Tau	τ^-	τ^+	1 784	0	0	0	+1	0	$< 4 \times 10^{-13}$	$\mu^- \bar{\nu}_\mu \nu_\tau$, $e^- \bar{\nu}_e \nu_\tau$
	Tau–neutrino	ν_τ	$\bar{\nu}_\tau$	< 30	0	0	0	+1	0	Stable	
Hadrons											
Mesons	Pion	π^+	π^-	139.6	0	0	0	0	0	2.60×10^{-8}	$\mu^+ \nu_\mu$
		π^0	Self	135.0	0	0	0	0	0	0.83×10^{-16}	2γ
	Kaon	K^+	K^-	493.7	0	0	0	0	+1	1.24×10^{-8}	$\mu^+ \nu_\mu$, $\pi^+ \pi^0$
		K^0_S	K^0_S	497.7	0	0	0	0	+1	0.89×10^{-10}	$\pi^+ \pi^-$, $2\pi^0$
		K^0_L	K^0_L	497.7	0	0	0	0	+1	5.2×10^{-8} $\pi^\pm \mu^\mp \bar{\nu}_\mu$	$\pi^\pm e^\mp \bar{\nu}_e$, $3\pi^0$
	Eta	η	Self	548.8	0	0	0	0	0	$< 10^{-18}$	2γ, 3π
		η'	Self	958	0	0	0	0	0	2.2×10^{-21}	$\eta\pi^+ \pi^-$
Baryons	Proton	p	$\bar{p}$	938.3	+1	0	0	0	0	Stable	
	Neutron	n	$\bar{n}$	939.6	+1	0	0	0	0	920	$pe^- \bar{\nu}_e$
	Lambda	Λ^0	$\bar{\Lambda}^0$	1 115.6	+1	0	0	0	-1	2.6×10^{-10}	$p\pi^-$, $n\pi0$
	Sigma	Σ^+	$\bar{\Sigma}^-$	1 189.4	+1	0	0	0	-1	0.80×10^{-10}	$p\pi^0$, $n\pi^+$
		Σ^0	$\bar{\Sigma}^0$	1 192.5	+1	0	0	0	-1	6×10^{-20}	$\Lambda^0 \gamma$
		Σ^-	$\bar{\Sigma}^+$	1 197.3	+1	0	0	0	-1	1.5×10^{-10}	$n\pi^-$
	Xi	Ξ^0	$\bar{\Xi}^0$	1 315	+1	0	0	0	-2	2.9×10^{-10}	$\Lambda^0 \pi^0$
		Ξ^-	Ξ^+	1 321	+1	0	0	0	-2	1.64×10^{-10}	$\Lambda^0 \pi^-$
	Omega	Ω^-	Ω^+	1 672	+1	0	0	0	-3	0.82×10^{-10}	$\Xi^0 \pi^-$, $\Lambda^0 K^-$

[a]Notations in this column, such as $p\pi^-$, $n\pi^0$, mean two possible decay modes. In this case the two possible decays are $\Lambda^0 \rightarrow p + \pi^-$ and $\Lambda^0 \rightarrow n + \pi^0$.

Leptons

Leptons (from the Greek *leptos*, meaning "small" or "light") are a group of particles that participate in the weak interaction. All leptons have a spin of $\frac{1}{2}$. Included in this group are electrons, muons, and neutrinos, which are all less massive than the lightest hadron. A muon is identical to an electron except that its mass is 207 times the electron mass. Although hadrons have size and structure, leptons appear to be truly elementary, with no structure down to the limit of resolution of experiment (about 10^{-19} m).

Unlike hadrons, the number of known leptons is small. Currently, scientists believe that there are only six leptons (each having an antiparticle): the electron, the muon, the tau, and a neutrino associated with each:

$$\begin{pmatrix} e^- \\ \nu_e \end{pmatrix} \quad \begin{pmatrix} \mu^- \\ \nu_\mu \end{pmatrix} \quad \begin{pmatrix} \tau^- \\ \nu_\tau \end{pmatrix}$$

The tau lepton, discovered in 1975, has a mass about twice that of the proton.

Although neutrinos have masses of about zero, there is strong indirect evidence that the electron neutrino has a nonzero mass of about 3 eV/c^2, or 1/180 000 of the electron mass. A firm knowledge of the neutrino's mass could have great significance in cosmological models and in our understanding of the future of the Universe.

30.6 Conservation Laws

A number of conservation laws are important in the study of elementary particles. Although those described here have no theoretical foundation, they are supported by abundant empirical evidence.

Baryon Number

The law of conservation of baryon number means that whenever a baryon is created in a reaction or decay, an antibaryon is also created. This information can be quantified by assigning a baryon number: $B = 1$ for all baryons, $B = -1$ for all antibaryons, and $B = 0$ for all other particles. Thus, the **law of conservation of baryon number** states that whenever a nuclear reaction or decay occurs, the sum of the baryon numbers before the process equals the sum of the baryon numbers after the process.

◀ Conservation of baryon number

Note that if the baryon number is absolutely conserved, the proton must be absolutely stable: if it were not for the law of conservation of baryon number, the proton could decay into a positron and a neutral pion. Such a decay, however, has never been observed. At present, we can only say that the proton has a half-life of at least 10^{31} years. (The estimated age of the Universe is about 10^{10} years.) In one version of a so-called grand unified theory, physicists predicted that the proton is actually unstable. According to this theory, the baryon number (sometimes called the *baryonic charge*) is not absolutely conserved, whereas electric charge is always conserved.

■ EXAMPLE 30.3 | **Checking Baryon Numbers**

GOAL Use conservation of baryon number to determine whether a given reaction can occur.

PROBLEM Determine whether the following reaction can occur based on the law of conservation of baryon number:

$$p + n \rightarrow p + p + n + \bar{p}$$

STRATEGY Count the baryons on both sides of the reaction, recalling that $B = 1$ for baryons and $B = -1$ for antibaryons.

SOLUTION

Count the baryons on the left:

The neutron and proton are both baryons; hence,
$1 + 1 = 2$.

Count the baryons on the right:

There are three baryons and one antibaryon, so
$1 + 1 + 1 + (-1) = 2$.

REMARKS Baryon number is conserved in this reaction, so it can occur provided that the incoming proton has sufficient energy.

QUESTION 30.3 True or False: A proton can't decay into a positron plus a neutrino.

EXERCISE 30.3 Can the following reaction occur, based on the law of conservation of baryon number?

$$p + n \rightarrow p + p + \bar{p}$$

ANSWER No. (Compute the baryon numbers on both sides and show that they're not equal.)

Lepton Number

There are three conservation laws involving lepton numbers, one for each variety of lepton. The **law of conservation of electron-lepton number** states that the sum of the electron-lepton numbers before a reaction or decay must equal the sum of the electron-lepton numbers after the reaction or decay. The electron and the electron neutrino are assigned a positive electron-lepton number $L_e = 1$, the anti-leptons e^+ and $\bar{\nu}_e$ are assigned the electron-lepton number $L_e = -1$, and all other particles have $L_e = 0$. For example, consider neutron decay:

◀ Conservation of lepton number

$$n \rightarrow p^+ + e^- + \bar{\nu}_e$$

◀ Neutron decay

Before the decay, the electron-lepton number is $L_e = 0$; after the decay, it is $0 + 1 + (-1) = 0$, so the electron-lepton number is conserved. It's important to recognize that baryon number must also be conserved. This can easily be seen by noting that before the decay $B = 1$, whereas after the decay $B = 1 + 0 + 0 = 1$.

Similarly, when a decay involves muons, the muon-lepton number L_μ is conserved. The μ^- and the ν_μ are assigned $L_\mu = +1$, the antimuons μ^+ and $\bar{\nu}_\mu$ are assigned $L_\mu = -1$, and all other particles have $L_\mu = 0$. Finally, the tau-lepton number L_τ is conserved, and similar assignments can be made for the τ lepton and its neutrino.

■ EXAMPLE 30.4 | Checking Lepton Numbers

GOAL Use conservation of lepton number to determine whether a given process is possible.

PROBLEM Determine which of the following decay schemes can occur on the basis of conservation of lepton number:

$$(1) \quad \mu^- \rightarrow e^- + \bar{\nu}_e + \nu_\mu$$
$$(2) \quad \pi^+ \rightarrow \mu^+ + \nu_\mu + \nu_e$$

STRATEGY Count the leptons on each side and see if the numbers are equal.

SOLUTION

Because decay 1 involves both a muon and an electron, L_μ and L_e must both be conserved. Before the decay, $L_\mu = +1$ and $L_e = 0$. After the decay, $L_\mu = 0 + 0 + 1 = +1$ and $L_e = +1 - 1 + 0 = 0$. Both lepton numbers are conserved, and on this basis, the decay mode is possible.

Before decay 2 occurs, $L_\mu = 0$ and $L_e = 0$. After the decay, $L_\mu = -1 + 1 + 0 = 0$, but $L_e = +1$. This decay isn't possible because the electron-lepton number is not conserved.

QUESTION 30.4 Can a neutron decay into a positron and an electron? Explain.

EXERCISE 30.4 Determine whether the decay $\tau^- \rightarrow \mu^- + \bar{\nu}_\mu$ can occur.

ANSWER No. (Compute lepton numbers on both sides and show that they're not equal in this case.)

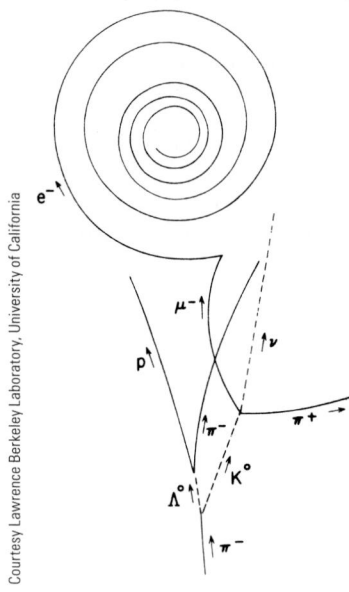

Figure 30.6 This drawing represents tracks of many events obtained by analyzing a bubble-chamber photograph. The strange particles Λ^0 and K^0 are formed (at the bottom) as the π^- interacts with a proton according to the interaction $\pi^- + p \rightarrow \Lambda^0 + K^0$. (Note that the neutral particles leave no tracks, as indicated by the dashed lines.) The Λ^0 and K^0 then decay according to the interactions $\Lambda^0 \rightarrow \pi + p$ and $K^0 \rightarrow \pi + \mu^- + \nu_\mu$.

Courtesy Lawrence Berkeley Laboratory, University of California

■ Quick Quiz

30.1 Which of the following reactions cannot occur?
(a) $p + p \rightarrow p + p + \bar{p}$ (b) $n \rightarrow p + e^- + \bar{\nu}_e$
(c) $\mu^+ \rightarrow e^+ + \nu_e + \bar{\nu}_\mu$ (d) $\pi^- \rightarrow \mu^- + \bar{\nu}_\mu$

30.2 Which of the following reactions cannot occur?
(a) $p + \bar{p} \rightarrow 2\gamma$ (b) $\gamma + p \rightarrow n + \pi^0$
(c) $\pi^0 + n \rightarrow K^+ + \Sigma^-$ (d) $\pi^+ + p \rightarrow K^+ + \Sigma^+$

Conservation of Strangeness

The K, Λ, and Σ particles exhibit unusual properties in their production and decay and hence are called *strange particles*.

One unusual property of strange particles is that they are always produced in pairs. For example, when a pion collides with a proton, two neutral strange particles are produced with high probability (Fig. 30.6) following the reaction:

$$\pi^- + p^+ \quad \rightarrow \quad K^0 + \Lambda^0$$

On the other hand, the reaction $\pi^- + p^+ \rightarrow K^0 + n$ has never occurred, even though it violates no known conservation laws and the energy of the pion is sufficient to initiate the reaction.

The second peculiar feature of strange particles is that although they are produced by the strong interaction at a high rate, they don't decay into particles that interact via the strong force at a very high rate. Instead, they decay very slowly, which is characteristic of the weak interaction. Their half-lives are in the range of 10^{-10} s to 10^{-8} s; most other particles that interact via the strong force have much shorter lifetimes on the order of 10^{-23} s.

To explain these unusual properties of strange particles, a law called *conservation of strangeness* was introduced, together with a new quantum number S called **strangeness**. The strangeness numbers for some particles are given in Table 30.2. The production of strange particles in pairs is explained by assigning $S = +1$ to one of the particles and $S = -1$ to the other. All nonstrange particles are assigned strangeness $S = 0$. The **law of conservation of strangeness** states that whenever a nuclear reaction or decay occurs, the sum of the strangeness numbers before the process must equal the sum of the strangeness numbers after the process.

The slow decay of strange particles can be explained by assuming the strong and electromagnetic interactions obey the law of conservation of strangeness, whereas the weak interaction does not. Because the decay reaction involves the loss of one strange particle, it violates strangeness conservation and hence proceeds slowly via the weak interaction.

In checking reactions for proper strangeness conservation, the same procedure as with baryon number conservation and lepton number conservation is followed. Using Table 30.2, count the strangeness on each side. If the two results are equal, the reaction conserves strangeness.

■ APPLYING PHYSICS 30.2 | **Breaking Conservation Laws**

A student claims to have observed a decay of an electron into two neutrinos traveling in opposite directions. What conservation laws would be violated by this decay?

EXPLANATION Several conservation laws would be violated. Conservation of electric charge would be violated because the negative charge of the electron has disappeared. Conservation of electron lepton number would also be violated because there is one lepton before the decay and two afterward. If both neutrinos were electron neutrinos, electron lepton number conservation would be violated in the final state. If one of the product neutrinos were other than an electron neutrino, however, another lepton conservation law would be violated because there were no other leptons in the initial state. Other conservation laws would be obeyed by this decay. Energy can be conserved; the rest energy of the electron appears as the kinetic energy (and possibly some small rest energy) of the neutrinos. The opposite directions of the two neutrinos' velocities allow for the conservation of momentum. Conservation of baryon number and conservation of other lepton numbers would also be upheld in this decay. ■

30.7 The Eightfold Way

Quantities such as spin, baryon number, lepton number, and strangeness are labels we associate with particles. Many classification schemes that group particles into families based on such labels have been proposed. First, consider the first eight baryons listed in Table 30.2, all having a spin of $\frac{1}{2}$. The family consists of the proton, the neutron, and six other particles. If we plot their strangeness versus their charge using a sloping coordinate system, as in Figure 30.7a, a fascinating pattern emerges: six of the baryons form a hexagon, and the remaining two are at the hexagon's center. (Particles with spin quantum number $\frac{1}{2}$ or $\frac{3}{2}$ are called *fermions*.)

Now consider the family of mesons listed in Table 30.2 with spins of zero. (Particles with spin quantum number 0 or 1 are called *bosons*.) If we count both particles and antiparticles, there are nine such mesons. Figure 30.7b is a plot of strangeness versus charge for this family. Again, a fascinating hexagonal pattern emerges. In this case the particles on the perimeter of the hexagon lie opposite their antiparticles, and the remaining three (which form their own antiparticles) are at its center. These and related symmetric patterns, called the **eightfold way**, were proposed independently in 1961 by Murray Gell-Mann and Yuval Ne'eman.

The groups of baryons and mesons can be displayed in many other symmetric patterns within the framework of the eightfold way. For example, the family of spin-$\frac{3}{2}$ baryons contains ten particles arranged in a pattern like the tenpins in a bowling alley. After the pattern was proposed, one of the particles was missing; it had yet to be discovered. Gell-Mann predicted that the missing particle, which he called the *omega minus* (Ω^-), should have a spin of $\frac{3}{2}$, a charge of -1, a strangeness of -3, and a mass of about 1 680 MeV/c^2. Shortly thereafter, in 1964, scientists at the Brookhaven National Laboratory found the missing particle through careful analyses of bubble-chamber photographs and confirmed all its predicted properties.

The patterns of the eightfold way in the field of particle physics have much in common with the periodic table. Whenever a vacancy (a missing particle or element) occurs in the organized patterns, experimentalists have a guide for their investigations.

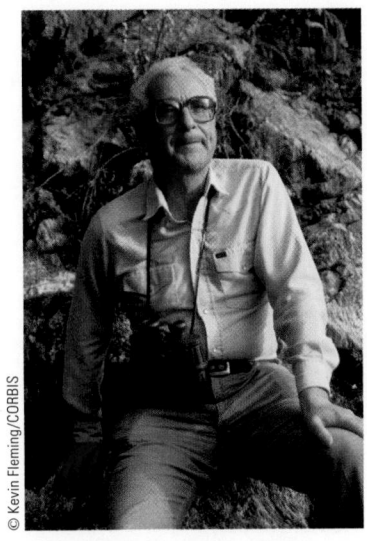

© Kevin Fleming/CORBIS

Murray Gell-Mann
American Physicist (b. 1929)
Gell-Mann was awarded the 1969 Nobel Prize in Physics for his theoretical studies dealing with subatomic particles.

30.8 Quarks and Color

Although leptons appear to be truly elementary particles without measurable size or structure, hadrons are more complex. There is strong evidence, including the scattering of electrons off nuclei, that hadrons are composed of more elementary particles called quarks.

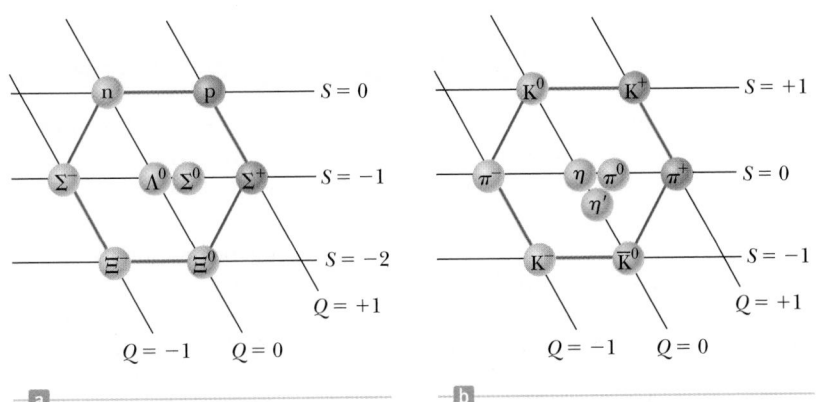

Figure 30.7 (a) The hexagonal eightfold-way pattern for the eight spin-$\frac{1}{2}$ baryons. This strangeness versus charge plot uses a horizontal axis for the strangeness values S, but a sloping axis for the charge number Q. (b) The eightfold-way pattern for the nine spin-zero mesons.

Table 30.3 Properties of Quarks and Antiquarks

Quarks

Name	Symbol	Spin	Charge	Baryon Number	Strangeness	Charm	Bottomness	Topness
Up	u	$\frac{1}{2}$	$+\frac{2}{3}e$	$\frac{1}{3}$	0	0	0	0
Down	d	$\frac{1}{2}$	$-\frac{1}{3}e$	$\frac{1}{3}$	0	0	0	0
Strange	s	$\frac{1}{2}$	$-\frac{1}{3}e$	$\frac{1}{3}$	-1	0	0	0
Charmed	c	$\frac{1}{2}$	$+\frac{2}{3}e$	$\frac{1}{3}$	0	$+1$	0	0
Bottom	b	$\frac{1}{2}$	$-\frac{1}{3}e$	$\frac{1}{3}$	0	0	$+1$	0
Top	t	$\frac{1}{2}$	$+\frac{2}{3}e$	$\frac{1}{3}$	0	0	0	$+1$

Antiquarks

Name	Symbol	Spin	Charge	Baryon Number	Strangeness	Charm	Bottomness	Topness
Anti-up	$\bar{u}$	$\frac{1}{2}$	$-\frac{2}{3}e$	$-\frac{1}{3}$	0	0	0	0
Anti-down	$\bar{d}$	$\frac{1}{2}$	$+\frac{1}{3}e$	$-\frac{1}{3}$	0	0	0	0
Anti-strange	$\bar{s}$	$\frac{1}{2}$	$+\frac{1}{3}e$	$-\frac{1}{3}$	$+1$	0	0	0
Anti-charmed	$\bar{c}$	$\frac{1}{2}$	$-\frac{2}{3}e$	$-\frac{1}{3}$	0	-1	0	0
Anti-bottom	$\bar{b}$	$\frac{1}{2}$	$+\frac{1}{3}e$	$-\frac{1}{3}$	0	0	-1	0
Anti-top	$\bar{t}$	$\frac{1}{2}$	$-\frac{2}{3}e$	$-\frac{1}{3}$	0	0	0	-1

Table 30.4 Quark Composition of Several Hadrons

Particle	Quark Composition
Mesons	
π^+	$\bar{d}u$
π^-	$\bar{u}d$
K^+	$\bar{s}u$
K^-	$\bar{u}s$
K^0	$\bar{s}d$
Baryons	
p	uud
n	udd
Λ^0	uds
Σ^+	uus
Σ^0	uds
Σ^-	dds
Ξ^0	uss
Ξ^-	dss
Ω^-	sss

The Quark Model

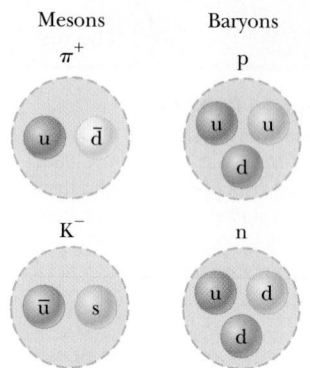

Mesons   Baryons
π^+ p

K^- n

Active Figure 30.8
Quark compositions of two mesons and two baryons. Note that the mesons on the left contain two quarks and that the baryons on the right contain three quarks.

According to the quark model, all hadrons are composite systems of two or three of six fundamental constituents called **quarks**, which rhymes with "sharks" (although some rhyme it with "forks"). These six quarks are given the arbitrary names *up*, *down*, *strange*, *charmed*, *bottom*, and *top*, designated by the letters u, d, s, c, b, and t.

Quarks have fractional electric charges, along with other properties, as shown in Table 30.3. Associated with each quark is an antiquark of opposite charge, baryon number, and strangeness. Mesons consist of a quark and an antiquark, whereas baryons consist of three quarks.

Table 30.4 lists the quark compositions of several mesons and baryons. Note that just two of the quarks, u and d, are contained in all hadrons encountered in ordinary matter (protons and neutrons). The third quark, s, is needed only to construct strange particles with a strangeness of either $+1$ or -1. Active Figure 30.8 is a pictorial representation of the quark compositions of several particles.

The charmed, bottom, and top quarks are more massive than the other quarks and occur in higher-energy interactions. Each has its own quantum number, called charm, bottomness, and topness, respectively. An example of a hadron formed from these quarks is the J/Ψ particle, also called charmonium, which is composed of a charmed quark and an anticharmed quark, $c\bar{c}$.

■ **APPLYING PHYSICS 30.3** | **Conservation of Meson Number**

We have seen a law of conservation of lepton number and a law of conservation of baryon number. Why isn't there a law of conservation of meson number?

EXPLANATION We can answer this question from the point of view of creating particle–antiparticle pairs from available energy. If energy is converted to the rest energy of a lepton–antilepton pair, there is no net change in lepton number because the lepton has a lepton number of +1 and the antilepton −1. Energy could also be transformed into the rest energy of a baryon-antibaryon pair. The baryon has baryon number +1, the antibaryon −1, and there is no net change in baryon number.

Now suppose energy is transformed into the rest energy of a quark–antiquark pair. By definition in quark theory, a quark–antiquark pair is a meson. In this reaction, therefore, the number of mesons increases from zero to one, so meson number is not conserved. ■

Color

Quarks have another property called **color** or **color charge**. This property isn't color in the visual sense; rather, it's just a label for something analogous to electric charge. Quarks are said to come in three colors: red, green, and blue. Antiquarks have the properties antired, antigreen, and antiblue.

Color was defined because some quark combinations appeared to violate the Pauli exclusion principle. An example is the omega-minus particle (Ω^-), which consists of three strange quarks, sss, that are all spin up, giving a spin of $\frac{3}{2}$. Each strange quark is assumed to have a different color and hence is in a distinct quantum state, satisfying the exclusion principle.

In general, quark combinations must be "colorless." A meson consists of a quark of one color and an antiquark of the corresponding anticolor. Baryons must consist of one red, one green, and one blue quark, or their anticolors.

The theory of how quarks interact with one another by means of color charge is called **quantum chromodynamics**, or QCD, to parallel quantum electrodynamics (the theory of interactions among electric charges). The strong force between quarks is often called the **color force**. The force is carried by massless particles called **gluons** (which are analogous to photons for the electromagnetic force). According to QCD, there are eight gluons, all with color charge, and their antigluons. When a quark emits or absorbs a gluon, its color changes. For example, a blue quark that emits a gluon may become a red quark, and a red quark that absorbs this gluon becomes a blue quark. The color force between quarks is analogous to the electric force between charges: like colors repel and opposite colors attract. Therefore, two red quarks repel each other, but a red quark will be attracted to an antired quark. The attraction between quarks of opposite color to form a meson ($q\bar{q}$) is indicated in Figure 30.9a.

Different-colored quarks also attract one another, but with less intensity than opposite colors of quark and antiquark. For example, a cluster of red, blue, and green quarks all attract one another to form baryons, as indicated in Figure 30.9b. Every baryon contains three quarks of three different colors.

Although the color force between two color-neutral hadrons (such as a proton and a neutron) is negligible at large separations, the strong color force between their constituent quarks does not exactly cancel at small separations of about 1 fm. **This residual strong force is in fact the nuclear force that binds protons and neutrons to form nuclei.** It is similar to the residual electromagnetic force that binds neutral atoms into molecules.

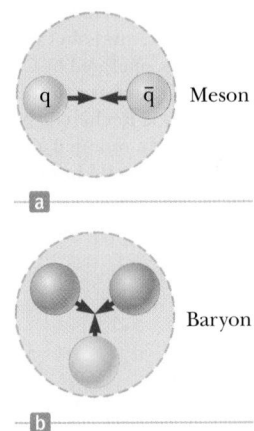

Figure 30.9 (a) A green quark is attracted to an antigreen quark to form a meson with quark structure ($q\bar{q}$). (b) Three different-colored quarks attract one another to form a baryon.

30.9 Electroweak Theory and the Standard Model

Recall that the weak interaction is an extremely short range force having an interaction distance of approximately 10^{-18} m. Such a short-range interaction implies that the quantized particles that carry the weak field (the spin 1 W^+, W^-, and Z^0 bosons) are extremely massive, as is indeed the case. These amazing bosons can be thought of as structureless, point-like particles as massive as krypton atoms! The weak interaction is responsible for the decay of the c, s, b, and t quarks into lighter, more stable u and d quarks, as well as the decay of the massive μ and τ leptons into (lighter) electrons. **The weak interaction is very important because it governs the stability of the basic particles of matter.**

A mysterious feature of the weak interaction is its lack of symmetry, especially when compared with the high degree of symmetry shown by the strong, electromagnetic, and gravitational interactions. For example, the weak interaction, unlike the strong interaction, is not symmetric under mirror reflection or charge exchange. (*Mirror reflection* means that all the quantities in a given particle reaction

An engineer tests the electronics associated with a superconducting magnet in the Large Hadron Collider at the European Laboratory for Particle Physics, operated by CERN. (The acronym stands for Conseil Européen pour la Recherche Nucléaire, and has been retained although "Conseil," or "Council," has been replaced by "Organisation".)

are exchanged as in a mirror reflection: left for right, an inward motion toward the mirror for an outward motion, and so forth. *Charge exchange* means that all the electric charges in a particle reaction are converted to their opposites: all positives to negatives and vice versa.) Not symmetric means that the reaction with all quantities changed occurs less frequently than the direct reaction. For example, the decay of the K^0, which is governed by the weak interaction, is not symmetric under charge exchange because the reaction $K^0 \rightarrow \pi^- + e^+ + \nu_e$ occurs much more frequently than the reaction $K^0 \rightarrow \pi^+ + e^- + \bar{\nu}_e$.

The **electroweak theory** unifies the electromagnetic and weak interactions. This theory postulates that the weak and electromagnetic interactions have the same strength at very high particle energies and are different manifestations of a single unifying electroweak interaction. The photon and the three massive bosons ($W^\pm$ and Z^0) play key roles in the electroweak theory. The theory makes many concrete predictions, such as the prediction of the masses of the W and Z particles at about 82 GeV/c^2 and 93 GeV/c^2, respectively. These predictions have been experimentally verified.

The combination of the electroweak theory and QCD for the strong interaction forms what is referred to in high-energy physics as the **Standard Model**. Although the details of the Standard Model are complex, its essential ingredients can be summarized with the help of Figure 30.10. The strong force, mediated by gluons, holds quarks together to form composite particles such as protons, neutrons, and mesons. Leptons participate only in the electromagnetic and weak interactions. The electromagnetic force is mediated by photons, and the weak force is mediated by W and Z bosons. Note that all fundamental forces are mediated by bosons (particles with spin 1) having properties given, to a large extent, by symmetries involved in the theories.

The Standard Model, however, doesn't answer all questions. A major question is why the photon has no mass although the W and Z bosons do. Because of this mass difference, the electromagnetic and weak forces are very different at low energies but become similar in nature at very high energies, where the rest energies of the W and Z bosons are insignificant fractions of their total energies. This behavior during the transition from high to low energies, called **symmetry breaking**, doesn't answer the question of the origin of particle masses. To resolve that problem, a hypothetical particle called the **Higgs boson**, which provides a mechanism for breaking the electroweak symmetry and bestowing different particle masses on different particles, has been proposed. The Standard Model, including the Higgs mechanism, provides a logically consistent explanation of the massive nature of the W and Z bosons. Unfortunately, the Higgs boson has not yet been found, but physicists predict that its mass should be less than 1 TeV/c^2 (10^{12} eV).

Following the success of the electroweak theory, scientists attempted to combine it with QCD in a **grand unification theory** (GUT). In this model the electroweak force was merged with the strong color force to form a grand unified force. One version of the theory considers leptons and quarks as members of the same family that are able to change into each other by exchanging an appropriate particle.

Figure 30.10 The Standard Model of particle physics.

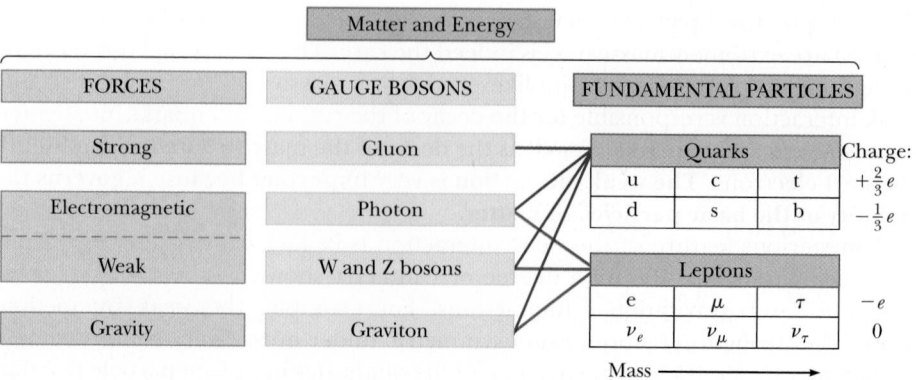

Matter and Energy		
FORCES	**GAUGE BOSONS**	**FUNDAMENTAL PARTICLES**

		Quarks			Charge:
Strong	Gluon	u	c	t	$+\frac{2}{3}e$
		d	s	b	$-\frac{1}{3}e$
Electromagnetic	Photon				
Weak	W and Z bosons	Leptons			
		e	μ	τ	$-e$
Gravity	Graviton	ν_e	ν_μ	ν_τ	0

Mass ⟶

Many GUT theories predict that protons are unstable and will decay with a lifetime of about 10^{31} years, a period far greater than the age of the Universe. As yet, proton decays have not been observed.

30.10 The Cosmic Connection

According to the Big Bang theory, the Universe erupted from an infinitely dense singularity about 15 billion to 20 billion years ago. The first few minutes after the Big Bang saw such extremes of energy that it is believed that all four interactions of physics were unified and all matter was contained in an undifferentiated "quark soup."

The evolution of the four fundamental forces from the Big Bang to the present is shown in Figure 30.11. During the first 10^{-43} s (the ultrahot epoch, with $T < 10^{32}$ K), the strong, electroweak, and gravitational forces were joined to form a completely unified force. In the first 10^{-35} s following the Big Bang (the hot epoch, with $T < 10^{29}$ K), gravity broke free of this unification and the strong and electroweak forces remained as one, described by a grand unification theory. During this period particle energies were so great ($> 10^{16}$ GeV) that very massive particles as well as quarks, leptons, and their antiparticles existed. Then, after 10^{-35} s, the Universe rapidly expanded and cooled (the warm epoch, with $T < 10^{29}$ to 10^{15} K), the strong and electroweak forces parted company, and the grand unification scheme was broken. As the Universe continued to cool, the electroweak force split into the weak force and the electromagnetic force about 10^{-10} s after the Big Bang.

George Gamow
Russian Physicist (1904–1968)
Gamow and two of his students, Ralph Alpher and Robert Herman, were the first to take the first half hour of the Universe seriously. In a mostly overlooked paper published in 1948, they made truly remarkable cosmological predictions. They correctly calculated the abundances of hydrogen and helium after the first half hour (75% H and 25% He) and predicted that radiation from the Big Bang should still be present and have an apparent temperature of about 5 K.

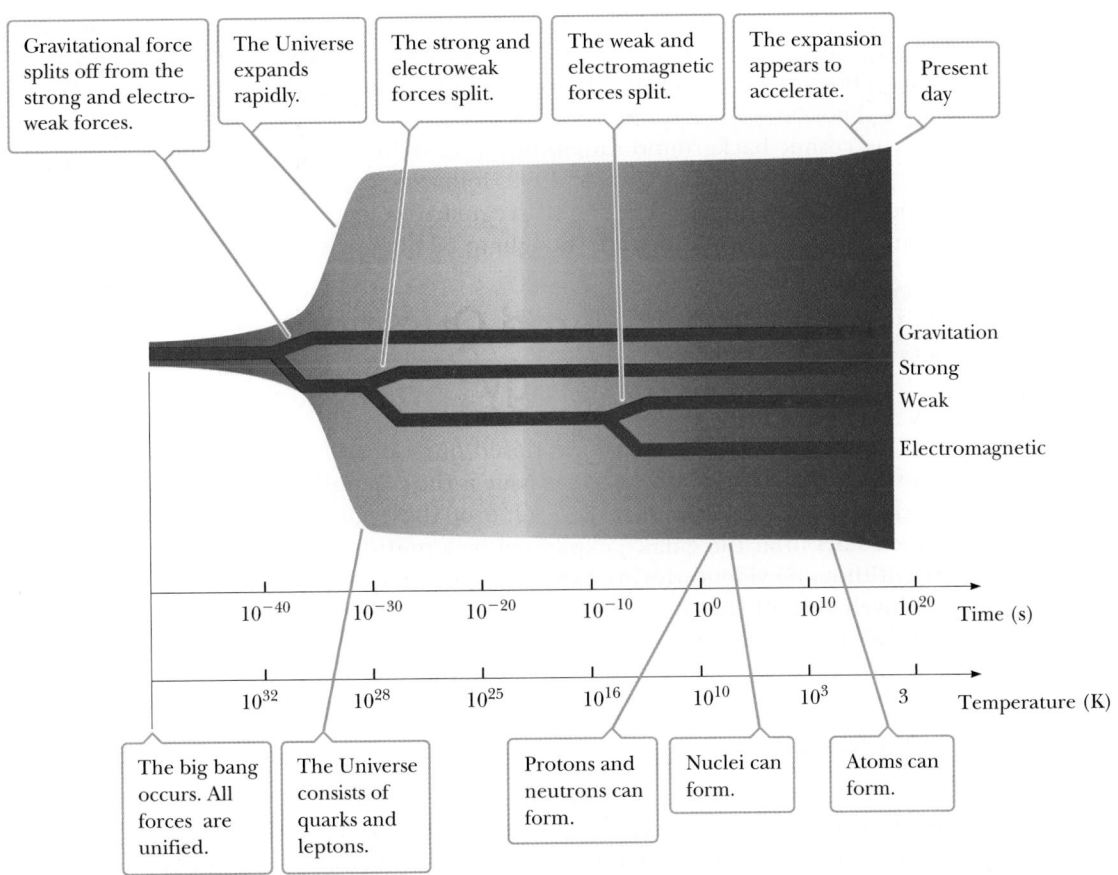

Figure 30.11 A brief history of the Universe from the Big Bang to the present. The four forces became distinguishable during the first microsecond. Then, all the quarks combined to form particles that interact via the strong force. The leptons remained separate, however, and exist as individually observable particles to this day.

Figure 30.12 Robert W. Wilson (*left*) and Arno A. Penzias (*right*), with Bell Telephone Laboratories' horn-reflector antenna.

The datum of Penzias and Wilson is indicated in blue.

Figure 30.13 Theoretical blackbody (rust-colored curve) and measured radiation spectra (black points) of the Big Bang. Most of the data were collected from the Cosmic Background Explorer (COBE) satellite.

After a few minutes, protons condensed out of the hot soup. For half an hour, the Universe underwent thermonuclear detonation, exploding like a hydrogen bomb and producing most of the helium nuclei now present. The Universe continued to expand, and its temperature dropped. Until about 700 000 years after the Big Bang, the Universe was dominated by radiation. Energetic radiation prevented matter from forming single hydrogen atoms because collisions would instantly ionize any atoms that might form. Photons underwent continuous Compton scattering from the vast number of free electrons, resulting in a Universe that was opaque to radiation. By the time the Universe was about 700 000 years old, it had expanded and cooled to about 3 000 K. Protons could now bind to electrons to form neutral hydrogen atoms, and the Universe suddenly became transparent to photons. Radiation no longer dominated the Universe, and clumps of neutral matter grew steadily: first atoms, followed by molecules, gas clouds, stars, and finally galaxies.

Observation of Radiation from the Primordial Fireball

In 1965 Arno A. Penzias (b. 1933) and Robert W. Wilson (b. 1936) of Bell Laboratories made an amazing discovery while testing a sensitive microwave receiver. A pesky signal producing a faint background hiss was interfering with their satellite communications experiments. Despite all their efforts, the signal remained. Ultimately, it became clear that they were observing microwave background radiation (at a wavelength of 7.35 cm) representing the leftover "glow" from the Big Bang.

The microwave horn that served as their receiving antenna is shown in Figure 30.12. The intensity of the detected signal remained unchanged as the antenna was pointed in different directions. The radiation had equal strength in all directions, which suggested that the entire Universe was the source of this radiation.

Subsequent experiments by other groups added intensity data at different wavelengths, as shown in Figure 30.13. The results confirm that the radiation is that of a blackbody at 2.9 K. This figure is perhaps the most clear-cut evidence for the Big Bang theory.

The cosmic background radiation was found to be too uniform to have led to the development of galaxies. In 1992, following a study using the Cosmic Background Explorer, or COBE, slight irregularities in the cosmic background were found. These irregularities are thought to be the seeds of galaxy formation.

30.11 Unanswered Questions in Cosmology

In the past decade new data have raised questions that many consider to be the most important in science today. At issue is the composition of the Universe, which is closely tied to its ultimate fate. One of these questions concerns the rate at which stars orbit the galaxy, explained by a postulated material called **dark matter**. Although evidence for its existence was noticed by Fritz Zwicky in 1933, only relatively recently has it become a dominant field of inquiry. The other question involves the accelerating expansion of the Universe discovered in 1998, attributed to an equally mysterious material called **dark energy**.

Dark Matter

When the velocities of stars in our galaxy are measured, it is found they are traveling too fast to remain bound by gravity to the Milky Way, if the mass of the galaxy is due to that found in luminous stars. Figure 30.14a shows the velocity versus radial distance curve for bodies circling the Sun. As the distance from the Sun increases, the velocity of planetary bodies decreases, a consequence of the inverse square law of gravitation. Figure 30.14b, on the other hand, shows the velocity curve of stars in the Milky Way galaxy. The curve increases and flattens out but doesn't decline,

Figure 30.14 (a) Velocity versus radial distance curve for bodies circling the Sun. (b) Velocity curve of stars in the Milky Way galaxy.

meaning the stars are traveling much faster than expected if primarily under the influence of gravitation from visible stars. Traveling at higher than the expected galactic escape speed, the stars should leave the galaxy, yet remain in their orbits. Similar observations have been made of stars in other galaxies.

Two general theories have been advanced to account for the behavior of too-rapidly moving stars: either there is a new form of dark matter that has not been directly observed, or the law of gravitation must become stronger than an inverse square at long range. From the velocity profile of stars, 90% of the matter in the galaxy would consist of the hypothetical dark matter. Among the candidates for dark matter are neutrinos, which due to "neutrino oscillation," the spontaneous changing from one type of neutrino into another, are now thought to have mass. All stars emit enormous numbers of neutrinos every second, so if neutrinos had even a small mass, they could account for the dark matter. Another hypothetical candidate is a WIMP, a weakly interacting massive particle left over from the Big Bang. Because other galaxies have rotation curves similar to the Milky Way's, it may well be that dark matter predominates over ordinary matter in the Universe at large.

The leading alternate explanation for the galactic rotation curves is that Newton's law of gravitation doesn't hold over large distances. That theory, called MOND (Modified Newtonian Dynamics), has received a great deal of attention but thus far has not worked well enough to gain widespread acceptance. Some researchers have also tried to account for the rotation curves of galaxies by using Einstein's theory of gravity, general relativity. Finally, it is entirely possible that the correct theory may require both new kinds of matter and a modification of gravity theory.

Dark Energy and the Accelerating Universe

By 1998 two groups of astronomers, one led by Brian Schmidt and Adam Riess and the other by Saul Perlmutter, had made highly accurate new measurements of the distances to other galaxies using Type 1a supernovae. Those observations showed that the Universe is both expanding and accelerating! The accelerated expansion can't be caused by normal matter nor by dark matter because they exert an attractive gravitational force. Instead, it is thought that a new kind of matter, called **dark energy**, exerts a repulsive force that causes the Universe to expand more rapidly than is predicted by Einstein's theory of general relativity. Figure 30.15 shows the theorized proportions of matter, dark matter, and dark energy. Normal atoms, the kind we're made of, comprise only about 4% of the Universe, whereas approximately 23% is dark matter and 73% is dark energy.

Einstein introduced a cosmological constant into his theory of general relativity in order to explain why the Universe appeared not to change with time. The cosmological constant provided a repulsive force sufficient to prevent the matter of the Universe from collapsing under the attractive influence of gravity. When Edwin Hubble's observations of the red shift of galaxies led to the notion of a dynamically expanding universe, Einstein called the cosmological constant "the

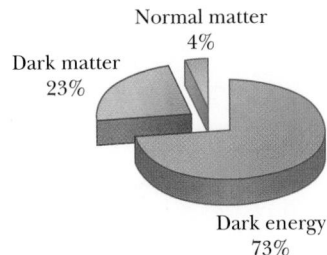

Figure 30.15 The theorized composition of the Universe. Normal matter, as found on Earth and in the Sun, comprises only about 4% of the material in the Universe. The unknown material causing increased gravitational attraction on the galactic scale is called dark matter, whereas the similarly unknown material causing the accelerated expansion of the Universe is called dark energy.

biggest blunder" of his life. That same cosmological constant can now produce a good model of the accelerating universe, turning his blunder into something of a triumph. The cosmological constant doesn't completely solve the mystery, however, because the origin of the cosmological constant hasn't been explained. As in the case of the galactic rotation curves, it isn't known whether the accelerating universe is a consequence of a new form of matter or energy, or an indication that the standard theories of cosmology derived from general relativity are in need of modification.

The Evolution and Fate of the Universe

Unsolved questions remain about the origin and early evolution of the Universe. Although the Big Bang model explains why galaxies seem to be flying away from us, several observational problems have emerged that can't be fully explained by the Big Bang hypothesis alone.

First of all, the Universe, as measured by the temperature of the microwave background, is altogether too uniform. It's as if the entire Universe were in equilibrium. For a system to be in equilibrium, its constituents must be able to exchange energy, arriving after a certain passage of time to a uniform temperature. How could this equilibrium be achieved, however, when different parts of the Universe are so far apart from each other that they could not possibly exchange energy? That mystery is called the horizon problem.

Second, the measurements of the cosmic microwave background strongly suggest that the Universe has a flat geometry. Figure 30.16 shows the standard three fates of the Universe, derived with Einstein's theory of general relativity by graphing the expansion factor, R, versus cosmic time. The expansion factor may be thought of as giving a measure of the size of the Universe, like a cosmic radius. A flat universe is expected to expand forever, although in the limit as time goes to infinity the expansion rate gradually slows to zero. A flat universe, however, is a state of unstable equilibrium, like a pencil standing on its point. With a small deviation one way or the other, either the Universe would collapse again as on the lower curve in Figure 30.16, or expand forever as in the upper curve in Figure 30.16. To be flat now, the Universe had to be flat also at the beginning of the Universe to extremely high accuracy. It is extremely improbable that the Universe was so finely tuned early in its evolution. That fine-tuning is called the flatness problem.

A third problem arises when particle theories are combined with cosmology. Studies of the standard model of particle physics in the early Universe show that large numbers of magnetic monopoles should have been created in the early Universe, so many that hundreds of thousands of them would pass through our bod-

Figure 30.16 The three fates of the Universe, according to Einstein's theory of general relativity. With a sufficient quantity of attractive matter, the universe would initially expand but eventually collapse back into a "big crunch." A flat universe would expand forever, with the expansion slowing to zero in the limit as cosmic time τ goes to infinity. A hyperbolic (or open) universe would accelerate forever. A dark energy universe, or equivalently, one due to a positive cosmological constant, would be similar to the hyperbolic universe but curve upward.

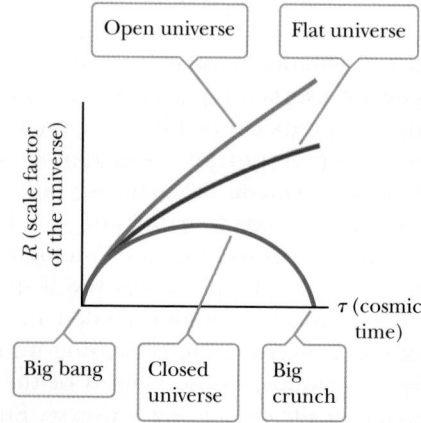

ies every second. Magnetic monopoles are tiny magnets consisting of an isolated north or south pole, and despite calculations predicting them to be common, they have never been observed. That is called the monopole problem.

In 1981 Alan Guth, now at MIT, proposed the inflationary model of the Universe to resolve these three problems with a single mechanism. In this model, an as yet unidentified field called the **inflaton field** caused the Universe to enter into a very rapid exponential inflation, expanding 10^{32} times in size in a tiny fraction of a second.

That accelerated expansion in the very early Universe would solve the monopole problem by making them so dilute that very few would exist in the observable Universe. Further, because the Universe was much smaller just prior to inflation, it would be in thermal equilibrium and, consequently, after the expansion would remain similar in all places and in all directions, solving the horizon problem. Finally, the rapid inflation would cause the curvature of spacetime to appear to flatten out, just as the Earth appears flat to those on its surface because only a very small portion of the entire Earth is visible in a given locality. That solves the flatness problem.

After the brief inflationary epoch the Universe could continue to expand normally. Whereas there is no definitive evidence that the inflationary Universe is correct, it is currently the most accepted working hypothesis for how the early Universe evolved. Some researchers have attempted to combine inflation and dark energy into a single theory called "quintessence." To date, however, no single theory explaining the origins of either early inflation or later universal acceleration has found general support among cosmologists.

30.12 Problems and Perspectives

While particle physicists have been exploring the realm of the very small, cosmologists have been exploring cosmic history back to the first microsecond of the Big Bang. Observation of the events that occur when two particles collide in an accelerator is essential in reconstructing the early moments in cosmic history. Perhaps the key to understanding the early Universe is first to understand the world of elementary particles.

Our understanding of physics at short and long distances is far from complete. Particle physicists are faced with many unanswered questions. Why is there so little antimatter in the Universe? Do neutrinos have a small mass, and if so, how much do they contribute to the "dark matter" holding the Universe together gravitationally? How can we understand the latest astronomical measurements, which show that the expansion of the Universe is accelerating and that there may be a kind of "antigravity force," or dark energy, acting between widely separated galaxies? Is it possible to unify the strong and electroweak theories in a logical and consistent manner? Why do quarks and leptons form three similar but distinct families? Are muons the same as electrons (apart from their different masses), or do they have subtle differences that have not been detected? Why are some particles charged and others neutral? Why do quarks carry a fractional charge? What determines the masses of the fundamental particles? The questions go on and on. Because of the rapid advances and new discoveries in the related fields of particle physics and cosmology, by the time you read this book some of these questions may have been resolved and others may have emerged.

An important question that remains is whether leptons and quarks have a substructure. Many physicists believe that the fundamental quantities are not infinitesimal points, but extremely tiny vibrating strings. Despite more than three decades of string theory research by thousands of physicists, however, a final Theory of Everything hasn't been found. Whether there is a limit to knowledge is an open question.

■ SUMMARY

30.1 Nuclear Fission

In **nuclear fission** the total mass of the products is always less than the original mass of the reactants. Nuclear fission occurs when a heavy nucleus splits, or fissions, into two smaller nuclei. The lost mass is transformed into energy, electromagnetic radiation, and the kinetic energy of daughter particles.

A **nuclear reactor** is a system designed to maintain a self-sustaining chain reaction. Nuclear reactors using controlled fission events are currently being used to generate electric power. A useful parameter for describing the level of reactor operation is the reproduction constant K, which is the average number of neutrons from each fission event that will cause another event. A self-sustaining reaction is achieved when $K = 1$.

30.2 Nuclear Fusion

In nuclear fusion two light nuclei combine to form a heavier nucleus. This type of nuclear reaction occurs in the Sun, assisted by a quantum tunneling process that helps particles get through the Coulomb barrier.

Controlled fusion events offer the hope of plentiful supplies of energy in the future. The nuclear fusion reactor is considered by many scientists to be the ultimate energy source because its fuel is water. **Lawson's criterion** states that a fusion reactor will provide a net output power if the product of the plasma ion density n and the plasma confinement time τ satisfies the following relationships:

$n\tau \geq 10^{14}$ s/cm^3 Deuterium–tritium interaction

$n\tau \geq 10^{16}$ s/cm^3 Deuterium–deuterium   [30.5]
interaction

30.3 Elementary Particles and the Fundamental Forces

There are four fundamental forces of nature: the **strong** (hadronic), **electromagnetic**, **weak**, and **gravitational** forces. The strong force is the force between nucleons that keeps the nucleus together. The weak force is responsible for beta decay. The electromagnetic and weak forces are now considered to be manifestations of a single force called the **electroweak** force.

Every fundamental interaction is said to be mediated by the exchange of field particles. The electromagnetic interaction is mediated by the photon, the weak interaction by the $W^\pm$ and Z^0 bosons, the gravitational interaction by gravitons, and the strong interaction by gluons.

30.4 Positrons and Other Antiparticles

An antiparticle and a particle have the same mass, but opposite charge, and may also have other properties with opposite values, such as lepton number and baryon number. It is possible to produce particle–antiparticle pairs in nuclear reactions if the available energy is greater than $2mc^2$, where m is the mass of the particle (or antiparticle).

30.5 Classification of Particles

Particles other than photons are classified as hadrons or leptons. **Hadrons** interact primarily through the strong force. They have size and structure and hence are not elementary particles. There are two types of hadrons: *baryons* and *mesons*. Mesons have a baryon number of zero and have either zero or integer spin. Baryons, which generally are the most massive particles, have nonzero baryon numbers and spins of $\frac{1}{2}$ or $\frac{3}{2}$. The neutron and proton are examples of baryons.

Leptons have no known structure, down to the limits of current resolution (about 10^{-19} m). Leptons interact only through the weak and electromagnetic forces. There are six leptons: the electron, e$^-$; the muon, μ^-; the tau, τ^-; and their associated neutrinos, ν_e, ν_μ, and ν_τ.

30.6 Conservation Laws

In all reactions and decays, quantities such as energy, linear momentum, angular momentum, electric charge, baryon number, and lepton number are strictly conserved. Certain particles have properties called **strangeness** and **charm**. These unusual properties are conserved only in those reactions and decays that occur via the strong force.

30.8 Quarks and Color

Recent theories postulate that all hadrons are composed of smaller units known as **quarks,** which have fractional electric charges and baryon numbers of $\frac{1}{3}$ and come in six "flavors": up, down, strange, charmed, top, and bottom. Each baryon contains three quarks, and each meson contains one quark and one antiquark.

According to the theory of **quantum chromodynamics**, quarks have a property called **color**, and the strong force between quarks is referred to as the **color force**. The color force increases as the distance between particles increases, so quarks are confined and are never observed in isolation. When two bound quarks are widely separated, a new quark–antiquark pair forms between them, and the single particle breaks into two new particles, each composed of a quark–antiquark pair.

30.10 The Cosmic Connection

Observation of background microwave radiation by Penzias and Wilson strongly confirmed that the Universe started with a Big Bang about 15 billion years ago and has been expanding ever since. The background radiation is equivalent to that of a blackbody at a temperature of about 3 K.

The cosmic microwave background has very small irregularities, corresponding to temperature variations of 0.000 3 K. Without these irregularities acting as nucleation sites, particles would never have clumped together to form galaxies and stars.

■ MULTIPLE-CHOICE QUESTIONS

WebAssign The multiple-choice questions in this chapter may be assigned online in Enhanced WebAssign.

1. In the first atomic bomb, a test carried out in New Mexico called Trinity, the energy released was equivalent to approximately 17 kilotons of TNT. Estimate the mass converted into energy in this event. *Note:* One ton of TNT has an energy equivalent of 4.0×10^9 J. (a) 20 kilotons (b) 0.1 kilotons (c) 1 kg (d) 1 g (e) 1 mg

2. When a neutron decays to a proton, electron, and neutrino, how much energy is released? (Neglect the energy of the neutrino.) (a) 0.784 MeV (b) 0.352 MeV (c) 4.31 MeV (d) 2.22 MeV (e) 1.70 MeV

3. The Ω^- particle is a baryon with spin $\frac{3}{2}$. Which of the following is true of this particle? (a) It has three possible spin states in a magnetic field. (b) It has four possible spin states. (c) It has three times the charge of a spin-$\frac{1}{2}$ particle. (d) It has three times the mass of a spin-$\frac{1}{2}$ particle. (e) Its decay products can't include a spin-$\frac{1}{2}$ particle.

4. Why can't a proton decay into a positron and a neutrino? (a) Charge conservation is violated. (b) Baryon number conservation is violated. (c) Conservation of energy is violated. (d) Lepton number conservation is violated. (e) Conservation of strangeness is violated.

5. Which particle is most likely to be captured by a ^{235}U nucleus and cause it to undergo fission? (a) an energetic proton (b) an energetic neutron (c) a slow-moving alpha particle (d) a slow-moving neutron (e) a fast-moving electron

6. If the moderator were suddenly removed from a nuclear reactor in an electric generating station, what is the most likely consequence? (a) The reactor would go supercritical, and a runaway reaction would occur. (b) The nuclear reactions would proceed as before, but the reactor would overheat. (c) The reactor would become subcritical, and the rate at which reactions occurred would diminish. (d) No change would occur in the reactor's operation. (e) The rate at which reactions occurred would increase, but the reactor wouldn't go supercritical.

7. When an electron and a positron meet at low speed in empty space, they annihilate each other to produce two 0.511-MeV gamma rays. What law would be violated if they produced one gamma ray with an energy of 1.02 MeV? (a) conservation of energy (b) conservation of momentum (c) conservation of charge (d) conservation of baryon number (e) conservation of electron-lepton number

8. In a fission reaction a ^{235}U nucleus captures a neutron, splitting the nucleus into ^{137}I and ^{96}Y. How many free neutrons result from this process? (a) 1 (b) 2 (c) 3 (d) 4 (e) 5

9. Which of the following particle reactions can't occur?
(a) $p + \bar{p} \to 2\gamma$
(b) $\pi^0 + n \to K_s^0 + \Sigma^0$
(c) $\gamma + p \to n + \pi^0$
(d) $\Omega^- \to 2\Xi^- + e^+ + \nu_e$
(e) $\pi^+ + p \to K^+ + \Sigma^+$

10. Which of the following particle reactions can't occur?
(a) $p + n \to p + p + \bar{p}$
(b) $n \to p + e^- + \bar{\nu}_e$
(c) $\mu^- \to e^- + \bar{\nu}_e + \nu_\mu$
(d) $\pi^- \to \mu^- + \bar{\nu}_\mu$
(e) $\tau^- \to e^- + \bar{\nu}_\tau + \bar{\nu}_e$

11. Which of the following fuel conditions are required in the operation of a self-sustained controlled fusion reactor? (a) The fuel must be at a sufficiently high temperature. (b) The fuel must be radioactive. (c) The fuel must be at a sufficiently high density. (d) The fuel must be confined for a sufficiently long period of time. (e) The fuel must consist of hydrogen isotopes, only.

12. If an alpha particle and an electron have the same kinetic energy, which undergoes the greater deflection when passed through a magnetic field? (a) The alpha particle does. (b) The electron does. (c) They undergo the same deflection. (d) Neither is deflected.

■ CONCEPTUAL QUESTIONS

WebAssign The conceptual questions in this chapter may be assigned online in Enhanced WebAssign.

1. If high-energy electrons with de Broglie wavelengths smaller than the size of the nucleus are scattered from nuclei, the behavior of the electrons is consistent with scattering from very massive structures much smaller in size than the nucleus, namely, quarks. How is this behavior similar to a classic experiment that detected small structures in an atom?

2. What factors make a fusion reaction difficult to achieve?

3. Doubly charged baryons are known to exist. Why are there no doubly charged mesons?

4. Why would a fusion reactor produce less radioactive waste than a fission reactor?

5. Why didn't atoms exist until hundreds of thousands of years after the Big Bang?

6. Particles known as resonances have very short half-lives, on the order of 10^{-23} s. Would you guess that they are hadrons or leptons? Explain.

7. Describe the quark model of hadrons, including the properties of quarks.

8. In the theory of quantum chromodynamics, quarks come in three colors. How would you justify the statement, "All baryons and mesons are colorless"?

9. Describe the properties of baryons and mesons and the important differences between them.

10. Identify the particle decays in Table 30.2 that occur by the electromagnetic interaction. Justify your answer.

11. Kaons all decay into final states that contain no protons or neutrons. What is the baryon number of kaons?

12. Why is a neutron stable inside the nucleus? (In free space the neutron decays in 900 s.)

13. Discuss the advantages and disadvantages of fission reactors from the point of view of safety, pollution, and resources. Make a comparison with power generated from the burning of fossil fuels.

■ PROBLEMS

ENHANCED
WebAssign The problems in this chapter may be assigned online in Enhanced WebAssign. Selected problems also have Watch It video solutions.

1. denotes straightforward problem; **2.** denotes intermediate problem;

3. denotes challenging problem

1. denotes full solution available in *Student Solutions Manual/ Study Guide*

1. denotes problems most often assigned in Enhanced WebAssign

BIO denotes biomedical problems

GP denotes guided problems

M denotes Master It tutorial available in Enhanced WebAssign

Q|C denotes asking for quantitative and conceptual reasoning

S denotes symbolic reasoning problem

30.1 Nuclear Fission

1. **M** If the average energy released in a fission event is 208 MeV, find the total number of fission events required to operate a 100-W lightbulb for 1.0 h.

2. Find the energy released in the fission reaction

$$n + {}^{235}_{92}U \rightarrow {}^{98}_{40}Zr + {}^{135}_{52}Te + 3n$$

The atomic masses of the fission products are 97.912 0 u for ${}^{98}_{40}Zr$ and 134.908 7 u for ${}^{135}_{52}Te$.

3. Find the energy released in the fission reaction

$${}^{1}_{0}n + {}^{235}_{92}U \rightarrow {}^{88}_{38}Sr + {}^{136}_{54}Xe + 12{}^{1}_{0}n$$

4. According to one estimate, the first atomic bomb released an energy equivalent to 20 kilotons of TNT. If 1 ton of TNT releases about 4.0×10^9 J, how much uranium was lost through fission in this bomb? (Assume 208 MeV released per fission.)

5. **M** Assume ordinary soil contains natural uranium in amounts of 1 part per million by mass. (a) How much uranium is in the top 1.00 m of soil on a 1-acre (43 560-ft²) plot of ground, assuming the specific gravity of soil is 4.00? (b) How much of the isotope ${}^{235}U$, appropriate for nuclear reactor fuel, is in this soil? *Hint:* See Appendix B for the percent abundance of ${}^{235}_{92}U$.

6. A typical nuclear fission power plant produces about 1.00 GW of electrical power. Assume the plant has an overall efficiency of 40.0% and each fission produces 200 MeV of thermal energy. Calculate the mass of ${}^{235}U$ consumed each day.

7. In order to minimize neutron leakage from a reactor, the ratio of the surface area to the volume must be as small as possible. Assume that a sphere of radius *a* and a cube both have the same volume. Find the surface-to-volume ratio for (a) the sphere and (b) the cube. (c) Which of these reactor shapes would have the minimum leakage?

8. **GP** According to one estimate, there are 4.4×10^6 metric tons of world uranium reserves extractable at \$130/kg or less. About 0.7% of naturally occurring uranium is the fissionable isotope ${}^{235}U$. (a) Calculate the mass of ${}^{235}U$ in this reserve in grams. (b) Find the number of moles of ${}^{235}U$ and convert to a number of atoms. (c) Assuming 208 MeV is obtained from each reaction and all this energy is captured, calculate the total energy that can be extracted from the reserve in joules. (d) Assuming world power consumption to be constant at 1.5×10^{13} J/s, how many years could the uranium reserves provide for all the world's energy needs using conventional reactors that don't generate nuclear fuel? (e) What conclusions can be drawn?

9. **M** An all-electric home uses approximately 2 000 kWh of electric energy per month. How much uranium-235 would be required to provide this house with its energy needs for one year? Assume 100% conversion efficiency and 208 MeV released per fission.

10. **Q|C** Seawater contains 3 mg of uranium per cubic meter. (a) Given that the average ocean depth is about 4 km and water covers two-thirds of Earth's surface, estimate the amount of uranium dissolved in the ocean. (b) Estimate how long this uranium could supply the world's energy needs at the current usage of 1.5×10^{13} J/s. (c) Where does the dissolved uranium come from? Is it a renewable energy source? Can uranium from the ocean satisfy our energy requirements? Discuss. *Note:* Breeder reactors increase the efficiency of nuclear fuel use by approximately two orders of magnitude.

30.2 Nuclear Fusion

11. When a star has exhausted its hydrogen fuel, it may fuse other nuclear fuels. At temperatures above 1.0×10^8 K, helium fusion can occur. Write the equations

for the following processes. (a) Two alpha particles fuse to produce a nucleus A and a gamma ray. What is nucleus A? (b) Nucleus A absorbs an alpha particle to produce a nucleus B and a gamma ray. What is nucleus B? (c) Find the total energy released in the reactions given in parts (a) and (b). *Note:* The mass of ^8_4Be = 8.005 305 u.

12. Find the energy released in the fusion reaction
$$^1_1\text{H} + {}^2_1\text{H} \rightarrow {}^3_2\text{He} + \gamma$$

13. Find the energy released in the fusion reaction
$$^2_1\text{H} + {}^2_1\text{H} \rightarrow {}^3_1\text{H} + {}^1_1\text{H}$$

14. **GP** Another series of nuclear reactions that can produce energy in the interior of stars is the cycle described below. This cycle is most efficient when the central temperature in a star is above 1.6×10^7 K. Because the temperature at the center of the Sun is only 1.5×10^7 K, the following cycle produces less than 10% of the Sun's energy. (a) A high-energy proton is absorbed by ^{12}C. Another nucleus, A, is produced in the reaction, along with a gamma ray. Identify nucleus A. (b) Nucleus A decays through positron emission to form nucleus B. Identify nucleus B. (c) Nucleus B absorbs a proton to produce nucleus C and a gamma ray. Identify nucleus C. (d) Nucleus C absorbs a proton to produce nucleus D and a gamma ray. Identify nucleus D. (e) Nucleus D decays through positron emission to produce nucleus E. Identify nucleus E. (f) Nucleus E absorbs a proton to produce nucleus F plus an alpha particle. What is nucleus F? *Note:* If nucleus F is not ^{12}C—that is, the nucleus you started with—you have made an error and should review the sequence of events.

15. Assume a deuteron and a triton are at rest when they fuse according to the reaction
$$^2_1\text{H} + {}^3_1\text{H} \rightarrow {}^4_2\text{He} + {}^1_0\text{n} + 17.6 \text{ MeV}$$
Neglecting relativistic corrections, determine the kinetic energy acquired by the neutron.

16. **Q|C** A reaction that has been considered as a source of energy is the absorption of a proton by a boron-11 nucleus to produce three alpha particles:
$$^1_1\text{H} + {}^{11}_5\text{B} \rightarrow 3({}^4_2\text{He})$$
This reaction is an attractive possibility because boron is easily obtained from Earth's crust. A disadvantage is that the protons and boron nuclei must have large kinetic energies for the reaction to take place. This requirement contrasts to the initiation of uranium fission by slow neutrons. (a) How much energy is released in each reaction? (b) Why must the reactant particles have high kinetic energies?

30.4 Positrons and Other Antiparticles

17. A photon produces a proton–antiproton pair according to the reaction $\gamma \rightarrow \text{p} + \bar{\text{p}}$. What is the minimum possible frequency of the photon? What is its wavelength?

18. **M** A photon with an energy of 2.09 GeV creates a proton–antiproton pair in which the proton has a kinetic energy of 95.0 MeV. What is the kinetic energy of the antiproton?

19. A neutral pion at rest decays into two photons according to
$$\pi^0 \rightarrow \gamma + \gamma$$
Find the energy, momentum, and frequency of each photon.

30.6 Conservation Laws

20. For the following two reactions, the first may occur but the second cannot. Explain.
$$\text{K}^0 \rightarrow \pi^+ + \pi^- \text{ (can occur)}$$
$$\Lambda^0 \rightarrow \pi^+ + \pi^- \text{ (cannot occur)}$$

21. Each of the following reactions is forbidden. Determine a conservation law that is violated for each reaction.
(a) $\text{p} + \bar{\text{p}} \rightarrow \mu^+ + \text{e}^-$
(b) $\pi^- + \text{p} \rightarrow \text{p} + \pi^+$
(c) $\text{p} + \text{p} \rightarrow \text{p} + \pi^+$
(d) $\text{p} + \text{p} \rightarrow \text{p} + \text{p} + \text{n}$
(e) $\gamma + \text{p} \rightarrow \text{n} + \pi^0$

22. Determine which of the reactions below can occur. For those that cannot occur, determine the conservation law (or laws) that each violates.
(a) $\text{p} \rightarrow \pi^+ + \pi^0$
(b) $\text{p} + \text{p} \rightarrow \text{p} + \text{p} + \pi^0$
(c) $\pi^+ \rightarrow \mu^+ + \nu_\mu$
(d) $\text{n} \rightarrow \text{p} + \text{e}^- + \bar{\nu}_e$
(e) $\pi^+ \rightarrow \mu^+ + \text{n}$

23. Which of the following processes are allowed by the strong interaction, the electromagnetic interaction, the weak interaction, or no interaction at all?
(a) $\pi^- + \text{p} \rightarrow 2\eta^0$
(b) $\text{K}^- + \text{n} \rightarrow \Lambda^0 + \pi^-$
(c) $\text{K}^- \rightarrow \pi^- + \pi^0$
(d) $\Omega^- \rightarrow \Xi^- + \pi^0$
(e) $\eta^0 \rightarrow 2\gamma$

24. **Q|C** (a) Show that baryon number and charge are conserved in the following reactions of a pion with a proton:
$$(1) \ \pi^+ + \text{p} \rightarrow \text{K}^+ + \Sigma^+$$
$$(2) \ \pi^+ + \text{p} \rightarrow \pi^+ + \Sigma^+$$
(b) The first reaction is observed, but the second never occurs. Explain these observations. (c) Could the second reaction happen if it created a third particle? If so, which particles in Table 30.2 might make it possible? Would the reaction require less energy or more energy than the reaction of Equation (1)? Why?

25. Determine whether or not strangeness is conserved in the following decays and reactions.
(a) $\Lambda^0 \rightarrow \text{p} + \pi^-$
(b) $\pi^- + \text{p} \rightarrow \Lambda^0 + \text{K}^0$
(c) $\bar{\text{p}} + \text{p} \rightarrow \bar{\Lambda}^0 + \Lambda^0$
(d) $\pi^- + \text{p} \rightarrow \pi^- + \Sigma^+$
(e) $\Xi^- \rightarrow \Lambda^0 + \pi^-$
(f) $\Xi^0 \rightarrow \text{p} + \pi^-$

30.8 Quarks and Color

26. The quark composition of the proton is uud, whereas that of the neutron is udd. Show that the charge, baryon number, and strangeness of these particles

equal the sums of these numbers for their quark constituents.

27. **M** Find the number of electrons, and of each species of quark, in 1 L of water.

28. The quark compositions of the K^0 and Λ^0 particles are $d\bar{s}$ and uds, respectively. Show that the charge, baryon number, and strangeness of these particles equal the sums of these numbers for their quark constituents.

29. Identify the particles corresponding to the quark states (a) suu, (b) $\bar{u}d$, (c) $\bar{s}d$, and (d) ssd.

30. What is the electrical charge of the baryons with the quark compositions (a) $\overline{uud}$ and (b) $\overline{udd}$? What are these baryons called?

Additional Problems

31. A Σ^0 particle traveling through matter strikes a proton. A Σ^+, a gamma ray, as well as a third particle, emerge. Use the quark model of each to determine the identity of the third particle.

32. Name at least one conservation law that prevents each of the following reactions from occurring.
    (a) $\pi^- + p \rightarrow \Sigma^+ + \pi^0$
    (b) $\mu^- \rightarrow \pi^- + \nu_e$
    (c) $p \rightarrow \pi^+ + \pi^+ + \pi^-$

33. Find the energy released in the fusion reaction
    $$_1^1H + _2^3He \rightarrow _2^4He + e^+ + \nu$$

34. Occasionally, high-energy muons collide with electrons and produce two neutrinos according to the reaction $\mu^+ + e^- \rightarrow 2\nu$. What kind of neutrinos are they?

35. Fill in the missing particle. Assume that (a) occurs via the strong interaction while (b) and (c) involve the weak interaction.
    (a) $K^+ + p \rightarrow ? + p$
    (b) $\Omega^- \rightarrow ? + \pi^-$
    (c) $K^+ \rightarrow ? + \mu^+ + \nu_\mu$

36. Two protons approach each other with 70.4 MeV of kinetic energy and engage in a reaction in which a proton and a positive pion emerge at rest. What third particle, obviously uncharged and therefore difficult to detect, must have been created?

37. A 2.0-MeV neutron is emitted in a fission reactor. If it loses one-half its kinetic energy in each collision with a moderator atom, how many collisions must it undergo to reach an energy associated with a gas at a room temperature of 20.0°C?

38. **QC** The fusion reaction $_1^2D + _1^2D \rightarrow _2^3He + _0^1n$ releases 3.27 MeV of energy. If a fusion reactor operates strictly on the basis of this reaction, (a) how much energy could it produce by completely reacting 1 kg of deu-

terium? (b) At eight cents a kilowatt-hour, how much would the produced energy be worth? (c) Heavy water (D_2O) costs about $300 per kilogram. Neglecting the cost of separating the deuterium from the oxygen via electrolysis, how much does 1 kg of deuterium cost, if derived from D_2O? (d) Would it be cost-effective to use deuterium as a source of energy? Discuss, assuming the cost of energy production is nine-tenths the value of energy produced.

39. (a) Show that about 1.0×10^{10} J would be released by the fusion of the deuterons in 1.0 gal of water. Note that 1 of every 6 500 hydrogen atoms is a deuteron. (b) The average energy consumption rate of a person living in the United States is about 1.0×10^4 J/s (an average power of 10 kW). At this rate, how long would the energy needs of one person be supplied by the fusion of the deuterons in 1.0 gal of water? Assume the energy released per deuteron is 1.64 MeV.

40. The oceans have a volume of 317 million cubic miles and contain 1.32×10^{21} kg of water. Of all the hydrogen nuclei in this water, 0.015 6% are deuterium. (a) If all of these deuterium nuclei were fused to helium via the first reaction in Equation 30.4, determine the total amount of energy that could be released. (b) Present world electric power consumption is about 7.00×10^{12} W. If consumption were 100 times greater, how many years would the energy supply calculated in (a) last?

41. A π-meson at rest decays according to
    $$\pi^- \rightarrow \mu^- + \bar{\nu}_\mu$$
    What is the energy carried off by the neutrino? Assume the neutrino has no mass and moves off with the speed of light. Take $m_\pi c^2 = 139.6$ MeV and $m_\mu c^2 = 105.7$ MeV. *Note:* Use relativity; see Equation 26.13.

42. The reaction $\pi^- + p \rightarrow K^0 + \Lambda^0$ occurs with high probability, whereas the reaction $\pi^- + p \rightarrow K^0 + n$ never occurs. Analyze these reactions at the quark level. Show that the first reaction conserves the total number of each type of quark and the second reaction does not.

43. The sun radiates energy at the rate of 3.85×10^{26} W. Suppose the net reaction
    $$4p + 2e^- \rightarrow \alpha + 2\nu_e + 6\gamma$$
    accounts for all the energy released. Calculate the number of protons fused per second. *Note:* Recall that an alpha particle is a helium-4 nucleus.

44. A K^0 particle at rest decays into a π^+ and a π^-. The mass of the K^0 is 497.7 MeV/c^2 and the mass of each pion is 139.6 MeV/c^2. What will be the speed of each of the pions?

■ AP* REVIEW QUESTIONS

1. Nuclear fission is a process that involves

   (A) the capture of free electrons by the nucleus.

   (B) combining two light nuclei to form a heavier nucleus.

   (C) splitting a heavy nucleus into smaller nuclei.

   (D) the emission of alpha particles.

   (E) turning neutrons into protons and electrons.

Questions 2–3

Questions 2–3 deal with the fission of Plutonium-239, according to the following equation.

$$^{239}_{94}\text{Pu} + ^{1}_{0}\text{n} \quad \rightarrow \quad ^{143}_{55}\text{Cs} + ^{95}_{39}\text{Y} + \underline{\qquad}$$

2. The number and type of particles released in this reaction are:

   (A) Two protons

   (B) Two neutrons

   (C) Three protons

   (D) Three neutrons

   (E) One proton and two neutrons

3. Which of the following statements is/are true?

   I. Electric charge is conserved.

   II. The total mass of the reactants is equal to the total mass of the products.

   III. The total number of protons and neutrons is conserved.

   (A) I only

   (B) I and II

   (C) I and III

   (D) II and III

   (E) I, II, and III

4. The fission of ^{235}U is utilized by nuclear reactors to produce energy. What must be done to keep the chain reaction from going supercritical and producing a runaway reaction?

   (A) Use heavy water to slow down fast neutrons

   (B) Use cooling towers to release excess heat

   (C) Use a fusion reaction to counter any runaway reactions

   (D) Use control rods to absorb excess neutrons

   (E) Use magnetic fields to contain the fission reaction

5. Which of the following comparisons between fission and fusion are true statements?

   I. Fusion produces more energy per unit mass than fission.

   II. Fission reactors are easier to build than fusion reactors.

   III. Fusion is the process by which stars produce energy.

   (A) I only

   (B) I and II

   (C) I and III

   (D) II and III

   (E) I, II, and III

6. In stars, the second step in the proton–proton cycle involves the fusion of a hydrogen-1 and helium-3, or two nuclei of helium-3. The nuclear equation for the first example is

   $$^{1}_{1}\text{H} + ^{3}_{2}\text{He} \quad \rightarrow \quad ^{4}_{2}\text{He} + \underline{\qquad} + \text{energy}$$

   Which of the following is the other product of the reaction?

   (A) One proton

   (B) One neutron

   (C) One electron

   (D) One positron

   (E) One photon

7. Which fundamental force is responsible for radioactivity?

   (A) Strong force

   (B) Weak force

   (C) Electromagnetic force

   (D) Gravitational force

   (E) Friction

8. Which two fundamental forces have been related and unified?

   (A) Weak and strong

   (B) Weak and electromagnetic

   (C) Electromagnetic and gravitational

   (D) Gravitational and strong

   (E) Strong and gravitational

9. Which of the following is the correct ranking of the fundamental forces, from the strongest to the weakest?

   (A) Gravity − strong − weak − electromagnetic

   (B) Electromagnetic − strong − gravity − weak

   (C) Weak − strong − gravity − electromagnetic

   (D) Strong − weak − electromagnetic − gravity

   (E) Strong − electromagnetic − weak − gravity

10. Which two fundamental forces are found only inside the nuclei of atoms?

    (A) Strong and weak

    (B) Strong and electromagnetic

    (C) Strong and gravitational

    (D) Weak and electromagnetic

    (E) Weak and gravitational

11. Pair production is the production of a particle and its antiparticle. If the mass of each particle is m, which of the following is true regarding the total amount of energy E required for pair production?

    (A) $E = mc^2$

    (B) $E < mc^2$

    (C) $E = 2mc^2$

    (D) $E > 2mc^2$

    (E) $mc^2 < E < 2mc^2$

12. Low-energy pair annihilation occurs when a particle interacts with its antiparticle at slow speeds. Which of the following are most commonly true of the two photons produced as a result of low-energy pair annihilation?

    I. The two photons have the same energies.

    II. The two photons go in opposite directions.

    III. The two photons have the same speed.

    (A) I only

    (B) I and II

    (C) I and III

    (D) II and III

    (E) I, II, and III

Mathematics Review

■ Appendix A

A.1 Mathematical Notation

Many mathematical symbols are used throughout this book. These symbols are described here, with examples illustrating their use.

Equals Sign: =

The symbol = denotes the mathematical equality of two quantities. In physics, it also makes a statement about the relationship of different physical concepts. An example is the equation $E = mc^2$. This famous equation says that a given mass m, *measured in kilograms*, is equivalent to a certain amount of energy, E, *measured in joules*. The speed of light squared, c^2, can be considered a constant of proportionality, neccessary because the units chosen for given quantities are rather arbitrary, based on historical circumstances.

Proportionality: ∝

The symbol $\propto$ denotes a proportionality. This symbol might be used when focusing on relationships rather than an exact mathematical equality. For example, we could write $E \propto m$, which says in words that "the energy E associated with an object is proportional to the mass m of the object." Another example is found in kinetic energy, which is the energy associated with an object's motion, defined by $KE = \frac{1}{2}mv^2$, where m is again the mass and v is the speed. Both m and v are variables in this expression. Hence, the kinetic energy KE is proportional to m, $KE \propto m$, and at the same time KE is proportional to the speed squared, $KE \propto v^2$. Another term used here is "directly proportional." The density ρ of an object is related to its mass and volume by $\rho = m/V$. Consequently, the density is said to be directly proportional to mass and inversely proportional to volume.

Inequalities

The symbol $<$ means "is less than," and $>$ means "is greater than." For example, $\rho_{Fe} > \rho_{Al}$ means that the density of iron, ρ_{Fe}, is greater than the density of aluminum, ρ_{Al}. If there is a line underneath the symbol, there is the possibility of equality: $\leq$ means "less than or equal to," whereas $\geq$ means "greater than or equal to." Any particle's speed v, for example, is less than or equal to the speed of light, c: $v \leq c$.

Sometimes the size of a given quantity greatly differs from the size of another quantity. Simple inequality doesn't convey vast differences. For such cases, the symbol $\ll$ means "is much less than" and $\gg$ means "is much greater than." The mass of the Sun, M_{Sun}, is much greater than the mass of the Earth, M_E: $M_{Sun} \gg M_E$. The mass of an electron, m_e, is much less than the mass of a proton, m_p: $m_e \ll m_p$.

Approximately Equal: ≈

The symbol $\approx$ indicates that two quantities are approximately equal to each other. The mass of a proton, m_p, is approximately the same as the mass of a neutron, m_n. This relationship can be written $m_p \approx m_n$.

Equivalence: ≡

The symbol $\equiv$ means "is defined as," which is a different statement than a simple $=$. It means that the quantity on the left—usually a single quantity—is another way of expressing the quantity or quantities on the right. The classical momentum of an object, p, is defined to be the mass of the object m times its velocity v, hence $p \equiv mv$. Because this equivalence is by definition, there is no possibility of p being equal to something else. Contrast this case with that of the expression for the velocity v of an object under constant acceleration, which is $v = at + v_0$. This equation would never be written with an equivalence sign because v in this context is not a defined quantity; rather it is an equality that holds true only under the assumption of constant acceleration. The expression for the classical momentum, however, is always true by definition, so it would be appropriate to write $p \equiv mv$ the first time the concept is introduced. After the introduction of a term, an ordinary equals sign generally suffices.

Differences: Δ

The Greek letter Δ (capital delta) is the symbol used to indicate the difference in a measured physical quantity, usually at two different times. The best example is a displacement along the x-axis, indicated by Δx (read as "delta x"). Note that Δx doesn't mean "the product of Δ and x." Suppose a person out for a morning stroll starts measuring her distance away from home when she is 10 m from her doorway. She then continues along a straight-line path and stops strolling 50 m from the door. Her change in position during the walk is $\Delta x = 50$ m $- 10$ m $= 40$ m. In symbolic form, such displacements can be written

$$\Delta x = x_f - x_i$$

In this equation, x_f is the final position and x_i is the initial position. There are numerous other examples of differences in physics, such as the difference (or change) in momentum, $\Delta p = p_f - p_i$; the change in kinetic energy, $\Delta K = K_f - K_i$; and the change in temperature, $\Delta T = T_f - T_i$.

Summation: Σ

In physics there are often contexts in which it's necessary to add several quantities. A useful abbreviation for representing such a sum is the Greek letter Σ (capital sigma). Suppose we wish to add a set of five numbers represented by $x_1, x_2, x_3, x_4,$ and x_5. In the abbreviated notation, we would write the sum as

$$x_1 + x_2 + x_3 + x_4 + x_5 = \sum_{i=1}^{5} x_i$$

where the subscript i on x represents any one of the numbers in the set. For example, if there are five masses in a system, $m_1, m_2, m_3, m_4,$ and m_5, the total mass of the system $M = m_1 + m_2 + m_3 + m_4 + m_5$ could be expressed as

$$M = \sum_{i=1}^{5} m_i$$

The x-coordinate of the center of mass of the five masses, meanwhile, could be written

$$x_{CM} = \frac{\sum_{i=1}^{5} m_i x_i}{M}$$

with similar expressions for the y- and z-coordinates of the center of mass.

Absolute Value: | |

The magnitude of a quantity x, written $|x|$, is simply the absolute value of that quantity. The sign of $|x|$ is always positive, regardless of the sign of x. For example, if $x = -5$, then $|x| = 5$; if $x = 8$, then $|x| = 8$. In physics this sign is useful whenever the magnitude of a quantity is more important than any direction that might be implied by a sign.

A.2 Scientific Notation

Many quantities in science have very large or very small values. The speed of light is about 300 000 000 m/s, and the ink required to make the dot over an i in this textbook has a mass of about 0.000 000 001 kg. It's very cumbersome to read, write, and keep track of such numbers because the decimal places have to be counted and because a number with one significant digit may require a large number of zeros. Scientific notation is a way of representing these numbers without having to write out so many zeros, which in general are only used to establish the magnitude of the number, not its accuracy. The key is to use powers of 10. The nonnegative powers of 10 are

$$10^0 = 1$$
$$10^1 = 10$$
$$10^2 = 10 \times 10 = 100$$
$$10^3 = 10 \times 10 \times 10 = 1\,000$$
$$10^4 = 10 \times 10 \times 10 \times 10 = 10\,000$$
$$10^5 = 10 \times 10 \times 10 \times 10 \times 10 = 100\,000$$

and so on. The number of decimal places following the first digit in the number and to the left of the decimal point corresponds to the power to which 10 is raised, called the **exponent** of 10. The speed of light, 300 000 000 m/s, can then be expressed as 3×10^8 m/s. Notice there are eight decimal places to the right of the leading digit, 3, and to the left of where the decimal point would be placed. In this method, some representative numbers smaller than 1 are

$$10^{-1} = \frac{1}{10} = 0.1$$
$$10^{-2} = \frac{1}{10 \times 10} = 0.01$$
$$10^{-3} = \frac{1}{10 \times 10 \times 10} = 0.001$$
$$10^{-4} = \frac{1}{10 \times 10 \times 10 \times 10} = 0.000\,1$$
$$10^{-5} = \frac{1}{10 \times 10 \times 10 \times 10 \times 10} = 0.000\,01$$

In these cases, the number of decimal places to the right of the decimal point up to and including only the first nonzero digit equals the value of the (negative) exponent.

Numbers expressed as some power of 10 multiplied by another number between 1 and 10 are said to be in **scientific notation**. For example, Coulomb's constant, which is associated with electric forces, is given by 8 987 551 789 N·m²/C² and is written in scientific notation as $8.987\,551\,789 \times 10^9$ N·m²/C². Newton's constant of gravitation is given by 0.000 000 000 066 731 N·m²/kg², written in scientific notation as $6.673\,1 \times 10^{-11}$ N·m²/kg².

When numbers expressed in scientific notation are being multiplied, the following general rule is very useful:

$$10^n \times 10^m = 10^{n+m} \qquad \text{[A.1]}$$

where n and m can be any numbers (not necessarily integers). For example, $10^2 \times 10^5 = 10^7$. The rule also applies if one of the exponents is negative: $10^3 \times 10^{-8} = 10^{-5}$.

When dividing numbers expressed in scientific notation, note that

$$\frac{10^n}{10^m} = 10^n \times 10^{-m} = 10^{n-m} \qquad [A.2]$$

Exercises

With help from the above rules, verify the answers to the following:

1. $86\,400 = 8.64 \times 10^4$
2. $9\,816\,762.5 = 9.816\,762\,5 \times 10^6$
3. $0.000\,000\,039\,8 = 3.98 \times 10^{-8}$
4. $(4 \times 10^8)(9 \times 10^9) = 3.6 \times 10^{18}$
5. $(3 \times 10^7)(6 \times 10^{-12}) = 1.8 \times 10^{-4}$
6. $\dfrac{75 \times 10^{-11}}{5 \times 10^{-3}} = 1.5 \times 10^{-7}$
7. $\dfrac{(3 \times 10^6)(8 \times 10^{-2})}{(2 \times 10^{17})(6 \times 10^5)} = 2 \times 10^{-18}$

A.3 Algebra

A. Some Basic Rules

When algebraic operations are performed, the laws of arithmetic apply. Symbols such as x, y, and z are usually used to represent quantities that are not specified, what are called the **unknowns**.

First, consider the equation

$$8x = 32$$

If we wish to solve for x, we can divide (or multiply) each side of the equation by the same factor without destroying the equality. In this case, if we divide both sides by 8, we have

$$\frac{8x}{8} = \frac{32}{8}$$
$$x = 4$$

Next consider the equation

$$x + 2 = 8$$

In this type of expression, we can add or subtract the same quantity from each side. If we subtract 2 from each side, we obtain

$$x + 2 - 2 = 8 - 2$$
$$x = 6$$

In general, if $x + a = b$, then $x = b - a$.

Now consider the equation

$$\frac{x}{5} = 9$$

If we multiply each side by 5, we are left with x on the left by itself and 45 on the right:

$$\left(\frac{x}{5}\right)(5) = 9 \times 5$$
$$x = 45$$

In all cases, **whatever operation is performed on the left side of the equality must also be performed on the right side.**

The following rules for multiplying, dividing, adding, and subtracting fractions should be recalled, where a, b, and c are three numbers:

	Rule	Example
Multiplying	$\left(\dfrac{a}{b}\right)\left(\dfrac{c}{d}\right) = \dfrac{ac}{bd}$	$\left(\dfrac{2}{3}\right)\left(\dfrac{4}{5}\right) = \dfrac{8}{15}$
Dividing	$\dfrac{(a/b)}{(c/d)} = \dfrac{ad}{bc}$	$\dfrac{2/3}{4/5} = \dfrac{(2)(5)}{(4)(3)} = \dfrac{10}{12} = \dfrac{5}{6}$
Adding	$\dfrac{a}{b} \pm \dfrac{c}{d} = \dfrac{ad \pm bc}{bd}$	$\dfrac{2}{3} - \dfrac{4}{5} = \dfrac{(2)(5) - (4)(3)}{(3)(5)} = -\dfrac{2}{15}$

Very often in physics we are called upon to manipulate symbolic expressions algebraically, a process most students find unfamiliar. It's very important, however, because substituting numbers into an equation too early can often obscure meaning. The following two examples illustrate how these kinds of algebraic manipulations are carried out.

■ EXAMPLE

A ball is dropped from the top of a building 50.0 m tall. How long does it take the ball to fall to a height of 25.0 m?

SOLUTION First, write the general ballistics equation for this situation:

$$x = \tfrac{1}{2}at^2 + v_0 t + x_0$$

Here, $a = -9.80 \text{ m/s}^2$ is the acceleration of gravity that causes the ball to fall, $v_0 = 0$ is the initial velocity, and $x_0 = 50.0$ m is the initial position. Substitute only the initial velocity, $v_0 = 0$, obtaining the following equation:

$$x = \tfrac{1}{2}at^2 + x_0$$

This equation must be solved for t. Subtract x_0 from both sides:

$$x - x_0 = \tfrac{1}{2}at^2 + x_0 - x_0 = \tfrac{1}{2}at^2$$

Multiply both sides by $2/a$:

$$\left(\frac{2}{a}\right)(x - x_0) = \left(\frac{2}{a}\right)\tfrac{1}{2}at^2 = t^2$$

It's customary to have the desired value on the left, so switch the equation around and take the square root of both sides:

$$t = \pm\sqrt{\left(\frac{2}{a}\right)(x - x_0)}$$

Only the positive root makes sense. Values could now be substituted to obtain a final answer.

■ EXAMPLE

A block of mass m slides over a frictionless surface in the positive x-direction. It encounters a patch of roughness having coefficient of kinetic friction μ_k. If the rough patch has length Δx, find the speed of the block after leaving the patch.

SOLUTION Using the work-energy theorem, we have

$$\tfrac{1}{2}mv^2 - \tfrac{1}{2}mv_0^2 = -\mu_k mg\,\Delta x$$

Add $\tfrac{1}{2}mv_0^2$ to both sides:

$$\tfrac{1}{2}mv^2 = \tfrac{1}{2}mv_0^2 - \mu_k mg\,\Delta x$$

(Continued)

Multiply both sides by $2/m$:

$$v^2 = v_0{}^2 - 2\mu_k g \,\Delta x$$

Finally, take the square root of both sides. Because the block is sliding in the positive x-direction, the positive square root is selected.

$$v = \sqrt{v_0{}^2 - 2\mu_k g \,\Delta x}$$

Exercises

In Exercises 1–4, solve for x:

Answers

1. $a = \dfrac{1}{1 + x}$
$x = \dfrac{1 - a}{a}$

2. $3x - 5 = 13$
$x = 6$

3. $ax - 5 = bx + 2$
$x = \dfrac{7}{a - b}$

4. $\dfrac{5}{2x + 6} = \dfrac{3}{4x + 8}$
$x = -\dfrac{11}{7}$

5. Solve the following equation for v_1:

$$P_1 + \tfrac{1}{2}\rho v_1{}^2 = P_2 + \tfrac{1}{2}\rho v_2{}^2$$

Answer: $v_1 = \pm\sqrt{\dfrac{2}{\rho}(P_2 - P_1) + v_2{}^2}$

B. Powers

When powers of a given quantity x are multiplied, the following rule applies:

$$x^n x^m = x^{n+m} \qquad \text{[A.3]}$$

For example, $x^2 x^4 = x^{2+4} = x^6$.

When dividing the powers of a given quantity, the rule is

$$\frac{x^n}{x^m} = x^{n-m} \qquad \text{[A.4]}$$

For example, $x^8/x^2 = x^{8-2} = x^6$.

A power that is a fraction, such as $\tfrac{1}{3}$, corresponds to a root as follows:

$$x^{1/n} = \sqrt[n]{x} \qquad \text{[A.5]}$$

For example, $4^{1/3} = \sqrt[3]{4} = 1.587\,4$. (A scientific calculator is useful for such calculations.)

Finally, any quantity x^n raised to the mth power is

$$(x^n)^m = x^{nm} \qquad \text{[A.6]}$$

Table A.1 summarizes the rules of exponents.

TABLE A.1 Rules of Exponents

$x^0 = 1$
$x^1 = x$
$x^n x^m = x^{n+m}$
$x^n / x^m = x^{n-m}$
$x^{1/n} = \sqrt[n]{x}$
$(x^n)^m = x^{nm}$

Exercises

Verify the following:

1. $3^2 \times 3^3 = 243$
2. $x^5 x^{-8} = x^{-3}$
3. $x^{10}/x^{-5} = x^{15}$
4. $5^{1/3} = 1.709\,975$ (Use your calculator.)
5. $60^{1/4} = 2.783\,158$ (Use your calculator.)
6. $(x^4)^3 = x^{12}$

C. Factoring

The following are some useful formulas for factoring an equation:

$$ax + ay + az = a(x + y + z) \qquad \text{common factor}$$

$$a^2 + 2ab + b^2 = (a + b)^2 \qquad \text{perfect square}$$

$$a^2 - b^2 = (a + b)(a - b) \qquad \text{differences of squares}$$

D. Quadratic Equations

The general form of a quadratic equation is

$$ax^2 + bx + c = 0 \qquad [\text{A.7}]$$

where x is the unknown quantity and a, b, and c are numerical factors referred to as coefficients of the equation. This equation has two roots, given by

$$x = \frac{-b \pm \sqrt{b^2 - 4ac}}{2a} \qquad [\text{A.8}]$$

If $b^2 - 4ac > 0$, the roots are real.

■ EXAMPLE

The equation $x^2 + 5x + 4 = 0$ has the following roots corresponding to the two signs of the square-root term:

$$x = \frac{-5 \pm \sqrt{5^2 - (4)(1)(4)}}{2(1)} = \frac{-5 \pm \sqrt{9}}{2} = \frac{-5 \pm 3}{2}$$

$$x_1 = \frac{-5 + 3}{2} = \boxed{-1} \qquad x_2 = \frac{-5 - 3}{2} = \boxed{-4}$$

where x_1 refers to the root corresponding to the positive sign and x_2 refers to the root corresponding to the negative sign.

■ EXAMPLE

A ball is projected upwards at 16.0 m/s. Use the quadratic formula to determine the time necessary for it to reach a height of 8.00 m above the point of release.

SOLUTION From the discussion of ballistics in Chapter 2, we can write

$$(1) \quad x = \tfrac{1}{2}at^2 + v_0 t + x_0$$

The acceleration is due to gravity, given by $a = -9.80$ m/s²; the initial velocity is $v_0 = 16.0$ m/s; and the initial position is the point of release, taken to be $x_0 = 0$. Substitute these values into Equation (1) and set $x = 8.00$ m, arriving at

$$x = -4.90t^2 + 16.00t = 8.00$$

where units have been suppressed for mathematical clarity. Rearrange this expression into the standard form of Equation A.7:

$$-4.90t^2 + 16.00t - 8.00 = 0$$

The equation is quadratic in the time, t. We have $a = -4.9$, $b = 16$, and $c = -8.00$. Substitute these values into Equation A.8:

$$t = \frac{-16.0 \pm \sqrt{16^2 - 4(-4.90)(-8.00)}}{2(-4.90)} = \frac{-16.0 \pm \sqrt{99.2}}{-9.80}$$

$$= 1.63 \mp \frac{\sqrt{99.2}}{9.80} = \boxed{0.614 \text{ s}, \ 2.65 \text{ s}}$$

Both solutions are valid in this case, one corresponding to reaching the point of interest on the way up and the other to reaching it on the way back down.

Exercises

Solve the following quadratic equations:

Answers

1. $x^2 + 2x - 3 = 0$ $x_1 = 1$ $x_2 = -3$
2. $2x^2 - 5x + 2 = 0$ $x_1 = 2$ $x_2 = \frac{1}{2}$
3. $2x^2 - 4x - 9 = 0$ $x_1 = 1 + \sqrt{22}/2$ $x_2 = 1 - \sqrt{22}/2$

4. Repeat the ballistics example for a height of 10.0 m above the point of release.
   Answer: $t_1 = 0.842$ s $t_2 = 2.42$ s

E. Linear Equations

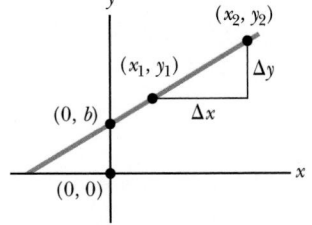

Figure A.1

A linear equation has the general form

$$y = mx + b \qquad \text{[A.9]}$$

where m and b are constants. This kind of equation is called linear because the graph of y versus x is a straight line, as shown in Figure A.1. The constant b, called the y-intercept, represents the value of y at which the straight line intersects the y-axis. The constant m is equal to the slope of the straight line. If any two points on the straight line are specified by the coordinates (x_1, y_1) and (x_2, y_2), as in Figure A.1, the slope of the straight line can be expressed as

$$\text{Slope} = \frac{y_2 - y_1}{x_2 - x_1} = \frac{\Delta y}{\Delta x} \qquad \text{[A.10]}$$

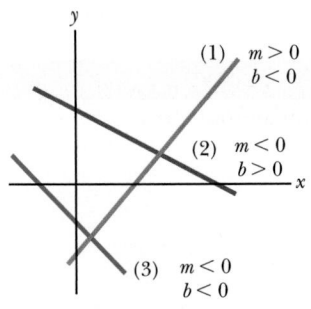

Figure A.2

Note that m and b can have either positive or negative values. If $m > 0$, the straight line has a positive slope, as in Figure A.1. If $m < 0$, the straight line has a negative slope. In Figure A.1, both m and b are positive. Three other possible situations are shown in Figure A.2.

■ EXAMPLE

Suppose the electrical resistance of a metal wire is 5.00 Ω at a temperature of 20.0°C and 6.14 Ω at 80.0°C. Assuming the resistance changes linearly, what is the resistance of the wire at 60.0°C?

SOLUTION   Find the equation of the line describing the resistance R and then substitute the new temperature into it. Two points on the graph of resistance versus temperature, (20.0°C, 5.00 Ω) and (80.0°C, 6.14 Ω), allow computation of the slope:

$$(1) \quad m = \frac{\Delta R}{\Delta T} = \frac{6.14\ \Omega - 5.00\ \Omega}{80.0°C - 20.0°C} = 1.90 \times 10^{-2}\ \Omega/°C$$

Now use the point-slope formulation of a line, with this slope and (20.0°C, 5.00 Ω):

$$(2) \quad R - R_0 = m(T - T_0)$$

$$(3) \quad R - 5.00\ \Omega = (1.90 \times 10^{-2}\ \Omega/°C)(T - 20.0°C)$$

Finally, substitute $T = 60.0°$ into Equation (3) and solve for R, getting $R = 5.76\ \Omega$.

Exercises

1. Draw graphs of the following straight lines:
       (a) $y = 5x + 3$ **(b)** $y = -2x + 4$ **(c)** $y = -3x - 6$
2. Find the slopes of the straight lines described in Exercise 1.
       Answers: (a) 5   **(b)** -2 **(c)** -3

3. Find the slopes of the straight lines that pass through the following sets of points: **(a)** $(0, -4)$ and $(4, 2)$ **(b)** $(0, 0)$ and $(2, -5)$ **(c)** $(-5, 2)$ and $(4, -2)$
Answers: (a) $3/2$ **(b)** $-5/2$ **(c)** $-4/9$

4. Suppose an experiment measures the following displacements (in meters) from equilibrium of a vertical spring due to attaching weights (in Newtons): $(0.025\ 0$ m, 22.0 N$)$, $(0.075\ 0$ m, 66.0 N$)$. Find the spring constant, which is the slope of the line in the graph of weight versus displacement.
Answer: 880 N/m

F. Solving Simultaneous Linear Equations

Consider the equation $3x + 5y = 15$, which has two unknowns, x and y. Such an equation doesn't have a unique solution. For example, note that $(x = 0, y = 3)$, $(x = 5, y = 0)$, and $(x = 2, y = 9/5)$ are all solutions to this equation.

If a problem has two unknowns, a unique solution is possible only if we have two equations. In general, if a problem has n unknowns, its solution requires n equations. To solve two simultaneous equations involving two unknowns, x and y, we solve one of the equations for x in terms of y and substitute this expression into the other equation.

▪ EXAMPLE

Solve the following two simultaneous equations:

$$(\mathbf{1})\quad 5x + y = -8 \qquad (\mathbf{2})\quad 2x - 2y = 4$$

SOLUTION From Equation (2), we find that $x = y + 2$. Substitution of this value into Equation (1) gives

$$5(y + 2) + y = -8$$
$$6y = -18$$
$$y = \boxed{-3}$$
$$x = y + 2 = \boxed{-1}$$

ALTERNATE SOLUTION Multiply each term in Equation (1) by the factor 2 and add the result to Equation (2):

$$10x + 2y = -16$$
$$\underline{2x - 2y = 4}$$
$$12x = -12$$
$$x = \boxed{-1}$$
$$y = x - 2 = \boxed{-3}$$

Two linear equations containing two unknowns can also be solved by a graphical method. If the straight lines corresponding to the two equations are plotted in a conventional coordinate system, the intersection of the two lines represents the solution. For example, consider the two equations

$$x - y = 2$$
$$x - 2y = -1$$

These equations are plotted in Figure A.3. The intersection of the two lines has the coordinates $x = 5$, $y = 3$, which represents the solution to the equations. You should check this solution by the analytical technique discussed above.

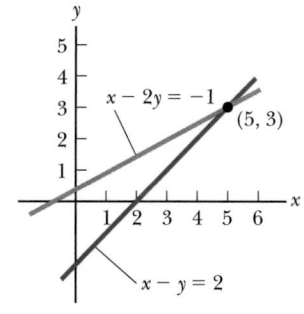

Figure A.3

▪ EXAMPLE

A block of mass $m = 2.00$ kg travels in the positive x-direction at $v_i = 5.00$ m/s, while a second block, of mass $M = 4.00$ kg and leading the first block, travels in the positive x-direction at 2.00 m/s. The surface is frictionless. What are the blocks' velocities after collision, if that collision is perfectly elastic?

SOLUTION As can be seen in Chapter 6, a perfectly elastic collision involves equations for the momentum and energy. With algebra, the energy equation, which is quadratic in v, can be recast as a linear equation. The two equations are given by

$$\textbf{(1)} \quad mv_i + MV_i = mv_f + MV_f$$

$$\textbf{(2)} \quad v_i - V_i = -(v_f - V_f)$$

Substitute the known quantities $v_i = 5.00$ m/s and $V_i = 2.00$ m/s into Equations (1) and (2):

$$\textbf{(3)} \quad 18 = 2v_f + 4V_f$$

$$\textbf{(4)} \quad 3 = -v_f + V_f$$

Multiply Equation (4) by 2 and add to Equation (3):

$$18 = 2v_f + 4V_f$$
$$\underline{6 = -2v_f + 2V_f}$$
$$24 = 6V_f \quad \rightarrow \quad V_f = \boxed{4.00 \text{ m/s}}$$

Substituting the solution for V_f back into Equation (4) yields $v_f = \boxed{1.00 \text{ m/s}}$.

Exercises

Solve the following pairs of simultaneous equations involving two unknowns:

		Answers
1.	$x + y = 8$	$x = 5, y = 3$
	$x - y = 2$	
2.	$98 - T = 10a$	$T = 65.3, a = 3.27$
	$T - 49 = 5a$	
3.	$6x + 2y = 6$	$x = 2, y = -3$
	$8x - 4y = 28$	

G. Logarithms and Exponentials

Suppose a quantity x is expressed as a power of some quantity a:

$$x = a^y \tag{A.11}$$

The number a is called the **base** number. The **logarithm** of x with respect to the base a is equal to the exponent to which the base must be raised so as to satisfy the expression $x = a^y$:

$$y = \log_a x \tag{A.12}$$

Conversely, the **antilogarithm** of y is the number x:

$$x = \text{antilog}_a y \tag{A.13}$$

The antilog expression is in fact identical to the exponential expression in Equation A.11, which is preferable for practical purposes.

In practice, the two bases most often used are base 10, called the *common* logarithm base, and base $e = 2.718\ldots$, called the *natural* logarithm base. When common logarithms are used,

$$y = \log_{10} x \quad (\text{or } x = 10^y) \tag{A.14}$$

When natural logarithms are used,

$$y = \ln x \qquad (\text{or } x = e^y) \qquad\qquad [\text{A.15}]$$

For example, $\log_{10} 52 = 1.716$, so $\text{antilog}_{10} 1.716 = 10^{1.716} = 52$. Likewise, $\ln_e 52 = 3.951$, so $\text{antiln}_e 3.951 = e^{3.951} = 52$.

In general, note that you can convert between base 10 and base e with the equality

$$\ln x = (2.302\ 585)\log_{10} x \qquad\qquad [\text{A.16}]$$

Finally, some useful properties of logarithms are

$$\log(ab) = \log a + \log b \qquad \ln e = 1$$

$$\log(a/b) = \log a - \log b \qquad \ln e^a = a$$

$$\log(a^n) = n \log a \qquad\qquad \ln\left(\frac{1}{a}\right) = -\ln a$$

Logarithms in college physics are used most notably in the definition of decibel level. Sound intensity varies across several orders of magnitude, making it awkward to compare different intensities. Decibel level converts these intensities to a more manageable logarithmic scale.

■ EXAMPLE | (Logs)

Suppose a jet testing its engines produces a sound intensity of $I = 0.750$ W at a given location in an airplane hangar. What decibel level corresponds to this sound intensity?

SOLUTION Decibel level β is defined by

$$\beta = 10 \log\left(\frac{I}{I_0}\right)$$

where $I_0 = 1 \times 10^{-12}$ W/m^2 is the standard reference intensity. Substitute the given information:

$$\beta = 10 \log\left(\frac{0.750 \text{ W/m}^2}{10^{-12} \text{ W/m}^2}\right) = 119 \text{ dB}$$

■ EXAMPLE | (Antilogs)

A collection of four identical machines creates a decibel level of $\beta = 87.0$ dB in a machine shop. What sound intensity would be created by only one such machine?

SOLUTION We use the equation of decibel level to find the total sound intensity of the four machines, and then we divide by 4. From Equation (1):

$$87.0 \text{ dB} = 10 \log\left(\frac{I}{10^{-12} \text{ W/m}^2}\right)$$

Divide both sides by 10 and take the antilog of both sides, which means, equivalently, to exponentiate:

$$10^{8.7} = 10^{\log(I/10^{-12})} = \frac{I}{10^{-12}}$$

$$I = 10^{-12} \cdot 10^{8.7} = 10^{-3.3} = 5.01 \times 10^{-4} \text{ W/m}^2\text{w}$$

There are four machines, so this result must be divided by 4 to get the intensity of one machine:

$$I = 1.25 \times 10^{-4} \text{ W/m}^2$$

EXAMPLE (Exponentials)

The half-life of tritium is 12.33 years. (Tritium is the heaviest isotope of hydrogen, with a nucleus consisting of a proton and two neutrons.) If a sample contains 3.0 g of tritium initially, how much remains after 20.0 years?

SOLUTION The equation giving the number of nuclei of a radioactive substance as a function of time is

$$N = N_0\left(\frac{1}{2}\right)^n$$

where N is the number of nuclei remaining, N_0 is the initial number of nuclei, and n is the number of half-lives. Note that this equation is an exponential expression with a base of $\frac{1}{2}$. The number of half-lives is given by $n = t/T_{1/2} = 20.0 \text{ yr}/12.33 \text{ yr} = 1.62$. The fractional amount of tritium that remains after 20.0 yr is therefore

$$\frac{N}{N_0} = \left(\frac{1}{2}\right)^{1.62} = 0.325$$

Hence, of the original 3.00 g of tritium, $0.325 \times 3.00 \text{ g} = 0.975 \text{ g}$ remains.

A.4 Geometry

Table A.2 gives the areas and volumes for several geometric shapes used throughout this text. These areas and volumes are important in numerous physics applications. A good example is the concept of pressure P, which is the force per unit area. As an equation, it is written $P = F/A$. Areas must also be calculated in problems involving the volume rate of fluid flow through a pipe using the equation of continuity, the tensile stress exerted on a cable by a weight, the rate of thermal energy transfer through a barrier, and the density of current through a wire. There are numerous other applications. Volumes are important in computing the buoyant force exerted by water on a submerged object, in calculating densities, and in determining the bulk stress of fluid or gas on an object, which affects its volume. Again, there are numerous other applications.

TABLE A.2 Useful Information for Geometry

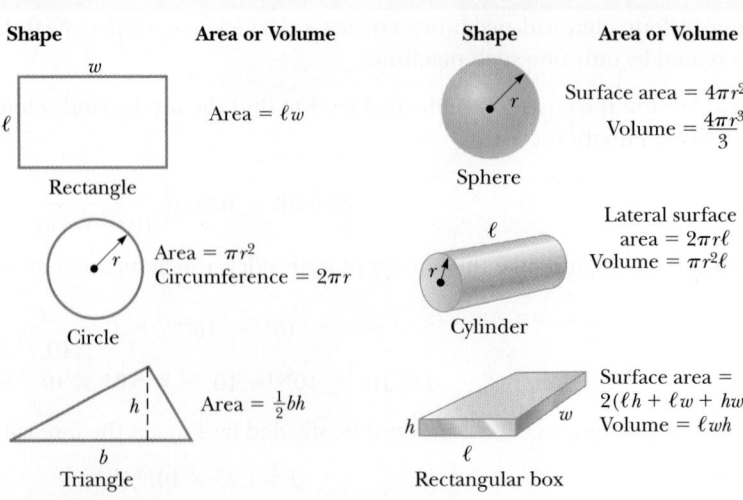

A.5 Trigonometry

Some of the most basic facts concerning trigonometry are presented in Chapter 1, and we encourage you to study the material presented there if you are having trouble with this branch of mathematics. The most important trigonometric concepts include the Pythagorean theorem:

$$\Delta s^2 = \Delta x^2 + \Delta y^2 \qquad [A.17]$$

This equation states that the square distance along the hypotenuse of a right triangle equals the sum of the squares of the legs. It can also be used to find distances between points in Cartesian coordinates and the length of a vector, where Δx is replaced by the x-component of the vector and Δy is replaced by the y-component of the vector. If the vector $\vec{A}$ has components A_x and A_y, the magnitude A of the vector satisfies

$$A^2 = A_x^2 + A_y^2 \qquad [A.18]$$

which has a form completely analogous to the form of the Pythagorean theorem. Also highly useful are the cosine and sine functions because they relate the length of a vector to its x- and y-components:

$$A_x = A \cos\theta \qquad [A.19]$$
$$A_y = A \sin\theta \qquad [A.20]$$

The direction θ of a vector in a plane can be determined by use of the tangent function:

$$\tan\theta = \frac{A_y}{A_x} \qquad [A.21]$$

A relative of the Pythagorean theorem is also frequently useful:

$$\sin^2\theta + \cos^2\theta = 1 \qquad [A.22]$$

Details on the above concepts can be found in the extensive discussions in Chapters 1 and 3. The following are some other trigonometric identities that can sometimes be useful:

$$\sin\theta = \cos(90° - \theta)$$
$$\cos\theta = \sin(90° - \theta)$$
$$\sin 2\theta = 2\sin\theta\cos\theta$$
$$\cos 2\theta = \cos^2\theta - \sin^2\theta$$
$$\sin(\theta \pm \phi) = \sin\theta\cos\phi \pm \cos\theta\sin\phi$$
$$\cos(\theta \pm \phi) = \cos\theta\cos\phi \pm \sin\theta\sin\phi$$

The following relationships apply to any triangle, as shown in Figure A.4:

$$\alpha + \beta + \gamma = 180°$$
$$a^2 = b^2 + c^2 - 2bc\cos\alpha$$
$$b^2 = a^2 + c^2 - 2ac\cos\beta \qquad \text{law of cosines}$$
$$c^2 = a^2 + b^2 - 2ab\cos\gamma$$
$$\frac{a}{\sin\alpha} = \frac{b}{\sin\beta} = \frac{c}{\sin\gamma} \qquad \text{law of sines}$$

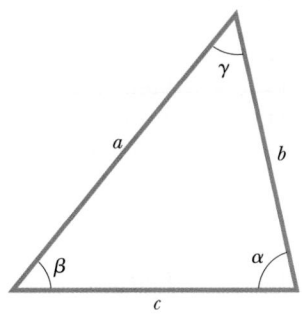

Figure A.4

▪ Appendix B *An Abbreviated Table of Isotopes*

Atomic Number Z	Element	Symbol	Chemical Atomic Mass (u)	Mass Number (* Indicates Radioactive) A	Atomic Mass (u)	Percent Abundance	Half-Life (If Radioactive) $T_{1/2}$
0	(Neutron)	n		1*	1.008 665		10.4 min
1	Hydrogen	H	1.007 94	1	1.007 825	99.988 5	
	Deuterium	D		2	2.014 102	0.011 5	
	Tritium	T		3*	3.016 049		12.33 yr
2	Helium	He	4.002 602	3	3.016 029	0.000 137	
				4	4.002 603	99.999 863	
3	Lithium	Li	6.941	6	6.015 122	7.5	
				7	7.016 004	92.5	
4	Beryllium	Be	9.012 182	7*	7.016 929		53.3 days
				9	9.012 182	100	
5	Boron	B	10.811	10	10.012 937	19.9	
				11	11.009 306	80.1	
6	Carbon	C	12.010 7	10*	10.016 853		19.3 s
				11*	11.011 434		20.4 min
				12	12.000 000	98.93	
				13	13.003 355	1.07	
				14*	14.003 242		5 730 yr
7	Nitrogen	N	14.006 7	13*	13.005 739		9.96 min
				14	14.003 074	99.632	
				15	15.000 109	0.368	
8	Oxygen	O	15.999 4	15*	15.003 065		122 s
				16	15.994 915	99.757	
				18	17.999 160	0.205	
9	Fluorine	F	18.998 403 2	19	18.998 403	100	
10	Neon	Ne	20.179 7	20	19.992 440	90.48	
				22	21.991 385	9.25	
11	Sodium	Na	22.989 77	22*	21.994 437		2.61 yr
				23	22.989 770	100	
				24*	23.990 963		14.96 h
12	Magnesium	Mg	24.305 0	24	23.985 042	78.99	
				25	24.985 837	10.00	
				26	25.982 593	11.01	
13	Aluminum	Al	26.981 538	27	26.981 539	100	
14	Silicon	Si	28.085 5	28	27.976 926	92.229 7	
15	Phosphorus	P	30.973 761	31	30.973 762	100	
				32*	31.973 907		14.26 days
16	Sulfur	S	32.066	32	31.972 071	94.93	
				35*	34.969 032		87.5 days
17	Chlorine	Cl	35.452 7	35	34.968 853	75.78	
				37	36.965 903	24.22	
18	Argon	Ar	39.948	40	39.962 383	99.600 3	
19	Potassium	K	39.098 3	39	38.963 707	93.258 1	
				40*	39.963 999	0.011 7	1.28×10^9 yr
20	Calcium	Ca	40.078	40	39.962 591	96.941	
21	Scandium	Sc	44.955 910	45	44.955 910	100	
22	Titanium	Ti	47.867	48	47.947 947	73.72	

Atomic Number Z	Element	Symbol	Chemical Atomic Mass (u)	Mass Number (* Indicates Radioactive) A	Atomic Mass (u)	Percent Abundance	Half-Life (If Radioactive) $T_{1/2}$
23	Vanadium	V	50.941 5	51	50.943 964	99.750	
24	Chromium	Cr	51.996 1	52	51.940 512	83.789	
25	Manganese	Mn	54.938 049	55	54.938 050	100	
26	Iron	Fe	55.845	56	55.934 942	91.754	
27	Cobalt	Co	58.933 200	59	58.933 200	100	
				60*	59.933 822		5.27 yr
28	Nickel	Ni	58.693 4	58	57.935 348	68.076 9	
				60	59.930 790	26.223 1	
29	Copper	Cu	63.546	63	62.929 601	69.17	
				65	64.927 794	30.83	
30	Zinc	Zn	65.39	64	63.929 147	48.63	
				66	65.926 037	27.90	
				68	67.924 848	18.75	
31	Gallium	Ga	69.723	69	68.925 581	60.108	
				71	70.924 705	39.892	
32	Germanium	Ge	72.61	70	69.924 250	20.84	
				72	71.922 076	27.54	
				74	73.921 178	36.28	
33	Arsenic	As	74.921 60	75	74.921 596	100	
34	Selenium	Se	78.96	78	77.917 310	23.77	
				80	79.916 522	49.61	
35	Bromine	Br	79.904	79	78.918 338	50.69	
				81	80.916 291	49.31	
36	Krypton	Kr	83.80	82	81.913 485	11.58	
				83	82.914 136	11.49	
				84	83.911 507	57.00	
				86	85.910 610	17.30	
37	Rubidium	Rb	85.467 8	85	84.911 789	72.17	
				87*	86.909 184	27.83	4.75×10^{10} yr
38	Strontium	Sr	87.62	86	85.909 262	9.86	
				88	87.905 614	82.58	
				90*	89.907 738		29.1 yr
39	Yttrium	Y	88.905 85	89	88.905 848	100	
40	Zirconium	Zr	91.224	90	89.904 704	51.45	
				91	90.905 645	11.22	
				92	91.905 040	17.15	
				94	93.906 316	17.38	
41	Niobium	Nb	92.906 38	93	92.906 378	100	
42	Molybdenum	Mo	95.94	92	91.906 810	14.84	
				95	94.905 842	15.92	
				96	95.904 679	16.68	
				98	97.905 408	24.13	

(Continued)

Atomic Number Z	Element	Symbol	Chemical Atomic Mass (u)	Mass Number (* Indicates Radioactive) A	Atomic Mass (u)	Percent Abundance	Half-Life (If Radioactive) $T_{1/2}$
43	Technetium	Tc		98*	97.907 216		4.2×10^6 yr
				99*	98.906 255		2.1×10^5 yr
44	Ruthenium	Ru	101.07	99	98.905 939	12.76	
				100	99.904 220	12.60	
				101	100.905 582	17.06	
				102	101.904 350	31.55	
				104	103.905 430	18.62	
45	Rhodium	Rh	102.905 50	103	102.905 504	100	
46	Palladium	Pd	106.42	104	103.904 035	11.14	
				105	104.905 084	22.33	
				106	105.903 483	27.33	
				108	107.903 894	26.46	
				110	109.905 152	11.72	
47	Silver	Ag	107.868 2	107	106.905 093	51.839	
				109	108.904 756	48.161	
48	Cadmium	Cd	112.411	110	109.903 006	12.49	
				111	110.904 182	12.80	
				112	111.902 757	24.13	
				113*	112.904 401	12.22	9.3×10^{15} yr
				114	113.903 358	28.73	
49	Indium	In	114.818	115*	114.903 878	95.71	4.4×10^{14} yr
50	Tin	Sn	118.710	116	115.901 744	14.54	
				118	117.901 606	24.22	
				120	119.902 197	32.58	
51	Antimony	Sb	121.760	121	120.903 818	57.21	
				123	122.904 216	42.79	
52	Tellurium	Te	127.60	126	125.903 306	18.84	
				128*	127.904 461	31.74	$> 8 \times 10^{24}$ yr
				130*	129.906 223	34.08	$\leq 1.25 \times 10^{21}$ yr
53	Iodine	I	126.904 47	127	126.904 468	100	
				129*	128.904 988		1.6×10^7 yr
54	Xenon	Xe	131.29	129	128.904 780	26.44	
				131	130.905 082	21.18	
				132	131.904 145	26.89	
				134	133.905 394	10.44	
				136*	135.907 220	8.87	$\geq 2.36 \times 10^{21}$ yr
55	Cesium	Cs	132.905 45	133	132.905 447	100	
56	Barium	Ba	137.327	137	136.905 821	11.232	
				138	137.905 241	71.698	
57	Lanthanum	La	138.905 5	139	138.906 349	99.910	
58	Cerium	Ce	140.116	140	139.905 434	88.450	
				142*	141.909 240	11.114	$> 5 \times 10^{16}$ yr
59	Praseodymium	Pr	140.907 65	141	140.907 648	100	
60	Neodymium	Nd	144.24	142	141.907 719	27.2	
				144*	143.910 083	23.8	2.3×10^{15} yr
				146	145.913 112	17.2	

Atomic Number Z	Element	Symbol	Chemical Atomic Mass (u)	Mass Number (* Indicates Radioactive) A	Atomic Mass (u)	Percent Abundance	Half-Life (If Radioactive) $T_{1/2}$
61	Promethium	Pm		145*	144.912 744		17.7 yr
62	Samarium	Sm	150.36	147*	146.914 893	14.99	1.06×10^{11} yr
				149*	148.917 180	13.82	$> 2 \times 10^{15}$ yr
				152	151.919 728	26.75	
				154	153.922 205	22.75	
63	Europium	Eu	151.964	151	150.919 846	47.81	
				153	152.921 226	52.19	
64	Gadolinium	Gd	157.25	156	155.922 120	20.47	
				158	157.924 100	24.84	
				160	159.927 051	21.86	
65	Terbium	Tb	158.925 34	159	158.925 343	100	
66	Dysprosium	Dy	162.50	162	161.926 796	25.51	
				163	162.928 728	24.90	
				164	163.929 171	28.18	
67	Holmium	Ho	164.930 32	165	164.930 320	100	
68	Erbium	Er	167.6	166	165.930 290	33.61	
				167	166.932 045	22.93	
				168	167.932 368	26.78	
69	Thulium	Tm	168.934 21	169	168.934 211	100	
70	Ytterbium	Yb	173.04	172	171.936 378	21.83	
				173	172.938 207	16.13	
				174	173.938 858	31.83	
71	Lutecium	Lu	174.967	175	174.940 768	97.41	
72	Hafnium	Hf	178.49	177	176.943 220	18.60	
				178	177.943 698	27.28	
				179	178.945 815	13.62	
				180	179.946 549	35.08	
73	Tantalum	Ta	180.947 9	181	180.947 996	99.988	
74	Tungsten (Wolfram)	W	183.84	182	181.948 206	26.50	
				183	182.950 224	14.31	
				184*	183.950 933	30.64	$> 3 \times 10^{17}$ yr
				186	185.954 362	28.43	
75	Rhenium	Re	186.207	185	184.952 956	37.40	
				187*	186.955 751	62.60	4.4×10^{10} yr
76	Osmium	Os	190.23	188	187.955 836	13.24	
				189	188.958 145	16.15	
				190	189.958 445	26.26	
				192	191.961 479	40.78	
77	Iridium	Ir	192.217	191	190.960 591	37.3	
				193	192.962 924	62.7	
78	Platinum	Pt	195.078	194	193.962 664	32.967	
				195	194.964 774	33.832	
				196	195.964 935	25.242	
79	Gold	Au	196.966 55	197	196.966 552	100	
80	Mercury	Hg	200.59	199	198.968 262	16.87	
				200	199.968 309	23.10	
				201	200.970 285	13.18	
				202	201.970 626	29.86	

(Continued)

Atomic Number Z	Element	Symbol	Chemical Atomic Mass (u)	Mass Number (* Indicates Radioactive) A	Atomic Mass (u)	Percent Abundance	Half-Life (If Radioactive) $T_{1/2}$
81	Thallium	Tl	204.383 3	203	202.972 329	29.524	
				205	204.974 412	70.476	
		(Th C″)		208*	207.982 005		3.053 min
		(Ra C″)		210*	209.990 066		1.30 min
82	Lead	Pb	207.2	204*	203.973 029	1.4	$\geq 1.4 \times 10^{17}$ yr
				206	205.974 449	24.1	
				207	206.975 881	22.1	
				208	207.976 636	52.4	
		(Ra D)		210*	209.984 173		22.3 yr
		(Ac B)		211*	210.988 732		36.1 min
		(Th B)		212*	211.991 888		10.64 h
		(Ra B)		214*	213.999 798		26.8 min
83	Bismuth	Bi	208.980 38	209	208.980 383	100	
		(Th C)		211*	210.987 258		2.14 min
84	Polonium	Po					
		(Ra F)		210*	209.982 857		138.38 days
		(Ra C′)		214*	213.995 186		164 μs
85	Astatine	At		218*	218.008 682		1.6 s
86	Radon	Rn		222*	222.017 570		3.823 days
87	Francium	Fr					
		(Ac K)		223*	223.019 731		22 min
88	Radium	Ra		226*	226.025 403		1 600 yr
		(Ms Th$_1$)		228*	228.031 064		5.75 yr
89	Actinium	Ac		227*	227.027 747		21.77 yr
90	Thorium	Th	232.038 1				
		(Rd Th)		228*	228.028 731		1.913 yr
		(Th)		232*	232.038 050	100	1.40×10^{10} yr
91	Protactinium	Pa	231.035 88	231*	231.035 879		32.760 yr
92	Uranium	U	238.028 9	232*	232.037 146		69 yr
				233*	233.039 628		1.59×10^5 yr
		(Ac U)		235*	235.043 923	0.720 0	7.04×10^8 yr
				236*	236.045 562		2.34×10^7 yr
		(UI)		238*	238.050 783	99.274 5	4.47×10^9 yr
93	Neptunium	Np		237*	237.048 167		2.14×10^6 yr
94	Plutonium	Pu		239*	239.052 156		2.412×10^4 yr
				242*	242.058 737		3.73×10^6 yr
				244*	244.064 198		8.1×10^7 yr

Sources: Chemical atomic masses are from T. B. Coplen, "Atomic Weights of the Elements 1999," a technical report to the International Union of Pure and Applied Chemistry, and published in *Pure and Applied Chemistry*, 73(4), 667–683, 2001. Atomic masses of the isotopes are from G. Audi and A. H. Wapstra, "The 1995 Update to the Atomic Mass Evaluation," *Nuclear Physics*, A595, vol. 4, 409–480, December 25, 1995. Percent abundance values are from K. J. R. Rosman and P. D. P. Taylor, "Isotopic Compositions of the Elements 1999," a technical report to the International Union of Pure and Applied Chemistry, and published in *Pure and Applied Chemistry*, 70(1), 217–236, 1998.

TABLE C.1 Mathematical Symbols Used in the Text and Their Meaning

Symbol	Meaning
$=$	is equal to
$\neq$	is not equal to
$\equiv$	is defined as
$\propto$	is proportional to
$>$	is greater than
$<$	is less than
$\gg$	is much greater than
$\ll$	is much less than
$\approx$	is approximately equal to
$\sim$	is on the order of magnitude of
Δx	change in x or uncertainty in x
Σx_i	sum of all quantities x_i
$\lvert x \rvert$	absolute value of x (always a positive quantity)

TABLE C.2 Standard Symbols for Units

Symbol	Unit	Symbol	Unit
A	ampere	kcal	kilocalorie
Å	angstrom	kg	kilogram
atm	atmosphere	km	kilometer
Bq	bequerel	kmol	kilomole
Btu	British thermal unit	L	liter
C	coulomb	lb	pound
°C	degree Celsius	ly	lightyear
cal	calorie	m	meter
cm	centimeter	min	minute
Ci	curie	mol	mole
d	day	N	newton
deg	degree (angle)	nm	nanometer
eV	electronvolt	Pa	pascal
°F	degree Fahrenheit	rad	radian
F	farad	rev	revolution
ft	foot	s	second
G	Gauss	T	tesla
g	gram	u	atomic mass unit
H	henry	V	volt
h	hour	W	watt
hp	horsepower	Wb	weber
Hz	hertz	yr	year
in.	inch	μm	micrometer
J	joule	Ω	ohm
K	kelvin		

TABLE C.3 The Greek Alphabet

Alpha	A	α	Nu	N	ν
Beta	B	β	Xi	Ξ	ξ
Gamma	Γ	γ	Omicron	O	o
Delta	Δ	δ	Pi	Π	π
Epsilon	E	ϵ	Rho	P	ρ
Zeta	Z	ζ	Sigma	Σ	σ
Eta	H	η	Tau	T	τ
Theta	Θ	θ	Upsilon	Y	υ
Iota	I	ι	Phi	Φ	ϕ
Kappa	K	κ	Chi	X	χ
Lambda	Λ	λ	Psi	Ψ	ψ
Mu	M	μ	Omega	Ω	ω

TABLE C.4 Physical Data Often Used[a]

Average Earth–Moon distance	3.84×10^8 m
Average Earth–Sun distance	1.496×10^{11} m
Equatorial radius of Earth	6.38×10^6 m
Density of air (20°C and 1 atm)	1.20 kg/m^3
Density of water (20°C and 1 atm)	1.00×10^3 kg/m^3
Free-fall acceleration	9.80 m/s^2
Mass of Earth	5.98×10^{24} kg
Mass of Moon	7.36×10^{22} kg
Mass of Sun	1.99×10^{30} kg
Standard atmospheric pressure	1.013×10^5 Pa

[a] These are the values of the constants as used in the text.

TABLE C.5 Some Fundamental Constants

Quantity	Symbol	Value[a]
Atomic mass unit	u	$1.660\ 538\ 782\ (83) \times 10^{-27}$ kg
		$931.494\ 028\ (23)$ MeV/c^2
Avogadro's number	N_A	$6.022\ 141\ 79\ (30) \times 10^{23}$ particles/mol
Bohr magneton	$\mu_B = \dfrac{e\hbar}{2m_e}$	$9.274\ 009\ 15\ (23) \times 10^{-24}$ J/T
Bohr radius	$a_0 = \dfrac{\hbar^2}{m_e e^2 k_e}$	$5.291\ 772\ 085\ 9\ (36) \times 10^{-11}$ m
Boltzmann's constant	$k_B = \dfrac{R}{N_A}$	$1.380\ 650\ 4\ (24) \times 10^{-23}$ J/K
Compton wavelength	$\lambda_C = \dfrac{h}{m_e c}$	$2.426\ 310\ 217\ 5\ (33) \times 10^{-12}$ m
Coulomb constant	$k_e = \dfrac{1}{4\pi\epsilon_0}$	$8.987\ 551\ 788 \ldots \times 10^9$ N·m²/C² (exact)
Deuteron mass	m_d	$3.343\ 583\ 20\ (17) \times 10^{-27}$ kg
		$2.013\ 553\ 212\ 724\ (78)$ u
Electron mass	m_e	$9.109\ 382\ 15\ (45) \times 10^{-31}$ kg
		$5.485\ 799\ 094\ 3\ (23) \times 10^{-4}$ u
		$0.510\ 998\ 910\ (13)$ MeV/c^2
Electron volt	eV	$1.602\ 176\ 487\ (40) \times 10^{-19}$ J
Elementary charge	e	$1.602\ 176\ 487\ (40) \times 10^{-19}$ C
Gas constant	R	$8.314\ 472\ (15)$ J/mol·K
Gravitational constant	G	$6.674\ 28\ (67) \times 10^{-11}$ N·m²/kg²
Neutron mass	m_n	$1.674\ 927\ 211\ (84) \times 10^{-27}$ kg
		$1.008\ 664\ 915\ 97\ (43)$ u
		$939.565\ 346\ (23)$ MeV/c^2
Nuclear magneton	$\mu_n = \dfrac{e\hbar}{2m_p}$	$5.050\ 783\ 24\ (13) \times 10^{-27}$ J/T
Permeability of free space	μ_0	$4\pi \times 10^{-7}$ T·m/A (exact)
Permittivity of free space	$\epsilon_0 = \dfrac{1}{\mu_0 c^2}$	$8.854\ 187\ 817 \ldots \times 10^{-12}$ C²/N·m² (exact)
Planck's constant	h	$6.626\ 068\ 96\ (33) \times 10^{-34}$ J·s
	$\hbar = \dfrac{h}{2\pi}$	$1.054\ 571\ 628\ (53) \times 10^{-34}$ J·s
Proton mass	m_p	$1.672\ 621\ 637\ (83) \times 10^{-27}$ kg
		$1.007\ 276\ 466\ 77\ (10)$ u
		$938.272\ 013\ (23)$ MeV/c^2
Rydberg constant	R_H	$1.097\ 373\ 156\ 852\ 7\ (73) \times 10^7$ m⁻¹
Speed of light in vacuum	c	$2.997\ 924\ 58 \times 10^8$ m/s (exact)

Note: These constants are the values recommended in 2006 by CODATA, based on a least-squares adjustment of data from different measurements. For a more complete list, see P. J. Mohr, B. N. Taylor, and D. B. Newell, "CODATA Recommended Values of the Fundamental Physical Constants: 2006." *Rev. Mod. Phys.* **80**:2, 633–730, 2008.

[a]The numbers in parentheses for the values represent the uncertainties of the last two digits.

SI Units

TABLE D.1 SI Base Units

Base Quantity	SI Base Unit Name	Symbol
Length	meter	m
Mass	kilogram	kg
Time	second	s
Electric current	ampere	A
Temperature	kelvin	K
Amount of substance	mole	mol
Luminous intensity	candela	cd

TABLE D.2 Derived SI Units

Quantity	Name	Symbol	Expression in Terms of Base Units	Expression in Terms of Other SI Units
Plane angle	radian	rad	m/m	
Frequency	hertz	Hz	s^{-1}	
Force	newton	N	$kg \cdot m/s^2$	J/m
Pressure	pascal	Pa	$kg/m \cdot s^2$	N/m^2
Energy: work	joule	J	$kg \cdot m^2/s^2$	$N \cdot m$
Power	watt	W	$kg \cdot m^2/s^3$	J/s
Electric charge	coulomb	C	$A \cdot s$	
Electric potential (emf)	volt	V	$kg \cdot m^2/A \cdot s^3$	W/A, J/C
Capacitance	farad	F	$A^2 \cdot s^4/kg \cdot m^2$	C/V
Electric resistance	ohm	Ω	$kg \cdot m^2/A^2 \cdot s^3$	V/A
Magnetic flux	weber	Wb	$kg \cdot m^2/A \cdot s^2$	$V \cdot s, T \cdot m^2$
Magnetic field intensity	tesla	T	$kg/A \cdot s^2$	Wb/m^2
Inductance	henry	H	$kg \cdot m^2/A^2 \cdot s^2$	Wb/A

Exam 1
Time—90 Minutes
7 Questions

Note: Please check with your teacher before writing in this textbook.

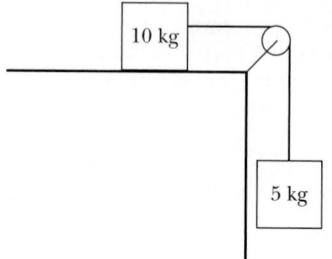

1. (15 points)

    A 10 kg block and a 5 kg block are connected by a light rope over a light, frictionless pulley. Initially, the 10 kg block sits at rest on a rough tabletop.

    (a) The dots below represent each block. Draw two similar dots and label the forces (not components) that act on each block while the system hangs at rest.

    (b) Calculate the coefficient of static friction between the 10 kg block and the tabletop that ensures the blocks remain at rest. If you need to draw anything other than what you have shown in part (a) to assist in your solution, use additional space on your answer sheet. Do <u>not</u> add anything to the figure you drew in part (a).

    The blocks are now given an initial velocity to the right. The coefficient of kinetic friction between the 10 kg block and the tabletop is 0.20.

    (c)

        i. Calculate the magnitude of the acceleration of the 10 kg block.

        ii. Draw a picture of the 10 kg block like the one below, then draw a vector representing the direction of the block's acceleration.

    (d)

        i. As the blocks accelerate, how does the tension T in the rope compare to the weight of the 5 kg block?

            ___ T is greater than the weight of the 5 kg block

            ___ T is less than the weight of the 5 kg block

            ___ T is equal to the weight of the 5 kg block

        ii. Justify your answer.

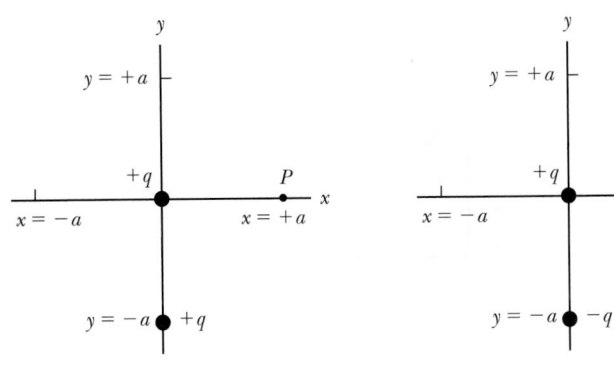

Arrangement 1   Arrangement 2

2. (10 points)

Two particles are fixed in a plane. The top particle is located at the origin of coordinates; the bottom particle is located on the y-axis at position $y = -a$. Point P is on the x-axis at position $x = +a$.

In arrangement 1, both particles have identical charge $+q$. In arrangement 2, the top particle has charge $+q$, while the bottom particle has charge $-q$.

(a)

    i. In which arrangement is the magnitude of the electric field E due to the charges at point P greater, or are the electric field magnitudes the same?

        ____ E is greater in arrangement 1

        ____ E is greater in arrangement 2

        ____ E is the same in both arrangements

    ii. Justify your answer.

(b) In which arrangement is the electric potential V greater, or are the electric potentials the same?

        ____ V is greater in arrangement 1

        ____ V is greater in arrangement 2

        ____ V is the same in both arrangements

Now consider arrangement 2 only.

(c) Derive an expression for the electric potential V at point P in arrangement 2 in terms of q, a, and fundamental constants.

(d)

    i. Draw a diagram similar to the diagram of arrangement 2 above, and then draw a vector representing the direction of the electric field at point P due to both charges. Label this vector **E**.

    ii. Explain how you determined the direction of **E**.

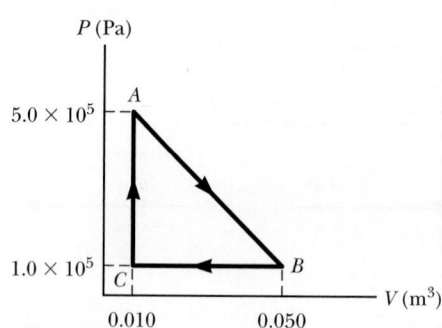

3. (15 points)

An ideal gas undergoes the cyclic process $A \rightarrow B \rightarrow C \rightarrow A$ as shown in the diagram above.

(a) Rank the temperature of the gas at states A, B, and C from highest to lowest. If two or more states have the same temperature, state that in your ranking.

Justify your answer.

(b) For each of the thermodynamic variables ΔU, Q, and W, indicate whether the variable is positive, negative, or zero for the process $A \rightarrow B$ only.

$A \rightarrow B$ ____ ΔU ____ Q ____ W

Justify your answer.

(c) Determine how much work, if any, was done on the gas in the process $A \rightarrow B$.

(d) Determine how much heat, if any, was added to the gas in the process $A \rightarrow B$.

(e) In the <u>entire</u> process $A \rightarrow B \rightarrow C \rightarrow A$, was heat added or removed from the gas, or neither?

___ heat was added

___ heat was removed

___ no heat was added or removed

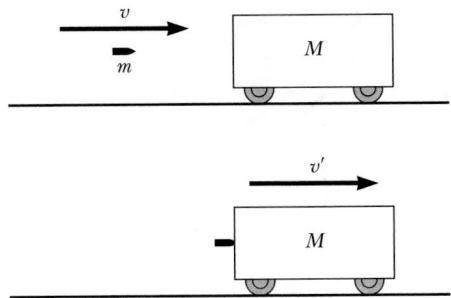

4. (10 points)

In an experiment, a projectile of mass m is shot with adjustable speed v toward a stationary cart of mass M. After each shot, the projectile lodges in the cart, and the combined objects move off with speed v'. Friction between the cart and the surface is negligible. Students repeat the experiment several times, varying the projectile's speed v and measuring the speed v'.

(a) Derive an expression for the speed v' in terms of m, M, and v.

The students obtain the data in the chart below.

Speed v (m/s)	Speed v' (m/s)
6	1.2
11	2.1
12	2.4
16	3.4
18	3.6
20	4.0

(b) On an axes similar to the one below, plot the data and draw a best-fit straight line. Label the axes and indicate a scale.

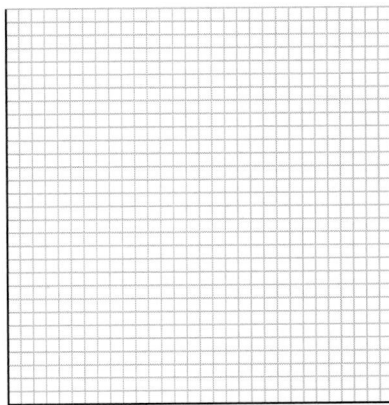

(c) The mass m of the projectile was known to be 100 g. Using your best-fit line, calculate the value of the cart's mass M.

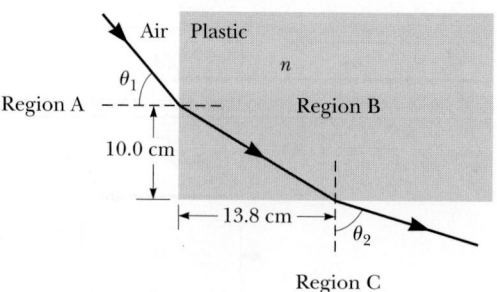

5. (10 points)

A green light ray of wavelength 520 nm in air enters the side of a rectangular block of plastic at an angle $\theta_1 = 45°$ and emerges from the bottom edge at an angle $\theta_2 = 76°$, as shown above. The distances of the beam's entrance and exit are labeled.

(a) Calculate the index of refraction n experienced by this light ray in the plastic.

(b) It is desired that the light beam undergo total internal reflection upon its exit from the plastic. Should θ_1 be increased or decreased?

___ increased   ___ decreased

Justify your answer.

(c) Determine the frequency of this light in the plastic.

(d) Rank the wavelength of this light in the three regions shown on the diagram. Rank from greatest to least, with number 1 being greatest. If the light has the same wavelength in several regions, give them the same ranking.

_____ Region A   _____ Region B   _____ Region C

Affixed to wall

12 Ω

24 V
+ −

Springs

Magnetic
field

5.0 cm

6. (10 points)

A 24 V battery and a 12 V resistor are fixed to a wall. They are connected to two identical springs, which suspend a straight wire of length 5.0 cm, mass 10.0 g, and negligible resistance. The springs each stretch a distance of 0.50 cm under the weight of the wire as the wire completes a circuit.

A magnetic field directed out of the page is then turned on in the region shown. The springs are observed to stretch an additional 0.30 cm.

(a) Determine the current produced by the battery.

(b) Calculate the spring constant of the left-hand spring.

(c) Calculate the magnitude of the applied magnetic field.

(d) Immediately after the magnetic field is turned on, the change in magnetic flux will, momentarily, cause the current in the circuit to change. Will the current increase or decrease during this brief interval? Justify your answer.

____ increase   ____ decrease

7. (10 points)

A pulsed ruby laser emits light at a wavelength of 694 nm in air. This laser produces a 14.0 ps pulse containing 3.00 J of energy.

(a)

    i. Calculate the physical length of the pulse as it travels through the air.

    ii. Which of the following objects has a length closest to the laser pulse length?

        ___ a classroom

        ___ the width of a piece of paper

        ___ an adult's arm

        ___ a fruit fly

(b) Calculate the number of photons in the pulse.

(c) You are asked to design a new laser that produces a pulse of the same duration with the same number of photons, but produces twice as much energy per pulse. Should this new laser have a wavelength that is greater than or less than that of the ruby laser?

    __ greater than   __ less than

Justify your answer.

Exam 2
Time—90 Minutes
6 Questions
Note: Please check with your teacher before writing in this textbook.

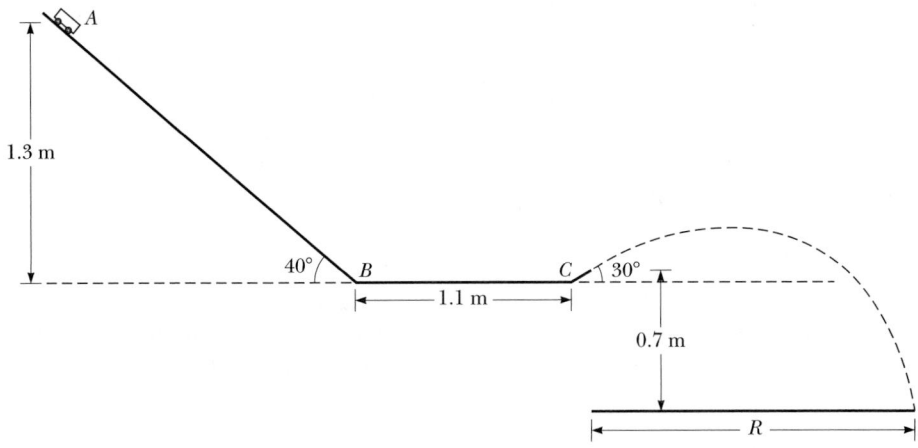

1. (15 points)

   A small cart is released from rest at point A on top of a track, as shown above. The track is angled $40°$ above the horizontal, and the cart starts 1.3 m vertically above a flat surface. Friction on the track and flat surface is negligible.

   (a) Calculate the speed of the cart at point B, when it reaches the flat surface.

   At point C, the cart is launched off of the track via a very short ramp angled at $30°$ above the horizontal. When the cart leaves the ramp, it continues with the same speed found in part (a). The ramp is at a height of 0.7 m above the floor.

   (b) Calculate the time for the cart to reach the floor after it leaves the ramp.

   (c) Calculate the horizontal distance R measured horizontally from the ramp to the cart's landing point on the floor.

   (d) Describe one simple modification to the contraption that would cause the distance R to increase. Justify your answer.

   (e) Imagine that the original contraption is transported to the surface of the Moon, where the free-fall acceleration g is 1/6 that on Earth. The same cart is once again released from rest. Would the distance R be increased, decreased, or unchanged? Justify your answer.

$T = 20.0°C$

2. (15 points)

An expandable cylinder has its top connected to a spring, as shown above. The lid of the cylinder has diameter 11 cm and negligible mass. The cylinder is filled with 5.0×10^{-3} m³ of gas with the spring relaxed at a pressure of 1.0 atm and a temperature of 20°C.

(a) Determine the number of moles of gas in the cylinder.

$T = 20.0°C$ $T = 250°C$

The temperature of the gas is now raised to 250°C. The piston rises a distance of 8.0 cm, as shown.

(b) Calculate the new pressure of the gas.

(c) Calculate the spring constant of the spring.

In an experiment, the temperature is varied continuously between 20°C and 250°C. A graph of pressure vs. temperature is produced.

(d) On an axes similar to the one below, sketch what the pressure vs. temperature graph would look like for the given temperature range.

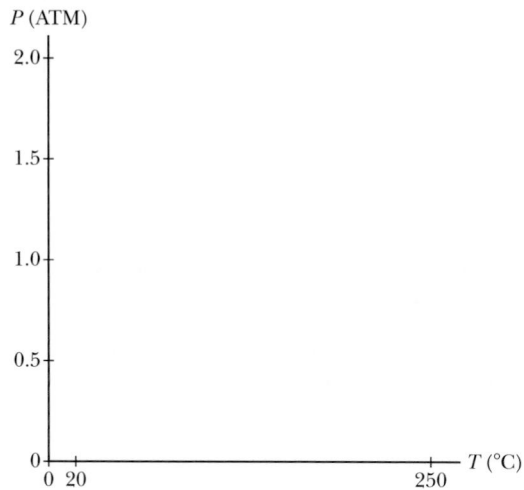

(e) Explain how the graph could be used to estimate the value of "absolute zero" temperature in units of °C.

3. (15 points)

A battery of emf ε and negligible internal resistance is connected to two resistors, as shown above. The resistance R is unknown.

(a) It is desired to connect a voltmeter and ammeter to measure the voltage across and current through the unknown resistor R. Redraw the circuit, including the voltmeter and ammeter.

When properly connected, the voltmeter reads 6.0 V, and the ammeter reads 3.0 mA. Consider the meters to be ideal.

(b) Calculate the value of R.

(c) Calculate the emf of the battery.

(d) Calculate the voltage across the 3.0 kΩ resistor.

(e) In this problem you assumed that the voltmeter was "ideal." Explain what it means for a voltmeter to be "ideal."

(f) On further investigation, it is found that the battery had an internal resistance of 10 Ω. Is the assumption of "negligible internal resistance" reasonable? Answer with reference to a calculation.

4. (10 points)

A spear fisherman sees a fish underwater. Light originating from the fish hits the smooth surface of the water at an angle of $\theta = 40°$ from the normal, as shown above. The index of refraction for water is 1.3.

(a)

    i. Calculate the angle of refraction θ_R for the light ray in the air.

    ii. Label this angle on a diagram similar to the one above with the variable θ_R.

Due to the refraction, the fisherman sees an image of the fish in the water. If he aims his spear at that image, he will miss the fish.

(b)

    i. Should the fisherman aim his spear above or below the image of the fish in order to hit the fish?

    ii. Justify your answer.

(c) In another area of the pond, a thin film of oil ($n = 1.4$) sits on the surface. The fisherman sees red light of wavelength 640 nm reflected when he is located directly above the thin film. Calculate two possible thicknesses of the oil film.

5. (10 points)

A 15 cm length of aluminum conductor, whose mass is 15 g, is aligned horizontally between two thin, vertical conductors. The horizontal conductor is free to move up and down with negligible friction. A uniform magnetic field is applied. When a 5.0 A current is directed as shown in the figure, the horizontal wire moves upward at constant velocity.

(a) On a separate sheet of paper, sketch the horizontal wire and draw and label the forces (not components) that act on the wire as it moves upward at constant velocity.

(b) Calculate the magnitude of the minimum magnetic field required to allow the wire to move at constant speed.

(c) In which direction should the magnetic field point to allow the horizontal wire to move at constant speed? Justify your answer.

(d) Now consider that the applied magnetic field was applied in the correct direction, but with a magnitude less than the value calculated in (b). Describe the resulting motion of the horizontal wire.

6. (15 points)

A nucleus of $^{27}_{13}\text{Al}$, initially at rest, decays via emission of a photon. The outgoing photon travels to the north and has energy 6.2 MeV.

(a) Determine the energy of the outgoing photon in units of joules.

(b) Determine the mass number A and proton number Z of the daughter nucleus. Justify your answer.

$A = $ _____ $Z = $ _____

(c) Which direction, if any, will the daughter nucleus be moving after the photon emission? Justify your answer.

(d) Determine the speed of the outgoing photon.

(e) Determine the speed of the daughter nucleus.

(f) Determine the total energy created by mass annihilation in this decay. Justify your answer.

Answers to Quick Quizzes, Example Questions, Odd-Numbered Multiple-Choice Questions, Conceptual Questions, and Problems

CHAPTER 1

Example Questions

1. False
2. True
3. 2.6×10^2 m^2
4. 28.0 m/s $= \left(28.0\dfrac{\cancel{m}}{\cancel{s}}\right)\left(\dfrac{2.24\ \text{mi/h}}{1.00\ \cancel{m/s}}\right) = 62.7$ mi/h

   The answer is slightly different because the different conversion factors were rounded, leading to small, unpredictable differences in the final answers.
5. $\left(\dfrac{60.0\ \text{min}}{1.00\ \text{h}}\right)^2$
6. An answer of 10^{12} cells is within an order of magnitude of the given answer, corresponding to slightly different choices in the volume estimations. Consequently, 10^{12} cells is also a reasonable estimate. An estimate of 10^9 cells would be suspect because (working backwards) it would imply cells that could be seen with the naked eye!
7. $\sim 4 \times 10^{11}$
8. $\sim 10^{12}$
9. Working backwards, $r = 4.998$, which further rounds to 5.00, whereas $\theta = 37.03°$, which further rounds to $37.0°$. The slight differences are caused by rounding.
10. Yes. The cosine function divided into the distance to the building will give the length of the hypotenuse of the triangle in question.
11. 540 km

Multiple-Choice Questions

1. (d)
3. (a)
5. (c)
7. (a) yes (b) no (c) yes (d) no (e) yes
9. (d)
11. (a)

Conceptual Questions

1. (a) ~ 0.1 m (b) ~ 1 m (c) Between 10 m and 100 m (d) ~ 10 m (e) ~ 100 m
3. $\sim 10^9$ s
5. (a) $\sim 10^6$ beats (b) $\sim 10^9$ beats
7. The length of a hand varies from person to person, so it isn't a useful standard of length.
9. (a) A dimensionally correct equation isn't necessarily true. For example, the equation 2 dogs = 5 dogs is dimensionally correct, but isn't true. (b) If an equation is not dimensionally correct, it cannot be true.
11. An estimate, even if imprecise by an order of magnitude, greatly reduces the range of plausible answers to a given question. The estimate gives guidance as to what corrective measures might be feasible. For example, if you estimate that 40 000 people in a country will die unless they have food assistance and if this number is reliable within an order of magnitude, you know that at most 400 000 people will need provisions.

Problems

3. (b) $A_{\text{cylinder}} = \pi R^2$, $A_{\text{rectangular plate}} = \text{length} \times \text{width}$
5. m^3/(kg $\cdot$ s^2)
7. 52 m^2
9. (a) three significant figures (b) four significant figures (c) three significant figures (d) two significant figures
11. (a) 35.7 cm^2 (b) 99.2 cm^3 (c) 17.7 cm^2, 99.5 cm^3 (d) In the rounding process, small amounts are either added to or subtracted from an answer to satisfy the rules of significant figures. For a given rounding, different small adjustments are made, introducing a certain amount of randomness in the last significant digit of the final answer.
13. 5.9×10^3 cm^3
15. 2×10^8 fathoms
17. 0.204 m^3
19. Yes. The speed of 38.0 m/s converts to a speed of 85.0 mi/h, so the driver exceeds the speed limit by 10 mi/h.
21. (a) 6.81 cm (b) 5.83×10^2 cm^2 (c) 1.32×10^3 cm^3
23. 6.71×10^8 mi/h
25. 3.08×10^4 m^3
27. 9.82 cm
29. $\sim 10^8$ breaths
31. (a) $\sim 10^{14}$. Other answers are possible. This answer assumes an intestinal length of about 7 m and average diameter of about 4 cm. There are probably more bacteria in your intestinal tract than there are cells in your body! (b) The large number means that they are probably not dangerous. Intestinal bacteria help digest food and provide important nutrients. Humans and bacteria enjoy a mutually beneficial symbiotic relationship.
33. $\sim 10^7$ rev
35. (2.0 m, 1.4 m)
37. $r = 2.2$ m, $\theta = 27°$
39. 5.69 m
41. (a) 6.71 m (b) 0.894 (c) 0.746
43. 3.41 m
45. (a) 3.00 (b) 3.00 (c) 0.800 (d) 0.800 (e) 1.33
47. 5.00/7.00; the angle itself is 35.5°
49. 70.0 m
51. (a) MLT^{-2} (b) kg $\cdot$ m/s^2
53. (a) 1.0×10^3 kg (b) $m_{\text{cell}} = 5.2 \times 10^{-16}$ kg (c) $m_{\text{kidney}} = 0.27$ kg (d) $m_{\text{fly}} = 1.3 \times 10^{-5}$ kg
55. The value of k, a dimensionless constant, cannot be found by dimensional analysis.
57. 152 μm
59. 1×10^{10} gal/yr
61. (a) 3.16×10^7 s (b) Between 10^{10} yr and 10^{11} yr
63. 1×10^5

CHAPTER 2

Quick Quizzes

1. (a) 200 yd (b) 0 (c) 0 (d) 8.00 yd/s
2. (a) False (b) True (c) True
3. The velocity vs. time graph (a) has a constant slope, indicating a constant acceleration, which is represented by the acceleration vs. time graph (e).

Graph (b) represents an object with increasing speed, but as time progresses, the lines drawn tangent to the curve have increasing slopes. Since the acceleration is equal to the slope of the tangent line, the acceleration must be increasing, and the acceleration vs. time graph that best indicates this behavior is (d).

Graph (c) depicts an object which first has a velocity that increases at a constant rate, which means that the object's acceleration is constant. The velocity then stops changing, which means that the acceleration of the object is zero. This behavior is best matched by graph (f).

4. (b)
5. (a) blue graph   (b) red graph   (c) green graph
6. (e)
7. (c)
8. (a) and (f)

Example Questions

1. No. The object may not be traveling in a straight line. If the initial and final positions are in the same place, for example, the displacement is zero regardless of the total distance traveled during the given time.
2. No. A vertical line in a position vs. time graph would mean that an object had somehow traversed all points along the given path instantaneously, which is physically impossible.
3. No. A vertical tangent line would correspond to an infinite acceleration, which is physically impossible.
4. 35.0 m/s
5. The graphical solution is the intersection of a straight line and a parabola.
6. The coasting displacement would double to 143 m, with a total displacement of 715 m.
7. The acceleration is zero wherever the tangent to the velocity versus time graph is horizontal. Visually, that occurs from −50 s to 0 s and then again at approximately 180 s, 320 s, and 330 s.
8. The upward jump would slightly increase the ball's initial velocity, slightly increasing the maximum height.
9. 6
10. The engine should be fired again at 235 m.

Multiple-Choice Questions

1. (d)
3. (b)
5. (b), (c)
7. (b)
9. (d)
11. (b)

Conceptual Questions

1. Yes. If the velocity of the particle is nonzero, the particle is in motion. If the acceleration is zero, the velocity of the particle is unchanging or is constant.
3. Yes. If this occurs, the acceleration of the car is opposite to the direction of motion, and the car will be slowing down.
5. No. Car B may be traveling at a lower velocity but have a greater acceleration at that instant.
7. (a) Yes.   (b) Yes.
9. (a) The car is moving to the east and speeding up.
   (b) The car is moving to the east but slowing down.
   (c) The car is moving to the east at constant speed.
   (d) The car is moving to the west but slowing down.
   (e) The car is moving to the west and speeding up.
   (f) The car is moving to the west at constant speed.
   (g) The car starts from rest and begins to speed up toward the east.
   (h) The car starts from rest and begins to speed up toward the west.

Problems

1. ≈ 0.02 s
3. (a) 52.9 km/h   (b) 90.0 km
5. (a) Boat A wins by 60 km   (b) 0
7. (a) 180 km   (b) 63.4 km/h
9. Yes. Taking the initial speed to be zero, the final speed as 75 m/s, and $a = 1.3$ m/s^2, we find that the distance the plane travels before takeoff is $x = v_{to}^2/2a = 2.2$ km, which is less than the length of the runway.
11. (a) 4.4 m/s^2 (b) 27 m
13. (a) 2.80 h   (b) 218 km
15. 274 km/h
17. (a) 5.00 m/s   (b) −2.50 m/s   (c) 0   (d) 5.00 m/s
19. 0.18 mi west of the flagpole
21. $|\bar{a}| = 1.34 \times 10^4$ m/s^2
23. 3.7 s
25. (a) 70.0 mi/h · s = 31.3 m/s^2 = 3.19g (b) 321 ft = 97.8 m
27. −16.0 cm/s^2
29. (a) 6.61 m/s   (b) −0.448 m/s^2
31. (a) 2.32 m/s^2 (b) 14.4 s
33. (a) 8.14 m/s^2 (b) 1.23 s   (c) Yes. For uniform acceleration, the velocity is a linear function of time.
35. There will be a collision only if the car and the van meet at the same place at some time. Writing expressions for the position versus time for each vehicle and equating the two gives a quadratic equation in t whose solution is either 11.4 s or 13.6 s. The first solution, 11.4 s, is the time of the collision. The collision occurs when the van is 212 m from the original position of Sue's car.
37. 200 m
39. (a) 1.5 m/s   (b) 32 m
41. 958 m
43. (a) 8.2 s   (b) 1.3×10^2 m
45. (a) 31.9 m   (b) 2.55 s   (c) 2.55 s   (d) −25.0 m/s
47. (a) −12.7 m/s   (b) 38.2 m
49. Hardwood floor: $a = 2.0 \times 10^3$ m/s^2, $\Delta t = 1.4$ ms; carpeted floor: $a = 3.9 \times 10^2$ m/s^2, $\Delta t = 7.1$ ms
51. (a) It is a freely falling object, so its acceleration is −9.80 m/s^2 (downward) while in flight.   (b) 0   (c) 9.80 m/s   (d) 4.90 m
53. (a) It continues upward, slowing under the influence of gravity until it reaches a maximum height, and then it falls to Earth.   (b) 308 m   (c) 8.51 s   (d) 16.4 s
55. 15.0 s
57. (a) -3.50×10^5 m/s^2 (b) 2.86×10^{-4} s
59. (a) 10.0 m/s upward   (b) 4.68 m/s downward
61. (a) 4.0 m/s   (b) 1.0 ms   (c) 0.82 m
63. 0.60 s
65. (a) 0.231 m   (b) 0.364 m   (c) 0.399 m   (d) 0.175 m
67. (a) 1.21 s after the first ball is dropped   (b) 7.18 m below the window
69. No. In the time interval equal to David's reaction time, the $1 bill (a freely falling object) falls a distance of $gt^2/2 \cong$ 20 cm, which is about twice the distance between the top of the bill and its center.
71. (a) $t_1 = 5.0$ s, $t_2 = 85$ s   (b) 200 ft/s   (c) 18 500 ft from starting point   (d) 10 s after starting to slow down (total trip time = 100 s)
73. (a) 5.5×10^3 ft   (b) 3.7×10^2 ft/s   (c) The plane would travel only 0.002 ft in the time it takes the light from the bolt to reach the eye.
75. (a) 7.82 m   (b) 0.782 s

CHAPTER 3

Quick Quizzes

1. (c)

2.
Vector	x-component	y-component
$\vec{A}$	−	+
$\vec{B}$	+	−
$\vec{A} + \vec{B}$	−	−

3. Vector $\vec{B}$
4. (b)
5. (a)
6. (c)
7. (b)

Example Questions

1. If the vectors point in the same direction, the sum of the magnitudes of the two vectors equals the magnitude of the resultant vector.
2. Because B_x, B_y, and B are all known, any of the trigonometric functions can be used to find the angle.
3. The hikers' displacement vectors are the same.
4. The initial and final velocity vectors are equal in magnitude because the x-component doesn't change and the y-component changes only by a sign.
5. To the pilot, the package appears to drop straight down because the x-components of velocity for the plane and package are the same.
6. False
7. 45°
8. False
9. False
10. To an observer on the ground, the ball drops straight down.
11. The angle decreases with increasing speed.
12. The angle is different because relative velocity depends on both the magnitude and the direction of the velocity vectors. In Example 3.12, the boat's velocity vector forms the hypotenuse of a right triangle, whereas in Example 3.11, that vector forms a leg of a right triangle.

Multiple-Choice Questions

1. (a)
3. (c)
5. (b), (d)
7. (a)
9. (b)
11. (b)
13. (a), (d)

Conceptual Questions

1. The magnitudes add when $\vec{A}$ and $\vec{B}$ are in the same direction. The resultant will be zero when the two vectors are equal in magnitude and opposite in direction.
3. (a) At the top of the projectile's flight, its velocity is horizontal and its acceleration is downward. This is the only point at which the velocity and acceleration vectors are perpendicular. (b) If the projectile is thrown straight up or down, then the velocity and acceleration will be parallel throughout the motion. For any other kind of projectile motion, the velocity and acceleration vectors are never parallel.
5. (a) The acceleration is zero, since both the magnitude and direction of the velocity remain constant. (b) The particle has an acceleration because the direction of $\vec{v}$ changes.
7. The spacecraft will follow a parabolic path equivalent to that of a projectile thrown off a cliff with a horizontal velocity. As regards the projectile, gravity provides an acceleration that is always perpendicular to the initial velocity, resulting in a parabolic path. As regards the spacecraft, the initial velocity plays the role of the horizontal velocity of the projectile, and the leaking gas plays the role that gravity plays in the case

of the projectile. If the orientation of the spacecraft were to change in response to the gas leak (which is by far the more likely result), then the acceleration would change direction and the motion could become very complicated.
9. For angles $\theta < 45°$, the projectile thrown at angle θ will be in the air for a shorter interval. For the smaller angle, the vertical component of the initial velocity is smaller than that for the larger angle. Thus, the projectile thrown at the smaller angle will not go as high into the air and will spend less time in the air before landing.
11. (a) Yes, the projectile is in free fall. (b) Its vertical component of acceleration is the downward acceleration of gravity. (c) Its horizontal component of acceleration is zero.

Problems

1. 43 units in the negative y-direction
3. (a) Approximately 5.0 units at −53° (b) Approximately 5.0 units at +53°
5. Approximately 421 ft at 3° below the horizontal
7. Approximately 310 km at 57° S of W
9. Approximately 15 m at 58° S of E
11. 28.7 units, −20.1 units
13. (a) 5.00 blocks at 53.1° N of E (b) 13.0 blocks
15. 47.2 units at 122° from the positive x-axis
17. 157 km
19. 245 km at 21.4° W of N
21. 4.64 m at 78.6° N of E
23. (a) $(x, y) = (0, 50.0 \text{ m})$ (b) $v_{0x} = 18.0$ m/s, $v_{0y} = 0$
    (c) $v_x = 18.0$ m/s, $v_y = -(9.80 \text{ m/s}^2)t$
    (d) $x = (18.0 \text{ m/s})t$, $y = -(4.90 \text{ m/s}^2)t^2 + 50.0$ m
    (e) 3.19 s (f) 36.1 m/s, −60.1°
25. 12 m/s
27. (a) The ball clears by 0.89 m (b) while descending
29. 25 m
31. (a) 32.5 m from the base of the cliff (b) 1.78 s
33. (a) 52.0 m/s horizontally (b) 212 m
35. (a) $(\vec{v}_{JA})_x = 3.00 \times 10^2$ mi/h, $(\vec{v}_{JA})_y = 0$,
    (b) $(\vec{v}_{AE})_x = 86.6$ mi/h, $(\vec{v}_{AE})_y = 50.0$ mi/h
    (c) $\vec{v}_{JA} = \vec{v}_{JE} - \vec{v}_{AE}$
    (d) $\vec{v}_{JE} = 3.90 \times 10^2$ mi/h, 7.36° N of E
37. (a) 9.80 m/s² down and 2.50 m/s² south (b) 9.80 m/s² down (c) The bolt moves on a parabola with a vertical axis.
39. (a) 1.26 h (b) 1.13 h (c) 1.19 h
41. (a) 2.02×10^3 s (b) 1.67×10^3 s (c) The time savings going downstream with the current is always less than the extra time required to go the same distance against the current.
43. (a) 6.80 km (b) 3.00 km vertically above the impact point (c) 66.2°
45. 18.0 s
47. (a) 40.5 m/s (b) Rather than falling like a rock, the skier glides through the air like a bird, prolonging the jump.
49. 68.6 km/h
51. (a) 1.53×10^3 m (b) 36.2 s (c) 4.04×10^3 m
53. (a) $R_{moon} = 18$ m (b) $R_{Mars} = 7.9$ m
55. (a) 42 m/s (b) 3.8 s (c) $v_x = 34$ m/s, $v_y = -13$ m/s; $v = 37$ m/s
57. (a) in the direction the ball was thrown (b) 7.5 m/s
61. $R/2$
63. 7.5 min
65. 10.8 m
67. (b) $y = Ax^2$ with $A = \dfrac{g}{2v_i^2}$ where v_i is the muzzle velocity
    (c) 14.5 m/s
69. (a) 35.1° or 54.9° (b) 42.2 m or 85.4 m, respectively
71. (a) 20.0° above the horizontal (b) 3.05 s
73. (a) 23 m/s (b) 360 m horizontally from the base of cliff

CHAPTER 4

Quick Quizzes

1. (a), (c), and (d) are true.
2. (b)
3. (a) False
   (b) True
   (c) False
   (d) False
4. (c); (d)
5. (c)
6. (c)
7. (b)
8. (b)
9. (b) By exerting an upward force component on the sled, you reduce the normal force on the ground and so reduce the force of kinetic friction.

Example Questions

1. Other than the forces mentioned in the problem, the force of gravity pulls downwards on the boat. Because the boat doesn't sink, a force exerted by the water on the boat must oppose the gravity force. (In Chapter 9 this force will be identified as the buoyancy force.)
2. False. The angles at which the forces are applied are also important in determining the magnitude of the acceleration vector.
3. 0.2 N
4. $3g$
5. The gravitational force of the Earth acts on the man, and an equal and opposite gravitational force of the man acts on the Earth. The normal force acts on the man, and the reaction force consists of the man pressing against the surface.
6. The tensions would double.
7. The magnitude of the tension force would be greater, and the magnitude of the normal force would be smaller.
8. Doubling the weight doubles the mass, which halves both the acceleration and displacement.
9. A gentler slope means a smaller angle and hence a smaller acceleration down the slope. Consequently, the car would take longer to reach the bottom of the hill.
10. The scale reading is greater than the weight of the fish during the first acceleration phase. When the velocity becomes constant, the scale reading is equal to the weight. When the elevator slows down, the scale reading is less than the weight.
11. Attach one end of the cable to the object to be lifted and the other end to a platform. Place lighter weights on the platform until the total mass of the weights and platform exceeds the mass of the heavy object.
12. A larger static friction coefficient would increase the maximum angle.
13. The coefficient of kinetic friction would be larger than in the example.
14. Both the acceleration and the tension increase when m_2 is increased.
15. The top block would slide off the back end of the lower block.

Multiple-Choice Questions

1. (a)
3. (b)
5. (d)
7. (b)
9. (a)
11. (b)
13. (c)
15. (b)

Conceptual Questions

1. The inertia of the suitcase would keep it moving forward as the bus stops. There would be no tendency for the suitcase to be thrown backward toward the passenger. The case should be dismissed.
3. (a) $w = mg$ and g decreases with altitude. Thus, to get a good buy, purchase it in Denver. (b) If gold were sold by mass, it would not matter where you bought it.
5. (a) Two external forces act on the ball. (i) One is a downward gravitational force exerted by Earth. (ii) The second force on the ball is an upward normal force exerted by the hand. The reactions to these forces are (i) an upward gravitational force exerted by the ball on Earth and (ii) a downward force exerted by the ball on the hand. (b) After the ball leaves the hand, the only external force acting on the ball is the gravitational force exerted by Earth. The reaction is an upward gravitational force exerted by the ball on Earth.
7. The force causing an automobile to move is the friction between the tires and the roadway as the automobile attempts to push the roadway backward. The force driving a propeller airplane forward is the reaction force exerted by the air on the propeller as the rotating propeller pushes the air backward (the action). In a rowboat, the rower pushes the water backward with the oars (the action). The water pushes forward on the oars and hence the boat (the reaction).
9. When the bus starts moving, Claudette's mass is accelerated by the force exerted by the back of the seat on her body. Clark is standing, however, and the only force acting on him is the friction between his shoes and the floor of the bus. Thus, when the bus starts moving, his feet accelerate forward, but the rest of his body experiences almost no accelerating force (only that due to his being attached to his accelerating feet!). As a consequence, his body tends to stay almost at rest, according to Newton's first law, relative to the ground. Relative to Claudette, however, he is moving toward her and falls into her lap. Both performers won Academy Awards.
11. (a) As the man takes the step, the action is the force his foot exerts on Earth; the reaction is the force exerted by Earth on his foot. (b) Here, the action is the force exerted by the snowball on the girl's back; the reaction is the force exerted by the girl's back on the snowball. (c) This action is the force exerted by the glove on the ball; the reaction is the force exerted by the ball on the glove. (d) This action is the force exerted by the air molecules on the window; the reaction is the force exerted by the window on the air molecules. In each case, we could equally well interchange the terms "action" and "reaction."
13. The tension in the rope is the maximum force that occurs in *both* directions. In this case, then, since both are pulling with a force of magnitude 200 N, the tension is 200 N. If the rope does not move, then the force on each athlete must equal zero. Therefore, each athlete exerts 200 N against the ground.

Problems

1. 2×10^4 N
3. (a) 12 N   (b) 3.0 m/s^2
5. 3.71 N, 58.7 N, 2.27 kg
7. 1.2 m/s^2 upward
9. (a) 13.5 m/s^2 (b) 1.42×10^3 N
11. (a) 0.200 m/s^2 (b) 10.0 m   (c) 2.00 m/s
13. 4.85 kN eastward
15. 1.1×10^4 N
17. (a) 600 N in vertical cable, 997 N in inclined cable, 796 N in horizontal cable (b) If the point of attachment were

moved higher up on the wall, the left cable would have a
y-component that would help support the cat burglar, thus
reducing the tension in the cable on the right.
19. 150 N in vertical cable, 75 N in right-side cable, 130 N in left-
    side cable
21. (a) $T_1 = 79.8$ N, $T_2 = 39.9$ N   (b) 2.34 m/s^2
23. 613 N
25. 64 N
27. (a) $T_1 = 3mg \sin \theta$ (b) $T_2 = 2mg \sin \theta$
29. (a) 7.0 m/s^2 horizontal and to the right   (b) 21 N   (c) 14 N
    horizontal and to the right
31. (a) 78.4 N   (b) 105 N
33. (a) 4.90 kN   (b) 607 N
35. (a) $T > w$ (b) $T = w$ (c) $T < w$ (d) 1.85×10^4 N; yes
    (e) 1.47×10^4 N; yes   (f) 1.25×10^4 N; yes
37. (a) 2.15×10^3 N forward   (b) 645 N forward   (c) 645 N
    rearward   (d) 1.02×10^4 N at 74.1° below horizontal and
    rearward
39. $\mu_s = 0.38$, $\mu_k = 0.31$
41. (a) 0.256   (b) 0.509 m/s^2
43. (a) 14.7 m   (b) Neither mass is necessary
45. $\mu_k = 0.287$
47. 32.1 N
49. (a) 33 m/s   (b) No. The object will speed up to 33 m/s
    from any lower speed and will slow down to 33 m/s from any
    higher speed.
51. (a) 1.78 m/s^2 (b) 0.368   (c) 9.37 N   (d) 2.67 m/s
53. (a) 1.11 s   (b) 0.875 s
55. (a) 0.404   (b) 45.8 lb
57. (a)

(b) 2.31 m/s^2, down for the 4.00-kg object, left for the
1.00-kg object, up for the 2.00-kg object (c) 30.0 N in the
left cord, 24.2 N in the right cord (d) Without friction, the
4-kg block falls more freely, so the tension T_1 in the string
attached to it is reduced. The 2-kg block is accelerated
upwards at a higher rate, hence the tension force T_2 acting
on it must be greater.
59. (a) 84.9 N upward   (b) 84.9 N downward
61. 50 m
63. (a) friction between box and truck   (b) 2.94 m/s^2
65. (a) 2.22 m   (b) 8.74 m/s down the incline
67. (a) 0.23 m/s^2 (b) 9.7 N
69. (a) 1.7 m/s^2, 17 N   (b) 0.69 m/s^2, 17 N
71. (a) 3.43 kN   (b) 0.967 m/s horizontally forward
    (c) Both would increase.
73. (a) 30.7°   (b) 0.843 N
75. 5.5×10^2 N
77. 72.0 N
79. (a) 7.1×10^2 N   (b) 8.1×10^2 N   (c) 7.1×10^2 N
    (d) 6.5×10^2 N
81. (a) 0.408 m/s^2 upward   (b) 83.3 N
83. (b) If θ is greater than $\tan^{-1} (1/\mu_s)$, motion is impossible.
85. $(M + m_1 + m_2)(m_1 g/m_2)$

CHAPTER 5

Quick Quizzes

1. (c)
2. (d)

3. (c)
4. (c)

Example Questions

1. As long as the same displacement is produced by the same
   force, doubling the load will not change the amount of work
   done by the applied force.
2. Doubling the displacement doubles the amount of work
   done in each case.
3. The wet road would reduce the coefficient of kinetic friction,
   so the final velocity would be greater.
4. (c)
5. In each case the velocity would have an additional horizontal component, meaning that the overall speed would be
   greater.
6. A smaller angle means that a larger initial speed would be
   required to allow the grasshopper to reach the indicated
   height.
7. In the presence of friction a different shape slide would
   result in different amounts of mechanical energy lost
   through friction, so the final answer would depend on the
   slide's shape.
8. In the crouching position there is less wind resistance.
   Crouching also lowers the skier's center of mass, making it
   easier to balance.
9. 73.5%
10. If the acrobat bends her legs and crouches immediately after
    contacting the springboard and then jumps as the platform
    pushes her back up, she can rebound to a height greater
    than her initial height.
11. The continuing vibration of the spring means that some
    energy wasn't transferred to the block. As a result, the block
    will go a slightly smaller distance up the ramp.
12. (a)
13. The work required would quadruple but time would double,
    so overall the average power would double.
14. The instantaneous power is 9.00×10^4 W, which is twice the
    average power.
15. False. The correct answer is one-quarter.
16. No. Using the same-size boxes is simply a matter of
    convenience.

Multiple-Choice Questions

1. (c)
3. (d)
5. (c)
7. (b)
9. (b)
11. (d)
13. (b)

Conceptual Questions

1. Because no motion is taking place, the rope undergoes no
   displacement and no work is done on it. For the same reason,
   no work is being done on the pullers or the ground. Work is
   being done only within the bodies of the pullers. For example, the heart of each puller is applying forces on the blood
   to move blood through the body.
3. (a) When the slide is frictionless, changing the length or
   shape of the slide will not make any difference in the final
   speed of the child, as long as the difference in the heights of
   the upper and lower ends of the slide is kept constant. (b) If
   friction must be considered, the path length along which
   the friction force does negative work will be greater when
   the slide is made longer or given bumps. Thus, the child will
   arrive at the lower end with less kinetic energy (and hence
   less speed).

5. If we ignore any effects due to rolling friction on the tires of the car, we find that the same amount of work would be done in driving up the switchback and in driving straight up the mountain because the weight of the car is moved upwards against gravity by the same vertical distance in each case. If we include friction, there is more work done in driving the switchback because the distance over which the friction force acts is much longer. So why do we use switchbacks? The answer lies in the force required, not the work. The force required from the engine to follow a gentle rise is much smaller than that required to drive straight up the hill. To negotiate roadways running straight uphill, engines would have to be redesigned to enable them to apply much larger forces. (It is for much the same reason that ramps are designed to move heavy objects into trucks, as opposed to lifting the objects vertically.)

7. (a) The tension in the supporting cord does no work, because the motion of the pendulum is always perpendicular to the cord and therefore to the tension force. (b) The air resistance does negative work at all times, because the air resistance is always acting in a direction opposite that of the motion. (c) The force of gravity always acts downwards; therefore, the work done by gravity is positive on the downswing and negative on the upswing.

9. During the time that the toe is in contact with the ball, the work done by the toe on the ball is given by

$$W_{\text{toe}} = \tfrac{1}{2}m_{\text{ball}}v^2 - 0 = \tfrac{1}{2}m_{\text{ball}}v^2$$

where v is the speed of the ball as it leaves the toe. After the ball loses contact with the toe, only the gravitational force and the retarding force due to air resistance continue to do work on the ball throughout its flight.

11. (a) Yes, the total mechanical energy of the system is conserved because the only forces acting are conservative: the force of gravity and the spring force. (b) There are two forms of potential energy in this case: gravitational potential energy and elastic potential energy stored in the spring.

13. Let's assume you lift the book slowly. In this case, there are two forces on the book that are almost equal in magnitude: the lifting force and the force of gravity. Thus, the positive work done by you and the negative work done by gravity cancel. There is no net work performed and no net change in the kinetic energy, so the work–energy theorem is satisfied.

15. As the satellite moves in a circular orbit about the Earth, its displacement during any small time interval is perpendicular to the gravitational force, which always acts toward the center of the Earth. Therefore, the work done by the gravitational force during any displacement is zero. (Recall that the work done by a force is defined to be $F\Delta x \cos \theta$, where θ is the angle between the force and the displacement. In this case, the angle is 90°, so the work done is zero.) Because the work–energy theorem says that the net work done on an object during any displacement is equal to the change in its kinetic energy, and the work done in this case is zero, the change in the satellite's kinetic energy is zero: hence, its speed remains constant.

Problems

1. 700 J
3. 2×10^4 J
5. (a) 61.3 J (b) −46.3 J (c) 0 (d) The work done by gravity would not change, the work done by the friction force would decrease, and the work done by the normal force would not change.
7. (a) 79.4 N (b) 1.49 kJ (c) −1.49 kJ
9. (a) 2.00 m/s (b) 200 N
11. (a) 879 J (b) His kinetic energy increases by a factor of 4.
13. (a) -5.6×10^2 J (b) 1.2 m

15. (a) 2.34×10^4 N (b) 1.91×10^{-4} s
17. (a) 4.68×10^9 J (b) -4.68×10^9 J (c) 1.87×10^6 N
19. (a) 2.5 J (b) −9.8 J (c) −12.3 J
21. 7.37 N/m
23. 878 kN up
25. $h = 6.94$ m
27. $W_{\text{biceps}} = 120$ J, $W_{\text{chin-up}} = 290$ J, additional muscles must be involved
29. (a) 4.30×10^5 J (b) -3.97×10^4 J (c) 115 m/s
31. (a) The mass, spring, and Earth (including the wall) constitute the system. The mass and Earth interact through the spring force, gravity, and the normal force. (b) the point of maximum extension, $x = 0.060\ 0$ m, and the equilibrium point, $x = 0$ (c) 1.53 J at $x = 6.00$ cm; 0 J at $x = 0$
   (d) $\tfrac{1}{2}mv_1^2 + \tfrac{1}{2}kx_1^2 = \tfrac{1}{2}mv_2^2 + \tfrac{1}{2}kx_2^2$
   $$\rightarrow \quad v_2 = \sqrt{v_1^2 + \frac{k}{m}(x_1^2 - x_2^2)},$$
   1.75 m/s (e) 1.51 m/s. This answer is not one-half the first answer because the equation is not linear.
33. 0.459 m
35. (a) 0.350 m (b) The result would be less than 0.350 m because some of the mechanical energy is lost as a result of the force of friction between the block and track.
37. (a) 10.9 m/s (b) 11.6 m/s
39. (a) Initially, all the energy is stored in the compressed spring. After the gun is fired and the projectile leaves the gun, the energy is transferred to the kinetic energy of the projectile, resulting in a small increase in gravitational potential energy. Once the projectile reaches its maximum height, the energy is all associated with its gravitational potential energy. (b) 544 N/m (c) 19.7 m/s
41. (a) Yes. There are no nonconservative forces acting on the child, so the total mechanical energy is conserved. (b) No. In the expression for conservation of mechanical energy, the mass of the child is included in every term and therefore cancels out. (c) The answer is the same in each case. (d) The expression would have to be modified to include the work done by the force of friction. (e) 15.3 m/s.
43. (a) 372 N (b) $T_1 = 372$ N, $T_2 = T_3 = 745$ N (c) 1.34 kJ
45. 3.8 m/s
47. 289 m
49. (a) 24.5 m/s (b) Yes (c) 206 m (d) Unrealistic; the actual retarding force will vary with speed.
51. 236 s or 3.93 min
53. 8.01 W
55. The power of the sports car is four times that of the older-model car.
57. (a) 2.38×10^4 W = 32.0 hp (b) 4.77×10^4 W =63.9 hp
59. (a) 24.0 J (b) −3.00 J (c) 21.0 J
61. (a) The graph is a straight line passing through the points (0 m, −16 N), (2 m, 0 N), and (3 m, 8 N). (b) −12.0 J
63. 0.265 m/s
65. (a) $PE_{Ⓐ} = 3.94 \times 10^5$ J, $PE_{Ⓑ} = 0$, $\Delta PE = -3.94 \times 10^5$ J
   (b) $PE_{Ⓐ} = 5.63 \times 10^5$ J, $PE_{Ⓑ} = 1.69 \times 10^5$ J, $\Delta PE = -3.94 \times 10^5$ J
67. (a) 575 N/m (b) 46.0 J
69. (a) 4.4 m/s (b) 1.5×10^5 N
71. (a) 3.13 m/s (b) 4.43 m/s (c) 1.00 m
73. (a) 0.588 J (b) 0.588 J (c) 2.42 m/s (d) $PE_C = 0.392$ J
   (e) $KE_C = 0.196$ J
75. (a) 0.020 4 m (b) 7.20×10^2 N/m
77. (a) 423 mi/gal (b) 776 mi/gal
79. (a) 28.0 m/s (b) 30.0 m (c) 88.9 m beyond the end of the track
81. (a) 101 J (b) 0.412 m (c) 2.84 m/s (d) −9.80 mm
   (e) 2.86 m/s
83. 914 N/m

85. (a) $W_{net} = 0$ (b) $W_{grav} = -2.0 \times 10^4$ J (c) $W_{normal} = 0$,
(d) $W_{friction} = 2.0 \times 10^4$ J
87. (a) 10.2 kW (b) 10.6 kW (c) 5.82×10^6 J
89. 4.3 m/s
91. between 25.2 km/h and 27.0 km/h

CHAPTER 6

Quick Quizzes

1. (b)
2. (c)
3. (c)
4. (a)
5. (a) Perfectly inelastic (b) Inelastic (c) Inelastic
6. (a)

Example Questions

1. 44 m/s
2. When one car is overtaking another, the relative velocity is small, so on impact the change in momentum is also small. In a head-on collision, however, the relative velocity is large because the cars are traveling in opposite directions. Consequently, the change in momentum of a passenger in a head-on collision is greater than when hit from behind, which implies a larger average force.
3. Assuming the kinetic energies of the two arrows are identical, the heavier arrow would have a greater momentum, because $p^2 = 2mK$. Greater arrow momentum means greater recoil speed for the archer.
4. The final velocity would be unaffected, but the change in kinetic energy would be doubled.
5. Energy can be lost due to friction in the mechanisms and associated thermal energy loss due to air drag and through emission of sound waves.
6. No. If that were the case, energy could not be conserved.
7. The blocks cannot both come to rest at the same time because then by Equation (1) momentum would not be conserved.
8. 45°
9. $m(a + g)$

Multiple-Choice Questions

1. (b)
3. (c)
5. (c)
7. (a)
9. (d)
11. (a)
13. (c)

Conceptual Questions

1. (a) No. It cannot carry more kinetic energy than it possesses. That would violate the law of energy conservation. (b) Yes. By bouncing from the object it strikes, it can deliver more momentum in a collision than it possesses in its flight.
3. If all the kinetic energy disappears, there must be no motion of either of the objects after the collision. If neither is moving, the final momentum of the system is zero, and the initial momentum of the system must also have been zero. A situation in which this could be true would be the head-on collision of two objects having momenta of equal magnitude but opposite direction.
5. Initially, the clay has momentum directed toward the wall. When it collides and sticks to the wall, neither the clay nor the wall appears to have any momentum. It is therefore tempting to (wrongfully) conclude that momentum is not conserved. The "lost" momentum, however, is actually imparted to the wall and the Earth, causing both to move.

Because of the Earth's enormous mass, its recoil speed is too small to detect.
7. As the water is forced out of the holes in the arm, the arm imparts a horizontal impulse to the water. The water then exerts an equal and opposite impulse on the spray arm, causing the spray arm to rotate in the direction opposite that of the spray.
9. It will be easiest to catch the medicine ball when its speed (and kinetic energy) is lowest. The first option—throwing the medicine ball at the same velocity—will be the most difficult, because the speed will not be reduced at all. The second option, throwing the medicine ball with the same momentum, will reduce the velocity by the ratio of the masses. Since $m_t v_t = m_m v_m$, it follows that

$$v_m = v_t \left(\frac{m_t}{m_m}\right)$$

The third option, throwing the medicine ball with the same kinetic energy, will also reduce the velocity, but only by the square root of the ratio of the masses. Since

$$\tfrac{1}{2} m_t v_t^{\,2} = \tfrac{1}{2} m_m v_m^{\,2}$$

it follows that

$$v_m = v_t \sqrt{\frac{m_t}{m_m}}$$

The slowest and easiest throw will be made when the momentum is held constant. If you wish to check this answer, try substituting in values of $v_t = 1$ m/s, $m_t = 1$ kg, and $m_m = 100$ kg. Then the same-momentum throw will be caught at 1 cm/s, while the same-energy throw will be caught at 10 cm/s.
11. It is the product mv that is the same for both the bullet and the gun. The bullet has a large velocity and a small mass, while the gun has a small velocity and a large mass. Furthermore, the bullet carries much more kinetic energy than the gun.
13. (a) The follow-through keeps the club in contact with the ball as long as possible, maximizing the impulse. Thus, the ball accrues a larger change in momentum than without the follow-through, and it leaves the club with a higher velocity and travels farther. (b) With a short shot to the green, the primary factor is control, not distance. Hence, there is little or no follow-through, allowing the golfer to have a better feel for how hard he or she is striking the ball.
15. No. Impulse, $\vec{\mathbf{F}}\Delta t$, depends on the force and the time interval during which it is applied.

Problems

1. (a) 8.35×10^{-21} kg · m/s (b) 4.50 kg · m/s (c) 750 kg · m/s
(d) 1.78×10^{29} kg · m/s
3. (a) 31.0 m/s (b) the bullet, 3.38×10^3 J versus 69.7 J
5. (a) 0.42 N downward (b) The hailstones would exert a larger average force on the roof because they would bounce off the roof, and the impulse acting on the hailstones would be greater than the impulse acting on the raindrops. Newton's third law then tells us that the hailstones exert a greater force on the roof.
7. (a) 22.0 m/s (b) 1.14 kg
9. (a) 10.4 kg · m/s in the direction of the final velocity of the ball (b) 173 N
11. 1.39 N · s up
13. (a) 364 kg · m/s forward (b) 438 N forward
15. (a) 8.0 N · s (b) 5.3 m/s (c) 3.3 m/s
17. (a) 12 N · s (b) 8.0 N · s (c) 8.0 m/s (d) 5.3 m/s
19. (a) 9.60×10^{-2} s (b) 3.65×10^5 N (c) 26.6g
21. 65 m/s

23. (a) 1.15 m/s   (b) 0.346 m/s directed opposite to girl's motion

25. (a) 154 m   (b) By Newton's third law, when the astronaut exerts a force on the tank, the tank exerts a force back on the astronaut. This reaction force accelerates the astronaut towards the spacecraft.

27. $v_{\text{thrower}} = 2.48$ m/s, $v_{\text{catcher}} = 2.25 \times 10^{-2}$ m/s

29. (a)

(b) The collision is best described as perfectly inelastic because the skaters remain in contact after the collision.
(c) $m_1 v_1 + m_2 v_2 = (m_1 + m_2) v_f$
(d) $v_f = (m_1 v_1 + m_2 v_2)/(m_1 + m_2)$ (e) 6.33 m/s

31. 15.6 m/s

33. (a) 1.80 m/s   (b) 2.16×10^4 J

35. (a) 1

37. 1.32 m

39. 57 m

41. 273 m/s

43. (a) He moves at a velocity of $\left(\dfrac{m_g}{m_b}\right) v_g$ toward the west.

(b) $KE_g = \frac{1}{2} m_g v_g{}^2$; $KE_b = \left(\dfrac{m_g{}^2}{2m_b}\right) v_g{}^2$ The ratio $\dfrac{KE_g}{KE_b} = \dfrac{m_b}{m_g}$

is greater than 1 because $m_b > m_g$. Hence, the girl has more kinetic energy. (c) Work is done by both the boy and girl as they push each other apart and the origin of this work is chemical energy in their bodies.

45. 17.1 cm/s (25.0-g object), 22.1 cm/s (10.0-g object)

47. (a) Over a very short time interval, external forces have no time to impart significant impulse to the players during the collision. The two players move together after the tackle, so the collision is completely inelastic. (b) 2.88 m/s at 32.3° (c) 785 J. (d) The lost kinetic energy is transformed into other forms of energy such as thermal energy and sound.

49. 5.59 m/s north

51. (a) 2.50 m/s at −60°   (b) elastic collision

53. 1.78×10^3 N on truck driver, 8.89×10^3 N on car driver

55. (a) 8/3 m/s (incident particle), 32/3 m/s (target particle)
(b) −16/3 m/s (incident particle), 8/3 m/s (target particle)
(c) 7.1×10^{-2} J in case (a), and 2.8×10^{-3} J in case (b). The incident particle loses more kinetic energy in case (a), in which the target mass is 1.0 g.

57. $v_1 = -1.7$ m/s (to the left); $v_2 = 1.1$ m/s (to the right)

59. 62 s

61. (a) 3   (b) 2

63. (a) −2.33 m/s, 4.67 m/s   (b) 0.277 m   (c) 2.98 m   (d) 1.49 m

65. (a) −0.667 m/s   (b) 0.952 m

67. (a) 3.54 m/s   (b) 1.77 m   (c) 3.54×10^4 N   (d) No, the normal force exerted by the rail contributes upward momentum to the system.

69. (a) 0.28 or 28%   (b) 1.1×10^{-13} J for the neutron, 4.5×10^{-14} J for carbon

71. (a) No. After colliding, the cars, moving as a unit, would travel northeast, so they couldn't damage property on the southeast corner. (b) x-component: 16.3 km/h, y-component: 9.17 km/h, angle: the final velocity of the car is 18.7 km/h at 29.4° north of east, consistent with part (a).

73. (a) 4.85 m/s   (b) 8.41 m

75. $v_0 = \left(\dfrac{M + m}{m}\right) \sqrt{2\mu gd}$

77. (a) 1.1 m/s at 30° below the positive x-axis   (b) 0.32 or 32%

79. (a) The momentum of the bullet-block system is conserved in the collision, so you can relate the speed of the block and bullet immediately after the collision to the initial speed of the bullet. Then, you can use conservation of mechanical energy for the bullet–block–Earth system to relate the speed after the collision to the maximum height.   (b) 521 m/s upward

CHAPTER 7

Quick Quizzes

1. (c)
2. (b)
3. (b)
4. (b)
5. (a)
6. 1. (e) 2. (a) 3. (b)
7. (c)
8. (b), (c)
9. (e)
10. (d)

Example Questions

1. Yes. The conversion factor is $(180°/\pi$ rad) or $57.3°$ s^{-1}.

2. All given quantities and answers are in angular units, so altering the radius of the wheel has no effect on the answers.

3. In this case, doubling the angular acceleration doubles the angular displacement. That is true here because the initial angular speed is zero.

4. The angular acceleration of a record player during play is zero. A CD player must have nonzero acceleration because the angular speed must change.

5. (b)

6. It would be increased.

7. The angle of the bank, the coefficient of friction, and the radius of the circle determine the minimum and maximum safe speeds.

8. The normal force is still zero.

9. Yes. The force of gravity acting on each billiard ball holds the balls against the table and assists in creating friction forces that allow the balls to roll. The gravity forces between the balls are insignificant, however.

10. First, most asteroids are irregular in shape, so Equation (1) will not apply because the acceleration may not be uniform. Second, the asteroid may be so small that there will be no significant or useful region where the acceleration is uniform. In that case, Newton's more general law of gravitation would be required.

11. (b)

12. Mechanical energy is conserved in this system. Because the potential energy at perigee is lower, the kinetic energy must be higher.

13. 5 days

Multiple-Choice Questions

1. (e)
3. (c)
5. (c)
7. (c)
9. (d)
11. (b)
13. (e)

Conceptual Questions

1. (a) The head will tend to lean toward the right shoulder (that is, toward the outside of the curve). (b) When there is no strap, tension in the neck muscles must produce the centripetal acceleration. (c) With a strap, the tension in the strap performs this function, allowing the neck muscles to remain relaxed.

3. The speedometer will be inaccurate. The speedometer measures the number of tire revolutions per second, so its readings will be too low.

5. (a) Point C. The total acceleration here is centripetal acceleration, straight up. (b) Point A. The speed at A is zero where the bob is reversing direction. The total acceleration here is tangential acceleration, to the right and downward perpendicular to the cord. (c) Point B. The total acceleration here is to the right and pointing in a direction somewhere in between the tangential and radial directions, depending on their relative magnitudes.

7. Consider an individual standing against the inside wall of the cylinder with her head pointed toward the axis of the cylinder. As the cylinder rotates, the person tends to move in a straight-line path tangent to the circular path followed by the cylinder wall. As a result, the person presses against the wall, and the normal force exerted on her provides the radial force required to keep her moving in a circular path. If the rotational speed is adjusted such that this normal force is equal in magnitude to her weight on Earth, she will not be able to distinguish between the artificial gravity of the colony and ordinary gravity.

9. The tendency of the water is to move in a straight-line path tangent to the circular path followed by the container. As a result, at the top of the circular path, the water presses against the bottom of the pail, and the normal force exerted by the pail on the water provides the radial force required to keep the water moving in its circular path.

11. Any object that moves such that the *direction* of its velocity changes has an acceleration. A car moving in a circular path will always have a centripetal acceleration.

13. The speed changes. The component of force tangential to the path causes a tangential acceleration.

Problems

1. (a) 7.27×10^{-5} rad/s (b) Because of its rotation about its axis, Earth bulges at the equator.

3. (a) 3.2×10^8 rad (b) 5.0×10^7 rev

5. (a) 821 rad/s^2 (b) 4.21×10^3 rad

7. (a) 3.5 rad (b) The angular displacement increases by a factor of 4 because Equation 7.9 is quadratic in the angular velocities.

9. Main rotor: 179 m/s $= 0.522 v_{sound}$
   Tail rotor: 221 m/s $= 0.644 v_{sound}$

11. (a) 116 rev (b) 62.1 rad/s

13. 13.7 rad/s^2

15. (a) 6.53 m/s (b) 0.285 m/s^2 directed toward the center of the circular arc

17. (a) 0.346 m/s^2 (b) 1.04 m/s (c) 0.346 m/s^2 (d) 0.943 m/s^2 (e) 1.00 m/s^2 at 20.1° forward with respect to the direction of $\vec{a}_c$

19. (a) 20.6 N (b) 3.35 m/s^2 downward tangent to the circle; 32.0 m/s^2 radially inward (c) 32.2 m/s^2 at 5.98° to the cord, pointing toward a location below the center of the circle. (d) No change. (e) If the object is swinging down it is gaining speed. If it is swinging up it is losing speed but its acceleration has the same magnitude and its direction can be described in the same terms.

21. (a) 1.10 kN (b) 2.04 times her weight

23. 22.6 m/s

25. (a) 18.0 m/s^2 (b) 900 N (c) 1.84; this large coefficient is unrealistic, and she will not be able to stay on the merry-go-round.

27. (a) 9.8 N (b) 9.8 N (c) 6.3 m/s

29. (a) The force of static friction acting toward the road's center of curvature causes the briefcase's centripetal acceleration. When the necessary centripetal force exceeds the maximum value of the static friction force, $\mu_s n$, the briefcase begins to slide. (b) 0.370

31. (a) 1.58 m/s^2 (b) 455 N upward (c) 329 N upward (d) 397 N directed inward and 80.8° above horizontal

33. 321 N toward Earth

35. 1.1×10^{-10} N at 72° above the $+x$-axis

37. (a) 2.50×10^{-5} N toward the 500-kg object (b) between the two objects and 0.245 m from the 500-kg object

39. (a) $r = \dfrac{9}{8} R_E = 7.18 \times 10^6$ m (b) 7.98×10^5 m

41. (a) 2.43 h (b) 6.59 km/s (c) 4.73 m/s^2 toward the Earth

43. 6.3×10^{23} kg

45. $\dfrac{T_B}{T_A} = \sqrt{\dfrac{27}{8}} = 1.84$

47. (a) 1.90×10^{27} kg (b) 1.89×10^{27} kg (c) yes

49. (a) 9.40 rev/s (b) 44.2 rev/s^2; $a_r = 2\,590$ m/s^2; $a_t = 206$ m/s^2 (c) $F_r = 515$ N; $F_t = 40.7$ N

51. (a) 2.51 m/s (b) 7.90 m/s^2 (c) 4.00 m/s

53. (a) 7.76×10^3 m/s (b) 89.3 min

55. (a) $n = m\left(g - \dfrac{v^2}{r}\right)$ (b) 17.1 m/s

57. (a) $F_{g,\,\text{true}} = F_{g,\,\text{apparent}} + m R_E \omega^2$ (b) 732 N (equator), 735 N (either pole)

59. 11.8 km/s

61. 0.835 rev/s

65. (a) 10.6 kN (b) 14.1 m/s

67. (a) 0.71 yr (b) The departure must be timed so that the spacecraft arrives at aphelion when the target planet is there.

69. (a) $t = \dfrac{2R\omega}{g}$ (b) $\omega = \sqrt{\dfrac{\pi g}{R}}$

71. (a) 109 N (b) 56.4 N

73. (a) 106 N (b) 0.396

75. 0.131

CHAPTER 8

Quick Quizzes

1. (d)
2. (b)
3. (b)
4. (a)
5. (c)
6. (a)

Example Questions

1. The revolving door begins to move counterclockwise instead of clockwise.

2. Placing the wedge closer to the doorknob increases its effectiveness.

3. If the woman leans backwards, the torque she exerts on the seesaw increases and she begins to descend.

4. (b)

5. The system would begin to rotate clockwise.

6. The angle made by the biceps force would still not vary much from 90° but the length of the moment arm would be doubled, so the required biceps force would be reduced by nearly half.

7. The tension in the cable would increase.

8. (c)

9. Lengthening the rod between balls 2 and 4 would create the larger change in the moment of inertia.

10. Stepping forward transfers the momentum of the pitcher's body to the ball. Without proper timing, the transfer will not take place or will have less effect.

11. The magnitude of the acceleration would decrease; that of the tension would increase.

12. Block, ball, cylinder

13. The final answer wouldn't change.

14. His angular speed remains the same.

15. Energy conservation is not violated. The positive net change occurs because the student is doing work on the system.

Multiple-Choice Questions

1. (b)
3. (a)
5. (d)
7. (b), (e)
9. (d)
11. (d)
13. (e)

Conceptual Questions

1. In order for you to remain in equilibrium, your center of gravity must always be over your point of support, the feet. If your heels are against a wall, your center of gravity cannot remain above your feet when you bend forward, so you lose your balance.
3. No, only if its angular velocity changes.
5. The long pole has a large moment of inertia about an axis along the rope. An unbalanced torque will then produce only a small angular acceleration of the performer–pole system, to extend the time available for getting back in balance. To keep the center of mass above the rope, the performer can shift the pole left or right, instead of having to bend his body around. The pole sags down at the ends to lower the system's center of gravity, increasing the relative stability of the system.
7. As the motorcycle leaves the ground, the friction between the tire and the ground suddenly disappears. If the motorcycle driver keeps the throttle open while leaving the ground, the rear tire will increase its angular speed and, hence, its angular momentum. The airborne motorcycle is now an isolated system, and its angular momentum must be conserved. The increase in angular momentum of the tire directed, say, clockwise must be compensated for by an increase in angular momentum of the entire motorcycle counterclockwise. This rotation results in the nose of the motorcycle rising and the tail dropping.
9. The angular momentum of the gas cloud is conserved. Thus, the product $I\omega$ remains constant. As the cloud shrinks in size, its moment of inertia decreases, so its angular speed ω must increase.
11. We can assume fairly accurately that the driving motor will run at a constant angular speed and at a constant torque. (a) As the radius of the take-up reel increases, the tension in the tape will decrease, in accordance with the equation.

$$T = \tau_{\text{const}}/R_{\text{take-up}} \qquad (1)$$

As the radius of the source reel decreases, given a decreasing tension, the torque in the source reel will decrease even faster, as the following equation shows:

$$\tau_{\text{source}} = TR_{\text{source}} = \tau_{\text{const}}R_{\text{source}}/R_{\text{take-up}} \qquad (2)$$

(b) In the case of a sudden jerk on the tape, the changing angular speed of the source reel becomes important. If the source reel is full, then the moment of inertia will be large and the tension in the tape will be large. If the source reel is nearly empty, then the angular acceleration will be large instead. Thus, the tape will be more likely to break when the source reel is nearly full. One sees the same effect in the case of paper towels: It is easier to snap a towel free when the roll is new than when it is nearly empty.
13. When a ladder leans against a wall, both the wall and the floor exert forces of friction on the ladder. If the floor is perfectly smooth, it can exert no frictional force in the horizontal direction to counterbalance the wall's normal force. Therefore, a ladder on a smooth floor cannot stand in equilibrium. However, a smooth wall can still exert a normal force to hold the ladder in equilibrium against horizontal motion. The counterclockwise torque of this force prevents rotation about the foot of the ladder. So you should choose a rough floor.

Problems

1. 168 N · m
3. (a) 30 N · m (counterclockwise)
   (b) 36 N · m (counterclockwise)
5. (a) 5.1 N · m (b) The torque increases, because the torque is proportional to the moment arm, $L \sin \theta$, and this factor increases as θ increases.
7. $F_t = 724$ N, $F_s = 716$ N
9. 312 N
11. $x_{\text{cg}} = 3.33$ ft, $y_{\text{cg}} = 1.67$ ft
13. $(-1.5$ m, -1.5 m$)$
15. 1.01 m in Figure P8.15b; 0.015 m toward the head in Figure P8.15c.
17. (a) $T = 2.71$ kN (b) $R_x = 2.65$ kN
19. (a) 443 N, (b) 222 N (to the right), 216 N (upward)
21. $T_1 = 501$ N, $T_2 = 672$ N, $T_3 = 384$ N
23. (a) $d = \dfrac{mg}{2k \tan \theta}$ (b) $R_x = \dfrac{mg}{2 \tan \theta}$; $R_y = mg$
25. $\theta = \tan^{-1}\left(\dfrac{w}{h}\right)$
27. $R = 107$ N, $T = 157$ N
29. 209 N
31. (a) 99.0 kg · m² (b) 44.0 kg · m² (c) 143 kg · m²
33. (a) 87.8 kg · m² (b) 1.61 × 10³ kg (c) 4.70 rad/s
35. (a) 3.92 m/s² (b) 9.80 rad/s² (c) As the rope leaves the cylinder, the mass of the cylinder decreases, also decreasing the cylinder's moment of inertia. At the same time, the mass of rope leaving the cylinder would increase the torque exerted on the cylinder. Hence, the acceleration of the system would increase in magnitude with time. (The increase would be slight in this case, given the large mass of the cylinder.)
37. (a) 24.0 N · m (b) 0.035 6 rad/s² (c) 1.07 m/s²
39. 177 N
41. 0.524
43. 276 J
45. (a) 5.47 J (b) 5.99 J
47. (a) 3.90 m/s (b) 15.6 rad/s
49. 149 rad/s
51. (a) 500 J (b) 250 J (c) 750 J
53. (a) 5.00 m (b) 2.31 × 10⁴ J (c) 1.79 × 10⁴ J (d) 9.27 m/s
55. (a) 7.08 × 10³³ J · s (b) 2.66 × 10⁴⁰ J · s
57. 17.5 J · s counterclockwise
59. (a) $7md^2/3$ (b) mgd counterclockwise (c) $3g/7d$ counterclockwise (d) $2g/7$ upward (e) mgd (f) $\sqrt{6g/7d}$
    (g) $m\sqrt{14gd^3}/3$ (h) $\sqrt{2gd/21}$
61. 6.73 rad/s
63. 5.99 × 10⁻² J
65. (a) $\omega = \left(\dfrac{I_1}{I_1 + I_2}\right)\omega_0$ (b) $\dfrac{KE_f}{KE_i} = \dfrac{I_1}{I_1 + I_2} < 1$
67. (a) 2.6 rad/s (b) 5.1 × 10⁵ kg · m² (c) 1.7 × 10⁶ J
69. (a) As the child walks to the right end of the boat, the boat moves left (toward the pier). (b) The boat moves 1.45 m closer to the pier, so the child will be 5.55 m from the pier. (c) No. He will be short of reaching the turtle by 0.45 m.
71. 36.9°
73. (a) Mvd (b) Mv^2 (c) Mvd (d) $2v$ (e) $4Mv^2$ (f) $3Mv^2$
75. (a) 6.73 N upward (b) $x = 0.389$ m
77. (a) 0 (b) 0; Because the monkey and the bananas are both moving upward with the same speed, the angular momentum of the system is zero. (c) The monkey won't reach the bananas until they become caught in the pulley.

79. 1.09 m

81. (a) $T = \dfrac{Mmg}{M + 4m}$ (b) $a_t = \dfrac{4mg}{M + 4m}$

83. 24.5 m/s

85. 9.3 kN

87. (a) 3.12 m/s^2 (b) $T_1 = 26.7$ N, $T_2 = 9.36$ N

89. (a) 0.73 m (b) 1.6 m/s

CHAPTER 9

Quick Quizzes

 1. (c)
 2. (a)
 3. (c)
 4. (b)
 5. (c)
 6. (b)
 7. (a)

Example Questions

 1. Because water is more dense than oil, the pressure exerted by a column of water is greater than the pressure exerted by a column of oil.
 2. Tungsten, steel, aluminum, rubber
 3. The lineman's skull and neck would undergo compressional stress.
 4. Steel, copper, mercury, water
 5. At higher altitude, the column of air above a given area is progressively shorter and less dense, so the weight of the air column is reduced. Pressure is caused by the weight of the air column, so the pressure is also reduced.
 6. As fluid pours out through a single opening, the air inside the can above the fluid expands into a larger volume, reducing the pressure to below atmospheric pressure. Air must then enter the same opening going the opposite direction, resulting in disrupted fluid flow. A separate opening for air intake maintains air pressure inside the can without disrupting the flow of the fluid.
 7. True
 8. False
 9. (a)
 10. The aluminum cube would float free of the bottom.
 11. The speed of the blood in the narrowed region increases.
 12. A factor of 2
 13. The speed slows with time.
 14. The limit is $v_1 = \sqrt{2gh}$, called Torricelli's Law. (See Example 9.13).
 15. The pressure difference across the wings depends linearly on the density of air. At higher altitude, the air's density decreases, so the lift force decreases as well.
 16. False
 17. No. There are many plants taller than 0.3 m, so there must be some additional explanation.
 18. A factor of 16
 19. False

Multiple-Choice Questions

 1. (c)
 3. (a)
 5. (c)
 7. (d)
 9. (c)
 11. (a), (c)
 13. (b)

Conceptual Questions

 1. She exerts enough pressure on the floor to dent or puncture the floor covering. The large pressure is caused by the fact that her weight is distributed over the very small cross-sectional area of her high heels. If you are the homeowner, you might want to suggest that she remove her high heels and put on some slippers.
 3. The density of air is lower in the mile-high city of Denver than it is at lower altitudes, so the effect of air drag is less in Denver than it would be in a city such as New York. The reduced air drag means a well-hit ball will go farther, benefiting home-run hitters. On the other hand, curve ball pitchers prefer to throw at lower altitudes where the higher-density air produces greater deflecting forces on a spinning ball.
 5. If you think of the grain stored in the silo as a fluid, the pressure the grain exerts on the walls of the silo increases with increasing depth, just as water pressure in a lake increases with increasing depth. Thus, the spacing between bands is made smaller at the lower portions to counterbalance the larger outward forces on the walls in these regions.
 7. In the ocean, the ship floats due to the buoyant force from *salt water*, which is denser than fresh water. As the ship is pulled up the river, the buoyant force from the fresh water in the river is not sufficient to support the weight of the ship, and it sinks.
 9. At lower elevation the water pressure is greater because pressure increases with increasing depth below the water surface in the reservoir (or water tower). The penthouse apartment is not so far below the water surface. The pressure behind a closed faucet is weaker there and the flow weaker from an open faucet. Your fire department likely has a record of the precise elevation of every fire hydrant.
 11. The two cans displace the same volume of water and hence are acted upon by buoyant forces of equal magnitude. The total weight of the can of diet cola must be less than this buoyant force, whereas the total weight of the can of regular cola is greater than the buoyant force. This is possible even though the two containers are identical and contain the same volume of liquid. Because of the difference in the quantities and densities of the sweeteners used, the volume V of the diet mixture will have less mass than an equal volume of the regular mixture.
 13. Opening the windows results in a smaller pressure difference between the exterior and interior of the house and, therefore, less tendency for severe damage to the structure due to the Bernoulli effect.

Problems

 1. $4.74\rho_0$
 3. (a) 2 550 N (b) 3.00×10^4 Pa (c) No. The pressure will be the same only if the acrobats all wear the same-size shoe.
 5. (a) $\sim 4 \times 10^{17}$ kg/m^3 (b) The density of an atom is about 10^{14} times greater than the density of iron and other common solids and liquids. This shows that an atom is mostly empty space. Liquids and solids, as well as gases, are mostly empty space.
 7. (a) 1.01×10^6 N (b) 3.88×10^5 N (c) 1.11×10^5 Pa
 9. 4.90 mm
 11. 1.05×10^7 Pa
 13. 3.5×10^8 Pa
 15. 4.4 mm
 17. 8.6×10^{-4} m
 19. 1.9 cm
 21. (a) 3.71×10^5 Pa (b) 3.57×10^4 N
 23. 0.133 m
 25. 1.05×10^5 Pa
 27. 27 N · m
 29. 0.258 N down
 31. 9.41 kN

33. (a) 408 kg/m³ (b) If the steel object's mass is just slightly greater than 0.310 kg, then the block is submerged but the steel object and the block do not sink to the bottom, the reason being that the steel object now starts to displace water and the buoyant force is now increasing. If the steel object is solid, it will displace a little more than 0.039 kg of water when fully submerged. The steel object and the block will sink to the bottom when the steel object's mass exceeds about 0.350 kg, and for values less than this, but greater than 0.310 kg, the block will be submerged and the steel object partially submerged.

35. (a) 1.43 kN upward (b) 1.28 kN upward (c) The balloon expands because the external pressure declines with increasing altitude.

37. (a) 4.0 kN (b) 2.2 kN (c) The air pressure at this high altitude is much lower than atmospheric pressure at the surface of Earth, so the balloons expanded and eventually burst.

39. (a) 7.00 cm (b) 2.80 kg

41. (a) 1.46×10^{-2} m³ (b) 2.10×10^3 kg/m³

43. 17.3 N (upper scale), 31.7 N (lower scale)

45. (a) 80 g/s (b) 0.27 mm/s

47. 12.6 m/s

49. (a) 9.43×10^3 Pa (b) 255 m/s (c) The density of air decreases with increasing height, resulting in a smaller pressure difference. Beyond the maximum operational altitude, the pressure difference can no longer support the aircraft.

51. (a) 0.553 s (b) 14.5 m/s (c) 0.145 m/s (d) 1.013×10^5 Pa (e) 2.06×10^5 Pa; gravity terms can be neglected. (f) 33.0 N

53. 9.00 cm

55. 1.47 cm

57. (a) 28.0 m/s (b) 28.0 m/s (c) 2.11 MPa

59. 8.3×10^{-2} N/m

61. 5.6×10^{-2} N/m

63. 8.6 N

65. 2.1 MPa

67. 2.8 μm

69. 0.21 mm

71. $RN = 4.3 \times 10^3$; turbulent flow

73. 1.8×10^{-3} kg/m³

75. 1.4×10^{-5} N · s/m²

77. (a) The buoyant forces are the same because the two blocks displace equal amounts of water. (b) The spring scale reads largest value for the iron block. (c) $B = 2.0 \times 10^3$ N for both blocks, $T_{iron} = 13 \times 10^3$ N, $T_{aluminum} = 3.3 \times 10^3$ N.

79. (b) 5.9 km

81. 2.5×10^7 capillaries

83. (a) 1.57 kPa, 1.55×10^{-2} atm, 11.8 mm of Hg (b) The fluid level in the tap should rise. (c) Blockage of flow of the cerebrospinal fluid

85. 2.25 m above the level of point B

87. 0.605 m

89. $F = \pi R^2 (P_0 - P)$

91. 17.0 cm above the floor

CHAPTER 10

Quick Quizzes

1. (c)
2. (b)
3. (c)
4. (c)
5. Unlike land-based ice, ocean-based ice already displaces water, so when it melts ocean levels won't change much.
6. (b)

Example Questions

1. A Celsius degree
2. True

3. When the temperature decreases, the tension in the wire increases.
4. The magnitude of the required temperature change would be larger because the linear expansion coefficient of steel is less than that of copper.
5. Glass, aluminum, ethyl alcohol, mercury
6. The balloon expands.
7. The pressure is slightly reduced.
8. The volume of air decreases.
9. The pressure would double.
10. True

Multiple-Choice Questions

1. (e)
3. (c)
5. (d)
7. (c)
9. (b)
11. (b)
13. (i) (b) (ii) (d)

Conceptual Questions

1. (a) An ordinary glass dish will usually break because of stresses that build up as the glass expands when heated. (b) The expansion coefficient for Pyrex glass is much lower than that of ordinary glass. Thus, the Pyrex dish will expand much less than the dish of ordinary glass and does not normally develop sufficient stress to cause breakage.

3. Mercury must have the larger coefficient of expansion. As the temperature of a thermometer rises, both the mercury and the glass expand. If they both had the same coefficient of linear expansion, the mercury and the cavity in the glass would expand by the same amount, and there would be no apparent movement of the end of the mercury column relative to the calibration scale on the glass. If the glass expanded more than the mercury, the reading would go down as the temperature went up! Now that we have argued this conceptually, we can look in a table and find that the coefficient for mercury is about 20 times as large as that for glass, so that the expansion of the glass can sometimes be ignored.

5. We can think of each bacterium as being a small bag of liquid containing bubbles of gas at a very high pressure. The ideal gas law indicates that if the bacterium is raised rapidly to the surface, then its volume must increase dramatically. In fact, the increase in volume is sufficient to rupture the bacterium.

7. Additional water vaporizes into the bubble, so that the number of moles n increases.

9. The bags of chips contain a sealed sample of air. When the bags are taken up the mountain, the external atmospheric pressure on them is reduced. As a result, the difference between the pressure of the air inside the bags and the reduced pressure outside results in a net force pushing the plastic of the bag outward.

11. The coefficient of expansion for metal is generally greater than that of glass; hence, the metal lid loosens because it expands more than the glass.

13. As the water rises in temperature, it expands or rises in pressure or both. The excess volume would spill out of the cooling system, or else the pressure would rise very high indeed. The expansion of the radiator itself provides only a little relief, because in general solids expand far less than liquids for a given positive change in temperature.

Problems

1. (a) −460°C (b) 37.0°C (c) −280°C
3. (a) −253°C (b) −423°F

9. (a) 107°F (b) Yes; the normal body temperature is 98.6°F, so the patient has a high fever that needs immediate attention.

11. 31 cm

13. 55.0°C

15. (a) −179°C (attainable) (b) −376°C (below 0 K, unattainable)

17. (a) $11.2 \times 10^3 \text{ kg/m}^3$ (b) No. Although the density of gold would be less on a warm day, the mass of the bar would be the same regardless of its temperature, and that is what you are paying for. (Note that the volume of the bar increases with increasing temperature, whereas its density decreases. Its mass, however, remains constant.)

19. 1.02×10^3 gallons

21. (a) 0.10 L (b) 2.009 L (c) 1.0 cm

23. $2.7 \times 10^2 \text{ N}$

25. 0.548 gal

27. (a) increases (b) 1.603 cm

29. (a) 627°C (b) 927°C

31. (a) 2.5×10^{19} molecules (b) 4.1×10^{-21} mol

33. 4.28 atm

35. 7.1 m

37. 16.0 cm^3

39. $6.21 \times 10^{-21} \text{ J}$

41. $6.64 \times 10^{-27} \text{ kg}$

43. (a) $2.01 \times 10^4 \text{ K}$ (b) 901 K

45. 16 N

47. 0.66 mm to the right at 78° below the horizontal

49. 3.55 L

51. 35.016 m

53. 6.57 MPa

55. (a) 99.8 mL (b) The change in volume of the flask is far smaller because Pyrex has a much smaller coefficient of expansion than acetone. Hence, the change in volume of the flask has a negligible effect on the answer.

57. (b) The expansion of the mercury is almost 20 times that of the flask (assuming Pyrex glass).

59. 2.7 m

61. (a) $\theta = \dfrac{(\alpha_2 - \alpha_1)L_0(\Delta T)}{\Delta r}$

(c) The bar bends in the opposite direction.

63. (a) No torque acts on the disk so its angular momentum is constant. Yes, the angular speed increases. As the disk cools, its radius, and hence, its moment of inertia, decreases. Conservation of angular momentum then requires that its angular speed increase. (b) 25.7 rad/s

CHAPTER 11

Quick Quizzes

1. (a) Water, glass, iron. (b) Iron, glass, water.

2. (b) The slopes are proportional to the reciprocal of the specific heat, so a larger specific heat results in a smaller slope, meaning more energy is required to achieve a given temperature change.

3. (c)

4. (b)

5. (a) 4 (b) 16 (c) 64

Example Questions

1. From the point of view of physics, faster repetitions don't affect the final answer; physiologically, however, the weightlifter's metabolic rate would increase.

2. (c)

3. No

4. (c)

5. No

6. The mass of ice melted would double.

7. Nickel–iron asteroids have a higher density and therefore a greater mass, which means they can deliver more energy on impact for a given speed.

8. A runner's metabolism is much higher when he is running than when he is at rest, and because muscles are only about 20% efficient, a great amount of random thermal energy is created through muscular exertion. Consequently, the runner needs to eliminate far more thermal energy when running than when resting. Once the run is over, muscular exertions cease and the metabolism starts to return to normal, so the runner begins to feel chilled.

9. (a)

10. (a)

Multiple-Choice Questions

1. (b)

3. (d)

5. (e)

7. (d)

9. (c)

11. (e)

Conceptual Questions

1. When you rub the surface, you increase the temperature of the rubbed region. With the metal surface, some of this energy is transferred away from the rubbed site by conduction. Consequently, the temperature in the rubbed area is not as high for the metal as it is for the wood, and it feels relatively cooler than the wood.

3. The fruit loses energy into the air by radiation and convection from its surface. Before ice crystals can form inside the fruit to rupture cell walls, all of the liquid water on the skin will have to freeze. The resulting time delay may prevent damage within the fruit throughout a frosty night. Further, a surface film of ice provides some insulation to slow subsequent energy loss by conduction from within the fruit.

5. One of the ways that objects transfer energy is by radiation. The top of the mailbox is oriented toward the clear sky. Radiation emitted by the top of the mailbox goes upward and into space. There is little radiation coming down from space to the top of the mailbox. Radiation leaving the sides of the mailbox is absorbed by the environment. Radiation from the environment (tree, houses, cars, etc.), however, can enter the sides of the mailbox, keeping them warmer than the top. As a result, the top is the coldest portion and frost forms there first.

7. (a) The operation of an immersion coil depends on the convection of water to maintain a safe temperature. As the water near a coil warms up, the warmed water floats to the top due to Archimedes' principle. The temperature of the coil cannot go higher than the boiling temperature of water, 100°C. If the coil is operated in air, convection is reduced, and the upper limit of 100°C is removed. As a result, the coil can become hot enough to be damaged. (b) If the coil is used in an attempt to warm a thick liquid like stew, convection cannot occur fast enough to carry energy away from the coil, so that it again may become hot enough to be damaged.

9. Tile is a better conductor of energy than carpet, so the tile conducts energy away from your feet more rapidly than does the carpeted floor.

11. The large amount of energy stored in the concrete during the day as the Sun falls on it is released at night, resulting in an overall higher average temperature in the city than in the countryside. The heated air in a city rises as it's displaced by cooler air moving in from the countryside, so evening breezes tend to blow from country to city.

Problems

1. 16.9°C
3. (a) 1.67×10^{18} J (b) 52.9 yr
5. (a) 25.8°C (b) No. Gravitational potential energy is proportional to the mass, just like the temperature change.
7. (a) 4.5×10^3 J (b) 910 W (c) 0.87 Cal/s (d) The excess thermal energy is transported by conduction and convection to the surface of the skin and disposed of through the evaporation of sweat.
9. 176°C
11. 88 W
13. 4.2×10^6 J
15. 0.845 kg
17. 80 g
19. (a) 1.82×10^3 J/kg·°C (b) We cannot make a definite identification. It might be beryllium. (c) The material might be an unknown alloy or a material not listed in the table.
21. 0.26 kg
23. (a) 21.3°C (b) 178 J/kg·K (c) $N_{Sn} = 2.03 \times 10^{24}$ atoms; $N_{Pb} = 1.16 \times 10^{24}$ atoms (d) $N_{Sn}/N_{Pb} = 1.75$; $c_{Sn}/c_{Pb} = 1.77$. The specific heat of an element is proportional to the number of atoms per unit mass of that element.
25. 16°C
27. 65°C
29. 2.3 km
31. 16°C
33. (a) t_{boil} = 2.8 min (b) $t_{evaporate}$ = 18 min
35. (a) all ice melts, T_f = 40°C (b) 8.0 g melts, T_f = 0°C
37. (a) The bullet loses all its kinetic energy as it is stopped by the ice. Also, thermal energy must be removed from the bullet to cool it from 30.0°C to 0°C. The sum of these two energies equals the energy it takes to melt part of the ice. The final temperature of the bullet is 0°C because not all the ice melts. (b) 0.294 g
39. 3×10^3 W
41. 402 MW
43. 709 s
45. 9.0 cm
47. 2.7×10^7 J
49. 16:1
51. 12 kW
53. 2.3 kg
55. 29°C
57. 8.00×10^2 J/kg·°C. This value differs from the tabulated value by 11%, so they agree within 15%.
59. 66.7 min
61. 51.2°C
63. (a) seven times (b) As the car stops, it transforms part of its kinetic energy into internal energy due to air resistance. As soon as the brakes rise above the air temperature, they transfer energy by heat into the air. If they reach a high temperature, they transfer energy very quickly.
65. (b) 2.7×10^3 J/kg·°C
67. 12 h
69. 3.85×10^{26} J
71. 1.4 kg
73. (a) 75.0°C (b) 36 kJ

CHAPTER 12

Quick Quizzes

1. (b)
2. A is isovolumetric, B is adiabatic, C is isothermal, D is isobaric.
3. (c)
4. (b)

5. The number 7 is the most probable outcome. The numbers 2 and 12 are the least probable outcomes.

Example Questions

1. No
2. No
3. True
4. True
5. The change in temperature must always be negative because the system does work on the environment at the expense of its internal energy and no thermal energy can be supplied to the system to compensate for the loss.
6. A diatomic gas does more work under these assumptions.
7. The carbon dioxide gas would have a final temperature lower than 380 K.
8. False
9. (a)
10. No. The efficiency improves only if the ratio $|Q_c/Q_h|$ becomes smaller. Further, too large an increase in Q_h will damage the engine, so there is a limit even if Q_c remains fixed.
11. If the path from B to C were a straight line, more work would be done per cycle.
12. No. The compressor does work and warms the kitchen. With the refrigerator door open, the compressor would run continuously.
13. False
14. Silver, lead, ice
15. False
16. The thermal energy created by your body during the exertion would be dissipated into the environment, increasing the entropy of the Universe.
17. Skipping meals can lower the basal metabolism, reducing the rate at which energy is used. When a large meal is eaten later, the lower metabolism means more food energy will be stored, and weight will be gained even if the same number of total calories is consumed in a day.

Multiple-Choice Questions

1. (c)
3. (c)
5. (e)
7. (b)
9. (d)
11. (c)
13. (b)
15. (b)
17. (b)

Conceptual Questions

1. First, the efficiency of the automobile engine cannot exceed the Carnot efficiency: it is limited by the temperature of the burning fuel and the temperature of the environment into which the exhaust is dumped. Second, the engine block cannot be allowed to exceed a certain temperature. Third, any practical engine has friction, incomplete burning of fuel, and limits set by timing and energy transfer by heat.
3. The energy that is leaving the body by work and heat is replaced by means of biological processes that transform chemical energy in the food that the individual ate into internal energy. Thus, the temperature of the body can be maintained.
5. If there is no change in internal energy, then, according to the first law of thermodynamics, the heat is equal to the negative of the work done on the gas (and thus equal to the work done by the gas). Thus, $Q = -W = W_{by\ gas}$.

7. Practically speaking, it isn't possible to create a heat engine that creates no thermal pollution, because there must be both a hot heat source (energy reservoir) and a cold heat sink (low-temperature energy reservoir). The heat engine will warm the cold heat sink and will cool down the heat source. If either of those two events is undesirable, then there will be thermal pollution.

Under some circumstances, the thermal pollution would be negligible. For example, suppose a satellite in space were to run a heat pump between its sunny side and its dark side. The satellite would intercept some of the energy that gathered on one side and would 'dump' it to the dark side. Since neither of those effects would be particularly undesirable, it could be said that such a heat pump produced no thermal pollution.

9. Although no energy is transferred into or out of the system by heat, work is done on the system as the result of the agitation. Consequently, both the temperature and the internal energy of the coffee increase.

11. The first law is a statement of conservation of energy that says that we cannot devise a cyclic process that produces more energy than we put into it. If the cyclic process takes in energy by heat and puts out work, we call the device a heat engine. In addition to the first law's limitation, the second law says that, during the operation of a heat engine, some energy must be ejected to the environment by heat. As a result, it is theoretically impossible to construct a heat engine that will work with 100% efficiency.

13. If the system is isolated, no energy enters or leaves the system by heat, work, or other transfer processes. Within the system energy can change from one form to another, but since energy is conserved these transformations cannot affect the total amount of energy. The total energy is constant.

Problems

1. (a) $-465\,\text{J}$ (b) The negative sign for work done on the gas indicates that the expanding gas does positive work on the surroundings.
3. (a) $-6.1 \times 10^5\,\text{J}$ (b) $4.6 \times 10^5\,\text{J}$
5. (a) $-810\,\text{J}$ (b) $-507\,\text{J}$ (c) $-203\,\text{J}$
7. $96.3\,\text{mg}$
9. (a) $1.09 \times 10^3\,\text{K}$ (b) $-6.81\,\text{kJ}$
13. (a) $-88.5\,\text{J}$ (b) $722\,\text{J}$
15. (a) $567\,\text{J}$ (b) $167\,\text{J}$
17. (a) $-180\,\text{J}$ (b) $+188\,\text{J}$
19. (a) $3.25\,\text{kJ}$ (b) 0 (c) $-3.25\,\text{kJ}$ (d) The internal energy would increase, resulting in an increase in temperature of the gas.
21. (a) $-4.58 \times 10^4\,\text{J}$ (b) $4.58 \times 10^4\,\text{J}$ (c) 0
23. (a) 40.6 moles (b) $506\,\text{J/K}$ (c) $W = 0$ (d) $16.0\,\text{kJ}$ (e) $31.6\,\text{K}$ (f) $332\,\text{K}$ (g) $5.53\,\text{atm}$
25. (a) $0.95\,\text{J}$ (b) $3.2 \times 10^5\,\text{J}$ (c) $3.2 \times 10^5\,\text{J}$
27. (b) $1.3 \times 10^{56}\,\text{K}$
29. $405\,\text{kJ}$
31. 0.540 (or 54.0%)
33. (a) 0.25 (or 25%) (b) $3/4$
35. (a) 0.672 (or 67.2%) (b) $58.8\,\text{kW}$
37. (a) 0.294 (or 29.4%) (b) $5.00 \times 10^2\,\text{J}$ (c) $1.67\,\text{kW}$
39. (a) $4.50 \times 10^6\,\text{J}$ (b) $2.84 \times 10^7\,\text{J}$ (c) $68.2\,\text{kg}$
41. $1/3$
43. (a) 30.6% (b) $985\,\text{MW}$
45. $143\,\text{J/K}$
47. (a) $-1.2\,\text{kJ/K}$ (b) $1.2\,\text{kJ/K}$
49. $57.2\,\text{J/K}$
51. $3.27\,\text{J/K}$
53. (a)

End Result	Possible Tosses	Total Number of Same Result
All H	HHHH	1
1T, 3H	HHHT, HHTH, HTHH, THHH	4
2T, 2H	HHTT, HTHT, THHT, HTTH, THTH, TTHH	6
3T, 1H	TTTH, TTHT, THTT, HTTT	4
All T	TTTT	1

(b) all H or all T (c) 2H and 2T
55. $-6.5\,\text{MJ}$
57. $1\,300\,\text{W}$
59. $18°\text{C}$
61. (a) $12.2\,\text{kJ}$ (b) $4.05\,\text{kJ}$ (c) $8.15\,\text{kJ}$
63. (a) $26\,\text{J}$ (b) $9.0 \times 10^5\,\text{J}$ (c) $9.0 \times 10^5\,\text{J}$
65. (a) $2.49\,\text{kJ}$ (b) $1.50\,\text{kJ}$ (c) $-990\,\text{J}$
67. (a) $T_{\text{Ⓐ}} = 1.20 \times 10^2\,\text{K}$; $T_{\text{Ⓑ}} = 722\,\text{K}$
(b) $1.10 \times 10^5\,\text{J}$ (c) $7.50 \times 10^4\,\text{J}$ (d) $1.85 \times 10^5\,\text{J}$
69. 0.146; $486\,\text{kcal}$
71. (a) 2.6×10^3 metric tons/day (b) $\$7.6 \times 10^6/\text{yr}$
(c) $4.1 \times 10^4\,\text{kg/s}$

CHAPTER 13

Quick Quizzes

1. (d)
2. (c)
3. (b)
4. (a)
5. (c)
6. (d)
7. (c), (b)
8. (a)
9. (b)

Example Questions

1. No. If a spring is stretched too far, it no longer satisfies Hooke's law and can become permanently deformed.
2. $k_{\text{eq}} = k_1 + k_2$
3. False
4. True
5. False
6. (b)
7. True
8. No
9. (a), (c)
10. The speed is doubled.

Multiple-Choice Questions

1. (c)
3. (a)
5. (b)
7. (a)
9. (e)
11. (d)
13. (c)

Conceptual Questions

1. No. Because the total energy is $E = \frac{1}{2}kA^2$, changing the mass of the object while keeping A constant has no effect on the total energy. When the object is at a displacement x from equilibrium, the potential energy is $\frac{1}{2}kx^2$, independent of the mass, and the kinetic energy is $KE = E - \frac{1}{2}kx^2$, also independent of the mass.

3. When the spring with two objects on opposite ends is set into oscillation in space, the coil at the exact center of the spring does not move. Thus, we can imagine clamping the center coil in place without affecting the motion. If we do this, we have two separate oscillating systems, one on each side of the clamp. The half-spring on each side of the clamp has twice the spring constant of the full spring, as shown by the following argument: The force exerted by a spring is proportional to the separation of the coils as the spring is extended. Imagine that we extend a spring by a given distance and measure the distance between coils. We then cut the spring in half. If one of the half-springs is now extended by the same distance, the coils will be twice as far apart as they were in the complete spring. Thus, it takes twice as much force to stretch the half-spring, from which we conclude that the half-spring has a spring constant which is twice that of the complete spring. Hence, our clamped system of objects on two half-springs will vibrate with a frequency that is higher than f by a factor of the square root of two.

5. We assume that the buoyant force acting on the sphere is negligible in comparison to its weight, even when the sphere is empty. We also assume that the bob is small compared with the pendulum length. Then, the frequency of the pendulum is $f = 1/T = (1/2\pi)\sqrt{g/L}$, which is independent of mass. Thus, the frequency will not change as the water leaks out.

7. (a) The bouncing ball is not an example of simple harmonic motion. The ball does not follow a sinusoidal function for its position as a function of time. (b) The daily movement of a student is also not simple harmonic motion, because the student stays at a fixed location, school, for a long time. If this motion were sinusoidal, the student would move more and more slowly as she approached her desk, and as soon as she sat down at the desk, she would start to move back toward home again.

9. The speed of a wave on a string is given by $v = \sqrt{F/\mu}$. This says the speed is independent of the frequency of the wave. Thus, doubling the frequency leaves the speed unaffected.

11. The kinetic energy is proportional to the square of the speed, and the potential energy is proportional to the square of the displacement. Therefore, both must be positive quantities.

Problems

1. (a) 17 N to the left (b) 28 m/s² to the left
3. (a) 6.58 N (b) 10.1 N
5. 0.242 kg
7. (a) 0.206 m (b) −0.042 1 m (c) The block oscillates around the unstretched position of the spring with an amplitude of 0.248 m.
9. (a) 60 J (b) 49 m/s
11. 2.94×10^3 N/m
13. 0.478 m
15. (a) 1 630 N/m (b) 47.0 J (c) 7.90 kg (d) 2.57 m/s (e) 26.1 J (f) 20.9 J (g) −0.201 m
17. (a) 0.28 m/s (b) 0.26 m/s (c) 0.26 m/s (d) 3.5 cm
19. 39.2 N
21. (a) 1.53 J (b) 1.75 m/s (c) 1.51 m/s
23. The horizontal displacement is described by $x(t) = A \cos \omega t$, where A is the distance from the center of the wheel to the crankpin.
25. 0.63 s
27. (a) 1.0 s (b) 0.28 m/s (c) 0.25 m/s
29. (a) 5.98 m/s (b) 206 N/m (c) 0.238 m
31. (a) 11.0 N toward the left (b) 0.881 oscillations
33. $v = \pm\omega A \sin \omega t$, $a = -\omega^2 A \cos \omega t$
35. (a) 1.46 s (b) 9.59 m/s²

37. (a) slow (b) 9:47
39. (a) $L_{Earth} = 25$ cm (b) $L_{Mars} = 9.4$ cm (c) $m_{Earth} = 0.25$ kg (d) $m_{Mars} = 0.25$ kg
41. (a) 4.13 cm (b) 10.4 cm (c) 5.56×10^{-2} s (d) 187 cm/s
43. (a) 5.45×10^{14} Hz (b) 1.83×10^{-15} s
45. 31.9 cm
47. 58.8 s
49. 80.0 N
51. 5.20×10^2 m/s
53. (a) 30.0 N (b) 25.8 m/s
55. 28.5 m/s
57. (a) 0.051 0 kg/m (b) 19.6 m/s
59. (a) 13.4 m/s (b) The worker could throw an object such as a snowball at one end of the line to set up a pulse and then use a stopwatch to measure the time it takes the pulse to travel the length of the line. From this measurement, the worker would have an estimate of the wave speed, which in turn can be used to estimate the tension.
61. (a) Constructive interference gives $A = 0.50$ m (b) Destructive interference gives $A = 0.10$ m
63. (a) 219 N/m (b) 6.12 kg
65. (a) 1.68 s (b) 16.8 N/m
67. (a) 588 N/m (b) 0.700 m/s
69. 6.62 cm
71. (a) Using s for the displacement from equilibrium along the arc, the restoring force on the balloon takes the form of Hooke's law: $F_{tangential} = -[(\rho_{air} - \rho_{He})Vg/L]s$ (b) $T = 1.40$ s
75. (a) 15.8 rad/s (b) 5.23 cm

CHAPTER 14

Quick Quizzes

1. (c)
2. (c)
3. (b)
4. (b), (e)
5. (d)
6. (a)
7. (b)

Example Questions

1. Rubber is easier to compress than solid aluminum, so aluminum must have the larger bulk modulus and by Equation 14.1, a higher sound speed.
2. 3.0 dB
3. You should increase your distance from the sound source by a factor of 5.
4. Yes. It changes because the speed of sound changes with temperature. Answer (b) is correct.
5. No
6. True
7. True
8. (b)
9. True
10. True
11. The notes are so different from each other in frequency that the beat frequency is very high and cannot be distinguished.

Multiple-Choice Questions

1. (b)
3. (a)
5. (d)
7. (d)
9. (e)
11. (b)
13. (e)
15. (c)

Conceptual Questions

1. (a) higher (b) lower

3. Yes. The speed of sound in air is proportional to the square root of the absolute temperature, $\sqrt{T}$. The speed of sound is greater in warmer air, so the pulse from the camera would return sooner than it would on a cooler day from an object at the same distance. The camera would interpret an object as being closer than it actually is on a hot day.

5. Sophisticated electronic devices break the frequency range used in telephone conversations into several frequency bands and then mix them in a predetermined pattern so that they become unintelligible. The descrambler moves the bands back into their proper order.

7. (a) The echo is Doppler shifted, and the shift is like both a moving source and a moving observer. The sound that leaves your horn in the forward direction is Doppler shifted to a higher frequency, because it is coming from a moving source. As the sound reflects back and comes toward you, you are a moving observer, so there is a second Doppler shift to an even higher frequency. (b) If the sound reflects from the spacecraft coming toward you, there is a different moving-source shift to an even higher frequency. The reflecting surface of the spacecraft acts as a moving source.

9. The bowstring is pulled away from equilibrium and released, in a manner similar to the way a guitar string is pulled and released when it is plucked. Thus, standing waves will be excited in the bowstring. If the arrow leaves from the exact center of the string, then a series of odd harmonics will be excited. Even harmonics will not be excited, because they have a node at the point where the string exhibits its maximum displacement.

11. The two engines are running at slightly different frequencies, thus producing a beat frequency between them.

Problems

1. (a) 5.56 km (b) No. The speed of light is much greater than the speed of sound, so the time interval required for the light to reach you is negligible compared to the time interval for the sound.

3. 358 m/s

5. 515 m

7. The wavelength decreases by 2.5 mm.

9. (a) The pulse that travels through the rail (b) 23.4 ms

11. 150 dB

13. 3.0×10^{-8} W/m^2

15. (a) 1.00×10^{-2} W/m^2 (b) 105 dB

17. 37 dB

19. (a) 1.3×10^2 W (b) 96 dB

23. (a) 75 Hz drop (b) 0.948 m

25. 596 Hz

27. 9.09 m/s

29. 19.7 m

31. (a) 56.3 s (b) 56.6 km farther along

33. At distances of 0.089 m, 0.303 m, 0.518 m, 0.732 m, 0.947 m, and 1.16 m from either speaker

35. 800 m

37. (a) 0.240 m (b) 0.855 m

39. (a) Nodes at 0, 2.67 m, 5.33 m, and 8.00 m; antinodes at 1.33 m, 4.00 m, and 6.67 m (b) 18.6 Hz

41. 378 Hz

43. (a) 1.85×10^{-2} kg/m (b) 90.6 m/s (c) 152 N (d) 2.20 m (e) 8.33 m

45. (a) 78.9 N (b) 211 Hz

47. 19.976 kHz

49. 58 Hz

51. 3.1 kHz

53. (a) 0.552 m (b) 316 Hz

55. 5.64 beats/s

57. 3.85 m/s away from the station or 3.77 m/s toward the station

59. (a) 1.99 beats/s (b) 3.38 m/s

61. 1.76 cm

63. (a) 0.642 W (b) 0.43%

65. 67.0 dB

67. $r_1 = 3.3$ m and $r_2 = 32.7$ m

69. 262 kHz

71. 64 dB

73. (a) 439 Hz (b) 441 Hz

75. 1.34×10^4 N

CHAPTER 15

Quick Quizzes

1. (b)

2. (b)

3. (c)

4. (a)

5. (c) and (d)

6. (a)

7. (c)

8. (b)

9. (d)

10. (b) and (d)

Example Questions

1. $\frac{1}{4}$

2. (a)

3. Fourth quadrant

4. The suspended droplet would accelerate downward at twice the acceleration of gravity.

5. The angle ϕ would increase.

6. (c)

7. The charge on the inner surface would be negative.

8. Zero

Multiple-Choice Questions

1. (b)

3. (a)

5. (b)

7. (d)

9. (e)

11. (e)

13. (a)

Conceptual Questions

1. Electrons have been removed from the glass object. Negative charge has been removed from the initially neutral rod, resulting in a net positive charge on the rod. The protons cannot be removed from the rod; protons are not mobile because they are within the nuclei of the atoms of the rod.

3. No. The charge on the metallic sphere resides on its outer surface, so the person is able to touch the surface without causing any charge transfer.

5. No. Life would be no different if electrons were + charged and protons were − charged. Opposite charges would still attract, and like charges would repel. The naming of + and − charge is merely a convention.

7. Move an object A with a net positive charge so it is near, but not touching, a neutral metallic object B that is insulated from the ground. The presence of A will polarize B, causing an excess negative charge to exist on the side nearest A and an excess positive charge of equal magnitude to exist on the side farthest from A. While A is still near B, touch B with your hand. Additional electrons will then flow from ground, through your body, and onto B. With A continuing to be near but not in contact with B, remove your hand from

B, thus trapping the excess electrons on B. When A is now removed, B is left with excess electrons, or a net negative charge. By means of mutual repulsion, this negative charge will now spread uniformly over the entire surface of B.

9. She is not shocked. She becomes part of the dome of the Van de Graaff, and charges flow onto her body. They do not jump to her body via a spark, however, so she is not shocked.

11. The dry paper is initially neutral. The comb attracts the paper because its electric field causes the molecules of the paper to become polarized—the paper as a whole cannot be polarized because it is an insulator. Each molecule is polarized so that its unlike-charged side is closer to the charged comb than its like-charged side, so the molecule experiences a net attractive force toward the comb. Once the paper comes in contact with the comb, like charge can be transferred from the comb to the paper, and if enough of this charge is transferred, the like-charged paper is then repelled by the like-charged comb.

13. The electric shielding effect of conductors depends on the fact that there are two kinds of charge: positive and negative. As a result, charges can move within the conductor so that the combination of positive and negative charges establishes an electric field that exactly cancels the external field within the conductor and any cavities inside the conductor. There is only one type of gravitation charge, however, because there is no negative mass. As a result, gravitational shielding is not possible. A room cannot be gravitationally shielded because mass is always positive or zero, never negative.

15. You can only conclude that the net charge inside the Gaussian surface is positive.

Problems

1. (a) 8.74×10^{-8} N   (b) repulsive
3. (a) 2.36×10^{-5} C (b) The charges induce opposite charges in the bulkheads, but the induced charge in the bulkhead near ball B is greater because of ball B's greater charge. The system therefore moves slowly toward the bulkhead closer to ball B.
5. (a) 36.8 N   (b) 5.54×10^{27} m/s^2
7. 49.3 N/m
9. (a) 2.2×10^{-5} N (attraction)   (b) 9.0×10^{-7} N (repulsion)
11. 1.38×10^{-5} N at 77.5° below the negative x-axis
13. 0.437 N at $-85.3°$ from the $+x$-axis.
15. 7.2 nC
17. 2.07×10^3 N/C down
19. 3.15 N due north
21. (a) $\dfrac{mg}{|Q|} \sin \theta$ (b) 3.19×10^3 N/C down the incline
23. (a) 6.12×10^{10} m/s^2 (b) 19.6 μs   (c) 11.8 m
    (d) 1.20×10^{-15} J
25. $E_x = (1 - \sqrt{2})k_e \dfrac{Q}{d^2}$, $E_y = \sqrt{2}k_e \dfrac{Q}{d^2}$
27. 1.8 m to the left of the -2.5-μC charge
29. zero
35. (a) 0 (b) 5 μC inside, -5 μC outside (c) 0 inside, -5 μC outside (d) 0 inside, -5 μC outside
37. 1.3×10^{-3} C
39. (a) 2.54×10^{-15} N   (b) 1.59×10^4 N/C radially outward
41. (a) 858 N · m^2/C   (b) 0   (c) 657 N · m^2/C
43. $-Q/\epsilon_0$ for S$_1$; 0 for S$_2$; $-2Q/\epsilon_0$ for S$_3$; 0 for S$_4$
45. (a) 0   (b) $k_e q/r^2$ outward
47. (a) -7.99 N/C   (b) 0   (c) 1.44 N/C (d) 2.00 nC on the inner surface; 1.00 nC on the outer surface
49. 115 N
51. 24 N/C in the positive x-direction
53. (a) $E = 2k_e qb \, (a^2 + b^2)^{-3/2}$ in the positive x-direction
    (b) $E = k_e Qb(a^2 + b^2)^{-3/2}$ in the positive x-direction

55. $F_x = (0.354)k_e \dfrac{Q^2}{d^2}$; $F_y = (1.65)k_e \dfrac{Q^2}{d^2}$
57. 4.4×10^5 N/C
59. 1.14×10^{-7} C on one sphere and 5.69×10^{-8} C on the other
61. (a) 0   (b) 7.99×10^7 N/C (outward)   (c) 0
    (d) 7.34×10^6 N/C (outward)
63. (a) 1.00×10^3 N/C   (b) 3.37×10^{-8} s   (c) accelerate at 1.76×10^{14} m/s^2 in the direction opposite that of the electric field

CHAPTER 16

Quick Quizzes

1. (b)
2. (a)
3. (b)
4. (d)
5. (d)
6. (c)
7. (a)
8. (c)
9. (a) C decreases. (b) Q stays the same. (c) E stays the same. (d) ΔV increases. (e) The energy stored increases.
10. (a) C increases. (b) Q increases. (c) E stays the same. (d) ΔV remains the same. (e) The energy stored increases.
11. (a)

Example Questions

1. True
2. True
3. False
4. (a)
5. Three
6. Each answer would be reduced by a factor of one-half.
7. One-quarter
8. The voltage drop is the smallest across the 24-μF capacitor and largest across the 3.0-μF capacitor.
9. The 3.0-μF capacitor
10. (c)
11. (b)
12. $C = \dfrac{\epsilon_0 A}{d}$

Multiple-Choice Questions

1. (b)
3. (d)
5. (b)
7. (a)
9. (a)
11. (c)

Conceptual Questions

1. (a) The proton moves in a straight line with constant acceleration in the direction of the electric field. (b) As its velocity increases, its kinetic energy increases, and the electric potential energy associated with the proton decreases.
3. The work done in pulling the capacitor plates farther apart is transferred into additional electric energy stored in the capacitor. The charge is constant, and the capacitance decreases, but the potential difference between the plates increases, which results in an increase in the stored electric energy.
5. If the power line makes electrical contact with the metal of the car, it will raise the potential of the car to 20 kV. It will also raise the potential of your body to 20 kV, because you are in contact with the car. In itself, this is not a problem. If you step out of the car, however, your body at 20 kV will make

contact with the ground, which is at zero volts. As a result, a current will pass through your body, and you will likely be injured. Thus, it is best to stay in the car until help arrives.

7. If two points on a conducting object were at different potentials, then free charges in the object would move, and we would not have static conditions, in contradiction to the initial assumption. (Free positive charges would migrate from locations of higher to locations of lower potential. Free electrons would rapidly move from locations of lower to locations of higher potential.) All of the charges would continue to move until the potential became equal everywhere in the conductor.

9. (a) The capacitor often remains charged long after the voltage source is disconnected. This residual charge can be lethal. (b) The capacitor can be safely handled after discharging the plates by short-circuiting the device with a conductor, such as a screwdriver with an insulating handle.

11. $D > C > B > A$

13. Not all connections are simple combinations of series and parallel circuits. As an example of such a complex circuit, consider the network of five capacitors, C_1, C_2, C_3, C_4, and C_5 shown below

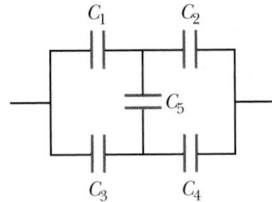

This combination cannot be reduced to a simple equivalent by the techniques of combining series and parallel capacitors.

Problems

1. (a) 1.92×10^{-18} J (b) -1.92×10^{-18} J (c) 2.05×10^6 m/s in the negative x-direction
3. 1.4×10^{-20} J
5. 1.7×10^6 N/C
7. (a) 1.13×10^5 N/C (b) 1.80×10^{-14} N (c) 4.37×10^{-17} J
9. (a) The spring stretches by 4.36 cm.
   (b) Equilibrium: $x = 2.18$ cm; $A = 2.18$ cm (c) $\Delta V = -\dfrac{2kA^2}{Q}$
11. (a) -5.75×10^{-7} V (b) -1.92×10^{-7} V, $\Delta V = 3.84 \times 10^{-7}$ V (c) No. Unless fixed in place, the electron would move in the opposite direction, increasing its distance from points A and B and lowering the potential difference between them.
13. (a) 2.67×10^6 V (b) 2.13×10^6 V
15. (a) 103 V (b) -3.85×10^{-7} J; positive work must be done to separate the charges.
17. -11.0 kV
19. (a) 3.84×10^{-14} J (b) 2.55×10^{-13} J (c) -2.17×10^{-13} J (d) 8.08×10^6 m/s (e) 1.24×10^7 m/s
21. (a) 0.294 J (b) 271 m/s
23. 2.74×10^{-14} m
25. (a) 1.1×10^{-8} F (b) 27 C
27. (a) 1.36 pF (b) 16.3 pC (c) 8.00×10^3 V/m
29. (a) 11.1 kV/m toward the negative plate (b) 3.74 pF (c) 74.8 pC and -74.8 pC
31. (a) 5.90×10^{-10} F (b) 3.54×10^{-9} C (c) 2.00×10^3 N/C (d) 1.77×10^{-8} C/m² (e) All the answers are reduced.
33. (a) $10.7\ \mu$C on each capacitor (b) $15.0\ \mu$C on the 2.50-μF capacitor and $37.5\ \mu$C on the 6.25-μF capacitor
35. (a) $2.67\ \mu$F (b) $24.0\ \mu$C on each 8.00-μF capacitor, $18.0\ \mu$C on the 6.00-μF capacitor, $6.00\ \mu$C on the 2.00-μF capacitor (c) 3.00 V across each capacitor
37. (a) $3.33\ \mu$F (b) $180\ \mu$C on the 3-μF and the 6-μF capacitors, $120\ \mu$C on the 2.00-μF and 4.00-μF capacitors (c) 60.0 V

across the 3-μF and the 2-μF capacitors, 30.0 V across the 6-μF and the 4-μF capacitors
39. $Q_1 = 16.0\ \mu$C, $Q_5 = 80.0\ \mu$C, $Q_8 = 64.0\ \mu$C, $Q_4 = 32.0\ \mu$C
41. (a) $Q_{25} = 1.25$ mC, $Q_{40} = 2.00$ mC (b) $Q'_{25} = 288\ \mu$C, $Q'_{40} = 462\ \mu$C (c) $\Delta V = 11.5$ V
43. $Q'_1 = 3.33\ \mu$C, $Q'_2 = 6.67\ \mu$C
45. 3.24×10^{-4} J
47. (a) $54.0\ \mu$J (b) $108\ \mu$J (c) $27.0\ \mu$J
49. (a) $\kappa = 3.4$. The material is probably nylon (see Table 16.1). (b) The voltage would lie somewhere between 25.0 V and 85.0 V.
51. (a) 8.1 nF (b) 2.4 kV
53. (a) volume 9.09×10^{-16} m³, area 4.54×10^{-10} m² (b) 2.01×10^{-13} F (c) 2.01×10^{-14} C, 1.26×10^5 electronic charges
59. 0.188 m²
61. $6.25\ \mu$F
63. 4.47 kV
65. 0.75 mC on C_1, 0.25 mC on C_2
67. Sphere A: $0.800\ \mu$C; sphere B: $1.20\ \mu$C

CHAPTER 17

Quick Quizzes

1. (d)
2. (b)
3. (c), (d)
4. (b)
5. (b)
6. (b)
7. (a)
8. (b)
9. (a)
10. (c)

Example Questions

1. No. Such a current corresponds to the passage of one electron every 2 seconds. The average current, however, can have any value.
2. True
3. Higher
4. (b)
5. (a)
6. (c)

Multiple-Choice Questions

1. (c)
3. (a)
5. (d)
7. (c)
9. (b)
11. (c)
13. (c)

Conceptual Questions

1. In the electrostatic case in which charges are stationary, the electric field inside a conductor must be zero. A non-zero field would produce a current (by interacting with the free electrons in the conductor), which would violate the condition of static equilibrium. In this chapter we deal with conductors that carry current, a nonelectrostatic situation. The current arises because of a potential difference applied between the ends of the conductor, which produces an internal electric field.

3. Because there are so many electrons in a conductor (approximately 10^{28} electrons/m³), the average velocity of charges is very slow. When you connect a wire to a potential difference, you establish an electric field everywhere in the wire nearly

instantaneously, to make electrons start drifting everywhere all at once.

5. We would conclude that the conductor is nonohmic.

7. A voltage is not something that "surges through" a completed circuit. A voltage is a potential difference that is applied across a device or a circuit. It would be more correct to say "1 ampere of electricity surged through the victim's body." Although this amount of current would have disastrous results on the human body, a value of 1 (ampere) doesn't sound as exciting for a newspaper article as 10 000 (volts). Another possibility is to write "10 000 volts of electricity were applied across the victim's body," which still doesn't sound quite as exciting.

9. The drift velocity might increase steadily as time goes on, because collisions between electrons and atoms in the wire would be essentially nonexistent and the conduction electrons would move with constant acceleration. The current would rise steadily without bound also, because I is proportional to the drift velocity.

11. Once the switch is closed, the line voltage is applied across the bulb. As the voltage is applied across the cold filament when it is first turned on, the resistance of the filament is low, the current is high, and a relatively large amount of power is delivered to the bulb. As the filament warms, its resistance rises and the current decreases. As a result, the power delivered to the bulb decreases. The large current spike at the beginning of the bulb's operation is the reason that lightbulbs often fail just after they are turned on.

Problems

1. (a) 3.00×10^{20} electrons (b) the direction opposite to the current

3. 1.05 mA

5. 0.678 mm

7. 27 yr

9. (a) 55.85×10^{-3} kg/mol (b) 1.41×10^5 mol/m³ (c) 8.49×10^{28} iron atoms/m³ (d) 1.70×10^{29} conduction electrons/m³ (e) 2.21×10^{-4} m/s

11. 32 V is 200 times larger than 0.16 V

13. (a) 13.0 Ω (b) 17.0 m

15. (a) 30 Ω (b) 4.7×10^{-4} Ω · m

17. silver ($\rho = 1.59 \times 10^{-8}$ Ω · m)

19. 256 Ω

23. 2.0 A

25. 2.71 MΩ

27. 26 mA

29. (a) 3.0 A (b) 2.9 A

31. (a) 1.2 Ω (b) 8.0×10^{-4} (a 0.080% increase)

33. (a) 8.33 A (b) 14.4 Ω

35. (a) 2.1 W (b) 3.42 W (c) The aluminum wire would not be as safe. If surrounded by thermal insulation, it would get much hotter than a copper wire.

37. 11.2 min

39. (a) $R_A = 576$ Ω; $R_B = 144$ Ω (b) 4.80 s. (c) The charge is the same. It is at a location that is lower in potential. (d) 0.040 0 s (e) Energy enters the lightbulb by electric transmission and leaves by heat and electromagnetic radiation. (f) $1.98

41. 1.6 cm

43. 15.0 μW

45. (a) 116 V (b) 12.8 kW

47. $\dfrac{d_A}{d_B} = \sqrt{3}$

49. 2.16×10^5 C

51. (a) 1.50 Ω (b) 6.00 A

53. 1.1 km

55. 1.47×10^{-6} Ω · m; differs by 2.0% from value in Table 17.1

57. (a) $3.06 (b) No. The circuit must be able to handle at least 26 A.

59. (a) 17.3 A (b) 22.4 MJ (c) $0.684

61. $3.77 \times 10^{28}/m^3$

63. 37 MΩ

65. 0.48 kg/s

CHAPTER 18

Quick Quizzes

1. True

2. Because of the battery's internal resistance, power is delivered to the battery material, raising its temperature.

3. (b)

4. (a)

5. (a)

6. (b)

7. *Parallel:* (a) unchanged (b) unchanged (c) increase (d) decrease

8. *Series:* (a) decrease (b) decrease (c) decrease (d) increase

9. (c)

Example Questions

1. As the resistors get warmer, their resistance increases, reducing the current.

2. (b)

3. The 8.00-Ω resistor

4. The answers would be negative, but they would have the same magnitude as before.

5. Yes

6. (a)

7. (a)

Multiple-Choice Questions

1. (b), (c)

3. (c)

5. (a)

7. (e)

9. (d)

11. (b), (e)

13. (d)

15. (a), (d)

Conceptual Questions

1. No. When a battery serves as a source and supplies current to a circuit, the direction of the current is from the negative terminal of the battery to the positive one. However, when a source having a larger emf than the battery is used to charge the battery, the direction of the current is from the positive terminal of the battery to the negative one.

3. The total amount of energy delivered by the battery will be less than W. Recall that a battery can be considered an ideal, resistanceless battery in series with the internal resistance. When the battery is being charged, the energy delivered to it includes the energy necessary to charge the ideal battery, plus the energy that goes into raising the temperature of the battery due to $I^2 r$ heating in the internal resistance. This latter energy is not available during discharge of the battery, when part of the reduced available energy again transforms into internal energy in the internal resistance, further reducing the available energy below W.

5. Connecting batteries in parallel does not increase the emf. A high-current device connected to two batteries in parallel can draw currents from both batteries. Thus, connecting the batteries in parallel increases the possible current output and, therefore, the possible power output.

7. The starter in the automobile draws a relatively large current from the battery. This large current causes a significant voltage drop across the internal resistance of the battery. As a

result, the terminal voltage of the battery is reduced, and the headlights dim accordingly.

9. The bird is resting on a wire of fixed potential. In order to be electrocuted, a large potential difference is required between the bird's feet. The potential difference between the bird's feet is too small to harm the bird.

11. She will not be electrocuted if she holds onto only one high-voltage wire, because she is not completing a circuit. There is no potential difference across her body as long as she clings to only one wire. However, she should release the wire immediately once it breaks, because she will become part of a closed circuit when she reaches the ground or comes into contact with another object.

13. The junction rule is a statement of conservation of charge. It says that the amount of charge that enters a junction in some time interval must equal the charge that leaves the junction in that time interval. The loop rule is a statement of conservation of energy. It says that the increases and decreases in potential around a closed loop in a circuit must add to zero.

Problems

1. $4.92\ \Omega$
3. (a) Your circuit diagram will consist of two 0.800-Ω resistors in series with the 192-Ω resistance of the bulb. (b) 73.8 W
5. (a) $17.1\ \Omega$ (b) 1.99 A for $4.00\ \Omega$ and $9.00\ \Omega$, 1.17 A for $7.00\ \Omega$, 0.820 A for $10.0\ \Omega$
7. $470\ \Omega$ and $220\ \Omega$
9. (a) 5.68 V (b) 0.227 A
11. $55\ \Omega$
13. 0.43 A
15. (a) Connect two 50-Ω resistors in parallel, and then connect this combination in series with a 20-Ω resistor. (b) Connect two 50-Ω resistors in parallel, connect two 20-V resistors in parallel, and then connect these two combinations in series with each other.
17. 0.714 A, 1.29 A, 12.6 V
19. 50.0 mA from a to e
21. (a) $I_1 = 1.00$ A upward in $200\ \Omega$; $I_4 = 4.00$ A upward in $70.0\ \Omega$; $I_2 = 3.00$ A upward in $80.0\ \Omega$; $I_3 = 8.00$ A downward in $20.0\ \Omega$; (b) 200 V
23. (a) 0.385 mA, 3.08 mA, 2.69 mA (b) 69.2 V, with c at the higher potential
25. (a) No. The only simplification is to note that the 2.0-Ω and 4.0-Ω resistors are in series and add to a resistance of $6.0\ \Omega$. Likewise, the 5.0-Ω and 1.0-Ω resistors are in series and add to a resistance of $6.0\ \Omega$. The circuit cannot be simplified any further. Kirchhoff's rules must be used to analyze the circuit. (b) $I_1 = 3.5$ A, $I_2 = 2.5$ A, $I_3 = 1.0$ A
27. (a) No. The multiloop circuit cannot be simplified any further. Kirchhoff's rules must be used to analyze the circuit. (b) $I_{30} = 0.353$ A directed to the right, $I_5 = 0.118$ A directed to the right, $I_{20} = 0.471$ A directed to the left
29. $\Delta V_2 = 3.05$ V, $\Delta V_3 = 4.57$ V, $\Delta V_4 = 7.38$ V, $\Delta V_5 = 1.62$ V
31. (a) 1.88 s (b) 1.90×10^{-4} C
33. (a) 5.00 s (b) 150 μC (c) 4.06 μA
35. (a) 0.432 s (b) 6.00 μF
37. 48 lightbulbs
39. (a) 6.25 A (b) 750 W
41. (a) 1.2×10^{-9} C, 7.3×10^9 K$^+$ ions. Not large, only $1e/(290\ \text{Å})^2$. (b) 1.7×10^{-9} C, 1.0×10^{10} Na$^+$ ions (c) 0.83 mA (d) 7.5×10^{-12} J
43. 11 nW
45. (a) 4.00 V (b) Point a is at the higher potential.
47. (a) $15\ \Omega$ (b) $I_1 = 1.0$ A, $I_2 = I_3 = 0.50$ A, $I_4 = 0.30$ A, and $I_5 = 0.20$ A (c) $(\Delta V)_{ac} = 6.0$ V, $(\Delta V)_{ce} = 1.2$ V, $(\Delta V)_{ed} = (\Delta V)_{fd} = 1.8$ V, $(\Delta V)_{cd} = 3.0$ V, $(\Delta V)_{db} = 6.0$ V (d) $P_{ac} = 6.0$ W, $P_{ce} = 0.60$ W, $P_{ed} = 0.54$ W, $P_{fd} = 0.36$ W, $P_{cd} = 1.5$ W, $P_{db} = 6.0$ W
49. $6.00\ \Omega$, $3.00\ \Omega$

51. (a) $R_{\text{eq}}^{\text{open}} = 3R$, $R_{\text{eq}}^{\text{closed}} = 2R$ (b) $P = \dfrac{\mathcal{E}^2}{3R}$, $P = \dfrac{\mathcal{E}^2}{2R}$
(c) Lamps A and B increase in brightness, lamp C goes out.
53. (a) 1.02 A down (b) 0.364 A down (c) 1.38 A up (d) 0 (e) 66.0 μC
55. (a) $R_x = R_2 - \frac{1}{4}R_1$ (b) $R_x = 2.8\ \Omega$ (inadequate grounding)
59. $P = \dfrac{(144\ \text{V}^2)R}{(R + 10.0\ \Omega)^2}$

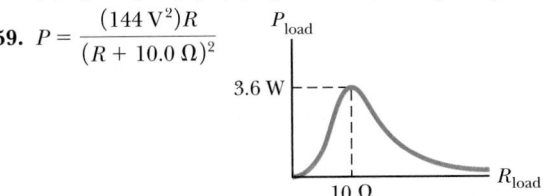

61. (a) 6.0×10^2 W (b) 1.2 J (c) 37 m
63. 0.395 A; 1.50 V
65. (a) 2.41×10^{-5} C (b) 1.61×10^{-5} C (c) 1.61×10^{-2} A

CHAPTER 19

Quick Quizzes

1. (b)
2. (c)
3. (c)
4. (a)
5. (a), (c)
6. (b)

Example Questions

1. The force on the electron is opposite the direction of the force on the proton, and the acceleration of the electron is far greater than the acceleration on the proton due to the electron's lower mass.
2. A magnetic field always exerts a force perpendicular to the velocity of a charged particle, so it can change the particle's direction but not its speed.
3. Zero
4. As the angle approaches 90°, the magnitude of the force increases. After going beyond 90°, it decreases.
5. The magnitude of the momentum remains constant. The direction of momentum changes, unless the particle's velocity is parallel or antiparallel to the magnetic field.
6. 20 m
7. (a) to the left (b) to the right
8. Earth's magnetic field is extremely weak, so the current carried by the car would have to be correspondingly very large. Such a current would be impractical to generate, and if generated, it would heat and melt the wires carrying it.
9. The proton would accelerate downward due to gravity while circling.

Multiple-Choice Questions

1. (a)
3. (c)
5. (e)
7. (e)
9. (c) and (e)
11. (a)
13. (b)
15. (a)
17. (c)

Conceptual Questions

1. The set should be oriented such that the beam is moving either toward the east or toward the west.

3. The magnetic force on a moving charged particle is always perpendicular to the particle's direction of motion. There is no magnetic force on the charge when it moves parallel to the direction of the magnetic field. However, the force on a charged particle moving in an electric field is never zero and is always parallel to the direction of the field. Therefore, by projecting the charged particle in different directions, it is possible to determine the nature of the field.

5. In the figure, the magnetic field created by wire 1 at the position of wire 2 is into the paper. Hence, the magnetic force on wire 2 is in direction (current down) × (field into the paper) = (force to the right), away from wire 1. Now wire 2 creates a magnetic field into the page at the location of wire 1, so wire 1 feels force (current up) × (field into the paper) = (force to the left), away from wire 2.

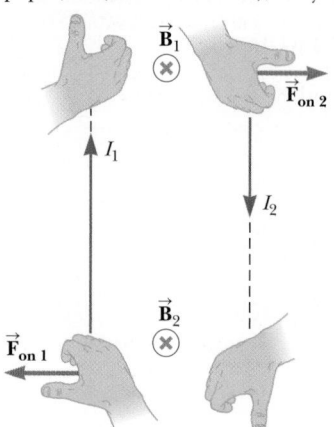

7. Such levitation could never occur. At the North Pole, where Earth's magnetic field is directed downward, toward the equivalent of a buried south pole, a coffin would be repelled if its south magnetic pole were directed downward. However, equilibrium would be only transitory, as any slight disturbance would upset the balance between the magnetic force and the gravitational force.

9. A compass does not detect currents in wires near light switches, for two reasons. The first is that, because the cable to the light switch contains two wires, one carrying current to the switch and the other carrying it away from the switch, the net magnetic field would be very small and would fall off rapidly with increasing distance. The second reason is that the current is alternating at 60 Hz. As a result, the magnetic field is oscillating at 60 Hz also. This frequency would be too fast for the compass to follow, so the effect on the compass reading would average to zero.

11. If you were moving along with the electrons, you would measure a zero current for the electrons, so they would not produce a magnetic field according to your observations. However, the fixed positive charges in the metal would now be moving backward relative to you, creating a current equivalent to the forward motion of the electrons when you were stationary. Thus, you would measure the same magnetic field as when you were stationary, but it would be due to the positive charges presumed to be moving from your point of view.

13. Each coil of the Slinky® will become a magnet, because a coil acts as a current loop. The sense of rotation of the current is the same in all coils, so each coil becomes a magnet with the same orientation of poles. Thus, all of the coils attract, and the Slinky® will compress.

15. There is no net force on the wires, but there is a torque. To understand this distinction, imagine a fixed vertical wire and a free horizontal wire (see the figure below). The vertical wire carries an upward current and creates a magnetic field that circles the vertical wire itself. To the right, the magnetic field of the vertical wire points into the page, while

on the left side it points out of the page, as indicated. Each segment of the horizontal wire (of length ℓ) carries current that interacts with the magnetic field according to the equation $F = BI\ell \sin \theta$. Apply the right-hand rule on the right side: point the fingers of your right hand in the direction of the horizontal current and curl them into the page in the direction of the magnetic field. Your thumb points downward, the direction of the force on the right side of the wire. Repeating the process on the left side gives a force upward on the left side of the wire. The two forces are equal in magnitude and opposite in direction, so the net force is zero, but they create a net torque around the point where the wires cross.

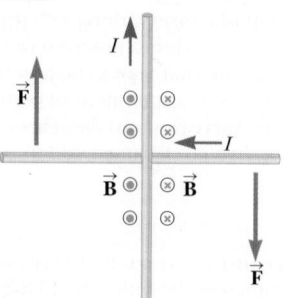

17. If they are projected in the same direction into the same magnetic field, the charges are of opposite sign.

Problems

1. (a) west (b) zero deflection (c) up (d) down
3. (a) into the page (b) toward the right (c) toward the bottom of the page
5. (a) 1.44×10^{-12} N (b) 8.62×10^{14} m/s² (c) A force would be exerted on the electron that had the same magnitude as the force on a proton, but in the opposite direction because of its negative charge. (d) The magnitude of the acceleration of the electron would be much greater than that of the proton because the mass of the electron is much smaller. The electron's acceleration would also be in the opposite direction.
7. 2.83×10^7 m/s west
9. 48.9° or 131°
11. $F_g = 8.93 \times 10^{-30}$ N (downward), $F_e = 1.60 \times 10^{-17}$ N (upward), $F_m = 4.80 \times 10^{-17}$ N (downward)
13. 8.0×10^{-3} T in the $+z$-direction
15. (a) into the page (b) toward the right (c) toward the bottom of the page
17. 7.50 N
19. 0.131 T (downward)
21. (a) The magnetic force and the force of gravity both act on the wire. When the magnetic force is upward and balances the downward force of gravity, the net force on the wire is zero, and the wire can move upward at constant velocity. (b) 0.20 T out of the page (c) If the field exceeds 0.20 T, the upward magnetic force exceeds the downward force of gravity, so the wire accelerates upward.
23. *ab*: 0, *bc*: 0.040 0 N in $-x$-direction, *cd*: 0.040 0 N in the $-z$-direction, *da*: 0.056 6 N parallel to the *xz*-plane and at 45° to both the $+x$- and the $+z$-directions
25. 118 μN · m
27. 9.05×10^{-4} N · m, tending to make the left-hand side of the loop move toward you and the right-hand side move away.
29. (a) 0.56 A (b) 0.064 N · m
31. (a) 3.97° (b) 3.39×10^{-3} N·m
33. (a) 8.51×10^5 m/s (b) 2.06×10^{-5} m
37. 1.77 cm
39. $r = 3R/4$
41. (a) 2.08×10^{-7} kg/C (b) 6.66×10^{-26} kg (c) Calcium
43. 20.0 μT

45. 2.0×10^{-10} A
47. 2.4 mm
49. 20.0 μT toward the bottom of page
51. 0.167 mT out of the page
53. (a) 4.00 m   (b) 7.50 nT   (c) 1.26 m   (d) zero
55. (a) 3.50×10^{-5} N/m   (b) repulsive
57. 4.5 mm
59. 31.8 mA
61. (a) 920 turns   (b) 12 cm
63. (a) 2.8 μT   (b) 0.89 mA
65. (a) 5.24 μT   (b) into the page   (c) 7.20 cm
67. (a) 0.500 μT out of the page   (b) 3.88 μT parallel to xy-plane and at 59.0° clockwise from $+x$-direction
69. (a) 1.33 m/s   (b) The sign of the emf is independent of the charge.
71. 53 μT toward the bottom of the page, 20 μT toward the bottom of the page, and 0
73. (a) -8.00×10^{-21} kg·m/s   (b) 8.90°
75. 1.41×10^{-6} N

CHAPTER 20

Quick Quizzes

1. *b, c, a*
2. (c)
3. (b)
4. (a)
5. (b)
6. (b)

Example Questions

1. False
2. 5.06×10^{-3} V; the current would be in the opposite direction.
3. (a), (e)
4. A magnetic force directed to the right will be exerted on the bar.
5. Doubling the frequency doubles the maximum induced emf.
6. (b)
7. (a)
8. 72.6 A
9. (b)
10. False

Multiple-Choice Questions

1. (c)
3. (d)
5. (c)
7. (b)
9. (b)
11. (a)

Conceptual Questions

1. As the spacecraft moves through space, it is apparently moving from a region of one magnetic field strength to a region of a different magnetic field strength. The changing magnetic field through the coil induces an emf and a corresponding current in the coil.
3. According to Faraday's law, an emf is induced in a wire loop if the magnetic flux through the loop changes with time. In this situation, an emf can be induced either by rotating the loop around an arbitrary axis or by changing the shape of the loop.
5. If the bar were moving to the left, the magnetic force on the negative charges in the bar would be upward, causing an accumulation of negative charges on the top and positive charges at the bottom. Hence, the electric field in the bar would be upward, as well.

7. If, for any reason, the magnetic field should change rapidly, a large emf could be induced in the bracelet. If the bracelet were not a continuous band, this emf would cause high-voltage arcs to occur at any gap in the band. If the bracelet were a continuous band, the induced emf would produce a large induced current and result in resistance heating of the bracelet.
11. As the aluminum plate moves into the field, eddy currents are induced in the metal by the changing magnetic field at the plate. The magnetic field of the electromagnet interacts with this current, producing a retarding force on the plate that slows it down. In a similar fashion, as the plate leaves the magnetic field, a current is induced, and once again there is an upward force to slow the plate.
13. Oscillating current in the solenoid produces an always-changing magnetic field. Vertical flux through the ring, alternately increasing and decreasing, produces current in it with a direction that is alternately clockwise and counterclockwise. The current through the ring's resistance converts electrically transmitted energy into internal energy at the rate I^2R.

Problems

1. 4.8×10^{-3} T · m^2
3. (a) 0.177 T   (b) 0
5. (a) $\Phi_{B,net} = 0$ (b) 0
7. (a) 3.1×10^{-3} T · m^2 (b) $\Phi_{B,net} = 0$
9. (a) zero, since the flux through the loop A doesn't change   (b) counterclockwise for loop B   (c) clockwise for loop C
11. 94 mV
13. 33 mV
15. (a) from left to right   (b) from right to left
17. (a) The current is zero, because the magnetic flux due to the current through the right side of the loop (into the page) is opposite the flux through the left side of the loop (out of the page), so net flux through the loop is always zero.   (b) Clockwise, because the flux due to the long wire through the loop is out of the page, and the induced current in the loop must be clockwise to compensate for the increasing external flux.
19. (a) 3.77×10^{-3} T   (b) 9.42×10^{-3} T   (c) 7.07×10^{-4} m^2 (d) 3.99×10^{-6} Wb   (e) 1.77×10^{-5} V; the average induced emf is equal to the instantaneous in this case because the current increases steadily.   (f) The induced emf is small, so the current in the 4-turn coil and its magnetic field will also be small.
21. 10.2 μV
23. 13.1 mV
25. 2.6 mV
27. (a) toward the east   (b) 4.58×10^{-4} V
29. 2.80 m/s
31. (a) 81.9 mV   (b) 105 mA
33. 1.9×10^{-11} V
35. (a) 60 V   (b) 57 V   (c) 0.13 s
37. (a) 18.1 μV   (b) 0
39. 4.0 mH
41. (a) 2.0 mH   (b) 38 A/s
43. (a) 5.33 A   (b) 2.67 s   (c) 8.00 s
45. (a) 2.4 V   (b) 75 mH   (c) 5.1 A   (d) $\Delta V_R = -1.5$ V   (e) $\Delta V_L = -0.9$ V
47. 1.92 Ω
49. (a) 0.208 mH   (b) 0.936 mJ
51. (a) 18 J   (b) 7.2 J
53. counterclockwise
55. (a) $F = N^2B^2w^2v/R$ to the left   (b) 0   (c) $F = N^2B^2w^2v/R$ to the left
57. (a) 20.0 ms   (b) 37.9 V   (c) 1.52 mV   (d) 51.8 mA
59. (a) 0.500 A   (b) 2.00 W   (c) 2.00 W
61. 115 kV

63. (a) 0.157 mV (end B is positive) (b) 5.89 mV (end A is positive)

65. (a) 9.00 A (b) 10.8 N (c) b is at the higher potential (d) No

67. (b) A larger resistance would make the current smaller, so the loop must reach higher speed before the magnitude of the magnetic force will equal the gravitational force. (c) The magnetic force is proportional to the product of the field and the current, while the current itself is proportional to the field. If B is cut in half, the speed must become four times larger to compensate and yield a magnetic force with magnitude equal to that of the gravitational force.

CHAPTER 21

Quick Quizzes

1. (c)
2. (b)
3. (b)
4. (a)
5. (a)
6. (b)
7. (b), (c)
8. (b), (d)

Example Questions

1. False
2. False
3. True
4. True
5. The average power will be zero if the phase angle is 90° or −90° (i.e., when $R = 0$).
6. False
7. (d)
8. Yes. When the roof is perpendicular to the Sun's rays, the amount of energy intercepted by the roof is a maximum. At other angles the amount is smaller.
9. (c)

Multiple-Choice Questions

1. (d)
3. (b)
5. (a)
7. (b)
9. (a)
11. (e)
13. (c)
15. (c) and (d)

Conceptual Questions

1. Different stations have transmitting antennas at different locations. For best reception align your rabbit ears perpendicular to the straight-line path from your TV to the transmitting antenna. The transmitted signals are also polarized. The polarization direction of the wave can be changed by reflection from surfaces—including the atmosphere—and through Kerr rotation—a change in polarization axis when passing through an organic substance. In your home, the plane of polarization is determined by your surroundings, so antennas need to be adjusted to align with the polarization of the wave.

3. The fundamental source of an electromagnetic wave is an accelerating charge. For example, in a transmitting antenna of a radio station, charges are caused to move up and down at the frequency of the radio station. These moving charges set up electric and magnetic fields, the electromagnetic wave, in the space around the antenna.

5. (a) The flashing of the light according to Morse code is a drastic amplitude modulation (AM)—the amplitude is changing from a maximum to zero. In this sense, it is similar to the on-and-off binary code used in computers and compact disks. (b) The carrier frequency is that of the light, on the order of 10^{14} Hz. (c) The frequency of the signal depends on the skill of the signal operator, but it is on the order of a single hertz, as the light is flashed on and off. (d) The broadcasting antenna for this modulated signal is the filament of the lightbulb in the signal source. (e) The receiving antenna is the eye.

7. The sail should be as reflective as possible, so that the maximum momentum is transferred to the sail from the reflection of sunlight.

9. No. The wire will emit electromagnetic waves only if the current varies in time. The radiation is the result of accelerating charges, which can occur only when the current is not constant.

11. Photographs created using infrared light make warmer areas of the face brighter; visible light photographs capture mainly reflected ambient light, and are not affected by temperature. Consequently, bright areas in infrared light would not necessarily be bright in visible light. Pupils, for example, are very bright in the infrared but dark in visible light.

13. It is far more economical to transmit power at a high voltage than at a low voltage because the I^2R loss on the transmission line is significantly lower at high voltage. Transmitting power at high voltage permits the use of step-down transformers to make "low" voltages and high currents available to the end user.

15. The resonance frequency is determined by the inductance and the capacitance in the circuit. If both L and C are doubled, the resonance frequency is reduced by a factor of two.

Problems

1. (a) 193 Ω (b) 145 Ω
3. 14.6 Hz
5. 6.76 W
7. (a) $f > 41.3$ Hz (b) $X_C < 87.5$ Ω
9. 4.0×10^2 Hz
11. 100 mA
13. 3.14 A
15. (a) 0.042 4 H (b) 942 rad/s
17. 0.450 T · m²
19. (a) 0.361 A (b) 18.1 V (c) 23.9 V (d) −53.0°
21. (a) 1.43 kΩ (b) 0.097 9 A (c) 51.1° (d) voltage leads current
23. (a) 17.4° (b) the voltage
25. 1.88 V
27. (a) 47.1 Ω (b) 637 Ω (c) 2.40 kΩ (d) 2.33 kΩ (e) −14.2°
29. (a) 103 V (b) 150 V (c) 127 V (d) 23.6 V
31. (a) 208 Ω (b) 40.0 Ω (c) 0.541 H
33. 8.00 W
35. (a) 1.8×10^2 Ω (b) 0.71 H
37. 1.82 pF
39. $C_{min} = 4.9$ nF, $C_{max} = 51$ nF
41. 3.60 kHz
43. 721 V
45. 0.18% is lost
47. (a) 1.1×10^3 kW (b) 3.1×10^2 A (c) 8.3×10^3 A
49. 1 000 km; there will always be better use for tax money.
51. (a) 6.30×10^{-6} Pa (b) Atmospheric pressure is 1.60×10^{10} times larger than the radiation pressure.
53. $f_{red} = 4.55 \times 10^{14}$ Hz, $f_{IR} = 3.19 \times 10^{14}$ Hz, $E_{max,f}/E_{max,i} = 0.57$
55. $B_{max} = 3.39 \times 10^{-6}$ T, $E_{max} = 1.02 \times 10^3$ V/m
57. 2.94×10^8 m/s
59. (a) 6.00 pm (b) 7.50 cm
61. (a) 188 m to 556 m (b) 2.78 m to 3.4 m
63. 5.2×10^{13} Hz, 5.8 μm
65. $4.299\ 999\ 84 \times 10^{14}$ Hz; The frequency decreases by 1.6×10^7 Hz.

67. 5.31×10^{-5} N/m^2
69. 1.7 cents
71. 99.6 mH
73. (a) 6.7×10^{-16} T   (b) 5.3×10^{-17} W/m^2 (c) 1.7×10^{-14} W
75. (a) 0.536 N   (b) 8.93×10^{-5} m/s^2 (c) 33.9 days

CHAPTER 22

Quick Quizzes

1. (a)
2. Beams 2 and 4 are reflected; beams 3 and 5 are refracted.
3. (b)
4. (c)

Example Questions

1. (a)
2. (b)
3. False
4. (c)
5. (b)
6. (b)

Multiple-Choice Questions

1. (c)
3. (e)
5. (b)
7. (b)
9. (c)

Conceptual Questions

1. The spectrum of the light sent back to you from a drop at the top of the rainbow arrives such that the red light (deviated by an angle of 42°) strikes the eye while the violet light (deviated by 40°) passes over your head. Thus, the top of the rainbow looks red. At the bottom of the rainbow, violet arrives at your eye and red light is deviated toward the ground. Thus, the bottom part of the rainbow appears violet.

3. $n_a > n_c > n_b$

5. On the one hand, a ball covered with mirrors sparkles by reflecting light from its surface. On the other hand, a faceted diamond lets in light at the top, reflects it by total internal reflection in the bottom half, and sends the light out through the top again. Because of its high index of refraction, the critical angle for diamond in air for total internal reflection, namely $\theta_c = \sin^{-1}(n_{air}/n_{diamond})$, is small. Thus, light rays enter through a large area and exit through a very small area with a much higher intensity. When a diamond is immersed in carbon disulfide, the critical angle is increased to $\theta_c = \sin^{-1}(n_{carbon\ disulfide}/n_{diamond})$. As a result, the light is emitted from the diamond over a larger area and appears less intense.

7. There is no dependence of the angle of reflection on wavelength, because the light does not enter deeply into the material during reflection—it reflects from the surface.

9. The color traveling slowest is bent the most. Thus, *X* travels more slowly in the glass prism.

11. Light rays coming from parts of the pencil under water are bent away from the normal as they emerge into the air above. The rays enter the eye (or camera) at angles closer to the horizontal, thus the parts of the pencil under water appear closer to the surface than they actually are, so the pencil appears bent.

13. Light travels through a vacuum at a speed of 3×10^8 m/s. Thus, an image we see from a distant star or galaxy must have been generated some time ago. For example, the star Altair is 16 light-years away; if we look at an image of Altair today, we know only what Altair looked like 16 years ago. This may not initially seem significant; however, astronomers who look at other galaxies can get an idea of what galaxies looked like when they were much younger. Thus, it does make sense to speak of "looking backward in time."

Problems

1. 3.00×10^8 m/s
3. (a) 2.07×10^3 eV   (b) 4.14 eV
5. (a) 2.25×10^8 m/s   (b) 1.97×10^8 m/s   (c) 1.24×10^8 m/s
7. (a) 29.0°   (b) 25.7°   (c) 32.0°
9. 19.5° above the horizontal
11. (a) 1.52   (b) 416 nm   (c) 4.74×10^{14} Hz   (d) 1.97×10^8 m/s
13. 110.6°
15. (a) 1.56×10^8 m/s   (b) 329.1 nm   (c) 4.74×10^{14} Hz
17. five times from the right-hand mirror and six times from the left
19. $\theta = 30.4°, \theta' = 22.3°$
21. (a) 4.84 cm   (b) 67.5°
23. (b) 4.73 cm
25. $\theta = \tan^{-1}(n_g)$
27. 3.39 m
29. (a) $\theta_{blue} = 47.79°$ (b) $\theta_{red} = 48.22°$
31. $\theta_{red} - \theta_{violet} = 0.32°$
33. (a) $\theta_{1i} = 30°, \theta_{1r} = 19°, \theta_{2i} = 41°, \theta_{2r} = 77°$ (b) First surface: $\theta_{reflection} = 30°$; second surface: $\theta_{reflection} = 41°$
35. (a) 66.1°   (b) 63.5°   (c) 59.7°
37. (a) 40.8°   (b) 60.6°
39. 1.414
41. (a) 10.7°   (b) air   (c) Sound falling on the wall from most directions is 100% reflected.
43. 27.5°
45. 22.0°
47. (a) 1.07 m   (b) 1.65 m
49. (a) 38.5°   (b) 1.44
53. 24.7°
55. 1.93
57. (a) 1.20   (b) 3.39 ns
59. (a) 53.1°   (b) $\theta_1 \geq 38.7°$
61. 15.9°

CHAPTER 23

Quick Quizzes

1. At *C*
2. (c)
3. (a) False (b) False (c) True
4. (b)
5. An infinite number
6. (a) False (b) True (c) False

Example Questions

1. No
2. (b)
3. True
4. (b)
5. (a)
6. (c)
7. The screen should be placed one focal length away from the lens.
8. No. The largest magnification would be 1, so a diverging lens would not make a good magnifying glass.
9. Upright
10. Yes, it's possible for a mirror to have a virtual object. Using the present system of mirror and lens, place the object to the right of the lens just outside the focal length. The image distance can be made as large as desired by moving the object toward the focal point, so at some point the lens's image will be located to the left of the mirror. That image behind the mirror forms a virtual object for the mirror.

Multiple-Choice Questions

1. (b), (c), (e)
3. (c)
5. (d)
7. (d), (e)
9. (c)
11. (b)

Conceptual Questions

1. You will not be able to focus your eyes on both the picture and your image at the same time. To focus on the picture, you must adjust your eyes so that an object several centimeters away (the picture) is in focus. Thus, you are focusing on the mirror surface. But your image in the mirror is as far behind the mirror as you are in front of it. Thus, you must focus your eyes beyond the mirror, twice as far away as the picture to bring the image into focus.

3. A single flat mirror forms a virtual image of an object due to two factors. First, the light rays from the object are necessarily diverging from the object, and second, the lack of curvature of the flat mirror cannot convert diverging rays to converging rays. If another optical element is first used to cause light rays to converge, then the flat mirror can be placed in the region in which the converging rays are present, and it will change the direction of the rays so that the real image is formed at a different location. For example, if a real image is formed by a convex lens, and the flat mirror is placed between the lens and the image position, the image formed by the mirror will be real.

5. An effect similar to a mirage is produced except the "mirage" is seen hovering in the air. Ghost lighthouses in the sky have been seen over bodies of water by this effect.

7. We consider the two trees to be two separate objects. The far tree is an object that is farther from the lens than the near tree. Thus, the image of the far tree will be closer to the lens than the image of the near tree. The screen must be moved closer to the lens to put the far tree in focus.

9. This is a possible scenario. When light crosses a boundary between air and ice, it will refract in the same manner as it does when crossing a boundary of the same shape between air and glass. Thus, a converging lens may be made from ice as well as glass. However, ice is such a strong absorber of infrared radiation that it is unlikely you will be able to start a fire with a small ice lens.

11. If a converging lens is placed in a liquid having an index of refraction larger than that of the lens material, the direction of refractions at the lens surfaces will be reversed, and the lens will diverge light. A mirror depends only on reflection that is independent of the surrounding material, so a converging mirror will be converging in any liquid.

13. The focal length for a mirror is determined by the law of reflection from the mirror surface. The law of reflection is independent of the material of which the mirror is made and of the surrounding medium. Thus, the focal length depends only on the radius of curvature and not on the material. The focal length of a lens depends on the indices of refraction of the lens material and surrounding medium. Thus, the focal length of a lens depends on the lens material.

15. Because when you look at the AMBULANCE in your rear view mirror, the apparent left-right inversion clearly displays the name of the AMBULANCE behind you.

Problems

1. (a) younger (b) on the order of 10^{-9} s
3. 10.0 ft, 30.0 ft, 40.0 ft
5. (a) $p_1 + h$, behind the lower mirror (b) virtual (c) upright (d) 1.00 (e) no

7. (a) The object should be placed 30.0 cm in front of the mirror. (b) 0.333
9. (a) The object is 10.0 cm in front of the mirror. (b) 2.00
11. 5.00 cm
13. 1.0 m
15. 8.05 cm
17. (a) 26.8 cm behind the mirror (b) upright (c) 0.026 8
19. (a) concave with focal length $f = 0.83$ m (b) Object must be 1.0 m in front of the mirror.
21. 38.2 cm below the upper surface of the ice
23. 3.8 mm
25. $n = 2.00$
27. (a) The image is 0.790 m from the outer surface of the glass pane, inside the water tank. (b) With a glass pane of negligible thickness, the image is 0.750 m inside the tank. (c) The thicker the glass, the greater the distance between the final image and the outer surface of the glass.
29. 20.0 cm
31. (a) 20.0 cm beyond the lens; real, inverted, $M = -1.00$ (b) No image is formed. Parallel rays leave the lens. (c) 10.0 cm in front of the lens; virtual, upright, $M = +2.00$
33. (i) (a) 13.3 cm in front of the lens (b) virtual (c) upright (d) +0.333 (ii) (a) 10.0 cm in front of the lens (b) virtual (c) upright (d) +0.500 (iii) (a) 6.67 cm in front of the lens (b) virtual (c) upright (d) +0.667
35. (a) either 9.63 cm or 3.27 cm (b) 2.10 cm
37. (a) 39.0 mm (b) 39.5 mm
39. 40.0 cm
41. 30.0 cm to the left of the second lens, $M = -3.00$
43. 7.47 cm in front of the second lens, 1.07 cm, virtual, upright
45. from 0.224 m to 18.2 m
47. real image, 5.71 cm in front of the mirror
49. (a) -34.7 cm (b) -36.1 cm
51. 160 cm to the left of the lens, inverted, $M = -0.800$
53. $q = 10.7$ cm
55. (a) 32.0 cm to the right of the second surface (b) real
57. (a) 20.0 cm to the right of the second lens, $M = -6.00$ (b) inverted (c) 6.67 cm to the right of the second lens, $M = -2.00$, inverted
59. (a) 1.99 (b) 10.0 cm to the left of the lens (c) inverted
61. (a) 5.45 m to the left of the lens (b) 8.24 m to the left of the lens (c) 17.1 m to the left of the lens (d) by surrounding the lens with a medium having a refractive index greater than that of the lens material
63. (a) 263 cm (b) 79.0 cm
65. 8.57 cm

CHAPTER 24

Quick Quizzes

1. (c)
2. (c)
3. (c)
4. (b)
5. (b)
6. The compact disc

Example Questions

1. False
2. The soap film is thicker in the region that reflects red light.
3. The coating should be thinner.
4. The wavelength is smaller in water than in air, so the distance between dark bands is also smaller.
5. False
6. Because the wavelength becomes smaller in water, the angles to the first maxima become smaller, resulting in a smaller central maximum.

7. The separation between principal maxima will be larger.

8. The additional polarizer must make an angle of 90° with respect to the previous polarizer.

Multiple-Choice Questions

1. (d)
3. (b)
5. (b)
7. (c)
9. (e)
11. (b)

Conceptual Questions

1. You will *not* see an interference pattern from the automobile headlights, for two reasons. The first is that the headlights are not coherent sources and are therefore incapable of producing sustained interference. Also, the headlights are so far apart in comparison to the wavelengths emitted that, even if they were made into coherent sources, the interference maxima and minima would be too closely spaced to be observable.

3. The result of the double slit is to redistribute the energy arriving at the screen. Although there is no energy at the location of a dark fringe, there is four times as much energy at the location of a bright fringe as there would be with only a single narrow slit. The total amount of energy arriving at the screen is twice as much as with a single slit, as it must be according to the law of conservation of energy.

5. One of the materials has a higher index of refraction than water, and the other has a lower index. The material with the higher index will appear black as it approaches zero thickness. There will be a 180° phase change for the light reflected from the upper surface, but no such phase change for the light reflected from the lower surface, because the index of refraction for water on the other side is lower than that of the film. Thus, the two reflections will be out of phase and will interfere destructively. The material with index of refraction lower than water will have a phase change for the light reflected from both the upper and the lower surface, so that the reflections from the zero-thickness film will be back in phase and the film will appear bright.

7. Because the light reflecting at the lower surface of the film undergoes a 180° phase change, while light reflecting from the upper surface of the film does not undergo such a change, the central spot (where the film has near zero thickness) will be dark. If the observed rings are not circular, the curved surface of the lens does not have a true spherical shape.

9. For regional communication at the Earth's surface, radio waves are typically broadcast from currents oscillating in tall vertical towers. These waves have vertical planes of polarization. Light originates from the vibrations of atoms or electronic transitions within atoms, which represent oscillations in all possible directions. Thus, light generally is not polarized.

11. Yes. In order to do this, first measure the radar reflectivity of the metal of your airplane. Then choose a light, durable material that has approximately half the radar reflectivity of the metal in your plane. Measure its index of refraction, and place onto the metal a coating equal in thickness to one-quarter of 3 cm, divided by that index. Sell the plane quickly, and then you can sell the supposed enemy new radars operating at 1.5 cm, which the coated metal will reflect with extra-high efficiency.

13. If you wish to perform an interference experiment, you need monochromatic coherent light. To obtain it, you must first pass light from an ordinary source through a prism or diffraction grating to disperse different colors into different directions. Using a single narrow slit, select a single color and make that light diffract to cover both slits for a Young's experiment. The procedure is much simpler with a laser because its output is already monochromatic and coherent.

Problems

1. 632 nm
3. (a) 2.6 mm   (b) 2.62 mm
5. (a) 36.2°   (b) 5.08 cm   (c) 5.08×10^{14} Hz
7. (a) 55.7 m   (b) 124 m
9. 662 nm
11. 11.3 m
13. 148 m
15. 75.0 m
17. 85.4 nm
19. 511 nm
21. 0.500 cm
23. (a) 238 nm   (b) λ will increase   (c) 328 nm
25. 78.4 μm
27. 4.75 μm
29. 617 nm, 441 nm, 343 nm
31. (a) 8.10 mm   (b) 4.05 mm
33. (a) 1.1 m   (b) 1.7 mm
35. 462 nm
37. 1.20 mm, 1.20 mm
39. (a) 479 nm, 647 nm, 698 nm   (b) 20.5°, 28.3°, 30.7°
41. 5.91° in first order; 13.2° in second order; and 26.5° in third order
43. 1.81 μm
45. 514 nm
47. 9.17 cm
49. (a) 3.53×10^3 grooves/cm   (b) 11 maxima
51. (a) 1.11   (b) 42.0°
53. (a) 56.7°   (b) 48.8°
55. (a) 55.6°   (b) 34.4°
59. 6.89 units
61. (a) 413.7 nm, 409.7 nm   (b) 8.6°
63. One slit 0.12 mm wide. The central maximum is twice as wide as the other maxima.
65. 0.156 mm
67. 2.50 mm
69. (a) 16.6 m   (b) 8.28 m
71. 127 m
73. 0.350 mm

CHAPTER 25

Quick Quizzes

1. (c)
2. (a)

Example Questions

1. True
2. True
3. A smaller focal length gives a greater magnification and should be selected.
4. True
5. Yes. Increasing the focal length of the mirror increases the magnification. Increasing the focal length of the eyepiece decreases the magnification.
6. More widely spaced eyes increase visual resolving power by effectively increasing the aperture size, D, in Equation 25.10. The limiting angle of resolution is thereby decreased, meaning finer details of distant objects can be resolved.
7. Resolution is better at the violet end of the visible spectrum.
8. True

Multiple-Choice Questions

1. (c)
3. (c)
5. (c)
7. (d)
9. (b)
11. (c)

Conceptual Questions

1. The observer is *not* using the lens as a simple magnifier. For a lens to be used as a simple magnifier, the object distance must be less than the focal length of the lens. Also, a simple magnifier produces a virtual image at the normal near point of the eye, or at an image distance of about $q = -25$ cm. With a large object distance and a relatively short image distance, the magnitude of the magnification by the lens would be considerably less than one. Most likely, the lens in this example is part of a lens combination being used as a telescope.

3. The image formed on the retina by the lens and cornea is already inverted.

5. For a lens to operate as a simple magnifier, the object should be located just inside the focal point of the lens. If the power of the lens is +20.0 diopters, its focal length is

$$f = (1.00 \text{ m})/P = (1.00 \text{ m})/+20.0 = 0.050\,0 \text{ m} = 5.00 \text{ cm}$$

The object should be placed slightly less than 5.00 cm in front of the lens.

7. You want a real image formed at the location of the paper. To form such an image, the object distance must be greater than the focal length of the lens.

9. In order for someone to see an object through a microscope, the wavelength of the light in the microscope must be smaller than the size of the object. An atom is much smaller than the wavelength of light in the visible spectrum, so an atom can never be seen with the use of visible light.

11. farsighted; converging

13. (a) The diffraction pattern of a hair is the same as the diffraction pattern produced by a single slit of the same width. (b) The central maximum is flanked by minima. Measure the width $2y$ of the central maximum between the minima bracketing it. Because the angle is small, you can use

$$\sin \theta_{\text{dark}} \approx \tan \theta_{\text{dark}}$$
$$m\lambda/a \approx y/L$$

to find the width a of the hair.

Problems

1. 7.0
3. 177 m
5. $f/1.4$
7. 8.0
9. (a) 42.9 cm (b) +2.33 diopters
11. 23.2 cm
13. (a) −2.00 diopters (b) 17.6 cm
15. +17.0 diopters
17. −2.50 diopters, a diverging lens
19. (a) 5.8 cm (b) $m = 4.3$
21. (a) 4.07 cm (b) $m = +7.14$
23. (a) $|M| = 1.22$ (b) $\theta/\theta_0 = 6.08$
25. 2.1 cm
27. 12.7
29. 3.38 min
31. (a) 2.53 cm (b) 88.5 cm
33. (b) $-fh/p$ (c) −1.07 mm
35. (a) 1.50 (b) 1.9
37. 492 km
39. 0.40 μrad
41. 5.40 mm
43. 9.8 km
45. No. A resolving power of 2.0×10^5 is needed, and that available is only 1.8×10^5.
47. 1.31×10^3
49. 50.4 μm
51. 40
53. (a) 8.00×10^2 (b) The image is inverted.
55. 15.4
57. (a) +2.67 diopters (b) 0.16 diopter too low
59. (a) +44.6 diopters (b) 3.03 diopters
61. (a) $m = 4.0$ (b) $m = 3.0$

CHAPTER 26

Quick Quizzes

1. False: the speed of light is c for all observers.
2. (a)
3. False
4. No. From your perspective you're at rest with respect to the cabin, so you will measure yourself as having your normal length, and will require a normal-sized cabin.
5. (i) (a), (e) (ii) (a), (e)
6. False
7. (a) False (b) False (c) True (d) False

Example Questions

1. 9.61 s
2. (c)
3. (a)
4. $-0.946c$
5. (a)
6. Very little of the mass is converted to other forms of energy in these reactions because the total number of neutrons and protons doesn't change. The energy liberated is only the energy associated with their interactions.

Multiple-Choice Questions

1. (d), (e)
3. (b), (c)
5. (c)
7. (e)
9. (d)
11. (b)

Conceptual Questions

1. An ellipsoid. The dimension in the direction of motion would be measured to be less than D.

3. No. The principle of relativity implies that nothing can travel faster than the speed of light in a *vacuum*, which is equal to 3.00×10^8 m/s.

5. As the object approaches the speed of light, its kinetic energy grows without limit. It would take an infinite investment of work to accelerate the object to the speed of light.

7. For a wonderful fictional exploration of this question, get a "Mr. Tompkins" book by George Gamow. All of the relativity effects would be obvious in our lives. Time dilation and length contraction would both occur. Driving home in a hurry, you would push on the gas pedal not to increase your speed very much, but to make the blocks shorter. Big Doppler shifts in wave frequencies would make red lights look green as you approached and make car horns and radios useless. High-speed transportation would be very expensive, requiring huge fuel purchases, as well as dangerous, since a speeding car could knock down a building. When you got home, hungry for lunch, you would find that you had missed dinner; there would be a five-day delay in transit when you

watch a live TV program originating in Australia. Finally, we would not be able to see the Milky Way, since the fireball of the Big Bang would surround us at the distance of Rigel or Deneb.

9. A photon transports energy. The relativistic equivalence of mass and energy is enough to give it momentum.

11. Suppose a railroad train is moving past you. One way to measure its length is this: you mark the tracks at the cowcatcher forming the front of the moving engine at 9:00:00 AM, while your assistant marks the tracks at the back of the caboose at the same time. Then you find the distance between the marks on the tracks with a tape measure. You and your assistant must make the marks simultaneously in your frame of reference, for otherwise the motion of the train would make its length different from the distance between marks.

Problems

1. (a) 1.38 yr   (b) 1.31 light-years
3. 0.103c
5. (a) 1.3×10^{-7} s   (b) 38 m   (c) 7.6 m
7. (a) 1.55×10^{-5} s   (b) 7.09   (c) 2.19×10^{-6} s   (d) 649 m
   (e) From the third observer's point of view, the muon is traveling faster, so according to the third observer, the muon's lifetime is longer than that measured by the observer at rest with respect to Earth.
9. 0.950c
11. Yes, with 19 m to spare
13. (a) $\dfrac{2\sqrt{2}}{3}c = 0.943c = 2.83 \times 10^8$ m/s   (b) The result would
    be the same.
15. 0.285c
17. 0.54c to the right
19. 0.357c
21. 0.998c toward the right
23. (a) 0.999 997c (b) 3.74×10^5 MeV
25. 0.786c
27. (a) 8.65×10^{22} J   (b) 9.61×10^5 kg
31. (a) 3.91×10^4 (b) 7.67 cm
33. (a) 0.979c (b) 0.065 2c (c) 0.914c
35. 0.917c
37. (a) $v/c = 1 - 1.13 \times 10^{-10}$ (b) 5.99×10^{27} J
    (c) \$2.16 $\times 10^{20}$
39. (a) 0.800c (b) 7.50×10^3 s   (c) 1.44×10^{12} m   (d) 0.385c
41. 0.80c
43. (a) $v = 0.141c$ (b) $v = 0.436c$
45. (a) 7.0 μs   (b) 1.1×10^4 muons
47. 5.5 yr; Goslo is older
49. (a) 17.4 m   (b) 3.30° with respect to the direction of motion

CHAPTER 27

Quick Quizzes

1. True
2. (b)
3. (c)
4. False
5. (c)

Example Questions

1. False
2. False
3. Some of the photon's energy is transferred to the electron.
4. Doubling the speed of a particle doubles its momentum, reducing the particle's wavelength by a factor of one-half. This answer is no longer true when the doubled speed is relativistic.
5. True

Multiple-Choice Questions

1. (b)
3. (b)
5. (a) and (c)
7. (e)
9. (b)
11. (a)

Conceptual Questions

1. The shape of an object is normally determined by observing the light reflecting from its surface. In a kiln, the object will be very hot and will be glowing red. The emitted radiation is far stronger than the reflected radiation, and the thermal radiation emitted is only slightly dependent on the material from which the object is made. Unlike reflected light, the emitted light comes from all surfaces with equal intensity, so contrast is lost and the shape of the object is harder to discern.

3. The "blackness" of a blackbody refers to its ideal property of absorbing all radiation incident on it. If an observed room temperature object in everyday life absorbs all radiation, we describe it as (visibly) black. The black appearance, however, is due to the fact that our eyes are sensitive only to visible light. If we could detect infrared light with our eyes, we would see the object emitting radiation. If the temperature of the blackbody is raised, Wien's law tells us that the emitted radiation will move into the visible range of the spectrum. Thus, the blackbody could appear as red, white, or blue, depending on its temperature.

5. All objects do radiate energy, but at room temperature this energy is primarily in the infrared region of the electromagnetic spectrum, which our eyes cannot detect. (Pit vipers have sensory organs that *are* sensitive to infrared radiation; thus, they can seek out their warm-blooded prey in what we would consider absolute darkness.)

7. We can picture higher frequency light as a stream of photons of higher energy. In a collision, one photon can give all of its energy to a single electron. The kinetic energy of such an electron is measured by the stopping potential. The reverse voltage (stopping voltage) required to stop the current is proportional to the frequency of the incoming light. More intense light consists of more photons striking a unit area each second, but atoms are so small that one emitted electron never gets a "kick" from more than one photon. Increasing the intensity of the light will generally increase the size of the current, but it will not change the energy of the individual electrons that are ejected. Thus, the stopping potential remains constant.

9. Wave theory predicts that the photoelectric effect should occur at any frequency, provided that the light intensity is high enough. However, as seen in photoelectric experiments, the light must have sufficiently high frequency for the effect to occur.

11. (a) Electrons are emitted only if the photon frequency is greater than the cutoff frequency.

13. No. Suppose that the incident light frequency at which you first observed the photoelectric effect is above the cutoff frequency of the first metal, but less than the cutoff frequency of the second metal. In that case, the photoelectric effect would not be observed at all in the second metal.

15. An electron has both classical-wave and classical-particle characteristics. In single- and double-slit diffraction and interference experiments, electrons behave like classical waves. An electron has mass and charge. It carries kinetic energy and momentum in parcels of definite size, as classical particles do. At the same time it has a particular wavelength and frequency. Since an electron displays characteristics of both classical waves and classical particles, it is neither a

classical wave nor a classical particle. It is customary to call it a *quantum particle,* but another invented term, such as "wavicle," could serve equally well.

Problems

1. (a) ≈ 3 000 K   (b) ≈ 20 000 K
3. 9.47 μm, which is in the infrared region of the spectrum
5. (a) 2.49×10^{-5} eV   (b) 2.49 eV   (c) 249 eV
7. (a) 2.57 eV   (b) 1.28×10^{-5} eV   (c) 1.91×10^{-7} eV
9. (a) 2.24 eV   (b) 555 nm   (c) 5.41×10^{14} Hz
11. (a) 1.02×10^{-18} J   (b) 1.53×10^{15} Hz   (c) 196 nm
    (d) 2.15 eV   (e) 2.15 V
13. 4.8×10^{14} Hz, 2.0 eV
15. 1.2×10^2 V and 1.2×10^7 V, respectively
17. 17.8 kV
19. 0.078 nm
21. 0.281 nm
23. 70.0°
25. (a) 1.18×10^{-23} kg·m/s   (b) 478 eV
27. (a) 1.46 km/s   (b) 7.28×10^{-11} m
29. 3.58×10^{-13} m
31. (a) 15 keV   (b) 1.2×10^2 keV
33. ~10^6 m/s
35. Within 1.16 mm for the electron, 5.28×10^{-32} m for the bullet
37. 3×10^{-29} J
39. (a) 2.21×10^{-32} kg·m/s   (b) 1.00×10^{10} Hz
    (c) 4.14×10^{-5} eV
41. 2.5×10^{20} photons
43. (a) 5 200 K (b) Clearly, a firefly is not at this temperature, so this is not blackbody radiation.
45. 1.36 eV
47. 2.00 eV
49. (a) 0.022 0c (b) 0.999 2c

CHAPTER 28

Quick Quizzes

1. (b)
2. (a) 5 (b) 9 (c) 25
3. (d)

Example Questions

1. The energy associated with the quantum number n increases with increasing quantum number n, going to zero in the limit of arbitrarily large n. A transition from a very high energy level to the ground state therefore results in the emission of photons approaching an energy of 13.6 eV, the same as the ionization energy.
2. The energy difference in the helium atom will be four times that of the same transition in hydrogen. Energy levels in hydrogen-like atoms are proportional to Z^2, where Z is the atomic number.
3. The quantum numbers n and ℓ are never negative.
4. No. The M shell is at a higher energy; hence, transitions from the M shell to the K shell will always result in more energetic photons than any transition from the L shell to the K shell.

Multiple-Choice Questions

1. (b)
3. (e)
5. (c)
7. (c)
9. (c)
11. (a)
13. (c)

Conceptual Questions

1. If the energy of the hydrogen atom were proportional to n (or any power of n), then the energy would become infinite as n grew to infinity. But the energy of the atom is inversely proportional to n^2. Thus, as n grows to infinity, the energy of the atom approaches a value that is above the ground state by a finite amount, namely, the ionization energy 13.6 eV. As the electron falls from one bound state to another, its energy loss is always less than the ionization energy. The energy and frequency of any emitted photon are finite.
3. The characteristic x-rays originate from transitions within the atoms of the target, such as an electron from the L shell making a transition to a vacancy in the K shell. The vacancy is caused when an accelerated electron in the x-ray tube supplies energy to the K shell electron to eject it from the atom. If the energy of the bombarding electrons were to be increased, the K shell electron will be ejected from the atom with more remaining kinetic energy. But the energy difference between the K and L shell has not changed, so the emitted x-ray has exactly the same wavelength.
5. A continuous spectrum without characteristic x-rays is possible. At a low accelerating potential difference for the electron, the electron may not have enough energy to eject an electron from a target atom. As a result, there will be no characteristic x-rays. The change in speed of the electron as it enters the target will result in the continuous spectrum.
7. The hologram is an interference pattern between light scattered from the object and the reference beam. If anything moves by a distance comparable to the wavelength of the light (or more), the pattern will wash out. The effect is just like making the slits vibrate in Young's experiment, to make the interference fringes vibrate wildly so that a photograph of the screen displays only the average intensity everywhere.
9. If the Pauli exclusion principle were not valid, the elements and their chemical behavior would be grossly different because every electron would end up in the lowest energy level of the atom. All matter would therefore be nearly alike in its chemistry and composition, since the shell structures of each element would be identical. Most materials would have a much higher density, and the spectra of atoms and molecules would be very simple, resulting in the existence of less color in the world.
11. The three elements have similar electronic configurations, with filled inner shells plus a single electron in an s orbital. Because atoms typically interact through their unfilled outer shells, and since the outer shells of these atoms are similar, the chemical interactions of the three atoms are also similar.
13. Each of the eight electrons must have at least one quantum number different from each of the others. They can differ (in m_s) by being spin-up or spin-down. They can differ (in ℓ) in angular momentum and in the general shape of the wave function. Those electrons with $\ell = 1$ can differ (in m_ℓ) in orientation of angular momentum.
15. Stimulated emission is the reason laser light is coherent and tends to travel in a well-defined parallel beam. When a photon passing by an excited atom stimulates that atom to emit a photon, the emitted photon is in phase with the original photon and travels in the same direction. As this process is repeated many times, an intense, parallel beam of coherent light is produced. Without stimulated emission, the excited atoms would return to the ground state by emitting photons at random times and in random directions. The resulting light would not have the useful properties of laser light.

Problems

1. (a) 121.5 nm, 102.5 nm, 97.20 nm   (b) Far ultraviolet
3. (a) 2.3×10^{-8} N   (b) −14 eV

5. (a) 1.6×10^6 m/s   (b) No. $v/c = 5.3 \times 10^{-3} \ll 1$
   (c) 0.45 nm   (d) Yes. The wavelength is roughly the same size as the atom.
7. (a) 0.212 nm   (b) 9.95×10^{-25} kg·m/s   (c) 2.11×10^{-34} J·s
   (d) 3.40 eV   (e) -6.80 eV   (f) -3.40 eV
11. $E = -1.51$ eV $(n = 3)$ to $E = -3.40$ eV $(n = 2)$
13. (a) 2.86 eV   (b) 0.472 eV
15. (a) 1.89 eV   (b) 658 nm   (c) 3.02 eV   (d) 412 nm
   (e) 366 nm
17. (a) 488 nm   (b) 0.814 m/s
19. (a) 3   (b) 520 km/s
21. (a) 0.476 nm   (b) 0.997 nm
23. (a) 0.026 5 nm   (b) 0.017 6 nm   (c) 0.013 2 nm
25. (a) 1.31 μm   (b) 164 nm
27.

n	ℓ	m_ℓ	m_s
3	2	2	$\frac{1}{2}$
3	2	2	$-\frac{1}{2}$
3	2	1	$\frac{1}{2}$
3	2	1	$-\frac{1}{2}$
3	2	0	$\frac{1}{2}$
3	2	0	$-\frac{1}{2}$
3	2	-1	$\frac{1}{2}$
3	2	-1	$-\frac{1}{2}$
3	2	-2	$\frac{1}{2}$
3	2	-2	$-\frac{1}{2}$

29. Fifteen possible states, as summarized in the following table:

n	3	3	3	3	3	3	3	3	3	3	3	3	3	3	3
ℓ	2	2	2	2	2	2	2	2	2	2	2	2	2	2	2
m_ℓ	2	2	2	1	1	1	0	0	0	-1	-1	-1	-2	-2	-2
m_s	1	0	-1	1	0	-1	1	0	-1	1	0	-1	1	0	-1

31. aluminum
33. (a) $n = 4$ and $\ell = 2$ (b) $m_\ell = (0, \pm 1, \pm 2)$, $m_s = \pm 1/2$
   (c) $1s^2 2s^2 2p^6 3s^2 3p^6 3d^{10} 4s^2 4p^6 4d^2 5s^2 = [\text{Kr}] \, 4d^2 5s^2$
35. (a) 14 keV   (b) 8.9×10^{-11} m
37. L shell: 11.7 keV; M shell: 10.0 keV; N shell: 2.30 keV
39. (a) 10.2 eV   (b) 7.88×10^4 K
41. (a) 5.40 keV   (b) 3.40 eV   (c) 5.40 keV
43. (a) 4.24×10^{15} W/m^2 (b) 1.20×10^{-12} J

CHAPTER 29

Quick Quizzes

1. False
2. (c)
3. (c)
4. (a) and (b)
5. (b)

Example Questions

1. Tritium has the greater binding energy. Unlike tritium, helium has two protons that exert a repulsive electrostatic force on each other. The helium-3 nucleus is therefore not as tightly bound as the tritium nucleus.
2. Doubling the initial mass of radioactive material doubles the initial activity. Doubling the mass has no effect on the half-life.
3. 7.794×10^{-13} J, 4.69×10^{11} J
4. The binding energy of carbon-14 should be greater than nitrogen-14 because nitrogen has more protons in its nucleus. The mutual repulsion of the protons means that the nitrogen nucleus would require less energy to break up than the carbon nucleus.
5. No
6. Reactions between helium and beryllium can be found in the Sun.

Multiple-Choice Questions

1. (d)
3. (e)
5. (c)
7. (a)
9. (c), (e)
11. (b)

Conceptual Questions

1. An alpha particle contains two protons and two neutrons. Because a hydrogen nucleus contains only one proton, it cannot emit an alpha particle.
3. Isotopes of a given element correspond to nuclei with different numbers of neutrons. This will result in a variety of different physical properties for the nuclei, including the obvious one of mass. The chemical behavior, however, is governed by the element's electrons. All isotopes of a given element have the same number of electrons and, therefore, the same chemical behavior.
5. Nucleus Y will be more unstable. The nucleus with the higher binding energy requires more energy to be disassembled into its constituent parts and has less available energy to release in a decay.
7. In alpha decay, there are only two final particles: the alpha particle and the daughter nucleus. There are also two conservation principles: of energy and of momentum. As a result, the alpha particle must be ejected with a discrete energy to satisfy both conservation principles. However, beta decay is a three-particle decay: the beta particle, the neutrino (or antineutron), and the daughter nucleus. As a result, the energy and momentum can be shared in a variety of ways among the three particles while still satisfying the two conservation principles. This allows a continuous range of energies for the beta particle.
11. The larger rest energy of the neutron means that a free proton in space will not spontaneously decay into a neutron and a positron. When the proton is in the nucleus, however, the important question is that of the total rest energy of the nucleus. If it is energetically favorable for the nucleus to have one less proton and one more neutron, then the decay process will occur to achieve this lower energy.
13. Carbon dating cannot generally be used to estimate the age of a rock, because the rock was not alive to receive carbon, and hence radioactive carbon-14, from the environment. Only the ages of objects that were once alive can be estimated with carbon dating.

Problems

1. (a) 1.5 fm   (b) 4.7 fm   (c) 7.0 fm   (d) 7.4 fm
3. 1.8×10^2 m
5. (a) 27.6 N   (b) 4.16×10^{27} m/s^2 (c) 1.73 MeV
7. (a) 1.9×10^7 m/s   (b) 7.1 MeV
9. (a) 8.26 MeV/nucleon   (b) 8.70 MeV/nucleon
11. 3.54 MeV
13. (a) 0.210 MeV/nucleon greater for $^{23}_{11}$Na   (b) attributable to less proton repulsion
15. 2.29 g
17. (a) 6.95×10^5 s   (b) 9.97×10^{-7} s^{-1} (c) 1.9×10^4 decays/s
   (d) 1.9×10^{10} nuclei   (e) 5, 0.200 mCi
19. 8.06 days
21. (a) 5.58×10^{-2} h^{-1}, 12.4 h   (b) 2.39×10^{13} nuclei
   (c) 1.9 mCi
23. (a) $^{208}_{81}$Tl   (b) $^{95}_{37}$Rb   (c) $^{144}_{60}$Nd
25. e^+ decay, $^{56}_{27}$Co $\rightarrow$ $^{56}_{26}$Fe $+ \, e^+ + \nu$
27. (a) cannot occur spontaneously   (b) can occur spontaneously
29. 18.6 keV
31. 4.22×10^3 yr
33. (a) $^{21}_{10}$Ne   (b) $^{144}_{54}$Xe   (c) X $= e^+$, X' $= \nu$

35. (a) $^{13}_{6}$C (b) $^{10}_{5}$B
37. (a) $^{197}_{79}$Au + n $\rightarrow$ $^{198}_{80}$Hg + e$^-$ + $\bar{\nu}$ (b) 7.89 MeV
39. (a) The product nucleus is $^{10}_{5}$B. (b) −2.79 MeV
41. 18.8 J
43. 24 d
45. (a) 8.97×10^{11} electrons (b) 0.100 J (c) 100 rad
47. (a) 3.18×10^{-7} mol (b) 1.91×10^{17} nuclei
(c) 1.08×10^{14} Bq (d) 8.92×10^{6} Bq
49. 46.5 d
51. (a) 4.0×10^{9} yr (b) It could be no older. (c) The rock
could be younger if some ^{87}Sr were initially present.
53. 54 μCi
55. 5.9 billion years

CHAPTER 30

Quick Quizzes

1. (a)
2. (b)

Example Questions

1. 1 mg/yr
2. 1.77×10^{12} J
3. True
4. No. That reaction violates conservation of baryon number.

Multiple-Choice Questions

1. (d)
3. (b)
5. (d)
7. (b)
9. (c) and (d)
11. (a), (c), and (d)

Conceptual Questions

1. The experiment described is a nice analogy to the Ruther-ford scattering experiment. In the Rutherford experiment, alpha particles were scattered from atoms and the scattering was consistent with a small structure in the atom containing the positive charge.
3. The largest quark charge is $2e/3$, so a combination of only two particles, a quark and an antiquark forming a meson, could not have an electric charge of $+2e$. Only particles containing three quarks, each with a charge of $2e/3$, can combine to produce a total charge of $2e$.
5. Until about 700 000 years after the Big Bang, the temperature of the Universe was high enough for any atoms that formed to be ionized by ambient radiation. Once the average radiation energy dropped below the hydrogen ionization energy of 13.6 eV, hydrogen atoms could form and remain as neutral atoms for relatively long period of time.
7. In the quark model, all hadrons are composed of smaller units called quarks. Quarks have a fractional electric charge and a baryon number of $\frac{1}{3}$. There are six flavors of quarks: up (u), down (d), strange (s), charmed (c), top (t), and bottom (b). All baryons contain three quarks, and all mesons contain one quark and one antiquark. Section 30.8 has a more detailed discussion of the quark model.
9. Baryons and mesons are hadrons, interacting primarily through the strong force. They are not elementary particles, being composed of either three quarks (baryons) or a quark and an antiquark (mesons). Baryons have a nonzero baryon number with a spin of either $\frac{1}{2}$ or $\frac{3}{2}$. Mesons have a baryon number of zero and a spin of either 0 or 1.

11. All stable particles other than protons and neutrons have baryon number zero. Since the baryon number must be conserved, and the final states of the kaon decay contain no protons or neutrons, the baryon number of all kaons must be *zero*.
13. Fission reactors do not emit greenhouse gases as combustion byproducts like fossil fuels—the only necessary environmental discharge is heat. The cost involved in producing fissile material is comparable to the cost of pumping, transporting, and refining fossil fuel. The cost per kilowatt hour of nuclear power is less than that of coal, and far less than that of oil or gas, which over time far outweighs the higher start up cost of nuclear power plants. Further, spent nuclear fuel can be recycled in breeder reactors, whereas when fossil fuel is spent, the waste is exhausted into the atmosphere. Finally, global reserves of uranium, if used in breeder reactors, will last much longer than the global supply of fossil fuel.

The disadvantage is that some of the products of a fission reaction are radioactive—and some of those have long half-lives. There will be a point at which enough fuel is spent that the fuel rods do not supply power economically and need to be replaced or recycled. The fuel rods are still radioactive after removal. Both the waste and the "spent" fuel rods present serious health and environmental hazards that can last for tens of thousands of years, if not handled properly or recycled in breeder reactors. The environmental hazards of nuclear reactor waste are probably much less than those due to burning fossil fuels.

Problems

1. 1.1×10^{16} fissions
3. 126 MeV
5. (a) 16.2 kg (b) 117 g
7. (a) $3/a$ (b) $3.72/a$ (c) The surface-to-volume ratio is lowest for the sphere; therefore, the sphere has the better shape for minimum leakage.
9. 1.01 g
11. (a) $^8_4$Be (b) $^{12}_6$C (c) 7.27 MeV
13. 4.03 MeV
15. 14.1 MeV
17. (a) 4.53×10^{23} Hz (b) 0.662 fm
19. 67.5 MeV, 67.5 MeV/c, 1.63×10^{22} Hz
21. (a) conservation of electron-lepton number and conservation of muon-lepton number (b) conservation of charge (c) conservation of baryon number (d) conservation of baryon number (e) conservation of charge
23. (a) Violates conservation of baryon number (not allowed). (b) This reaction may occur via the strong interaction. (c) This reaction may occur via the weak interaction only. (d) This reaction may occur by the weak interaction only. (e) This reaction may occur via the electromagnetic interaction.
25. (a) not conserved (b) conserved (c) conserved (d) not conserved (e) not conserved (f) not conserved
27. 3.34×10^{26} electrons, 9.36×10^{26} up quarks, 8.70×10^{26} down quarks
29. (a) Σ^+ (b) π^- (c) K^0 (d) Ξ^-
31. a neutron, udd
33. 18.8 MeV
35. (a) K$^+$ (b) Ξ^0 (c) π^0
37. 26
39. (b) 12 days
41. 29.8 MeV
43. 3.60×10^{38} protons/s

Note: Page numbers followed by *f* and *t* refer to figures and tables respectively.

■ PHYSICAL CONSTANTS

Quantity	Symbol	Value	SI unit
Avogadro's number	N_A	6.02×10^{23}	particles/mol
Bohr radius	a_0	5.29×10^{-11}	m
Boltzmann's constant	k_B	1.38×10^{-23}	J/K
Coulomb constant, $1/4\pi\epsilon_0$	k_e	8.99×10^9	$N \cdot m^2/C^2$
Electron Compton wavelength	$h/m_e c$	2.43×10^{-12}	m
Electron mass	m_e	9.11×10^{-31}	kg
		5.49×10^{-4}	u
		$0.511 \text{ MeV}/c^2$	
Elementary charge	e	1.60×10^{-19}	C
Gravitational constant	G	6.67×10^{-11}	$N \cdot m^2/kg^2$
Mass of Earth	M_E	5.98×10^{24}	kg
Mass of Moon	M_M	7.36×10^{22}	kg
Molar volume of ideal gas at STP	V	22.4	L/mol
		2.24×10^{-2}	m^3/mol
Neutron mass	m_n	$1.674\,93 \times 10^{-27}$	kg
		$1.008\,665$	u
		$939.565 \text{ MeV}/c^2$	
Permeability of free space	μ_0	1.26×10^{-6}	$T \cdot m/A$
		($4\pi \times 10^{-7}$ exactly)	
Permittivity of free space	ϵ_0	8.85×10^{-12}	$C^2/N \cdot m^2$
Planck's constant	h	6.63×10^{-34}	$J \cdot s$
	$\hbar = h/2\pi$	1.05×10^{-34}	$J \cdot s$
Proton mass	m_p	$1.672\,62 \times 10^{-27}$	kg
		$1.007\,276$	u
		$938.272 \text{ MeV}/c^2$	
Radius of Earth (at equator)	R_E	6.38×10^6	m
Radius of Moon	R_M	1.74×10^6	m
Rydberg constant	R_H	1.10×10^7	m^{-1}
Speed of light in vacuum	c	3.00×10^8	m/s
Standard free-fall acceleration	g	9.80	m/s^2
Stefan-Boltzmann constant	σ	5.67×10^{-8}	$W/m^2 \cdot K^4$
Universal gas constant	R	8.31	$J/mol \cdot K$

The values presented in this table are those used in computations in the text. Generally, the physical constants are known to much better precision.